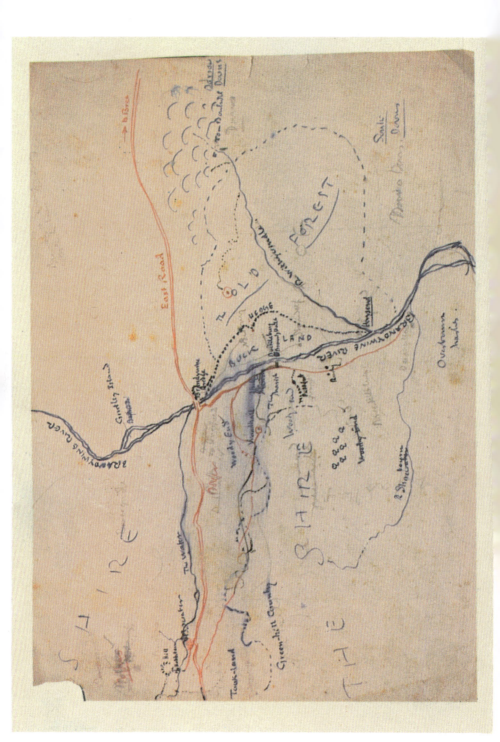

THE HISTORY OF MIDDLE-EARTH II

Works by J.R.R. Tolkien
THE HOBBIT
LEAF BY NIGGLE
ON FAIRY-STORIES
FARMER GILES OF HAM
THE HOMECOMING OF BEORHTNOTH
THE LORD OF THE RINGS
THE ADVENTURES OF TOM BOMBADIL
THE ROAD GOES EVER ON (WITH DONALD SWANN)
SMITH OF WOOTTON MAJOR

Works published posthumously
SIR GAWAIN AND THE GREEN KNIGHT, PEARL AND SIR ORFEO*
THE FATHER CHRISTMAS LETTERS
THE SILMARILLION*
PICTURES BY J.R.R. TOLKIEN*
UNFINISHED TALES*
THE LETTERS OF J.R.R. TOLKIEN*
FINN AND HENGEST
MR BLISS
THE MONSTERS AND THE CRITICS & OTHER ESSAYS*
ROVERANDOM
THE CHILDREN OF HÚRIN*
THE LEGEND OF SIGURD AND GUDRÚN*
THE FALL OF ARTHUR*
BEOWULF: A TRANSLATION AND COMMENTARY*
THE STORY OF KULLERVO
THE LAY OF AOTROU AND ITROUN
BEREN AND LÚTHIEN*
THE FALL OF GONDOLIN*
THE NATURE OF MIDDLE-EARTH
THE FALL OF NÚMENOR

The History of Middle-earth – by Christopher Tolkien
I THE BOOK OF LOST TALES, PART ONE
II THE BOOK OF LOST TALES, PART TWO
III THE LAYS OF BELERIAND
IV THE SHAPING OF MIDDLE-EARTH
V THE LOST ROAD AND OTHER WRITINGS
VI THE RETURN OF THE SHADOW
VII THE TREASON OF ISENGARD
VIII THE WAR OF THE RING
IX SAURON DEFEATED
X MORGOTH'S RING
XI THE WAR OF THE JEWELS
XII THE PEOPLES OF MIDDLE-EARTH

* Edited by Christopher Tolkien

TOLKIEN

The History of Middle-earth II

VI The Return of the Shadow
VII The Treason of Isengard
VIII The War of the Ring
IX Sauron Defeated

CHRISTOPHER TOLKIEN

HarperCollins*Publishers*

HarperCollins*Publishers* Ltd
1 London Bridge Street,
London SE1 9GF

HarperCollins*Publishers*
Macken House, 39/40 Mayor Street Upper,
Dublin 1, D01 C9W8, Ireland

www.tolkien.co.uk
www.tolkienestate.com

This edition published by HarperCollins*Publishers* 2002
15

First published by HarperCollins*Publishers* 2000

The Return of the Shadow first published in Great Britain by
Unwin Hyman 1988
The Treason of Isengard first published in Great Britain by
Unwin Hyman 1989
The War of the Ring first published in Great Britain by
Unwin Hyman 1990
Sauron Defeated first published in Great Britain by
HarperCollins*Publishers* 1992

Copyright © The Tolkien Estate Limited and C.R. Tolkien
1988, 1989, 1990 and 1992
This edition Copyright © HarperCollins*Publishers* 2002

ISBN 978-0-00-714916-2

☨® and 'Tolkien'® are registered trade marks of
The Tolkien Estate Limited

Set in Imprint

Printed and bound in Italy by ROTOLITO S.p.A.

All rights reserved. No part of this publication may be reproduced,
stored in a retrieval system, or transmitted in any form or by any means,
electronic, mechanical, photocopying, recording or otherwise,
without the prior permission of the publishers.

This book is produced from independently certified FSC™ paper
to ensure responsible forest management.
For more information visit: www.harpercollins.co.uk/green

THE RETURN OF THE SHADOW
THE HISTORY OF THE LORD OF THE RINGS, PART ONE

J. R. R. TOLKIEN

The Return of the Shadow

The History of
The Lord of the Rings

PART ONE

Christopher Tolkien

To
RAYNER UNWIN

I met a lot of things on the way that astonished me. Tom Bombadil I knew already; but I had never been to Bree. Strider sitting in the corner at the inn was a shock, and I had no more idea who he was than had Frodo. The Mines of Moria had been a mere name; and of Lothlórien no word had reached my mortal ears till I came there. Far away I knew there were the Horse-lords on the confines of an ancient Kingdom of Men, but Fangorn Forest was an unforeseen adventure. I had never heard of the House of Eorl nor of the Stewards of Gondor. Most disquieting of all, Saruman had never been revealed to me, and I was as mystified as Frodo at Gandalf's failure to appear on September 22.

J. R. R. Tolkien, in a letter to
W. H. Auden, 7 June 1955

CONTENTS

Foreword   *page* 1

THE FIRST PHASE

I	A LONG-EXPECTED PARTY	11
II	FROM HOBBITON TO THE WOODY END	45
III	OF GOLLUM AND THE RING	73
IV	TO MAGGOT'S FARM AND BUCKLAND	88
V	THE OLD FOREST AND THE WITHYWINDLE	110
VI	TOM BOMBADIL	117
VII	THE BARROW-WIGHT	125
VIII	ARRIVAL AT BREE	132
IX	TROTTER AND THE JOURNEY TO WEATHERTOP	148
X	THE ATTACK ON WEATHERTOP	177
XI	FROM WEATHERTOP TO THE FORD	190
XII	AT RIVENDELL	206
XIII	'QUERIES AND ALTERATIONS'	220

THE SECOND PHASE

XIV	RETURN TO HOBBITON	233
XV	ANCIENT HISTORY	250
XVI	DELAYS ARE DANGEROUS	273
XVII	A SHORT CUT TO MUSHROOMS	286
XVIII	AGAIN FROM BUCKLAND TO THE WITHYWINDLE	298

THE THIRD PHASE

XIX	THE THIRD PHASE (1): THE JOURNEY TO BREE	309

xii   THE RETURN OF THE SHADOW

page

XX   THE THIRD PHASE (2):
        AT THE SIGN OF THE PRANCING PONY   331

XXI   THE THIRD PHASE (3):
        TO WEATHERTOP AND RIVENDELL   352

XXII   NEW UNCERTAINTIES AND NEW
        PROJECTIONS   369

THE STORY CONTINUED

XXIII   IN THE HOUSE OF ELROND   391
XXIV   THE RING GOES SOUTH   415
XXV   THE MINES OF MORIA   442

Index   468

ILLUSTRATIONS

Map of the Shire   *frontispiece*
The original opening page of *The Lord of the Rings*   12
The original description of the writing on the Ring   257
The Ring-verse, and the emergence of the Ruling Ring in
   the narrative   259
Plan of Bree   335
The emergence of Treebeard   383
The earliest map of the lands south of the Map of Wilderland
   in *The Hobbit*   439
The inscription of the West Gate of Moria 450

FOREWORD

As is well known, the manuscripts and typescripts of *The Lord of the Rings* were sold by J. R. R. Tolkien to Marquette University, Milwaukee, a few years after its publication, together with those of *The Hobbit* and *Farmer Giles of Ham*, and also *Mr. Bliss*. A long time elapsed between the shipment of these latter papers, which reached Marquette in July 1957, and that of *The Lord of the Rings*, which did not arrive until the following year. The reason for this was that my father had undertaken to sort, annotate, and date the multifarious manuscripts of *The Lord of the Rings*, but found it impossible at that time to do the work required. It is clear that he never did so, and in the end let the papers go just as they were; it was noted when they reached Marquette that they were 'in no order'. Had he done so, he must have seen at that time that, very large though the manuscript collection was, it was nonetheless incomplete.

Seven years later, in 1965, when he was working on the revision of *The Lord of the Rings*, he wrote to the Director of Libraries at Marquette, asking if a certain scheme of dates and events in the narrative was to be found there, since he had 'never made out any full schedule or note of the papers transferred to you.' In this letter he explained that the transfer had taken place at a time when his papers were dispersed between his house in Headington (Oxford) and his rooms in Merton College; and he also said that he now found himself still in possession of 'written matter' that 'should belong to you': when he had finished the revision of *The Lord of the Rings* he would look into the question. But he did not do so.

These papers passed to me on his death eight years later; but though Humphrey Carpenter made reference to them in his *Biography* (1977) and cited from them some early notes, I neglected them for many years, being absorbed in the long work of tracing the evolution of the narratives of the Elder Days, the legends of Beleriand and Valinor. The publication of Volume III of 'The History of Middle-earth' was already approaching before I had any idea that the 'History' might extend to an account of the writing of *The Lord of the Rings*. During the last three years, however, I have been engaged at intervals in the decipherment and analysis of *The Lord of the Rings* manuscripts in my possession

2   THE RETURN OF THE SHADOW

(a task still far from completed). It has emerged from this that the papers left behind in 1958 consist largely of the earliest phases of composition, although in some cases (and most notably in the first chapter, which was rewritten many times over) successive versions found among these papers bring the narrative to an advanced state. In general, however, it was only the initial notes and earliest drafts, with outlines for the further course of the story, that remained in England when the great bulk of the papers went to Marquette.

I do not of course know how it came about that these particular manuscripts came to be left out of the consignment to Marquette; but I think that an explanation in general terms can be found readily enough. Immensely prolific as my father was ('I found not being able to use a pen or pencil as defeating as the loss of her beak would be to a hen,' he wrote to Stanley Unwin in 1963, when suffering from an ailment in his right arm), constantly revising, re-using, beginning again, but never throwing any of his writing away, his papers became inextricably complex, disorganised, and dispersed. It does not seem likely that at the time of the transfer to Marquette he would have been greatly concerned with or have had any precise recollection of the early drafts, some of them supplanted and overtaken as much as twenty years before; and no doubt they had long since been set aside, forgotten, and buried.

However this may be, it is self-evidently desirable that the separated manuscripts should be joined together again, and the whole corpus preserved in one place. This must have been my father's intention at the time of the original sale; and accordingly the manuscripts at present in my keeping will be handed over to Marquette University.

The greater part of the material cited or described in this book is found in the papers that remained behind; but the third section of the book (called 'The Third Phase') constituted a difficult problem, because in this case the manuscripts were divided. Most of the chapters in this 'phase' of composition went to Marquette in 1958, but substantial parts of several of them did not. These parts had become separated because my father had rejected them, while using the remainder as constituent elements in new versions. The interpretation of this part of the history would have been altogether impossible without very full co-operation from Marquette, and this I have abundantly received. Above all, Mr Taum Santoski has engaged with great skill and care in a complex operation in

FOREWORD

which we have exchanged over many months annotated copies of the texts; and it has been possible in this way to determine the textual history, and to reconstruct the original manuscripts which my father himself dismembered nearly half a century ago. I record with pleasure and deep appreciation the generous assistance that I have received from him, and also from Mr Charles B. Elston, the Archivist of the Memorial Library at Marquette, from Mr John D. Rateliff, and from Miss Tracy Muench.

This attempt to give an account of the first stages in the writing of *The Lord of the Rings* has been beset by other difficulties than the fact of the manuscripts being widely sundered; difficulties primarily in the interpretation of the sequence of writing, but also in the presentation of the results in a printed book.

Briefly, the writing proceeded in a series of 'waves' or (as I have called them in this book) 'phases'. The first chapter was itself reconstituted three times before the hobbits ever left Hobbiton, but the story then went all the way to Rivendell before the impulse failed. My father then started again from the beginning (the 'second phase'), and then again (the 'third phase'); and as new narrative elements and new names and relations among the characters appeared they were written into previous drafts, at different times. Parts of a text were taken out and used elsewhere. Alternative versions were incorporated into the same manuscript, so that the story could be read in more than one way according to the directions given. To determine the sequence of these exceedingly complex movements with demonstrable correctness at all points is scarcely possible. One or two dates that my father wrote in are insufficient to give more than very limited assistance, and references to the progress of the work in his letters are unclear and hard to interpret. Differences of script can be very misleading. Thus the determination of the history of composition has to be based very largely on clues afforded by the evolution of names and motives in the narrative itself; but in this there is every possibility of going astray through mistaking the relative dates of additions and alterations. Exemplification of these problems will be found throughout the book. I do not suppose for one moment that I have succeeded in determining the history correctly at every point: indeed there remain several cases where the evidence appears to be contradictory and I can offer no solution. The nature of the manuscripts is such that they will probably always admit of differing interpretations. But the sequence of composition that I

THE RETURN OF THE SHADOW

propose, after much experimentation with alternative theories, seems to me to fit the evidence very much the best.

The earliest plot-outlines and narrative drafts are often barely legible, and become more difficult as the work proceeded. Using any scrap of the wretched paper of the war years that came to hand – sometimes writing not merely on the backs of examination scripts but across the scripts themselves – my father would dash down elliptically his thoughts for the story to come, and his first formulations of narrative, at tearing speed. In the handwriting that he used for rapid drafts and sketches, not intended to endure long before he turned to them again and gave them a more workable form, letters are so loosely formed that a word which cannot be deduced or guessed at from the context or from later versions can prove perfectly opaque after long examination; and if, as he often did, he used a soft pencil much has now become blurred and faint. This must be borne in mind throughout: the earliest drafts were put urgently to paper just as the first words came to mind and before the thought dissolved, whereas the printed text (apart from a sprinkling of dots and queries in the face of illegibility) inevitably conveys an air of calm and ordered composition, the phrasing weighed and intended.

Turning to the way in which the material is presented in this book, the most intractable problem lies in the development of the story through successive drafts, always changing but always closely dependent on what preceded. In the rather extreme case of the opening chapter 'A Long-expected Party', there are in this book six main texts to be considered and a number of abandoned openings. A complete presentation of all the material for this one chapter would almost constitute a book in itself, not to speak of a mass of repetition or near-repetition. On the other hand, a succession of texts reduced to extracts and short citations (where the versions differ significantly from their predecessors) is not easy to follow, and if the development is traced at all closely this method also takes up much space. There is no really satisfactory solution to this. The editor must take responsibility for selecting and emphasizing those elements that he considers most interesting and most significant. In general I give the earliest narrative complete, or nearly complete, in each chapter, as the basis to which subsequent development can be referred. Different treatment of the manuscripts calls for different arrangement of the editorial element: where texts are given more or less in full much use is

FOREWORD

made of numbered notes (which may constitute an important part of the presentation of a complex text), but where they are not the chapter proceeds rather as a discussion with citations.

My father bestowed immense pains on the creation of *The Lord of the Rings*, and my intention has been that this record of his first years of work on it should reflect those pains. The first part of the story, before the Ring left Rivendell, took by far the most labour to achieve (hence the length of this book in relation to the whole story); and the doubts, indecisions, unpickings, restructurings, and false starts have been described. The result is necessarily extremely intricate; but whereas it would be possible to recount the history in a greatly reduced and abbreviated form, I am convinced that to omit difficult detail or to oversimplify problems and explanations would rob the study of its essential interest.

My object has been to give an account of the *writing* of *The Lord of the Rings*, to exhibit the subtle process of change that could transform the significance of events and the identity of persons while preserving those scenes and the words that were spoken from the earliest drafts. I therefore (for example) pursue in detail the history of the two hobbits who ultimately issued in Peregrin Took and Fredegar Bolger, but only after the most extraordinary permutations and coalescences of name, character, and rôle; on the other hand I refrain from all discussion that is not directly relevant to the evolution of the narrative.

In the nature of the book, I assume conversance with *The Fellowship of the Ring*, and comparison is made throughout of course with the published work. Page-references to *The Fellowship of the Ring* (abbreviated FR) are given to the three-volume hardback edition of *The Lord of the Rings* (LR) published by George Allen and Unwin (now Unwin Hyman) and Houghton Mifflin Company, this being the edition common to both England and America, but I think that it will be found in fact that almost all such references can be readily traced in any edition, since the precise point referred to in the final form of the story is nearly always evident from the context.

In the 'first phase' of writing, which took the story to Rivendell, most of the chapters were title-less, and subsequently there was much shifting in the division of the story into chapters, with variation in titles and numbers. I have thought it best therefore to avoid confusion by giving many of my chapters simple descriptive titles, such as 'From Hobbiton to the Woody End', indicating the content rather than relating them to the chapter-titles in *The*

6   THE RETURN OF THE SHADOW

Fellowship of the Ring. As a title for the book it seemed suitable to take one of my father's own suggested but abandoned titles for the first volume of *The Lord of the Rings*. In a letter to Rayner Unwin of 8 August 1953 (*The Letters of J. R. R. Tolkien*, no. 139) he proposed *The Return of the Shadow*.

No account is given in this book of the history of the writing of *The Hobbit* up to its original publication in 1937, although, from the nature of its relationship to *The Lord of the Rings*, the published work is constantly referred to. That relationship is curious and complex. My father several times expressed his view of it, but most fully and (as I think) most accurately in the course of a long letter to Christopher Bretherton written in July 1964 (*Letters* no. 257).

I returned to Oxford in Jan. 1926, and by the time *The Hobbit* appeared (1937) this 'matter of the Elder Days' was in coherent form. *The Hobbit* was not intended to have anything to do with it. I had the habit while my children were still young of inventing and telling orally, sometimes of writing down, 'children's stories' for their private amusement . . . *The Hobbit* was intended to be one of them. It had no necessary connexion with the 'mythology', but naturally became attracted towards this dominant construction in my mind, causing the tale to become larger and more heroic as it proceeded. Even so it could really stand quite apart, except for the references (unnecessary, though they give an impression of historical depth) to the Fall of Gondolin, the branches of the Elfkin, and the quarrel of King Thingol, Lúthien's father, with the Dwarves. . . .

The magic ring was the one obvious thing in *The Hobbit* that could be connected with my mythology. To be the burden of a large story it had to be of supreme importance. I then linked it with the (originally) quite casual reference to the Necromancer, whose function was hardly more than to provide a reason for Gandalf going away and leaving Bilbo and the Dwarves to fend for themselves, which was necessary for the tale. From *The Hobbit* are also derived the matter of the Dwarves, Durin their prime ancestor, and Moria; and Elrond. The passage in Ch. iii relating him to the Half-elven of the mythology was a fortunate accident, due to the difficulty of constantly inventing good names for new characters. I gave him the name Elrond casually, but as this came from the mythology (Elros and Elrond the two sons of Eärendel) I made him half-elven. Only in *The Lord* was

FOREWORD

he identified with the son of Eärendel, and so the great-grandson of Lúthien and Beren, a great power and a Ringholder.

How my father saw *The Hobbit* – specifically in relation to 'The Silmarillion' – at the time of its publication is shown clearly in the letter that he wrote to G. E. Selby on 14 December 1937:

> I don't much approve of *The Hobbit* myself, preferring my own mythology (which is just touched on) with its consistent nomenclature – Elrond, Gondolin, and Esgaroth have escaped out of it – and organized history, to this rabble of Eddaic-named dwarves out of Völuspá, newfangled hobbits and gollums (invented in an idle hour) and Anglo-Saxon runes.

The importance of *The Hobbit* in *the history of the evolution* of Middle-earth lies then, at this time, in the fact that it was published, and that a sequel to it was demanded. As a result, from the nature of *The Lord of the Rings* as it evolved, *The Hobbit* was *drawn into* Middle-earth – and transformed it; but as it stood in 1937 it was not a part of it. Its significance for Middle-earth lies in what it would do, not in what it was.

Later, *The Lord of the Rings* in turn reacted upon *The Hobbit* itself, in published and in (far more extensive) unpublished revisions of the text; but all that lies of course far in the future at the point which this History has reached.

In the manuscripts of *The Lord of the Rings* there is extreme inconsistency in such matters as the use of capital letters and hyphens, and the separation of elements in compound names. In my representation of the texts I have not imposed any standardization in this respect, though using consistent forms in my own discussions.

THE FIRST PHASE

I

A LONG-EXPECTED PARTY

(i)

The First Version

The original written starting-point of *The Lord of the Rings* – its 'first germ', as my father scribbled on the text long after – has been preserved: a manuscript of five pages entitled *A long-expected party*. I think that it must have been to this (rather than to a second, unfinished, draft that soon followed it) that my father referred when on 19 December 1937 he wrote to Charles Furth at Allen and Unwin: 'I have written the first chapter of a new story about Hobbits – "A long expected party".' Only three days before he had written to Stanley Unwin:

> I think it is plain that . . . a sequel or successor to The Hobbit is called for. I promise to give this thought and attention. But I am sure you will sympathize when I say that the construction of elaborate and consistent mythology (and two languages) rather occupies the mind, and the Silmarils are in my heart. So that goodness knows what will happen. Mr Baggins began as a comic tale among conventional Grimm's fairy-tale dwarves, and got drawn into the edge of it – so that even Sauron the terrible peeped over the edge. And what more can hobbits do? They can be comic, but their comedy is suburban unless it is set against things more elemental.

From this it seems plain that on the 16th of December he had not only not begun writing, but in all probability had not even given thought to the substance of 'a new story about Hobbits'. Not long before he had parted with the manuscript of the third version of *The Silmarillion* to Allen and Unwin; it was unfinished, and he was still deeply immersed in it. In a postscript to this letter to Stanley Unwin he acknowledged, in fact, the return of *The Silmarillion* (and other things) later on that day. Nonetheless, he must have begun on the new story there and then.

When he first put pen to paper he wrote in large letters 'When M', but he stopped before completing the final stroke of the M and wrote instead 'When Bilbo . . .' The text begins in a handsome script, but the writing becomes progessively faster and deteriorates at the end into a rapid scrawl not at all points legible. There are a good many alterations to the manuscript. The text that follows represents the original form as I judge it to have been, granting that what is 'original' and what is not cannot be perfectly distinguished. Some changes can be seen to have been made at the moment of writing, and these are taken up into the text; but others

When N

When Bilbo, son of Bungo of the family of Baggins, celebrated his seventieth birthday there was for a day or two some talk in the neighbourhood. He had once had a little fleeting fame among the people of Hobbiton and Bywater — he had disappeared after breakfast one April 30th and not reappeared until lunchtime on June 22nd in the following year. A very odd proceeding for which he had never given any good reason, and of which he wrote a nonsensical account. After that he returned to normal ways; and the shaken confidence of the district was gradually restored, especially as Bilbo seemed by some unexplained method to have become more than comfortably off — if not positively wealthy. Indeed it was the magnificence of the party rather than the fleeting fame that at first caused the talk — after all that other odd business had happened some twenty years before and was becoming decently forgotten. The magnificence of the impar-

The original opening page of *The Lord of the Rings*

First Version   A LONG-EXPECTED PARTY   13

are characteristic anticipations of the following version, and these are ignored. In any case it is highly probable that my father wrote the versions of this opening chapter in quick succession. Notes to this version follow immediately on the end of the text (p. 17).

A *long-expected party*[1]

When Bilbo, son of Bungo of the family of Baggins, [had celebrated >] prepared to celebrate his seventieth birthday there was for a day or two some talk in the neighbourhood. He had once had a little fleeting fame among the people of Hobbiton and Bywater – he had disappeared after breakfast one April 30th and not reappeared until lunchtime on June 22nd in the following year. A very odd proceeding for which he had never given any good reason, and of which he wrote a nonsensical account. After that he returned to normal ways; and the shaken confidence of the district was gradually restored, especially as Bilbo seemed by some unexplained method to have become more than comfortably off, if not positively wealthy. Indeed it was the magnificence of the party rather than the fleeting fame that at first caused the talk – after all that other odd business had happened some twenty years before and was becoming decently forgotten. The magnificence of the preparations for the party, I should say. The field to the south of his front door was being covered with pavilions. Invitations were being sent out to all the Bagginses and all the Tooks (his relatives on his mother's side), and to the Grubbs (only remotely connected); and to the Burroweses, the Boffinses, the Chubbses and the Proudfeet: none of whom were connected at all within the memory of the local historians – some of them lived on the other side of the shire; but they were all, of course, hobbits. Even the Sackville-Bagginses, his cousins on his father's side, were not forgotten. There had been a feud between them and Mr Bilbo Baggins, as some of you may remember. But so splendid was the invitation-card, all written in gold, that they were induced to accept; besides, their cousin had been specializing in good food for a long time, and his tables had a high reputation even in that time and country when food was still what it ought to be and abundant enough for all folk to practise on.

Everyone expected a pleasant feast; though they rather dreaded the after-dinner speech of their host. He was liable to drag in bits of what he called poetry, and even to allude, after a glass or two, to the absurd adventures he said he had had long ago during his

14 THE RETURN OF THE SHADOW

ridiculous vanishment. They had a *very* pleasant feast: indeed an engrossing entertainment. The purchase of provisions fell almost to zero throughout the whole shire during the ensuing week; but as Mr Baggins' catering had emptied all the stores, cellars and warehouses for miles around, that did not matter. Then came the speech. Most of the assembled hobbits were now in a tolerant mood, and their former fears were forgotten. They were prepared to listen to anything, and to cheer at every full stop. But they were not prepared to be startled. But they were – completely and unprecedentedly startled; some even had indigestion.

'My dear people,' began Mr Baggins. 'Hear, hear!' they replied in chorus. 'My dear Bagginses,' he went on, standing now on his chair, so that the light of the lanterns that illuminated the enormous pavilion flashed upon the gold buttons of his embroidered waistcoat for all to see. 'And my dear Tooks, and Grubbs, and Chubbs, and Burroweses, and Boffinses, and Proudfoots.'[2] 'Proudfeet' shouted an elderly hobbit from the back. His name of course was Proudfoot, and merited; his feet were large, exceptionally furry, and both were on the table. 'Also my dear Sackville-Bagginses that I welcome back at last to Bag-end,' Bilbo continued. 'Today is my seventieth birthday.' 'Hurray hurray and many happy returns!' they shouted. That was the sort of stuff they liked: short, obvious, uncontroversial.

'I hope you are all enjoying yourselves as much as I am.' Deafening cheers, cries of yes (and no), and noises of trumpets and whistles. There were a great many junior hobbits present, as hobbits were indulgent to their children, especially if there was a chance of an extra meal. Hundreds of musical crackers had been pulled. Most of them were labelled 'Made in Dale'. What that meant only Bilbo and a few of his Took-nephews knew; but they were very marvellous crackers. 'I have called you all together,' Bilbo went on when the last cheer died away, and something in his voice made a few of the Tooks prick up their ears. 'First of all to tell you that I am immensely fond of you, and that seventy years is too short a time to live among such excellent and charming hobbits' – 'hear hear!' 'I don't know half of you half as well as I should like, and less than half of you half as well as you deserve.' No cheers, a few claps – most of them were trying to work it out. 'Secondly to celebrate my birthday and the twentieth year of my return' – an uncomfortable rustle. 'Lastly to make an *Announcement*.' He said this very loud and everybody sat up who could. 'Goodbye! I am going away after dinner. Also I am going to get married.'

First Version   A LONG-EXPECTED PARTY   15

He sat down. The silence was flabbergastation. It was broken only by Mr Proudfoot, who kicked over the table; Mrs Proudfoot choked in the middle of a drink.

That's that. It merely serves to explain that Bilbo Baggins got married and had many children, because I am going to tell you a story about one of his descendants, and if you had only read his memoirs up to the date of Balin's visit – ten years at least before this birthday party – you might have been puzzled.[3]

As a matter of fact Bilbo Baggins disappeared silently and unnoticed – the ring was in his hand even while he made his speech – in the middle of the confused outburst of talk that followed the flabbergasted silence. He was never seen in Hobbiton again. When the carriages came for the guests there was no one to say good-bye to. The carriages rolled away, one after another, filled with full but oddly unsatisfied hobbits. Gardeners came (by appointment) and cleared away in wheelbarrows those that had inadvertently remained. Night settled down and passed. The sun rose. People came to clear away the pavilions and the tables and the chairs and the lanterns and the flowering trees in boxes, and the spoons and knives and plates and forks, and crumbs, and the uneaten food – a very small parcel. Lots of other people came too. Bagginses and Sackville-Bagginses and Tooks, and people with even less business. By the middle of the morning (when even the best-fed were out and about again) there was quite a crowd at Bag-end, uninvited but not unexpected. ENTER was painted on a large white board outside the great front-door. The door was open. On everything inside there was a label tied. 'For Mungo Took, with love from Bilbo'; 'For Semolina Baggins, with love from her nephew', on a waste-paper basket – she had written him a deal of letters (mostly of good advice). 'For Caramella Took, with kind remembrances from her uncle', on a clock in the hall. Though unpunctual she had been a niece he rather liked, until coming late one day to tea she had declared his clock was fast. Bilbo's clocks were never either slow or fast, and he did not forget it. 'For Obo Took-Took, from his great-nephew', on a feather bed; Obo was seldom awake before 12 noon or after tea, and snored. 'For Gorboduc Grubb with best wishes from B. Baggins' – on a gold fountain-pen; he never answered letters. 'For Angelica's use' on a mirror – she was a young Baggins and thought herself very comely.[4] 'For Inigo Grubb-Took', on a complete dinner-service – he was the greediest hobbit known to history. 'For

16 THE RETURN OF THE SHADOW

Amalda Sackville-Baggins *as a present*', on a case of silver spoons. She was the wife of Bilbo's cousin, the one he had discovered years ago on his return measuring his dining-room (you may remember his suspicions about disappearing spoons: anyway neither he nor Amalda had forgotten).[5]

Of course there were a thousand and one things in Bilbo's house, and all had labels – most of them with some point (which sank in after a time). The whole house-furniture was disposed of, but not a penny piece of money, nor a brass ring of jewelry, was to be found. Amalda was the only Sackville-Baggins remembered with a label – but then there was a notice in the hall saying that Mr Bilbo Baggins made over the desirable property or dwelling-hole known as Bag-end Underhill together with all lands thereto belonging or annexed to Sago Sackville-Baggins and his wife Amalda for them to have hold possess occupy or otherwise dispose of at their pleasure and discretion as from September 22nd next. It was then September 21st (Bilbo's birthday being on the 20th of that pleasant month). So the Sackville-Bagginses did live in Bag-end after all – though they had had to wait some twenty years. And they had a great deal of difficulty too getting all the labelled stuff out – labels got torn and mixed, and people tried to do swaps in the hall, and some tried to make off with stuff that was [not] being carefully watched; and various prying folk began knocking holes in walls and burrowing in cellars before they could be ejected. They were still worrying about the money and the jewelry. How Bilbo would have laughed. Indeed he was – he had foreseen how it would all fall out, and was enjoying the joke quite privately.

There, I suppose it has become all too plain. The fact is, in spite of his after-dinner speech, he had grown suddenly very tired of them all. The Tookishness (not of course that all Tooks ever had much of this wayward quality) had quite suddenly and uncomfortably come to life again. Also another secret – after he had blowed his last fifty ducats on the party he had not got *any money or jewelry left*, except the ring, and the gold buttons on his waistcoat. He had spent it all in twenty years (even the proceeds of his beautiful . . . . which he had sold a few years back).[6]

Then how could he get married? He was not going to just then – he merely said 'I am going to get married'. I cannot quite say why. It came suddenly into his head. Also he thought it was an event that might occur in the future – if he travelled again amongst other folk, or found a more rare and more beautiful race of hobbits somewhere. Also it was a kind of explanation. Hobbits had a

First Version A LONG-EXPECTED PARTY 17

curious habit in their weddings. They kept it (always officially and very often actually) a dead secret for years who they were going to marry, even when they knew. Then they suddenly went and got married and went off without an address for a week or two (or even longer). When Bilbo had disappeared this is what at first his neighbours thought. 'He has gone and got married. Now who can it be? – no one else has disappeared, as far as we know.' Even after a year they would have been less surprised if he had come back with a wife. For a long while some folk thought he was keeping one in hiding, and quite a legend about the poor Mrs Bilbo who was too ugly to be seen grew up for a while.

So now Bilbo said before he disappeared: 'I am going to get married.' He thought that that – together with all the fuss about the house (or hole) and furniture – would keep them all busy and satisfied for a long while, so that no one would bother to hunt for him for a bit. And he was right – or nearly right. For no one ever bothered to hunt for him at all. They decided he had gone mad, and run off till he met a pool or a river or a steep fall, and there was one Baggins the less. Most of them, that is. He was deeply regretted by a few of his younger friends of course (. . . Angelica and Sar . . . . . .). But he had not said good-bye to all of them – O no. That is easily explained.

NOTES

1 The title was written in subsequently, but no doubt before the chapter was finished, since my father referred to it by this title in his letter of 19 December 1937 (p. 11).

2 After 'Burroweses' followed 'and Ogdens', but this was struck out – almost certainly at the time of writing. 'Proudfoots' was first written 'Proudfeet', as earlier in the chapter, but as the next sentence shows it was changed in the act of writing.

3 The reference is to the conclusion of *The Hobbit*, when Gandalf and Balin called at Bag End 'some years afterwards'.

4 At this point a present to Inigo Baggins of a case of hairbrushes was mentioned, but struck out, evidently at the time of writing, since the present to another Inigo (Grubb-Took) immediately follows.

5 Various changes were made to the names and other details in this passage, not all of which were taken up in the third version (the second ends before this point). Mungo Took's gift (an umbrella) was specified; and Caramella Took was changed from niece to cousin. Gorboduc Grubb became Orlando Grubb. Pencilled proposals for the name of Mrs Sackville-Baggins, replacing Amalda, are Lonicera

18   THE RETURN OF THE SHADOW

(Honeysuckle) and Griselda, and her husband Sago (named in the next paragraph of the text) became Cosmo.

6   Cf. the end of *The Hobbit*: 'His gold and silver was mostly [*afterwards changed to* largely] spent in presents, both useful and extravagant'. The illegible word here might possibly be *arms*, but it does not look like it, and cf. the same passage in *The Hobbit*: 'His coat of mail was arranged on a stand in the hall (until he lent it to a Museum).'

★

Writing of this draft in his *Biography*, Humphrey Carpenter says (p. 185):

The reason for his disappearance, as given in this first draft, is that Bilbo 'had not got any money or jewels left' and was going off in search of more dragon-gold. At this point the first version of the opening chapter breaks off, unfinished.

But it may be argued that it was in fact finished: for the next completed draft of the chapter (the third – the second seems certainly unfinished, and breaks off at a much earlier point) ends only a very little further on in the narrative (p. 34), and shortly before the end has:

But not all of them had said good-bye to him. That is easily explained, and soon will be.

And the explanation is not given, but reserved for the next chapter. Nor is it made so explicit in the first draft that Bilbo was 'going off in search of more dragon-gold'. That lack of money was a reason for leaving his home is certainly the case, but a sudden Tookish disgust with hobbit dulness and conventionality is also emphasized; and in fact there is not so much as a hint of what Bilbo was planning to do. It may well be that on 19 December 1937 my father had no idea. The rapidly-written conclusion of the text strongly suggests uncertain direction (and indeed he had said earlier in the chapter that the story was going to be about one of Bilbo's descendants).

But while there is no sign of Gandalf, most of the essentials and many of the details of the actual party as it is described in *The Fellowship of the Ring* (FR) emerge right at the beginning, and even some phrases remained. The Chubbs (or Chubbses, p. 13), the Boffinses, and the Proudfoots now appear – the families named Burrowes (Burrows in FR) and Grubb had been mentioned at the end of *The Hobbit*, in the names of the auctioneers at the sale of Bag End; and the hobbits' land is for the first time called 'the shire' (see, however, p. 31). But the first names of the hobbits were only at the beginning of their protean variations – such names as Sago and Semolina would be rejected as unsuitable, others (Amalda, Inigo, Obo) would have no place in the final genealogies, and yet others (Mungo, Gorboduc) would be given to different persons; only the vain Angelica Baggins survived.

★

Second Version   A LONG-EXPECTED PARTY   19

(ii)

The Second Version

The next manuscript, while closely based on the first, introduced much new material – most notably the arrival of Gandalf, and the fireworks. This version breaks off at the words 'Morning went on' (FR p. 45).

The manuscript was much emended, and it is very difficult to distinguish those changes made at the time of composition from those made subsequently: in any case the third version no doubt followed hard upon the second, superseding it before it was completed. I give this second text also in full, so far as it goes, but in this case I include virtually all the emendations made to it (in some cases the original reading is given in the notes which follow the text on p. 25).

Chapter 1

A long-expected party

When Bilbo, son of Bungo, of the respectable family of Baggins prepared to celebrate his seventy-first[1] birthday there was some little talk in the neighbourhood, and people polished up their memories.[2] Bilbo had once had some brief notoriety among the hobbits of Hobbiton and Bywater – he had disappeared after breakfast one April 30th and had not reappeared until lunch-time on June 22nd in the following year. A very odd proceeding, and one for which he had never accounted satisfactorily. He wrote a book about it, of course: but even those who had read it never took that seriously. It is no good talking to hobbits about dragons: they either disbelieve you, or feel uncomfortable; and in either case tend to avoid you afterwards. Mr Baggins, however, had soon returned to more or less normal ways; and though the shaken confidence of the countryside was never quite restored, in time the hobbits agreed to pardon the past, and Bilbo was on calling-terms again with all his relatives and neighbours, except of course the Sackville-Bagginses. For one thing Bilbo seemed by some unexplained method to have become more than comfortably off, in fact positively wealthy. Indeed it was the magnificence of the preparations for his birthday-party far more than his brief and distant fame that caused the talk. After all that other odd business had happened some twenty years ago and was all but forgotten; the party was going to happen that very month of September. The weather was fine, and there was talk of a display of fireworks such as had not been seen since the days of Old Took.

20   THE RETURN OF THE SHADOW

Time drew nearer. Odd-looking carts with odd-looking packages began to toil up the Hill to Bag-end (the residence of Mr Bilbo
Baggins). They arrived by night, and startled folk peered out of
their doors to gape at them. Some were driven by outlandish folk
singing strange songs, elves, or heavily hooded dwarves. There
was one huge creaking wain with great lumbering tow-haired Men
on it that caused quite a commotion. It bore a large B under a
crown.[3] It could not get across the bridge by the mill, and the Men
carried the goods on their backs up the hill – stumping on the
hobbit road like elephants. All the beer at the inn vanished as if
down a drain when they came downhill again. Later in the week a
cart came trotting in in broad daylight. An old man was driving it
all alone. He wore a tall pointed blue hat and a long grey cloak.
Hobbit boys and girls ran after the cart all the way up the hill. It
had a cargo of fireworks, that they could see when it began to
unload: great bundles of them, labelled with a red G.

'G for grand,' they shouted; and that was as good a guess as they
could make at its meaning. Not many of their elders guessed
better: hobbits have rather short memories as a rule. As for the
little old man,[4] he vanished inside Bilbo's front door and never
reappeared.

There might have been some grumbling about 'dealing locally';
but suddenly orders began to pour out from Bag-end, and into
every shop in the neighbourhood (even widely measured). Then
people stopped being merely curious, and became enthusiastic.
They began to tick off the days on the calendar till Bilbo's
birthday, and they began to watch for the postman, hoping for
invitations.

Then the invitations began pouring out, and the post-office
of Hobbiton was blocked, and Bywater post-office was snowed
under, and voluntary postmen were called for. There was a
constant stream of them going up The Hill to Bag-end carrying
letters containing hundreds of polite variations on 'thank-you, I
shall certainly come.' During all this time, for days and days,
indeed since September [10th >] 8th, Bilbo had not been seen out
or about by anyone. He either did not answer the bell, or came to
the door and cried 'Sorry – Busy!' round the edge of it. They
thought he was only writing invitation cards, but they were not
quite right.

Finally the field to the south of his front door – it was bordered
by his kitchen garden on one side and the Hill road on the other –

Second Version   A LONG-EXPECTED PARTY   21

began to be covered with tents and pavilions. The three hobbit-families of Bagshot Row just below it were immensely excited. There was one specially large pavilion, so large that the tree that stood in the field was inside it, standing growing in the middle.[5] It was hung all over with lanterns. Even more promising was the erection of a huge kitchen in a corner of the field. A draught of cooks arrived. Excitement rose to its height. Then the weather clouded over. That was on Friday, the eve of the party. Anxiety grew intense. Then Saturday September [20th >] 22nd[6] actually dawned. The sun got up, the clouds vanished, flags were unfurled, and the fun began.

Mr Baggins called it a party – but it was several rolled into one and mixed up. Practically everybody near at hand was invited to something or other – very few were forgotten (by accident), and as they turned up anyhow it did not matter. Bilbo met the guests (and additions) at the gate in person. He gave away presents to all and sundry – the latter were those that went out again by the back way and came in again by the front for a second helping. He began with the youngest and smallest, and came back again quickly to the smallest and youngest. Hobbits give presents to other people on their birthdays: not very expensive ones, of course. But it was not a bad system. Actually in Hobbiton and Bywater, since every day in the year was somebody's birthday, it meant that every hobbit got a present (and sometimes more) almost every day of his life. But they did not get tired of them. On this occasion the hobbit-fry were wildly excited – there were toys the like of which they had never seen before. As you have guessed, they came from Dale.

When they got inside the grounds the guests had songs, dances, games – and of course food and drink. There were three official meals: lunch, tea, and dinner (or supper); but lunch and tea were marked chiefly by the fact that at those times everybody was sitting down and eating at the same time. Drinking never stopped. Eating went on pretty continuously from elevenses to six o'clock, when the fireworks started.

The fireworks of course (as you at any rate have guessed) were by Gandalf, and brought by him in person, and let off by him – the main ones: there was generous distribution of squibs, crackers, sparklers, torches, dwarf-candles, elf-fountains, goblin-barkers and thunderclaps. They were of course superb. The art of Gandalf naturally got the older the better. There were rockets like a flight of scintillating birds singing with sweet voices; there were green trees with trunks of twisted smoke: their leaves opened like a

22   THE RETURN OF THE SHADOW

whole spring unfolding in a few minutes, and their shining branches dropped glowing flowers down upon the astonished hobbits – only to disappear in a sweet scent before they touched head hat or bonnet. There were fountains of butterflies that flew into the trees; there were pillars of coloured fires that turned into hovering eagles, or sailing ships, or a flight of swans; there were red thunderstorms and showers of yellow rain; there was a forest of silver spears that went suddenly up into the air with a yell like a charging army and came down into The Water with a hiss like a hundred hot snakes. And there was also one last thing in which Gandalf rather overdid it – after all, he knew a great deal about hobbits and their beliefs. The lights went out, a great smoke went up, it shaped itself like a mountain, it began to glow at the top, it burst into flames of scarlet and green, out flew a red-golden dragon (not life-size, of course, but terribly life-like): fire came out of its mouth, its eyes glared down, there was a roar and it whizzed three times round the crowd. Everyone ducked and some fell flat. The dragon passed like an express train and burst over Bywater with a deafening explosion.

'That means it is dinner-time,' said Gandalf. A fortunate re-mark, for the pain and alarm vanished like magic. Now really we must hurry on, for all this is not as important as it seemed. There was a supper for all the guests. But there was also a very special dinner-party in the great pavilion with the tree. To that party invitations had been limited to twelve dozen, or one gross (in addition to Gandalf and the host), made up of all the chief hobbits, and their elder children, to whom Bilbo was related or with whom he was connected, or by whom he had been well-treated at any time, or for whom he felt some special affection. Nearly all the living Baggins[es] had been invited; a quantity of Tooks (his relations on his mother's side); a number of Grubbs (connections of his grandfather's), dozens of Brandybucks (connections of his grandmother's), and various Chubbs and Burrowses and Boffins and Proudfeet – some of whom were not connected with Bilbo at all, within the memory of the local historians; some even lived right on the other side of the Shire; but they were all, of course, hobbits. Even the Sackville-Bagginses, his first cousins on his father's side, were not omitted. There had been some coolness between them and Mr Baggins, as you may remember, dating from some 20 years back. But so splendid was the invitation card, written all in gold, that they felt it was impossible to refuse. Besides, their cousin had been specializing in

Second Version   A LONG-EXPECTED PARTY   23

food for a good many years, and his tables had a high reputation even in that time and country, when food was still all that it ought to be, and abundant enough for all folk to practise both discrimination and satisfaction.

All the 144 special guests expected a pleasant feast; though they rather dreaded the after-dinner speech of their host. He was liable to drag in bits of what he called 'poetry'; and sometimes, after a glass or two, would allude to the absurd adventures he said he had had long ago – during his ridiculous vanishment. Not one of the 144 were disappointed: they had a *very* pleasant feast, indeed an engrossing entertainment: rich, abundant, varied, and prolonged. The purchase of provisions fell almost to zero throughout the district during the ensuing week; but as Mr Baggins' catering had depleted most of the stores, cellars, and warehouses for miles around, that did not matter much.

After the feast (more or less) came the Speech. Most of the assembled hobbits were now in a tolerant mood – at that delicious stage which they called filling up the 'corners' (with sips of their favourite drinks and nips of their favourite sweetmeats): their former fears were forgotten. They were prepared to listen to anything, and to cheer at every full stop. But they were not prepared to be startled. Yet startled they certainly were: indeed, completely blowed: some even got indigestion.

My dear people, began Mr Baggins, rising in his place.

'Hear, hear, hear!' they answered in chorus, and seemed reluctant to follow their own advice. Meanwhile Bilbo left his place and went and stood on a chair under the illuminated tree. The lantern light fell upon his beaming face; the gold buttons shone on his flowered waistcoat. They could all see him. One hand was in his pocket. He raised the other.

My dear Bagginses! he began again. *And my dear Tooks and Brandybucks and Grubbs and Chubbs and Burroweses and Bracegirdles and Boffinses and Proudfoots.*

'Proud*feet*!' shouted an elderly hobbit from the back. His name, of course, was Proudfoot, and merited: his feet were large, exceptionally furry, and both were on the table.

Also my good Sackville-Bagginses that I welcome back at last to Bag-end. Today is my seventy-first birthday!

'Hurray, hurray! Many Happy Returns!' they shouted, and they hammered joyously on the tables. Bilbo was doing splendidly. That was the sort of stuff they liked: short, obvious, uncontroversial.

I hope you are all enjoying yourselves as much as I am. Deafening cheers. Cries of Yes (and No). Noises of horns and trumpets, pipes and flutes, and other musical instruments. There were many junior hobbits present, for hobbits were easygoing with their children in the matter of sitting up late – especially if there was a chance of getting them an extra meal free (bringing up young hobbits took a great deal of provender). Hundreds of musical crackers had been pulled. Most of them bore the mark *Dale* on them somewhere or other, inside or out. What that meant only Bilbo and a few of his close friends knew (and you of course); but they were very marvellous crackers. They contained instruments small but of perfect make and enchanting tone. Indeed in one corner some of the younger Tooks and Brandybucks, supposing Bilbo to have finished his speech (having said all that was needed), now got up an impromptu orchestra, and began a merry dance tune. Young Prospero Brandybuck[7] and Melba Took got on a table and started to dance the flip-flap, a pretty thing if rather vigorous. But Bilbo had *not* finished.

Seizing a horn from one of the children he blew three very loud notes. The noise subsided. *I shall not keep you long,* he cried. Cheering broke out again. *BUT I have called you all together for a Purpose.*

Something in his voice made a few of the Tooks prick up their ears. *Indeed for three Purposes. First of all, to tell you that I am immensely fond of you all; and that seventy-one years is too short a time to live among such excellent and admirable hobbits.*

Tremendous outburst of approval.

I don't know half of you half as well as I would like, and less than half of you half as well as you deserve.

No cheers this time: it was a bit too difficult. There was some scattered clapping; but not all of them had yet had time to work it out and see if it came to a compliment in the end.

Secondly, to celebrate my birthday, and the twentieth anniversary of my return. No cheers; there was some uncomfortable rustling.

Lastly, to make an Announcement. He said this so loudly and suddenly that everyone sat up who could. *I regret to announce that – though, as I have said, 71 years is far too short a time among you – this is the END. I am going. I am leaving after dinner. Goodbye!*

He stepped down. One hundred and forty-four flabbergasted hobbits sat back speechless. Mr Proudfoot removed his feet from

Second Version   A LONG-EXPECTED PARTY   25

the table. Mrs Proudfoot swallowed a large chocolate and choked. Then there was complete silence for quite forty winks, until suddenly every Baggins, Took, Brandybuck, Chubb, Grubb, Burrowes, Bracegirdle, Boffin and Proudfoot began to talk at once.

'The hobbit's mad. Always said so. Bad taste in jokes. Trying to pull the fur off our toes (a hobbit idiom). Spoiling a good dinner. Where's my handkerchief. Won't drink his health now. Shall drink my own. Where's that bottle. Is he going to get married? Not to anyone here tonight. Who would take him? Why good-bye? Where is there to *go* to? What is he leaving?' And so on. At last old Rory Brandybuck[8] (well-filled but still pretty bright) was heard to shout: 'Where is he now, anyway? Where's Bilbo?'

There was not a sign of their host anywhere.

As a matter of fact Bilbo Baggins had disappeared silently and unnoticed in the midst of all the talk. While he was speaking he had already been fingering a small ring[9] in his trouser-pocket. As he stepped down he had slipped it on – and he was never seen in Hobbiton again.

When the carriages came for the guests there was no one to say good-bye to. The carriages rolled away, one after another, filled with full but oddly unsatisfied hobbits. Gardeners came (by arrangement) and cleared away in wheelbarrows those that had inadvertently remained behind, asleep or immoveable. Night settled down and passed. The sun rose. The hobbits rose rather later. Morning went on.

NOTES

1 *seventy-first* emended from *seventieth*; but *seventy-first* in the text of Bilbo's farewell speech as first written.

2 At this point my father wrote at first:

> Twice before this he had been a matter of local news: a rare achievement for a Baggins. The first time was when he was left an orphan, when barely forty years old, by the untimely death of his father and mother (in a boating accident). The second time was more remarkable.

Such a fate in store for Bungo Baggins and his wife seems most improbable in the light of the words of the first chapter of *The Hobbit*:

> Not that Belladonna Took ever had any adventures after she became Mrs Bungo Baggins. Bungo, that was Bilbo's father, built the most luxurious hobbit-hole for her . . . and there they remained to the end of their days.

26   THE RETURN OF THE SHADOW

They seem an unlikely couple to have gone 'fooling about with boats', in Gaffer Gamgee's phrase, and his recognition of this was no doubt the reason why my father immediately struck the passage out; but the boating accident was not forgotten, and it became the fate of (Rollo Bolger >) Drogo Baggins and his Brandybuck wife, Primula, for whom it was a less improbable end (see p. 37).

3   At this stage only 20 years separated Bilbo's adventure in *The Hobbit* and his farewell party, and my father clearly intended the B on the waggon to stand for Bard, King of Dale. Later, when the years had been greatly lengthened out, it would be Bain son of Bard who ruled in Dale at this time.

4   In the original *Hobbit* Gandalf at his first appearance was described as 'a little old man', but afterwards the word 'little' was removed. See p. 315.

5   The single tree in the field below Bag End was already in the illustration of Hobbiton that appeared as the frontispiece to *The Hobbit*, as also were Bilbo's kitchen-garden and the hobbit-holes of Bagshot Row (though that name first appears here).

6   September 20th was the date of Bilbo's birthday in the first version (p. 16).

7   Prospero Brandybuck was first written Orlando Brandybuck, the second bearer of the name: in the list of Bilbo's gifts in the first version (p. 17 note 5) Gorboduc Grubb had been changed to Orlando Grubb.

8   A very similar passage, indicating the outraged comments of the guests, was added to the manuscript of the original draft at this point, but it was Inigo Grubb-Took who shouted 'Where is he now, anyway?' It was the greedy Inigo Grubb-Took who received the dinner-service (p. 15), and in this respect he survived into the third version of the chapter.

9   *a small ring*: emended from *his famous ring*.

★

I have given this text in full, since taken together with the first it provides a basis of reference in describing those that follow, from which only extracts are given; but it will be seen that the Party – the preparations for it, the fireworks, the feast – had already reached the form it retains in FR (pp. 34–9), save in a few and quite minor features of the narrative (and here and there in tone). This is the more striking when we realize that at this stage my father still had very little idea of where he was going: it was a beginning without a destination (but see pp. 42–3).

Certain changes made to the manuscript towards its end have not been taken up in the text given above. In Bilbo's speech, his words 'Secondly, to celebrate my birthday, and the twentieth anniversary of my return'

Second Version   A LONG-EXPECTED PARTY   27

and the comment 'No cheers; there was some uncomfortable rustling' were removed, and the following expanded passage substituted:

> *Secondly, to celebrate OUR birthdays: mine and my honourable and gallant father's.* Uncomfortable and apprehensive silence. *I am only half the man that he is: I am 72, he is 144. Your numbers are chosen to do honour to each of his honourable years.* This was really dreadful – a regular braintwister, and some of them felt insulted, like leap-days shoved in to fill up a calendar.

This change gives every appearance of belonging closely with the writing of the manuscript: it is clearly written in ink, and seems distinct from various scattered scribbles in pencil. But the appearance is misleading. Why should Bilbo thus refer to old Bungo Baggins, underground these many years? Bungo was pure Baggins, 'solid and comfortable' (as he is described in *The Hobbit*), and surely died solidly in his bed at Bag End. To call him 'gallant' seems odd, and for Bilbo to say 'I am half the man that he *is*' and 'he *is* 144' rather tastelessly whimsical.

The explanation is in fact simple: it was not Bilbo who said it, but his son, Bingo Baggins, who enters in the third version of 'A Long-expected Party'. The textual point would not be worth mentioning here were it not so striking an example of my father's way of using one manuscript as the matrix of the next version, but not correcting it coherently throughout: so in this case, he made no structural alterations to the earlier part of the story, but pencilled in the name 'Bingo' against 'Bilbo' on the last pages of the manuscript, and (to the severe initial confusion of the editor) carefully rewrote a passage of Bilbo's speech to make it seem that Bilbo had taken leave of his senses. It is clear, I think, that it was the sudden emergence of this radical new idea that caused him to abandon this version.

Other hasty changes altered 'seventy-first' to 'seventy-second' and '71' to '72' at each occurrence, and these belong also with the new story that was emerging. In this text, Bilbo's age in the opening sentence was 70, as in the first version, but it was changed to 71 in the course of the chapter (note 1 above). The number of guests at the dinner-party was already 144 in the text as first written, but nothing is made of this figure; that it was chosen for a particular reason only appears from the expanded passage of the speech given above: 'I am 72, he is 144. Your numbers are chosen to do honour to each of his honourable years.' It seems clear that the change of 71 to 72 was made because 72 is half of 144. The number of guests came first, when the story was still told of Bilbo, and at first had no significance beyond its being a dozen dozens, a gross.

A few other points may be noticed. Gandalf was present at the dinner-party; Gaffer Gamgee had not yet emerged, but 'old Rory Brandybuck' makes his appearance (in place of Inigo Grubb-Took, note 8 above); and Bilbo does not disappear with a blinding flash. At each stage the number of hobbit clans named is increased: so here the Brandybucks emerge, and

28 THE RETURN OF THE SHADOW

the Bracegirdles were pencilled in, to appear in the third version as written.

★

(iii)

The Third Version

The third draft of 'A Long-expected Party' is complete, and is a good clear manuscript with relatively little later correction. In this section numbered notes again appear at the end (p. 34).

Discussion of the change made to Bilbo's speech in the second version has already indicated the central new feature of the third: the story is now told *not of Bilbo, but of his son*. On this substitution Humphrey Carpenter remarked (*Biography* p. 185):

> Tolkien had as yet no clear idea of what the new story was going to be about. At the end of *The Hobbit* he had stated that Bilbo 'remained very happy to the end of his days, and those were extraordinarily long.' So how could the hobbit have any new adventures worth the name without this being contradicted? And had he not explored most of the possibilities in Bilbo's character? He decided to introduce a new hobbit, Bilbo's son – and to give him the name of a family of toy koala bears owned by his children, 'The Bingos'.[1] So he crossed out 'Bilbo' in the first draft and above it wrote 'Bingo'.[2]

This explanation is plausible. In the first draft, however, my father wrote that the story of the birthday party 'merely serves to explain that Bilbo Baggins got married and had many children, *because I am going to tell you a story about one of his descendants*' (in the second version we are given no indication at all of what was going to happen after the party – though there is possibly a suggestion of something similar in the words (p. 22) 'Now really we must hurry on, for all this is not as important as it seemed'). On the other hand, there are explicit statements in early notes (p. 41) that for a time it was indeed going to be Bilbo who had the new 'adventure'.

The first part of the third version is almost wholly different from the two preceding, and I give it here in full, with a few early changes incorporated.

A long-expected party

When Bingo, son of Bilbo, of the well-known Baggins family, prepared to celebrate his [fifty-fifth >] seventy-second[3] birthday there was some talk in the neighbourhood, and people polished up their memories. The Bagginses were fairly numerous in those

Third Version   A LONG-EXPECTED PARTY   29

parts, and generally respected; but Bingo belonged to a branch of the family that was a bit peculiar, and there were some odd stories about them. Bingo's father, as some still remembered, had once made quite a stir in Hobbiton and Bywater – he had disappeared one April 30th after breakfast, and had not reappeared until lunch-time on June 22nd in the following year. A very odd proceeding, and one for which he had never accounted satisfactorily. He wrote a book about it, of course; but even those who had read it never took that seriously. It is no good telling hobbits about dragons: they either disbelieve you, or feel uncomfortable; and in either case tend to avoid you afterwards.

Bilbo Baggins, it is true, had soon returned to normal ways (more or less), and though his reputation was never quite restored, he became an accepted figure in the neighbourhood. He was never perhaps again regarded as a 'safe hobbit', but he was undoubtedly a 'warm' one. In some mysterious way he appeared to have become more than comfortably off, in fact positively wealthy; so naturally, he was on visiting terms with all his neighbours and relatives (except, of course, the Sackville-Bagginses). He did two more things that caused tongues to wag: he got married when seventy-one (a little but not too late for a hobbit), choosing a bride from the other side of the Shire, and giving a wedding-feast of memorable splendour; he disappeared (together with his wife) shortly before his hundred-and-eleventh birthday, and was never seen again. The folk of Hobbiton and Bywater were cheated of a funeral (not that they had expected his for many a year yet), so they had a good deal to say. His residence, his wealth, his position (and the dubious regard of the neighbourhood) were inherited by his son Bingo, just before his own birthday (which happened to be the same as his father's). Bingo was, of course, a mere youngster of 39, who had hardly cut his wisdom-teeth; but he at once began to carry on his father's reputation for oddity: he never went into mourning for his parents, and said he did not think they were dead. To the obvious question: 'Where are they then?' he merely winked. He lived alone, and was often away from home. He went about a lot with the least well-behaved members of the Took family (his grandmother's people and his father's friends), and he was also fond of some of the Brandybucks. They were his mother's relatives. She was Primula Brandybuck[4] of the Brandybucks of Buckland, across Brandywine River on the other side of the Shire and on the edge of the Old Forest – a dubious region.[5] Folk in Hobbiton did not know

30   THE RETURN OF THE SHADOW

much about it, or about the Brandybucks either; though some had heard it said that they were rich, and would have been richer, but for a certain 'recklessness' – generosity, that is, if any came your way.

Anyway, Bingo had lived at Bag-end Underhill now for some [16 >] 33 years[6] without giving any scandal. His parties were sometimes a bit noisy, perhaps, but hobbits don't mind that kind of noise now and again. He spent his money freely and mostly locally. Now the neighbourhood understood that he was planning something quite unusual in the way of parties. Naturally their memories awoke and their tongues wagged, and Bingo's wealth was again guessed and re-calculated at every fireside. Indeed the magnificence of the preparations quite overshadowed the tales of the old folk about his father's vanishments.

'After all,' as old Gaffer Gamgee of Bagshot Row[7] remarked, 'them goings-on are old affairs and over; this here party is going to happen this very month as is.' It was early September and as fine as you could wish. Somebody started a rumour about fireworks. Very soon it was accepted that there were going to be fireworks such as had not been seen for over a century, not since the Old Took died.

It is interesting to see the figures 111 and 33 emerging, though afterwards they would be differently achieved: here, Bilbo was 111 when he left the Shire, and Bingo lived on at Bag End for 33 years before his farewell party; afterwards, 111 was Bilbo's age at the time of the party – when it had become his party again – and 33 Bingo's (Frodo's) age at the same time.

In this passage we also see the emergence of a very important piece of topography and toponymy: Buckland, the Brandywine, and the Old Forest. For the names first written here see note 5.

For the account in this version of the preparations for the Party, the Party itself, and its immediate aftermath, my father followed the emended second version (pp. 19–25) extremely closely, adding a detail here and there, but for the most part doing little more than copy it out (and of course changing 'Bilbo' to 'Bingo' where necessary). I give here a list of interesting – though mostly extremely minor – shifts in the new narrative. The page references are to those of the second version.

(20–1)   'B under a crown' on the waggon driven by Men becomes 'B painted in yellow', and 'B' was emended on the text to 'D' (i.e. 'Dale').

When the Men came down the Hill again, it is added that 'the elves and dwarves did not return'; and 'the draught of cooks'

Third Version   A LONG-EXPECTED PARTY   31

who arrived were 'to supplement the elves and dwarves (who seemed to be staying at Bag-end and doing a lot of mysterious work)'.

The notice refusing admittance on the door of Bag End now appears, and 'a special entrance was cut in the bank leading to the road; wide steps and a large white gate were built' (as in FR). Gaffer Gamgee comes in again: 'he stopped even pretending to garden.'

The day of the party was still a Saturday (September 22nd).

Many of the toys ('some obviously magical') that had come from Dale were 'genuinely dwarf-made'.

(22)   It is Bingo, not Gandalf, who at the end of the fireworks says 'That is the signal for supper!'; and though it was said at first, as in the second version, that the total of 144 guests did not include the host and Gandalf, this was struck out (see p. 106, note 12).

A new Hobbit family-name enters in the list of guests: 'and various Burroweses, Slocums, Bracegirdles, Boffinses and Proudfoots'; but 'Slocums' was then changed to 'Hornblowers', which was also added in to the text at subsequent points in the chapter. The Bolgers appear in pencilled additions, and are present from the start in the fourth version. In his letter to the *Observer* newspaper published on 20 February 1938 (*Letters* no. 25) my father said: 'The full list of their wealthier families is: Baggins, Boffin, Bolger, Bracegirdle, Brandybuck, Burrowes, Chubb, Grubb, Hornblower, Proudfoot, Sackville, and Took.' – The Grubbs, connexions of Bingo's grandfather, became by a pencilled change connexions of his grandmother; and the Chubbs, in a reverse change, were first said to be connexions of his grandmother and then of his grandfather.

Where in the first and second versions it is said that some of the hobbits at the party came from 'the other side of the shire', it is now said that some of them 'did not even live in that county', changed to 'in that Shire'; and 'in that Shire' was retained in the fourth version. The use of 'that' rather than 'the' suggests that the later use (cf. the Prologue to LR, p. 14: 'The Hobbits named it the Shire, as the region of the authority of their Thain') was only in the process of emergence.

The coldness between the Bagginses of Bag End and the Sackville-Bagginses had now lasted, not 20 years as in the first two versions, but 'some seventy-five years and more': this figure depends on 111 (Bilbo's age when he finally disappeared) less 51 (he was 'about fifty years old or so' at the time of his great adventure, according to *The Hobbit*), plus the 16 years

32   THE RETURN OF THE SHADOW

of Bingo's solitary residence at Bag End. 'Seventy-five' was emended to 'ninety' (a round figure), which belongs with the change of 16 to 33 (p. 30).

(23)   Bingo was liable to allude to 'the absurd adventures of his "gallant and famous" father'.

(24)   The two young hobbits who got on the table and danced are still Prospero Brandybuck and Melba Took, but Melba was changed in pencil first to Arabella and then to Amanda.

Bingo now said, as did Bilbo in FR (p. 38), '*I like* less than half of you half as well as you deserve.'

Bingo's 'second purpose' is expressed in exactly the words written into the second version (see p. 27): 'to celebrate OUR birthdays: mine and my honourable and gallant father's. I am only half the man he is: I am 72, and he is 144', &c.

Bingo's last words, 'I am leaving after dinner' were corrected on the manuscript to 'I am leaving now.'

(25)   The collected comments after Bingo's concluding remarks now begin: 'The hobbit's mad. Always said so. And his father. He's been dead 33 years, I know. 144, all rubbish.' And Rory Brandybuck shouts: 'Where is Bilbo – confound it, Bingo I mean. Where is he?'

After 'he was never seen in Hobbiton again' is added: 'The ring was his father's parting gift.'

From the point where the second version ends at the words 'Morning went on' the third goes back to the original draft (p. 15) and follows it closely until near the end, using pretty well the same phrases, and largely retaining the original list (as emended, p. 17 note 5) of names and labels for the recipients of presents from Bag End – these being now, of course, presents from Bilbo's son Bingo.

Semolina Baggins is called 'an aunt, or first cousin once removed';

Caramella Took (changed later to *Bolger*) 'had been favoured among [Bingo's] junior and remoter cousins';

Obo Took-Took who received a feather-bed remained as a great-uncle, but *Obo* was emended on the manuscript to *Rollo*;

Gorboduc (> Orlando) Grubb of the first draft, recipient of a gold fountain-pen, becomes *Orlando Burrowes*;

Mungo Took, Inigo Grubb-Took, and *Angelica Baggins* remain; and two new beneficiaries are named before Mrs Sackville-Baggins at the end of the list:

For the collection of Hugo Bracegirdle, from a contributor: on an (empty) bookcase. Hugo was a great borrower of books, but a small returner.

Third Version   A LONG-EXPECTED PARTY   33

For Cosimo Chubb, treat it as your own, Bingo: on the barometer. Cosimo used to bang it with a large fat finger whenever he came to call. He was afraid of getting wet, and wore a scarf and macintosh all the year round.

For Grimalda [> *Lobelia*] *Sackville-Baggins, as a present:* on a case of silver spoons. It was believed by Bilbo Baggins that she had acquired a good many of his spoons while he was away – ninety odd years before. Bingo inherited the belief, and Grimalda [> Lobelia] knew it.

It is also mentioned that 'Bingo had very carefully disposed of his treasures: books, pictures, and a collection of toys. For his wines he found a very good (if temporary) home. Most of them went to Marmaduke Brandybuck' (predecessor of Meriadoc). The original draft is closely followed in the absence of any money or jewelry, and in the legal notice disposing of Bag End to the Sackville-Bagginses (but Bilbo's cousin now becomes Otho, and their occupancy is to start from September 24th) – 'and they got Bag-end after all, though they had to wait 93 years longer for it than they had once expected': 111 less 51 plus 33, see pp. 31–2.[8] Sancho Proudfoot appears, excavating in the pantry where he thought there was an echo (as in FR, p. 48); physically attacked by Otho Sackville-Baggins, he was only finally ejected by the lawyers, first called 'Grubbs and Burrowes', as in *The Hobbit*, then changed to 'Messrs. Iago Grubb and Folco Burrowes (Bingo's lawyers)'.

The conclusion of the third version I give in full.

The fact is Bingo's money had become a legend, and everybody was puzzled and anxious – though still hopeful. How he would have laughed. Indeed he was as near laughing as he dared at that very moment, for he was inside a large cupboard outside the dining-room door, and heard most of the racket. He was inside, of course, not for concealment, but to avoid being bumped into, being totally invisible. He had to laugh rather privately and silently, but all the same he was enjoying his joke: it was turning out so much like his expectation.

I suppose it is now becoming all too plain to everyone but the anxious and grabsome hobbits. The fact is that (in spite of certain things in his after-dinner speech) Bingo had grown suddenly tired of them all. A violent fit of Tookishness had come over him – not of course that all Tooks had much of this wayward quality, their mothers being Chubbs, Hornblowers, Bolgers, Bracegirdles, Grubbs and what not; but Tooks were on the whole the most jocular and unexpected of Hobbits. Also I can tell you something more, in case you have not guessed: Bingo had no money or

34 THE RETURN OF THE SHADOW

jewelry left! Practically none, that is. Nothing worth digging up a nice hobbit-hole for. Money went a prodigious way in those days, and one could get quite a lot of things without it; but he had blown his last 500 ducats on the birthday party. That was Brandybucksome of him. After that he had nothing left but the buttons on his waistcoat, a small bag-purse of silver, and his ring. In the course of 33 years he had contrived to spend all the rest – what was left, that is, by his father, who had done a bit of spending in fifty years[9] (and had required some travelling-expenses).

Well, there it is. All things come to an end. Evening came on. Bag-end was left empty and gloomy. People went away – haggling and arguing, most of them. You could hear their voices coming up the Hill in the dusk. Very few gave a thought to Bingo. They decided he had gone mad, and run off, and that was one Baggins the less, and that was that. They were annoyed about the legendary money, of course, but meanwhile there was tea waiting for them. There were some, of course, who regretted his sudden disappearance – a few of his younger friends were really distressed. But not all of them had said good-bye to him. That is easily explained, and soon will be.

Bingo stepped out of the cupboard. It was getting dim. His watch said six. The door was open, as he had kept the key in his pocket. He went out, locked the door (leaving the key), and looked at the sky. Stars were coming out.

'It is going to be a fine night,' he said. 'What a lark! Well, I must not keep them waiting. Now we're off. Goodbye!' He trotted down the garden, jumped the fence, and took to the fields, and passed like an invisible rustle in the grasses.

NOTES

1   I find it difficult to believe this, yet if it is not so the coincidence is strange. If Bingo Baggins did get his name from this source, I can only suppose that the demonic character (composed of monomaniac religious despotism and a lust for destruction through high explosive) of the chief Bingo (not to mention that of his appalling wife), by which my sister and I now remember them, developed somewhat later.

2   The substitution was not made in the first draft, but in pencilled corrections to the end of the second version (p. 27).

3   The change of 'fifty-fifth' to 'seventy-second' was made at the same time as the 16 years during which Bingo lived at Bag End after his

Third Version   A LONG-EXPECTED PARTY   35

parents' departure were changed to 33 (note 6). These changes were made before the chapter was finished, since later in it, in Bingo's farewell speech, the revised figures are present from the first writing. When at the outset he wrote 'fifty-fifth birthday' and '16 years' my father was presumably intending to get rid of the idea, appearing in rewriting of the second version (see p. 27), that the number of 144 guests was chosen for an inner reason, since on Bingo's 55th birthday his father Bilbo would have been 127 (having left the Shire 16 years before at the age of 111, when Bingo was 39).

4   *Primula* was first written *Amalda*. In the first version (p. 16) Amalda was the name of Mrs Sackville-Baggins. In the fourth version of 'A long-expected party', when Bilbo had returned to his bachelor state, Primula Brandybuck, no longer his wife, remained Bingo's mother.

5   My father first wrote here: 'the Brandybucks of Wood Eaton on the other side of the shire, on the edge of Buckwood – a dubious region.' He first changed (certainly at the time of writing) the name of the Brandybuck stronghold from Wood Eaton (a village in the Cherwell valley near Oxford) to Bury Underwood (where 'Bury' is the very common English place-name element derived from Old English *byrig*, the dative of *burg* 'fortified place, town'); then he introduced the name of the river, replaced Bury Underwood by Buckland, and replaced Buckwood by the Old Forest.

6   This change was made at the same time as '55' to '72' for Bingo's years at the time of the birthday party; see note 3.

7   This is the first appearance of Gaffer Gamgee, living in Bagshot Row (first mentioned in the second version, p. 21).

8   As mentioned in note 3, the later figure of 72 for 55 as Bingo's age on this birthday, and 33 for 16 as the number of years in which he lived on alone at Bag End after Bilbo's departure, which appear as emendations in the early part of the text, are in the later part of the chapter present from the first writing.

9   One would expect 'sixty' (111 less 51): see pp. 31, 252.

Note on Hobbit-names

It will be seen that delight in the names and relations of the hobbit-families of the Shire from which the ramifying genealogies would spring was present from the start. In no respect did my father chop and change more copiously. Already we have met, apart from Bilbo and Bungo Baggins and Belladonna Took who appeared in *The Hobbit*:

Baggins: Angelica; Inigo; Semolina
Bolger: Caramella (replacing Caramella Took)
Bracegirdle: Hugo
Brandybuck: Amalda > Primula; Marmaduke; Orlando > Prospero;
   Rory

36 THE RETURN OF THE SHADOW

Burrowes: Folco; Orlando (replacing Orlando Grubb)
Chubb: Cosimo
Grubb: Gorboduc > Orlando; Iago
Grubb-Took: Inigo
Proudfoot: Sancho
Sackville-Baggins: Amalda > Lonicera or Griselda > Grimalda >
 Lobelia; Sago > Cosmo > Otho
Took: Caramella; Melba > Arabella > Amanda; Mungo
Took-Took: Obo > Rollo

★

(iv)

The Fourth Version

Two further changes, embodying an important shift, were made to the
manuscript of the third version. They were carefully made, in red ink,
but concomitant changes later in the text were not made. In the first
sentence of the chapter (p. 28) 'Bingo, son of Bilbo' was altered to 'Bingo
Bolger-Baggins'; and in the third sentence 'Bingo's father' was altered to
'Bingo's uncle (and guardian), Bilbo Baggins.'

We come now therefore to a further stage, where the 'long-expected
party' is still Bingo's, not Bilbo's, but Bingo is his nephew, not his son,
and Bilbo's marriage (as was inevitable, I think) has been rejected.

The fourth version is a typescript, made by my father. It was emended
very heavily later on, but these changes belong to the second phase of the
writing of *The Fellowship of the Ring*, and here I ignore them. The
alterations to the third version just referred to were now incorporated
into the text (which therefore now begins: 'When Bingo Bolger-Baggins
of the well-known Baggins family prepared to celebrate his seventy-
second birthday . . .'), but otherwise it proceeds as an exact copy of the
third version as far as 'he was on visiting terms with all his neighbours
and relatives (except, of course, the Sackville-Bagginses)' (p. 29). Here it
diverges.

But folk did not bother him much. He was frequently out. And if
he was in, you never knew who you would find with him: hobbits
of quite poor families, or folk from distant villages, dwarves, and
even sometimes elves.

He did two more things that caused tongues to wag. At the age
of ninety-nine he adopted his nephew – or to be accurate (Bilbo
scattered the titles nephew and niece about rather recklessly) his
first cousin once removed, Bingo Bolger, a lad of twenty-seven.
They had heard very little about him, and that not too good (they

Fourth Version   A LONG-EXPECTED PARTY   37

said). As a matter of fact Bingo was the son of Primula Brandy-buck (and Rollo Bolger, who was quite unimportant); and she was the daughter of Mirabella Took (and Gorboduc Brandybuck, who was rather important); and she was one of three remarkable daughters of the Old Took, for long the head of the hobbits who lived across The Water. And so the Tooks come in again – always a disturbing element, especially when mixed with Brandybuck. For Primula was a Brandybuck of Buckland, across the Brandywine River, on the other side of the Shire and at the edge of the Old Forest – a dubious region. Folk in Hobbiton did not know much about it, or about the Brandybucks either; though some had heard it said that they were rich, and would have been richer, if they had not been reckless. What had happened to Primula and her husband was not known for certain in Hobbiton. There was rumour of a boating accident on the Brandywine River – the sort of thing that Brandybucks would go in for. Some said that Rollo Bolger had died young of overeating; others said that it was his weight that had sunk the boat.

Anyway, Bilbo Baggins adopted Master Bolger, announced that he would make him his heir, changed his name to Bolger-Baggins, and still further offended the Sackville-Bagginses. Then shortly before his hundred-and-eleventh birthday Bilbo disappeared finally and was never seen in Hobbiton again. His relatives and neighbours lost the chance of a funeral, and they had a good deal to say. But it made no difference: Bilbo's residence, his wealth, his position (and the dubious regard of the more influential hobbits), were inherited by Bingo Bolger-Baggins.

Bingo was a mere youngster of thirty-nine and had hardly cut his wisdom-teeth; but he at once began to carry on his uncle's reputation for oddity. He refused to go into mourning, and within a week gave a birthday-party – for himself and his uncle (their birthdays happened to be on the same day). At first people were shocked, but he kept up the custom year after year, until they got used to it. He said he did not think Bilbo Baggins was dead. When they asked the obvious question: 'Where is he then?' he merely winked. He lived alone, and was often away from home. He went about a good deal with the least well-behaved members of the Took family (his grandmother's people); and he was also fond of the Brandybucks (his mother's relatives).

Anyway, Bingo Bolger-Baggins had been the master of Bag-end Underhill now for thirty-three years without doing anything outrageous. His parties were sometimes a bit noisy . . .

38 THE RETURN OF THE SHADOW

With Gorboduc Brandybuck and Mirabella Took (one of 'the three remarkable daughters of the Old Took' who had been mentioned in *The Hobbit*) the genealogy now becomes that of LR, except that Primula Brandybuck's husband (Bilbo in the third version) is Rollo Bolger, not Drogo Baggins; and the boating accident reappears (see p. 25, note 2).

From here to the end the typescript follows the third version (as emended) very closely, and there is little further to add. Bilbo becomes Bingo's 'uncle' throughout, of course; Bingo was liable to allude to 'the absurd adventures of his "gallant and famous" uncle' (see p. 32). But, with this change, Bingo's remarks in his speech on the ages of himself and his uncle and the number of guests at the party remain exactly the same, and 'The ring was his uncle's parting gift' (*ibid.*).

Small changes of wording move the text towards the final form in FR; for example, where in the third version Rory Brandybuck is described as 'well-filled but still brighter than many', it is now said of him that his 'wits neither old age, nor surprise, nor an enormous dinner, had quite clouded'. But to set out even a portion of such developments in expression between closely related versions would obviously be quite impracticable. There are however a few minor narrative shifts which I collect in the following notes, with page-references indicating where the relevant passages in earlier versions are to be found.

(30) Gaffer Gamgee had a little more to say:

'. . . A very nice well-spoken gentlehobbit is Mr Bolger-Baggins, as I've always said.' And that was perfectly true; for Bingo had always been very polite to Gaffer Gamgee, calling him Mr Gamgee, and discussing potatoes with him over the hedge.

(21, 31) The day of the party now becomes Thursday (not Saturday) 22 September (a change made to the typescript, but carefully over an erasure and clearly belonging to the time of typing).

(31) There is no further reference to Gandalf in the chapter, after the fireworks.

(24, 32) The young hobbits who danced on the table are Prospero Took and Melissa Brandybuck.

(32–3) Several names are changed among the recipients of gifts from Bag End, Caramella (Took >) Bolger becomes Caramella Chubb; the comatose Rollo Took-Took becomes Fosco Bolger (and is Bingo's uncle); Inigo Grubb-Took the glutton, who had survived from the first draft, is now Inigo Grubb; and Cosimo Chubb the barometer-tapper becomes Cosimo Hornblower.

(33) It is now added that 'The poorer hobbits did very well, especially old Gaffer Gamgee, who got about half a ton of potatoes'; that Bingo had a collection of *magical* toys; and that he and his friends drank

Fourth Version A LONG-EXPECTED PARTY 39

nearly all the wine, the remainder still going to Marmaduke Brandy-buck.

(16, 33) The legal notice in the hall at Bag End is extended, and followed by a new passage:

> *Bingo Bolger-Baggins Esqre. departing hereby devises delivers and makes over by free gift the desirable property and messuage or dwelling-hole known as Bag-end Underhill with all lands thereto belonging and annexed to Otho Sackville-Baggins Esqre. and his wife Lobelia for them jointly to have hold possess occupy let on lease or otherwise dispose of at their pleasure as from September the twenty fourth in the seventy second year of the aforesaid Bingo Bolger-Baggins and the one hundred and forty fourth year of Bilbo Baggins who as former rightful owners hereby relinquish all claims to the abovesaid property as from the date aforesaid.*

The notice was signed *Bingo Bolger-Baggins for self and uncle*. Bingo was not a lawyer, and he merely put things that way to please Otho Sackville-Baggins, who was a lawyer. Otho certainly was pleased, but whether by the language or the property is difficult to say. Anyway, as soon as he had read the notice he shouted: 'Ours at last!' So I suppose it was all right, at least according to the legal notions of hobbits. And that is how the Sackville-Bagginses got Bag-end in the end, though they had to wait ninety-three years longer for it than they had once expected.

(33) The lawyers who ejected Sancho Proudfoot do not appear.

An addition is made to the passage describing the character of the Tooks: 'and since they had inherited both enormous wealth and no little courage from the Old Took, they carried things off with a pretty high hand at times.'

(34) The reference to Bilbo's having 'done a bit of spending in fifty years' was changed; the text now reads: '– what was left him by his Uncle, that is; for Bilbo had done a bit of spending in his time.'

'A few were distressed at his sudden disappearance; one or two were not distressed, because they were in the know – but they were not at Bag-end.'

Thus it is never explained why Bingo (or Bilbo in the first version), for whom money was now a severe problem (and one of the reasons for his departure), simply handed over 'the desirable property known as Bag-end' to the Sackville-Bagginses 'by free gift'.

There were further twists still to come in this amazingly sinuous evolution before the final structure was reached, but this was how the opening chapter stood for some time, and Bingo Bolger-Baggins, 'nephew' or more properly first cousin once removed of Bilbo Baggins,

40　　　　THE RETURN OF THE SHADOW

is present throughout the original form of Book I of *The Fellowship of the Ring*. I set out briefly here the major shifts and stages encountered thus far.

A Long-expected party

Version I　　Bilbo gives the party, aged 70. ('I am going to tell you a story about one of his descendants')

Version II　　Bilbo gives the party, aged 71.

Version III　　Bilbo married, and disappeared from Hobbiton with his wife (Primula Brandybuck) when he was 111.
His son Bingo Baggins gives the party, aged 72.

Version IV　　Bilbo, unmarried, adopted his young cousin Bingo Bolger (son of Primula Brandybuck), changed his name to Bingo Bolger-Baggins, and disappeared from Hobbiton when he was 111.
His adopted cousin Bingo Bolger-Baggins gives the party, aged 72.

★

(v)

'The Tale that is Brewing'

It was to the fourth version (writing on the typescript shows that it went to Allen and Unwin) that my father referred in a letter to Charles Furth on 1 February 1938, six weeks after he began the new book:

> Would you ask Mr Unwin whether his son [Rayner Unwin, then twelve years old], a very reliable critic, would care to read the first chapter of the sequel to *The Hobbit*? I have typed it. I have no confidence in it, but if he thought it a promising beginning, could add to it the tale that is brewing.

What was 'the tale that is brewing'? The texts of 'A Long-expected Party' provide no clues, except that the end of the third version (p. 34) makes it clear that when Bingo left Bag End he was going to meet, and go off with, some of his younger friends – and this is hinted at already at the end of the first draft (p. 17); in the fourth version this is repeated, and 'one or two' of his friends were 'in the know' – and 'they were not at Bag-end' (p. 39). Of course it is clear, too, that Bilbo is not dead; and (with knowledge of what was in fact to come) we may count the references to Buckland and the Old Forest (pp. 29, 37) as further hints.

But there are some jottings from this time, written on two sides of a single sheet of paper, that do give some inkling of what was 'brewing'. The first of these reads:

A LONG-EXPECTED PARTY   41

Bilbo goes off with 3 Took nephews: Odo, Frodo, and Drogo [*changed to* Odo, Drogo, and Frodo]. He has only a small bag of money. They walk all night – East. Adventures: troll-like: witch-house on way to Rivendell. Elrond again [*added*: (by advice of Gandalf?)]. A tale in Elrond's house.

Where is G[andalf] asks Odo – said I was old and foolish enough now to take care of myself said B. But I dare say he will turn up, he is apt to.

There follows a note to the effect that while Odo believed no more than a quarter of 'B.'s stories', Drogo was less sceptical, and Frodo believed them 'almost completely'. The character of this last nephew was early established, though he was destined to disappear (see p. 70): he is *not* the forerunner of Frodo in LR. All this seems to have been written at one time. On the face of it, it must belong with the second (unfinished) version of 'A Long-expected Party', since it is Bilbo who 'goes off' (afterwards my father bracketed the words 'Bilbo goes off with 3 Took nephews' and wrote 'Bingo' above). The implication is presumably that when Bilbo set out with his nephews Gandalf was no longer present.

Then follows, in pencil: 'Make return of ring a motive.' This no doubt refers to the statement in the third version that 'The ring was his [Bingo's] father's parting gift' (p. 32).

After a note suggesting the coming of a dragon to Hobbiton and a more heroic rôle for hobbits, a suggestion rejected with a pencilled 'No', there follows, apparently all written at one time (but with a later pencilled heading 'Conversation of Bingo and Bilbo'):

'No one,' said B., 'can escape quite unscathed from dragons. The only thing is to shun them (if you can) like the Hobbitonians, though not nec[essarily] to disbelieve in them (or refuse to remember them) like the H[obbitonians]. Now I have spent all my money which seemed once to me too much and my own has gone after it [*sic*]. And I don't like being without after [?having] – in fact I am being lured. Well, well, twice one is not always two, as my father used to say. But at any rate I think I would rather wander as a poor man than sit and shiver. And Hobbiton rather grows on you in 20 years, don't you think; grows too heavy to bear, I mean. Anyway, we are off – and it's autumn. I enjoy autumn wandering.'

Asks Elrond what he can do to heal his money-wish and unsettlement. Elrond tells him of an island. Britain? Far west where the Elves still reign. Journey to perilous isle.

I want to look again on a live dragon.

This is certainly Bilbo, and the passage (though not of course the pencilled heading) precedes the third version, as the reference to '20 years' shows (see pp. 22, 31). – At the foot of the page are these faint pencilled scrawls:

42　THE RETURN OF THE SHADOW

Bingo goes to find his father.
You said you . . . . end your days in contentment – *so I hope to*
The illegible word might possibly be 'want'. – On the reverse of the page
is the following coherent passage in ink:

> *The Ring:* whence its origin. Necromancer? Not very dangerous, when
> used for good purpose. But it exacts its penalty. You must either lose
> it, or *yourself*. Bilbo could not bring himself to lose it. He starts on a
> holiday [*struck out:* with his wife] handing over ring to Bingo. But he
> vanishes. Bingo worried. Resists desire to go and find him – though he
> does travel round a lot looking for news. Won't lose ring as he feels it
> will ultimately bring him to his father.
>   At last he meets Gandalf. Gandalf's advice. You must stage a
> *disappearance*, and the ring may then be cheated into letting you
> follow a similar path. But you have got to *really disappear* and give up
> the past. Hence the 'party'.
>   Bingo confides in his friends. Odo, Frodo, and Vigo (?) insist on
> coming too. Gandalf rather dubious. You will share the same fate as
> Bingo, he said, if you dare the ring. Look what happened to Primula.

A couple of pencilled changes were made to this: above 'Vigo(?)' my
father wrote 'Marmaduke'; and he bracketed the last sentence. – Since
Bingo is here Bilbo's son this note belongs with the third version. But the
watery death of Primula Brandybuck (no longer Bilbo's wife, but still
Bingo's mother) is first recorded in the fourth version (p. 37), and the
Ring could not possibly be associated with that event; so that the
reference to 'Primula' here must refer to something else of which there is
no other trace.

Particularly noteworthy is the suggestion that the idea of the Party
arose from Gandalf's advice to Bingo concerning the Ring. It is indeed
remarkable that already at this stage, when my father was still working on
the opening chapter, so much of the Ring's nature was already present in
embryo. – The final two notes are in pencil. The first reads:

> Bilbo goes to Elrond to cure dragon-longing, and settles down in
> Rivendell. Hence Bingo's frequent absences from home. The dragon-
> longing comes on Bingo. Also ring-lure.

With Bingo's 'frequent absences from home' cf. 'he was often away from
home' in the third version (p. 29), and 'Resists desire to go and find him –
though he does travel round a lot looking for news' in the note on the Ring
given above. And the last:

> Make dubious regions – Old Forest on way to Rivendell. South of
> River. They turn aside to call up Frodo Br[andybuck] [*written above:*
> Marmaduke], get lost and caught by Willowman and by Barrow-
> wights. T. Bombadil comes in.

'South' was changed from 'North', and 'East' is written in the margin.

A LONG-EXPECTED PARTY

43

On a separate page (in fact on the back of my father's earliest surviving map of the Shire) is a brief 'scheme' that is closely associated with these last notes; at the head of it my father afterwards wrote *Genesis of 'Lord of the Rings'*.

B.B. sets out with 2 nephews. They turn S[outh]ward to collect Frodo Brandybuck. Get lost in Old Forest. Adventure with Willowman and Barrow-wights. T. Bombadil.

Reach Rivendell and find Bilbo. Bilbo had had a sudden desire to visit the Wild again. But meets Gandalf at Rivendell. Learns about [*sic; here presumably the narrative idea changes*] Gandalf had turned up at Bag-end. Bilbo tells him of desire for Wild and gold. Dragon curse working. He goes to Rivendell between the worlds and settles down.

Ring must eventually go back to Maker, or draw you towards it. Rather a dirty trick handing it on?

It is interesting to see the idea already present that Bingo and his companions would turn aside to 'collect' or 'call up' another hobbit, at first named Frodo Brandybuck, but changed to Marmaduke (Brandybuck). Frodo Brandybuck also appears in initial drafting for the second chapter (p. 45) as one of Bingo's three companions on his departure from Hobbiton. There are various ways of combining all these references to the three (or two) nephews, so as to present a series of successive formulations, but names and rôles were still entirely fluid and ephemeral and no certainty is possible. Only in the first full text of the second chapter does the story become clear (for a time): Bingo set out with two companions, Odo Took and Frodo Took.

It is to be noted that Tom Bombadil, the Willow-man, and the Barrow-wights were already in existence years before my father began *The Lord of the Rings*; see p. 115.

★

On 11 February 1938 Stanley Unwin reported to my father that his son Rayner had read the first chapter and was delighted with it. On 17 February my father wrote to Charles Furth at Allen and Unwin:

They say it is the first step that costs the effort. I do not find it so. I am sure I could write unlimited 'first chapters'. I have indeed written many. The Hobbit sequel is still where it was, and I have only the vaguest notions of how to proceed. Not ever intending any sequel, I fear I squandered all my favourite 'motifs' and characters on the original 'Hobbit'.

And on the following day he replied to Stanley Unwin:

I am most grateful to your son Rayner: and am encouraged. At the same time I find it only too easy to write opening chapters – and for the

44   THE RETURN OF THE SHADOW

moment the story is not unfolding. I have unfortunately very little time, made shorter by a rather disastrous Christmas vacation. I squandered so much on the original 'Hobbit' (which was not meant to have a sequel) that it is difficult to find anything new in that world.

But on 4 March 1938, in the course of a long letter to Stanley Unwin on another subject, he said:

> The sequel to *The Hobbit* has now progressed as far as the end of the third chapter. But stories tend to get out of hand, and this has taken an unpremeditated turn. Mr Lewis and my youngest boy are reading it in bits as a serial. I hesitate to bother your son, though I should value his criticism. At any rate if he would like to read it in serial form he can.

The 'unpremeditated turn', beyond any doubt, was the appearance of the Black Riders.

II
FROM HOBBITON TO THE WOODY END

The original manuscript drafts for the second chapter of *The Lord of the Rings* do not constitute a completed narrative, however rough, but rather, disconnected parts of the narrative, in places in more than one version, as the story expanded and changed in the writing. The fact that my father had typed out the first chapter by 1 February 1938 (p. 40), but on 17 February wrote (p. 43) that while first chapters came easily to him 'the Hobbit sequel is still where it was,' suggests strongly that the original drafting of this second chapter followed the typing of the fourth version of 'A Long-expected Party'.

There followed a typescript text, with a title 'Three's Company and Four's More'; this will be given in full, but before doing so earlier stages of the story (one of them of the utmost interest) must be looked at.

The first rough manuscript begins with Odo and Frodo Took (but Frodo at once changed to Drogo) sitting on a gate at night and talking about the events at Bag End that afternoon, while 'Frodo Brandybuck was sitting on a pile of haversacks and packs and looking at the stars.' Frodo Brandybuck, it seems, was brought in here from the rôle prepared for him in the notes given on pp. 42–3, in one of which he was replaced by Marmaduke (Brandybuck). Bingo, coming up behind silently and invisibly, pushed Odo and Drogo off the gate; and after the ensuing raillery the draft continues:

'Have you three any idea where we are going to?' said Bingo.

'None whatever,' said Frodo, '– if you mean, where we are going to land finally. With such a captain it would be quite impossible to guess that. But we all know where we are making for first.'

'What we don't know,' put in Drogo, 'is how long it is going to take us on foot. Do you? You have usually taken a pony.'

'That is not much faster, though it is less tiring. Let me see – I have never done the journey in a hurry before, and have usually taken five and a half weeks (with plenty of rests). Actually I have *always* had some adventure, milder or less so, every time I have taken the road to Rivendell.'

'Very well,' said Frodo, 'let's put a bit of the way behind us tonight. It is jolly under the stars, and cool.'

46   THE RETURN OF THE SHADOW

'Better turn in soon and make an early start,' said Odo (who was fond of bed). 'We shall do more tomorrow if we begin fresh.'

'I back councillor Frodo,' said Bingo. So they started, shouldering packs, and gripping long sticks. They went very quietly over fields and along hedgerows and the fringes of small coppices until night fell, and in their dark [?green] cloaks they were quite invisible without any rings. And of course being Hobbits they could not be heard – not even by Hobbits. At last Hobbiton was far behind, and the lights in the windows of the last farmhouse were twinkling on a hilltop a long way away. Bingo turned and waved a hand in farewell.

At the bottom of a slight hill they struck the main road East – rolling away pale grey into the darkness, between high hedges and dark wind-stirred trees. Now they marched along two by two; talking a little, occasionally humming, often tramping in time for a mile or so without saying anything. The stars swung overhead, and the night got late.

Odo gave a big yawn and slowed down. 'I am so sleepy,' he said, 'that I shall fall down on the road. What about a place for the night?'

Here the original opening draft ends. Notably, the hobbits are setting out expressly for Rivendell, and Bingo has been there several times before; cf. the note given on p. 42: 'Bilbo . . . settles down in Rivendell. Hence Bingo's frequent absences from home.' But there is no indication, nor has there been any, why they should be in any particular hurry.

It is clear that when the hobbits struck the East Road they took to it and walked eastward along it. At this stage there is no suggestion of a side road to Buckland, nor indeed that Buckland played any part in their plans.

A revised beginning followed. Drogo Took was dropped, leaving Odo and Frodo as Bingo's companions (Frodo now in all probability a Took). The passage concerning Rivendell has gone, and instead the plan to go first 'to pick up Marmaduke' appears. The description of the walk from Hobbiton is now much fuller, and largely reaches the form in the typescript text (p. 50); it is interesting to observe here the point of emergence of the road to Buckland:

After a rest on a bank under some thinly clad birches they went on again, until they struck a narrow road. It went rolling away, pale grey in the dark, up and down – but all the time gently climbing southward. It was the road to Buckland, climbing away from the main East Road in the Water Valley, and winding away past the skirts of the Green Hills towards the south-east corner of

FROM HOBBITON TO THE WOODY END 47

the Shire, the Wood-end as the Hobbits called it. They marched along it, until it plunged between high hedges and dark trees rustling their dry leaves gently in the night airs.

Comparison of this with the description of the East Road in the first draft ('rolling away pale grey into the darkness, between high hedges and dark wind-stirred trees') shows that the one was derived from the other. Perhaps as a result, the crossing of the East Road is omitted; it is merely said that the Buckland road diverged from it (contrast FR p. 80).

After Odo's words (typescript text p. 50) 'Or are you fellows going to sleep on your legs?' there follows:

> *The Road goes ever on and on*
> *down from the Door where it began:*
> *before us far the Road has gone,*
> *and we come after it, who can;*
> *pursuing it with weary feet,*
> *until it joins some larger way,*
> *where many paths and errands meet,*
> *and whither then? – we cannot say.*

There is no indication, in the manuscript as written, who spoke the verse (for which there is also a good deal of rough working); in the typescript text (pp. 52–3) it is given to Frodo and displaced to a later point in the story.

The second draft then jumps to the following day, and takes up in the middle of a sentence:

. . . on the flat among tall trees growing in scattered fashion in the grasslands, when Frodo said: 'I can hear a horse coming along the road behind!'

They looked back, but the windings of the road hid the traveller.

'I think we had better get out of sight,' said Bingo; 'or you fellows at any rate. Of course it doesn't matter very much, but I would rather not be met by anyone we know.'

They [*written above at the same time:* Odo & F.] ran quickly to the left down into a little hollow beside the road, and lay flat. Bingo slipped on his ring and sat down a few yards from the track. The sound of hoofs drew nearer. Round a turn came a white horse, and on it sat a bundle – or that is what it looked like: a small man wrapped entirely in a great cloak and hood so that only his eyes peered out, and his boots in the stirrups below.

The horse stopped when it came level with Bingo. The figure uncovered its nose and sniffed; and then sat silent as if listening. Suddenly a laugh came from inside the hood.

'Bingo my boy!' said Gandalf, throwing aside his wrappings.

48   THE RETURN OF THE SHADOW

'You and your lads are somewhere about. Come along now and show up, I want a word with you!' He turned his horse and rode straight to the hollow where Odo and Frodo lay. 'Hullo! hullo!' he said. 'Tired already? Aren't you going any further today?'

At that moment Bingo reappeared again. 'Well I'm blest,' said he. 'What are you doing along this way, Gandalf? I thought you had gone back with the elves and dwarves. And how did you know where we were?'

'Easy,' said Gandalf. 'No magic. I saw you from the top of the hill, and knew how far ahead you were. As soon as I turned the corner and saw the straight piece in front was empty I knew you had turned aside somewhere about here. And you have made a track in the long grass that I can see, at any rate when I am looking for it.'

Here this draft stops, at the foot of a page, and if my father continued beyond this point the manuscript is lost; but I think it far more likely that he abandoned it because he abandoned the idea that the rider was Gandalf as soon as written. It is most curious to see how directly the description of Gandalf led into that of the Black Rider – and that the original sniff was Gandalf's! In fact the conversion of the one to the other was first carried out by pencilled changes on the draft text, thus:

> Round a turn came a white [> black] horse, and on it sat a bundle – or that is what it looked like: a small [> short] man wrapped entirely in a great [*added:* black] cloak and hood so that only his eyes peered out [> so that his face was entirely shadowed] . . .

If the description of Gandalf in the draft is compared with that of the Black Rider in the typescript text (p. 54) it will be seen that with further refinement the one still remains very closely based on the other. The new turn in the story was indeed 'unpremeditated' (p. 44).

Further rough drafting begins again with the workings for the song *Upon the hearth the fire is red* and continues through the second appearance of the Black Rider and the coming of the Elves to the end of the chapter. This material was followed very closely indeed in the typescript text and need not be further considered (one or two minor points of interest in the development of the narrative are mentioned in the Notes). There is however a separate section in manuscript which was not taken up into the typescript, and this very interesting passage will be given separately (see p. 73).

I give here the typescript text – which became an extremely complex and now very battered document. It is clear that as soon as, or before, he had finished it my father began revising it, in some cases retyping pages (the rejected pages being retained), and also writing in many other changes here and there, most of these being very minor alterations of

FROM HOBBITON TO THE WOODY END   49

wording.[1] In the text that follows I take up all these revisions silently, but some earlier readings of interest are detailed in the Notes at the end of it (pp. 65 ff.).

II

Three's Company and Four's More[2]

Odo Took was sitting on a gate whistling softly. His cousin Frodo was lying on the ground beside a pile of packs and haversacks, looking up at the stars, and sniffing the cool air of the autumn twilight.

'I hope Bingo has not got locked up in the cupboard, or something,' said Odo. 'He's late: it's after six.'

'There's no need to worry,' said Frodo. 'He'll turn up when he thinks fit. He may have thought of some last irresistible joke, or something: he's very Brandybucksome. But he'll come all right; quite reliable in the long run is Uncle Bingo.'

There was a chuckle behind him. 'I'm glad to hear it,' said Bingo suddenly becoming visible; 'for this is going to be a very Long Run. Well, you fellows, are you quite ready to depart?'

'It's not fair sneaking up with that ring on,' said Odo. 'One day you will hear what *I* think of you, and you won't be so glad.'

'I know already,' said Bingo laughing, 'and yet I remain quite cheerful. Where's my pack and stick?'

'Here you are!' said Frodo jumping up. 'This is your little lot: pack, bag, cloak, stick.'

'I'm sure you have given me all the heaviest stuff,' puffed Bingo, struggling into the straps. He was a bit on the stout side.

'Now then!' said Odo. 'Don't start being Bolger-like. There's nothing there, except what you told us to pack. You'll feel the weight less, when you have walked off a bit of your own.'

'Be kind to a poor ruined hobbit!' laughed Bingo. 'I shall be thin as a willow-wand, I'm sure, before a week is out. But now what about it? Let's have a council! What shall we do first?'

'I thought that was settled,' said Odo. 'Surely we have got to pick up Marmaduke first of all?'

'O yes! I didn't mean that,' said Bingo. 'I meant: what about this evening? Shall we walk a little or a lot? All night or not at all?'

'We'd better find some snug corner in a haystack, or somewhere, and turn in soon,' said Odo. 'We shall do more tomorrow, if we start fresh.'

'Let's put a bit of the road behind us to-night,' said Frodo. 'I

50   THE RETURN OF THE SHADOW

want to get away from Hobbiton. Beside it's jolly under the stars,
and cool.'

'I vote for Frodo,' said Bingo. And so they started, shouldering
their packs, and swinging their stout sticks. They went very
quietly over fields and along hedgerows and the borders of coppices, until night fell. In their dark grey cloaks they were invisible
without the help of any magic rings, and since they were all
hobbits, they made no noise that even hobbits could hear (or
indeed even wild creatures in the woods and fields).

After some time they crossed The Water, west of Hobbiton,
where it was no more than a winding ribbon of black, lined with
leaning alders. They were now in Tookland; and they began to
climb into the Green Hill Country south of Hobbiton.[3] They
could see the village twinkling away down in the gentle valley of
The Water. Soon it disappeared in the folds of the darkened land,
and was followed by Bywater beside its grey pool. When the light
of the last farmhouse was far behind, peeping out of the trees,
Bingo turned and waved a hand in farewell.

'Now we're really off,' he said. 'I wonder if we shall ever look
down into that valley again.'

After they had walked for about two hours they rested. The
night was clear, cool, and starry, but smoky wisps of mist were
creeping up the hills from the streams and deep meadows. Thin-
clad birches swaying in a cold breeze above their heads made a
black net against the pale sky. They ate a very frugal supper (for
hobbits), and then went on again. Odo was reluctant, but the rest
of the council pointed out that this bare hillside was no place for
passing the night. Soon they struck a narrow road. It went rolling
up and down until it faded grey into the gathering dark. It was the
road to Buckland, climbing away from the main East Road in the
Water-valley, and winding over the skirts of the Green Hills
towards the south-eastern corner of the Shire, the Woody End as
the hobbits called it. Not many of them lived in that part.

Along this road they marched. Soon it plunged into a deeply
cloven track between tall trees that rustled their dry leaves in the
night. It was very dark. At first they talked, or hummed a tune
softly together: then they marched on in silence, and Odo began to
lag behind. At last he stopped, and gave a big yawn.

'I am so sleepy,' he said, 'that soon I shall fall down on the road.
What about a place for the night? Or are you fellows going to sleep
on your legs?'[4]

FROM HOBBITON TO THE WOODY END 51

'When does Marmaduke expect us?' asked Frodo. 'Tomorrow night?'

'No,' said Bingo. 'We should not get there by tomorrow night, even with a forced march, unless we went on many more miles now. And I must say I don't feel like it. It is getting on for midnight already. But it is all right. I told Marmaduke to expect us the night after tomorrow; so there is no hurry.'

'The wind's in the West,' said Odo. 'If we go down the other side of this hill we are climbing, we ought to find a spot fairly dry and sheltered.'

At the top of the hill over which the road ran they came upon a patch of fir-wood, dry and resin-scented. Leaving the road they went into the deep darkness of the wood, and gathered dead sticks and cones to make a fire. Soon they had a merry crackle of flame at the foot of a great fir, and sat round it for a while, until they began to nod with sleep. Then each in an angle of the great tree's roots they curled up in their cloaks and blankets, and were soon fast asleep.

There was no danger: for they were still in the Shire. A few creatures came and looked at them, when the fire had died away. A fox passing through the wood on business of his own stopped several minutes and sniffed. 'Hobbits!' he thought. 'Well, what next? I have heard a good many tales of queer goings on in this Shire; but I have never heard of a hobbit sleeping out of doors under a tree! Three of them! There's something mighty queer behind this.' He was quite right, but he never found out any more about it.

The morning came rather pale and clammy. Bingo woke up first, and found that a tree-root had made a hole in his back and that his neck was stiff. It did not seem such a lark as it had the day before. 'Why on earth did I give that beautiful feather-bed to that old pudding Fosco?'⁵ he thought. 'The tree-roots would have been much better for him.' 'Wake up, hobbits!' he cried. 'It's a beautiful morning!'

'What's beautiful about it?' said Odo, peering over the edge of his blanket with one eye. 'Have you got the bath-water hot? Get breakfast ready for half past nine.'

Bingo stripped the blanket off him, and rolled him over on top of Frodo; and then he left them scuffling and walked to the edge of the wood. Away eastward the sun was rising red out of the mists that lay thick on the world. Touched with gold and red the autumn trees in the distance seemed to be sailing rootless in a

52   THE RETURN OF THE SHADOW

shadowy sea. A little below him to the left the road plunged down
into a hollow between two slopes and vanished.

When he got back the other two had got a good fire going.
'Water!' they shouted. 'Where's the water?'

'I don't keep water in my pockets,' said Bingo.

'I thought you had gone to find some,' said Odo. 'You had better
go now.'

'Why?' asked Bingo. 'We had enough left for breakfast last
night; or I thought we had.'

'Well, you thought wrong,' said Frodo. 'Odo drank the last
drop, I saw him.'

'Then he can go and find some more, and not put it on Uncle
Bingo. There's a stream at the foot of the slope; the road crosses it
just below where we turned aside last night.'

In the end, of course, they all went with their water-bottles and
the small kettle they had brought with them. They filled them in
the stream where it fell a foot or two over a small outcrop of grey
stone in its path. The water was icy cold; and Odo spluttered as he
bathed his face and hands. Luckily hobbits grow no beards (and
would not shave if they did).

By the time their breakfast was over, and their packs all trussed
up again, it was ten o'clock at least, and beginning to turn into a
day even finer and hotter than the day of Bingo's birthday, that
already seemed quite a long while past. They went down the
slope, across the stream, and up the next slope, and by that time
their cloaks, blankets, water, food, spare clothes and other gear
already seemed a heavy load. The day's march was going to be
something quite different from a country walk.

After a time the road ceased to roll up and down: it climbed to
the top of a steep bank in a tired zigzagging sort of way, and then
prepared to go down for the last time. In front of them they saw
the lower lands dotted with small clumps of trees that melted away
in the distance to a hazy woodland brown. They were looking
across the Woody End towards the Brandywine River. The road
wound away before them like a piece of string.

'The road goes on for ever,' said Odo, 'but I can't without a rest.
It is high time for lunch.'

Frodo sat down on the bank at the side of the road and looked
away east into the haze, beyond which lay the River and the end of
the Shire in which he had spent all his life. Suddenly he spoke, as
if half to himself:

FROM HOBBITON TO THE WOODY END 53

The Road goes ever on and on
Down from the door where it began.
Now far ahead the Road has gone,
And we must follow if we can,
Pursuing it with weary feet,
Until it joins some larger way,
Where many paths and errands meet.
And whither then? We cannot say.[6]

'That sounds like a bit of Old Bilbo's rhyming,' said Odo. 'Or is it one of Bingo's imitations? It does not sound altogether encouraging.'

'No, *I* made it up, or at any rate it came to me,' said Frodo.

'I've never heard it before, certainly,' said Bingo. 'But it reminds me very much of Bilbo in the last years, before he went away. He used often to say that there was only one Road in all the land; that it was like a great river: its springs were at every doorstep, and every path was its tributary. "It's a dangerous business, Bingo, going out of your door," he used to say. "You step into the Road, and if you don't keep your feet, there is no knowing where you might get swept off to. Do you realize that this is the very path that goes through Mirkwood, and that if you let it, it might take you to even farther and worse places than the Lonely Mountain?" He used to say that on the path outside the front-door at Bag-end, especially after he had been out for a walk.'

'Well, the Road won't sweep me anywhere for an hour at least,' said Odo, unslinging his pack. The others followed his example, putting their packs against the bank and their legs out into the road. After a rest they had lunch (a frugal one) and then more rest.

The sun was beginning to get lower and the light of afternoon was on the land as they went down the hill. So far they had not met a soul on the road. This way was not much used, and the ordinary way to Buckland was along the East Road to the meeting of the Water and the Brandywine River, where there was a bridge, and then south along the River. They had been jogging along again for an hour or more, when Frodo stopped a moment as if listening. They were now on level ground, and the road, after much winding, lay straight ahead through grassland sprinkled with tall trees, outliers of the approaching woods.

'I can hear a horse or a pony coming along the road behind,' said Frodo.

54   THE RETURN OF THE SHADOW

They looked back, but the turn of the road prevented them from seeing far.

'I think we had better get out of sight,' said Bingo; 'or you two at any rate. Of course, it does not matter much, but I have a feeling that I would rather not be seen by anyone just now.'

Odo and Frodo ran quickly to the left, down into a little hollow not far from the road, and lay flat. Bingo slipped on his ring and stepped behind a tree. The sound of hoofs drew nearer. Round the turn came a black horse, no hobbit-pony but a full-sized horse; and on it sat a bundle, or that is what it looked like: a broad squat man, completely wrapped in a great black cloak and hood, so that only his boots in the stirrups showed below: his face was shadowed and invisible.

When it came on a level with Bingo, the horse stopped. The riding figure sat quite still, as if listening. From inside the hood came a noise as of someone sniffing to catch an elusive scent; the head turned from side to side of the road. At last the horse moved on again, walking slowly at first, and then taking to a gentle trot.

Bingo slipped to the edge of the road and watched the rider, until he dwindled in the distance. He could not be quite sure, but it seemed to him that suddenly, before they passed out of sight, the horse and rider turned aside and rode into the trees.

'Well, I call that very queer, and even a little disturbing,' said Bingo to himself, as he walked back to his companions. They had remained flat in the grass, and had seen nothing; so Bingo described to them the rider and his strange behaviour. 'I can't say why, but I felt perfectly certain he was looking or *smelling* for me: and also I felt very clearly that I did not want him to discover me. I've never seen or felt anything quite like it in the Shire before.'

'But what has one of the Big People got to do with us?' said Odo. 'And what is he doing in this part of the world at all? Except for those Men from Dale the other day[7] I haven't seen one of that Kind in our Shire for years.'[8]

'I have though,' said Frodo, who had listened intently to Bingo's description of the black rider. 'It reminds me of something I had almost forgotten. I was walking away up in the North Moor – you know, right up on the northern borders of the Shire – early last spring, when a similar rider met me. He was riding south, and he stopped and spoke, though he did not seem able to speak our language very well; he asked me if I knew where a place called Hobbiton was, and if there were any folk called Baggins there. I thought it very queer at the time; and I had a queer uncomfortable

FROM HOBBITON TO THE WOODY END

55

feeling, too. I could not see any face under his hood. I never heard whether he turned up in Hobbiton or not. If I did not tell you, I meant to.'

'You didn't tell me, and I wish you had,' said Bingo. 'I should have asked Gandalf about it; and probably we should have taken more care on the road.'

'Then you know or guess something about the rider?' said Frodo. 'What is he?'

'I don't know, and I don't want to guess,' said Bingo. 'But somehow I don't believe either of these riders (if there are two) was really one of the Big People, not one of the kind like Dalemen, I mean. I wish Gandalf was here; but now it will be a long time before we find him. In a way I suppose I ought to be pleased; but I am not quite prepared for adventures yet, and I was not expecting any in our own Shire. Do you two wish to go on with the journey?'

'Of course!' said Frodo. 'I am not going to turn back, not for an army of goblins.'

'I shall go where Uncle Bingo goes,' said Odo. 'But what is the next thing to do? Shall we go on at once, or stay here and have some food?[9] I should like a bite and a sip, but somehow I think we had better move on from here. Your talk of sniffing riders with invisible noses has made me feel quite uncomfortable.'

'I think we will move on now,' said Bingo; 'but not on the road, in case that rider comes back, or another one follows him. We ought to do a good step more today; Buckland is still miles away.'

The shadows of the trees were long and thin on the grass, as they started off again. They now kept a stone's throw to the left of the road, but their going was slow, for the grass was thick and tussocky and the ground uneven. The sun had gone down red behind the hills at their back, and evening was coming on, by the time they had come to the end of the straight stretch. There the road bent southward, and began to wind again as it entered a wood of ancient scattered oak trees.[10]

Close to the road they came on the huge hulk of an aged tree.[11] It was still alive and had leaves on small branches that it had put out round the broken stumps of its long fallen limbs; but it was hollow, and could be entered by a great crack on the far side. The hobbits went in and sat upon the floor of old leaves and decayed wood. There they rested and had a meal, talking quietly and listening in between.

56 THE RETURN OF THE SHADOW

They had just finished and were thinking of setting out again, when they heard quite clearly the sound of hoofs walking slow along the road outside. They did not move. The hoofs stopped, as far as they could judge, on the road beside their tree, but only for a moment. Soon they went on again and faded away – down the road, in the direction of Buckland. When Bingo at last stole out of the tree and peered up and down the road, there was nothing to be seen.

'Most peculiar!' he said, coming back to the others. 'I think we had better wait inside here for a bit.'

It grew almost dark inside the tree-trunk. 'I really think we shall have to go on now,' said Bingo. 'We have done very little to-day and we shan't get to Buckland tomorrow night at this rate.'

Twilight was about them, when they crept out. There was no living sound, not even a bird-call in the wood. The West wind was sighing in the branches. They stepped into the road and looked up and down again.

'We had better risk the road,' said Odo. 'The ground is much too rough off the track, especially in a fading light. We are probably making a fuss about nothing. It is very likely only a wandering stranger who has got lost; and if he met us, he would just ask us the way to Buckland or Brandywine Bridge, and ride on.'

'I hope you are right,' said Bingo. 'But anyway there is nothing for it but the open road. Luckily it winds a good deal.'

'What if he stops us and asks if we know where Mr Bolger-Baggins lives?' said Frodo.

'Give him the true answer: *Nowhere*,' said Bingo. 'Forward!'

They were now entering the Woody End, and the road began to fall gently but steadily, making south-east towards the lowlands of the Brandywine River. A star came out in the darkening East. They went abreast and in step, and their spirits rose; the uncomfortable feeling vanished, and they no longer listened for the sound of hoofs. After a mile or two they began to hum softly, as hobbits have a way of doing when twilight closes in and the stars come out. With most hobbits it is a bed-song or a supper-song; but these hobbits hummed a walking-song (though not, of course, without any mention of bed and supper). Bilbo Baggins had made the words (the tune was as old as the hills), and taught it to Bingo as they walked in the lanes of the Water-valley and talked about Adventure.

FROM HOBBITON TO THE WOODY END

Upon the hearth the fire is red,
Beneath the roof there is a bed;
But not yet weary are our feet,
Still round the corner we may meet
A sudden tree or standing stone
That none have seen, but we alone.
Tree and flower and leaf and grass,
　　Let them pass! Let them pass!
Hill and water under sky,
　　Pass them by! Pass them by!

Still round the corner there may wait
A new road or a secret gate,
And even if we pass them by,
We still shall know which way they lie,
And whether hidden pathways run
Towards the Moon or to the Sun.
Apple, thorn, and nut and sloe,
　　Let them go! Let them go!
Sand and stone and pool and dell,
　　Fare you well! Fare you well!

Home is behind, the world ahead,
And there are many paths to tread
Through shadow to the edge of night,
Until the stars are all alight.
Then world behind and home ahead,
We'll wander back to fire and bed.
Mist and twilight, cloud and shade,
　　Away shall fade! Away shall fade!
Fire and lamp and meat and bread,
　　And then to bed! And then to bed![12]

The song ended. 'And *now* to bed! And *now* to bed!' sang Odo in a loud voice. 'Hush!' said Frodo. 'I think I hear hoofs again.'

They stopped suddenly, and stood as silent as tree-shadows, listening. There was a sound of hoofs on the road some way behind, but coming slow and clear in the stillness of the evening. Quickly and quietly they slipped off the road and ran into the deeper shade under the oak-trees.

'Don't let's go too far!' said Bingo. 'I don't want to be seen, but I want to see what I can this time.'

'Very well!' said Odo; 'but don't forget the sniffing!'

58   THE RETURN OF THE SHADOW

The hoofs drew nearer. They had no time to find any hiding-place[13] better than the general darkness under the trees; so Odo and Frodo lay behind a large tree-trunk, while Bingo slipped on his ring and crept forward a few yards towards the road. It showed grey and pale, a line of fading light through the wood. Above it the stars were now coming out thick in the dim sky, but there was no moon.

The sound of hoofs ceased. As Bingo watched he saw something dark pass across the lighter space between two trees, and then halt. It looked like the black shade of a horse led by a smaller black shadow. The black shadow stood close to the point where they had left the road, and it swayed from side to side. Bingo thought he heard the sound of sniffing. The shadow bent to the ground, and then began to crawl towards him.

At that moment there came a sound like mingled song and laughter. Voices clear and fair rose and fell in the starlit air. The black shadow straightened and retreated.[14] It climbed on to the shadowy horse and seemed to vanish across the road into the darkness on the other side. Bingo breathed again.

'Elves!' said Frodo in an excited whisper behind him. 'Elves! How wonderful! I have always wished to hear elves singing under the stars; but I did not know any lived in the Shire.'

'Oh yes!' said Bingo. 'Old Bilbo knew there were some down in the Woody End. They don't really live here, though; but they often come across the river in spring and autumn. I am very glad they do!'

'Why?' said Odo.

'You didn't see, of course,' said Bingo; 'but that black rider (or another of the same sort) stopped just here and was actually crawling towards us, when the song started. As soon as he heard the voices he slipped away.'

'Did he sniff?' asked Odo.

'He did,' said Bingo. 'It is mysterious, uncomfortably mysterious.'

'Let's find the Elves, if we can,' said Frodo.

'Listen! They are coming this way,' said Bingo. 'We have only to wait by the road.'

The singing drew nearer. One clear voice rose above the others. It seemed to be singing in the secret elf-tongue, of which Bingo knew only a little, and the others knew nothing, yet the sound of the words blending with the tune seemed to turn into words in their own listening thought, which they only partly understood.

FROM HOBBITON TO THE WOODY END 59

Frodo and Bingo afterwards agreed that the song went something like this:

Snow-white! Snow-white! O Lady clear!
O Queen beyond the Western Seas!
O Light to us that wander here
Amid the world of woven trees!

Gilthoniel! O Elbereth!
Clear are thy eyes and cold thy breath!
Snow-white! Snow-white! We sing to thee
In a far land beyond the Sea.

O Stars that in the Sunless Year
With shining hand by her were sown,
In windy fields now bright and clear
We see your silver blossom blown!

O Elbereth! Gilthoniel!
We still remember, we who dwell
In this far land beneath the trees,
Thy starlight on the Western Seas.[15]

The hobbits sat in shadow by the roadside. Before long the Elves came down the road towards the valley. They passed slowly and the hobbits could see the starlight glimmering on their hair and in their eyes.[16] They bore no lights, yet as they walked a shimmer, like the light of the moon above the rim of the hills before it rises, seemed to fall about their feet. They had stopped singing, and as the last elf passed he turned and looked towards the hobbits, and laughed.

'Hail Bingo!' he said. 'You are out late – or are you perhaps lost?' Then he called aloud in the elf-tongue, and all the company stopped and gathered round.

'Well! Isn't this wonderful!' they said. 'Three hobbits in a wood at night! What is the meaning of this? We haven't seen anything like it, since dear Bilbo went away.'

'The meaning of this, my good Elves,' said Bingo, 'is simply that we seem to be going the same way as you are. I was brought up by Bilbo, so I like walking, even under the stars. And I can put up with Elves for lack of other company!'

'But we have no need of other company, and hobbits are so dull,' they laughed. 'Come along now, tell us all about it! We see

THE RETURN OF THE SHADOW

you are simply swelling with secrets we should like to hear. Though some we know, of course, and some we guess. Many Happy Returns of yesterday – we have heard all about that, of course, from the Rivendell people.'[17]

'Then who are you, and who is your lord?' said Bingo.

'I am Gildor,' said the Elf who had hailed him. 'Gildor Inglorion of the house of Finrod. We are exiles, one of the few companies that still remain east of the Sea, for our kindred went back to the West long ago. We are Wise-elves, and the elves of Rivendell are our kinsfolk.'[18]

'O Wise People,' said Frodo, 'tell us about the Black Rider!'

'The Black Rider!' they said in low voices. 'Why do you ask about the Black Rider?'

'Because three Black Riders have overtaken us today, or one three times,'[19] said Bingo; 'and only a few moments ago one slipped away as you drew near.'

The Elves did not answer at once, but spoke together softly in the elf-tongue. At last Gildor turned to the hobbits: 'We will not speak more of this here,' he said. 'We think you had better come with us. As you know, it is not our custom; but for Bilbo's sake we will take you on our road, and you shall lodge with us to-night, if you wish.'

'I thank you indeed, Gildor Inglorion,' said Bingo bowing. 'O Fair Folk! This is a good fortune beyond my best hope,' said Frodo. Odo also bowed, but said nothing aloud. 'Rather good luck?' he whispered to Bingo. 'I suppose we shall get a really good bed and supper?'

'You can reckon your luck in the morning,' said Gildor, as if he had been spoken to. 'We shall do what we can, though we have heard that hobbits are hard to satisfy.'

'I beg your pardon,' stammered Odo. Bingo laughed: 'You must be careful of Elvish ears, Odo!' 'We count our luck already,' he said to the Elves; 'and I think that you will find that we are very easy to please (for hobbits).' He added in the elf-tongue a greeting that Bilbo had taught him: 'The stars shine on the hour of our meeting.'

'Be careful, friends!' cried Gildor laughing. 'Speak no secrets! Here is a scholar in the elf-latin.[20] Bilbo was indeed a good master! Hail! elf-friend,' he said, bowing to Bingo, 'come now and join our company![21] You had best walk in the middle, so that you will not stray. You may be weary before we halt.'

'Why? Where are you going?' asked Bingo.

FROM HOBBITON TO THE WOODY END 61

'To the woods near Woodhall down in the valley. It is some miles; but it will shorten your journey to Buckland to-morrow.'

They marched along in silence, and passed like shadows and faint lights; for both Elves and hobbits could walk when they wished without a sound. They sang no more songs. Odo began to feel sleepy, and stumbled once or twice; but each time a tall elf by his side put out his arm and saved him from a fall.

The woods on either side became denser; the trees were younger and more thick, and as the road went lower there were many deep brakes of hazel. At last they turned right from the road: a green ride lay almost unseen through the thicket This they followed until they came suddenly to a wide space of grass, grey under the night. The wood bordered it on three sides; but on the east the ground fell steeply, and the tops of the dark trees growing in the fold below were level with their feet. Beyond them the low land lay dim and flat under the stars. Nearer at hand there was a twinkle of lights: the village of Woodhall.

The Elves sat on the grass, and seemed to take no further notice of the hobbits. They spoke together in soft voices. The hobbits wrapped themselves in cloak and blankets, and drowsiness crept over them. The night drew on, and the lights in the valley went out. Odo fell asleep, pillowed on a smooth hillock.

Out of the mists away eastward a pale gold light went up. The yellow moon rose; springing swiftly out of the shadow, and then climbing round and slow into the sky. The Elves all burst into song. Suddenly under the trees to one side a fire sprang up with a red light.

'Come!' the Elves called to the hobbits. 'Come! Now is the time for speech and merriment.'

Odo sat up and rubbed his eyes. He shivered. 'Come, little Odo!' said an elf. 'There is a fire in the hall, and some food for hungry guests.'

On the south side of the green-sward the wood drew close. Here there was a space green-floored, but entirely overshadowed by tall trees. Their trunks ran like pillars down each side, and their interlaced branches made a roof above. In the middle there was a wood-fire blazing; upon the sides of the tree-pillars torches with lights of gold and silver were burning steadily without smoke. The Elves sat round the fire upon the grass or upon the sawn rings of old trunks. Some went to and fro bearing cups and pouring drink;

62   THE RETURN OF THE SHADOW

others brought food on heaped plates and dishes, and set them on the grass.

'This is poor fare,' they said to the hobbits; 'for we are lodging in the greenwood far from our halls. If ever you are our guests at home, we will treat you better.'

'It seems to me good enough for a birthday party,' said Bingo.

Actually it was Odo that ate the least after all. The drink in his cup seemed sweet and fragrant; he drained it, and felt all weariness slip away, and yet sleep came softly down upon him. He was already half wrapped in warm dreams as he ate; and afterwards he could remember nothing more than the taste of bread – yet a bread that was like the best hobbit-bread ever baked (and that was Bread indeed) eaten after a long fast, only this bread was better. Frodo afterwards recalled little of either food or drink, for his mind was filled with the light under the trees, the elf-faces, the sound of voices so various and so beautiful that he felt in a waking dream. But he remembered taking a draught that had the warmth of a golden autumn afternoon and the cool of a clear fountain; and he remembered too the taste of fruits, sweet as wild berries, richer than the tended fruits of hobbit-gardens (and those are fruits indeed).

Bingo sat and ate and drank and talked, and simply remembered having had something of all the foods he liked best; but his mind was chiefly on the talk. He knew something of the elf-tongue, and listened eagerly. Now and again he spoke to those that served him and thanked them in their own language. They smiled on him and said laughing: 'Here is a jewel among hobbits!'[22]

After a while Odo and Frodo fell fast asleep, and were lifted up and borne away to bowers under the trees; they were laid there upon soft beds and slept the night away. But Bingo remained talking with Gildor, the leader of the Elves.[23]

'Why did you choose this moment to set out?' asked Gildor.

'Well, really it chose itself,' answered Bingo. 'I had come to the end of my treasure. It had always held me back from the Journey which half of my heart wished for, ever since Bilbo went away; but now it was gone. So I said to my stay-at-home half: "There is nothing to keep you here. The Journey *might* bring you some more treasure, as it did for old Bilbo; and anyway on the road you will be able to live more easily without any. Of course if you like to stay in Hobbiton and earn your living as a gardener or a carpenter, you can." The stay-at-home half surrendered; it did not want to make other people's chairs or grow other people's potatoes. It was

FROM HOBBITON TO THE WOODY END 63

soft and fat. I think the Journey will do it good. But of course the other half is not really looking for treasure, but for Adventure – later rather than sooner. At the moment it also is soft and fat, and finding walking over the Shire quite enough.'

'Yes!' laughed Gildor. 'You still *look* just like an ordinary hobbit!'

'I daresay,' said Bingo. 'But my birthday the day before yesterday[24] seems already a long way behind. Still a hobbit I am, and a hobbit I shall always be.'

'I only said *look*,' replied the Elf. 'You seem to me a most peculiar hobbit inside, quite as peculiar as Bilbo; and I think strange things will happen to you and your friends. If you go looking for Adventure, you usually find as much of it as you can manage. And it often happens that when you think it is ahead, it comes on you unexpectedly from behind.'

'So it seems,' said Bingo. 'But I did not expect it ahead or behind so soon – not in our own Shire.'

'But it is not your Shire alone, nor for ever,' said Gildor. 'The Wide World is all about it. You can fence yourselves in, but you have no means of fencing it out.'

'All the same, it is disturbing,' said Bingo. 'I want to get to Rivendell, if I can – though I hear the road has not grown easier of late years. Can you tell me anything to guide me or help me?'

'I do not think you will find the road too hard. But if you are thinking of what you call the Black Rider, that is another matter. Have you told me all your reasons for leaving secretly? Did Gandalf tell you nothing?'

'Not even a hint, at least none that I understood. I seldom saw him after Bilbo went away, twice a year at most. I saw him last spring, when he turned up unexpectedly one night; and I told him then of the plan I was beginning to make for the Journey. He seemed pleased, and told me not to put it off later than the autumn. He came again to help me with the Party, but we were too busy then to talk much, and he went off with the dwarves and the Rivendell elves as soon as the fireworks were over. He did hint that I might meet him again in Rivendell, and suggested that I should make for that place first.'

'Not later than the autumn!' said Gildor. 'I wonder. He may all the same not have known that they were in the Shire; yet he knows more about them than we do. If he did not tell you any more, I do not feel inclined to do so, for fear of frightening you from the Journey. Because I think it is clear that your Journey started none

64 THE RETURN OF THE SHADOW

too soon; by what seems strange good luck you went just in time. You ought to go on, and not turn back, though you have met adventure, and danger, much sooner than you expected. You ought to go quickly; but you must be careful, and look not only ahead, but also behind, and even perhaps to both sides as well.'

'I wish you would say things plainer,' said Bingo. 'But I am glad to be told that I ought to go on; for that is what I want to do. Only I now rather wonder if I ought to take Odo and Frodo. The original plan was just a Journey, a sort of prolonged (and perhaps permanent) holiday from Hobbiton, and I am sure they did not expect any more adventures for a long time than getting wet and hungry. We had no idea we should be *pursued*.'

'O come! They must have known that if you intend to go wandering out of the Shire into the Wide World, you must be prepared for anything. I cannot see that it makes so much difference, if *something* has turned up rather soon. Are they not willing to go on?'

'Yes, they say so.'

'Then let them go on![25] They are lucky to be your companions: and you are lucky to have them. They are a great protection to you.'

'What do you mean?'

'I think the Riders do not know that they are with you, and their presence has confused the scent, and puzzled them.'

'Dear me! It is all very mysterious. It is like solving riddles. But I have always heard that talking to Elves is like that.'

'It is,' laughed Gildor. 'And Elves seldom give advice; but when they do, it is good. I have advised you to go to Rivendell with speed and care. Nothing else that I could tell you would make that advice any better.[26] We have our own business and our own sorrows, and those have little to do with the ways of hobbits or of other creatures. Our paths cross those ways seldom, and mostly by accident. In our meeting there is perhaps something more than accident, yet I do not feel sure that I ought to interfere. But I will add a little more advice: if a Rider finds you or speaks to you, do not answer, and do not name yourself. Also do not again use the ring to escape from his search. I do not know,[27] but I guess that the use of the ring helps them more than you.'

'More and more mysterious!' said Bingo. 'I can't imagine what information would be more frightening than your hints; but I suppose you know best.'

'I do indeed,' said Gildor, 'and I will say no more.'

FROM HOBBITON TO THE WOODY END   65

'Very well!' said Bingo. 'I am now all of a twitter; but I am much obliged to you.'

'Be of good heart!' said Gildor. 'Sleep now! In the morning we shall have gone; but we will send our messages through the land. The wandering Companies shall know of you and your Journey. I name you elf-friend, and wish you well. Seldom have we had such delight in strangers; and it is pleasant to hear words of our own tongue from the lips of other wanderers in the World.'

Bingo felt sleep coming upon him, even as Gildor finished speaking. 'I will sleep now,' he said. Gildor led him to a bower beside Odo and Frodo, and he threw himself upon a bed, and fell at once into a dreamless slumber.

NOTES

1 For emendation of the typescript at this stage my father used black ink. This was fortunate, for otherwise the historical unravelling of the text would be scarcely possible: in a later phase of the work he returned to it and covered it with corrections in blue and red inks, blue chalk and pencil. In one case, however, an addition in black ink belongs demonstrably to the later phase. It is possible therefore that some of the emendations which I have adopted into the text are really later; but none seem to me to be so, and in any case all changes of any narrative significance are detailed in the following notes.

2 The meaning of this title is not clear. The phrase 'Three's company, but four's more' is used however by Marmaduke Brandybuck during the conversation in Buckland, where he asserts that he will certainly be one of the party (p. 103). Conceivably, therefore, my father gave the original second chapter this title because he believed that it would extend as far as the arrival in Buckland. Subsequently he crossed out the words 'and Four's More', but it cannot be said when this was done.

3 In the second draft of the opening of the chapter, which had reached virtually the form of the typescript text in this passage, the crossing of the East Road was omitted, and the omission remains here (see p. 47).

4 In the draft text the verse *The Road goes ever on and on* is placed here (see p. 47).

5 Fosco Bolger, Bingo's uncle: see p. 38.

6 In FR (pp. 82–3) the verse has *I* for *we* in lines 4 and 8, but is otherwise the same; there, however, it is an echo from Bilbo's speaking it in Chapter 1 (FR p. 44). For the earliest form see p. 47; and see further p. 246 note 18.

7 *Men from Dale:* see pp. 20, 30.

66   THE RETURN OF THE SHADOW

8   The next portion of the narrative, from *'I have though,' said Frodo* and extending to the end of the song *Upon the hearth the fire is red* (p. 57), was early re-typed to replace two pages of the original typescript, and a substantial alteration and expansion of the story was introduced (see notes 9 and 11).

9   This first part of the re-typed section (see note 8) was not greatly changed from the earlier form. In the earlier, Frodo described his encounter with a Black Rider 'up in the North Moors' in the previous spring in almost exactly the same words; but Bingo's response was somewhat different:

> 'That makes it even queerer,' said Bingo. 'I am glad I had the fancy not to be seen on the road. But, somehow, I don't believe either of these riders was one of the Big People, not of the kind like the Dale-men, I mean. I wonder what they were? I rather wish Gandalf was here. But, of course, he went away immediately after the fireworks with the elves and dwarves, and it will be ages before we see him now.'
>
> 'Shall we go on now, or stay here and have some food?' asked Odo . . .

In the later versions of *A Long-expected Party* there is no reference to Gandalf after the fireworks (see pp. 31, 38; 63).

10   *There the road bent southward:* on the map of the Shire in FR the road does not bend southward 'at the end of the straight stretch'; it bends left or northward, while a side road goes on to Woodhall. But at this stage there was only one road, and at the place where the hobbits met the Elves it was falling steadily, 'making south-east towards the lowlands of the Brandywine River' (p. 56). Certainly by oversight, the present passage was preserved with little change in the original edition of FR (p. 86):

> The sun had gone down red behind the hills at their backs, and evening was coming on before they came to the end of the long level over which the road ran straight. At that point it bent somewhat southward, and began to wind again, as it entered a wood of ancient oak-trees.

It was not until the second edition of 1966 that my father changed the text to agree with the map:

> At that point it bent *left* and went down into the lowlands of the Yale making for Stock; but *a lane branched right*, winding through a wood of ancient oak-trees on its way to Woodhall. 'That is the way for us,' said Frodo.
>
> Not far from *the road-meeting* they came on the huge hulk of a tree . . .

This is also the reason for change in the second edition of 'road' to 'lane' (also 'path', 'way') at almost all the many subsequent occurrences in FR pp. 86–90: it was the 'lane' to Woodhall they were on, not the 'road' to Stock.

FROM HOBBITON TO THE WOODY END   67

11 The entire passage from 'Close to the road they came on the huge hulk of an aged tree' is an expansion in the replacement typescript (see note 8) of a few sentences in the earlier:

> Inside the huge hollow trunk of an aged tree, broken and stumpy but still alive and in leaf, they rested and had a meal. Twilight was about them when they came out and prepared to go on again. 'I am going to risk the road now,' said Bingo, who had stubbed his toes several times against hidden roots and stones in the grass. 'We are probably making a fuss about nothing.'

Though the enlarged description of the hollow tree was preserved in FR (p. 86), the second passage of a Black Rider was not, and the tree has again no importance beyond being the scene of the hobbits' meal. In the third chapter Bingo, talking to Marmaduke in Buckland, refers to this story of a Rider heard while they sat inside the tree (p. 103); see also note 19 below.

12 The version of the song in the rejected typescript (see note 8) had the second and third verses thus:

> *Home is behind, the world ahead,*
> *And there are many paths to tread;*
> *And round the corner there may wait*
> *A new road or a secret gate,*
> *And hidden pathways there may run*
> *Towards the Moon or to the Sun.*
>   *Apple, thorn, &c.*
>
> *Down hill, up hill walks the way*
> *From sunrise to the falling day,*
> *Through shadow to the edge of night,*
> *Until the stars are all alight; &c.*

13 In the initial drafting for this passage Bingo proposed that they stow their burdens in the hollow of an old broken oak and then climb it, but this was rejected as soon as written. This was no doubt where the 'hollow tree' motive first appeared.

14 In the original draft my father first wrote here: 'Suddenly there was a sound of laughter and a creak of wheels on the road. The shadow straightened up and retreated.' This was soon replaced, without the creak of wheels being explained; but it suggests that he had some intervention other than Elves in mind.

15 This was another portion that was re-typed. The passage immediately preceding the Elves' song was different in the earlier form:

> It seemed to be singing in the secret elf-tongue, and yet as they listened the sounds, or the sounds and the tune together, seemed to turn into strange words in their own thought, which they only partly understood. Frodo afterwards said that he thought he heard words like these:

68 THE RETURN OF THE SHADOW

The song also had certain differences, including a second verse that was rejected.

> *O Elbereth! O Elbereth!*
> *O Queen beyond the Western Seas!*
> *O Light to him that wandereth*
> *Amid the world of woven trees!*
>
> *O Stars that in the Sunless Year*
> *Were kindled by her silver hand,*
> *That under Night the shade of Fear*
> *Should fly like shadow from the land!*
>
> *O Elbereth! Gilthonieth!*
> *Clear are thy eyes, and cold thy breath! &c.*

In the last verse the form is *Gilthoniel*. Extensive rough workings are also found, in which the first line of the song appears also as *O Elberil! O Elberil!* (and the third *O Light to us that wander still*); from these is also seen the meaning of *the Sunless Year*, since my father first wrote *the Flowering Years* (with reference to the Two Trees; see the *Quenta Silmarillion* §19, V.212). – It seems to have been here that the name *Elbereth* was first applied to Varda, having been previously that of one of the sons of Dior Thingol's Heir: see V.351.

16 In the original draft it was added here that the Elves 'were crowned with red and yellow leaves'; rejected, no doubt, because it was dark and they bore no lights.

17 At an earlier point in the chapter (p. 52) the typescript read 'a day even finer and hotter than the day before (Bingo's birthday, that already seemed quite a long while past).' It was of course on the evening of the day following the birthday party that Bingo and his companions set out, and my father realising this simply changed 'before' to 'of' and removed the brackets, as in the text printed. Here, however, he neglected to change 'yesterday' (see also note 24). These slips are odd, but do not seem to have any particular significance.

It is seen subsequently how these Elves could have 'heard all about that from the Rivendell people', for Bingo tells Gildor (p. 63) that Gandalf 'went off with the dwarves *and the Rivendell elves* as soon as the fireworks were over.' The meeting between them is in fact mentioned later (p. 101).

18 The typescript runs straight on from *we have heard all about that, of course, from the Rivendell people* to 'O Wise People,' said Frodo, and the passage beginning *'Then who are you, and who is your lord?' said Bingo* is an addition. In the typescript as typed the leader of the Elves is not named until towards the end, where after they had eaten

FROM HOBBITON TO THE WOODY END   69

'Bingo remained talking with Gildor, the leader of the Elves' (p. 62); all references to *Gildor* before that are corrections in ink

19 As the text was typed, Bingo said: 'Because we have seen two Black Riders, or one twice over, today.' The changed text accompanies the story of the Rider who paused momentarily beside the hollow tree (see note 11).

20 For the 'elf-latin' (*Qenya*) see the *Lhammas* §4, V.172.

21 This passage is an alteration of the text as typed, which read:
    . . . we are very easy to please (for hobbits). For myself I can only say that the delight of meeting you has already made this a day of bright Adventure.'
        'Bilbo was a good master,' said the Elf bowing. 'Come now, join our company, and we will go. You had best walk in the middle . . .'

22 This sentence replaced the following:
    'Be careful, friends,' said one laughing. 'Speak no secrets! Here is a scholar in the elf-latin and all the dialects. Bilbo was indeed a good master.'
    See note 21 and the altered passage referred to there.

23 This is the first occurrence of the name *Gildor* in the text as typed; see note 18.

24 For *my birthday the day before yesterday* the text as typed had *yesterday*; see note 17.

25 The conversation between Bingo and Gildor to this point, beginning at *You can fence yourselves in, but you have no means of fencing it out* (p. 63), is the last of the replacement typescript pages. The differences from the earlier form are in fact very slight, except in these points. Bingo did not say that Gandalf had told him not to put off his journey later than the autumn, but simply 'He helped me, and seemed to think it a good idea'; and Gildor's reply therefore begins differently: 'I wonder. He may not have known they were in the Shire; yet he knows more about them than we do.' And Bingo said that Odo and Frodo 'only know that I am on a Journey – on a sort of prolonged (and possibly permanent) holiday from Hobbiton; and making for Rivendell to begin with.'

26 Struck from the typescript here: 'and it might prevent you from taking it.'

27 Struck from the typescript here: '(for the matter is outside the concern of such Elves as we are).'

★

It is characteristic that while the *dramatis personae* are not the same, and the story possesses as yet none of the dimension, the gravity, and the sense of vast danger, imparted by the second chapter of *The Fellowship of the Ring*, a good part of 'Three is Company' was already in being; for

70   THE RETURN OF THE SHADOW

once the journey has started not only the structure of the final narrative but much of the detail is present, though countless modifications in expression were to come, and in several substantial passages the chapter was scarcely changed afterwards.

While 'Bingo' is directly equatable with the later 'Frodo', the other relations are more complex. It is true that, comparing the text as it was at this stage with the final form in FR, it may be said simply that 'Odo' became 'Pippin' while Frodo Took disappeared: of the individual speeches in this chapter which remained into FR almost every remark made by Odo was afterwards given to Pippin. But the way in which this came about was in fact strangely tortuous, and was by no means a simple substitution of one name for another (see further pp. 323–4). Frodo Took is seen as a less limited and more aware being than Odo, more susceptible to the beauty and otherness of the Elves; it is he who speaks *The Road goes ever on and on*, and it is to him that the recollection of the words of the song to Elbereth is first attributed (note 15). Some element of him might be said to be preserved in Sam Gamgee (who of course imparts a new and entirely distinctive air to the developed form of the chapter); it was Frodo Took who with bated breath whispered *Elves!* when their voices were first heard coming down the road.

Most remarkable is the fact that when the story of the beginning of the Journey, the coming of the Black Riders, and the meeting with Gildor and his company, was written, and written so that its content would not in essentials be changed afterwards, Bingo has no faintest inkling of what the Riders want with him. Gandalf has told him nothing. He has no reason to associate the Riders with his ring, and no reason to regard it as more than a highly convenient magical device – he slips it on each time a Rider passes, naturally.

Of course, the fact that Bingo is wholly ignorant of the nature of the pursuing menace, utterly baffled by the black horsemen, does not imply that my father was also. There are several suggestions that new ideas had arisen in the background, not explicitly conveyed in the narrative, but deliberately reduced to dark hints of danger in the words of Gildor (that this was so will be seen more clearly at the beginning of the next chapter). It may be that it was the 'unpremeditated' conversion of the cloaked and muffled horseman who overtook them on the road from Gandalf to a 'black rider' (p. 48), combining with the idea already present that Bilbo's ring was of dark origin and strange properties (pp. 42–3) that was the impulse of the new conceptions.

From the early rewriting of the conversation between Gildor and Bingo (see p. 63 and note 25) it emerges that Gandalf had warned Bingo not to delay his departure beyond the autumn (though without, apparently, giving him any reason for the warning), and in both forms of the text Gildor evidently knows something about the Riders, says that 'by what seems strange good luck you went just in time', and associates them with the Ring: warning Bingo against using it again to escape them,

FROM HOBBITON TO THE WOODY END 71

and suggesting that the use of it 'helps them more than you.' (The Ring had not been mentioned in their conversation, but we can suppose that Bingo had previously told Gildor that he had used it when the Riders came by).

The idea of the Riders and the Ring was no doubt evolving as my father wrote. I think it very possible that when he first described the halts of the black horsemen beside the hiding hobbits he imagined them as drawn by scent alone (see p. 75); and it is not clear in any case in what way the use of the Ring would 'help them more than you.' As I have said, it is deeply characteristic that these scenes emerged at once in the clear and memorable form that was never changed, but that their bearing and significance would afterwards be enormously enlarged. The 'event' (one might say) was fixed, but its meaning capable of indefinite extension; and this is seen, over and over again, as a prime mark of my father's writing. In FR, from the intervening chapter *The Shadow of the Past*, we have some notion of what that other feeling was which struggled with Frodo's desire to hide, of why Gandalf had so urgently forbidden him to use the Ring, and of why he was driven irresistibly to put it on; and when we have read further we know what would have happened if he had. The scenes here are empty by comparison, yet they are the same scenes. Even such slight remarks as Bingo's 'I don't know, and I don't want to guess' (p. 55) – in the context, a mere expression of doubt and discomfort, if with a suggestion that Gandalf must have said *something*, or rather, that my father was beginning to think that Gandalf must have said something – survived to take on a much more menacing significance in FR (p. 85), where we have a very good idea of what Frodo chose not to guess about.

Frodo Took's story of his meeting with a Rider on the moors in the North of the Shire in the previous spring is the forerunner of Sam's sudden remembering that a Rider had come to Hobbiton and spoken with Gaffer Gamgee on the evening of their departure; but it seems strange that the beginning of the hunt for 'Baggins' should be set so long before (see p. 74 and note 4).

The striking out of Gildor's words 'for the matter is outside the concern of such Elves as we are' (note 27) is interesting. At first, I think, my father thought of these Elves as 'Dark-elves'; but he now decided that they (and also the Elves of Rivendell) were indeed 'High Elves of the West', and he added in Gildor's words to Bingo on p. 60 (see note 18): they were 'Wise-elves' (Noldor or Gnomes), 'one of the few companies that still remain east of the Sea', and he himself is Gildor Inglorion of the house of Finrod. With these words of Gildor's cf. the *Quenta Silmarillion* §28, in V.332:

Yet not all the Eldalië were willing to forsake the Hither Lands where they had long suffered and long dwelt; and some lingered many an age in the West and North . . . But ever as the ages drew on and the Elf-folk

72   THE RETURN OF THE SHADOW

faded upon earth, they would set sail at eve from the western shores of this world, as still they do, until now there linger few anywhere of their lonely companies.

At this time Finrod was the name of the third son of Finwë (first Lord of the Noldor). This was later changed to Finarfin, when Inglor Felagund his son took over the name Finrod (see I.44), but my father did not change 'of the house of Finrod' here (FR p. 89) to 'of the house of Finarfin' in the second edition of *The Lord of the Rings*. See further p. 188 (end of note 9).

The geography of the Shire was now taking more substantial shape. In this chapter there emerge the North Moor(s); the Green Hill Country lying to the south of Hobbiton; the Pool of Bywater (described in rough drafting for the passage as a 'little lake'); the East Road to the Brandywine Bridge, where the Water joined the Brandywine; the road branching off from it southward and leading in a direct line to Buckland; and the hamlet of Woodhall in the Woody End.

III

OF GOLLUM AND THE RING

I have suggested that by this stage my father knew a good deal more about the Riders and the Ring than Bingo did, or than he permitted Gildor to tell; and evidence for this is found in the manuscript draft referred to on p. 48. This begins, at any rate, as a draft for a part of the conversation between Bingo and Gildor, but the talk here moves into topics which my father excluded from the typescript version (pp. 62–5). Gildor is not yet named, in fact, and indeed it was apparently in this text that he emerged as an individual: at first the conversation is between Bingo and an undifferentiated plural 'they'.

The passage begins with an apparently disconnected sentence: 'Since he did not tell his companions what he discovered I think I shall not tell you.' (Does this refer to what Bingo discovered from the Elves?) Then follows:

'Of course,' they said, 'we know that you are in search of Adventure; but it often happens that when you think it is ahead, it comes up unexpectedly from behind. Why did you choose this moment to set out?'

'Well, the moment was really inevitable, you know,' said Bingo. 'I had come to the end of my treasure. And by wandering I thought I *might* find some more, like old Bilbo, and at least should be able more easily to live without any. I thought too it might be good for me. I was getting rather soft and fat.'

'Yes,' they laughed, 'you *look* just like an ordinary hobbit.'

'But though I can do a few things – like carpentry and gardening: I did not feel inclined somehow to make other people's chairs, or grow other people's vegetables for a living. I suppose some tiny touch of dragon-curse came to me. I am gold-lazy.'

'Then Gandalf did not tell you anything? You were not actually escaping.'

'What do you mean? What from?'

'Well, this black rider,' they said.

'I don't understand them at all.'

'Then Gandalf told you nothing?'

'Not about them. He warned Bilbo a long time ago about the Ring, of course.[1] "Don't use it too much!" he used to say. "And

74   THE RETURN OF THE SHADOW

only use it for proper purposes. I mean, do not use it except for jest, or for escaping from danger and annoyance – don't use it for harm, or for finding out other people's secrets, and of course not for theft or worse things. Because it may get the better of you." I did not understand.

'I seldom saw Gandalf after Bilbo went away. But about a year ago he came one night, and I told him of the plan I was beginning to make for leaving Bag-end. "What about the Ring?" he asked. "Are you being careful? Do be careful: otherwise you will be overcome by it." I had as a matter of fact hardly ever used it – and I did not use it again after that talk until my birthday party.'

'Does anyone else know about it?'

'I cannot say; but I don't think so. Bilbo kept it very secret. He always told me that I was the only one who knew about it (in the Shire).[2] I never told anyone else except Odo and Frodo who are my best friends. I have tried to be to them what Bilbo was to me. But even to them I never spoke of the Ring until they agreed to come with me on this Journey a few months ago. They would not tell anyone – though we often speak of it among ourselves. – Well, what do you make of it all? I can see you are bursting with secrets, but I cannot guess any of them.'

'Well,' said the Elf. 'I don't know much about this. You must find Gandalf as quick as you can – Rivendell I think is the place to go to. But it is my belief that the Lord of the Ring[3] is looking for you.'

'Is that bad or good?'

'Bad; but how bad I cannot say. Bad enough if he only wants the ring back (which is unlikely); worse, if he wants payment; very bad indeed if he wants you as well (which is quite likely). We fancy that he must at last after many years have found out that Bilbo had it. Hence the asking for Baggins.[4] But somehow the search for Baggins failed, and then something must have been discovered about you. But by strange luck you must have held your party and vanished just as they found out where you lived. You put off the scent; but they are hot on it now.'

'Who are they?'

'Servants of the Lord of the Ring – [?people] who have passed through the Ring.'

This ends a sheet, and the following sheet is not continuous with what precedes; but as found among my father's papers they were placed together, and on both of them he wrote (later) 'About Ring-wraiths'. The second passage is also part of a conversation, but there is no indication of

OF GOLLUM AND THE RING

who the speaker is (whoever it is, he is obviously speaking to Bingo). It was written at great speed and is extremely difficult to make out.

Yes, if the Ring overcomes you, you yourself become permanently invisible – and it is a horrible cold feeling. Everything becomes very faint like grey ghost pictures against the black background in which you live; but you can smell more clearly than you can hear or see.[5] You have no power however like a Ring of making other things invisible: you are a ringwraith. You can wear clothes. [> you are just a ringwraith; and your clothes are visible, unless the Lord lends you a ring.] But you are under the command of the Lord of the Rings.[6]

I expect that one (or more) of these Ringwraiths have been sent to get the ring away from hobbits.

In the very ancient days the Ring-lord made many of these Rings: and sent them out through the world to snare people. He sent them to all sorts of folk – the Elves had many, and there are now many elfwraiths in the world, but the Ring-lord cannot rule them; the goblins got many, and the invisible goblins are very evil and wholly under the Lord; dwarves I don't believe had any; some say the rings don't work on them: they are too solid. Men had few, but they were most quickly overcome and . . . . . The men-wraiths are also servants of the Lord. Other creatures got them. Do you remember Bilbo's story of Gollum?[7] We don't know where Gollum comes in – certainly not elf, nor goblin; he is probably not dwarf; we rather believe he really belongs to an ancient sort of hobbit. Because the ring seems to act just the same for him and you. Long ago [?he belonged] . . . . to a wise, cleverhanded and quietfooted little family. But he disappeared underground, and though he used the ring often the Lord evidently lost track of it. Until Bilbo brought it out to light again.

Of course Gollum himself may have heard news – all the mountains were full of it after the battle – and tried to get back the ring, or told the Lord.

At this point the manuscript stops. Here is a first glimpse of an earlier history of Gollum; a suggestion of how the hunt for the Ring originated; and a first sketching of the idea that the Dark Lord gave out Rings among the peoples of Middle-earth. The Rings conferred invisibility, and (it is at least implied) this invisibility was associated with the fate (or at least the peril) of the bearers of the Rings: that they become 'wraiths' and – in the case of goblins and men – servants of the Dark Lord.

76   THE RETURN OF THE SHADOW

Now at some very early stage my father wrote a chapter, without number or title, in which he made use of the passage just given; and this is the first drafting of (a part of) what ultimately became Chapter 2, 'The Shadow of the Past'. As I have noticed, in the second of these two passages marked 'About Ring-wraiths' it is not clear who is speaking. It may be Gildor, or it may be Gandalf, or (perhaps most likely) neither the one nor the other, but indeterminate; but in any case I think that my father decided when writing the draft text of the second chapter that he would not have Gildor discussing these matters with Bingo (as he certainly does in the first of these 'Ring-wraith' passages, p. 74), but would reserve them for Gandalf's instruction, and that this was the starting-point of the chapter which I now give, in which as I have said he made use of the second 'Ring-wraith' passage. Whether he wrote this text at once, before going on to the third chapter (IV in this book), seems impossible to say; but the fact that Marmaduke is mentioned shows that it preceded 'In the House of Tom Bombadil', where 'Meriadoc' and 'Merry' first appear. This, at any rate, is a convenient place to put it.

Subsequently my father referred to it as a 'foreword' (see p. 224), and it is clear that it was written as a possible new beginning for the book, in which Gandalf tells Bingo at Bag End, not long before the Party, something of the history and nature of his Ring, of his danger, and of the need for him to leave his home. It was composed very rapidly and is hard to read. I have introduced punctuation where needed, and occasionally put in silently necessary connective words. There are many pencilled alterations and additions which are here ignored, for they are anticipations of a later version of the chapter; but changes belonging to the time of composition are adopted into the text. There is no title.

One day long ago two people were sitting talking in a small room. One was a wizard and the other was a hobbit, and the room was the sitting-room of the comfortable and well-furnished hobbit-hole known as Bag-end, Underhill, on the outskirts of Hobbiton in the middle of the Shire. The wizard was of course Gandalf and he looked much the same as he had always done, though ninety years and more[8] had gone by since he last came into any story that is now remembered. The hobbit was Bingo Bolger-Baggins, the nephew (or really first cousin once removed) of old Bilbo Baggins, and his adopted heir. Bilbo had quietly disappeared many years before, but he was not forgotten in Hobbiton.

Bingo of course was always thinking about him; and when Gandalf paid him a visit their talk usually came back to Bilbo. Gandalf had not been to Hobbiton for some time: since Bilbo disappeared his visits had become fewer and more secret. The people of Hobbiton had not in fact seen or at any rate noticed him

OF GOLLUM AND THE RING

for many years: he used to come quietly up to the door of Bag-end in the twilight and step in without knocking, and only Bingo (and one or two of his closest friends) knew he had been in the Shire. This evening he had slipped in in his usual way, and Bingo was more than usually glad to see him. For he was worried, and wanted explanations and advice.[9] They were now talking of Bilbo, and his disappearance, and particularly about the Ring (which he had left behind with Bingo) – and about certain strange signs and portents of trouble brewing after a long time of peace and quiet.[10]

'It is all very peculiar – and most disturbing and in fact terrifying,' said Bingo. Gandalf was sitting smoking in a high chair, and Bingo near his feet was huddled on a stool warming his hands by a small wood-fire as if he felt chilly, though actually it was rather a warm evening for the time of the year [*written above:* at the end of August].[11] Gandalf grunted – the sound might have meant 'I quite agree, but it can't be helped,' or else possibly 'What a silly thing to say.' There was a long silence. 'How long have you known all this?' asked Bingo at length; 'and did you ever talk about it to Bilbo?'

'I guessed a good deal immediately,' answered Gandalf slowly, as if searching back in memory. Already to him the days of the journey and the Dragon and the Battle of Five Armies began to seem far off – in an almost legendary past. Perhaps even he was at last getting to feel his age a little; and in any case many dark and curious adventures had befallen him since then. 'I guessed much,' he said, 'but soon I learnt more, for I went, as Bilbo may have told you, to the land of the Necromancer.'[12] For a moment his voice faded to a whisper. 'But I knew that all was well with Bilbo,' he went on. 'Bilbo was safe, for that kind of power was powerless over him – or so I thought, and I was right in a way (if not quite right). I kept an eye on him and it, of course, but perhaps I was not careful enough.'

'I am sure you did your best,' said Bingo, meaning to console him. 'O dearest and best friend of our house, may your beard never grow less! But it must have been rather a blow when Bilbo disappeared.'

'Not at all,' said Gandalf, with a sudden return to his ordinary tones. He sent out a great jet of smoke with an indignant *poof* and it coiled round his head like a cloud on a mountain. 'That did not worry me. Bilbo is all right. It is you and all these other dear, silly, charming, idiotic, helpless hobbits that trouble me! It would be a

78   THE RETURN OF THE SHADOW

mortal blow if the dark power should overcome the Shire, and all these jolly, greedy, stupid Bolgers, Bagginses, Brandybucks, Hornblowers, Proudfoots and whatnot became Wraiths.'

Bingo shuddered. 'But why should we?' he asked; 'and why should the Lord want such servants, and what has all this to do with me and the Ring?'

'It is the only Ring left,' said Gandalf. 'And hobbits are the only people of whom the Lord has not yet mastered any one.

'In[13] the ancient days the dark master made many Rings, and he dealt them out lavishly, so that they might be spread abroad to ensnare folk. The elves had many, and there are now many elf-wraiths in the world; the goblins had some and their wraiths are very evil and wholly under the command of the Lord. The dwarves it is said had seven, but nothing could make them invisible. In them it only kindled to flames the fire of greed, and the foundation of each of the seven hoards of the Dwarves of old was a golden ring. In this way the master controlled them. But these hoards are destroyed, and the dragons have devoured them, and the rings are melted, or so some say.[14] Men had three rings, and others they found in secret places cast away by the elf-wraiths: the men-wraiths are servants of the Lord, and they brought all their rings back to him; till at last he had gathered all into his hands again that had not been destroyed by fire – all save one.

'It fell from the hand of an elf as he swam across a river; and it betrayed him, for he was flying from pursuit in the old wars, and he became visible to his enemies, and the goblins slew him.[15] But a fish took the ring and was filled with madness, and swam upstream, leaping over rocks and up waterfalls until it cast itself on a bank and spat out the ring and died.

'There was long ago living by the bank of the stream a wise, cleverhanded and quietfooted little family.[16] I guess they were of hobbit-kind, or akin to the fathers of the fathers of the hobbits. The most inquisitive and curious-minded of that family was called Dígol. He was interested in roots and beginnings; he dived in deep pools, he burrowed under trees and growing plants, he tunnelled into green mounds, and he ceased to look up at flowers, and hill-tops, or the birds that are in the upper air: his head and eyes were downward. He found the ring in the mud of the river-bank under the roots of a thorn tree; and he put it on; and when he returned home none of his family saw him while he wore it. He was pleased with his discovery and concealed it, and he used it to discover secrets, and put his knowledge to malicious use, and became

OF GOLLUM AND THE RING

sharp-eyed and keen-eared for all that was unpleasant. It is not to be wondered at that he became very unpopular, and was shunned (when visible) by all his relatives. They kicked him, and he bit their feet. He took to muttering to himself and gurgling in his throat. So they called him Gollum, and cursed him, and told him to go far away. He wandered in loneliness up the stream and caught fish with his fingers in deep pools and ate them raw. One day it was very hot, and as he was bending over a pool he felt a burning on the back of his head, and a dazzling light from the water pained his eyes. He wondered, for he had almost forgotten about the sun; and for the last time he looked up and shook his fist at it; but as he lowered his eyes again he saw far ahead the tops of the Misty Mountains. And he thought suddenly: "It would be cool and shady under those mountains. The sun could never find me there. And the roots of those peaks must be roots indeed; there must be great secrets buried there which have not been discovered since the beginning." So he journeyed by night towards the mountains, and found a hole out of which a stream issued; and he wormed his way in like a maggot in the heart of the hills, and disappeared from all knowledge. And the ring went into the shadows with him, and even the Master lost it. But whenever he counted his rings, besides the seven rings that the Dwarves had held and lost, there was also one missing.'

'Gollum!' said Bingo. 'Do you mean that Gollum that Bilbo met? Is that his history? How very horrible and sad. I hate to think that he was connected with hobbits, however distantly.'

'But that surely was plain from Bilbo's own account,' said Gandalf. 'It is the only thing that explains the events – or partly explains them. There was a lot in the background of both their minds and memories that was very similar – they understood one another really (if you think of it) better than hobbits ever understood dwarves, elves, or goblins.'

'Still, Gollum must have been, or be, very much older than the oldest hobbit that ever lived in field or burrow,' said Bingo.

'That was the Ring,' said Gandalf. 'Of course it is a poor sort of long life that the Ring gives, a kind of stretched life rather than a continued growing – a sort of thinning and thinning. Frightfully wearisome, Bingo, in fact finally tormenting. Even Gollum came at last to feel it, to feel he could not bear it, and to understand dimly the cause of the torment. He had even made up his mind to get rid of it. But he was too full of malice. If you want to know, I believe he had begun to make a plan that he had not the courage

80 THE RETURN OF THE SHADOW

left to carry out. There was nothing new to find out; nothing left but darkness, nothing to do but cold eating, and regretful remembering. He wanted to slip out and leave the mountains, and smell the open air even if it killed him – as he thought it probably would. But that would have meant leaving the Ring. And that is not easy to do. The longer you have had one the harder it is. It was especially hard for Gollum, as he had had a Ring for ages, and it hurt him and he hated it, and he wanted, when he could no longer bear to keep it, to hand it on to someone else to whom it would become a burden – [?bind] itself as a blessing and turn to a curse.[17] That is in fact the best way of getting rid of its power.'

'Why not give it to the goblins, then?' asked Bingo.

'I don't think Gollum would have found that amusing enough,' said Gandalf. 'The goblins are already so beastly and miserable that it was wasting malice on them. Also it would have been difficult to escape from the hunters if there was an invisible goblin to reckon with. But I suppose he might have put it in their path in the end (if he had plucked up enough courage to do anything); but for the unexpected arrival of Bilbo. You remember how surprised he was. But as soon as the riddles started a plan formed in his mind – or half-formed. I dare say his old bad habits would have beaten his resolves and he would have eaten Bilbo if it had proved easy. But there was the sword, you remember. In his heart, I fancy, he never seriously expected to get a chance of eating Bilbo.'

'But he never gave Bilbo the ring,' said Bingo. 'Bilbo had got it already!'

'I know,' said Gandalf. 'And that is why I said that Gollum's ancestry only partly explained events. There was, of course, something much more mysterious behind the whole thing – something quite beyond the Lord of the Rings himself, peculiar to Bilbo and his great Adventure. There was a queer fate over these rings, and especially over [?this] one. They got lost occasionally, and turned up in strange places. This one had already slipped away from its owner treacherously once before. It had slipped away from Gollum too. That is why I let Bilbo keep the ring so long.[18] But for the moment I am trying to explain Gollum.'

'I see,' said Bingo doubtfully. 'But do you know what happened afterwards?'

'Not very clearly,' said Gandalf. 'I have heard a little, and can guess more. I think it certain that Gollum knew in the end that Bilbo had somehow got the Ring. He may well have guessed it soon. But in any case the news of the later events went all over

OF GOLLUM AND THE RING

Wilderland and far beyond, East, West, and South and North. The mountains were full of whispers and reports; and that would give Gollum enough to think about.[19] Anyway, it is said that Gollum left the mountains – for the goblins had become very few there, and the deep places more than ever dark and lonely, and the power of the ring had left him. He was probably feeling old, very old, but less timid. But I do not think he became less wicked. There is no news of what happened to him afterwards. Of course, it is quite likely that wind and the mere shadow of sunlight killed him pretty quickly. But it is possible that it did not. He was cunning. He could hide from daylight or moonlight till he slowly grew more used to things. I have in fact a horrible fancy that he made his slow sneaking way bit by bit to the dark tower, to the Necromancer, the Lord of the Rings. I think that Gollum is very likely the beginning of our present trouble; and that through him the Lord found out where to look for this last and most precious and potent of his Rings.'

'What a pity Bilbo did not stab the beastly creature when he said goodbye,' said Bingo . . . .

'What nonsense you do talk sometimes, Bingo,' said Gandalf. 'Pity! It was pity that prevented him. And he could not do so, without doing wrong. It was against the rules. If he had done so he would not have had the ring, the ring would have had him at once. He might have been a wraith on the spot.'

'Of course, of course,' said Bingo. 'What a thing to say of Bilbo. Dear old Bilbo! But why did *he* keep the thing, or why did you let him? Didn't you warn him about it?'

'Yes,' said Gandalf. 'But even over Bilbo it had *some* power. Sentiment . . . . He liked to keep it as a memento. Let us be frank – he continued to be proud of his Great Adventure, and to look on the ring now and again warmed his memory, and made him feel just a trifle heroic. But he could hardly have helped himself anyway: if you think for a moment, it is not really very easy to get rid of a Ring once you have got it.'

'Why not?' said Bingo, after thinking for a moment. 'You can give it away, throw it away, or destroy it.'

'Yes,' said Gandalf – 'or you can surrender it: to the Master. That is if you wish to serve him, and to fall into his power, and to greatly increase his power.'

'But no one would wish to do that,' said Bingo, horrified.

'Nobody that you can imagine, perhaps,' answered Gandalf. 'Certainly not Bilbo. That is what made it difficult for him. He

82   THE RETURN OF THE SHADOW

dared not throw it away lest it get into evil hands, and be misused, and find its way back to the Master after doing much evil. He would not give it away to bad folk for the same reason; and he would not give it away to good folk or people he knew and trusted because he did not wish to burden them with it, any sooner than he was obliged. And he could not destroy it.'

'Why not?'

'Well, how would you destroy it? Have *you* ever tried?'

'No; but I suppose one could hammer it, or melt it, or do both.'

'Try them,' said Gandalf, 'and you will find out what Bilbo found out long ago.'

Bingo drew the Ring out of an inner pocket, and looked at it. It was plain and smooth without device, emblem, or rune; but it was of gold, and as he looked at it it seemed to Bingo that its colour was rich and beautiful, and its roundness perfect. It was very admirable and wholly precious. He had thought of throwing it into the hot embers of the fire. He found he could not do so without a struggle. He weighed the Ring in his hand, and then with an effort of will he made a movement as if to throw it in the fire; but he found he had put it back in his pocket.

Gandalf laughed. 'You see? You have always regarded it as a great treasure, and an heirloom from Bilbo. Now you cannot easily get rid of it. Though as a matter of fact, even if you took it to an anvil and summoned enough will to strike it with a heavy hammer, you would make no dint on it. Your little wood-fire, of course, even if you blew all night with a bellows would hardly melt any gold. But old Adam Hornblower the smith down the road could not melt it in his furnace. They say only dragonfire can melt them – but I wonder if that is not a legend, or at any rate if there are any dragons now left in which the old fire is hot enough. I fancy you would have to find one of the Cracks of Earth in the depths of the Fiery Mountain, and drop it down into the Secret Fire, if you really wanted to destroy it.'[20]

'After all your talk,' said Bingo, half solemnly and half in pretended annoyance, 'I really do want to destroy it. I cannot think how Bilbo put up with it for so long, if he knew as much – but he actually used it sometimes, and joked about it to me.'

'The only thing to do with such perilous treasures that Adventure has bestowed on you is to take them lightheartedly,' said Gandalf. 'Bilbo never used the ring for any serious purpose after he came back. He knew that it was too serious a matter. And I

OF GOLLUM AND THE RING

83

think he taught you well – after he had chosen you as his heir from among all the hobbits of his kindred.'

There was a long silence again, while Gandalf puffed at his pipe in apparent content, though under his lids his eyes were watching Bingo intently. Bingo gazed at the red embers, that began to glow as the light faded and the room grew slowly dark. He was thinking about the fabled Cracks of Earth and the terror of the Fiery Mountain.

'Well?' said Gandalf at last. 'What are you thinking about? Are you making any plans or getting any ideas?'

'No,' said Bingo coming back to himself, and finding to his surprise that he was in the dark. 'Or perhaps yes! As far as I can see I have got to leave Hobbiton, leave the Shire, leave everything and go away and draw the danger after me. I must save the Shire somehow, though there have been times when I thought it too stupid and dull for anything, and fancied a big explosion or an invasion of dragons might do it good! But I don't feel like that now. I feel that as long as the Shire lies behind safe and comfortable, I shall find wandering and adventures bearable. I shall feel there is some foothold somewhere, even if I can't ever stand on it myself again. But I suppose I must go alone. I feel rather minute, don't you know, and extremely uprooted, and, well, frightened, I suppose. Help me, Gandalf, best of friends.'

'Cheer up, Bingo, my lad,' said Gandalf, throwing two small logs of wood on the fire and puffing it with his mouth. Immediately the wood blazed up and filled the room with dancing light. 'No, I don't think you need or should go alone. Why not ask your three best friends to, beg them to, order them to (if you must) – I mean the three, the only three who you have (perhaps indiscreetly but perhaps with wise choice) told about your secret Ring: Odo, Frodo, and Marmaduke [*written above:* Meriadoc]. But you must go quickly – and make it a joke, Bingo, a joke, a huge joke, a resounding jest. Don't be mournful and serious. Jokes are really in your line. That's what Bilbo liked about you (among other things), if you care to know.'

'And where shall we go, and what shall we steer by, and what shall be our quest?' said Bingo, without a trace of a smile or the glimmer of a jest. 'When the huge joke is over, what then?'

'At present I have no idea,' said Gandalf, quite seriously and much to Bingo's surprise and dismay. 'But it will be just the opposite of Bilbo's adventure – to begin with, at any rate. You will set out on a journey without any known destination; and as far as

84   THE RETURN OF THE SHADOW

you have any object it will not be to win new treasure but to get rid of a treasure that belongs (one might say) inevitably to you. But you cannot even start without going East, West, South, or North; and which shall we choose? Towards danger, and yet not too rashly or too straight towards it. Go East. Yes, yes, I have it. Make first for Rivendell, and then we shall see. Yes, we shall see then. Indeed, I begin to see already!' Suddenly Gandalf began to chuckle. He rubbed his long gnarled hands together and cracked the finger-joints. He leant forward to Bingo. 'I have thought of a joke,' he said. 'Just a rough plan – you can set your comic wits to work on it.' And his beard wagged backwards and forwards as he whispered long in Bingo's ear. The fire burned low again – but suddenly in the darkness an unexpected sound rang out. Bingo was rocking with laughter.

NOTES

1   My father's own thought is surely transparent here. Bingo introduces the subject of the Ring as if it had some connection with the Riders, whereas he is obviously intended to appear as quite unable even to guess at their significance; and there is no suggestion in the drafts that the Ring had been mentioned before this point.

2   *(in the Shire):* my father first wrote 'except Gandalf'. The words *'(in the Shire)'* probably mean no more than that: i.e., no one save Bilbo and Bingo, and outside the Shire only Gandalf, and anyone else whom Gandalf might possibly have told.

3   This is probably the first time that the expression *The Lord of the Ring* was used; and *The Lord of the Rings* occurs below (note 6). (My father gave *The Lord of the Ring* as the title of the new work in a letter to Allen and Unwin of 31 August 1938).

4   *Hence the asking for Baggins:* this is not mentioned in the manuscript drafts, but see the typescript version, p. 54 and note 9. The following sentence, 'But somehow the search for Baggins failed, and then something must have been discovered about you' perhaps explains the story that Frodo Took met a Black Rider on the North Moor as early as the previous spring (see p. 71).

5   My father first wrote here that the clothing of one who has thus become permanently invisible was invisible also, but rejected the statement as soon as written.

6   This seems to be the first appearance of the expression *The Lord of the Rings*; see note 3.

7   After this sentence my father wrote: 'Gollum I think some sort of distant kinsman of the goblin sort.' Since this is contradicted in the

OF GOLLUM AND THE RING 85

next sentence it was obviously rejected in the act of writing; he crossed it out later.

8 *ninety years and more:* see pp. 31–3.

9 At no point in this text is there any further mention of Bingo's 'worry'; and the advice that he asks is entirely based on what . Gandalf now tells him and which is obviously entirely new to him. There is also no further reference to the 'strange signs and portents of trouble brewing' spoken of in the next sentence, nor any explanation of Gandalf's remark (p. 81) that 'Gollum is very likely the beginning of *our present trouble.*'

10 This ends the first page of the manuscript. At the head of the second page my father wrote in pencil: 'Gandalf and Bingo discuss Rings and Gollum', and 'Draft: Later used in Chapter II', and he numbered the pages (previously unnumbered) in Greek letters, beginning at this point. Thus the first page is left out. But these pencillings were clearly put in long after, and in my view they cast no doubt on the validity of the opening section as an integral part of the text. May be it had at one time become separated and mislaid; but as the papers were found it was placed with the rest.

11 Rumour of the Party – decided on between Gandalf and Bingo at the end of this text – began to circulate early in September (p. 30).

12 In *The Hobbit* (Chapter I) Gandalf told Thorin at Bag End that he found his father Thrain 'in the dungeons of the Necromancer'. In the Tale of Years in LR Appendix B this, Gandalf's second visit to Dol Guldur, took place in the year 2850, forty years before Bilbo's birth; it was then that he 'discovered that its master was indeed Sauron' (cf. FR p. 263). But here the meaning is clearly that Gandalf went to the land of the Necromancer *after* Bilbo's acquisition of the Ring. Later my father altered the text in pencil to read: 'for I went back once more to the land of the Necromancer.'

13 Here the earlier draft concerning the Rings is used: see p. 75.

14 See FR p. 60 and LR Appendix A pp. 357–8.

15 This is the first germ of the story of the death of Isildur.

16 This is also derived from the text referred to in note 13.

17 This sentence as first written ended: 'and he wanted to hand it on to someone else.' It is to this that the following sentence refers.

18 The passage beginning 'There was a queer fate' was an addition, and 'That is why I let Bilbo keep the ring so long' refers to the sentence ending '. . . peculiar to Bilbo and his great Adventure.'

19 Cf. the draft passage given on p. 75: 'Of course Gollum himself may have heard news – all the mountains were full of it after the battle – and tried to get back the ring.'

20 The first mention of the Fiery Mountain and the Cracks of Earth in its depths.

★

86   THE RETURN OF THE SHADOW

It will be seen that a part of the 'Gollum' element in 'The Shadow of the Past' (Chapter 2 in FR) was at once very largely achieved, even though Dígol* (later Déagol) is Gollum himself, and not his friend whom he murdered, though Gandalf had never seen him (and so no explanation is given of how he knows his history, which of its nature could only be derived from Gollum's own words), and though it is only surmised that he went at last to the Dark Lord.

It is important to realise that when my father wrote this, he was working within the constraints of the story as originally told in *The Hobbit*. As *The Hobbit* first appeared, and until 1951, the story was that Gollum, encountering Bilbo at the edge of the subterranean lake, proposed the riddle game on these conditions: 'If precious asks, and it doesn't answer, we eats it, my preciousss. If it asks us, and we doesn't answer, we gives it a present, gollum!' When Bilbo won the contest, Gollum held to his promise, and went back in his boat to his island in the lake to find his treasure, the ring which was to be his present to Bilbo. He could not find it, for Bilbo had it in his pocket, and coming back to Bilbo he begged his pardon many times: 'He kept on saying: "We are ssorry: we didn't mean to cheat, we meant to give it our only present, if it won the competition".' '"Never mind!" he [Bilbo] said. "The ring would have been mine now, if you had found it; so you would have lost it anyway. And I will let you off on one condition." "Yes, what iss it? What does it wish us to do, my precious?" "Help me to get out of these places", said Bilbo.' And Gollum did so; and Bilbo 'said good-bye to the nasty miserable creature.' On the way up through the tunnels Bilbo slipped on the ring, and Gollum at once missed him, so that Bilbo perceived that the ring was as Gollum had told him – it made you invisible.

This is why, in the present text, Gandalf says 'I think it certain that Gollum knew in the end that Bilbo had got the ring'; and why my father had Gandalf develop a theory that Gollum was actually ready to give the ring away: 'he wanted . . . to hand it on to someone else . . . I suppose he might have put it in [the goblins'] path in the end . . . but for the unexpected arrival of Bilbo . . . as soon as the riddles started a plan formed in his mind.' This is all carefully conceived in relation to the text of *The Hobbit* as it then was, to meet the formidable difficulty: if the Ring were of such a nature as my father now conceived it, how *could* Gollum have really intended to give it away to a stranger who won a riddle contest? – and the original text of *The Hobbit* left no doubt that that was indeed his serious intention. But it is interesting to observe that Gandalf's remarks about the affinity of mind between Gollum and Bilbo, which survived into FR (pp. 63–4), originally arose in this context, of explaining how it was that Gollum was willing to let his treasure go.

---

*Old English *dígol*, *déagol*, etc. 'secret, hidden'; cf. LR Appendix F (p. 415).

OF GOLLUM AND THE RING

87

Turning to what is told of the Rings in this text, the original idea (p. 75) that the Elves had many Rings, and that there were many 'Elf-wraiths' in the world, is still present, but the phrase 'the Ring-lord cannot rule them' is not. The Dwarves, on the other hand, at first said not to have had any, now had seven, each the foundation of one of 'the seven hoards of the Dwarves', and their distinctive response to the corruptive power of the Rings enters (though this was already foreshadowed in the first rough draft on the subject: 'some say the rings don't work on them: they are too solid.') Men, at first said to have had 'few', now had three – but 'others they found in secret places cast away by the elf-wraiths' (thus allowing for more than three Black Riders). But the central conception of the Ruling Ring is not yet present, though it was, so to say, waiting in the wings: for it is said that Gollum's Ring was not only the only one that had not returned to the Dark Lord (other than those lost by the Dwarves) – it was the *most precious and potent* of his Rings' (p. 81). But in what its peculiar potency lay we are not told; nor indeed do we learn more here of the relation between the invisibility conferred by the Rings, the torment-ing longevity (which now first appears), and the decline of their bearers into 'wraiths'.

The element of moral will required in one possessed of a Ring to resist its power is strongly asserted. This is seen in Gandalf's advice to Bilbo in the original draft (p. 74): 'don't use it for harm, or for finding out other people's secrets, and of course not for theft or for worse things. *Because it may get the better of you*'; and still more expressly in his rebuke to Bingo, who said that it was a pity that Bilbo did not kill Gollum: 'He could not do so, without doing wrong. It was against the rules. If he had done so he would not have had the ring, *the ring would have had him at once*' (p. 81). This element remains in FR (pp. 68–9), but is more guardedly expressed: 'Be sure that he took so little hurt from the evil, and escaped in the end, because he began his ownership of the Ring so.'

The end of the chapter – with Gandalf actually himself proposing the Birthday Party and Bingo's 'resounding jest' – was to be quickly rejected, and is never heard of again.

IV

TO MAGGOT'S FARM AND BUCKLAND

The third of the original consecutive chapters exists in complete form only in a typescript, where it bears the number 'III' but has no title; there are also however incomplete and very rough manuscript drafts, which were filled out and improved in the typescript but in all essentials left unchanged. Near the end the typescript ceases (note 16), not at the foot of a page, and the remainder of the chapter is in manuscript; for this part also rough drafting exists.

I again give the text in full, since in this chapter the original narrative was far removed from what finally went into print. Subsequent emendation was here very slight. I take up into the text a few manuscript changes that seem to me to be in all probability contemporary with the making of the typescript.

The end of the chapter corresponds to FR Chapter 5 'A Conspiracy Unmasked'; at this stage there was no conspiracy.

III

In the morning Bingo woke refreshed. He was lying in a bower made by a living tree with branches laced and drooping to the ground; his bed was of fern and grass, deep and soft and strangely fragrant. The sun was shining through the fluttering leaves, which were still green upon the tree. He jumped up and went out.

Odo and Frodo were sitting on the grass near the edge of the wood; there was no sign of any elves.

'They have left us fruit and drink, and bread,' said Odo. 'Come and have breakfast! The bread tastes almost as good as last night.'

Bingo sat down beside them. 'Well?' said Odo. 'Did you find anything out?'

'No, nothing,' said Bingo. 'Only hints and riddles. But as far as I could make them out, it seems to me that Gildor thinks there are several Riders; that they are after *me*; that they are now ahead and behind and on both sides of us; that it is no use going back (at least not for me); that we ought to make for Rivendell as quickly as possible, and if we find Gandalf there so much the better; and that we shall have an exciting and dangerous time getting there.'

TO MAGGOT'S FARM AND BUCKLAND

'I call that a lot more than nothing,' said Odo. 'But what about the sniffing?'

'We did not discuss it,' said Bingo with his mouth full.

'You should have,' said Odo. 'I am sure it is very important.'

'In that case I am sure Gildor would have told me nothing about it. But he did say that he thought you might as well come with me. I gathered that the riders are not after you, and that you rather bother them.'

'Splendid! Odo and Frodo are to take care of Uncle Bingo. They won't let him be sniffed at.'

'All right!' said Bingo. 'That's settled. What about the method of advance?'

'What do you mean?' said Odo. 'Shall we hop, skip, run, crawl on our stomachs, or just walk singing along?'

'Exactly. And shall we follow the road, or risk a cross-country cut? There is no choice in the matter of time; we must go in daylight, because Marmaduke is expecting us to-night. In fact we must get off as soon as possible; we have slept late, and there are still quite eighteen miles to go.'

'*You* have slept late, you mean,' said Odo. 'We have been up a long time.'

So far Frodo had said nothing. He was looking out over the tree-tops eastward. He now turned towards them. 'I vote for striking across country,' he said. 'The land is not so wild between here and the River. It ought not to be difficult to mark our direction before we leave this hill, and to keep pretty well to it. Buckland is almost exactly south-east from Woodhall[1] down there in the trees. We should cut off quite a corner, because the road bears away to the left – you can see a bit of it over there – and then sweeps round south when it gets nearer to the River.[2] We could strike it above Buckland before it gets really dark.'

'Short cuts make long delays,' said Odo; 'and I don't see that a Rider is any worse on the road than in the woods.'

'Except that he probably won't be able to see so well, and may not be able to ride so fast,' said Bingo. 'I am also in favour of leaving the road.'

'All right!' said Odo. 'I will follow you into every bog and ditch. You two are as bad as Marmaduke. I suppose I shall be outvoted by three to one, instead of two to one, when we collect him, if we ever do.'

The sun was now hot again; but clouds were beginning to come up from the West. It looked likely to turn to rain, if the wind fell. The hobbits scrambled down a steep green bank and struck into the trees below. Their line was taken to leave Woodhall on their left, and there was some thickish wood immediately in front of them, though after a mile or two it had looked from above as if the land became more open. There was a good deal of undergrowth, and they did not get on very fast. At the bottom of the slope they found a stream running in a deeply dug bed with steep slippery banks overhung with brambles. They could not jump across, and they had the choice of going back and taking a new line, or of turning aside to the left and following the stream until it became easier to cross. Odo looked back. Through the trees they could see the top of the bank which fell from the high green which they had just left. 'Look!' he said, clutching Bingo by the arm. On the top of the slope a black rider sat on a horse; he seemed to be swaying from side to side, as if sweeping all the land eastward with his gaze.

The hobbits gave up any idea of going back, and plunged quickly and silently into the thickest bushes by the stream. They were cut off from the West wind down in the hollow, and very soon they were hot and tired. Bushes, brambles, rough ground, and their packs, all did what they could to hold them back.

'Whew!' said Bingo. 'Both parties were right! The short cut has gone crooked; but we got under cover only just in time. Yours are the sharpest ears, Frodo. Can you hear – can you hear *anything* behind?'

They stopped and looked and listened; but there was no sign or sound of pursuit. They went on again, until the banks of the stream sank and its bed became broad and shallow. They waded across and hurried into the wood on the other side, no longer quite sure of the line they should take. There were no paths, but the ground was fairly level and open. A tall growth of young oaks, mixed with ash and elm, was all round them, so that they could not see far. The leaves of the trees blew upwards in sudden gusts, and spots of rain began to fall; then the wind died away, and the rain came down steadily.

They trudged along fast through thick leaves, while all about them the rain pattered and trickled; they did not talk, but kept glancing from side to side, and sometimes behind. After about an hour Frodo said: 'I suppose we have not struck too much to the south, and are not walking longwise through this wood? From above it looked like a narrow belt, and we ought to have crossed it by now, I should have thought.'

TO MAGGOT'S FARM AND BUCKLAND

'It is no good starting going in zigzags now,' said Bingo. 'Let's keep on. The clouds seem to be breaking, and we may get a helpful glimpse of the sun again before long.'

He was right. By the time they had gone another mile, the sun gleamed out of ragged clouds; and they saw that they were in fact heading too much to the south. They bore a little to their left; but before long they decided by their feelings as much as by the sun that it was time for a mid-day halt and some food.

The rain was still falling at intervals; so they sat under an elm-tree, whose leaves were still thick, though they were fast turning yellow. They found that the Elves had filled their water-bottles with some clear golden drink: it had the scent rather than the taste of honey made of many flowers, and was mightily refreshing. They made a merry meal, and soon were laughing and snapping their fingers at rain and black riders. The next few miles they felt would soon be put behind them. With his back to the tree-trunk Odo began to sing softly to himself:

> *Ho! ho! ho! To my bottle I go*
> *To heal my heart and drown my woe.*
> *Rain may fall and wind may blow,*
> *And many miles be still to go,*
> *But under the elm-tree I will lie*
> *And let the clouds go sailing by!*
>
> *Ho! ho! ho!* ———

It will never be known whether the next verse was any better than the first; for just at the moment there was a noise like a sneeze or a sniff. Odo never finished his song. The noise came again: sniff, sniff, sniff; it seemed to be quite close. They sprang to their feet, and looked quickly about; but there was nothing to be seen anywhere near their tree.[3]

Odo had no more thought of lying and watching the clouds go by. He was the first to be packed and ready to start. In a few minutes from the last sniff they were off again as fast as they could go. The wood soon came to an end; but they were not particularly pleased, for the land became soft and boggy, and hobbits (even on a Journey) don't like mud and clay on their feet. The sun was shining again, and they felt both too hot and too exposed to view away from the trees. Far back now behind them lay the high green where they had breakfasted; every time they looked back towards it they expected to see the distant figure of a horseman against the

92   THE RETURN OF THE SHADOW

sky. But none appeared; and as they went on the land about them got steadily more tame. There were hedges and gates and dikes for drainage; everything looked quiet and peaceful, just an ordinary corner of the Shire.

'I think I recognize these fields,' said Frodo suddenly. 'They belong to old Farmer Maggot,[4] unless I am quite lost. There ought to be a lane somewhere near, that leads from his place into the road a mile or two above Buckland.'[5]

'Does he live in a hole or a house?' asked Odo, who did not know this part of the country.

It was a curious thing about the hobbits of those days that this was an important distinction. All hobbits had, of course, originally lived in holes; but now only the best and the poorest hobbits did so, as a rule. Important hobbits lived in luxurious versions of the simple holes of olden times; but the sites for really good hobbit-holes were not to be found everywhere. Even in Hobbiton, one of the most important villages, there were houses. These were specially favoured by the farmers, millers, blacksmiths, carpenters, and people of that sort. The custom of building houses was supposed to have started among the hobbits of the woody riverside regions, where the land was heavy and wet and had no good hills or convenient banks. They began making artificial holes of mud (and later of brick), roofed with thatch in imitation of natural grass. That was a long time ago, and on the edge of history; but houses were still considered an innovation. The poorest hobbits still lived in holes of the most ancient sort – in fact just holes, with only one window, or even none.[6] But Odo was not thinking about hobbit-history. He merely wanted to know where to look for the farm. If Farmer Maggot had lived in a hole, there would have been rising ground somewhere near; but the land ahead looked perfectly flat.

'He lives in a house,' answered Frodo. 'There are very few holes in these parts. They say houses were invented here. Of course the Brandybucks have that great burrow of theirs at Bucklebury in the high bank across the River; but most of their people live in houses. There are lots of those new-fashioned brick houses – not too bad, I suppose, in their way; though they look very naked, if you know what I mean: no decent turf-covering, all bare and bony.'

'Fancy climbing upstairs to bed!' said Odo. 'That seems to me most inconvenient. Hobbits aren't birds.'

'I don't know,' said Bingo. 'It isn't as bad as it sounds; though personally I never like looking out of upstairs windows, it makes

TO MAGGOT'S FARM AND BUCKLAND 93

me a bit giddy. There are some houses that have three stages, bedrooms above bedrooms. I slept in one once long ago on a holiday; the wind kept me awake all night.'

'What a nuisance, if you want a handkerchief or something when you are downstairs, and find it is upstairs,' said Odo.

'You could keep handkerchiefs downstairs, if you wished,' said Frodo.

'You could, but I don't believe anybody does.'

'That is not the houses' fault,' said Bingo; 'it is just the silliness of the hobbits that live in them. The old tales tell that the Wise Elves used to build tall towers; and only went up their long stairs when they wished to sing or look out of the windows at the sky, or even perhaps the sea. They kept everything downstairs, or in deep halls dug beneath the feet of the towers. I have always fancied that the idea of building came largely from the Elves, though we use it very differently. There used to be three elftowers standing in the land away west beyond the edge of the Shire. I saw them once. They shone white in the Moon. The tallest was furthest away, standing alone on a hill. It was told that you could see the sea from the top of that tower; but I don't believe any hobbit has ever climbed it.[7] If ever I live in a house, I shall keep everything I want downstairs, and only go up when I don't want anything; or perhaps I shall have a cold supper upstairs in the dark on a starry night.'

'And have to carry plates and things downstairs, if you don't fall all the way down,' laughed Odo.

'No!' said Bingo. 'I shall have wooden plates and bowls, and throw them out of the window. There will be thick grass all round my house.'

'But you would still have to carry your supper *up*stairs,' said Odo.

'O well then, perhaps I should not have supper upstairs,' said Bingo. 'It was only just an idea. I don't suppose I shall ever live in a house. As far as I can see, I am going to be just a wandering beggar.'

This very hobbit-like conversation went on for some time. It shows that the three were beginning to feel quite comfortable again, as they got back into tame and familiar country. But even invisible sniffs could not damp for long the spirits of these excellent and peculiarly adventurous hobbits, not in any kind of country.

While they talked they plodded steadily on. It was already late

94   THE RETURN OF THE SHADOW

afternoon when they saw the roof of a house peeping out of a clump of trees ahead and to their left.

'There is Farmer Maggot's!' said Frodo.

'I think we will go round it,' said Bingo, 'and strike the lane on the far side of the house. I am supposed to have vanished, and I would rather not be seen sneaking off in the direction of Buckland, even by good Farmer Maggot.'

They went on, leaving the farmhouse away on their left, hidden in the trees several fields away. Suddenly a small dog came through a gap in a hedge, and ran barking towards them.

'Here! Here! Gip! Gip!' said a voice. Bingo slipped on his ring. There was no chance for the others to hide. Over the top of the low hedge appeared a large round hobbit-face.

'Hullo! Hullo! And who may you be, and what may you be doing?' he asked.

'Good evening, Farmer Maggot!' said Frodo. 'Just a couple of Tooks, from away back yonder; and doing no harm, I hope.'

'Well now, let me see – you'll be Mr Frodo Took, Mr Folco Took's son, if I'm not mistook (and I seldom am: I've a rare memory for faces). You used to stay with young Mr Marmaduke. Any friend of Mr Marmaduke Brandybuck is welcome. You'll excuse my speaking sharp, before I recognized you. We get some strange folk in these parts at times. Too near the river,' he said, jerking back his head. 'There's been a very funny customer round here only an hour back. That's why I'm out with the dog.'

'What kind of a customer?' asked Frodo.

'A funny customer and asking funny questions,' said Farmer Maggot, shaking his head. 'Come along to my house and have a drink and we'll pass the news more comfortably like, if you and your friend are willing, Mr Took.'

It seemed plain that Farmer Maggot would only pass the news in his own time and place, and they guessed that it might be interesting; so Frodo and Odo went along with him. The dog remained behind jumping and frisking round Bingo to his annoyance.

'What's come to the dog?' said the farmer, looking back. 'Here, Gip! Heel!' he called. To Bingo's relief the dog obeyed, though it turned back once and barked.

'What's the matter with you?' growled Farmer Maggot. 'There seems to be something queer abroad this day. Gip went near off his head when that stranger came along, and now you'd think he could see or smell something that ain't there.'

TO MAGGOT'S FARM AND BUCKLAND 95

They went into the farmer's kitchen and sat by the wide fireplace. Mrs Maggot brought them beer in large earthenware mugs. It was a good brew, and Odo found himself wishing that they were going to stay the night in the house.

'I hear there have been fine goings on up Hobbiton way,' said Farmer Maggot. 'Fireworks and all; and this Mr Bolger-Baggins disappearing, and giving everything away. Oddest thing I have heard tell of in my time. I suppose it all comes of living with that Mr Bilbo Baggins. My mother used to tell me queer tales of him, when I was a boy: not but what he seemed a very nice gentleman. I have seen him wandering down this way many a time when I was a lad, and that Mr Bingo with him. Now we take an interest in him in these parts, seeing as he belongs here, being half Brandybuck, as you might say. We never thought any good would come of his going away to Hobbiton, and folk are a bit queer back there, if you'll pardon me. I was forgetting you come from those parts.'

'O, folk are queer enough in Hobbiton – and Tookland,' said Frodo. 'We don't mind. But we know, I mean knew, Mr Bingo very well. I don't think any harm's come to him. It really was a very marvellous party, and I can't see that anyone has anything to complain of.' He gave the farmer a full and amusing account of the proceedings, which pleased him mightily. He stamped his feet and slapped his legs, and called for more beer; and made them tell his wife most of the tale over again, especially about the fireworks. Neither of the Maggots had ever seen fireworks.

'It must be a sight to do your eyes good,' said the farmer.

'No dragons for me!' said Mrs Maggot. 'But I would have liked to have been at that supper. Let's hope old Mr Rory Brandybuck will take the idea and give a party down in these parts for his next birthday. – And what did you say has become of Mr Bolger-Baggins?' she said, turning to Frodo.

'Well – er, well, he's vanished, don't you know,' said Frodo. He half thought he heard the ghost of a chuckle somewhere not far from his ear, but he was not sure.

'There now – that reminds me!' said Farmer Maggot. 'What do you think that funny customer said?'

'What?' said Odo and Frodo together.

'Well, he comes riding in at the gate and up to the door on a big black horse; all black he was himself too, and cloaked and hooded up as if he didn't want to be known. "Good Heavens!" I said to myself. "Here's one of the Big People! Now what in the Shire can he want?" We don't see many of the Big People down here, though they come over the River at times; but I've never heard tell of any like this black chap. "Good day to you," I says. "This lane don't go no further, and wherever you be going your quickest way will be back to the road." I did not like the look of him, and when Gip came out he took one sniff and let out a howl as if he had been bitten; he put down his tail and bolted howling all the way.

'"I come from over yonder," he answered stiff and slow like, pointing back West, over *my* fields, Woodhall-way. "Have you ever seen Mist-er Bolg-er Bagg-ins?" he asked in a queer voice and bent down towards me, but I could see no face, his hood fell so low. I had a sort of shiver down my back; but I didn't see why he should come riding so bold over my land. "Be off!" I said. "Mr Bolger-Baggins has vanished, disappeared, if you take my meaning: gone into the blue, and you can follow him!"

'He gave a sort of hiss, seeming angry and startled like, it seemed to me; and he spurred his great horse right at me. I was standing by the gate, but I jumped out of the way mighty quick, and he rode through it and down the lane like mad. What do you think of that?'

'I don't know what to think,' said Frodo.

'Well, I'll tell you what to think,' said the farmer. 'This Mr Bingo has got himself mixed up in some trouble, and disappeared *a purpose*. There are plainly some folk as are mighty eager to find him. Mark my words, it'll all be along of some of those doings of old Mr Bilbo's. He ought to have stuck at Bolger and not gone tacking on Baggins. They are queer folk up Hobbiton way, begging your pardon. It's the Baggins that has got him into trouble, mark my words!'

'That certainly is an idea,' said Frodo. 'Very interesting, what you tell us. I suppose you've never seen any of these – er – black chaps before?'

'Not that I remember,' said Farmer Maggot, 'and I don't want to see any again. Now I hope you and your friend will stay and have a bite and a sup with me and the wife.'

'Thank you very much!' said Odo regretfully, 'but I am afraid we ought to go on.'

'Yes,' said Frodo, 'we have some way to go before night, and really we have already rested too long. But it is very kind of you all the same.'

'Well! Here's your health and good luck!' said the farmer, reaching for his mug. But at that moment the mug left the table, rose, tilted in the air, and then returned empty to its place.

TO MAGGOT'S FARM AND BUCKLAND 97

'Help and save us!' cried the farmer jumping up. 'Did you see that? This is a queer day and no mistake. First the dog and then me seeing things that ain't.'

'Oh, I saw the mug too,' said Odo, unable to hide a grin.

'You did, did you!' said the farmer. 'I don't see no cause to laugh.' He looked quickly and queerly at Odo and Frodo, and now seemed only too glad that they were going. They said good-bye politely but hurriedly, and ran down the steps and out of the gate. Farmer Maggot and his wife stood whispering at their door and watched them out of sight.

'What did you want to play that silly trick for?' said Odo when the farmhouse was well behind. 'The old man had done you a good turn with that Rider, or so it seemed to me.'

'I daresay,' said a voice behind him. 'But you did me a pretty poor turn, going inside and drinking and talking, and leaving me in the cold. As it was I only got half a mug. And now we are late. I shall make you trot after this.'

'Show us how to trot!' said Odo.

Bingo immediately reappeared and went off as fast as he could down the lane. The others hurried after him. 'Look!' said Frodo pointing to one side. Along the edge of the lane, in the mud made by the day's rain, there were deep hoofmarks.

'Never mind!' said Bingo. 'We knew from old Maggot's talk that he went this way. It can't be helped. Come along!'

They met nothing in the lane. The afternoon faded and the sun went down into low clouds behind them. The light was already failing when they reached the end of the lane and came at last back to the road.[8] It was growing chilly and thin strands of mist were crawling over the fields. The twilight was clammy.

'Not too bad,' said Frodo. 'It is four miles from here to the landing stage opposite Bucklebury. We shall make it before it is quite dark.'

They now turned right along the road, which here ran quite straight, drawing steadily nearer to the River. There was no sign of any other traveller upon the way. Soon they could see lights in the distance ahead and to their left, beyond the dim line of the shadowy willow-trees along the borders of the river, where the far bank rose almost into a low hill.

'There's Bucklebury!' said Frodo.

'Thank goodness!' said Odo. 'My feet are sore, sticky, and mud-tired. Also it is getting chilly.' He stumbled into a puddle and

98   THE RETURN OF THE SHADOW

splashed up a fountain of dirty water. 'Drat it!' he said. 'I've nearly had enough of to-day's walk. Do you think there is any chance of a bath to-night?' Without waiting for an answer he suddenly began a hobbit bathroom song.

> *O Water warm and water hot!*
> *O Water boiled in pan and pot!*
> *O Water blue and water green,*
> *O Water silver-clear and clean,*
>   *Of bath I sing my song!*
> *O praise the steam expectant nose!*
> *O bless the tub my weary toes!*
> *O happy fingers come and play!*
> *O arms and legs, you here may stay,*
>   *And wallow warm and long!*
> *Put mire away! Forget the clay!*
> *Shut out the night! Wash off the day!*
> *In water lapping chin and knees,*
> *In water kind now lie at ease,*
>   *Until the dinner gong!*

'Really you might wait till you are *in* the bath!' said Frodo.

'I warn you,' added Bingo, 'that you will have yours last, or else you will not wallow very long.'

'Very well,' said Odo; 'only I warn *you* that if you go first you must not take all the hot water, or I shall drown you in your own bath. I want a hot bath and a clean one.'

'You may not get any,' said Bingo. 'I don't know what Marmaduke has arranged, or where we are sleeping. I didn't order baths, and if we get them they will be our last for some time, I expect.'

Their talk flagged. They were now getting really tired, and went along with their chins down and their eyes in front of their toes. They were quite startled when suddenly a voice behind them cried: 'Hi!' It then burst into a loud song:

> *As I was sitting by the way,*
>   *I saw three hobbits walking:*
> *One was dumb with naught to say,*
>   *The others were not talking.*

> *'Good night!' I said. 'Good night to you!'*
>   *They heeded not my greeting:*
> *One was deaf like the other two.*
>   *It was a merry meeting!*

TO MAGGOT'S FARM AND BUCKLAND 99

'Marmaduke!' cried Bingo turning round. 'Where did you spring from?'

'You passed me sitting at the road-side,' said Marmaduke. 'Perhaps I ought to have lain down in the road; but then you would have just trodden on me and passed gaily on.'

'We are tired,' said Bingo.

'So it seems. I told you you would be – but you were so proud and stiff. "Ponies! Pooh!" you said. "Just a little leg-stretcher before the real business begins."'

'As it happens ponies would not have helped much,' said Bingo. 'We have been having *adventures*.' He stopped suddenly and looked up and down the dark road. 'We will tell you later.'

'Bless me!' said Marmaduke. 'But how mean of you! You shouldn't have adventures without me. And what are you peering about for? Are there some big bad rabbits loose?'

'Don't be so Marmadukish all at once! I can't bear it at the end of the day,' said Odo. 'Let's get off our legs and have some food, and then you shall hear a tale. Can I have a bath?'

'What?' said Marmaduke. 'A bath? That would put you right out of training again. A bath! I am surprised at such a question. Now lift up your chins and follow me!'

A few yards further on there was a turning to the left. They went down a path, neat and well-kept and edged with large white stones. It led them quickly to the river-bank. There there was a landing-stage big enough for several boats. Its white posts glimmered in the gloom. The mists were beginning to gather almost hedge-high in the fields, but the water before them was dark with only a few curling wisps of grey like steam among the reeds at the sides. The Brandywine River flowed slow and broad. On the other side two lamps twinkled upon another landing-stage with many steps going up the high bank beyond. Behind it the low hill loomed, and out of the hill through stray strands of mist shone many round hobbit-windows, red and yellow. They were the lights of Brandy Hall, the ancient home of the Brandybucks.

Long, long ago the Brandybucks had crossed the River (the original boundary of the Shire on this side), attracted by the high bank and the drier rolling ground behind. But their family (one of the oldest hobbit families) grew, and grew, until Brandy Hall occupied the whole of the low hill, and had three large front doors, several back doors, and at least fifty windows. The Brandybucks and their numerous dependants then began to burrow and later to build all round about. That was the origin of the village of Bucklebury-by-the-River. A great deal of the land on the west side of the river still belonged to the family, almost as far as Woodhall, but most of the actual Brandybucks lived in Buckland: a thickly inhabited strip between the River and the Old Forest, a sort of colony from the old Shire.

The people of the old Shire, of course, told strange tales of the Bucklanders; but as a matter of fact the Bucklanders were hobbits, and not really very different from other hobbits of the North, South, or West – except in one point: they were fond of boats and some of them could swim. Also they were unprotected from the East except by a hedge, THE HEDGE. It had been planted ages ago. It now ran all the way from Brandywine Bridge to Haysend in a big loop, furthest from the River behind Bucklebury, something like forty miles from end to end.[9] It was thick and tall, and was constantly tended. But of course it was not a complete protection. The Bucklanders kept their doors locked, and that also was not usual in the Shire.

Marmaduke helped his friends into a small boat that lay at the stage. He then cast off and taking a pair of oars pulled across the river. Frodo and Bingo had often been to Buckland before. Bingo's mother was a Brandybuck. Marmaduke was Frodo's cousin, since his mother Yolanda was Folco Took's sister, and Folco was Frodo's father. Marmaduke was thus Took plus Brandybuck, and that was apt to be a lively blend.[10] But Odo had never been so far East before. He had a queer feeling as they crossed the slow silent river, as if he had now at last started, as if he was crossing a boundary and leaving his old life on the other shore.

They stepped quietly out of the boat. Marmaduke was tying it up, when Frodo said suddenly in a whisper: 'I say, look back! Do you see anything?'

On the stage they had left they seemed to see a dark black bundle sitting in the gloom; it seemed to be peering, or sniffing, this way and that at the ground they had trodden.

'What in the Shire is that?' said Marmaduke.

'Our Adventure, that we have been and left behind on the other side; or at least I hope so,' said Bingo. 'Can horses get across the River?'

'What have horses got to do with it? They can get across, I suppose, if they can swim; but I have never seen them do it here. There are bridges. But what have horses to do with it?'

TO MAGGOT'S FARM AND BUCKLAND

'A great deal!' said Bingo. 'But let's get away!' He took Marmaduke by the arm and hurried him up the steps on to the path above the landing. Frodo looked back, but the far shore was now shrouded in mist and nothing more could be seen.

'Where are you taking us for the night?' asked Odo. 'Not to Brandy Hall?'

'Indeed not!' said Marmaduke. 'It's crowded. And anyway I thought you wanted to be secret. I am taking you to a nice little house on the far side of Bucklebury. It's a mile more, I am afraid, but it is quite cosy and out of the way. I don't expect anyone will notice us. You wouldn't want to meet old Rory just now, Bingo! He is in a ramping mood still, about your behaviour. They treated him badly at the inn at Bywater on the party night (they were more full up than Brandy Hall); and then his carriage broke down on the way home, on the hill above Woodhall, and he blames you for these accidents as well.'

'I don't want to see him, and I don't much mind what he says or thinks,' said Bingo. 'I wanted to get out of the Shire unseen, just to complete the joke, but now I have other reasons for wanting to be secret. Let's hurry.'

They came at length to a little low one-storied house. It was an old-fashioned building, as much like a hobbit-hole as possible: it had a round door and round windows and a low rounded roof of turf. It was reached by a narrow green path, and surrounded by a circle of green lawn, round which close bushes grew. It showed no lights.

Marmaduke unlocked the door, and light streamed out in friendly fashion. They slipped quickly in, and shut the light and themselves inside. They were in a wide hall from which several doors opened. 'Here we are!' said Marmaduke. 'Not a bad little place. We often use it for guests, since Brandy Hall is so frightfully full of Brandybucks. I have got it quietly ready in the last day or two.'

'Splendid fellow!' said Bingo. 'I was dreadfully sorry you had to miss that supper.'

'So was I,' said Marmaduke. 'And after hearing the accounts of Rory and Melissa[11] (both entirely different, but I expect equally true), I am sorrier still. But I had a merry ride with Gandalf and the dwarves and Elves.[12] We met some more Elves on the way,[13] and there was some fine singing. I have never heard anything like it before.'

'Did Gandalf send me any message?' asked Bingo.

'No, nothing special. I asked him, when we got to Brandywine Bridge, if he wouldn't come along with me and wait for you, so as to be a guide and helping hand. But he said he was in a hurry. In fact, if you want to know, he said: "Bingo is now old enough and foolish enough to look after himself for a bit."'[14]

"I hope he is right,' said Bingo.

The hobbits hung up their cloaks and sticks, and piled their packs on the floor. Marmaduke went forward and flung open a closed door. Firelight came out and a puff of steam.

'Bath!' cried Odo. 'O blessed Marmaduke!'

'Which way shall we go: eldest first, or quickest first? You will be last either way, Odo,' said Frodo.

'Ha! ha!' said Marmaduke. 'What kind of an innkeeper do you think I am? In that room there are three tubs; and also a copper over a merry furnace that seems to be nearly on the boil. There are also towels, soap, mats, jugs, and what not. Get inside!'

The three rushed in and shut the door. Marmaduke went into the kitchen, and while he was busy there he heard snatches of competing songs mixed with the sound of splashing and wallowing. Over all the rest Odo's voice suddenly rose in a chant:

> *Bless the water O my feet and toes!*
> *Bless it O my ten fingers!*
> *Bless the water, O Odo!*
> *And praise the name of Marmaduke!*[15]

Marmaduke knocked on the door. 'All Bucklebury will know you have arrived before long,' he said. 'Also there is such a thing as supper. I cannot live on praise much longer.'

Bingo came out. 'Lawks!' said Marmaduke looking in. The stone floor was all in pools. Frodo was drying in front of the fire; Odo was still wallowing.

'Come on, Bingo!' said Marmaduke. 'Let's begin supper, and leave them!'

They had supper in the kitchen on a table near the open fire. The others soon arrived. Odo was the last, but he quickly made up for lost time. When they had finished Marmaduke pushed back the table, and drew chairs round the fire. 'We'll clear up later,' he said. 'Now tell me all about it!'[16]

Bingo stretched his legs and yawned. 'It's easy in here,' he said, 'and somehow our adventure seems rather absurd, and not so

TO MAGGOT'S FARM AND BUCKLAND 103

important as it did out there. But this is what happened. A Black Rider came up behind us yesterday afternoon (it seems a week ago), and I am sure he was looking for us, or me. After that he kept on reappearing (always behind). Let me see, yes, we saw him four times altogether, counting the figure on the landing-stage, and once we heard his horse,[17] and once we thought we heard just a sniff.'

'What are you talking about?' said Marmaduke. 'What is a black rider?'

'A black figure on a horse,' said Bingo. 'But I will tell you all about it.' He gave a pretty good account of their journey, with occasional additions and interruptions by Frodo and Odo. Only Odo was still positive that the sniff they thought they heard was really part of the mystery.

'I should think you were making it all up, if I had not seen that queer shape this evening,' said Marmaduke. 'What is it all about, I wonder?'

'So do we!' said Frodo. 'Do you think anything of Farmer Maggot's guess, that it has something to do with Bilbo?'

'Well, it was only a guess anyway,' said Bingo. 'I am sure old Maggot does not know anything. I should have expected the Elves to tell me, if the Riders had anything to do with Bilbo's adventures.'

'Old Maggot is rather a shrewd fellow,' said Marmaduke. 'A good deal goes on behind his round face which does not come out in his talk. He used to go into the Old Forest at one time, and had the reputation of knowing a thing or two outside the Shire. Anyway I can guess no better. What are you going to do about it?'

'There is nothing to do, ' said Bingo, 'except to go home. Which is difficult for me, as I haven't got one now. I shall just have to go on, as the Elves advised. But you need not come, of course.'

'Of course not,' said Marmaduke. 'I joined the party just for fun, and I am certainly not going to leave it now. Besides, you will need me. Three's company, but four's more. And if the hints of the Elves mean what you think, there are at least four Riders, not to mention an invisible sniff, and a black bundle on the landing-stage. My advice is: let us start off even earlier tomorrow than we planned, and see if we can't get a good start. I rather fancy Riders will have to go round by the bridges to get across the River.'

'But we shall have to go much the same way,' said Bingo. 'We shall have to strike the East Road near Brandywine Bridge.'

'That's not my idea,' said Marmaduke. 'I think we should avoid

104 THE RETURN OF THE SHADOW

the road at present. It's a waste of time. We should actually be going back westward if we made for the road-meeting near the Bridge. We must make a short cut north-east through the Old Forest. I will guide you.'

'How can you?' asked Odo. 'Have you ever been there?'

'O yes,' said Marmaduke. 'All the Brandybucks go there occasionally, when the fit takes them. I often go – only in daylight, of course, when the woods are fairly quiet and sleepy. Still I know my way about. If we start early and push along we ought to be quite safe and clear of the Forest before tomorrow night. I have got five good ponies waiting – sturdy little beasts: not speedy of course, but good for a long day's work. They're stabled in a shed out in the fields behind this house.'

'I don't like the idea at all,' said Odo. 'I would rather meet these Riders (if we must meet them) on a road, where there is a chance of meeting ordinary honest travellers as well. I don't like woods, and I have heard queer tales of the Old Forest. I think Black Riders will be very much more at home there than we shall.'

'But we shall probably be out of it again before they get in,' said Marmaduke. 'It seems to me silly, anyway, when you are beginning an adventurous journey to start by going back and jogging along a dull river-side road – in full view of all the numerous hobbits of Buckland.[18] Perhaps you would like to call and take leave of old Rory at the Hall. It would be polite and proper; and he might lend you a carriage.'

'I knew you would propose something rash,' said Odo. 'But I am not going to argue any more, if the others agree. Let's vote – though I am sure I shall be the odd man out.'

He was – though Bingo and Frodo took some time to make up their minds.

'There you are!' said Odo. 'What did I say this morning? Three to one! Well, I only hope it comes off all right.'

'Now that's settled,' said Marmaduke, 'we had better get to bed. But first we must clear up, and do all the packing we can. Come on!'

It was some time before the hobbits finished putting things away, tidying up, and packing what they needed in the way of stores for their journey. At last they went to bed – and slept in proper beds (but without sheets) for the last time for many a long day.[19] Bingo could not go to sleep for some time: his legs ached. He was glad he was riding in the morning. At last he fell asleep into a vague dream, in which he seemed to be lying under a window

TO MAGGOT'S FARM AND BUCKLAND 105

that looked out into a sea of tangled trees: outside there was a snuffling.

NOTES

1 It is at first sight puzzling that Frodo should say that 'Buckland is almost exactly south-east from Woodhall', and again immediately below that they could strike the road again 'above Buckland', since later in this chapter (p. 100) Buckland is described as 'a thickly inhabited strip between the River and the Old Forest', defended by the Hedge some forty miles long – clearly too large an area to be described as 'almost exactly south-east from Woodhall'. The explanation must be, however, that my father changed the meaning of the name *Buckland* in the course of the chapter. At first *Buckland* was a place, a village, rather than a region (at its first occurrence it replaced *Bury Underwood*, which in turn replaced *Wood Eaton*, p. 35 note 5), and it still was so here; but further on in the chapter the village of Bucklebury-by-the-River emerged (p. 92), and Buckland then became the name of the Brandybucks' land beyond the River. See note 5, and the note on the Shire Map, p. 107.

2 See the note on the Shire Map, p. 107.

3 A hastily pencilled note on the typescript here reads: 'Sound of hoofs going by not far off.' See p. 287.

4 *Maggot* was later struck out in pencil and replaced by *Puddifoot*, but only in this one instance. On the earliest map of the Shire (see p. 107) the farm is marked, in ink, *Puddifoot*, changed in pencil to *Maggot*. The Puddifoots of Stock are mentioned in FR, p. 101.

5 Here again *Buckland* still signifies the village (see note 1); but *Bucklebury* appears shortly after (p. 92), the name being typed over an erasure.

6 The substance of this passage about hobbit-holes and hobbit-houses was afterwards placed in the Prologue. See further pp. 294, 312.

7 Towers built on the western coasts of Middle-earth by exiles of Númenor are mentioned in the second version of *The Fall of Númenor* (V.28, 30). – The substance of this passage was also afterwards placed in the Prologue (see note 6), and there also the towers are called 'Elf-towers'. Cf. *Of the Rings of Power* in *The Silmarillion*, p. 292: 'It is said that the towers of Emyn Beraid were not built indeed by the exiles of Númenor, but were raised by Gil-galad for Elendil, his friend.'

8 *came at last back to the road:* this is of course the road they had been walking on originally, 'the road to Buckland'; at this time there was no causeway road running south from the Brandywine Bridge on the west bank of the river (and no village of Stock).

9 In FR (p. 109) the distance is 'well over twenty miles from end to end.' See p. 298.

106   THE RETURN OF THE SHADOW

10   This genealogy was afterwards wholly abandoned, of course, but the mother of Meriadoc (Marmaduke) remained a Took (Esmeralda, who married Saradoc Brandybuck, known as 'Scattergold').

11   Melissa Brandybuck appeared in the fourth version of 'A Long-expected Party', on which occasion she danced on a table with Prospero Took (p. 38).

12   Bingo told Gildor (p. 63) that Gandalf 'went off with the dwarves and the Rivendell elves as soon as the fireworks were over.' This is the first appearance of the story that Marmaduke/Meriadoc had been at Hobbiton but had left early.

13   *We met some more Elves on the way:* these were the Elves of Gildor's company, who thus already knew about the Party when Bingo, Frodo and Odo encountered them (p. 68, note 17).

14   Cf. the note cited on p. 41: 'Where is G[andalf] asks Odo – said I was old and foolish enough now to take care of myself said B.'

15   This 'chant' was emended on the typescript thus:

> *Bless the water, O my feet and toes!*
> *Praise the bath, O my ten fingers!*
> *Bless the water, O my knees and shoulders!*
> *Praise the bath, O my ribs, and rejoice!*
> *Let Odo praise the house of Brandybuck,*
> *And praise the name of Marmaduke for ever.*

This new version belongs to the time of the manuscript portion at the end of the chapter (note 16).

16   Here the typescript ends, and the remainder is in manuscript; see p. 109.

17   *and once we heard his horse:* this is a reference to the revised passage in the second chapter, where it is told that a Black Rider stopped his horse for a moment on the road beside the tree in which the hobbits were sitting (p. 55 and note 11).

18   This is a reference to the road within Buckland. Cf. p. 53: 'the ordinary way to Buckland was along the East Road to the meeting of the Water and the Brandywine River, where there was a bridge, *and then south along the River.*'

19   It is clear from this that my father had not yet foreseen the hobbits' visit to the house of Tom Bombadil.

Note on the Shire Map

There are four extant maps of the Shire made by my father, and two which I made, but only one of them, I think, can contain an element or layer that goes back to the time when these chapters were written (the first months of 1938). This is however a convenient place to give some indications concerning all of them.

TO MAGGOT'S FARM AND BUCKLAND   107

I   An extremely rough map (reproduced as the frontispiece), built up in stages, and done in pencil and red, blue, and black inks; extending from Hobbiton in the West to the Barrow-downs in the East. In its inception this was the first, or at least the first that survives. Some features were first marked in pencil and then inked over.

II A map on a smaller scale in faint pencil and blue and red chalks, extending to the Far Downs in the West, but showing little more than the courses of roads and rivers.

III A map of roads and rivers on a larger scale than II, extending from Michel Delving in the West to the Hedge of Buckland, but without any names (see on map V below).

IV A small scale map extending from the Green Hill Country to Bree, carefully drawn in ink and coloured chalks, but soon abandoned and marking only a few features.

V   An elaborate map in pencil and coloured chalks which I made in 1943 (see p. 200), for which III (showing only the courses of roads and rivers) was very clearly the basis and which I followed closely. No doubt III was made by my father for this purpose.

VI The map which was published in *The Fellowship of the Ring*; this I made not long before its publication (that is to say, some ten years after map V).

In what follows I consider only certain features arising in the course of this chapter.

Buckland is almost exactly south-east from Woodhall (p. 89). *Buckland* was still here the name of the village (see note 1 above); *Bucklebury* first appears on p. 92. On map I Bucklebury does indeed lie south-east (or strictly east-south-east) from Woodhall, but on map II the Ferry is due east, and on III it is east-north-east, whence the representation on my maps V and VI. In the original edition of FR (p. 97) the text had here 'The Ferry is south-east from Woodhall', which was corrected to 'east' in the revised edition (second impression 1967) when my father observed the discrepancy with the published map. The shifting had clearly come about unintentionally. (It may be noticed incidentally that all the maps show Woodhall on a side road (the 'lane') going off from that to Buckland; see p. 66, note 10).

The road bears away to the left . . . and then sweeps round south when it gets nearer to the River (p. 89). This southward sweep is strongly marked on map I (and repeated on map II), where the Buckland road joins the causeway road above the village of Stock (as Frodo says in FR, p. 97: 'It goes round the north of the Marish so as to strike the causeway from the Bridge above Stock'). At the time when this chapter was written there was no causeway road (note 8). This is another case where the text of FR accords with map I, but not with the published map (VI); in this case, however, my father did not correct the text. On map III the Buckland road does not 'sweep round south': but after bearing away to

108   THE RETURN OF THE SHADOW

the left or north (before reaching Woodhall) it runs *in a straight line due east* to meet the road from the Bridge. This I followed on my map V; but the village of Stock was not marked on III, which only shows roads and rivers, and I placed the road-meeting actually in the village, not to the north of it. Although, as I clearly recollect, map V was made in his study and in conversation with him, my father cannot have noticed my error in this point. The published map simply follows V.

One other point may be noticed here. Marmaduke twice (pp. 100, 103) refers to 'bridges' over the Brandywine, but none of the maps shows any other bridge but that which carried the East Road, the Brandywine Bridge.

★

My father's letter to Stanley Unwin quoted on page 44 shows that he had finished this chapter by 4 March 1938. Three months later, on 4 June 1938, he wrote to Stanley Unwin saying:

I meant long ago to have thanked Rayner for bothering to read the tentative chapters, and for his excellent criticism. It agrees strikingly with Mr Lewis', which is therefore confirmed. I must plainly bow to my two chief (and most well-disposed) critics. The trouble is that 'hobbit talk'* amuses me privately (and to a certain degree also my boy Christopher) more than adventures; but I must curb this severely. Although longing to do so, I have not had a chance to touch any story-writing since the Christmas vacation.

And he added that he could not 'see any loophole left for months.' On 24 July he said in a letter to Charles Furth at Allen and Unwin:

The sequel to *the Hobbit* has remained where it stopped. It has lost my favour, and I have no idea what to do with it. For one thing the original *Hobbit* was never intended to have a sequel – Bilbo 'remained very happy to the end of his days and those were extraordinarily long': a sentence I find an almost insuperable obstacle to a satisfactory link. For another nearly all the 'motives' that I can use were packed into the original book, so that a sequel will appear either 'thinner' or merely repetitional. For a third: I am personally immensely amused by hobbits as such, and can contemplate them eating and making their rather fatuous jokes indefinitely; but I find that is not the case with even my most devoted 'fans' (such as Mr Lewis, and ?Rayner Unwin). Mr Lewis says hobbits are only amusing when in unhobbitlike situations. For a last: my mind on the 'story' side is really preoccupied with the 'pure' fairy stories or mythologies of the *Silmarillion*, into which even Mr Baggins got dragged against my original will, and I do not

---

*Rayner Unwin had said that the second and third chapters 'have I think a little too much conversation and "hobbit talk" which tends to make it lag a little.'

TO MAGGOT'S FARM AND BUCKLAND 109

think I shall be able to move much outside it – unless it is finished (and perhaps published) – which has a releasing effect.

At the beginning of this extract my father was repeating what he had said in his letters of 17 and 18 February quoted on pp. 43–4, when he had written no more than 'A Long-expected Party'. But it is very hard to see why he said here that he found the sentence in *The Hobbit*, that Bilbo 'remained very happy to the end of his days and those were extraordinarily long', 'an almost insuperable obstacle to a satisfactory link'; since what he had written at this stage was not about Bilbo but about his 'nephew' Bingo, and in so far as Bilbo was mentioned nothing had been said to show that he did not remain happy till the end of his extraordinarily long days.

This then is where the narrative stopped, and stayed stopped through some six months or more. With abundant 'hobbit-talk' on the way, he had got Bingo, Frodo, and Odo to Buckland on the way to Rivendell, whither Gandalf had preceded them. They had encountered the Black Riders, Gildor and his company of Elves, and Farmer Maggot, where their visit ended in a much less satisfactory way than it would do later, through an outrageous practical joke on Bingo's part (the comic potential of which had by no means been exhausted); they had crossed the Brandywine, and arrived at the little house prepared for them by Marmaduke Brandybuck. In his letter to Charles Furth just cited he said that he had 'no idea what to do with it'; but Tom Bombadil, the Willowman and the Barrow-wights were already envisaged as possibilities (see pp. 42–3).

On 31 August 1938 he wrote again to Charles Furth, and now a great change had taken place:

> In the last two or three days . . . I have begun again on the sequel to the 'Hobbit' – The Lord of the Ring. It is now flowing along, and getting quite out of hand. It has reached about Chapter VII and progresses towards quite unforeseen goals.

He said 'about Chapter VII' on account of uncertainty over chapter-divisions (see p. 132).

The passage in manuscript at the end of the present chapter (see note 16 above) was (I feel certain) added to the typescript at this time, and was the beginning of this new burst of narrative energy. My father had now decided that the hobbits' journey would take them into the Old Forest, that 'dubious region' which had appeared in the third version of 'A Long-expected Party' (p. 29), and where he had already suggested in early notes (p. 43) that the hobbits should become lost and caught by the Willow-man. And 'the sequel to *The Hobbit*' is given – for the first time, it seems – a title: *The Lord of the Ring* (see p. 74 and note 3).

V

THE OLD FOREST AND THE WITHYWINDLE

In the letter of 31 August 1938 quoted at the end of the last chapter my father said that 'in the last two or three days' he had turned again to the book, that it was 'flowing along, and getting quite out of hand', and that it had reached 'about Chapter VII'. It is clear that in those few days the hobbits had passed through the Old Forest by way of the Withywindle valley, stayed in the house of Tom Bombadil, escaped from the Barrow-wight, and reached Bree,

There is very little preliminary sketching of the original fourth chapter, and such as there is I give here. There is first a page dashed down in soft pencil and now very difficult to read; I introduce some necessary punctuation and small connective words that were omitted, and expand the initial letters that stand for names.

They got on to the ponies and rode off into the mist. After riding more than an hour they came to the Hedge. It was tall and netted over with silver cobwebs.

'How do we get through this?' said Odo.

'There is a way,' said Marmaduke. Following him along the Hedge they came to a small brick-lined tunnel. It went down a gully and dived right under the Hedge, coming out some twenty yards at the far side, where it was closed by a gate of close iron bars. Marmaduke unlocked this, let them out, and locked it again. As it snapped back they all felt a sudden pang.

'There,' said Marmaduke. 'You have now left the Shire – and are [?outside] and close to the edge of the Old Forest.'

'Are the stories about it true?' said Odo.

'I don't know what stories you mean – if you mean the old bogey stories our nurses used to tell us, about goblins and wolves and things of that sort, no. But it is queer. Everything in the Old Forest is very much more alive, more aware of what is going on, than in the Shire. And they don't like strangers. The trees watch you. But they don't do much in daylight. [?Occasionally] the most malicious ones may drop a branch or stick a root out or grasp at you with long trailers. But at night things can get most disturbing – I am told. I have only once been in the Old Forest, and then only

THE OLD FOREST AND THE WITHYWINDLE   111

near the edge, after dark. I thought the trees were all whispering to each other although there was no wind, and the branches waved about and groped. They do say the trees actually move and can surround strangers and hem them in. They used long ago to attack the Hedge, come and plant themselves right by it and lean over it. But we burn[t] the ground all along the east side for miles and they gave it up. There are also queer things living deep in the Forest and on the far side. But I have not heard that they are very fierce – at least not in daytime. But something makes paths and keeps them open. There is the beginning of a great and broad one that goes more or less in our direction. That is the one I am making for.'

The ground was rising steadily and as their ponies plodded along the trees became darker and thicker and taller. There was no sound, save an occasional drip; but they all got an uncomfortable feeling which steadily increased that they were being watched – with disapproval if not dislike. Marmaduke tried to sing, but his voice soon fell to a hum and then died away. A small branch fell from an old tree with a crack on the ground behind them. They stopped, startled, and looked round.

'The trees seem to object to my singing,' said Marmaduke cheerfully. 'All right, we'll wait till we get to a more open point.'

Clearing   hillock   view   sun up   mist goes   turns hot
Trees bar way.   They turn [?always . . . . . . side]
Willowman.   Meeting with Tombombadil.
[*Struck out:* Barrow-wights]
Camp on the downs

Whereas this piece begins as narrative and tails off into notes, another page is expressly a 'sketch' of the story to be written:

The path winds on and they get tired. They cannot get any view. At last they see a bare hillock (crowned by a few pines) ahead looking down onto the path. They reach this and find the mist gone, and the sun very hot and nearly above. 11 o'clock. They rest and eat. But they can see only forest all round, and cannot make out either Hedge or line of the road northward, but the bare downland East and South lies green-grey in the distance. Beyond the hillock the path turns *southwards*. They determine to leave it and strike N.E. by the sun. But trees bar the way. They are going downhill, and brambles and bushes, hazels and whatnot block them. Every . . . . . [?opening] leads them away to their right. Eventually when it is already afternoon they find themselves

112   THE RETURN OF THE SHADOW

coming to a willow-bordered river – the Withywindle.[1] Marmaduke knows this flows through the forest from the downs to join the Brandywine at Haysend. There seems some sort of rough path going upstream. But a great sleepiness comes on them. Odo and Bingo cannot go on without a rest. They sit down with their backs to a great willow, while Frodo and Marmaduke attend to the ponies. Willowman traps Bingo and Odo. Suddenly a singing is heard in the distance. (Tom Bombadil not named). The Willow relaxes its hold.

They get through to end of forest as evening comes on, and climb on to the downs. It gets very cold – mist is followed by a chilly drizzle. They shelter under a big barrow. Barrow-wight takes them inside. They wake to find themselves buried alive. They shout. At last Marmaduke and Bingo begin a song. An answering song outside. Tom Bombadil opens the stone door and lets them out. They go to his house for the night – two Barrow-wights come [?galloping] after them, but stop every time Tom Bombadil turns and looks at them.

At this stage, then, their first encounter with Tom Bombadil was to be very brief, and they would not be his guests until after their escape from the barrow up on the downs; but no narrative of this form is found, and doubtless none was written.

It is of course possible that other preliminary drafting has been lost, but the earliest extant text of the original fourth chapter (numbered 'IV' but with no title) looks like composition *ab initio*, with many words and sentences and even whole pages rejected and replaced at the time of writing. For most of its length, however, this is an orderly and legible manuscript, though rapidly written, and increasingly so as it proceeds (see note 3). It is then remarkable that this text reaches at a stroke the narrative as published in FR (Chapter 6, 'The Old Forest'), with only the most minor differences – other than the different cast of characters (largely a matter of names) and different attribution of 'parts', and often and for substantial stretches with almost exactly the wording of the final form. My father might well say that *The Lord of the Ring* was 'now flowing along'.

There are a few particular points to notice. First, as regards the characters, the 'spoken parts' are variously distributed as between the first form and the final. Fredegar Bolger is of course not present to see them off at the entrance to the tunnel under the Hedge, and his question 'How are you going to get through this?' (FR p. 120) is given to Odo ('How do we get through this?', cf. p. 110). The verse *O! Wanderers in the shadowed land*,[2] Frodo's in FR (p. 123), is here Marmaduke's, but changed, probably immediately, to Frodo Took's. Pippin's objection to taking the path by the Withywindle (FR pp. 126–7) is Bingo's; and in the

THE OLD FOREST AND THE WITHYWINDLE 113

scene with Old Man Willow the parts are quite distinct. In the original version it is Bingo and Odo who are totally overcome by sleep and lay themselves against the willow-trunk, and it is Marmaduke who is more resistant and alarmed at the onset of drowsiness. Frodo Took ('more adventurous') goes down to the river-bank (as does Frodo Baggins in FR), and falling asleep at the Willow's feet is tipped into the water and held under by a root, while Marmaduke plays the later part of Sam in rounding up the ponies, rescuing Frodo (Took or Baggins) from the river, and discussing with him how to release the prisoners from the tree. Yet despite the later redistribution of parts in this scene, and the advent of Sam Gamgee, the old text is very close to the final form, as may be seen from this example (cf. FR p. 128).

Marmaduke gripped him [Frodo Took] by the back of his jacket, and dragged him from under the tree-root, and laid him on the bank. Almost at once he woke, and coughed and spluttered.

'Do you know,' he said, 'the beast *threw* me in! I felt it and saw it: the big root just twizzled round and threw me in.'

'You were dreaming,' said Marmaduke. 'I left you asleep, though I thought it rather a silly place to sit in.'

'What about the other two?' asked Frodo. 'I wonder what sort of dreams *they've* had?'

They went round to the landward side. Marmaduke then understood the click. Odo had vanished. The crack he lay in had closed to, so that not a chink could be seen. Bingo was trapped; for his crack had closed to about his waist . . .

There are also a few minor points of topography to mention. It is said in the outline (p. 111) that the hillock was crowned with pines, and this was retained: it had 'a knot of pine-trees at the top', under which the hobbits sat. In FR (p. 124) the hill is likened to a bald head, and the trees about it to 'thick hair that ended sharply in a circle round a shaven crown.' – When later they came to the end of the gully and looked out from the trees at the Withywindle, they were at the top of a cliff:

Suddenly the woodland trees came to an end, and the gully ended at the top of a bank that was almost a cliff. Over this the stream dived, and fell in a series of small waterfalls. Looking down they saw that below them was a wide space of grass and reeds . . .

Marmaduke scrambled down to the river, and disappeared into the long grass and low bushes. After a while he reappeared and called up to them from a patch of turf some thirty feet below. He reported that there was fairly solid ground between the bank and the river . . .

In FR (p. 126) it is clear that the hobbits, following the little stream down the gully, had reached the level of the Withywindle valley while still in the deep woodland:

114   THE RETURN OF THE SHADOW

Coming to the opening they found that they had made their way down through a cleft in a high steep bank, almost a cliff. At its feet was a wide space of grass and reeds . . .

[Merry] passed out into the sunshine and disappeared into the long grasses. After a while he reappeared, and reported . . .

Subsequently, in the original version, there is anxiety about the descent of the ponies from the cliff; they got down in fact without difficulty, but Frodo Took 'put too much weight on a grassy lump that stuck out like a step, and went down with his head over heels for the last fifteen feet or so; but he came to no great harm at the bottom, for the ground was soft.' In FR (p. 127) the hobbits merely 'filed out' from the trees.

The last part of the chapter, in which Tom Bombadil appears, and which ends with the same words as in FR ('a golden light was all about them'), is so close to the final form[3] that only one small matter need be mentioned. It is made just as clear here as in FR that the path which the hobbits followed beside the Withywindle lay on the north side of the river, the side from which they descended out of the forest, and it is therefore strange that the approach to Tom Bombadil's house should be described thus:

The grass under their feet was smooth and short, and seemed to be mown and shaven. The forest edge behind them was as clipped and trim as a hedge. The path was edged with white stones; and *turning sharp to the left went over a little bridge*. It then wound up onto the top of a round knoll . . .

But the path was already on the left side of the river as it went upstream. Later on, this text was very heavily corrected, and the FR version all but achieved; yet this detail was retained: 'The path was bordered with white stones; and turning sharp to the left it led them over a wooden bridge.' Later again, the word 'left' was changed to 'right', implying that Tom Bombadil's house lay on the south side of the Withywindle. In FR there is no mention of a bridge. My father's map of the Shire (see p. 107: map I) probably shows that he changed his mind on this point; for the underlying pencil shows 'TB', with a dark mark beside it, on the south side, whereas the ink overlay shows the house to the north of the stream. See further pp. 327–8.

NOTES

1   The first occurrence of the name *Withywindle*.
2   The verse has *shadow-land* for *shadowed land* in the first line, but is otherwise as in FR. Rough working for a verse in this place is also found. My father first wrote: 'O wanderers in the land of trees / despair not for there is no wood', but this was broken off and the following suggested:

think not of hearth that lies behind
but set your hearts on distant hills

THE OLD FOREST AND THE WITHYWINDLE   115

> *beyond the rising of the sun.*
> *The journey is but new begun,*
> *the road goes ever on before*
> *past many a house and many a door*
> *over water and under wood*

3   Towards the end of the chapter the manuscript becomes extremely confused. From the point where Marmaduke and Frodo Took discover that Bingo and Odo are trapped by the Willow-man my father changed from ink to pencil, and degenerating into a rapid scribble the chapter seems to have petered out in the course of their rescue by Tom Bombadil; but he subsequently erased most of the pencilled text, or overwrote it in ink, and continued on in ink to the end of the chapter. This concluding portion departs from the preliminary sketch given on p. 112, where the hobbits after their rescue went up on to the Downs and were captured by the Barrow-wight; here, as in FR, Tom invites them to come to his house, and goes on ahead up the path beside the Withywindle. The last part of the manuscript is probably, strictly speaking, a subsequent addition; but the matter is of slight importance, since all this writing obviously belongs to the same period of work, at the end of August 1938.

Note on Tom Bombadil

Tom Bombadil, Goldberry, Old Man Willow, and the Barrow-wight had already existed for some time, appearing in print in the pages of *The Oxford Magazine* (Vol. LII, no. 13, 15 February 1934). In a letter of 1954 my father said:

> I don't think Tom needs philosophizing about, and is not improved by it. But many have found him an odd or indeed discordant ingredient. In historical fact I put him in because I had already 'invented' him independently (he first appeared in the Oxford Magazine) and wanted an 'adventure' on the way.[*]

On a small isolated piece of paper are found the following verses. At the top of the page my father wrote: 'Date unknown – germ of Tom Bombadil so evidently in mid 1930s'; and this note was written at the same time as the text, which is certainly quite late. There is no trace of the text from which it was copied.

> *(Said I)*
> *'Ho! Tom Bombadil*
> *Whither are you going*
> *With John Pompador*
> *Down the River rowing?'*

---

[*]*The Letters of J. R. R. Tolkien*, no. 153. Some major observations on Tom Bombadil are found in this letter and in no. 144.

THE RETURN OF THE SHADOW

(Said he)
'Through Long Congleby,
   Stoke Canonicorum,†
Past King's Singleton
   To Bumby Cocalorum –

To call Bill Willoughby
   Whatever he be doing,
And ax Harry Larraby
   What beer he is a-brewing.'

(And he sang)
'Go, boat! Row! The willows are a-bending,
   reeds are leaning, wind is in the grasses.
Flow, stream, flow! The ripples are unending;
   green they gleam, and shimmer as it passes.

Run, fair Sun, through heaven all the morning,
   rolling golden! Merry is our singing!
Cool the pools, though summer be a-burning;
   in shady glades let laughter run a-ringing!'

The poem published in *The Oxford Magazine* in 1934 bore the title *The Adventures of Tom Bombadil* (in earlier forms it was *The History of Tom Bombadil*). Many years later (1962) my father made it the first poem in the collection to which it gave the title (and added also a new poem, *Bombadil Goes Boating*, in which he meets Farmer Maggot in the Marish). Various changes were made in this later version, and references to the Withywindle were introduced, but the old poem was very largely preserved. In it are to be found the origin of many things in this and the following chapters – the closing crack in the Great Willow (though in the poem it was Tom himself who was caught in it), the supper of 'yellow cream and honeycomb, and white bread, and butter', the 'nightly noises' that included the tapping of the branches of Old Man Willow on the window-pane, the words of the Barrow-wight (who in the poem was inside Tom's house) 'I am waiting for you', and much else.

†Mediaeval name of what is now Stoke Canon in Devonshire.

VI

TOM BOMBADIL

A very brief outline shows my father's first thoughts for the next stage of the hobbits' journey: their visit to the house of Tom Bombadil.

Tom Bombadil rescues them from Willow Man. He says it was lucky he came that way – he had gone to the water-lily pool for some white water-lilies for Goldberry (my wife).

He turns out to know Farmer Maggot. (Make Maggot not a hobbit, but some other kind of creature – not dwarf, but akin to Tom Bombadil). They rest at his house. He says *only* way out is along his path beside the Withywindle. Description of feast and [?willow] fire. *Many noises at night.*

Tom Bombadil wakes them singing *derry dol*, and opening all the windows (he lives in a little house under the down-side facing the forest edge and the [?east corner] of the wood). He tells them to go north but avoid the high Downs and barrows. *He warns them of barrow-wights*; tells them a song to sing if the barrow-wights frighten them or

A cold day. The mist thickens and they get lost.

This scheme was written at great speed in pencil. As will be seen shortly, at this stage the hobbits only spent the one night with Tom Bombadil, and left the following morning. Another set of notes, also obviously preceding the first actual narrative text, is also very difficult to read:

Water-lily motive – last lilies of summer for Goldberry.

Relation of Tom Bombadil to Farmer Maggot (Maggot not a hobbit?)

Tom Bombadil is an 'aborigine' – he knew the land before men, before hobbits, before barrow-wights, yes before the necromancer – before the elves came to this quarter of the world.

Goldberry says he is 'master of water, wood and hill'. Does all this land belong to him? No! The land and the things belong to themselves. He is not the possessor but the master, because he belongs to himself.

Description of Goldberry, with her hair as yellow as the flag-lilies, her green gown and light feet.

118 THE RETURN OF THE SHADOW

Barrow-wights related to Black-riders. Are Black-riders actually horsed Barrow-wights?

The guests sleep – there is a noise as of wind surging in the edges of the forest and . . . . . through the panes and gables and the doors. Galloping of [?horses] round the house.

The first actual narrative (incomplete) of this chapter is a very rough and difficult manuscript in ink, becoming very rough indeed before it peters out on the first morning at Bombadil's house. It has no title, but is rather oddly numbered 'V or VI'. Here, even more than in the last chapter, the final form – until just at the end – is already present in all but detail of expression.

Most interesting is the story of the hobbits' dreams during the night, which is told thus:

In the dead night Bingo woke and heard noises: a sudden fear came over him [?so that] he did not speak but lay listening breathless. He heard a sound like a strong wind curling round the house and shaking it, and down the wind came a galloping, a galloping, a galloping: hooves seemed to come charging down the hillside from the east, up to the walls and round and round, hooves thudding and wind blowing, and then dying away back up the hill and into the darkness.

'Black riders,' thought Bingo. 'Black riders, a black host of riders,' and he wondered if he would ever again have the courage even in the morning to leave the safety of these good stone walls. He lay and listened for a while, but all had become quiet again, and after a while he fell asleep. At his side Odo lay dreaming. He turned and groaned, and woke to the darkness, and yet the dream went on. Tap, tap, squeak: the noise was like branches fretting in the wind, twigs like fingers scraping wall and window . . . [*&c. as in FR p. 138*].

It was the sound of water that Frodo heard falling into his sleep and slowly waking him. Water streaming gently down at first, and then spreading all round the house, gurgling under the walls . . . [*&c. as in FR p. 139*].

Meriadoc[1] slept on through the night in deep content.

As told here, there seems no reason not to understand that Black Riders (or Barrow-wights) actually came and rode round Tom Bombadil's house during the night. It will be seen that it is said explicitly that Bingo *woke*, and after a while *fell asleep*. In the initial sketch given on p. 112 (where the hobbits only went to stay with Tom after their capture by a Barrow-wight up on the Downs) 'Two Barrow-wights come

TOM BOMBADIL 119

[?galloping] after them'; cf. also the note on p. 118: 'Barrow-wights related to Black-riders. Are Black-riders actually horsed Barrow-wights?' – followed by 'Galloping of [?horses] round the house.' In any case, the end of the present text (unhappily so eccentrically scribbled as to make its interpretation extremely difficult) is explicit. Here, as in the later story, Bingo waking looks out of the east window of their room on to the kitchen-garden grey with dew.

He had expected to see turf right up to the walls, turf all pocked with hoof-marks. Actually his view was screened by a tall line of green beans on poles, but above and far beyond them the grey top of the hill loomed up against the sunrise. It was a grey morning with soft clouds, behind which were deeps of yellow and pale red. The light was broadening quickly and the red flowers on the beans began to shine against the wet green leaves.

Frodo looks from the western window, as does Pippin in FR, and sees the Withywindle disappearing into the mist below, and the flower-garden: 'there was no willow-tree to be seen.'

'Good morning, merry friends!' said Tom, opening the east window wide. A cool air flowed in. 'The sun will [?heat] you when the day is older. I have been walking far, leaping on the hill-tops, since the grey twilight [?came] and the night foundered, wet grass underfoot . . . .'

When they were dressed [*struck out as written:* Tom took them up the hillside] the sun was already risen over the hill, and the clouds were melting away. In the forest valley trees were appearing like tall heads rising out of the curling sea of mist. They were glad of breakfast – indeed they were glad to be awake and safe and at the merry end of a day again. The thought of going was heavy on them – and not only for fear of the road. Had it been a [?merry] road and the road home they would still have wished to tarry there.

But they knew that could not be. Bingo too found in his heart that the noise of hoofs was not only dream. They must escape quickly or else . . . [?pursued] here. So he made up his mind to get such help and advice as [?old] Bombadil could or would give.

'Master,' he said, 'we cannot thank you for your kindness for it has been beyond thanks. But we must go, against our wish and quickly. For I heard horsemen in the night and fear we are pursued.'

Tom looked at him. 'Horsemen,' he said. 'Dead men [?riding the wind. 'Tis long since they came hence.] What ails the Barrow-

120   THE RETURN OF THE SHADOW

wights to leave their old mounds? You are strange folk to come out of the Shire, [?even stranger than my news told me.] Now you had best tell me all – and I will give you counsel.'

Here the text ends, but following it are these notes in pencil:

Make it sudden rainy day. They spend it at Tom's house, and tell him the tale; and he of Willow-man and the . . . . . .[2] He is concerned about the riders; but says he will think of counsel. Next day is fine. He takes them to the hilltop. They . . . . the barrows.

This is where the story of the wet second day spent in long talk with Bombadil entered; before this the weather was to have become fine, and the hobbits were to have left when they had told Tom their story and received his advice. In this earliest narrative Bingo was so convinced of the reality of what he had heard in the night that he raised the matter with Tom, and Tom seems to take him seriously; and in this context the word 'Actually' (retained in FR) in 'Actually his view was screened by a tall line of beans on poles' suggests that if it had not been for this he would indeed have seen the turf 'all pocked with hoof-prints.'

A second narrative followed, obviously written immediately after the first, and this is complete. Here the chapter is numbered 'V', still without title. The first text was now refined and ordered in expression, the morning bodes rain, and the new version becomes, to the point where the first ended, scarcely distinguishable from that of FR, except in the matter of the 'dreams'. These are still told in the same unambiguous language as if they were real events in the night; but nothing more is said of them afterwards than is said in FR. In the final story Frodo's dream is a vision of Gandalf standing on the pinnacle of Orthanc and of the descent of Gwaihir to bear him away, but that vision is still accompanied by the sound of the Black Riders galloping out of the East; and it was that sound that woke him. It is still said that he thought in the morning to find the ground round the house marked by hoofs, but this is now no more than a way of emphasising the vividness of his experience in the night.

The remainder of the second version of the chapter generally approaches extraordinarily closely to the final form,[3] but there are not a few interesting differences.

In Tom Bombadil's long talk with the hobbits on the second day, his voice is described as 'always in a sing-song or actually singing' (cf. FR p. 140: 'Often his voice would turn to song'). The passage concerning Old Man Willow was first written thus:

Amongst his talk there was here and there much said of Old Man Willow, and Merry learned enough to content him[4] (more than enough, for it was not comfortable lore), though not enough for him to understand how that grey thirsty earth-bound spirit had

TOM BOMBADIL 121

become imprisoned in the greatest Willow of the Forest. The tree did not die, though its heart went rotten, while the malice of the Old Man drew power out of earth and water, and spread like a net, like fine root-threads in the ground, and invisible twig-fingers in the air, till it had infected or subjugated nearly all the trees on both sides of the valley.[5]

Bombadil's talk about the Barrow-wights of the Barrow-downs remained almost word for word into FR (pp. 141–2), with one difference: for FR 'A shadow came out of dark places far away' this text has 'A dark shadow came up out of the middle of the world'; in the underlying pencilled text (see note 3) can be read 'a dark shadow came up out of the South.' At the end of his talk, where FR has 'still on and back Tom went singing out into ancient starlight', the present version has 'and still further Tom went singing back before the Sun and before the Moon, out into the old starlight.'

A detail worth remarking is the sentence in the old version: 'Whether the morning and evening of one day or of many days had passed Bingo could not tell (nor did he ever discover for certain).' The bracketed words were soon to be removed, when the dating of the journey to Bree became precise; the hobbits stayed with Bombadil on the 26th and 27th of September, and left on the morning of the 28th (see p. 160).

Tom Bombadil's answer to Bingo's question 'Who are you, Master?' has some interesting differences from the final form (FR p. 142):

'Eh, what?' said Tom sitting up, and his eyes glinted in the gloom. 'I am an Aborigine, that's what I am, the Aborigine of this land. [*Struck out at once:* I have spoken a mort[6] of languages and called myself by many names.] Mark my words, my merry friends: Tom was here before the River or the Trees. Tom remembers the first acorn and the first rain-drop. He made paths before the Big People, and saw the Little People arriving. He was here before the kings and the graves and the [ghosts >] Barrow-wights. When the Elves passed westward Tom was here already – before the seas were bent. He saw the Sun rise in the West and the Moon following, before the new order of days was made. He knew the dark under the stars when it was fearless – before the Dark Lord came from Outside.'

In FR Tom Bombadil calls himself 'Eldest', not 'Aborigine' (cf. the notes given on p. 117: 'Tom Bombadil is an "aborigine"'); and the reference here to his having seen 'the Sun rise in the West and the Moon following' was dropped (though 'Tom remembers the first acorn and the first rain-drop', which was retained, says the same). These words are extremely surprising; for in the *Quenta Silmarillion* which my father had

122 THE RETURN OF THE SHADOW

only set aside at the end of the previous year it is told that 'Rana [the Moon] was first wrought and made ready, and first rose into the region of the stars, and was the elder of the lights, as was Silpion of the Trees' (V.240); and the Moon first rose as Fingolfin set foot upon Middle-earth, but the Sun when he entered Mithrim (V.250).

Tom Bombadil was 'there' during the Ages of the Stars, before Morgoth came back to Middle-earth after the destruction of the Trees; is it to this event that he referred in his words (retained in FR) 'He knew the dark under the stars when it was fearless – *before the Dark Lord came from Outside*'? It must be said that it seems unlikely that Bombadil would refer to Valinor across the Great Sea as 'Outside', especially since this was long ages 'before the seas were bent', when Númenor was drowned; it would seem much more natural to interpret the word as meaning 'the Outer Dark', 'the Void' beyond the Walls of the World. But in the mythology as it was when my father began *The Lord of the Rings* Melkor entered 'the World' with the other Valar, and never left it until his final defeat. It was only with his return to *The Silmarillion* after *The Lord of the Rings* was completed that there entered the account found in the published work (pp. 35–7) of the First War, in which Melkor was defeated by Tulkas and driven into the Outer Dark, from which he returned in secret while the Valar were resting from their labours on the Isle of Almaren, and overthrew the Lamps, ending the Spring of Arda. It seems then that either Bombadil must in fact refer to Morgoth's return from Valinor to Middle-earth, in company with Ungoliant and bearing the Silmarils, or else that my father had already at this date developed a new conception of the earliest history of Melkor.

After the reference to Farmer Maggot, from whom Tom Bombadil got his knowledge of the Shire, and whom he 'seemed to regard as a person of more importance than they had fancied' (FR p. 143), this text adds: 'We are kinsfolk, he and I. In a way of speaking: distantly and far back, but near enough for friendship' (in the original draft: 'We are akin, he said, distantly, very distantly, but near enough to count'). Cf. the notes given on p. 117, concerning the possibility that Farmer Maggot was not a hobbit at all, but a being of a wholly different kind, and akin to Bombadil.[7] At the end of this passage, the reference in FR to Tom's dealings with Elves, and to his having had news of the flight of Frodo (Bingo) from Gildor, is absent from the present text. (Tom indeed said earlier, FR p. 137, that he and Goldberry had heard of their wandering, and 'guessed you'd come ere long down to the water', and this is found in both the original texts).

Of Tom's questioning of Bingo it is said here that Bingo 'found himself telling him more about Bilbo Baggins and his own history and about the business of his sudden flight than he told before even to his three friends'; in FR (p. 144) this became 'telling him more about Bilbo and his own hopes and fears than he had told before even to Gandalf.' It may be noted that in the old narrative thus far there has been no suggestion that Bingo's

TOM BOMBADIL

departure from Hobbiton was a 'sudden flight' – except perhaps in the 'foreword' given in Chapter III, where Gandalf said to him before the Party 'But you must go quickly' (p. 83).

The episode of Tom and the Ring is told in virtually the same words as in FR, the only and very slight difference being that when Bingo put on the Ring Tom cried: 'Hey, come Bingo there, where be you a-going? What be you a-grinning at? Are you tired of talking? Take off that Ring of yours and sit down a moment. We must talk a while more . . .' Against this my father wrote later: 'Make the seeing clearer', and substituted (after 'where be you a-going?'): 'Did you think I should not see when you had the Ring on? Ha, Tom Bombadil's not as blind as that yet. Take off your golden Ring, and sit down a moment.'

Lastly, at the very end of the chapter, the rhyme that Tom Bombadil taught the hobbits to sing if in need of him is different from that in FR:

> *Ho! Tom Bombadil! Whither do you wander?*
> *Up, down, near or far? Here, there, or yonder?*
> *By hill that stands, wood that grows, and by the water falling,*
> *Here now we summon you! Can you hear us calling?*

This rhyme was at first present in the next chapter, when Bingo sang it in the barrow; but it was replaced there at the time of writing by *Ho! Tom Bombadil, Tom Bombadillo!* etc., as in FR (p. 153). In the present passage my father wrote in the margin: 'Or substitute rhyme in chapter VI', and that was done (FR p. 145).

NOTES

1   This is the first occurrence of *Meriadoc* for *Marmaduke* in a manuscript as originally written.

2   The word looks very much like *badgers*. If this is so, it must be a reference to the badgers who captured Tom Bombadil in the poem ('By the coat they caught him, pulled Tom inside the hole, down their tunnels brought him'); see *The Adventures of Tom Bombadil* (1962), pp. 12–13 (the verses describing Tom's encounter with the badgers were left virtually unchanged in the later version). In the next text of this chapter Tom was telling the hobbits 'an absurd story about badgers and their odd ways' when Bingo slipped on the Ring; and this was retained in FR.

3   The story of the wet second day at Bombadil's was written *ab initio* in pencil, then a part of the manuscript overwritten in ink; for the last part of the chapter, from supper on the second day, there is both pencilled draft and manuscript in ink. But it is clear that all this work was continuous and overlapping.

4   The question about Old Man Willow on the night before is asked by Merry (by Frodo in FR); i.e. by one who had not been imprisoned in the tree.

124   THE RETURN OF THE SHADOW

5 A passage very close to that in FR (from 'Tom's words laid bare the
   hearts of trees') was substituted, probably while the manuscript was
   in progress or very soon after.
6 *a mort:* a great many.
7 Conceivably, some pencilled emendations to the typescript of the
   third chapter were added at this time and in this connection. Frodo
   Took's words of Farmer Maggot, 'He lives in a house' (p. 92), were
   thus extended: 'He is not a hobbit – not a pure hobbit anyway. He is
   rather large and has hair under his chin. But his family has had these
   fields time out of mind.' And when Maggot appears (p. 94), 'a large
   round hobbit-face' was changed to 'a large round hair-framed face.'
   Afterwards, in the Prologue to LR, the hobbits of the Eastfarthing
   were decribed as being 'rather large and heavy-legged': 'they were
   well known to be Stoors in a large part of their blood, as indeed was
   shown by the down that many grew on their chins. No Harfoot or
   Fallohide had any trace of a beard.' See p. 294.
      There has already been a hint earlier that Farmer Maggot was not
   altogether what he appeared to be, in Merry's remark (p. 103): 'He
   used to go into the Old Forest at one time, and had the reputation of
   knowing a thing or two outside the Shire.' This was retained in FR
   (p. 113).

VII

THE BARROW-WIGHT

My father's earliest thoughts on the encounter with the Barrow-wight (written down while he was working on the story of the hobbits in the Old Forest) have been given on p. 112. When he came to write this chapter he began with a pencilled draft[1] that took the story as far as the hobbits' waking beside the standing stone in the hollow circle on the Downs, and leading their ponies down from it into the fog (FR p. 149). Like many of his preliminary drafts, this would be virtually illegible had he not followed it closely in the first full manuscript (in ink), for words that could be interpreted in a dozen ways without context can then be identified at once. In this case he did no more than improve the hasty wording of the draft, and add the passage describing the view northwards from the stone pillar, with the dark line in the distance that Merry took for trees bordering the East Road.

If the draft continued beyond this point it is lost now; but in fact the manuscript in ink could well be the primary composition. There is however a very rough pencilled plot-outline for the story from the point where 'Bingo comes to himself inside a barrow', and this outline continues the story to Rivendell. This is so rapidly written and now so faint that I cannot after much effort make it all out. The worst part, however, is at the beginning, extending from Bingo's finding himself in the barrow to Tom's waking Odo, Frodo, and Merry, and from what is legible it can be seen that while very concise and limited all the essentials of the narrative were present. I shall not therefore try to represent this part, but give the remainder of the outline in full in this place, since it is of great interest in showing my father's thoughts on the further course of the story at this juncture – i.e. before the 'Barrow-wight' chapter had been completed.

Tom sings a song over Odo Frodo Merry. Wake now my merry . . .!

. . . .[2] of the [?pillar] and how they became separated. Tom puts a blessing or a curse on the gold and lays it on the top of the mound. None of the hobbits will have any but Tom takes a brooch for Goldberry.

Tom says he will go with them, after chiding them for sleeping by the stone pillar. They soon find the Road and the way seems short. They turn along the Road. [?Gallops] come after them. Tom turns and holds up his hand. They fly back.[3] As dusk falls

126   THE RETURN OF THE SHADOW

they see a . . . light. Tom says goodbye – for Goldberry will be waiting.

They sleep at the inn and hear news of Gandalf. Jolly landlord. Drinking song.

Pass rapidly over rest of journey to Rivendell. Any riders on the Road? Make them foolishly turn aside to visit Troll Stones. This delays them. One day at last they halted on a rise and looked forward to the Ford. Galloping behind. Seven (3? 4?) Blackriders hastening along the Road. They have gold rings and crowns. Flight over Ford. Bingo [*written above:* Gandalf?] flings a stone and imitates Tom Bombadil. Go back and ride away! The Riders halt as if astonished, and looking up at the hobbits on the bank the hobbits can see no faces in their hoods. Go back says Bingo, but he is not Tom Bombadil, and the riders ride into the ford. But just then a rumbling rush is heard and a great [?wall] of water bowling stones roars down the river from the mountains. *Elves arrive.*

The Riders draw back just in time in dismay. The hobbits ride as hard as they can to Rivendell.

At Rivendell   *sleeping Bilbo*   Gandalf. Some explanations. Ringmail of Bingo in barrow and the dark rocks – (the 3 hobbits had dashed *past* the rocks when suddenly they all became [?shut] off??) Gandalf had sent the water down with Elrond's permission.

Gandalf astonished to hear about Tom.

Consultation of hobbits with Elrond and Gandalf.

The Quest of the Fiery Mountain.

This projection ends here. While my father had already conceived the scene at the Ford, with the sudden rising of the Bruinen (and the cry of Bingo/Frodo to the Riders: Go back!), Strider (not at first called Strider) would only emerge with the greatly increased significance of the Inn (which here first appears) at Bree in the next chapter; and there is no hint of Weathertop. If the 'dark rocks' are the 'two huge standing stones' through which Bingo/Frodo passed in the fog on the Downs (FR p. 150) – they are called 'standing rocks' in the first version – it is odd that discussion of this was postponed till the hobbits reached Rivendell; but possibly the words 'some explanations' imply that Gandalf was able to throw light on what had happened.[4] On the 'Ringmail of Bingo in barrow' see p. 223. The Cracks of Earth in the depths of the Fiery Mountain are named by Gandalf as the only heat great enough to destroy Bilbo's ring (p. 82); here for the first time the Fiery Mountain enters the story as the goal for which they will in the end be bound.

THE BARROW-WIGHT 127

The first full manuscript of this chapter (simply headed 'VI' and as usual at this stage without title) is fully legible for most of its length, but as so frequently becomes quicker and rougher, ending in rapid pencil. This my father went over here and there in ink, partly to improve the expression, partly to clarify his own writing; this certainly belongs to the same period, but after he had started on the next chapter.

As with the previous two chapters, the final form of FR Chapter 8 ('Fog on the Barrow-downs') is very largely present: for most of its length only very minor alterations were made afterwards. In what follows I note points of difference that seem to me of interest, though most are very slight.

In the opening paragraph the song and vision 'in dreams or out of them' is told in the same words in the old text, but is ascribed not to Bingo (Frodo in FR) alone, but to all the hobbits.

When they looked back over the forest and saw the knoll on which they had rested before their descent to the Withywindle valley, 'the fir-trees growing there could be seen now small and dark in the West' (see p. 113).

When the hobbits became separated in the fog, and Bingo cried out miserably 'Where are you?' (FR p. 150), my father at first had a quite different story in mind:

'Here! Here!' came the voices suddenly plain and not far to the right. Plunging blindly towards them he bumped suddenly into the tail of a pony. An undoubted hobbit-voice (it was Odo's) gave a shriek of fright, and [he] fell over something on the ground. The something kicked him, and gave a yell. 'Help!' it cried in the undoubted voice of Odo.

'Thank goodness,' said Bingo, rolling on the ground in Odo's arms. 'Thank goodness I have found you!'

'Thank goodness indeed!' said Odo in a relieved voice; 'but need you really run away without warning and then jump down out of the sky on top of me?'

My father rejected this as soon as written, and wrote instead, as in FR: 'There was no reply. He stood listening', etc.

A first version of the Barrow-wight's incantation was rejected and replaced by the form that appears in FR (p. 152); but the changes made were very slight except in line 7, where for 'till the dark lord lifts his hand' the first version had 'till the king of the dark tower lifts his hand.'[5] In the rough workings for this verse my father wrote: 'The dark lord sits in the tower and looks over the dark seas and the dark world', and also 'his hand stretches over the cold sea and the dead world.'

The arm 'walking on its fingers' crept towards Frodo Took (Sam in FR); and where in FR 'Frodo fell forward over Merry, and Merry's face felt cold', in the old version Bingo fell forward over Frodo Took. There is

128   THE RETURN OF THE SHADOW

no evident pattern in the changed ascriptions when the 'cast of characters' was altered; so later in the chapter Odo says 'Where are my clothes?'
(Sam in FR), and when Tom Bombadil says 'You won't find your clothes
again' it is Frodo Took who asks 'What do you mean?' (Pippin in FR).
In general I do not further note such points unless they seem significant.

On the rejected form of the rhyme taught to the hobbits by Tom
Bombadil and sung by Bingo in the barrow see p. 123. The first two
lines of the rejected rhyme were used later in the chapter, when Tom
goes off after the ponies (FR p. 155).

When Merry said 'What in the name of wonder?' as he felt the gold
circlet that had slipped over one eye, the old version continues: 'Then he
stopped, and a shadow came over his face. "I begin to remember," he
said. "I thought I was dead – but don't let us speak of it."' There is no
mention of the Men of Carn Dûm (FR p. 154).

Tom Bombadil's names for the ponies go back to the beginning, with
the exception of 'Sharp-ears', who was first called 'Four-foot'! When he
bade the treasures lying in the sun on the top of the mound lie there 'free
to all finders, bird, beast, elves or men and all kind creatures', he added:
'For the makers and owners of these things are not here, and their day is
long past, and the makers cannot claim them again until the world is
mended.' And when he took the brooch for Goldberry he said: 'Fair was
she who long ago wore this on her shoulder, and Goldberry shall wear it
now, and we shall not forget them, the vanished folk, the old kings, the
children and the maidens, and all those who walked the earth when the
world was younger.'

While in the outline given on p. 125 the hobbits refuse to take anything
from the treasure in the mound, in the first text the story is that Tom
chose for them 'bronze swords, short, leaf-shaped and keen', but nothing
further is said in description of them (cf. FR p. 157), though the
following was added in pencil and perhaps belongs to the time of the
writing of the manuscript: 'These, he said, were made many ages ago by
men out of the West. They were foes of the Ring-lord.' The manuscript
continues:

and they hung them from the leather belts beneath their jackets;
though they did not yet see the purpose of them. Fighting had not
occurred to any of them as among the possible adventures that
their flight might bring them to. As far as Bingo could remember
even the great and heroic Bilbo had somehow avoided using his
small sword even on goblins – and then he remembered the
spiders of Mirkwood and tightened his belt.

Of the hints in Tom's words in FR concerning the history of Angmar and
the coming of Aragorn there is of course no suggestion.

As already noted, the end of the chapter is roughly pencilled and here
and there overwritten in ink. The crossing of the dyke – boundary of an

THE BARROW-WIGHT 129

old kingdom, about which 'Tom seemed to remember something un-happy and would not say much' – and their coming at last to the Road is much as in FR (p. 158), but the remainder is best given in full, as originally pencilled, so far as that can be made out.

Bingo rode down onto the track and looked both ways. There was no one in sight. 'Well, here we are again at last!' he said. 'I suppose we haven't lost more than a day by Merry's short cut. We had better stick to the beaten way after this.'

'You had better,' said Tom, 'and ride fast.'

Bingo looked at him. Black riders came back into his thought. He looked a little anxiously back towards the setting sun, but the road was brown and empty. 'Do you think,' he asked hesitatingly, 'do you think we shall be – er, pursued tonight?'

'Not tonight,' said Tom. 'No, not tonight. Not perhaps the next day. Not perhaps for days to come.

The next passage is very confused and little can be made out (of the first pencilled text); as overwritten in ink it reads:

But I cannot say for certain. Tom is not master of the Riders that come out of the Black Land far beyond his country.' All the same the hobbits wished that Tom was coming with them. They felt that he would know how to deal with them – if anyone did. They were now at last going forward into lands wholly strange to them, and beyond all but the most distant legends of the Shire, and they began to feel really lonely, exiled, and rather helpless. But Tom was now wishing them a final farewell, bidding them have good heart, and ride till dark without halting.

The pencilled text continues:

But he encouraged them – a little – by telling them that he guessed the Riders (or some of them) were seeking now among the mounds. For he seemed to think that the Riders and Barrow-wights had some kind of kinship or understanding. If that were so, it might prove in the end well that they had been captured. They learned from him that some miles away along the road was the old village of Bree, on the west side of Bree-hill.[6] It had an inn that could be trusted: the White Horse [*written above:* Prancing Pony]. The keeper was a good man and not unknown to Tom. 'Just you mention my name and he will treat you fairly. There you can sleep sound, and after that the morning will speed you well upon your way. Go now with my blessing.' They begged him to come as far as the inn and drink once more with them. But he

130 THE RETURN OF THE SHADOW

laughed and refused, saying: 'Tom has his house to mind, and Goldberry is waiting.' Then he turned, tossed up his hat, leaped on Lumpkin's back, and rode over the bank and away singing into the gathering dusk.

This passage, as far as 'Go now with my blessing', was rejected, and a new version written in ink on a separate sheet; this second text is the same as Tom's farewell speech in FR p. 159 ('Tom will give you good advice . . .'), but it is here written out in verse-lines, and with these differences: the 'worthy keeper' is Barnabas Butterbur, not Barliman, and the reference to him is followed by:

> *He knows Tom Bombadil, and Tom's name will help you.*
> *Say 'Tom sent us here' and he will treat you kindly.*
> *There you can sleep sound, and afterwards the morning*
> *Will speed you upon your way. Go now with my blessing!*
> *Keep up your merry hearts, and ride to meet your fortune!*

That these revisions are later than the first pencilled draft of the next chapter is seen from the fact that throughout that draft the innkeeper's name was Timothy Titus, not yet Barnabas Butterbur (p. 140 note 3).

The end of this chapter is again overwritten in ink, but so far as I can make out this was only to clarify the almost illegible pencilled text:

The hobbits stood and watched him out of sight. Then, feeling heavy at heart (in spite of his encouragement), they mounted their ponies, not without some glances back along the Road, and went off slowly into the evening. They did not sing, or talk, or discuss the events of the night before, but plodded silently along. Bingo and Merry rode in front, Odo and Frodo, leading the spare pony, were behind.

It was quite dark before they saw lights twinkling some distance ahead. Before them rose Bree Hill, barring the way, a dark slope against the misty stars, and under it and on its western side nestled the little village.

NOTES

1 This draft is in fact continuous with that for the Bombadil chapter (p. 123 note 3), but my father soon after drew a line on the pencilled text between 'and led them with candles back to their bedroom' and 'That night they heard no noises', entering the chapter-number 'VI?'.
2 The illegible word begins *Expl* but the remainder does not seem to be *(Expl)anation.*
3 Cf. the outline given on p. 112: 'two Barrow-wights come [?galloping] after them, but stop every time Tom Bombadil turns and looks at them.'

THE BARROW-WIGHT   131

4   In a very early form of the chapter 'Many Meetings' (a passage
    retained word for word in FR, pp. 231–2) Bingo says to Gandalf at
    Rivendell: 'You seem to know a great deal already. I have not spoken
    to the others about the Barrow. At first it was too horrible, and
    afterwards there were other things to think about. How did you know
    about it?' And Gandalf replies: 'You have talked long in your sleep,
    Bingo.' But I doubt that this is relevant.

5   The 'dark tower' of the Necromancer is referred to by Gandalf in the
    text given in Chapter III (p. 81), and indeed goes back to *The Hobbit*,
    where at the end of Chapter VII 'Queer Lodgings' Gandalf speaks of
    the 'dark tower' of the Necromancer, in the south of Mirkwood. But it
    is difficult to feel sure where at this stage my father imagined the Dark
    Tower to stand. Tom Bombadil says (p. 129) that he 'is not master of
    the Riders that come out of the Black Land far beyond his country',
    and the name *Mordor* had certainly arisen: cf. the second version of
    The Fall of Númenor (V.29, 31), 'And they came at last even to
    Mordor the Black Country, where Sauron, that is in the Gnomish
    tongue named Thû, has rebuilt his fortresses.' See further p. 218
    note 17.

6   My father first put 'an old village which had an inn', but the change to
    'the old village of Bree, on the west side of Bree-hill. It had an inn' was
    almost certainly made as he wrote (and 'Prancing Pony' above 'White
    Horse' likewise). This is where the name first appears, based on Brill
    in Buckinghamshire, a place which he knew well, for it sits on a hill in
    the Little Kingdom of Farmer Giles of Ham (see Carpenter, *Bio-
    graphy*, p. 160). The name *Brill* is derived from the old British word
    bre 'hill', to which the English added their own word *hyll*; cf. LR
    Appendix F (p. 414), and the *Guide to the Names in The Lord of the
    Rings* (in Lobdell, *A Tolkien Compass*, 1975), entry *Archet*.

VIII

ARRIVAL AT BREE

My father continued on into a description of the Breelanders without a break. Subsequently he wrote over the original pencilled text in ink, and in that form, necessarily, I give it here.[1]

Little in a sense – it had perhaps some 50 houses on the hillside, and a large inn because of the goings and comings on the Road (though those were now less than they had once been). But it was actually a village built by Big People – mainly (the nearest settled habitation of that large and mysterious race to the Shire). Not many lived as far West as that in those days, and the Bree-folk (together with the neighbouring villages of Staddle and Crick) were an odd and rather isolated community, belonging to nobody but themselves (and more accustomed to dealing with hobbits, dwarves, and the other odd inhabitants of the world than Big People were or are). They were brown-faced, dark-haired, broad, shortish, cheerful and independent. They nor any one else knew why or when they had settled where they were. The land thereabouts and for many miles eastward was pretty empty in those days. There were hobbits about, of course – some higher up on the slopes of Bree-hill itself, and many in the valley of Combe on the east side. For not all hobbits lived in the Shire by any means. But the Outsiders were a rustic, not to say (though in the Shire it was often said) uncivilized sort. Some were in fact no better than tramps and wanderers, ready to dig a hole in any bank, and to stay there just as long or short a time as it suited them. So the folk of Bree were, you see, familiar enough with hobbits, civilized or otherwise – for Brandywine Bridge was not so far off. But our hobbits were not familiar with Bree-folk, and the houses seemed strange, large and tall (almost hillocks), as they trotted in on their ponies.

My father then struck this out, and began again. He was still numbering the pages continuously from the beginning of Chapter VI (the story of the Barrow-wight), but when he reached Bingo's song at the inn he realised that he was well into a new chapter, and wrote in 'VII' at this point, i.e. at the beginning of this new account of the people of Bree. Once again there is no title.

ARRIVAL AT BREE 133

The manuscript of this chapter is an exceedingly complicated document: pencil overlaid with ink (sometimes remaining partly legible, sometimes not at all), pencil not overlaid but struck through, pencil allowed to stand, and fresh composition in ink, together with riders on slips and complex directions for insertions. There is no reason to suppose that the 'layers' are significantly separated in time, but the story was evolving as my father wrote: and the only way to present a coherent text is to give the manuscript in its last form. The chapter is given almost in full, since although much was retained it can only be seen clearly from a complete text just what the story was; but for convenience I divide it into two chapters in this book, breaking the narrative at the point where FR Chapter 9 'At the Sign of *The Prancing Pony*' ends and 10 'Strider' begins.

The interrelations of chapter-structure in the following part of the story are inevitably complex, and can best be seen from a table:

	Original text	*This Book*	
VII	Arrival at Bree, and Bingo's song	VIII	9 'At the Sign of *The Prancing Pony*'
	Conversation with Trotter and Butterbur	IX	10 'Strider'
	Attack on the inn		11 'A Knife in the Dark'
	Journey to Weathertop		
VIII	Attack on Weathertop	X	
	Weathertop to Rivendell	XI	12 'Flight to the Ford'

It will be seen at the beginning of this text that the presence of Men at Bree had been temporarily abandoned, and the description of their appearance in the rejected passage just given is now applied to the hobbits of the Bree-land; the innkeeper is a hobbit, and *The Prancing Pony* has a round front door leading into the side of Bree-hill.

They were hobbit-folk of course that lived in Bree (and the neighbouring villages of Combe and Archet).[2] Not all the hobbits lived in the Shire by any means, but the Outsiders were a rustic, not to say (though in the Shire it was often said) uncivilized lot, and not held in much account. There were probably a good many more of them scattered about in the West of the world in those days than people in the Shire imagined, though many were indeed no better than tramps and wanderers, ready to dig a rough hole in any bank, and stay only as long as it suited them. The villagers of Bree, Combe, and Archet, however, were settled folk (in reality not more rustic than most of their distant relations in Hobbiton) –

134   THE RETURN OF THE SHADOW

but they were rather odd and independent, and belonged to nobody but themselves. They were browner-skinned, darker-haired, slightly stouter, a good deal broader (and perhaps a trifle tougher) than the average hobbit of the Shire. Neither they nor anyone else knew why or when they had settled just there; but there they were, moderately prosperous and content. The land all round about was very empty for leagues and leagues in those days, and few folk (Big or Little) would be seen in a day's march. Owing to the Road the inn at Bree was fairly large; but the comings and goings, East or West, were less than they had been, and the inn was now chiefly used as a meeting-place for the idle, talkative, sociable or inquisitive inhabitants of the villages and the odd inhabitants of the wilder country round about.

When our four hobbits at last rode into Bree they were very glad. The inn door was open. It was a large round door leading into the side of Bree-hill, at which the road turned, looping to the right, and disappeared in the darkness. Light streamed into the road from the door, over which there was a lamp swinging and beneath that a sign – a fat white pony standing on his hind legs. Over the door was painted in white letters: The Prancing Pony by Barnabas Butterbur.[3] Someone was singing a song inside.

As the hobbits got off their ponies the song ended and there was a burst of laughter. Bingo stepped inside, and nearly bumped into the largest and fattest hobbit that he had ever set eyes on in all his days in the well-fed Shire. It was obviously Mr Butterbur himself. He had on a white apron and was scuttling out of one door and in through another with a tray full of full mugs. 'Can we . . . ?' said Bingo.

'Half a moment if you please,' the landlord shouted over his shoulder, and vanished into a babel of voices and a cloud of smoke beyond the door. In a moment he was out again wiping his hands on his apron. 'Good evening, master,' he said. 'What may you be wanting?'

'Beds for four and stabling for five ponies,' said Bingo, 'if that can be managed. We have come far today. Are you Mr Butterbur, perhaps?'

'That's right,' he answered, 'Barnabas is my name, Barnabas Butterbur at your service – if it is possible. But the house is nearly full, and so are the stables.'

'I was afraid it might be,' said Bingo. 'I hear it is an excellent house. We were specially recommended to stop here by our friend Tom Bombadil.'

ARRIVAL AT BREE 135

'In that case *anything* can be managed!' said Mr Butterbur, slapping his thighs and beaming. 'Come right inside! And how is the old fellow? Mad and merry, but merrier than mad, I'll be bound! Why didn't he come along too, and then we should have had some fun! Hi! Nob![4] Come here! Where are you, you woolly-footed slow-coach? Take the guests' bags! Where's Bob? You don't know? Well, find out! Double sharp. I haven't got six legs, nor six arms, nor six eyes either. Tell Bob there's five ponies that have to be stabled. And well, mind you. Well, you must make room then, if they have to go in bedrooms![5] Come right inside, sirs, all of you. Pleased to meet you! What names did you say? Mr Hill, Mr Rivers, Mr Green, and Mr Brown.[6] Can't say I have heard those names before, but I am pleased to meet you and hear them now.' Bingo had made them up, of course, on the spur of the moment, suddenly feeling that it would not be at all wise to publish their real names in a hobbit-inn on the high road. Hill, Rivers, Green, Brown sounded much stranger as names to hob-bits than they do to us, and Mr Butterbur had his own reasons for thinking them unlikely. However, he said nothing about that yet. 'But there,' he went on, 'I dare say there are lots of queer names and queer folk that we never hear of in these parts. We don't see so many Shire-folk in these days. Time was when the Tooks, now, often came along to have a crack with me or my old dad. Rare good people were the Tooks. They say they had Bree blood in 'em, and were not quite like other Shire-folk, but I don't know the rights of it. But there! I must be running off. But wait a minute now! Four riders and five ponies? Let me see, what does that remind me of? Never mind, it will come back. All in good time. One thing drives out another, as they say. I am a bit busy tonight. Lots of folk have dropped in, unexpected. Hi, Nob! Take these bags to the guests' rooms. That's right. Seven to ten down the west passage. Be quick now! And will you be wanting supper? You will. I thought so. Soon, I shouldn't wonder. Very well, masters, soon it shall be. This way now! Here's a room will suit you nicely, I hope. Excuse me, now. I must be trotting. 'Tis hard work for two legs, but I don't get thinner. I'll look in again later. If you want anything, ring the hand-bell, and Nob will come. If he don't, shout!'

Off he went, leaving them feeling a little breathless. He had not stopped talking to them (mixed with the giving of orders and instructions to other scuttling hobbits in the passages) from the time that he welcomed Bingo, until he ushered them into a small but cosy private parlour. There was a bit of bright fire burning;

136   THE RETURN OF THE SHADOW

there were some very comfortable chairs, and there was a round table, already spread with a white cloth. On it was a large handbell. But Nob, a small round curly-haired red-faced hobbit, came bustling back long before they thought of using it.

'Will you be wanting anything to drink, masters?' he asked. 'Or shall I show you your rooms, while supper is making?'

They were washed, and in the middle of a good deep mug of beer each, before Mr Butterbur came trotting in again, followed by Nob. A fine smell came with them. In a twinkling the table was laid. Hot soup, cold meats, new loaves, mounds of butter, cheese and fresh fruits, all the good solid plain food dear to hobbit-hearts, was set before them in plenty. They went at it with a will – not without a passing thought (in Bingo's mind especially) that it had to be paid for, and that they had no endless store of money. The time would come all too soon when they would have to pass good inns (even if they could find them).[7] Mr Butterbur hovered round for a bit, and then prepared to leave. 'I don't know whether you would care to join the company after supper,' he said, standing in the door. 'But perhaps you would rather find your beds. Still, the company would be pleased to welcome you, if you had a mind. We don't get travellers from the Shire – outsiders we call 'em, begging your pardon – too often in these days; and we like to hear the news, or any new song you may have in mind. But as you like, sirs. Ring the bell, if you wish for anything.'

There was nothing omitted that they could wish for, so they did not need to ring the bell. So refreshed and encouraged did they feel at the end of their supper (about 55 minutes steady going, not hindered by unnecessary talk) that they decided to join the company. At least Odo, Frodo, and Bingo did. Merry said he thought it would be too stuffy. 'I shall either sit here quietly by the fire, or else go out for a snuff of the air outside. Mind your Ps and Qs, and don't forget that you are supposed to be escaping in secret, and are Mr Hill, Mr Green, and Mr Brown.' 'All right,' they said. 'Mind yourself! Don't get lost, and don't forget that it is safest indoors.' Then they went and joined the company in the big meeting-room of the inn. The gathering was large, as they discovered as soon as their eyes became used to the light. This came chiefly from a large fire on a wide hearth, for the rather dim rays of three lamps hanging from the roof were clouded with smoke. Barnabas Butterbur was standing near the fire. He introduced them, so quickly that they did not catch half the names he mentioned, nor discover to whom the names they caught be-

ARRIVAL AT BREE
137

longed. There seemed to be several Mugworts (an odd name to their way of thinking), and also other rather botanical names like Rushlight, Heathertoes, Ferny, and Appledore (not to mention Butterbur);[8] there were also some (to hobbits) natural names like Banks, Longholes, Brockhouse, Sandheaver, and Tunnelly, which were not unknown among the more rustic inhabitants of the Shire.

But they got on well enough without surnames (which were very little used in that company). On the other side the company, as soon as they discovered that the strangers were from the Shire, were disposed to be friendly, and curious. Bingo had not attempted to conceal where they came from, knowing that their clothes and talk would give them away at once. But he gave out that he was interested in history and geography, at which there was much wagging of heads (although neither of these words were familiar in Bree-dialect); and that he was writing a book (at which there was silent astonishment); and that he and his friends were going to try and find out something about the various scattered eastern hobbits. At this a regular chorus of voices broke out, and if Bingo had really been going to write such a book (and had had many ears and sufficient patience) he would have learned a good deal in a few minutes, and also obtained lots of advice on who to apply to for more and profounder information.

But after a time, as Bingo did not show any sign of writing a book on the spot, the company returned to more recent and engaging topics, and Bingo sat in a corner, listening and looking round. Odo and Frodo made themselves very quickly at home, and were soon (rather to Bingo's disquiet) giving lively accounts of recent events in the Shire. There was some laughter and wagging of heads, and some questions. Suddenly Bingo noticed that a queer-looking, brown-faced hobbit, sitting in the shadows behind the others, was also listening intently. He had an enormous mug (more like a jug) in front of him, and was smoking a broken-stemmed pipe right under his rather long nose. He was dressed in dark rough brown cloth, and had a hood on, in spite of the warmth, – and, very remarkably, he had wooden shoes! Bingo could see them sticking out under the table in front of him.

'Who is that over there?' said Bingo, when he got a chance to whisper to Mr Butterbur. 'I don't think you introduced him.'

'Him?' said Barnabas, cocking an eye without turning his head. 'O! that is one of the wild folk – rangers we call 'em. He has been coming in now and again (in autumn and winter mostly) the last

138   THE RETURN OF THE SHADOW

few years; but he seldom talks. Not but what he can tell some rare tales when he has a mind, you take my word. What his right name is I never heard, but he's known round here as Trotter. You can hear him coming along the road in those shoes: clitter-clap – when he walks on a path, which isn't often. Why does he wear 'em? Well, that I can't say. But there ain't no accounting for East or West, as we say here, meaning the Rangers and the Shire-folk, begging your pardon.' Mr Butterbur was called away at that moment, or he might have whispered on in that fashion indefinitely.

Bingo found Trotter looking at him, as if he had heard or guessed all that was said. Presently the Ranger, with a click and a jerk of his hand, invited Bingo to come over to him; and as Bingo sat down beside him he threw back his hood, showing a long shaggy head of hair, some of which hung over his forehead. But it did not hide a pair of keen dark eyes. 'I'm Trotter,' he said in a low voice. 'I am very pleased to meet you, Mr — Hill, if old Barnabas had your name right?'⁹ 'He had,' said Bingo, rather stiffly: he was feeling far from comfortable under the stare of those dark eyes.

'Well, Mr Hill,' said Trotter, 'if I were you, I should stop your young friends from talking too much. Drink, fire, and chance meetings are well enough, but – well, this is not the Shire. There are queer folk about – though I say it as shouldn't,' he added with a grin, seeing Bingo's look. 'And there have been queer travellers through Bree not long back,' he went on, peering at Bingo's face.

Bingo peered back, but Trotter made no further sign. He seemed suddenly to be listening to Odo. Odo was now giving a comic account of the Farewell Party, and was just reaching Bingo's disappearing act. There was a hush of expectation. Bingo felt seriously annoyed. What was the good of vanishing out of the Shire, if the ass went away and gave their names to a mixed crowd in an inn on the highway! Even now Odo had said enough to set shrewd wits (Trotter's for instance) guessing; and it would soon become obvious that 'Hill' was no other than Bolger-Baggins (of Bag-end Underhill). And Bingo somehow felt that it would be dangerous, even disastrous, if Odo mentioned the Ring.

'You had better do something quick!' said Trotter in his ear.

Bingo jumped on the table, and began to talk. The attention was shifted from Odo at once, and several of the hobbits laughed and clapped (thinking possibly that Mr Hill had been taking as much ale as was good for him). Bingo suddenly felt very nervous, and found himself, as was his habit when making a speech, fingering

ARRIVAL AT BREE 139

the things in his pocket. Vaguely he felt the chain and the Ring there, and jingled it against a few copper coins; but this did not help him much, and after a few suitable words, as they would have said in the Shire (such as 'We are all very much gratified by the kindness of your reception', and things of that sort), he stopped and coughed. 'A song! A song!' they shouted. 'Come on now, Master, sing us something.' In desperation Bingo began an absurd song, which Bilbo had been fond of (he probably wrote it).[10]

[Song][11]

There was loud applause. Bingo had a good voice, and the company was not over particular. 'Where's old Barney?' they cried. 'He ought to hear this. He ought to larn his cat the fiddle, and then we'd have a dance. Bring in some more ale, and let's have it again!' They made Bingo have another drink and then sing the song once more, while many of them joined in; for the tune was well-known and they were quick at picking up words.

Much encouraged Bingo capered about on the table; and when he came a second time to 'the cow jumped over the moon', he jumped in the air. Much too vigorously:[12] for he came down bang into a tray full of mugs, and then slipped and rolled off the table with a crash, clatter, and bump. But what interested the company far more and stopped their cheers and laughter dead was his vanishing. As Bingo rolled off the table he simply disappeared with a crash as if he had thudded through the floor without making a hole.

The local hobbits sprang to their feet and shouted for Barnabas. They drew away from Odo and Frodo, who found themselves left alone in a corner and eyed darkly and doubtfully from a distance, as if they were the companions of a travelling wizard of dubious origin and unknown powers and purpose. There was one swarthy-faced fellow who stood looking at them with a knowing sort of look that made them feel uncomfortable. Very soon he slipped out of the door followed by one of his friends: not a well-favoured pair.[13] Bingo in the meanwhile feeling a fool (quite rightly) and not knowing what else to do crawled away under the tables to the corner by Trotter, who was sitting still quite unconcerned. He then sat back against the wall, and took off the Ring. By bad luck he had been fingering it in his pocket just at the fatal moment, and had slipped it on in his sudden surprise at falling.

'Hullo!' said Trotter. 'What did you mean by that? Worse than

140   THE RETURN OF THE SHADOW

anything your friends could have said. You've fair put your foot and finger in it, haven't you?'

'I don't know what you mean,' said Bingo (annoyed and alarmed).

'O yes you do,' said Trotter. 'But we had better wait till the uproar has died down. Then, if you don't mind, Mr Bolger-Baggins, I should like a quiet word with you.'

'What about?' said Bingo, pretending not to notice the sudden use of his proper name. 'O, wizards, and that sort of thing,' said Trotter with a grin. 'You'll hear something to your advantage.' 'Very well,' said Bingo. 'I'll see you later.'

In the meantime argument in a chorus of voices had been going on by the fireplace. Mr Butterbur had come trotting in, and was trying to listen to many conflicting accounts at the same time.

The next part of the text, as far as the end of Chapter 9 in FR, is almost word for word the same as in the final version, with only such differences as are to be expected: 'Mr Underhill' of FR is 'Mr Hill'; 'There's Mr Took, now: he's not vanished' is 'There's Mr Green and Mr Brown, now: they've not vanished'; and there is no mention of the Men of Bree, of the Dwarves, or of the strange Men – it is simply 'the company' that went off in a huff. But at the end, when Bingo said to the landlord: 'Will you see that our ponies are ready?', the old narrative differs:

'There now!' said the landlord, snapping his fingers. 'Half a moment. It's come back to me, as I said it would. Bless me! Four hobbits and five ponies!'

As already explained, though I end this chapter here the earliest version goes on into what was afterwards Chapter 10 'Strider' without a break; see the table on p. 133.

NOTES

1   Bits of the underlying text can in fact be made out: enough to show that the conception of Bree as a village of Men, though with 'hobbits about', was present.

2   *Crick* (p. 132) has disappeared for good (but cf. 'Crickhollow'); *Staddle* also, but only temporarily.

3   *Barnabas Butterbur* is written in ink over the original name in pencil: *Timothy Titus*. Timothy Titus was the name of the inn-keeper in the underlying pencilled text throughout the chapter. This was a name that survived from an old story of my father's, of

ARRIVAL AT BREE
141

which only a couple of pages exist (no doubt all that was ever written down); but that Timothy Titus bore no resemblance whatsoever to Mr Butterbur.

4 Nob was at first called Lob; this survived into the inked manuscript stage and was then changed.

5 The original pencilled text went on from here:

Come right inside. Pleased to meet you. Mr Took, did you say? Lor now, I remember that name. Time was when Tooks would think nothing of riding out here just to have a crack with my old dad or me. Mr Odo Took, Mr Frodo Took, Mr Merry Brandy-buck, Mr Bingo Baggins. Lemme see, what does that remind me of? Never mind, it will come back. One thing drives out another. Bit busy tonight. Lots of folk dropped in. Hi, Nob! Take these bags (etc.)

My father struck this out, noting 'hobbits must hide their names', and wrote these two passages on an added slip in pencil:

Mr Frodo Walker, Mr Odo Walker – can't say I have met that name before. (Bingo had made it up on the spur of the moment, suddenly realizing that it would not be wise to publish their real names in a hobbit-inn on the high road).

What name did you say – all Walkers, Mr Ben Walker and three nephews. Can't say I have met that name before, but I'm pleased to meet you.

These also were struck out, and the passage that follows in the text ('Come right inside, sirs, all of you . . .'), in pencil overwritten in ink, was adopted.

6 In the underlying pencilled text of this passage my father wrote *Ferny* but at once changed it to *Hill*; and in the text in ink he wrote *Fellowes* but changed it to *Green*. Later on, in rejected pencilled drafting, Mr Butterbur says: 'You don't say, Mr Mugwort. Well, as long as Mr Rivers and the two Mr Fellowes don't vanish too (without paying the bill) he is welcome' (i.e. to vanish into thin air, as Mugwort has asserted that he did: FR p. 173).

7 Cf. Bingo's words to Gildor, p. 62: 'I had come to the end of my treasure.' The present passage was rejected and does not appear in FR: but cf. p. 172 note 3.

8 *Appledore*: 'apple-tree' (Old English *apuldor*). – In FR (p. 167) these 'botanical' names are primarily names of families of Men in Bree.

9 The underlying pencilled text still had here: 'I am very pleased to meet Mr Bingo Baggins'; and Trotter's next words began: 'Well, Mr Bingo . . .' See note 5.

10 Here follows: 'It went to a well-known tune, and the company joined in the chorus', referring to the song which was originally given to Bingo here (see note 11), where there is a chorus; the sentence was struck out when 'The Cat and the Fiddle' was chosen instead.

142   THE RETURN OF THE SHADOW

11   My father first wrote here 'Troll Song', and a rough and unfinished
      version of it is found in the manuscript at this point. He apparently
      decided almost at once to substitute 'The Cat and the Fiddle', and
      there are also two texts of that song included in the manuscript, each
      preceded by the words (as in FR p. 170):
          It was about an Inn, and I suppose that is what brought it to
          Bingo's mind. Here it is in full, though only a few words of it are
          now generally remembered.
      For the history and early forms of these songs see the *Note on the
      Songs at the Prancing Pony* that follows. – That there was to be a
      song at Bree is already foreseen in the primitive outline given on
      p. 126: 'They sleep at the inn and hear news of Gandalf. Jolly
      landlord. Drinking song.'
12   In the original text, where the song was to be the Troll Song, the
      comments of the audience on the cat and the fiddle are of course
      absent. Instead, after 'the company was not over particular', there
      followed:
          They made him have a drink and then sing it all over again. Much
          encouraged Bingo capered about on the table, and when he came
          a second time to 'his boot to bear where needed' he kicked in the
          air. Much too realistically: he overbalanced and fell . . .
      The line *His boot to bear where needed* is found in the version of the
      Troll Song written for this episode.
13   As the people of Bree were conceived at this stage, the ill-favoured
      pair would presumably be hobbits; and indeed in the next chapter
      Bill Ferny is explicitly so (p. 165). His companion here is the origin
      of the 'squint-eyed Southerner' who had come up the Greenway
      (FR p. 168); but there is no suggestion as yet of that element in what
      was still a very limited canvas.

Note on the Songs at the Prancing Pony

(i) The Troll Song

    When my father came to the scene where Bingo sings a song in *The
Prancing Pony* he first used the 'Troll Song' (note 11 above). The
original version of this, called *The Root of the Boot*, goes back to his time
at the University of Leeds; it was privately printed in a booklet with the
title *Songs for the Philologists*, University College, London, 1936 (for
the history of this publication see pp. 144–5). My father was extremely
fond of this song, which went to the tune of *The fox went out on a winter's
night*, and my delight in the line *If bonfire there be, 'tis underneath* is
among my very early recollections. Two copies of this booklet came into
my father's possession later (in 1940–1), and at some time undetermin-
able he corrected the text, removing some minor errors that had crept in.
I give the text here as printed in *Songs for the Philologists*, with these
corrections.

ARRIVAL AT BREE

THE ROOT OF THE BOOT

A troll sat alone on his seat of stone,
And munched and mumbled a bare old bone;
And long and long he had sat there lone
  And seen no man nor mortal –
    Ortal! Portal!
And long and long he had sat there lone
  And seen no man nor mortal.

Up came Tom with his big boots on;
'Hallo!' says he, 'pray what is yon?
It looks like the leg o' me nuncle John
  As should be a-lyin' in churchyard.
    Searchyard, Birchyard! etc.

'Young man,' says the troll, 'that bone I stole;
But what be bones, when mayhap the soul
In heaven on high hath an aureole
  As big and as bright as a bonfire?
    On fire, yon fire!'

Says Tom: 'Oddsteeth! 'tis my belief,
If bonfire there be, 'tis underneath;
For old man John was as proper a thief
  As ever wore black on a Sunday –
    Grundy, Monday!

But still I doan't see what is that to thee,
Wi' me kith and me kin a-makin' free:
So get to hell and ax leave o' he,
  Afore thou gnaws me nuncle!
    Uncle, Buncle!'

In the proper place upon the base
Tom boots him right – but, alas! that race
Hath a stonier seat than its stony face;
  So he rued that root on the rumpo,
    Lumpo, Bumpo!

Now Tom goes lame since home he came,
And his bootless foot is grievous game;
But troll's old seat is much the same,
  And the bone he boned* from its owner!
    Donor, Boner!

---

*bone: steal, make off with.

144 THE RETURN OF THE SHADOW

In addition to correcting errors in the text printed in *Songs for the Philologists* my father also changed the third line in verse 3 to *Hath a halo in heaven upon its poll.*

The original pencilled manuscript of the song is still extant. The title was *Pēro & Pōdex* ('Boot and Bottom'), and verse 6 as first written went:

> *In the proper place upon the base*
> *Tom boots him right – but, alas! that race*
> *Hath as stony a seat as it is in face,*
> *And Pero was punished by Podex.*
> *Odex! Codex!*

My father made a new version of the song for Bingo to sing in *The Prancing Pony*, suitable to the intended context, and as already mentioned this is found in the manuscript of the present chapter; but it is still in a rough state, and uncertain, and was abandoned when still incomplete. When he decided that he would not after all use it in this place he did not at once reintroduce it into *The Lord of the Rings*; it will be seen in Chapter XI that while the visit of the hobbits to the scene of Bilbo's encounter with the three Trolls was fully present from the first version, there was no song. It was only introduced here later; but the earlier drafts of Sam's 'Troll Song' proceed in series from the version intended for Bingo at Bree.

Songs for the Philologists.

The origin of the material in this little booklet goes back to Leeds University in the 1920s, when Professor E. V. Gordon (my father's colleague and close friend, who died most untimely in the summer of this same year, 1938) made typescripts for the use of students in the Department of English. 'His sources', in my father's words, 'were MSS of my own verses and his . . . with many additions of modern and traditional Icelandic songs taken mostly from Icelandic student songbooks.'

In 1935 or 1936 Dr. A. H. Smith of London University (formerly a student at Leeds) gave one of these typescripts (uncorrected) to a group of Honours students there for them to set up on the Elizabethan printing-press. The result was a booklet bearing the title

SONGS FOR THE PHILOLOGISTS

By J. R. R. Tolkien, E. V. Gordon & Others

Privately Printed in the Department of
English at University College, London
MCMXXXVI

In November 1940 Winifred Husbands of University College wrote to my father and explained that 'when the books were ready, Dr Smith realised that he had never asked your permission or that of Professor

ARRIVAL AT BREE 145

Gordon, and he said that the books must not be distributed till that had been done – but, so far as I know, he has never written or spoken to you on the subject, though I spoke of it to him more than once. The sad result is that most of the copies printed, being left undistributed in our rooms in Gower Street, have perished like the press itself in the fire which destroyed that part of the College building.' My father was therefore asked to give his retrospective permission. At that time there were 13 copies known to her, but subsequently she found more, I do not know how many; my father received two (p. 142).

There are 30 *Songs for the Philologists*, in Gothic, Icelandic, Old, Middle and Modern English, and Latin, and some poems in a macaronic mixture of languages. My father was the author of 13 (6 in Modern English, 6 in Old English, 1 in Gothic), and E. V. Gordon of two. Three of my father's Old English poems, and the one in Gothic, are printed with translations as an appendix to Professor T. A. Shippey's *The Road to Middle-earth* (1982).*

(ii) The Cat and the Fiddle

'The Cat and the Fiddle', which became Bingo's song at *The Prancing Pony*, was published in 1923 in *Yorkshire Poetry*, Vol. II no. 19 (Leeds, the Swan Press). I give here the text as it is found in the original manuscript, written on Leeds University paper.

THE CAT AND THE FIDDLE,
or
A Nursery Rhyme Undone and its Scandalous Secret
Unlocked

They say there's a little crooked inn
Behind an old grey hill,
Where they brew a beer so very brown
The man in the moon himself comes down,
And sometimes drinks his fill.

---

*This is a convenient place to cite my father's explanation of the significance of the Birch-tree that appears in two of the poems given by Professor Shippey (see his book pp. 206–7); cf. also 'Birchyard' in the chorus to verse 2 of *The Root of the Boot*. In a note on one of his copies of *Songs for the Philologists* my father wrote: 'ᛒ, B, Bee and (because of the runic name of ᛒ) Birch all symbolize mediaeval and philological studies (including Icelandic); while A, and Āc (oak = ᚫ) denote 'modern literature'. This more pleasing heraldry (and friendly rivalry and raillery) grew out of the grim assertion in the Syllabus that studies should be "divided into two Schemes, Scheme A and Scheme B". A was mainly modern and B mainly mediaeval and philological. Songs, festivities and other gaieties were however mainly confined to ᛒ.'

And there the ostler has a cat
 That plays a five-stringed fiddle;
Mine host a little dog so clever
He laughs at any joke whatever,
 And sometimes in the middle.

They also keep a hornéd cow,
 'Tis said, with golden hooves –
But music turns her head like ale,
And makes her wave her tufted tail,
 And dance upon the rooves.

But O! the rows of silver dishes
 And the store of silver spoons:
For Sunday there's a special pair,
And these they polish up with care
 On Saturday afternoons.

The man in the moon had drunk too deep,
 The ostler's cat was totty,*
A dish made love to a Sunday spoon,
The little dog saw all the jokes too soon,
 And the cow was dancing-dotty.

The man in the moon had another mug
 And fell beneath his chair,
And there he called for still more ale,
Though the stars were fading thin and pale,
 And the dawn was on the stair.

Then the ostler said to his tipsy cat:
 'The white horses of the Moon,
They neigh and champ their silver bits,
For their master's been and drowned his wits,
 And the Sun'll be rising soon –

Come play on your fiddle a hey-diddle-diddle,
 A jig to wake the dead.'
So the cat played a terrible drunken tune,
While the landlord shook the man in the moon:
 "Tis after three,' he said.

They rolled him slowly up the hill
 And bundled him in the moon,
And his horses galloped up in rear,
And the cow came capering like a deer,
 And the dish embraced the spoon.

---

*totty: tottery, shaky, dizzy.

ARRIVAL AT BREE 147

The cat then suddenly changed the tune,
  The dog began to roar,
The horses stood upon their heads,
The guests all bounded from their beds,
  And danced upon the floor.

The cat broke all his fiddle-strings,
  The cow jumped over the moon,
The little dog howled to see such fun,
In the middle the Saturday dish did run
  Away with the Sunday spoon.

The round moon rolled off down the hill,
  But only just in time,
For the Sun looked up with fiery head,
And ordered everyone back to bed,
  And the ending of the rhyme.

The two versions found in the manuscript of the present chapter move progressively towards the final form, and with emendations made to the second of them it is virtually attained (FR pp. 170–2).

IX

TROTTER AND THE JOURNEY TO WEATHERTOP

The original titleless chapter VII continues without a break through what became in FR Chapter 10 'Strider', ending part way through FR Chapter 11 'A Knife in the Dark'; but the first part of the narrative to be given now exists in two structurally quite distinct forms (both written legibly in ink). These my father marked 'Short' and 'Alternative', but for the purposes of this chapter I shall call them A ('Alternative') and B ('Short'). The relation between the two is a textual conundrum, though I think it can be explained;[1] the question is however of no great importance for the history of the narrative, since the two versions obviously belong to the same time. I give first the alternative A (on which my father subsequently wrote 'Use this version').

'There now!' said the landlord, snapping his fingers. 'Half a moment. It's come back to me, as I said it would. Bless me! Four hobbits and five ponies! There's been some enquiries for a party of your description in the last few days; and perhaps I might have a word with you.'

'Yes, certainly!' said Bingo with a sinking feeling. 'But not here. Won't you come to our room?'

'As you wish,' said the landlord. 'I'll be coming along to bid you good night and see that Nob has brought all you need, as soon as I've seen to a thing or two: we may have a word then.'

Bingo, Odo, and Frodo made their way back to their parlour.[2] There was no light. Merry was not there, and the fire had burned low. It was not until they had puffed up the embers into a blaze and put on a faggot that they discovered Trotter had come with them. There he was calmly sitting in a chair in the corner.

'Hullo!' said Odo. 'What do you want?'

'This is Trotter,' said Bingo hastily. 'I believe he wants a word with me too.'

'I do and I don't,' said Trotter. 'That is: I have my price.'

'What do you mean?' asked Bingo, puzzled and alarmed.

'Don't be frightened. I mean just this: I will tell you what I know, and give you what I've got, and what's more I'll keep your secret under my hood (which is closer than you or your friends keep it) – but I shall want my reward.'

TROTTER AND THE JOURNEY TO WEATHERTOP   149

'And what will that be, pray?' said Bingo, angrily; he not unnaturally suspected that they had met a rascal, and he thought uncomfortably of his small remaining purse of money.[3] All of it would hardly satisfy a rascal, and he could not spare any of it.

'Not much,' answered Trotter with an amused grin. 'Just this: you must take me along with you, until I want to leave you!'

'Oh, indeed!' replied Bingo, surprised but not much relieved. 'But even if I was likely to say yes, I would not promise any such thing until I knew a lot more about you, and your news, Mr Trotter.'

'Excellent!' said Trotter, crossing his legs. 'You seem to be coming to your senses again; and that is all to the good. You have not been half suspicious enough so far. Very well then: I will tell you what I know, and leave the rest to you. That's fair enough.'

'Go on then!' said Bingo. 'What do you know?'

'Well, it's like this,' said Trotter, dropping his voice; he got up and went to the door, opened it quickly, looked out, and then shut it quietly and sat down again. 'I have quick ears, and though I can't disappear into thin air, I can take care no one sees me, when I don't wish them to. I was behind a hedge when a party of travellers was halted by the Road not far west from here. There was a cart and horses and ponies; a whole pack of dwarves, one or two elves, and – a wizard. Gandalf, of course; there's no mistaking him, you'll agree. They were talking about a certain Mr Bingo Bolger-Baggins and his three friends, that were supposed to be riding on the Road behind. A bit incautious of Gandalf, I must say; but then, he was speaking low and I have quick ears, and was lying pretty close.

'I followed him and his party here to this inn. There was a fine commotion for a Sunday morning, I can tell you, and old Barnabas was running round in rings; but they kept themselves to themselves and did not talk outside closed doors. That would be five days ago.[4] They went away next morning. Now up comes a hobbit and three friends out of the Shire, and though he gives out the name of Hill, he and his friends seem to know a lot of the doings of Gandalf and of Mr Bolger-Baggins of Underhill. I can put two and two together. But that need not trouble you: for I am going to keep the answer under my hood, as I said. Maybe Mr Bolger-Baggins has his own good reasons for leaving his name behind. But if so, I should advise him to remember that there are more folk than Trotter that can add two and two together; and not all are to be trusted.'

150   THE RETURN OF THE SHADOW

'I am obliged to you,' said Bingo, feeling relieved, for Trotter did not seem to know anything very serious. 'I *have* my reasons for leaving my name behind, as you put it; but I can't quite see how any one else would guess my real name from what has occurred, unless he had your skill in eavesdropping, in – er – collecting information. Nor what use my real name would be to anybody in Bree.'

'Can't you?' said Trotter rather grimly; 'but eavesdropping, as you put it, is not unknown in Bree, and besides, I have not told you all yet.'

But at that moment he was interrupted by a knock on the door. Mr Barnabas Butterbur was there, with a tray of candles, and Nob behind him with jugs of hot water. 'Thinking you might wish to give some orders before you went to bed,' said the landlord, putting the candles on the table, 'I've come to wish you a good night. Nob! Take the water to the rooms.' He came in and shut the door.

'It's like this, Mr – er – Hill,' he said. 'I've been asked more than once to look out for a party of four hobbits from the Shire, four hobbits with five ponies. Hullo, Trotter, you here!'

'It's all right,' said Bingo. 'Say what you want. Trotter has my leave to stay.' Trotter grinned.

'Well,' began Mr Butterbur again, 'it's like this. Five days ago (yes, that's right, it would be Sunday morning, when all was quiet and peaceful) up rode a whole pack of travellers. Queer folk, dwarves and what not, with a cart and horses. And old Mr Gandalf was with them. Now says I to myself, there's been some doings in the Shire; and they'll be returning from the Party.'

'From the Party?' said Bingo. 'What Party?'

'Lor bless you, yes, sir! From the party your Mr Green was telling of. Mr Bolger-Baggins' party. A rare lot of traffic went westward through here earlier in the month. Some Men there were too. Great Big Folk. There hasn't been anything like it in my time. Those that would say anything gave out that they were going or taking stuff to a Mr Bolger-Baggins' birthday party. It seems he was a relation of that Mr Bilbo Baggins there was once strange tales about. Indeed they are still told in Bree, sir; though I daresay they are forgotten in the Shire. But we are slower-moving in Bree, so to speak, and like to hear old tales again. Not that I believe all these stories, mind you. Legends, I call 'em. They may be true, and then again mayhap they ain't. Now, where was I? Yes. Last Sunday morning in came old Mr Gandalf and his dwarves and all.

TROTTER AND THE JOURNEY TO WEATHERTOP 151

"Good morning," said I. "And where may you be going to, and where may you be coming from?" says I pleasant like. But he winks at me, and says nothing, and neither did any of his folk. But later on he drew me aside, and he said: "Butterbur," said he, "I have some friends behind that will be passing your way before long. They should be here by Tuesday,[5] if they can follow a plain road. They are hobbits: one is a round-bellied little chap (begging your pardon, sir) with red cheeks, and the others just young hobbits. They'll be riding on ponies. Just tell them to push along, will you? I'll go on slow from here, and they had best catch me up, if they can. Now don't go telling anybody else, and don't encourage them to stop here for a holiday. Your beer's good; but they must take what they can quick, and move on. See?"'

'Thankyou,' said Bingo, thinking Mr Butterbur had finished; and relieved again to find that there seemed nothing very serious behind the mystery.

'Ah, but wait a minute,' said Barnabas Butterbur, dropping his voice. 'That wasn't the end of it. There was others that enquired after four hobbits; and that's what is puzzling me. On Monday evening there came riding in a big fellow on a great black horse. All hooded and cloaked he was. I was standing by my door, and he spoke to me. Very strange I thought his voice, and could hardly make out his talk at first. I did not like the looks of him at all. But sure enough he was asking for news of four hobbits with five ponies[6] that were riding out of the Shire. There's something funny here, thought I; but remembering what old Mr Gandalf said, I gave him no satisfaction. "I haven't seen any such party," I said. "What may you be wanting with them, or with me?" At that he whipped up his horse without another word, and rode off eastward. The dogs were all yammering, and the geese a-screaming, as he went through the village. I was not sorry to see him go, I can tell you. But I heard tell later that three were seen going along the road towards Combe behind the hill, though where the other two sprang from no one could say.

'But will you believe me, they came back, or some others as like 'em as night and dark followed after them. On Tuesday evening, there was a bang at the door, and my dog in the yard set up a yelping and a howling. "It's another of they black Men," said Nob coming to fetch me with his hair all on end. Sure enough it was, when I went to the door: not one though, but four of 'em; and one was sitting there in the twilight with his horse nigh on my doorstep. He stooped down at me, and spoke in a sort of whisper.

THE RETURN OF THE SHADOW

It made me go queer down me back, if you understand me, as if someone had poured cold water behind me collar.[7] It was the same story: he wanted news of four hobbits with five ponies. But he seemed more pressing and eager like. Indeed to tell you the truth he offered me a tidy bit of gold and silver if I would tell him which way they had gone, or promise to watch out for them.

'"There's lots of hobbits and ponies round here and on the Road," said I (thinking things mighty curious, and not liking the sound of his voice). "But I haven't seen any party of that sort. If you give me a name, maybe I could give a message, if they happen to call at my house." At that he sat silent for a moment. And then, sir, he says: "The name is Baggins, Bolger-Baggins," and he hissed out the end of it like a snake. "Any message?" says I, all of a twitter. "Nay, just tell him that we are seeking him in haste," he hissed; "you may see us again, perhaps," and with that he and his fellows rode away, and disappeared quick in the darkness, being all wrapped up in black, like.

'Now what do you make of that, Mr Hill? I must say that it comes in my mind to wonder if that is your right name, begging your pardon. But I hope I have done right: for it seems to me that those black fellows mean no good by Mr Bolger-Baggins, if that is who you are.'

'Yes! He is Mr Bolger-Baggins all right,' said Trotter suddenly. 'And he ought to be grateful to you. He has only himself and his friends to thank, if all the village knows his name by now.'

'I *am* grateful,' said Bingo. 'I am sorry I cannot tell you the whole story, Mr Butterbur. I am very tired, and rather worried. But to put it briefly, these – er – black riders are just what I'm trying to escape. I should be very grateful (and so also will Gandalf be, and I expect old Tom Bombadil as well) if you would forget that anyone but Mr Hill passed this way; though I hope these abominable riders won't bother you any more.'

'I hope not indeed!' said Barnabas.

'Well, now good night!' said Bingo. 'Thankyou again for your kindness.'

'Good night, Mr Hill. Good night, Trotter!' said Barnabas. 'Good night, Mr Brown, sir, and Mr Green. Bless me now, where's Mr Rivers?'

'I don't know,' said Bingo; 'but I expect he is outside. He said something about going out for a breath of air. He'll be in before long.'

'Very well. I'll not go locking him out,' said the landlord. 'Good

TROTTER AND THE JOURNEY TO WEATHERTOP 153

night to you all!' With that he went out, and his feet died away down the passage.

'There now!' said Trotter, before Bingo could speak. 'Old Barnabas has told you a good deal of what I still had to say. I saw the Riders myself. There are seven at least. That rather alters things, doesn't it?'

'Yes,' said Bingo, hiding his alarm as well as he could. 'But we knew already that they were after us; and they did not find out anything new, it seems. How lucky that they came *before* we arrived!'

'I should not be sure,' said Trotter. 'I've still some more to add. [*Added in pencil:* I first saw the Riders last Saturday away west of Bree, before I ran across Gandalf. I am not at all sure they were not following *his* trail, too. I also saw those that called on Barnabas. And] on Tuesday night I was lying on a bank under the hedge of Bill Ferny's garden; and I heard Bill Ferny talking. He is a queer fellow, and his friends are like him. You may have noticed him among the company: a swarthy fellow with a scowl. He slipped out just after the song and the 'accident'. I wouldn't trust him. He would sell *anything* to *anybody*. Do you take my meaning? I did not see who Ferny was talking to, nor did I hear what was said: the voices were hisses and whispers. That is the end of my news. You must do what you like about my 'reward'. But as for my coming with you, I will say just this: I know all the lands between the Shire and the Mountains, for I've wandered over most of them in the course of my life; and I'm older now than I look. I might prove useful. For I fancy you'll have to leave the open Road after tonight's accident. I don't think somehow that you will be wanting to meet any of these Black-riders, if you can help it. They give me the creeps.' He shuddered, and they saw with surprise that he had drawn his hood over his face which was buried in his hands. The room seemed very still and quiet and the lights dim.

'There! It has passed!' he said after a moment, throwing back his hood and pushing his hair from his face. 'Perhaps I know or guess more about these Riders then even you do. You do not fear them enough – yet. But it seems likely enough to me that news of you will reach them before the night is old. Tomorrow you will have to go swiftly and secretly (if possible). But Trotter can take you by ways that are little trod. Will you have him?'

Bingo made no answer. He looked at Trotter: grim and wild

THE RETURN OF THE SHADOW

and rough-clad. It was hard to know what to do. He did not doubt that most of his tale was true (borne out as it was by the landlord's account); but it was less easy to feel sure of his good intent. He had a dark look – and yet there was something in it, and in his speech which often strayed from the rustic manner of the rangers and Bree-folk, that seemed friendly, and even familiar. The silence grew, and still Bingo could not make up his mind.

'Well, I'm for Trotter, if you want any help in deciding,' said Frodo at last. 'In any case I daresay he could follow us wherever we went, even if we refused.'

'Thankyou!' said Trotter, smiling at Frodo. 'I could, and I should, for I should feel it my duty. But here is a letter which I have for you – I daresay it will help you to make up your mind.'

To Bingo's amazement he took from a pocket a small sealed letter and handed it over. On the outside it was inscribed: 'B from G ⚊'

'Read it,' said Trotter.[8]

Bingo looked carefully at the seal before he broke it. It seemed undoubtedly to be Gandalf's, as was the writing and the Rune ⚊. Inside was the following message. Bingo read it aloud.

Monday morning Sept. 26. Dear B. Don't stop long in Bree – not for the night, if you can help it. Have learned some news on the way. Pursuit is getting close: there are 7 at least, perhaps more. On no account use It again, not even for a joke. Don't move in dark or mist. Push along by day! Try and catch me up. I cannot wait here for you; but I shall go slow for a day or two. Look out for our camp on Weathertop Hill.[9] I shall wait there as long as I dare. I am giving this to a ranger (wild hobbit) known as Trotter: he is dark, long-haired, has wooden shoes! You can trust him. He is an old friend of mine and knows a great deal. He will guide you to Weathertop and further if necessary. Push along! Yours

ᚷᚠᚾᛗᚠᛚᚣ *Gandalf* ⚊ [10]

Bingo looked at the trailing handwriting – it seemed as plainly genuine as the seal. 'Well, Trotter!' he said, 'if you had told me right away that you had this letter, it would have smoothed things out a lot, and saved a lot of talk. But why did you invent all that about eavesdropping?'

'I did not,' laughed Trotter. 'I gave old Gandalf quite a start when I popped up from behind the hedge. I told him he was lucky that it was an old friend. We had a long talk, about various things – Bilbo and Bingo and the [*added in pencil:* Riders and the] Ring, if

TROTTER AND THE JOURNEY TO WEATHERTOP 155

you want to know. He was very pleased to see me, as he was in a hurry and yet anxious to get in touch with you.'

'Well, I must admit I am glad to have a word from him,' said Bingo. 'And if you are a friend of Gandalf's then we are lucky to meet you. I am sorry if I was unnecessarily suspicious.'

'You weren't,' said Trotter. 'You weren't half suspicious enough. If you had had previous experience of your present enemy, you would not trust your own hands without a good look, once you knew that he was on your track. Now I *am* suspicious: and I had to make quite sure that *you* were genuine first, before handing over any letter. I've heard of shadow-parties picking up messages that were not meant for them – it has been done by enemies before now. Also, if you want to know, it amused me to see if I could induce you to take me on – just by my gifts of persuasion. It would have been nice (though quite wrong) if you had accepted me for my manners without testimonial! But there, I suppose my looks are against me!'

'They are!' said Odo laughing. 'But handsome is as handsome does, we say in the Shire, and anyway I daresay we shall all look much the same before long, after lying in hedges and ditches.'

'It will take more than a few days (or weeks or years) wandering in the world to make you look like Trotter,' he answered, and Odo subsided. 'You would die first, unless you are made of tougher stuff than you look to be.'

'What are we to do?' said Bingo. 'I don't altogether understand his letter. Gandalf said "don't stay in Bree." Is Barnabas Butterbur all right?'

'Perfectly!' said Trotter. 'As sound a hobbit as you would find between the West Towers and Rivendell. Faithful, kind, shrewd enough in his plain business; but not overcurious about anything but the daily events among the simple Bree-folk. If anything strange happens he just invents an explanation or else forgets it. "Queer," he says, and scratches his head, and goes back to his larder, or his brewhouse. That is just as well for you! I expect he has now convinced himself that there was "some mistake", and that the light was tricky, and that all the hobbits in the room merely imagined that "Mr Hill" disappeared. The black riders will become ordinary travellers looking for a friend, in a week or two – if they don't come back.'

'Well, is it safe then to stay the night here?' said Bingo, with a look at the comfortable fire and the candle-light. 'I mean, Gandalf said: "push along"; but also: "don't move in the dark".'

156 THE RETURN OF THE SHADOW

It is here that the alternative version B (see p. 148 and note 1) joins or merges with version A just given (though before this point, as will be seen, there are substantial passages in common). The beginning of the narrative is here quite different:

'There now!' said the landlord, snapping his fingers. 'Half a moment. It's come back to me, as I said it would. Bless me! Four hobbits and five ponies! I think I have a letter for your party.'

'A letter!' said Bingo, holding out his hand.

'Well,' said he, hesitating; 'he did say that I must be careful to deliver it to the right hands. So perhaps, if you don't mind, you would be so good as to tell me, who you might expect a message from.'

'Gandalf?' said Bingo. 'An old – er– man' (he thought perhaps *wizard* was an inadvisable word) 'with a tall hat and a long beard?'

'Gandalf it was,' said Butterbur; 'and old he is, but there is no call to describe him. All folk know *him*. A wizard they say he is; but that's as may be. But what may your first name be, if you will excuse my asking, sir?'

'Bingo.'

'Ah!' said Barnabas.[11] 'Well, that seems all right; though he did say that you should be here by Tuesday, not Thursday, as it is.[12] Here is the letter.' From his pocket he drew a small sealed envelope, on which was written: *To Bingo from G.* ※ *by the hand of Mr B. Butterbur, landlord of the Prancing Pony, Bree.*

'Thankyou very much, Mr Butterbur,' said Bingo, pocketing the letter. 'Now, if you will excuse me, I will say good night. I am very tired.'

'Good night, Mr Hill! I'll be sending water and candles to your room as soon as may be.' He trotted off; and Bingo, Frodo, and Odo made their way back to their parlour.

Version B now agrees with version A virtually word for word from here (p. 148) to Trotter's words 'but eavesdropping, as you put it, is not unknown in Bree, and besides, I have not told you all yet' (p. 150), at which point in A he was interrupted by the arrival of Mr Butterbur; thus in B also, Trotter tells them of his overhearing Gandalf talking about Bingo with the Dwarves and Elves on the Road west of Bree. B now diverges again:

. . . Besides, I have not yet told you the most important part. There were *other* folk enquiring after four hobbits.'

Bingo's heart sank: he guessed what was coming. 'Go on,' he said quietly.

TROTTER AND THE JOURNEY TO WEATHERTOP 157

'On Monday evening at the west end of the village I nearly ran into a horse and rider going fast in the dusk: all hooded and cloaked in black he was, and his horse was tall and black. I hailed him with a curse, not liking the looks of him; and he halted and spoke. He had a strange voice, and I could hardly make out his talk at first. Sure enough, he was asking for news of four hobbits with five ponies that were riding out of the Shire. I stood still and did not answer; and he brought his horse step by step nearer to me. When he was quite close he stooped and sniffed. Then he hissed, and rode off through the village, eastward. I heard the dogs yammering, and geese screaming. From the talk in the inn that night I gathered that *three* riders had been seen in the dusk going along the Road towards Combe behind the hill; though I don't know where the other two sprang from.

'On Tuesday I was on the look-out all day. Sure enough, as evening drew in, I saw the same riders again, or others as like them as night is to darkness – coming down the Road from the West again. Four this time, though, not three. I hailed them from behind a hedge as they passed; and they all halted suddenly, and turned towards my voice. One of them – he seemed larger and mounted on a taller horse – came forward in my direction. "Where are you going, and what is your business?" I said. The rider leaned forward as if he was peering – or smelling; and then riding to the hedge he spoke in a sort of whisper. I felt cold shivers run down my back. It was the same story: he wanted news of four hobbits and five ponies. But he seemed more pressing and eager. Indeed (and it is that that is worrying me at the moment) he offered a deal of silver and gold, if I could tell him which way they had gone, or promise to watch out for them. "I have seen no such party," I said, "and I am a wanderer myself, and maybe shall be far West or East by tomorrow. But if you give me a name, maybe I could give a message, if I happen to meet such folk in my way." At that he sat silent for a while; and then he said suddenly: "The name is Baggins, Bolger-Baggins," and he hissed out the end of it like a snake. "What message?" I asked all trembling. "Just tell him that we are seeking him in haste," he hissed; and with that he rode away with his companions, and their black robes were quickly swallowed up in the dark. What do you think of that? It rather alters things, doesn't it?'

'Yes,' said Bingo, hiding his alarm as well as he could. 'But we knew already that they were after us; and they do not seem to have found out anything new.'

158   THE RETURN OF THE SHADOW

'If you can trust me!' said Trotter, with a look at Bingo. 'But even so, I should not be too sure. I've a little more to tell. On Tuesday night I was lying on a bank under the hedge of Bill Ferny's garden . . .

Here version B returns again to the other (p. 153), and is almost word for word the same as far as 'The silence grew, and still Bingo could not make up his mind' (p. 154), the only difference being that after 'Bingo did not doubt that most of his tale was true' the words '(borne out as it was by the landlord's account)' are necessarily absent, since in this version Mr Butterbur has not encountered the Riders. Now follows in B:

'I should take a look at that letter of Gandalf's, if I were you,' said Trotter quietly. 'It might help you to make up your mind.'

Bingo took the letter, which he had almost forgotten, out of his pocket. He looked at the seal carefully before he broke it. It seemed certainly to be Gandalf's, as was the writing, and the runic ⓧ. He opened it, and read it aloud.

The letter is the same as in version A, except at the end, since in this story Gandalf gave the letter not to Trotter but to the landlord:[13]

> . . . *If you meet a ranger (wild hobbit: dark, long-haired, has wooden shoes!) known as Trotter, stick to him. You can trust him. Old friend of mine: I have seen him, and told him to look out for you. He knows a lot. He will guide you to Weathertop and further if necessary. Push along! Yours*
> ᚷᚨᚾᛞᚨᛚᚠ *Gandalf* ⓧ.

Bingo looked at the trailing handwriting. It seemed as plainly genuine as the seal. 'Well, Trotter,' he said, 'if you had told me right away that you had seen Gandalf to speak to, and that he had written this letter, it would have smoothed things out a lot, and saved a lot of talk.'

'As for the letter,' said Trotter, 'I knew nothing about it, till old Barnabas brought it out. Gandalf put two strings to his bow. I expect he was afraid I might miss you.'

'But why did you invent all that tale about eavesdropping?'

'I did not invent it,' laughed Trotter. 'It was true. I gave old Gandalf quite a start when I popped up from behind the hedge.

The two texts coincide again from this point (p. 154) – except of course that Trotter does not say here 'I had to make quite sure that *you* were genuine first, before handing over any letter', but simply 'I had to make sure that *you* were genuine.' But when Bingo says 'I don't altogether

TROTTER AND THE JOURNEY TO WEATHERTOP   159

understand this letter. He says "don't stop in Bree"' (p. 155), in version B he gets no further, for:

At that moment there came a knock on the door. Mr Butterbur was there again, with a tray of candles, and Nob behind him with jugs of hot water. 'Here's your water and lights, if you be wishing for your beds,' said he. 'But your Mr Rivers has not come in yet. I hope he will not be long, for I've a mind for bed myself, but I won't leave the locking-up to anyone else tonight; not with these pestering black foreigners about.'

'Where can Merry have got to?' said Frodo. 'I hope he's all right.'

'Give him a few more minutes, Mr Butterbur,' said Bingo. 'I am sorry to bother you.' 'Very good,' he said, putting the candles on the table. 'Nob, take the water to the rooms! Good night, sirs.' He shut the door.

'What I was going to say,' Bingo went on quietly after a moment, 'was: why not stop in Bree? Is Butterbur all right? Of course, Tom Bombadil said so; but I'm learning to be suspicious.'

'Old Barnabas!' said Trotter. 'He's perfectly all right. As sound a hobbit as there is between the West Towers and Rivendell. Gandalf was only afraid you might be too comfortable here! Barney is faithful, kind, shrewd in plain business – and not overcurious about anything but the daily events among his Bree-folk. If anything strange happens, he just invents an explanation, or puts it out of his mind as soon as possible. "Queer," he says, and scratches his head, and then goes back to his larder or his brewhouse.'

'Well, is it safe to stay the night here?' said Bingo, with a look at the comfortable fire and the candles. 'At any rate Gandalf said "Don't move in the dark".'

At this point the two versions finally merge. It will be seen that the essential differences of B from A are these. In B, Butterbur has Gandalf's letter and gives it to Bingo at the outset (though Bingo does not read it there and then). Trotter not only, as in A, 'eavesdrops' on Gandalf and his companions on the Road west of Bree, but he, not Butterbur, has the encounter with the Riders, and not of course at the inn door but on the road. The 'material' of the two accounts is closely similar, allowing for the Butterburian quality of the one, and the difference of place.

In version A Trotter, to help him make up his mind, gives Bingo the letter when Mr Butterbur has gone; in B, he reminds Bingo about it (as in FR p. 181). And in B, Butterbur only now comes into the parlour, so that the realisation that Merry has not come back is postponed.

160 THE RETURN OF THE SHADOW

A characteristic combination of, or selection from, these divergent accounts is found in the relation between the final story in FR and the two original variants; for A is followed in making Mr Butterbur enter in the middle of the conversation between the hobbits and Trotter/Strider – but B in making it Butterbur who has Gandalf's letter. It is extremely characteristic, again, that Trotter's 'eavesdropping' on Gandalf and his companions behind the hedge on the Road west of Bree survives in FR (p. 176), but becomes the eavesdropping of Strider on the hobbits themselves – for of course in FR Gandalf had been in Bree and left the letter long before, at the end of June, and at the time of the Birthday Party was far away. But while the relative chronology, as between Gandalf's movements and those of the hobbits, would be entirely reconstructed, that of the latter was never changed.

Thurs.	Sept. 22	Birthday Party	Gandalf and Merry, with Dwarves and Elves, left Hobbiton (after the fireworks)
Fri.	Sept. 23	Bingo, Frodo, and Odo left Hobbiton and slept out	
Sat.	Sept. 24	The hobbits passed the night with Gildor and the Elves	
Sun.	Sept. 25	The hobbits reached Buckland at night	Gandalf and his companions arrived at Bree in the morning
Mon.	Sept. 26	The hobbits in the Old Forest; first night with Tom Bombadil	Gandalf and his companions left Bree, Gandalf leaving letter for Bingo. Black Rider comes to the inn (*or* encounters Trotter on the Road)
Tues.	Sept. 27	Second night with Tom Bombadil	Four Riders come to the inn (*or* Trotter encounters them on the Road)
Wed.	Sept. 28	Hobbits captured by Barrow-wight	
Thurs. Sept. 29		Hobbits arrive at Bree	

The same dates for the hobbits' movements appear in The Tale of Years in LR Appendix B (p. 372). That the 22nd of September, the day of the Birthday Party, was a Thursday first appears in the fourth version

TROTTER AND THE JOURNEY TO WEATHERTOP   161

of 'A Long-expected Party' (FR p. 34); originally it was a Saturday (see pp. 21, 38).

For the significance of the additions in pencil on pp. 153–4, whereby Trotter is made to have seen the Riders 'away west of Bree' already on the Saturday, before Gandalf arrived there, and to have spoken with Gandalf about them when they met, see p. 217, note 11.

From the point where the two versions join, the text (in ink over pencil) proceeds thus. I give it in full, since though much was retained in FR there are a very great many differences in detail.

'You mustn't,' said Trotter; 'and so you can't help staying here tonight. What has been done can't be helped; and we must hope that all will be well. I don't think anything will get inside this inn, once it is locked. But, of course, we must get off as early as may be in the morning. I shall be up and about sooner than the Sun and I'll see all is ready. You are two or three days behind – somehow. Perhaps you will tell me as we go along what you have been up to. Unless you start early, and go fast, I doubt if you'll find any camp on Weathertop.'

'In that case let's get to bed now!' said Odo yawning. 'Where's that silly fellow Merry? It would be too much, if we had to go out now and look for him.'

At that very moment they heard a door slam, and feet running in the passage. Merry came in with a rush, shut the door hastily, and leaned against it. He was out of breath. They stared at him in alarm for a moment; then he gasped: 'I've seen one, Bingo. I've seen one!'

'What?' they cried all together.

'A Black Rider!'

'Where?' said Bingo.

'Here. In the village,' he answered. 'I had come back from a stroll, and was standing just outside the light from the door, looking at the stars: it is a fine night, but dark. I felt something coming towards, if you know what I mean: there was a sort of dark shadow; and then I saw him for a second,[14] just as he passed through the beam of light from the door. He was leading his horse along the grass-edge on the other side of the Road, and hardly made a sound.'

'Which way did he go?' asked Trotter.

Merry started, noticing the stranger for the first time. 'Go on,' said Bingo. 'This is a messenger from Gandalf. He will help us.'

'I followed him,' said Merry. 'He went through the village, right to the east end, where the Road turns round the foot of the hill.

162   THE RETURN OF THE SHADOW

Suddenly he stopped under a dark hedge; and I thought I heard him speaking, or whispering, to someone on the other side. I wasn't sure, though I crept as near as I dared. But I'm afraid I came over all queer and trembling suddenly, and bolted back.'

'What's to be done?' said Bingo, turning to Trotter.

'Don't go to your rooms!' said Trotter at once. 'That must have been Bill Ferny – for his hole is at the east end of Bree; and it is more than likely that he will have found out which rooms you have got. They have small windows looking back west and the outside walls are not very thick. We'll all stay in here, bar the door and window, and take turns to watch.[15] But first we had better fetch your baggage – and arrange the beds!'

At this point my father interrupted his original pencilled draft text to set down a sketch of the story to come, and since he did not overwrite this part of the manuscript in ink it can be read – or could be, if it were not written in a scribble at the very limit of legibility and beyond.

That was done. Pillows put in beds. Nothing happens that night – but in the morning windows open, pillows on floor. The ponies have all vanished. Timothy [i.e. Timothy Titus the landlord] in a great state. They . . . . . [?a bill]. He pays for ponies [?but there are] no more to be had. Shortage in the village. They go on with Trotter on foot. Trotter takes them to a wild hobbit hole, and [?gets his friend] to run on ahead and send a message to Weather-top by pony? Trotter [?guides them by quiet paths off the . . . .] road and going through the woods. Once far in distance on a hill which looked down on to a piece of the road they thought they saw a Black Rider sitting on his horse [?scanning] the road [?and the country round].

. . . . . Weathertop [?about] 50 [written beside: 100] miles from Bree.

Commanding view all round.

Gandalf had gone, but left a pile of stones – message. Waited two days. Must go on. Push on for ford. Help will be easy from Rivendell, if I get there.

They come to Troll Stones . . . . . of Road. Here owing to River ahead they [?are obliged] to go back to Road. Black Riders evidently expect them to visit Troll-wood [> Trollshaw] and are waiting on road where path joined it.

At this stage, then, my father did not at all foresee the attack on the hobbits at Weathertop, just as in the earlier sketch given on p. 126 he did not foresee the attack on the inn. The visit to the Troll Stones had already

TROTTER AND THE JOURNEY TO WEATHERTOP 163

been envisaged in that sketch (there described as 'foolish'), and there as
here the Riders would only finally come upon them at the Ford.

This is the first occurrence of the name *Trollshaw*, which appears on
the LR map (*Trollshaws*) but nowhere in the text.

The text in ink continues:

Trotter was now accepted as a member of the party, indeed as
their guide. They at once did as he suggested; and creeping to
their bedrooms they disordered the clothes, and put a pillow
longwise in each bed. Odo added a brown fur mat, a more realistic
substitute for his head. When they were all gathered in the sitting-
room again, they piled their things on the floor, pushed a low chair
against the door, and shut the window. Peeping out Bingo saw it
was still a clear night: he then closed and barred the heavy inside
shutters, drew the curtains, and blew out the candles. The hobbits
lay on their blankets with their feet towards the fire. Trotter lay in
the chair against the door. They did not talk much, but fell asleep
one by one.[16] Nothing happened in the night to disturb them.
Both Merry and Bingo woke up once in the early and still dark
hours, fancying they had heard or felt something moving; but
soon they fell asleep again. They noticed that Trotter seemed to be
sitting awake in his chair with his eyes open. It was also Trotter
that drew the curtains and opened the shutters and let in the early
light. He seemed to be able to do with next to no sleep. As soon as
he had roused them they tiptoed along the passage to their
bedrooms.

There they found how good Trotter's advice had been. The
windows were open and swinging, and the curtains were flapping.
The beds were tossed about, and the pillows flung on the floor –
ripped open. Odo's mat was torn to pieces.

Trotter promptly went in search of Mr Butterbur, and roused
him out of bed. What exactly he said to him he did not tell Bingo;
but the landlord appeared very quickly, and he seemed very
frightened, and very apologetic.

'Never has such a thing happened in my time, or my dad's,' said
he, raising his hands in horror. 'Guests unable to sleep in their
beds, and all. What are we coming to? But this has been a queer
week, and no mistake.' He did not seem surprised that they were
anxious to leave as soon as possible, before folk were up and about;
and bustled off to get them some breakfast at once, and have their
ponies got ready.

But before long he came back in dismay. The ponies had
vanished! The stabledoors had been broken open in the night, and

164   THE RETURN OF THE SHADOW

they were gone, and all the other ponies in the place as well. This was crushing news. They were already probably too late to overtake Gandalf. On foot there was no hope of it – they could not reach Weathertop for days, nor Rivendell for weeks.

'What *can* we do, Mr Butterbur?' asked Bingo desperately. 'Can we borrow any more ponies in the village, or the neighbourhood? Or hire them?' he added rather doubtfully.

'I doubt it,' said Mr Butterbur. 'I doubt if there be four riding-ponies left in all Bree; and I don't suppose one of them is for sale or hire. Bill Ferny has one, a poor overworked creature; but he won't part with that for less than thrice its worth, not if I know him. But I'll do what I can. I'll rout out Bob and send him round right away.'

In the end, after an hour and more's delay, it turned out that only *one* pony could be got – and that had to be bought for six silver pennies (a high price for those parts). But Mr Barnabas Butterbur was an honest hobbit, and a generous one (not but what he could afford to be both); and he insisted on paying Mr Rivers (that is Merry) for the lost five animals, 20 silver pennies,[17] less the cost of their food and lodging. That made a very valuable addition to their travelling funds, since silver pennies were very valuable in those days; but it was not at the moment much comfort for their loss and delay. It must have been rather a serious blow for poor old Barnabas, even though he was comfortably off.*

Of course all this bother about the ponies not only took time, but brought the hobbits and their affairs very much into public notice. There was no chance of keeping their departure secret any longer – much to their dismay, and to Trotter's. Indeed they did not get off until after nine o'clock, and by that time all the Bree-folk were out to watch them go. After saying farewell to Nob and Rob,[18] and taking leave of Mr Butterbur, they tramped off,

---

*Footnote. Still, I believe he came out on the right side in the end; for it turned out that the ponies, wild with terror, had escaped, and having a great deal of sense eventually made their way to find old Fatty Lumpkin. And that proved useful. For Tom Bombadil saw them, and was afraid that disaster had befallen the hobbits. So he went off to Bree to find out what he could; and there he learned all that Barnabas could tell him (and a bit more). Also he bought the ponies off Barnabas (as they belonged to him now). That was very much to the delight of Fatty Lumpkin, who now had friends to whom he could tell tales, and (as they were his juniors) on to whom he could shift most of the little work there was to do.

TROTTER AND THE JOURNEY TO WEATHERTOP 165

anxious and downhearted. Trotter walked in front leading their only pony, which was laden with the greater part of their luggage. Trotter was chewing an apple: he seemed to have a pocketful of them. Apples and tobacco, he said, were the things he most missed when he could not get them. They took no notice of the many inquisitive heads poking out of doors or popping over fences as they passed through the village; but as they drew near to the east end, Bingo saw a squat sullen-faced hobbit (rather goblinish, he thought to himself): he was looking over a hedge. He had black eyes, a large mouth, and an unpleasant leer, and was smoking a blackened pipe. He took the pipe out of his mouth, and spat back over his shoulder as they went by.

'Morning, Trotter!' he said. 'Found some new friends?' Trotter nodded, but did not answer.

'Morning, gentles!' he said to the hobbits. 'I suppose you know who you are going with? That's dirty Trotter, that is; or so he calls himself – though I have heard other names not so pretty. But maybe a ranger is good enough for you.'

Trotter turned round quickly. 'Bill Ferny!' he said. 'You put your ugly face out of sight, or you'll get it broken. Not that that'll do it much harm.' With a sudden flick, quick as lightning, half an apple left his hand and hit Bill square on the nose. He ducked and vanished with a yowk;[19] and they did not listen to the curses that came from behind the hedge.

After leaving the village they went along the Road for some miles. It wound to the right, round the south side of Bree hill, and then began to run downwards into wooded country.[20] Away north of the Road they could see first Archet on some higher ground like an island in the trees; and then down in a deep hollow, to the east of Archet, wisps of rising smoke that showed where Combe lay. After the Road had run down some way and left Bree hill behind, they came on a narrow track that ran northward away from the Road. 'This is where we leave the open, and take to cover!' said Trotter. '*Not* a short cut, I hope,' said Bingo. 'It was a short cut through woods that made us two days late before.' 'Ah, but you had not got me with you,' said Trotter. 'My cuts, short or long, don't go wrong.' His plan, as far as they could gather, not knowing the country, was to pass near Combe[21] and keep under cover of the woods while the Road was still near, and then to steer as straight as they could over the wild country to Weathertop Hill. They would in that way (if all went well) cut off a great loop of the Road, which further on bent away south to avoid the Flymarshes [*written*

166   THE RETURN OF THE SHADOW

above: Midgewater]. Trotter also had a notion that if he came across any of his friends among the wild hobbits, one that he could trust, they might send him on ahead on the pony to Weathertop. But the others did not think well of his plan, as it would mean carrying heavy packs, and thought the Flymarshes [*written above:* Midgewater] would prove bad enough (from Trotter's description) without that. [22] However, in the meantime walking was not unpleasant. Indeed, if it had not been for the disturbing events of the night before, they would have enjoyed this part of the journey better than any up to that time. The sun was shining, clear but not hot. The woods were still leafy and full of colour, and seemed peaceful, clean, and wholesome. Trotter guided them confidently among the many crossing ways, although very soon they themselves lost all sense of direction; but as he explained to them, they were not yet going in a straight line, but making a zig-zag course, to put off any pursuit.

'Bill Ferny will have watched where we left the Road, for certain,' he said; 'but I don't think he will follow us far himself, though he knows the land round here well enough. It's what he tells other – people that matters. If they think we have made for Combe, so much the better.' Whether because of Trotter's skill or for some other reason, they saw no sign, and heard no sound, of any other living thing all that day, and all the next day: neither two-footed (save birds), nor four-footed (except foxes and rabbits). On the third day out from Bree they came out of the woodlands. Their way had trended downwards all the time, and now they came to flatter and more difficult country.

They were on the borders of the Midgewater Marshes. The ground became damper, in places boggy, and here and there there were pools, and wide stretches of reeds and rushes, full of hidden warbling birds. They had to pick their way carefully to keep both dry-footed and on their line. At first they made fair progress: in fact they were probably going quite as quickly on foot as they could have done mounted. But as they went on their way became slower and more dangerous. The marshes were wide and treacherous, and across them there was only a winding ranger-trail, which it taxed Trotter's skill to find. The flies became a torment: particularly the clouds of tiny midges that crept up their sleeves and breeches and under their hair.

'I'm being eaten alive!' said Odo. 'Midgewater! There are more midges than water. What do they live on, when they can't get hobbits?'

TROTTER AND THE JOURNEY TO WEATHERTOP   167

They were two miserable days in this lonely and unpleasant country. Their camping places were damp and cold, for there was no good fuel. Armfuls of dry reeds and rush and grass blazed away all too soon. And of course the biting things would not let them sleep. There were also some abominable over-grown cousins of the cricket that squeaked all round, and nearly drove Bingo wild. He hated crickets, even when he was not kept awake by bites to listen to them. But these crickets were shriller than any cricket he had met, and even more persistent. They were more than glad, when early on the fifth day from Bree they saw the land before them slowly rising again, sloping up until in the distance it became a line of low hills.[23]

To the right of the line there was a tall conical hill with a slightly flattened top. 'That is Weathertop,' said Trotter. 'The old Road, which we have left far away on our right, runs to the south of it, and passes not far from its foot. We might reach it by noon tomorrow; and I suppose we had better make for it.'

'What do you mean?' asked Bingo.

'I mean: when we do get there, it is not certain what we shall find. It is close to the Road.'

'But was not Gandalf going to camp there?'

'Yes – but what with one thing and another, you are already three or even four days behind the time when he expected you to get there. You will be four or five days late by the time we reach the top. I wonder very much if we shall find *him* there. On the other hand, if certain persons were warned that you went east out of Bree, and have failed to find us in the wilderness, they may not unlikely make for Weathertop themselves. It commands a wide view of the lands all round. Indeed there are many birds and beasts in this country that could see us as we stand here from that hill-top. There are even some of the rangers that on a clear day could spy us from there, if we moved. And not all the rangers are to be trusted, nor all the birds and beasts.'

The hobbits looked anxiously at the distant hill. Odo looked up in the pale sky, as if he feared to see hawks or eagles hovering over them. 'You make me feel most uncomfortable,' said Bingo; 'but I suppose it is all for our good. We ought to realize what danger we are in. What do you advise us to do?'

'I think,' answered Trotter slowly and as if he was for the first time not quite sure of his plans, 'I think the best thing is to go straight forward, or as straight as we can, from this point, and make for the line of hills. There we can strike certain paths that I

168   THE RETURN OF THE SHADOW

know, and in fact will bring us to Weathertop from the North, and less openly. Then we shall see what we shall see.'

There seemed nothing else to do. In any case they could not stop in that comfortless land, and the line of march that Trotter proposed was more or less in the direction that they must take, if ever they were to get to Rivendell. All that day they plodded along, until the cold and early evening came down. The land became drier and more barren; but mists and vapours lay behind them on the wide marshes. A few melancholy birds were piping, until the round red sun sank slowly into the western shadows. They thought how its soft light would be glancing through the cheerful windows looking on to the garden at Bag-end far away. They came upon a stream that wandered down from the hills to lose itself in the stagnant marshland, and this they followed while the light lasted. It was already nearly dark when they camped under some stunted alder-trees on the stony banks of the stream; now dark before them loomed the bare side of the nearest hill, bleak and barren. They set a watch that night, but those that were not watching slept uneasily. The moon was waxing, and in the early night hours a grey cold light lay on the land.

Next morning they set out again soon after sunrise. There was a frost in the air, and the sky was a pale clear blue. They felt refreshed, as if they had had a night of good sleep, and were glad to have left the damp heavy air of the marshes. Already they were getting used to much walking, and to short commons (or shorter at any rate than they would have thought possible to walk on in the Shire). Odo declared that Bingo was looking twice the hobbit that he was.

'Very odd,' said Bingo, tightening his belt, 'considering that there is actually a great deal less of me. I hope the thinning-process won't go on indefinitely, or I shall become a wraith.'

'Don't speak of such things!' said Trotter quickly, and with surprising earnestness.

Before long they reached the feet of the hills; and there they found, for the first time since they left the Road, a track plain to see. This they took, turning and following it south-west.[24] It led them up and down, following a line of country that contrived to keep them hidden as often and as long as possible from view, either from the hill-tops above, or from the flats to the West. It dived into dells, and hugged steep banks, and found crossings over the streams, and ways round the bogs that these made in

TROTTER AND THE JOURNEY TO WEATHERTOP 169

hollow places. Where it crossed a flatter and more open space it often had lines of large boulders on either side, screening the marchers almost like a hedge.

'I wonder who made this path, and what for?' said Frodo, as they passed along one of these avenues, where the stones were unusually large and closely set. 'I am not sure I quite like it – it has a, well, rather barrow-wightish look? Is there any barrow on Weathertop?'

'No!' said Trotter. 'There is no barrow on Weathertop nor on any of these hills. The Men of the West did not live here. I do not know who made this path, nor how long ago, but it was made to provide a way to Weathertop that could be defended. It is told by some that Gilgalad and Valandil [later > Elendil] made a fort and strong place here in the Ancient Days, when they marched East.'

'Who was Gilgalad?' asked Frodo; but Trotter did not answer, and seemed to be lost in thought.[25]

It was already mid-day when they came towards the south-eastern end of the line of hills, and saw before them, in the pale clear light of the October sun, a green-grey ridge leading up like a sagging bridge on to the northward side of the tall conical hill. They decided to make for the top at once, while the day was broad. Concealment was no longer possible, and they could only hope for the best. Nothing could be seen moving on the hill.

After an hour's slow plodding climb, Trotter reached the crown of the hill. Bingo and Merry followed, tired and breathless. The last slope had been steep and stony. Odo and Frodo were left below with the baggage and the pony, in a sheltered hollow under the western flank of the hill. On the top they found only a pile of stones – a cairn of long forgotten meaning. There was no sign of Gandalf, or of any living thing. All about and below them was a wide view, for the most part of a land empty, deserted, and featureless – except for patches of woodland away to the south, where they caught also the occasional glint of distant water. Beneath them, on the southward side, ran the ribbon of the Old Road, coming out of the West and winding up and down until it faded behind a ridge of dark land in the East. It too was empty. Nothing was moving on it. Following its line eastward they beheld the Mountains – now plain to see, the nearer foothills brown and brooding, with taller greyer shapes behind, and behind them again the high white peaks glimmering out of clouds.

'Well, here we are!' said Merry. 'And very cheerless and un-

170   THE RETURN OF THE SHADOW

inviting it all looks. There is no water, and no shelter. I don't blame Gandalf for not waiting here! He would have to leave the waggon, and horses, and most of his companions, too, I expect, down near the Road.'

'I wonder,' said Trotter thoughtfully. 'He must certainly have come here, since he said he would. It is not like him to leave no sign. I hope nothing has happened to him – though it is not easy to imagine *him* coming to grief.' He pushed the pile of stones with his foot, and the topmost stones fell down with a clatter. Something white, set free, began to flutter in the wind. It was a piece of paper. Trotter seized it eagerly, and read out the message scrawled on it:

Waited three days. Must go. What has happened to you. Push on for the Ford beyond Troll-shaw, as fast as you can. Help will come there from Rivendell, as soon as I can manage it. Be watchful. G. ✕✕

'Three days!' said Trotter. 'Then he must have left while we were still in the marshes. I suppose we were too far away for any glimpse of our miserable fires.'

'How far is the Ford, and Rivendell?' said Bingo wearily. The world looked wild and wide from the hill-top.

'Let me think!' said Trotter. 'I don't know if the Road has ever been measured beyond the Forsaken Inn – a day's journey east of Bree. But the stages, in days taken by waggon, pony, or horse, or on foot, are pretty well known, of course. I should reckon it is about 120 long-miles from Bree to Weathertop – by the Road, which loops south and north. We have come a shorter but not quicker way: between 80 and 90 miles in the last six days. It is nearer 40 than 30 miles from Brandywine Bridge to Bree. I don't know, but I should make the count of miles from your Bridge to the Ford under the Misty Mountains a deal over 300 miles. So it must be close on 200 from Weathertop to the Ford. I have heard it said that from Bridge to Ford can be done in a fortnight going hard with fair weather; but I have never met any that had made the journey in that time. Most take nigh on a month, and poor hobbit-folk on foot take more.

This passage, from 'But the stages, in days taken by waggon, pony, or horse, or on foot', was enclosed within square brackets; and against it my father wrote: '? Cut out – as this though it can be kept as a narrative time guide is too cut and dried and spoils the feeling. ?' He then wrote the following replacement on a slip (cf. FR p. 200):

TROTTER AND THE JOURNEY TO WEATHERTOP   171

Some say it is so far, and some say otherwise. It is a queer Road. And folk are glad to reach their journey's end, be the time longer or shorter. But I know how long it would take me, with fair weather and no illfortune, just a poor ranger on his own feet: between three weeks and a month going hard from Brandywine Bridge to the Ford under the Misty Mountains. More than two days from the Bridge to Bree, a week from Bree to Weathertop. We have made it in that time, but we have come by a shorter way, for the Road bends south and north. Say ten days. Then we have a fortnight before us, maybe less, but more likely more.'

'A fortnight!' said Bingo. 'A lot may happen in that time.' They all fell silent. Bingo felt for the first time in that lonely place the full realization of his danger and exile. He wished that his fortune had left him in the quiet and beloved Shire. He stared at the hateful Road – leading back westward – to his old home. Suddenly he was aware that two black specks were moving along the ribbon, going westward, and looking closer he saw now that several more were crawling slowly eastward to meet them. He gave a cry and clutched Trotter's arm. 'Look!' he said, pointing.

'Get down!' cried Trotter, pulling Bingo flat on the ground beside him. Merry flung himself alongside. 'What is it?' he whispered. 'I don't know, but I fear,' said Trotter. They wormed their way to the edge of the flat hilltop and peered out from behind a stony outcrop. The light was not bright, for the clear morning had faded, and clouds crawled slowly out of the East and had now caught the sun, as it began to go west. They could see the black specks, but neither Bingo nor Merry could make out their shape for certain. Yet something told them that there below were Black Riders assembling on the Road, beyond the hill's foot. 'Yes,' said Trotter, whose keener sight left him in no doubt. 'The enemy is here.'

Hastily they crawled away, and slipped down the north side of the hill to find Odo and Frodo.

Here the original Chapter VII, which I have divided into two, ends.

NOTES

1   Of the original pencilled draft, overwritten by version B, little can now be read; it was dashed down in faint pencil, and except here and there the text in ink effectively obliterates it. Enough can be seen, however, to show that the story was that of version B (in which

172   THE RETURN OF THE SHADOW

Gandalf's letter was given to the landlord of the inn, not to Trotter); and though this is less certain, I suspect that at this stage there was no mention of Black Riders having come to Bree before Bingo, Merry, Frodo, and Odo arrived. On the other hand, it is perfectly clear that when my father wrote out version B on top of the original draft he had version A in front of him.

The explanation of this odd situation can be seen, I think, in the fact that version B is much longer than the pencilled draft and not at all closely associated with it; some of it is on slips added in. I think that my father wrote out version A *first*, on the basis of the pencilled draft, but changed the story as he did so (by giving Gandalf's letter to Trotter, and introducing Butterbur's story of the Riders who came to the inn); he *then* returned to the pencilled draft and wrote version B on top of it, going back to the story that the letter had been entrusted to Butterbur, and again introducing the story of the Black Riders at Bree but ascribing it now to Trotter, who encountered them on the Road. For this text he used version A and followed it very closely so far as the changed story allowed. Thus the textual history was:

(1)   Original pencilled draft: Gandalf's letter left with Butterbur; (probably) no story as yet of Black Riders having already come to Bree.

(2)   Version A: the story changed: Gandalf's letter left with Trotter; Butterbur tells of the coming of the Riders to the inn.

(3)   Version B, written over the original draft, but using much of the wording of A: Gandalf's letter left with Butterbur; Trotter tells of his encounters with the Riders on the Road.

Finally, some new phrases in B were written back into A.

2   It is with this sentence that Chapter 10 'Strider' begins in FR, but I include the preceding passage here since it forms part of the narrative which is treated in alternative ways (see p. 156).

3   Cf. p. 141 note 7. But even though the old idea that Bingo 'had come to the end of his treasure' (and that a vague object of his 'Journey' was that it might bring him some more, p. 62) disappeared, it remained in FR (p. 175) that 'he had brought only a little money with him.'

4   *That would be five days ago:* see the chronology given on p. 160. Gandalf and his companions arrived at the inn on Sunday morning, and it was now Thursday night.

5   *They should be here by Tuesday:* Gandalf had assumed that they would follow the Road from the Brandywine Bridge to Bree, and take two days over it. Cf. Trotter's calculations (pp. 170–1): 'It is nearer 40 than 30 miles from Brandywine Bridge to Bree', and 'More than two days from the Bridge to Bree' (on foot).

6   How did the Black Riders know this? See p. 350, note 7.

TROTTER AND THE JOURNEY TO WEATHERTOP 173

7 Here my father wrote: 'Now he described your party very exactly, sir, more exactly than Mr Gandalf did: colour of your ponies, look of your faces,' but struck it out as soon as written, probably because it was not consistent with his conception of the Black Riders: he had already said (p. 75) that for Ring-wraiths 'Everything becomes very faint like grey ghost pictures against the black background in which you live; but you can smell better than you can hear or see.' It seems very likely that the idea of the 'wraith-world', into which in some sense the bearer of a Ring entered if he put it on his finger, and in which he then became fully visible to the denizens of that world, had already arisen; a hint of this appears in Gildor's words (p. 64) 'I guess that the use of the ring helps them more than you', and in Gandalf's letter in the present chapter he is urgent that Bingo should never wear the Ring for any purpose – now that he has learned that the Riders are in pursuit.

8 These words are at the bottom of a manuscript page. At the bottom my father scribbled in pencil:

> Nov. 19 Motive *trailing Gandalf*. Gandalf drawing them off. *No camp at Weathertop* or again Gandalf leads them off.

With this cf. the pencilled addition on p. 153: 'I first saw the Riders last Saturday away west of Bree, before I ran across Gandalf. I am not at all sure they were not following *his* trail too.'

'Nov. 19' presumably refers to the date of the note, i.e. 19 November 1938; by then my father had got well beyond this point in the narrative, judging by what he said in a letter to Stanley Unwin of 13 October 1938: 'I have worked very hard for a month . . . on a sequel to *The Hobbit*. It has reached Chapter XI (though in rather an illegible state) . . .'

9 The first mention of Weathertop Hill; the actual first occurrence of the name must be in the original pencilled draft of Gandalf's letter, which can be partly made out (note 13).

10 The runes are the Old English runes, as in *The Hobbit*. Gandalf uses the English (Common Germanic) rune ᚷ for G in writing his name, but uses also as a sign for himself a rune ᛤ. In the *Angerthas* (LR Appendix E pp. 401–4) this rune meant (in the usage of the Dwarves of Moria) [ng].

11 Oddly, the manuscript in ink has here *Timothy*, not *Barnabas*; but it can only be a slip, returning momentarily to the landlord's original name (p. 140 note 3).

12 *Tuesday, not Thursday:* see note 5.

13 The ending of the letter can be read in the pencilled draft:

> *Don't be out after dark or in mist. Push along. Am so anxious that I shall wait [?two] days for you . . . . . Weathertop Hill. If you meet a ranger (wild hobbit) called Trotter, stick to him. I have told him to look out. He will guide you to Weathertop and further if necessary. Push along.*

174   THE RETURN OF THE SHADOW

14   The text as first written here (in ink: the pencilled text beneath is illegible) had: 'I felt something moving behind me, and when I turned I saw one going along the Road.' – For 'coming towards' in the revised sentence perhaps read 'coming towards me'.

15   *bar the door and window* was written in above *and take turns to watch*, which was not struck out. See note 16.

16   The underlying pencilled text can be read here:
> They did not talk much but fell asleep one by one. Trotter watched for three hours; he said he could do with very little sleep. Next came Merry. Nothing happened . . .

A first version in ink reads:
> He could do with very little (he said): 'give me three hours, and then wake me, and I will watch for the rest of the time.' Bingo took the first watch; the others talked for a while and then fell asleep.

At this point FR Chapter 10 'Strider' ends, and Chapter 11 'A Knife in the Dark' begins – where that chapter takes up the story at Bree again: of the attack by the Black Riders on the house at Crickhollow with which it begins there is as yet no trace.

17   *20* (silver pennies) was later changed to *25*.

18   *Rob:* at previous occurrences (pp. 135, 164) the name of the ostler at *The Prancing Pony* is certainly *Bob*, as in FR.

19   *a yowk:* the verb *yowk* 'howl, bawl, yelp' is given in Joseph Wright, *The English Dialect Dictionary*.

20   A tiny pencilled sketch in the body of the manuscript, belonging with the underlying draft, shows the Road, after it has curved down round the south side of Bree-hill, bending up north again and continuing the same line east of Bree as it had to the west of the village.

21   *Combe* changed in pencil to *Archet* (as in FR, p. 193).

22   These two sentences, from *Trotter also had a notion*, were enclosed in square brackets, probably at the time of writing. Cf. the outline (p. 162): 'Trotter takes them to a wild hobbit hole, and gets his friend to run on ahead and send a message to Weathertop by pony?'.

23   The pencilled text beneath the ink can be read sufficiently to show that the passage of the marshes (unnamed) was described in a couple of sentences.

24   Since at the end of the next sentence my father wrote 'from the flats to the East', which is an obvious slip and which he later corrected to 'West', it seems likely that the 'south-west' course of the track along the feet of the hills is also a slip for 'south-east'; a little later it is said that 'they came towards the south-eastern end of the line of hills.'

25   For the story of Gil-galad and Elendil and the Last Alliance as it was at this time see the second version of *The Fall of Númenor* §14 (V.28–9) and pp. 215–16. Though Elendil is present in *The Fall of Númenor* my father does not seem to have been entirely satisfied

TROTTER AND THE JOURNEY TO WEATHERTOP 175

with the name: here he wrote *Valandil* first, and in the original draft of the next chapter he changed *Elendil* temporarily to *Orendil* (p. 197 note 3). In *The Lost Road* Valandil was the name of Elendil's father (V.60, 69), and in a later version of *The Fall of Númenor* Valandil is Elendil's brother (V.33).

★

In the latter part of this chapter, from the point where the variant versions join (pp. 159, 161), all the essential structure of the immediate narrative in FR (pp. 185–201) is in place, though the larger bearings and the glimpses of ancient history are conspicuously absent. The narrative runs in a narrower dimension in any case, from the fact that there are no Men in the story: Butterbur is a hobbit, the wild 'rangers', of whom Trotter is one, are hobbits, Bill Ferny is a hobbit (p. 165) – though it is true that the range of hobbit character is greatly extended by these 'Outsiders' who live beyond the Shire's borders.

A few specific points of difference may be briefly mentioned. The pony bought in Bree is not in fact said to be Ferny's (p. 164), though it seems to be implied; and the subsequent history of the five ponies from Buckland, recorded in the footnote to the text (p. 164), was afterwards largely changed (FR p. 191). The encounter of Merry with the Black Rider outside the inn at Bree does not end with his being attacked; and it is Trotter who plays the later part of Sam in having a pocketful of apples and discomfiting Bill Ferny with one on the nose.

The journey from Bree to Weathertop has the same structure as that in FR (pp. 194–7), except at the end. The chronology is:

Days out of Bree	Date	Place
1	Fri. Sept. 30	In the woods (Chetwood)
2	Sat. Oct. 1	In the woods
3	Sun. Oct. 2	First day and camp in the marshes
4	Mon. Oct. 3	Second day and camp in the marshes
5	Tues. Oct. 4	Camp by the stream under alders

But in FR the hobbits made another night camp at the feet of the western slopes of the Weather Hills – and that was 'the night of the fifth of October, and they were six days out from Bree' (p. 197); this camp is not in the original version, and thus they reached Weathertop on Wednesday October 5. Trotter on Weathertop says that they have covered between 80 and 90 miles 'in the last six days': he was including that day also, for it was already after noon.

In the old story Gandalf stayed on Weathertop for three days, and he left there a note in a pile of stones, written on paper. This message ('Help

176   THE RETURN OF THE SHADOW

will come there [i.e. to the Ford] from Rivendell, as soon as I can manage it') gives the first clear indication in the story of what Gandalf's intentions were; and with this can be taken the words scribbled on the manuscript that are given in note 8. Gandalf was trying to lure the Riders after *him*.

Looking back over the whole of the original Chapter VII, the story from the hobbits' arrival in Bree to the sight of the Black Riders on the Road far below the summit of Weathertop, there appears again and in the most striking form the characteristic of my father's writing that elements emerge suddenly and clearly conceived, but with their 'meaning' and context still to undergo huge further development, or even complete transformation, in the later narrative (cf. p. 71). A small example here is the face that Bingo thought 'goblinish' as they walked out of Bree (p. 165) – which is here the face of Bill Ferny (a hobbit): in FR (p. 193) it will be that of 'the squint-eyed southerner' whom Frodo glimpsed through the window of Ferny's house, and thought that he looked 'more than half like a goblin.' In a 'chrysalis' state are the 'Rangers', wanderers in the wilderness, and Trotter is a Ranger, grim and weatherworn, deeply learned in the lore of the wild, and in many other matters; but they are hobbits, and of any further or larger significance that they might have in the history of Middle-earth there is no hint. Trotter is at once so fully realized that his tone in this part of the narrative (indeed not a few of his actual words) was never changed afterwards; yet such little as is glimpsed of his history at this stage bears no relation whatsoever to that of Aragorn son of Arathorn. He is a hobbit, marked out by wearing wooden shoes (whence his name Trotter); there seems to be something in his history that gives him a special knowledge of, and horror of, the Ring-wraiths (p. 153); and Bingo finds something about him that distinguishes him from other 'Rangers', and is in a way familiar (p. 154). These things will be explained later, before they are finally swept away.

X
THE ATTACK ON WEATHERTOP

This chapter, numbered VIII, and titleless as usual (though later my father pencilled in 'A Knife in the Dark'), begins on the same manuscript page as the end of the last; it was obviously continuous work, and the manuscript proceeds as before, in ink, rapid but always legible, over pencilled drafts of which only words or phrases here and there are visible (see p. 188). The text goes on through FR Chapter 12 'Flight to the Ford' without any sort of break, but as with the original Chapter VII I divide it into two (see the table on p. 133).

There was a hollow dell beneath the north-west shoulder of Weathertop, right under the long ridge that joined it to the hills behind. There Odo and Frodo had been left to wait for them. They had found the signs of a recent camp and fire, and, a great (and most unexpected) boon, behind a large rock was piled a small store of fire-wood. Better still, under the fuel they found a wooden case with some food in it. It was mostly cram-cakes, but there was some bacon, and some dried fruits. There was also some tobacco!

Cram was, as you may remember, a word in the language of the men of Dale and the Long-lake – to describe a special food they made for long journeys. It kept good indefinitely and was very sustaining, but not entertaining, as it took a lot of chewing and had no particular taste. Bilbo Baggins brought back the recipe – he used *cram* after he got home on some of his long and mysterious walks. Gandalf also took to using it on his perpetual journeys. He said he liked it softened in water (but that is hard to believe). But *cram* was not to be despised in the wilderness, and the hobbits were extremely grateful for Gandalf's thoughtfulness. They were still more grateful when the three others came down with their alarming news, and they all realized that they had a long journey still ahead, before they could expect to get help. They immediately held a council, and found it hard to decide what to do. It was the presence of the fire-wood (of which they could not have carried much away) that finally decided them to go no further that day, and to camp for that night in the dell.[1] It seemed unsafe, not to say desperate, to go on at once, or until they found out whether their

178   THE RETURN OF THE SHADOW

arrival at the hill was known or expected. For, unless they were to
make a long detour back north-west along the hills, and abandon
the direction of Rivendell altogether for a while, it would not be
easy to find any cover or concealment. The Road itself was
impossible; but they must at least cross it, if they were to get into
the more broken land, full of bushy thickets, immediately to the
south of it. To the north of the Road, beyond the hills, the land
was bare and flat for many miles.

'Can the – er – enemy *see*?' asked Merry. 'I mean, they seem
usually to have *smelt* rather than seen, at least in the daytime. But
you made us lie down flat.'

'I don't know,' said Trotter, 'how they perceive what they seek;
but I fear them. And their horses can see.'[2]

It was now already late afternoon. They had had no food since
breakfast. In spite of their fear and uncertainty they were very
hungry. So down in the dell where all was still and quiet they made
a meal – as good a meal as they dared take, after they had examined
their stores. But for Gandalf's present they would not have dared
to have more than a bite. They had left behind the countries where
inns or villages could be found. There were Big People (so Trotter
said) away to the South of them. But North and East the neighbouring lands were empty of all save birds and beasts, unfriendly
places deserted by all the races of the world: Elves, Men,
Dwarves, or Hobbits, and even by goblins. The more adventurous Rangers journeyed occasionally into those regions, but
they passed and did not stay. Other wanderers were rare, and of no
good sort: Trolls might stray at times down out of the further hills
and Mountains. Only on the Road would travellers be found, Big
People rarely in those days, Elves perhaps sometimes, most often
Dwarves hurrying along on business, and with no help and few
words to spare for strangers.

So now – since Gandalf had gone – they had to depend on what
they carried with them – probably until they found their way at
last to Rivendell. For water they were obliged to trust to chance.
For food they could perhaps just have managed to go ten or eleven
days; and now with Gandalf's additions they could with economy
probably hold out for more than a fortnight. It might have been
worse. But starving was not their only fear.

It became very cold as evening fell. There was some mist again
over the distant marshes; but the sky above cleared again, and the
clouds were blown away by a chill east wind. Looking out from the
lip of the dale [*read* dell] they could see nothing but a grey land

THE ATTACK ON WEATHERTOP 179

quickly vanishing in shadows, under an open sky filling slowly with twinkling stars.

They lit a small fire down at the lowest point in the hollow, and sat round it clothed and wrapped in every garment and blanket they possessed: at least Bingo and his companions did so. Trotter seemed content with a single blanket, and sat some little way from the fire puffing his short pipe. They took it in turns to sit on guard on the edge of the dell, at a point where the steep sides of Weathertop Hill, and the gentler slope down from the ridge, could be seen – as far as anything could be seen in the gathering dusk.

As the evening deepened Trotter began to tell them tales to keep their minds from fear. He knew much lore concerning wild animals, and claimed to speak some of their languages; and he had strange stories to tell of their lives and little known adventures. He knew also many histories and legends of the ancient days, of hobbits when the Shire was still wild, and of things beyond the mists of memory out of which the hobbits came. They wondered where he had learned all his lore.

'Tell us of Gil-galad!' said Frodo – 'you spoke that name not long ago,[3] and it is still ringing in my ears. Who was he?'

'Don't you know!' said Trotter. 'Gil-galad was the last of the great Elf-kings: Gil-galad is Starlight in their tongue. He over-threw the Enemy, but he himself perished. But I will not tell that tale now; though you will hear it, I think, in Rivendell, when we get there. Elrond should tell it, for he knows it well. But I will tell you the tale of Tinúviel – in brief, for in full it is a long tale of which the end is not known, and there is no one that remembers it in full as it was told of old, unless it be Elrond. But even in brief it is a fair tale – the fairest that has come out of the oldest days.' He fell silent for a moment, and then he began not to speak, but to chant softly:

Put in *Light on Linden Tree* [*sic*] emended. Or the alliterative lines. Follow with brief Tinúviel story.

My father then went straight on in the manuscript to the beginning of a prose résumé of the story of Beren and Lúthien. He had not gone far with this, however, when he abandoned it, and returning to Trotter's words about the story changed the end of them to: 'It is a fair tale, though it is sad as are the tales of Middle-earth, and yet it may lift up the hearts of the enemies of the Enemy.' He then wrote:

Lo Beren Gamlost the boldhearted[4]

but struck this out also. He had suggested just above that 'the alliterative

180   THE RETURN OF THE SHADOW

lines' might be used. He was referring to the passage of alliterative verse
that preceded *Light as Leaf on Lindentree* as published in *The Gryphon*
(Leeds University) in 1925,[5] a passage itself closely related to lines in the
second version of the alliterative *Lay of the Children of Húrin*, 355 ff.,
where Halog, one of Túrin's guides on the journey to Doriath, sang this
song 'for hearts' uplifting' as they wandered in the forest. But he now
decided against the alliterative lines for this place, and wrote in the
manuscript a new version of *Light as Leaf on Lindentree*. This text of the
poem moves it far towards the final version in FR pp. 204–5, but has
elements surviving from the old poem that were afterwards lost, and
elements common to neither. There are many later emendations to the
text, and many alternative readings (mostly taken up into the final
version) written at the time of composition; but here I give the primary
text without variants or later corrections.

> *The leaves were long, the grass was thin,*
> *The fall of many years lay thick,*
> *The tree-roots twisted out and in,*
> *The rising moon was glimmering.*
> *Her feet went lilting light and quick*
> *To the silver flute of Ilverin:*[6]
> *Beneath the hemlock-umbels thick*
> *Tinúviel was shimmering.*
>
> *The noiseless moths their wings did fold,*
> *The light was lost among the leaves,*
> *As Beren there from mountains cold*
> *Came wandering and sorrowing.*
> *He peered between the hemlock leaves*
> *And saw in wonder flowers of gold*
> *Upon her mantle and her sleeves,*
> *And her hair like shadow following.*
>
> *Enchantment took his weary feet,*
> *That over stone were doomed to roam,*
> *And forth he hastened, strong and fleet,*
> *And grasped at moonbeams glistening.*
> *Through woven woods of Elvenhome*
> *They fled on swiftly dancing feet,*
> *And left him lonely still to roam,*
> *In the silent forest listening.*
>
> *He heard at times the flying sound*
> *Of feet as light as linden leaves,*
> *Or music welling underground*

THE ATTACK ON WEATHERTOP   181

In the hidden halls of Doriath.
But withered were the hemlock sheaves,
*   And one by one with sighing sound*
Whispering fell the beechen leaves
In the wintry woods of Doriath.

He sought her ever, wandering far
*   Where leaves of years were thickly strewn,*
By light of moon and ray of star
*   In frosty heavens shivering.*
Her mantle glistened in the moon,
*   As on a hill-top high and far*
She danced, and at her feet was strewn
*   A mist of silver quivering.*

When winter passed she came again,
*   And her song released the sudden spring,*
Like rising lark, and falling rain,
*   And melting water bubbling.*
There high and clear he heard her sing,
*   And from him fell the winter's chain;*
No more he feared by her to spring
*   Upon the grass untroubling.*

Again she fled, but clear he called:
*   Tinúviel, Tinúviel.*
She halted by his voice enthralled
*   And stood before him shimmering.*
Her doom at last there on her fell,
*   As in the hills the echoes called;*
Tinúviel, Tinúviel,
*   In the arms of Beren glimmering.*

As Beren looked into her eyes
*   Within the shadows of her hair*
The trembling starlight of the skies
*   He saw there mirrored shimmering.*
Tinúviel! O elven-fair!
*   Immortal maiden elven-wise,*
About him cast her shadowy hair
*   And white her arms were glimmering.*

Long was the way that fate them bore
*   O'er stony mountains cold and grey,*

182   THE RETURN OF THE SHADOW

Through halls of iron and darkling door
And woods of night-shade morrowless.
The Sundering Seas between them lay
And yet at last they met once more,
And long ago they passed away
In the forest singing sorrowless.

He paused before he spoke again. 'That is a song,' he said, 'that tells of the meeting of Beren the mortal and Lúthien Tinúviel, which is but the beginning of the tale.

'Lúthien was the daughter of the elven-king Thingol of Doriath in the West of the Middle-world, when the earth was young. Her mother was Melian, who was not of the Elf-race but came out of the Far West from the land of the Gods and the Blessed Realm of Valinor. It is said that the daughter of Thingol and Melian was the most fair maiden that ever was or shall be among all the children of the world. No limbs so fair shall again run upon the green earth, no face so beautiful shall look upon the sky, till all things are changed.

The passage in praise of Lúthien that follows is almost word for word the same as that in the *Quenta Silmarillion* (1937), largely retained in the published work (p. 165, 'Blue was her raiment . . .').

'But Beren was son of Barahir the Bold. In those days the fathers of the fathers of Men came out of the East; and some there were that journeyed even to the West of Middle-earth, and there they met the Elves, and were taught by them, and became wise, but they were mortal and shortlived, for such is their fate. Yet many of them aided the Elves in their wars. For in that time the Elves besieged the Enemy in his dreadful fortress in the North. Angband it was called, the Halls of Iron beneath the thunderous towers of the black mountain Thangorodrim.

'But he broke the siege, and drove Elves and Men ever southward; and Barahir was slain. Ruin came upon the West-lands, but Doriath long endured because of the power and enchantment of Melian the Queen that fenced it about so that no evil could come within. In the song it is told[7] how Beren flying southward through many perils came at last into the hidden kingdom and beheld Lúthien. Tinúviel he called her, which is Nightingale, for he did not yet know her name.

'But Thingol the Elven-king was wroth, despising him as a mortal, and a fugitive; and he sent Beren upon a hopeless quest ere

THE ATTACK ON WEATHERTOP 183

he could win Lúthien. For he commanded him to bring him one of the three jewels from the crown of the King of Angband, out of the deeps of the Iron Halls. These were the Silmarils renowned in song, filled with power and a holy light, for they had been made by the Elves in the Blessed Realm, but the Enemy had stolen them, and guarded them with all his strength. Yet Beren achieved that Quest, for Lúthien fled from her father's realm and followed after him; and with the aid of Húan hound of the Gods, who came out of Valinor, she found him once again; and together thereafter they passed through peril and darkness; and they came even to Angband and beguiled the Enemy, and overthrew him, and took a Silmaril and fled.

'But the wolf-warden of the dark gate of Angband bit off the hand of Beren that held the Silmaril, and he came near to death. Yet it is told that at length Lúthien and Beren escaped and returned to Doriath, and the king and all his people marvelled. But Thingol reminded Beren that he had vowed not to return save with a Silmaril in his hand.

'"It is in my hand even now," he answered.

'"Show it to me!" said the king.

'"That I cannot do," said Beren, "for my hand is not here," and he held up his maimed arm. And from that hour he was named Beren Erhamion the Onehanded.

'Then the tale of the Quest was told in the king's hall and his mood was softened, and Lúthien laid her hand in Beren's before the throne of her father.

'But soon fear came upon Doriath. For the dread wolf-warden of Angband, being maddened by the fire of the Silmaril that consumed his evil flesh within, roamed through the world, wild and terrible. And by fate and the power of the jewel he passed the guarded borders and came ravening even into Doriath; and all things fled before him. Thus befell the Wolf-hunt of Doriath, and to that hunt went King Thingol, and Beren Erhamion, and Beleg the Bowman and Mablung the heavy-handed, and Húan the hound.

'And the great wolf leaped upon Beren and felled him and grievously wounded him; and Húan slew the wolf but himself was slain. And Mablung cut the Silmaril from the belly of the wolf, and gave it to Beren, and Beren gave it to Thingol. Then they bore Beren back with Húan at his side to the king's hall. And Lúthien bade him farewell before the gates, bidding him await her beyond the Great Seas; and he died in her arms.

184   THE RETURN OF THE SHADOW

'But the spirit of Lúthien fell down into darkness, for such was the doom upon the elven-maid for her love of a mortal man; and she faded slowly, as the Elves do under the burden of a grief unbearable. Her fair body lay like a flower that is suddenly cut off and lies for a while unwithered on the grass;[8] but her spirit journeyed over the Great Seas. And it is said that she sang before the Gods, and her song was made of the sorrows of the two kindreds, of Elves and Men. So fair was she and so moving was her song that they were moved to pity. But they had not the power long to withhold within the confines of the world the spirits of mortal men that died; nor to change the sundered fate of the two kindreds.

'Therefore they gave this choice to Lúthien. Because of her sorrow and of the Silmaril that was regained from the Enemy, and because her mother Melian came from Valinor, she should be released from the Halls of Waiting, and return not to the woes of Middle-earth, but go to the Blessed Realm and dwell with the Gods until the world's end, forgetting all sadness that her life had known. Thither Beren could not come. The other choice was this. She might return to earth, and take with her Beren for a while, there to dwell with him again, but without certitude of life or joy. Then she would become mortal even as he; and ere long she should leave the world for ever, and her beauty become only a memory of song, until that too faded. This doom she chose, forsaking the Blessed Realm, and thus they met again, Beren and Tinúviel, beyond the Great Seas, as she had said; and their paths led together, and passed long ago beyond the confines of the world. So it was that Lúthien alone of all the Elven-kin has died indeed. But by her choice the Two Kindreds were joined, and she is the fore-mother of many in whom the Elves see yet, though the world changeth, the likeness of Lúthien the beloved whom they have lost.'[9]

As Trotter was speaking, the darkness closed in; night fell on the world. They could see his queer eager face dimly lit in the glow of the red wood-fire. Above him was a black starry sky. Suddenly a pale light appeared behind the crown of Weathertop behind him. The moon, now nearly half-full, was climbing slowly above the hill that overshadowed them. The stars above its top grew pale.

The story ended. The hobbits moved and stretched. 'Look!' said Merry. 'The moon is rising. It must be getting late.' The others looked up. Even as they did so they saw something small and dark on the hill-top against the glimmer of the moonlight. It

THE ATTACK ON WEATHERTOP   185

was perhaps only a large stone or jutting rock shown up by the pale light.

At that moment Odo, who had been on guard (being less reluctant than the others to miss Trotter's tale-telling) came hurrying down to the fire. 'I don't know what it is,' he said, 'but I *feel* that something is creeping up the hill. And I *thought* (I couldn't be sure) that away there, westwards, where the moon-light is falling, there were two or three black shapes. They seemed to be moving this way.'

'Keep close beside the fire, with your faces outwards!' said Trotter. 'Get some of these pine-wood sticks ready in your hands!'

For a long while they sat there silent and alert with their backs turned to the little fire, which was thus almost entirely screened. Nothing happened. There was no sound or movement. Bingo was just about to whisper a question to Trotter, who sat next to him, when Frodo gasped: 'What's that?' '*Sh*,' said Trotter.

It was just as Odo had said: over the lip of the hollow, on the side away from the hill, they *felt* a shadow rise, one shadow or more than one. They strained their eyes, and the shadows seemed to grow. Soon there could be no doubt: three or four tall black figures were standing there, on the slope above them. Bingo fancied that he heard faintly a sound like breath being drawn in with a hiss. Then the shapes advanced slowly.

Terror seized Odo and Frodo, and they threw themselves flat on the ground. Merry shrank to Bingo's side. Bingo was no less afraid; he was quaking as if he was bitter cold. But his fear was swallowed up in a sudden temptation to put on the Ring. It seized him, and he could think of nothing else. He did not forget the Barrow, nor the message of Gandalf, but he felt a desperate desire to disregard all warnings. Something seemed to be compelling him; he longed to yield. Not with the hope of escaping, or of doing anything, good or bad. He simply felt that he must take the Ring, and put it on his finger. He could not speak. He struggled for a while, but resistance became unbearable; and at last he slowly drew out the chain, unfastened the Ring, and put it on the fore-finger of his left hand.

Immediately – though everything else remained as before, dim and dark – the shapes became terribly clear. He seemed able to see beneath their black wrapping. There were three tall figures: in their white faces burned keen and merciless eyes; under their black mantles were long grey robes, upon their grey hair were helms of silver;[10] in their haggard hands were swords of steel.

186 THE RETURN OF THE SHADOW

Their eyes fell upon him and pierced him, as they rushed towards him. Desperate, he drew his own sword; and it seemed to him that it flickered redly as if it was a fire-brand. Two of the figures halted. But the third was taller than the others. His hair was long and gleaming, and on it was a crown. The hand that held the long sword glowed with a pale light. He sprang forward and bore down upon Bingo.

At that moment Bingo threw himself forward onto the ground, and he heard himself crying aloud (though he did not know why): *Elbereth! Gilthoniel! Gurth i Morthu.*[11] At the same time he struck at the feet of his enemy. A shrill cry rang out in the night; and he felt a pain like a dart of poisoned ice touch his [*added:* left] shoulder. Even as he swooned Bingo caught a glimpse of Trotter leaping out of the darkness with a flaming fire-brand in each hand. With a last effort he slipped the Ring from his finger, and closed his hand on it.

NOTES

1 This passage, from 'Better still, under the fuel they found a wooden case', is an insertion on a slip, certainly written at the same time as the main text, replacing the (ink) text as first written:

> Gandalf, it would seem, had taken thought for them. It was the presence of fuel that decided them to go no further that day, and to make their camp in the dell.

With the passage here about *cram*, not found in FR, cf. *The Hobbit*, Chapter XIII 'Not at Home':

> If you want to know what *cram* is, I can only say that I don't know the recipe, but it is biscuitish, keeps good indefinitely, is supposed to be sustaining, and is certainly not entertaining, being in fact very uninteresting except as a chewing exercise. It was made by the Lake-men for long journeys.

In the *Etymologies* (V.365) *cram*, defined as 'cake of compressed flour or meal (often containing honey and milk) used on long journeys', appears as a Noldorin word (stem KRAB- 'press'). – In FR the fire-wood, alone of the stores found on Weathertop, survived, but it had been left by Rangers, not by Gandalf.

2 Strider gives a much more elaborate and informed account of the perceptions of the Ring-wraiths in FR (p. 202). See p. 173, note 7.

3 See p. 169 and note 25.

4 Beren's name *Camlost* or *Gamlost* ('Empty-handed') occurs in the *Quenta Silmarillion* (interrupted at the end of 1937); for the variation in the initial consonant see V.298, 301.

THE ATTACK ON WEATHERTOP   187

5   For the text and textual history of *Light as Leaf on Lindentree* see III.108–10, 120–3.

6   *To the silver flute of Ilverin:* in *Light as Leaf on Lindentree* (III.108) Dairon is named here. The name Ilverin occurs in *The Book of Lost Tales* as one of the many names of Littleheart, the 'Gong-warden' of Mar Vanwa Tyaliéva (I.46, 255), but there seems no basis to seek any kind of connection. In the margin my father at some point pencilled other names: *Neldorín, Elberin, Diarin*. See note 9, at end.

7   Trotter has mentioned no song, but it is of course the *Lay of Leithian* that is meant.

8   Struck out at the time of writing:

> But her spirit came to the Halls of Waiting, where are the places appointed for the Elven-kin beyond the Blessed Realms in the West, on the confines of the world. And she knelt before the Lord [of the Halls of Waiting]

9   This concluding paragraph of Trotter's tale is very close to the account of the Choices of Lúthien that my father had written while the *Quenta Silmarillion* was with the publishers at the end of 1937, and which appears in the published *Silmarillion* on p. 187; see V.293, 303–4.

There are other very roughly written texts giving a résumé of a part of 'The Silmarillion' found among the papers at this point. They attempt to condense a much greater part of the history of the Elder Days than that strictly concerned with the story of Beren and Lúthien, and have interesting features which must be mentioned, though their discussion scarcely falls within the history of the writing of *The Lord of the Rings*. Most notable is the following passage:

> For as it is told the Blessed Realms of the West were illumined by the Two Trees, Galathilion the Silver Cherry, and Galagloriel that is Golden Rain. But Morgoth, the greatest of the Powers, made war upon the Gods, and he destroyed the Trees, and fled. And he took with him the immortal gems, the Silmarils, that were made by the Elves of the light of the Trees, and in which alone now the ancient radiance of the days of bliss remained. In the north of the Middle-earth he set up his throne Angband, the Halls of Iron under Thangorodrim the Mountain of Thunder; and he grew in strength and darkness; and he brought forth the Orcs and goblins, and the Balrogs, demons of fire. But the High Elves of the West forsook the land of the Gods and returned to the earth, and made war upon him to regain the jewels.

The names *Galathilion* and *Galadlóriel* first appear in the *Quenta Silmarillion* (V.209–10) as the Gnomish names for Silpion and Laurelin. 'Silver Cherry' and 'Golden Rain' are not the actual meanings of the names (as seems to be implied here): see the

188   THE RETURN OF THE SHADOW

Etymologies in Vol. V, stems GALAD- (where the form *Galagloriel* is also given), LAWAR-, THIL-. That the blossom of Silpion was like that of a cherry-tree, and the flowers of Laurelin like those of the laburnum ('Golden Rain') was however often said (see e.g. V.209).

On Morgoth 'the greatest of the Powers' see V.157 and note 4. Very curious is the statement here that when Morgoth returned to Middle-earth after the destruction of the Trees 'he brought forth the Orcs and goblins, *and the Balrogs, demons of fire.*' It was certainly my father's view at this period that the Orcs were then first engendered (see V.233, §62 and commentary), but the Balrogs were far older in their beginning (V.212, §18), and indeed came to rescue Morgoth from Ungoliantë at the time of his return: 'to his aid there came the Balrogs that lived yet in the deepest places of his ancient fortress.'

The term 'High Elves' is here used to mean the Elves of Valinor, not, as in the *Quenta Silmarillion*, the First Kindred (*Lindar, Vanyar*): see V.214, §25 and commentary.

A very surprising point is the mention, a little later in this text, of *Finrod Inglor the fair* (see p. 72). In the first edition of LR (Appendices) *Finrod* was still the name of third son of Finwë, as in the *Quenta Silmarillion*, and his son was *Felagund* (in QS also named *Inglor*); it was not till the second edition of 1966 that Finrod son of Finwë became Finarfin, and his son Inglor Felagund became *Finrod Felagund*.

In another of these drafts the minstrel of Doriath is named *Iverin*, not Dairon; see note 6.

10 My father first wrote here: 'upon their long grey hair were crowns and helms of pale gold'. This was no doubt changed at once, with the emergence immediately below of the tall king, a crown on his long hair. See p. 198 note 6.

11 For *Morthu* see V.393, stem THUS-.

★

My father's practice at this time of overwriting his first pencilled drafts largely denies the possibility of seeing the earliest forms of the narrative. In this chapter the underlying text can only be made out here and there and with great difficulty; but at least it can be seen that the opening passage quickly declined into an abbreviated outline for the story. Trotter's tales were only to be concerned with animals of the wild; and then follows at once: 'Fight in dell', with a sketch in a few lines, scribbled down at great speed, of which however something can be disinterred:

Bingo is tempted to put on ring. He does so. The riders [?come] at him. He sees them plain – fell white faces . . . . . He draws his sword

THE ATTACK ON WEATHERTOP 189

and it shines like fire. They draw back but one Rider with long silver hair and a [?red hand] leaps forward. Bingo . . . . . hears himself shouting *Elbereth Gilthoniel* . . . . . struck at the leg of the Rider. He felt . . . . . cold [?pain] in the shoulder. There was a flash . . . . .

The attack on the dell entered before the idea that Trotter should chant to them, and tell them a tale of ancient days; and the material of his tale remains in this manuscript in a very rough state, the primary stage of composition, obviously demanding the compression that it afterwards received.

More developed pencilled drafting takes up again from the point where Trotter comes to an end, and from what can be read it seems that the final story of the attack by the Ring-wraiths was now fully present. Then, apart from a few details (as that there are three Ring-wraiths, not five), the text written in ink on top of the draft achieved the finished story: no element in the potent scene, the fearful suspense on the cold hillside in the moonlight, the dark shapes looking down on the hobbits huddled round the fire, the irresistible demand on the Ringbearer to reveal himself, and the final revelation of what lay beneath the black cloaks of the Riders, is absent – and all is told virtually in the very words of *The Fellowship of the Ring*. The significance of the Ring, in its power to reveal and to be revealed, its operation as a bridge between two worlds, two modes of being, has been attained, once and for all.

The completeness, and the resonance, of this scene on Weathertop Hill is the more remarkable, when we consider that (in relation to *The Lord of the Rings* as it was ultimately achieved) all was still extremely restricted in scope. If the nature of the Ring in its effect on the bearer was now fully conceived, there is as yet no suggestion that the fate of Middle-earth lay within its tiny circle. It is indeed far from certain that the idea of the Ruling Ring had yet arisen. Of the great lands and histories east and south of the Misty Mountains – of Lothlórien, Fangorn, Isengard, Rohan, the Númenórean kingdoms – there is no shadow of a hint. I very much doubt that when the Ring-wraiths rose up over the lip of the dell beneath Weathertop my father foresaw any more of the Journey than that the Ring must pass over the Mountains and find its end in the depths of the Fiery Mountain (p. 126). In October 1938 he could still say to Stanley Unwin (see p. 173) that he had hopes of being able to submit the new story early in the following year.

XI

FROM WEATHERTOP TO THE FORD

The manuscript of the original Chapter VIII continues, without any break, in the same form, ink over pencil. While in the earlier part of this chapter I have given the full original text even in the concluding passage, where there is scarcely any material difference from FR (since the attack of the Ring-wraiths is a scene of exceptional importance), in this part I do not do so throughout. The narrative is very close to that of FR Chapter 12, 'Flight to the Ford' (with a fair number of minor differences and some less minor), and for much of its length the wording almost the same. In those parts where the original text is not given, however, it can be understood that all differences of any significance are remarked.

After it is told that the hobbits (Sam in FR) heard Bingo's voice crying out strange words, it is further said that they 'had seen a red flash; and Trotter came dashing up with flaming wood.' So also in the fragmentary outline given on pp. 188–9 'There was a flash'; but this is absent in FR. Perhaps the reference is to Bingo's sword that 'flickered redly as if it was a firebrand' (p. 186), a detail preserved in FR p. 208. Trotter's first return to the dell is slightly differently told, but this is chiefly because Sam's distrust of Strider is of course absent, and there is nothing in the old version corresponding to Strider's words to Sam apart (FR pp. 209–10). When Trotter lifted the black cloak from the ground he said only: 'That was the stroke of your sword. What harm it did to the Rider I do not know. Fire is better.'

Athelas is not said to have been brought by Men of the West to Middle-earth: 'it is a healing plant, known only to Elves, and to some of those who walk in the wild: *athelas* they name it.'[1] A curious detail is that when *athelas* was applied to Bingo's wound he 'felt the pain and the sense of frozen cold lessen in his right side'; and again later in the chapter 'his right arm was lifeless' (FR p. 215). Similarly, when Bingo drew his sword and faced the Riders at the Ford, my father first wrote: 'His sword he had hung at his right side; with his left hand he gripped the hilt and drew it', though this he struck out. He evidently decided that it was Bingo's left shoulder that was stabbed, and therefore wrote in the word 'left' in the description of the actual wounding (p. 186); but he did not correct the occurrences of 'right' just mentioned.

When they left the dell beneath Weathertop they took Gandalf's firewood with them ('For Trotter said that from now onwards fire-wood must always be a part of their stores, when they were away from trees').

FROM WEATHERTOP TO THE FORD 191

Nothing is said of the rejuvenation of Bill Ferny's pony (if indeed it was Bill Ferny's, p. 175). The distant cries of Black Riders which they heard as they crossed the Road in FR (p. 211) are absent from the old version.

The description of the eastward journey from Weathertop is at first fairly close to that in FR, though the timing is slightly different; but the geography was to be significantly altered. I give the passage following the words 'Even Trotter seemed tired and dejected' (FR p. 212) in full.

Before the first day's march was over Bingo's pain began to grow again, but for a long time he did not speak of it. In this way three or four days passed without the ground or the scene changing much, except that behind them Weathertop slowly sank, and before them the distant mountains loomed a little nearer. The weather remained dry, but was grey with cloud; and they were oppressed with the fear of pursuit. But of this there was no sign by day; and though they kept watch by night nothing happened. They dreaded to see black shapes stalking in the dim grey night under the waxing moon veiled by thin cloud; but they saw nothing, and heard nothing, but the sigh of withering leaves and grass. It seemed that, as they had hardly dared to hope, their swift crossing of the Road had not been marked, and their enemy had for the moment lost their trail.

At the end of the fourth day the ground began once more to rise slowly out of the wide shallow valley into which they had come. Trotter now bent their course again towards the north-east; and before long, as they reached the top of a slow-climbing slope, they saw ahead a huddle of wooded hills. Late on the fifth day they came to a ridge on which a few gaunt fir-trees stood. A little below them the Road could be seen curving away towards a small river that gleamed pale in a thin ray of sunshine, far away on their right. Next day, early in the morning, they again crossed the Road. Looking anxiously along it, westward and eastward, they hurried quickly across, and went towards the wooded hills.

Trotter was still leading them in as straight a line as the country allowed towards the distant Ford. In the hills their path would be more uncertain, but they could no longer keep to the south side of the Road, because the land became bare and stony and ahead lay the river. 'That river,' he said, 'comes down out of the Mountains, and flows through Rivendell.[2] It is not wide, but it is deep and strong, being fed by the many small torrents that come out of the wooded hills. Over these the Road goes by little fords or bridges; but there is no ford or bridge over the river until we come to the Ford under the Mountains.' The hobbits looked at the dark hills

192   THE RETURN OF THE SHADOW

ahead, and though they were glad to leave the cheerless lands behind them, the land ahead seemed threatening and unfriendly.

In the developed geography, the Road traverses two rivers between Weathertop and Rivendell: the Hoarwell or Mitheithel that flowed down out of the Ettenmoors, crossed by the Last Bridge, and the Loudwater or Bruinen, crossed by the Ford of Rivendell; these rivers joined a long way to the south, becoming the Greyflood. In the original story, on the other hand, there is only one river, not named, flowing down through Rivendell and crossed at the Ford.

In FR the travellers came down, early in the morning on the seventh day out from Weathertop, to the Road (i.e. approaching it from the south), and went along it for a mile or two to the Last Bridge, where Strider found the elf-stone lying in the mud; they crossed the bridge, and after a further mile turned off the Road to the left and went up into the hills. In the original story, they came to the Road early on the sixth day and crossed it, going up into the hills; there is no river (Hoarwell) and no bridge. Some sort of explanation is given why they had to cross the Road here and stay no longer to the south of it: 'the land became bare and stony and ahead lay the river.' But the fact of there being no ford or bridge over the river except that below Rivendell only meant that that is where they would have to cross; it does not in itself explain why they could not stay south of the Road until they got there. Thus it is only the 'bare and stony' nature of the land south of the Road that really offers an explanation: Trotter sought to pass through country that provided more concealment? The 'real' explanation, it might be said, why they crossed the Road and went up into the wooded hills is quite other: my father had already suggested, when sketching out the story from the Barrow-downs to Rivendell (p. 126), that the hobbits should 'foolishly turn aside to visit Troll Stones'. On the other hand, Trotter was taking the straightest line to the Ford that he could (p. 191), and the sketches on p. 201 show clearly that the great southward loop of the Road (already mentioned in the original text, p. 199) must force him to cross it and go up into the hills to the north. – On the different chronology in the two versions see the Note on Chronology, p. 219.

When they came into the hills, the conversation with Trotter arising from their sight of the ruined towers is somewhat different from that with Strider in FR (pp. 213–14):

'Who lives in this land?' he [Bingo] asked; 'and who built these towers? Is this troll-country?'

'No,' said Trotter; 'trolls do not build. No one lives in this land. Men once dwelt here, ages ago. But none now remain. They were an evil people, as far as tales and legends tell; for they came under the sway of the Dark Lord. It is said that they were overthrown by Elendil, as King of Western Men, who aided Gilgalad, when they

FROM WEATHERTOP TO THE FORD   193

made war on the Dark Lord.[3] But that was so long ago that the hills have forgotten them, though a shadow still lies on the land.'

'Where did you learn such tales?' asked Frodo, 'if all the land is empty and forgetful? The birds and beasts do not tell tales of that sort.'

'Many things are remembered in Rivendell,' said Trotter.

'Have you often been to Rivendell?' said Bingo.

'I have,' said Trotter; 'many a time; and I wonder now that I was ever so foolish as to leave it. But it is not my fate to sit quiet, even in the fair house of Elrond.'

The journey in the hills north of the Road had lasted for three days when the weather turned to rain, but two in FR (p. 214); thus the shorter journey from Weathertop till the return to the Road is made up, though there is still a difference of one day, since they had reached Weathertop a day earlier in the original story (p. 175): as I understand it, the first morning after the rain (FR p. 215) was in the old version that of October 16, but in FR that of October 17. When the rain stopped, on the eleventh day from Weathertop, and Trotter climbed up to see the lie of the land, he said when he came back:

'We have got too far to the North; and we *must* find some way to turn southwards, or at least sharp to the East. If we keep on as we are going, we shall get into impassable country among the skirts of the Mountains. Somehow or other we must strike the Road again before it reaches the Ford. But even if we manage that fairly quickly, we still cannot hope to get to Rivendell for some days yet, four or even five I fear.'

In the night spent up on the ridge (FR pp. 215–16) Sam's questioning of Strider concerning Frodo's wound is given to Merry; and Frodo's dream that 'endless dark wings were sweeping over him, and that on the wings rode pursuers seeking for him in all the hollows of the hills' is present. It is not said in the original text that 'the trees about him seemed shadowy and dim', nor on the following day that 'a mist seemed to obscure his sight' (FR pp. 215, 217); but later, when Glorfindel searched Bingo's wound with his finger (FR p. 223), 'he saw his friends' faces more clearly, though all day he had been troubled by the feeling that a shadow or a mist was coming between him and them.'

When they came to the old trolls turned to stone, 'Trotter walked forward unconcernedly. "Hullo, William!" he said, and slapped the stooping troll soundly.' And he said: '"In any case you might have noticed that Bert has got a bird's nest behind his ear."' In FR the trolls' names from *The Hobbit* were excluded.

After 'They rested in the clearing for a while, and had their midday

194   THE RETURN OF THE SHADOW

meal right under the shadow of the trolls' large legs' the original narrative goes straight on with 'In the afternoon they went on down through the woods'; there is no suggestion that the Troll Song would be introduced here (see p. 144). Their return to the Road is thus described:

Eventually they came out upon the top of a high bank above the Road. This was now beginning to bend rather away from the river, and clung to the feet of the hills, some way up the side of the narrow valley at the bottom of which the river ran. Not far from the borders of the Road Trotter pointed out a stone in the grass; on it roughly cut and much weathered could still be seen two runic letters G · B in a circle: (x ʙ)

'That,' he said, 'is the stone that once marked the place where Gandalf and Bilbo hid the trolls' gold.' Bingo looked at it – rather sadly: Bilbo and he himself had long ago spent all that gold.

The Road, bending now northward, lay quiet under the shadows of early evening. There was no sign of any other travellers to be seen.

Only minor differences (except in one matter) are to be recorded in the encounter with Glorfindel: the whole scene was present, and in very much the same words, from the beginning. The sentence in FR (p. 221) 'To Frodo it appeared that a white light was shining through the form and raiment of the rider, as if through a thin veil' is absent.[4] To Trotter Glorfindel cried out: *Ai Padathir, Padathir! Mai govannen!*[5] But it is not said subsequently that he spoke to Trotter 'in the elf-tongue' (FR p. 224); rather he spoke 'in a low tone.' The drink that Glorfindel gave them instantly reminded the hobbits of the drink in Bombadil's house, 'for the drink they took was refreshing like spring-water, but filled them also with a sense of warm vigour.' 'Cram-cake' is mentioned together with the stale bread and dried fruit which is all they had to eat.

The conversation with Glorfindel on the road is different from that in FR (p. 222), for the number of the Black Riders was not known to anybody at this stage (not even to my father), and in FR Gandalf had not yet reached Rivendell when Glorfindel and others were sent out by Elrond nine days before – Elrond having heard news from the Elves led by Gildor whom the hobbits encountered in the Shire. The element of Glorfindel's leaving the jewel on the Last Bridge is also of course absent (p. 192).

'This is Glorfindel, one of those that dwell in Rivendell,' said Trotter. 'He has news for us.'

'Hail and well met at last!' said Glorfindel to Bingo. 'I was sent from Rivendell to look on the Road for your coming. Gandalf was anxious and afraid, for unless something evil had befallen you, you should have come there days ago.'

FROM WEATHERTOP TO THE FORD 195

'We have not been on the Road for many, many days until this day,' said Bingo.

'Well, now you must return to it, and go with all speed,' said Glorfindel. 'A day's swift riding back westward there is a company of evil horsemen, and they are travelling this way with all the haste that frequent search of the land upon either side of the Road allows them. You must not halt here, nor anywhere tonight, but must journey on as long and far as you are able. For when they find your trail, where it rejoined the Road, they will search no longer but ride after you like the wind. I do not think they will miss your footsteps where the path runs down from Trolls-wood; for they have a dreadful skill in hunting by scent, and darkness helps and does not hinder them.'

'Then why must we go on now by night, against the warning of Gandalf?' asked Merry.

'Do not fear Gandalf's warning now,' answered Glorfindel. 'Speed is your chief hope; and now I will go with you. And I do not think that there is any peril ahead; but the pursuit is hard behind.'

'But Bingo is wounded and sick and weary,' said Merry. 'He should not ride any more without rest!'

Glorfindel shook his head and looked grave, when he heard the account of the attack upon the dell under Weathertop, and the hurt to Bingo's arm. He looked at the knife-hilt that Trotter had kept, and now drew out to show him. He shuddered.

'There are evil things written on that hilt,' he said, 'though maybe they are not for your eyes to see. Keep it till we get to Rivendell, Padathir, but be wary, and handle it as little as you may.'

The chief structural difference in the narrative of this chapter from that in FR appears in Glorfindel's words 'I do not think that there is any peril ahead'; contrast FR (p. 222): 'There are five behind us . . . Where the other four may be, I do not know. I fear that we may find the Ford is already held against us.'

Only three Riders (at first) came out of the tree-hung cutting through which the Road passed before the flat mile to the Ford, not five as in FR (p. 225). The story is the same that Bingo halted, feeling the command of the Riders upon him to wait, but filled with sudden hatred drew his sword; and that Glorfindel cried to his horse, so that it sped away towards the Ford. But all the Riders were behind; there was no ambush by four of them lying in wait at the Ford. The conclusion of the chapter I give in full.

THE RETURN OF THE SHADOW

'Ride on! Ride on!' cried Glorfindel and Trotter; and then Glorfindel spoke a word in the elf-tongue: *nora-lim, nora-lim*. At once the white horse sprang away and sped along the last lap of the Road. At the same moment the black horses of the Riders leaped down in pursuit; and others following came flying out of the wood. Bingo looking back over his shoulder thought he could count [as many as twelve >] at least seven. They seemed to run like the wind, and to grow swiftly larger and darker as they overtook him stride by stride. He could no longer see his friends. Through them and over them the Riders must now be hurtling. Bingo turned and lay forward, encouraging with urgent words. The Ford still seemed far ahead. Once more he looked back. It seemed to him that the Riders had cast aside their hoods and black cloaks; they appeared now to be robed in white and grey. Swords were in their pale hands, helm and crown were on their heads;[6] their cold eyes glittered from afar.

Fear now swallowed up Bingo's mind. He thought no longer of his sword. No cry came from him. He shut his eyes and clung to the mane of the horse. The wind whistled in his ears, and wildly the bells rang, clear and shrill. It seemed bitter cold.

Suddenly he heard the splash of water. It foamed about his feet. He felt the stumbling scramble of the horse as it struggled up the stony path, climbing the steep further bank of the river. He was across the Ford! But the Riders were now hard behind.

At the top of the bank the horse halted snorting. Bingo turned about and opened his eyes. [*Struck out as soon as written:* Forgetting that the horse belonged to the folk of Rivendell and knew all that land, he determined to face his enemies, thinking it useless to] He felt that it was useless to try to escape over the long uncertain path from the Ford to the lip of Rivendell – if once the Riders crossed. Though they had all thought of the Ford as the goal of their flight and the end of peril, it came to him now that he knew of nothing that would prevent the dread Riders from crossing as easily as he. In any case he felt now commanded urgently to halt, and though again hatred stirred in him he had no longer the strength to refuse. He saw the horse of the foremost Rider check at the water, and rear up. With a great effort he stood in his stirrups and brandished his sword.

'Go back!' he cried. 'Go back to the Dark Lord and follow me no more.'[7] His voice sounded shrill in his ears. The Riders halted, but Bingo had not the power of Tom Bombadil.[8] They laughed – a harsh chilling laughter. 'Come back! Come back!' they called. 'To

FROM WEATHERTOP TO THE FORD 197

Mordor we will take you.'[9] 'Go back,' he whispered. 'The Ring, the Ring,' they cried with deadly voices, and immediately their leader rode forward into the water, closely followed by two others.

'By Elbereth and Lúthien the fair,'[10] said Bingo with a last effort, lifting up his sword, 'you shall have neither me nor it.' Then the leader, who was now half across the river, stood up menacing in his stirrup and raised up his hand. Bingo grew dumb; he felt his tongue cleave to his mouth, and his eyes grow misty. His sword broke and fell out of his shaking hand. The horse under him reared and snorted, as the foremost of the black horses came near the shore.

Even at that moment there came a roaring and a rushing: a noise of loud waters rolling many stones. Dimly he saw the river rise, and come galloping down along its course in a plumed cavalry of waves. The three Riders that were still upon the Ford disappeared, overwhelmed and buried under angry foam. Those that were behind drew back in dismay.

With his last failing sense Bingo heard cries, and it seemed to him that behind the Riders there appeared suddenly one shining white figure followed by other smaller and more shadowy figures waving flames. Redly they flamed in the white mist that was over all. Two of the Riders turned and rode wildly away to the left down the bank of the river; the others borne by their plunging horses were driven into the flood, and carried away. Then Bingo heard a roaring in his ears and felt himself falling, as if the flood had reached up to the high bank, and engulfed him with his enemies. He heard and saw no more.

NOTES

1 In the *Lay of Leithian* my father wrote *athelas* against the passage where

> Huan came and bore a leaf,
> of all the herbs of healing chief,
> that evergreen in woodland glade
> there grew with broad and hoary blade

for the allaying of Beren's wound (III.266, 269).

2 *That river . . . flows through Rivendell:* see the note on Rivendell, pp. 204–5.

3 In the underlying pencilled text, which is here visible for a stretch, Trotter's words about the 'Big People' who used to live in those regions are much the same, but he says that they were overthrown by *Elendil Orendil* and Gil-galad; apparently *Orendil* was substi-

198   THE RETURN OF THE SHADOW

tuted for *Elendil* in the act of writing. Both names were struck out, and then *Elendil* again written in. See p. 174 note 25.

4   The 'bit and bridle' of Glorfindel's horse flickered and flashed, as in the First Edition, where the Second Edition has 'headstall'. Cf. *Letters* no. 211, p. 279 (14 October 1958):

> . . . *bridle* was casually and carelessly used for what I suppose should have been called a *headstall*. Or rather, since *bit* was added (I.221) long ago (Chapter I 12 was written very early) I had not considered the natural ways of elves with animals. Glorfindel's horse would have an ornamental *headstall*, carrying a plume, and with the straps studded with jewels and small bells; but Glorfindel would certainly not use a *bit*. I will change *bridle and bit* to *headstall*.

5   The pencilled text, after various forms struck out, had *Ai Rimbedir*; this was then changed to *Ai Padathir*, etc., with a translation 'Hail Trotter, Trotter, well met.'

6   *helm and crown were on their heads:* in the story of the attack on Weathertop my father first wrote that all three Ringwraiths were crowned, but changed the text to say that only the leader ('the pale king' as Bingo called him) wore a crown (pp. 185–6 and note 10). Cf. the citation in note 8 below.

7   The pencilled draft has: 'Ride back to the Dark Tower of your lord.' For early references to the Dark Tower see p. 131 note 5.

8   It is interesting to look back to the earliest sketch for the flight over the Ford (p. 126):

> One day at last they halted on a rise and looked forward to the Ford. Galloping behind. Seven (3? 4?) Black-riders hastening along the Road. They have gold rings and crowns. Flight over Ford. Bingo flings a stone *and imitates Tom Bombadil*. Go back and ride away! The Riders halt as if astonished, and looking up at the hobbits on the bank the hobbits can see no faces in their hoods. Go back says Bingo, *but he is not Tom Bombadil*, and the riders ride into the ford.

At that stage my father envisaged the hobbits crossing the Ford together; and the rising of the river does not destroy the Riders: they 'draw back just in time in dismay.'

The words in the present text, retained in FR, 'Bingo (Frodo) had not the power of Tom Bombadil', must now refer to Bombadil's rout of the Barrow-wight; but behind them surely lies the unused idea of his power to arrest the onset of the evil beings by raising his hand in authority: cf. the outline given on p. 112, 'two Barrow-wights come galloping after them, but stop every time Tom Bombadil turns and looks at them', and the earlier part of the outline just cited (p. 125), where when they reach the Road west of Bree 'Tom turns and holds up his hand. They fly back.'

FROM WEATHERTOP TO THE FORD   199

9 This is the first occurrence of the name *Mordor* in *The Lord of the Rings*; see p. 131 note 5.
10 In the pencilled text visible beneath the ink, Bingo took the names of Gil-galad and Elendil, together with that of Lúthien.

★

In this chapter it is made plain that the commands of the Ring-wraiths are communicated wordlessly to the bearer of the Ring, and that they have great power over his will. Moreover the idea has now entered that the wound of the Ring-wraith's knife produces, or begins to produce, a similar effect to that brought about by putting on the Ring: the world becomes shadowy and dim to Bingo, and at the end of the chapter he can see the Riders plain, beneath the black wrappings that to others cloak their invisibility.

Note on the course of the Road between Weathertop and Rivendell

This was an element in the geography to which my father made various alterations in the Revised Edition of *The Lord of the Rings* (1966). I set out first three passages from the chapter 'Flight to the Ford' for comparison.

(1) Page 212.
     Original text:
     (the original text has no passage corresponding)
     First Edition: 'That is Loudwater, the Bruinen of Rivendell,' answered Strider. 'The Road runs along it for many leagues to the Ford.'
     Second Edition: 'That is Loudwater, the Bruinen of Rivendell,' answered Strider. 'The Road runs along the edge of the hills for many miles from the Bridge to the Ford of Bruinen.'

(2) Page 214.
     Original text: The hills now shut them in. The Road looped away southward, towards the river; but both were now lost to view.
     First Edition: The hills now began to shut them in. The Road bent back again southward towards the River, but both were now hidden from view.
     Second Edition: The hills now began to shut them in. The Road behind held on its way to the River Bruinen, but both were now hidden from view.

(3) Page 220.
     Original text (p. 194): Eventually they came out upon the top of a high bank above the Road. This was now beginning to bend rather away from the river, and clung to the feet of the hills,

200   THE RETURN OF THE SHADOW

some way up the side of the narrow valley at the bottom of which the river ran.

First Edition: After a few miles they came out on the top of a high bank above the Road. At this point the Road had turned away from the river down in its narrow valley, and now clung close to the feet of the hills, rolling and winding northward among woods and heather-covered slopes towards the Ford and the Mountains.

Second Edition: After a few miles they came out on the top of a high bank above the Road. At this point the Road had left the Hoarwell far behind in its narrow valley, and now clung close to the feet of the hills, rolling and winding eastward among woods (etc.)

Taking first citation (2), from small-scale and large-scale maps made by my father there is no question that the Road after passing south of Weathertop made first a great swing or loop to the North-east: cf. FR p. 211 – when they left Weathertop it was Strider's plan 'to shorten their journey by cutting across another great loop of the Road: east beyond Weathertop it changed its course and took a wide bend northwards.' This goes back to the original text. The Road then made a great bend southwards, round the feet of the Trollshaws, as stated in the original text and in the First Edition in citation (2). All my father's maps show the same course for the Road in respect of these two great curves. The two sketches on p. 201 are redrawn from very rough large-scale maps which he made (the second in particular is extremely hard to interpret owing to the multiplicity of lines made as he pondered different configurations).

In 1943 I made an elaborate map in pencil and coloured chalks for *The Lord of the Rings*, and a similar map of the Shire (see p. 107, item V). These maps are referred to in *Letters* nos. 74 and 98 (pp. 86, 112). On my LR map the course of the Road from Weathertop to the Ford is shown exactly as on my father's maps, with the great northward and southward swings. On the map that I made in 1954 (published in the first two volumes of *The Lord of the Rings*), however, the Road has only a feeble northward curve between Weathertop and the Hoarwell Bridge, and then runs in a straight line to the Ford. This was obviously simply carelessness due to haste on my part. My father doubtless observed it at the time but felt that on so small a scale the error was not very grievous: in any case the map was made, and it had been a matter of urgency. But I think that this error was the reason for the change in the Second Edition given in citation (2), from 'the Road bent back again southward towards the River' to 'the Road behind held on its way to the River Bruinen': my father was making the discrepancy with the map less obvious. A similar instance has been seen already in the change that he made in the Second Edition in respect of the direction of Bucklebury Ferry from Woodhall, p. 107. In his letter to Austin Olney of Houghton Mifflin, 28 July 1965

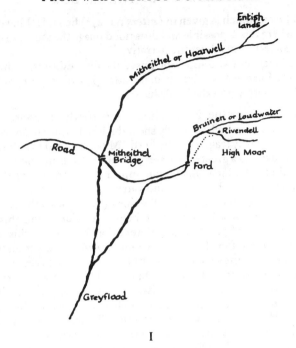

I

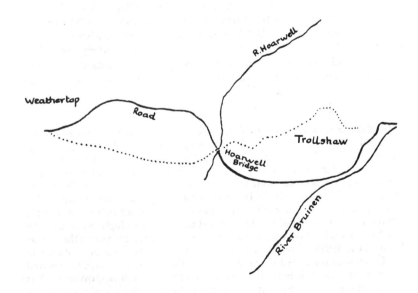

II

202   THE RETURN OF THE SHADOW

(an extract from which is given in *Letters* no. 274) he said: 'I have finally decided, where this is possible and does not damage the story, to take the *maps* as "correct" and adjust the narrative.'

Barbara Strachey (who apparently used the First Edition) deduced the course of the Road very accurately in her atlas, *Journeys of Frodo* (1981), map 13 'Weathertop and the Trollshaws'.

Citation (1) from the First Edition is perfectly illustrated in the sketches on p. 201, which precisely show the Road running alongside the Loudwater 'for many leagues to the Ford.' My father made various small-scale maps covering a greater or lesser part of the lands in *The Lord of the Rings*, on three of which this region appears; and on two of these the Road is shown approaching the Loudwater at a fairly acute angle, but by no means running alongside it. On the third (the earliest) the Road runs close to the river for a long distance before the Ford; and this is less because the course of the Road is different than because on this map the river flows at first (after the Ford) in a more westerly direction towards the Hoarwell (as in the sketch-maps).* On my 1943 map (see above) this is also and very markedly the case. On the published map, on the other hand, the Road approaches the river at a wide angle; and this was another error. It is clear, I think, that the changed Second Edition text in citation (1), with 'runs along the edge of the hills' instead of 'runs along it [the Loudwater]', was again made to save the appearance of the map.

Citation (3) in the First Edition seems to contradict (1): the Road runs along the Loudwater for many leagues to the Ford (1), but when the travellers came down to the Road out of the Trollshaws it had turned away from the river (3). But it is probably less a contradiction than a question of how closely 'runs along the Loudwater' is interpreted. The second sketch-map seems clear at least to this extent, that it shows the Road approaching the river, running alongside it for a stretch, and then

---

*Barbara Strachey makes the Loudwater bend sharply west just below the Ford and flow in this direction (before turning south) much further than on my father's maps, so that the land between the Hoarwell and the Loudwater (called 'the Angle' in LR Appendix A, p. 320) ceases to be at all triangular. She makes this assumption because from the high ground above the Last Bridge the travellers could see not only the Hoarwell but also the Loudwater, whereas going by the published map the rivers 'would have been some 100 miles apart and the hill [on which they stood] would have had to have been a high mountain for it [the Loudwater] to have been visible.' By bringing this river so far to the west on her map the distance from the hill above the Last Bridge to the nearest point of the Loudwater is reduced to about 27 miles. On my father's maps the shortest distance from the Bridge to the Loudwater varies between (approximately) 45 (on the earliest), 60, and 62 miles; on the published map it is about 75 miles. Thus the objection that the Loudwater was too far away to be seen is real; but it cannot be resolved in this way.

FROM WEATHERTOP TO THE FORD   203

bending somewhat away and 'clinging to the feet of the hills' before returning to it at the Ford.

The changed reading of the Second Edition in (3) – made so as not to alter the amount of text – makes the words 'narrow valley' refer to the Hoarwell, and there is no longer any statement at this point about the course of the Road in relation to the Loudwater. This was clearly another accommodation to the published map (and is not an entirely happy solution), as also was 'northward' (cf. Sketch II) to 'eastward'.

Note on the River Hoarwell

The absence of the River Hoarwell (p. 192), which had still not emerged in the next version of this part of the story (p. 360), is interesting. In the original story in Chapter II of *The Hobbit*, when Bilbo, Gandalf, and the Dwarves were approaching the hills crowned with old castles on an evening of heavy rain, they came to a river:

. . . it began to get dark. Wind got up, and the willows along the river-bank [*no river has been mentioned*] bent and sighed. I don't know what river it was, a rushing red one, swollen with the rains of the last few days, that came down from the hills and mountains in front of them.

Soon it was nearly dark. The winds broke up the grey clouds . . .

The river here ran *alongside* the road (described as 'a very muddy track'); they only crossed it finally by a ford, beyond which was the great slope up into the Mountains (beginning of Chapter III, 'A Short Rest'). In the third edition (1966) the passage quoted was changed:

. . . it began to get dark as they went down into a deep valley with a river at the bottom. Wind got up, and willows along its banks bent and sighed. Fortunately the road went over an ancient stone bridge, for the river, swollen with the rains, came rushing down from the hills and mountains in the north.

It was nearly night when they had crossed over. The wind broke up the grey clouds . . .

The river now becomes the Hoarwell, over which the road passed by the Last Bridge (and the river which they forded before climbing up towards Rivendell becomes distinct (the Loudwater), by changing 'they forded the river' to 'they forded a river'.) But my father did nothing to change what follows in the original story. There, the company stopped for the night where they did because that is where they were when it got dark, and it was beside a river. From that spot the light of the Trolls' fire became visible. By the introduction of the Last Bridge at this point into the old narrative, while everything else is left untouched, the company stops for the night as soon as they have crossed it – near enough to the river for one of the ponies to break loose and dash into the water, so that most of the food was lost – and the Trolls' fire is therefore visible from the Bridge, or very near it. And at the end of the chapter the pots of gold from

204   THE RETURN OF THE SHADOW

the Trolls' lair are still buried 'not far from the track by the river' – a
phrase unchanged from the original story, when the river flowed alongside the track.

Karen Fonstad puts the matter clearly (*The Atlas of Middle-earth*,
1981, p. 97), noting the inconsistency between *The Hobbit* (as it is now)
and *The Lord of the Rings* as to the distance between the river and the
Trolls' clearing:

> The Trolls' fire was so close to the river that it could be seen 'some way
> off', and it probably took the Dwarves no more than an hour to reach;
> whereas Strider led the Hobbits north of the road [turning off a mile
> beyond the Bridge], where they lost their way and spent almost six days
> reaching the clearing where they found the Stone-trolls. Lost or not, it
> seems almost impossible that the time-pressed Ranger would have
> spent six days reaching a point the Dwarves found in an hour.

Earlier, apparently in 1960, in an elaborate rewriting of *The Hobbit*
Chapter II which was never used,* my father had introduced the Last
Bridge at the same point in the narrative; but there the passage of the
river took place in the morning, and the camp from which the Trolls' fire
was seen was made at the end of the day and many miles further east. The
present text of *The Hobbit*, deriving from corrections made in 1965 and
first published in 1966, here introduces an element from *The Lord of the
Rings* but fails to harmonise the two geographies. This highly uncharacteristic lapse is no doubt to be attributed simply to the haste with which
my father worked under the extreme pressure imposed on him in 1965.

Note on the river of Rivendell

Trotter says expressly that the river which the Road crosses at the Ford
flows through Rivendell (p. 191). In the corresponding passage in FR
(p. 212) Strider names the river: 'That is Loudwater, the Bruinen of
Rivendell.' Later, in 'Many Meetings' (FR p. 250), it is said that Bilbo's
room 'opened on to the gardens and looked south across the ravine of the
Bruinen'; and at the beginning of 'The Council of Elrond' (FR p. 252)
Frodo 'walked along the terraces above the loud-flowing Bruinen.' This
is quite unambiguous; the maps, however, are not in this point perfectly
clear.

In the map of Wilderland in *The Hobbit* (endpaper), the unnamed
river receives, some way north of the Ford, a tributary stream, and
Elrond's house is placed between them, near the confluence, and nearer

---

*My father was greatly concerned to harmonise Bilbo's journey with the
geography of *The Lord of the Rings*, especially in respect of the distance and time
taken: in terms of *The Lord of the Rings* Gandalf, Bilbo, and the Dwarves took far
too long, seeing that they were mounted (see Karen Fonstad's discussion in *The
Atlas of Middle-earth*, p. 97). But he never brought this work to a definitive
solution.

FROM WEATHERTOP TO THE FORD

205

the tributary – exactly as in Sketch I on p. 201.* On one of his copies of *The Hobbit* my father pencilled in a few later names on the map of Wilderland, and these included *Bruinen or Loudwater* against the river north of the house (again as in Sketch I), and *Merrill* against the tributary flowing just to the south of it.† When therefore in *The Hobbit* (Chapter III) the elf said to Gandalf:

> You are a little out of your way: that is, if you are making for the only path across the water and to the house beyond. We will set you right, but you had best get on foot, until you are over the bridge

it would seem to be the Merrill that must be crossed by the bridge. Barbara Strachey (*Journeys of Frodo*, maps 15–16) shows very unambiguously the ravine of Rivendell as the ravine of the tributary stream, Elrond's house being some mile and a half from its confluence with the Loudwater; while Karen Fonstad (*The Atlas of Middle-earth*, pp. 80, 101, etc.) likewise places Rivendell on the southerly stream – calling it (p. 127) the Bruinen.

The lines of rivers and Road in Sketch I were first drawn in ink, and subsequently coloured over in blue and red chalk. When my father did this he changed the course of the 'tributary stream' south of Elrond's house by bending it up northwards and joining it to the Bruinen some way to the east; thus the house at Rivendell is at the western end of land enclosed between two streams coming down from the Mountains, parting, and then joining again. It might therefore be supposed that both were called 'Bruinen' (discounting the name 'Merrill' written on the Wilderland map in *The Hobbit*). But I do not think that detailed conclusions can be drawn from this sketch-map.

Note on the Entish Lands

The name *Entish Lands* on Sketch I needs a word of explanation. Originally the region in which the Hoarwell rose was called *Dimrilldale(s)* (p. 360), but when that name was displaced it was briefly called *Hoardale* (p. 432 note 3), and then *Entish Dales, Entish Lands. Entish* here was used in the Old English sense of *ent*, 'giant'; the *Entish Lands* were the 'troll-lands' (cf. the later names *Ettendales* and *Ettenmoors* of this region in FR, containing Old English *eoten* 'giant'), and are in no way associated with the *Ents* of *The Lord of the Rings*.

*In two of my father's small-scale maps the tributary stream is not marked, and Rivendell is a point on or beside the Bruinen; the third is too rubbed and faint to be sure of, but probably shows the tributary, and Rivendell between the two streams, as in the *Hobbit* map, and as my 1943 map certainly does (and that published in *The Lord of the Rings*).

†This name, which I have found nowhere else, is unfortunately not quite clear, though *Me-* and *-ll* are certain, and it is hard to read it in any other way. – Another name added to the Wilderland map was *Rhimdath* 'Rushdown', the river flowing from the Misty Mountains into Anduin north of the Carrock (see the Index to Vol. V, p. 446).

XII

AT RIVENDELL

Some preliminary ideas for this chapter (which in FR is Book II, Chapter 1, 'Many Meetings') have been given on p. 126. The original narrative draft is extant in a very rough manuscript, first in ink, then in pencil and petering out. It was variously emended and added to, but I give it here as my father seems to have set it down – granting that there is often no clear distinction between changes made at once and changes made after (and probably no significant distinction in time, in any case). This and the two following drafts all bear the number 'IX' without title.

He awoke to find himself lying in bed; and also feeling a great deal better. 'Where am I and what's the time?' he said aloud to the ceiling. Its dark carved beams were touched by sunlight. Distantly he heard the sound of a waterfall.

'In Elrond's house, and it is ten o'clock in the morning: the morning of October 24th to be exact,'[1] said a voice.

'Gandalf!' said Bingo sitting up. There was the wizard sitting in a chair by the open window.

'Yes,' said the wizard. 'I'm here all right – and you're lucky to be here too, after all the absurd things you have done since you left home.'

Bingo felt too peaceful and comfortable to argue – and in any case he did not imagine he would get the best of the argument: the memory came back to him of the disastrous short cut through the Old Forest, of his own stupidity in the inn, and of his nearly fatal madness in putting on the ring on Weathertop Hill.

There was a long silence broken only by the soft puffs of Gandalf's pipe as he blew smoke-rings out of the window.

'What happened at the Ford?' asked Bingo at last. 'It all seemed so dim somehow, and it still does.'

'Yes!' answered Gandalf. 'You were beginning to fade. They would have made a wraith of you before long – certainly if you had put on the Ring[2] again. How does the arm and side feel now?'

'I don't know,' said Bingo. 'It does not feel at all, which is better than aching, but' – he made an effort – 'I can move it a little again: yes: it feels as if it were coming back to life. It is not cold now,' he added, touching his right hand with his left.[3]

AT RIVENDELL   207

'Good!' said Gandalf. 'Elrond bathed and doctored it for hours last night after you were brought in. He has great power and skill, but I was very anxious, for the craft and malice of the Enemy is very great.'

'Brought in?' said Bingo. 'Of course: the last I remember was the rush of water. What happened? Where are the others? Do tell me, Gandalf!'

'What happened – as far as I can make out from Glorfindel and Trotter (who both have some wits in their different ways) – was this: the pursuers made straight for you (as Glorfindel expected they would). The others might have been trampled down, but Glorfindel made them leap out of the way off the road. Nothing could save you if the white elf-horse could not; so they followed cautiously behind on foot, keeping out of sight as much as they could behind bushes and rocks. When they had got as near to the Ford as they dared go, they made a fire hastily, and rushed out on the Riders with flaming brands, just at the moment when the flood came down. Between the fire and water these pursuers were destroyed – if they can be wholly destroyed by such means – all but two that vanished into the wild.

'The rest of your party and the elf then crossed the ford, with some difficulty as it is too deep for hobbits and deep even for a horse. But Glorfindel crossed on your pony and regained his horse. They found you lying on your face in the grass at the top of the slope: pale and cold. At first they feared you were dead. They carried you towards Rivendell: a slow business, and I don't know when they would have arrived, if Elrond had not sent some Elves out to help you, at the same time as the water was released.'

'Did Elrond make the flood then?' asked Bingo.

'No, I did,'[4] said Gandalf. 'It is not very difficult magic, in a stream that comes down from the mountains. The sun has been fairly hot today. But I was surprised to find how well the river responded. The roar and rush was tremendous.'

'It was,' said Bingo. 'Did you also send Glorfindel?'

'Yes,' said Gandalf, '– or rather, I asked Elrond to lend him to me. He is a wise and noble elf. Bilbo is – was – very fond of him. I also sent Rimbedir[5] (as they call him here) – that Trotter fellow. From what Merry tells me I gather he has been useful.'

'I should think he has,' said Bingo. 'I was very suspicious of him at first – but we should never have got here without him. I have grown very fond of him. I wish indeed that he was going to go on wandering with me as long as I must wander. It is an odd thing,

208 THE RETURN OF THE SHADOW

you know, but I keep on feeling that I have seen him somewhere before.'

'I daresay you do,' said Gandalf. 'I often have that feeling when I look at a hobbit – they all seem to remind me of one another, don't you know. Really they are extraordinarily alike!'

'Nonsense,' said Bingo. 'Trotter is most peculiar. However I feel extremely hobbit-like myself, and I could wish that I was not doomed to wander. I have now had more than a month of it, and that is about 28 days too much for me.' He fell silent again, and began to doze. 'What did those dreadful pursuers do to me in Weathertop dell?' he said half to himself, on the edge of a shadowy dream.

'They attempted to pierce you with the sword of the Necromancer,' said Gandalf. 'But by some grace of fortune, or by your own courage (I have heard an account of the fight) and by the confusion caused by the elf-name which you cried, only your shoulder was grazed. But that was dangerous enough – especially with the ring on. For while the ring was on, you yourself were in the wraith-world, and subject to their weapons.[6] They could see you, and you them.'

'Why can we see their horses?'

'Because they are real horses. Just as the black robes they wear to give shape to their nothingness are real robes.'

'Then why, when all other animals – dogs, horses, ponies – are filled with terror of them, do these horses endure them on their backs?'

'Because they are born and bred under the power of the evil Lord in the dark kingdom. Not all his servants and chattels are wraiths!'

'It is all very threatening and confusing,' said Bingo sleepily.

'Well, you are quite safe for the present,' said Gandalf, 'and are mending rapidly. I should not worry about anything now, if I were you.'

'All right,' said Bingo, and fell fast asleep.[7]

Bingo was now as you know in the Last Homely House west of the Mountains, on the edge of the wild, the house of Elrond: that house was (as Bilbo Baggins had long ago reported) 'a perfect house, whether you like food or sleep or work or story-telling or singing, or just sitting and thinking, best, or a pleasant mixture of them all.' Merely to be there was a cure for weariness and sadness. As evening drew on Bingo woke up and found that he no longer

AT RIVENDELL

209

felt like sleep but had a mind for food and drink, story-telling and singing. So he got up, and found his arm already nearly as useful as ever it had been. As soon as he was dressed he went in search of his friends. They were sitting in the porch of the house that faced west: shadows were fallen in the valley, but the light was still upon high eastern faces of the hills far above, and the air was warm. It was seldom cold in the fair valley of Rivendell. The sound of the waterfalls was loud in the stillness. There was a scent of trees and flowers [?in harmony].

'Hullo,' said Merry, 'here is our noble uncle. Three cheers for Bingo Lord of the Ring!'

'Hush!' said Gandalf. 'Evil things do not come into this valley, but nonetheless we should not name them. The Lord of the Ring is not Bingo, but the Lord of the Dark Tower of Mordor,[8] whose power is growing again, and we are here sitting only in a fortress of peace. Outside it is getting dark.'

'Gandalf has been saying lots of cheerful things like that,' said Odo. 'Just to keep us in order: but it seems impossible somehow to feel gloomy or depressed in Elrond's house. I feel I could sing – if I knew how: only I never was any good at making up words or tunes.'

'You never were,' said Bingo, 'but I daresay even that could be cured in time, if you stayed here long enough. I feel much the same myself. Though at the moment I feel more hungry than anything else.'

His hunger was soon cured. For before long they were summoned to the evening meal. The hall was filled with many folk: elves for the most part, though there were a few guests and travellers of various sort. Elrond sat in the high seat, and next to him sat Gandalf. Bingo did not see Trotter or Glorfindel: they were probably at one of the other halls among their friends, but to his surprise he found sitting next to him a dwarf of venerable appearance and rich dress – his beard was white, nearly as white as the snow-white cloth of his garments; he wore a belt of silver and a chain of silver and diamonds.

'Welcome and well met,' said the dwarf, rising and bowing. 'Glóin at your service!' and he bowed again.

'Bingo Bolger-Baggins at your service and your family's,' replied Bingo. 'Am I right in imagining that you are *the* Glóin, one of the twelve companions of the great Thorin?'

'You are,' said he. 'And I need not ask, since I have already been told that you are the friend and adopted son of our dear friend

210   THE RETURN OF THE SHADOW

Bilbo Baggins. I wonder much what brings *four* hobbits so far
from their homes. Nothing like it has occurred since Bilbo left
Hobbiton. But perhaps I should not ask this; since Elrond and
Gandalf do not seem disposed to tell?'

'I think we will not speak of such things, at any rate yet,' said
Bingo politely – he wanted to forget about his troubles for the
moment. 'Though I am equally curious to know what brings so
important a dwarf so far from the Mountain.'

Glóin looked at him and laughed – indeed he actually winked. 'I
am no spoil-sport,' he said. 'So I will not tell you – yet. But there
are many other things to tell.'

Throughout the meal they talked together. Bingo told news of
the Shire, but he listened more than he talked, for Glóin had much
to tell of the Dwarf-kingdom under the Mountain, and of Dale.
There Dáin was still king of the dwarfs,[9] and was now ancient
(some 200 years old), venerable, and fabulously rich. Of the ten
companions that had survived the battle, seven were still with
him: Dwalin, Dori, Nori, Bifur and Bofur and Bombur.[10] But the
last was now so fat that he could not move himself from his couch
to his chair, and it took four young dwarves to lift him. In Dale the
grandson of Bard, Brand son of Bain, was lord.

My father stopped here, and scribbled down a few notes before at once
beginning the chapter anew. The notes at the end of the first draft
include the following:

What of Balin etc. They went to colonize (Ring needed to found
colony?) Bilbo must be seen. Who is Trotter?

The second text is a clear manuscript, but it had proceeded no farther
than Gandalf's account of the flood in the Bruinen when my father again
stopped and started again. This is an intermediate text much nearer to
the third than to the first, and need not be considered more closely.

The third text, the last in this phase of the work, but again abandoned
before its conclusion (going in fact scarcely any farther than the first
draft), is very close to 'Many Meetings' in FR, but there are many minor
differences (quite apart, of course, from those that are constant at this
stage, as Trotter/Strider-Aragorn and the absence of Sam). The opening
is now almost identical to that in FR, but the date is October 26, and
Gandalf adds, after 'You were beginning to fade', 'Trotter noticed it, to
his great alarm – though of course he said nothing.' But after Gandalf's 'It
is no small feat . . .' (FR p. 232) the old narrative goes on:

'. . . But I am delighted to have you all here safe. I am really rather
to blame. I knew there were some risks – but if I had known more
before I left the Shire I should have arranged matters differently.

AT RIVENDELL   211

But things are moving fast,' he added in a lower voice as if to himself, 'even faster than I feared. I *had* to get here quickly. But if I had known the Riders were already out!'

'Did not you know that?' asked Bingo.

'No I did not – not until we came to Bree. It was Trotter that told me.[11] And if I had not known Trotter and trusted him, I should have waited for you there. And as it has turned out, he saved you and brought you through in the end.'

'We should never have got here without him,' said Bingo. 'I was very suspicious of him at first, but I have grown very fond of him. Though he is rather queer. I wish that he was going to go on wandering with me – as long as I must wander. It is an odd thing, you know, but I keep on feeling that I have seen him somewhere before – that, that I ought to be able to put a name to him, a name different to Trotter.'

'I dare say you do,' laughed Gandalf. 'I often have that feeling when I look at a hobbit: they all seem to remind me of one another, if you know what I mean. They are wonderfully alike!'

'Nonsense!' said Bingo, sitting up again in protest. 'Trotter is most peculiar. And he has shoes! However, I am feeling a very ordinary hobbit myself at the moment. I wish now that I need not go any further. I have had more than a month of exile and adventures, and that is about four weeks more than enough for me.'[12]

The text now becomes very close to that of FR pp. 233–4, but there are several differences. As in FR, Bingo cannot understand how he can be out in his reckoning of the date, but in this version Gandalf has told him that it is the 26th of October (not as in FR the 24th), and he calculates that they must have reached the Ford on the 23rd (the 20th in FR). On this question see the Note on Chronology on p. 219. In contrast to the first draft, where Gandalf says that Bingo was brought in to Rivendell 'last night', he has been unconscious for a long time, and the mortal danger of his wound is emphasized. Gandalf calls the weapon that was used 'a deadly blade, the knife of the Necromancer which remains in the wound', not 'a Morgul-knife', and he explains to Bingo that 'You would have become a Ring-wraith (the only hobbit Ring-wraith) and you would have been under the dominion of the Dark Lord. Also they would have got possession of the Ring. And the Dark Lord would have found some way of tormenting you for trying to keep it from him, and of striking at all your friends and kinsfolk through you, if he could.' He says that the Riders wear black robes 'to give shape to their nothingness in our world'; and he includes among the servants of the Dark Lord 'orcs and goblins' and 'kings, warriors, and wizards.'

212   THE RETURN OF THE SHADOW

Gandalf's reply to Bingo's question 'Is Rivendell safe?' is similar to that in FR (pp. 234–5), but has some notable features:

'Yes, I hope so. He has seldom overcome any of the Elves in the past; and all Elves now are his enemies. The Elves of Rivendell are indeed descendants of his chief foes: the Gnomes, the Elven-wise ones, that came out of the Far West, and whom Elbereth Gilthoniel still protects.[13] They fear no Ring-wraiths, for they live at once in both worlds, and each world has only half power over them, while they have double power over both. But such places as Rivendell (or the Shire in its own way) will soon become besieged islands, if things go on as they are going. The Dark Lord is moving again. Dreadful is the power of the Necromancer. Still,' he said, standing suddenly up and sticking out his chin while his beard stuck out like bristling wire, 'the Wise say that he is doomed in the end. We will keep up our courage. You are mending rapidly, and you need not worry about anything at the moment.'

The passage in which Gandalf looked closely at Frodo, and then spoke to himself, is lacking; but his story of the events at the Ford is in all essentials the same as in FR, with a few features still retained from the first draft – most important, Gandalf still says that two of the Riders escaped into the wild. The difficult passage of the deep ford is still described, as in the first draft, and Gandalf still says 'I was surprised to find how well the river responded to a little simple magic.' But Elrond's power over the river, and Gandalf's waves like white horses with white riders, now enter. The end of Bingo's talk with Gandalf, however, has differences:

'. . . I thought I was drowning – and all my friends and enemies together. It is wonderful that Elrond and Glorfindel and such great people should take all this trouble over me – not to mention Trotter.'

'Well – there are many reasons for that. I am one good reason. You may discover others.[14] For one thing they are – were – very fond of Bilbo Baggins.'

'What do you mean – "are fond of Bilbo"?' said Bingo sleepily.

'Did I say that? Just a slip of the tongue,' answered Gandalf. 'I thought I said "were".'

'I wish old Bilbo could have been here and heard all about this,' murmured Bingo. 'I could have made him laugh. The cow jumped over the moon. Hullo William!' he said. 'Poor old troll!' and then he fell asleep.

The next section of the narrative follows the first draft (p. 208) pretty

AT RIVENDELL 213

closely, but Bingo's discovery of green garments laid out for him now enters the story, with a further addition that only survived in part in FR:

He put on his own best waistcoat with the gold buttons (which he had brought in his luggage as his only remaining treasure). But it seemed very loose. Looking in a little mirror he was startled to see a very much thinner reflection of Bingo than he had seen for a long while. It looked remarkably like the young nephew of Bilbo that used to go tramping with his uncle in the Shire, though it was a bit pale in the face. 'And I feel like it,' he said, slapping his chest and tightening his waistcoat strap. Then he went in search of his friends.

There is nothing corresponding to Sam's entering Frodo's room.

The feast in Elrond's house moves far to the final text. The descriptions of Elrond, Gandalf, and Glorfindel now appear (they were written on an inserted slip, but it seems to belong to the same time) and in almost the same words as in FR (p. 239) – but there is mention of Elrond's smile, 'like the summer sun', and his laughter. There is no mention of Arwen. Bingo 'could not see Trotter, nor his nephews. They had been led to other tables.'

The conversation with Glóin proceeds as in the first draft, with some touches and phrases that move it to the final text (FR p. 240). Glóin is now described as 'a dwarf of solemn dignity and rich dress', but he still winks (as he does not in FR).

At the point where the first draft ends (p. 210) my father only added a further couple of lines before again stopping:

In Dale the grandson of Bard the Bowman ruled, Brand son of Bain son of Bard, and he was become a strong king whose realm included Esgaroth, and much land to the south of the great falls.[15]

On the reverse of the sheet the conversation continues in a different script and a different ink: Glóin gives an account of Balin's history (his return to Moria) – but it is Frodo, not Bingo, that he is speaking with, and this side of the page belongs to a later phase in the writing of the book (see pp. 369, 391).

A passage on a detached slip, forming part of Gandalf's conversation with Bingo, seems to belong to the time of the third draft of this chapter. There is no direction for its insertion into the text, and there is no echo of it in FR.

Things work out oddly. But for that 'short cut' you would not have met old Bombadil, nor had the one kind of sword the Riders fear.[16] Why did not I think of Bombadil before! If only he was not so far away, I would go straight back now and consult him. We have

214   THE RETURN OF THE SHADOW

never had much to do with one another up till now. I don't think he quite approves of me somehow. He belongs to a much older generation, and my ways are not his. He keeps himself to himself and does not believe in travel. But I fancy somehow that we shall all need his help in the end – and that he may have to take an interest in things outside his own country.

Among my father's earliest ideas for this part of the story (p. 126) appears: 'Gandalf astonished to hear about Tom.' – Another brief passage on the same slip of paper was struck out at the time of writing:

Not to mention courage – and also swords and a strange and ancient name. Later on I must be told about that curious sword of yours, and how you knew the name of Elbereth.'
    'I thought you knew everything.'
    'No,' said Gandalf. 'You

Some notes that were scribbled down at Sidmouth in Devon in the late summer of 1938 (see Carpenter, *Biography*, p. 187) on a page of doodles evidently represent my father's thoughts for the next stages of the story at this time:

    Consultation. Over M[isty] M[ountains]. Down Great River to Mordor. Dark Tower. Beyond (?) which is the Fiery Hill.
    Story of Gilgalad told by Elrond? Who is Trotter? Glorfindel tells of his ancestry in Gondolin.

'The Quest of the Fiery Mountain' (preceded by 'Consultation of hobbits with Elrond and Gandalf') was mentioned in the outline given on p. 126, but here is the first hint of the journey that was to be undertaken from Rivendell, and the first mention of the Great River in the context of *The Lord of the Rings*.

My father had already asked the question 'Who is Trotter?' and he would ask it again. A hint of one solution, in the end rejected, has been met already in Bingo's words to Gandalf in this chapter: 'I keep on feeling that I have seen him somewhere before – that, that I ought to be able to put a name to him, a name different to Trotter'; and indeed earlier, in the inn at Bree (p. 154): 'He had a dark look – and yet there was something in it . . . that seemed friendly, and even familiar.'

Also very notable is 'Glorfindel tells of his ancestry in Gondolin.' Years later, long after the publication of *The Lord of the Rings*, my father gave a great deal of thought to the matter of Glorfindel, and at that time he wrote: '[The use of *Glorfindel*] in *The Lord of the Rings* is one of the cases of the somewhat random use of the names found in the older legends, now referred to as *The Silmarillion*, which escaped reconsideration in the final published form of *The Lord of the Rings*.' He came to the conclusion that Glorfindel of Gondolin, who fell to his death in combat

AT RIVENDELL

215

with a Balrog after the sack of the city (II.192–4, IV.145), and Glorfindel of Rivendell were one and the same: he was released from Mandos and returned to Middle-earth in the Second Age.

A single loose page, which has nothing to connect it with any other writing, is perhaps the 'story of Gilgalad told by Elrond' mentioned in these notes, and I give it here. Other than the first, the changes noted were made subsequently, in pencil on the manuscript written in ink.

'Now in the dark days Sauron the Magician [*first written* Necromancer, *then* Necromancer *written again above* Magician] had been very powerful in the Great Lands, and nearly all living things had served him out of fear. And he pursued the Elves that lived on this side of the Sundering Sea with especial hatred, for they did not serve him, although they were afraid. And there were some Men that were friends of the Elves, though not many in the darkest of days.'

'And how,' said Bingo, 'did his overthrow come about [> was his power made less]?'

'It was in this way,' said Elrond. 'The lands and islands in the North-west of the Great Lands of the Old World were called long ago Beleriand. Here the Elves of the West had dwelt for a long while until [> during] the wars with the Power of darkness, in which the Power was defeated but the land destroyed. Sauron alone of his chief servants escaped. But still after the Elves had mostly departed [> Although most of the Elves returned] again into the West, there were many Elves and Elf-friends that dwelt [> still dwelt in after days] in that region. And thither came many of the Great Men of old out of the Far West Island which was called by the Elves Númenor (but by some Avallon) [> out of the land of Westernesse (that they called Númenor)]; for Sauron had destroyed their island [> land], and they were exiles and hated him. There was a king in Beleriand of Númenórean race and he was called Elendil, that is Elf-friend. And he made an alliance with the Elf-king of those lands, whose name is Gilgalad (Starlight), a descendant of Fëanor the renowned. I remember well their council – for it reminded me of the great days of the ancient war, so many fair princes and captains were there, yet not so many or so fair as once had been.'

'You remember?' said Bingo, looking astonished at Elrond. 'But I thought this tale was of days very long ago.'

'So it is,' said Elrond laughing. 'But my memory reaches back a long way [> to long ago]. My father was Eärendel who was born in Gondolin seven years before it fell, and my mother was Elwing

216   THE RETURN OF THE SHADOW

daughter of Lúthien daughter of King Thingol of Doriath, and I have seen many ages in the West of the world. I was at the council I speak of, for I was the minstrel and counsellor of Gilgalad. The armies of Elves and Men were joined once more, and we marched eastward, and crossed the Misty Mountains, and passed into the inner lands far from the memory of the Sea. And we became weary, and sickness was heavy on us, made by the spells of Sauron – for we had come at last to Mordor, the Black Country, where Sauron had rebuilt his fortress. It is on part of that dreary land that the Forest of Mirkwood now stands,[17] and it derives its darkness and dread from the ancient evil [added: of the soil]. Sauron could not drive us away, for the power of the Elves was in those days still very great, though waning; and we besieged his stronghold for 7 [> 10] years. And at last Sauron came out in person, and wrestled with Gilgalad, and Elendil came to his rescue, and both were mortally wounded; but Sauron was thrown down, and his bodily shape was destroyed. His servants were dispelled and the host of Beleriand broke his stronghold and razed it to the ground. Gilgalad and Elendil died. But Sauron's evil spirit fled away and was hidden for a long while in waste places. Yet after an age he took shape again, and has long troubled the northern world [added: but his power is less than of old].

   If this extremely interesting piece is compared with the end of the second version of *The Fall of Númenor* ('FN II') in V.28–9 it will be seen that while an important new element has entered the two texts are closely related and have closely similar phrases: citing the form in FN II, 'in Beleriand there arose a king, who was of Númenórean race, and he was named Elendil, that is Elf-friend'; the hosts of the Alliance 'passed the mountains and came into inner lands far from the Sea'; 'they came at last even to Mordor the Black Country, where Sauron . . . had rebuilt his fortresses'; 'Thû was thrown down, and his bodily shape destroyed, and his servants were dispelled, and the host of Beleriand destroyed his dwelling'; 'Thû's spirit fled far away, and was hidden in waste places.' Moreover in both texts Gil-galad is descended from Fëanor. The new element is the appearance of Elrond as the minstrel and counsellor of Gil-galad (in FN II §2 Elrond was the first King of Númenor, and a mortal; a conception now of course abandoned, with the emergence of Elros his brother, V.332, §28). There is no suggestion here that any sort of 'Council' was in progress: it seems rather that Elrond was recounting the tale to Bingo, as Trotter had said on Weathertop (p. 179): 'you will hear it, I think, in Rivendell, when we get there. Elrond should tell it, for he knows it well.' But an element survived into FR (II) Chapter 2, 'The Council of Elrond': Bingo's amazement at the vast age of Elrond, and

AT RIVENDELL 217

Elrond's reply, naming his lineage and recollecting the hosts of the Last Alliance.[18]

NOTES

1 On this puzzling date see the Note on Chronology, p. 219.

2 *the Ring:* changed from *that ring.*

3 *touching his right hand with his left:* on the wound having been originally in Bingo's right shoulder see p. 190.

4 *'No, I did'* changed from *'Yes'.* Cf. the original sketch of the story (p. 126): 'Gandalf had sent the water down with Elrond's permission.'

5 *Rimbedir* as the Elvish name for Trotter appears in the pencilled draft of the last chapter, p. 198 note 5 (*Padathir* in the overwritten text in ink). This shows that the present text was written before my father had rewritten the last chapter, or at least before he had completed it. Later he replaced *Rimbedir* by *Padathir* in the present passage. – By 'I also sent Rimbedir' Gandalf must mean that he sent Trotter to them at *The Prancing Pony.*

6 This passage was changed in the following text to the form in FR (p. 234), i.e. 'you yourself were *half* in the wraith-world, and they might have seized you', with the words 'and subject to their weapons' removed.

7 From this point the manuscript was continued in rapid pencil.

8 *the Dark Tower of Mordor:* see note 17.

9 On the plural form *dwarfs* see V.277.

10 Glóin is missed out (so also in the third text, where his name was inserted subsequently). The companions of Thorin not named are (as in FR) Balin, Ori, and Óin.

11 *It was Trotter that told me:* Gandalf left a letter for Bingo at Bree before he left on Monday 26 September, and in this he said that he had *'learned some news on the way'* (from Hobbiton): 'Pursuit is getting close: there are 7 at least, perhaps more' (p. 154). When my father wrote this he cannot have had in mind Trotter's meeting with Gandalf on the Road on the Sunday morning (pp. 149, 154), because the first Black Rider did not come to Bree until the Monday evening (pp. 151, 157). It was no doubt when he decided that Gandalf learnt about the Black Riders from Trotter that he added the passages on p. 153, where Trotter says 'I first saw the Riders last Saturday away west of Bree, before I ran across Gandalf', and on p. 154, where he says that their conversation also included the Black Riders.

12 *more than a month* (as in the first draft) replaced *30 odd days* at the time of writing. See the Note on Chronology on p. 219.

13 *The Elves of Rivendell are indeed descendants of his chief foes: the Gnomes, the Elvenwise ones:* see p. 71.

218   THE RETURN OF THE SHADOW

14 My father added in pencil at the foot of the page, but it is impossible
    to say when: 'The Ring is another, and is becoming more and more
    important.'
15 Cf. *The Hobbit*, Chapter X 'A Warm Welcome':
    At the southern end [of the Long Lake] the doubled waters [of
    the Running River and the Forest River] poured out again over
    high waterfalls and ran away hurriedly to unknown lands. In the
    still evening air the noise of the falls could be heard like a distant
    roar.
16 An isolated note says: 'What of the sword of the Barrow-wights?
    Why did the Black Riders fear it? – because it belonged to Western
    Men.' Cf. *The Two Towers* III. 1, p. 17.
17 Elrond's statement here that Mirkwood is itself in Mordor, 'the
    Black Country', and that the forest 'derives its darkness from the
    ancient evil' of the time when Sauron had his fortress in that region
    is interesting. Both here and in the very similar passage in the
    second version of *The Fall of Númenor* (V.29) Sauron is said to have
    'rebuilt' his fortress(es) in Mordor, and I take this to mean that
    it was in Mordor that he established himself after the downfall
    of Morgoth and the destruction of Angband. That fortress was
    destroyed by the hosts of the Last Alliance; and in the first version of
    The Fall of Númenor (V.18) when Thû was defeated and his
    dwelling destroyed 'he fled to a dark forest, and hid himself.' In *The
    Hobbit* the 'dark tower' of the Necromancer was in southern Mirk-
    wood. At the end of *The Hobbit* it is told that the white wizards 'had
    at last driven the Necromancer from his dark hold in the south of
    Mirkwood', but it is not said that it was destroyed. If 'it is on part of
    that dreary land [Mordor] that the Forest of Mirkwood now stands',
    it might be argued that (at this stage of the development of the story)
    Sauron had returned there, to 'the Dark Tower of Mordor' – in the
    south of Mirkwood. (There seems no positive evidence that the
    geography of Middle-earth had yet been extended south and east of
    the map of Wilderland in *The Hobbit*, beyond the conception of the
    Fiery Mountain, whose actual placing seems to be entirely vague;
    and it certainly cannot be assumed that my father yet conceived of
    the mountain-defended land of Mordor far away in the South-east.)
        But I do not think this at all probable. Not long after the point
    we have reached, my father wrote in the chapter 'Ancient History'
    (p. 253) that the Necromancer 'had flown from Mirkwood [i.e. after
    his expulsion by the white wizards] *only to reoccupy his ancient
    stronghold in the South*, near the midst of the world in those days, in
    the Land of Mordor; and it was rumoured that the Black Tower had
    been raised anew.' 'His ancient stronghold' was of course the
    fortress destroyed in the War of the Last Alliance.
18 For previous references to the story of Gil-galad and Elendil in the
    texts thus far see pp. 169, 179, 192.

AT RIVENDELL   219

Note on the Chronology

In the first draft of this chapter Gandalf tells Bingo when he wakes up in Elrond's house that it is the morning of October 24; but this seems to be at variance with all the indications of date that have been given. (October 24 is the date in FR, p. 231, but this was differently achieved.)

At Weathertop there is one day's difference between the original chronology and that of FR: they reached it on October 5 in the old version, but on October 6 in FR (see p. 175). The hobbits came back to the Road again from the lands to the south, and crossed it, on the sixth day from Weathertop (p. 192), i.e. October 11, whereas in FR they took an extra day (contrast 'At the end of the fourth day the ground began once more to rise' in the old version, p. 191, with FR p. 212, 'At the end of the fifth day'): thus there is now a lag of two days between the two accounts, and in FR they came back to the Road and crossed the Last Bridge on October 13. In the hills to the north of the Road, on the other hand, they took a day longer in the old version (see p. 193), and thus came down out of the hills, and met Glorfindel, on the evening of the 17th (the 18th in FR). There are no further differences in respect of chronology in this chapter, and therefore in the original story they reached the Ford on October 19 (October 20 in FR). How then can it be the 24th of October when Bingo wakes in Rivendell, if, as Gandalf says, he was 'brought in last night'?

In the second and third versions of the opening of this chapter the date on which Bingo woke up in Elrond's house becomes October 26, and he says that it ought to be the 24th: 'unless I lost count somewhere, we must have reached the Ford on the 23rd.' Gandalf tells him that Elrond tended him for 'three nights and two days, to be exact. The Elves brought you to Rivendell at night on the 23rd, and that is where you lost your count'; and he refers to Bingo's having borne the splinter of the blade for 'fifteen days or more' (seventeen in FR). This does not help at all with the chronological puzzle, for in all the drafts for the opening of Chapter IX my father was assuming that the hobbits reached the Ford on October 23, and not, as the actual narrative seems clearly to show, on October 19. It is equally odd that Gandalf should say that Bingo had borne the splinter of the blade for 'fifteen days or more', if the crossing of the Ford actually was on the 23rd and Elrond finally removed the shard 'last night' (October 25): the total should be 20 (October 6 to 25); in FR the number is seventeen days (October 7 to 23).

XIII

'QUERIES AND ALTERATIONS'

In this chapter I give a series of notes which my father headed *Queries and Alterations*. I think that it can be shown clearly that they come from the time we have now reached.

He had abandoned his third draft for Chapter IX (later to be called 'Many Meetings') at the point where Glóin was telling Bingo about King Brand of Dale; this is at the bottom of a page that bears the number IX.8. I have already noticed (p. 213) that on the reverse of this page, numbered IX.9, the conversation continues – but it is obviously discontinuous with what precedes, being written in different ink and a different script, and Glóin is now talking to 'Frodo', not 'Bingo'; and in fact, after this point in the narrative of *The Lord of the Rings* 'Bingo' never appears again.

Now the first of these *Queries and Alterations* is concerned precisely with the conversation of Bingo and Glóin, and actually refers to the last page of the 'Bingo' part of the chapter, IX.8 (perhaps it had just been written). In another of these notes my father was for the first time considering the substitution of 'Frodo' for 'Bingo'; but he here decided against it – and when he came to write a new version of 'A Long-expected Party' (a question discussed in these same notes) Bilbo's heir was still 'Bingo', not 'Frodo'.

I conclude, therefore, that it was just at the time when he abandoned Chapter IX that he wrote *Queries and Alterations*; that when he abandoned it he returned again to the beginning of the book; and that it was some considerable time – during which 'Bingo' became 'Frodo' – before he took up again the conversation with Glóin at Rivendell.

There are two pages of these notes, mostly set out in ink in an orderly and legible way; but there are also many hasty pencilled additions, and these may or may not, in particular cases, belong to the same time (granting that the intervals of time are not likely to be great: but in attempting to trace this history it is 'layers' and 'phases' that are significant rather than weeks or months). Some of the suggestions embodied in these notes had no future, but others are of the utmost interest in showing the actual emergence of new ideas.

I set them out in what seems to be the order in which they were written down, taking in the additions as convenient and relevant, and adding one or two other notes that belong to this time.

'QUERIES AND ALTERATIONS'

(1) Dale Men and Dwarfs at Party – is this good? Rather spoils meeting of Bingo and Glóin (IX.8). Also unwise to bring Big People to Hobbiton. Simply make Gandalf and dwarfs bring things from Dale.

For the 'great lumbering tow-haired Men' who went 'stumping on the hobbit road like elephants' and drank all the beer in the inn at Hobbiton see p. 20 (the account of them had survived without change into the fourth version of 'A Long-expected Party'). By 'Dale Men and Dwarfs at Party' my father meant 'in Hobbiton at that time', not of course that they were present at the Party. The Men would be abandoned in the next version of 'A Long-expected Party', but the Dwarves remained into FR (p. 33). Perhaps my father felt that whereas the Men would certainly have told Bingo the news from Dale, the Dwarves need have no particular connection with the Lonely Mountain.

(2) *Too many hobbits*. Also Bingo Bolger-Baggins a bad name. Let Bingo = Frodo, a son of Primula Brandybuck but of father Drogo Baggins (Bilbo's first cousin). So Frodo (= Bingo) is Bilbo's first cousin once removed both on Took side and on Baggins. Also he has as proper name *Baggins*.

[Frodo *struck out*] No – I am now too used to Bingo.

Frodo [*i.e.* Took] and Odo are in the know and see Bingo off at gate after the Party. Would it not be well to cancel *sale*, and have Odo as heir and in charge? – though many things could be given away. The Sackville-Bagginses could quarrel with Odo?

Frodo (and possibly Odo) go on the first stage of road (because Frodo's news about Black Riders is necessary) [see pp. 54–5].

But Frodo says goodbye at Bucklebury. Only Merry and Bingo ride on into exile – because *Merry insists*. Bingo originally intended to go alone.

Probably best would be to have only Frodo Took – who sees Bingo to Bucklebury; and then Merry. *Cut out Odo*. Even better to have Frodo and *Merry* at the gate: Frodo says goodbye then, and is left in charge of the Shire [i.e. 'in the Shire', at Bag End]. *Merry* see Black Riders in North.

All of this, from 'No – I am now too used to Bingo', was struck out in pencil, and at the same time my father wrote 'Sam Gamgee' in the margin, and to 'Bingo originally intended to go alone' he added 'with Sam'. It may be that this is where he first set down Sam Gamgee's name.

There is a first hint here, in 'Frodo says goodbye at Bucklebury', of the hobbit who would remain behind at Crickhollow when the others entered the Old Forest; while 'Too many hobbits' and 'Cut out Odo' are the first signs of what before long would become a major problem and an almost impenetrable confusion.

The genealogy as it now stood in the fourth version of 'A Long-

222   THE RETURN OF THE SHADOW

expected Party' is found on p. 37. Bingo was already Bilbo's first cousin once removed on the Took side, but his father was Rollo Bolger (and when Bilbo adopted him he changed his name from Bolger to Bolger-Baggins). With the appearance of Drogo Baggins, Bingo would become Bilbo's first cousin once removed on the Baggins side also: we must suppose that Drogo's father was to be brother of Bilbo's father Bungo Baggins. In the later genealogy Drogo became Bilbo's second cousin, as Gaffer Gamgee explained to his audience at *The Ivy Bush*: 'so Mr. Frodo is [Mr. Bilbo's] first *and* second cousin, once removed either way, as the saying is, if you follow me' (FR p. 31).

An abandoned genealogy on one of these pages shows my father evolving the Baggins pedigree. This little table begins with Inigo Baggins (for a previous holder of this name see p. 17), whose son was Mungo Baggins, father of Bungo: Mungo, first appearing here, survived into the final family tree. Bungo has a sister Rosa, who married 'Young Took'; Rosa also survived, but not as Bilbo's aunt – she became Bungo's first cousin, still with a Took husband (Hildigrim). In this table Drogo is Bungo's brother, but it was at this point that the table was abandoned.

The reference in this note to the 'sale' is on the face of it very puzzling. 'A Long-expected Party' was still in its fourth version – when the Party was given by Bingo Bolger-Baggins, and the major revision whereby it reverted to Bilbo had not yet been undertaken. Then what 'sale' is referred to? There has been no sale of Bag End: Bingo 'devised delivered and made over by free gift the desirable property' to the Sackville-Bagginses (p. 39). The sale of Bag End to the Sackville-Bagginses only arose with the changed story. There is however another reference to the *sale*, in a scribbled list of the days of the hobbits' journey from Hobbiton found on the manuscript of the Troll Song which Bingo was to sing at Bree (p. 142 note 11): this list begins 'Party *Thursday, Friday* "Sale" and departure of Odo, Frodo, and Bingo,' etc. The fact that the word is here enclosed in inverted commas may suggest that my father merely had in mind the auction of Bag End to which Bilbo returned at the end of *The Hobbit*: the earlier clear-out of Bilbo's home, which was a sale, made the word a convenient if misleading shorthand for the clear-out in the new story, which was not a sale.

At the foot of the page the following note was hastily jotted in pencil, and then struck out:

(3)   Gandalf is against Bingo's telling *anyone* where he is off to. Bingo is to take *Merry*. Bingo is reluctant to give pain to Odo and Frodo. He tells them – suddenly saying goodbye, and Frodo (Odo) meets what looks like a *hobbit* on the way up hill. He asks after Bingo – and Frodo or Odo tells him he is off to Bucklebury. So Black Riders know and ride after Bingo.

'QUERIES AND ALTERATIONS' 223

This is the embryo of the final story, that a Rider came and spoke to Gaffer Gamgee, who sent him on to Bucklebury (FR p. 85).

(4) *Sting.* Did Bilbo take this? What of the armour? Various possibilities: (a) Bingo has armour, but loses it in Barrow; (b) Gandalf urges him to take armour, but it is heavy and he leaves it at Bucklebury; (c) he likes it, and it saves him in the Barrow, but is *stolen* at Bree.

The point is, of course, that he cannot be wearing armour on Weathertop. With this note compare the mention in the original 'scheme' for Chapter IX (p. 126) of 'Ring-mail of Bingo in barrow' – this was apparently to be an element in 'some explanations' when the hobbits reached Rivendell.

Another note, on another page, is almost the same as this, but asserts that Bilbo did take Sting, and says that if Bingo's armour was stolen at Bree 'discovery of the burgled rooms is before night.' The meaning of this is presumably that according to the existing story (pp. 162–3) the hobbits had taken all their belongings out of the bedrooms into their parlour before the attack, and that this would have to be changed.

In FR (pp. 290–1) Bilbo gave Sting to Frodo at Rivendell, together with the coat of mithril.

(5) Bree-folk are *not* to be hobbits. Bring in bit about the *upstairs windows*. As a result of the hobbits not liking it, landlord gives them rooms on side of the house where second floor is level with ground owing to hill-slope.

The 'bit about the upstairs windows' is presumably the passage in the original Chapter III (pp. 92–3) where the hobbits, approaching Farmer Maggot's, discuss the inconveniences of living on more than one floor. – In fact, in the original beginning of the *Prancing Pony* chapter (p. 132) the people of Bree were primarily Men (with 'hobbits about', 'some higher up on the slopes of Bree-hill itself, and many in the valley of Combe on the east side'); so that this new idea was, to some extent, a reversion. But a pencilled note on the same page, added in afterthought, asks: 'What is to happen at Bree now? What kind of talk can give away Mr Hill?' – and I take the implication of this to be that the Bree-folk were now to be exclusively Men (for they would be less curious and less informed about the Shire). See p. 236.

(6) Rangers are best *not* as hobbits, perhaps. But either Trotter (as a ranger) must be *not* a hobbit, or someone very well known: e.g. Bilbo. But the latter is awkward in view of 'happily ever after'. I thought of making Trotter into Fosco Took (Bilbo's first cousin) who vanished when a lad, owing to Gandalf. Who is Trotter? He must have had some bitter acquaintance with Ring-wraiths &c.

224   THE RETURN OF THE SHADOW

This note on Trotter is to be taken with Bingo's feeling that he had met Trotter before, and should be able to think of his true name (see p. 214). Bilbo's first cousin Fosco Took has not been mentioned before; possibly he was to be the son of Bilbo's aunt Rosa Baggins, who married a Took, according to the little genealogical table described above (p. 222). The ascription of Fosco Took's vanishing to Gandalf looks back to the beginning of *The Hobbit*, where Bilbo says to him: 'Not the Gandalf who was responsible for so many quiet lads and lasses going off into the Blue for mad adventures?'

There is here the first suggestion that my father, in his pondering of the mystery of Trotter, saw the possibility of his not being a hobbit. But this note, like several of the others, is elliptically expressed. The meaning is, I think: If rangers are not hobbits, then Trotter is not; but if nonetheless he *is* both, he must be a hobbit very well known.

(7) Bingo must NOT put on his Ring when Black Riders go by – in view of later developments. He must *think* of doing so but somehow be prevented. Each time the temptation must grow stronger.

This refers to the original second chapter, pp. 54, 58. For the ways in which in the later story Frodo was prevented from putting on the Ring see FR pp. 84, 88. 'Later developments' refers of course to the evolution of the concept of the Ring that had by now supervened: the Riders could see the Ringbearer, as he could see them, when he put it on his finger. The temptation to do so arose from the Ring-wraiths' power to communicate their command to the Ringbearer and make it appear to him that it was his own urgent desire (see p. 199); but Bingo must not be allowed to surrender to the temptation until the disaster in the dell under Weathertop.

(8) Some reason for Gandalf's uneasiness and the flight of Bingo which does not include Black Riders must be found. Gandalf knew of their existence (of course), but had no idea they were out yet. But Gandalf might give some kind of warning against use of Ring (after he leaves Shire?). Perhaps the idea of suddenly using Ring at party as a final joke should be a Bingoism, and contrary to Gandalf (not approved, as in my foreword).

The 'foreword' referred to here is the text given on pp. 76 ff., earliest form of FR Chapter 2 'The Shadow of the Past', – where indeed Gandalf does not merely 'approve' the idea, but actually suggests it (p. 84).

As regards the first sentence of this note, in the 'foreword' there is a reference to 'certain strange signs and portents of trouble brewing after a long time of peace and quiet', but there is no indication of what they were (p. 85 note 9). In the same text Gandalf says that 'Gollum is very likely the beginning of our present trouble'; but if 'our present trouble' was the fact that the Dark Lord was known to Gandalf to be seeking the only

'QUERIES AND ALTERATIONS' 225

missing Ring in the direction of the Shire, it is in no way explained how he knew this. This was a very serious problem in the narrative structure: Gandalf cannot know of the coming of the Ring-wraiths, for if he had he would never have allowed Bingo and his companions to set off alone. The solution would require complex restructuring of parts of the opening narrative as it now stood, in respect of Gandalf's movements in the summer of that year (these in turn involved with the changed story of the Birthday Party); and would ultimately lead to Isengard.

(9)   Why was Gandalf hurrying? Because Dark Lord knew of *him* and hated him. He had to get quick to Rivendell, and thought he was drawing pursuit off Bingo. Also he knew there was a council called at Rivendell for mid-September (Glóin &c. coming to see Bilbo?). It was postponed when the news of the Black Riders reached Rivendell and was not held till Bingo arrived.

For the idea that Gandalf was attempting to draw off the pursuit of the Black Riders see p. 173 note 8; cf. also his words to Bingo at Rivendell (p. 211): 'But things are moving fast, even faster than I feared. I *had* to get here quickly. But if I had known the Riders were already out!'
    This is probably the point at which the idea of the Council of Elrond arose, though there have been previous mentions of a 'consultation' with Elrond when the hobbits reached Rivendell (pp. 126, 214).

(10)   Should the Elves have Necromancer-rings? See note about their 'being in both worlds'. But perhaps only the High Elves of the West? Also perhaps Elves – if corrupted – would use rings differently: normally they were *visible in both worlds* all the time and equally with a ring they could appear *only in one* if they chose.

In the earliest statement about Elves and the Rings (p. 75) it is said that 'the Elves had many, and there are now many elfwraiths in the world, but the Ring-lord cannot rule them'; this was repeated exactly in the 'foreword' (p. 78), but without the words 'but the Ring-lord cannot rule them.' I have found no 'note' about the Elves 'being in both worlds', but my father may have been referring to Gandalf's words in the last chapter (p. 212): '[The Elves of Rivendell] fear no Ring-wraiths, for they live at once in both worlds, and each world has only half power over them, while they have double power over both.' With his remark here 'But perhaps only the High Elves of the West [are in both worlds]?' cf. the final form of this same passage in FR (p. 235): 'They do not fear the Ringwraiths, for *those who have dwelt in the Blessed Realm live at once in both worlds*, and against both the Seen and the Unseen they have great power.'

(11)   At Rivendell Bilbo must be seen by Bingo &c.
       Sleeping – in retirement?
       Shadows gathering in the South. Lord of Dale is suspected of being secretly corrupted. Strange men are seen in Dale?

226   THE RETURN OF THE SHADOW

What happened to Balin, Ori, and Óin? They went out to colonize
– being told of rich hills in the South. But after a time no word was
heard of them. Dáin feared the Dark Lord – rumour of his
movements reached him. (One idea was that dwarves need *a Ring*
as foundation of their hoard, and either Balin or Dáin sent to
Bilbo to discover what had become of it. The dwarves might have
received threatening messages from Mordor – for the Lord suspected that the One Ring was in their hoards.)

The thought that Trotter was really Bilbo is obviously not present here;
and cf the early outline given on p. 126: 'At Rivendell *sleeping Bilbo*'.

An isolated note elsewhere* says: 'Glóin has come to see Bilbo. News
of the world. Loss of the colony of Balin &c.' But the 'rich hills in the
South' in note (11) are probably the first appearance of the idea of Moria,
deriving from *The Hobbit* – though the absence of the name here might
suggest that the identification had not yet been made. Cf. also the notes at
the end of the abandoned first draft of the last chapter (p. 210): 'What of
Balin etc. They went to colonize (Ring needed to found colony?). In the
earliest account of the Rings (p. 75) it was said that the Dwarves
probably had none ('some say the rings don't work on them: they are too
solid'); but in the 'foreword' (p. 78) Gandalf tells Bingo that the Dwarves
were said to have had seven, 'but nothing could make them invisible. In
them it only kindled to flames the fire of greed, and the foundation of
each of the seven hoards of the Dwarves of old was a golden ring.'

Above the words *One Ring* at the end of note (11) my father wrote
missing. He may therefore have meant only 'the one missing Ring', but
the fact that he used capital letters suggests its great importance – and in
the 'foreword' the missing Ring is the 'most precious and potent of his
Rings' (pp. 81, 87).

(12)   Bilbo's ring proved to be the *one missing Ring* – all others had
        come back to Mordor: but this one had been lost.
        Make it taken from the Lord himself when Gilgalad wrestled with
        him, and taken by a flying Elf. It was more powerful than all the
        other rings. Why did the Dark Lord desire it so?

That Bilbo's Ring was the one missing Ring, and that it was the most
potent of them all, is (as just noted) stated in the 'foreword' – the first
sentence of note (12) is the restatement of an existing idea. What is new is
the linking up of its earlier history to Gil-galad's wrestling with the
Necromancer (see p. 216); in the 'foreword' (p. 78) Gollum's Ring had
fallen 'from the hand of an elf as he swam across a river; and it betrayed
him, for he was flying from pursuit in the old wars, and he became visible

---

*This note was in fact written in ink across the faint pencilled outline for the
story of the Barrow-wight (p. 125), and is presumably a thought that came to my
father while he was thinking about the story of the arrival in Rivendell which
comes at the end of this outline (p. 126).

'QUERIES AND ALTERATIONS' 227

to his enemies, and the goblins slew him.' This is where the story of Isildur began; but now the Elf (later to become Isildur the Númenórean) has it from Gil-galad, who took it from the Dark Lord. And the question is asked: 'Why did the Dark Lord desire it so?' Which means, since it is already conceived to be the most potent of the Rings and therefore self-evidently a chief object of the Dark Lord's desire, 'In what did its potency consist?'*

Subsequently my father pencilled rapid additions to the note. He marked the words 'all others had come back to Mordor' for rejection; and to the words 'It was more powerful than all the other rings' he added:

> though its power depended on the user – and its danger: the simpler the user and the less he used it. To Gollum it just helped him to hunt (but made him wretched). To Bilbo it was useful, but drove him wandering again. To Bingo as Bilbo. Gandalf could have trebled his power – but he dare not use it (not after he found out all about it). An Elf would have grown nearly as mighty as the Lord, but would have become dark.

At this time also he underlined the words 'Why did the Dark Lord desire it so?', put an exclamation mark against them, and wrote:

> Because if he had it he could see where all the others were, and would be master of their masters – control all the dwarf-hoards, and the dragons, and know the secrets of the Elf-kings, and the secret [?plans] of evil men.

Here the central idea of the Ruling Ring is clearly present at last, and it may be that it was here that it first emerged. But the note in ink and the pencilled addition (a faint scribble now only just legible) were obviously written at different times.

On the reverse of the second page of these notes is the following in pencil:

(13)   Simpler Story.

Bilbo disappears on his 100th [*written above:* 111] Birthday

---

*Humphrey Carpenter (*Biography*, p. 188) cites this note, but interprets it to be the moment at which the idea of the Ruling Ring emerged:

> There was also the problem of why the Ring seemed so important to everyone – this had not yet been established clearly. Suddenly an idea occurred to him, and he wrote: 'Bilbo's ring proved to be the *one ruling Ring* – all others had come back to Mordor: but this one had been lost.' The one ruling ring that controlled all the others . . .

But the note in question most certainly says 'Bilbo's ring proved to be the *one missing Ring*' (as the following words show in any case), not 'the *one ruling Ring*'. There would be no need to ask 'Why did the Dark Lord desire it so?' if the conception of the Ruling Ring emerged here.

228   THE RETURN OF THE SHADOW

> party. Bingo is his heir – much to the annoyance of the Sackville-
> Bagginses.
> ['If you want to know what lay behind these mysterious events
> we must go back a month or two.' Then have a conversation of
> Bilbo and Gandalf.]
> The talk dies down; and Gandalf is seldom seen again in
> Hobbiton.
> Next chapter begins with Bingo's life. Gandalf's furtive visits.
> Conversation. Bingo is bored by Shire (ring-restlessness?): and
> makes up his mind to go and look for Bilbo. Also he has been
> rather reckless and the money is running out. So he sells Bag-
> end to the Sackville-Bagginses who thus get it 90 years too late,
> pockets the money, and goes off when 72 (144) – same tendency
> to longevity as Bilbo had had. Gandalf encourages him for
> reasons of his own. But warns him not to use the Ring outside
> the Shire – if he can help it [cf. note (8)]. Bilbo used it for a last
> big jest, but you had better not. (Bingo does not tell Gandalf
> that looking for Bilbo was his motive).

All this was subsequently struck through; and the passage which is here
enclosed in square brackets was struck out separately, perhaps at the time
of writing.

The narrative structure in its principal relations is now that of the final
story:

> Bilbo disappears (putting on the Ring) at his 111th birthday party, and
> leaves Bingo as his heir.
> Years after, Gandalf talks to Bingo at Bag End; Bingo is anxious to
> leave for his own reasons, and Gandalf encourages him to go (but
> apparently without telling him much, though he warns him against
> using the Ring).

Although the Party now reverts to Bilbo, and is held on his 111th
birthday – his age when he departed out of the Shire in the existing
version of 'A Long-expected Party' (p. 40), Bingo still leaves at the age of
72 – his age when it was he who gave the Party. The bracketed figure 144
is presumably Bilbo's age at the time, as in the existing version, from
which it follows that at the time of Bilbo's Farewell Party Bingo was 39;
the total of their two ages was 150. But what my father had in mind on
this point cannot be said, for he never wrote the story in this form.

The bracketed passage suggests that some account would be given, in a
conversation between Bilbo and Gandalf a month or two *before* the party,
of what had led up to Bilbo's decision to leave the Shire in this way; and
this account would *follow* the opening chapter describing the festivity.
What this conversation would be about is suggested by another note,
doubtless written at the same time:

> Place 'Gollum' chapter after 'Long-expected party': with a heading: 'If

'QUERIES AND ALTERATIONS'

you want to know what lay behind these mysterious events, we must go back a month or two.'

This presumably means that my father was thinking of making the conversation between Bilbo and Gandalf before the Party (but standing in the narrative after it) cover the story of Gollum and the Ring. The 'Gollum chapter' would thus be in its final place, though the context here suggested for it would be entirely changed.

Lastly, a scribbled note reads:

(14)   Bilbo carries off 'memoirs' to Rivendell.

THE SECOND PHASE

XIV
RETURN TO HOBBITON

My father now settled at last for the 'simpler story' which he had roughed out in the *Queries and Alterations* (note 13); and so the Birthday Party at Bag End returns again to Bilbo, with whom it had begun (pp. 13, 19, 40). The following rough outline no doubt immediately preceded the rewriting of the opening chapter: the fifth version, and an exceedingly complicated document.

Bilbo disappears on his 111th birthday. 'Long-expected Party' chapter[1] suitably altered up to point where Gandalf disappears into Bag-End. Then a short conversation between Gandalf and Bilbo inside.
Bilbo says it is becoming wearisome – stretched feeling. He must get rid of it. Also he is tired of Hobbiton, he feels a great desire to go away. Dragon gold curse? or Ring. Where are you going? I don't know. Take care! I don't care. He gets Gandalf to promise to hand on Ring to his heir Bingo. He leaves it to him – but I don't want him to worry or to try and follow: not yet. So he does not even tell Bingo of the joke. At end of chapter make Bilbo say goodbye to Gandalf at gate, hand him a package (with Ring) for Bingo, and disappear.
Chapter II is then Bingo. Furtive visits of Gandalf. Gandalf urges him to go off – for reasons of his own. Bingo on his side never tells Gandalf that looking for Bilbo is his great desire. Gandalf does not [?tell ?talk] of the Ring. The Gollum business must come in later (at Rivendell) – after Bingo has met Bilbo; and Gandalf has now found out much more. It will probably be necessary to run this Chapter II on to head of present II 'Two's company – and three's more'.[2]

The fourth version of 'A Long-expected Party' had in fact reached quite an advanced stage in most respects – in some respects virtually the final form; but the Party was Bingo's on his 72nd birthday, Bilbo having quietly disappeared out of the Shire for good thirty-three years before, when he was 111 and Bingo was 39, and apart from providing the fireworks Gandalf played no part in the chapter at all.
The outline just given says that the chapter must be 'suitably altered up to the point where Gandalf disappears into Bag-End', and the story

234   THE RETURN OF THE SHADOW

now begins: 'When Bilbo Baggins of the well-known Hobbiton family prepared to celebrate his one-hundred-and-eleventh (or eleventy-first) birthday, there was some talk in the neighbourhood,' etc. (see pp. 28, 36). The fourth version is then followed[3] as far as 'And if he was in, you never knew who you would find with him: hobbits of quite poor families, or folk from distant villages, dwarves, and even sometimes elves' (p. 36); here a new passage concerning Gandalf and Bilbo was introduced.

Gandalf the wizard, too, was sometimes seen going up the hill. People said Gandalf 'encouraged' him, and accused him in turn of 'encouraging' some of his more lively nephews (and removed cousins), especially on the Took side; but what exactly they meant was not clear. They may have been referring to the mysterious absences from home, and to the strange habit Bilbo and his encouraged young friends had of walking all over the Shire in untidy clothes.

As time wore on the prolonged vigour, not to say youthfulness, of Mr Bilbo Baggins also became the subject of comment. At ninety he seemed much the same as ever he had been. At 99 they began to call him 'well-preserved'; but 'unchanged' would have been nearer the mark. Nevertheless he surprised them all that year by making a considerable change in his habits: he adopted as his heir his favourite and most completely 'encouraged' nephew, Bingo. Bingo Baggins was then a mere lad of 27,[4] and was strictly speaking not Bilbo's nephew (a title he used rather loosely), but both his first and his second cousin, once removed in each case,[5] but he happened to have the same birthday, September 22, as Bilbo, which seemed an additional link between them.[6] He was the son of poor Primula Brandybuck and [> who married late and as last resort] Drogo Baggins (Bilbo's second cousin but otherwise quite unimportant).

In *Queries and Alterations*, note 2, my father had said that he was 'too used to Bingo' to change his name to Frodo, but he was now following up the suggestions in that note that *Bolger-Baggins* ('a bad name') should be got rid of, and that Bingo should be a Baggins in his own right. Later in this passage Drogo takes over the rumoured boating accident on the Brandywine from Rollo Bolger (see p. 37): 'some said that Drogo Baggins had died of over-eating while staying with the old gormandizer Gorboduc; others said that it was his weight that had sunk the boat.' It is now told that Bingo was twelve years old at the time, and that he

afterwards lived mostly with his grandfather [Gorboduc Brandybuck, p. 37] and his mother's hundred and one relatives in the Great Hole of Bucklebury,[7] the ancestral and very overcrowded

RETURN TO HOBBITON 235

residence of the gregarious Brandybucks. But his visits to 'Uncle' Bilbo became more and more frequent, until at last, as has been said, Bilbo adopted him, when he was a lad of 27.

But all that was old history. People had become in the last 12 years used to having Bingo about. Neither Bilbo nor Bingo did anything outrageous. Their parties were sometimes a bit noisy (and not too select), perhaps; but hobbits don't mind that kind of noise now and again. Bilbo – now in his turn 'encouraged' by Bingo – spent his money freely, and his wealth became a local legend. It was popularly believed that most of the Hill was full of tunnels stuffed with gold and silver. Now it was suddenly given out that Bilbo, perhaps struck with the curiosity of the number 111, was planning to give something quite unusual in the way of birthday-parties. 111 was a respectable age even for hobbits.[8] Naturally tongues wagged, and old memories were stirred, and new expectations aroused. Bilbo's wealth was guessed afresh . . . (*etc. as before, see p. 30*).

In the account of the comings and goings at Bag End there are a few slight changes. The Men and the waggon painted with a D (pp. 20, 30) have been removed, as proposed in *Queries and Alterations* (note 1), but Elves as well as Dwarves are still mentioned. The bundles of fireworks were labelled not only with a big red G but also with ⚡ – 'That was Gandalf's mark' (the same rune appears in his letter at Bree and in his note left on Weathertop). The disappointed children given pennies but no fireworks are introduced (FR p. 33); and now at last appears the 'short conversation between Gandalf and Bilbo inside Bag-End' sketched in the outline on p. 233.

Inside Bag-End Bilbo and Gandalf were sitting at the open window of the sitting-room looking west onto the garden. The late afternoon was bright and peaceful; the flowers were red and golden; snapdragons, and sunflowers, and nasturtians trailing all over the turf walls and peeping in at the windows.

'How bright your garden is!' said Gandalf.

'Yes,' said Bilbo. 'I am very fond indeed of it, and of all the dear old Shire; but I think the time has come.'

'You mean to go on with your plan then?' asked Gandalf.

'Yes, I do,' Bilbo answered. 'I have made up my mind at last. I really must get rid of It.[9] "Well-preserved" indeed!' he snorted. 'Why, I feel all thin – sort of stretched, if you know what I mean: like a string that won't quite go round the parcel, or – or – butter that is scraped over too much bread. And that can't be right.'

'No!' said Gandalf thoughtfully. 'No. I daresay your plan is the

236   THE RETURN OF THE SHADOW

best, at any rate for you. At least at present I know nothing against it, and can think of nothing better.'

'Yes, I suppose it may seem a bit hard on Bingo,' said Bilbo. 'But what can I do? I can't destroy it, and after what you have told me I am not going to throw it away; but I don't want it, in fact I can't abide it any more. But you did promise me, didn't you, to keep an eye on him, and help him if he needs it later on? Otherwise, of course, I should have to.'

'I will do what I can for him,' said Gandalf. 'But I hope you will take care of yourself.'

'Take care! I don't care!' said Bilbo, and then going suddenly into verse (as was becoming his habit more and more) he went on in a low voice looking out of the window with a far-away look in his eyes:

The Road etc. as II.5

(This is a reference to the typescript of 'Three's Company', p. 53). All of this new passage, from the words 'I really must get rid of It', was struck out in pencil and marked 'Later' (see pp. 237 and 239–40).

The text continues: 'More carts rolled up the Hill next day, and still more carts. There might have been some grumbling about "dealing locally",' etc. (p. 20). From this point in the fourth version (essentially the same as the third and second, pp. 31, 38, and as FR) the fifth of course very largely follows the old drafts, 'Bingo' being changed to 'Bilbo' where necessary. To the guests at the select dinner party are now added members of the families of Gawkroger[10] (Goodbody in FR) and Brockhouse: the latter 'did not live in the Shire at all, but in Combe-under-Bree, a village on the Eastern Road beyond Brandywine. They were supposed to be remotely connected with the Tooks, but were also friends Bilbo had made in the course of his travels.' On this see *Queries and Alterations* note 5, and my comment on it; cf. also the original Chapter VII (p. 137), of the hobbits at *The Prancing Pony*: 'there were also some (to hobbits) natural names like Banks, Longholes, Brockhouse . . . which were not unknown among the more rustic inhabitants of the Shire.'

A curious point is that at this stage there were 'eight score or one hundred and sixty' guests at the dinner party in the pavilion under the tree, not 144; and in his speech Bilbo said: 'For it is of course also the birthday of my heir and nephew, Bingo. Together we score one hundred and sixty. Your numbers were chosen to fit this remarkable total.' Emendations to the preceding part of the chapter relate to this: Bingo's age at his adoption was changed from 27 to 37, so that when Bilbo was 111 (twelve years later) Bingo was 49 – totalling 160. My father had of course decided – the party being Bilbo's, and both he and Bingo being present – that the significance of the number of guests must now relate, not as previously to the elder hobbit's years, but to the total of their

RETURN TO HOBBITON

237

combined ages; but why he did not stick to 144 and reduce Bingo's age accordingly to 144 minus 111 I cannot say.

Bilbo now refers to its being the anniversary of his arrival by barrel at Lake-town; but there is still no flash when he stepped down and vanished.

This part of the text was soon revised – indeed before the story had gone much further,[11] and in a rewritten version of Bilbo's speech the number of guests reverts to 144, Bingo becomes 33 (which is the year of his 'coming of age'), and there is a blinding flash of light when he vanishes. Emendation to the earlier part of the text now changed Bingo's age at adoption once more, and finally, to 21.

In the hubbub that followed Bilbo's disappearance

there was one person harder hit than all the rest: and that was Bingo. He sat for some time quite silent in his seat beside the empty chair of his uncle, ignoring all remarks and questions; and then abandoning the party to look after itself he slipped out of the pavilion unnoticed.[12]

'What do we do now?' This question became more and more popular, and louder and louder. Suddenly old Rory Brandybuck, whose wits neither old age, nor surprise, nor an enormous dinner, had quite clouded was heard to shout: 'I never saw him go. Where is he now, anyway? Where is Bilbo – and Bingo, too, confound him?' There was no sign of their hosts, anywhere.

As a matter of fact, Bilbo Baggins, even while he was making his speech, had been fingering a small ring in his pocket: his magic ring, that he had kept secret for so many years. As he stepped down he slipped it on – and was never seen in Hobbiton again.

There now enters a wholly new element in the narrative, and it was clearly at this time that the passage of conversation between Gandalf and Bilbo inside Bag End before the party was largely struck out and marked 'Later' (pp. 235–6); at this time also that that conversation was re-extended from the point where Bilbo says 'Yes, I do. I have made up my mind at last', as follows (cf. FR pp. 33–4):

'Very well,' said Gandalf. 'I can see you mean to have your own way. I hope it will turn out all right – for all of us.'

'I hope so,' said Bilbo. 'Anyway I mean to enjoy myself on Thursday, and have my little joke in my own way.'

'Well, I hope you will still be laughing this time next year,' said Gandalf.

'And I hope you will, too,' retorted Bilbo.

The new version continues (from 'and was never seen in Hobbiton again'):

238   THE RETURN OF THE SHADOW

He walked briskly back to his hole, and stood listening with a smile for a moment to the sounds of merrymaking going on in various parts of the field. Then he went in. He took off his party clothes, folded up and wrapped in tissue paper his embroidered waistcoat with the silk [> gold] buttons and put it away. Then he put on some old and untidy garments,[13] and from a locked bottom drawer (reeking of mothballs) he got out an old cloak and an old hood that seemed to have been laid up as carefully as if they were very precious, though they were so weatherstained and mended that their original colour (probably dark green) could hardly be guessed. They were rather too big for him. He put a large bulky envelope on the mantelpiece, on which was written BINGO.

He chose his favourite thick stick from the hall stand, and then whistled. Several dwarves appeared from various rooms where they had been busy.

'Is everything ready?' Bilbo asked. 'Everything packed up [*added:* and labelled]?'

'Everything,' they said.

'Well, let's start then. Lofar, you are stopping behind, of course [*added:* for Gandalf]: please make sure that Bingo gets the letter on the dining room mantelpiece as soon as he comes in. Nar, Anar, Hannar, are you ready?[14] Right. Off we go.'

He stepped out of the front door. It was a fine clear night, and the black sky was full of stars. He looked up, sniffing the air. 'What fun!' he said. 'What fun to be off again – on the Road with dwarves: this is what I have really been longing for for years.' He waved his hand to the door: 'Goodbye,' he said. He turned away from the lights and voices in the field and the tents, and followed by his three companions went round to the garden on the west side of Bag-End, and trotted down the long sloping path. They jumped the low place in the hedge at the bottom and took to the meadows, passing like a rustle in the grasses.

At the bottom of the Hill they came to a gate opening on to a narrow lane. As they climbed over, a dark figure in a tall hat rose up from under the hedge.

'Hullo, Gandalf!' cried Bilbo. 'I wondered if you would turn up.'

'And I wondered if *you* would,' replied the wizard; 'or if you would think better of it.[15] I suppose you feel that everything has gone off splendidly, and just as you intended?'

'Yes,' said Bilbo. 'Though that flash was surprising: it quite

RETURN TO HOBBITON

239

startled *me*, let alone the others. A little addition of yours, I suppose?'

'It was,' answered Gandalf. 'You have wisely kept that Ring secret all these years; and it seemed to me necessary to give them all some reason to explain their not noticing your sudden vanishment [> to give them all something they would think explained your sudden vanishment].'

'You are an interfering old busybody,' laughed Bilbo; 'but I expect you know best, as usual.'

'I do,' said Gandalf, 'when I know anything. But I do not feel too sure about the whole affair. Still, it has now come to the final point. You have had your joke, and successfully alarmed or offended all your friends and relations, and given the whole Shire something to talk about for nine days (or ninety-nine more likely). Are you going to go any further?'

'Yes, I am,' answered Bilbo.[16] 'I really must get rid of It, Gandalf. *Well-preserved*, indeed,' he snorted. 'Why, I feel all thin – sort of stretched, if you know what I mean: like string that won't quite go round a parcel, or, or, butter that is scraped over too much bread. And that can't be right.'

'No,' said Gandalf thoughtfully. 'No. I was afraid it might come to that. I dare say your plan is the best, at any rate for you. At least at present I do not feel I know enough to say anything definite against it.'

'What else can I do? I can't destroy the thing, and after what you have told me I am not going to throw it away. Oddly enough I find that impossible to make up my mind to do – I simply put it back in my pocket. I find it very hard even to leave behind! And yet I don't want it, indeed I can't abide it any more. But you did promise to keep an eye on Bingo, didn't you, and to help him if he needs it, later on? Otherwise, of course, I should hardly be able to go. I should have to stop and put up with it.'

'I will do what I can for him,' said Gandalf. 'What have you done with it meanwhile?'

'It is in the envelope with my will and other papers. Lofar is giving it to Bingo as soon as he comes in.'

'My dear Bilbo! And with Otho Sackville-Baggins about the place, and that Lobelia wife of his! Really you *are* getting reckless. And I suppose you left the door unlocked as usual?'

'Yes, I am afraid I did. I rather fancy Bingo will be creeping off home before anyone else.'

240   THE RETURN OF THE SHADOW

'Fancy is not safe enough! But you may be right. He knows about it, of course?'

'He knows that I have, or had, the Ring: he has read my private memoirs,[17] for one thing; and he also has some idea [> he may have an inkling] that it has some other – er – effects than just making you invisible on occasion. But he doesn't, or didn't, know quite what I was beginning to feel about it. But after all, as it cannot be destroyed, and can only be handed on – it had best be handed on to him: I chose him as the best in all the Shire: and he is my heir. He knows that I am leaving that to him with all the rest. I don't suppose he would ask to be excused this responsibility, and take only the money.'

'He will miss you pretty badly, you know?'

'Yes, I found it very hard to make up my mind. It is hard on him – but not too hard, I think. The time has come for him to be his own master. After all, if things had been more – er – normal, he would have been losing me soon anyway, if he had not already done so. I am sorry to cheat all my dear people of a grand funeral – how they all did enjoy Old Took's – but there it is.'

'Does he know where you are going?'

'No! I am not sure myself, really. And I think that is just as well for everybody. He might want to *follow* me.'

'So might I. I hope you will take care of yourself!'

'Take care! I don't care. And don't be unhappy about me: I am as happy as ever I have been, and that is saying a lot. But the time has come. I am being swept off my feet,' he added mysteriously, and then in a low voice as if to himself he sang softly in the darkness.

> *The Road goes ever on and on*
>   *Down from the Door where it began.*
> *Now far ahead the Road has gone,*
>   *And I must follow if I can,*
> *Pursuing it with weary feet,*
>   *Until it joins some larger way,*
> *Where many paths and errands meet.*
>   *And whither then? I cannot say.*[18]

He stopped silent a moment. Then 'Goodbye, Gandalf!' he cried, and made off into the night. Nar, Anar, and Hannar followed him.[19] Gandalf remained by the gate for a little, and then sprang over it and made his way up the Hill.[20]

RETURN TO HOBBITON   241

It will be seen that in this passage, far different from that which occupies the same narrative place in FR pp. 40–4, my father was thinking about the effect of the Ring on its possessor on very much the same lines as in the chapter on Gollum (the 'foreword'), pp. 79–80. Moreover in FR the conversation – and quarrel – between Bilbo and Gandalf takes place in Bag End, so that the elements in the present version of Gandalf's anxiety about the Ring, left unguarded in an envelope at Bag End, and his going up the Hill to find Bingo, do not arise; Gandalf was sitting there waiting for him when he came in.

The clearing up of the party follows the earlier version, of course (FR p. 45); but the end of the chapter exists in two variant forms, marked as such. One of the variants, very much longer than the other and preceding it, is itself heavily modified. To look at this first: the list of presents remains the same, with some further changes in the names.[21] With 'Of course, this was only a selection of the presents' the new text advances very close to the form in FR (pp. 46–7), with the reflections on the cluttered nature of hobbit-holes (on which Bingo had remarked: 'We soon shan't be able to sit down for stools or tell the time for clocks in Bag-End'), and the gifts to Gaffer Gamgee (but Bilbo's collection of magical toys, pp. 33, 38, still remains); the dozen bottles of Old Winyards go to Rory Brandybuck, and are said to come from 'the south Shire', not yet the Southfarthing.

From 'not a penny piece or a brass farthing was given away' there is a rejected text and a replacement, differing from each other chiefly in the arrangement of the elements. As written first, the Sackville-Bagginses are introduced immediately, demanding to see the will – which is given at length;[22] then follows the rumour that the entire contents of Bag End were being distributed, and 'in the middle of the commotion' Bingo finds Lobelia investigating, ejects the three young hobbits, and has a fight with Sancho Proudfoot;[23] and the passage concludes with 'The fact is that Bilbo's money had become a legend . . .' (FR p. 48).

In the replacement text the structure in FR (pp. 47-8) is reached, with the sole important difference that Merry's rôle is taken by the dwarf Lofar, who had stayed behind after Bilbo's departure (p. 238); and the only minor differences from FR are that Otho Sackville-Baggins is still a lawyer, the date of Bingo's entry into his inheritance is stated (midnight on 22 September), the witnessing of the will was by three hobbits of more than 33 years old, according to the custom, and the Sackville-Bagginses 'more than hinted that he or the wizard (or the pair of them together) were at the bottom of the whole business.' The exchange between Frodo and Merry on the subject of Lobelia's calling Frodo a Brandybuck is of course not present – Bingo merely 'shut the door behind her with a grimace.'

The short variant is very short, and was not adopted. The large crowd who arrived at Bag End on the morning after the party does no more than go away again when they see a notice on the gate saying: 'Mr Bilbo

242 THE RETURN OF THE SHADOW

Baggins has gone away. There is no further news. Unless your business is urgent, please do not knock or ring. Bingo Baggins.' The Sackville-Bagginses 'thought that their business was urgent. They knocked and rang several times.' Admitted by Lofar the Dwarf, the remainder of the passage is the same as in the (revised) long variant and FR – the interview between Bingo and the Sackville-Bagginses in the study, ending with Bingo's telling Lofar not to open the front door even against battering-rams (and omitting the mopping-up operations against the three young hobbits and Sancho Proudfoot). Thus the entire 'business' of the presents, and the invasion of Bag End, was in this variant removed. For my father's intention here see p.276.

The reappearance of Gandalf at Bag End now enters the story, and begins pretty well exactly as in FR (p.48), but soon significant differences enter the conversation, from the point where Gandalf says to Bingo 'What do you know already?' (FR p.49):

'Only Bilbo's tale of how he got it,[24] from that Gollum creature, and how he used it afterwards, on his journey I mean. I don't think he used it much after he came home; though he used to disappear (or not be findable) rather mysteriously sometimes, if things were a bit inconvenient. We saw the Sackville-Bagginses coming when we were out walking one day, and he disappeared, and came out from behind a hedge after they had gone by.[25] Being invisible has its advantages.'

'But it also has its disadvantages. It does not do much harm as a joke, nor even to avoid "inconveniences" – but even these things have to be paid for. Also making you invisible, when you wish, is not the only property of the Ring.'

'I know what you mean,' said Bingo; 'Bilbo did not seem to change much. They called him well-preserved. But I must say that also seems to me to have its advantages. I cannot make out why the dear old thing left the Ring behind.'

'No, I expect you cannot yet. But you may find out the disadvantages of that as well, in time. For instance, Bilbo seemed a bit restless of late years, didn't he?'

'Yes, for quite a long time,'

'Well, I think that was a symptom too. I don't want to alarm you, but I want you to be careful. Take care of the Ring, and take care of yourself, and watch yourself. Don't use the Ring,[26] or let it get any more, er, *power* over you than you can help. Keep it *secret*, and let me know, if you hear, see, or feel anything at all odd.'

'All right. But what is all this about?'

'I am not quite sure. I begin to guess, and I don't like the guesses. But I am now going off to find out as much as I can.

RETURN TO HOBBITON 243

Before I have done so, I am not going to say any more, except to warn you, and to promise you what help I can give.'

'But you say you are going off?'

'Yes, for a bit. But you'll be safe for a year or two, in any case. Don't worry. I shall come and see you again as soon as I can – quietly, you know. I don't think I shall be visiting the Shire openly again very much. I find I have become rather unpopular: they say I am a nuisance and a disturber of the peace; and some people are accusing me of spiriting Bilbo away. It is supposed to be a little plot between me and you (if you want to know).'

'That sounds like Otho and Lobelia.[27] How outrageous! I only wish I knew why and where old Bilbo has gone. Do you? Do you think I could catch him up or find him if I went off at once? I would give Bag-end and everything in it to the Sackville-Bagginses if I could do that.'

'I don't think I should try. Let poor Bilbo get rid of the Ring – which he could only do (reluctantly) by handing it on to you, for a bit.[28] Do what he wished and hoped you would.'

'What is that?'

'Live on here; keep up Bag-end; guard the Ring – and wait.'

'All right – I will try; but I should prefer to go after Bilbo.[29] I don't know if that is a symptom, as you call it – though I have only had the Ring a day or less?'

'No, not yet. It merely means you were fond of Bilbo. He knew it was hard on you. He hated leaving you. But there it is. We may all understand this better before the end. I must say goodbye now. Look out for me – at any time, especially unlikely ones. If you really need me send a message to the nearest dwarves: I shall try and give them some knowledge of where I am.[30] Goodbye!'

Bingo saw him off. The dwarf Lofar went with him carrying a large bag. They walked away down the path to the gate at a surprising pace,[31] but Bingo thought the wizard looked rather bent, almost as if bowed under a heavy burden. The evening was closing in, and he soon vanished into the twilight. Bingo did not see him again for a long time.

About this time my father wrote a new experimental opening to the chapter, in which the facts and assertions about the family history were communicated through the talk of Gaffer Gamgee, Old Noakes, and Sandyman the miller in *The Ivy Bush*. The mention of Sam Gamgee as the Bag End gardener shows that it was in fact written after the second chapter, 'Ancient History', which now follows; for if this text had been already in existence my father would not have given an explanation of

244   THE RETURN OF THE SHADOW

who Sam Gamgee was when he appears in 'Ancient History' (p. 253). But it is convenient to notice it here.

This version of the conversation had still a good way to go before it reached the form in FR (pp. 30–2). The opening of the chapter was now to be greatly compressed:

When Mr Bilbo Baggins of Bag-end, Under-hill, announced that he would shortly be celebrating his eleventy-first birthday with a party of special magnificence, there was much talk and excitement in Hobbiton. Before long rumour of the event travelled all over the Shire, and the history and character of Mr Baggins became once again the most popular topic of conversation. The older folk who remembered something of the strange happenings sixty years before found their reminiscences suddenly in demand, and rose to the gratifying occasion with entertaining invention when mere facts failed them.

No one had a more attentive audience than old Ham Gamgee, commonly known as the Gaffer. He held forth at the *Ivy Bush*,[32] a small inn on the Bywater Road; and he spoke with some authority, for he had tended the garden at Bag-end for half a century, and had helped his father in the same job before that. Now that he was grown old and creaky in the joints he had passed the job on to one of his own sons, Sam Gamgee.

The subject of Bingo is treated thus:

'And what about this Mr Bingo Baggins that lives with him?' asked old Noakes of Bywater.[33] 'I hear he is coming of age on the same day.'

'That's right,' said the Gaffer. 'He has the same birthday as Mr Bilbo, September the twenty-second. It is a sort of link between them, as you might say. Not but what they get on remarkably well, and have done all the last twelve years, since Mr Bingo came to Bag-end. Very much alike in every way, they are, being closely related. Though Mr Bingo is half a Brandybuck by rights, and that's a queer breed, as I've heard tell. They fool about with boats and water, and that isn't natural. Small wonder that trouble came of it, I say.'

For the rest, Mr Twofoot of Bagshot Row does not appear; Gorboduc Brandybuck is called by the Gaffer 'the head of the family, and mighty important down in Buckland, I'm told'; the miller does not suggest that there was anything more sinister in the drowning of Drogo Baggins and his wife than Drogo's weight; the hobbit who introduces the topic of the tunnels packed with treasure inside the Hill is not 'a visitor from Michel

RETURN TO HOBBITON 245

Delving' but 'one of the Bywater hobbits'; and there are many differences of phrasing.

NOTES

1 My father actually wrote '"Unex[pected]P[arty]" chapter' – thinking of the first chapter of *The Hobbit*. Cf. my suggestion about his use of the word 'sale' in *Queries and Alterations*, note 2.

2 The actual title of Chapter II was 'Three's Company and Four's More' (p. 49). – A pencilled note on the same page says: 'Should Bingo spend all his money? Is it not better he should be sacrificing something? Though he must give out that he has spent it.'

3 The passage about Bilbo's book and the reception accorded to it, which had survived unchanged from the second version (p. 19), was at first repeated here, but subsequently replaced by the following:
He told many tales of his adventures, of course, to those who would listen. But most of the hobbits soon got tired of them, and only one or two of his younger friends ever took them seriously. It is no good telling ordinary hobbits about dragons: they either disbelieve you or want to disbelieve you, and in either case stop listening. As he grew older Bilbo wrote his adventures in a private book of memoirs, in which he recounted some things that he had never spoken about (such as the magic ring); but that book was never published in the Shire, and he never showed it to anyone, except his favourite 'nephew' Bingo.

4 This was Bingo's age at the time of his adoption in the fourth version (p. 36), but it was changed in the course of the writing of the present text (see p. 236).

5 In *Queries and Alterations* (note 2) the suggestion was that Drogo Baggins should be Bilbo's first cousin.

6 This remark about Bilbo and Bingo having the same birthday was a pencilled addition, but the idea goes back to the third version (p. 29),when Bingo was Bilbo's son.

7 *The Great Hole of Bucklebury:* Brandy Hall has been named and described in the original version of 'A Short Cut to Mushrooms' (p. 99).

8 Added in pencil:
and the Old Took himself had only reached the age of 125 (though the title Old was bestowed on him, it is true, not so much for his age as for his oddity, and because of the enormous number of the young, younger, and youngest Tooks).

9 This was to be the first, intentionally obscure, reference to the Ring in the story. With the shortening and alteration of this initial converation between Gandalf and Bilbo before the Party (p. 237) this reference was removed, and it is then first spoken of only after Bilbo's vanishment.

246   THE RETURN OF THE SHADOW

10   *Gawkroger* is an English (Yorkshire) surname, meaning 'clumsy Roger'.

11   The textual situation is in fact of fearful complexity in this part, the manuscript being constituted from two 'layers', and the earlier of the two being constituted partly from new manuscript and partly from the typescript of the fourth version. With the actual texts in front of one it can be worked out how my father was proceeding, but to present the detail in a printed book is neither possible nor necessary. It is demonstrable that the second 'layer', with revised dating of Bingo's life and the flash which accompanied Bilbo's vanishing, entered in the course of the composition of the chapter.

12   This perhaps suggests that Bingo had not been told of Bilbo's 'joke'; cf. the outline on p. 233: 'So he does not even tell Bingo of the joke.' A pencilled correction and addition changed the passage towards that in FR (p. 39).
    The only one who said nothing was Bingo, the most concerned. His feelings were mixed. On the one hand he appreciated the joke (if no one else did). It was quite after his own heart: he would have liked to laugh and dance with mirth; and was grateful that he had been allowed to get the full and delicious suspense, for on the other hand he would have liked to weep. He was immensely fond of Bilbo, and the blow was crushing. Was he really never to see him again – not even to take another farewell? He sat for some time quite silent in his seat . . .

13   Added later:
    and fastened on a leather belt round his waist. On it hung a short sword in an old black leather scabbard.
    Cf. *Queries and Alterations*, note 4, on the subject of Sting.

14   My father took all these four Dwarf-names from the same source in the Old Norse *Elder Edda* as those in *The Hobbit*.

15   Added later:
    But I want just a final word with you. Now, my good dwarves, just walk on down the lane a bit. I shan't keep you long!' He turned back to Bilbo. 'Well,' he said in a lowered voice.

16   From this point the earlier, rejected conversation between Bilbo and Gandalf before the Party (pp. 235–6, there marked 'Later') is taken up again, though not in the same form, and much extended.

17   A pencilled addition here probably says: '(the only one who has)'; see note 3.

18   This verse came into existence in the original form of the chapter 'Three is Company' (pp. 47, 53), where it will now become a recollection of Bilbo's verse from years before. The two versions are the same, except that in lines 4 and 8 Bilbo's form here has *I* for *we*. In FR (pp. 44, 82) both versions have *I*, not *we*; but Bilbo's has *eager* in the 5th line where Frodo's has *weary*. In the present text

RETURN TO HOBBITON   247

eager is written above *weary*, and with this change the final form is reached in this instance (see p. 284 note 10).

19   This sentence was struck out when the addition given in note 15 was made.

20   The remainder of this part of the text is in very rough pencilled form, with alteration of the last passage in ink preceding it:

'Goodbye, Gandalf!' he cried, and made off into the night. Gandalf remained by the gate for a moment, staring into the dark after him. '*Adieu*, my dear Bilbo,' he said, '— or *au revoir*.' [This was marked with an X: Gandalf would not use French, however useful the distinction.] And then he jumped over the low gate and made his way quickly up the Hill. 'If I find Lobelia sneaking round,' he muttered, 'I'll turn her into a weasel!'

But he need not have worried. At Bag-End he found Bingo sitting on a chair in the hall with the envelope in his hand. He refused to have any more to do with the party.

21   The umbrella now goes, not to Mungo Took, but to Uffo Took (Adelard Took in FR). Semolina Baggins becomes Drogo's sister, aged 92 (in FR she is Dora Baggins, aged 99). The feather-bed goes now not to Fosco Bolger (who had been Bingo's uncle when he was still a Bolger), but to Rollo Bolger (an equally suitable recipient), 'from his friend'; Rollo Bolger has survived his displacement from Primula Brandybuck's husband and death by drowning in the Brandywine. The 'rather florid' dinner-service goes to Primo (not Inigo) Grubb; and the Hornblower who received the barometer now changes from Cosimo (by way of Carambo) to Colombo. Caramella Chubb, Orlando Burrows (so spelt), Angelica Baggins, Hugo Bracegirdle, and of course Lobelia Sackville-Baggins, remain, and their gifts. For the earlier lists see pp. 15, 32–3, 38.

22   'This is how the will ran:

Bilbo (son of Bungo son of Mungo son of Inigo) Baggins hereinafter called the testator, now departing being the rightful owner of all properties and goods hereinafter named hereby devises, makes over, and bequeathes the property and messuage or dwelling-hole known as Bag-End Underhill near Hobbiton with all lands thereto belonging and annexed to his cousin and adopted heir Bingo (son of Drogo son of Togo son of Bingo son of Inigo) Baggins hereinafter called the heir, for him to have hold possess occupy let on lease sell or otherwise dispose of at his pleasure as from midnight of the twenty-second day of September in the one hundred and eleventh or eleventy-first year of the aforesaid Bilbo Baggins. Moreover the aforesaid testator devises and bequeathes to the aforesaid heir all monies in gold silver copper brass or tin and all trinkets, armours, weapons, uncoined metals, gems, jewels, or precious stones and all furniture appurtenances goods perishable or imperishable and chattels movable and immovable belonging to the testator and

THE RETURN OF THE SHADOW

after his departure found housed kept stored or secreted in any part of the said hole and residence of Bag-end or of the lands thereto annexed, save only such goods or movable chattels as are contained in the subjoined schedule which are selected and directed as parting gifts to the friends of the testator and which the heir shall dispatch deliver or hand over according to his convenience. The testator hereby relinquishes all rights or claims to all these properties lands monies goods or chattels and wishes all his friends farewell. Signed Bilbo Baggins.

Otho, who was a lawyer, read this document carefully, and snorted. It was apparently correct and incontestable, according to the legal notions of hobbits. "Foiled again!" he said to his wife . . .' (etc. as in FR p. 47).

23 'Old Proudfoot's son' (in FR 'old Odo Proudfoot's grandson', p. 48).

24 This sentence was extended in pencil as follows:

'Just what Bilbo's parting letter said: "Here's the Ring. Please accept it. Take care of it, and yourself. Ask Gandalf, if you want to know more." And of course I have read and heard Bilbo's tale of how he got it . . .'

25 This mention of Bilbo's disappearance when he saw the Sackville-Bagginses approaching was struck out in pencil, with the note 'Put in later'. See p. 300.

26 'Don't use the Ring' was struck out in pencil, with 'If you take my advice you will not use the Ring' substituted; and before the words 'Keep it *secret*' in the next sentence was added 'But have it by you always.'

27 In this version, Otho and Lobelia have as good as said this to Bingo (p. 241) – a passage not in FR.

28 This was rewritten in pencil: 'I don't think I should try. I don't think it would please or help Bilbo. Let him get rid of the Ring – which he can only do, if you will accept it, for a bit.'

29 This was rewritten in pencil: 'All right – I will try. But I want to follow Bilbo. I think I shall in the end, anyway, if it is not then too late ever to find him again.'

30 This sentence ('If you really need me . . .') was bracketed (in ink) for probable exclusion.

31 This was rewritten in pencil:

Bingo saw Gandalf to the door. There the dwarf Lofar was waiting. He popped up when the door was opened, and picked up a large bag that was standing in the porch. 'Goodbye, Bingo,' he said, bowing low. 'I am going with Gandalf.' 'Goodbye,' said Bingo. Gandalf gave a final wave of his hand, and with the dwarf at his side walked off down the path at a surprising pace . . .

At the end of the chapter my father wrote: 'Perhaps alter this – Gandalf *has ring*. Meeting at gate prearranged: ring handed over there. Gandalf's last visit is to give it to Bingo?' He struck this out and wrote 'No' against it. This had in fact been his idea when he wrote the outline given on p. 233, where Bilbo is to 'say goodbye to Gandalf at gate, hand him a package (with Ring) for Bingo, and disappear.'

32 *Ivy Bush:* changed at the time of writing from *Green Dragon*. See note 33.

33 *old Noakes of Bywater:* changed at the time of writing from *Ted Sandyman, the miller's son*. This is a further indication that this version of the opening of 'A Long-expected Party' followed 'Ancient History', where the miller's son was named Tom until the very end of it (p. 269, note 9). The conversation between Sam Gamgee and Ted Sandyman in 'Ancient History' was in *The Green Dragon* at Bywater, and my father probably changed the rendezvous of Gaffer Gamgee's cronies to *The Ivy Bush* (note 32) for the same reason as he replaced the miller's son by Old Noakes.

★

I give here as much of the genealogy of Bilbo and Bingo as is established from the text at this time. The Baggins ancestry is derived from Bilbo's will (note 22); the names in brackets are those that differ in LR Appendix C, *Baggins of Hobbiton*.

The Old Took was evidently already known to have had many children beside his 'three remarkable daughters' (see note 8).

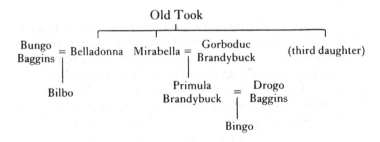

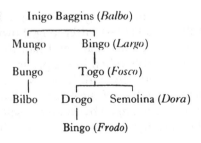

XV
ANCIENT HISTORY

A chapter titled 'II: Ancient History', precursor of 'The Shadow of the Past' in FR, was now introduced to follow 'A Long-expected Party'. It is of central importance in the evolution of *The Lord of the Rings*: for it was here that there emerged in the actual narrative the concept of the Ruling Ring, and Sam Gamgee as the companion of Bingo (Frodo) on his great journey. There is no trace of earlier drafting, save for a few notes so scrappy and disjointed that they can scarcely be reproduced. In these my father scribbled down salient features of Bingo's life after Bilbo's disappearance, and first devised the story of Bingo's own departure 17 years later, celebrated by a dinner party for Merry, Frodo, and Odo (here apparently said to have been given on the proceeds of the sale of Bag End). Against these notes my father wrote: 'Sam Gamgee to replace Odo' (cf. *Queries and Alterations*, p. 221).

The manuscript is rough, and in places very rough indeed, but legible virtually throughout. There is some emendation from a later phase, here ignored, and a good deal of pencilled change that can in some cases be seen to have been made while the chapter was in progress. These latter I adopt into the text, but in some cases refer in the notes to the text as first written.

The talk did not die down in nine or even ninety-nine days. The second and final disappearance of Mr Bilbo Baggins was discussed in Hobbiton and Bywater, and indeed all over the Shire, for a year and a day, and was remembered much longer than that. It became a fireside story for young hobbits; and eventually (a century or so later) Mad Baggins, who used to disappear with a bang and a flash and reappear with bags of gold and jewels, became a favourite character of legend and lived on long after all the true events were forgotten.

But in the meantime sober grown-ups gradually settled to the opinion that Bilbo had at last (after long showing symptoms of its coming on) gone suddenly mad, and had run off into the blue; where he had inevitably fallen into a pit or a pool, and come to a tragic but hardly untimely end. There was one Baggins the less and that was that.[1] In face of the evidence that this disappearance had been timed and arranged by Bilbo himself, Bingo was eventually relieved of suspicion. It was also plain that the departure of

ANCIENT HISTORY

Bilbo was a grief to him – more than to any other even of Bilbo's closest friends. But Gandalf was held finally responsible for inciting and encouraging 'poor old Mr Bilbo', for dark and unknown ends of his own.

'If only that wizard will leave young Bingo alone, perhaps he will settle down and grow some hobbit-sense,' they said. And to all appearances the wizard did leave Bingo alone, and he did settle down, though the growth of hobbit-sense was not so noticeable. Indeed Bingo at once carried on his uncle's reputation for oddity. He refused to go into mourning; and the next year he gave a party in honour of Bilbo's 112th birthday, which he called the Hundred-weight Party; although only a few friends were invited and they hardly ate a hundredweight between them. People were rather pained; but he kept up the custom of giving 'Bilbo's birthday party' year after year, until they got used to it. He said he did not think Bilbo was dead. When they asked: 'Where is he, then?' he shrugged his shoulders.[2] He lived alone, but he went about a lot with certain younger hobbits that Bilbo had been fond of, and continued to 'encourage' them. The chief of these were Meriadoc Brandybuck (usually called Merry), Frodo Took, and Odo Bolger.[3] Merry was the son of Caradoc Brandybuck (Bingo's cousin) and Yolanda Took, and so the cousin of Frodo, son of Folco (whose sister was Yolanda). Frodo, or Frodo the Second, was the great-great-grandson of Frodo the First (otherwise known as the Old Took), and the heir and rather desperate hope of the Hole of Took, as the clan was called. Odo also had a Took mother and was a third cousin of the other two.[4] With these Bingo went about (often in untidy clothes) and walked all over the Shire. He was often away from home. But he continued to spend his money lavishly, indeed more lavishly than Bilbo had. And there still seemed to be plenty of it, so naturally his oddities were overlooked, as far as possible. As time went on it is true that they began to notice that Bingo also showed signs of good 'preservation': outwardly he retained the appearance of a strong and rather large and well-built hobbit just out of his 'tweens'. 'Some people have all the luck,' they said, meaning this enviable combination of cash and preservation; but they did not attach any particular significance to it, not even when Bingo began to approach the more sober age of 50.

Bingo himself, after the first shock of loss and change, rather enjoyed being his own master, and *the* Mr Baggins of Bag-end.

252   THE RETURN OF THE SHADOW

For a while, indeed several years, he was very happy, and did not think much about the future. He knew, of course, if no one else did, that the money was not unlimited, and was fast disappearing. Money went a prodigious long way in those days, and one could also get many things without it; but Bilbo had made great inroads on his inheritance and his acquired treasures in the course of sixty years, and had blown at least 500 pieces of gold on that last Party.[5] So an end would come sooner or later. But Bingo did not worry: down inside though suppressed there still remained his desire to follow Bilbo, or at all events to leave the Shire and go off into the Blue, or wherever chance took him.

One day, he thought, he would do it. As he approached 50 – a number he somehow felt was significant (or ominous), it was at any rate at that age that adventure had first come upon Bilbo – he began to think more seriously of it. He felt restless. He used to look at maps and wonder what it was like beyond the edges: hobbit maps made in the Shire did not extend very far east or west of its borders. And he began to feel, sometimes, a sort of thin feeling, as if he was being stretched out over a lot of days, and weeks, and months, but was not fully there, somehow. He could not explain any better than that to Gandalf, though he tried to. Gandalf nodded thoughtfully.

Gandalf had taken to slipping in to see him again – quietly and secretly, and usually when no one was about. He would tap an agreed signal on the window or door, and be let in: it was usually dark when he arrived, and while he was there he did not go out. He went off again, often without warning, either at night or in the very early morning before sunrise. The only people besides Bingo who knew of these visits were Frodo and Merry; though no doubt folk out in the country caught sight of him going along the road or over the fields, and scratched their heads either trying to remember who he was, or wondering what he was doing.

Gandalf turned up again first about three years after Bilbo's departure, took a look at Bingo, listened to the small news of the Shire, and went off again soon, seeing that Bingo was still quite settled. But he returned once or twice every year (except for one other long gap of nearly two years) until the fourteenth year. Bingo was then 47. After that he came frequently and stayed longer.[6] He began to be worried about Bingo; and also odd things were happening. Rumour of them had begun to reach the ears of even the deafest and most parochial hobbits. Bingo had heard a good deal more than any other hobbit of the Shire, for of course he

ANCIENT HISTORY

253

continued Bilbo's habit of welcoming dwarves and odd strangers, and even occasionally of visiting elves. It was believed by his close friends Merry and Frodo at any rate that elves were friendly to him [*bracketed at the time of writing:* and that he knew some of their few haunts. This was in fact quite true. Bilbo had taught Bingo all that he knew, and had even instructed him in what he had learned of the two elf-languages used in those times and places (by the elves among themselves). There were very few elves actually in the Shire, and they were very seldom seen by anyone but Bilbo, and Bingo. *This was replaced at the time of writing by:*] and that he knew something of their secret languages – learned probably from Bilbo. And they were quite right.

Both elves and dwarves were troubled, especially those that occasionally arrived or passed by coming from a distance, from East or South. They would seldom, however, say anything very definite. But they constantly mentioned the Necromancer, or the [Dark Lord >] Enemy; and sometimes referred to the Land of Mor-dor and the Black Tower. It seemed that the Necromancer was moving again, and that Gandalf's confidence that the North would be freed from him for many an age had not been justified.[7] He had flown from Mirkwood only to reoccupy his ancient stronghold in the South, near the midst of the world in those days, in the Land of Mordor; and it was rumoured that the Black Tower had been raised anew. Already his power was creeping out over the lands again and the mountains and woods were darkened. Men were restless and moving North and West, and many seemed now to be partly or wholly under the dominion of the Dark Lord. There were wars, and there was much burning and ruin. The dwarves were growing afraid. Goblins were multiplying again and reappearing. Trolls of a new and most malevolent kind were abroad; giants were spoken of, a Big Folk only far bigger and stronger than Men the [?ordinary] Big Folk, and no stupider, indeed often full of cunning and wizardry. And there were vague hints of things or creatures more terrible than goblins, trolls, or giants. Elves were vanishing, or wandering steadily westward.

In Hobbiton there began to be some talk about the odd folk that were abroad, and often strayed over the borders. The following report of a conversation in the *Green Dragon* at Bywater one evening [about this time >] in the spring of Bingo's 49th? 50th? [*sic*] year[8] will give some idea of the feeling in the air.

Sam Gamgee (old Gaffer Gamgee's [eldest >] youngest and a good jobbing gardener) was sitting in one corner by the fire,

254   THE RETURN OF THE SHADOW

and opposite him was Ted Sandyman[9] the miller's son from Hobbiton; and there were various other rustic hobbits listening.

'Queer things you do hear these days, to be sure, Ted,' said Sam.

There follows in the manuscript the original draft, written very roughly and rapidly, of the conversation at *The Green Dragon* found in FR, pp. 53–5; and it was scarcely altered afterwards save in little details of phrasing. The hobbit who saw the Tree-man beyond the North Moors (in FR Sam's cousin Halfast Gamgee, who worked for Mr Boffin at Overhill) is here 'Jo Button, him that works for the Gawkrogers [see p. 236] and goes up North for the hunting.' Sam's reference to 'queer folk' being turned back by the Bounders on the Shire-borders is absent; he speaks of the Elves journeying to the harbours 'out away West, away beyond the Towers',[10] but the reference to the Grey Havens is lacking.

Most interesting is the reference to the Tree-men. As my father first wrote Sam's words, he said: 'But what about these what do you call 'em – giants? They do say as one nigh as big as a tower or leastways a tree was seen up away beyond the North Moors not long back.' This was changed at the time of writing to: 'But what about these Tree-Men, these here – giants? They do say one nigh as big as a tower was seen,' etc. (Was this passage (preserved in FR, p. 53) the first premonition of the Ents? But long before my father had referred to 'Tree-men' in connection with the voyages of Eärendel: II.254, 261).

Sam's words about the Bagginses at the end of the conversation are different (and explain why the egregious Ted Sandyman used the word 'cracked' in FR):

'Well, I dunno. But that Mr Baggins of Bag-End, he thinks it is true; he told me and my dad so; and both he and old Mr Bilbo know a bit about Elves, or so my dad says and he ought to know. He's known the Bag-End folk since he was a lad, and he worked in their gardens till his joints cracked too much for bending, and I took on.'

'And they're both cracked . . .'

After Ted Sandyman's last words,

Sam sat silent and said no more. He was due for a job of work in Bingo's garden next day, and was thinking he might have a chance of a word with Bingo, to whom he had transferred the reverence of his dad for old Bilbo. It was April and the sky was high and clear after much rain. The sun was gone, and a cool pallid sky was fading slowly. He went home through Hobbiton and up the hill whistling softly and thoughtfully.

ANCIENT HISTORY   255

About the same time Gandalf was quietly slipping in through the half-open front door of Bag-End.

Next morning after breakfast two people, Gandalf and Bingo, were sitting near the open window. A bright fire was on the hearth; but the sun was warm, and the wind was southerly: everything looked fresh, and the new green of Spring was shimmering in the fields and on the tips of the trees' fingers. Gandalf was thinking of a spring nearly 80 years before, when Bilbo had run out of Bag-end without a handkerchief. Gandalf's hair was perhaps whiter than it had been then, and his beard and eyebrows were perhaps longer and face wiser; but his eyes were no less bright and powerful, and he smoked and blew smoke-rings with as great vigour and delight as ever. He was smoking now in silence, for they had been talking about Bilbo (as they often did), and [other things >] the Necromancer and the Ring.

'It is all most disturbing, and in fact terrifying,' said Bingo. Gandalf grunted: the sound apparently meant 'I quite agree, but your remark is not helpful.' There was another silence. The sound of Sam Gamgee giving the lawn its first cut came from the garden.

'How long have you known all this?' asked Bingo at length. 'And did you tell Bilbo?'

'I guessed a good deal immediately,' answered Gandalf slowly . . .

My father had now returned to the text given on pp. 76 ff, the 'foreword' as he called it (see p. 224), which I have discussed on pp. 86–7, and in which of course the story was present that Bingo gave the Party: the conversation with Gandalf took place a few weeks before it, and it was indeed Gandalf's own idea. But my father followed parts of the old text closely, while extending it in certain very important ways.

In Gandalf's reply to Bingo's question (original text p. 77) he says:

'I guessed much, but at first I said little. I thought that all was well with Bilbo, and that he was safe enough, for that kind of power was powerless over him. So I thought, and I was right in a way; but not quite right. I kept an eye on him, of course, but perhaps I was not careful enough. I did not then know which of the many Rings this one was. Had I known I might have done differently – but perhaps not. But I know now.' His voice faded to a whisper. 'For I went back to the land of the Necromancer – twice.'[11]

'I am sure you have done everything you could,' said Bingo . . .

Gandalf says rather more about Bilbo: 'I was not greatly worried about Bilbo – his education was nearly complete, and I no longer felt respon-

256   THE RETURN OF THE SHADOW

sible for him. He had to follow his own mind, when he had made it up.'
And he speaks of the hobbits of the Shire being 'enslaved' (as in FR,
p. 58), not 'becoming Wraiths.'

But with Gandalf's reply to Bingo's 'I do not quite understand what all
this has got to do with me and Bilbo and the Ring' my father departed
altogether from the original text.

'To tell you the truth,' answered Gandalf, 'I believe he has
hitherto, *hitherto* mind you, entirely overlooked the existence of
hobbits – as Smaug the dragon had. For which you may be
thankful. And I don't think even now that he particularly wants
them: they would be obedient (perhaps), but not terribly useful
servants. But there is such a thing as malice and revenge. Miserable hobbits would please him more than happy ones. As for what
it has to do with you and the Ring: I think I can explain that –
partly at any rate. I do not yet know quite all. Give me the Ring a
minute.'

Bingo took it from his trouser pocket where it was clasped on a
chain that went round him like a belt. 'Good,' said Gandalf. 'I see
you keep it always on you. Go on doing so.' Bingo unclasped it and
handed it to Gandalf. It felt heavy, as if either it, or Bingo, were in
some curious way reluctant for Gandalf to touch it. It looked to be
made of pure and solid gold, thick, flattened, and unjointed.[12]
Gandalf held it up.

'Can you see any markings on it?' he said. 'No!' said Bingo. 'It is
quite plain, and does not even show any scratches or signs of
wear.'

'Well then, look,' said Gandalf, and to Bingo's astonishment
and distress the wizard threw it into the middle of a hot patch in
the fire. Bingo gave a cry and groped for the poker; but Gandalf
held him back. 'Wait!' he said in commanding tones, giving Bingo
a quick look from under his eyebrows.

No apparent change came over the Ring. After a while Gandalf
got up, closed the shutters outside the round window, and drew
the curtain. The room became dark and silent. The clack of Sam's
shears, now nearer the hole, could be heard outside. Gandalf
stood for a moment looking at the fire; then he stooped and
removed the Ring with the tongs, and at once picked it up. Bingo
gasped.

'It is quite cold,' said Gandalf. 'Take it!'

Bingo received it on his shrinking palm: it seemed colder and
even heavier than before. 'Hold it up!' said Gandalf, 'and look
inside.' As Bingo did so he saw fine lines, more fine than the finest

The original description of the writing on the Ring

258   THE RETURN OF THE SHADOW

pen strokes, running along the inside of the Ring – lines of fire that seemed to form the letters of a strange alphabet. They shone bright, piercingly bright, and yet it seemed remotely, as if out of a great depth.

'I cannot read the fiery letters,' said Bingo in a quavering voice. 'No,' said Gandalf; 'but I can – now. The writing says:

> *One Ring to rule them all, One Ring to find them,*
> *One Ring to bring them all, and in the darkness bind them.*[13]

That is part of a verse that I know now in full.

> *Three rings for the Elven-kings under the sky,*
> *Seven for the Dwarf-lords in their halls of stone,*
> *Nine for Mortal Men doomed to die,*
> *One for the Dark Lord on his dark throne*
>   *In the Land of Mor-dor where the shadows lie.*
> *One Ring to rule them all, One Ring to find them,*
> *One Ring to bring them all, and in the darkness bind them,*
>   *In the land of Mor-dor where the shadows lie.*[14]

'This,' said Gandalf, 'is the Master-ring: the One Ring to Rule them all! This is the One Ring that he lost many ages ago – to the great weakening of his power; and that he still so greatly desires.[15] But he must *not* get it!'

Bingo sat silent and motionless. Fear seemed to stretch out a vast hand like a dark cloud, rising out of the East and looming up to engulf him. 'This Ring?' he stammered. 'How on earth did it come to me?'

'I can tell you the part of the story that I know,' answered Gandalf. 'In ancient days the Necromancer, the Dark Lord Sauron,[16] made many magic rings of various properties that gave various powers to their possessors. He dealt them out lavishly and sowed them abroad to ensnare all peoples, but specially Elves and Men. For those that used the rings, according to their strength and will and hearts, fell quicker or slower under the power of the rings, and the dominion of their maker.[17] Three, Seven, Nine and One he made of special potency:[18] for their possessors became not only invisible to all in this world, if they wished, but could see both the world under the sun and the other side in which invisible things move.[19] And they had (what is called) good luck, and (what seemed) endless life. Though, as I say, what power the Rings conferred on each possessor depended on what use they made of them – on what they were themselves, and what they desired.

The Ring-verse, and the emergence of the Ruling Ring in the narrative

260 THE RETURN OF THE SHADOW

'But the Rings were under the command of the maker and were always drawing the possessors back to him. For he retained the ruling Ring, which, when *he* wore it, enabled him to see all the others, and to see even the thoughts of those that possessed them.[20] But he lost this Ring, and consequently lost control of all the others. Slowly through the years he has been gathering them and seeking them out – hoping to find the lost One. But the Elves resist his power more than all other races; and the high-elves of the West, of whom some still remain in the middle-world, perceive and dwell at once both [in] this world and the other side without the aid of rings.[21] And they having suffered and fought long against Sauron are not easily drawn into his net, or deluded by him. What has become of the Three Rings of earth, air, and sky I do not know.[22] Some say they have been carried far over the sea. Others say that hidden Elf-kings still keep them. The dwarves too proved tough and intractable: for they do not lightly endure any obedience or domination (even of their own kind). Nor are they easily made into shadows. With the dwarves the chief power of the Rings was to kindle in their hearts the fire of greed (whence evil has come that has aided Sauron). It is said that the foundation of each of the Seven Great Hoards of the dwarves of old was a golden Ring. But it is said that those hoards are plundered and the dragons have devoured them, and the Rings have perished molten in their fire; yet it is also said that not all the hoards have been broken, and that still some of the Seven Rings are guarded.

'But all the Nine Rings of Men have gone back to Sauron, and borne with them their possessors, kings, warriors, and wizards of old,[23] who became Ring-wraiths and served the maker, and were his most terrible servants. Men indeed have most often been under his dominion, and are now again throughout the middle-earth[24] falling under his power, especially in the East and South of the world, where the Elves are few.'

'Ring-wraiths!' exclaimed Bingo. 'What are they?'

'We will not speak of them now,' said Gandalf. 'Let us not speak of horrible things without need. They belong to the ancient days, and let us hope that they will never again arise. At least Gilgalad accomplished that.'[25]

'Who was Gilgalad?' asked Bingo.

'The one who bereft the Dark Lord of the One Ring,' answered Gandalf. 'He was the last in middle-earth of the great Elf-kings of the high western race, and he made alliance with Orendil[26] King of the Island who came back to the middle-world in those days. But I

ANCIENT HISTORY   261

will not tell all that tale now. One day perhaps you may hear it from one who knows it truly. It is enough to say that they marched against Sauron and besieged him in his tower; and he came forth and wrestled with Gilgalad and Orendil, and was overthrown. But he forsook his bodily shape and fled like a ghost to waste places until he rested in Mirkwood and took shape again in the darkness. Gilgalad and Orendil were both mortally hurt and perished in the land of Mordor; but Isildor son of Orendil cut the One Ring from the finger of Sauron and took it for his own.[27]

'But when he marched back from Mordor, Isildor's host was overwhelmed by Goblins that swarmed down out of the mountains. And it is told that Isildor put on the Ring and vanished from their sight, but they trailed him by slot and scent, until he came to the banks of a wide river. Then Isildor plunged in and swam across, but the Ring betrayed him,[28] and slipped from his hand, and he became visible to his enemies; and they killed him with their arrows.[29] But a fish took the Ring and was filled with a madness, and swam up stream leaping over rocks and up waterfalls until it cast itself upon a bank, and spat out the Ring and died.' Gandalf paused. 'And there,' he said, 'the Ring passed out of knowledge and legend; and even so much of the story is now known and remembered by few. Yet I can now add to it, I think.

'Long after, but still very long ago, there lived by the bank of a stream on the edge of Wilderland a wise clever-handed and quiet-footed little family. . . .

For Gollum's earlier history my father followed the original text (pp. 78–9) very closely indeed, only introducing a slight change of wording here and there: thus Dígol is still Gollum himself, and not his friend. At the end of the passage the words 'and even the Master lost it' become 'and even the maker, when his power had grown again, could learn nothing of it', and the following sentence, about the Necromancer counting his rings and always finding one missing, is of course removed.

Gandalf's discussion of Gollum's mind and motives at the time of Bilbo's encounter with him (still of course based on the original story in *The Hobbit*, see p. 86) also remains very close to the old version (pp. 79–80). There are indeed many small improvements in the phrasing; but only two changes need be noticed. Gandalf's words about the longevity afforded to the possessor of the Ring (p. 79) are thus interestingly extended:

. . . Frightfully wearisome, Bingo, in fact finally tormenting (even if you do not become a Wraith). Only Elves can stand it, and even they fade.

262   THE RETURN OF THE SHADOW

And when Gandalf speaks of 'the unexpected arrival of Bilbo' (p. 80) he now goes on:

. . . You remember how surprised he was, and how soon he began talking of a present, though he gave himself a chance of keeping it if luck went that way. Even so I dare say his old habits might have beaten him in the end, and he might have tried to eat Bilbo, if it had been easy. But I am not sure: I guess he was using the Riddle Game (at which even a Gollum dare hardly cheat, as it is sacred and of immense antiquity) as a kind of toss-up to decide for him. And anyway Bilbo had the sword Sting, if you remember, so it was not easy.

But from the point where Bingo objects that Gollum never gave Bilbo the Ring, for Bilbo had it already, Gandalf's story takes a great step forward, with his announcement that he himself had found Gollum (in the original text there is no explanation of how he knew Gollum's history). I give the next part of the chapter, much of which is in a very rough state, in full.

'I know,' said Gandalf. 'And that is why I said that Gollum's ancestry only partly explained events. There was, of course, something much more mysterious behind the whole affair – something probably quite beyond the design of the Lord of the Rings himself, peculiar to Bilbo and his private Adventure. I can put it no clearer than by saying that *Bilbo was 'meant' to have the Ring*, and that he perhaps got involved in the Quest of the treasure mainly for that reason. In which case you were meant to have it. Which may (or may not) be a comforting thought. And there has also always been a queer fate over the Rings on their own account. They get lost, and turn up in strange places. The One had already slipped once from its owner and betrayed him to death. It had now slipped away from Gollum. But the evil they work according to their maker's design turns often to good that he did not intend, and even to his loss and defeat.[30] And that too may be a comforting thought, or not.'

'I don't find either of your thoughts very encouraging,' said Bingo; 'though I don't really understand what you mean. But how do you come to know or guess so much about Gollum?'

'As for the guessing, or the putting of one and one and one together, much of that has not been very difficult,' said Gandalf. 'The Ring that you had of Bilbo, and Bilbo had of Gollum, is shown by the fire-writing to be the One Ring. And concerning that the tale of Gilgalad and Isildor is known – to the wise. The filling

ANCIENT HISTORY

in of the tale of Gollum and fitting it into the gap presents no special difficulty: to one who knows much about the history and the minds and ways of the creatures of middle-earth that he does not tell you. What was the first riddle Gollum asked: do you remember?'

'Yes,' said Bingo, thinking.

> *What has roots that nobody sees,*
> *Is higher than trees,*
> *Up, up it goes,*
> *And yet never grows?*

'More or less right!' said Gandalf. 'Roots and mountains! But as a matter of fact, I have not had to do much guessing from hints of that kind.[31] I know. I know because I found Gollum.'

'You found Gollum!' said Bingo astonished.

'The obvious thing to try to do, surely,' said Gandalf.

'Then what happened after Bilbo left? Do you know that?'

'Not so clearly. What I have told you Gollum was willing to tell; though not of course in the way I have reported it – he thought he was misunderstood and ill-treated, and he was full of tears for himself, and hatred of all other things. But after the Riddle Game he was unwilling to say anything, except in dark hints. One gathered that somehow or other Gollum was going to get his own back, and that people would see if he could be kicked and despised and stuck in a hole, and starved and *robbed*. They might get worse coming their way; for Gollum now had friends, powerful friends. You can imagine the spiteful stuff. He had found out eventually that Bilbo had in some way got "his" Ring, and what his name was.'

'How?' asked Bingo.

'I asked him, but he only leered and chuckled, and said "Gollum issn't deaf iss he, no Gollum, and he hass eyes, hassn't he, yes my preciouss, yes Gollum." But [32] one can imagine various ways in which that might happen. He could, for instance, have overheard the goblins talking about the escape of Bilbo from the gate. And the news of the later events went all over Wilderland, and would give Gollum plenty to think about. Anyway, after having been "robbed and cheated", as he put it, he left the Mountains: the goblins there became few and wary after the Battle; hunting was poor, and the deep places were more than ever dark and lonely. Also the power of the Ring had left him: he was no longer bound by it. He was feeling old, very old, but less timid, though he did not become less malicious.

264   THE RETURN OF THE SHADOW

'One might have expected wind and even the mere shadow of sunlight to kill him pretty quickly. But he was cunning. He could hide from daylight or moonlight, and travel softly and swiftly by night with his long pale eyes – and catch small frightened and unwary things. Indeed he grew for a while stronger with new food and new air. He crept into Mirkwood, which is not surprising.'

'Did you find him there?'

'Yes – I followed him there: he had left a trail of horrible stories behind him, among the beasts and birds and even the Woodmen of Wilderland. He had developed a skill in climbing trees to find nests, and creeping into houses to find cradles. He boasted of it to me.

'But his trail also ran away south, far south of where I actually came upon him – with the help finally of the Wood-elves. He would not explain that. He just grinned and leered, and said *Gollum*, rubbing his horrible hands together gleefully. But I have a suspicion – it is now much more than a suspicion – that he made his slow sneaking way bit by bit long ago down to the land of – *Mordor*,' said Gandalf almost in a whisper. 'Such creatures go naturally that way; and in that land he would soon learn much, and soon himself be discovered, and examined. I think indeed that Gollum is the beginning of our present troubles;[33] for if I guess right, through him the Necromancer discovered what became of the One Ring he had lost. He has even, one may fear, at last heard of the existence of hobbits, and may now be seeking the Shire, if he has not already found out where it is. Indeed I fear that he may even have heard[34] of the humble and long unnoticeable name of – Baggins.'

'But this is terrible!' cried Bingo. 'Far worse than I feared! O Gandalf, what am I to do, for now I am really afraid? What a pity that Bilbo didn't stab the beastly creature, when he said goodbye!'

'What nonsense you do talk sometimes, Bingo!' said Gandalf. 'Pity! It was pity that prevented him. And he could not do so, without doing wrong. It was against the Rules. If he had done so, he would not have had the Ring – the Ring would have had him at once. He would have been enslaved under the Necromancer.'

'Of course, of course,' said Bingo. 'What a thing to say of Bilbo! Dear old Bilbo! But I am frightened – and I cannot feel any pity for that vile Gollum. Do you mean to say that you, and the Elves, let him live on, after all those horrible stories? Now at any rate he is worse than a goblin, and just an enemy.'

'Yes, he deserved to die,' said Gandalf; 'but we did not kill him.

ANCIENT HISTORY

He is very old, and very wretched. The Wood-elves have him in prison, and treat [him] with such kindness as they can find in their wise hearts. They feed him on clean food. But I do not think much can be done to cure him: yet even Gollum might prove useful for good before the end.'[35]

'Well anyway,' said Bingo. 'if Gollum could not be killed, I wish you had not let Bilbo keep the Ring. Why did he? Why did you let him? Did you tell him all this?'

'Yes, I let him,' said Gandalf. 'But at first of course I did not even imagine that it was [one] of the nineteen[36] Rings of Power: I thought he had got nothing more dangerous than one of the lesser magic rings that were once more common – and were used (as their maker intended) chiefly by minor rogues and villains, for mean wickednesses. I was not frightened of Bilbo being affected by *their* power. But when I began to suspect that the matter was more serious than that, I told him as much as my suspicions warranted. He knew that it came in the long run from the Necromancer. But you must remember there was the Ring itself to reckon with. Even Bilbo could not wholly escape the power of the Ruling Ring. He developed – a sentiment. He would keep it as a memento. Frankly – he became rather proud of his Great Adventure, and used to look at the Ring now and again (and oftener as time went on) to warm his memory: it made him feel rather heroic, though he never lost his power of laughing at the feeling.

'But in the end it got a hold of him in that way. He knew eventually that it was giving him "long life", and thinning him. He grew weary of it – "I can't abide it any longer", he said – but to get rid of it was not so easy. He found it hard to bring himself to it. If you think for a moment: it is not really very easy to get rid of the Ring once you have got it.'[37]

From this point the text again follows the old (pp. 81–2) very closely. Bingo now of course draws the Ring out of his pocket 'again', and means to throw it 'back again' into the fire; and Gandalf says (as in FR, p. 70) that 'This Ring at any rate has already passed through your fire and come out unscathed, and even unheated.' Adam Hornblower the Hobbiton smith remains. Gandalf says here that 'you would have to find one of the Cracks of Earth in the depth of the Fiery Mountain, and drop it in there, if you really did wish to destroy it – or to place it out of all reach until the End.' Against 'Cracks of Earth' (the name in the original text, p. 82) my father wrote in the margin, at the same time, '? Cracks of Doom'; at the second occurrence of the name he wrote 'Cracks of Doom', but put 'Earth' above 'Doom'.

266   THE RETURN OF THE SHADOW

The original text is developed and extended from the point where Bingo says 'I really do wish to destroy it' (p. 82):

. . . I cannot think how Bilbo put up with it for so long. And also, I must say, I cannot help wondering why he passed it on to me. I knew, of course, that he had it – though I was the only one who did or does know; but he spoke of it jokingly, and on the only two or three occasions when I ever caught him using it he used it more or less as a joke – especially the last time.'

'Bilbo would: and when your fate has bestowed on you such perilous treasures it is not a bad way to take them – as long as you can do so. But as for passing it on to you: he did so only because he thought you were safe: safe not to misuse it; safe not to let it get into evil hands; safe from its power, for a while; and safe, as an unknown and unimportant hobbit in the heart of the quiet and easily overlooked little Shire, from the – enemy. I promised him, too, to help and advise you, if any difficulty arose. Also, I may say that I did not discover the letters of fire, or guess that this ring was the One Ring, until he had already decided to go away and leave it.[38] And I did not tell him, for then he would not have burdened you, or gone away. But for his own sake, I knew he ought to go. He had had that Ring for 60 years, and it was telling on him, Bingo. You have tried before now to describe to me your own feeling – the stretched feeling.[39] His was much stronger. The Ring would have worn him down in the end. Yet the only sure way of ridding him of it was to let someone else take on the burden, for a while. He is free. But you are his heir. And now that I have (since that time) discovered much more, I know that you have a heavy inheritance. I wish it could be otherwise. But do not blame Bilbo – or me, if you can help it. Let us bear what is laid upon us (if we can). But we must do something soon. The enemy is moving.'

There was a long silence. Gandalf puffed at his pipe in apparent content . . .

The new version then develops the old text (p. 83) almost to the form in FR (pp. 71–2), with Bingo's saying that he had often thought of going off, but imagined it as a kind of holiday, and his sudden strong desire, not communicated to Gandalf, to follow Bilbo and perhaps to find him, and to run out of Bag End there and then. The new text continues:

'My dear Bingo!' said Gandalf. 'Bilbo made no mistake in choosing you as his heir. Yes, I think you will have to go – before long, though not at once or without a little thought and care. And I am not sure you need go alone: not if you know of anyone you could trust, and who would be willing to go by your side – and who you would be willing to take into unknown dangers. But be careful in choosing, and in what you say even to your closest friends. The enemy has many spies, and many ways of hearing.' Suddenly he stopped as if listening.

The remainder of the chapter (the surprising of Sam outside the window, and Gandalf's decision that he should be Bingo's companion – cf. *Queries and Alterations* note 2, p. 221) is almost word for word the final form (FR pp. 72–3), which was reached almost at a stroke[40] and never changed.

NOTES

1 This passage goes back to the original version of 'A Long-expected Party' (p. 17).
2 This passage goes back to the fourth version of 'A Long-expected Party' (p. 37), and indeed in part to the third (p. 29), when Bilbo was Bingo's father.
3 *Odo Bolger:* hitherto Odo has been Odo Took – or, at least, he was still Odo Took when his surname was last mentioned, which was in the original text of the 'Bree' chapter (p. 141, note 5). At the beginning, Odo Took could tell Bingo not to be 'Bolger-like' (p. 49); but perhaps my father felt that Odo had developed strong Bolger traits as the story proceeded. He retains, however, a Took mother.
4 This passage, from 'Merry was the son of Caradoc Brandybuck', was placed within square brackets, apparently at the time of writing. The genealogy (part of which has appeared before, p. 100) is of course very different from the final form, but when it is seen that Frodo Took occupies the place in the 'tree' afterwards taken by Peregrin Took (Pippin) it becomes at once much closer. In the following table the names in LR (Appendix C, *Took of Great Smials*) are given in brackets.

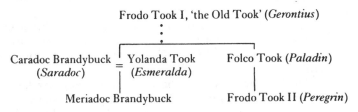

Since Caradoc Brandybuck, Merry's father, is here said to be Bingo's cousin, it can be presumed that the genealogy given in the family tree of the Brandybucks in LR was already present, i.e. Caradoc was the son of Old Rory, the brother of Bingo's mother Primula. That Rory Brandybuck was Bingo's uncle is never actually

268   THE RETURN OF THE SHADOW

said in LR, though of course it appears in the family tree, but it does appear in rejected versions of the Farmer Maggot episode (pp. 289, 296), and again later (pp. 385–6).

Merry Brandybuck and Frodo Took are the great-great-grandsons of the Old Took, as are Merry and Pippin in LR.

5   This passage goes back to the third version of 'A Long-expected Party' (p. 34). '500 pieces of gold' was later changed to '500 double-dragons (gold pieces of the highest value in the Shire)'; but this was not taken up into the next version of 'Ancient History', which returns to '500 gold pieces'. *sixty years:* 111 less 51 (see p. 31).

6   *Gandalf's visits to Hobbiton.* In *The Tale of Years* (LR Appendix B) Bilbo's Farewell Party took place in 3001; Gandalf visited Frodo in the years 3004–8, the last visit being in the autumn of 3008; and returned finally in April 3018 (after 9 and a half years): Frodo's 50th birthday was in September of that year, when he left Bag End. Cf. FR p. 55.

In the present text there was likewise a gap of three years after the Party before Gandalf came again; but then he came once or twice every year, with one gap of two years, till the 14th year after the Party, when Bingo was 47, and after that 'frequently'. The passage was subsequently rewritten to read:

... seeing that Bingo was still quite settled. After that he returned several times, until he suddenly disappeared. Bingo heard no news of him between the 7th and 14th years after Bilbo's departure, when Gandalf suddenly reappeared one winter's night. After that the wizard came frequently and stayed longer.

For the year in which the conversation in 'Ancient History' took place (it was in the month of April, p. 254) see note 8.

7   This is a reference to *The Hobbit*, Chapter XIX 'The Last Stage':

... they had at last driven the Necromancer from his dark hold in the south of Mirkwood.

'Ere long now,' Gandalf was saying, 'the Forest will grow somewhat more wholesome. The North is freed from that horror for many an age.

On his copy of the sixth impression (1954) my father changed Gandalf's words to read: The North *will be* freed from that horror for many *long years, I hope.* This is the text from the third edition (1966).

The following passage is the first clear, if very general, statement of where the Land of Mordor lay; see p. 218, note 17. Cf. also Gandalf's account of Gollum's journey (p. 264): 'his trail also ran away south, far south of where I actually came upon him' (which was in Mirkwood).

8   *in the spring of Bingo's 49th? 50th? year.* At the beginning of the next chapter in this 'phase' it is said that Bingo decided to leave Bag End on September 22nd 'in this (his 50th) year.'

ANCIENT HISTORY   269

9   My father first made the miller's son Tom Tunnelly, changing it as
    he wrote to Tom Sandyman; *Tom* was changed to *Ted* in pencil,
    before the chapter was finished, for *Ted* appears, as first written, at
    the end of it. See p. 249, note 33.

10 It is a very old conception that appears here; see II.323 and note 44.
    – Bingo describes the Elf-towers to his companions on the walk to
    Farmer Maggot's: he says that he saw them once, shining white in
    the light of the Moon (p. 93). Trotter at Bree calls them the West
    Towers (pp. 155, 159).

11 On Gandalf's visits to the land of the Necromancer see p. 85,
    note 12.

12 Here my father wrote: 'Bingo had never seen it on any finger but his
    own forefinger', but at once struck it out.

13 My father first wrote 'One ring to bind them', changing it in pencil
    to 'and in the darkness bind them', which is the form as written from
    the first in the whole verse that immediately follows.

14 *The text of the verse of the Rings.* My father's original workings for
    this verse are extant. The first complete form reads:

> *Nine for the Elven-kings under moon and star,*
> *Seven for the Dwarf-lords in their halls of stone,*
> *Three for Mortal Men that wander far,*
> *One for the Dark Lord on his dark throne*
> *In the Land of Mor-dor where the shadows are.*
> *One Ring to rule them all, One Ring to find them,*
> *One Ring to bring them all and in the darkness bind them*
> *In the Land of Mor-dor where the shadows are.*

He was at this time still uncertain as to the disposition of the Rings
among the different peoples. The verse in the text of the present
chapter as first written also had 'Nine rings for the Elven-kings' and
'Three for Mortal Men' (in the original text, p. 78, 'the Elves had
many', and 'Men had three rings', but 'others they found in secret
places cast away by the elf-wraiths'). But he wrote in the margin (in
ink and at the same time as the verse itself) '3' against 'Nine' and '9'
against 'Three', subsequently changing the words in the verse itself:
see note 22.

Another preliminary version of the verse has:

> *Twelve for Mortal Men doomed to die,*
> *Nine for the Dwarf-lords in their halls of stone,*
> *Three for the Elven-kings of earth, sea, and sky,*
> *One for the Dark Lord on his dark throne.*

'Twelve' and 'Nine' were then changed to 'Nine' and 'Seven'. On
there being at one time twelve Black Riders see p. 196. In the text of
the chapter (p. 260) the Three Rings are called the Rings 'of earth,
air, and sky'.

270   THE RETURN OF THE SHADOW

15   The text as first written here was 'and now that he knows or guesses where it is he desires so greatly.'

16   My father wrote here: 'In ancient days the Necromancer [servant of ???] the Dark Lord Sauron.' The brackets and queries were put in at the time of writing or very soon after. I can only explain this on the assumption that he was momentarily thinking of Morgoth as the Dark Lord, before he wrote the name Sauron; but it is odd that he did not simply strike out the words 'servant of'.

17   Against this passage my father wrote in the margin: 'Ring-wraiths later' (see p. 260). In the original text (p. 78, and cf. the draft on which that was based, p. 75) the Wraiths are mentioned at this point.

18   My father wrote 'Nine, Seven, Three, and One', reversing 'Nine' and 'Three' in pencil. – Here appears explicitly for the first time the distinction between the lesser Rings and the Rings of Power.

19   The text as written, but probably changed immediately, was: 'but could see both the world under the sun and the phantom world [> the world of shadow] in which the invisible creatures of the Lord moved.'

20   With this account of the relation of the power of the Rings to the innate qualities of those who bore them, and of the potency of the One Ring in the hand of its maker, compare *Queries and Alterations*, note 12 (p. 227), where the idea of the Ruling Ring first explicitly appears.

21   Cf. p. 212, and *Queries and Alterations*, note 10 (p. 225).

22   Here the *Three* Rings of the Elves appear in the text as first written (and the *Nine* Rings of Men in the next paragraph): see note 14. In the draft of the Ring-verse given at the end of note 14 the Three Rings are 'of earth, sea, and sky', whereas here they are 'of earth, air, and sky.'

23   *wizards:* cf. p. 211, where Gandalf at Rivendell likewise includes 'wizards' among the servants of the Dark Lord.

24   *the middle-earth* was changed from *the middle-world*, which is used earlier in this passage and again subsequently.

25   The meaning appears to be that after the loss of the Ruling Ring to the Necromancer, the Ring-wraiths could no longer function as his servants; they were not definitively destroyed, but they had no effective existence. Gandalf was soon to be proved wrong in this opinion, of course; and it may be that my father introduced it here to explain Gandalf's failure to take them into account. In FR he is less confident: 'It is many a year since the Nine walked abroad. Yet who knows? As the Shadow grows once more, they too may walk again.'

26   The name of the King of Men was first written *Valandil*; above this my father wrote *E* and *Orendil*. The next part of Gandalf's story was constantly changed in the act of composition, and at subsequent occurrences the name of the King varies between *Valandil* >

ANCIENT HISTORY 271

Orendil/Elendil, Elendil > Orendil, and then *Orendil* unchanged; I read *Orendil* throughout. For previous hesitation over the name see p. 174 note 25 and p. 197 note 3.

27 Here my father first wrote: 'but ere he fell Gilgalad cut the One Ring from the hand finger of Sauron, and gave it to Ithildor that stood by, but Ithildor took it for his own.' This was changed at the time of writing to the text given. *hand finger* was left thus; I read *finger* because that is the word used in the next text of this chapter. – *Ithildor* was changed to *Isildor* at each occurrence until the last in this passage, where *Isildor* was the form first written. See note 29.

28 The original reading here was: 'but the Ring [or >] and his fate betrayed him'.

29 The story of the One Ring now moves further. In the original text (p. 78) it was simply that the Ring 'fell from the hand of an elf as he swam across a river; and it betrayed him, for he was flying from pursuit in the old wars, and he became visible to his enemies, and the goblins slew him.' In *Queries and Alterations* note 12 (p. 226) a new element was proposed: that the Ring was 'taken from the Lord himself when Gilgalad wrestled with him, and taken by a flying Elf'; the implication clearly being that Gilgalad took it (as said at first in the present text, see note 27). Now the Elf becomes Isildor son of Orendil (Elendil: note 26).

30 This passage, from 'And there has also always been a queer fate', was enclosed in brackets with a query; and the last sentence, 'But the evil they work . . .', additionally enclosed in double brackets with a double query. The sentences immediately following (Gandalf's 'And that too may be a comforting thought, or not', and the first part of Bingo's reply) are a pencilled addition. But it is not clear to me why Bingo should be discouraged by the suggestion that the evil wrought by the Rings could turn to good and against the design of their maker.

31 Bingo's version has slight deviations from the text in *The Hobbit*. – It is not very evident what Gandalf had deduced from Gollum's first riddle.

32 In place of this passage, from 'He had found out eventually', the text as first written had (much as in the original version, p. 80): 'I think it is certain that Gollum knew after a time that Bilbo had in some way got "his" Ring. One can imagine . . .'
With the pencilled extension Gandalf's explanation of how Gollum knew that the hobbit had got the Ring is extended to cover the fact that Gollum also found out what his name was. But this is odd, since in the original story in *The Hobbit* as in the revised version Bilbo told Gollum his name: '"What iss he, my precious?" whisperered Gollum. "I am Mr Bilbo Baggins . . ."' See further note 34 (and cf. FR p. 66).

33 This phrase of Gandalf's, 'I think indeed that Gollum is the

272   THE RETURN OF THE SHADOW

beginning of our present troubles', is repeated from the original text
(p. 81), and here as there seems to refer to the fact that the Dark
Lord was known to Gandalf to be seeking the Ring in the direction
of the Shire. But it is still not really explained what kind of searching
could lead Gandalf to describe it as 'our present trouble', since he
knew nothing of the Black Riders (see *Queries and Alterations*, p.
224). He can hardly be referring to those things mentioned earlier in
the chapter (p. 253): Men moving North and West, goblins multiplying, new kinds of trolls; for these were surely large manifestations of the growing power of the Dark Lord, rather than of the
search for the Ring.

34   Here follows: '(for his ears are keen and his spies legion)', marked in
pencil for deletion. This change perhaps goes with the puzzling
addition referred to in note 32, where Gandalf suggests that Gollum
had eventually found out Bilbo's name; for in that case, if Gollum
had indeed been to Mordor, he himself could have told the Necromancer that 'Baggins' had taken the Ring.

35   From this point the text is written in faint pencil.

36   Above 'nineteen' is pencilled '20'. This is the first occurrence of the
term 'Rings of Power'.

37   From this point the text is again in ink, a good clear manuscript to
the end of the chapter.

38   The meaning must surely be that Gandalf *had* 'discovered the
letters of fire' on the Ring before Bilbo left Hobbiton; which is
curious, since Gandalf also says that he did not tell Bilbo, and it is
hard to imagine him conducting the test without Bilbo knowing of
it. In FR (p. 65), when Frodo asked him when he discovered the
fire-writing, he replied: 'Just now in this room, of course. But I
expected to find it. I have come back from dark journeys and long
search to make that final test.' Gandalf's words on p. 256 could be
taken to mean that he did not know for certain until now: 'I do not
yet know quite all. Give me the Ring a minute.' But they cannot
mean this; and he refers (p. 262) to the fire-writing on the Ring as if
it had been one of the main pieces of evidence in his deduction of the
story which he now told to Bingo.
     My father later pencilled an 'X' in the margin of the text here, and
scribbled 'did not know until recently'.

39   See p. 252.

40   The original drafting for the episode is extant, scribbled faintly at
the end of the manuscript of the original version of the chapter, and
is naturally less finished; but already in this draft the final text is
fully present except in details of expression.

XVI

DELAYS ARE DANGEROUS

From 'Ancient History' my father proceeded to the revision of the original second chapter, which had been given the title 'Three's Company and Four's More' (p. 49); this new version becomes Chapter III, but was given no title. Later, he scribbled in at the head of the text 'Delays are Dangerous' (which is the title *ab initio* of the following version of the chapter), and it is convenient to adopt this here.

Some exceedingly rough and fluid notes – the continuation of those mentioned at the beginning of the last chapter, p. 250 – are all that exist by way of preparatory writing for this revision. I have already noticed (p. 250) that the story of Bingo's dinner-party for Merry, Frodo Took, and Odo Bolger on the eve of departure was devised here, and that against this my father wrote 'Sam Gamgee to replace Odo' (these notes preceded the writing of 'Ancient History', where Sam Gamgee first emerged). But Odo could not be got rid of so easily. The notes continue:

Gandalf was *supposed to come to party* but did *not* turn up. Bingo waits till Friday [September 23] but foolishly did not wait any longer, as Sackville-Bagginses threaten to turn him out: but sets off on Friday night. Gives out he is going to stay with Merry and return to his Brandybuck relations.

A rejected suggestion that Odo remained at Hobbiton 'to give news to Gandalf' shows my father already pondering this question, which after a long history of change would ultimately lead to Fredegar Bolger remaining at Crickhollow (FR p. 118). In these notes a Brandybuck with the Arthurian name of Lanorac (changed from Bercilak), a cousin of Merry's, 'has been ordered to have all ready' in Buckland; and there is a suggestion for the story after they leave Buckland and enter the Old Forest: 'Frodo wants to come but is told *no*: to give news to Gandalf. Merry says nothing – but *does* come: locks door and throws key over hedge.' With this cf. *Queries and Alterations*, note 2 (p. 221): 'Frodo says goodbye at Bucklebury. Only Merry and Bingo ride on into exile – because *Merry insists*. Bingo originally intended to go alone' (this was written before Sam Gamgee entered).

The text of the new version of this chapter is the most complicated document yet encountered. It begins as manuscript, in which part of the narrative is in two variant forms, and then turns back to the original typescript (given in full on pp. 49–65), which was heavily corrected in two forms (with different inks to cover different versions): some of the more extensive changes are on inserted slips. At the end my father

274   THE RETURN OF THE SHADOW

abandoned the old typescript and concluded the chapter in a new manuscript – the first part of it in three versions. To present the whole complex in this book is obviously impossible, and is in any case in no way necessary for the understanding of the development of the narrative.

The initial portion in manuscript extends as far as the beginning of the hobbits' walk on the first night ('They went very quietly over fields and along hedgerows and the borders of coppices, until night fell', p. 50), and the opening of the chapter presents an entirely new narrative. Leaving aside for the moment the passage existing in variant forms, the new text while very rough reaches in all essentials the final form in FR, pp. 74–80. There are many differences still in wording, and the chapter begins with the local gossip about the sale of Bag End and then proceeds to Bingo's discussion with Gandalf about his departure, rather than the other way about;[1] but differences of substance are few and mostly slight. More emphasis is placed on the fact that the 22nd of September was in that year again a Thursday (as it was in FR, p. 77): 'that seemed to [Bingo's] fancy to mark the date as the proper one for setting out to follow Bilbo.' Gandalf's tone to Bingo is a bit grimmer, and has more asperity; and he does not refer to the possibility that it may, or may not, be Bingo's task to find the Cracks of Doom. His parting words to him are significantly different from what he says in FR; and Bingo's state of mind on the eve of his own departure is given a different emphasis. I give here a portion of the text, taking it up from the point where Gandalf says that the direction which Bingo takes when he leaves Hobbiton should not be known (FR p. 74, at bottom).

'Well now,' said Bingo, 'do you know I have mostly thought just about going, and have never decided on the direction! For where shall I go, and by what shall I steer, and what is to be my quest? This will indeed be the opposite of Bilbo's adventure: setting out without any known destination, and to get rid of a treasure, not to find one.'

'And to go *there* but not come *back again*, likely enough,' added Gandalf grimly.

'That I know,' said Bingo, pretending not to be impressed. 'But seriously, in what direction shall I start?'

'Towards danger, but not too rashly, nor too straight towards it,' answered Gandalf. 'Make first for Rivendell, if you will at least take that much advice. After that we shall see – if you ever get there: the Road is not as easy as it was.'

'Rivendell!' said Bingo. 'Very good. That will please Sam.' He did not add that it pleased him too; and that though he had not decided, he had often thought of making for the house of Elrond; if only because he thought that perhaps Bilbo, after he had become free again, had chosen that way too.

DELAYS ARE DANGEROUS 275

The decision to go Eastwards directed Bingo's later plans. It was for this reason that he gave out that he was removing to Buckland, and actually did ask his Brandybuck cousins, Merry and Lanorac and the rest, to look out for a little place for him to live in.[2] In the meantime he went on much as usual, and the summer passed. Gandalf had gone off again. But he was invited to the farewell party, and had promised to arrive on the day before, or at latest on the 22nd itself. 'Don't go till you see me, Bingo,' he said, as he took his leave one wet dark evening in May. 'I may have news, and useful information about the Road. And I may want to come with you.'[3]

The autumn came on. No news came from Gandalf. There began to be signs of activity at Bag-End. Two covered carts went off laden. They were understood to be conveying such furniture as Mr Baggins had not sold to the Sackville-Bagginses to his new house in Buckland by way of the Brandywine Bridge. Odo Bolger, Merry Brandybuck, and Frodo Took were staying there with Bingo. The four of them seemed to be busy packing and the hole was all upside-down. On Wednesday September 21 Bingo began to look out anxiously for Gandalf, but there was no sign of him. His birthday morning September 22 dawned, as fair and clear as it had for Bilbo's party long ago (as it now seemed to Bingo). But still Gandalf did not appear. In the evening Bingo gave his farewell party. The absence of Gandalf rather worried Bingo and a little damped his spirits, which had been steadily rising – as every cool and misty autumn morning brought him closer to the day of his going. The only wrench now was parting from his young friends. The danger did not seem so threatening. He wanted to be off – at once. Everyone had been told that he was leaving for Bucklebury as soon as possible after his birthday. The Sackville-Bagginses got possession after midnight on the 23rd. All the same, he wanted to see Gandalf first. But his three friends were in high spirits . . .

From the end of Bingo's birthday dinner to the beginning of the hobbits' night walk the new text is almost the same as that in FR (pp. 77–80), apart from the different hobbits present (and still leaving aside the part existing in variant forms). The third cart, bearing 'the remaining and more valuable things', went off as in FR on the morning of the 23rd; at first Odo Bolger was said to be in charge of this, but he was changed, apparently at once, to Merry Brandybuck. (In FR Merry was accompanied by Fredegar Bolger, and my father queried in the margin here: 'Merry and Odo?'). Now enters the story of Bingo's overhearing Gaffer Gamgee talking (in almost the same words as in FR) to a stranger

276   THE RETURN OF THE SHADOW

at the end of Bagshot Row: the first germ of this has been seen in *Queries and Alterations*, note 3 (p. 222). The only real difference is that the old discussion among the hobbits (p. 49) whether to walk far or not is still present, Odo disagreeing with Frodo and Bingo; but there are now four of them, and Bingo asks Sam for his opinion:

'Well, sir,' he answered, taking off his hat and looking up at the sky, 'I do guess that it may be pretty warm tomorrow. And walking in the sun, even at this time o' year, with a load on your back, can be wearisome, like. I votes with Mr Frodo, if you ask me.'

The variant section was written continuously with the preceding narrative – that is to say, it is the story as my father first intended to tell it, and the other version was written subsequently, at first as an alternative. The divergence begins after Merry's departure for Buckland on Friday September 23, Bingo's last day at Bag End.

After lunch people began to arrive – some by invitation, others brought by rumour and curiosity. They found the door open, and Bingo on the mat in the hall waiting to greet them. Inside the hall was piled an assortment of packages, bric-a-brac and small articles of furniture. On every package and item there was a label tied. . . .

On the manuscript my father wrote later that 'this variant depending on shortening in Chapter I and the transference of parting gifts etc. to III' was now rejected. The shortening of Chapter I proposed is in fact the short variant of the story of the aftermath of Bilbo's party which has been described on pp. 241–2: as I noted there, 'the entire "business" of the presents, and the invasion of Bag End, was in this variant removed', for it was now to be transferred to *Bingo's* departure – or at least, was under the option of being so transferred. Thus a further twist is given to the serpentine history of this element in *The Lord of the Rings*: for what is involved is not of course a simple reversion to the story as it was at the end of the 'first phase' of 'A Long-expected Party', where also the gifts were Bingo's, not Bilbo's. The new idea was that the gifts,[4] the invasion of Bag End, the ejection of the hobbits excavating in the pantry, and the fight with Sancho Proudfoot (his adversary here being Cosimo Sackville-Baggins,[5] supported by his mother, who broke her umbrella on Sancho's head) – that all this took place not after the great Birthday Party (which was now Bilbo's), but after *Bingo's* own discreet birthday party before *his* departure.

It is possible and even probable that my father's intention in this was to reduce the element of Hobbiton comedy that confronts the reader at the outset, and introduce sooner, in 'Ancient History', the very much

DELAYS ARE DANGEROUS 277

weightier matters that had come into being since 'A Long-expected Party' was first written.

In this version the story of Bingo's walking a little way from Bag End, and so hearing Gaffer Gamgee talking to the Black Rider, was not yet present; and when he has sent Sam off with the key to his father, he leaves by himself. There is no mention of Odo Bolger and Frodo Took before the variant text ends, with Bingo going down the garden path, jumping the fence at the bottom, and passing into the twilight. I cannot say for certain whether this is significant or not. It seems unlikely to be a mere casual oversight; but if it is not, it means presumably that my father was contemplating a wholly new course for the story: Bingo and Sam journeying through the Shire alone. He had certainly contemplated something of the sort earlier. However this may be, nothing came of it; and he passed on at once to the second version of this part of the narrative (the form in FR), where Bingo after listening to Gaffer Gamgee talking to the stranger returns to Bag End and finds Odo and Frodo (Pippin in FR) sitting on their packs in the porch.

Effectively, then, the third chapter of FR, as far as the departure of Bingo (Frodo) from Bag End, was now achieved. My father here, as I have said, turned back to the original typescript, and used it as the physical basis for his new text until near the end of the chapter. He emended it in different inks, and added this note on the typescript: *Corrections in black are for any version. Those in red are for the revised version (with Bilbo as party-giver and including Sam).*[6] In the new material, corrections and additions, he distinguished very carefully between the two types of change: in one case he wrote 'red emendation' against the first part of a new passage, and 'black emendation' against the next part, continuous with the first (the passage is given in note 11, and the reason for the distinction is very clear). It is hard to see why he should have gone to all this trouble, unless at this stage he was still (remarkably enough) uncertain about the new story, with 'Bilbo as party-giver and including Sam', and saw the possibility of returning to the old.

As I have said, the presentation of the results of this procedure here is impossible,[7] and unnecessary even if possible. The effect of all the emendations is to bring the original version very close indeed to the form in FR (pp. 80 ff.). In places the new version is a halfway house between the two, and in the latter part the corrections are less thoroughgoing, but only here and there is there anything of narrative importance to note; and in what follows it can be assumed unless the contrary is said that the FR text was already present in all particulars other than the choice of phrasing. But the hobbits are now four: Bingo, Frodo Took, Odo Bolger, and Sam Gamgee, so that there is in this respect also an intervening stage here between the original story (where there are three, Bingo, Frodo Took, and Odo Took) and FR (where there are again only three, but a different three, Frodo Baggins, Peregrin Took, and Sam

278   THE RETURN OF THE SHADOW

Gamgee), and some variation between the versions in the attribution of remarks to different characters (on this matter see p. 70). But things said by Sam in FR are said by him in this text also.[8]

At the beginning of this part of the chapter, where the old text (p. 50) had: 'They were now in Tookland; and they began to climb into the Green Hill Country south of Hobbiton', the new reads: 'They were now in Tookland and going southwards; but a mile or two further on they crossed the main road from Much Hemlock (in the Hornblower country) to Bywater and Brandywine Bridge. Then they struck eastward and began to climb . . .'[9] Beside this my father wrote: '?Michel Delving (the chief town of the Shire back west on the White Downs).' This is the first appearance of Michel Delving, and of the White Downs (see p. 295). 'Much Hemlock' echoes the name Much Wenlock in Shropshire (*Much* 'Great', as *Michel*).

The Woody End is not called 'a wild corner of the Eastfarthing' – the 'Farthings' had not yet been devised – but it is added that 'Not many of them [hobbits] lived in that part.'

The verse *The Road goes ever on and on*, now ascribed to Bingo and not to Frodo Took, is still as in the original version (p. 53).[10]

A slight difference from FR is present at the first appearance of the Black Rider on the road (old version p. 54):

Odo and Frodo ran quickly to the left, and down into a little hollow not far from the road. There they lay flat. Bingo hesitated for a second: curiosity or some other impulse was struggling with his desire to hide. Sam waited for his master to move. The sound of hoofs drew nearer. 'Get down, Sam!' said Bingo, just in time. They threw themselves flat in a patch of long grass behind a tree that overshadowed the road.[11]

In the discussion that followed the departure of the first Black Rider my father retained at this time the old version (p. 54), in which Frodo Took told of his encounter with a Black Rider in the north of the Shire:

. . . I haven't seen one of that Kind in our Shire for years.'

'There are Men about, all the same,' said Bingo; 'and I have heard many reports of strange folk on our borders, and within them, of late. Down in the south Shire they have had some trouble with Big People, I am told. But I have heard of nothing like this rider.'

'I have though,' said Frodo, who had listened intently to Bingo's description of the Black Rider. 'I remember now something I had quite forgotten. I was walking away up in the North Moor – you know, right up on the northern borders of the Shire –

DELAYS ARE DANGEROUS

this very summer, when a tall black-cloaked rider met me. He was riding south, and he stopped and spoke, though he did not seem able to speak our language very well; he asked me if I knew whether there were any folk called Baggins in those parts. I thought it very queer at the time; and I had a queer uncomfortable feeling, too. I could not see any face under his hood. I said *no*, not liking the look of him. As far as I heard, he never found his way to Hobbiton and the Baggins country.'

'Begging your pardon,' put in Sam suddenly, 'but he found his way to Hobbiton all right, him or another like him. Anyway it's from Hobbiton as this here Black Rider comes – and I know where he's going to.'

'What do you mean?' said Bingo, turning sharply. 'Why didn't you speak up before?'

Sam's report of the Gaffer's account to him of the Rider who came to Hobbiton is exactly as in FR, p. 85. Then follows:

'Your father can't be blamed anyway,' said Bingo. 'But I should have taken more care on the road, if you had told me this before. I wish I had waited for Gandalf,' he muttered; 'but perhaps that would have only made matters worse.'

'Then you know or guess something about the rider?' said Frodo, who had caught the muttered words. 'What is he?'

'I don't know, and I would rather not guess,' said Bingo. 'But I don't believe either this rider (or yours, or Sam's – if they are all different) was really one of the Big People, not an ordinary Man, I mean. I wish Gandalf was here; but now the most we can hope is that he will come quick to Bucklebury. Whoever would have expected a quiet walk from Hobbiton to Buckland to turn out so queer. I had no idea that I was letting you folk in for anything dangerous.'

'Dangerous?' said Frodo. 'So you think it is dangerous, do you? You are rather close, aren't you, Uncle Bingo? Never mind – we shall get your secret out of you some time. But if it is dangerous, then I am glad we are with you.'

'Hear, hear!' said Odo. 'But what is the next thing to do? Shall we go on at once, or stay here and have some food? . . .

My father still retained the development (see pp. 55–6 and note 11) that a Black Rider came past, and briefly stopped beside, the great hollow tree in which the hobbits sat, and only changed this story at its end:

. . . We are probably making a fuss about nothing [said Odo]. This

280   THE RETURN OF THE SHADOW

second rider, at any rate, was very likely only a wandering stranger who has got lost; and if he met us, he would just ask us the way to Buckland or Brandywine Bridge, and ride on.'

'What if he stops us and asks if we know where Mr Baggins of Bag-end is?' said Frodo.

'Give him a true answer,' said Bingo. 'Either say: *Back in Hobbiton*, where there are hundreds; or say *Nowhere*. For Mr Bingo Baggins has left Bag-end, and not yet found any other home. Indeed I think he has vanished; here and now I become Mr Hill of Faraway.'

An alternative version is provided:

'What if he stops us and asks if we know where Mr Baggins of Bag-end is?' said Frodo.

'Tell him that he has vanished!' said Odo. 'After all one Baggins of Bag-end has vanished, and how should we know that it is not old Bilbo that he wants to pay a belated call on? Bilbo made some queer friends in his travels, by his own account.'

Bingo looked quickly at Odo. 'That is an idea,' he said. 'But I hope we shall not be asked that question; and if we are, I have a feeling that silence will be the best answer. Now let us get on. I am glad the road is winding.'

This entire element was removed in FR (p. 86).

When the singing of the Elves is heard (old version p. 58) Bingo still attributes to Bilbo his knowledge that there were sometimes Elves in the Woody End (cf. the passage in 'Ancient History', p. 253), and he says that they wander into the Shire in spring and autumn 'out of their own lands far beyond the river'; in FR (p. 88) Frodo knows independently of Bilbo that Elves may be met with in the Woody End, and says that they come 'out of their own lands away beyond the Tower Hills.' The conception of Elvish lands west of the Shire was of course fully present at this time: cf. Sam's words about Elves 'going to the harbours, out away West, away beyond the Towers' (p. 254). The hymn to Elbereth has the last emendation needed to bring it to the final form (see p. 59): *cold* to *bright* in the second line of the second verse. It is still said to be sung 'in the secret elf-tongue'. At its end, Bingo speaks of the High Elves as Frodo does in FR (p. 89), though without saying 'They spoke the name of Elbereth!' – thus it is not explained how he knows they are High Elves.[12]

Odo's unfortunate remark ('I suppose we shall get a really good bed and supper?') is retained, and Bingo's greeting that Bilbo had taught him, 'The stars shine on the hour of our meeting', remains only in translation. Gildor in his reply refers to Bingo's being 'a scholar in the elf-tongue', changed from 'the elf-latin' (p. 60), where FR has 'the Ancient

DELAYS ARE DANGEROUS 281

Tongue'. It is still the Moon, and not the autumn stars, that is seen in the sky; and the different recollections by the hobbits of the meal eaten with the Elves are retained from the old text, with the addition of the passage about Sam (FR p. 92).

From this point my father abandoned the old typescript, and though returning to it just at the end continued the text in manuscript. The beginning of Bingo's conversation with Gildor is extant in three forms. All three begin as in FR, p. 92 ('They spoke of many things, old and new'), but in the first Gildor goes on from 'The secret will not reach the Enemy from us' with 'But why did you not go before?' – the first thing that he says to Bingo in the original version ('Why did you choose this moment to set out?', p. 62). Bingo replies with a very brief reference to his divided mind about leaving the Shire, and then Gildor explains him to himself:

'That I can understand,' said Gildor. 'Half your heart wished to go, but the other half held you back; for its home was in the Shire, and its delight in bed and board and the voices of friends, and in the changing of the gentle seasons among the fields and trees. But since you are a hobbit that half is the stronger, as it was even in Bilbo. What has made it surrender?'

'Yes, I am an ordinary hobbit, and so I always shall be, I imagine,' said Bingo. 'But a most un-hobbitlike fate has been laid upon me.'

'Then you are not an ordinary hobbit,' said Gildor, 'for otherwise that could not be so. But the half that is plain hobbit will suffer much I fear from being forced to follow the other half which is worthy of the strange fate, until it too becomes worthy (and yet remains hobbit). For that must be the purpose of your fate, or the purpose of that part of your fate which concerns you yourself. The hobbit half that loves the Shire is not to be despised but it has to be trained, and to rediscover the changing seasons and voices of friends when they have been lost.'

Here the text ends. The second of these abandoned versions is nearer to FR, but has Gildor speak severely about Bingo's lateness on the road:

'Has Gandalf told you nothing?'

'Nothing about such creatures.'

'Is it not by his advice, then, that you have left your home? Did he not even urge you to make haste?'

'Yes. He wished me to go sooner in the year. He said that delay might prove dangerous; and I begin to fear that it has.'

'Why did you not go before?'

282   THE RETURN OF THE SHADOW

Bingo then speaks about his two 'halves', though without comment, moves into an explanation of why he lingered till autumn, and speaks of his dismay at the danger that is already threatening.

The third text is very close to and quite largely word for word the same as the final form until near the end of the conversation, where the matter though essentially the same is somewhat differently arranged. Gildor's advice about taking companions is more explicit than in FR ('Take such friends as are trusty and willing', p. 94): here he says 'If there are any whom you can wholly trust, and who are willing to share your peril, take them with you.' He is referring to Bingo's present companions; for he goes on (much as in the old version, p. 64): 'They will protect you. I think it likely that your three companions have already helped you to escape: the Riders did not know that they were with you, and their presence has for the time being confused the scent.' But at the very end there occurs this passage:

. . . In this meeting there may be more than chance; but the purpose is not clear to me, and I fear to say too much. But' – and he paused and looked intently at Bingo – 'have you perhaps Bilbo's ring with you?'

'Yes, I have,' said Bingo, taken aback.

'Then I will add this last word. If a Rider approaches or pursues you hard – do not use the ring to escape from his search. I guess that the ring will help him more than you.'

'More mysteries!' said Bingo. 'How can a ring that makes me invisible help a Black Rider to find me?'

'I will answer only this,' said Gildor: 'the ring came in the beginning from the Enemy, and was not made to delude his servants.'

'But Bilbo used his ring to escape from goblins, and evil creatures,' said Bingo.

'Black Riders are not goblins,' said the Elf. 'Ask no more of me. But my heart forebodes that ere all is ended you Bingo son of Drogo will know more of these fell things than Gildor Inglorion. May Elbereth protect you!'

'You are far worse than Gandalf,' cried Bingo; 'and I am now more completely terrified than I have ever been in my life. But I am deeply grateful to you.'

The end of the chapter is virtually the same in the old version, the present text, and FR; but now Gildor adds the salutation: 'and may the stars shine upon the end of your road.'

DELAYS ARE DANGEROUS 283

NOTES

1 The different arrangement of the opening of the chapter introduces Bingo's intention to go and live in Buckland *before* it actually arose as a result of his conversation with Gandalf. It may be that my father afterwards reversed the order of these narrative elements in order to avoid this.

2 This passage, from 'and actually did ask his Brandybuck cousins', was struck out in pencil and replaced by the following:

With the help of his Brandybuck cousin Merry he chose and bought a little house [*added subsequently:* at Crickhollow] in the country behind Bucklebury, and began to make preparations for a removal.

3 Gandalf's words were changed in pencil thus:

'I shall want to see you before you set out, Bingo,' he said, as he took his leave one wet dark evening in May. 'I may have news, and useful information about the Road.' Bingo was not clear whether Gandalf intended to go with him to Rivendell or not.

4 There is no new list of presents in this variant: my father contented himself with a reference to the latest version of 'A Long-expected party', which was to be 'suitably emended' (p. 247, note 21).

5 The Sackville-Bagginses' son now first appears. It is said in both variants that Lobelia 'and her pimply son Cosimo (and his over-shadowed wife Miranda) lived at Bag-end for a long while afterwards / for many a year after.' Lobelia was in both versions 92 years old at this time, and had had to wait seventy-seven years (as in FR) for Bag-end, which makes her a grasping fifteen year old when Bilbo came back at the end of *The Hobbit* to find her measuring his rooms; in FR she was a hundred years old, and in the second of these variant versions '92' is changed to '102'. In FR her son is 'sandy-haired Lotho', and no wife is named.

6 The corrections are in fact in blue, black, and red inks. I have said earlier (p. 48 and note 1) that those in black ink belong to a very early stage of revision. Those in blue and red were made at the present stage; but in his note on the subject my father no doubt meant by 'corrections in black' to include all those that were not in red.

7 I give an example, however, to show the nature of the procedure (original version p. 51):

'The wind's in the West,' said Odo. 'If we go down the other side of this hill we are climbing, we ought to find a spot fairly dry and sheltered.'

The red ink corrections are given here in italics; other changes from the original text are in black (actually blue, see note 6) ink.

'The wind's in the West,' said *Sam*. 'If we go down the other side of this hill we are climbing, we shall find a spot that is sheltered and snug enough, *sir*. There is a dry fir-wood just

284 THE RETURN OF THE SHADOW

ahead, if I remember rightly.' *Sam knew the land well within about twenty miles of Hobbiton, but that was the limit of his geography.*
See also note 11.

8 The text is actually rendered still more complicated by a layer of later emendation arising from my father's intention to get rid of Odo altogether, leaving Bingo, Frodo Took, and Sam, but this is here ignored.

9 In the original texts the crossing of the East Road had been omitted (see pp. 46–7, 50). – With 'Michel Delving' for 'Much Hemlock (in the Hornblower country)' and 'south-east' for 'eastward', this is the reading of FR – in the first edition of LR. In the second edition (1966) the text was changed to read:

A mile or two further south they hastily crossed the great road from the Brandywine Bridge; they were now in the Tookland and bending south-eastwards they made for the Green Hill Country. As they began to climb its first slopes they looked back and saw the lamps in Hobbiton far off twinkling . . .

Robert Foster, in *The Complete Guide to Middle-earth*, entry *Hornblower*, says that 'all or most' of the Hornblowers 'dwelt in the Southfarthing'; this seems to be based only on the statement in the Prologue to LR that Tobold Hornblower, first grower of pipeweed, lived at Longbottom in the Southfarthing, but may well be a legitimate deduction. A few hobbit 'family territories' are marked on my father's map of the Shire (p. 107, item I), but the Hornblowers are not among them. (The Bracegirdles are placed west of Girdley Island in the Brandywine; the Bolgers south of the East Road and north of the Woody End; the Boffins north of Hobbiton Hill – cf. Mr Boffin of Overhill, FR p. 53; and the Tooks in Tookland, south of Hobbiton.) See p. 304, note 1.

10 See p. 246, note 18. The verse is now a repetition, for Bilbo had sung it before he left Bag End (p. 240); but whereas in FR (pp. 82–3) the only difference between the two recitations is that Bilbo says 'eager feet' in the 5th line and Frodo 'weary feet', here Bingo has also 'we' for 'I' in the 4th and 8th lines (retained from the original text, p. 53).

11 This passage interestingly exemplifies the 'two-tier' system of emendation which my father employed in this text (see p. 277). The new passage in which Bingo wonders if it is Gandalf coming after them and proposes to surprise him, though feeling certain that it is not him – exactly as in FR pp. 83–4 – is a 'red' emendation: because according to the new story Gandalf might well be expected to have just missed them at Hobbiton and be following on their heels, whereas according to the old story – in which the Birthday Party was Bingo's – Gandalf left immediately after the fireworks and went east (see p. 101 and note 12).

DELAYS ARE DANGEROUS

The remainder of the new passage (cited in the text), describing Bingo's conflicting desires to hide and not to hide, is a 'black' emendation (i.e. covering both 'old' and 'new' stories) – as is the addition almost immediately following, in which Bingo feels an urgent desire to put on the Ring, but does not: because, whatever version is followed, the nature of the Ring demands these changes (cf. *Queries and Alterations*, note 7 (p. 224): 'Bingo must NOT put on his Ring when Black Riders go by – in view of later developments. He must *think* of doing so but somehow be prevented.')

12 The text of FR here, 'I did not know that any of that fairest folk were ever seen in the Shire', was emended in the second edition to 'Few of that fairest folk are ever seen in the Shire.' – For previous references to the High Elves (which means now the Elves of Valinor) see pp. 187, 225, 260.

XVII

A SHORT CUT TO MUSHROOMS

The third of the original chapters (pp. 88 ff.) was now rewritten, numbered 'IV', and given a title, 'A Short Cut to Mushrooms'. This is a readily legible but much altered manuscript, with a great deal of variant and rejected material. The final result, however, as achieved already at this time (if a long variant version of the Farmer Maggot interlude, not at once rejected, is ignored for the moment), is virtually Chapter 5 in *The Fellowship of the Ring*, to a very great extent word for word, and there is not much that needs to be said about it.

The chief difference from FR lies of course in the fact that there were still Frodo Took and Odo Bolger and not simply Pippin. Pippin's part and all the things he says in FR are present in almost exactly the same form; but where in FR it is Pippin who is familiar with the region and who knows Farmer Maggot, in the present text (as also in the original version) this is Frodo Took's part, and once they have got down into the flat country Odo is in the background.

A good deal of new geography enters with the discussion whether to take a short cut or not (FR p. 97). While the wet low-lying land is described in the original story (pp. 91–2), it is now called the Marish, and the northward curve of the road (p. 89) is explained: 'to get round the north of the Marish.' The way south from Brandywine Bridge now appears – first called 'the raised road', then 'the banked road', then 'the causeway': 'the causeway that runs from the Bridge through Stock and past the Ferry down along the River to Deephallow.' Here the village of Stock is first named (and its inn the *Golden Perch*, where according to Odo there used to be the best beer in 'the East Shire'), and also Deephallow, which though marked on my father's map of the Shire and on the map in FR is never mentioned in the text of *The Lord of the Rings*. (In the original version of this chapter there is no suggestion of the causeway road, and the hobbits leaving Maggot's lane came out on to the road they had left, shortly before it reached the Ferry: see p. 97 and note 8. Stock had not then been devised. Later in the old version Marmaduke, arguing for going through the Old Forest, says that it would be silly of them to start their journey by 'jogging along a dull river-side road – in full view of all the numerous hobbits of Buckland', but he is speaking of the road within Buckland, on the east side of the Brandywine: p. 106, note 18).

The argument about which way to go is mainly between Odo and Frodo, and is somewhat different from the final form. Odo, not knowing

A SHORT CUT TO MUSHROOMS   287

the country, argued that there would be 'all kinds of obstacles' when they got down into the Marish, to which Frodo replied that he did know it, and that the Marish was now 'all tamed and drained' (in FR Pippin, who takes Frodo Took's part in that he does know the country, but Odo's in that he has his eye on the *Golden Perch*, argues with Frodo (Baggins) that in the Marish 'there are bogs and all kinds of difficulties').[1]

The stream that barred their passage is now identified as the Stockbrook. The only other feature to mention before coming to Farmer Maggot is a rejected passage that was to take the place of the mysterious sniffing that interrupted Odo's song in praise of the bottle in the original version (p. 91). There, a pencilled note on the manuscript (p. 105, note 3) said: 'Sound of hoofs going by not far off.'

Ho! ho! ho! they began again louder. 'Hush!' said Sam. 'I think I can hear something.' They stopped short. Bingo sat up. Listening he caught or thought he caught the sound of hoofs, some way off, going at a trot. They sat silent for some while after the sound had died away; but at last Frodo spoke. 'That's very odd,' he said. 'There is not any road that I know of anywhere near, yet the hoofs were not going on turf or leaves – if they were hoofs.' 'But if they were, it does not follow that it was the sound of a Black Rider,' said Odo. 'The land is not quite uninhabited round here: there are farms and villages.'

This was replaced by the terrible signal cries, exactly as in FR (pp. 99–100). From a rejected page a little later, when they came into the 'tame and well-ordered lands', it is clear that the hoof-beats they heard were not in fact so mysterious: 'They were just beginning to think that they had imagined the sound of hoofs, when they came to a gate: beyond it a rutted lane wound away towards a distant clump of trees' (i.e. Farmer Maggot's). The horseman they heard was the Black Rider who came to Maggot's door.

When my father came in this version to Farmer Maggot, he followed the old story in this: Bingo put on the Ring in the lane outside the farm, then entered the house invisibly, and drank Farmer Maggot's beer, so that the departure of the others was highly embarrassing and unhappy. Considering all that had now been said concerning the Ring this is remarkable; but I think that my father was reluctant to lose this interlude (see also note 13), and although at this time he also wrote the story of the visit to Maggot's in exactly the form it has in FR, he retained this first, entirely different account of what happened in Maggot's house and marked it as a variant.

In it, Maggot becomes a violent and intransigeant character, with a black hatred of all Bagginses – a development clearly arising, as I think, from the need to explain the intensity of Bingo's alarm when he learns

288   THE RETURN OF THE SHADOW

who is the owner of the farm, an alarm great enough (coupled with the ferocious dogs) to explain in turn how he could put the Ring on in the face of all counsel. In the original version Bingo put on the Ring as a matter of course, as he put it on when the Black Riders came by. Moreover, as the story stood then Frodo and Odo were perfectly familiar with his possession of a magic ring that conferred invisibility, and after they left Farmer Maggot's Odo addressed Bingo while he was still invisible, calling his behaviour 'a silly trick' (p. 97). But now they were not (cf. p. 245, note 3: 'Bilbo wrote his adventures in a private book of memoirs, in which he recounted some things that he had never spoken about (such as the magic ring); but that book was never published in the Shire, and he never showed it to anyone, except his favourite "nephew" Bingo.') The great problem now with this story, my father noted in the margin of the manuscript, was that it would necessitate making Odo, Frodo, and Sam all aware of Bingo's ring – 'which is a pity'; or else, he added, 'making the others equally astonished with Farmer Maggot – which is difficult.' He was even prepared, however, as he noted in the same place, to consider altering the structure to the extent of getting rid of Odo and Frodo from this episode by making them the advance party to Buckland, while Bingo's walk from Hobbiton would be with Merry and Sam – which seems to imply that Merry had been let into the secret of the Ring. Sam might be supposed to have known of it from his eavesdropping under the window of Bag End at the end of the chapter 'Ancient History'; and my father also revised the text here and there in pencil in order to 'allow this version to stand if Bingo's ring is *unknown* to any but Sam.' A point he did not make here is the distinction between the others knowing about the Ring and Bingo's knowing that they knew; and when he reached the conversation in the house in Buckland (not much later, for the text of the two chapters is continuous in the manuscript) he had decided that they did know, but had kept the knowledge to themselves (as in FR, p. 114).

I give now the greater part of this first variant version.

They came to a gate, beyond which a rutted lane ran between low hedges towards a distant clump of trees. Frodo stopped. 'I know these fields!' he said. 'They are part of old Farmer Maggot's land.[2] That must be his farm away there in the trees.'

'One trouble after another!' said Bingo, looking nearly as much alarmed as if Frodo had declared the lane to be the slot leading to a dragon's lair. The others looked at him in astonishment.

'What's wrong with old Maggot?' asked Frodo.[3]

'I don't like him, and he doesn't like me,' said Bingo. 'If I had thought my short cut would bring me near his farm today, I would have gone by the long road. I haven't been near it for years and years.'

A SHORT CUT TO MUSHROOMS   289

'Why ever not?' said Frodo. 'He's all right, if you get on the right side of him. I thought he was friendly to all the Brandybuck clan. Though he is a terror to trespassers, and he does keep some ferocious-looking dogs. But after all we are near the borders here and folk have to be more on their guard.'

'That's just it,' said Bingo. 'I used to trespass on his land when I was a youngster at Bucklebury. His fields used to grow the best mushrooms.⁴ I killed one of his dogs once. I broke its head with a heavy stone. A lucky shot, for I was terrified, and I believe it would have mauled me. He beat me, and told me he would kill me next time I put a foot over his boundaries. "I'd kill you now," he said, "if you were not Mr Rory's nephew,⁵ more's the pity and shame to the Brandybucks."'

'But that's long ago,' said Frodo. 'He won't kill Mr Bingo Baggins, late of Bag-end, because of his misdeeds when he was one of the many young rascals of Brandy Hall. Even if he remembers about it.'

'I don't fancy Maggot is a good forgetter,' said Bingo, 'especially not where his dogs are concerned. They used to say he loved his dogs more than his children. And Bilbo told me (only a year or two before he left the Shire) that he was once down this way and called at the farm to get a bite and drink. When he gave his name old Maggot ordered him off. "I'll have no Baggins over my doorstep. A lot of thievish murderous rascals. You get back where you belong," he said, and threatened him with a stick. He's shaken his fist at me, if we passed on the road, many a time since.'⁶

'Well I'm blest,' said Odo. 'So now I suppose we shall all get beaten or bitten, if we are seen with the marauding Bingo.'

'Nonsense!' said Frodo. 'Get into the lane, and then you won't be trespassing. Maggot used to be quite friendly with Merry and me. I'll talk to him.'

They went along the lane, until they saw the thatched roofs of a large house and farm-buildings peeping out among the trees ahead. The Maggots and the Puddifoots of Stock and most of the folk of the Marish were house-dwellers . . .

At this point a long digression was introduced (following that in the original version, p. 92) on the subject of hobbits living in houses; see pp. 294–5.

. . . and this farm was stoutly built of brick and had a high wall all round it. There was a strong wooden gate in the wall opening on to the lane. Bingo lagged behind. Suddenly as they drew nearer a

290   THE RETURN OF THE SHADOW

terrific baying and barking broke out, and a loud voice was heard
shouting: 'Grip! Fang! Wolf! Go on, lads! Go on!'

This was too much for Bingo. He slipped on the Ring, and
vanished. 'It can't do any harm this once,' he thought. 'I am sure
Bilbo would have done the same.'

He was only just in time. The gate opened and three huge dogs
came pelting out into the lane, and dashed towards the travellers.
Odo and Sam shrank against the wall, while two large grey
wolvish-looking dogs sniffed at them. The third dog halted near
Bingo sniffing and growling with the hair rising on its neck,
and a puzzled look in its eyes. Frodo walked on a few paces unmolested.

Through the gate came a broad thickset hobbit with a round red
face[7] and a soft high-crowned hat. 'Hullo! hullo! And who may
you be, and what may you be doing?' he asked.

'Good afternoon, Farmer Maggot!' said Frodo.

The farmer looked at him closely. 'Well now,' he said. 'Let me
see – you'll be Mr Frodo Took, Mr Folco's son, if I am not
mistook. I seldom am, I've a rare memory for faces. It's some time
since I saw you round here, with Mr Merry Brandybuck . . .

The opening encounter with Maggot is then exactly as in the other
variant of the episode, which is to say exactly as in FR p. 102, as far as 'to
the great relief of Odo and Sam the dogs let them go free.' Then follows:

Odo and Frodo at once went through the gate, but Sam hesitated.
So did the third dog. He remained standing growling and bristling.

This was altered in pencil to read:

Odo joined Frodo at the gate, but Sam hesitated in the lane. Frodo
looked back to beckon Bingo, and wondered how to introduce
him, whether to give his name, or hope that Maggot's memory was
less good than he boasted, and say nothing; but there was no sign
of Bingo to be seen. Sam was watching one of the dogs. It was still
standing growling and bristling. It all seemed rather queer.

This was one of the changes made 'to allow this version to stand if
Bingo's ring is unknown to any but Sam' (p. 288).

'Here, Wolf!' cried Farmer Maggot, looking back. 'Dang it,
what's come to the dog. Heel, Wolf!'

The dog obeyed reluctantly, and at the gate turned back and
barked.

A SHORT CUT TO MUSHROOMS
291

'What's the matter with you?' said the farmer. 'This is a queer day, and no mistake. Wolf went near off his head when that fellow came riding up, and now you'd think he could see or smell something that ain't there.'

They went into the farmer's kitchen, and sat by the wide fireplace. The dogs were shut up, as neither Odo nor Sam concealed their uneasiness while they were about. 'They won't harm you,' said the farmer, 'not unless I tell them to.' Mrs Maggot brought out beer and filled four large earthenware mugs. It was a good brew, and Odo found himself fully compensated for missing the *Golden Perch*. Sam would have enjoyed it better, if he had not been anxious about his master.

'And where might you be coming from and going to, Mr Frodo?' asked Farmer Maggot with a shrewd look. 'Were you coming to visit me? For if so you had gone past my gate without my seeing you.'

'Well, no,' said Frodo. 'To tell you the truth (since you guess it already) we had been on your fields. But it was quite by accident. We lost our way back near Woodhall trying to take a short cut to the causeway near the Ferry. We are in rather a hurry to get over into Buckland.'

'Then the road would have served you better,' said the farmer. 'But you and Mr Merry have my leave to walk on my land, as long as you do no damage. Not like those thievish folk from way back West – begging your pardon, I was forgetting you were a Took by name, and only half a Brandybuck as you might say.[8] But you aren't a Baggins or you'd not be inside here. That Mr Bingo Baggins he killed one of my dogs once, he did. It's more than 30 years ago, but I haven't forgotten it, and I'll remind him of it sharp too if ever he dares to come round here. I hear tell that he is coming back to live in Buckland. More's the pity. I can't think why the Brandybucks allow it.'

'But Mr Bingo's half a Brandybuck too,' said Odo (trying to keep from smiling). 'He's quite a nice fellow when you get on the right side of him; though he will go walking across country and he is fond of mushrooms.'

There seemed to be a breath, the ghost of an exclamation, not far from Odo's ear, though he could not be quite sure.[9]

'That's just it,' said the farmer. 'He used to take mine though I beat him for it. And I'll beat him again, if I catch him at it. But that reminds me: what do you think that funny customer asked me?'

292   THE RETURN OF THE SHADOW

Farmer Maggot then turns to his account of the funny customer, and his report, though briefer, goes pretty well as in the other variant version and in FR,[10] with this difference:

'. . . I had a sort of shiver down my back. But that question was too much for me. "Be off," I said. "There are no Bagginses here, and won't be while I am on my legs. If you are a friend of theirs you are not welcome. I give you one minute before I call my dogs."

From '"I don't know what to think," said Frodo' the story in this version moves in the direction of farce.

'Then I'll tell you what to think,' said Maggot. 'This Mr Bingo Baggins has got into some trouble. I hear tell that he has lost or wasted most of the money he got from old Bilbo Baggins. And *that* was got in some queer fashion, in foreign parts, too, they say. Mark my words, this all comes of some of those doings of old Mr Bilbo's. Maybe there is some that want to know what has become of the gold and what not that he left behind. Mark my words.'

'I certainly will,' said Frodo, rather taken aback by old Maggot's guessing.[11]

'And if you'll take my advice, too,' said the farmer, 'you'll steer clear of Mr Bingo, or you'll be getting into more trouble yourself than you bargain for.'

There was no mistaking the breath and the suppressed gasp by Frodo's ear on this occasion.[12]

'I'll remember the advice,' said Frodo. 'But now we must be getting to Bucklebury. Mr Merry Brandybuck is expecting us this evening.'

'Now that's a pity,' said the farmer. 'I was going to ask if you and your friends would stay and have a bite and sup with me and my wife.'

'It is very kind of you,' said Frodo; 'but I am afraid we must be off now – we want to get to the Ferry before dark.'

'Well then, one more drink!' said the farmer, and his wife poured out some beer. 'Here's your health and good luck!' he said, reaching for his mug. But at that moment the mug left the table, rose, tilted in the air, and then returned empty to its place.

'Help us and save us!' cried the farmer jumping up and gaping. 'This day is bewitched. First the dog and then me: seeing things that ain't.'

'But I saw the mug get up too,' said Odo indiscreetly, and not fully hiding a grin.

A SHORT CUT TO MUSHROOMS

This last sentence was struck out in pencil, as being unwanted 'if Bingo's ring is unknown to any but Sam.' The remainder of this version was written on that basis.

Odo and Frodo sat and stared. Sam looked anxious and worried. 'You did not ask me to have a bite or a sup,' said a voice coming apparently from the middle of the room. Farmer Maggot backed towards the fire-place; his wife screamed. 'And that's a pity,' went on the voice, which Frodo to his bewilderment now recognized as Bingo's, 'because I like your beer. But don't boast again that no Baggins will ever come inside your house. There's one inside now. A thievish Baggins. A very angry Baggins.' There was a pause. 'In fact BINGO!' the voice suddenly yelled just by the farmer's ear. At the same time something gave him a push in the waistcoat, and he fell over with a crash among the fire-irons. He sat up again just in time to see his own hat leave the settle where he had thrown it down, and sail out of the door, which opened to let it pass.

'Hi! here!' yelled the farmer, leaping to his feet. 'Hey, Grip, Fang, Wolf!' At that the hat went off at a great speed towards the gate; but as the farmer ran after it, it came sailing back through the air and fell at his feet. He picked it up gingerly, and looked at it in astonishment. The dogs released by Mrs Maggot came bounding up; but the farmer gave them no command. He stood still scratching his head and turning his hat over and over, as if he expected to find it had grown wings.[13]

Odo and Frodo followed by Sam came out of the house.

'Well, if that ain't the queerest thing that ever happened in my house!' said the farmer. 'Talk about ghosts! I suppose you haven't been playing any tricks on me, have you?' he said suddenly, looking hard at them in turn.

'We?' said Frodo. 'Why, we were as startled as you were. I can't make mugs drain themselves, or hats walk out of the house.'

'Well, it is mighty queer,' said the farmer, not seeming quite satisfied. 'First this rider asks for Mr Baggins. Then you folk come along; and while you are in the house Mr Baggins' voice starts playing tricks. And you are friends of his, seemingly. "Quite a nice fellow," you said. If there ain't some connexion between all these bewitchments, I'll eat this very hat. You can tell him from me to keep his voice at home, or I'll come and gag him, if I have to swim the River and hunt him all through Bucklebury. And now you'd best be going back to your friends, and leave me in peace. Good day to you.'

294 THE RETURN OF THE SHADOW

He watched them with a thoughtful scowl on his face until they turned a corner of the lane and passed out of his sight.

'What do you make of that?' asked Odo as they went along. 'And where on earth is Bingo?'

'What I make of it,' answered Frodo, 'is that Uncle Bingo has taken leave of his senses; and I fancy we shall run into him in this lane before long.'

'You won't run into me because I'm just behind,' said Bingo. There he was by Sam Gamgee's side.

This version of the episode ends here, with the note: 'This variant would proceed much as in older typed Chapter III' – i.e. in respect of the hobbits getting from Farmer Maggot's to the Ferry, if they are not driven there in Maggot's cart (see pp. 97–9).

Apart from any other considerations (which there may well have been), I think that it was primarily the difficulty with the Ring that killed this version. In the next chapter it turns out that the other hobbits had known about the Ring, but that Bingo had not known that they knew. So the ferocious Farmer Maggot, prone to ill-will, had already disappeared, and with him the last (more or less) light-hearted use of the Ring.[14] The second version of the Maggot episode in this manuscript evidently followed quite closely on the first, and this, as I have said, is (names apart) identical save for a word here and there with the story in FR.

There remains to notice the passage about hobbit architecture mentioned above (p. 289). Against it my father wrote 'Put in Foreword',[15] and in the second version of the Maggot story it is not included. It was somewhat developed from that in the original form of the chapter (p. 92), but has less detail than that in the Prologue to FR (pp. 15–16, in the first edition 16–17). The division of hobbits into Harfoots, Fallohides, and Stoors had not yet arisen, and the fact that some of the people in the Marish were 'rather large, and heavy-legged, and a few actually had a little down under their chins' is ascribed to their not being of pure hobbit-breed. In this account the art of house-building still originated, or was thought to have originated, among the hobbits themselves, down in the riverside regions (in the Prologue it is suggested that it was derived from the Dúnedain, or even from the Elves); but it 'had long been altered (and perhaps improved) by taking wrinkles from dwarves and elves and even Big Folk, and other people outside the Shire.'

The passage in the Prologue concerning the presence of houses in many hobbit villages is present, and here Tuckborough first appears. As this passage was first drafted it read:

Even in Hobbiton and Bywater, and in Tuckborough away in Tookland, and on the chalky Indowns in the centre of the Shire where there was a large population

A SHORT CUT TO MUSHROOMS 295

My father then struck out *Indowns*, presumably meaning to include *on the chalky* as well, and substituted [*Much* >] *Micheldelving*, before abandoning the sentence and starting again. Michel Delving on the White Downs has appeared in the last chapter (p. 278), replacing 'Much Hemlock (in the Hornblower country)'. He was probably going to write 'Much Hemlock' here too. It seems that up till now he had not decided that the chief town was in the west of the Shire, if indeed there were any chief town; but he at once rewrote the passage, and it was very probably at this point that Michel Delving on the White Downs came into existence (and was then written into 'Delays are Dangerous'). As finally written, the sentence reads:

> In Hobbiton, in Tuckborough away in Tookland, and even in the most populous [village >] town of the Shire, Micheldelving, on the White Downs in the West, there were many houses of stone and wood and brick.

The name *Indowns* does not occur again; cf. the *Inlands* (*Mittalmar*), the central region of Númenor, *Unfinished Tales* p. 165.

The text of this chapter, following the arrangement of the original version, continues straight on without break from 'Suddenly Bingo laughed: from the covered basket he held the scent of mushrooms was rising', which ends Chapter 4 in FR, to '"Now we'd better get home ourselves," said Merry', which in FR begins Chapter 5; but not long after my father broke the text at this point, inserting the number 'V' and the title 'A Conspiracy is Unmasked', and I follow this arrangement here.

NOTES

1 This passage of discussion was much rewritten. In rejected versions Odo proposes that they split up: 'Why all go the same way? Those who vote for short cuts, cut. Those who don't, go round – and they (mark you) will reach the *Golden Perch* at Stock before sundown'; and Frodo argues for going across country by saying 'Merry won't worry if we are late.' In another, Odo says: 'Then I must fall in behind, or go alone. Well, I don't think Black Riders will do anything to me. It's you, Bingo, they are sniffing for. If they ask after you, I shall say: I have quarrelled with Mr Baggins and left him. He lodged with the Elves last night – ask them.'

    A minute point in connection with the geography may be mentioned here. In 'the woods that clustered along the eastern side of the hill', FR p. 98 line 5, 'hill' should be 'hills', as it is in the present text.

2 At this first mention of the farmer in this text, he is called *Farmer Puddifoot*, but this was changed at once to *Maggot*, and *Maggot* is his name subsequently throughout. At the same place in the original

296   THE RETURN OF THE SHADOW

typescript, and only at that place, *Maggot* was changed to *Puddifoot* (p. 105, note 4).

3 Frodo continued: 'Of course these people down in the Marish are a bit queer and unfriendly, but the Brandybucks get on all right with them', but this was struck out as soon as written.

4 This is where the mushrooms entered the story: there is no mention of mushrooms in the original version.

5 On Bingo's being the nephew of Rory Brandybuck (Merry's grand-father) see p. 267, note 4.

6 Another version of Bingo's account makes it Bilbo and Bingo who had the encounter with Maggot, and the farmer a real ogre:

> 'That's just it,' said Bingo. 'I got on the wrong side of him, and of his hedge. We were trespassing, as he called it. We had been in the Shirebourn valley, and were making a cross-country line towards Stock – rather like today – when we got on to his land. It was getting dark, and a white fog came on, and we got lost. We climbed through a hedge and found ourselves in a garden; and Maggot found us. He set a great dog on us, more like a wolf. I fell down with the dog over me, and Bilbo broke its head with that thick stick of his. Maggot was violent. He is a strong fellow, and while Bilbo ws trying to explain who we were and how we came there he picked him up and flung him over the hedge into a ditch. Then he picked me up and had a good look at me. He recognized me as one of the Brandybuck clan, though I had not been to his farm since I was a youngster. "I was going to break your neck," he said, "and I will yet, whether you be Mr Rory's nephew or not, if I catch you round here again. Get out before I do you an injury!" He dropped me over the hedge on top of Bilbo.
>
> 'Bilbo got up and said: "I shall come around next time with something sharper than a stick. Neither you nor your dogs would be any loss to the countryside." Maggot laughed. "I have a weapon or two myself," he said; 'and next time you kill one of my dogs, I'll kill you. Be off now, or I'll kill you tonight." That'll be 20 years ago. But I don't imagine Maggot is a good forgetter. Ours would not be a friendly meeting.'

Frodo Took's reception of this story was strangely mild. 'How very unfortunate!' [he said.] 'Nobody seems to have been much to blame. After all, Bingo, you must remember that this is near the Borders, and people round here are a deal more suspicious than up in the Baggins country.'

Like Deephallow (p. 286), the Shirebourn, mentioned in this passage, is never named in LR, though marked both on my father's map of the Shire and on that published in FR (both are mentioned in *The Adventures of Tom Bombadil*, p. 9).

7 Farmer Maggot is again unambiguously a hobbit: see p. 122 and note 7.

A SHORT CUT TO MUSHROOMS   297

8   There has in fact been no indication that Frodo Took's mother was a Brandybuck, as is seen to be the case from Maggot's remark here, supported also by Frodo's knowledge of the Marish and Maggot's familiarity with him as a companion of Merry Brandybuck. In LR the mother of Peregrin (who is related to Meriadoc as Frodo Took is at this stage, see p. 267, note 4) was Eglantine Banks.

9   This sentence is marked in pencil for deletion.

10 In this version the Black Rider does not say anything beyond 'Have you seen Mist-er Bagg-ins?' In the second version his words are almost as in FR, though he still calls him 'Mister Baggins'.

11 In the second version, as in FR (p. 104) 'the shrewd guesses of the farmer were rather disconcerting' to Bingo (Frodo); but here Maggot's guesses disconcert Frodo Took, which would suggest that he knew what the Black Riders were after.

12 This sentence is marked in pencil for deletion; cf. note 9.

13 Pencilled changes in this passage substitute the beer jug for Farmer Maggot's hat: 'He sat up again just in time to see the jug (still holding some beer) leave the table where he had lain it down, and sail out of the door . . . At that the jug went off at a great speed towards the gate, spilling beer in the yard; but as the farmer ran after it, it suddenly stopped and came to rest on the gatepost . . . He stood still scratching his head and turning the jug round and round . . .' (and 'jug' for 'hat' subsequently).

In the margin of the manuscript my father wrote: 'Christopher queries – why was not *hat* invisible if Bingo's clothes were?' The story must have been that Bingo was actually wearing Maggot's hat, for otherwise the objection seems easily answered (the hat was an object external to the wearer of the Ring just as much as the beer-jug, or as anything else would be, whatever its purpose). Clearly, a subtle question arises if the Ring is put to such uses, a question my father sidestepped by substituting the jug. – I was greatly delighted by the story of Bingo's turning the tables on Farmer Maggot, and while I retain now only a dim half-memory I believe I was much opposed to its loss: which may perhaps explain my father's retaining it after it had become apparent that it introduced serious difficulties.

14 Unless the episode in Tom Bombadil's house (FR p. 144) can be so described.

15 The passage in the 'Foreword' is given on pp. 312–13.

XVIII

AGAIN FROM BUCKLAND TO THE WITHYWINDLE

(i)

A Conspiracy is Unmasked

The text of 'A Short Cut to Mushrooms', as I have said, continues without break, but my father added in (not much later, see p. 302) a new chapter number 'V' and the title 'A Conspiracy is Unmasked'. The text now becomes very close indeed to FR Chapter 5 (apart of course from the number of and names of the hobbits), and there are only a few particular points to notice in it. For the earliest form see pp. 99 ff.

The history of the Brandybucks does not yet know Gorhendad Oldbuck as the founder (FR p. 108). As the manuscript was first written, the village was called Bucklebury-beyond-the-River, and (developing the original text, p. 100) 'the authority of the head of the Brandybucks was still acknowledged by the farmers as far west as Woodhall (which was reckoned to be in the Boffin-country)';[1] this was changed to 'still acknowledged by the farmers between Stock and Rushey,' as in FR. Rushey here first appears.[2]

It was in this passage that the Four Farthings of the Shire were first devised, as the wording shows: 'They were not very different from the other hobbits of the Four Farthings (North, West, South, and East), as the quarters of the Shire were called.' Here too occur for the first time the names Buck Hill and the High Hay – but Haysend goes back to the original version, p. 100. The great hedge is still 'something over forty miles from end to end.'[3] In answer to Bingo's question 'Can horses cross the river?' Merry answers: 'They can go fifteen miles to Brandywine Bridge', with '20?' pencilled over 'fifteen'. In FR the High Hay is 'well over *twenty* miles from end to end', yet Merry still says: 'They can go *twenty* miles north to Brandywine Bridge.' Barbara Strachey (*Journeys of Frodo*, Map 6) points out this difficulty, and assumes that Merry 'meant 20 miles in all – 10 miles north to the Bridge and 10 miles south on the other side'; but this is to strain the language: Merry did not mean that. It is in fact an error which my father never observed: when the length of Buckland from north to south was reduced, Merry's estimate of the distance from the Bridge to the Ferry should have been changed commensurately.[4]

The main road within Buckland is described (on a rejected page only) as running 'from the Bridge to Standelf and Haysend.' Standelf is never

AGAIN FROM BUCKLAND TO THE WITHYWINDLE 299

mentioned in the text of LR, though marked on my father's map of the Shire and on both of mine; on all three the road stops there and does not continue to Haysend, which is not shown as a village or any sort of habitation.[5]

At the first two occurrences of Crickhollow in this chapter the name was first *Ringhay*, changed to *Crickhollow* (in the passage cited in note 2 on p. 283 the name is a later addition to the text). At the third occurrence here *Crickhollow* was the name first written. *Ringhay* refers to the 'wide circle of lawn surrounded by a belt of trees inside the outer hedge.'[6]

The most important development in this chapter is that after the words 'the far shore seemed to be shrouded in mist and nothing could be seen' (FR p. 109) my father interrupted the narrative with the following note before proceeding:

From here onwards Odo is presumed to have gone with Merry ahead. The preliminary journey was Frodo, Bingo and Sam only. Frodo has a character a little more like Odo once had. Odo is now rather silent (and greedy).

Against this my father wrote: 'Christopher wants Odo kept.' Unhappily I have now only a very shadowy recollection of those conversations of half a century ago; and it is not clear to me what the issue really was. On the face of it, my 'wanting Odo kept' should mean that I wanted him kept as a member of the party that walked from Hobbiton, since my father had not proposed that Odo be dropped absolutely; on the other hand, since he had in mind the blending of 'Odo' elements into the character of Frodo Took, it may very well be that he was planning to cut him out of the expedition after the hobbits left Crickhollow. Perhaps the idea that Odo should remain on at Crickhollow was already present as a possibility, and 'Christopher wants Odo kept' was a plea for his survival in the larger narrative, as a member of the major expedition. This is no more than guesswork, but if there is anything in it, it seems that my objection temporarily won the day, since at the end of the chapter Odo is fully re-established, and prepared to go with the others into the Old Forest – as indeed he does, in the revision of that chapter in this 'phase'.

The situation in the text that follows this note on Odo is in any case extraordinarily difficult to interpret. As first written, Merry says that he will ride on and tell *Olo* that they are coming; when Bingo knocked on the door of (Ringhay) Crickhollow it was opened by Olo Bolger, and Merry refers to 'Olo and I' having got to Crickhollow with the last cartload on the day before; Merry and Olo prepared the supper in the kitchen. 'Olo' here plays the part of Fatty (Fredegar) Bolger in FR (pp. 110–11), but after these mentions he disappears from the text (and never appears again). In red ink my father noted: 'If Odo is kept alter in red,' and for a short distance some red ink alterations were made, changing 'You'll be last either way, Frodo' (concerning the order of entry into the bath) to

300   THE RETURN OF THE SHADOW

'Odo', changing 'three tubs' to 'four tubs', and cutting out the references to 'Olo'.[7]

The best explanation seems to be that when Odo was to be removed from the walking party and attached to Merry his name was to be changed also. Some alterations were made to preserve the option of retaining the received story. But from the moment when they sat down to supper Odo reappears in the text as first written; not merely as being present (which would only show that *Olo* had been rejected and *Odo* restored) but as having walked from Hobbiton (though in this case his name was bracketed). But Frodo Took now makes 'Odo-Pippin' remarks (as 'Oh! That was poetry!' FR p. 116 – he would hardly have said such a thing previously). See further pp. 323–4.

The bath-song (here sung by Frodo in his new Odoesque character) is all but identical to that which Pippin sings in FR; but in a red ink addition to the text (one of the optional additions made to bring Odo back in his original rôle) specimens of the 'competing songs' (FR p. 111) sung by Bingo and Odo are given: the first verse of the bath-song which Odo sang as they walked from Farmer Maggot's to the Ferry in the original version (p. 98) and which is thus no longer used, and the first two lines of the bath-chant sung by Odo when they reached their destination (p. 102), these last being struck out.

The revelation of the conspiracy is almost exactly as in FR, the burden of its exposition being taken here as there by Merry (Pippin's intervention 'You do not understand! . . .' being given here to Frodo Took). As in FR, Merry recounts the story of how he discovered the existence of Bilbo's ring, which was previously set in a quite different context (see p. 242 and note 25), and tells that he had had a rapid glance at Bilbo's 'memoirs' ('secret book' in FR).[8]

The report of what Gildor had said, here referred to by Merry rather than by Sam himself, on the subject of Bingo's taking companions reflects the text of that episode at this time (see p. 282): 'I know you have been advised to take us. Gildor told you to, and you can't deny it!'

The song that Merry and Pippin sang in FR (p. 116) is here sung by Merry, Frodo Took, and Odo,[9] and is very different:

> *Farewell! farewell, now hearth and hall!*
> *Though wind may blow and rain may fall,*
> *We must away ere break of day*
> *Far over wood and mountain tall.*

> *The hunt is up! Across the land*
> *The Shadow stretches forth its hand.*
> *We must away ere break of day*
> *To where the Towers of Darkness stand.*

AGAIN FROM BUCKLAND TO THE WITHYWINDLE 301

With foes behind and foes ahead,
Beneath the sky shall be our bed,
Until at last the Ring is cast
In Fire beneath the Mountain Red.

We must away, we must away,
We ride before the break of day.

In a rejected version of his answer to Bingo's question whether it would be safe to wait one day at Crickhollow for Gandalf (FR p. 117), a passage rewritten several times, Merry refers to the gate-guards getting a message through to 'my father the Master of the Hall.' Merry's father was Caradoc Brandybuck (Saradoc 'Scattergold' in LR); see p. 251 and note 4.

When Bingo raises the question of going through the Old Forest, it is Odo who, filled with horror at the thought, voices the objections given in FR to Fatty Bolger (who is going to stay behind).

The end of the chapter is different from that in FR, and belongs rather with the original version (p. 104). (Merry does not mention, incidentally, that Bingo had ever been into the Forest).

'. . . I have often been in – only in the daylight, of course, when the trees are fairly quiet and sleepy. Still, I have some some knowledge of it, and I will try and guide you.'

Odo was not convinced, and was plainly far less frightened of meeting a troop of Riders on the open road than of venturing into the dubious Forest. Even Frodo was against the plan.

'I hate the idea,' said Odo. 'I would rather risk pursuers on the Road, where there is a chance of meeting ordinary honest travellers as well. I don't like woods, and the stories about the Old Forest have always terrified me. I am sure Black Riders will be very much more at home in that gloomy place than we shall.' Even Frodo on this occasion sided with Odo.

'But we shall probably be out of it again before they ever find out or guess that we have gone in,' said Bingo. 'In any case, if you wish to come with me, it is no good taking fright at the first danger: there are almost certainly far worse things than the Old Forest ahead of you. Do you follow Captain Bingo, or do you stay at home?'

'We follow Captain Bingo,' they said at once.

'Well, that's settled!' said Merry. 'Now we must tidy up and put the finishing touches to the packing. And then to bed. I shall call you all well before the break of day.'

When at last he got to bed Bingo could not sleep for some time.

302 THE RETURN OF THE SHADOW

His legs ached. He was glad that he was riding in the morning. At last he fell into a vague dream: in which he seemed to be looking out of a window over a dark sea of tangled trees. Down below among the roots there was a sound of something crawling and snuffling.

A note on the manuscript earlier says 'Pencillings = Odo stays behind.' These pencillings are in fact confined to the section just given. 'Even Frodo on this occasion sided with Odo' is bracketed and replaced by further words of Odo's: 'Also I feel certain it is wrong not to wait for Gandalf.' And after '"We follow Captain Bingo," they said at once' is inserted:

'I will follow Captain Bingo,' said Merry, and Frodo, and Sam. Odo was silent. 'Look here!' he said, after a pause. 'I don't mind admitting I am frightened of the Forest, but I also think you ought to try and get in touch with Gandalf. I will stay behind here and keep off inquisitive folk. When Gandalf comes as he is sure to I will tell him what you have done, and I will come on after you with him, if he will bring me.' Merry and Frodo agreed that that was a good plan.

This would be an important development, though ultimately rejected. These alterations derive, however, from a somewhat later stage.

(ii)

The Old Forest

Having completed 'A Conspiracy is Unmasked', my father continued his revision into the next chapter, afterwards called 'The Old Forest'. In this case he did not make a new manuscript, but merely made corrections to the original text (described on pp. 112–14), which as I have said had reached with only the most minor differences the form of the published narrative. The chapter was at this time renumbered, from IV to VI, showing that Chapter V 'A Conspiracy is Unmasked' had been separated off from 'A Short Cut to Mushrooms'. Extensive emendations, made in red ink to the original manuscript, bring the text still closer in detail of wording to that of FR (but the topographical differences noticed on pp. 113–14 remain). The parts played in the Willow-man episode are changed by the presence of Sam Gamgee in the party. Bingo and Odo are still the two who are caught in the cracks of the tree, and Frodo Took is still the one pushed into the river; but whereas in the original story it was Marmaduke (i.e. Merry) who rounded up the ponies and rescued Frodo Took from the water, Sam now takes over this part (as in FR), while Merry 'lay like a log.'

AGAIN FROM BUCKLAND TO THE WITHYWINDLE   303

(iii)

Tom Bombadil

The manuscript of the Tom Bombadil chapter, the number changed from V to VII but still title-less, underwent (with one important exception) minimal revision at this stage (there were indeed few changes ever made to it): scarcely more than a mention of Sam sleeping, with Merry, like a log, and the changing of the number of hobbits from four to five. The points of difference noticed on pp. 120–3 were nearly all left as they were; but Bombadil's remark about Farmer Maggot ('We are kinsfolk, he and I . . .') was marked with an X, probably at this time.

The one substantial change made is of great interest. On the manuscript my father marked 'Insert' before the passage concerning the hobbits' dreams on the first night in Tom Bombadil's house; and that the insertion belongs to this phase is made clear by the fact that Crickhollow was *empty* (i.e. Odo had gone with the others into the Old Forest).

As they slept there in the house of Tom Bombadil, darkness lay on Buckland. Mist strayed in the hollow places. The house at Crickhollow stood silent and lonely: deserted so soon after being made ready for a new master.

The gate in the hedge opened, and up the path, quietly but in haste, a grey man came, wrapped in a great cloak. He halted looking at the dark house. He knocked softly on the door, and waited; and then passed from window to window, and finally disappeared round the corner of the house-end. There was silence again. After a long time a sound of hoofs was heard in the lane approaching swiftly. Horses were coming. Outside the gate they stopped; and then swiftly up the path there came three more figures, hooded, swathed in black, and stooping low towards the ground. One went to the door, one to the corners of the house-end at either side; and there they stood silent as the shadows of black yew-trees, while time went slowly on, and the house and the trees about it seemed to be waiting breathlessly.

Suddenly there was a movement. It was dark, and hardly a star was shining, but the blade that was drawn gleamed suddenly, as if it brought with it a chill light, keen and menacing. There was a blow, soft but heavy, and the door shuddered. 'Open to the servants of the Lord!' said a voice, thin, cold, and clear. At a second blow the door yielded and fell back, its lock broken.

At that moment there rang out behind the house a horn. It rent the night like fire on a hill-top. Loud and brazen it shouted, echoing over field and hill: *Awake, awake, fear, fire, foe! Awake!*

Round the corner of the house came the grey man. His cloak

304 THE RETURN OF THE SHADOW

and hat were cast aside. His beard streamed wide. In one hand was a horn, in the other a wand. A splendour of light flashed out before him. There was a wail and cry as of fell hunting beasts that are smitten suddenly, and turn to fly in wrath and anguish.

In the lane the sound of hoofs broke out, and gathering rapidly to a gallop raced madly into the darkness. Far away answering horns were heard. Distant sounds of waking and alarm rose up. Along the roads folk were riding and running northward. But before them all there galloped a white horse. On it sat an old man with long silver hair and flowing beard. His horn sounded over hill and dale. In his hand his wand flared and flickered like a sheaf of lightning. Gandalf was riding to the North Gate with the speed of thunder.

Against the end of this inserted text my father wrote in pencil: 'This will require altering if Odo is left behind'; see the pencilled passage added at the end of the last chapter (p. 302). And at the end of the text, after the words 'a sheaf of lightning', he added in: 'Behind clung a small figure with flying cloak', and the name 'Odo'. The significance of this will become clear later.

NOTES

1 On my father's map of the Shire the Boffins are placed north of Hobbiton, and the Bolgers north of the Woody End (p. 284, note 9), but this was an alteration of what he first wrote: the underlying names can be seen to be in the reverse positions.

2 The spelling *Rushy* on the published map of the Shire is an error, made first on my elaborate early map (p. 107, item V) through misreading of my father's. The second element is Old English *ey* 'island'.

3 On my father's original map it can be roughly calculated (since Bingo estimated that they had eighteen miles to go in a straight line from the place where they passed the night with the Elves to Bucklebury Ferry) that the High Hay was about 43 miles measured in a straight line from its northern to its southern end.

4 On my father's later maps (see p. 107) measurement can only be very approximate, but on the same basis as the calculation in note 3 the High Hay cannot in these be much more than 20 miles (in a straight line between its ends).

5 *Standelf* means 'stone-quarry' (Old English *stān-(ge)delf*, surviving in the place-name *Stonydelph* in Warwickshire).

6 Just as in FR, the hobbits leaving the Ferry passed Buck Hill and Brandy Hall on their left, struck the main road of Buckland, turned

AGAIN FROM BUCKLAND TO THE WITHYWINDLE 305

north along it for half a mile, and then took the lane to Crickhollow. On my original map of the Shire, made in 1943 (p. 107), the text – which was never changed here – was already wrongly represented, since the main road is shown as passing between the River and Brandy Hall (and the lane to Crickhollow leaves the road south of the hall, so that the hobbits would in fact, according to this map, still pass it on their left). This must have been a simple misinterpretation of the text which my father did not notice (cf. p. 108); and it reappeared on my map published in the first edition of FR. My father referred to the error in his letter to Austin Olney of Houghton Mifflin, 28 July 1965 (*Letters* no. 274); and it was corrected, after a fashion, on the map as published in the second edition. Karen Fonstad (*The Atlas of Middle-earth*, p. 121) and Barbara Strachey (*Journeys of Frodo*, Map 7) show the correct topography clearly.

7   These alterations to bring Odo back were made at the same time as the notes on the retention of the story that Bingo entered Farmer Maggot's house invisibly (p. 288); cf. p. 297, note 13.

8   In this text Merry says 'I was only in my tweens', whereas in FR he says 'teens'. In LR (Appendix C) Merry was born in (1382 =) 2982, and so in the year before the Farewell Party he was 18. Here, Merry is conceived to be somewhat older. – To Merry's question about Bilbo's book ('Have you got it, Bingo?') Bingo replies: 'No! He took it away, or so it seems.' Cf. the last note in *Queries and Alterations* (p. 229): 'Bilbo carries off "memoirs" to Rivendell.'

9   Changed from 'Merry and Frodo'.

THE THIRD PHASE

XIX
THE THIRD PHASE (1):
THE JOURNEY TO BREE

It seems to me extremely probable that the 'second phase' of writing, beginning with the fifth version of 'A Long-expected Party' (Chapter XIV in this book) now petered out, and once again a new start was made on the whole work. This 'third phase' is constituted by a long series of homogeneous manuscripts carrying the story from a sixth version of 'A Long-expected Party' right through to Rivendell. Though subsequently overwritten, interleaved, struck through, or 'cannibalised' to form parts of later texts, these manuscripts were at first clear and neat, and their rather distinctive, regular script makes it possible to reconstitute the series quite precisely despite the punishment they received later, and despite the fact that some parts remained in England when others went to Marquette University. They were indeed fair copies of the now chaotic existing texts, and few important narrative changes were made. But in these new texts 'Bingo' is finally supplanted by 'Frodo', and 'Frodo Took' becomes in turn 'Folco Took', taking over what had been his father's name (see pp. 251, 290). In describing these third phase versions I restrict myself here almost exclusively to the form they had when first written, and ignore the fearsome complexities of their later treatment.

There are three pieces of evidence available for the determination of the 'external' date. One is my father's letter of 13 October 1938, in which he said that the book 'has reached Chapter XI (though in rather an illegible state)' (*Letters* no. 34). Another is his letter of 2 February 1939, in which he recorded that although he had not been able to touch it since the previous December, it had by then 'reached Chapter 12 (and had been re-written several times), running to over 300 MS pages of the same size as this paper and written generally as closely.' The third is a set of notes, plot-outlines and brief narrative drafts all bearing the date 'August 1939': from these, as will be seen later, it is apparent that the third phase was already in being.

My guess – it can hardly be more – is that in October 1938 the third phase had not been begun, or had not proceeded far, since the book was 'in rather an illegible state'; while when my father wrote of having had to set the work aside in December 1938 it was to the third phase that he was referring: hence he said that it had been 're-written several times' (moreover 'Chapter XII' of this phase is the arrival at Rivendell, and it is here – as I think – that the new version was interrupted).

310   THE RETURN OF THE SHADOW

The third phase can be described quite rapidly, as far as the end of 'Fog on the Barrow-downs'; but first there is an interesting new text to be given. This my father called a *Foreword* (precursor of the *Prologue* in the published work). There is no preparatory material for it extant, but for a section of it he took up the passage concerning hobbit architecture from the second version of 'A Short Cut to Mushrooms', against which he had directed 'Put in Foreword' (see pp. 294–5). This was scarcely changed for its place in the *Foreword*, but there was now added a reference to the 'Elf-towers', which goes back to the earliest form of the 'architecture' passage in the original version of the chapter (pp. 92–3), where Bingo says that he had once seen the towers himself.

A number of changes were made to the manuscript of the *Foreword*, but apart from those that seem clearly to belong to the time of writing I ignore them here and print the text as it was first written.

FOREWORD

Concerning Hobbits

This book is largely concerned with hobbits, and it is possible to find out from it what they are (or were), and whether they are worth hearing about or not. But finding out things as you trudge along a road or plod through a story is rather tiring, even when it is (as occasionally happens) interesting or exciting. Those who wish to have things clear from the beginning will find some useful information in the brief account of Mr Bilbo Baggins' great Adventure, which led to the even more difficult and dangerous adventures recorded in this book. This account was called *The Hobbit* or *There and Back again*, because it was chiefly concerned with the most famous of all the old legendary hobbits, Bilbo; and because he went to the Lonely Mountain and came back again to his own home. But one story may well be all that readers have time or taste for. So I will put down some items of useful information here.

Hobbits are a very ancient people, once upon a time more numerous, alas! than they are to-day, when (or so I hear it sadly rumoured) they are vanishing rapidly; for they are fond of peace and quiet, and good tilled earth: a well-ordered and well-farmed countryside is their natural haunt. They are quite useless with machines more complicated than a bellows or a water-mill; though they are fairly handy with tools. They were always rather shy of the Big People (as they call us), and now they are positively scared of us.

THE JOURNEY TO BREE   311

And yet plainly they must be relatives of ours: nearer to us than elves are, or even dwarves. For one thing, they spoke a very similar language (or languages), and liked or disliked much the same things as we used to. What exactly the relationship is would be difficult to say. To answer that question one would have to re-discover a great deal of the now wholly lost history and legends of the Earliest Days;[1] and that is not likely to happen, for only the Elves preserve any traditions about the Earliest Days, and their traditions are mostly about themselves – not unnaturally: the Elves were much the most important people of those times. But even their traditions are incomplete: Men only come in to them occasionally, and Hobbits are not mentioned. Elves, Dwarves, Men, and other creatures only became aware of Hobbits after they had actually existed, jogging along in their uneventful fashion, for many ages. And they continued, as a rule, to jog along, keeping to themselves and keeping out of stories. In the days of Bilbo (and Frodo his heir) they became for a time very important, by what is called accident, and the great persons of the world, even the Necromancer, were obliged to take them into account, as these stories show. Though Hobbits had then already had a long history (of a quiet kind), those days are now very long ago, and geography (and many other things) were then very different. But the lands in which they lived, changed though they now are, must have been more or less in the same place as the lands in which they still linger: the North-west of the old world.

They are (or were) a small people, smaller than dwarves: less stout and stocky, that is, even when they were not in fact much shorter. Their height was, like the height of us Big People, rather variable, ranging between two and four feet (of our length): three feet was more or less an average. Very few hobbits, outside their own more fantastic legends, touched three foot six. Only Bandobras Took, son of Isengrim the First, known usually as the Bullroarer, of all the hobbits of history exceeded four feet. He was four foot five and rode a horse.[2]

There is, and always has been, very little magic about hobbits. Of course they possess the power which we sometimes confuse with real magic – it is really only a kind of professional skill, that has become uncanny through long practice, aided by close friend-ship with the earth and all things that grow on it: the power of disappearing quietly and quickly when large stupid folk like us come blundering along, making noises like elephants, which they can hear a mile off. Even long ago their great desire was to avoid

312   THE RETURN OF THE SHADOW

trouble; and they were quick in hearing, and sharpsighted. And they were neat and deft in their movements, though they were inclined to be fat in the stomach, and did not hurry unnecessarily.

They dressed in bright colours, being particularly fond of green and yellow; but they wore no shoes, because their feet grew natural leathery soles and thick warm brown hair, curly like the brown hair of their heads. The only trade unknown among them was consequently shoemaking; but they had long clever brown fingers and could make many other useful things. They had good-natured faces, being as a rule good-natured; and they laughed long and deeply, being fond of simple jests at all times, but especially after dinner (which they had twice a day, when they could get it). They were fond of presents, and gave them away freely, and accepted them readily.

All hobbits had originally lived in holes in the ground, or so they believed; although actually already in Bilbo's time it was as a rule only the richest and the poorest hobbits that still did so. The poorest hobbits went on living in holes of the most antiquated kind – in fact just holes, with only one window, or even none. The most important families continued to live (when they could) in luxurious versions of the simple excavations of olden times. But suitable sites for these large and ramifying tunnels were not to be found everywhere. In Hobbiton, in Tuckborough in Tookland, and even in the one really populous town of their Shire, Michel-Delving on the White Downs, there were many houses of stone and wood and brick. These were specially favoured by the millers, blacksmiths, wheelwrights, and people of that sort: for even when they had holes to live in hobbits used to put up sheds and barns for workshops and storehouses.

The custom of building farms and dwelling-houses was believed to have begun among the inhabitants of the river-side regions (especially the Marish down by the Brandywine), where the land was flat and wet; and where perhaps the hobbit-breed was not quite pure. Some of the hobbits of the Marish in the East-farthing at any rate were rather large and heavy-legged; a few actually had a little down under their chins (no pure-bred hobbit had a beard); and one or two even wore boots in muddy weather.

It is possible that the idea of building, as of so many other things, came originally from the Elves. There were still in Bilbo's time three Elf-towers just beyond the western borders of the Shire. They shone in the moonlight. The tallest was furthest away, standing alone on a hill. The hobbits of the Westfarthing

THE JOURNEY TO BREE

said that you could see the Sea from the top of that tower: but no hobbit had ever been known to climb it. But even if the notion of building came originally from the Elves, the hobbits used it in their own fashion. They did not go in much for towers. Their houses were usually long and low, and comfortable. The oldest kind were really artificial holes of mud (and later of brick), thatched with dry grass or straw, or roofed with turf; and the walls were slightly bulged. But, of course, that stage belonged to very ancient history. Hobbit-building had long been altered (and perhaps improved) by the taking of wrinkles from dwarves and even Big People, and other folk outside the Shire. A preference for round windows, and also (but to a less extent) for round doors, was the chief remaining characteristic of hobbit-architecture.

Both the houses and the holes of hobbits were usually large and inhabited by large families. (Bilbo and Frodo Baggins were in this point, as in many others, rather exceptional.) Sometimes, as in the case of the Brandybucks of Brandy Hall, many generations of relations lived in (comparative) peace together in one ancestral and ramifying mansion. All hobbits were, in any case, clannish, and reckoned up their relationships with great care. They drew long and elaborate family-trees with many branches. In dealing with hobbits it is most important to remember who is related to whom, and how, and why.

It would be impossible to set out in this book a family-tree that included even the more important members of the more important families of the Shire at the time we speak of. It would take a whole book, and everyone but hobbits would find it dull. (Hobbits would love it, if it was accurate: they like to have books full of things they already know set out fair and square with no contradictions.) The Shire was their own name for the very pleasant little corner of the world in which the most numerous, thoroughbred, and representative kind of hobbits lived in Bilbo's time. It was the only part of the world, indeed, at that time in which the two-legged inhabitants were all Hobbits, and in which Dwarves, Big People (and even Elves) were merely strangers and occasional visitors. The Shire was divided into four quarters, called the Four Farthings, the North, South, East and West Farthings; and also into a number of folklands, which bore the names of the important families, although by this time these names were no longer found only in their proper folklands. Nearly all Tooks still lived in Tookland, but that was not so true of other families, like the Bagginses or the Boffins. A map of the Shire will be found in this

314   THE RETURN OF THE SHADOW

book, in the hope that it will be useful (and be approved as reasonably correct by those hobbits that go in for hobbit-history).

To complete the information some (abridged) family-trees are also given, which will show in what way the hobbit-persons mentioned are related to one another, and what their various ages were at the time when the story opens. This will at any rate make clear the connexions between Bilbo and Frodo, and between Folco Took and Meriadoc Brandybuck (usually called Merry) and the other chief characters.[3]

Frodo Baggins became Bilbo's heir by adoption: heir not only to what was left of Bilbo's considerable wealth, but also to his most mysterious treasure: a magic ring. This ring came from a cave in the Misty Mountains, far away in the East. It had belonged to a sad and rather loathsome creature called Gollum, of whom more will be heard in this story, though I hope some will find time to read the account of his riddle-competition with Bilbo in *The Hobbit*. It is important to this tale, as the wizard Gandalf tried to explain to Frodo. The ring had the power of making its wearer invisible. It had also other powers, which Bilbo did not discover until long after he had come back and settled down at home again. Consequently they are not spoken of in the story of his journey. But this later story is concerned chiefly with the ring, and so no more need be said about them here.

Bilbo it is told 'remained very happy to the end of his days and those were extraordinarily long.' They were. How extraordinarily long you may now discover, and you may also learn that remaining happy did not mean continuing to live for ever at Bag-end. Bilbo returned home on June 22nd in his fifty-second year, and nothing very notable occurred in the Shire for another sixty years, when Bilbo began to make preparations for the celebration of his hundred and eleventh birthday. At which point the present tale of the Ring begins.

Chapter I: 'A Long-expected Party'

At the beginning of this sixth embodiment of the opening chapter the revised passage about Bilbo's book (p. 245, note 3) was now removed, and replaced by: 'He was supposed to be writing a book, containing a full account of his year's mysterious adventures, which no one was allowed to see.'

The conversation at *The Ivy Bush* is taken up from the preliminary version described on pp. 244–5, and now reaches virtually the form it has

THE JOURNEY TO BREE   315

in FR; but at this stage the Gaffer's instruction on the subject of Bilbo and Frodo and their antecedents was still recounted in advance by the narrator also.[4]

The 'odd-looking waggons laden with odd-looking packages', driven by 'elves or heavily hooded dwarves,' which had survived from the second version of the chapter (p. 20), were now reduced to a single waggon, driven by dwarves, and no elves appear (see p. 235); but Gandalf's mark on the fireworks, here called 'runic', still remains, and he is still 'a little old man'. The guests still included the Gaukrogers (so spelt), but the remark that the Brockhouses had come in from Combe-under-Bree (p. 236) is dropped. The young Took who danced on the table changes his name from Prospero to Everard (as in FR), but his partner remains Melissa Brandybuck (Melilot in FR).

The pencilled addition to the fifth version (p. 246, note 12), showing that Bingo/Frodo was fully aware of what Bilbo intended to do, was taken up (but as in FR Frodo stays on long enough at the dinner-table to satisfy Rory Brandybuck's thirst: 'Hey, Frodo, just send that decanter round again!'); as also was the passage about Bilbo's taking Sting with him (p. 246, note 13). Bilbo now (as in FR) takes a leather-bound manuscript from a strong-box (though not the 'bundle wrapped in old cloths'), but gives the bulky envelope, which he addresses to Frodo and into which he puts the Ring, to the dwarf Lofar, asking him to put it in Frodo's room.

Gandalf still meets Bilbo at the bottom of the Hill after he has left Bag End with the Dwarves (still named Nar, Anar, and Hannar), and their conversation remains as it was (pp. 238–40): in answer to Gandalf's question 'He [Frodo] knows about it, of course?' Bilbo replies: 'He knows that I have a Ring. He has read my private memoirs (the only one I have ever allowed to read them).' Gandalf's return to Bag End after saying good-bye to Bilbo is incorporated from the very rough form in the fifth version (p. 247, note 20), the only difference being that Frodo is now actually reading Bilbo's letter as he sits in the hall.

The list of Bilbo's parting presents (p. 247, note 21) is now further changed by the loss of Caramella Chubb and her clock and Primo Grubb and his dinner-service (survivors from the original draft, p. 15, when they were Caramella Took and Inigo Grubb-Took); Colombo Hornblower and the barometer also disappear. Lofar still plays the rôle of Merry Brandybuck on the day following the Party, and Gandalf's conversation with Frodo on that day remains the same, with various later additions and omissions made to the fifth version (p. 248, notes 24–6, 28–30) incorporated: thus Bingo's reference to Bilbo's use of the Ring to escape from the Sackville-Bagginses is of course removed, in view of its use in 'A Conspiracy is Unmasked' (p. 300), as is Gandalf's suggestion that Bingo might be able to get in touch with him if necessary through 'the nearest dwarves'.

316   THE RETURN OF THE SHADOW

Genealogy of the Tooks

On the reverse of one of the pages of this manuscript of 'A Long-expected Party' is the most substantial genealogy of the Tooks that has yet appeared.

The figures attached to the names are at first glance very puzzling: they are obviously neither dates according to an independent calendar, nor ages at death. The key is provided by 'Bilbo Baggins 111', and by the statement in the *Foreword* (p. 314) that the family-trees (of which this is the only one that survives, or was made at this time) would show 'what their various ages were at the time when the story opens.' The basis is the year of the Party, which is zero; and the figures are the ages of the persons *relative to the Party*. As between any two figures, the relative ages of the persons are given. Thus 311 against Ferumbras and 266 against Fortinbras means that Ferumbras was born 45 years before his son; Isengrim the First was born 374 years before Meriadoc Brandybuck eight generations later; Drogo Baggins was 23 years younger than Bilbo, and if he had not been drowned in the Brandywine and had been able to come to the Party would have been 88; and so on. The daggers of course show persons who were dead at the time of the Party.

A few of the figures were changed on the manuscript, the later ones being: Isengrim II 172, Isambard 160, Flambard 167, Rosa Baggins 151, Bungo Baggins 155, Yolanda 60, Folco Took 23, Meriadoc 25, Odo 24.

It will be seen that while there is no external chronological structure, the internal or relative structure is not so very different from that of the family tree of *Took of Great Smials* in LR Appendix C. In LR Meriadoc was born 362 years after Isengrim II (= Isengrim I in the old tree) and eight generations later.

Bandobras the Bullroarer (see p. 311 and note 2) is here the son of Isengrim, first of the Took line in the tree; and in the *Prologue* to LR (p. 11) he is likewise the son of that Isengrim (the Second). This was overlooked when the final Took tree was made, for Bandobras is there moved down by a generation, becoming the son (not the brother) of Isengrim's son Isumbras (III).[5]

The Old Took now acquires the name Gerontius, as in LR (earlier he was 'Frodo the First', p. 251). Four sons are named here; in LR he had nine. Rosa Baggins, wife of one of them (Flambard), has appeared in the little genealogy found in *Queries and Alterations* (p. 222): there she is the sister of Bungo Baggins, and she married 'Young Took'. The tree given on p. 267 is maintained here in respect of Merry's parents; Frodo Took has become Folco Took, and his father Folcard (see p. 309). Odo, here with a double-barrelled name Took-Bolger, was said earlier (p. 251) to have a Took mother and to be a third cousin of Merry and Frodo (Folco), as is shown in this tree.

Donnamira Took, second of the Old Took's daughters, is now named,

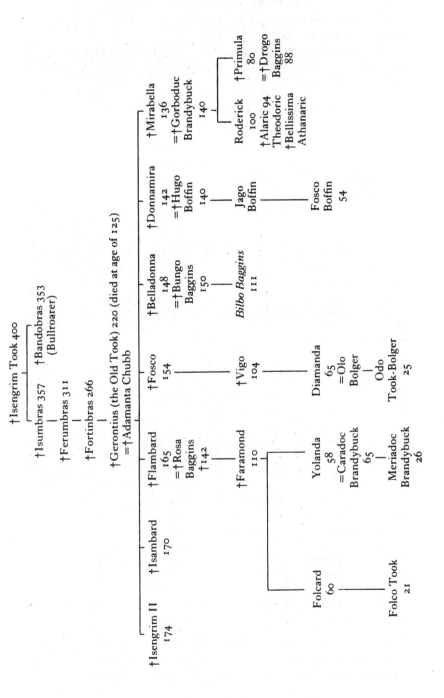

318   THE RETURN OF THE SHADOW

and is the wife of Hugo Boffin, as in LR, where however no issue is recorded in the tree: on this see p. 386.

Lastly, five further children (six in LR) of Mirabella Took and Gorboduc Brandybuck are given in addition to Primula, one of them being Rory Brandybuck (see p. 267, note 4), whose true name is here Roderick (Rorimac in LR); the other sons have Visigothic names altogether different from those in the Brandybuck tree in LR.

Chapter II: 'Ancient History'

The earlier forms of this chapter are found on pp. 76 ff. and pp. 250 ff. The version in the third phase is in places difficult to interpret, for it was a good deal changed in the act of composition and very heavily altered afterwards, and it is not easy to distinguish the 'layers'; moreover, it became divided up, with some of its pages remaining in England and some going to Marquette University.

In general, the substance of the narrative remains remarkably close to that of the preceding version; my father had that before him, of course, and he was largely content merely to alter the expression as he went along – ubiquitously, but leaving the existing story little affected.

Of the younger hobbits that Frodo went about with, the chief are now Meriadoc Brandybuck, Folco Took, and Odo Bolger (on *Folco* for *Frodo* see p. 309); genealogical information about them is not provided (cf. p. 251). Frodo no longer 'walked all over the Shire,' nor was he 'often away from home'; rather, 'he did not go far afield, and after Bilbo left his walks gradually grew shorter and circled more and more round his own hole.' When he thought of leaving the Shire, and wondered what lay beyond its borders, 'half of him was now unwilling, and began to be afraid of walks abroad, lest the mud on his feet should carry him off.' The 'thin feeling' mentioned in the previous version (p. 252), 'as if he was being stretched out over a lot of days, and weeks, and months, but was not fully there', is no longer referred to, and Gandalf does not do so later in the chapter (cf. p. 266).

In the account of Gandalf's visits to Hobbiton, the passage in the previous version describing his secret comings and taps on the window is moved, so that it refers to the earlier time when he came often (cf. FR p. 55), before his long absence of seven years (p. 268, note 6). The wizard reappeared 'about fifteen years after Bilbo's departure', and 'during the last year he had often come and stayed a long time.' The conversation at *The Green Dragon* took place in 'the spring of Frodo's forty-ninth year' (at the beginning of the next chapter in this phase Frodo decides to leave Bag End in September of 'this (his fiftieth) year': see p. 253 and note 8).

In the passage concerning the rumours of trouble and the migrations in the wide world the site of Sauron's ancient stronghold in the South 'near the midst of the world in those days' (p. 253) becomes 'near the

THE JOURNEY TO BREE 319

middle of the Great Land', but this was at once struck out; and the passage concerning giants becomes: 'Trolls and giants were abroad, of a new and more malevolent kind, no longer dull-witted but full of cunning and wizardry.' In the talk at the inn, the passage about the Grey Havens now appears, and the whole conversation moves almost to the form in FR (p. 54); but it is still Jo Button who saw the 'Tree-men' beyond the North Moors, though he works now for 'Mr Fosco Boffin' – with 'of Northope' added later, and then changed to 'at Overhill'. Fosco Boffin, Bilbo's first cousin once removed, appears in the Took genealogy given on p. 317; see p. 386.

The opening of the conversation between Gandalf and Frodo at Bag End was changed, probably at or very soon after the time of composition, from a form very close to that of the preceding version (p. 255) and still including Gandalf's mention of his two visits to the land of the Necromancer. The new form reads:

'You say the ring is dangerous, far more dangerous than I guess,' said Frodo at length. 'How long have you known that? And did Bilbo know? I wish you would tell me more now.'

'At first I knew very little,' answered Gandalf slowly, as if searching back in memory. Already the days of the journey and the Dragon and the Battle of Five Armies began to seem dim and far-off. Perhaps even he was at last beginning to feel his age; and in any case many dark and strange adventures had befallen him since. 'Then after I came back from the South and the White Council, I began to wonder what kind of magic ring he possessed; but I said nothing to Bilbo. All seemed well with him, and I thought that that kind of power was powerless over him. So I thought; and I was right in a way; but not quite right. I ought perhaps to have found out more, sooner than I did, and then I should have warned him earlier. But before he left I told him what I could – by that time I had begun to suspect the truth, but I knew very little for certain.'

'I am sure you did all you could,' said Frodo. 'You have been a good friend, and a wise counsellor to us. But it must have been a great blow to you when Bilbo disappeared.'

In Gandalf's account of the Rings (p. 260) he now says: 'Slowly through the years he has been seeking for them, hoping to recall their power into his own hands, and hoping always to find the One'; and his words concerning the Three Rings were early changed from their form in the second version (p. 260, but with 'earth, sea, and sky' for 'earth, air, and sky'):

What use they made of the Three Rings of Earth, Sea, and Sky, I

320   THE RETURN OF THE SHADOW

do not know; nor do I know what has now become of them. Some say that hidden Elf-kings still keep them in fast places of the Middle-earth; but I believe they have long been carried far over the Great Sea.

Gandalf, again by early or immediate change, now concludes his remarks about the Seven Rings of the Dwarves, which some say have perished in the fire of the dragons, with the words: 'Yet that account, maybe, is not wholly true'; he does not now refer to the belief that some of the Seven Rings are preserved, though no doubt he implies it (cf. the first draft for the Council of Elrond, p. 398).

As my father first wrote here the passage about Gil-galad, he began by following the former text almost exactly, with 'Valandil, King of the Island' (see p. 260 and note 26), but he changed it in the act of writing to: 'and he made an alliance with Valandil, King of the men of Númenor, who came back over the sea from Westernesse into Middle-earth in those days.' *Valandil* was then changed to *Elendil*, probably almost immediately, and also at the subsequent occurrences of the name in this passage. *Isildor* of the second text is now written *Isildur*. Isildur's host was overwhelmed by 'Orcs', not 'Goblins' (see p. 437, note 35).

To Gandalf's story of Gollum nothing is added or altered from the preceding version (see p. 261), save that 'his grandmother who ruled all the family turned him out of her hole.'

The purport of Gandalf's discussion of Gollum's character and motives in respect of the Ring remains unchanged from the second version, though of course with continual slight development in expression, and in some passages with considerable expansion. The words 'Only Elves can stand it, and even they fade' (p. 261) are now omitted. Gandalf's meaning in his reply to Frodo's objection that Gollum never gave Bilbo the Ring is now made clearer:

'But he never gave Bilbo the Ring,' said Frodo. 'Bilbo had already found it lying on the floor.'

'I know, answered Gandalf, 'and I have always thought that that was one of the strangest things about Bilbo's adventure. That is why I said that Gollum's ancestry only partly explained what happened . . .'

It is still Gandalf himself who found Gollum, though Frodo's exclamation 'You found Gollum!' (p. 263) was subsequently changed to 'You have seen Gollum!', and Gandalf's reply to Frodo's question 'Did you find him there [in Mirkwood]?' (p. 264) was changed to 'I saw him there, but it was friends of mine who actually tracked him down, with the help of the Wood-elves.' Cf. the first version of the Council of Elrond, p. 401 and note 20. – Gandalf's account of Gollum's own story is expanded thus:

THE JOURNEY TO BREE 321

What I have told you, Gollum was willing to tell – though not, of course, in the way I have reported it. Gollum is a liar, and you have to sift his words. For instance, you may remember that he told Bilbo he had the Ring as a birthday-present. Very unlikely on the face of it: incredible when one suspects what kind of ring it really was. It was said merely to make Bilbo willing to accept it as a harmless kind of toy – one of Gollum's hobbit-like thoughts. He repeated this nonsense to me, but I laughed at him. He then told me the truer story, with a lot of snivelling and snarling. He thought he was misunderstood and ill-treated . . .

Gandalf still says, oddly, that Gollum 'had found out eventually, of course, that Bilbo had in some way got his Ring, and what his name was, and where he came from' (see p. 263 and note 32); indeed the point is now made more emphatically: 'And the news of later events went all over Wilderland, and *Bilbo's name was spoken* far and wide.'

When Gandalf pauses after saying 'he made his slow sneaking way bit by bit, years ago, down to the Land of Mordor' the heavy silence mentioned in FR p. 68 falls, and 'there was now no sound of Sam's shears.' The phrase 'I think indeed that Gollum is the beginning of our present troubles' is retained: see p. 271, note 33.

From '"Well anyway," said Frodo, "if Gollum could not be killed"' my father at first followed the earlier text (p. 265) very closely, but then rewrote it in a changed form.

'Well anyway,' said Frodo, 'if Gollum could not be killed, I wish Bilbo had not kept the Ring. Why did he?'

'Is not that clear from what you have now heard?' answered Gandalf. 'I remember you saying, when it first came to you, that it had its advantages, and that you wondered why Bilbo went off without it [see p. 242]. He had possessed it a long while before we knew that it was specially important. After that it was too late: there was the Ring itself to reckon with. It has a power and purpose of its own that clouds wise counsel. Even Bilbo could not altogether escape its influence. He developed a sentiment. Even when he knew that it came ultimately from the Necromancer he wished to keep it as a memento . . .'

Lastly, the passage beginning 'I really do wish to destroy it!' (p. 266) was changed and amplified:

'I really do wish to destroy it!' cried Frodo. 'But I wish more that the Ring need never have come to me. Why was I chosen?'

'Bilbo passed it on to you to save himself from destruction; and because he could find no one else. He did so reluctantly, but

322 THE RETURN OF THE SHADOW

believing that, when you knew more, you would accept the burden for a while out of love for him. He thought you were safe: safe not to misuse it or to let it get into evil hands; safe from its power for a time; and safe in the quiet Shire of the hobbits from the knowledge of its maker. And I promised him to help you. He relied on that. Indeed for your sake and for his I have taken many perilous journeys.

'Also I may say that I did not discover the letters of fire or their meaning or know for certain that this was the Ruling Ring until he had already decided to go. I did not tell him, for then he would not have burdened you. I let him go. He had had the Ring for sixty years, and it was telling on him, Frodo. It would have worn him down in the end, and I dare not guess what might then have happened.

'But now, alas! I know more. I have seen Gollum. I have journeyed even to the Land of Mordor. I fear that the Enemy is searching. You are in a far graver peril than ever Bilbo dreamed of. So do not blame him.'

'But I am not strong enough!' said Frodo. 'You are wise and powerful. Will you not take the Ring?'

'No!' said Gandalf springing to his feet. 'With that Ring I should have power too great and terrible. And over me it would gain a power still greater and more deadly.' His eyes flashed and his face was lit as by a fire within. 'Do not tempt me! For I do not wish to become like the Dark Lord himself. Yet the way of the Ring to my heart is by pity for weakness and the desire of strength to do good. Do not tempt me!'

He went to the window and drew aside the curtain and shutters. Sunlight streamed back again into the room. Sam passed along the path outside, whistling. 'In any case,' said the wizard, turning back to Frodo, 'it is now too late. You would hate me and call me a thief; and our friendship would cease. Such is the power of the Ring. But together we will shoulder the burden that is laid on us.' He came and laid his hand on Frodo's shoulder. 'But we must do something soon,' he said. 'The Enemy is moving.'

The same curious idea is still present here that Gandalf discovered the letters of fire on Bilbo's ring, and knew that it was the Ruling Ring, *before* Bilbo left but *without* telling him (i.e. without Bilbo's knowledge that this test had been made): see p. 266 and note 38. – Gandalf's remark (p. 321) 'I think indeed that Gollum is the beginning of our present troubles', retained from the second version, now perhaps becomes less

THE JOURNEY TO BREE 323

obscure (see p. 271, note 33): 'I have been to the Land of Mordor. I fear that the Enemy is searching.'

Chapter III: 'Delays are Dangerous'

The new text of the third chapter, now given this title (which had been scribbled in on the second version), was another fine clear manuscript, replacing its appallingly difficult predecessor (pp. 273 ff.).

The chapter still begins with the gossip in *The Ivy Bush* and *The Green Dragon* (p. 274 and note 1) before turning to the conversation between Gandalf and Frodo. In that conversation Gandalf does now refer, as in FR, to the possibility that it may be Frodo's task to find the Cracks of Doom – indeed he goes further:

'And to go *there* but not come *back again*,' added Gandalf grimly. 'For in the end I think you must come to the Fiery Mountain, though you are not yet ready to make that your goal.'

That with Merry's help[6] Frodo had chosen a little house at Crick-hollow (see p. 299) is now taken up from the pencilled change to the previous version (p. 283, note 2). Gandalf still leaves Hobbiton 'one wet dark evening in May'.

But a major change enters the story with the departure of Odo Bolger (not Took-Bolger, as in the family tree, p. 317) with Merry Brandybuck in the third cart from Hobbiton. My father had proposed this earlier (p. 299): 'From here onwards [i.e. after the arrival in Buckland] Odo is presumed to have gone with Merry ahead. The preliminary journey was Frodo [Took], Bingo and Sam only. Frodo has a character a little more like Odo once had. Odo is now rather silent (and greedy).' But the text that followed this direction was obscure and contradictory, apparently on account of my opposition to the proposal (see p. 299). Now the deed was done properly.

In the earlier versions of the chapter the young hobbits Frodo and Odo had distinct characters (see p. 70). The removal of Odo from the expedition does not mean, however, that Odo's character was removed; because my father always worked on the basis of preceding drafts, and a great deal of the original material of this chapter survived. Though Frodo Took, now renamed Folco Took (since Bingo had become Frodo), was the one who remained in the new narrative, he had to become the speaker of the things that the absent Odo had said – unless my father was to rewrite what he had written in a far more drastic way than he wished to. Despite the early note 'Sam Gamgee to replace Odo' (p. 250), Sam was too particularly conceived from the outset to be at all suitable to take up Odo's nonchalance. Moreover, in this version of the

324 THE RETURN OF THE SHADOW

chapter the original contribution of Folco (Frodo) Took was in any case further reduced. The verse *The Road goes ever on and on* had already been given to Bingo in the second version (p. 278); now his account of meeting a Black Rider up on the North Moors was dropped, and his exclamation of delight when the singing of the Elves was heard ('Elves! How wonderful! I have always wished to hear elves singing under stars') was cut out apparently in the act of writing and replaced by Sam's hoarse whisper: 'Elves!' So Folco Took, with a diminished part of 'his own', and acquiring much of 'Odo's', becomes 'Odo' more completely than my father apparently foresaw when he said 'Frodo [Took] has a character a little more like Odo once had.'[7]

Yet Folco's *genealogical* place remains; for Odo himself (once surnamed Took but now a Bolger with a Took mother) has gone on ahead to Buckland, where a separate and distinct adventure (already glimpsed in advance, pp. 302, 304) will overtake him, while into Folco's place in the family tree of the Tooks, as first cousin of Merry Brandybuck (pp. 267, 317), will later step Peregrin Took (Pippin).

Cosimo Sackville-Baggins' 'overshadowed wife Miranda' disappears again, together with the remark that he and his mother Lobelia lived at Bag End 'for many a year after' (p. 283, note 5). – *The Road goes ever on and on* now attains the final form (p. 284, note 10). – At the first appearance of the Black Rider on the road, in the passage cited on p. 278, 'Odo and Frodo' become 'Folco and Sam', and the text of FR (p. 84) is reached.

As already noticed, Frodo Took's account of his meeting with a Black Rider on the North Moors of the Shire (p. 278) is now dropped, and the conversation between Bingo and Frodo Took on the subject of the Black Riders (p. 279) that follows Sam's revelation moves on to precisely the form in FR (p. 85), with of course Folco for Pippin. The brief halt of the Rider by the decayed tree in which the hobbits ate their supper is however retained in this version, and in the ensuing conversation Frodo still says, as did Bingo, that he will take the name of Mr Hill of Faraway.

When the singing of the Elves is heard Frodo says, as in FR p. 88: 'One can meet them sometimes in the Woody End', but he still says as in the preceding version (p. 280) that they come in spring and autumn 'out of their own lands far beyond the River'. As in FR, the hymn to Elbereth is now said to be sung 'in the fair Elven-tongue', and at the end of it Frodo says: 'These are High-elves! They speak the name of Elbereth!'

Odo's indiscreet remark about their good luck in landing unexpectedly good food and lodging disappears and is not handed on to Folco. Frodo's 'The stars shine on the hour of our meeting' was at first given as before (p. 280) only in translation, but my father changed this, clearly in the act of writing the manuscript, by the introduction of the Elvish words as well, *Eleni silir lúmesse omentiemman*, and then again to *Elen silë* . . . , 'A

THE JOURNEY TO BREE 325

star shines . . .' At this Gildor says, as in FR, 'Here is a scholar in the Ancient Tongue.'

It is still the Moon that rouses the Elves to song; but the old wording ('The yellow moon rose; springing swiftly out of the shadow, and then climbing round and slow into the sky') surviving from the original version of the chapter (p. 61), was changed, apparently at or very near the time of writing, to: 'Above the mists away in the East the thin silver rind of the New Moon appeared, and rising swift and clear out of the shadow it swung gleaming in the sky.' My father no doubt made this change on account of what he had said elsewhere about the Moon; for there was a waxing moon as the hobbits approached Weathertop, and it was 'nearly half-full' on the night of the attack (pp. 168, 184): the attack was on 5 October (p. 175), and there could not be a full or nearly full Moon on 24 September, the night passed with the Elves in the Woody End (see p. 160). On that night it must have been almost New Moon. The dates of the phases of the Moon in the autumn and early winter of that year cited on p. 434, note 19, in fact give New Moon on 25 September, the First Quarter (half-full) on 2 October, and Full Moon on 10 October. But it is an odd and uncharacteristic aberration that my father envisaged a New Moon rising late at night in the East.[8] In FR, of course, there is no mention of the Moon in this passage: it was 'the Swordsman of the Sky, Menelvagor with his shining belt' that caused the Elves to burst into song.

In the passage describing the memories of the meal eaten with the Elves the text of FR is reached, with Folco retaining those of Frodo Took together with Odo's recollection of the bread.

Gildor's advice to Bingo (Frodo) that he should take trusty companions, and his opinion that his present companions have already confused the Riders, is retained (see p. 282); but at the end there is now no mention of the Ring, and their talk ends as in FR (p. 94).

Chapter IV: 'A Short Cut to Mushrooms'

In this new version of the chapter there is only to notice the curious result of the exclusion of Odo Bolger: with Folco Took adding Odo's part to that which he retained from Frodo Took's in the former narrative. In the previous version Odo argued against taking a short cut to the Ferry, because, while he did not know the country, he did know *The Golden Perch* at Stock, and Frodo Took argued for it – because he did know the country.[9] Now, the Frodo-element in Folco, retaining a knowledge of the country, uses it to support the desire of the Odo-element in him for the beer at Stock, and his opponent in the argument is Frodo (Baggins); thus Folco is here, and throughout the chapter, Pippin in all but name (see pp. 286–7).

Deephallow now disappears from the text (see p. 286).

326   THE RETURN OF THE SHADOW

Chapter V: 'A Conspiracy Unmasked'

This chapter had already reached in the second version (pp. 298 ff.) a form very close to that in FR, but there remained the confusion over whether Odo had been on the walk from Hobbiton or whether he had gone on ahead to Buckland with Merry (see pp. 299, 323). Following the new version of Chapter III, this is now resolved, of course: Odo is at Crickhollow, opens the door when they arrive, and cooks the supper with Merry – in fact, until the end of the chapter, he has become Fredegar (Fatty) Bolger. The text now reaches, until the end of the chapter, the form in FR, down to the smallest particulars of expression, with these differences only: the passage about Gorhendad Oldbuck is still not present (p. 298); the Hedge is still forty miles from end to end (*ibid.*); and the 'dwarf-song' *Farewell! farewell, now hearth and hall!* still retains the form in the previous version (pp. 300–1).[10]

The end of the chapter still differs altogether from that in FR, however. The form in the second version was preserved, with the pencilled additions incorporated (p. 302). Odo says 'But *we shan't* have any luck in the Old Forest' (whereas in FR Fredegar says 'But *you won't* have any luck'), because he is still potentially a member of the further expedition, even though my father had in fact decided that he would stay at Crickhollow till Gandalf came. I give the text from 'Do you follow Captain Frodo, or do you stay at home?'

'We follow Captain Frodo,' said Merry and Folco (and of course Sam). Odo was silent. 'Look here!' he said after a pause. 'I don't mind admitting that I am more terrified of the Forest than of anything I know about. I dislike woods of any kind, but the stories about the Old Forest are a nightmare. But I also think that you ought to try and keep in touch with Gandalf, who I guess knows more about the Black Riders than you do. I will stay behind here and keep off inquisitive folk. When Gandalf comes, as I think he is sure to, I will tell him what you have done, and I will come on after you with him, if he will bring me.'

The others agreed that this seemed on the whole an excellent plan; and Frodo at once wrote a brief letter to Gandalf, and gave it to Odo.

'Well, that's settled,' said Merry.

The rest of the chapter is as in the previous version.

A curious trace of this stage survives in the published text. Since Odo's staying behind had not formed part of the 'conspiracy', Merry had prepared six ponies, five for the five hobbits and one for the baggage. When the story changed, and Fredegar Bolger's task 'according to the original plans of the conspirators' (FR p. 118) was expressly to stay

THE JOURNEY TO BREE 327

behind, this detail was overlooked, and the six ponies remained at this point (FR p. 117).

Chapter VI: 'The Old Forest'

The chapter now at last receives its title. Odo now said farewell to the others at the entrance to the tunnel under the Hedge in these words:

'I wish you were not going into the Forest. I don't believe you will get safely through; and I think it is very necessary that someone should warn Gandalf that you have gone in. I'm sure you will need rescuing before to-day is out. Still I wish you luck and I hope, perhaps, I shall catch you up again one day.'

The hill rising out of the forest was still crowned with a knot of trees (p. 113), but this was changed to the 'bald head' of FR in the act of writing this manuscript. The gully which the hobbits were forced to follow downwards because they could not climb out of it still ends as before (*ibid.*):

Suddenly the woodland trees came to an end, and the gully became deep and sheer-sided; its bottom was almost wholly filled by the noisy hurrying water. It ran down finally to a narrow shelf at the top of a rocky bank, over which the stream dived and fell in a series of small waterfalls. Looking down they saw that below them was a wide space of grass and reeds . . .

The old story of the descent down the thirty-foot bank is thus still present, with Folco falling the last fifteen feet.

In the original form of the story of the encounter with Old Man Willow (p. 113) Bingo and Odo were trapped in the tree, and Merry (then called Marmaduke) was the one who rounded up the ponies and rescued Frodo Took from the river. In the next stage (p. 302) this was changed to the extent that Sam took over Merry's part, and Merry simply 'lay like a log'. Now, with Frodo Took and Odo 'reduced' to Folco Took, it is still Frodo Baggins and Folco who are imprisoned in the tree, but Merry steps into Frodo Took's rôle as the one pushed into the river.

In the oldest version the path beside the Withywindle puzzlingly turned sharply to the left below Tom Bombadil's house and went over a little bridge; and in later revision this was retained, with, later again, the word 'left' changed to 'right', implying that Bombadil's house was on the south side of the Withywindle (see p. 114). The present text read at first here:

[The path] turned sharply to the right, and took them over a wooden bridge that crossed another smaller stream that came chattering down.

328   THE RETURN OF THE SHADOW

This retains the turn in the path and the bridge, but the bridge being over a tributary stream Bombadil's house is on the north side of the Withywindle. My father struck the passage out, however, apparently as he wrote.

Chapter VII: 'In the House of Tom Bombadil'

Like the last, this chapter now receives its title. The episode of the attack on Crickhollow (pp. 303–4) is now a part of the text, and was repeated from the earlier form with scarcely any significant change and almost word for word. The 'grey man' came up the path leading a white horse, but that Gandalf had a white horse appears later in the first version. More important, my father at first repeated the words 'Suddenly there was a movement', but struck them out and substituted: 'A curtain in one of the windows stirred. Then suddenly the figure by the door moved swiftly' (this change clearly belongs with the writing of the manuscript). Odo was in the house, of course. To the words pencilled at the end of the first version of the episode, 'Behind clung a small figure with flying cloak', and 'Odo', there is nothing corresponding in the next, and I think that they had not, in fact, yet been written in on the former; at this stage, it seems, my father had no further plans for Odo. But there is a pencilled addition to the second text of which, though it was erased, Mr Taum Santoski has been able to make out the following: 'Behind him ran Odo . . . and . . . wind. Cf. IX.22.' On this question see p. 336.

The dreams. The content of Frodo's dream remains the same, almost word for word, as Bingo's in the original version (p. 118), except that after the words 'hoofs thudding and wind blowing' there follows 'and faint and far the echo of a horn': this obviously echoes Gandalf's blowing of the horn at Crickhollow, which in this text immediately precedes Frodo's dream. But whereas in the story as told in the first phase 'Bingo woke' and then 'fell asleep again' (on the reality of the sounds he heard see p. 119), in this version Frodo 'lay in a dream without light': this is as in FR, but nothing is said here to suggest that he woke (contrast FR: '"Black Riders!" thought Frodo as he wakened.') On the other hand the passage in the present text ends as in FR: 'at last he turned and fell asleep again or wandered into some other unremembered dream.' Folco dreams what was originally Odo's dream, and like Pippin in FR 'woke, or thought he had waked', and then 'went to sleep again.' Merry takes over Frodo Took's dream of water, with the words 'falling into his quiet sleep and slowly waking him' retained from the old version, though struck out, probably at once; this passage ends, as in FR, 'He breathed deep and fell asleep again.' Sam 'slept through the night in deep content, if logs are contented.'

In Tom's talk with the hobbits on the second day, the old phrase 'A dark shadow came up out of the middle of the world' is retained (see p. 121); and Tom's reply to Frodo's question 'Who are you, Master?' is

THE JOURNEY TO BREE 329

almost exactly as in the old version (p. 121): he says 'I am Ab-Origine, that's what I am,' and the words 'He saw the Sun rise in the West and the Moon following, before the new order of days was made' are retained (see my discussion of this passage, pp. 121–2).

In all the other minor differences mentioned on pp. 122–3 the present text reaches the final form.

Chapter VIII: 'Fog on the Barrow-downs'

There is little that need be said about this chapter, which followed on the original text (pp. 127–30), and which now received its title. The 'arm walking on its fingers' in the barrow crept towards Folco, and Frodo fell forward upon him (p. 127). Merry's words when he woke remain unchanged (p. 128); and nothing more is said of the bronze swords that Tom Bombadil chose for the hobbits from the treasures of the mound than the words added to the original text: Tom said that 'they were made many ages ago by men out of the West: they were foes of the dark Lord.'

The conclusion of the chapter moves some way to the final form, but features of the original version are retained (pp. 129–30). Thus Frodo, riding down onto the Road, still says: 'I hope we shall be able to stick to the beaten track after this,' to which Bombadil replies: 'That's what you ought to do, as long as you are able: hold to the beaten way, but ride fast and wary.' In his parting advice he still says: 'Barnabas Butterbur is the worthy keeper: he knows Tom Bombadil, and Tom's name will help you. Say "Tom sent us here", and he will treat you kindly.' After he has gone there is no conversation among the hobbits recorded, and the chapter ends much as in the original text. Sam rode with Frodo in front, Merry and Folco behind, leading the spare pony; and Bree is still 'a little village'.

NOTES

1 *Earliest Days*, occurring twice in this passage, was changed later to *Elder Days*. The latter expression occurs once in the *Quenta Silmarillion*, where it is not capitalised (V.259); cf. also *Elder Years* (V.90), *eldest years* (V.245).

2 Bandobras the Bullroarer reappears from *The Hobbit* (Chapter I); see further pp. 316–17.

3 Only one such tree is known to me, perhaps the only one made by my father at this time; see pp. 316–18.

4 Thus whereas in the preliminary version of the talk in *The Ivy Bush* (p. 244) the narrator's opening was to be reduced to a brief paragraph, my father was now both retaining the account of past history from earlier versions of the chapter and also adding Gaffer Gamgee's

330   THE RETURN OF THE SHADOW

own characteristic mode of retailing it. In FR the Gaffer becomes the sole source.

5 In *The Hobbit* Bandobras is called Bilbo's great-grand-uncle, but Bilbo himself calls him his great-great-great-grand-uncle – as he is in the present tree.

6 His cousin Lanorac Brandybuck (p. 275) has disappeared.

7 The discussion whether to walk far or not on the first night was still present (see p. 276), but Folco does not take on Odo's reluctance; the result is that all three of them agree, and the discussion being now rather pointless my father struck it out and replaced it with the words of FR (p. 80): 'Well, we all like walking in the dark, so let's put some miles behind us before bed.'

8 It is indeed so extraordinary, in view of his deep and constant awareness of all such modes and appearances, that one seeks for an explanation: can he have intended 'the Old Moon' but have written 'the New Moon' because he was thinking of the crescent form (characteristically 'the New Moon') rather than the phase? This seems unlikely; and in any case an 'old Moon' as a 'thin silver rind' is not seen till near dawn, for the Moon to have this appearance must be very near to the Sun.

9 In the earlier, abandoned variant of the Farmer Maggot episode in the previous version of the chapter Maggot says that Frodo Took is 'half a Brandybuck' (p. 291). This was already omitted in the second variant; but he was Merry Brandybuck's first cousin, and he tells Bingo that Maggot 'is a friend of Merry's, and I used to come here with him a good deal at one time' – just as Pippin tells Frodo in FR, p. 101.

10 My father first wrote that it was sung by Merry, Folco, and Odo, but Odo's name was no doubt due to its presence in the previous version (p. 300), and he struck it out at once.

XX

THE THIRD PHASE (2):
AT THE SIGN OF THE
PRANCING PONY

With Chapter IX, now given the title 'At the Sign of the Prancing Pony', the narrative of this phase underwent a much more substantial development, but not at all in the direction of the final story in FR. Before coming to this, however, there is a curious feature in the opening of the chapter to be considered.

The opening now advanced far from the early forms given on pp. 132–4: an initial account in which Bree was a village of Men, but where 'there were hobbits about', changed to the story that there were only hobbits in Bree, and Mr Butterbur was himself a hobbit. A later note (p. 223) said however that 'Bree-folk are *not* to be hobbits.' Now my father resolved the question by returning, more or less, to the original idea: Men and Hobbits lived together in Bree. But he found it difficult to achieve a form of the opening with which he could be satisfied, and there is version after version soon tailing off, to be replaced by the next. All these drafts are very similar, differing in the ordering of the material and in the admission or omission of detail; all obviously belong to the same time; and there is no need to look at them closely, except in one particular. All the drafts contain the passage in FR (p. 161) concerning the origin of the Men of Bree – one of them adding that they were 'descendants of the sons of Bëor' – and the return of the Kings of Men over the Great Seas.[1] The passage that follows, as in FR, concerns the Rangers, and is almost the same in all the draft forms of it:

No other Men lived now so far West, nor so near the Shire by a hundred leagues and more. No settled people, that is: for there were the Rangers, mysterious wanderers that the Men of Bree regarded with deep respect (and a little fear), since they were said to be the last remnant of the kingly people from beyond the Seas. But the Rangers were few and seldom seen, and roamed at will in the wild lands eastward, even as far as the Misty Mountains.

The curious thing is that in the form of the chapter-opening that was allowed to stand the account of the Rangers is quite different, and does not follow on from the words 'No other Men lived at that time so far West, nor so near by a hundred leagues to the Shire', but is placed

332 THE RETURN OF THE SHADOW

further on (after 'There was Bree-blood in the Brandybuck family by all accounts', FR p. 162). This version reads:

In the wild lands east of Bree there roamed a few unsettled folk (men and hobbits). These the people of the Bree-land called Rangers. Some of them were well-known in Bree, which they visited fairly frequently, and were welcome as bringers of news and tellers of strange tales.

Later in the chapter, Butterbur answers Frodo's question about Trotter thus:

I don't rightly know. He is one of the wandering folk – Rangers, we call them. Not that he really is a Ranger, if you understand me, though he behaves like one. He seems to be a hobbit of some kind. He has been coming in pretty often during the past twelve months, especially since last spring; but he seldom talks.

In the original version at this place (p. 137) Butterbur says: 'O! that is one of the wild folk – rangers we call 'em.' And Gandalf in his letter to Frodo still refers in the third phase text, as in the old version, to Trotter as 'a ranger . . . dark rather lean hobbit, wears wooden shoes' (p. 352).

With these extracts compare the note in *Queries and Alterations* (p. 223): 'Rangers are best *not* as hobbits, perhaps.'

It is difficult to interpret this. In the third phase we find the statement (in draft versions) that Rangers are 'the last remnant of the kingly people from beyond the Seas'; and also the statements that Rangers are both men and hobbits, that one particular hobbit is a Ranger (so Gandalf), and that this same hobbit is 'not really a Ranger, though he behaves like one' (so Butterbur). The simplest explanation is to suppose that the Númenórean origin of the Rangers was an idea that my father was considering in the drafts, but which he set aside when he wrote the text of the chapter and the subsequent narrative (see further p. 393). Whatever the explanation, it is clear that the finished conception of the Rangers had a difficult emergence; and it is characteristic that even when the idea of the Rangers as the last descendants of the Númenórean exiles had arisen, and a place thus prepared, as it were, for Trotter, he did not at once move into that place.

The village of Staddle now reappears (see p. 132), on the other side of the hill; and Combe is set 'in a deep valley a little further eastward', Archet 'on the edge of Chetwood' – all as in FR p. 161. That Bree stood at an old meeting of the ways, the East Road and the Greenway running north and south, now appears. In the only one of the draft versions of the opening to reach the actual narrative, the hobbits

passed one or two detached houses before they came to the inn, and Sam and Folco stared at these in wonder. Sam was filled with

AT THE SIGN OF THE PRANCING PONY 333

deep suspicion, and doubted the wisdom of seeking any lodging in such an outlandish place. 'Fancy having to climb up a ladder to bed!' he said. 'What do they do it for? They aren't birds.'

'It's airier,' said Frodo, 'and safer too in wilder country. There is no fence around Bree that I can see.'

Here my father stopped; probably at that moment he decided that this was improbable. In the completed text of the chapter dike, hedge, and gate appear.

Frodo and his companions came at last to the Greenway-crossing and drew near the village. They found that it was surrounded by a deep ditch with a hedge and fence on the inner side. Over this the Road ran, but it was closed (as was the custom after nightfall) by a great gate of loose bars laid across strong posts on either side.

A little sketch-map, reproduced on p. 335, very likely belongs to just this time. Written beside the line marking the outer circuit of Bree is 'ditch & f', i.e. 'fence'. (For an earlier, very simple sketch-plan of Bree see p. 174, note 20).

The text continues:

There was a house just beyond the barrier, and a man was sitting at the door. He jumped up and fetched a lantern, and looked down over the gate at them in surprise.

'We are making for the inn here,' said Frodo in answer to his questions. 'We are journeying east, and cannot go further tonight.'

'Hobbits!' said the man. 'And what's more, Shire-hobbits from the sound of your talk! Well, if that is not a wonder: Shire-folk riding by night and journeying east!'

He removed the bars slowly and let them ride through. 'And what makes it stranger,' he went on: 'there's been more than one traveller in the last few days going the same way, and enquiring after a party of four hobbits on ponies. But I laughed at them and said there had been no such party and was never likely to be. And here you are! But if you go on to old Butterbur's I don't doubt you'll find a welcome, and more news of your friends, maybe.'

They wished him goodnight; but Frodo made no comment on his talk, though he could see in the lantern-light that the man was eyeing them curiously. He was glad to hear the bars dropped in their places behind them as they rode forward. One Black Rider at least was now ahead of them, or so he guessed from the man's words, but it was likely enough that others were still behind. And

334   THE RETURN OF THE SHADOW

what about Gandalf? Had he, too, passed through, trying to catch
them up while they were delayed in the Forest and Downs?

The hobbits rode on up a gentle slope, passing a few detached
houses, and drew up outside the inn. . . .

The account of Sam's dismay at the sight of the tall houses, of the
structure of the inn, and of their arrival, is almost word for word as in FR
p. 164; and Barnabas Butterbur is now a man, not a hobbit. But the
passage in the original version in which Bingo (Frodo) refers to Tom
Bombadil's recommendation of *The Prancing Pony* and is then made
welcome by the landlord (pp. 134–5) is retained. Frodo now introduces
them by their correct names, except that he calls himself 'Mr Hill of
Faraway' (see pp. 280, 324). Butterbur replies much as in the old version
(p. 135), but his remarks there about the Tooks are now applied to the
Brandybucks, and not merely in the general context of the Shire-folk but
because Merry has been introduced as Mr Brandybuck; and he now
mentions the strangers who had come up the Greenway the night before.
The passage about their supply of money (see p. 136 and note 7) is
retained, though the urgency is made less ('Frodo had brought some
money with him, of course, as much as was safe or convenient; but it
would not cover the expenses of good inns indefinitely.')

From 'The landlord hovered round for a little, and then prepared[2] to
leave them' the new chapter reaches the final form for a long stretch with
only minor differences and for the most part in the same words. The
people in the common-room of the inn (including the strangers from the
South, who 'stared curiously') are as in FR (and the botanical names of
the Men of Bree, see p. 137 and note 8); but 'among the company
[Frodo] noticed the gate-keeper, and wondered vaguely if it was his night
off duty.' The 'squint-eyed ill-favoured fellow' who in FR foretold that
many more people would be coming north in the near future is here
simply 'one of the travellers' who had come up the Greenway. Folco
Took is now of course 'the ridiculous young Took'; but he does not yet
tell the tale of the collapse of the roof of the Town Hole in Michel
Delving. Frodo 'heard someone ask what part the Hills lived in and
where Faraway was; and he hoped Sam and Folco would be careful.'

As already noticed, Trotter remains a hobbit;[3] and the description of
him in fact follows the original version (p. 137) closely, including the
wooden shoes; his pipe was changed from 'broken' to 'short-stemmed' in
the act of writing, and he had 'an enormous mug (large even for a man)' in
front of him. In Frodo's first conversation with Trotter, and in all that
follows to the end of Chapter 9 in FR, the present text moves almost to
the final form (which has in any case been virtually attained, in the latter
part, already in the original version, see p. 140). Frodo's feeling that the
suggestion that he put on the Ring came to him 'from outside, from
someone or something in the room' is present. At first my father wrote
simply that the 'swarthy-faced fellow' (Bill Ferney)[4] 'slipped out of the

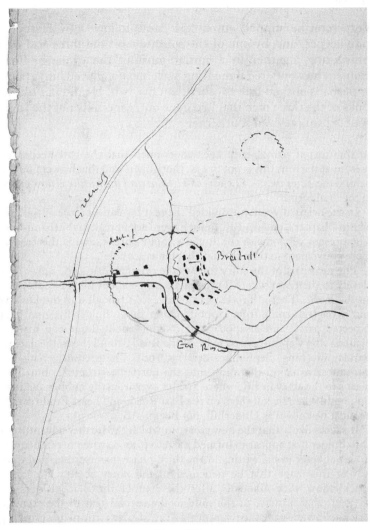

Plan of Bree

336   THE RETURN OF THE SHADOW

door, followed by one of the southerners: not a well-favoured pair'; but by a change that seems little later than the writing of the manuscript this became:

Very soon he slipped out of the door, followed by Harry the gate-keeper, and by one of the southerners: the three had been whispering together in a corner most of the evening. For a moment he wondered if the Ring itself had not played him a trick – or perhaps obeyed orders other than his own. He did not like the looks of the three men that had gone out, especially not the [dark-eyed >] squint-eyed southerner.

In this text it has already been mentioned that the gate-keeper was present at the inn; this is not in FR, though it is said that he went out just behind the other two. – The text of *The Cat and the Fiddle* is now exactly in the final form.

In the original version I divided the text for convenience at the point where Chapter 9 ends in FR, though there is no break in the manuscript. The present version also continues without a break, and in this case it is more convenient to treat the old chapter as a whole.

The next part of the story follows the original form (pp. 148–9) very closely to the point where Trotter tells Bingo about his 'eavesdropping' on the Road. There, Trotter had overheard Gandalf and the Dwarves and Elves (returning from Hobbiton after Bingo Bolger-Baggins' 'long-expected party' and disappearance) talking about Bingo and his companions who were supposed to be on the Road behind them: the date was Sunday morning, September 25th (p. 160). The present version here introduces a major alteration into the narrative structure, but by no means to the story in FR, where Strider overhears the hobbits talking to Bombadil when he left them on the East Road (and hears Frodo say that he must be known as Underhill, not Baggins).

It seems likely that the new story, in which the further adventures of Odo Bolger first appear in formed narrative, arose when my father came to this chapter in his writing of the third phase manuscripts, and that it was at this stage that he pencilled in the notes about Odo leaving Crickhollow with Gandalf[5] after the rout of the Black Riders (see p. 328): that is why, in the note to the second text of the attack on Crickhollow, he gave the reference 'IX.22'. IX.22 is the manuscript page in which Trotter's story of his eavesdropping on Gandalf *and Odo* on the East Road appears in the present chapter.

It will be seen that version 'A' of the original story is used: see pp. 148 and 171 note 1.

The opening of this section of the story is duplicated, both versions appearing to belong to the same time of writing, and neither being struck out; but the second form given here was preferred. The one reads:

AT THE SIGN OF THE PRANCING PONY   337

. . . I was behind a hedge, when a man on a horse halted on the Road not far [west of Bree > *(at time of writing)*] east of Bree. To my surprise there was a hobbit riding behind him on the same horse! They got off to take a meal, and started talking. Now, oddly enough, they were discussing a certain Frodo Baggins and his three companions. I gathered that these four strange folk were hobbits that had bolted out of the Shire (by a back-door, as you might say) last Monday, and ought to be on the Road somewhere. The travellers were very worried about Mr Baggins, and wondered whether he was on the Road or off it, in front of them or behind. They wanted to find him and *warn* him.

'A bit incautious, I must say, of Gandalf – there now! Gandalf it was, of course: there's no mistaking him, you'll agree – to go talking like that by the Road-side. But actually he was speaking low, and I happened to be lying very close. That would be yesterday noon: Wednesday.

The other reads:

. . . I was hiding under a hedge, by the Road some way west of Bree, trying to shelter from the rain, when a man on horseback halted close by. To my surprise there was a hobbit riding behind him on the same horse! They got off to rest, and take a little food, and they started talking. If you want to know, they were discussing a certain Frodo Baggins and his three companions. I gathered that these were four hobbits that had left the Shire in a great hurry the previous day. The horseman was trying to catch them up, but he was not sure if they were on the Road or off it, in front or behind. He seemed very worried, but hoped to find them at Bree. I thought it very strange, for it is not often that Gandalf's plans go wrong.'

Frodo stirred suddenly at the mention of the name, and Trotter smiled. 'Yes, Gandalf!' he said. 'I know what he looks like, and once seen never forgotten, you'll agree. He was speaking very low, but he had no idea that old Trotter was so close. That was on Tuesday evening, just as the light was failing.

The hobbits left Crickhollow early in the morning of Monday 26 September, and arrived in Bree at nightfall on Thursday 29 September (p. 160). The first of these variants makes Trotter see Gandalf and Odo on the road east of Bree on the Wednesday, i.e. after passing through the village; the second places the encounter a day earlier, on the Tuesday evening, before they reached Bree. Therefore Frodo calculates, in the passage that now follows, that Gandalf had reached Crickhollow 'on the

338   THE RETURN OF THE SHADOW

Monday, after they had left,' since Bree was a day's riding from the Brandywine Bridge. The rain on the Tuesday from which Trotter was sheltering was the rain that fell during the hobbits' second day in the house of Tom Bombadil. The text continues:

Now up comes a hobbit and three friends out of the Shire, and though he gives out the name of Hill, his friends call him Frodo, and they all seem to know a good deal about the doings of Gandalf and the Bagginses of Hobbiton. I can put two and two together, when it is as easy as that. But don't let it trouble you: I shall keep the answer to myself. Maybe, Mr Baggins has a good honest reason for leaving his name behind. But if so, I should advise him to remember that there are others besides Trotter that can do such easy sums – and not all are to be trusted.'

'I am obliged to you,' said Frodo, greatly relieved. Here at any rate was news of Gandalf; and of Odo too, apparently. Gandalf must have turned up at Crickhollow on the Monday, after they had left. But Frodo was still suspicious of Trotter, and was determined to pretend that the affair was of no special importance. 'I have not left my name behind, as you put it,' he said stiffly. 'I called myself Hill at this inn merely to avoid idle questions. Mr Butterbur has quite enough to say as it is. I don't quite see how anyone would guess my real name from what has occurred, unless he had your skill in eavesdropping. And I don't see, either, what special interest my name has for anybody in Bree, or for you, for that matter.'

Trotter laughed at him. 'Don't you?' he said grimly. 'But eavesdropping, as you put it, is not unknown in Bree. And besides, I have not told you all about myself yet.'

At that moment he was interrupted by a knock on the door. Mr Butterbur was there with a tray of candles, and Nob behind him with cans of hot water. 'I've come to wish you a good night,' said the landlord, putting the candles on the table. 'Nob! Take the water to the rooms.' He came in and shut the door. 'It's like this, Mr Hill,' he began: 'I've been asked more than once to look out for a party of four hobbits and five ponies. Hullo, Trotter! You here?'

'It's all right,' said Frodo. 'Say what you wish! Trotter has my leave to stay.' Trotter grinned.

'Well,' began Mr Butterbur again, 'it's like this: a couple of days ago, yes, it would be late on Tuesday night, just as I was going to lock up, there came a ring at the bell in the yard. Who should be standing at the door but old Gandalf, if you know who I mean! All wet through he was: it had been raining heavens hard all day.

AT THE SIGN OF THE PRANCING PONY 339

There was a hobbit with him, and a white horse – very tired the poor beast was; for it had carried both of them a long way, it seemed. "Bless me, Gandalf!" says I. " What are you doing out in this weather at this time of night? And who's your little friend?" But he winked at me, and didn't answer my questions. "Hot drinks and warm beds!" he croaked, and stumbled up the steps.

'Later on he sent for me. "Butterbur," says he. "I'm looking for some friends: four hobbits. One is a round-bellied little fellow with red cheeks" – begging your pardon – "and the others just young hobbits. They should have five ponies and a good deal of baggage. Have you seen them? They ought to have passed through Bree some time today,[6] unless they have stopped here."

'He seemed very put out, when I said no such party was at *The Pony*, and none had passed through, to my certain knowledge. "That's bad news!" he said, tugging at his beard. "Will you do two things for me? If this party turns up, give them a message: *Hurry on! Gandalf is ahead*. Just that. Don't forget, because it's important! And if anyone – anyone, mind you, however strange – enquires after a hobbit called Baggins, tell them Baggins has gone east with Gandalf. Don't forget that either, and I shall be grateful to you."' The landlord paused, looking hard at Frodo.

'Thankyou very much!' said Frodo, thinking Mr Butterbur had finished, and relieved to find that his story was much the same as Trotter's, and no more alarming. All the same he was extremely puzzled by Gandalf's mysterious words about *Baggins*. He wondered if Butterbur had got it all wrong.

'Ah! But wait a minute!' said the landlord, lowering his voice. 'That wasn't the end of it. And that's what is puzzling me. On Monday a big black fellow went through Bree on a great black horse, and all the folk were talking about it. The dogs were all yammering and the geese screaming as he rode through the village. I heard later that three of these riders were seen on the Road by Combe; though where the other two had sprung from I couldn't say.

'Gandalf and his little friend Baggins went off yesterday, after sleeping late, about the middle of the morning. In the evening, just before the road-gate was shut, in rode the black fellows again, or others as like them as night and dark. "There's the Black Man at the door!" shouted Nob, running to fetch me with his hair all on end. Sure enough, it was: not one nor three, though, but four of them! One was sitting there in the twilight with his big black horse

340   THE RETURN OF THE SHADOW

almost on my door-step. All hooded and cloaked he was. He bent
down and spoke to me, and very cold I thought his voice sounded.
And what do you think? He was asking for news of *four hobbits*
riding east out of the Shire![7]

'I didn't like the sound or the looks of him, and I answered him
short. "I haven't seen any such party," I said, "and I'm not likely
to, either. What may you be wanting with them, or with me?"

'At that he sent out a breath that set me shivering. "We want
news of them. We are seeking *Baggins*," he said, hissing out the
name like a snake. "Baggins is with them. If he comes, you will tell
us, and we will repay you with gold. If you do not tell us, we will
repay you – otherwise."

'"Baggins!" said I. "He ain't with them. If you are looking for a
hobbit of that name, he went off east this morning with Gandalf."

'At that name he drew in his breath and sat up. Then he stooped
at me again. "Is that truth?" he said, very hard and quiet. "Do not
lie to us!"

'I was all of a twitter, I can tell you, but I answered up as bold as
I could: "Of course it's the truth! I know Gandalf, and he and his
friend were here last night, I tell you." At that the four of them
turned their horses and rode off into the darkness without another
word.

'Now, Mr Hill, what do you make of all that? I hope I've done
right. If it hadn't been for Gandalf's orders, I'd never have given
them news of Baggins, nor of anyone else. For these Black Men
mean no good to anyone, I'll be bound.'

'You've done quite right, as far as I can see,' said Frodo. 'From
what I know of Gandalf, it is usually best to do what he asks.'

'Yes,' said the landlord, 'but I am puzzled all the same. How
came these Black Men to think Baggins was one of *your* party?
And I must say, from what I've heard and seen tonight, I wonder
if maybe they aren't right. But Baggins or no, you are welcome to
any help I can give to a friend of old Tom, and of Gandalf.'

'I'm very grateful,' said Frodo. 'I am sorry I can't tell you the
whole story, Mr Butterbur. I am very tired, and very worried. But
if you want to know, I *am* Frodo Baggins. I have no idea what
Gandalf meant by saying that Baggins had gone east with him; for
I think the hobbit's name was Bolger. But these – er – Black Riders
are hunting us, and we are in danger. I am very grateful for your
help; but I hope you won't get into any trouble yourself on our
account. I hope these abominable Riders won't come here again.'

'I hope not indeed!' said Butterbur with a shiver.

AT THE SIGN OF THE PRANCING PONY 341

'If they do, you must not risk their anger for my sake. They are dangerous. Once we have got clear away, you can do us little harm, if you tell them that a party of four hobbits *has* passed through Bree. Good night, Mr Butterbur! Thankyou again for your kindness. One day perhaps Gandalf will tell you what it is all about.'

'Good night, Mr Baggins – Mr Hill, I should say! Good night, Mr Took! Bless me! Where's Mr Brandybuck?'

'I don't know,' said Folco; 'but I expect he's outside. He said something about going out for a breath of air. He ought to be in before long.'

'Very good!' said Mr Butterbur. 'I'll see that he is not locked out. Good night to you all!' With a puzzled look at Trotter, and a shake of his head, he went out and his footsteps died away in the passage.

'There you go again!' said Trotter before Frodo could speak. 'Too trusting still! Why tell old Barnabas all that about being hunted; and why tell him the other hobbit was a Bolger?'

'Isn't he safe?' asked Frodo. 'Tom Bombadil said he was, and Gandalf seems to have trusted him.'

'Is he safe?' cried Trotter, throwing up his hands. 'Yes, he's safe, safer than houses. But why give him any more to puzzle about than is necessary? And why interfere with Gandalf's plan? You're not very quick, or it would have been plain at once to you that Gandalf wanted it *believed* that the hobbit with him was Baggins – precisely so that you would have a better chance, if you were still behind. And what about me? Am I safe? You're not sure (I know that), and yet you talk to Butterbur in front of me! However, I know now all that he had to say; and at least it will cut short what I still had to tell you – which was mostly about those Black Riders, as you call them. I saw them myself. I should say that seven all told have passed through Bree since Monday. You won't pretend any longer that you can't imagine what interest your real name might have. There is a reward offered for anyone who can report that four hobbits are here, and that one of them is probably a Baggins after all.'

'Yes, yes,' said Frodo. 'I see all that. But I knew already that They were after me; and so far at any rate they seem to have been sent off on a false scent.'

'I should not be too sure that they have all gone right away,' said Trotter; 'or that they are all ahead of you, and chasing after

342   THE RETURN OF THE SHADOW

Gandalf. They are cunning, and they divide their forces. I can still
tell you a few things you have not heard from Butterbur. I first saw
a Rider on Monday night, east of Bree as I was coming in out of the
wilds. I nearly ran into him, going fast along the Road in the dark.
I hailed him with a curse, for he had almost run over me; and he
pulled up and came back. I stood still and made no sound, but he
brought his horse step by step towards me. When he was quite
close he stooped and sniffed. Then he hissed, and turned his horse
and rode off.[8] Yesterday I saw the four that called at this inn. Last
night I was on the look-out. I was lying on a bank under the hedge
of Bill Ferney's garden; and I heard Bill Ferney talking. He is a
surly fellow, and has a bad name in the Bree-land, and queer folk
are known to call at his house sometimes. You must have noticed
him among the company: a swarthy man with a scowl. He was
very close tonight with Harry Goatleaf, the west-gate keeper (a
mean old curmudgeon); and with one of the southern strangers.
They slipped out together just after your song and accident. I
don't trust Ferney. He would sell *anything* to *anybody*, if you
understand me.'

'I don't understand you,' said Frodo.

'Well, I'm not going to say it plainer,' said Trotter. 'I just
wonder whether this unusual arrival of strange travellers up the
Greenway, and the appearance of the hunting horsemen come
together by mere chance. Both might be looking for the same
thing – or person. Anyway, I heard Bill Ferney talking last night. I
know his voice, though I could not catch what was said. The other
voice was whispering, or hissing. And that's all I have to tell you.
You must do as you like about my reward. But as for my coming
with you, I will say this: I know all the lands between the Shire
and the Misty Mountains, for I've wandered over them many
times in the course of my life – and I'm older now than I look. I
might prove useful. You'll have to leave the open Road after
tonight; for if you ask me, I should say that these Riders are
patrolling it – and still looking for your party. I don't fancy that
you wish to meet them. I don't! They give me the creeps!' he
ended suddenly with a shudder.

The others looked at him and saw with surprise that his face was
buried in his hands, and his hood was drawn right down. The
room was very quiet and still and the lights seemed to have grown
dim.

'There!' he cried after a moment, throwing back his hood and
pushing the hair from his face. 'Perhaps I know more about these

AT THE SIGN OF THE PRANCING PONY 343

pursuers than you do. You do not fear them enough – yet. It seems to me only too likely that news of you will reach them before this night is over. Tomorrow you will have to go swiftly, and secretly – if you can. But Trotter can take you by paths that are seldom trodden. Will you have him?'

Frodo made no answer. He looked at Trotter: grim and wild and rough-clad. It was hard to know what to do. He did not doubt that most of his tale was true; but it was less easy to feel sure of his good will. Why was he so interested? He had a dark look – and yet there was something in it that seemed friendly and even curiously attractive. And his speech had changed as he talked, from the unfamiliar tones of the Outsiders to something more familiar, something that seemed to remind Frodo of somebody.⁹ The silence grew, and still he could not make up his mind.

'Well, I'm for Trotter, if you want any help in deciding,' said Folco suddenly. 'In any case, I daresay he could follow us wherever we went, even if we refused.'

'Thankyou!' said Trotter smiling at Folco. 'I could and I should; for I should feel it was my duty. But here is a letter which I have for you – that ought to make up your mind for you.' To Frodo's amazement he took from his pocket a small sealed letter and handed it over. On the outside was written: *F. from G.* ⚔

'Read it!' said Trotter.

Here the chapter ends. It will be seen that in this narrative, despite the radical differences in what Trotter and Butterbur communicated, the original form of the story (in the 'A' version, but see note 8) was still closely followed.

The manuscript of this chapter subsequently underwent immensely intricate alteration, with long insertions and deletions, for my father used the original text for two distinct developments, both involving major structural change. The one he called the 'red' version, marked out and paginated in red, the other the 'blue'; thus a rider on an inserted slip bears the number 'rider to IX.3(g) = red IX.9 = blue IX.4'! The relations can in fact be worked out perfectly satisfactorily. The 'blue' version is the later, and peters out towards the end; this represents a later plot, in which all reference to the visit of Gandalf and Odo to *The Prancing Pony* is cut out. The 'red' version, on the other hand, may well be contemporary or nearly contemporary with the primary text; it is carefully written (the alterations constituting the 'blue' version being much rougher), and it tells the same story of Gandalf and Odo – but tells it quite differently. It takes up from the end of the description of Bree, and begins with Gandalf's arrival there with Odo, now told directly and not in Butterburian narrative.

344 THE RETURN OF THE SHADOW

The Tuesday had been a day of heavy rain. Night had fallen some hours ago, and it was still pouring down. It was so dark that nothing could be heard but the seething noise of the rain, and the ripple of flood-rivers running down the hill – and the sound of hoofs splashing on the Road. A horse was slowly climbing up the long slope towards the village of Bree.

Suddenly a great gate loomed up: it stretched right across the Road from one strong post to another, and it was shut. There was a small house beyond it, dark and grey. The horse halted with its nose over the top bar of the gate, and the rider, an old man, dismounted stiffly, and lifted down a small figure that had been riding on a pillion behind him. The old man beat on the gate, and was just beginning to climb over it, when the door of the house opened and a man came out with a lantern, muttering and grumbling.

'A fine night to come hammering on the gate and getting a man out of his bed!' he said.

'And a fine night to be out in, wet through and cold, and on the wrong side of a gate!' replied the rider. 'Come on now, Harry! Get it open quick!'

'Bless me!' cried the gate-keeper, holding up the lantern. 'Gandalf it is – and I might have guessed it. There's never no knowing when you'll turn up next.' He opened the gate slowly, peering in surprise at the small bedraggled figure at Gandalf's side.

'Thank you!' said Gandalf, leading his horse forward. 'This is a friend of mine, a hobbit out of the Shire. Have you seen any more on the Road? There ought to be four of them ahead, a party on ponies.'

'There hasn't been any such party through, while I've been about,' said Harry. 'There *might* have been up to mid-day, for I was away in Staddle, and my brother was here. But I've heard no talk of it. Not that we watch the Road much between sunrise and nightfall, while the gate's open. But we shall have to be more heedful, I'm thinking.'

'Why?' asked Gandalf. 'Have any strange folk been about?'

'I should say so! Mighty queer folk. Black men on horses; and a lot of foreigners out of the South came up the Greenway at dusk. But if you're going to *The Pony*, I should get on before they lock up. You'll hear all the news there. I'll be getting back to my bed, and wish you good night.' He shut the gate and went in.

'Good night!' said Gandalf, and walked on into the village, leading his horse. The hobbit stumbled along beside him.

AT THE SIGN OF THE PRANCING PONY 345

There was a lamp still shining over the entrance to the inn, but the door was closed. Gandalf rang the bell in the yard, and after a little delay a large fat man, in his shirt sleeves and with slippers on his feet, opened the door a crack and peered out.

'Good evening, Butterbur!' said the wizard. 'Any room for an old friend?'

'Heavens above, if they aren't all washed away!' cried the landlord. 'Gandalf! And what are you doing out in this weather and at this time of night? And who's your little friend?'

Gandalf winked at him. 'Hot drinks and warm beds – that's what we want, and not too many questions,' he said, and stumped up the steps.

'What about the horse?' asked the landlord.

'Give him the best you've got!' answered Gandalf. 'And if Bob grumbles at being got up again at this hour, tell him the beast deserves it: Narothal[10] has carried us both, fast and far today. I'll repay Bob in the morning according as my horse reports of him!'

A little later the wizard and his companion were sitting before the hot embers of a fire in Mr Butterbur's own room, warming and drying themselves and drinking mulled ale. The landlord came in to say that a room was ready for them.

'Don't you hurry yourselves!' said he, 'but when you're ready, I'll be going to my own bed. There's been an unusual lot of travellers in here today, more than I remember for years, and I'm tired.'

'Any hobbits among them?' asked Gandalf. 'I'm looking for four of them – a friend of mine out of the Shire and three companions.' He described Frodo carefully, but did not give his name. 'They should have five ponies and a fair amoung of baggage; and they ought to have reached Bree today. Harry hasn't seen them; but I hoped they might have come in without his noticing them.'

'Nay,' said the landlord, 'a party like that would have been heard of even by Harry, dull old grumbler though he be. We don't get many Outsiders from the Shire to Bree these days. There's no such party at *The Pony*, and there's been none along the Road to my certain knowledge.'

'That's bad news!' said Gandalf, tugging at his beard. 'I wonder where they have got to!'[11] He was silent for a moment. 'Look here, Butterbur!' he went on. 'You and I are old friends. You have eyes and ears in your head, and though you say a lot, you know what to

346 THE RETURN OF THE SHADOW

leave unsaid. I want to be private while I'm here, and if I see no one but you and Bob I'll be pleased. Don't tell everyone that I've asked after this party! But keep your eyes open, and if they turn up after I've gone, give them this message: *Hurry on! Gandalf's ahead.* Just that. Don't forget, because it's important. And if anyone – anyone, mind you, however strange – enquires after a hobbit called *Baggins*, tell them Baggins has gone east with Gandalf. Don't forget that, either, and I shall be grateful to you!'

'Right you are!' said Mr Butterbur. 'I hope I'll not forget, though one thing drives out another, when I'm busy with guests in the house. Baggins, you say? Let me see – I remember that name. Wasn't there a Bilbo Baggins that they told some strange tales about over in the Shire? My dad told me that he had stayed in this house more than once. But your friend won't be him – he disappeared in some funny way nigh on twenty years back: vanished with a bang while he was talking, or so I've heard. Not that I believe all the tales that come out of the West.'

'No need to,' said Gandalf, laughing. 'Anyway my young friend here is not old Bilbo Baggins. Just a relation.'

'That's right!' said the hobbit. 'Just a relation – a cousin in fact.'

'I see,' said the landlord. 'Well, it does you credit. Bilbo was a fine little fellow, and rich as a king into the bargain, if half I've heard is true. I'll give your messages, if the chance comes, Gandalf; and I'll ask no questions, strange though it all seems to me. But you know your own business best, and you've done me many a good turn.'

'Thankyou Barnabas!' said Gandalf. 'And now I'll do you another – let you go to your bed at once.' He drained his mug and stood up. The landlord put out the lights, and holding a candle in each hand led them to their room.

In the morning Gandalf and his friend got up late. They breakfasted in a private room, and spoke to no one but Mr Barnabas Butterbur. It was close on eleven before Gandalf called for his reckoning, and for his horse.

'Tell Bob to take him up the lane and wait for me near the Greenway,' he said. 'I'm not going along the Road to be gaped at this morning.'

He took his leave of the landlord at a side-door. 'Goodbye, my friend,' he said. 'Don't forget the messages! One day, perhaps, I'll tell you the whole story, and repay you, too, with something better

AT THE SIGN OF THE PRANCING PONY 347

even than good news – that is, I will, if the whole story does not come to a bad end. Goodbye!'

He walked off with the hobbit up a narrow lane that ran north from the inn over the ditch round the village and on towards the Greenway.[12] Bob the ostler was waiting outside the village boundary. The white horse was glossy and well-groomed, and seemed thoroughly rested and eager for another day's journey. Gandalf called to him by name, and Narothal[13] whinnied, tossing up his head, and trotting back to his master, and nuzzling against his face.

'A good report, Bob!' said Gandalf, giving the ostler a silver piece. He mounted; and Bob helped the hobbit up on to a cushion behind the wizard, then he stood back with his cap in his hand, grinning broadly.

'That's right, my lad!' laughed Gandalf. 'We look a funny pair, I daresay. But we're not as funny as we look. When we've gone, remember that we've gone east, but forget that we set out along this lane. See? Goodbye!' He rode off and left Bob scratching his head.

'Curry me! if these aren't queer days!' he said to himself. 'Black men riding out of nowhere, and folk on the Greenway, and old Gandalf with a hobbit on a pillion and all! Things are beginning to move in Bree! But you watch yourself, Bob my lad – old Gandalf can hand out something hotter than silver.'

The fair morning that had followed the rain gave way later to cloud and mist. Nothing more happened in Bree that day until dusk was falling. Then out of the fog four horsemen rode though the gate. Harry peered through a window, and then hurriedly withdrew. He had been thinking of going out and shutting the gate, but he changed his mind. The horsemen were all clad and muffled in black, and rode high black horses. Some of the same sort had been seen in Bree two days before and wild stories were going about. Some said they were not human, and even the dogs were afeared of them. Harry locked the door and stood quaking behind it.

But the riders halted, and one dismounted and came and smote on the door. 'What do you want?' called Harry from inside.

'We want news!' hissed a cold voice through the keyhole.

'What of?' he answered, shaking in his boots.

'News of four hobbits,[14] riding on ponies out of the Shire. Have they passed?'

348   THE RETURN OF THE SHADOW

Harry wished they had, for it might have satisfied these riders, if he could have said *yes*. There was a threat and urgency in the cold voice: but he dared not risk a *yes* that was not true. 'No sir!' he said in a quavering voice. 'There's been no hobbits on ponies through Bree, and there isn't likely to be any. But there was a hobbit riding behind an old man on a white horse, last night. They went to *The Pony*.'

'Do you know their names?' said the voice.

'The old man was Gandalf,' said Harry.

A hiss came through the keyhole, and Harry started back, feeling as if something icy cold had touched him. 'You have our thanks', said the voice. 'You will keep watch for four hobbits, if you still wish to please us. We will return.'

Harry heard the sound of hoofs going off towards the village. He unlocked the door stealthily, and then crept out, and peered up the road. It was too foggy and already too dark to see much. But he heard the hoofs halt at the bend of the Road by the inn. He waited a while, and then quietly shut and locked the gate. He was just returning to his house, when in the misty air he heard the sound of hoofs again, starting up by the inn and dying away round the corner and down the Road eastward. It was turning very cold, he thought. He shivered and hurried indoors, bolting and barring the door.

The next morning, Thursday, was clear again, with a warm sun and the wind turning towards the South. Towards evening a dozen dwarves came walking out of the East into Bree with heavy packs on their backs. They were sullen and had few words for anybody. But no traveller came past the western gate all day. Night fell and Harry shut the gate, but he kept on going to his door. He was afraid of the threat in the cold voice, if he missed any strange hobbits.

It was dark and white stars were shining when Frodo and his companions came at last to the Greenway-crossing and drew near the village. They found that it was surrounded by a deep ditch with a hedge and fence on the inner side. Over and through this the Road ran, but it was now barred by the great gate. They saw a house on the other side, and a man sitting at the door. He jumped up and fetched a lantern, and looked down over the gate at them in surprise.

'What do you want and where do you come from?' he asked gruffly.

AT THE SIGN OF THE PRANCING PONY   349

'We are making for the inn here,' answered Frodo. 'We are journeying east and cannot go further tonight.'

'Hobbits! Four hobbits! And what's more, out of the Shire from the sound of their talk,' said the gate-keeper, quietly and almost as if he was speaking to himself. He stared at them darkly for a moment, and then slowly opened the gate and let them ride through.

'We don't often see Shire-folk riding on the Road by night,' he went on, as they halted for a moment by his door. 'You'll pardon me wondering what business takes you away east of Bree.'

'I do,' said Frodo, 'though it does not seem very wonderful to us. But this does not seem a good place to talk of our business.'

'Ah well, your business is your own, no doubt,' said the gate-keeper. 'But you'll find maybe that there are more folk than old Harry at the gate that will ask questions. Are you expecting to meet any friends here?'

'What do you mean?' asked Frodo in surprise. 'Why should we?'

'And why not? Many folk meet at Bree even in these days. If you go on to *The Pony*, you may find you are not the only guests.'

Frodo wished him good night and made no further answer, though he could see in the lantern-light that the man was still eyeing them curiously. He was glad to hear the gate clang to behind them, as they rode forward. He wondered what the man had meant by 'meeting friends'. Could anyone have been asking for news of four hobbits? Gandalf, perhaps? He might have passed through, while they were delayed in the Forest and the Downs. But a Black Rider was more likely. There was something in the look and tone of the gate-keeper that filled him with suspicion.

Harry stared after them for a moment, and then he went to his door. 'Ned!' he called. 'I've business up at *The Pony*, and it may keep me a while. You must be on the gate, till I come back.'

From this point the 'red version' is only different from the first text in that Butterbur's story of Gandalf's visit is of course very greatly reduced from the form given on pp. 338–9.

NOTES

1 The drafts have 'Few had survived the turmoils of the Earliest Days', an expression used in the *Foreword* (p. 329, note 1), where FR has 'Elder Days'; the earliest form of the passage has: 'Few had

350   THE RETURN OF THE SHADOW

survived the turmoils of those old and forgotten days, and the wars of the Elves and Goblins'.

2 *prepared:* FR has '*proposed* to leave them', but this is an error that arose at the typescript stage.

3 My father wrote 'a queer-looking brown-faced hobbit', struck out 'hobbit', and then wrote 'hobbit' again.

4 In this phase *Ferney* is spelt thus; *Ferny* in the original version and in FR.

5 The word *ran* in the erased note to the second text of the attack on Crickhollow ('Behind him ran Odo . . .', p. 328) is rather surprising, since it seems pointless: if Odo was to accompany Gandalf there seems no reason why he should not ride pillion from the first – and in any case he would have been quickly left far behind.

6 It is perhaps surprising that Gandalf should expect Frodo and his companions to have passed through Bree on the Tuesday, since he knew from Odo that they left the house at Crickhollow on the Monday morning and had gone into the Old Forest. When they would get to Bree was presumably now far more uncertain than if they had taken the Road (hostile interventions apart). Possibly this survives from the old form of the story – 'They should be here by Tuesday, if they can follow a plain road', p. 151 – when Gandalf had no reason to think that they had not simply ridden the East Road from the Brandywine Bridge. See note 11.

7 How did the Riders know that there were *four* hobbits? (In the old variant versions, pp. 152, 157, they knew even that the four hobbits had five ponies). Presumably they surmised it: they knew that three had come to Bucklebury Ferry and been met there by another. Beyond that they had no knowledge (on the Wednesday night when they came to the inn) of Frodo and his companions. – At some point my father struck out the word *four*; see note 14.

8 This episode derives from the old 'B' version, p. 157; but there the Rider questioned Trotter, who did not answer. The relations between the versions here are:
Old version 'A' (p. 151):
  (Monday) One Rider questions Butterbur at the inn-door
  (Tuesday) Four Riders come to the inn-door, and one questions Butterbur
Old version 'B' (p. 157):
  (Monday) One Rider questions Trotter on the Road
  (Tuesday) Four riders meet Trotter on the Road, and one questions him
The present version:
  (Monday) One Rider goes through Bree (p. 339), and meets Trotter on the Road east of Bree without speech (p. 342)
  (Wednesday) Four Riders come to the inn-door, and one questions Butterbur (pp. 339–40); they are seen by Trotter (p. 342)

AT THE SIGN OF THE PRANCING PONY 351

9 The change in Trotter's speech remarked by Frodo, deriving from the original form of the story (p. 154), survived in FR (p. 178), though the significance is there quite different: 'I think you are not really as you choose to look. You began to talk to me like the Bree-folk, but your voice has changed.'

10 *Narothal* ('Firefoot'), the first name given to Gandalf's white horse, was replaced later in pencil by the suggestions: 'Fairfax, Snowfax', and pencilled in the margin is 'Firefoot Arod? Aragorn', but these latter were struck out. *Arod* became in LR the name of a horse of Rohan.

11 A pencilled note on the manuscript says: 'Since he has been to Crickhollow he must know of Old Forest' – i.e. Gandalf must know from Odo that the other hobbits went into the Old Forest. At the same time my father pencilled into the text at this point: 'I trusted Tom Bombadil to keep them out of trouble.'

12 This lane is marked on the sketch-map of Bree given on p. 335.

13 'Narothal' changed in pencil to 'Fairfax'; see note 10.

14 *four hobbits:* see note 7. Subsequently my father struck out *four*, and wrote instead: *hobbits, three or more*.

XXI
THE THIRD PHASE (3):
TO WEATHERTOP AND RIVENDELL

The next chapter, numbered X and with the title 'Wild Ways to Weather-top', belongs with the base-form of 'At the Sign of the Prancing Pony' and is continuous with it; but it begins by repeating almost exactly the end of that chapter, from 'Frodo made no answer' to '"Read it!" said Trotter' (p. 343). Then follows:

Frodo looked carefully at the seal before he broke it. It seemed certainly to be Gandalf's, as did the writing also, and the runic G ⚌. Inside was the following message. Frodo read it and then repeated it aloud for the benefit of Folco and Sam.

The Prancing Pony, Wednesday, Sept. 28. Dear F. Where on earth are you? Not still in the Forest, I hope! Could not help being late, but explanations must wait. If you ever get this letter, I shall be ahead of you. Hurry on, and don't stop anywhere! Things are worse than I thought and pursuit is close. Look out for horsemen in black, and avoid them. They are perilous: your worst enemies. Don't use It again, not on any account. Don't move in the dark. Try and catch me up. I dare not wait here, but I shall halt at a place known to the bearer, and look out for you there. I am giving this to a ranger known as Trotter: dark rather lean hobbit, wears wooden shoes. He is an old friend of mine, and knows a great deal. You can trust him. He will guide you to appointed place through wild country. N.B. Odo Baggins is with me. Hurry on! Yours ✕ ᚠ ᚤ ᛗ ᚠ ᚱ ᚣ. ⦂ ⚌ ⦂

Frodo looked at the trailing handwriting: it seemed as plainly genuine as the seal. 'It is dated Wednesday and from this house,' he said. 'How did you come by it?'

'I met Gandalf by appointment near Archet,' answered Trotter. 'He did not leave Bree by the Road, but went up a side lane and round the hill the other way.'

'Well, Trotter,' said Frodo after a pause, 'it would have made things easier and saved a lot of time and talk, if you had produced

TO WEATHERTOP AND RIVENDELL 353

this letter at once. Why did you invent all that tale about eaves-dropping?'

'I didn't invent it,' laughed Trotter. 'I gave old Gandalf quite a shock when I popped up from behind the hedge. But he was very glad when he saw who I was. He said it was the first bit of luck he had had for some while. It was then that we arranged that I was to wait about here in case you were behind, while he pushed on and tried to draw the Riders after him. I know all about your troubles – including the Ring, I may say.'

'Then there's nothing more for me to say,' said Frodo, 'except that I am glad we have found you. I am sorry if I have been unnecessarily suspicious.'

The conversation proceeds very much as in the original story (p. 155), as far as the 'subsidence' of Folco (Odo) beneath Trotter's opinion of him.[1] Then follows:

'We shall all perish, tough or not, unless we have strange good luck, as far as I can see,' said Frodo. 'I cannot understand why you want to be mixed up in our troubles, Trotter.'

'One reason is that Gandalf asked me to help you,' he replied quietly.

'What do you advise then?' asked Frodo. 'I don't quite under-stand this letter: *don't stop anywhere* it says, and yet *don't move in the dark*. Is it safe to stop here till morning?' Frodo looked at the comfortable fire and the soft candlelight in the room, and sighed.

'No, it probably isn't safe – but it would be far more dangerous to start off by night. So we must wait for daylight and hope for the best. But we had better start early – it is a long way to Weathertop.'

'Weathertop?' said Folco. 'Where and what is that?'

'The *appointed place* mentioned in the letter,' Trotter replied. 'It is a hill, just north of the Road, somewhere about halfway to Rivendell from here.[2] It commands a very wide view all round. But you will start nearly two days behind Gandalf, and you'll have to go fast or you won't find him there.'

'In that case let's get to bed now, while there is still some night left!' said Folco yawning. 'Where's that silly fellow Merry? It would be too much, if we had to go out now and look for him.'

Merry's story of the Black Rider whom he saw outside the inn and followed differs in this, that whereas in the original version (pp. 161–2) the Rider went through the village from west to east and stopped at Bill Ferny's house (hole), here

'He was coming *from* the east,' Merry went on. 'I followed him

354　　　　THE RETURN OF THE SHADOW

down the Road almost to the gate. He stopped there at the keeper's house, and I thought I heard him talking to someone. I tried to creep near, but I did not dare to get very close. In fact, I am afraid I suddenly began to shiver and shake, and bolted back here.'

'What's to be done?' said Frodo, turning to Trotter.

'Don't go to your rooms!' he answered at once. 'I don't like this at all. Harry Goatleaf was here tonight and went off with Bill Ferney. It's quite likely that they have found out which rooms you have got.

While in the remainder of the chapter there are advances in detail to the text of FR (from p. 186, the end of Chapter 10 'Strider', to p. 201, in the course of Chapter 11 'A Knife in the Dark'), the narrative of this third phase version follows the original (pp. 162–71) closely in almost all points where that differed from FR, and ends at the same point.

It is now Trotter who imitated Frodo's head in the bed with a mat. The pony is expressly said to be Bill Ferney's, and is described as 'a bony, underfed, and rather dispirited animal.' There were two men looking over the hedge round Ferney's house: Ferney himself, and 'a southerner with a sallow face, and a sly and almost goblinish look in his slanting eyes.' This latter is not identified with the 'squint-eyed southerner' who left the inn the night before with Ferney and the gate-keeper (p. 336). In the old story (p. 165) it was Bill Ferny standing there alone, whom Bingo thought 'goblinish'. It is still Trotter who has the apples, and who hits Ferney on the nose with one. Archet, Combe, and Staddle are referred to as in FR (p. 193), in keeping with what is said of them in the description of the Bree-land at the opening of Chapter IX (p. 332), and Trotter's plan is now to make for Archet and pass it on the east (cf. p. 165 and note 21).

The lights in the eastern sky seen by the travellers from the Midge-water Marshes do not appear until the whole story of Gandalf's movements at this time had been changed. Trotter replies to Frodo's question 'But surely we were hoping to find Gandalf there?' (FR p. 195, original version p. 167) thus:

'Yes – but my hope is rather faint. It is four days since we left Bree, and if Gandalf has managed to get to Weathertop himself without being too hotly pursued, he must have arrived at least two days ago. I doubt if he has dared to wait so long, on the mere chance of your following him: he does not know for certain that you are behind or have got his messages . . .'

He still says: 'There are even some of the Rangers that on a clear day could spy us from there, if we moved. And not all the Rangers are to be trusted . . .'

TO WEATHERTOP AND RIVENDELL 355

The chronology is thus (cf. p. 175):

Wed.	Sept.	28	Gandalf and Odo left Bree
Thurs.	Sept.	29	Frodo and companions reached Bree
Fri.	Sept.	30	Trotter, Frodo and companions left Bree; night in Chetwood
Sat.	Oct.	1	Night in Chetwood
Sun.	Oct.	2	First day and camp in marshes
Mon.	Oct.	3	Second day and camp in marshes
Tues.	Oct.	4	Leaving the marshes. Camp by stream under alders.

On this day Trotter calculated that Gandalf, if he reached Weathertop, must have arrived there 'at least two days ago', i.e. on Sunday 2 October, which allows as much as four days and nights for the journey from Bree on horseback.

In the original version they reached Weathertop on 5 October, whereas in FR they camped at the feet of the hills that night (see p. 175). In the present text my father retained the former story, but then changed it to that of FR:

By night they had reached the feet of the hills, and there they camped. It was the night of October the fifth, and they were six days out from Bree. In the morning they found, for the first time since they left the Bree-land [> Chetwood], a track plain to see.

It will be seen shortly that this change was made before the chapter was finished.

The passage following Folco's question 'Is there any barrow on Weathertop?' (FR p. 197) remains exactly as in the original text (p. 169), with *Elendil* for *Valandil*; and when they reach the summit all remains as before, with only the necessary change of Merry's 'I don't blame Gandalf for not waiting here! He would have to leave the waggon, and horses, and most of his companions, too, I expect, down near the Road' to 'I don't blame Gandalf for not waiting long – if he ever came here.' But the paper that flutters from the cairn bears a different message (see p. 170):

Wednesday Oct. 5. Bad news. We arrived late Monday. Odo vanished last night. I must go at once to Rivendell. Make for Ford beyond Trollshaw with all speed, but look out. Enemies may attempt to guard it.   G ⨯⨯[3]

'Odo!' cried Merry. 'Does that mean that the Riders have got him? How horrible!'

356 THE RETURN OF THE SHADOW

'Our missing Gandalf has turned out disastrous,' said Frodo. 'Poor Odo! I expect this is the result of pretending to be Baggins. If only we could all have been together!'

'Monday!' said Trotter. 'Then they arrived when we were in the marshes, and Gandalf did not leave till we were already close to the hills. They cannot have caught any glimpse of our miserable little fires on Monday, or on Tuesday. I wonder what happened here that night. Still it is no good guessing: there is nothing we can do but make for Rivendell as best we may.'[4]

'How far is Rivendell?' asked Frodo, looking round wearily. The world looked wild and wide from Weathertop.

From here the text follows the old version (pp. 170–1) almost exactly – with the revised form of Trotter's answer concerning the distance to Rivendell, p. 171 – to the end of the chapter, with Trotter, Frodo, and Merry slipping down from the summit of Weathertop to find Sam and Folco in the dell (where the original Chapter VII also ended).

Since Gandalf and Odo left Bree on the morning of Wednesday 28 September but did not reach Weathertop till late on Monday 3 October, they took longer even than Trotter had calculated (p. 355): nearly six days on horseback, whereas Trotter says (in this text as in the old, p. 171) that it would take 'a ranger on his own feet' about a week from Bree to Weathertop (in the rejected passage of the old text, p. 170, Trotter said that he reckoned it was 'about 120 long-miles' by the Road). Trotter's words 'I wonder what happened here that night', referring to the night on which Odo vanished (Tuesday 4 October), show that the night camp at the foot of the hills on 5 October had entered the narrative, and that it was now Thursday 6 October, for he would not say 'that night' if he meant 'last night'. The chronology given on p. 355 can therefore be completed for this stage of the development of the narrative thus:

Mon.	Oct. 3	Second day and camp in the marshes
		Gandalf and Odo reach Weathertop late
Tues.	Oct. 4	Leaving the marshes. Camp by stream under alders
		Odo disappears from Weathertop at night
Wed.	Oct. 5	Camp at feet of hills
		Gandalf leaves Weathertop
Thurs.	Oct. 6	Trotter, Frodo and companions reach Weathertop

★

The next chapter, numbered XI but without title,[5] begins with an account of what Sam and Folco had been doing (FR p. 201), which is

TO WEATHERTOP AND RIVENDELL   357

where the corresponding chapter VIII in the original version began (p. 177).

Sam and Folco had not been idle. They had explored the small dell and the surrounding valley. Not far away they had found a spring of clear water, and near it footprints not more than a day or two old. In the dell itself they had found recent traces of a fire and other signs of a small camp. But the most unexpected and most welcome discovery was made by Sam. There were some large fallen rocks at the edge of the dell nearest to the hill-side. Behind them Sam came upon a small store of fire-wood neatly stacked; and under the wood was a bag containing food. It was mostly cakes of *cram*[6] packed in two small wooden boxes, but there was also a little bacon, and some dried fruits.

'Old Gandalf has been here, then,' said Sam to Folco. 'These packets of *cram* show that. I never heard tell of anyone but the two Bagginses and the wizard using that stuff. Better than dying of hunger, they say, but not much better.'

'I wonder if it was left for us, or if Gandalf is still about somewhere near,' said Folco. 'I wish Frodo and the other two would come back.'

Sam was more grateful for the *cram* when the others did return, hurrying back to the dell with their alarming news. There was a long journey ahead of them before they could expect to get help; and it seemed plain that Gandalf had left what food he could spare in case their own supplies were short.

'It is probably some that he did not need after poor Odo's disappearance,' said Frodo. 'But what about the wood?'

'I think they must have collected it on the Tuesday,' said Trotter, 'and were preparing to wait here in camp for some time. They would have to go some distance for it, as there are no trees close at hand.'

It was already late afternoon, and the sun was sinking. They debated for some while what they ought to do. It was the store of fuel that finally decided them to go no further that day, and to camp for the night in the dell.

The text now follows the old version (pp. 177–9) fairly closely. To Merry's question 'Can the enemies *see*?' Trotter now replies: 'Their horses can see. They do not themselves see the world of light as we do; but they are not blind, and in the dark they are most to be feared.' Trotter no longer says that there were Men dwelling in the lands away to the South of them; nor is it told that they took it in turns to sit on guard at the

358   THE RETURN OF THE SHADOW

edge of the dell. The passage describing Trotter's tales is a characteristic blending of the old version (p. 179) with new elements that would survive into FR (p. 203):

As night fell and the light of the fire began to shine out brightly, Trotter began to tell them tales to keep their minds from fear. He knew much lore concerning wild animals, and understood something of their languages; and he had strange tales to tell of their hidden lives and little known adventures. He knew also many histories and legends of the ancient days, of hobbits when the Shire was still unexplored, and of things beyond the mists of memory out of which the hobbits came. They wondered how old he was, and where he had learned all this lore.

'Tell us of Gilgalad,' said Merry suddenly, when he paused at the end of a story of the Elf-kingdoms. 'You spoke that name not long ago, and it is still ringing in my ears. I seem to remember hearing it before, but I cannot remember anything else about it.'

'You should ask the possessor of the Ring about that name,' answered Trotter in a low voice. Merry and Folco looked at Frodo, who was staring into the fire.

From this point the manuscript is defective, two sheets being missing; but a rejected page carries the story a little further before tailing off:

'I know only the little that Gandalf told me,' he said. 'Gilgalad was the last of the great elf-kings. Gilgalad is *Starlight* in their tongue. With the aid of King Elendil, the Elf-friend, he overthrew the Enemy, but they both perished. And I would gladly hear more if Trotter will tell us. It was the son of Elendil that carried off the Ring. But I cannot tell that tale. Tell us more, Trotter, if you will.'

'No,' said Trotter. 'I will not tell that tale now, in this time and place with the servants of the Enemy at hand. Perhaps in the house of Elrond you will hear it. For Elrond knows it in full.'

'Then tell us some other tale of old,' said Merry . . .

Trotter's song, and his story of Beren and Lúthien, are thus missing here; and the manuscript takes up again at 'As Trotter was speaking they watched his strange eager face . . .' From this point the text of FR, as far as the end of Chapter 11 'A Knife in the Dark', was achieved, with scarcely any difference even of wording, except for these points: Folco stands for Pippin; there were still three Riders, not five, in the attack on the dell; and Frodo as he threw himself on the ground cried out *Elbereth! Elbereth!*

At this point Chapter 12 'Flight to the Ford' begins in FR, but as in the original text (p. 190) the present version continues without break to the

TO WEATHERTOP AND RIVENDELL 359

Ford of Rivendell. The relations of chapter-structure between the
present phase and FR can be shown thus (and cf. the table on p. 133):

The present 'phase'	*FR*
IX *At the Sign of the Prancing Pony.* Ends with Trotter giving Frodo the letter from Gandalf.	9 *At the Sign of the Prancing Pony.* Ends with Frodo, Pippin and Sam returning to their room at the inn.
X *Wild Ways to Weathertop.* Conclusion of conversation with Trotter. Attack on the inn, departure from Bree; ends with sight of the Riders below Weathertop.	10 *Strider.* Conversations with Strider and Butterbur.
	11 *A Knife in the Dark.* Attack on the inn, departure from Bree; ends with the attack on Weathertop.
XI *No title.* Attack on Weathertop. Journey from Weathertop to the Ford.	12 *Flight to the Ford.*

As is characteristic of these third phase chapters, the present text
advances largely towards the form in FR in detail of wording and
description, but retains many features of the original version; thus the
'red flash' seen at the moment of the attack on Weathertop survives, of
the slash in the black robe Trotter still says only 'What harm it did to the
Black Rider I do not know', and the distant cries of the Riders as they
crossed the Road are not heard, while on the other hand the firewood left
by Gandalf is no longer said to have been taken with them, and the
rejuvenation of Bill Ferney's pony is described (for these elements in
the narrative see pp. 190–1). Trotter now speaks aside to Sam, but what
he says is different:

'I think I understand things better now,' he said in a low voice.
'Our enemies knew the Ring was here; perhaps because they have
captured Odo, and certainly because they can feel its presence.
They are no longer pursuing Gandalf. But they have now drawn
off from us for the time, because we are many and more bold than
they expected, but especially because they think they have slain or
mortally wounded your master – so that the Ring will inevitably
come soon into their power.'

The rest of his words to Sam are as in FR (p. 210). – In the discussion
of what it were best to do now (FR p. 211) the present version reads:

The others were discussing this very question. They decided to
leave Weathertop as soon as possible. It was already Friday
morning, and the two days that Gandalf's message had asked for
would soon be up. In any case it was no good remaining in so bare
and indefensible a place, now that their enemies had discovered

360   THE RETURN OF THE SHADOW

them, and knew also that Frodo had the Ring. As soon as the daylight was full they had some hurried food and packed.

For 'the two days that Gandalf's message had asked for' see notes 3 and 4.

The chronology of the journey remains as in the original text (see pp. 192–3, 219): they still recrossed the Road on the morning of the sixth day from Weathertop (the seventh in FR), and spent three days in the hills before the weather turned to rain (two in FR). But the lag of one day that remained between the original text and FR (owing to their earlier arrival on Weathertop), so that they reached the Ford of Rivendell on 19 October, is no longer present (see p. 356).

The rain that Trotter judged had fallen some two days before at the place where they crossed the Road again (FR p. 213) is now mentioned, but the River Hoarwell (Mitheithel) and the Last Bridge have still not emerged. The river which they could see in the distance, unnamed in the first version (p. 191), is now given a name: 'the Riven River, that came down out of the Mountains and flowed through Rivendell' (later in the chapter it is called 'the Rivendell River').

The conversation between Trotter, Folco and Frodo arising from the ruined towers in the hills remains as in the first version (pp. 192–3; FR p. 214).

When the rain stopped, and Trotter climbed up to see the lie of the land, he observed in the first version (p. 193) that 'if we keep on as we are going, we shall get into impassable country among the skirts of the Mountains.' This now becomes: 'we shall get up into the [Dimrill-lands >] Dimrill-dales far north of Rivendell.'[7] He continues, approaching Strider's words in FR:

'It is a troll-country, I have heard, though I have not been there. We could perhaps find our way through and come round to Rivendell from the north; but it would take long, and our food would not last. Anyway we ought to follow Gandalf's last message and make for the Rivendell Ford. So somehow or other we must strike the Road again.'

The encounter with the Stone Trolls follows the first version: Trotter slapped the stooping troll, called him William, and pointed out the bird's nest behind Bert's ear. There is still no suggestion of Sam's *Troll Song*; and when Frodo saw the memorial stone he 'wished that Bilbo had brought home no treasure more perilous than stolen money rescued from trolls.' The description of the Road here is nearly that of the First Edition of FR (see p. 200): 'At this point the Road had turned away from the river, leaving it at the bottom of a narrow valley, and clung close to the feet of the hills, rolling and winding northward among woods and heather-covered slopes towards the Ford and the Mountains.'

TO WEATHERTOP AND RIVENDELL 361

Glorfindel now calls Trotter not *Padathir* (p. 194) but *Du-finnion*, calling out *Ai, Du-finnion! Mai govannen!* The passage beginning with Trotter's signalling to Frodo and the others to come down to the road is found in two forms, the second to all appearance immediately replacing the first. The first runs:

'Hail and well met at last!' said Glorfindel to Frodo. 'I was sent from Rivendell to look for your coming. Gandalf feared that you might follow the Road.'

'Gandalf has arrived at Rivendell then?' cried Merry. 'Has he found Odo?'

'Certainly there is a hobbit of that name with him,' said Glorfindel; 'but I did not hear that he had been lost. He rode behind Gandalf from the north out of Dimrildale.'

'Out of Dimrildale?' exclaimed Frodo.

'Yes,' said the elf; 'and we thought that you also might go that way to avoid the peril of the Road. Some have been sent to seek for you in that country. But come! There is no time now for news or debate, until we halt. We must go on with all speed, and save our breath. Hardly a day's ride back westward there are horsemen, searching for your trail along the Road and in the lands on either side . . .

Glorfindel continues as in the first version (p. 195). The replacement passage differs mostly in small points: Glorfindel does not say of Odo 'but I did not hear that he had been lost'; *Dimrilldale* is so spelt (cf. p. 360), in place of *Dimrildale* in the rejected text; and the interjections of Merry and Frodo are reversed. The important difference lies in Glorfindel's words:

'There are horsemen back westward searching for your trail along the Road, and when they find the place where you came down from the hills, they will ride after us like the wind. But they are not all: there are others, who may be before us now, or upon either hand. Unless we go with all speed and good fortune, we shall find the Ford guarded against us by the enemy.'

From Frodo's faintness and Sam's objection to Glorfindel's urging the text of FR to the end of the chapter is achieved almost to the last word.[8] Yet there remain certain differences. Only three Riders came out of the tree-hung cutting behind the fugitives; and 'out from the trees and rocks away on the left other Riders came flying. Three rode towards Frodo; three galloped madly towards the Ford to cut off his escape.' And at the very end 'Three of the Riders turned and rode wildly away to the left down the bank of the River; the others, borne by their terrified and

362   THE RETURN OF THE SHADOW

plunging horses, were driven into the flood and carried away.' This is
derived from the first version (p. 197), where however there were only
two Riders that escaped the flood. The manuscript was changed to the
reading of the final paragraph of the chapter in FR, where no Riders
escaped, and this was done before or in the course of the writing of the
next chapter (see p. 364).

★

The first part of the next chapter, numbered XII, is the direct
development of the original title-less chapter IX, extant in three texts,
none of which goes further than the conversation between Bingo and
Glóin at the feast in Rivendell (pp. 206 ff., 210 ff.). The new version is
given the title 'The Council of Elrond'; see pp. 399–400. Here, for
reasons that will appear presently, I describe only that portion of the
chapter which derives from Chapter IX of the 'first phase'. In this, the
text of FR Book II, Chapter 1, 'Many Meetings' is achieved for long
stretches with only the most minor differences of wording, if any; on the
other hand there is still much preserved from the original text. In what
follows it can be understood that where no comment is made the FR text
was present at this time either exactly or in a close approximation.

The date of Frodo's awakening in the house of Elrond is now October
24th, and all the details of date are precisely as in FR (see pp. 219, 360).
The references to Sam in the FR text are none of them present in this
version as written until the feast itself, but were added in to the
manuscript probably after no very long interval.

Gandalf now adds, after 'You were beginning to fade' (p. 210, FR
p. 231), 'Glorfindel noticed it, though he did not speak of it to anyone but
Trotter'; and he still says (see p. 206) 'You would have become a wraith
before long – certainly, if you had put on the Ring again after you were
wounded.' Following his words 'It is no small feat to have come so far and
through such dangers, still bearing the Ring' (FR p. 232) the conversation is developed from the earlier text (p. 210) in a very interesting
way, naturally still far from the form in FR:

'. . . You ought never to have left the Shire without me.'

'I know – but you never came to my party, as was arranged; and
I did not know what to do.'

'I was delayed,' said Gandalf, 'and that nearly proved our ruin –
as was intended. Still after all it has turned out better than any
plan I should have dared to make, and we have defeated the black
horsemen.'

'I wish you would tell me what happened!'

'All in good time! You are not supposed to talk or worry about
anything today, by Elrond's orders.'

TO WEATHERTOP AND RIVENDELL 363

'But talking would stop me thinking and wondering, which are quite as tiring,' said Frodo. 'I am wide awake now, and remember so many things that want explaining. Why were you delayed? You ought to tell me that, at least.'

'You will soon hear all you wish to know,' said Gandalf. 'We shall have a Council, as soon as you are well enough. At the moment I will only say that I was held captive.'

'You!' cried Frodo.

'Yes!' laughed Gandalf. 'There are many powers greater than mine, for good and evil, in the world. I was caught in Fangorn and spent many weary days as a prisoner of the Giant Treebeard. It was a desperately anxious time, for I was hurrying back to the Shire to help you. I had just learned that the horsemen had been sent out.'

'Then you did not know of the Black Riders before.'

'Yes, I knew of them. I spoke of them once to you: for what you call the Black Riders are the Ring-wraiths, the Nine Servants of the Lord of the Ring. But I did not know that they had arisen again, and were let loose on the world once more – until I saw them. I have tried to find you ever since – but if I had not met Trotter, I don't suppose I ever should have done so. He has saved us all.'

'We should never have got here without him,' said Frodo. 'I was suspicious of him at first, but now I am very fond of him, though he is rather mysterious. It is an odd thing, you know, but I keep on feeling that I have seen him somewhere before; that – that I ought to be able to put a name to him, a name different to Trotter.'

'I daresay you do,' laughed Gandalf. 'I often have that feeling myself, when I look at a hobbit: they all remind me of one another, if you know what I mean.'

'Nonsense!' said Frodo, sitting up again in protest. 'Trotter is most peculiar. And he wears shoes! But I see you are in one of your tiresome moods.' He lay down again. 'I shall have to be patient. And it is rather pleasant resting, after all. To be perfectly honest I wish I need go no further than Rivendell. I have had a month of exile and adventures, and that is nearly four weeks more than enough for me.'

He fell silent and shut his eyes.

For the remainder of Frodo's conversation with Gandalf this text is mostly very close indeed to FR, and only a few differences need be noticed.

The 'Morgul-knife' (FR p. 234) is still the 'knife of the Necromancer'

364 THE RETURN OF THE SHADOW

(p. 211), and Gandalf says here: 'You would have become a wraith, and under the dominion of the Dark Lord. But you would have had no ring of your own, as the Nine have; for your Ring is the Ruling Ring, and the Necromancer would have taken that, and would have tormented you for trying to keep it – if any torment greater than being robbed of it was possible.'

Among the servants of the Dark Lord Gandalf still includes, as in the previous version, 'orcs and goblins' and 'kings, warriors, and wizards' (p. 211).

Gandalf's reply to Frodo's question 'Is Rivendell safe?' derives from the former text, but moves also towards that of FR:

'Yes, I hope so. He has less power over Elves than over any other creature: they have suffered too much in the past to be deceived or cowed by him now. And the Elves of Rivendell are descendants of his chief foes: the Gnomes, the Elvenwise, that came out of the West; and the Queen Elbereth Gilthoniel, Lady of the Stars, still protects them. They fear no Ring-wraiths, for those that have dwelt in the Blessed Realm beyond the Seas live at once in both worlds; and each world has only half power over them, while they have double power over both.'[9]

'I thought I saw a white figure that shone and did not grow dim like the others. Was that Glorfindel then?'

'Yes, you saw him for a moment as he is upon the other side: one of the mighty of the Elder Race. He is an elf-lord of a house of princes.'

'Then there are still some powers left that can withstand the Lord of Mordor,' said Frodo.

'Yes, there is power in Rivendell,' answered Gandalf, 'and there is a power, too, of another kind in the Shire. . . .

At the end of this passage Gandalf still says: 'the Wise say that he is doomed in the End, though that is far away' (see p. 212).

In Gandalf's story of what happened at the Ford he says, as in FR, 'Three were carried off by the first assault of the flood; the others were now hurled into the water by their horses and overwhelmed.' It thus appears that the rewriting of the end of the preceding chapter (p. 362) had already been carried out.

At the end of his conversation with Gandalf the story of Odo reappears:

'Yes, it all comes back to me now,' said Frodo: 'the tremendous roaring. I thought I was drowning, together with my friends and enemies. But now we are all safe! And Odo, too. At least, Glorfindel said so. How did you find him again?'

TO WEATHERTOP AND RIVENDELL 365

Gandalf looked [oddly >] quickly at Frodo, but he had shut his eyes. 'Yes, Odo is safe,' the wizard said. 'You will see him soon, and hear his account. There will be feasting and merrymaking to celebrate the victory of the Ford, and you will all be there in places of honour.'

Gandalf's 'odd' or 'quick' look at Frodo can only relate to his question about Odo, but since the story of Odo's vanishing from Weathertop and his subsequent reappearance (rescue?) was never told it is impossible to know what lay behind it. There is a suggestion that there was something odd about the story of his disappearance. Gandalf's tone, when taken with his 'look' at Frodo, seems to have a slightly quizzical air. Glorfindel says (p. 361): 'Certainly there is a hobbit of that name with him; but I did not hear that he had been lost': yet surely the capture of a hobbit by the Black Riders and his subsequent recovery was a matter of the utmost interest to those concerned with the Ring-wraiths? But whatever the story was, it seems to be something that will never be known. – It is curious that the wizard's sudden quick look at Frodo was preserved in FR (p. 236), when the Odo-story had of course disappeared, and Frodo's words that gave rise to the look were 'But now we are safe!'

Gandalf's slip of the tongue ('The people of Rivendell are very fond of Bilbo') and Frodo's noticing it are retained from the first version (p. 212), as is Frodo's recollection of Trotter's words to the troll as he fell asleep.

When Frodo goes down to find his friends in a porch of the house[10] the conversation is retained almost exactly from the original form (p. 209). Odo takes over from Merry 'Three cheers for Frodo, lord of the Ring!' and further says, as does Pippin in FR, 'You have shown your usual cunning in getting up just in time for a meal'; but despite Odo's increased prominence in Frodo's reception (in FR given to Pippin) there is no reference to his adventures. Frodo might surely be expected to make some remark about Odo's extremely perilous and altogether unlooked-for experiences since he had last seen him at the entrance into the Old Forest, especially since Gandalf had refrained from telling him what had happened on Weathertop and after.

The description of Elrond, Gandalf, and Glorfindel at the banquet had already appeared in almost the final form in the earlier text. The mention of Elrond's smile and laughter (p. 213) was at this time still retained; and there is of course still no hint of Arwen. In the description of the seating, the statement in the former version (*ibid.*) that Bingo 'could not see Trotter, nor his nephews. They had been led to other tables' was retained; but when Frodo 'began to look about him' he did see them, though not Trotter (the latter passage surviving into FR):

The feast was merry and all that his hunger could desire. He could not see Trotter, or the other hobbits, and supposed they

366   THE RETURN OF THE SHADOW

were at one of the side tables. It was some time before he began to look about him. Sam had begged to be allowed to wait on his master, but was told that he was for this night a guest of honour. Frodo could see him sitting with Odo, Folco and Merry at the upper end of one of the side tables, close to the dais. He could not see Trotter.

Frodo's conversation with Glóin proceeds exactly as in FR as far as 'But I am equally curious to know what brings so important a dwarf so far from the Lonely Mountain.' In the original texts Glóin said that he wondered much what could have brought *four* hobbits on so long a journey (Bingo, Frodo Took, Odo, Merry; Trotter being excluded – presumably as being so altogether distinct, and not a hobbit of the Shire). The number is four in FR (Frodo, Sam, Pippin, Merry); but four is also found in the present text, where the hobbits (excluding Trotter) were now five: Frodo, Sam, Folco, Odo, Merry. Either 'four' was a slip, or Glóin excluded Odo since he knew that Odo had not arrived at Rivendell with the others. Glóin's reply to Frodo's question remains less grave than in FR:

Glóin looked at him, and laughed, indeed he winked. 'You'll soon find out,' he said; 'but I am not allowed to tell you – yet. So we will not speak of that either! But there are many other things to hear and tell.'

The conversation (so far as it goes in the portion of the manuscript dealt with here) remains almost exactly as it was, with the short extension at the end of the third of the early texts (p. 213), the only difference of any substance being that Dáin had now, as in FR, 'passed his two-hundred-and-fiftieth-year'.

It will be seen that from the series of once fine manuscripts that constitute the 'third phase' of the writing of *The Lord of the Rings* a wholly coherent story emerges. The following are essential points in that story in respect of the intricate later evolution:

- Gandalf did not return to Hobbiton in time for Frodo's small final party.
- Merry and Odo Bolger went off to Buckland in advance.
- Frodo, Sam, and Folco Took walked from Hobbiton to Buckland.
- At Buckland, Odo decided not to go with the others into the Old Forest, but to stay behind at Crickhollow and wait for Gandalf to come.
- Gandalf came to Crickhollow at night on the day that Frodo and his companions left (Monday 26 September), drove off the Riders, and rode after them with Odo on his horse.
- Gandalf and Odo (whose name was given out to be Odo Baggins)

TO WEATHERTOP AND RIVENDELL   367

spent the night of Tuesday 27 September at Bree. Near Bree they encountered Trotter.

- Gandalf and Odo left Bree on Wednesday 28 September, meeting Trotter near Archet, as had been arranged.
- Frodo, Sam, Merry and Folco arrived at Bree on Thursday 29 September, and met Trotter, who gave Frodo Gandalf's letter.
- Trotter was a hobbit; Frodo found him curiously familiar without being able to say why, but there is no hint of who he might really be.
- Gandalf reached Weathertop on Monday 3 October, and left on 5 October.
- Trotter, Frodo and the others reached Weathertop on Thursday 6 October and found Gandalf's note telling that Odo had disappeared.
- They learned from Glorfindel that Gandalf had reached Rivendell, with Odo, coming down from the north by way of 'Dimrilldale'.
- At Rivendell, Gandalf explained that he had been delayed in his return to Hobbiton (having learned that the Ring-wraiths were abroad) through having been held prisoner in Fangorn by Giant Treebeard.
- The Shire hobbits at Rivendell are Frodo, Sam, Merry, Folco, and Odo.

NOTES

1   After 'I had to make quite sure that you were genuine first, before I handed over the letter. I've heard of shadow-parties picking up messages that weren't meant for them . . .' Trotter now adds: 'Gandalf's letter was worded carefully in case of accidents, but I didn't know that.' Thus Gandalf no longer names Weathertop in the letter, but calls it the 'appointed place'.

2   Barbara Strachey, in *Journeys of Frodo* (Map 11) says:
At this point I must note what I believe to be a real discrepancy in the text itself. In Bree . . . Aragorn tells Sam that Weathertop is halfway to *Rivendell*. I am sure that this was a slip of the tongue and that he meant halfway to *The Last Bridge*. Everything falls into place on this assumption, since the travellers took 7 days between Bree and Weathertop (involving a detour to the north) and 7 days from Weathertop to the Bridge (with Frodo in a wounded condition and unable to hurry) while there was a *further* stretch of 7 days from the Bridge to Rivendell. Aragorn was well aware of the distance, as he said later (A Knife in the Dark; Bk. I), when they reached Weathertop, that it would then take them 14 days to the Ford of Bruinen although it normally took him only 12.

368   THE RETURN OF THE SHADOW

But it is now seen that Aragorn's words 'about halfway from here (Bree) to Rivendell' in FR go back to Trotter's here; and at this stage the River Hoarwell and the Last Bridge on the East Road did not yet exist (p. 360). I think that Trotter (Aragorn) was merely giving Folco (Sam) a rough but sufficient idea of the distances before them. – The relative distances go back to the original version (see pp. 170–1): about 120 miles from Bree to Weathertop, close on 200 from Weathertop to the Ford.

3   A draft for Gandalf's message has: 'Last night Odo vanished: suspect capture by horsemen.'

The message was changed in pencil to read:

Wednesday morning Oct. 5. Bad news. We arrived late Monday. Baggins vanished last night. I must go and look for him. Wait for me here for [a day or two >] two days. I shall return if possible. If not go to Rivendell by the Ford on the Road.

Merry then says: 'Baggins! Does that mean that the Riders have got Odo?'

Gandalf's message that he would return to Weathertop if he could may have been intended as an explanation of why they decided to stay there; see note 4. This pencilled revision preceded the writing of the next chapter; see p. 359.

4   This was changed in pencil to read:

there is nothing we can do but] wait at least until tomorrow, which will be two days since Gandalf wrote the note [see note 3]. After that if he does not turn up we must [make for Rivendell as best we may.

5   The title 'A Knife in the Dark' was pencilled in later, as also on the original chapter, VIII (p. 177).

6   The passage about *cram* was retained in this text, but placed in a footnote.

7   On *Dimrill-dale* see pp. 432–3, notes 3, 13.

8   It may be noted that the name *Asfaloth* of Glorfindel's horse now appears.

9.   On the conclusion of this passage see p. 225.

10   The porch still faced west (p. 209), not east as in FR, and the odd statement that the evening light shone on the eastern faces of the hills far above was repeated, though struck out, probably in the act of writing.

XXII
NEW UNCERTAINTIES AND
NEW PROJECTIONS

The first phase or original wave of composition of *The Lord of the Rings* carried the story to Rivendell, and broke off in the middle of the original Chapter IX, at Glóin's account to Bingo Bolger-Baggins of the realm of Dale (p. 213):

> In Dale the grandson of Bard the Bowman ruled, Brand son of Bain son of Bard, and he was become a strong king whose realm included Esgaroth, and much land to the south of the great falls.

This sentence ended a manuscript page; on the reverse side, as noted on p. 213, the text was continued, but in a different script and a different ink, and it begins:

> 'And what has become of Balin and Ori and Óin?' asked Frodo.

Since in the second phase Bingo was still the name of Bilbo's heir, and since 'Bingo' never appears in any narrative writing falling later in the story than the feast at Rivendell, it is certain that there was a significant gap between 'much land to the south of the great falls' and 'And what has become of Balin and Ori and Óin?'

It is therefore very curious that in Chapter XII of the third phase there is a marked change of script at precisely the same point. Though still neatly and carefully written, it is immediately obvious to the eye that '"And what has become of Balin and Ori and Óin?" asked Frodo' and the subsequent text was not continuous with what preceded. Moreover, the latter part of this Chapter XII is not coherent with what precedes, either: for Bilbo says – as my father first wrote out the manuscript – 'I shall have to get that fellow *Aragorn* to help me' (cf. FR p. 243: 'I shall have to get my friend the Dúnadan to help me.')

I do not think that it can possibly be a mere coincidence that both versions halt at precisely the same point; and I conclude that the third phase, in the sense of a fine continuous manuscript series, ended at the same place as the first phase had done – and did so precisely *because* that is where the first phase ended. For this reason I stopped at this point in the previous chapter. I have suggested earlier (p. 309) that when my father said (in February 1939) that by December 1938 *The Lord of the Rings* had reached Chapter XII 'and has been rewritten several times' it was to the third phase that he was referring.

The textual-chronological questions that now arise are of peculiar difficulty, and I doubt whether a solution demonstrably correct at all points could be reached. There is no external evidence for many months

370   THE RETURN OF THE SHADOW

after February 1939, and nothing to show what my father achieved during that time; but we get at last an unambiguous date, 'August 1939', written (most unusually) on every page of a collection of rough papers containing plot-outlines, questionings, and portions of text. These show my father at a halt, even at a loss, to the point of a lack of confidence in radical components of the narrative structure that had been built up with such pains. The only external evidence that I know of to cast light on this is a letter, dispirited in tone, which he wrote to Stanley Unwin on 15 September 1939, twelve days after the entry of England into war with Germany, apologising for his 'silence about the state of the proposed sequel to the Hobbit, which you enquired about as long ago as June 21st.' 'I do not suppose,' he said, 'this any longer interests you greatly – though I still hope to finish it eventually. It is only about ¾ written. I have not had much time, quite apart from the gloom of approaching disaster, and have been unwell most of this year . . .' There is nothing in the 'August 1939' papers themselves to show why he should have thought that the existing structure of the story was in need of such radical transformation.

Proposals made at this time for new articulations of the plot were set down in such haste and so elliptically expressed that it is sometimes not easy to understand their bearings (here and there one may suspect a confusion between what had been written in the latest wave of composition and what had been written earlier); and determination of the order in which these notes and outlines were set down is impossible. To take first the most drastic proposals:

(1) New Plot. *Bilbo* is the hero all through. Merry and Frodo his companions. This helps with Gollum (though Gollum probably gets new ring in Mordor). Or Bilbo just takes a 'holiday' – and never returns, and the surprise party [i.e. the party that ended in a surprise] is Frodo's. In which case Gandalf is *not* present to let off fireworks.

The astonishing suggestion in the first part of this note ignores the problem of 'lived happily ever after', which had bulked so large earlier (see pp. 108–9). For a brief while, at any rate, my father was prepared to envisage the demolition of the entire Bilbo-Frodo structure – the now established and essential idea that Bilbo vanished 'with a bang and a flash' at the end of his hundred-and-eleventh birthday party and that Frodo followed him out of the Shire, more discreetly, seventeen years later. Happily, he did not spend long on this – though he did go so far as to begin a new text, headed:

New version – with Bilbo as hero. Aug. 1939

The Lord of the Rings

This begins: '"It is all most disturbing and in fact rather alarming," said Bilbo Baggins,' and the matter is the same as in 'Ancient History' – with

NEW UNCERTAINTIES AND NEW PROJECTIONS   371

Sam's shears audible outside – altered only as was necessary since Gandalf was here speaking to Bilbo, not Frodo; but this text peters out after a couple of sides.

The second part of this note is little less drastic: a return to the story as it was at the end of the first phase of work on this chapter, where Bilbo merely disappeared quietly from the Shire shortly before his 111th birthday, and the party was given by Bingo (Bolger-Baggins); see p. 40. This idea is developed in the following outline:

(2)   Go back to original idea. Make Frodo (or Bingo) a more comic character.

Bilbo is not overcome by Ring – he very seldom used it. He lived long and then said goodbye, put on his old clothes and rode off. He would not say where he was going – except that he was going across the River. He had 2 favourite 'nephews', Peregrin Boffin and Frodo [*written above:* Folco] Baggins. Peregrin was the elder. Peregrin went off and Bilbo was blamed, and after that the young folk were kept away from him – only Folco remained faithful.

Bilbo left all his possessions to Folco (who thus inherited with interest all the dislike of the Sackville-Bagginses).

Bilbo lived long, 111 – he tells Gandalf he is feeling tired, and discusses what to do. He is worried about the Ring. Says he is reluctant to leave it and thinks of taking it. Gandalf looks at him.

In the end he leaves it behind, but puts on Sting and his elf-armour under his old patched green cloak. He also takes his book. Last whimsical saying was 'I think I shall look for a place where there is more peace and quiet, and I can finish my book.'

'Nobody will read it!'

'O, they may – in years to come.'

Ring begins to have an effect on Folco. He gets restless. And plans to go off 'following Bilbo'. His friends are Odo Bolger and Merry Brandybuck.

Conversation with Gandalf as in Tale.

Folco gives the unexpected [*read* long-expected][1] party and vanishes as in original draft of the Tale.[2] But bring in Black Riders.

Cut out whole part of Gandalf being *supposed to come*. Make Gandalf pursue the fugitives since he has found out about Black Riders (the scene at Crickhollow will do – but without Odo complication).

Make Gandalf looking for Folco (in that case Gandalf will *not* be at final party) – and send Trotter.

Find Bilbo at Rivendell. There Bilbo offers to take up burden of the Ring (reluctantly) but Gandalf supports Folco in offering to carry it on.

Trotter turns out to be Peregrin, who had been to Mordor.

372   THE RETURN OF THE SHADOW

Not the least curious feature of these notes is the renewed uncertainty
about names: thus we have 'Frodo (or Bingo)', then 'Frodo' changed to
'Folco' (and at one of the occurrences of 'Folco' my father first wrote a
'B'); see also §§5 and 9. For long I assumed that it was at the very time of
the writing of these notes that 'Bingo' became 'Frodo', and that they
therefore preceded the third phase of the work. Those third phase
manuscripts were so orderly and so suggestive of secure purpose that
it seemed hard to imagine that such radical uncertainty could have
succeeded them: rather they seemed like a confident new start when the
doubts had been dissipated. But this cannot possibly be so. This is the
first mention of Bilbo's taking his 'elf-armour' (cf. p. 223, §4), and it is
only by later revision to the third phase version of 'A Long-expected
Party' that the story that Bilbo took it with him enters the narrative (see
p. 315; in FR, p. 40, he packed it in his bag, the 'bundle wrapped in old
cloths' which he took from the strong-box). Similarly, Bilbo's saying that
he wanted to find peace in which to finish his book and Gandalf's
rejoinder 'Nobody will read it!' only appear in the *revision* of the third
phase version of the first chapter (surviving into FR p. 41). Or again, the
reference to 'the scene at Crickhollow – but without Odo complication'
shows that the third phase was in being (see p. 336). Other evidence
elsewhere in these 'August 1939' papers is equally clear. It must therefore
be concluded that the temporary confusion and loss of direction from
which my father suffered at this time extended even to established
names: 'Bingo' might be brought back, or 'Frodo' changed to 'Folco'.

The words 'But bring in Black Riders' are puzzling, since the Black
Riders were of course very much present 'in the original draft of the
Tale'; but I suspect that my father meant 'But bring in Black Rider' in the
singular, i.e. the Rider who came to Hobbiton and spoke to Gaffer
Gamgee. The changed story which my father was so elliptically discuss-
ing in these notes can presumably be shown in essentials thus:

(I)	Fourth version of 'A Long-expected Party', last in the 'first phase'; see p. 40	Bilbo departs quietly from Hobbiton at the age of 111. *Bingo* gives the party 33 years later and vanishes at the end of it. Gandalf leaves Hobbiton after the fire-works at the Party and goes ahead towards Rivendell.
(II)	The existing state of the story	*Bilbo* gives the Party at the age of 111 and vanishes at the end of it. Frodo departs quietly from Hobbiton with his friends 17 years later. Gandalf fails to come as he promised before Frodo leaves. A Black Rider comes to Hobbiton on the last evening.

NEW UNCERTAINTIES AND NEW PROJECTIONS 373

Gandalf arrives at Crickhollow after the hobbits have left.

(III) Projected plot — Bilbo departs quietly from Hobbiton at the age of 111.
Frodo ('Folco') gives the Party and vanishes at the end of it.
Gandalf is not present at the Party.
A Black Rider comes to Hobbiton.
Gandalf arrives at Crickhollow after the hobbits have left.

If I am right in my interpretation of 'But bring in Black Riders', the point is that while in a fundamental feature of its structure (III) would return to (I), the coming of the Rider would be retained – so that he would arrive in the aftermath of the Party. And unlike (I), Gandalf would no longer come to the Party (so that, as mentioned in §1, there would be no fireworks, or at least not of the Gandalfian kind), but would follow hard on the hobbits ('the fugitives'), 'since he has found out about the Black Riders'.

Here again, and again happily, my father did not in the event allow himself to be diverted to yet another restructuring (and consequent very tricky rewriting at many points) of the narrative that had been achieved.

Most interesting are the statements that Trotter was Peregrin Boffin, standing in the same sort of relationship to Bilbo as did Frodo, but older than Frodo, and that running off into the wide world he had found his way to Mordor. Earlier (p. 223, §6) my father had noted: 'I thought of making Trotter into Fosco Took (Bilbo's first cousin) who vanished when a lad, owing to Gandalf. He must have had some bitter acquaintance with Ring-wraiths &c.' See further pp. 385–6.

(3) In some points it is still harder to feel sure of the meaning of another outline dated 'August 1939'. This begins with a proposal to 'alter names'.

Frodo > ? Peregrin Faramond
Odo   >   Fredegar Hamilcar Bolger

My father subsequently added (but struck out): 'Too many hobbits. Sam, Merry, and Faramond (= Frodo) are quite enough.' He was evidently dissatisfied with the name 'Frodo' for his central character. In §2 he changed 'Frodo' to 'Folco', in §2, §5, and §9 'Bingo' reappears, and here he considers the possibility of 'Faramond'. – This seems to be the first occurrence of either name, Fredegar or Hamilcar.

The text that follows on the same page, seeming quite at variance with these notes on names, reads thus:

Alterations of Plot
(1) Less emphasis on longevity caused by the Ring, until the story has progressed.

374   THE RETURN OF THE SHADOW

(2) *Important*. (a) Neither Bilbo nor Gandalf must know much about the Ring, when Bilbo departs. Bilbo's motive is simply *tiredness*, an unexplained restlessness (and longing to see Rivendell again, but this is not said – finding him at Rivendell must be a surprise).

(b) Gandalf does *not* tell Frodo to leave Shire – only mere hint that Lord may look for Shire. The plan for leaving was entirely Frodo's. Dreams or some other cause [*added:* restlessness] have made him decide to go journeying (to find Cracks of Doom? after seeking counsel of Elrond). Gandalf simply vanishes for years. They are not trying to catch up Gandalf. Gandalf is simply trying to *find* them, and is desperately upset when he discovers Frodo has left Hobbiton. Odo must be cut out or altered (blended with Folco), and go with F[rodo] on his ride. Only Meriadoc goes ahead.

In that case alteration of plot at Bree. Who is Trotter? A Ranger or a Hobbit? Peregrin? If Gandalf is only looking for Frodo, Trotter will have to be an old associate.[3] Thus if a Hobbit, make him one who went off under Gandalf's influence (cf. introduction to *Hobbit*).[4] E.g. –

After Bilbo's little escapade Gandalf was little seen, and only one disappearance was recorded during many years. This was the curious case of Peregrin Boffin –

Since he was a close relation of Bilbo's, Bilbo was blamed for putting notions into the boy's head with his silly fairy-stories; and visits of the young to Bag-End were discouraged by many of the elders in spite of Bilbo's generosity. But he had several faithful young friends. The chief of these was Frodo (Bilbo's cousin).

As regards (1) and (2) (a), these ideas were taken up. In 'A Long-expected Party' as it was at this time (see p. 239: preserved without significant change in the third phase version) the Ring is the only motive that Bilbo refers to in explanation of his decision to leave the Shire; and he clearly associates his longevity with possession of it: 'I really must get rid of It, Gandalf. *Well-preserved*, indeed. Why, I feel all thin – sort of stretched, if you know what I mean.' *Revisions made to the third phase version* brought the text in these respects to the form in FR (pp. 41–3), where it is clear that the Ring is not consciously a motive in Bilbo's mind (however strongly the reader is made aware of the sinister influence it was in fact exerting): he speaks of his need for 'a holiday, a very long holiday' (cf. §1 above: 'Bilbo just takes a "holiday"'), and his wish 'to see the wild country again before I die, and the Mountains.' He still says '*Well-preserved*, indeed! Why I feel all thin, sort of *stretched*, if you know what I mean', but his sense of great age is now not in any way associated with possession of the Ring; and so later, *in revision to the third phase version* of 'Ancient History', Gandalf says to Frodo: 'He certainly did not begin to connect his long life and outward youthfulness with the ring' (cf. FR p. 56: 'But as for his long life, Bilbo never connected it with the ring at all. He took all the credit for that to himself, and was very proud of it.')

NEW UNCERTAINTIES AND NEW PROJECTIONS   375

The notes under (2) (b) outline a new idea in respect of Gandalf's movements: for many years before Frodo left he had never come back at all to Hobbiton, and Frodo's leaving was entirely independent of the wizard. Learning (we may suppose) that the Ring-wraiths were abroad, Gandalf hastened back at last to the Shire, where he heard to his horror that Frodo had gone. This idea was not taken up, of course (and against it my father wrote: 'But in this case the Sam chapter is spoilt' – he was referring to the end of 'Ancient History', where Sam is discovered by Gandalf eavesdropping outside the window of Bag End).

The words 'They are not trying to catch up Gandalf' are difficult to understand. It seems incredible that my father would be referring now to the first phase version of the story, in which Gandalf had left the Party (given by Bingo) after letting off the fireworks, and was known to be ahead of Frodo and his friends on the journey east; yet in the subsequent versions all that is known of him is that he did not come, as he had promised, to the small farewell party given by Bingo/Frodo before he left Bag End, and was supposed (rightly) to be behind them rather than ahead.

Still more baffling is the passage concerning Odo ('Odo must be cut out or altered (blended with Folco) and go with F[rodo] on his ride. Only Meriadoc goes ahead'). If the meaning of this is that the entire 'Odo-story' of the third phase (his journey with Gandalf from Crickhollow through Bree, the pseudonym of 'Baggins', his disappearance from Weathertop, and his unexplained arrival with Gandalf at Rivendell) was to be abandoned, how (one may ask) can he be 'blended with Folco', since 'Folco' is already a blend of the original 'Frodo and Odo', with the advantage heavily to 'Odo'? It must be remembered that these notes were in no way the logical expression of an ordered programme, but are rather the vestiges of rapidly-changing thoughts. The withdrawal of Odo, in the third phase, from the adventures of the other hobbits had caused Folco (formerly Frodo) Took to take over Odo's part and character in the narrative of those adventures, since that narrative already existed from the earlier phases, and Odo had played a large part in the hobbits' conversation (see pp. 323–4). But the *retention* of Odo in the background, with adventures of his own, would mean that when he re-emerged into the foreground again at Rivendell there would be two 'Odo' characters – the rather ironic result of getting rid of him!

The proposal here is presumably that 'Odo Bolger' and 'Folco Took' should now be definitively joined together as one character, under the latter name. 'Folco' seems indeed now too much 'Odo' for 'blending' to have much meaning; but my father may not have felt this (nor perhaps did he have so clear a picture of the intricate evolutions of his story as can be attained from long study of the manuscripts). In 'go with F[rodo] on his ride', 'ride' is perhaps a mere slip for 'walk': the meaning being that the resultant 'blend' accompanies Frodo and does not 'go ahead' with Merry to Buckland. This is all very fine-spun, but it reflects the

376   THE RETURN OF THE SHADOW

extraordinarily intricate nature of my father's changing construction.

With 'Who is Trotter? A Ranger or a Hobbit?' cf. pp. 331–2. The story that Trotter was Peregrin Boffin is now definitively present and would be fully developed in revision to the third phase text of 'A Long-expected party' (pp. 384–6).

(4) The remaining papers in this 'August 1939' collection that are concerned with the opening part of the story perhaps followed the others. These pages of very rough narrative drafting are headed *Conversation of Bilbo and Frodo* – a relationship never otherwise seen at close quarters, before they met long afterwards at Rivendell. The conversation takes place at Bag End before Bilbo's Farewell Party; he speaks to Frodo of the Ring for the first time, only to discover to his genuine amazement and mock indignation, that Frodo knew about it already, and had looked at Bilbo's secret book. This is a different story to that in 'A Long-expected Party', where Frodo had read Bilbo's memoirs with his permission (pp. 240, 315).

Conversation of Bilbo and Frodo

'Well, my lad, we have got on very well – and I am sorry to leave, in a way. But I am going on a holiday, a very long holiday. In fact I have no intention of coming back. I am tired. I am going to cross the Rivers.[5] So be prepared for surprises at this party. I may say that I am leaving everything, practically, to you – all except a few oddments.'

★

Mr Bilbo Baggins, of Bag-end, Underhill (Hobbiton) was sitting in his west sitting-room one summer afternoon.

'Well, that's my little plan, Frodo,' said Bilbo Baggins. 'It's a dead secret, mind you! I've kept it from everyone but you and Gandalf. I needed Gandalf's help; and I've told you because I hope you'll enjoy the joke all the better for being in the know – and of course you're closely concerned.'

'I don't like it at all,' said the other hobbit, looking rather puzzled and downcast. 'But I've known you long enough to know that it's no good trying to talk you out of your little plans.'

★

'Well, the time has come to say goodbye, my dear lad,' said Bilbo.

'I suppose so,' said Frodo sadly. 'Though I don't at all under-

NEW UNCERTAINTIES AND NEW PROJECTIONS   377

stand why. [But I know you too well to think of trying to talk you out of your little plans – especially after they have gone so far.]'

'I can't explain it any clearer,' answered Bilbo, 'because I am not quite clear myself. But I hope this is clear: I am leaving everything (except a few oddments) to you. My bit of money will keep you nicely as it did me in the old days; and besides there is a bit of my treasure left – you know where. Not so much now, but a pretty nest-egg still. And there's one thing more, There's a ring.'

'The magic ring?' asked Frodo incautiously.

'Eh, what?' said Bilbo. 'Who said magic ring?'

'I did,' said Frodo blushing. 'My dear old hobbit, you don't allow for the inquisitiveness of young nephews.'

'I do allow for it,' said Bilbo, 'or I thought I had. And in any case don't call me a dear old hobbit.'

'I have known about the existence of your Ring for years.'

'Have you indeed?' said Bilbo. 'How, I should like to know! Come on, then: you had better make a clean breast of it before I go.'

'Well, it was like this. It was the Sackville-Bagginses that were your undoing.'

'They would be,' grunted Bilbo.

Frodo then tells the story of his observing Bilbo's escape, by becoming invisible, from the Sackville-Bagginses while out walking one day. This, in very brief form, had been used in the fifth version of 'A Long-expected Party' (p. 242), when Bingo told it to Gandalf after the Party – there, merely as an example of how Bilbo had used the Ring for small-scale disappearances to avoid boredom and inconvenience (for of course in the 'received' story Bingo knew about the Ring because Bilbo had told him about it). It was then, in more elaborate form, given to Merry in 'A Conspiracy is Unmasked' (p. 300) as an explanation of how Merry knew of the existence of the Ring (and so was dropped from the sixth version of 'A Long-expected Party', p. 315). Now, in the present text, my father simply lifted the story word for word from 'A Conspiracy (is) Unmasked' and gave it to Frodo, as his explanation to Bilbo of how *he* learnt about the Ring; and Frodo continues here, again almost word for word, with Merry's account of how he got a sight of Bilbo's book:

'That doesn't explain it all,' said Bilbo, with a gleam in his eye. 'Come on, out with it, whatever it is!'

'Well, after that I kept my eyes open,' stammered Frodo. 'I – er – in fact I rather kept a watch on you. But you must admit it was very intriguing – and I was only in my early tweens. So one day I came across your book.'

378   THE RETURN OF THE SHADOW

'My book!' said Bilbo. 'Good heavens above. Is nothing safe!'

'Not too safe,' said Frodo. 'But I only got one rapid glance. You never left the book about, except just that once: you were called out of the study, and I came in and found it lying open. I should like a rather longer look, Bilbo. I suppose you are leaving it to me now?'

'No I am not!' said Bilbo decisively. 'It isn't finished. Why, one of my chief reasons for leaving is to go somewhere where I can get on with it in peace without a parcel of rascally nephews prying round the place, and a string of confounded visitors hanging on to the bell.'

'You shouldn't be so kind to everyone,' said Frodo. 'I am sure you needn't go away.

'Well, I am going,' said Bilbo. 'And about that Ring: I suppose I needn't describe it now, or how I got it. I thought of giving it to you.'

At this point my father interrupted the text and wrote across the page: 'This won't do because of the use of the Ring at the party!' – i.e., Bilbo could not have the intention to give it to Frodo then, before the Party. But without changing anything that he had written he went on with the story thus:

He fumbled in his pocket and drew out a small golden ring attached by another ring to a fine chain. He unfastened it, laid it in the palm of his hand, and looked long at it.

'Here it is!' he said with sigh.

Frodo held out his hand. But Bilbo put the ring straight back in his pocket. [A puzzled look >] An odd look came over his face. 'Er, well,' he stammered, 'I'll give it you I expect last thing before I go – or leave it in my locked drawer or something.'

Frodo looked puzzled and stared at him, but said nothing.

The last lines of the text come after the Party:

Bilbo . . . . goes and dresses as in the older version (but with *armour* under his cloak)[6] and says goodbye. 'The – er – ring,' he said, 'is in the drawer' – and vanished into [the] darkness.

I think that this new version is to be associated with the opening notes under 'Alterations of Plot' in §3 above: it represents a movement away from the idea that Bilbo was troubled about the Ring, that it was his prime motive for leaving (rather, his tiredness, his desire for peace, is mentioned). He has never even spoken to Frodo about it. It seems that my father's intention had been that Bilbo should simply hand it to Frodo

NEW UNCERTAINTIES AND NEW PROJECTIONS   379

there and then, without any suggestion of inner struggle; but he only realised, as he wrote, that 'This won't do' – because Bilbo must retain the Ring till the actual moment of his departure. The gift would therefore have to be postponed from the present occasion; and it was only now that he took up the suggestion in 'A Long-expected Party', where Bilbo said to Gandalf: 'I am not going to throw it away. In any case I find it impossible to make myself do that – *I simply put it back in my pocket.*'[7] The curious result is that the scene actually ends now with a demonstration, in Bilbo's embarrassed and ambiguous behaviour, precisely of the sinister effect that the Ring has in fact had on its owner; and this would be developed into the quarrel with Gandalf in FR, pp. 41–3.

(5)   Turning now to those papers dated August 1939 that are concerned with larger projections of the story to come after the sojourn in Rivendell, there is first a suggestion that a Dragon should come to the Shire and that by its coming the hobbits should be led to show that they are made of 'sterner stuff', and that 'Frodo (Bingo)' should 'actually come near the end of his money – now it was *dragon* gold. He is "lured"?' There is here a reference to 'Bilbo remarks on old sheet of notes' – obviously those given on pp. 41–2 (where the same suggestion of a Dragon coming to Hobbiton was made).

(6)   Following these notes on the same page is a brief list of narrative elements that might enter much further on:

> Island in sea. Take Frodo there in end.
> Radagast?[8]
> Battle is raging far off between armies of Elves and Men v[ersus the] Lord.
> Adventures . . Stone-Men.

With the first of these cf. the note given on p. 41: 'Elrond tells him [Bilbo] of an island', etc. The reference to the 'battle raging' probably belongs to the end of the story, when the Ring goes into the Crack of Doom.

Most interesting is the last item here. A note by my father found with the LR papers states that he looked through (some, at least of) the material in 1964; and it was very probably at that time that he scrawled against the words 'Adventures . . Stone-Men':

> Thought of as just an 'adventure'. The whole of the matter of Gondor (Stone-land) grew from this note. (Aragorn, still called Trotter, had no connexion with it then, and was at first conceived as one of the hobbits that had wanderlust.)

(7)   This is a convenient place to give a page of pencilled notes which bears no date and in which 'Bingo' appears. At the head of the page stand the words: 'City of Stone and civilized men'. Then follows an extremely abbreviated outline of the end of the story.

380 THE RETURN OF THE SHADOW

At end

When Bingo [*written above:* Frodo] at last reaches Crack and Fiery Mountain *he cannot make himself throw the Ring away.* ? He hears Necromancer's voice offering him great reward – to share power with him, if he will keep it.

At that moment Gollum – who had seemed to reform and had guided them by secret ways through Mordor – comes up and treacherously tries to take Ring. They wrestle and Gollum *takes Ring* and falls into the Crack.

The mountain begins to rumble.

Bingo flies away [i.e. flees away].

Eruption.

Mordor vanishes like a dark cloud. Elves are seen riding like lights rolling away a dark cloud.

The City of Stone is covered in ashes.

Journey back to Rivendell.

What of Shire? Sackville-Baggins . . . . lands. . . . . the four quarters.

Bingo makes peace, and settles down in a little hut on the high green ridge – until one day he goes with the Elves west beyond the towers.

Better – no land was tilled, all the hobbits were busy making swords.

The illegible words might just possibly be interpreted thus: 'Sackville-Baggins [and] his friends hurt [the] lands. There was war between the four quarters.'

Since there is here a reference to 'the City of Stone', while my father said in 1964 that the whole idea of Gondor arose from the reference to 'Stone-Men' in a note dated August 1939, it would have to be concluded on a strict interpretation that this outline comes from that time or later; on the other hand, the hero is still 'Bingo', so that this outline would seem to be the earlier. I think, however, that the contradiction may be only apparent, since in other notes dated August 1939 my father seems still to have been hesitant about the name 'Bingo', and I would therefore ascribe the outline just given to much the same time as the rest of these notes.

It obviously leaves out some things that my father must already have known (more or less): such as how Gollum reappeared. But it is most remarkable to find here – when there is no suggestion of the vast structure still to be built – that the corruption of the Shire, and the crucial presence of Gollum on the Fiery Mountain, were very early elements in the whole.

(8) On the reverse of the page bearing this outline is the following:

'The ring is destroyed,' said Bilbo, 'and I am feeling sleepy. We must say goodbye, Bingo [*written above:* Frodo] – but it is a good place to say goodbye, in the House of Elrond, where memory is long and kind. I am leaving the book of my small deeds here. And I don't think I shall go to rest till I have written down your tale too.

NEW UNCERTAINTIES AND NEW PROJECTIONS   381

Elrond will keep it – no doubt after all hobbits have gone their ways into the past. Well, Bingo my lad, you and I were very small creatures, but we've played our part. We've played our part. An odd fate we have shared, to be sure.'

It seems then that at this time my father foresaw that Bilbo died in Rivendell.

(9)   There is one further page dated 'August 1939', and this is of great interest. It is a series of pencilled notes like the others, and is headed 'Plot from XII on'.

Have to wait till Spring? Or have to go at once.
They go south along the Mountains. Later or early? Snowstorm in the Red Pass. Journey down the R. Redway.
Adventure with Giant Tree Beard in Forest.
Mines of Moria. These again deserted – except for *Goblins*.
Land of Ond. Siege of the City.
They draw near the borders of Mordor.
In dark Gollum comes up. He feigns reform? Or tries to throttle Frodo? – but Gollum has now a magic ring given by Lord and is invisible. Frodo dare not use his own.
Cavalcade of evil led by seven Black Riders.
See Dark Tower on the horizon. Horrible feeling of an Eye searching for him.
Fiery Mountain.
Eruption of Fiery Mountain causes destruction of Tower.

A pencilled marginal note asks whether 'Bingo' (with 'Frodo' written beside) should be captured by the Dark Lord and questioned, but be saved 'by Sam?'.

Subsequently my father emended these notes in ink. In the first line, against 'Or have to go at once', he wrote 'at once'; he directed that 'Mines of Moria . . .' should precede 'Adventure with Giant Tree Beard in Forest' and come between 'Snowstorm in the Red Pass' and 'Journey down the R. Redway'; and after 'These again deserted – except for *Goblins*' he added 'Loss of Gandalf'.

Some features of this outline have occurred already; the feigned reform of Gollum, his attack on Frodo, and the eruption of the Fiery Mountain, in §7; the acquisition of a ring by Gollum in Mordor in §1. But we meet here for the first time other major ingredients in the later work. The Ring crosses the Misty Mountains by 'the Red Pass', which will survive in the Redhorn Pass, or Redhorn Gate. The Mines of Moria now first reappear from *The Hobbit* – at any rate under that name: the mention in *Queries and Alterations* note 11 (p. 226) of the colony founded by the Dwarves Balin, Óri, and Óin from the Lonely Mountain in 'rich hills in the South' does not show that the identification had been

382   THE RETURN OF THE SHADOW

made. The actual link lay no doubt in Elrond's words in *The Hobbit* (Chapter III, 'A Short Rest'): 'I have heard that there are still forgotten treasures to be found in the deserted caverns of the mines of Moria, since the dwarf and goblin war'; and the words here 'These again deserted – except for Goblins', taken with those in *Queries and Alterations* (*ibid.*) 'But after a time no word was heard of them', clearly imply the story in *The Lord of the Rings*. The land of the Stone-Men (see §6) is the 'Land of Ond', and the 'City of Stone' (§7) will be besieged. Here also there is the first hint of the story of the capture of Frodo and his rescue by Sam Gamgee from the tower of Cirith Ungol; and most notable of all, perhaps, the first mention of the Searching Eye in the Dark Tower.

These are references to narrative 'moments' which my father foresaw: they do not constitute an articulated narrative scheme. They may very well not be in the succession that he even then perceived. Thus in this outline Gollum's treachery is brought in long before Frodo reaches the Fiery Mountain, which in view of what is said in §7 can hardly have been his meaning; and the Mines of Moria are named after the passage of the Misty Mountains. This was corrected later in ink, but it may not have been his conception when he wrote these notes: for in none of the (six) mentions of the Mines of Moria in *The Hobbit* is there any suggestion of where they were (cf. his letter to W. H. Auden in 1955: 'The Mines of Moria had been a mere name', *Letters* no. 163).

(10)   Something must be said here of 'Giant Treebeard', for he emerged into a scrap of actual narrative at this time (and had been mentioned by Gandalf to Frodo in Rivendell. p. 363: 'I was caught in Fangorn and spent many weary days as a prisoner of the Giant Treebeard'). There exists a single sheet of manuscript, which began as a letter dated 'July 27–29th 1939', but which my father covered on both sides with fine ornamental script (one side of the sheet is reproduced opposite). Among the writings on the page are the words 'July Summer Diversions' and lines from Chaucer's *Reeve's Tale* – for these 'Diversions' were a series of public entertainments held at Oxford in the course of which my father, attired as Chaucer, recited that Tale. But the page is chiefly taken up with a text on which he afterwards pencilled *Tree Beard*.

When Frodo heard the voice he looked up, but he could see nothing through the thick entangled branches. Suddenly he felt a quiver in the gnarled tree-trunk against which he was leaning, and before he could spring away he was pushed, or kicked, forward onto his knees. Picking himself up he looked at the tree, and even as he looked, it took a stride towards him. He scrambled out of the way, and a deep rumbling chuckle came down out of the tree-top.

'Where are you, little beetle?' said the voice. 'If you don't let me know where you are, you can't blame me for treading on you. And please, don't tickle my leg!'

NEW UNCERTAINTIES AND NEW PROJECTIONS

When Frodo heard the voice he looked up, but he could see nothing through the thick entangled branches Suddenly he felt a quiver in the gnarled tree-trunk against which he was leaning, and before he could spring away he was pushed, or kicked, forward on to his knees. Picking himself up he looked at the tree, and even as he looked, it took a stride towards him. He scrambled out of the way, and a deep rumbling chuckle came down out of the tree-top.

"Where are you, little beetle?" said the voice. 'If you don't let me know where you are, you can't blame me for treading on you. And please, don't tickle my leg!"

JRR JRRTolkien.

The emergence of Treebeard

384   THE RETURN OF THE SHADOW

'I can't see any leg,' said Frodo. 'And where are you?' 'You must be blind,' said the voice. 'I am here.' 'Who are you?' 'I am Treebeard,' the voice answered. 'If you haven't heard of me before, you ought to have done; and anyway you are in my garden.'

'I can't see any garden,' said Frodo. 'Do you know what a garden looks like?' 'I have one of my own: there are flowers and plants in it, and a fence round it; but there is nothing of the kind here.' 'O yes! there is. Only you have walked through the fence without noticing it; and you can't see the plants, because you are down underneath them by their roots.'

It was only then when Frodo looked closer that he saw that what he had taken for smooth tree-stems were the stalks of gigantic flowers – and what he had thought was the stem of a monstrous oaktree was really a thick gnarled leg with a rootlike foot and many branching toes.

This is the first image of Treebeard: seeming in its air to come rather from the old *Hobbit* than the new. Six lines in Elvish *tengwar* are also written here, which transliterated read:

Fragment from The Lord of the Rings, sequel to The Hobbit.
Frodo meets Giant Treebeard in the Forest of Neldoreth while seeking for his lost companions: he is deceived by the giant who pretends to be friendly, but is really in league with the Enemy.

The forest of Neldoreth, forming the northern part of Doriath, had appeared in the later *Annals of Beleriand* (V.126, 148); the name from the old legends (like that of Glorfindel, see p. 214) was to be re-used.

Six months earlier, in a letter of 2 February 1939, my father had said that 'though there is no dragon (so far) there is going to be a Giant' (*Letters* no. 35, footnote to the text). If my suggested analysis of the chronology is correct (see p. 309) 'Giant Treebeard' had already appeared, as Gandalf's captor, at the end of the third phase (p. 363).

(11)   There remains one further text (extant in two versions) to be given in this chapter; this is the story of Peregrin Boffin (see under §§2, 3 above). One form of it is found as part of a rather roughly written two-page manuscript that begins as a new text of 'A Long-expected Party': very closely related to the sixth or third phase version of that chapter, but certainly following it. I take it up from the point 'At ninety he seemed much the same as ever' (FR p. 29).

At ninety-nine they began to call him *well-preserved*, though *unchanged* would have been nearer the mark. Some were heard to say that it was too much of a good thing, this combination of apparently perpetual youth with seemingly inexhaustible wealth.

NEW UNCERTAINTIES AND NEW PROJECTIONS 385

'It will have to be paid for,' they said. 'It isn't natural, and trouble will come of it!'

But trouble had not yet come, and Mr Baggins was extremely generous with his money, so most people (and especially the poorer and less important hobbits) pardoned his oddities. In a way the inhabitants of Hobbiton were (secretly) rather proud of him: the wealth that he had brought back from his travels became a local legend, and it was widely believed, whatever the old folk might say, that most of the Hill was full of tunnels stuffed with treasure.

'He may be peculiar, but he does no harm,' said the younger folk. But not all of his more important relatives agreed. They were suspicious of his influence on their children, and especially of their sons meeting Gandalf at his house. Their suspicions were much increased by the unfortunate affair of Peregrin Boffin.

Peregrin was the grandson of Bilbo's mother's second sister Donnamira Took. He was a mere babe, five years old, when Bilbo came back from his journey; but he grew up a dark-haired and (for a hobbit) lanky lad, very much more of a Took than a Boffin. He was always trotting round to Hobbiton, for his father, Paladin Boffin, lived at Northope, only a mile or two behind the Hill. When Peregrin began to talk about mountains and dwarves, and forests and wolves, Paladin became alarmed, and finally forbade his son to go near Bag-end, and shut his door on Bilbo.

Bilbo took this to heart, for he was extremely fond of Peregrin, but he did nothing to encourage him to visit Bag-end secretly. Peregrin then ran away from home and was found wandering about half-starved up on the moors of the Northfarthing. Finally, the day after he came of age (in the spring of Bilbo's eightieth year)[9] he disappeared, and was never found in spite of a search all over the Shire.

In former times Gandalf had always been held responsible for the occasional regrettable accidents of this kind; but now Bilbo got a large share of the blame, and after Peregrin's disappearance most of his younger relations were kept away from him. Though in fact Bilbo was probably more troubled by the loss of Peregrin than all the Boffins put together.

He had, however, other young friends, who for one reason or another were not kept away from him. His favourite soon became Frodo Baggins, grandson of Mirabella the third of the Old Took's remarkable daughters, and son of Drogo (one of Bilbo's second cousins). Just about the time of Peregrin's disappearance Frodo

386   THE RETURN OF THE SHADOW

was left an orphan, when only a child of twelve, and so he had no anxious parents to keep him out of bad company. He lived with his uncle Rory Brandybuck, and his mother's hundred and one relatives in the Great Hole of Bucklebury: Brandy Hall.

Here this new opening ends. A slightly shorter version is found as a rider to the manuscript of the third phase version itself: there are some differences of wording but none of substance. Bilbo is here said to have taken the delinquent back to Northope and apologised to Paladin Boffin, when Peregrin 'sneaked round to him secretly'; and Bilbo 'stoutly denied having anything to do with the events.'

The village of *Northope* later became *Overhill*, and was so corrected on the second of these texts.[10] – *Paladin* is already fixed as the name of the father of *Peregrin*: these Boffins are – as names – the origin of Paladin and Peregrin Took in LR. Donnamira Took, second of the Old Took's daughters, appears in the family tree of the Tooks given on p. 317, where she is the wife of Hugo Boffin (as in LR, but there without recorded issue): their son was Jago Boffin, and his son was Fosco, Bilbo's first cousin (once removed), who was 54 at the time of the Party. In the third phase version of 'Ancient History' (p. 319) Jo Button, who saw the 'Tree-men' beyond the North Moors, is said to have worked for Fosco Boffin of Northope, and this is presumably the same person as the Fosco Boffin of the family tree, grandson of Donnamira. In this case Peregrin Boffin (Trotter) – who was 64 at the time of the Party (see note 9), though of course he had then long since disappeared from the Shire – has stepped into Fosco's genealogical place, and his father Paladin into that of Jago. But only into the genealogical place: the Boffin of Northope for whom Jo Button was working has obviously nothing to do with the renegade Peregrin.

It will be seen that in this account Frodo and Trotter were second cousins, and both were first cousins once removed of Bilbo.[11]

NOTES

1 With 'unexpected party' for 'long-expected party' cf. p. 245, note 1.
2 Actually, the third and fourth drafts of the first phase: by 'original draft of the Tale' my father meant the form of 'A Long-expected Party' as it stood when submitted to Allen and Unwin (see p. 40).
3 I do not understand the force of this sentence.
4 The reference to *The Hobbit* is to Chapter I 'An Unexpected Party', a passage already cited (p. 224).
5 *the Rivers:* the plural form is clear.
6 That Bilbo wore his 'elf-armour' under his cloak when he went is said in §2; see pp. 371–2.
7 This is the wording of the sixth (third phase) version, little changed from that of the fifth (p. 239).

NEW UNCERTAINTIES AND NEW PROJECTIONS 387

8 Radagast had occurred in *The Hobbit*: in Chapter VII 'Queer Lodgings' Gandalf spoke to Beorn of 'my good cousin Radagast who lives near the Southern borders of Mirkwood.'

9 Peregrin Boffin was five years old when Bilbo returned from his great adventure. The calculation is: 51 to 79 ('the spring of his eightieth year') = 28, plus 5 = 33 ('coming of age'). According to this story Peregrin/Trotter was 81 years old when Frodo and his companions met him at Bree (Bilbo finally departed when he was 111; Peregrin/Trotter was then 64, and Frodo left the Shire 17 years later). As he said at Bree, 'I'm older now than I look' (pp. 153, 342); Aragorn was 87 when he said the same thing (FR p. 177).

10 *Northope > Overhill* also on p. 319. – The name *Northope* appears here on my father's original map of the Shire (p. 107, item I), but it was struck out and replaced, not by Overhill, but by *The Yale*. This is a convenient place to notice the history of this name. Long after, my father wrote in *The Yale* on the Shire map in a copy of the First Edition of FR, placing it south of Whitfurrows in the Eastfarthing, in such a way as to show that he intended a region, like 'The Marish', not a particular place of settlement (the road to Stock runs through it); and at the same time, on the same copy, he expanded the text in FR p. 86, introducing the name: 'the lowlands of the Yale' (for the reason for this change of text, which was published in the Second Edition, see p. 66, note 10). The Shire map in the Second Edition has *The Yale* added here, but in relation to a small black square, as if it were the name of a farm or small hamlet; this must have been a misunderstanding. I cannot explain the meaning of *The Yale*. *Northope* contains a place-name element *hope* that usually means 'a small enclosed valley'.

11 My father's earlier suggestion concerning Trotter (p. 223) also made him Bilbo's first cousin (Fosco Took).

THE STORY
CONTINUED

XXIII

IN THE HOUSE OF ELROND

In the next stage of the work it is difficult to deduce the chronology of composition, or to relate it to important further revisions made to the 'third phase' of the story as far as Rivendell. Determination of the chronology depends on the form taken by certain key elements, and if these happen to be absent certainty becomes impossible.

At any rate, after 'Bingo' had become 'Frodo' my father continued Frodo's interrupted conversation with Glóin at the feast in the house of Elrond (see p. 369). This continuation is in two forms, the second closely following the first, and already in the first form the latter part of 'Many Meetings' in FR is quite closely approached; but there are certain major differences. I give here the second form (in part).[1]

'And what has become of Balin and Ori and Óin?' asked Frodo.

A shadow passed over Glóin's face. 'Balin took to travelling again,' he answered. 'You may have heard that he visited Bilbo in Hobbiton many years ago:[2] well, not very long after that he went away for two or three years. Then he returned to the Mountain with a great number of dwarves that he discovered wandering masterless in the South and East. He wanted Dáin to go back to Moria – or at least to allow him to found a colony there and reopen the great mines. As you probably know, Moria was the ancestral home of the dwarves of the race of Durin, and the forefathers of Thorin and Dáin dwelt there, until they were driven by the goblin invasions far into the North. Now Balin reported that Moria was again wholly deserted, since the great defeat of the goblins, but the mines were still rich, especially in silver. Dáin was not willing to leave the Mountain and the tomb of Thorin, but he allowed Balin to go, and he took with him many of the folk of the Mountain as well as his own following; and Ori and Óin went with him. For many years things went well, and the colony throve; there was traffic once more between Moria and the Mountain, and many gifts of silver were sent to Dáin. Then fortune changed. Our messengers were attacked and robbed by cruel Men, well-armed. No messengers came from Moria; but rumour reached us that the mines and dwarf-city were again deserted. For long we could not learn what had become of Balin and his people – but now we have

392 THE RETURN OF THE SHADOW

news, and it is evil. It is to tell these tidings and to ask for the counsel of – of those that dwell in Rivendell that I have come. But to-night let us speak of merrier things!'

At the head of the page my father wrote the words that stand in this place in FR (p. 241): '"We do not know," he answered. "It is largely on his account that I have come to ask for the counsel of – of those that dwell in Rivendell. But for to-night let us speak of merrier things."' In FR the story of Balin was taken up into 'The Council of Elrond' and greatly enlarged.

Glóin's account of the works of the Dwarves in Dale and under the Lonely Mountain (FR pp. 241–2) is present in the old version.[3] At the end, when Glóin said: 'You were very fond of Bilbo, weren't you?' Frodo replied simply 'Yes', and then 'they went on to talk about the old adventures of Bilbo with the dwarves, in Mirkwood, and among the Wood-elves, and in the caverns of the Mountain.'

The entrance into the Hall of Fire, and the discovery and recognition of Bilbo, are already very close to FR (for early references to Bilbo at Rivendell see pp. 126, 225). The Hall of Fire is said in both texts to be nearly as large as the 'Hall of Feasting' or 'Great Hall'; in the second this hall 'appeared to have no windows'; and in both there were many fires burning: Bilbo sat beside the furthest, with his cup and bread on a low table beside him (in FR there were no tables).

Bilbo says 'I shall have to get that fellow Peregrin to help me' (cf. p. 369) and Elrond replies that he will have *Ethelion*[4] found (in Chapter XI of the 'third phase' Glorfindel calls Trotter *Du-finnion*, p. 361). 'Messengers were sent to find Bilbo's friend. It was said that he had been in the kitchens, for his help was as much esteemed by the cooks as by the poets.' It had been said in the earlier part of the chapter (p. 365) that Frodo could not see Trotter at the feast, and his absence survived into FR (p. 243), but with a very different reason for it.

Whatever Bilbo may have had to say of himself is not reported in the original story. The entire passage (FR pp. 243–4) in which Bilbo tells of his journey to Dale, of his life in Rivendell, and his interest in the Ring – and the distressing incident when he asks to see it – is absent.

They were so deep in the doings of the Shire that they did not notice the arrival of another hobbit. For several minutes he stood by them, looking at them with a smile. Suddenly they looked up. 'Ah, there you are, Peregrin!' said Bilbo. 'Trotter!' said Frodo.

'Both right!' laughed Trotter.

'Well, that is tiresome of Gandalf!' exclaimed Frodo. 'I knew you reminded me of some one, and he laughed at me.[5] Of course, you remind me of yourself, and of Folco, and of all the Tooks. You came once to Buckland when I was very small, but I never

IN THE HOUSE OF ELROND
393

quite forgot it, because you talked to Old Rory about lands outside the Shire, and about Bilbo who you were not allowed to see. I have wondered what became of you. But I was puzzled by your shoes. Why do you wear them?'

'I shall not tell you the reason now,' said Trotter quietly.

'No, Frodo, don't ask that yet,' said Bilbo, looking rather unhappy. 'Come on, Perry! I want your help. This song of mine has got to be finished this evening.'

At this point, while in the middle of writing the second text, my father wrote across it: '?? Trotter had better not be a hobbit – but a Ranger, remainder of Western Men, as originally planned.' Of course, looking back over the texts from Trotter's first appearance, there is no possibility that my father had 'originally planned' to make Trotter anything but a hobbit. The first suggestion that he might not be appears in *Queries and Alterations* (p. 223, §6). But by 'originally planned' my father may well have been thinking no further back than to the drafts for the opening of the 'Bree' chapter in the third phase (p. 331), where the idea that the Rangers were Men, 'the last remnant of the kingly people from beyond the Seas', first emerged, though this was not taken up in the chapter as actually written at that time. It may be that he had felt for some time that Trotter should not be a hobbit, but (as he said of the name 'Bingo', p. 221) he was now too used to the idea to change it. Even now, he did not follow up his directive, and Trotter remains Peregrin Boffin.

As in FR, Frodo sits alone and falls asleep during the music; but the song *Eärendil was a mariner* is not present (though the word '?Messenger' written at the top of the page is a hint of it).[6]

He woke to the sound of ringing laughter. There was no longer any music, but on the edge of his waking sense was the echo of a voice that had just stopped singing. He looked, and saw that Bilbo was seated on his stool, set now near to the middle fire, in the centre of a circle of listeners.

'Come now, tell us, Bilbo!' said one of the Elves, 'which is the line which Peregrin put in?'

'No!' laughed Bilbo. 'I leave you to guess – you pride yourselves on your judgement of words.'

'But it is difficult to discriminate between two hobbits,' they laughed.

'Nonsense!' said Bilbo. 'But I won't argue the matter. I'm sleepy, after so much sound and song!' He got up and bowed and came back beside Frodo.

'Well, that's that,' he said. 'It went off better than I expected. As a matter of fact, quite a lot of it was Peregrin's.'

394 THE RETURN OF THE SHADOW

'I am sorry I did not hear it,' said Frodo. 'I heard the Elves laughing as I woke up.'

'Never mind,' said Bilbo. 'You'll hear it again, very likely. Just a lot of nonsense, anyway. But it is difficult to keep awake here, until you get used to it – not that hobbits ever acquire the Elves' appetite for song and poetry and tales of all sorts. They will be going on for a long while yet. . . .

The words of the chant to Elbereth (identical in both texts) are different from the form in FR:

> *Elbereth Gilthoniel sir evrin pennar oriel*
> *dir avos-eithen miriel*
> *bel daurion sel aurinon*
> *pennáros evrin ériol.*

The sweet syllables fell like clear jewels of mingled word and sound, and he halted for a moment looking back.

'That is the opening of the chant to Elbereth,' said Bilbo. 'They will sing that and other songs of the Blessed Realm many times tonight.'

Bilbo led Frodo back to his upper room. There they sat for some while, looking at the bright stars through the window, and talking softly. They spoke no longer of the small and happy news of the Shire far away, but of the Elves, and of the wide world, and its perils, and of the burden and mystery of the Ring.

When Sam came to the door (at the end of the chapter in FR) Bilbo said:

'Quite right, Sam! Though I never expected to live long enough to be ordered about by Ham Gamgee's boy. Bless me, I am near 150 and old enough to be your great-grandfather.'

'No sir, and I never expected to be doing it.'

'It is Gandalf's fault, said Frodo. 'He chose Sam to be my companion in adventure, and Sam takes his task seriously.'

This was replaced at the time of writing by the ending in FR. Bilbo was in fact 128.

Both texts continue on briefly into what became 'The Council of Elrond' in FR (the title that my father had given to the 'third phase' text Chapter XII, p. 362, afterwards called 'Many Meetings', when he anticipated that it would contain the Council as well as the 'many meetings' that preceded it).

IN THE HOUSE OF ELROND

Frodo awoke early next day, feeling refreshed and well. Sam brought him breakfast, and would not allow him to get up till he had eaten it. Then Bilbo and Gandalf came and talked for a while. Suddenly a single bell rang out. [*All the remainder of the text from this point was struck out; see p. 399.*]

'Bless me!' said Gandalf. 'The council is in half an hour. That is the warning. I must be off. Bilbo will bring you to the place, as soon as you are ready. Sam had better come with you.'

The council was held in a high glade among the trees on the valley-side far above the house. A falling stream ran at the side of the meeting place, and with the trickling and bubbling of the water was mingled the sound of many birds. There were twelve seats of carved stone in a wide circle; and behind them many other smaller seats of wood. The ground was strewn with many red and yellow leaves, but the trees above were still clothed with fading green; a clear sky of pale blue hung high above, filled with the light of morning.

When Bilbo, Frodo and Sam arrived Elrond was already seated, and beside him, as at the feast, were Gandalf and Glorfindel. Glóin was there also with [an attendant >] a younger dwarf, whom Frodo later discovered was Burin son of Balin.[7] A strange elf, a messenger from the king of the Wood-elves . . . Eastern Mirkwood was seated beside Burin.[8] Trotter (as Frodo continued to call him instead of Peregrin or the Elvish equivalent Ethelion) was there, and all the rest of the hobbit party, Merry, Folco, and Odo. There were besides three other counsellors attendant on Elrond, one an Elf named Erestor, and two other kinsmen of Elrond, of that half-elvish folk whom the Elves named the children of Lúthien.[9] And seated alone and silent was a Man of noble face, but dark and sad.

'This is Boromir,' said Elrond. 'He arrived only yesterday, in the evening. He comes from far away in the South, and his tidings may be of use to us.'

It would take long to tell of all that was spoken in that council under the fair trees of Rivendell. The sun climbed to noon and was turning westward before all the tidings were recounted. Then Elves brought food and drink for the company. The sun had fallen low and its slanting light was red in the valley before an end was made of the debate and they rose and returned down the long path to the house.

396   THE RETURN OF THE SHADOW

Both texts end at this point. At the end of the second my father wrote:
'(The Council must be behind closed doors. Frodo invited to presence of
Elrond. Tidings of the world. They decide Ring must be destroyed.)'

While Trotter is Peregrin Boffin, and the long-awaited 'recognition'
between Trotter and Frodo takes place, Odo is still present: but in the
papers dated August 1939, where the identification of Trotter with
Peregrin Boffin first appears, Odo appears to be emphatically abandoned. Once again, Odo seems to have proved unsinkable, even though,
as discussed on p. 375, Folco had effectively assumed his character. – Of
course, these 'Rivendell' manuscripts may very well belong to the same
time, and a step-by-step reconstruction cannot be expected. In any case,
the removal of Odo and (much more) the identity of Trotter were
questions long revolved, and such notes as 'Trotter had better not be a
hobbit' or 'Odo must be cut out' are rather the traces of a long debate
than a series of clear-cut, successive decisions.

The text just given was continued in a further manuscript of different
form, in which appears the first complete version of the Council of
Elrond; but before going on to this, two sides of a single isolated page
seem undoubtedly to represent my father's first expressed ideas for the
Council. It was written in pencil so faint and rapid that it would be
largely illegible had my father not gone over it in ink; and he himself
could not be sure in places of what he had written, but had to make
guesses at words, marking them with queries. In representing this
extraordinarily interesting text I give these guessed words of his in italic
within brackets. At the head of the page is an isolated direction that the
'Weathertop business' must be 'simplified'. It would be interesting to
know what he had in mind: the only 'complication' that was, in the event,
removed was the disappearance of Odo, and it may be that this is what he
was referring to. It is clear from the first line of this text that the 'third
phase' story of Odo was present.

Ring Wraiths. They will get *(no? new?)* horses *(in time?)*. Odo's
capturing explained.

Ring offered to Elrond. He refuses. 'It is a peril to all possessors: more to myself than all others. It is fate that the *hobbits*
should rid the world of it.'

'What will then become of the other rings?' 'They will lose their
power. But we must sacrifice that power in order to destroy the
Lord. As long as anyone in the world holds the Ruling Ring there
is a chance for *him* to get it back again. Two things can be done.
We can send it West, or we can destroy it. If we had sent it West
long ago that would have been well enough. But now the power of
the Lord is grown too great, and he is fully awake. It would be too

IN THE HOUSE OF ELROND

397

perilous – and his war would come over the Shire and destroy the Havens.'[10] [*In the margin is written* Radagast.]

They decide that the Ring must be taken to the Fiery Mountain. How? – it can hardly be reached except by passing over the borders of the Land of Mordor. Bilbo? No – 'It would kill me now. My years are stretched, and I shall live some time yet. But I have no longer strength for the Ring.'

Frodo volunteers to go.

Who shall go with him? Gandalf. Trotter. Sam. Odo. Folco. Merry. (7)   Glorfindel and Frár [*written beneath:* Burin] son of Balin.

South along mountains. Over the Red Pass down the Redway to the Great River.

'Beware!' said Gandalf 'of the Giant Treebeard, who haunts the Forest between the River and the South Mts.' Fangorn?

After a time of rest they set out. Bilbo bids farewell; gives him Sting and his armour. The others are armed.

Snow storm.

The reverse of the page, while not continuous with the first side, was certainly written at the same time, and is again in ink over faint pencil:

First he was asked to give as complete an account of the journey as possible. The story of their dealings with Tom Bombadil seemed to interest Elrond and Gandalf most.

Much that was said was now known already to Frodo. Gandalf spoke long, making clear to all the history of the Ring, and the reason why the Dark Lord so greatly desired it. 'For not only does he desire to discover and control the lost rings, those of the Elves and dwarves – but without the Ring he is still shorn of much power. He put into that Ring much of his own power, and without it is weaker than of old [and obliged to lean more on servants].[11] Of old he could guess or half see what were the hidden purposes of the Elflords, but now he is blind as far as they are concerned. He cannot make rings until he has regained the master ring. And also his mind is moved by revenge and hatred of the Elves and Men that (*disputed him?*).

'Now is the time for true speaking. Tell me, Elrond, if the *Three* Rings still are? And tell me, Glóin, if you know it, whether any of the *Seven* remain?'

'Yes, the Three still are,' said Elrond, 'and it would be ill indeed if Sauron should discover where they be, or have power over their

398 THE RETURN OF THE SHADOW

rulers; for then perhaps his shadow would stretch even to the Blessed Realm.'

'Yes! Some of the Seven remain,' said Glóin. 'I do not know whether I have the right to reveal this, for Dáin did not give me orders concerning it. But Thráin of old had one that descended from his sires. We do not now know where it is. We think it was taken from him, ere you found him in the dungeons long ago [or maybe it was lost in Moria].[12] Yet of late we have received secret messages from Mordor demanding all such rings as we have or know of. But there are others still in our power. Dáin has one – and on that his fortune is founded: his age, his wealth, and (. . . . . . .?) future. Yet of late we have received secret messages from Mordor bidding us yield up the rings to the Master, and threatening us and all our allies of Dale with war.[13] It is on this account that I am now come to Rivendell. For the messages have asked often concerning *one Bilbo*, and offered us peace if we would obtain from him (willing or unwilling) his ring. That they said they would accept in lieu of all. I now understand why. But our hearts are troubled, for we guess that King Brand's heart is afraid, and that the Dark Lord will *(move?)* eastern men to some evil. Already there is war upon the *(southern?)* borders. And *(of course that matter whereof?)* I seek counsel, the disappearance of Balin and his people, is now *(revealed?)* as part of the same evil.'

Boromir the *(lord? Land?)* of Ond. These men are besieged by wild men out of the East. They send to the *(F . . . . . ?)* of Balin of Moria. He promised assistance.

Here this text ends. Against the passage beginning '"Yes! Some of the Seven remain," said Glóin' my father wrote: 'No! This won't do – otherwise the dwarves would have been more suspicious of Bilbo.'

In this text, again, there is an apparent contradiction of the 'August 1939' papers: Bilbo gives his mailcoat to Frodo at Rivendell, and had therefore taken it with him when he left Bag End – a story that first appears under the date August 1939 (p. 371, §2), whereas it is also proposed there that the 'Odo-story' be abandoned – a story that is expressly present here. – The Fellowship of the Ring is to consist of five 'Shire hobbits', Frodo, Sam, Merry, Folco, and Odo, with Trotter, Gandalf, Glorfindel, and the dwarf Frár (> Burin).

Whatever the relative age of these texts, and they can scarcely be far apart, there have now appeared the younger Dwarf, Balin's son, who had come with Glóin – precursor of Gimli Glóin's son in LR; the Elf from Mirkwood, precursor of Legolas; Erestor, counsellor of Elrond; two kinsmen of Elrond; and Boromir – so named unhesitatingly from the start[14] – from the Land of Ond far in the South. The Land of Ond is

IN THE HOUSE OF ELROND 399

named in an outline dated August 1939 (p. 381). Treebeard is no longer placed in 'the Forest of Neldoreth' (p. 384), but in 'the Forest between the [Great] River and the South Mountains' – the first mention of the mountains that would afterwards be Ered Nimrais, the White Mountains; and Gandalf warns against him (as well he might, having been his captive, 'in Fangorn', p. 363).

The passage concerning the Three Rings of the Elves and the Seven Rings of the Dwarves is to be compared with a passage in the third phase version of 'Ancient History', p. 320, where Gandalf says that he does not know what has become of 'the Three Rings of Earth, Sea, and Sky', but believes that 'they have long been carried far over the Great Sea' – which is to be associated no doubt with Elrond's words in the present text: 'it would be ill indeed if Sauron should discover where they be, or have power over their rulers; for then perhaps his shadow would stretch even to the Blessed Realm.' In the same passage of 'Ancient History' Gandalf says that 'the foundation of each of the Seven Hoards of the dwarves of old was a golden ring', and that it is said that all the Seven Rings perished in the fire of the dragons: 'Yet that account, maybe, is not wholly true.'

With the menacing messages to King Dáin out of Mordor here cf. *Queries and Alterations* (p. 226, §11): 'The dwarves might have received threatening messages from Mordor – for the Lord suspected that the One Ring was in their hoards.' In the same note it is said that 'after a time no word was heard of them [Balin and his companions]. Dáin feared the Dark Lord'; so also Glóin says here that 'the disappearance of Balin and his people is now revealed as part of the same evil.' At this time the story was that Sauron demanded the return of the Rings which the Dwarves still possessed – or Bilbo's Ring 'in lieu of all'; in FR (p. 254) they were offered the return of three of the ancient Rings of the Dwarves if they could obtain Bilbo's Ring.

The reference to Thráin, father of Thorin Oakenshield, in the dungeons of the Necromancer, where Gandalf found him, goes back to *The Hobbit* (Chapter I); but the story emerges here that he possessed one of the Rings of the Dwarves, and that it was taken from him after his capture (see FR pp. 281–2, and LR Appendix A (iii), pp. 353–4, 357–8).

The 'Many Meetings' text (extant in two forms) given on pp. 391 ff. continued into the beginning of an account of the Council of Elrond, held in the open in a glade above the house; but from the words '"Bless me!" said Gandalf. "The council is in half an hour"' (p. 395) my father struck it through, and added the note at the end saying that the Council must be held 'behind closed doors' (p. 396). A new manuscript now begins, taking up at '"Bless me!" said Gandalf', and in this is found the first complete narrative of the deliberations of the Council. This was originally paginated 'XII' with page-numbers consecutive from 'Suddenly a single bell rang out' (p. 395). As noticed before, my father at this stage

400   THE RETURN OF THE SHADOW

saw all the meetings and discussions at Rivendell as constituting a single chapter, and had given the number and title 'XII. The Council of Elrond' to the third phase chapter which begins with Frodo waking up at Rivendell (p. 362).

The manuscript is partly in ink and partly in pencil, but though very rough is legible throughout. Being in the first stage of composition it is full of alterations, phrases or whole passages constantly rewritten in the act of composition; and many other corrections, made to passages which at the time of writing had been allowed to stand, are probably pretty well contemporary. In general I give the text in its final form, but with more important changes indicated.

'Bless me!' said Gandalf. 'That is the warning bell for the council. We had better make our way there at once.'

Bilbo and Frodo (and Sam [added: uninvited]) followed him down many stairs and passages towards the western wing of the house, until they came to the porch where Frodo had found his friends the evening before. But now the light of a clear autumn morning was glowing in the valley. The sky was high and cool above the hill-tops; and in the bright air below a few golden leaves were fluttering from the trees. The noise of bubbling waters came up from the foaming river-bed. Birds were singing and a wholesome peace lay on the land, and to Frodo his dangerous flight and the rumours of the dark shadow growing in the world outside seemed now only like memories of a troubled dream.

But the faces that were turned to meet him were grave.[15] Elrond was there and several others were already seated about him in silence. Frodo saw Glorfindel and Glóin, and Trotter (sitting in a corner).

Elrond welcomed Frodo and drew him to a seat at his knee and presented him to the company, saying: 'Here my friends is the hobbit who by fortune and courage has brought the Ring to Rivendell. This is Frodo son of Drogo.' He then pointed out and named those whom Frodo had not seen before. There was a younger dwarf at Glóin's side, [Burin the son of Balin >] his son Gimli.[16] There were three counsellors of Elrond's own household: Erestor his kinsman (a man of the same half-elvish folk known as the children of Lúthien), [17] and beside him two elflords of Rivendell. There was a strange elf clad in green and brown, Galdor, a messenger from the King of the Wood-elves in Eastern Mirkwood.[18] And seated a little apart was a tall man of noble face, but dark and sad.

'Here,' said Elrond, turning to Gandalf, 'is Boromir from the

IN THE HOUSE OF ELROND
401

Land of Ond, far in the South. He arrived in the night, and brings tidings that must be considered.'

It would take long to tell of all the things that were spoken in that council. Many of them were known already to Frodo. Gandalf spoke long, making clear to those who did not already know the tale in full the ancient history of the Ring, and the reasons why the Dark Lord so greatly desired it. Bilbo then gave an account of the finding of the Ring in the cave of the Misty Mountains, and Trotter described his search for Gollum that he had made with Gandalf's help, and told of his perilous adventures in Mordor. Thus it was that Frodo learned how Trotter had tracked Gollum as he wandered southwards, through Fangorn Forest, and past the Dead Marshes,[19] until he had himself been caught and imprisoned by the Dark Lord. 'Ever since I have worn shoes,' said Trotter with a shudder, and though he said no more Frodo knew that he had been tortured and his feet hurt in some way. But he had been rescued by Gandalf and saved from death.[20]

In this way the tale was brought slowly down to the spring morning when Gandalf had revealed the history of the Ring to Frodo. Then Frodo was summoned to take up the tale, and he gave a full account of all his adventures from the moment of his flight from Hobbiton. Step by step they questioned him, and every detail that he could tell concerning the Black Riders was examined.[21]

Elrond was also deeply interested in the events in the Old Forest and on the Barrow-downs. 'The Barrow-wights I knew of,' he said, 'for they are closely akin to the Riders;[22] and I marvel at your escape from them. But never before have I heard tell of this strange Bombadil. I would like to know more of him. Did you know of him, Gandalf?'

'Yes,' answered the wizard. 'And I sought him out at once, as soon as I found that the hobbits had disappeared from Buckland. When I had chased the Riders from Crickhollow I turned back to visit him. I daresay he would have kept the travellers longer in his home, if he had known that I was near. But I am not sure of it: he is a strange creature, and follows his own counsels, which few can fathom.'[23]

'Could we not even now send messages to him and obtain his help?' asked Erestor. 'It seems that he has a power even over the Ring.'

'That is not quite the way of it,' said Gandalf. 'The Ring has no

402   THE RETURN OF THE SHADOW

power over *him* or for him: it can neither harm nor serve him: he is his own master. But he has no power over it, and he cannot alter the Ring itself, not break its power over others. And I think that the mastery of Tom Bombadil is seen only on his own ground – from which he has never stepped within my memory.'[24]

'But on his own ground nothing seems to dismay him,' said Erestor. 'Would he not perhaps take the Ring and keep it there for ever harmless?'

'He would, perhaps, if all the free folk of the world begged him to do so,' said Gandalf. 'But he would not do so willingly. For it would only postpone the evil day. In time the Lord of the Ring would find out its hiding-place, and in the end he would come in person.[25] I doubt whether Tom Bombadil, even on his own ground, could withstand that power; but I am sure that we should not leave him to face it. Besides, he lives too far away and the Ring has come from his land only at great hazard. It would have to pass through greater danger to return. If the Ring is to be hidden – surely it is here in Rivendell that it should be kept: if Elrond has might to withstand the coming of Sauron in all his power?'

'I have not,' said Elrond.

'In that case,' said Erestor,[26] 'there are but two things for us to attempt: we may send the Ring West over the Sea, or we may try to destroy it. If the Ring had gone to the West long ago that would have perhaps been well. But now the power of the Lord is grown great again, and he is awake, and he knows where the Ring is. The journey to the Havens would be fraught with the greatest peril. On the other hand we cannot by our own skill or strength destroy the Ring; and the journey to the Fiery Mountain would seem still more perilous, leading as it does towards the stronghold of the Enemy. Who can read this riddle for us?'

'None here can do so,' said Elrond gravely.[27] 'None can foretell which road leads to safety, if that is what you mean. But I can choose which road it is right to take, as it seems to me – and indeed the choice is clear. The Ring must be sent to the Fire. The peril is greater on the western road; for my heart tells me that is the road which Sauron will expect us to take when he hears what has befallen. And if we take it he will pursue us swiftly and surely, since we must make for the Havens beyond the Towers. Those he would certainly destroy, even if he found us not, and there would be thereafter no way of escape for the Elves from the darkening world.'

IN THE HOUSE OF ELROND 403

'And the Shire too would be destroyed,' said Trotter in a low voice, looking towards Bilbo and Frodo.

'But on the other road,' said Elrond, 'with speed and skill the travellers might go far unmarked. I do not say there is great hope in the quest; but only in this way could any lasting good be achieved. In the Ring is hidden much of the ancient power of Sauron. Even though he does not hold it that power still lives and works for him and towards him. As long as the Ring lives on land or sea he will not be overcome. While the Ring lasts he will grow, and have hope, and the fear lest the Ring come into his hand again will ever weigh on the world. War will never cease while that fear lives, and all Men will be turned to him.'

'I do not understand this,' said Boromir. 'Why should the Elves and their friends not use the Great Ring to defeat Sauron? And I say that all men will *not* join him: the men of Ond will never submit.'

'Never is a long word, O Boromir,' said Elrond. 'The men of Ond are valiant and still faithful amid a host of foes; but valour alone cannot withstand Sauron for ever. Many of his servants are as valiant. But as for the Ruling Ring – it belongs to Sauron and is filled with his spirit. Its might is too great for those of lesser strength, as Bilbo and Frodo have found, and in the end it must lead them captive to him if they keep it. For those who have power of their own, its danger is far greater. With it they might perchance overthrow the Dark Lord, but they would set themselves in his throne. Then they would become as evil as he, or worse. For nothing is evil in the beginning. Even Sauron was not so. I dare not take the Ring to wield it.'

'Nor I,' said Gandalf.

'But is it not true, as I have heard said, O Elrond,' said Boromir, 'that the Elves keep yet and wield Three Rings, and yet these too came from Sauron in the ancient days? And the dwarves, too, had rings, it is said. Tell me, Glóin, if you know it, whether any of the Seven Rings remain?'

'I do not know,' said Glóin. 'It was said in secret that Thráin (father of Thrór father of Thorin[28] who fell in battle) possessed one that had descended from his sires. Some said it was the last. But where it is no dwarf now knows. We think maybe it was taken from him, ere Gandalf found him in the dungeons of Mordor long ago[29] – or maybe it was lost in Moria. Yet of late we have received secret messages from Mordor offering us rings again. It was partly on this account that I came to Rivendell; for the messages asked

404   THE RETURN OF THE SHADOW

concerning one *Bilbo*, and commanded us to obtain from him (willing or unwilling) the ring that he possessed. For this ring we were offered [seven >] three such as our fathers had of old. Even for news of where he might be found we were offered friendship for ever and great wealth.[30] Our hearts are troubled, for we perceive that King Brand in Dale is afraid, and if we do not answer Sauron will move other men to evil against him. Already there are threats of war upon the south.'

'It would seem that the Seven Rings are lost or have returned to their Lord,' said Boromir. 'What of the Three?'

'The Three Rings remain still,' said Elrond. 'They have conferred great power on the Elves, but they have never yet availed them in their strife with Sauron. For they came from Sauron himself, and can give no skill or knowledge that he did not already possess at their making. And to each race the rings of the Lord bring such powers as each desires and is capable of wielding. The Elves desired not strength or domination or riches, but subtlety of craft and lore, and knowledge of the secrets of the world's being. These things they have gained, yet with sorrow. But they will turn to evil if Sauron regains the Ruling Ring; for then all that the Elves have devised or learned with the power of the rings will become his, as was his purpose.'

Against this passage concerning the Three Rings of the Elves my father wrote later; '*Elfrings* made by *Elves* for themselves. The 7 and 9 were made by Sauron – to cheat men and dwarves. They originally accepted them because they believed they were *elfrings*.' And he also wrote, separately but against the same passage: 'Alter this: make the Elfrings their own and Sauron's made in answer.' This is the first appearance of this central idea concerning the origin and nature of the Rings; but since it does not emerge in actual narrative until considerably later these notes cannot be contemporary with the text. – In FR it is Glóin, not Boromir, who raises the question of the Three Rings of the Elves; but he also, like Boromir in the present text, asserts that they were made by the Dark Lord. Elrond corrects Glóin's error; yet earlier in the Council (FR p. 255) Elrond has expressly said that Celebrimbor made the Three, and that Sauron forged the One in secret to be their master. Glóin's assertion (FR p. 282) is thus not appropriate, and is probably an echo of my father's original conception of the Rings. The text continues:

'What then would happen, if the Ruling Ring were destroyed?' asked Boromir.

'The Elves would not lose what they have already won,'

IN THE HOUSE OF ELROND

answered Elrond; 'but the Three Rings would lose all power thereafter.'

'Yet that loss,' said Glorfindel, 'all Elves would gladly suffer, if by it the power of Sauron might be broken.'

'Thus we return again to the point whence we started,' said Erestor. 'The Ring should be destroyed; but we cannot destroy it, save by the perilous journey to the Fire. What strength or cunning have we for that task?'

'In this task it is plain that great power will not avail,' said Elrond. 'It must be attempted by the weak. Such is the way of things. In this great matter fate seems already to have pointed the way for us.'

'Very well, very well, Master Elrond!' said Bilbo suddenly.[31] 'Say no more! It is plain at least what *you* are pointing at. Bilbo the hobbit started this affair, and Bilbo had better finish it, or himself. I was very comfortable here, and getting on with my book. If you want to know, I am just writing an ending for it. I had thought of putting "and he lived happily ever afterward to the end of his days": which is a good ending, and none the worse for having been used before. Now I shall have to alter that – it does not look like being true, and anyway there will have to be several more chapters, even if I don't write them myself. It is a frightful nuisance! When ought I to start?'

Elrond smiled, and Gandalf laughed loudly. 'Of course,' said the wizard, 'if you had really started the affair, my dear Bilbo, you would be expected to finish it. But *starting* is a strong word. I have often tried to suggest to you that you only came in (accidentally, as you might say) in the *middle* of a long story, that was not made up for your sake only. That is, of course, true enough of all heroes and all adventures, but never mind that now. As for you, if you want my opinion once more, I should say that your part is finished – except as a recorder. Finish your book and leave the ending! But get ready to write a sequel, when they come back.'

Bilbo laughed in his turn. 'I have never known you to give pleasant advice before, Gandalf,' he said, 'or to tell me to do what I really wanted to do. Since all your unpleasant advice has usually been good, I wonder if this is not bad. Yet it is true that my years are stretched and getting thin, and I do not think I have strength for the Ring. But tell me: who do you mean by "they"?'

'The adventurers who are sent with the Ring.'

'Exactly, and who are they to be? That seems to me precisely what this council now has to decide.'

406 THE RETURN OF THE SHADOW

There was a long silence. Frodo glanced round at all the faces, but no one looked at him – except Sam; in whose eyes there was a strange mixture of hope and fear. All the others sat as if in deep thought with their eyes closed or upon the ground. A great dread fell on Frodo, and he felt an overmastering longing to remain at peace by Bilbo's side in Rivendell.

These words stand at the foot of a page. The next page, beginning 'At last with an effort he spoke', continues only a brief way, and was replaced by another beginning with the same words. I give both forms.

At last with an effort he spoke. 'If this task is fated to fall to the weak,' he said, 'I will attempt it. But I shall need the help of the strong and the wise.'

'I think, Frodo,' said Elrond, looking keenly at him, 'that this task is appointed for you. But it is very well that you should offer yourself unbidden. All the help that we can contrive shall be yours.'

'But you won't send him alone, surely, master!' cried Sam.

'No indeed,' said Elrond, turning to him. 'You at least shall go – since you are here although I do not think you were summoned. It seems difficult to separate you from your master Frodo.'

Sam subsided, but whispered to Frodo: 'How far is this Mountain? A nice pickle we have landed ourselves in, Mr. Frodo!'[32]

'Taking care of hobbits is not a task that everyone would like,' said Gandalf, 'but I am used to it. I suggest Frodo and his Sam, Merry, Faramond, and myself. That is five. And Glorfindel, if he will come and lend us the wisdom of the Elves: we shall need it. That is six.'

'And Trotter!' said Peregrin from the corner. 'That is seven, and a fitting number. The Ring-bearer will have good company.'

Here this version of the passage ends. Pencilled beneath is an unfinished sentence: 'The choice is good,' said Elrond. 'Though

Other very rough pencillings read: 'Alter this. Hobbits only, including Trotter. Gandalf as [?guide] in early stages. Gandalf says he will go all way? No Glorfindel.' And below these notes, the single isolated name Boromir. – On the back of this page is a remarkable sketch of events to come; for this see p. 410.

The replacement page treats the selection of the Company quite differently:

At last with an effort he spoke. 'I will take the Ring,' he said. 'Though I don't know the way.'

Elrond looked keenly at him. 'If I understand all the tale that I

IN THE HOUSE OF ELROND 407

have heard,' he said, 'I think that this task is appointed for you, Frodo, and that if you do not find the way, no other will.'

'But you won't send him off alone surely, master!' cried Sam, unable to contain himself.

'No indeed!' said Elrond, turning towards him with a smile. 'You at least shall go with him, since it is hardly possible to separate you from him – even when he is summoned to a secret council and you are not.'

Sam subsided, but whispered to Frodo: 'How far is this Mountain? A nice pickle we have landed ourselves in, Mr. Frodo!'

'When shall I start?' asked Frodo.

'First you shall rest and recover full strength,' answered Elrond, guessing his mind. 'Rivendell is a fair place, and we will not send you away, until you know it better. And meanwhile we will make plans for your guidance.'

Later in the afternoon of the council Frodo was strolling in the woods with his friends. Merry and Faramond were indignant when they heard that Sam had crept into the council, and been chosen as Frodo's companion. 'Not the only one!' said Merry. 'I have come so far and I am not going to be left behind now. Someone with intelligence ought to be in the party.'

'I don't see that your inclusion will help much in that way,' said Faramond. 'But, of course, you must go, and I must too. We hobbits must stick together. We seem to have become mighty important these days. It would be a bit of an eye-opener for the people back in the Shire!'

'I doubt it!' said Frodo. 'Hardly any of them would believe a word of it. I wish I was one of them, and back in Hobbiton. Anyone who wants can have all my importance.'

'Quite accidental! Quite accidental, as I keep on telling you,' said a voice behind them. They turned to see Gandalf hurrying round a bend in the path. 'Hobbit voices carry a long way,' he said. 'All right in Rivendell (or I hope so); but I should not discuss matters so loud outside the house. Your importance is accidental, Frodo – by which I mean, someone else might have been chosen and done as well – but it is real. No one else can have it now. So be careful – you can't be too careful! As for you two, if I let you come, you'll have to do just what you are told. And I shall make other arrangements for the supply of intelligence.'

'Ah, now we know who really is important,' laughed Merry. 'Gandalf is never in doubt about that, and does not let anyone else

408   THE RETURN OF THE SHADOW

doubt it. So you are making all the arrangements already, are you?'

'Of course!' said Gandalf. 'But if you hobbits wish to stick together I shall raise no objection. You two and Sam can go – if you are really willing. Trotter would also be useful[33] – he has journeyed South before. Boromir may well join the company, since your road leads through his own land. That will be about as large a party as will be at all safe.'

'Who is to be the brains of the party?' asked Frodo. 'Trotter, I suppose. Boromir is only one of the Big Folk, and they are not as wise as hobbits.'

'Boromir has more than strength and valour,' answered Gandalf. 'He comes of an ancient race that the people of the Shire have not seen, at least not since days that they have forgotten. And Trotter has learned many things in his wanderings that are not known in the Shire.[34] They both know something of the road: but more than that will be needed. I think *I* shall have to come with you!'

So great was the delight of the hobbits at this announcement that Gandalf took off his hat and bowed. 'I am used to taking care of hobbits,' he said, 'when they wait for me and don't run off on their own. But I only said: I *think* I shall have to come. It may only be for part of the way. We have not made any definite plans yet. Very likely we shan't be able to make any.'

'How soon do you think we shall start?' asked Frodo.

'I don't know. It depends on what news we get. Scouts will have to go out and find out what they can – especially about the Black Riders.'

'I thought they were all destroyed in the flood!' said Merry.

'You cannot destroy the Ringwraiths so easily,' said Gandalf. 'The power of their master is in them, and they stand or fall by him. They were unhorsed, and unmasked, and will be less dangerous for a while; yet it would be well to find out if we can what they are doing. In time they will get new steeds and fresh disguise. But for the present you should put all troubles out of your thoughts, if you can.'

The hobbits did not find this easy to do. They continued to think and talk mainly of the journey and the perils ahead of them. Yet such was the virtue of the land of Elrond that in all their thoughts there came no shadow of fear. Hope and courage grew in their hearts, and strength in their bodies. In every meal, and in every word and song they found delight. The very breathing of the

IN THE HOUSE OF ELROND 409

air became a joy no less sweet because the time of their stay was short.

The days slipped by, though autumn was fast waning, and each morning dawned bright and fair. But slowly the golden light grew silver, and the leaves fell from the trees. The winds blew cold from the Misty Mountains in the East. The Hunters' Moon grew round in the evening sky, putting to flight the lesser stars, and glittering in the falls and pools of the River. But low in the South one star shone red. Every night as the moon waned again it shone brighter. Frodo could see it through his window deep in the sky, burning like a wrathful eye watching, and waiting for him to set out.

At the end of the text my father wrote: 'New Moon Oct. 24. Hunters' Moon Full Nov. 8'. See p. 434, note 19.

The manuscript is interrupted here by a heading, 'The Ring Goes South', but without new chapter number, and what follows was written continuously with what precedes.

It will be seen that by far the greater part of the content of the 'The Council of Elrond' in FR is absent; but while the past and present texture of the world is so much thinner in the original form, the discussion of what to do with the Ring is in its essential pattern of argument already present.

Gandalf says that the road to the Fiery Mountain lies through Boromir's land. It may well be that at this stage the geography of the lands south and east of the Misty Mountains was still fairly sketchy, even though Fangorn Forest, the Dead Marshes, the Land of Ond (Gondor), and 'the South Mountains' have appeared in name (pp. 397–8, 401). Further aspects of this question appear in the next chapter.

It is curious that although Elrond says at the outset that Boromir brings tidings that must be considered, we are not told what these tidings were. In the original draft for the Council (p. 398) it is said that the men of Ond 'are besieged by wild men out of the East'; and in the text just given (p. 403) Elrond says that they are 'still faithful amid a host of foes'.

Odo Bolger has at long last disappeared (at least by that name); and Folco has been renamed *Faramond*. That name has appeared in the papers dated August 1939, but there it was proposed for Frodo himself (p. 373). The Fellowship of the Ring now changes again, and not for the last time: as may readily be supposed, the achievement of the final composition of the 'Nine Walkers' caused my father great difficulty. In the first draft for the Council of Elro..d (p. 397) there were to be:

Gandalf. Trotter. Frodo. Sam. Merry. Folco. Odo. Glorfindel. Burin son of Balin. (9)

In the rejected page of the text just given (p. 406) the Company becomes:

Gandalf. Trotter. Frodo. Sam. Merry. Faramond. Glorfindel. (7)

A note to this page proposes that the Company consist only of hobbits,

410   THE RETURN OF THE SHADOW

with Gandalf at least at first, but without Glorfindel. In the replacement
text (p. 408) Gandalf suggests:

Gandalf. Trotter. Frodo. Sam. Merry. Faramond. Boromir. (7)
– and this was indeed the composition in the original narrative of the
southward journey as far as Moria.

The continuation of the story in the original manuscript ('The Ring
Goes South') is given in the next chapter; but before concluding this,
there must be given the remarkable outline of future events found on the
back of a rejected page of the text of the Council of Elrond (see p. 406).
This clearly belongs in time with the manuscript in which it is included.
In the outline of the further course of the story dated August 1939
(p. 381, §9) there is no suggestion of the reappearance of Gollum before
Mordor is reached; and the reference in this one to Frodo's hearing the
patter of Gollum's feet in the Mines shows that it preceded the first draft
of the Moria chapter.

Gollum must reappear at or after Moria. Frodo hears patter.

Fangorn Forest. In some way – hears voice, or sees something
off path, or ? alarmed by Gollum – Frodo must get separated from
the rest.

Fangorn is an evergreen (oak holly?) forest. Trees of *vast*
height. (*Beleghir* [*pencilled above: Anduin*] Great River divides
into many channels.) Say 500–1000 feet. It runs right up to the
[Blue >] Black Mountains, which are not very high (run NEN –
SWW [*i.e. North-east by North – South-west by West*]) but very
steep on N. side.

If Treebeard comes in at all – let him be kindly and rather good?
About 50 feet high with barky skin. Hair and beard rather like
twigs. Clothed in dark green like a mail of short shining leaves. He
has a castle in the Black Mountains and many thanes and followers.
They look like young trees [?when] they stand.

Make Frodo be terrified of Gollum after a meeting in which
Gollum pretended to make friends, but tried to strangle Frodo in
his sleep and steal the Ring. Treebeard finds him lost and carries
him up into the Black Mountains. It is only here that Frodo finds
he is friendly.

Treebeard brings him on the way to Ond. His scouts report that
Ond is besieged, and that Trotter and four [*written above:* 3?]
others have been captured. Where is Sam? (Sam is found in the
Forest. He had refused to go on without Frodo and had remained
looking for him.)

The tree-giants assail the besiegers and rescue Trotter &c. and
raise siege.

IN THE HOUSE OF ELROND   411

(If this plot is used it will be better to have no Boromir in party. Substitute Gimli? son of Glóin – who was killed in Moria. But Frodo can bear messages from Boromir to his father the K[ing] of Ond.)

Next stage – they set out for the Fire Mountain. They have to skirt Mordor on its west edge.

In this brief sketch we see the very starting-point, in written expression, of two fundamental 'moments' in the narrative of *The Lord of the Rings*: the separation of Frodo from the Company (subsequently rejoined by Sam), and the assault by the 'tree-giants' of Fangorn on the enemies of Gondor; but such narrative frame as they were given here was entirely ephemeral. We meet also a further early image of Giant Treebeard: still of vast height, as in the text given on pp. 382–4, where his voice came down to Frodo 'out of the tree-top', but no longer hostile, the captor of Gandalf (p. 363), 'pretending to be friendly but really in league with the enemy' (p. 384). Boromir is now said to be the son of the King of Ond; but the death of Gimli in Moria was an idea never further developed. Here is the first appearance of an Elvish name, *Beleghir*, of the Great River, which flowed through Fangorn Forest (see p. 410). The Forest 'runs right up to the [Blue >] Black Mountains'; cf. the outline for the Council of Elrond (p. 397), in which Gandalf says that Giant Treebeard 'haunts the Forest between the River and the South Mountains'. But of Lothlórien and Rohan there is as yet not a hint.

NOTES

1   The last sheet of the original chapter (see p. 213) had ended with the words 'a strong king whose realm included Esgaroth, and much land to the south of the great falls' at the foot of the page (numbered 'IX.8'), and the reverse was left blank. The first version of the continuation was written out (in a rapid scribble in ink) independently of the old text; the second, also very rough and nearly all in pencil, starts on the unused verso side of 'IX.8', on which however my father wrote in preparation 'IX.9', although at that time he did not use the page. When he returned to it later he did not change the chapter-number but continued the numeration 'IX.10' etc.; this however was mere absentmindedness, since the chapter could not possibly at this time still be numbered 'IX'.

2   The reference is to the end of *The Hobbit*; cf. p. 15 and note 3.

3   In the first version Glóin does not admit to any falling short of the skill of the forefathers: 'He began to speak of new inventions and of the great works at which the folk of the Mountain were now labouring; of armour of surpassing strength and beauty, swords more keen and strong . . .' – The sentence 'You should see the

412   THE RETURN OF THE SHADOW

waterways of Dale, Frodo, and the fountains and the pools!' goes
back to the first draft; in FR (p. 242) the word 'mountains' is an
obvious error which has never been corrected.

4   This name is found only in the first of the two texts, but it appears
later on in the second (p. 395).

5   Cf. pp. 211, 214, 363. – Peregrin disappeared out of the Shire when
he was 33, at which time Frodo was only two years old (see p. 387,
note 9).

6   When my father wrote this passage he evidently had in mind, at least
as one possibility, a comic song, received with the 'ringing laughter'
that wakened Frodo; for at the top of the page he wrote 'Troll Song'
– a passing idea before it was given far more appositely to Sam in the
Trollshaws. But he also wrote 'Let B[ilbo] sing *Tinúviel*', and the
word '?Messenger'. This is a reference to the poem *Errantry*
(published in *The Oxford Magazine* 9 November 1933, and with
many further changes in *The Adventures of Tom Bombadil* (1962)).
Bilbo's song *Eärendil was a mariner* derived (in a sense) from
Errantry, and the earliest text of it still begins:

> There was a merry messenger,
> a passenger, a mariner,
> he built a boat and gilded her
> and silver oars he fashioned her . . .

7   In the first text the dwarf with Glóin is named *Frár*; in the margin is
pencilled *Burin son of Balin*. Frár appears also in the outline for the
Council of Elrond on p. 397, again replaced by Burin.

8   The presence of an Elf of Mirkwood was an addition to the second
text.

9   As written, the first text read here: 'two of Elrond's own kinsfolk the
Pereldar or halfelven folk . . .' *Pereldar* was struck out, probably at
once. In the *Quenta Silmarillion* the *Pereldar* or 'Half-eldar' are the
Danas (Green-elves): V.215. The Danas were also called 'the
Lovers of Lúthien' (*ibid.*). In LR (Appendix A I (i)) Elros and
Elrond are called *Peredhil* 'Half-elven'; an earlier name for them was
Peringol, Peringiul (V.152).

10   The Grey Havens are first named in the third phase version of
'Ancient History', p. 319.

11   The square brackets are in the original.

12   As note 11.

13   The text stands thus, with two passages both beginning 'Yet of
late we have received secret messages from Mordor', but neither
rejected.

14   The name *Boromir* of the second son of Bor, killed in the Battle of
Unnumbered Tears, had appeared in the later *Annals of Beleriand*
and in the *Quenta Silmarillion* (V.134, 287, 310). For the
etymology of the name see V.353, 373.

IN THE HOUSE OF ELROND   413

15 This sentence is a subsequent correction of 'But the faces of those that were seated in the room were grave.' In a rejected opening of the text Gandalf says: 'We had better make our way to Elrond's chamber at once', and in the western wing of the house he knocks at a door and enters 'a small room, the western side of which opened onto a porch beyond which the ground fell sheer to the foaming river.' In the revised opening as printed the Council of Elrond takes place in the porch (as in FR, p. 252), though it was still described here as a 'room', until this correction was made.

16 This first appearance of Gimli son of Glóin was a pencilled alteration, but not from much later.

17 In the previous account of those present at the Council (p. 395) the three counsellors of Rivendell are Erestor, called 'an Elf', and 'two other kinsmen of Elrond, of that half-elvish folk whom the Elves named the children of Lúthien' – which seems however to imply that Erestor also was Elrond's kinsman.

18 In FR (p. 253) Galdor, here the precursor of Legolas, is the name of the Elf from the Grey Havens who bore the errand of Círdan. *Galdor* had not at this time become the name of the father of Húrin and Huor; in the *Quenta Silmarillion* he was still named *Gumlin*.

19 The first reference to the Dead Marshes.

20 My father bracketed the passage from 'Ever since I have worn shoes' to 'hurt in some way', and wrote in the margin (with a query) that it should be revealed later that Trotter had wooden feet. – This is the first appearance of the story that it was Trotter who found Gollum (in the version of 'Ancient History' in the third phase (p. 320) Gandalf still told Frodo that he had himself found Gollum, in Mirkwood); and Trotter's experience of Mordor, several times mentioned or hinted at (see pp. 223, 371), is explained at the same time.

21 Written in the margin against this paragraph: 'Gandalf's captivity'.

22 See pp. 118–20.

23 An earlier form of this passage makes Gandalf reply to Elrond: 'I knew of him. But I had quite forgotten him. I must go and see him as soon as there is a chance.' This was changed – at the time of writing – to the passage given, in which Gandalf says that he actually visited Tom Bombadil after the attack on Crickhollow – the first appearance of an idea that will be met again, though the meeting of Gandalf and Bombadil never (alas!) reached narrative form. Cf. the isolated passage given on pp. 213–14, where Gandalf says at Rivendell: 'Why did I not think of Bombadil before! If only he was not so far away, I would go straight back now and consult him.' Cf. also p. 345 and note 11. – Gandalf does not mention Odo here, and it becomes clear at the end of this chapter that he had been removed from Rivendell (see pp. 407, 409).

414   THE RETURN OF THE SHADOW

24 In the third phase version of 'At the Sign of the Prancing Pony' it is still apparent that Tom Bombadil was known to visit the inn at Bree (p. 334).

25 In rough drafting of this passage my father wrote: 'and in the end he would come in person; and the Barrow-wights would', striking out these last words as he wrote and changing them to: 'and even on his own ground Tom Bombadil alone could not withstand that onset unscathed.' – 'Lord of the Ring' was first written 'Lord of the Rings', but changed immediately.

26 *Erestor* changed from *Glorfindel*, which was changed from *Elrond*. Cf. p. 396.

27 This reply to Erestor was first given to Gandalf, for Erestor addressed his question to him: 'Can you solve this riddle, Gandalf?' To which Gandalf answered: 'No! I cannot. But I can choose, if you wish me to choose.' The passage was then changed at once to the form given.

28 In *The Hobbit* Thráin was not the father of Thrór, but his son. This is a complex question which will be discussed in Vol. VII.

29 In the dungeons of Dol Guldur in Mirkwood in FR (p. 282).

30 As this passage was first written, Glóin says that the messages from Mordor offered the Dwarves 'a ring'; and that they were offered peace and friendship if they could obtain Bilbo's ring, or even tell where he was to be found. As altered subsequently, his words approach what he tells in FR (p. 254); and the story in the first draft for the Council (p. 398), that the Dwarves still possessed some of their ancient Rings, that Dáin had one, and that Sauron was demanding them back, has already been abandoned.

31 Cf. p. 371, at the end of the outline §2.

32 The chapter 'The Council of Elrond' in FR (II.2) ends here.

33 'Trotter would also be useful' was changed to 'Trotter will also be essential'; and probably at the same time my father wrote in the margin: 'Trotter is connected with the Ring.' This alteration thus comes from somewhat later, when he was reaching the conception of Aragorn and his ancestry. See note 34.

34 Trotter was of course still a hobbit. In the margin my father wrote against this passage: 'Correct this. Only Trotter is of ancient race' (i.e. Trotter is a Númenórean, but Boromir is not).

XXIV

THE RING GOES SOUTH

As I have said, this next stage in the story was written continuously on from the first version of 'The Council of Elrond'. After the description of the red star in the South (FR p. 287) there is a heading 'The Ring Goes South', but no new chapter-number, and the pagination is continuous with what precedes.

I give now the text of this earliest version of 'The Ring Goes South' (which extends somewhat into the next chapter in FR, II.4 'A Journey in the Dark'). This is an outstandingly difficult manuscript, and difficult to represent. I think that it was *not* based on any preliminary notes or sketches, except in one passage,[1] that my father wrote it *ab initio* as a full narrative; and this being so it is remarkable how much of its wording survived into the final form, despite the radical differences that Trotter was still the hobbit Peregrin and that neither Dwarf nor Elf was present. The company, as already noticed, consisted of Gandalf, Boromir, and five hobbits – even though one of them, to be sure, was no inexperienced hobbit of the Shire.

My father wrote nearly all of it in ink, but he wrote extremely fast (though with patience – and some aid from the text of FR – all but a few words can be puzzled out), so fast that he often left to stand what he had written but rejected, while racing on to a new phrasing or formulation; and the expression is often rough and unfinished. Subsequently he went over it in pencil, but the great majority of these pencilled alterations belong, I feel sure, to a time very close to the original writing, and some of them demonstrably so. A few are certainly later, and introduce references to Gimli and Legolas that are chronologically and structurally irrelevant. There are also some alterations in red ink, but these only concern certain place-names.

In the text as printed here, I adopt pencilled alterations that seem certainly 'early': few affect the narrative in any important respect, and where they do the original text is given in the notes. The notes are here an integral part of the representation of the manuscript.

The Ring goes South

When Frodo had been about a fortnight in Rivendell and November was already a week old or more[2] the scouts began to return. Some had been northwards as far as the Dimrill-dales,[3] and some had gone southwards almost as far as the River Redway. A few

416   THE RETURN OF THE SHADOW

had passed the mountains both by the High Pass and Goblin Gate (Annerchin), and by the passage at the sources of the Gladden. These were the last to return, for they had descended into Wilderland as far as the Gladden Fields,[4] and that was a great way from Rivendell even for the swiftest Elves. But neither they nor those who had received the aid of the Eagles near Goblin 'Gate[5] had discovered any news – except that the wild wolves called wargs were gathering again and were hunting once more between the Mountains and Mirkwood. No sign of the Black Riders had been found – except on the rocks below the Ford the bodies of four [*written above:* several] drowned horses, and [?one] long black cloak slashed and tattered.

'One can never tell,' said Gandalf, 'but it does look as if the Riders were dispersed – and have had to make their way as best they could back to Mordor. In that case there will still be a long while before the hunt begins again. And it will have to come back here to pick up the trail – if we are lucky and careful, and they do not get news of us on the way. We had better get off as soon as possible now – and as quietly.'

Elrond agreed, and warned them to journey by dusk and dark as often as might be, and to lie hid when they could in the broad daylight. 'When the news reaches Sauron,' he said, 'of the discomfiture of the Nine Riders, he will be filled with a great anger. When the hunt begins again, it will be far greater and more ravenous.'

'Are there still more Black Riders then?' asked Frodo.

'No! There are but Nine Ringwraiths. But when they come forth again, I fear they will bring a host of evil things in their train, and set their spies wide over the lands. Even of the sky above you must beware as you go your way.'

There came a cold grey day in mid November.[6] The East wind was streaming through the bare branches of the trees, and seething in the firtrees on the hills. The hurrying clouds were low and sunless. As the cheerless shadows of the early evening began to fall, the adventurers made ready to depart. Their farewells had all been said by the fire in the great hall, and they were waiting only for Gandalf, who was still in the house speaking some last words in private with Elrond. Their spare food and clothes and other necessaries were laden on two sure-footed ponies. The travellers themselves were to go on foot; for their course was set through lands where there were few roads and paths were rough and

THE RING GOES SOUTH   417

difficult. Sooner or later they would have to cross the Mountains. Also they were going to journey for the most part by dusk or dark.[7] Sam was standing by the two pack-ponies sucking his teeth and staring moodily at the house – his desire for adventure was at a low ebb. But in that hour none of the hobbits had any heart for their journey – a chill was in their hearts, and a cold wind in their faces. A gleam of firelight came from the open doors; lights were glowing in many windows, and the world outside seemed empty and cold. Bilbo huddled in his cloak stood silent on the doorstep beside Frodo. Trotter sat with his head bowed to his knees.[8]

At last Elrond came out with Gandalf. 'Farewell now!' he said. 'May the blessing of Elves and Men and all free folk go with you. And may white stars shine on your journey!'

'Good . . . good luck!' said Bilbo, stuttering a little (from the cold perhaps). 'I don't suppose you will be able to keep a diary, Frodo my lad, but I shall expect a full account when you get back. And don't be too long: I have lived longer than I expected already. Farewell!'

Many others of Elrond's household stood in the shadows and watched them go, bidding them farewell with soft voices. There was no laughter, and no songs or music. Silently at last they turned away, and leading their ponies they faded swiftly into the gathering dusk.

They crossed the bridge and wound slowly up the long steep paths out of the cloven vale of Rivendell, and came at length to the high moors, grey and formless under misty stars. Then with one last look down at the lights of the Last Homely House below they strode on, far on into the night.

At the Ford they left the west road that crossed the River; and turning left went on by narrow paths among the folded lands. They were going South. Their purpose was to hold this course for many miles and days on the western side of the Misty Mountains. The country was much wilder and rougher than in the green valley of the Great River in Wilderland on the eastern side of the range and their going would be much slower; but they hoped in this way to escape the notice of enemies. The spies of Sauron had hitherto seldom been seen in the western regions; and the paths were little known except to the people of Rivendell. Gandalf walked in front and with him went Trotter who knew this country even in the dark. Boromir as rearguard walked behind.

The first part of their journey was cheerless and grim and Frodo

418   THE RETURN OF THE SHADOW

remembered little of it, except the cold wind. It blew icy from the
eastern mountains for many sunless days and no garment seemed
able to keep out its searching fingers. They had been well furnished with warm clothes in Rivendell, and had jackets and cloaks
lined with fur as well as many blankets, but they seldom felt warm
either moving or at rest. They slept uneasily during the middle of
the day, in some hollow of the land, or hidden under the tangled
thorn-bushes that grew in great thickets in those parts. In the late
afternoon they were roused, and had their chief meal: usually cold
and cheerless and with little talk, for they seldom risked the
lighting of a fire. In the evening they went on again, as nearly due
south as they could find a way.

At first it seemed to the hobbits that they were creeping like
snails and getting nowhere; for each day the land looked much as
it had done the day before. Yet all the while the Mountains which
south of Rivendell bent westward were drawing nearer. More and
more often they found no paths and had to make wide turns
to avoid either steep places, or thickets, or sullen treacherous
swamps. The land was tumbled in barren hills and deep valleys
filled with turbulent waters.

But when they had been about ten days on the road the weather
grew better. The wind suddenly veered southward. The swift
flowing clouds lifted and melted away, and the sun came out.

There came a dawn at the end of a long stumbling night march.
The travellers reached a low ridge crowned with ancient holly
trees, whose pale fluted trunks seemed to have been formed out of
the very stone of the hills. Their berries shone red in the light of
the rising sun. Far away south Frodo saw the dim shapes of
mountains, that seemed now to lie across their path. To the left of
this distant range a tall peak stood up like a tooth: it was tipped
with snow but its bare western shoulder glowed redly in the
growing light.

Gandalf stood by Frodo's side and looked out under his hand.
'We have done well,' he said. 'We have reached the borders of the
country called Hollin: many Elves lived here once in happier days.
Eighty leagues we have come,[9] if we have come a mile, and we have
marched quicker than winter from the North. The land and
weather will be milder now -- but perhaps all the more dangerous.'

'Danger or not, a real sunrise is mighty welcome,' said Frodo,
throwing back his hood and letting the morning light play on his
face.

THE RING GOES SOUTH   419

'Mountains ahead!' said Faramond. 'We seemed to have turned eastward.'

'No, it is the mountains that have turned,' said Gandalf.[10] 'Don't you remember Elrond's map in Rivendell?'

'No, I did not look very carefully at it,' said Faramond. 'Frodo has a better head for things of that sort.'

'Well, anyone who did look at the map,' said Gandalf, 'would see that away there stands Taragaer or Ruddyhorn,[11] – that mountain with the red side. The Misty Mountains divide there and between their arms lies the land[12] of Caron-dûn the Red Valley.[13] Our way lies there: over the Red Pass of Cris-caron,[14] under Taragaer's side, and into Caron-dûn and down the River Redway[15] – to the Great River, and . . .' He stopped.

'Yes, and where then?' asked Merry.

'To the end of the journey – in the end,' said Gandalf. 'But at first the evergreen forest of Fangorn, through the midst of which runs the Great River.[16] But we will not look too far ahead. Let us be glad that the first stage is safely over. I think we will rest here for a whole day. There is a wholesome air about Hollin. Much evil must befall any country before it wholly forgets the Elves, if once they have dwelt there.'

That morning they lit a fire in a deep hollow shrouded by two great holly trees, and their supper was merrier than it had been since they left the house of Elrond. They did not hurry to bed afterwards, for they had all the night to sleep in and did not mean to go on until the evening of next day. Only Trotter was moody and restless. After a while he left the company and wandered about on the ridge, looking out on the lands south and west. He came back and stood looking at them.

'What is the matter?' said Merry. 'Do you miss the east wind?'

'No indeed,' answered Trotter. 'But I miss something. I know Hollin fairly well, and have been here in many seasons. No people dwell here now, but many other things live here, or used to – especially birds. But now it is very silent. I can feel it. There is no sound for miles round, and your voices seem to make the ground echo. I cannot make it out.'

Gandalf looked up quickly. 'But what do you *think* the reason is?' he asked. 'Is there more in it than surprise at seeing a whole party of hobbits (not to mention Boromir and me) where people are so seldom seen?'

'I hope that is it,' said Trotter. 'But I get a feeling of watchfulness and of fear that I have never had here before.'

'Very well! Let us be more careful,' said Gandalf. 'If you bring a Ranger with you, it is best to pay attention to him – especially if the Ranger is Trotter, as I have found before. There are some things that even an experienced wizard does not notice. We had better stop talking now, and rest quietly and set a look-out.'

It was Sam's turn to take the first watch, but Trotter joined him. The others soon fell asleep, one by one. The silence grew till even Sam felt it. The breathing of the sleepers could be plainly heard. The swish of a pony's tail and the occasional movements of his feet became loud noises. Sam seemed to hear his very joints creaking if he stirred or moved. Over all hung a blue sky as the sun rode high and clear. The last clouds melted. But away in the south-east a dark patch grew and divided, flying like smoke to the north and west.

'What's that?' said Sam in a whisper to Trotter. Trotter made no answer, for he was gazing intently at the sky, but before long Sam could see what it was for himself. The clouds were flocks of birds going at great speed – wheeling and circling, and traversing all the land as if they were searching for something.

'Lie flat and still,' hissed Trotter, drawing Sam down into the shade of a holly-bush – for a whole regiment of birds had separated from the western flock and came back flying low right over the ridge where the travellers lay. Sam thought they were some kind of crows of a large size. As they passed overhead one harsh croak was heard.

Not till they had dwindled in the distance would Trotter move. Then he went and wakened Gandalf.

'Regiments of black crows are flying to and fro over Hollin,' he said. 'They are not natives to this place. I do not know what they are after – possibly there is some trouble going on away south: but I think they are spying out the land. I think too that I have seen hawks flying higher in the sky. That would account for the silence.[17] We ought to move again this evening. I am afraid that Hollin is no longer wholesome for us: it is being watched.'

'And in that case so is the Red Pass, and how we can get over it without being seen I don't know,' said Gandalf. 'But we will think about that when we get nearer. About moving on from here tonight: I am afraid you are right.'

'It is as well that we let our fire make little smoke,' said Trotter.

THE RING GOES SOUTH 421

'It was out again (I think) before the birds came over. It must not be lit again.'

'Well, if that is not disappointing!' said Faramond. The news had been broken to him as soon as he woke (in the late afternoon): no fire, and a move again by night. 'I had looked forward to a real good meal tonight, something hot. All because of a pack of crows!'

'Well, you can go on looking forward,' said Gandalf. 'There may be many unexpected feasts ahead of you! Personally I should like a pipe of tobacco in comfort, and warmer feet. However, we are certain of one thing, at any rate: it will get warmer as we go south.'

'Too warm, I shouldn't wonder!' said Sam to Frodo. 'Not but what I would be glad to see that Fiery Mountain, and see the road's end ahead, so to speak. I thought that there Ruddyhorn or whatever its name is might be it, till Mr. Gandalf said not.' Maps conveyed nothing to Sam, and all distances in these strange lands seemed so vast that he was quite out of his reckonings.

The travellers remained hidden all that day. The birds passed over every now and again; but as the westering sun grew red they vanished southwards.[18] Soon afterwards the party set out again; and turned now a little eastward making for the peak of Taragaer which still glowed dully red in the distance. Frodo thought of Elrond's warning to watch even the sky above, but the sky was now clear and empty overhead, and one by one white stars sprang forth as the last gleams of sunset faded.

Guided by Trotter and Gandalf as usual they struck a good path. It looked to Frodo, as far as he could guess in the gathering dark, like the remains of an ancient road that had once run broad and well-planned from now deserted Hollin to the pass beneath Taragaer. A crescent moon rose over the mountains, and cast a pale light which was helpful – but was not welcomed by Trotter or Gandalf. It stayed but a little while and left them to the stars.[19] At midnight they had been going on again for an hour or more from their first halt. Frodo kept looking up at the sky, partly because of its beauty, partly because of Elrond's words. Suddenly he saw or felt a shadow pass over the stars – as if they faded and flashed out again. He shivered.

'Did you see anything?' he said to Gandalf, who was just in front.

'No, but I felt it, whatever it was,' said the wizard. 'It *may* be

422   THE RETURN OF THE SHADOW

nothing, just a wisp of thin cloud.' It did not sound as if he thought much of his own explanation.[20]

Nothing more happened that night. The next morning was even brighter than before, but the wind was turning back eastward and the air was chill. For three more nights they marched on, climbing steadily and ever more slowly as their road wound into the hills and the mountains drew nearer and nearer. On the third morning Taragaer towered up before them, a mighty peak tipped with snow like silver, but with sheer naked sides dull red as if stained with blood.

There was a black look in the air, and the sun was wan. The wind was now gone towards the North. Gandalf sniffed and looked back. 'Winter is behind,' he said quietly to Trotter. 'The peaks behind are whiter than they were.'

'And tonight,' said Trotter, 'we shall be high up on our way to the red pass of Cris-caron. What do you think of our course now? If we are not seen in that narrow place – and waylaid by some evil, as would be easy there – the weather may prove as bad an enemy.'[21]

'I think no good of any part of our course, as you know well, Master Peregrin,' snapped Gandalf. 'Still we have to go on. It is no good whatever our trying to cross further south into the land of Rohan. The Horse-kings have long been in the service of Sauron.'[22]

'No, I know that. But there is a way – not *over* Cris-caron, as you are well aware.'

'Of course I am. But I am not going to risk that, until I am quite sure there is no other way. I shall think things out while the others rest and sleep.'[23]

In the late afternoon, before preparations were made for moving, Gandalf spoke to the travellers. 'We have now come to our first serious difficulty and doubt,' he said. 'The pass that we ought to take is up there ahead' – he waved his hand towards Taragaer: its sides were now dark and sullen, for the sun had gone, and its head was in grey cloud. 'It will take us at least two marches to get near the top of the pass. From certain signs we have seen recently I fear it may be watched or guarded; and in any case Trotter and I have doubts of the weather, on this wind. But I am afraid we must go on. We can't go back into the winter; and further south the passes are held. Tonight we must push along as hard as we can.'

The hearts of the travellers sank at his words. But they hurried

THE RING GOES SOUTH 423

with their preparations, and started off at as good a pace as they could make. It was heavy going.[24] The winding and twisting road had long been neglected and in places was blocked with fallen stones, over which they had great difficulty in finding any way to lead the pack ponies.[25] The night grew deadly dark under the great clouds; a bitter wind swirled among the rocks. By midnight they had already climbed to the very knees of the great mountains, and were going straight up under a mountain-side, with a deep ravine guessed but unseen on their right. Suddenly Frodo felt soft cold touches on his face. He put out his arm, and saw white snowflakes settle on his sleeve. Before long they were falling fast, swirling from every direction into his eyes, and filling all the air. The dark shapes of Gandalf and Trotter, a few paces in front, could hardly be seen.

'I don't like this,' panted Sam just behind. 'Snow is all right on a fine morning, seen from a window; but I like to be in bed while it's falling.' As a matter of fact snow fell very seldom in most parts of the Shire except the moors of the Northfarthing. There would occasionally, in January or February, be a thin white dusting of it, but [it] soon vanished, and only rarely in cold winters was there a real fall – enough to make snowballs of.

Gandalf halted. Frodo thought as he came up by him that he already looked almost like a snow-man. Snow was white on his hood and bowed shoulders, and it was already getting thick on the ground under foot.

'This is a bad business!' said the wizard. 'I never bargained for this, and left snow out of my plans. It seldom falls as far south as this except on the high peaks, and here we are not halfway up even to the high pass. I wonder if the Enemy has anything to do with it. He has strange powers and many allies.'

'We had better get all the party together,' said Trotter. 'We don't want to lose anyone on a night like this.'

For a while they struggled on. The snow became a blinding blizzard, and soon it was in places almost knee-deep. 'It'll be up over my head before long,' said Merry. Faramond was dragging behind and needed what help Merry and Sam could give him. Frodo felt his own legs like lead at every step.

Suddenly they heard strange sounds: they may have been but tricks of the rising wind in cracks and gullies of the rocks, but it sounded like hoarse cries and howls of harsh laughter. Then stones began to fall whirling like leaves on the wind, and crashing onto the path and the rocks on either hand. Every now and again

424   THE RETURN OF THE SHADOW

they heard in the darkness a dull rumble as a great boulder rolled down thunderously from hidden heights in the dark above.

The party halted. 'We can't get any further tonight,' said Trotter. 'You can call it the wind if you like, but I call it voices and those stones are aimed at us, or at least at the path.'

'I do call it the wind,' said Gandalf; 'but that does not make the rest untrue. Not all the servants of the Enemy have bodies or arms and legs.'[26]

'What can we do?' asked Frodo. His heart suddenly failed him, and he felt alone and lost in dark and driving snow, mocked at by demons of the mountains.

'Stop here or go back,' answered Gandalf. 'We are protected at present by the high wall on our left, and a deep gully on the right. Further up there is a wide shallow valley, and the road runs at the bottom of two long slopes. We should now hardly get through there without damage, quite apart from the snow.'[27]

After some debate they retreated to a spot they had passed just before the snow came on. There the path passed under a low overhanging cliff. It faced southwards and they hoped it would give them some protection from the wind. But the eddying blasts whirled in from either side, and the snow came down thicker than ever. They huddled together with their backs to the wall. The two ponies stood dejected but patiently in front of them and served as some kind of screen, but before long the snow was up to their bellies and still mounting. The hobbits crouching behind were nearly buried. A great sleepiness came over Frodo, and he felt himself fast sinking into a warm and hazy dream. He thought a fire was warming his toes, and out of the shadows he heard Bilbo's voice speaking. 'I don't think much of your diary,' he heard him say. 'Snow(storm) on December 2nd:[28] there was no need to come back to report that.'

Suddenly he felt himself violently shaken, and came back painfully to wakefulness. Boromir had lifted him right off the ground. 'This snow will be the death of the hobbits, Gandalf,' he said. 'We must do something.'

'Give them this,' said Gandalf, fumbling in his pack that lay beside him, and drawing out a leather flagon. 'Just a little each – for all of us. It is very precious: one of Elrond's cordials, and I did not expect to have to use it so soon.'

As soon as Frodo had swallowed a little of the potent cordial, he felt new strength of heart, and the heavy sleepiness left his limbs. The others revived as quickly.

THE RING GOES SOUTH 425

Boromir now endeavoured to clear away the snow and make a free space under the rock-wall. Finding his hands and feet slow tools, and his sword not much better, he took a faggot from the fuel that they carried on one of the ponies, in case they should need fire in places where there was no wood. He bound it tight and thrust a staff in the midst, so that it looked like a large mallet; but he used it as a ram to thrust back the soft snow, till it was packed hard into a wall before them and could not be pushed further away. For the moment things looked better, and in the small cleared space the travellers stood and took short paces, stamping to keep their limbs awake. But the snow continued to fall unrelenting; and it became plain that they were likely enough to be all buried in snow again before the night was out.[29]

'What about a fire?' said Trotter suddenly. 'As for giving ourselves away: personally I think our whereabouts is pretty well known or guessed already – by somebody.'

In desperation they decided to light a fire if they could, even if it meant sacrificing all the fuel that they had with them. It taxed even Gandalf's power to kindle the wet wood in that windy place. Ordinary methods were of no use, though each of the travellers had tinder and flint. They had brought some fir cones and little bundles of dried grass for kindling, but no fire would catch in them, until Gandalf thrust his wand into the midst of them and caused a great spark of blue and green flame to spring out.

'Well, if any enemy is watching,' he said, 'that will give *me* away. Let us hope other eyes are as blinded by the storm as ours. But anyway a fire is a good thing to see.' The wood now burned merrily and kept a clear circle all round it in which the travellers gathered somewhat heartened; but looking round Gandalf saw anxious eyes revealed by the dancing flames. The wood was burning fast, and the snow was not yet lessening.

'Daylight will soon be showing,' said Gandalf as cheerily as he could, but added: 'if any daylight can get through the snow-clouds.'

The fire burned low and the last faggot was thrown on. Trotter stood up and stared into the blackness above. 'I believe it is getting less,' he said. For a long while the others gazed at the flakes coming . . . . . down out of the darkness, to be revealed for a moment white in the light of the fire; but they could see little difference. After a while, however, it became plain that Trotter was right. The flakes became fewer and fewer. The wind grew less. The daylight began to grow pale grey and diffused. Then the snow ceased altogether.

426   THE RETURN OF THE SHADOW

As the light grew stronger it showed a shapeless world all about them. The high places were hid in clouds (that threatened still more snow), but below them they could see dim white hills and domes and valleys in which the path they had come by seemed altogether lost.

'The sooner we make a move, and get down again, the better,' said Trotter.[30] 'There is more snow still to fall up here!' But much as they all desired to get down again it was easier to speak of it than to manage it. The snow round about was already some feet deep: up to the necks of the hobbits or over their heads in places; and it was still soft. If they had [had] northern sledges or snowshoes [they] would have been of little use. Gandalf could only just manage to get forward with labour, more like swimming (and burrowing) than walking. Boromir was the tallest of the party: being some six feet high and broad-shouldered as well. He went ahead a little way to test the path. The snow was everywhere above even his knees, and in many places he sank up to the waist. The situation looked fairly desperate.

'I will go on down if I can,' he said.[31] 'As far as I can make out our course of last night, the path seems to turn right round a shoulder of rock down there. And if I remember rightly, a furlong or two below the turn we ought to come on to a flat space at the top of a long steep slope – very heavy going it was coming up. From there I may be able to get some view and some idea of how the snow lies further down.' He struggled forward slowly, and after a while disappeared round the turn.

It was nearly an hour before he came back, tired but with some encouraging news. 'There is a deep wind drift just the other side of the turn, and I was nearly buried in it; but beyond that the snow quickly gets less. At the top of the slope it is no more than ankle-deep and it is only sprinkled on the ground from there down: or so it seems.'

'It may be only sprinkled further down,' grunted Gandalf; 'but it is not sprinkled up here. Even the snow seems to have been aimed specially at us.'

'How are *we* to get to the turn?' asked Trotter.

'I don't know!' said Boromir. 'It is a pity Gandalf can't produce flame enough to melt us a pathway.'

'I daresay it is,' snapped Gandalf; 'but even I need a few materials to work upon. I can kindle fire not feed it. What you want is a dragon not a wizard.'

'Indeed I think a tame dragon would actually be more useful at

THE RING GOES SOUTH   427

the moment than a wild wizard,' said Boromir – with a laugh that
did not in any way appease Gandalf.

'At the moment, at the moment,' he replied. 'Later on we may
see. I am old enough to be your great-grandfather's ancestor – but
I am not doddery yet. It will serve you right if you meet a wild
dragon.'[32]

'Well, well! *When heads are at a loss bodies must serve* they say
in my country,' said Boromir. 'We must just try and thrust our
way through. Put the little folk on the ponies, two on each. I will
carry the smallest; you go behind, Gandalf, and I will go in front.'

At once he set about unloading the ponies of their burdens. 'I
will come back for these when we have forced a passage,' he said.
Frodo and Sam were mounted on one of the ponies, Merry and
Trotter on the other. Then picking up Faramond Boromir strode
forward.

Slowly they ploughed their way forward. It took some time to
reach the bend, but they did so without mishap. After a short halt
they laboured on to the edge of the drift. Suddenly Boromir
stumbled on some hidden stone, and fell headlong. Faramond was
thrown from his shoulder into deep snow and disappeared. The
pony behind reared and then fell also, tumbling both Frodo and
Sam into the drift. Trotter however managed to hold back the
second pony.

For some moments all was confusion. But Boromir got up,
shaking the snow from his face and eyes, and went to the head of
the floundering and kicking pony. When he had got it onto its feet
again, he went to the rescue of the hobbits who had vanished into
deep holes in the yielding snow. Picking up first Faramond and
then Frodo he ploughed his way through the remainder of the
drift and set them on their feet beyond. He then returned for the
pony and Sam. 'Follow now in my track!' he cried to the remaining three. 'The worst is over!'

At last they all came to the head of the long slope. Gandalf
bowed to Boromir. 'If I was testy,' he said, 'forgive me. Even the
wisest wizard does not like to see his plans go awry. Thank
goodness for plain strength and good sense. We are grateful to
you, Boromir of Ond.'[33]

They looked out from the high place where they stood over the
lands. Daylight was now as full as it would be, unless the heavy
clouds were broken. Far below, and over the tumbled country
falling away from the foot of the incline, Frodo thought he could
see the dell from which they had started to climb the night before.

428   THE RETURN OF THE SHADOW

His legs ached and his head was dizzy as he thought of the long painful march down again. In the distance, below him but still high above the lower hills, he saw many black specks moving in the air. 'The birds again,' he said in a low voice, pointing.

'It can't be helped now, said Gandalf. 'Whether they are good or bad, or nothing to do with us, we must go on down at once.' The wind was blowing stiffly again over the pass hidden in the clouds behind; and already some snowflakes were drifting down.

It was late in the afternoon, and the grey light was already again waning fast when they got back to their camp of the previous night. They were weary and very hungry. The mountains were veiled in a deepening dusk full of snow: even there in the foothills snow was falling gently. The birds had vanished.

They had no fuel for a fire, and made themselves as warm as they could with all their spare furs and blankets. Gandalf spared them each one more mouthful of the cordial. When they had eaten, Gandalf called a council.

'We cannot of course go on again tonight,' he said. 'We all need a good rest, and I think we had better stay here till tomorrow evening.'

'And when we move where are we to go to?' asked Frodo. 'It is no use trying the pass again; but you said yourself last night in this very spot that we could not now cross the passes further north because of winter, nor further south because of enemies.'

'There is no need to remind me,' said Gandalf. 'The choice is now between going on with our journey – by some road or other – or returning to Rivendell.'

The faces of the hobbits revealed plainly enough the pleasure they felt at the mere mention of returning to Rivendell. Sam's face brightened visibly, and he glanced at his master. But Frodo looked troubled.

'I wish I was back in Rivendell,' he acknowledged. 'But would not that be going back also on all that was spoken and decided there?' he asked.

'Yes,' replied Gandalf. 'Our journey was already delayed perhaps too long. After the winter it would be quite vain. If we return it will mean the siege of Rivendell, and likely enough its fall and destruction.'

'Then we must go on,' said Frodo with a sigh, and Sam sank back into gloom. 'We must go on – if there is any road to take.'

'There is, or there may be,' said Gandalf. 'But I have not mentioned it to you before, and have hardly even thought of it

THE RING GOES SOUTH

while there was hope of the pass of Cris-caron. For it is not a pleasant road.'

'If it is worse than the pass of Cris-caron it must be very nasty indeed,' said Merry. 'But you had better now tell us about it.'

'Have you ever heard of the Mines of Moria or the Black Gulf?'[34] asked Gandalf.

'Yes,' answered Frodo. 'I think so. I seem to remember Bilbo speaking of them long ago, when he told me tales of the dwarves and goblins. But I have no idea where they are.'

'They are not far away,' said the wizard. 'They are in these mountains. They were made by the Dwarves of Durin's clan many hundreds of years ago, when elves dwelt in Hollin, and there was peace between the two races. In those ancient days Durin dwelt in Caron-dûn, and there was traffic on the Great River. But the Goblins – fierce orcs[35] in great number – drove them out after many wars, and most of the dwarves that escaped removed far into the North. They have often tried to regain these mines, but never so far as I know have they succeeded. King Thrór was killed there after he fled from Dale when the dragon came, as you may remember from Bilbo's tales. As Glóin told us, the dwarves of Dale think Balin came here, but no news has come from him.'[36]

'How can the mines [of the] Black Gulf help us?' asked Boromir. 'It sounds a name of ill-omen.'

'It is so, or has become so,' answered Gandalf. 'But one must tread the path need chooses. If there are orcs in the mines, it will prove ill for us. But most of the goblins of the Misty Mountains were destroyed in the Battle of Five Armies at the Lonely Mountain. There is a chance that the mines are still deserted. There is even a chance that dwarves are there, and that Balin lives in secret in some deep hall. If either of these chances prove true, then we may get through. For the mines go right through and under this western arm of the mountains. The tunnels of Moria were of old the most famous in the northern world. There were two secret gates on the western side, though the chief entrance was on the East looking upon Caron-dûn.[37] I passed right through, many years ago, when I was looking for Thrór and Thráin. But I have never been since – I have never wished to repeat the experience.'[38]

'And I don't wish for it even once,' said Merry. 'Nor me,' muttered Sam.

'Of course not,' said Gandalf. 'Who would? But the question is, will you follow me, if I take the risk?'

430   THE RETURN OF THE SHADOW

There was no answer for some time. 'How far are the western gates?' asked Frodo at length.

'About ten[39] miles south of Cris-caron,' said Trotter.

'Then you know of Moria?' said Frodo, looking at him in surprise.

'Yes, I know of the mines,' said Trotter quietly. 'I went there once, and the memory is evil; but if you want to know, I was always in favour of trying that way rather than an open pass.[40] I will follow Gandalf – though I should have followed him more willingly if we could have come to the gate of Moria more secretly.'

'Well, come now,' said Gandalf. 'I would not put such a choice to you, if there were any hope in other roads, or any hope in retreat. Will you try Moria, or go back to Rivendell?'

'We must risk the Mines,' said Frodo.

As I have said, it is remarkable how substantially the structure of the story was achieved at the very beginning, while the differences in the *dramatis personae* are so great. It is indeed very curious, that before my father had even written the first complete draft of 'The Council of Elrond' he had decided that the Company should include an Elf and a Dwarf (p. 397), as seems now so natural and inevitable, and yet in 'The Ring Goes South' we have only Gandalf and Boromir and five hobbits (one of whom, admittedly, is the most unusually far-travelled and widely experienced Trotter).

But as often in the history of *The Lord of the Rings* much of the earliest writing remained, for example in the detail of conversation, and yet such conversation appears later shifted into new contexts, given to different speakers, and acquiring new resonance as the 'world' and its history grew and expanded. A striking example is given in note 8, where in the original text 'Trotter sat with his head bowed to his knees' as they waited to depart from Rivendell, while in FR 'Aragorn sat with his head bowed to his knees; *only Elrond knew fully what this hour meant to him.*' The question presents itself: what is really the relation between Trotter = Peregrin Boffin and Strider = Aragorn?

It would obviously not be true to say merely that there was a rôle to be played in the story, and that at first this rôle was played by a Hobbit but afterwards by a Man. In particular cases, looked at narrowly without the larger context, this might seem a sufficient or nearly sufficient account: the necessary or fixed action was that Sam Gamgee's companion should hiss 'Lie flat and still' and pull him down into the shade of a holly-bush (p. 420, FR p. 298). But this says very little. I would be inclined to think that the original figure (the mysterious person who encounters the hobbits in the inn at Bree) was capable of development in different directions without losing important elements of his 'identity' as a recognisable character – even though the choice of one direction or another

THE RING GOES SOUTH 431

would lead to quite different historical and racial 'identities' in Middle-earth. So Trotter was not simply switched from Hobbit to Man – though such a switch could take place in the case of Mr. Butterbur with very little disturbance. Rather, he had been potentially Aragorn for a long time; and when my father decided that Trotter *was* Aragorn and *was not* Peregrin Boffin his stature and his history were totally changed, but a great deal of the 'indivisible' Trotter remained in Aragorn and determined his nature.

It may also be thought that in the story of the attempt on Cris-caron Trotter is diminished from the rôle he had played in the narrative of the journey from Bree to Rivendell, in which, though a hobbit, he is set altogether apart from the others, a wise and resourceful leader of great experience in whom all their hope rests. Now, in these physical circumstances, and beside Boromir, he is one of the helpless 'little folk', as Boromir says, to be set on a pony. Of course, this question cannot be approached without hindsight; if Trotter had in fact remained a hobbit in *The Lord of the Rings* it would not arise. Yet considerations along these lines may have been an element in the decision about him which my father would now shortly take.

NOTES

1 An isolated page, certainly of this time, does give a preliminary sketch of the passage that begins approximately at 'As the light grew stronger' on p. 426. The writing is at the extreme limit of legibility, in rapid pencil now very faint.

Grey light grew revealing a snow . . . world in which the path by which they had climbed could scarcely be seen. The snow was no longer falling but the sky threatened more to come.

'The sooner we move and begin to get down the better,' said Gandalf. This was easier said than done. Hobbits. One on each journey. [*Struck out:* Boromir carries Frodo (. . precious burden).] Boromir and Gandalf go ahead and feel the way. In places Boromir vanished almost to his neck. They began to despair for the snow was soft. . . . . With great labour they had gone only ¼ mile down and were all getting exhausted. But suddenly they found the snow less thick – 'even that seems to have been specially aimed at us' said Gandalf. Boromir strode ahead and came back reporting that it was [?soon only white]. At last when daylight was broad they came back to places almost clear of snow.

G. points out the place they had started from the evening before. Council. What is to be done. Moria.

The page continues with some preliminary strokes for the scene outside the West Gate of Moria; see p. 444.

432 THE RETURN OF THE SHADOW

2 Dates were put in marginally against this sentence: 'Nov. 7th?' and 'Nov. 10–11'; in addition, 'a fortnight' was changed to '3 weeks' and 'a week old or more' to 'nearly 2 weeks old'.

3 After 'as far as' my father first wrote *Dimbar*, perhaps intending 'Dimbar in the Dimrill-dales'. The name *Dimbar* had appeared in the *Quenta Silmarillion* (V.261), of the empty land between the rivers Sirion and Mindeb.

For this application of *Dimrill-dale(s)* (north of Rivendell) see p. 360. When the name *Dimrill-dale* was transferred southwards and to the other side of the Misty Mountains it was replaced in the north by *Hoardale*, and this name was pencilled later on the text here.

4 This is the first occurrence of the names *Gladden* (River) and *Gladden* Fields. The river had been shown on the Map of Wilderland in *The Hobbit*, with marshy land at its confluence with the Great River, suggesting a region where 'gladdens' would grow.

At the foot of the page is a note that applies to the names in this passage: 'These names are given in Hobbit [fashion >] translation. Their real names were *Tum Dincelon*; *Arad Dain (Annerchin)*; *Crandir* Redway; and *Palathrin (Palath* = Iris).' *Tum Dincelon* is *Dimrill-dale*, in the original application (note 3). I do not understand the reference of '*Arad Dain (Annerchin)*'. My father first wrote *Tar* and struck it out before writing *Arad*. For the names of the River Redway see note 15. In the *Etymologies* the Noldorin word *palath* = 'surface' (V.380).

5 Cf. the Map of Wilderland in *The Hobbit*; 'Goblin Gate and Eyrie.'

6 According to *The Tale of Years* in LR (Appendix B) the Company left Rivendell on 25 December.

7 This passage was rewritten over and over again, and it is impossible to interpret the sequence precisely: but it is clear that my father first envisaged the Company as mounted, with Boromir's 'great brown horse', Gandalf's white horse, and seven ponies, five for the five hobbits, and two pack-animals (see note 25). An intermediate stage saw Boromir alone on foot: 'There were ponies for all the hobbits to ride where the road allowed, and Gandalf of course had his horse; but Boromir strode on foot, as he had come. The men of his race did not ride horses.' The text printed is certainly the final formulation at this stage, and is of course different from that in FR (p. 293), where the sole beast of burden was Bill Ferny's pony, whom Sam called Bill.

8 Cf. FR p. 293: 'Aragorn sat with his head bowed to his knees; only Elrond knew fully what this hour meant to him.' See p. 430.

9 This is the first occurrence of *Hollin*; but the Elvish name *Eregion* does not appear. In the *Etymologies* (V.356) the Elvish name of Hollin is *Regornion*. – In FR (p. 296) Gandalf says that they have

THE RING GOES SOUTH
433

come 45 leagues, but that was as the crow flies: 'many long miles further our feet have walked.'

10 See the Note on Geography, pp. 440–1.

11 At the first occurrence the name of the 'red horn mountain' was replaced over and over again: first it was *Bliscarn*, then *Carnbeleg* or *Ruddyhorn*, then *Taragaer* (see the *Etymologies*, V.391); also written on the margins of the page are *Caradras = Ruddihorn*, and *Rhascaron*. All these names appear on the contemporary map (p. 439). At the next occurrence *Carnbeleg* was replaced by *Taragaer*, and subsequently the name first written was *Caradras* replaced by *Taragaer*, and finally *Taragaer*. I give *Taragaer* throughout, as being apparently the preferred name at this stage. Changes made in red ink at some later stage brought back *Caradras*.

12 On the dividing of the Misty Mountains into an eastern and a western arm see the Note on Geography, p. 438. My father wrote here first 'the great vale', and the replacement word is probably but not certainly 'land'.

13 The name of the vale was first *Carndoom the Red Valley*; above was written *Carondûn* and *Doon-Caron*, but these were struck out. Elsewhere on this page is *Narodûm = Red Vale*; and the name in the text was corrected in red ink to *Dimrill-dale: Nanduhiriath* (in FR *Nanduhirion*). On the former application of *Dimrill-dale* see note 3. At subsequent occurrences the name is *Carndoom*, *Caron-doom*, *Caron-dûn*, *Dûn Caron*, and at the last the name was replaced in red ink by *Glassmere in Dimrilldale* (note 37). Among these forms, all meaning 'Red Valley', I have rather arbitrarily chosen *Caron-dûn* to stand as the consistent form in the text.

14 The name of the pass was first written *Criscarn*, with *Cris-caron* as a rejected alternative; at subsequent occurrences both appear, but with the preference to *Cris-caron* (also *Cris-carron*, *Cris Caron*), which I adopt. *Dimrill-stair* replaces it twice in red ink, in the present passage thus: 'over the pass that was [*read* is] called Dimrill-stair (*Pendrethdulur*) under the side of Caradras.' The pass was afterwards called the Redhorn Gate, the Dimrill-stair being the descent from the pass on the eastern side; cf. note 21. With *Pendrethdulur* cf. the *Etymologies*, V.380, *pendrath* 'passage up or down a slope, stairway'.

15 The River Redway, the later Silverlode, has been referred to in an outline dated August 1939 (p. 381), and at its occurrence at the beginning of the chapter the Elvish name *Crandir* is given (note 4). Here, above *Redway*, are written the names *Rathgarn* (struck out); *Rathcarn*; *Nenning* (struck out); and *Caradras or Redway*. Written in the margin is also *Narosîr = Redway*. At this time *Nenning* had not yet appeared in *The Silmarillion* and the *Annals of Beleriand* as the name of the river in Beleriand west of Narog, which was

434   THE RETURN OF THE SHADOW

still called *Eglor*. In red ink the name *Celebrin* was substituted (*Celebrant* in FR). The river is called *Caradras* on the contemporary map (p. 439).

16 It was said in the outline given on p. 410 that Beleghir the Great River divided into many channels in Fangorn Forest. See the map, p. 439.

17 While in FR (p. 298) Aragorn says that he has seen hawks flying high up, he does not say, as Trotter does here, 'That would account for the silence.'

18 *southwards:* changed in pencil from *northwards*.

19 It was now 28 November (since they walked for three nights after this and attempted Cris-caron on 2 December, pp. 422, 424). In notes on phases of the Moon (found on the back of a page in the previous section of this manuscript) my father gave the following dates, showing that on the night of the 28th the Moon was in its first quarter:

Last Quarter	New Moon	First Quarter	Full Moon
Sept. 18	Sept. 25	Oct. 2	Oct. 10
Oct. 17	Oct. 24	Oct. 31	Nov. 8
Nov. 15	Nov. 22	Nov. 29	Dec. 7

20 This incident was retained in FR, but it is not explained. The Winged Nazgûl had not yet crossed the River (*The Two Towers* pp. 101, 201).

21 As written in ink, and before changes in pencil produced the passage given, Gandalf said: 'Winter is behind. There is snow coming. In fact it has come. The peaks behind are whiter than they were.' Trotter's reply is the same, but he ends: 'we may get caught in a blizzard before we get over the pass.' In the margin my father wrote: '? Cut out prophecy of snow – let it come suddenly.' He struck this out, but the passage as emended makes the threat of snow seem less certain.

  The words 'on our way to the red pass of Cris-caron' were emended in red ink to 'on our way up the Dimrill-stair'; see note 14.

22 My father first wrote here (emending it to the text given at the time of writing): 'But we have to go on, and we have to cross the mountains here or go back. The passes further south are too far away, and were all guarded years ago – they lead straight into the country of the [Beardless Men Mani Aroman >] Horsemen.' In the rewritten passage, the reference to the passes further south is removed, but it reappears a little later: 'further south the passes are held' (cf. FR p. 300: 'Further south there are no passes, till one comes to the Gap of Rohan').

  Before the name *Rohan* was reached several others were written, *Thanador, Ulthanador, Borthendor, Orothan*[*ador*]. After *Rohan* is written: [= *Rochan(dor)* = Horseland]. This is unquestionably

THE RING GOES SOUTH   435

the point at which the name *Rohan* arose. Cf. the *Etymologies*, V.384: Quenya *rokko*, Noldorin *roch*, horse.

A scribble in the margin seems to change 'The Horse-kings have long been in the service of Sauron' to 'Rohan where the Horsekings or Horselords are.' Cf. FR p. 300: 'Who knows which side now the marshals of the Horse-lords serve?'

23 In the original story Trotter favoured the passage of Moria and Gandalf the pass; in FR (p. 300) it was Aragorn who favoured the pass.

24 This passage, from 'Trotter and I have doubts of the weather', is a rewriting in pencil of a much longer passage in which Gandalf introduced at this point the subject of Moria. Gandalf says:

'Trotter thinks we are likely to be caught in a heavy snow-storm before we get across [see note 21]. I think we shall have to attempt it, all the same. But there is another way, or there used to be. I don't know whether you have heard of the Mines of Moria, or the Black [Pit >] Gulf?'

Gandalf then describes Moria; and after this the original text continues:

The hearts of the travellers sank at his words. All of them would have voted at once for the cold and perils of the high pass rather than for the black gulfs of Moria. But Gandalf did not ask for a vote. After a silence he said: 'There is no need to ask you to decide. I know which way you would choose, and I choose the same. We will try the pass.'

The introduction of Moria was postponed until after the Company had been forced back from the pass by the snowstorm; and Gandalf's words about it reappear there in closely similar form (see p. 429 and note 38). The second occurrence of the passage is in ink and an integral part of the chapter.

25 'pack ponies' is a pencilled emendation from 'horses and ponies'; see note 7. But when the travellers halt under the overhanging cliff the reference to 'the two ponies' (p. 424) is in the text as first written.

26 This sentence was marked with a query and enclosed within square brackets at the time of writing. Later my father wrote here: 'Not all evil things are Sauron['s]', and 'The hawks' (referring presumably to the hawks which Trotter saw high up over Hollin, and said 'accounted for the silence', p. 420); and in the margin: 'Gimli says Caradras had an ill name even in days when Sauron was of little account' (see FR p. 303).

27 As first written (but at once rejected) the content of these speeches (from '"This is hopeless," said Gandalf. "You can call it the wind if you like . . ."') was more condensed and was given entirely to Gandalf.

28 In the same passage in FR (p. 303) the date is 12 January; the Company had left Rivendell on 25 December, and so had been in

436   THE RETURN OF THE SHADOW

the wilderness for nineteen nights. But in the original story the journey was shorter: 'when they had been about ten days on the road the weather grew better' (p. 418), whereas FR (p. 295) has 'a fortnight'.

29 This sentence replaced (probably at once): 'But the snow continued to fall unrelenting, and at length Gandalf had to admit that being buried in snow was at the moment the chief danger.' With the words *had to admit* cf. notes 23 and 30.

30 'Trotter' was changed in pencil to 'Gandalf'. In the context of the story at this stage Trotter would be the more likely to say this (see notes 23 and 29), but in the rough preliminary draft given in note 1 it is said by Gandalf.

31 My father pencilled here: 'Boromir knows snow from the Black Mountains. He was born a mountaineer'; but he struck this out. It is said in the outline given on p. 410 that Fangorn Forest extended up to the Black Mountains (changed from Blue Mountains, which are referred to on the contemporary map).

32 Pencilled changes altered the speakers in this passage, but I believe that these are later. The question 'How are *we* to get to the turn?' is taken from Trotter and given to Merry (probably because my father had decided that Trotter was a Man), who goes on 'It is a pity Gandalf can't produce flame enough to melt us a pathway'; and it is Merry, not Boromir, who makes the remark about a tame dragon and a wild wizard. But since subsequently it is to Boromir that Gandalf apologises for his irritability, these changes were casual and not fully integrated into the narrative. Either at this time or later the remark about Gandalf's melting them a path was transferred to Legolas (cf. FR p. 305), and this is obviously a structurally irrelevant addition, like that concerning Gimli in note 26.

33 The descent of the Company through the deep snow was first told quite differently, though the version given replaced the other before it was completed. As first written, Gandalf relented at once towards Boromir (after 'It will serve you right if you meet a wild dragon') and since he appeared already tired gave him a further sip of Elrond's cordial. Boromir was to carry each hobbit down separately (cf. the preliminary sketch given in note 1) and began with Frodo; at the drift he stumbled on a hidden stone and Frodo was thrown into the deep snow and disappeared, but Boromir 'soon recovered him'. Sam was brought down next ('he had disapproved greatly of his master (with the Ring) being left alone and out of reach in any sudden danger'). Boromir was then too tired to repeat the ascent and descent three times more, and this version ends with hasty notes telling that Trotter, Faramond, and Merry were put on the ponies, while Gandalf behind and Boromir ahead, carrying the baggage, 'ploughed their way down dragging and thrusting the ponies forward.'

THE RING GOES SOUTH 437

My father then wrote: 'Or alter all above', and proposed that the whole Company should go down together. In the second version, given in the text, he neglected to mention that Boromir returned once more to bring down the baggage. The story in FR is of course entirely different since Trotter has become Aragorn.

34 *Moria* is translated 'Black Gulf' in the first, rejected occurrence of this passage (note 24). An isolated note earlier in the MS has *'Moria* = Black Gulf', with the etymology *yagō, ia*; here 'Gulf' is a correction of some other word which I cannot interpret. Cf. the *Etymologies*, V.400, stem YAG 'yawn, gape', where *Moria* is translated 'Black Gulf'.

35 This is not the first use of the word *Orcs* in the LR papers: Gandalf refers to 'orcs and goblins' among the servants of the Dark Lord, pp. 211, 364; cf. also pp. 187, 320. But the rarity of the usage at this stage is remarkable. The word *Orc* goes back to the *Lost Tales*, and had been pervasive in all my father's subsequent writings. In the *Lost Tales* the two terms were used as equivalents, though sometimes apparently distinguished (see II.364, entry *Goblins*). A clue may be found in a passage that occurs in both the earlier and the later *Quenta* (IV.82, V.233): 'Goblins they may be called, *but in ancient days they were strong and fell.*' At this stage it seems that 'Orcs' are to be regarded as a more formidable kind of 'Goblin'; so in the preliminary sketch for 'The Mines of Moria' (p. 443) Gandalf says 'there are goblins – of very evil kind, larger than usual, *real orcs.*' – It is incidentally notable that in the first edition of *The Hobbit* the word *Orcs* is used only once (at the end of Chapter VII 'Queer Lodgings'), while in the published LR *goblins* is hardly ever used.

36 Strangely, this is not at all in agreement with what Glóin had said at Rivendell (p. 391): 'For many years things went well, and the colony throve; there was traffic once more between Moria and the Mountain, and many gifts of silver were sent to Dáin.'

37 It is here that the emendation in red ink to *Glassmere in Dimrilldale* is made (note 13). This is the first appearance of the lake in Dimrill Dale; on the contemporary map it is marked and named *Mirrormere*.

38 Gandalf's account of Moria here differs from the earlier form (see note 24) only in that here there is mention of Durin, of the peace between Elves and Dwarves, and of Orcs (see note 35) – the rejected version refers only to goblins. In that version it is said that the Dwarves of Caron-dûn 'sent their goods down the Great River.'

39 'ten' changed in pencil to '20'. In FR (p. 311) Gandalf says: 'There was a door south-west of Caradhras, some fifteen miles as the crow flies, and maybe twenty as the wolf runs.'

40 See note 23. In the margin, probably made at the time of writing of the manuscript, is a note: 'Trotter was caught there.' This contrasts with what was said earlier, at the Council of Elrond (p. 401): 'Thus

438   THE RETURN OF THE SHADOW

it was that Frodo learned how Trotter had tracked Gollum as he wandered southwards, through Fangorn Forest, and past the Dead Marshes, until he had himself been caught and imprisoned by the Dark Lord.'

Note on the Geography and the contemporary Map

The extremely rapid, rough, and now tattered map reproduced on p. 439 can with complete certainty, I think, be ascribed to the time of the original writing of this chapter. It was my father's first representation of Middle-earth south of the Map of Wilderland in *The Hobbit* – which he had before him, as the courses of the rivers show.

Going from North to South on the map, there is *Carrock* at the top; and *Gladden* (River) and *Gl[adden] Fields* (see p. 416 and note 4). *Hollin* is named and roughly marked with a broken line; and the names, struck out, to the right of the mountains are *Taragaer, Caradras* (with the final form *Caradras* beside it in pencil), *Carnbeleg*, and *Rhascarn* (see note 11). The pass is called *Dimrill*, with (probably) *Cris-caron* struck out (note 14); and *Mirrormere* is marked, the first occurrence of the name (see note 37). West of the mere *Moria* is marked; below are two illegible names and below them *Bliscarn* (note 11) and again *Carnbeleg*, all struck out.

The division of the Misty Mountains into two arms here, referred to by Gandalf in the present text (pp. 419, 429) and by Gimli in FR (p. 296), is shown far more markedly on this original map than it is on my father's later ones – where the eastern arm is shown as actually less extensive than it is on mine published in LR. For the names of the valley between the arms of the mountains see note 13.

The vast westward swing of the Great River (marked *great bend*) is already in being, but the placing of *Fangorn Forest* (in which my father's writing of the word *Forest* is a sample of his more rapid script) would later be wholly changed. That the Great River flowed through the midst of Fangorn is stated by Gandalf (p. 419 and note 16). The name *Belfalas* in the North-east of Fangorn is in red ink (the only item that is); afterwards Belfalas was a coastal region of Gondor, and since *falas* ('shore') was one of the most ancient of Elvish words (see I.253) it is hard to see how it could be used to refer to a region of forest far inland. I suspect that my father wrote it on the page after, or before, the making of this extremely rapid map and without any reference to it, so that it has no significance in this context.

For the various proposed names of the river *Redway* in the text see note 15; among them is *Caradras*, which is written on the map (but struck through in pencil).

Across the Misty Mountains further south is written 'Place this pass into *Rohan* further south' (on passes over the Mountains south of Caradras see note 22). At the bottom of the map on the left is written:

THE RING GOES SOUTH 439

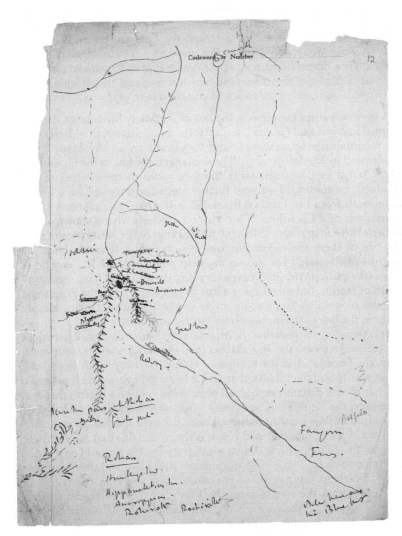

The earliest map of the lands south of the
Map of Wilderland in *The Hobbit*

440   THE RETURN OF THE SHADOW

'Rohan. Horsekings land Hippanaletians . . . [possibly *kn* standing for *kingdom*] Anaxippians Rohiroth Rochiroth.' The *Hippanaletians* and *Anaxippians* ('Horse-lords') are surprising.

At the right-hand corner is: *Below here are the Blue Mts.* Compare Gandalf's words in the first sketching of 'The Council of Elrond' (p. 397): 'Giant Treebeard, who haunts the Forest between the River and *the South Mountains*'; the outline given on p. 410 in which it is said that Fangorn Forest runs up into the *Blue (> Black) Mountains*; and the rejected note to the present text in which it was said that Boromir was 'born a mountaineer' in the *Black Mountains* (note 31).

A question arises concerning the line of the Misty Mountains. In this original text it is said (p. 418), as in FR (p. 295), that south of Rivendell the mountains bent westward; and this is shown on the Map of the Wilderland in *The Hobbit*. It will be seen that if the line of the mountains where it leaves that map, some distance south of the sources of the Gladden, be continued without further westward curving, a track running south from the Ford of Rivendell will strike the mountain chain somewhere near Caradhras. This is in fact precisely what is shown on my father's three maps that exhibit the whole range of the Misty Mountains. On two of them the mountains run in a straight line from about the latitude of Rivendell (as also on my map published in LR); on one of them (the earliest) the line curves very slightly westward from some way north of Hollin; but on all three a line drawn south from the Ford must cut the mountains at an acute angle in the region of Hollin, simply because the line of the mountains is south-south-west.

It is therefore curious that the original sketch-map discussed here does not really agree with the original text (p. 418). The travellers went south from the Ford; and on the borders of Hollin 'far away south Frodo saw the dim shapes of mountains, that seemed now to lie across their path. To the left of this distant range a tall peak stood up like a tooth': that was Taragaer, the Redhorn (Caradhras). And when Faramond said that he thought that they must have turned east, since the mountains were now in front of them, Gandalf said No, it is the mountains that have turned. But on the old map, a line drawn south from the Ford would only strike the mountains far south of Moria and the Red Pass; and this is because my father bent the mountain-line almost due south in the region of Hollin, so that the course from the Ford and the mountain-line then become nearly parallel. This is possibly no more than a consequence of the speed and roughness with which the map was made – the merest guide; but it is curious that the dotted line marking the route of the travellers does actually turn strongly south-east towards the pass – as Faramond thought that it had!

Barbara Strachey, writing on this question in *Journeys of Frodo* (Map 17), remarks: 'The mountains bent westward as they went; more so, in my opinion, than appears in the maps of Middle-earth, especially south

THE RING GOES SOUTH 441

of the Redhorn Pass. Frodo said that they seemed to "stand across the path" that the Companions were taking' (FR p. 295). This is arguable; but the point is strengthened by Gandalf's reply to Pippin, who has said that they must have turned east: 'No, but you see further ahead in the clear light. *Beyond those peaks* [i.e. the Mountains of Moria] *the range bends round south-west'* (FR p. 296). On none of my father's maps is there a change in the direction of the main mountain-chain south of Caradhras. But all show some degree of mountainous extension westwards from the main chain at the point where the Glanduin flows down towards Greyflood: very slight in one (and so represented on my map in LR), more marked on a second, and on the third (the earliest) amounting to a virtual division of the range, with a broad arm of mountains running southwest. On the elaborate map in coloured chalks that I made in 1943 (see p. 200) this is again a strongly marked feature.* It may be that it was to this that Gandalf was referring.

In this connection it may be mentioned that on my map published in LR the mountainous heights shown extending from the main range westwards north of Hollin are badly exaggerated from what my father intended: 'about the feet of the main range there was tumbled an ever wider land of bleak hills, and deep valleys filled with turbulent waters' (FR p. 295).

---

*The map referred to here as 'the earliest' (cf. also p. 202) is my father's original elaborate working map of *The Lord of the Rings* (on which my 1943 map was closely based). This map will be studied in Vol. VII.

XXV
THE MINES OF MORIA

I have little doubt that the first draft of this chapter was written continuously from the end of 'The Ring Goes South', both from internal evidence and external (the nature of the manuscript). But there is also a very interesting two-page 'Sketch of the Mines of Moria chapter' which, I think, immediately preceded the writing of it. This 'Sketch' is extremely difficult to read, and some words can only be guessed at.

Their adventures must be made different from Lonely Mountain. Tunnels leading in every direction, sloping up and running steeply down. stairs. pits. noise of water in darkness.

Gandalf guided mainly by the general sense of direction. They had brought one bundle of torches in case of need, 2 each. Gandalf won't use them until necessary. Faint spark from his staff. Glamdring does not glow, therefore no goblins near.

How far to go. How long will it take. Gandalf reckons at least 2 days, perhaps more. Thought of a night (or two!) in Moria terrifies them. Frodo feels dread growing. Perhaps his adventures with the Ring have made him sensitive. While others are keeping up spirits with hopeful talk he feels the certainty of evil creeping over him, but says nothing. He constantly fancies he hears patter of feet of [?some creature] behind – [?this] is Gollum as it proves long after.

It was about ten o'clock in the morning when they entered. They had had little rest. They went on (with 2 halts) until too weary to go much further. They came to a dark arch leading to 3 passages all leading in same general direction, but the left down, the right up, the centre (apparently) level. Gandalf unable to choose: he does not remember the place.

They halt for the night in a small chamber (almost like a guard-room watching the entrances) just to [?their] left. A deep pit to right. A loose stone falls in. Several minutes before they hear a noise of it reach bottom. After that some of them fancy a far off echo of small knocks at intervals (like signals?). But nothing further happens that night. Gandalf sleeps little trying to choose the road. [?In end] chooses the right hand upward way. They go for nearly 8 hours exclusive of halts.[1]

THE MINES OF MORIA 443

Come to a great chamber. Door in [?south] wall. Dim light – a [?high ?huge] chimney like shaft slanting up. Far up a gleam of daylight. The gleam falls on a great square table of stone [*written above*: a tomb].

There is another door in west [*written above*: east] wall. There are lances and swords and [? broken lying] by both doors.

The gleam of light shows carved letters. Here lies Balin son of Burin, Lord of Moria. In the recesses are chests and a few swords and shields. Chests empty except one. Here is a book with some dwarf writing.

Tells how Balin came to Moria. Then hand changes and tells how he died – of [?an] arrow that came unawares. Then how 'enemies' invaded the east gates. We cannot get out of the west gates because of the 'dweller in the water'. Brief account of siege. Last scrawl says 'they are coming'.

I think we had better be going, said Gandalf. At that moment there is a noise like a great boom far underneath. Then a terrible noise like a horn echoed endlessly. Gandalf springs to door. Noise like goblin feet.

Gandalf lets out a blinding flash and cries Who comes there? Ripple of . . . . . laughter – and some deep voices.

Gandalf says there are goblins – of very evil kind, larger than usual, real orcs.[2] Also certainly some kind of troll is leading them.

Plan of defence. They gather at east door. But [?south] door is propped ajar with wedges. Great arm and shoulder appear by the . . . . . door. Gandalf hews it with Glamdring. Frodo stabs foot with Sting. Horrible cry. Arrows whistle in through crack.

Orcs leap in but are killed.

[?Boom] as great rocks hit door.

They rush out through east door – opens outwards – and slam it. [?They fly] up a long wide tunnel. Noise soon shows east door is broken down. Pursuit is after them.

Here follows the loss of Gandalf.

In pencil in the margin against the account of the attack on the chamber is written:

Black-mailed orc leaps in and goes for Frodo with spear – he is saved by the elfmail and strikes down the orc.

This is a very striking example of an important narrative passage in *The Lord of the Rings* at its actual moment of emergence. Here as elsewhere many of the most essential elements were present from the first: the junction of three roads, Gandalf's doubt, the guardroom, the

444   THE RETURN OF THE SHADOW

falling stone and the subterranean tapping that followed, the chamber of
Balin's tomb, the writing in the book, the troll, and much else. That
Gollum should be following them in Moria had been proposed in the
outline given on p. 410: 'Gollum must reappear at or after Moria. Frodo
hears patter.'

Gandalf's sword *Glamdring* (Foe-hammer), which he took from the
trolls' lair and which (so Elrond told him) 'the king of Gondolin once
wore', now reappears from *The Hobbit*.

Balin's father (Fundin in *The Hobbit* as in LR) is here surprisingly
Burin; this dwarf-name (found in Old Norse) had previously been
given to Balin's son, in the first drafts for 'The Council of Elrond'
(pp. 395, 397), before he was replaced by Gimli son of Glóin (p.
400).

The story that Bilbo gave Sting and his 'elf-mail' to Frodo before he
left Rivendell (FR pp. 290–1) entered in the sketch given on p. 397.

This is not the first reference to the loss of Gandalf; see p. 381, and for
the first sketch of the event see p. 462.

This 'Sketch' begins when the Company is already inside Moria. For
the story of their approach to the West Gate and the opening of the door
there seems to be only the following by way of preparatory outline
(though the 'dweller in the water' before the West Gate appears in the
'Sketch', p. 443, in the words of the book found in the chamber of Balin's
tomb). It follows and was written at the same time as the sketch of the
descent from the Red Pass in the snow (p. 431, note 1).

Moria's west gates are dwarf-gates (closed like the Lonely
Mountain); but openable not at a set time but by a [?special
?speech] spell. Gandalf knows or [?thinks] it must be one of
[?three] in ancient tongue – for the Elves of Hollin wrought the
spell.
   Holly bushes grow before these gates. Then Gandalf knows it
is an elf-spell.

I give now the first draft text of the chapter. It was numbered from the
outset 'XIV', presumably because my father had decided that 'The Ring
Goes South' was a separate chapter and so should be numbered 'XIII',
though he never wrote that number on the manuscript. My description
of the text of 'The Ring Goes South' (p. 415) can be repeated here still
more emphatically. The writing, again in ink not pencil, is even faster
and more often indecipherable, the amount of rejected material (often
not struck out) even greater; many passages are chaotic. There is also a
certain amount of pencilled correction, probably made at different times,
and some of it obviously belonging to a later stage. In one case, my father
made a quite careful insertion in ink, saying that Gimli was of little help
to Gandalf in finding a way through Moria (cf. FR p. 324), though he put

THE MINES OF MORIA 445

in no mention of Gimli anywhere else. The text is thus difficult to interpret and still more difficult to represent.

It will be seen that the entire story of the attack by the Wargs in the night after the Company came down from the pass (FR pp. 310–13) is absent.

THE MINES OF MORIA

Next day the weather changed again, almost as if it obeyed the orders of some power that had now given up the idea of snow, since they had retreated from Cris-caron. The wind had turned southward in the night. In the morning it was veering west, and rain was beginning to fall. The travellers pitched a tent in a sheltered hollow and remained quiet all the day till the afternoon was drawing towards evening.

All the day they had heard no sound and seen no sign of any living thing. As soon as the light began to fade they started off again. A light rain was still falling, but that did not trouble them much at first. Gandalf and Trotter led them in a detour away from the Mountains, for they planned to come at Moria up the course of a stream that ran out from the feet of the hills not far from the hidden gates. But it seemed that somehow or other they must have gone astray in the dark, for it was a black night under an overcast sky. In any case, they did not strike the stream, and morning found them wandering and floundering in wet and marshy places filled with red pools, for there was much clay in the hollows.[3]

They were somewhat comforted by a change in the weather: the clouds broke and the rain stopped. The sun came out in gleams. But Gandalf was fretted by the delay, and decided to move on again by day, after only a few hours' rest. There were no birds in the sky or other ominous signs. They steered now straight back towards the mountains, but both Gandalf and Trotter were much puzzled by their failure to find the stream.

When they had come back again to the foothills and lower slopes they struck a narrow watercourse in a deep channel; but it was dry, and there was now no water among [the] reddish stones in the bed. There was, however, still something like an open path on the left bank.

'This is where the stream used to run, I feel sure,' said Gandalf. 'Sirannon the Gatestream[4] they used to call it. Anyway our road lies up this course.' The night was now falling, but though they were already tired, especially the hobbits, Gandalf urged them to press on.

446   THE RETURN OF THE SHADOW

'Are you thinking of climbing to the top of the mountains tonight, in time to get an early view of the dawn?' asked Merry.

'I should think of it if there was any chance of doing it!' said Gandalf. 'But no one can scale the mountains here. The gates are not high up, but in a certain place near the foot of a great cliff. I hope I can find it – but things seem oddly changed, since I was last here.'

Before the night was old the moon, now only two days off the full,[5] rose through the clouds that lay on the eastern peaks, and shone fitfully down over the western lands. They trudged on with their weary feet stumbling among the stones, until suddenly they came to a wall of rock some thirty feet high. Over it ran a trickling fall of water, but plainly the fall had once been much stronger. 'Ah! Now I know where we are!' cried Gandalf. 'This is where the Stair-falls were. I wonder what has happened to them. But if I am right there is a stairway cut in the stone at the left: the main path goes further round and up an incline. There is or was a wide and shallow valley above the falls through which the Sirannon flowed.'

Very soon they found the stairway, and followed by Frodo and Trotter Gandalf climbed quickly up. When they got to the top they discovered the reason of the drying up of the stream.

The moon was now sinking westwards. It shone out brightly for a while, and they saw stretched before their feet a dark still lake, glinting in the moonlight. The Gate-stream had been dammed, and had filled all the valley. Only a trickle of water escaped over the old falls, for the main outlet of the lake was now away at the southern end.[6]

Before them, dim and grey across the dark water, stood a cliff. The moonlight lay pale upon it, and it looked cold and forbidding: a final bar to all passage. Frodo could see no sign of any gate or entrance in the frowning stone.

'This way is blocked!' said Gandalf. 'At least it is, as far as can be seen by night. I don't suppose anyone wants to try and swim across by moonlight – or any other light. The pool has an unwholesome look. When it was made or why I do not know, but not for any good purpose, I guess.'

'We must try and find a way round by the main path,' said Trotter. 'Even if there was no lake we could not get our ponies up the narrow stair.'

'And even if we could, they would not be able to go into the Mines,' said Gandalf. 'Our road there under the mountains will take us by paths where they cannot go – even if we can.'

THE MINES OF MORIA

447

'I wondered if you had thought of that drawback,' said Trotter. 'I supposed you had, though you did not mention it.'

'No need to mention it, until necessary,' answered the wizard. 'We will take them as far as we can. It remains to be seen if the [?other] road is not drowned as well: in which case we may not be able to get at the gates at all.'

'If the gates are still there,' said Trotter.

They had no great difficulty in finding the old path. It turned away from the falls and wound northward for some way, before bending east again, and climbed up a long slope. When they reached the top of this they saw the lake lying on the right. The path skirted its very edge, but was not submerged. For the most part it was just above the water; but in one place, at the northernmost end of the lake, where there was a slimy and stagnant pool, it disappeared for a short distance, before bending south again toward the foot of the great cliff.

When they reached this point Boromir went forward, and found that the path was only just awash. Carefully they threaded their way in single file behind him. The footing was slippery and treacherous; Frodo felt a curious disgust at the very feel of the dark water on his feet.

As Faramond the last of the party stepped onto the dry land, there was a soft sound, a swish followed by a plop, as if a fish had disturbed the still surface of the water. Turning swiftly they saw in the moonlight ripples sharpened [?with] dark shadows: great rings were widening outwards from some point near the middle of the pool.[7] They halted; and at that very moment the light went out, as the moon fell and vanished into low clouds. There was a soft bubbling noise in the lake, and then silence.

It was too dark to seek for the gate in that changed valley, and the rest of the night the travellers spent unhappily, sitting watchful between the cliff and the dark water which they could no longer see. None of them slept more than briefly and uneasily.

But with the morning their spirits revived. Slowly the light reached the lake: its dark surface was still and unruffled by any breeze. The sky was clear above, and slowly the sun rose above the mountains at their back, and shone on the western lands before them. They ate a little food, and rested for a while after the cheerless night, until the sun reached the south and its warm rays slanted down, driving away the shadows of the great wall behind. Then Gandalf stood up and said that it was high time to begin to search for the gates. The strip of dry land left by the lake was quite

448 THE RETURN OF THE SHADOW

narrow, and their path took them close under the face of the cliff. When they had gone for almost a mile southward they came to some holly-trees. There were stumps and dead logs rotting in the water – the remains of old thickets, or of a hedge that had once lined the submerged road across the drowned valley. But close under the cliff there stood, still living and strong, two tall trees with great roots that spread from the wall to the water's edge. From far across under the other side in the fitful moon Frodo had thought them mere bushes on piles of stone: but now they towered above his head: stiff, silent, dark except for their clustered berries: standing like sentinels or pillars at the end of a road.

'Well, here we are at last!' said Gandalf. 'This is where the elf-way from Hollin ended. The holly-trees were planted by the elves in the old days to mark the end of their domains – the westgates were made chiefly for their use in their traffic with the dwarves. This is the end of our path – and now I am afraid we must say farewell to our ponies. The good beasts would go almost anywhere we told them to; but I do not think we could get them to go into the dark passages of Moria. And in any case there are behind the west gate many steep stairs, and many difficult and dangerous places where ponies could not pass, or would be a perilous handicap. If we are to win through we must travel lighter. Much of the stuff we have brought against bitter weather will not be wanted inside, nor when we get to the other side and turn south.'

'But surely you aren't going to leave the poor beasts in this forsaken place, Mr Gandalf!' protested Sam, who was specially fond of ponies.

'Don't you worry, Sam! They'll find their way back home in time. They have wiser noses even than most of their kind, and these two have returned to Elrond from far away before now. I expect they'll make off west and then work back northward through country where they can find grass.'

'I'd be happier if I might lead them back past the wash and down to the old falls,' said Sam, '– I'd like to sort of say goodbye and set them on the road as it were.'

'Very well, you can,' said Gandalf. 'But first let us unlade them and distribute the goods we mean to keep.'

When each member of the party had been given a share according to his size – most of the foodstuffs and the waterskins – the remainder was secured again on the ponies' backs. In each bundle Gandalf put a brief message to Elrond written in secret runes, telling him of the snowstorm and their turning aside to Moria.

THE MINES OF MORIA   449

Then Sam and Trotter led the horses off.

'Now let us have a look at the gates!' said Gandalf.[8]

'I do not see any gates,' said Merry.

'Dwarf-gates are not made to be seen,' said the wizard. 'Many are quite invisible, and their own masters cannot find them if their secret is lost. But these gates were not made to be wholly[9] secret, and unless things are altogether changed eyes that know what to look for may discover the signs. Let us go and see!'

He strode forward to the cliff-wall. There was a smooth space right in the middle of the shade of the trees, and over this he passed his hands to and fro, muttering words under his breath. Then he stepped back. 'Look!' he said. 'Can you see anything now?' The sun shone across the face of the wall, and as the travellers stared at it, it seemed to them that on the surface where Gandalf's hand had passed faint lines appeared like slender veins of silver running in the stone; at first they seemed like pale threads of gossamer so fine as only to be seen fitfully where the sun caught them; but slowly they broadened and their design could be guessed. At the top, as high as Gandalf could reach, was an arch of interlacing letters in the elvish character; below it seemed (though the drawing was in places blurred and broken) that there was the outline of an anvil and hammer, and above that a crown and a crescent moon. More clearly than all else there shone forth palely three stars with many rays.[10]

'Those are the emblems of Durin and of the Elves,' said Gandalf. 'They are of some silver substance that is seen only when touched by one who knows certain words – at night under the moon they shine most bright.[11] Now you can see that we have certainly found the west gate of Moria.'

'What does the writing say?' asked Frodo, who was trying to puzzle out the inscription. 'I thought I knew the elf-letters, but I cannot read these, they are so tangled.'

'The words are in the elf-tongue, not in ordinary language,' said Gandalf. 'But they do not say anything of much importance to us. Certainly they don't tell the opening-spell, if that is what you are thinking. They merely say: The Doors of Durin Lord of Moria. Speak friends and enter. And underneath very small and now faint is: Narfi made them.[12] Celebrimbor of Hollin drew these signs.'

'What does it mean by "speak friends and enter"?' asked Frodo.

'That is plain enough,' said Gandalf, '– if you are friends speak the password, and then the door will open and you can enter. Some dwarf-gates will open only at special times, or for particular

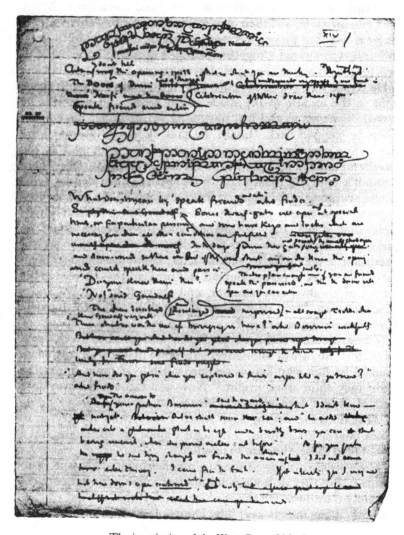

The inscription of the West Gate of Moria

THE MINES OF MORIA

persons; and some have keys and locks which are necessary even when all other conditions are fulfilled. In the days of Durin these gates were not secret: they usually stood open and door-wards sat here. But if they were shut anyone who knew the opening words could speak them and pass in.'

'Do you know them then?'

'No!' said Gandalf.

The others looked surprised and dismayed – all except Trotter, who knew Gandalf very well. 'Then what was the use of bringing us here?' asked Boromir wrathfully.

'And how did you get in when you explored the Mines, as you told us just now?' asked Frodo.

'The answer to your question, Boromir,' said the wizard, 'is that I don't know – not yet. But we shall soon see; and,' he added, with a glint in his eyes under bristling brows, 'you can start being uncivil, when it is proved useless: not before. As for your question,' he said, turning sharply on Frodo, 'the answer is obvious: I did not enter this way. I came from the East. If it interests you I may add that these doors open *outwards* with a push, but nothing can open them inwards. They can swing out, or they can be broken if you have enough force.'

'What are you going to do then?' asked Merry,[13] who was not much disturbed by Gandalf's bristling brows; and in his heart hoped that the doors would prove impossible to open.

'I am going to try and find the opening words. I once knew every formula and spell in any language of elves, dwarves, or goblins that was ever used for such purposes. I can still remember two or three hundreds without racking my brains. But I think only a few trials should be necessary. The opening words were in Elvish, like the written words – I feel certain: from the signs on the doors, from the holly trees, and because of the use for which the road and gates were originally made.' He stepped up to the rock and lightly touched with his wand the silver star that was near the middle of the emblems, just above the crown.

Annon porennin diragas·venwed
diragath·telwen porannin nithrad[14]

he said. The silver letters faded, but the grey blank stone did not stir. Many many times he tried other formulas one after another, but nothing further happened. Then he tried single words spoken in commanding tones, and finally (seeming to lose his temper) he

452   THE RETURN OF THE SHADOW

shouted *Édro, édro!* and followed it with *open!* in every language he could remember. Then he sat down in silence.

Boromir was smiling broadly behind his back. 'It looks as if we may be wanting those ponies back,' he said in an undertone. 'It would have been wiser to have kept them till the gates were open.'[15] If Gandalf heard he made no sign.

Suddenly in the silence Frodo heard a soft swish and bubble in the water[16] as on the evening before, only softer. Turning quickly he saw faint ripples on the surface of the lake – and at the same time saw that Sam and Trotter in the distance [were] crossing the wash on their return. The ripples on the water seemed to be moving in their direction.

'I don't like this place,' said Merry, who had also seen the ripples. 'I wish we could go back, or that Gandalf would do something and we could go on – if we must.'

'I have a queer feeling,' said Frodo slowly, '– a dread either of the gates or of something else. But I don't think Gandalf is defeated: he is thinking hard, I fancy.'

It appeared that Frodo was right; for the wizard suddenly sprang to his feet with a laugh. 'I have it!' he cried. 'Of course, of course! Absurdly simple – when you think of it!' Raising his wand he stood before the rock and said in a clear voice: *Mellyn!* (or *Meldir!*)[17]

The three stars shone briefly and went out again. Then silently a great door was outlined, though not the finest crack or joint had been visible before. Slowly it began to swing outwards, inch by inch until it lay right back against the wall.[18] Behind, the foot of a shadowy stairway could be seen climbing up into the gloom within. All the party stood and stared in wonder.

'I was wrong after all,' said Gandalf. 'The opening word was inscribed there all the time. *Speak friends and enter* it said, and when I spoke the elvish word for *friends*, it opened. Quite simple! And now we can enter.'

But at that moment Frodo felt something seize his ankle and he fell. At the same moment Sam and Trotter who had just come back gave a yell as they ran up. Turning suddenly the others saw that a long arm, sinuous as a tentacle, was thrust out from the lake's dark edge. It was pale green-grey and wet: its fingered end had hold of Frodo's foot and was dragging him towards the water.

Sam dashed up with a drawn knife and slashed at it. The fingers let go of Frodo and Sam dragged him away; but immediately the waters of the lake began to heave and boil, and twenty more

THE MINES OF MORIA 453

writhing arms came rippling out, making for the travellers as if directed by something in the deep pools that could see them all.

'Into the gateway! Quick! Up the stairs!' shouted Gandalf, rousing them from the horror that had held them rooted.

There was just time. Gandalf saw them all inside, and then sprang back upon the heels of Trotter, but he was no more than four steps up when the crawling fingers of the dweller in the pool reached the cliff.[19]

He paused. But if he was pondering how to close the door, or what word would move them from within, there was no need. For the arms seized the door, and with dreadful strength swung it round. With a shattering echo it slammed behind them; and they halted on the stairs in dismay as the sounds of rending and crashing came dully through the stones from outside. Gandalf ran down to the door and thrust up . . . . and spoke the . . . . words;[20] but though the door groaned it did not stir.

'I am afraid the door is blocked behind us now,' he said. 'If I guess right, the trees are thrown down across it, and boulders have been rolled against it. I am sorry for the trees – they were beautiful and old and had . . . . . so long.[21] Well now, we can only go on – there is nothing left to do.'

'I am mighty glad I saw those poor beasts safe first,' said Sam.

'I felt that something evil was near,' said Frodo. 'What was it, Gandalf?'

'I could not say,' said Gandalf, '– there was not time enough to look at the arms. They all belong to one creature, I should say, from the way they moved – but that is all I can say. Something that has . . . . . crept, or been driven out of the dark waters under ground, I guess. There are older and fouler things than goblins in the dark places of the world.' He did not speak aloud his uncomfortable thought that the Dweller in the Pool had not seized on Frodo among all the party by accident.[22]

Gandalf now went ahead and allowed his wand to glow faintly to prevent them from walking into unseen dangers in the dark. But the great stairway was sound and undamaged. There were two hundred steps, broad and shallow; and at the top they found the floor level before them.

'Let us have something to eat here on the landing, since we can't find a dining-room,' said Frodo. He had recovered from the terror of the clutching arm, and was feeling unusually hungry. The idea was welcome to all. After they had eaten Gandalf again gave them a taste of the cordial.

454   THE RETURN OF THE SHADOW

'It won't last much longer,' he said, 'but I think we need it after that business at the gate. And we shall need all that is left before we get through, unless we have luck. Go carefully with the water too! There are streams and wells in the Mines, but they should not be touched. We shan't get a chance of filling our bottles till we come down in Dunruin.'[23]

'How long are we going to take to get through?' asked Frodo.

'I don't know that,' answered Gandalf. 'It all depends. But going straight (without mishaps, or losing our way) we should take at least three or four marches. It cannot be less than forty miles from West-doors to Eastgate in a straight line, and we may not find the most direct passages.'

They rested now only for a short while, as all were eager to get the journey over as quickly as possible, and were willing, tired as they were, to go on still for several hours. They had no fuel or means of making torches, and would be obliged to find the way mostly in the dark.[24] Gandalf went in front holding in his left hand his wand, the pale light of which was sufficient to show the ground before his feet. In his right hand he held the sword Glamdring, which he had kept ever since it was discovered in the trolls' lair.[25] No gleam came from it – which was some comfort; for being a sword of ancient elvish make it shone with a cold light, if goblins were at hand.

He led them forward first along the passage in which they had halted. As the light of his wand dimly lit their dark openings other passages and tunnels could be seen or guessed: sloping up, or running steeply down, or turning suddenly round hidden corners. It was most bewildering. Gandalf was guided mainly by his general sense of direction: and anyone who had been on a journey with him knew that he never lost that by dark or day, underground or above it: being better at steering in a tunnel than a goblin, and less likely to be lost in a wood than a hobbit, and surer of finding the way through night as black as the Pit than the cats of Queen Beruthiel.[26] Had that not been so, it is more than doubtful if the party would have gone a mile without disaster. For there were not only many paths to choose from, there were in many places pits at the sides of the tunnel, and dark wells in which far under the gurgling of water could be heard. Rotting strands of rope dangled above them from broken winches. There were dangerous chasms and fissures in the rock, and sometimes a chasm would open right across their path. One was so wide that Gandalf himself nearly stumbled into it. It was quite ten feet wide, and Sam stumbled in

THE MINES OF MORIA

455

his jump and would have fallen back on the further bank if Frodo had not grabbed his hand and [?jerked] him forward.

Their march was slow, and it began to feel never-ending. They grew very weary; and yet there was no comfort in the thought of halting anywhere. Frodo's spirits had risen for a while after his escape from the water-monster; but now a deep sense of disquiet, growing to dread, crept over him once more. Though he had been healed in Rivendell of the knife stroke, it is probable that that grim adventure had left its mark, and that he was specially sensitive; and in any case he it was that bore the Ring upon its chain against his breast.[27] He felt the certainty of evil ahead, and of evil following. But he said nothing.

The travellers spoke seldom and then only in hurried whispers. There was no sound but the sound of their own feet. If they stopped for a moment they heard nothing at all, unless it were occasionally a faint sound of water trickling or dripping. Only Frodo began to hear or imagine that he heard something else: like the faint fall of soft feet following. It was never loud or near enough for him to feel certain that he heard it; but once it had started it never stopped, unless they did. And it was not an echo, for when they halted (as they did from time to time) it pattered on for some time, and then grew still.

It was about 10 o'clock in the morning when they entered the Mines.[28] They had been going for many hours (with brief halts) when Gandalf came to his first serious doubt. They had come to a wide dark arch opening into three passages: all three led in the same general direction, East, but the left hand passage seemed to plunge down, the right hand to climb up, while the middle way seemed to run level (but was very narrow).

'I have no memory of this place at all!' said Gandalf, standing uncertainly under the arch. He held up his wand in the hope of finding some direction marks or an inscription that might help. But nothing of the kind was to be seen.

'I am too tired to choose,' he said, shaking his head; 'and I expect you are all as weary as I am or wearier. We had better halt here for the night – if you know what I mean. It is all night of course inside, but outside I fancy the night is already come. It is quite ten hours since we left the gate.'[29]

They groped about in the darkness looking for a place where they could rest with some feeling of security. To the left of the great arch was a lower opening, and when they explored it closer they discovered that it was a stone door that was half closed, but swung

456   THE RETURN OF THE SHADOW

back easily to a gentle thrust. Beyond there seemed to be a chamber or chambers cut in the rock.

'Steady, steady!' said Gandalf as Merry and Faramond pushed forward, glad to find somewhere where they could rest with some sort of security. 'Steady! You don't know what may be inside. I will go first.'

He went cautiously in followed by the rest. 'There!' he said, pointing with his wand to the middle of the floor. They saw before their feet a round hole like the mouth of a well. Rotting strands of rope lay at the edge and trailed down into the dark pit; fragments of broken stone lay near.

'One of you might have fallen in and still be waiting to hit the bottom,' said the wizard to Merry. 'Look before your feet! This seems to have been a kind of guard-room placed to watch those passages,' he went on. 'The hole I expect is a well, and was doubtless once covered with a stone lid. But that is broken now, and you had better be careful of the fall.'

Sam[30] felt curiously attracted by the well; and while the others were making beds of blankets in dark corners of the room, as far as possible from the well, he crept to the edge and peered over. A chill air seemed to mount up to his face from the invisible depths. Moved by a sudden impulse, he groped for a loose stone, and let it drop.

It seemed almost a whole minute before there was any sound – then far below there was a *plunk*, as if the stone had fallen into deep water in a cavernous place – very distant, but magnified and repeated in the hollow rock.

'What's that?' cried Gandalf. He was relieved when Sam confessed what he had done; but he was angry, and Sam could see his eyes glint in the dark. 'Fool of a fellow!' he growled. 'This is a serious journey, not a hobbit school treat. Throw yourself in next time, and then you'll be no further nuisance. Now be quiet!'

There was nothing to hear for several minutes; but then there came out of the depths faint knocks, that stopped, and were dimly echoed, and then after a short silence were repeated. It sounded strangely like signals of some sort. But after a while the knocks died away altogether and were heard no more.

'It may have nothing to do with that stone,' said Gandalf; 'and in any case it may have nothing to do with us – but of course it may be anything. Don't do anything like that again. Let's hope we get some rest undisturbed. You Sam can go on the first watch. And stay near the door, well away from the well,' he grunted, as he rolled himself in a blanket.

THE MINES OF MORIA 457

Sam sat miserably by the door in the pitch dark, but kept on turning round, for fear some unknown thing should crawl out of the well. He wished he could cover the hole, if only with a blanket; but he dared not go near, even though Gandalf seemed to be snoring.

Gandalf was actually not asleep, and the snores came from Boromir, who lay next him. The wizard was thinking hard again trying to recall every memory he could of his former journey in the Mines, and trying to make up his mind about the next course to take. After about an hour he got up and came over to Sam.

'Get into a blanket and have a sleep, my lad!' he said in a more kindly tone. 'You could sleep, I guess. I can't, so I may as well do the watching.'

'I know what is the matter with me,' he muttered. 'I need a pipe; and I think I'll risk it.' The last thing Sam saw before sleep took him was a vision of the old wizard squatting on the floor shielding a blazing chip in his gnarled hands between his knees. The flicker for a moment showed his sharp nose and the puffs of smoke.

It was Gandalf who roused them all from sleep. He had watched all alone for about six hours and let the others rest. 'And in the meantime I have made up my mind,' he said. 'I don't like the feel of the middle way, and I don't like the smell of the left hand – there is foul air down there, or I am no guide. I shall take the right hand way – it's time we began to go up again.'

For eight dark hours, not counting two brief halts, they marched on, and met no danger, and heard nothing and saw nothing but the faint gleam of the wizard's light bobbing like a will-o'-the-wisp in front of them. The passage they had chosen wound steadily upwards, going, as far as they could judge, in great curves, and growing steadily wider. On neither side were there now any openings to other galleries or tunnels, and the floor, though rough in many places, was sound and without pits or cracks. They went quicker than the day before, and must have covered some twenty miles or more, perhaps fifteen in a straight line eastwards. As they went upwards Frodo's spirits rose a little; but still he felt oppressed, and still at times he heard or thought he heard away behind and through the patter of their own feet a following footfall that was not an echo.

They had gone nearly as far as the hobbits could endure without rest and sleep, and they were all thinking of a place to halt for the night, when suddenly the walls to right and left vanished. They halted. Gandalf seemed well pleased. 'I think we have reached the

458 THE RETURN OF THE SHADOW

habitable parts,' he said, 'and are no great way from the eastern side. I can feel a change in the air, and guess we are in a wide hall. I think I will risk a little light.'[31]

He raised his wand and for a brief moment it blazed out like a flash of lightning. Great shadows leapt up and fled, and for a second or two they saw a vast roof high above their heads. On every side stretched a huge empty hall with straight hewn walls. Four entrances they glimpsed: dark arches in the walls: one at the west by which they had come, one before them in the east, and one on either side. Then the light went out.

'That is all I shall venture on for the present,' said the wizard. 'There used to be great windows on the mountain-side, and shafts leading out to the light and the upper reaches of the mines. I think that is where we are. But it is night now, and we cannot tell till morning. If I am right, tomorrow we may actually see the morning peeping in. But in the meanwhile we had better go no further without exploration. There will still be a good way to go before we are through – the East Gates are on a much lower level than this, and it is a long road down. Let us rest if we can.'

They spent that night in the great empty hall, huddled in a corner to escape the draught – there seemed to be a steady flow of chill air in through the eastern archway. The vastness and immensity of the tunnels and excavations filled the hobbits with bewilderment.[32] 'There must have been a mighty tribe o' dwarves here at one time,' said Sam; 'and every one as busy as a badger for a hundred years to make all this – and most in hard rock too. What did they do it all for? They didn't live in these darksome holes, surely?'

'Not for long,' said Gandalf;[33] 'though the miners often took long spells underground, I believe. They found precious metals, and jewels – very abundantly in the earlier days. But the mines were most renowned for the metal which was only found here in any quantity: Moria-silver, or true-silver as some call it. *Ithil*[34] the Elves call it, and value it still above gold.[35] It is nearly as heavy as lead, and malleable as copper, but the dwarves could by some secret of theirs make it as hard as steel. It surpasses common silver in all save beauty, and even in that it is its equal. In their day the dwarflords of Uruktharbun[36] were more wealthy than any of the Kings of Men.'

'Well, *we* haven't clapped eyes on any kind of silver since we came in,' grunted Sam; 'nor any jewels neither. Nor on any dwarves.'

THE MINES OF MORIA 459

'I don't think we are likely to until we get further up[37] and nearer to the eastern entrances,' said Gandalf.

'I hope we do find dwarves in the end,' said Frodo. 'I would give a great deal to see old Balin. Bilbo was fond of him and would be delighted to have news of him. He visited him in Hobbiton once long ago, but that was before I went to live there.'

But these words carried his thoughts far away from the darkness; and memories of Bag-end while Bilbo was still there crowded [?thickly] into his mind. He wished with all his heart that he was back there, mowing the lawn, or pottering among the flowers, and that he had never heard of the Ring.[38] It was his turn to watch. As silence fell and one by one the others fell asleep he felt the strange dread assail him again. But though he listened endlessly through the slow hours till he was relieved he heard no sound of any footfall. Only once, far away where he guessed the western archway stood, he fancied he saw two pale points of light – almost like luminous eyes. He started – 'I must have nearly fallen asleep,' he thought; 'I was on the edge of a dream.' He rubbed his eyes and stood up, and remained standing peering into the dark until he was relieved by Merry. He quickly fell asleep, but after a while it seemed to him in his dream that he heard whispers, and saw two pale points of light approaching. He woke – and found that the others were speaking softly near him, and that a dim light was actually falling on his face. High up above the eastern arch, through a shaft near the roof, came a grey gleam. And across the hall through the northern arch light also glimmered faint and distantly.

Frodo sat up. 'Good morning!' said Gandalf. 'For morning it is again at last. I was right, you see. Before today's over we ought to get to the Eastern Gate and see the waters of Helevorn in the Dimrilldale before us.'[39]

All the same the wizard felt some doubt as to their exact position – they might be far to the north or the south of the Gates. The eastern arch was the most likely exit to choose, and the draught that flowed through it seemed to promise a passage leading before long to the outer air; but beyond the opening there was no trace of light. 'If I could only see out of one of these shafts,' he said, 'I should know better what to do. We might wander backwards and forwards endlessly, and just miss the way out. We had better explore a little before we start. And let us go first towards the light.'

Passing under the northern arch they went down a wide

460   THE RETURN OF THE SHADOW

corridor and as they went the glimmer of light grew stronger. Turning a sharp corner they came to a great door on their right. It was half open, and beyond there was a large square chamber. It was only dimly lit, but to their eyes, after so long in the dark, it seemed almost dazzlingly light, and they blinked as they entered. Their feet disturbed deep dust and stumbled amongst things lying on the floor within the doorway whose shapes they could not at first make out.

They saw now that the chamber was lit by a wide shaft high up in the far wall – it slanted upwards and far above a small square patch of sky could be seen where it issued outwards. The light fell directly on a table in the midst of the chamber, a square block some three feet high upon which was laid a great slab of whitened stone.

'It looks like a tomb!' [muttered >] thought Frodo, and went forward to look at it more closely with a curious sense of foreboding. Gandalf came quickly to his side. On the slab was deeply cut in Runes:[40]

BALIN SON OF BURIN LORD OF MORIA

Gandalf and Frodo looked at one another. 'He is dead then. I feared it somehow,' said Frodo.

Although the outline for the story of the passage of Moria continues well beyond this point (p. 443), this first draft of the narrative stopped here. My father pencilled some barely legible notes on the blank remainder of the page, and years later (when, as I think, the page had become detached from the rest of the chapter: see note 40) he deciphered them as follows.

Balin son of *Burin* was changed to Balin son of *Fundin*, as in *The Hobbit* (see p. 444).

At the end of the narrative in ink is written, as in FR: 'Gimli cast his hood over his face.'

'Runes of ?Dwarves'

'(they) look about and see broken swords and ?axe-heads and cloven shields'

'The ?trodden book is bloodstained & tossed in a corner. Only some can be read. Balin was slain in ?fray in Dimrill dale. They have taken the gates they are coming'

On the back of the page is a first scribbled sketch of a 'Page of Balin's Book' (see note 40).

THE MINES OF MORIA

It may be that my father did not at this time feel that he had reached the end of a chapter, and intended to continue the story; but it is known from his own words in the Foreword to the Second Edition (1966), in which he set down some recollections of the stages in the writing of the book, that he stopped for a long time at precisely this point. He said there that by the end of 1939 'the tale had not yet reached the end of Book I' (and it is clear that he referred to Book I of FR, not to Volume I of *The Lord of the Rings*); and that

> In spite of the darkness of the next five years I found that the story could not now be wholly abandoned, and I plodded on, mostly by night, till I stood by Balin's tomb in Moria. There I halted for a long while. It was almost a year later when I went on and so came to Lothlórien and the Great River late in 1941.

This can only mean that the story was broken off in Moria late in 1940.

It seems impossible to accommodate these dates to such other evidence as exists on the subject. I think it extremely probable, even virtually certain, that these last chapters, taking the story from Rivendell to Moria, belong to the latter part of 1939; and indeed my father himself said, in a letter to Stanley Unwin dated 19 December 1939, that he had 'never quite ceased work' on *The Lord of the Rings*, and that 'it has reached Chapter XVI' (*Letters* no. 37). The chapter-numbers at this stage are unfortunately so erratic that the evidence they provide is very difficult to use; but when it is observed that the number 'XV' was pencilled on the original manuscript of 'The Council of Elrond', and that the chapter which afterwards continued the story from the point where the present text ends – originally called 'The Mines of Moria (ii)' and afterwards 'The Bridge of Khazad-dûm' – is numbered 'XVII', it seems probable that it was to 'The Mines of Moria' that my father referred in the letter of December 1939. In any case 'Chapter XVI' could not by any reckoning be one of the chapters of Book I in FR. I feel sure, therefore, that – more than a quarter of a century later – he erred in his recollection of the year. But it would be out of the question that he should err in his recollection that he 'halted for a long while by Balin's tomb in Moria.' Internal evidence in any case suggests that the 'wave' of composition which had carried the story from the Council of Elrond to the chamber of Balin's tomb came to an end here. All subsequent texts rest on a developed form of the Council and a different composition of the Company of the Ring.

There this history halts also. But before ending there remains another outline scrap, found on the same isolated page as bears the preliminary sketches for the descent from the Red Pass (p. 431, note 1) and the spell that held the West Gate of Moria (p. 444). It is in fact a continuation of the 'Sketch of the Moria chapter' given on pp. 442–3, which ends with the words: 'Pursuit is after them. Here follows the loss of Gandalf.' Written in a faint pencilled scribble it is extremely difficult to read.

462 THE RETURN OF THE SHADOW

They are pursued by goblins and a B[lack] R[ider] [*written above:* a Balrog] after escaping from Balin's Tomb – they come to a bridge of slender stone over a gulf.

Gandalf turns back and holds off [?enemy], they cross the bridge but the B[lack] R[ider] leaps forward and wrestles with Gandalf. The bridge cracks under them and the last they see is Gandalf falling into the pit with the B[lack] R[ider]. There is a flash of fire and blue light up from abyss.

Their grief. Trotter now guides party.

(Of course Gandalf must reappear later – probably fall is not as deep as it seemed. Gandalf thrusts Balrog under him and so . . . . and eventually following the subterranean stream in the gulf he found a way out – but he does not turn up until they have had many adventures: not indeed until they are on [?borders] of Mordor and the King of Ond is being beaten in battle.)

This seems to show clearly that before ever the story of the fall of Gandalf from the Bridge of Khazad-dûm was written, my father fully intended that he should return.

NOTES

1 To this point the text of this 'Sketch' was struck through, but the remainder was not.

2 See p. 437, note 35; and cf. the corresponding passage in FR (p. 338), where Gandalf says: 'There are Orcs, very many of them. And some are large and evil: black Uruks of Mordor.'

3 In FR (p. 313) the Company moved south towards Moria by day, and they 'wandered and scrambled in a barren country of red stones. Nowhere could they see any gleam of water . . .'

4 My father first wrote here (changing it at once): '*Caradras dilthen* the Little Redway'. For *Caradras* as the name of the river Redway (later Silverlode) on the other side of the Mountains see p. 433, note 15.

5 It was now the night of 5 December, and full moon was on the 7th (see p. 434, note 19).

6 This sentence was enclosed within square brackets, and the concluding words 'from whence they heard the splash of running water' struck out. These changes belong with the writing of the manuscript.

7 Though the word 'pool' is used, the reference is clearly to the lake and not to the 'pool' which they had just walked through. The 'soft bubbling noise' comes from the 'lake'.

THE MINES OF MORIA   463

8   The whole passage from 'Well, here we are at last' on p. 448 to this point is a rider on a slip, replacing the following in the original text:
    'Here is the gate,' said Gandalf. 'This is where the road from Hollin ended, and the elves planted these trees in old days; for the west-gates were made chiefly for their use in their traffic with the dwarves.'
    The replacement certainly belongs with the first writing of the chapter, for the dispatch of the ponies by Sam and Trotter is subsequently referred to in the text as written.

9   The word 'wholly' is enclosed in square brackets.

10 In FR (p. 318) the hammer and anvil are 'surmounted by a crown with seven stars', and 'more clearly than all else there shone forth in the middle of the door a single star with many rays.' The original draft has no mention of the two trees bearing crescent moons.

11 In FR the inscription on the doors is of *ithildin* which mirrors only starlight and moonlight (p. 318). In this original draft, of course, the time-scheme is different – the middle of the day, not early night (see note 28).

12 This was first written: 'Narfi made the Doors'.

13 Merry replaced Frodo, who replaced Boromir; it was apparently said of Boromir that he was not much disturbed by Gandalf's bristling brows, and that he secretly wished that the doors might stay shut.

14 I cannot interpret this. In FR (p. 320) Gandalf's invocation means: 'Elvish gate open now for us; doorway of the Dwarf-folk listen to the word [*beth*] of my tongue.'

15 The text of this passage, from 'Then he sat down in silence', as first written read:
    Only Trotter seemed troubled. Boromir was smiling broadly behind his back. Sam ventured to whisper in Frodo's ear: 'I've never seen old Gandalf at a loss for words before,' he said. 'It looks as if we were not *meant* to pass these gates, somehow.'
    'I have a feeling of dread,' said Frodo slowly, 'either of the gates or of something else. But I do not think Gandalf is beaten – he is thinking hard, I fancy.'
    Subsequently Sam's whispered speech to Frodo was given to Merry, with the addition: 'He ought not to have sent off the ponies till he got them open.'

16 Written in pencil here: 'Sound of wolves far off at same time as swish in water'. But this would have been added when the time of their entry into the Mines had been altered; cf. FR p. 321 and note 28.

17 These words were struck out in pencil and the form *Melin* substituted. In the *Etymologies* (V.372), stem MEL, are given Noldorin *mellon* and *meldir* 'friend', and also Quenya *melin* 'dear'.

18 In FR there are two doors; and despite the single door described here, the inscription bears the words 'The Doors of Durin'; Gandalf

464   THE RETURN OF THE SHADOW

tells them: 'these doors open outwards, but nothing can open them inwards. They can swing out, or they can be broken . . .'

19   As first written (and not struck out) this passage read: 'They had just time; Trotter who came last was not more than four steps up when the arms of the creature in the water came feeling and fingering the wall.'

20   In the first of these lacunas the text seems to read *in it*, or possibly *with* (in which case *his wand* was omitted; cf. FR p. 322, 'he thrust his staff against the doors'). In the second, the word looks like *open* (perhaps for *opening*).

21   The illegible word is just a series of wiggles; certainly not *stood*, the word here in FR. Just possibly, *survived*.

22   The actual reading here is '– not by accident'. The sentence was enclosed in square brackets at the time of writing, but a similar sentence remains in FR.

23   *Dunruin* replaced, apparently at the time of writing, *Carondoom* (see p. 433, note 13). Subsequently *Dimrilldale* was written in in pencil.

24   This sentence was a replacement (to all appearance made at the time of writing; see note 31) of: 'In the confusion of the attack at the Westgate some of the bundles and packages had been left on the ground; but they had still with them one bundle of torches which they had brought with them in case of need, but never yet useu.'

25   The words following *Glamdring* are enclosed in square brackets. Glamdring has appeared in the 'Sketch' for the chapter; see pp. 442–4.

26   This sentence was changed in the act of writing, the successive stages not being crossed out: 'than any cat that ever walked', 'than is the cat of Benish Armon', 'than the cats of Queen [?Tamar >] Margoliantë   Beruthiel' – both these names being left to stand.

27   The original passage that follows here was enclosed in square brackets and later struck out in pencil:

While the others were trying to keep up their spirits with hopeful talk, and were asking whispered questions concerning the lands [*struck out:* of Dunruin and Fangorn] beyond the mountains, the vale of Redway, the forest of Fangorn, and beyond, he felt the certainty . . .

This derives from the 'Sketch' for the chapter (see p. 442).

28   In the 'Sketch' (p. 442) it is said, as here, that 'it was about 10 o'clock in the morning' when they entered the Mines. This does not agree with what is said on p. 447, that when 'the sun *reached the south*' Gandalf 'stood up and said that it was high time to begin to search for the gates', and the sun was shining across the face of the cliff when he made the signs appear. This suggests that the door was opened in the early afternoon. The sentence in the text here was altered in pencil to 'five o'clock in the evening', but it is hard to say

THE MINES OF MORIA 465

to what form of the story this refers. In FR it was fully dark – 'the countless stars were kindled' – when they entered the Mines (pp. 320, 326), and though it was early December it was surely after five o'clock. A few lines below in the present text, however, another change in the time-scheme clearly introduces that of FR; see note 29.

29 The words 'the night is already come' were changed in pencil to 'the night is already old'; and the following sentence, which had been enclosed in square brackets, was struck out. As written, the text agrees with the story that they went into the Mines at about ten in the morning – it would now be about 8 p.m. (see note 28). As changed, it agrees with FR, p. 326 ('outside the late Moon is riding westward and the middle-night has passed').

30 'Sam' replaced 'Merry' at the time of writing, since at the end of this episode it is Sam, not changed from Merry, who takes the first watch as a punishment for casting the stone into the well.

31 This passage was much changed in the course of composition. At first 'Gandalf allowed two torches to be lit to help in exploration. Their light found no roof, but was sufficient to show that they had come (as they had guessed) into a wide space high and broad like a great hall.' It has however been said, by a change apparently made during the initial composition (see note 24), that they had neither torches nor means of making them.

32 The passage in FR p. 329 from 'All about them as they lay hung the darkness . . .' to 'the actual dread and wonder of Moria' was first drafted in the margin of the manuscript here, perhaps quite soon after the writing of the main text.

33 'Gandalf' is an early emendation from 'Trotter', and in the following speech.

34 *Ithil* is an early, perhaps immediate, change from *Erceleb*.

35 This passage was changed in the act of writing from:
> – very abundantly in the earlier days, and especially the silver. Moria-silver was (and still is) renowned; and many held it a precious

This is where the conception of *mithril* first emerged, though not yet the name (see note 34). The reference to *mithril* in *The Hobbit* (Chapter XIII, 'Not at Home') entered in the third edition of 1966: until then the text read: 'It was of silvered steel, and ornamented with pearls, and with it went a belt of pearls and crystals.' This was changed to: 'It was of silver-steel, which the elves call *mithril*, and with it went a belt of pearls and crystals.'

36 Against *Uruktharbun* is pencilled *Azanulbizâr*, which in FR is the Dwarvish name of Dimrill-dale. If *Uruktharbun* is Moria (and the next revision of this text has 'the dwarflords of Khazad-dûm'), *Azanulbizâr* may have been intended to replace it and to have referred at first to Moria; on the other hand, my father may perhaps

466   THE RETURN OF THE SHADOW

have wished to name the 'dwarflords' as lords in the Dimrill-dale. It may be mentioned that placed in this manuscript, though written on different paper and presumably belonging to a later stage when Gimli had become a member of the Company, is a sheet of primary workings for his song in Moria; and in these occur the lines:

> *When Durin came to Azanûl*
> *and found and named the nameless pool.*

In notes written years later (after the publication of *The Lord of the Rings*) my father observed that 'the interpretation of the Dwarf names (owing to scanty knowledge of Khuzdul) is largely uncertain, except that, since this region [i.e. Moria and Dimrill-dale] was originally a Dwarf-home and primarily named by them, the Sindarin and Westron names are probably in origin of similar senses.' He interpreted (hesitantly) *Azanulbizar* as containing ZN 'dark, dim', *ûl* 'streams', and *bizar* a dale or valley, the whole thus meaning 'Vale of Dim Streams'.

The name *Khazad-dûm* had already appeared in the *Quenta Silmarillion* (V.274), where it was the name of the Dwarf-city in the Blue Mountains which the Elves called *Nogrod*.

37   The word *up* here is odd (and my father later put a query against it), since the statement that the East Gates were on a much lower level than the great hall where they now were is part of the original composition.

38   This passage survives in FR (pp. 331–2), but there Frodo's thoughts turn to Bilbo and Bag End for a different reason – the mention by Gandalf of Bilbo's corslet of mithril-rings. Moria-silver had only just emerged (note 35), and the connection with Bilbo's mailcoat had not been made.

39   In the previous chapter the name *Dimrilldale* appears as a correction (p. 433, note 13), together with the first mention of the lake in the dale, there called *Glassmere*; *Mirrormere* is named on the map reproduced on p. 439. The Elvish name *Helevorn* (in the *Etymologies*, V.365, translated 'black-glass') given to it here had appeared in the *Quenta Silmarillion* as the name of the lake in Thargelion beside which dwelt Cranthir, son of Fëanor. No other Elvish name for Mirrormere is recorded in published writing, but in the notes referred to in note 36 my father said that the Sindarin name, not given in LR, was in fact *Nen Cenedril* 'Lake Looking-glass'. Translating *Kheled-zâram* as 'probably "glass-pool"', he noted: '*kheled* was certainly a Dwarf word for "glass", and seems to be the origin of Sindarin *heleð* "glass". Cf. Lake *Hele(ð)vorn* near the Dwarf-regions in the north of Dor Caranthir [Thargelion]: it means "black glass", and is probably also a translation of a Dwarf-name (given by the Dwarves: the same is probably the case in the Moria region) such as *Narag-zâram* (that NRG was Khuzdul for "black" is seen in the Dwarf-name for Mordor: *Nargûn*).'

THE MINES OF MORIA 467

40   As the manuscript of this chapter was found among my father's papers it ended at the foot of a page, at the words 'a great slab of whitened stone' on p. 460. I had assumed that this was where my father broke off, until, a few days before the typescript of this book was due to go to the printers, I came most unexpectedly upon a further page, beginning at the words '"It looks like a tomb!" thought Frodo', which had evidently been separated from the rest of the chapter long ago, on account of the inscriptions. It was of course too late to reproduce these in this book, but an account of the runic alphabets as my father conceived them at this time and of the writing on Balin's tomb and in the Book of Mazarbul will, I hope, be published in Volume VII.

It may be noticed here, however, that it was at this point that my father decided to abandon the Old English (or 'Hobbit') runes and to use the real runes of Beleriand, which were already in a developed form. The inscription on the tomb (*Balin Son of Burin Lord of Moria*) was first written in the former, and then immediately below in 'Angerthas', twice, with the same words but in runes that differ in certain points.

On the back of this newly discovered page, and as I think very probably dating from the same time, is a very roughly pencilled design of a 'Page of Balin's Book', in runes representing English spelt phonetically, which reads thus:

> We drove out the Orcs fro(m) . . . guard
> . . . . (f)irst hall. We slew many under the bright sun
> in the dale. Flói was killed by an arrow . . . .
> We did . . . .
> . . . . We have occupied the twenty-first hall of
> . . . . . north end. There there is . . . .
> . . . . shaft is . . . .
> (B)alin has set up his chair in the chamber of Mazar
> bul . . . . Balin is Lord of
> Moria . . . .

And on the right-hand bottom corner of the page, torn off from the rest, is the name *Kazaddūm*.

INDEX

This Index is made on the same lines as those of the previous volumes, but the extreme fluidity of names in this case, especially among the hobbits, has proved taxing, as a glance at the entries under *Took* will show. The complexity of the matter to be indexed scarcely allows of a consistent presentation.

Certain names appear constantly throughout the book, and where possible I have reduced the more intimidating blocks of references by using the word *passim* to mean that a name is missing only from a single page here and there in a long series.

Forms are standardized, and no account is taken of the innumerable variants in capitalization, hyphenation, and separation of elements that occur in the texts.

Names appearing in the reproductions of pages from the original manuscripts are not indexed.

Allen and Unwin   11, 40, 43, 84, 108, 386
Almaren, Isle of   122
Anar   One of the Dwarves who accompanied Bilbo from Bag End. 238, 240, 315
Ancient Days   169, 179, 260, 358. See *Earliest Days*, *Elder Days*.
Anduin   205, 410. See *Beleghir*, *Great River*.
Angband   182-3, 187, 218; *King of Angband* 183; *Halls of Iron* 182, 187; *Iron Halls* 183
Angerthas   173, 467
Angle, The   Land between the rivers Hoarwell and Loudwater. 202
Angmar   128
Annals of Beleriand   384, 412, 433
Annerchin   Goblin Gate (in the Misty Mountains). 416, 432
Appledore   Family name in Bree. 137, 141
Arad Dain   See 432.
Aragorn   (1) Suggested name for Gandalf's horse. 351. (2) Aragorn son of Arathorn. 128, 176, 210, 367-9, 379, 387, 414, 430-2, 434-5, 437
Arathorn   Father of Aragorn. 176
Archet   Village of the Bree-land. 133, 165, 174, 332, 352, 354, 367
Arda   122 (*the Spring of Arda*).
Arod   (1) Suggested name for Gandalf's horse. 351. (2) Name of a horse of Rohan. 351
Arwen   213, 365
Asfaloth   Glorfindel's horse. 368

INDEX

469

As I was sitting by the way 98
Athelas Healing plant. 190, 197
Auden, W. H. 382
Avallon Númenor. 215
Azanulbizâr Dwarvish name: Dimrill-dale. 465–6; *'Vale of Dim Streams'* 466; *Azanûl* 466

Bag End 14–18, 20, 23, 26–7, 30–5, 38–40, 43, 45, 53, 74, 76–7, 85, 168, 221–2, 228, 233–5, 237–8, 240–4, 247–8, 250–1, 254–5, 266, 268, 274–7, 280, 283–4, 288–9, 314–15, 318–19, 324, 374–6, 385, 398, 459, 466; *Bag End Underhill* 16, 30, 37, 39, 76, 138, 244, 247, 376
Baggins family, Bagginses 13–15, 17, 19, 22–3, 25, 27–8, 31, 34, 36, 54, 78, 96, 221–2, 234, 249–50, 254, 264, 279–80, 287, 289, 291–3, 313, 338, 357; *Baggins country* 279, 296
Baggins, Angelica 15, 17–18, 32, 35, 247
~ *Balbo* Bilbo's great-grandfather in LR. 249. (Replaced *Inigo Baggins* (2).)
~ *Bilbo* 11, 13–42, 46, 53, 56, 58–60, 62–3, 65, 69–70, 73–7, 79–87, 95–6, 103, 108–9, 122, 126, 128, 139, 144, 150, 154, 177, 194, 203–4, 207–8, 210, 212–13, 220–9, 233–56, 261–8, 271–2, 274–7, 280–4, 288–90, 292, 300, 305, 310–22, 330, 346, 357, 360, 365, 369–81 *passim*, 384–7, 391–406 *passim*, 412, 414, 417, 424, 429, 444, 459, 466. *Mad Baggins* 250; Bilbo's book, memoirs 13, 19, 29, 229, 240, 245, 288, 300, 305, 314–15, 371–2, 376–8, 380, 405; his marriage 17, 29, 36; Primula Brandybuck his wife 29, 42
~ *Bingo* (1) Son of Bilbo. 27–36, 40–3, 245, 267; origin of the name 28, 34. (2) Bilbo's cousin (see also under *Bolger, Bolger-Baggins*), son of Drogo Baggins. 221–5, 227–8, 233–302 *passim*, 305, 309; references after *Bingo* > *Frodo*, 315, 323–5, 330, 369, 371–3, 375, 377, 379–81, 391, 393. (3) Grandfather of Drogo. 247, 249 (replaced by *Largo Baggins*).
~ *Bungo* Bilbo's father. 13, 19, 25, 27, 35, 222, 247, 249, 316–17
~ *Dora* Frodo's aunt (in LR). 247, 249. (Replaced *Semolina Baggins.*)
~ *Drogo* Father of Bingo > Frodo. 26, 38, 221–2, 234, 244–5, 247, 249, 282, 316–17, 385, 400. (Replaced *Rollo Bolger*.)
~ *Faramond* Passing replacement of Frodo Baggins. 373, 409
~ *Folco* Passing replacement of Frodo Baggins. 371–3
~ *Fosco* Father of Drogo (in LR). 249. (Replaced *Togo Baggins*.)
~ *Frodo* (references in this book before the change Bingo > Frodo is reached) 30, 41, 66, 70–1, 107, 112–13, 120, 122–3, 126–7, 176, 193–4, 198, 204, 212–13, 220–4, 234, 241, 246, 250, 268, 272, 277, 280, 284, 287, 297; (after the change) 309, 311, 313–87 *passim*, 391–8, 400–1, 403, 406–24 *passim*, 427–31, 436, 438, 440–60 *passim*, 463, 467

THE RETURN OF THE SHADOW

~ *Inigo* (1) A contemporary of Bilbo's. 17, 35. (2) Bilbo's great-grandfather. 222, 247, 249

~ *Largo* Frodo's great-grandfather (in LR). 249. (Replaced *Bingo Baggins* (3).)

~ *Mungo* Bilbo's grandfather. 222, 247, 249

~ *Rosa* (1) Bilbo's aunt. 222, 224, 316–17. (2) Bilbo's cousin (in LR). 222

~ *Semolina* (1) Bilbo's aunt or cousin. 15, 18, 32, 35. (2) Drogo's sister, aunt of Bingo > Frodo. 247, 249. (Replaced by *Dora Baggins*.)

~ *Togo* Father of Drogo. 247, 249. (Replaced by *Fosco Baggins*.)

Bagshot Row 21, 26, 30, 35, 244, 276

Bain Son of Bard, King of Dale. 26, 210, 213, 369

Balin Dwarf, companion of Thorin Oakenshield. 15, 17, 210, 213, 217, 226, 369, 381, 391–2, 395, 397–400, 409, 412, 429, 443–4, 459–60, 467; *Lord of Moria* 443, 460, 467; *son of Burin* 443–4, 460, 467; *son of Fundin* 444, 460; Balin's tomb 443–4, 460–2, 467; *Balin's Book* 460, 467 (see *Mazarbul*).

Balrog(s) 187–8, 215, 462

Banks Hobbit family name. 137, 236. *Eglantine Banks* 297

Barahir Called 'the Bold', father of Beren. 182

Bard Called 'the Bowman', King of Dale. 26, 210, 213, 369

Barrow-downs (including references to *the Downs*) 107, 111–12, 115, 117–18, 121, 125–6, 192, 334, 349, 401

Barrow-wight(s) 42–3, 109–12, 115–19, 121, 125, 127, 129–30, 132, 160, 169, 198, 218, 226, 401, 414; relation to Black Riders 118–20, 401

Battle of Five Armies 77, 210, 263, 319, 429

Battle of Unnumbered Tears 412

Beardless Men See 434.

Beleg Called 'the Bowman', Elf of Doriath. 183

Beleghir Early name of the Great River. 410–11, 434

Beleriand 215–16, 433; Runes of Beleriand 467

Belfalas See 438.

Benish Armon See 464.

Bëor Father of Men. *Sons of Bëor* 331

Beorn 387

Beren 179–84, 186–7, 197, 358; called *Camlost, Gamlost* 179, 186, *Erhamion* 183

Bert One of the Trolls turned to stone. 193, 360

Beruthiel, Queen 454

Bifur Dwarf, companion of Thorin Oakenshield. 210

Big Folk, Big People Men (as seen by hobbits). 54–5, 66, 95, 121, 132, 134, 150, 178, 197, 221, 253, 278–9, 294, 310–11, 313, 408

Bilbo Baggins See *Baggins*.

Bill the pony 432. See *Ferny, Bill*.

INDEX 471

Birthday Party See *Party*.

Black Country Mordor. 131, 216, 218; *Black Land* 129, 131

Black Gulf Moria. 429, 435, 437; *Black Pit* 435

Black Mountains Range south of the Misty Mountains. 410–11, 436, 440. See *Blue Mountains, South Mountains*.

Black Riders (including references to *Riders, (black) horsemen, black men*, &c.) 44, 48, 54–5, 58, 60, 63–4, 66–7, 69–71, 73, 84, 87–91, 95–7, 100, 103–4, 106, 109, 118–20, 126, 129, 131, 151–5, 157–63, 171–6, 178, 185–6, 188–91, 194–9, 207–8, 211–13, 217–18, 221–5, 269, 272, 277–9, 281–2, 285, 287–8, 291–3, 295, 297, 301, 303, 324–6, 328, 336, 339–44, 347–50, 353–68 *passim*, 371–3, 381, 401, 408, 416, 462. See *Ring-wraiths, (the) Nine*.

Black Tower 218, 253. See *Dark Tower*.

Blessed Realm 182–4, 187, 225, 364, 394, 398–9; *Blessed Realms* 187

Bliscarn Early name for Caradhras. 433, 438

Blue Mountains (1) Eredlindon. 466. (2) Range south of the Misty Mountains. 410–11, 436, 440. See *Black Mountains, South Mountains*.

Bob The ostler at Bree. 135, 164, 174, 345–7; also called *Rob*, 164, 174

Boffin family 25, 31; *Boffinses* 13–14, 18, 23, 31; *Boffins* 22, 284, 304, 313, 385; *Boffin-country* 298; *Mr Boffin of Overhill* 254, 284

Boffin, Fosco Cousin of Bilbo; son of Jago Boffin. 317, 319, 386

~ *Hugo* Husband of Donnamira Took. 317–18, 386

~ *Jago* Son of Donnamira Took and Hugo Boffin. 317, 386

~ *Paladin* Father of Peregrin Boffin. 385–6

~ *Peregrin* Grandson of Donnamira Took; known in Bree as *Trotter*. 371, 373–4, 376, 384–7, 392–3, 395–6, 406, 412, 415, 422, 430–1; called *Perry* 393

Bofur Dwarf, companion of Thorin Oakenshield. 210

Bolger family, Bolgers 31, 33, 49, 78, 96, 267, 284, 304

Bolger, Bingo Bingo Bolger-Baggins before his adoption by Bilbo. 36–7, 40

~ *Caramella* A relative of Bilbo's (formerly a Took, subsequently a Chubb). 32, 35, 38

~ *Fosco* Bingo's somnolent uncle. 38, 51, 65, 247

~ *Fredegar* Called *Fatty*. 112, 273, 275, 299, 301, 326, 373

~ *Hamilcar* 373. (Replaced by *Fredegar Bolger*.)

~ *Odo* (including all references to Odo both as Took and later as Bolger, see p. 267 note 3). 41–66 *passim*, 69–70, 74, 83, 88–104, 106, 109–10, 112–13, 115, 118, 125, 127–8, 130, 136–9, 141, 148, 155–6, 160–1, 163, 166–9, 171–2, 177, 185, 209, 221–2, 250–1, 267, 273, 275–80, 283–95 *passim*, 299–305, 316–18, 323–8, 330, 336–57 *passim*, 359, 361, 364–8, 371–5, 395–8, 409, 413. Called *Odo Took-Bolger* 316–17, 323; passes as 'Baggins' 339–41, 347, 352, 356, 366, 368, 375

472   THE RETURN OF THE SHADOW

On the history of 'Odo' see 221, 250, 273, 299–303, 323–4, 374–5, 396, 409

~ *Olo* (1) = Odo Bolger. 299–300. (2) Odo's father. 317

~ *Rollo* (1) Precursor of Drogo Baggins. 26, 37–8, 222, 234. (2) A friend of Bilbo's. 247

Bolger-Baggins, Bingo (before he became Bingo Baggins (2)). 36–40, 45–106 *passim*, 109, 112–13, 115, 118–45 *passim*, 148–74 *passim*, 176, 179, 185–6, 188–99, 206–17, 219–23, 226, 233–4, 247, 267, 277, 284, 310, 327–8, 334, 336, 354, 362, 365–6, 369, 371–2, 375. On Bingo's sword see 128, 186, 190, 213–14

Bombadil See *Tom Bombadil.*

Bombur Dwarf, companion of Thorin Oakenshield. 210

Book of Lost Tales 187, 437

Bor Man of the Elder Days. 412

Boromir (1) Son of Bor, slain in the Battle of Unnumbered Tears. 412. (2) Man of Ond. 395, 398, 400, 403–4, 406, 408–11, 414–15, 417, 419, 424–7, 429–32, 436–7, 440, 447, 451, 457, 463; his horse 432

Borthendor See *Rohan.*

Bounders (of the Shire-borders) 254

Bracegirdle Hobbit family name. 23, 25, 28, 31, 33, 284

Bracegirdle, Hugo 32, 35, 247

Brand Son of Bain son of Bard, King of Dale. 210, 213, 220, 369, 398, 404

Brandybuck family, Brandybucks 22–5, 27, 29–31, 34–5, 37, 49, 78, 92, 95, 99–101, 104–6, 235, 241, 244, 267, 273, 275, 283, 289, 291, 296–8, 313, 318, 330, 332, 334

Brandybuck, Alaric Son of Gorboduc Brandybuck. 317

~ *Amalda* 35. (Replaced by *Primula Brandybuck*.)

~ *Athanaric* Son of Gorboduc Brandybuck. 317

~ *Bellissima* Daughter of Gorboduc Brandybuck. 317

~ *Bercilak* 273. (Replaced by *Lanorac Brandybuck*.)

~ *Caradoc* Father of Meriadoc. 251, 267, 301, 317. (Replaced by *Saradoc Brandybuck*.)

~ *Frodo* See 42–3, 45–6.

~ *Gorboduc* Grandfather of Bingo > Frodo. 37–8, 234, 244, 249, 317–18

~ *Lanorac* Cousin of Meriadoc and Bingo. 273, 275, 330

~ *Marmaduke* Earlier name for Meriadoc. 33, 35, 39, 42–3, 45–6, 49, 51, 65, 67, 76, 83, 89, 94, 98–104, 106, 108–13, 115, 123, 286, 302, 327

~ *Melilot* 315. (Replaced *Melissa Brandybuck*.)

~ *Melissa* 38, 101, 106, 315. (Replaced by *Melilot Brandybuck*.)

~ *Meriadoc* (including references to *Merry*) 33, 76, 83, 106, 114, 118, 120, 123–5, 127–30, 136, 141, 148, 159–61, 163–4, 169, 171–2, 174–5, 178, 184–5, 193, 195, 207, 209, 221–2, 241, 250–3, 267–8, 273, 275–6, 283, 288–9, 291–2, 295–303, 305, 314–17,

INDEX 473

323–4, 326–30, 334, 341, 353–8, 361, 365–8, 370–1, 373–5, 395, 397–8, 406–10, 419, 423, 427, 429, 436, 446, 449, 451–2, 456, 459, 463, 465. (Replaced *Marmaduke Brandybuck.*)

~ *Orlando* 26, 35. (Replaced by *Prospero Brandybuck.*)

~ *Primula* 26, 29, 35, 37–8, 40, 42, 221, 234, 244, 247, 249, 267, 317–18, 386; as Bilbo's wife 29, 40

~ *Prospero* 24, 26, 32, 35. (Replaced *Orlando Brandybuck*, replaced by *Prospero Took.*)

~ *Roderick* = Rory Brandybuck. 317–18

~ *Rorimac* = Rory Brandybuck (in LR). 318

~ *Rory* Grandfather of Meriadoc; often called *Old Rory.* 25, 27, 32, 35, 38, 95, 101, 104, 237, 241, 267, 288, 296, 315, 318, 386, 393

~ *Saradoc 'Scattergold'* Father of Meriadoc (in LR). 106, 267, 301. (Replaced *Caradoc Brandybuck.*)

~ *Theodoric* Son of Gorboduc Brandybuck. 317

Brandy Hall 99, 101, 104, 245, 289, 304–5, 313, 386; *Master of the Hall* 301. See *Bucklebury.*

Brandywine Bridge 53, 56, 72, 100, 102–8, 132, 170–2, 275, 278, 280, 284, 286, 298, 338, 350

Brandywine River (including references to *the River*) 29–30, 35, 37, 42, 52–3, 56, 58, 66, 72, 89, 92, 94, 96–7, 99–100, 103, 105–9, 112, 121, 236, 247, 280, 284, 286, 293, 298, 305, 312, 316, 324, 371, 376

Bree 107, 110, 121, 126, 129, 131–5, 138, 140–2, 144, 150, 153–7, 159–62, 164–7, 170–6, 198, 211, 214, 217, 222–3, 235, 269, 329, 331–3, 337–56 *passim*, 359, 367–8, 374–5, 387, 414, 430–1. On the people of Bree see 132–4, 223, 331, and see *Bree-folk.*

Bree-folk 132, 154–5, 159, 164, 223, 331, 351; *Bree-dialect* 137

Bree-hill 129–34, 165, 174, 223. See *Brill.*

Bree-land 133, 332, 342, 354–5; *Breelanders* 132

Brill Village in Buckinghamshire ('Bree-hill'). 131

Britain 41. *British* (language) 131

Brockhouse Hobbit family name. 137, 236, 315

Brown, Mr. Assumed name of Frodo Took at Bree. 135–6, 140, 152

Bruinen The river of Rivendell (Loudwater). 126, 192, 199–201, 204–5, 210; *Ford of Bruinen* 199, 367. See *Loudwater, River of Rivendell.*

Buck Hill The hill in which was Brandy Hall. 298, 304

Buckland (village; see 105) 29–30, 35, 37, 40, 46, 53, 55–6, 61, 65, 89, 92, 105–7; (region) 65, 67, 94, 100, 104–5, 107, 109, 160, 175, 244, 273, 275–6, 279–80, 283, 286, 288, 291, 298, 303, 323–4, 326, 366, 375, 392, 401; *Bucklanders* 100.

Road to Buckland 46–7, 50, 66, 72, 89, 92, 97, 105, 107, 288, 291; road within Buckland 104, 106, 286, 298, 304; causeway road 105, 107, 286, 291; *North Gate* 304

Bucklebury 92, 97, 100–2, 105, 107, 221–3, 273, 275, 279, 283, 289,

474 THE RETURN OF THE SHADOW

292–3; *Bucklebury-by-the-River* 100, 105, *-beyond-the-River* 298; *Great Hole of Bucklebury* 234, 245, 386 (see *Brandy Hall*).

Bucklebury Ferry (including references to *the Ferry*) 107, 200, 286, 291–2, 294, 298, 300, 304, 325, 350

Buckwood Original name of the Old Forest. 35

Burin Dwarf. (1) Son of Balin. 395, 397–8, 400, 409, 412, 444. (2) Father of Balin. 443–4, 460, 467 (see *Fundin*).

Burrowes Hobbit family name. 18, 25, 31; *Burrows* 18; plural *Burroweses* 13–14, 17, 23, 31, *Burrowses* 22

Burrowes, Folco Lawyer. 33, 36

~ *Orlando* Friend of Bilbo's. 32, 36; spelt *Burrows* 247. (Replaced *Orlando Grubb*.)

Bury Underwood Early name of Buckland (as village). 35, 105. (Replaced *Wood Eaton*.)

Butterbur, Barnabas 130, 133–41, 148–56, 158–60, 163–4, 172–3, 175, 329, 331–4, 338–43, 345–6, 349–50, 359, 431; called *Barney* 139, 159; later name *Barliman Butterbur* 130. (Replaced *Timothy Titus*.)

Button, Jo Hobbit who saw a Tree-man beyond the North Moors. 254, 319, 386

Bywater 13, 19–22, 29, 50, 101, 244–5, 249–50, 253, 278, 294; *Bywater Pool* 50, 72; *Bywater Road* 244

Camlost 'Empty-handed'; see *Beren*.

Caradras (1) The Redhorn. 433, 435, 438; later form *Caradhras* 437, 440–1. For other names see 433. (2) The River Redway (later Silverlode). 433–4, 438, 462. For other names see 433.

Caradras dilthen The Little Redway, first name for Sirannon the Gate-stream of Moria. 462

Carnbeleg Early name for Caradhras. 433, 438

Carndoom The Red Valley; early name for Dimrill-dale. 433. For other names see 433, and *Dunruin*.

Carn Dûm The stronghold of the Witch-king of Angmar. 128

Caron-dûn The Red Valley; early name for Dimrill-dale. 419, 429, 433, 437; *Caron-doom* 433, 464. For other names see 433, and *Dunruin*.

Carpenter, Humphrey Biography. 18, 28, 131, 214, 227

Carrock, The Great rock in the Anduin. 205, 438

Cat and the Fiddle, The 141–2, 145–7, 336

Celebrant The river Silverlode. 434

Celebrimbor of Hollin 404, 449

Celebrin Early name of the Silverlode. 434

Chaucer, Geoffrey 382 (*The Reeve's Tale*).

Cherwell, River 35

Chetwood 175, 332, 355

Children of Lúthien The Half-elven. 395, 400, 413

INDEX 475

Children of the World 182

Chronology (1) within the narrative. 160, 175, 193, 211, 219, 337–8, 355–6, 360, 362, 432, 434–6. (2) of writing (external dating). 11, 40, 43–4, 108–10, 309, 369–70, 461

Chubb family, Chubbs 14, 18, 22–3, 25, 31, 33; *Chubbses* 13, 18

Chubb, Adamanta Wife of the Old Took. 317

~ *Caramella* 38, 247, 315. (Replaced *Caramella Bolger*.)

~ *Cosimo* A friend of Bilbo's. 33, 36, 38. (Replaced by *Cosimo Hornblower*.)

Círdan 413

Cirith Ungol 382

City of Stone City of the Land of Ond. 379–82. See *Stone-land*.

Combe Village of the Bree-land. 132–3, 151, 157, 165–6, 174, 223, 332, 339, 354; *Combe-under-Bree* 236, 315

Company (of the Ring) 406, 409, 411, 419, 430, 432, 435–7, 444–5, 461–2, 466

Council of Elrond 216, 225, 363, 395–6, 399–401, 404–5, 407, 409–14, 437, 461

Crack(s) of Doom 265, 274, 323, 374, 379–80

Cracks of Earth 82–3, 85, 126, 265

Cram 177, 186, 194, 357, 368

Crandir The River Redway (later Silverlode). 432–3

Cranthir Son of Fëanor. 466

Crick Village of the Bree-land. 132, 140

Crickhollow 140, 174, 221, 273, 283, 299, 301, 303–4, 323, 326, 328, 336–8, 350–1, 366, 371–3, 375, 401, 413. See *Ringhay*.

Cris-caron The Red Pass. 419, 422, 429–31, 433–4, 438, 445; also *Cris Caron*, *Cris-carron*, *Criscarn* 433

Dáin King under the Mountain. 210, 226, 366, 391, 398–9, 414, 437

Dairon Minstrel of Doriath. 187–8

Dale 14, 21, 24, 26, 30–1, 54–5, 65–6, 177, 210, 213, 220–1, 225, 369, 392, 398, 404, 412, 429; *Lord of Dale* 225; *Dale-men*, *Men of Dale* 54–5, 65–6, 177 (language), 221

Danas Green-elves. 412

Dark-elves 71

Dark Kingdom Mordor. 208

Dark Lord 75, 86–7, 121–2, 127, 192–3, 196, 211–12, 224–7, 253, 258, 260, 269–70, 272, 322, 329, 364, 381, 397–9, 401, 403–4, 437–8; *Dark Master* 78, *the Master* 78–9, 81–2, 261, 398; *Dark Power* 78. See *(the) Lord*, *Lord of the Ring(s)*, *Necromancer*, *Sauron*, *Thû*.

Dark Tower 81, 127, 131, 198, 209, 214, 217–18, 381–2. See *Black Tower*.

Dead Marshes 401, 409, 413, 438

Déagol Gollum's friend, finder of the Ring. 86. See *Dígol*.

476   THE RETURN OF THE SHADOW

Deephallow   Village in the Eastfarthing. 286, 296, 325

Diarin   See *Ilverin*.

Digol   Gollum. 78, 86, 261

Dimbar   (1) Land between Sirion and Mindeb in the Elder Days. 432. (2) A region north of Rivendell. 432

Dimrill-dale(s)   (1) Troll-country north of Rivendell. 205, 360–1, 367–8, 415, 432; *Dimrill-lands* 360. See *Entish Lands*, *Hoardale*, *Tum Dincelon*. (2) In later sense, Nanduhirion. 432–3, 437, 459–60, 464–6

Dimrill-stair   (1) Name of the pass beneath Caradhras (later the Redhorn Gate). 433–4; *Dimrill* 438. See *Pendrethdulur*. (2) Later sense, the descent from the pass on the eastern side. 433

Dior Thingol's Heir   68

Dol Guldur   85, 414

Doon-Caron, *Dûn Caron*   The Red Valley; early name for Dimrill-dale. 433. See *Carndoom*, *Caron-dûn*.

Dor Caranthir   The land of C(a)ranthir son of Fëanor (Thargelion). 466

Dori   Dwarf, companion of Thorin Oakenshield. 210

Doriath   180–3, 188, 216, 384

Dragon(s)   19, 22, 29, 41, 78, 82–3, 227, 245, 260, 320, 379, 384, 399; referring to Smaug 77, 256, 319, 429; *dragon-gold*, *dragon-curse* 18, 43, 73, 233, 379, and cf. 42.

Du-finnion   Elvish name of Trotter. 361, 392. See *Ethelion*, *Padathir*, *Rimbedir*.

Dúnedain   294; *the Dúnadan* (Aragorn) 369

Dunruin   The Red Valley; early name of Dimrill-dale. 454, 464

Durin   429, 437, 449, 451, 466; *Lord of Moria* 449; *Durin's race*, *clan* 391, 429; *Doors of Durin* 449, 463

Dwalin   Dwarf, companion of Thorin Oakenshield. 210

Dwarves   Visitors to Hobbiton 20, 30–1, 36, 48, 63, 66, 101, 106, 149–50, 156, 160, 221, 234–5, 238, 246, 253, 315, 336; companions of Bilbo 203–4, 392, 398; Dwarves of Moria 173, 226, 391, 429, 437, 448, 458–9, 463; of the Lonely Mountain 31, 210, 226, 381, 391–2, 398–9, 411, 414, 429; other references 75, 79, 87, 117, 132, 140, 178, 243, 253, 294, 311, 313, 315, 348, 385, 429, and see *Hoards of the Dwarves*, *Rings of the Dwarves*.

    Dwarfs 210, 217, 221; *Dwarf and Goblin War* 382; *Dwarf-city* 391, 466; *Dwarf-folk* 463; *Dwarf-gates* 444, 449; *Dwarf-home* 466; *Dwarf-kingdom* 210; *Dwarf-lords* 258, 269, 458, 465–6; *Dwarf-regions* 466; *Dwarf-writing* 443, Runes 460; Dwarf-names and language 246, 444, 451, 466

Dwarvish   (of language) 465

Dweller in the Water   443–4; *Dweller in the Pool* 453; *the water-monster* 455

INDEX   477

Eagles 416

Eärendel 215, 254

Eärendil was a mariner 393, 412

Earliest Days 311, 329, 349; *oldest days* 179. See *Ancient Days, Elder Days.*

Eastfarthing 124, 278, 298, 312–13, 387; *East Shire* 286

East Gate(s) of Moria 443, 454, 458–60, 466; 'the chief entrance was on the East' 429

East Road (including many references to *the Road*) 46–7, 50, 53, 65, 72, 103–4, 106, 108, 125–6, 129–30, 132, 134, 149, 152–3, 156–7, 159–62, 165–72, 174, 176, 178, 191–6, 198–205, 217, 219, 236, 274–5, 278, 283–4, 301, 329, 332–3, 336–7, 339, 341–56 *passim*, 359–61, 368; *the Old Road* 167, 169; *the west road* 417. Course of the Road 192, 199–203; distances along the Road 170–1, 356, 367–8

East, The 182, 398, 409

Eglor, River In Beleriand. 434

Elbereth (1) Son of Dior Thingol's Heir. 68. (2) Varda. 59, 68, 70, 186, 189, 197, 212, 214, 280, 282, 324, 358, 364, 394; *Elberil* 68

Elberin See *Ilverin.*

Eldalië 71

Elder Days 187, 329, 349. See *Ancient Days, Earliest Days.*

Elder Edda 246

Elder Race The Elves. 364

Elendil 105, 169, 174–5, 192, 197–9, 215–16, 218, 271, 320, 355, 358; 'Elf-friend' 215–16, 358. See *Orendil, Valandil.*

Elf-, Elven- Elf-armour (Bilbo's) 371–2, 386 (see *Mailcoat*); *Elven-fair* 181; *Elf-folk* 71; *Elf-horse* 207; *Elven-kin* 184, 187; *Elf-king(s)* 179, 215, 227, 260, 320, 358, *Elven-king(s)* 182, 258, 269; *Elf-kingdoms* 358; *Elf-letters* 449; *Elf-lord(s)* 364, 397, 400; *Elf-mail* (Bilbo's) 443–4 (see *Mailcoat*); *Elven-maid* 184; *Elf-name* 208; *Elf-race* 182; *Elf-rings* 404 (see *Rings of the Elves*); *Elf-spell* 444; *Elf-stone* 192; *Elf-way* 448; *Elvenwise* 181, (with reference to the Gnomes) 212, 217, 364

Elf-friend(s) 60, 65, 215–16, 358. See *Elendil.*

Elf-latin 60, 69, 280

Elf-tongue 58–60, 62, 67, 194, 196, 280, 449; *Elven-tongue* 324; *Ancient Tongue* 280–1, 325; *two Elf-languages* 253; called 'secret' 58, 67, 253, 280. See *Elvish.*

Elf-towers 93, 105, 269, 310, 312–13. See *Towers, West Towers.*

Elf-wraiths 75, 78, 87, 225, 269

Elrond (many references are to Elrond's house in Rivendell) 41–2, 126, 179, 193–4, 204–10, 212–19, 225, 274, 358, 362, 365, 374, 379–82, 391, 395–409, 411–14, 416–17, 419, 421, 424, 430, 432, 436, 444, 448; *Kinsmen of Elrond* 395, 398. See *Council of Elrond.*

Elros 216, 412

478 THE RETURN OF THE SHADOW

Elvenhome 180

Elves Visitors to Hobbiton from Rivendell 20, 30–1, 48, 60, 63, 66, 68, 101, 106, 149, 156, 160, 235, 315, 336; to Bingo/Frodo at Bag End 36, 234, 253; in the Shire 58, 253, 280; Elves of Rivendell 60, 71, 126, 207, 209, 212, 217, 225, 364, 393–5, 416; of Gildor's company 48, 58–62, 66–71, 73, 88, 91, 101, 103, 106, 109, 160, 194, 280–1, 295, 304, 324–5; of Hollin 418, 429, 437, 444, 448–9, 463; few in South and East of the world 260; wars of the Elves and Goblins 350; in relation to hobbits 79, 93, 294, 311–13; fading (on account of the Ring) 261, 320; other references 41, 61, 64, 70, 75, 78, 87, 117, 121–2, 178, 182–4, 187–8, 190, 198, 212, 215–16, 227, 253–4, 260, 311, 364, 379–80, 394–5, 397, 402–6, 412–13, 417, 419, 451, 458, 466. See *High Elves, Wood-elves*; *Rings of the Elves, Elf-wraiths*.

Elvish (of language) 217, 324, 395, 411, 432–3, 438, 451–2, 466; (of letters) 384, 449; (with other reference) 280, 454, 463. Elvish speech cited, 194, 196, 324, 361, 394, 451–2

Elwing 215

Emyn Beraid The Tower Hills. 105

Enemy, The 179, 182–4, 207, 253, 266, 281–2, 322–3, 358, 384, 402, 423–4

Entish Lands Troll-country north of Rivendell. 201, 205; *Entish Dales* 205. (Replaced by *Ettenmoors, Ettendales*.) See *Dimrill-dale, Hoardale*.

Ents 205, 254

Erceleb The first name for *mithril* or Moria-silver. 465. See *Ithil*.

Ered Nimrais The White Mountains. 399

Eregion Hollin. 432. See *Regornion*.

Erestor Elf of Rivendell, Elrond's kinsman and counsellor. 395, 398, 400–2, 405, 413–14

Erhamion 'Onehanded'; see *Beren*.

Errantry (poem) 412

Esgaroth Lake-town. 213, 369, 411

Ethelion Elvish name of Peregrin Boffin (Trotter). 392, 395. See *Dufinnion, Padathir, Rimbedir*.

Ettenmoors 192, 205; *Ettendales* 205. See *Entish Lands*.

Etymologies In Vol. V. 186, 188, 432–3, 435, 437, 463, 466

Eye, The The Eye of Sauron. 381–2

Fairfax ('Fair-mane'), suggested name for Gandalf's horse. 351

Fair Folk The Elves. 60; cf. 285

Fallohides 124, 294

Fang One of Farmer Maggot's dogs. 290, 293

Fangorn Forest (including references to *the Forest*) 189, 363, 367, 381–2, 397, 399, 401, 409–11, 419, 434, 436, 438, 440, 464. See *Neldoreth* (2).

Faraway Fictitious home of Bingo/Frodo Baggins. 280, 324, 334

INDEX

Far Downs 107

Farewell! farewell, now hearth and hall! 300–1, 326

Farewell Party See *Party*.

Farmer Giles of Ham 131

Farthings 278; *Four Farthings* 298, 313; *Four Quarters* 313, 380

Fathers of Men 182

Fëanor 215–16, 466

Felagund See *Finrod* (2), *Inglor*.

Fellowes Assumed name of Odo and Frodo Took at Bree. 141

Fellowship of the Ring 398, 409

Ferny Family name in Bree. 137; cf. 141

Ferny, Bill (139), 142, 153, 158, 162, 164–6, 175–6, 191, 350, 353–4; spelt *Ferney* 334, 342, 350, 354, 359; his pony 164, 175, 191, 354, 359, 432

Fiery Mountain 82–3, 85, 126, 189, 214, 218, 265, 323, 380–2, 397, 402, 406–7, 409, 421; *Fiery Hill* 214; *Fire Mountain* 411; *the Fire* 402, 405; *the Mountain Red* 301; eruption of the mountain 380–1

Finarfin 72, 188

Fingolfin 122

Finrod (1) Third son of Finwë, later *Finarfin*. 60, 71–2, 188. (2) Finrod Felagund, son of Finarfin. 72, 188; *Finrod Inglor* 188

Finwë 72, 188

Firefoot Suggested name for Gandalf's horse (see *Narothal*). 351

First Kindred (of the Elves). 188

First War of the Gods 122

Flói Dwarf, companion of Balin in Moria. 467

Flymarshes First name of the Midgewater Marshes. 165–6

Fonstad, Karen The Atlas of Middle-earth. 204–5, 305

Ford (of Rivendell) 126, 163, 170–1, 176, 190–3, 195–204, 206–7, 211–12, 219, 355, 359–61, 364–5, 368, 416–17, 440; *Ford of Bruinen* 199, 367

Forest River 218

Forsaken Inn 170

Foster, Robert The Complete Guide to Middle-earth. 284

Four Farthings See *Farthings*.

Frár Dwarf (son of Balin?) accompanying Glóin at Rivendell (replaced by Burin). 397–8, 412

French 247

Frodo Baggins, Frodo Took See *Baggins, Took*.

Fundin Father of Balin. 444, 460. See *Burin* (2).

Furth, Charles 11, 40, 43, 108–9

Galadlóriel Gnomish name of Laurelin. 187; *Galagloriel* 187–8

Galathilion Gnomish name of Silpion (Telperion). 187

Galdor (1) Father of Húrin. 413. (2) Elf of Mirkwood (precursor of Legolas). 400, 413. (3) Elf of the Grey Havens. 413

480   THE RETURN OF THE SHADOW

Gamgee, Gaffer   26–7, 30–1, 35, 38, 71, 222–3, 241, 243–4, 249, 253–4, 275, 277, 279, 315, 329–30, 372; *Ham Gamgee* 244, 394

Gamgee, Halfast   254

Gamgee, Sam   70–1, 113, 127–8, 144, 175, 190, 193, 210, 213, 221, 243–4, 249–50, 253–6, 267, 273–84 and 287–94 *passim*, 299–300, 302–3, 321–4, 326–9, 332–4, 352, 356–7, 359–62, 366–8, 371, 373, 375, 381–2, 394–5, 397–8, 400, 406–12, 417, 420–1, 423, 427–30, 432, 436, 448–9, 452–4, 456–8, 463, 465

Gamlost   'Empty-handed'; see *Beren.*

Gandalf   17–22, 26–7, 31, 38, 41–3, 47–8, 55, 63, 66, 68–71, 73–4, 76–88, 101–2, 106, 109, 120, 122–3, 126, 131, 142, 149–64 and 167–78 *passim*, 185–6, 190, 194–5, 203–14, 217, 219, 221–9, 233–75 *passim*, 279, 281–4, 301–4, 314–15, 318–23, 326–8, 332, 334, 336–87 *passim*, 392–465 *passim*. Letters from Gandalf 154, 156, 158–60, 170, 172–3, 352, 355, 368; the loss of Gandalf 381, 443, 462

Gate-stream   See *Caradras dilthen, Sirannon.*

Gawkroger   Hobbit family name. 236, 246, 254; *Gaukrogers* 315

Giants   253–4, 319, 384; and see *Treebeard.*

Gildor   60, 62–5, 68–71, 73, 76, 88–9, 106, 109, 122, 141, 160, 173, 194, 280–2, 300, 325; *Gildor Inglorion* 60, 71, 282

Gil-galad   105, 169, 174, 179, 192, 197, 199, 214–16, 218, 226–7, 260–2, 271, 320, 358; translated 'Starlight' 179, 215, 358; descendant of Fëanor 215–16

Gilthoniel   Varda. 59, 68, 186, 189, 212, 364, 394; *Gilthonieth* 68

Gimli   Dwarf, son of Glóin. 398, 400, 411, 413, 415, 435–6, 438, 444–5, 460, 466

Gip   Farmer Maggot's dog. 94, 96

Girdley Island   In the Brandywine River. 284

Gladden Fields   416, 432, 438

Gladden River   416, 432, 438, 440. See *Palathrin.*

Glamdring   'Foe-hammer', Gandalf's sword. 442–4, 454, 464

Glanduin, River   (flowing from the Misty Mountains to the Greyflood above Tharbad) 441

Glassmere in Dimrill-dale   Earliest name of Mirrormere. 433, 437, 466. See *Helevorn.*

Glóin   Dwarf, companion of Thorin Oakenshield. 209–10, 213, 217, 220–1, 225–6, 362, 366, 369, 391–2, 395, 397–400, 403–4, 411–14, 429, 437, 444

Glorfindel   Elf of Rivendell. 193–6, 198, 207, 209, 212–15, 361–2, 364–5, 367–8, 384, 392, 395, 397–8, 400, 405–6, 409–10, 414; on the identity of Glorfindel of Rivendell and Glorfindel of Gondolin see 214–15.

Gnomes   71, 212, 217, 364. See *Noldor, Wise-elves.*

Gnomish   (tongue) 131, 187. See *Noldorin.*

INDEX 481

Goatleaf, Harry Keeper of the west-gate of Bree. (333–4), 336, 342, 344–5, 347–9, 354; his brother (Ned?) 344, 349

Goblin Gate In the Misty Mountains. 416, 432. See *Annerchin*.

Goblins 55, 75, 78–81, 84, 86, 110, 128, 176, 178, 187–8, 211, 227, 253, 261, 263–4, 271–2, 282, 320, 364, 381–2, 391, 429, 437, ·442–3, 451, 453–4, 462; *goblinish* 165, 176, 354; *Wars of the Elves and Goblins* 350; *Dwarf and Goblin War* 391, *Goblin invasions* 391; language 451; Goblins as Ring-wraiths 75, 78. On the relation of *Orcs* and *Goblins* see 437, 443.

Gods 184, 187; *land of the Gods* 182, 187; *hound of the Gods* 183

Goldberry 115, 117, 122, 125–6, 128, 130

Golden Perch The inn at Stock. 286–7, 291, 295, 325

Gollum 75, 79–81, 84–7, 224, 226–9, 233, 241–2, 261–5, 268, 271–2, 314, 320–2, 370, 380–2, 401, 410, 413, 438, 442, 444; his relation to hobbits 75, 78–9; his grandmother 320; his (second) ring 370, 381. See *Dígol*.

Gondolin 214–15; *King of Gondolin* 444

Gondor 379–80, 409, 411, 438; *'Stone-land'* 379. See *Ond*.

Goodbody Hobbit family name. 236

Gordon, E.V. 144–5

Gothic 145

Great Hole of Bucklebury 234, 245, 386. See *Brandy Hall*.

Great Lands 215; *Great Land* 319

Great Men Númenóreans (cf. V.376, stem NDŪ). 215

Great River (also *the River*) 214, 397, 399, 410–11, 417, 419, 429, 432, 434, 437–8, 440, 461. See *Anduin, Beleghir*.

Great Sea 122, 320, 399; *Great Seas* 183–4, 331. See *(the) Sea, Western Seas*.

Green Dragon The inn at Bywater. 249, 253–4, 318, 323

Green-elves 412

Green Hill Country 50, 72, 107, 278, 284; *Green Hills* 46, 50

Green, Mr. Assumed name of Odo Took at Bree. 135–6, 140–1, 150, 152

Greenway 142, 332–4, 342, 346–8

Greyflood, River 192, 201, 441

Grey Havens 254, 319, 412–13; *the Havens* 397, 402

Grip One of Farmer Maggot's dogs. 290, 293

Grubb family, Grubbs 13–14, 18, 22–3, 25, 31, 33

Grubb, Gorboduc A friend of Bilbo's. 15, 17–18, 26, 32, 36. (Replaced by *Orlando Grubb*.)

~ *Iago* Lawyer. 33, 36

~ *Inigo* A great glutton. 38, 247; earlier called *Inigo Grubb-Took*, 15, 17–18, 26–7, 32, 36, 38, 315. (Replaced by *Primo Grubb*.)

~ *Orlando* 17, 26, 32, 36. (Replaced *Gorboduc Grubb*; replaced by *Orlando Burrowes*.)

~ *Primo* 247, 315. (Replaced *Inigo Grubb*.)

482   THE RETURN OF THE SHADOW

Gumlin   Father of Húrin. 413. See *Galdor*.
Gwaihir   Lord of Eagles. 120

Half-elvish   395, 400, 413; *Half-elven* 412; *Half-eldar* 412
Hall of Fire   In Elrond's house. 392. *Hall of Feasting* in Elrond's house, also called the *Great Hall*. 392
Halls of Iron   See *Angband*.
Halls of Waiting   184, 187
Halog   Túrin's guardian. 180
Hannar   One of the Dwarves who accompanied Bilbo from Bag End. 238, 240, 315
Harfoots   124, 294
Haysend   The southern end of the High Hay. 100, 112, 298–9
Heathertoes   Family name in Bree. 137
Hedge, The   Fencing Buckland from the Old Forest. 100, 105, 107, 110–12, 327. See *High Hay*.
Helevorn   (1) Lake in Thargelion. 466. (2) Early name for Mirrormere. 459, 466. See *Glassmere*.
Hidden Kingdom   Doriath. 182
High Elves   Elves of Valinor. 188, 280, 285, 324; *High Elves of the West* 71, 187, 225, 260. The High Elves 'live in both worlds', 212, 225, 260, 364
High Hay   The Hedge of Buckland. 298, 304
High Moor   South of Rivendell. 201; *high moors* 417
High Pass   Pass over the Misty Mountains east of Rivendell. 416
Hill, Mr.   Assumed name of Bingo/Frodo at Bree. 135–6, 138, 140–1, 149–50, 152, 155–6, 223, 280, 324, 334, 338, 340–1
Hill, The   20, 30, 34, 222, 234–6, 238, 240–1, 244, 247, 315, 385; *Hobbiton Hill* 284
Hither Lands   Middle-earth. 71
Hoardale   Briefly replaced *Dimrill-dale* in the earlier sense. 205, 432
Hoards of the Dwarves   78, 87, 226–7, 260, 399
Hoarwell, River   192, 200–5, 360, 368; *Hoarwell Bridge* 200–1. See *Mitheithel, Last Bridge*.
Hobbiton   13, 15, 19–21, 25–6, 29, 32, 37, 40–1, 43, 46, 50, 54–5, 62, 64, 69, 71–2, 76, 83, 92, 95–6, 106–7, 123, 133, 160, 210, 217, 221–2, 228, 233–4, 237, 244, 247, 249–50, 253–4, 265, 268, 272–4, 276, 278–80, 284, 288, 294–5, 299–300, 304, 312, 318, 323, 326, 336, 338, 366–7, 372–6, 379, 385, 391, 401, 407, 459; *Hobbitonians* 41
Hobbits   (Selected references). Stature 311; beardlessness 52, 294, 312; shoelessness 312; silence of movement 46, 50, 61, 311; short memories 20; weddings 17; and their children 14, 24; and dragons 19, 29, 41; presents 21, 312; money (ducats, double-dragons, silver pennies) 16, 34, 164, 174, 252, 268; houses, holes (architecture) 92, 289, 294, 310, 312–13; families and their lands 313; maps 252;

INDEX
483

language 311; 'Hobbit translation' of Elvish names = English 432. A general account of hobbits 310–14. *Wild Hobbits, see Rangers*.

Hobbit, The   11, 17–18, 25–8, 31, 33, 35, 38, 43–4, 85–6, 108–9, 131, 173, 186, 193, 203–5, 218, 222, 224, 226, 245–6, 261, 268, 271, 283, 310, 314, 329–30, 374, 381–2, 384, 387, 399, 411, 414, 432, 437–8, 440, 444, 460, 465; *'sequel to The Hobbit'* 40, 43–5, 108–9, 173, 370, 384

Ho! ho! ho! To my bottle I go   91, 287

Hollin   418–21, 429, 432, 435, 438, 440–1, 444, 448–9, 463. See *Eregion, Regornion*.

Hornblower family, Hornblowers   31, 33, 78, 284; *Hornblower country* 278, 284, 295

Hornblower, Adam   The Hobbiton blacksmith. 82, 265

~ *Carambo*, ~ *Colombo*   247, 315. (Replaced *Cosimo Hornblower*.)

~ *Cosimo*   38, 247. (Replaced *Cosimo Chubb*.)

~ *Tobold*   First grower of pipeweed in the Shire. 284

Horse-kings   422, 435, 440; *Horse-lords* 435, 440; *Horsemen* 434; *Horseland* 434. See *Rohan, Rohiroth*.

Ho! Tom Bombadil/Whither are you going   115–16

Houghton Mifflin Company   200, 305

Húan   183 (*hound of the Gods*), 197

Hundredweight Party   251

Huor   413

Húrin   413

Husbands, Winifred   144–5

Icelandic   144–5

Ilverin   (1) Minstrel of Doriath (in the place of Dairon). 180, 187. Other names *Neldorin, Elberin, Diarin* 187. See *Iverin*. (2) A name of Littleheart of Mar Vanwa Tyaliéva. 187

Indowns   In the Shire. 294–5

Inglor Felagund   72, 188. See *Finrod* (2).

Inglorion   See *Gildor*.

Inlands   The Mittalmar, central region of Númenor. 295

Iron Halls   See *Angband*.

Isengard   189, 225

Isildur   85, 227, 320; *Isildor* 261–2, 271, 320; *Ithildor* 271; *son of Elendil* 358. Earliest germ of the story of his death 78

Ithil   Moria-silver, *mithril*. 458, 465. See *Erceleb*.

Ithildin   Element from which the design on the West Gate of Moria was made. 463

Ithildor   See *Isildur*.

Iverin   Minstrel of Doriath. 188. See *Ilverin*.

Ivy Bush   Inn on the Bywater road. 222, 243–4, 249, 314, 323, 329

484 THE RETURN OF THE SHADOW

Khazad-dûm (1) Dwarf-city in Eredlindon; Elvish *Nogrod*. 466. (2)
 Moria. 462 (*the Bridge of Khazad-dûm*), 465–6; *Kazaddûm* 467
Kheled-zâram Mirrormere. 466
Khuzdul Language of the Dwarves. 466
Kings of Men Númenóreans. 331, 458

Lady of the Stars Varda. 364
Lake-men Men of the Long Lake. 186
Lake-town 237. See *Esgaroth*.
Lamps, The 122
Last Alliance 174, 216–18, 260, 320
Last Bridge 192, 194, 199, 202–4, 219, 360, 367–8; *Hoarwell Bridge*
 200–1; *Mitheithel Bridge* 201
Last Homely House Elrond's house at Rivendell. 208, 417
Latin 145
Laurelin 187–8. See *Galadlóriel*.
Lay of Leithian 187, 197
Lay of the Children of Húrin 180
Leeds, University of 142, 144–5, 180
Legolas Elf of Mirkwood. 398, 413, 415, 436. See *Galdor* (2).
Lewis, C. S. 44, 108
Lhammas, The 69
Light as Leaf on Lindentree 179–80, 187. See *Tinúviel*.
Lindar The First Kindred of the Elves. 188
Little Folk, Little People Hobbits. 121, 134, 427, 431
Littleheart The Gong-warden of Mar Vanwa Tyaliéva. 187
Lofar Dwarf who stayed at Bag End after the Party. 238–9, 241–3,
 248, 315
Lonely Mountain (in many references *the Mountain*) 53, 210, 221, 310,
 366, 381, 391–2, 411, 429, 437, 442, 444
Longbottom In the Southfarthing. 284
Longholes Hobbit family name. 137, 236
Long Lake 177, 218
Lord of the Ring 74, 84, 209, 363, 402, 414; *The Lord of the Ring* as title
 of the book 84, 109, 112
Lord of the Rings (not as title of the book) 75, 80–1, 84, 262, 414; *the
 Ring-lord* 75, 87, 128, 225
Lord, The Sauron. 75, 78, 81, 226, 270–1, 303, 374, 379, 381, 396,
 399, 402, 404; *the evil Lord* 208; *the Lord of the Dark Tower* 209.
 See *Dark Lord*.
Lost Road, The 175
Lost Tales See *Book of Lost Tales*.
Lothlórien 189, 411, 461
Loudwater, River 192, 199, 201–5. See *Bruinen, River of Rivendell*.
Lovers of Lúthien The Danas, Green-elves. 412

INDEX

485

Lumpkin   Tom Bombadil's pony. (128), 130, 164

Lúthien   179, 182–4, 187, 197, 199, 216, 358; *the Choices of Lúthien* 187. See *Children of Lúthien, Lovers of Lúthien*.

Mablung   Elf of Doriath; called 'the heavy-handed'. 183

Maggots   Hobbit family of the Marish. 289

Maggot, Farmer   92, 94–7, 103, 105, 109, 116–17, 122, 124, 223, 268–9, 286–97, 300, 303, 305, 330; see especially 117, 122. *Mrs. Maggot* 95–7, 291–3

Mailcoat (Bilbo's)   Referred to also as his *ring-mail, elf-armour, elf-mail*, etc. 18, 126, 223, (315), 371–2, 378, 386, 397–8, 443–4, 466

Mandos   The abode of the Vala Mandos. 215

Mani Aroman   See 434.

Maps   See *Shire, Wilderland*. Maps of *The Lord of the Rings* 163, 200–2, 205, 438–41

Margoliantë, Queen   See 464.

Marish, The   107, 116, 286–7, 289, 294, 296–7, 312, 387

Marquette University   309, 318

Mar Vanwa Tyaliéva   The Cottage of Lost Play. 187

Master, The   See *Dark Lord*.

Mazarbul   Book of (443–4, 460), 467; *Chamber of* (443–4, 460), 467

Melian   Queen of Doriath. 182, 184

Melkor   122

Mellyn, Meldir, Melin   Forms of the Elvish word for 'friends' spoken by Gandalf before the Gate of Moria. 452, 463

Men   Visitors to Hobbiton 20, 30, 54–5, 150, 221, 235; in Bree 132–3, 140–1, 223, 331, 334; *Men (out) of the West, Western Men* 128, 169, 190, 192, 218, 329, 393; *Eastern Men* 398; other references 175, 178, 182, 184, 192, 215–16, 225, 253, 260, 272, 278, 311, 357, 379, 391, 397, 403–4, 417. See *Rings of Men, Men-wraiths; Big Folk, Wild Men*.

Menelvagor   Orion. 325

Men-wraiths   75, 78

Meriadoc Brandybuck, Merry   See *Brandybuck*.

Merrill   The stream of Rivendell. 205

Michel Delving   107, 244–5, 278, 284, 295, 312, 334. (Replaced *Much Hemlock*.)

Middle-earth, the Middle-earth   75, 105, 122, 176, 179, 182, 184, 187–90, 215, 218, 260, 263, 270, 320, 431, 438, 440; *the Middle-world* 182, 260, 270

Middle English   145

Midgewater Marshes   166, 354; the marshes 170, 174–5, 178, 355–6. (Replaced *Flymarshes*.)

Mindeb, River   432

Mines of Moria   See *Moria*.

Mirkwood   53, 128, 131, 216, 218, 253, 261, 264, 268, 320, 387,

486   THE RETURN OF THE SHADOW

392, 398, 412–14, 416; *Eastern Mirkwood* 395, 400. Mirkwood in Mordor 216, 218

Mirrormere   437–8, 466. See *Glassmere, Helevorn, Nen Cenedril.*

Misty Mountains   (including many references to *the Mountains*) 79, 153, 169–71, 178, 189, 191, 193, 200, 203, 205, 207–8, 214, 216, 263, 314, 331, 342, 360, 374, 381–2, 397, 401, 409, 416–19, 422–4, 429, 432–4, 438, 440–1, 445–6, 448, 462; demons of the mountains 424. Passes south of the Red Pass 422, 428, 434, 438; configuration of the Mountains 440–1

Mitheithel   The River Hoarwell. 192, 201, 360; *Mitheithel Bridge* 201. See *Hoarwell, Last Bridge.*

Mithril   223, 465–6. See *Erceleb, Ithil, Moria-silver.*

Mithrim   122

Mittalmar   The 'Inlands' of Númenor. 295

Moon, The   57, 121–2, 329; on the West Gate of Moria 449. References to the Moon's phases 58, 61, 168, 184, 191, 281, 325, 330, 409, 421, 434, 446, 462; *Hunter's Moon* 409

Mordor   131, 197, 199, 209, 214, 216–18, 226–7, 253, 258, 261, 264, 268–9, 272, 321–3, 370–1, 373, 380–1, 397–9, 401, 403, 410–14, 416, 462, 466; *Lord of Mordor* 364. See *Black Country.*

Morgoth   122, 187–8, 218, 270

Morgul-knife   211, 363

Moria   (including references to *the Mines of Moria, the Mines*) 173, 213, 226, 381–2, 391, 398, 403, 410–11, 429–31, 435, 437–8, 440, 442–6, 448–9, 451, 454–5, 457–8, 460–6; *Lord of Moria* 449 (Durin), 443, 460, 467 (Balin). See *East Gate(s), West Gate(s), of Moria.*

Moria-silver   (391), 458, 465–6; *true-silver* 458. See *Erceleb, Ithil, Mithril.*

Morthu   'Black Thû', Sauron. 186, 188

Mountains of Moria   441

Much Hemlock   278, 284, 295. (Replaced by *Michel Delving.*)

Much Wenlock, Shropshire   278

Mugwort   Family name in Bree. 137. *Mr. Mugwort* 141

Nanduhiriath   Dimrill-dale. 433. *Nanduhirion* 433

Nar   One of the Dwarves who accompanied Bilbo from Bag End. 238, 240, 315

Narag-zâram   Dwarvish name, probable origin of *Helevorn*. 466

Narfi   Dwarf, maker of the West Doors of Moria. 449, 463

Nargûn   Dwarvish name of Mordor. 466

Narodûm   The Red Vale; early name of Dimrill-dale. 433

Narog, River   In Beleriand. 433

Narosîr   The River Redway (later Silverlode). 433

Narothal   'Firefoot', earliest name of Gandalf's horse. 345, 347, 351

Nazgûl   434 (*Winged Nazgûl*).

INDEX 487

Necromancer, The 42, 81, 85, 117, 131, 208, 211–12, 215, 218, 226, 253, 255, 258, 261, 264–5, 268, 270, 272, 311, 321, 363–4, 380, 399; *land of the Necromancer* 77, 85, 255, 269, 319; *Necromancer-rings* 225

Neldoreth, Forest of (1) The northern part of Doriath. 384. (2) Passing name for Fangorn. 384, 399

Neldorín See *Ilverin*.

Nen Cenedril Mirrormere. 466

Nenning (1) River in Beleriand (replacing Eglor). 433. (2) Passing name for the River Redway. 433

Nine Rings See *Rings of Men*. Nine Rings of the Elves, and of the Dwarves, 269

Nine, The 270, 364; *the Nine Servants of the Lord of the Ring* 363; *the Nine Riders, Nine Ring-wraiths* 416

Nine Walkers 409

Noakes Hobbit family name. *Old Noakes (of Bywater)* 243–4, 249

Nob Servant at *The Prancing Pony*. 135–6, 141, 148, 150–1, 159, 164, 338–9; originally called *Lob* 141

Nogrod Dwarf-city in Eredlindon. 466. See *Khazad-dûm*.

Noldor 71–2. See *Gnomes, Wise-elves*.

Noldorin (tongue) 186, 432, 435, 463. See *Gnomish*.

Nori Dwarf, companion of Thorin Oakenshield. 210

Northfarthing 298, 313, 385, 423

North Moor(s) 54, 66, (71), 72, 84, 254, 278, 319, 324, 386; *moors of the Northfarthing* 385, 423

Northope Village north of Hobbiton Hill. 319, 385–7. (Replaced by *Overhill*.)

Númenor 105, 122, 215–16, 295, 320; *the Island* 260, 320, *the Far West Island* 215; '*The Fall of Númenor*' 105, 131, 174–5, 216, 218. See *Avallon, Westernesse*.

Númenórean 215–16, 227, 332, 414; Númenórean kingdoms in Middle-earth 189

Odo (including *Odo Took* and *Odo Bolger*) See *Bolger*.

Ogden Hobbit family name. 17

Óin Dwarf, companion of Thorin Oakenshield. 217, 226, 369, 381, 391

Oldbuck, Gorhendad Founder of the Brandybuck clan. 298, 326

Old English 35, 86, 131, 141, 145, 173, 205, 304; Runes 467

Old Forest (also often *the Forest*) 29–30, 35, 37, 40, 42–3, 100, 103–5, 109–12, 121, 124–5, 160, 206, 221, 273, 286, 299, 301–3, 326–7, 334, 349–52, 365–6, 401. See *Buckwood*.

Old Man Willow See *Willow-man*.

Old Norse 246, 444

Old Took See *Took, Frodo* (1) and *Took, Gerontius*.

Old Winyards Wine of the Southfarthing. 241

488   THE RETURN OF THE SHADOW

Old World   (after the Cataclysm) 215, 311

Olney, Austin   200, 305

Ond   Earliest name of Gondor. *(Land of) Ond* 381–2, 398, 401, 409–10, 427; *Men of Ond* 403, 409; *King of Ond* (father of Boromir) 411, 462. See *Stone-land*, *City of Stone*.

Orcs   187–8, 211, 320, 364, 429, 437, 443, 462, 467. See especially 437, 443; and see *Goblins*.

Orendil   Name varying with *Elendil*. 175, 197, 260–1, 270–1. See *Valandil*.

Ori   Dwarf, companion of Thorin Oakenshield. 217, 226, 369, 381, 391

Orothanador   See *Rohan*.

Orthanc   120

Outer Dark   122. *Outside* 121–2

Outsiders   Hobbits not of the Shire. 132–3, 175, 343; Hobbits not of the Bree-land 136, 345

Overhill   Village north of Hobbiton Hill. 254, 284, 319, 386–7. (Replaced *Northope*.)

O! Wanderers in the shadowed land   112, 114

O Water warm and water hot!   98

Oxford   35, 382; *Oxford Magazine* 115–16, 412

Padathir   Elvish name of Trotter. 194–5, 198, 217, 361. See *Dufinnion, Ethelion, Rimbedir*.

Palathrin   The Gladden River. 432

Party, The   (including references to *Birthday Party, Farewell Party*). Given by Bilbo: 13–15, 19–26, 40; (later story) 160, 225, 227–9, 233, 236–7, 245, 247, 252, 268, 276–7, 305, 315–16, 370, 372, 376–8, 386. Given by Bingo: 30–2, 36, 40, 42, 63, 74, 76, 85, 87, 106, 123, 138, 150, 160, 221–2, 224, 228, 233, 255, 284, 336, 371–2, 375. Given by Frodo (or 'Folco'): 370–1, 373

Pendrethdulur   The Dimrill-stair. 433

Peredhil   The Half-elven (Elrond and Elros). 412

Peregrin Took, Pippin   See *Took*.

Pereldar   Half-elven, 'Elrond's kinsfolk'. 412. See *Children of Lúthien*.

Peringol, Peringiul   The Half-elven (Elrond and Elros). 412

Powers, The   187–8; *the Power of darkness* 215

Prancing Pony, The   (including references to *The Pony* and to *the inn*) 126, 129, 131–4, 142, 144–5, 149, 156–7, 159–62, 172, 174–5, 206, 214, 217, 223, 236, 333–4, 338–9, 342–54 *passim*, 359, 414, 430. See *White Horse*.

Prologue   (to *The Lord of the Rings*) 31, 105, 124, 284, 294, 310, 316

Proudfoot   Hobbit family name. 14, 23, 25, 31; *Proudfeet* 13–14, 17, 22–3; *Proudfoots* 14, 17–18, 23, 31, 78; *Mr. and Mrs. Proudfoot* 15, 23–5; *Old Proudfoot* 248; *old Odo Proudfoot* 248

Proudfoot, Sancho   33, 36, 39, 241–2, 276

INDEX 489

Puddifoots of Stock   Hobbit family of the Marish. 105, 289
Puddifoot, Farmer   105, 295–6

Qenya, Quenya   69, 435, 463
Quenta (Noldorinwa)   437; *Quenta Silmarillion*, see *Silmarillion*.

Radagast   379, 387, 397
Rana   The Moon. 122
Rangers   137–8, 154, 158, 165–7, 171, 173, 175–6, 178, 186, 204, 223–4, 331–2, 352, 354, 356, 374, 376, 393, 420; identified as *wild folk* 137, *wild hobbits* 154, 158, 173 (other references to *wild hobbits* 162, 166, 174). See especially 223–4, 331–2.
Rathcarn, Rathgarn   The River Redway (later Silverlode). 433
Redhorn Gate   The pass beneath Caradhras. 381, 433; *Redhorn Pass* 381, 441
Redhorn, The   Caradhras. 440. See *Ruddyhorn*.
Red Pass   Earlier name of the pass beneath Caradhras. 381, 397, 419–20, 422, 434, 440, 444, 461. See *Cris-caron, Dimrill-stair*.
Red Valley   Earlier name of Dimrill-dale. 419, 433; *Red Vale* 433; *vale of Redway* 464. For Elvish names see 433, and *Dunruin*.
Redway, River   Earlier name of the Silverlode. 381, 397, 415, 419, 432–3, 438, 462, 464. For Elvish names see 433–4. *Little Redway*, see *Caradras dilthen*.
Regornion   Hollin. 432. See *Eregion*.
Rhascaron   Early name for Caradhras. 433; *Rhascarn* 438
Rhimdath   The River Rushdown. 205
Riddle-game   80, 86, 262–3, 314
Rimbedir   Elvish name of Trotter. 198, 207, 217. See *Du-finnion, Ethelion, Padathir*.
Ringbearer, The   189, 199, 224, 406
Ringhay   Original name of the house at Crickhollow. 299
Ring-lord   See *Lord of the Rings*.
Rings   75, 78, 80–2, 85, 87, 173, 225–7, 255, 258, 260–2, 265, 269–71, 319, 364, 396–7, 404. See *Lord of the Rings*.
Rings of Men   75, 78, 87, 258, 260, 269–70, 404
Rings of Power   265, 270, 272
Rings of the Dwarves   75, 78–9, 87, 210, 226, 258, 260, 269, 320, 397–9, 403–4, 414
Rings of the Elves   75, 78, 87, 225, 258, 260, 269–70, 319, 397, 399, 403–5. See especially 225, 404.
Rings of the Goblins   75, 78
Ring, The   15–16, 25–6, 32, 34, 38, 41–3, 47, 49, 54, 58, 64, 70–1, 73–87, 94, 123, 126, 138–9, 154, 173, 185–6, 188–9, 197, 199, 206, 208, 211, 217–18, 224–9, 233, 237, 239–43, 245, 248–9, 255–6, 258, 261–6, 271–2, 282, 285, 287–8, 290, 293–4, 297, 300–1, 314–15, 319–22, 325, 334, 336, 352–3, 358–60, 362, 364–5, 371,

490   THE RETURN OF THE SHADOW

373–4, 376–81, 392, 394, 396–406, 409–10, 414, 436, 442, 455, 459, 461. See especially 42–3, 64, 73–5, 78–82, 87, 226–7, 396–7.

Ring, The One   226, 258, 260–2, 264, 266, 269–71, 319, 399, 404; *the Master-ring* 258, 397; *the Great Ring* 403. See *Ruling Ring*.

Ring-verse, The   258–9, 269–70

Ring-wraiths   74–6, 173, 176, 186, 189–90, 198–9, 211–12, 223–5, 260, 270, 363–5, 367, 373, 375, 396, 408, 416; *Wraiths* 78, 81, 87, 168, 206, 208, 256, 261, 270, 362, 364; *wraith-world* 208, 217. See *Elf-wraiths*, *Men-wraiths*; *Black Riders, (the) Nine*.

Rivendell   41–3, 45–6, 60, 63–4, 68–9, 74, 84, 88, 106, 109, 125–6, 131, 133, 155, 159, 162, 164, 168, 170, 176, 178–9, 191–217 *passim*, 220, 223, 225–6, 229, 233, 270, 274, 283, 305, 309, 353, 355–6, 359–76 *passim*, 379–82, 391–2, 395–6, 398, 400, 402–3, 406–7, 413, 415–19, 428, 430–2, 435, 437, 440, 444, 455, 461. See *Elves*.

Riven River   The river of Rivendell. 360

River of Rivendell   204; *Rivendell River* 360; unnamed 126, 162, 191–2, 196–8, 200, 204, 207, 212, 360–1, 400, 409, 417. See especially 204–5; and see *Bruinen, Loudwater*.

Rivers, Mr.   Assumed name of Merry Brandybuck at Bree. 135, 141, 152, 159, 164

Road goes ever on and on, The   47, 53, 65, 70, 236, 240, 246–7, 278, 284, 324

Road, The   See *East Road*.

Rohan   189, 351, 411, 422, 434–5, 438, 440; *Rochan(dor)* 'Horseland' 434; *Gap of Rohan* 434. Other names *Borthendor, Orothanador, Thanador, Ulthanador* 434

Rohiroth, Rochiroth   The Horse-lords. 440. See *Horse-kings*.

Root of the Boot, The   The original 'Troll Song'. 142–4

Ruddyhorn   Caradhras. 419, 421, 433; *Ruddihorn* 433. See *Redhorn*, and for early Elvish names see 433.

Ruling Ring, The   87, 189, 227, 250, 258, 260, 265, 270, 322, 364, 396, 403–4. See *Ring, The One*.

Runes   82, 145, 154, 156, 158, 170, 173, 194, 235, 343, 352, 355, 448, 460, 467

Running River   218

Rushdown, River   Rhimdath, a tributary of the Anduin. 205

Rushey   Village in the Marish. 298, 304; *Rushy* (erroneous) 304

Rushlight   Family name in Bree. 137

Sackville   Hobbit family name. 31

Sackville-Bagginses   13–16, 19, 22–3, 29, 31, 33, 36–7, 39, 221–2, 228, 241–3, 248, 273, 275, 283, 315, 371, 377

Sackville-Baggins, Amalda   Earliest name of Lobelia. 16–18, 35–6

~   *Cosimo*   Son of Lobelia and Otho. 276, 283, 324, 380. (Replaced by *Lotho*.)

INDEX   491

~ *Cosmo*   Early name of Otho. 18, 36. (Replaced *Sago*.)
~ *Grimalda, Griselda*   Early names of Lobelia. 18, 33, 36
~ *Lobelia*   32–3, 36, 39, 239, 241, 243, 247–8, 276, 283, 324
~ *Lonicera*   Early name of Lobelia. 17, 36
~ *Lotho*   Son of Lobelia and Otho. 283. (Replaced *Cosimo*.)
~ *Miranda*   Wife of Cosimo. 283, 324
~ *Otho*   33, 36, 39, 239, 241, 243, 248
~ *Sago*   Earliest name of Otho. 16, 18, 36
Sam Gamgee   See *Gamgee*.
Sandheaver   Hobbit family name. 137
Sandyman   The Hobbiton miller. 243–4
Sandyman, Ted   Son of the Hobbiton miller. 249, 254, 269; earlier
   Tom Sandyman 249, 269 (replaced *Tom Tunnelly*).
Santoski, T. J. R.   328
Sauron   11, 85, 131, 215–16, 218, 258, 260–1, 270–1, 318, 397, 399,
   402–5, 414, 416–17, 422, 435; called *the Magician* 215. See *Dark
   Lord, (the) Lord, Lord of the Ring(s), Necromancer, Thû*.
Sea, The   59–60, 71, 93, 216, 260, 313, 320, 402; *the Seas* 331–2, 364,
   393; the bending of the seas 121–2. See *Great Sea, Western Seas*.
Second Age   215
Secret Fire   In the Fiery Mountain. 82
Seven Rings   See *Rings of the Dwarves*.
Shadow, The   270, 300, 398, 400
Shippey, T. A.   *The Road to Middle-earth*. 145
Shire, The   13–14, 18, 22, 29–31, 35, 37, 47, 50–2, 54–5, 58, 63–4, 69,
   71–2, 74, 76–8, 83–4, 92–3, 95, 99–101, 103, 110, 120, 122, 124,
   129, 132–4, 136–9, 149–51, 153, 155, 157, 168, 171, 175, 179, 194,
   210, 212–13, 221, 223–5, 228, 233–6, 239–40, 243–5, 250–4, 256,
   264, 266, 268, 272, 277–8, 280–1, 285, 288–9, 294–5, 298, 312–14,
   318, 322, 324, 331, 337–8, 340, 342, 344–7, 349, 358, 362–4,
   366–7, 370–1, 374–5, 379–80, 385–7, 392–4, 397–8, 403, 407–8,
   412, 415, 423; see especially 31.
   Shire-folk 135, 138, 333–4, 349; *South Shire* 241, 278; *East Shire*
   286. Maps of the Shire 43, 66, 105–8, 114, 200, 202, 284, 296, 299,
   304–5, 313, 387
Shirebourn   River in the Shire. 296
Sidmouth, Devon   214
Silmarillion, The   105, 108, 122, 187, 214, 433; *Quenta Silmarillion* 11,
   68, 71, 121, 182, 186–8, 329, 412–13, 432, 437, 466
Silmarils   122, 183–4, 187
Silpion   The White Tree of Valinor   122, 187–8
Silverlode, River   433, 462. See *Redway*.
Sindarin   466
Sirannon   The Gate-stream of Moria. 445–6. See *Caradras dilthen*.
Sirion, River   432
Slocum   Hobbit family name. 31

492 THE RETURN OF THE SHADOW

Smaug 256. See *Dragon(s)*.

Smith, A. H. 144

Snowfax 'Snow-mane', suggested name for Gandalf's horse. 351

Snow-white! Snow-white! O Lady clear! 59, 68, 280

Songs for the Philologists 142–5

Southerner The 'squint-eyed Southerner' at Bree. 142, 176, 334, 336, 342, 354

Southfarthing 241, 284, 298, 313; *South Shire* 241, 278

South Mountains Range south of the Misty Mountains. 397, 399, 409, 411, 440. See *Black Mountains, Blue Mountains*.

Staddle Village of the Bree-land. 132, 140, 332, 344, 354

Stair-falls Falls in the Gate-stream below the West Gate of Moria. 446–8

Standelf Village in Buckland. 298–9, 304

Stars *Ages of the Stars* 122. *Lady of the Stars* (Varda) 364. Red star in the South seen from Rivendell 409, 415

Sting Bilbo's sword. 223, 246, 262, 315, 371, 397, 443–4

Stock Village in the Marish. 66, 105, 107–8, 286, 289, 295–6, 298, 325, 387

Stock-brook 287

Stone-land Gondor. 379. See *City of Stone, Ond*.

Stone-Men Men of Ond. 379–80, 382

Stonydelph, Warwickshire 304

Stoors 124, 294

Strachey, Barbara *Journeys of Frodo*. 202, 205, 298, 305, 367, 440

Strider 126, 160, 186, 190, 192–3, 199–200, 204, 210, 336, 359–60, 430

Sundering Sea(s) 182, 215

Sun, The 57, 121–2, 329; *the Sunless Year* 59, 68

Tale of Years 85, 160

Taragaer Early name for Caradhras. 419, 421–2, 433, 438, 440

Tengwar 384

Thain of the Shire 31

Thanador See *Rohan*.

Thangorodrim 182, 187; *the black mountain* 182, *the Mountain of Thunder* 187

Thargelion 466

Thingol 182–3, 216; *Thingol's Heir* 68

Thorin Oakenshield 85, 209, 217, 391, 399, 403

Thráin Son of Thrór (but said to be his father, 403). 85, 398–9, 403, 414, 429

Three Rings See *Rings of the Elves*. Three Rings of Men 78, 269

Thrór Father of Thráin (but said to be his son, and the father of Thorin Oakenshield, 403). 403, 414, 429

Thû 131, 216, 218. See *Morthu*.

INDEX   493

Tinúviel   179–82, 184; as name of the song *Light as Leaf on Lindentree*
   412
Titus, Timothy   Landlord of the inn at Bree (replaced by *Barnabas
   Butterbur*). 130, 140–1, 162, 173
Tolkien, C. R.   44, 106–8, 142, 200, 297, 299, 304–5, 323, 441
Tolkien, J. R. R.   *Letters:* 11, 17, 31, 40, 43–4, 84, 108–10, 115, 173,
   198, 200, 202, 305, 309, 370, 382, 384, 461. (Works are indexed
   separately.)
Tom Bombadil   (including references to *Tom* and *Bombadil*) 42–3, 106,
   109–31 *passim*, 134–5, 152, 159–60, 164, 194, 196, 198, 213–14,
   297, 303, 327–9, 334, 336, 338, 340–1, 351, 397, 401–2, 413–14;
   'Aborigine' 117, 121, 329; *'Eldest'* 121. *The Adventures of Tom
   Bombadil* 116, 123, 296, 412; *Bombadil Goes Boating* 116; *Ho! Tom
   Bombadil/Whither are you going* 115–16. On Gandalf and Bombadil
   see 126, 213–14, 397, 401, 413
Took family, Tooks   13–16, 22–5, 29, 31, 33, 37, 39, 94, 100, 106, 135,
   141, 221–2, 224, 234, 236, 245, 251, 267, 284, 291, 313, 316–17
   (genealogical table), 319, 324, 334, 385–6, 392; *Tookish(ness)* 16,
   18, 33; *Hole of Took* (clan-name) 251
Took, Adelard   247. (Replaced *Uffo Took*.)
~   *Amanda*   32, 36. (Replaced *Arabella Took*.)
~   *Arabella*   32, 36. (Replaced *Melba Took*.)
~   *Bandobras, the Bullroarer*   311, 316–17, 329–30
~   *Belladonna*   Married Bungo Baggins; Bilbo's mother. 25, 35,
   249, 317
~   *Caramella*   A relative of Bilbo's. 15, 17, 32, 35–6, 38, 315. (See
   Caramella Bolger.)
~   *Diamanda*   Married Olo Bolger (2); Odo's mother. 317
~   *Donnamira*   Married Hugo Boffin; grandmother of Peregrin
   Boffin (Trotter). 316–17, 385–6
~   *Drogo*   See 41, 45–6.
~   *Esmeralda*   Married Saradoc Brandybuck; Meriadoc's mother.
   106, 267. (Replaced *Yolanda Took*.)
~   *Everard*   315. (Replaced *Prospero Took*.)
~   *Faramond*   (1) Grandfather of Folco Took (2) and Merry
   Brandybuck. 317. (2) Replaced Folco Took (2) as Frodo's friend
   and companion of his journey. 406–7, 409–10, 419, 421, 423, 427,
   436, 440, 447, 456
~   *Ferumbras*   Grandfather of the Old Took. 316–17
~   *Flambard*   Son of the Old Took. 316–17
~   *Folcard*   Father of Folco Took (2). 316–17
~   *Folco*   (1)   Father of Frodo Took (2). 94, 100, 251, 267, 290,
   309
~   *Folco*   (2)   Replaced Frodo Took (2) (Bingo's friend and com-
   panion of his journey) when Bingo became Frodo (Baggins). 309,
   314, 316–18, 323–30, 332, 334, 341, 343, 352–3, 355–8, 360,

494   THE RETURN OF THE SHADOW

366–8, 374–5, 392, 395–8, 409; see especially 323–4. (Replaced by *Faramond Took* (2).)

~ *Fortinbras* Father of the Old Took. 316–17

~ *Fosco* (1) Bilbo's first cousin, a candidate for 'Trotter' in his earlier life. 223–4, 373, 387. (2) Bilbo's uncle, son of the Old Took. 317

~ *Frodo* (1), *Frodo the First* The Old Took. 19, 30, 37–9, 240, 245, 249, 251, 267–8, 316. (Replaced by *Gerontius Took*.)

~ *Frodo* (2), *Frodo the Second* Bingo's friend and companion of his journey; replaced by Folco Took (2). 41–71 *passim*, 74, 83–4, 88–106 *passim*, 109, 112–15, 118–19, 124–5, 127–8, 130, 136–7, 139, 141, 148, 154, 156, 159–60, 169, 171–2, 177, 179, 185, 193, 221–2, 250–3, 267–8, 273, 275–80, 284–302 *passim*, 305, 309; references after *Frodo > Folco* 316, 323–5, 327–8, 330, 366, 375. See especially 70, 299–300, 323–4.

~ *Gerontius* The Old Took. 267, 316–17, 385–6. (Replaced *Frodo Took* (1).)

~ *Hildigrim* Son of the Old Took. 222

~ *Isambard* Son of the Old Took. 316–17

~ *Isengrim the First* Earliest recorded Took in the old genealogy (in LR *Isengrim II*, 316). 311, 316–17

~ *Isengrim the Second* Son of the Old Took (in LR *Isengrim III*). 316–17

~ *Isumbras* Son of Isengrim the First (in LR *Isumbras III*, 316). 316–17

~ *Melba* 24, 32, 36. (Replaced by *Arabella Took*.)

~ *Mirabella* Married Gorboduc Brandybuck. 37–8, 249, 317–18, 385

~ *Mungo* 15, 17–18, 32, 36, 247. (Replaced by *Uffo Took*.)

~ *Odo* See *Bolger, Odo*.

~ *the Old* See *Took, Frodo I* and *Took, Gerontius*.

~ *Paladin* Father of Peregrin (Pippin). 267, 386

~ *Peregrin* (including references to *Pippin*) 70, 112, 119, 128, 140, 267–8, 277, 286–7, 297, 300, 324–5, 328, 330, 358–9, 365–6, 386, 441; see especially 267, 324

~ *Prospero* 38, 106, 315. (Replaced *Prospero Brandybuck*, replaced by *Everard Took*.)

~ *Uffo* 247. (Replaced *Mungo Took*, replaced by *Adelard Took*.)

~ *Vigo* Odo's grandfather. 317.

~ *Yolanda* Married Caradoc Brandybuck; mother of (Marmaduke >) Meriadoc. 100, 251, 267, 316–17. (Replaced by *Esmeralda Took*.)

~ *Young* 222, 316

Tookland 50, 95, 278, 284, 294–5, 312–13

Took-Took, Obo Bilbo's great-uncle. 15, 18, 32, 36. (Replaced by *Rollo Took-Took*.)

INDEX

495

Took-Took, Rollo 32, 36, 38. (Replaced *Obo Took-Took*, replaced by *Fosco Bolger*.)

Tower Hills 280. See *Emyn Beraid*.

Towers of Darkness 300

Towers, The 254, 280, 380, 402. See *Elf-towers*, *West Towers*.

Treebeard (in most references called *Giant Treebeard*) 363, 367, 381–2, 384, 397, 399, 410–11, 440

Tree-giants 410–11. *Tree-men* 254, 319, 386

Troll-country 192, 360; *Troll-lands* 205

Trolls References to the three Trolls of *The Hobbit* (also *Troll Stones*, *Stone Trolls*) 126, 144, 162, 192–4, 203–4, 212, 360, 365, 444, 454. Other references 178, 192, 253, 272, 319, 443–4

Trollshaw(s) 162–3, 170, 200–2, 355, 412; *Troll-wood* 162, *Trolls-wood* 195

Troll Song 142–4, 194, 222, 360, 412

Trotter 133, 138–41, 148–79 *passim*, 182, 184–98, 204, 207–14, 216–17, 223–4, 226, 269, 332, 336–9, 341–3, 350–63, 365–8, 371, 373–4, 376, 379, 386–7, 392–403 *passim*, 406, 408–10, 413–27 *passim*, 430–1, 434–8, 445–7, 449, 451–3, 462–5.
On the history of Trotter see 214, 223–4, 332, 371, 373–4, 376, 384–6, 392–3, 414, 430–1; and see *Boffin, Peregrin*.

Tuckborough Chief place of the Tookland. 294, 312

Tulkas 122

Tum Dincelon Dimrill-dale in the original application (north of Rivendell). 432

Tunnelly Hobbit family name. 137

Tunnelly, Tom Original name of the Hobbiton miller's son. 269

Túrin 180

Twelve Rings of Men 269

Twofoot, Mr. Hobbit of Bagshot Row, Hobbiton. 244

Two Kindreds Elves and Men. 184

Two Trees 68, 122, 187–8

Ulthanador See *Rohan*.

Underhill 149. See *Bag End*.

Underhill, Mr. Assumed name of Frodo at Bree (in LR). 140, 336. See *Hill, Mr.*

Unfinished Tales 295

Ungoliant 122; *Ungoliantë* 188

University College, London 142, 144

Unwin, Rayner 40, 43, 108

Unwin, Stanley 11, 40, 43–4, 108, 173, 189, 370, 461

Upon the hearth the fire is red 48, 57, 66–7

Uruks 462

496 THE RETURN OF THE SHADOW

Uruktharbun   Dwarvish name, probably of Dimrill-dale, preceding
  Azanulbizâr. 458, 465

Valandil   (1) Elendil's father in *The Lost Road*. 175. (2) Elendil's
  brother in *The Fall of Númenor*. 175. (3) Preceding or varying with
  Elendil. 169, 175, 270, 320, 355. See *Orendil*.
Valar   122
Valinor   122, 182–4, 188, 285
Vanyar   The First Kindred of the Elves. 188
Varda   68. See *Elbereth*, *Gilthoniel*.
Void, The   122

Walker   Name assumed by the hobbits at Bree. 141
Walls of the World   122
Wandering Companies   (of Elves) 65; cf. 60, 72
Wargs   416, 445
Water, The   22, 37, 46, 50, 56, 72, 106
Weather Hills   175; unnamed 167–9, 174, 177–8, 355
Weathertop (Hill)   126, 133, 154, 158, 161–79 *passim*, 184, 186,
  189–93, 195, 198–202, 206, 208, 216, 219, 223–4, 325, 353–6,
  359–60, 365, 367–8, 375, 396
Westernesse   Númenor. 215, 320
Western Seas   59, 68. See *Great Sea*, *(the) Sea*.
Westfarthing   298, 312–13
West Gate(s) of Moria   (including references to *the gate(s)*) 430–1,
  443–9, 451–2, 454–5, 461, 463–4; '*two secret gates on the western
  side*' 429; *West-doors* 454; 437. The design on the Gate 450, 463
West-lands   (of Middle-earth) 182
Westron   466
West, The   60, 71, 187, 215, 225, 260, 364, 396, 402; *the Far West* 182,
  212; *the Far West Island*, Númenor, 215; the West of Middle-earth
  182. See *Men*.
West Towers   155, 159, 269. See *Elf-towers*, *Towers*.
White Council   319
White Downs   278, 295, 312
White Horse   Original name of the inn at Bree. 129, 131
White Mountains   Ered Nimrais. 399
White Wizards   218
Whitfurrows   Village in the Eastfarthing. 387
Wide World, The   63–4
Wilderland   Lands east of the Misty Mountains. 81, 261, 263–4, 321,
  416–17; *the Wild* 43, 208. Map of Wilderland in *The Hobbit* 204–5,
  218, 432, 438, 440
Wild Hobbits   See *Rangers*.
Wild Men out of the East   398, 409; *Eastern Men* 398
William   One of the Trolls turned to stone. 193, 212, 360

INDEX 497

Willow-man 42–3, 109, 111–12, 115, 117, 120, 302; *Old Man Willow*
113, 115–16, 120, 123, 327; *the Old Man* 121; *the Willow* 112–13;
the Great Willow 116

Wise-elves Noldor. 60, 71, 93; *the Elvenwise* 212, 217, 364

Wise, The 212, 262, 364

Withywindle, River 110, 112–17, 119, 127, 327–8

Wizards References to wizards other than Gandalf: 211, 260, 270,
364; *White Wizards* 318

Wolf One of Farmer Maggot's dogs. 290, 293

Wood Eaton Earliest name of Buckland (as village). 35, 105. (Replaced by *Bury Underwood*.)

Wood-elves (of Mirkwood) 264–5, 320, 392; *King of the Wood-elves*
395, 400

Woodhall Village in the Eastfarthing. 61, 66, 72, 89–90, 96, 100–1,
105, 107–8, 200, 291, 298

Woodmen of Wilderland 264

Woody End 50, 52, 56, 58, 72, 278, 280, 284, 304, 324–5; earliest form
Wood-end 47

Wraiths See *Elf-wraiths*, *Men-wraiths*, *Ring-wraiths*.

Yale, The Region of the Eastfarthing. 66, 387

Yorkshire 246; *Yorkshire Poetry* 145

THE TREASON OF ISENGARD
THE HISTORY OF THE LORD OF THE RINGS,
PART TWO

J. R. R. TOLKIEN

The Treason of Isengard

The History of
The Lord of the Rings
PART TWO

Christopher Tolkien

CONTENTS

Foreword		*page*	1
I	GANDALF'S DELAY		5
II	THE FOURTH PHASE (1): FROM HOBBITON TO BREE		18
III	THE FOURTH PHASE (2): FROM BREE TO THE FORD OF RIVENDELL		40
IV	OF HAMILCAR, GANDALF, AND SARUMAN		67
V	BILBO'S SONG AT RIVENDELL: *ERRANTRY* AND *EÄRENDILLINWË*		81
VI	THE COUNCIL OF ELROND (1)		110
VII	THE COUNCIL OF ELROND (2)		141
VIII	THE RING GOES SOUTH		161
IX	THE MINES OF MORIA (1): THE LORD OF MORIA		176
X	THE MINES OF MORIA (2): THE BRIDGE		190
XI	THE STORY FORESEEN FROM MORIA		207
XII	LOTHLÓRIEN		217
XIII	GALADRIEL		245
XIV	FAREWELL TO LÓRIEN		267
XV	THE FIRST MAP OF THE LORD OF THE RINGS		295
XVI	THE STORY FORESEEN FROM LÓRIEN		324
XVII	THE GREAT RIVER		350
XVIII	THE BREAKING OF THE FELLOWSHIP		370
XIX	THE DEPARTURE OF BOROMIR		378
XX	THE RIDERS OF ROHAN		389
XXI	THE URUK-HAI		408
XXII	TREEBEARD		411
XXIII	NOTES ON VARIOUS TOPICS		422

THE TREASON OF ISENGARD

vi

XXIV THE WHITE RIDER   *page* 425
XXV THE STORY FORESEEN FROM FANGORN   434
XXVI THE KING OF THE GOLDEN HALL   441

APPENDIX ON RUNES   452

Index   466

ILLUSTRATIONS

Orthanc	*frontispiece*
The West Gate of Moria	182
Runic Inscription on Balin's Tomb	186
The First Map of The Lord of the Rings Construction of the Map	297

  Redrawn maps: Map I 302; I^A 303; II 305; III^A 308;
  III 309; IV^A 314; IV^B, IV^C 317; IV^{D-E} 319

Sketch for the Gate of Minas Morgul	342
Sketch-plan of the scene of the Breaking of the Fellowship	383
Runes	460–5

Note:
Owing to the limitations of printing on 'India' paper, it has been necessary to reproduce in black and white the originally coloured frontispiece illustration.

FOREWORD

In 'The History of Middle-earth' I have tried to make each book as much an independent entity as possible, and not merely a section cut off when the book had reached a certain size; but in the history of the writing of *The Lord of the Rings* this has proved difficult. In *The Return of the Shadow* I was able to bring the story to the point where my father, as he said, 'halted for a long while' while the Company of the Ring stood before the tomb of Balin in the mines of Khazad-dûm; but this meant leaving till later the further complex restructurings of earlier parts of *The Fellowship of the Ring* that belong to that period.

In this volume my hope and intention was to reach the second major halt in the writing of *The Lord of the Rings*. In the Foreword to the Second Edition my father said that in 1942 he 'wrote the first drafts of the matter that now stands as Book III [the story from 'The Departure of Boromir' to 'The Palantír'], and the beginnings of Chapters 1 and 3 of Book V ['Minas Tirith' and 'The Muster of Rohan']; and there as the beacons flared in Anórien and Théoden came to Harrowdale I stopped. Foresight had failed and there was no time for thought.' It seems to have been around the end of 1942 that he stopped, and he began again ('I forced myself to tackle the journey of Frodo to Mordor') at the beginning of April 1944, after an interval of well over a year.

For this reason I chose as a title for this book *The Treason of Isengard*, that being a title my father had proposed for Book III (the first Book of *The Two Towers*) in a letter to Rayner Unwin of March 1953 (*The Letters of J. R. R. Tolkien* no. 136). But I have found repeatedly that a history of the writing of *The Lord of the Rings* tends to set its own pace and scale, and that there comes a sort of critical point beyond which condensation of the intricacies of the evolving structure is not possible, without changing the nature of the enterprise. Finding that the story was not moving rapidly enough to reach the great ride of Gandalf with Pippin on Shadowfax before I ran out of space, I rewrote a great part of the book in an attempt to shorten it; but I found

2   THE TREASON OF ISENGARD

that if I rejected material as being less essential or of less interest I was always confronted at a later point with the need for explanations that destroyed my gains. Finally I decided that 'The King of the Golden Hall' does in fact provide a very suitable stopping-place, not in terms of the movement of composition but in terms of the movement of the story; and I have retained the title *The Treason of Isengard*, because that was the central new element in this part of *The Lord of the Rings*, even though in this book the account of the destruction of Isengard and the reward of Saruman's betrayal is only reached in a preliminary outline.

Of course it would be possible to shorten my account very considerably by treating such matters as the chronology and geography far more superficially, but as I know well there are some who find these often exceedingly complex questions of great interest, and those who do not can easily pass them by. Or I might have omitted some passages of original writing where it is not very distinctively different from the published work; but it has been my intention throughout this 'History' that the author's own voice should be largely heard.

The way in which *The Return of the Shadow* was constructed has meant that the first part of *The Treason of Isengard* must deal at some length with further developments in *The Fellowship of the Ring* up to the point reached in the first book, and this part is of necessity a continuation of the account in *The Return of the Shadow* and stands in very close relation to it – though most of the many page-references made to it are no more than references and need not be looked up in order to follow the discussion.

This book is again very largely descriptive in intent; and in general I have thought it more useful to explain why I believe the narrative to have evolved as I describe it than to enlarge on my own views of the significance of particular features.

As the writing of *The Lord of the Rings* proceeds the initial draftings become more and more difficult to read; but for obvious reasons I have not hesitated to try to present even the most formidable examples, such as the original description of Frodo's vision on Amon Hen (pp. 372–3), though the result must be peppered all over with dots and queries.

In the preparation of this book I have again been greatly indebted to the help of Mr Taum Santoski generously and unfailingly given, and to that of Mr John D. Rateliff who has

FOREWORD 3

assisted in the analysis of manuscripts in the possession of Marquette University. I thank also Mr Charles B. Elston, the Archivist of the Memorial Library at Marquette, for providing photographs of the designs on the West Gate of Moria and the inscription on Balin's Tomb, and Miss Tracy Muench, who has been responsible for the photocopying of many manuscripts.

Mr Charles Noad very kindly undertook an additional and independent reading of the proofs, together with a meticulous checking of all references and citations from published works. In this connection I must explain, what I should have explained in *The Return of the Shadow*, a perhaps rather misleading device that I have employed in these books: when relating an earlier text to the published form I often treat passages as identical although the wording actually differs in unimportant ways. Thus for example (p. 370) 'Sam broke in on the discussion... with "Begging your pardons, but I don't think you understand Mr Frodo at all" (FR p. 419)' is not a misquotation of *The Fellowship of the Ring* (which has ' "Begging your pardon," said Sam. "I don't think you understand my master at all"'), but a 'shorthand' by which I indicate the precise point in *The Fellowship of the Ring* but also cite accurately the reading of the earlier text. I do this also when relating successive early versions to each other.

The illustration of Orthanc in the Ring of Isengard reproduced as the frontispiece is the earliest of successive conceptions of the tower, and may be taken to represent my father's image of it at the time when the texts in this book were written. It was done on the back of an examination script in 1942, and was found, together with other drawings, among the original drafts of 'The Road to Isengard'. The evolution of Orthanc will be described in Volume VIII, but it seemed suitable to use this picture as the frontispiece to *The Treason of Isengard*.

As in *The Return of the Shadow*, when citing texts I follow my father's representation of names, which was very inconsistent, especially in the use of capital letters. I abbreviate *The Fellowship of the Ring* as FR, *The Two Towers* as TT, and *The Lord of the Rings* as LR; and I refer to the previous volumes in this 'History', listed on the title-page, as (e.g.) 'II.189, V.226'.

I take this opportunity to explain an error in *The Return of the Shadow* (not present in the first American printing). After correction of the second proofs, lines 11–12 on page 32 of that

4   THE TREASON OF ISENGARD

book came to be repeated in lines 15–16 in place of the correct text, which should read:

Bingo's last words, 'I am leaving after dinner', were corrected on the manuscript to 'I am leaving now.'

I

GANDALF'S DELAY

In *The Return of the Shadow*, after citing and discussing the remarkable notes and plot-outlines bearing the date August 1939 (Chapter XXII: 'New Uncertainties and New Projections'), I turned to the continuation of the story at Rivendell and after, as far as Moria. But at this time (towards the end of 1939) my father was also engaged in substantial further revision to what ultimately became Book I of *The Fellowship of the Ring* (FR), arising primarily from a changed story of Gandalf's movements, and an explanation of his delay. I doubt that it would be possible to deduce a perfectly clear and coherent, step-by-step chronology of this period in the narrative evolution, or to relate precisely the development of the early chapters of what became Book II to the new work on Book I; for my father moved back and forth, trying out new conceptions and then perhaps abandoning them, and producing such a tangle of change as cannot always be untied: and even if it could be, it would require a vast amount of space to make it all remotely comprehensible without the manuscripts. However, granting that many uncertainties remain, I do not think that they constitute a real impediment to understanding the development in all essentials.

Most of this new work on the story as far as Rivendell can be treated in terms of the individual chapters, but some outlines, time-schemes, and notes are best collected together, though I cannot certainly determine the order in which they were set down. These are the subject of this chapter.

(1) This slip of paper begins 'State of Plot assumed after XI. (Much of explanation in XII and of incident in Bree chapter will have to be rewritten.)' The reference is clearly to Chapter XII 'The Council of Elrond', which at this stage included the narrative afterwards separated off as 'Many Meetings' (see VI.399–400). Then follows:

> Bilbo gives Party and goes off. At that time he does not know anything about the ring's powers or origin (other than invisibility). Motive writing book (bring in his wry expression about 'living happily to end of [his] days') – and a restlessness: desire to see either Sea or Mountains while his days last. Confesses to a slight reluctance to leave the ring, mixed with an oddly opposite feeling. Says to Gandalf he sometimes feels it is like an eye looking at [him].

6   THE TREASON OF ISENGARD

These two things give Gandalf food for thought. He helps Bilbo therefore with his preparations – but keeps an eye on the Ring.

(Cut out a lot of the genealogical stuff and most of the Sackville-Baggins stuff.)

Then Gandalf goes off and is absent for 3 and 7 years. At the end of the last absence (14–15 years after Bilbo's disappearance) Gandalf returns and actually stays with Frodo. Then he explains what he has discovered. But he does *not* advise Frodo yet to go off, though he does mention the Cracks of Doom and the Fiery Mountain.

He departs again; and Frodo becomes restless. As Gandalf does not come back for a year and more Frodo forms the idea of going *perhaps* to the Cracks of Doom, but at any rate to Rivendell. There he will get advice. He finally makes his plans with his friends Merry and [Folco >] Faramond[1] (no Odo) and Sam. They go off just as the Black Riders come to Hobbiton.

Gandalf finds out about the Black Riders but is delayed, because the Dark Lord is hunting him (or because of Treebeard). He is alarmed at finding Frodo gone and immediately rides off to Buckland, but is again too late. He loses their trail owing to the Old Forest escapade, and actually gets ahead. He falls in with Trotter. Who is Trotter?

At the end of this sketch my father for a moment contemplated an entirely novel answer to this question: that Trotter was 'a disguised elf – friend of Bilbo's in Rivendell.' He was one of the Rivendell scouts, of whom many were sent out, and he 'pretends to be a ranger'. This was struck out, probably as soon as written.

If this is compared with the note dated August 1939 given in VI.374 it will be seen that a passage in the latter bears a distinct similarity to what is said here:

Gandalf does *not* tell Frodo to leave Shire ... The plan for leaving was entirely Frodo's. Dreams or some other cause [*added:* restlessness] have made him decide to go journeying (to find Cracks of Doom? after seeking counsel of Elrond). Gandalf simply vanishes for years. ... Gandalf is simply trying to *find* them, and is desperately upset when he discovers Frodo has left Hobbiton.

That Treebeard was a hostile being, and that he held Gandalf in captivity during the crucial time, appeared in the 'third phase' Chapter XII (VI.363); cf. also VI.384, 397.

(2) In another undated scrap is seen the actual emergence of 'Trotter's' true name – as a Man: *Aragorn.*

Trotter is a man of Elrond's race descendant of [*struck out at once:* Túrin][2] the ancient men of the North, and one of Elrond's house-

GANDALF'S DELAY 7

hold. He was a hunter and wanderer. He became a friend of Bilbo. He knew Gandalf. He was intrigued by Bilbo's story, and found Gollum.[3] When Gandalf went off on the last perilous quest – really to find out about Black Riders and whether the Dark Lord would attack the Shire – he [> Gandalf and Bilbo] arranged with Trotter (real name [*other unfinished names struck out in the act of writing*: Bara / Rho / Dam] Aragorn son of Aramir) to go towards the Shire and keep a lookout on the road from East (Gandalf was going South). He gives Aragorn a letter to Frodo. Aragorn pretends he is a Ranger and hangs about Bree. (He also warns Tom Bombadil.)

Reason of wooden shoes – no need in this case because Aragorn is a man.[4] Hence there is no need for Gandalf...[5] The cache of food at Weathertop is Aragorn's. Aragorn steers them to Weathertop as a good lookout.

But how could Trotter miss Gandalf?

What delayed Gandalf? Black Riders or other hunters. Treebeard.

Aragorn did not miss Gandalf and arranged tryst on Weathertop.

At the end is written very emphatically and twice underlined: NO ODO.

The likeness of what is said of Trotter/Aragorn here (he was a man of Elrond's race and household, he became a friend of Bilbo's, and he 'pretends he is a Ranger') to the proposal at the end of §1 (Trotter was 'a disguised elf', one of the Rivendell scouts, a friend of Bilbo's in Rivendell, and he 'pretends to be a ranger') may suggest that the one arose directly from the other. On the other hand, my father had still not finally decided the question; for on the reverse of this piece of paper and undoubtedly at the same time he wrote:

Alternative function for Trotter. Trotter is Peregrin Boffin that Bilbo took away with him or who ran off with Bilbo – but this rather duplicates things – unless you cut out all Frodo's friends.[6]

If Trotter is Peregrin Boffin then Bilbo must go off quietly and Peregrin simply vanish *about the same time*.

This is followed by a brief passage sketching a rough narrative on these lines:

There was peace in Hobbiton for many years. Gandalf came seldom and then very quietly and mainly to visit Bilbo. He seemed to have given up trying to persuade even [?young] Tooks to go off on mad adventures out of the Shire. Then suddenly things began to happen. Bilbo Baggins disappeared again – that is hardly exact: he walked off without saying a word except to Gandalf (and to his nephews Peregrin and Frodo,[7] it may be supposed). It was a great blow to Frodo. He found Bilbo had left everything he possessed to himself and Peregrin. But Peregrin also disappeared, leaving a will in which his share

8 THE TREASON OF ISENGARD

Here these notes end, the idea abandoned. Perhaps it was here that Trotter ceased finally to be a hobbit, Peregrin Boffin.

(3) A page of clear notes in ink, agreeing in part with features of §1 and §2, is headed optimistically *Final decisions. Oct. 8 1939.* This was subsequently emended in pencil, but I give it first as it was written.

(1) General plot as at present. Bilbo vanishes at party (but all that chapter will have to be reduced, especially the Sackville-Baggins business). (Begin with a conversation between Bilbo and Frodo?)[8]
(2) Gandalf *not* expected by Frodo. Gandalf had not been seen for 2/3 *years.* Frodo grew restless and went off – although Gandalf had really not wished him to go till he returned.
(3) When Bilbo went Gandalf *not* sure of nature of Ring. Bilbo's longevity had made him suspicious – and he induced Bilbo *not* to take Ring with him. Bilbo had no idea that Ring was dangerous – hence simplify all Bilbo's motives, and remove the difficulty of his burdening Frodo with it.
(4) Frodo's friends are Meriadoc Brandybuck and Peregrin Boffin called Merry and Perry (only; no Odo). Peregrin drops off at Crickhollow. Merry at Rivendell. Sam only goes on to end.
(5) Trotter is not a hobbit but a real *ranger* who had gone to live in Rivendell after much wandering. Cut out shoes.

In (4) it is seen that despite the decision – which was indeed final – that Trotter was a Man, 'Peregrin Boffin' survived the loss of his *alter ego,* remaining an intimate of the owner of Bag End in a later generation; and for a brief moment may be said to step into the shoes of Odo Bolger – since he 'drops off at Crickhollow'.

Pencilled emendations were made to (4) and (5). To (4) was first added: 'Peregrin stays at Hobbiton and tells Gandalf.' This was struck out, and the first sentence of the note was changed to read: 'Frodo's friends are Meriadoc Brandybuck and Ham [ilcar] Bolger and Faramond Took, called Merry, Ham, and Far', with the further addition: 'Ham drops off at Crickhollow, but is picked up by Gandalf and used as a decoy. ?' (On this see under §6 below, p. 13.) Thus once more 'Odo Bolger' will bounce back, but now under the name of Hamilcar of that ilk. 'Hamilcar' has appeared hitherto only in a note dated August 1939, where it is proposed that 'Odo' be changed to 'Hamilcar' or 'Fredegar' (VI.373). 'Peregrin Boffin' disappears again – but only temporarily.

To (5) was added in pencil, after 'a real *ranger*': 'descendant of Elendil. Tarkil.' The name *Tarkil* appears in the *Etymologies* in V.364 (stem KHIL 'follow'): **tāra-khil*, in which the second element evidently bears the sense 'mortal man' (*Hildi* 'the Followers', an Elvish name for Men, V.245).

(4) A page of very rough notes in pencil, covered with emendations

GANDALF'S DELAY

and additions, is dated 'Autumn 1939' and headed *New Plot*. There now enters a very important development: a far more explicit account of what had caused Gandalf's delay than anything that has been said hitherto; and the evil figure of 'Giant Treebeard', his captor, disappears – though not for good (see p. 72).

Time Scheme won't work out for Gandalf to be ahead.

(1) Crickhollow scene – only Hamilcar [*struck out:* or Folco][9] there. He blows horn and startles the Riders' horses, which bolt. They run out of the house, and find a way[10] as the hue and cry wakes.

(2) Gandalf is *behind* at Bree. He knows Trotter (real name Aragorn). Trotter helped him track Gollum. He brings Trotter back in April 1418 to keep watch especially S.E. of Shire. It was a message of Trotter's in July (?) that took Gandalf away[11] – fearing Black Riders. He meets Trotter at Sarn Ford.[12] He then tells him of Frodo's intended departure on Sept. 22. Begs him to watch East Road in case anything happens to Gandalf himself. He visits Bree on way back to Shire on Sept. [*date illegible*]. But is pursued and tries to get round to west of Shire.

Black Riders pursue them [*read* him] – Gandalf has insufficient magic to cope with Black Riders unaided, whose king is a wizard. They pursue him over Sarn Ford and he cannot (or dare not) go back to Shire.

Eventually he is besieged in the *Western Tower*. He cannot get away while they guard it with five Riders. But when Black Riders have located Frodo and found that he has gone off without Gandalf they ride away. Three are ahead. Three follow Frodo, but miss him and get ahead at Bree. Three come behind.[13] Gandalf follows after – meets Peregrin [*written above:* news from Gaffer].

The remainder of this outline is a very rough and much corrected chronology of Gandalf's subsequent movements, which is best considered together with other chronologies of this time (§6).

A remarkable feature of this 'New Plot' is the date April 1418, for this is the first appearance of any 'exterior' chronology; moreover 1418 is the year in LR, Appendix B – according to the Shire Reckoning, i.e. 3018 of the Third Age. At the present time, at any rate, I am unable to cast any light on the chronology underlying this date, or to make any suggestion as to the process by which it had arisen.

(5) On the reverse of the page bearing this 'New Plot' is a series of notes on unconnected topics.

(1) Some mention of Bill Ferney's pony. Does this remain at Rivendell? [The question is answered 'Yes'.]

(2) Real name of Trotter? [Pencilled against this: 'Aragorn'. See §§ 2, 4.]

10 THE TREASON OF ISENGARD

(3) Elrond should tell more of Gilgalad?

(4) New name of Dimrilldale (now transferred to South). River Hoarwell flowing out of ? Hoardale. Nen fimred. Wolfdale [*written above:* Entishdale]. The region west of the Misty Mountains north of Rivendell is called the Entishlands – home of Trolls.[14]

(5) Gandalf says Tom Bombadil never leaves his own ground. How then known to Butterbur? Tom's boundaries are from Bree to High Hay?[15] [Against the words 'How then known to Butterbur?' my father pencilled 'Not'.]

(6) Trotter is a Ranger – descendant of Elendil? – he is known to Bilbo, and Gandalf. He has previously been to Mordor and been tormented (caught in Moria). Gandalf brought him back towards borders of Shire in April. It was a message from Trotter that fetched Gandalf away in summer before Frodo left.

(7) Note Frodo's red sword is broken. Hence he accepts Sting.[16]

A final note was added in pencil: '(8) Not *Barnabas* Butterbur.' – In the remarks about Trotter here the only point that has not appeared in notes already given is that Trotter was captured in Moria: cf. the original story of the Council of Elrond (VI.401): 'Trotter had tracked Gollum as he wandered southwards, through Fangorn Forest, and past the Dead Marshes, until he had himself been caught and imprisoned by the Dark Lord.' It is seen here that the story of Trotter's capture and torturing survived his change from hobbit to man.

Since Trotter's real name is not yet known these notes evidently preceded those in §2 and §4; but no doubt they all come from the same time.

(6) *Time-schemes.* In this section I attempt to present four chronologies of Gandalf's movements, which I label A, B, C, D. A is the conclusion of the 'New Plot' given in §4 above, and was probably the first to be set down. The schemes vary among themselves, each one giving slightly different chronologies; and it is hard to be sure to what extent the story differed in each, since my father was more explicit and less explicit at different points in the different schemes. They were working chronologies, much confused by alternatives and additions, and they cannot be usefully reproduced as they stand, but in the table on p. 12 I set out comparatively the (final) dates in each, with statements in the original wording or closely based on it. The dates of Frodo's journey from Hobbiton to Weathertop remain of course unchanged, but I repeat them here for convenience:

Thurs. Sept.	22	Frodo's party
Fri.	23	Frodo and his friends leave Hobbiton
Sat.	24	Night with the Elves
Sun.	25	Farmer Maggot; reach Crickhollow
Mon.	26	Old Forest; first night with Bombadil

GANDALF'S DELAY

Tues.		27	Second night with Bombadil
Wed.		28	Leave Bombadil; Barrow-downs
Thurs.		29	Reach Bree
Fri.		30	Leave Bree; in Chetwood
Sat.	Oct.	1	In Chetwood
Sun.		2	In the Midgewater Marshes
Mon.		3	Second day in the Marshes
Tues.		4	Camp by stream under alders
Wed.		5	Camp at feet of the hills
Thurs.		6	Reach Weathertop; attack at night

Notes on the Time-schemes (table on p. 12).

The relative chronology of Gandalf's movements is much the same in all four, though the actual dates differ; but in C he takes longer from Hobbiton to Crickhollow, and in D he takes a day less from Bree to Weathertop. In A and B the date of Gandalf's escape from the Tower was first given as 24 September, the night that Frodo and his companions passed with the Elves in the Woody End, and in B there is a suggestion, struck out, that Frodo 'dreamt his dream at night with the Elves'; as is seen from the other schemes, he dreamed of Gandalf in the Western Tower. In C it is said that Frodo dreamt of the Tower when 'with the Elves near Woodhall', but against this my father wrote: 'No – at Crickhollow'; he also noted here that the attack on Crickhollow should be told on the night of *The Prancing Pony* (whence the 'doubled' opening of FR Chapter 11, 'A Knife in the Dark'). In D the placing of Frodo's 'vision of Gandalf' or 'Dream of the Tower' hesitates between the night he spent with the Elves, the night at Crickhollow, and the first night at Bombadil's house. – For the remarkable history of the dream see pp. 33–6.

The mention in A and B of Gandalf's meeting with Peregrin Boffin (Perry) at Hobbiton after his escape belongs with the addition made to the 'final decisions' given in §3 above: 'Peregrin stays at Hobbiton and tells Gandalf.' This was a short-lived idea – indeed already in the 'New Plot' (§4) my father scribbled in here 'news from Gaffer': a reference to the story that will appear in the next phase of work on 'The Council of Elrond' (p. 135; FR p. 276).

Scheme A makes no mention of what happened at Crickhollow, but the 'New Plot' that precedes it begins with the statement that only Hamilcar Bolger was there, and that the horses of the Riders bolted when he blew a horn: which presumably means that the attack took place before Gandalf arrived. An addition to B (contradicting the chronology of that scheme) says that

> The Black Riders creep into Buckland, but too late to see Frodo depart. They track him to Crickhollow and guard it, and see Gandalf enter. But Gandalf (and Ham pretending to be Frodo) burst out on night of Sept. 29.

Journeys of Gandalf

	A	B	C	D
Sun. Sept. 25	Escapes from Tower	Escapes from Tower at dawn	Leaves White Tower at dawn	
Tues. Sept. 27		Reaches Hobbiton; sees Perry Boffin (morning)	Reaches Hobbiton	
Wed. Sept. 28	Reaches Hobbiton; sees Perry Boffin	Reaches Crickhollow late		Returns to Shire
Thurs. Sept. 29	Crickhollow	Leaves Crickhollow early, goes to Bombadil	Reaches Crickhollow via Bridge, evening. Riders attack at night	Riders attack Crickhollow; carry off Ham, pursued by Gandalf (midnight)
Fri. Sept. 30	Leaves Crickhollow, goes to Bombadil	Leaves Bombadil, reaches Bree late, 'very tired'	Dawn: breaks out with Ham and 'rides off' to Bombadil	Early morning: rescues Ham, goes to Bombadil
Sat. Oct. 1	Leaves Bombadil; reaches Bree	Leaves Bree early	Reaches Bree in evening	Leaves Bombadil early, reaches Bree
Sun. Oct. 2	Leaves Bree in morning		Leaves Bree	Leaves Bree with Ham early
Mon. Oct. 3		Reaches Weathertop late		Reaches Weathertop in evening. Holds out during night
Tues. Oct. 4	Breaks through Riders and reaches Weathertop	Pursued by Riders leaves Weathertop early	Reaches Weathertop in evening. Leaves during night	Flies from Weathertop pursued by Riders

GANDALF'S DELAY
13

With this cf. the addition to §3 above: 'Ham drops off at Crickhollow, but is picked up by Gandalf and used as a decoy.' Scheme C says that it was at dawn on the 30th (the morning on which the hobbits left Bree with Trotter after the attack on the inn) that 'Gandalf broke out with Ham'; he then 'rode off to Tom' (which way did he go?).

A different story is seen in D, in which it is told that at midnight on the 29th/30th Black Riders crossed the Brandywine by the Ferry, attacked the house at Crickhollow, and *carried off* Ham, 'pursued by Gandalf'; and that in the early morning of the 30th Gandalf *rescued* Ham, the Black Riders fled in terror to their King, and Gandalf went on to visit Tom.

For narrative drafts reflecting these versions of the events at Crickhollow see pp. 53–6, 68–70.

All the schemes agree that Gandalf went from Buckland to visit Tom Bombadil; cf. the original version of 'The Council of Elrond', VI.401, where Gandalf says that 'when I had chased the Riders from Crickhollow I turned back to visit him.'

Scheme D has a note that 'Trotter reaches the Shire border Sept. 14 and hears ill news on morning of 25th from Elves.' This scheme also provides an account of the movements of the individual Riders, who are identified by the letters A to I. It was D who came to Hobbiton on 23 September, the night on which Frodo left, and it was D and E who trailed the hobbits in the Shire, while G H I were on the East Road and F was to the southward. On the 25th, the day that Frodo reached Crickhollow, D E G H I assembled at the Brandywine Bridge; G waited there while H and I passed through Bree on Monday the 26th. On the 27th D and E 'got into Buckland and looked for Baggins'; on the 28th they 'located' him and went to get the help of G. On the night of the 29th D E G crossed the River by the Ferry; and on the same night H and I returned and attacked *The Prancing Pony*. Pursued by Gandalf from Crickhollow D E G fled to the King. A B C D E F G 'rode East after Gandalf and the supposed Baggins' on 1 October; F and G were sent direct to Weathertop, and the other five, together with H and I, rode through Bree at night, throwing down the gates, and from the inn (where Gandalf was) the noise of their passage was heard like a wind. F and G reached Weathertop on the 2nd; Gandalf was pursued North from Weathertop by C D E, while A B F G H I patrolled the East Road.

Of these four time-schemes only D treats fully the chronology from Weathertop to the Ford. A mentions that Gandalf went North 'via Entish Lands' and reached Rivendell on 14 October; two Riders pursued him 'towards Entish Dale; these are they that came from the flank at the Ford.'[17] B also has Gandalf reach Rivendell on the 14th, and says:

> But messages from the Elves of the Shire have travelled swiftly since Sept. 24. Already Elrond has heard in Rivendell that the Ring had

14   THE TREASON OF ISENGARD

set out alone, and that Gandalf is missing, and the Ringwraiths are out. He sends out scouts North, South, and West. These scouts are Elves of power. Glorfindel goes along the Road. He reaches the Bridge of *Mitheithel*[18] at dawn on Oct. 12 and drives off the Black Riders and pursues them West till they escape. On Oct. 14 he turns and searches for traces of Frodo's party for several days (2/3), finds them, and then comes after them, catching them up on the evening of Oct. 18.

In Scheme D the final chronology for this part of the story, agreeing (except in one point) with that in LR Appendix B though fuller, was attained. For earlier phases of the development see VI.219, 360.

October

Wed.	5	Camp near hills	
Thurs.	6	Attack on camp at Weathertop	
Fri.	7	Frodo leaves Weathertop	
Sat.	8		News reaches Elrond
Sun.	9	Frodo in the Cheerless Lands	Glorfindel leaves Rivendell
Mon.	10		
Tues.	11		Gandalf at Hoarwell (Mitheithel) Rain. Glorfindel at Bridge of Mitheithel
Wed.	12	Frodo and Trotter see Road and rivers	
Thurs.	13	Frodo crosses Last Bridge	
Fri.	14	Frodo in hills	Glorfindel finds tracks
Sat.	15	Hills (wet)	
Sun.	16	Hills (shelf) [See FR p. 214: 'a stony shelf']	
Mon.	17	Troll-ridge	
Tues.	18	Trolls	Gandalf and Ham reach Rivendell Glorfindel finds Trotter etc.
Wed.	19	Bend [See FR p. 224: 'the Road bent right']	
Thurs.	20	Battle at Ford of Bruinen[19]	
Fri.	21		
Sat.	22	Frodo unconscious	
Sun.	23		
Mon.	24	Frodo wakes	
Tues.	25		
Wed.	26	Council of Elrond	

The only point in which this differs from the final chronology is that a whole day passes between Frodo's waking and the Council of Elrond, which thus takes place here on the 26th of October, not on the 25th.

GANDALF'S DELAY

15

But this is not a slip, for the same appears in other closely related chronologies of this period.

NOTES

1 *Faramond Took* replaced *Folco Took* in the original version of 'The Council of Elrond', VI.406 and subsequently.

2 Túrin of course had no descendants. Possibly *Túrin* was a slip for *Tuor*, grandfather of Elrond.

3 That it was Trotter who found Gollum appears in the original version of 'The Council of Elrond' (VI.401 and note 20).

4 The meaning of this very elliptical remark is possibly that when Trotter was a hobbit the injury to his feet caused him to wear shoes, which for a hobbit was highly unusual; but if he was a man that would not be the case.

5 From its appearance the illegible word could well be *otiose*, but that does not seem likely. If however this is what it is, 'Hence there is no need for' must be a sentence left in the air, followed by 'Gandalf otiose' – i.e. Gandalf need have nothing to do with Weathertop: Aragorn 'steered them to Weathertop' simply because it was 'a good lookout'. But the whole passage is very obscure.

6 I.e., if Bilbo went off with Peregrin Boffin there would be a duplication when Frodo in his turn went off with younger companions.

7 Cf. the story of Peregrin Boffin in VI.385–6: there Peregrin and Frodo stood in the same relationship (first cousins once removed) to Bilbo.

8 The bracketed sentence was struck out, with the note: 'No, because that would give away suspense.' On the same piece of paper as these 'final decisions' there is a sketch of such a conversation, although in this there is no suggestion of a party:

'I am going for a holiday, a long holiday!' said Bilbo Baggins to his young 'nephew' Frodo. 'What is more, I am going tomorrow. It will be April 30th, my anniversary and a good day to start on. Also the weather is fine!'

Bilbo had made this announcement a great many times before; but each time he made it, and it became plainer that he really meant it, Frodo's heart sank lower. He had lived with Bilbo for nearly 12 years and known him longer, and he was devoted to him. 'Where are you going?' he asked, but he did not expect any answer, as he had also asked this question often before and got no satisfactory reply.

'I would tell you if I knew myself for certain – or perhaps I would,' answered Bilbo as usual. 'To the Sea maybe, or the

16   THE TREASON OF ISENGARD

Mountains. Mountains, I think; yes, Mountains,' he said, as if to himself.

'Could I come with you?' asked Frodo. He had never said that before; and he had not really any desire to leave Bag-End or the Shire that he loved; but that night with Bilbo's departure so near

Here this fragment ends.

9   *or Folco*: cf. §3 (4): 'Peregrin [Boffin] drops off at Crickhollow.'

10   *find a way* is clear, but my father possibly intended *ride away*, or *flee away*, or something similar.

11   In the 'third phase' version Gandalf still left Bag End 'one wet dark evening in May' (VI.323). In FR (p. 76) he left at the end of June.

12   The name *Sarn Ford* is here met for the first time. It is found on the most original part of the original LR map (pp. 299, 305).

13   The numbers were first written two ahead, four following Frodo, three behind. The passage was bracketed with a note: 'No, see Black Riders' movements': this is a reference to the full account in Scheme D (see p. 13).

14   For the transference of *Dimrill-dale* to the South and the other side of the Misty Mountains and its replacement by *Hoardale* see VI.432–3, notes 3 and 13. The present note is very probably where the River *Hoarwell* (see VI.192, 360) rising in *Hoardale*, and the *Entish Lands*, first emerged. No doubt it was at this time that *Hoardale* was written on the manuscript of the first version of 'The Ring Goes South' (VI.432, note 3); but *Entish Dale* evidently soon replaced it – it is found in one of the Time-schemes (p. 13) and was written in on the present note. On *Ent* as used in these names, in the sense of Old English *ent* 'giant', the *Ents* of Fangorn not having yet arisen, see VI.205.

15   In the 'third phase' narrative Tom Bombadil was still thought of as visiting *The Prancing Pony* (VI.334), but in the first version of 'The Council of Elrond' (VI.402) Gandalf says that 'the mastery of Tom Bombadil is seen only on his own ground – from which he has never stepped within my memory.'

16   Bilbo's gift to Frodo of Sting is first mentioned in the initial draft for 'The Council of Elrond' (VI.397), and Frodo's possession of it in the sketch for the Moria story (VI.443). – Why is Frodo's sword called 'red'? In another isolated note, written much later, this reappears: 'What happened to the red sword[s] of the Barrows? In Frodo's case it is broken at the Ford and he has Sting.' In the 'third phase' version of 'Fog on the Barrow-downs' they were 'bronze swords, short, leaf-shaped and keen' (VI.128, 329); at some later time the reading of FR (p. 157), according to which they were 'damasked with serpent-forms in red and gold', was entered on that manuscript.

GANDALF'S DELAY

17 On *Entish Dale* see note 14. – In the 'third phase' version of the story there were six Riders in ambush at the Ford (VI.361); in FR there were four (cf. p. 62).

18 This is the first appearance in the texts of the Elvish name *Mitheithel* of the River Hoarwell (see note 14) and of the Last Bridge, by which the East Road crossed the river (but they are found on the sketch-maps redrawn in Vol. VI, p. 201).

19 This is the first occurrence of the name *Bruinen*, other than on one of the sketch-maps mentioned in note 18.

II

THE FOURTH PHASE (1):
FROM HOBBITON TO BREE

The rethinking and rewriting of this period led to an extremely complex situation in the actual constituent chapter-manuscripts of the book as it stood. Some of the manuscripts of the 'third phase' were now in their turn covered with corrections and deletions and interspersed with inserted riders, so that they became chaotic (cf. VI.309). In this case, however, since substantial parts of those manuscripts were in no need of correction, or of very little, my father wrote out fair only those parts of the chapters that had been much affected by revision, and added to these the unaffected portions of the original 'third phase' texts. For this 'fourth' phase, therefore, some of the manuscripts are textually hybrids, while others remain common to both 'phases' (no doubt a somewhat artificial conception).

The rejected parts of the 'third phase' manuscripts were separated and set aside and in a sense 'lost', so that when the 'fourth phase' series was sent to Marquette University some eighteen years later these superseded pages – and a good deal of preliminary draft writing for their replacement – remained in England. To put it all together again, and to work out the intricacies of the whole complex become so widely separated, has been far from easy; but I have no doubt that in the result the history of these texts has been correctly ascertained.[1]

Where necessary to distinguish rough revision in draft and the fair copy manuscript based on it I shall call the former 'A' and the latter 'B' for the purpose of this chapter.

The revision of this period came very near to attaining the text of FR Book I through a great part of its length, though with certain major and notable exceptions; and in what follows a host of minor changes is to be presupposed, since there would be little purpose in spelling them out. It is indeed remarkable to see that by the end of 1939 the story as far as Rivendell had been brought, after so many and such meticulous revisions, to a point where one could read the greater part of it and scarcely suspect any difference from FR without careful comparison; yet at this time my father was without any clear conception of what lay before him.

In my account chapter by chapter of the 'fourth phase' I shall concentrate on the major elements of reconstruction that belong to this time.

THE FOURTH PHASE (1)   19

Chapter I: 'A Long-expected Party'

The sixth or 'third phase' version of this chapter (VI.314–15) was heavily reworked in certain passages, bringing the story at almost all points virtually to the form in FR. The substantial rider added at the beginning, introducing the story of the youth of Peregrin Boffin or Trotter (see VI.384–6), was rejected when the decision was finally taken that Trotter was a Man, and does not appear in the fair copy B.

Many changes reflect suggestions in the notes dated August 1939 given in VI.370 ff., and some new features derive from the notes and outlines given in Chapter I of this book. Thus Bilbo took with him 'a bundle wrapped in old cloths': his 'elf-armour' (see VI.371–2). Now, just as in FR (p. 40), he put the envelope on the mantlepiece (but suddenly took it down and stuck it in his pocket), and Gandalf entered at that moment (changing the previous story, in which Gandalf met Bilbo at the bottom of the hill, VI.315). Their conversation (for the form of it before this revision see VI.238–40) becomes exactly as in FR, as far as 'It's time he was his own master now' (p. 41), and this clearly derives from the 'August 1939' note given in VI.374: 'Neither Bilbo nor Gandalf must know much about the Ring, when Bilbo departs. Bilbo's motive is simply *tiredness*, an unexplained restlessness...' Bilbo's words about his book, which Gandalf says nobody will read, are taken up from the note given in VI.371.[2] But here this 'fourth phase' version shows a significant difference from FR: for there is *no quarrel* between them as yet, though it hovers on the verge of being devised (on the first germ of the quarrel see VI.378–9). I give the passage in the form of the fair copy B (which the draft A approaches very closely):

'Everything?' said Gandalf. 'The ring as well?'

'Well, or yes I suppose so,' stammered Bilbo.

'Where is it?'

'I put it in an envelope for him, and put it on the mantle – well no! Isn't that odd now! Here it is in my pocket!'

Gandalf looked again very hard at Bilbo, and his eyes glinted. 'I think, Bilbo,' he said quietly, 'I should leave it with him. Don't you want to?'

'Well yes – and yet it seems very difficult to part with it somehow. Why do you want me to leave it behind?' he asked, and a curious note of suspicion came into his voice. 'You are always worrying about it lately, but you have never bothered me about the other things I got on my journey.'

'Magic rings are – well, *magic*,' answered Gandalf; 'and they are not, nowadays, very common. Let's say that I am professionally interested in your ring, and would like to know where it

20 THE TREASON OF ISENGARD

is. Also I think *you* have had it long enough. You won't want it any more, Bilbo, unless I am quite mistaken.'

'Oh, very well,' said Bilbo. 'It would be a relief, in a way, not to be bothered with it. It has been rather growing on my mind lately. Sometimes I have felt that it was like an eye looking at me;[3] and I am always wanting to put it on and disappear, don't you know, or wondering if it is safe and pulling it out to make sure. I tried leaving it locked up, but I found I couldn't rest without it in my pocket. I don't know why. Well! Now I must be starting, or somebody else will catch me. I have said good-bye, and I couldn't bear to do it all over again.' He picked up his bag and moved towards the door.

'You have still got the ring in your pocket,' said the wizard.

'So I have, and my will and all the other documents too!' cried Bilbo. 'I had better give them to you to deliver to Frodo. That will be safest.' He held out the envelope, but just as Gandalf was about to take it, Bilbo's hand jerked and the envelope fell on the floor. Quick as lightning the wizard stooped and seized it, before Bilbo could pick it up. An odd look passed over the hobbit's face, almost like anger. Suddenly it gave way to a look of relief and a smile.

'Well, that's that!' he said. 'Now I'm off!'

From this point the revision brings the narrative almost to the final form. The dwarves, now three and no longer named, play only the same rôle as in FR; and when Frodo returns to Bag End he finds Gandalf sitting in the dark, whereupon the conversation between them in FR (pp. 44–5) follows. A minute but characteristically subtle difference remaining is that it is not said, in the passage just cited, that when the envelope fell to the floor Gandalf 'set it in its place' on the mantlepiece; and now Gandalf says to Frodo: 'He left a packet with me to give to you. Here it is!' Then Frodo took the envelope from the wizard. In FR Gandalf pointed to it on the mantlepiece; he would not sit waiting for Frodo with the envelope containing the Ring in his hand.

Once again the list of Bilbo's labelled legacies changes (see VI.247), in that Uffo Took now receives the final name Adelard, while the somnolent Rollo Bolger, recipient of the feather-bed, makes his last appearance, his first name changed to Odovacar, in A; in B he has gone.

The conversation between Gandalf and Frodo at Bag End on the following day (see VI.242–3) now becomes precisely as in FR with, of course, the one major difference that there is no reference to the variant stories which Bilbo had told concerning his acquisition of the

THE FOURTH PHASE (1)   21

Ring (p. 49). The rewriting of this conversation again clearly springs from the note of August 1939 (VI.374) referred to above, to the effect that Gandalf still did not know very much about the Ring at this time; for Gandalf now knows less about it than he had done. He no longer warns Frodo against allowing it to gain power over him, nor is there now any mention in their conversation of Bilbo's state of 'preservation', and his restlessness, as concomitants of his possession of the Ring.

The revision got rid of the Dwarf Lofar, who had previously remained at Bag End after Bilbo's departure with the other Dwarves, but at first provided no clear substitute for Frodo's aide-de-camp whose task (as it turned out) was to receive the Sackville-Bagginses. In the fair copy B this is Merry, as in FR; but in the draft revision A my father replaced Lofar by one scribbled name after another: 'Merry' > 'Peregrin Boffin' > 'Folco Took'; at subsequent occurrences in this episode 'Peregrin Boffin' > 'Folco', and once 'Peregrin' retained. 'Peregrin Boffin' had been moved from the rôle of Trotter in his youth, but survived as one of Frodo's intimates: as such we have already met him (pp. 8, 11). See further pp. 30–2.

Chapter II: 'Ancient History'

This chapter (ultimately one of the most worked upon in all *The Lord of the Rings*) underwent very substantial rewriting at this time in certain passages, but remained still in important respects far different from 'The Shadow of the Past' in FR. The 'third phase' manuscript (VI.318 ff.), not much changed in substance from the second version (VI.250 ff.), was reduced to a wreck in the process; and here again my father made a new text (B) of the chapter, taking up all this rough correction and new writing (A), but incorporated into the new manuscript those parts of the old that were retained more or less intact, so that the new version is again textually a hybrid.

In draft revision of the beginning of the chapter Frodo's 'closest companions were Folco Took [*pencilled above:* Faramond] and Meriadoc Brandybuck (usually called Merry), both a few years younger than himself' (cf. VI.318); in B his companions become Faramond Took, Peregrin Boffin, and Hamilcar Bolger, while his closest friend was Merry Brandybuck. With this cf. the notes given on p. 8. In the drafts (A) the names Folco, Faramond, Peregrin, shift and replace each other at every occurrence, and it is scarcely possible to say whether characters or merely names are in question.

Otherwise, the new version reaches the final form in most respects for a long stretch. The chronology of Gandalf's visits to Bag End, from the Party to the time of this chapter, becomes precisely that of FR (p. 55); but the passage (FR pp. 52–3) concerning the 'rumours of strange

22   THE TREASON OF ISENGARD

things happening in the world outside' was at this stage left virtually unchanged – which means that it still essentially took the form it had in the second version, VI.253.

The first part of the conversation between Gandalf and Frodo now takes a great step towards that in FR (pp. 55–6; cf. VI.319), but Gandalf as yet says nothing of the making of rings 'in Eregion long ago', nor does he speak here of the Great Rings, the Rings of Power. Though his words are the same as in FR, they apply only to the ring in Frodo's possession: thus he says 'Those who keep this ring do not die,' &c. His account of Bilbo's knowledge of and feeling about his ring are very much as in FR, but he says here that Bilbo 'knew, of course, that it made one invisible, if it encircled any part of the body.' In rejected drafts for this passage occur the following:

> He certainly had not yet begun to connect his long life and 'good preservation' with the ring – but he had begun to feel the restlessness that is the first symptom of the stretching of the days.

> On that last evening I saw plainly that the ring was trying to keep hold of him and prevent his parting with it. But he was not yet conscious of it himself. And certainly he had no idea that it would have made him permanently invisible, nor that his long life and 'good preservation' – how the expression annoyed him! – had anything to do with it.

From Frodo's question at the end of Gandalf's remarks about Bilbo, the new version retains the existing text (VI.319) concerning Gandalf's memories, but is then developed quite differently, though still far from that of FR (p. 57):

> 'How long have you known?' asked Frodo again.
> 'I knew very little of these things at first,' answered Gandalf slowly, as if searching back in memory. The days of Bilbo's journey and the Dragon and the Battle of Five Armies seemed dim and far off, and many other dark and strange adventures had befallen him since. 'Let me see – it was after the White Council in the South that I first began to give serious thought to Bilbo's ring. There was much talk of rings at the Council: even wizards have much to learn as long as they live, however long that may be. There are many sorts of ring, of course. Some are no more than toys (though dangerous ones to my mind), and not difficult to contrive if you go in for such things – they are not in my line. But what I heard made me think a good deal, though I said nothing to Bilbo. All seemed well with him. I thought he was safe enough from any evil of that sort. I was nearly right but not quite right. Perhaps I should have been

THE FOURTH PHASE (1) 23

more suspicious, and have found out the truth sooner than I did – yet if I had, I don't know what else could have been done.

'Then, of course, I noticed that he did not seem to grow older. But the whole thing seemed so unlikely that I did not get seriously alarmed, never until the night he left this house. He said and did things then that were unmistakeable signs of something wrong.[4] From that moment my chief anxiety was to get him to go and give up the ring. And I have spent most of the years since in finding out the truth about it.'

'There wasn't any permanent harm done, was there?' asked Frodo anxiously. 'He would get right in time, wouldn't he – be able to rest in peace, I mean?'

'That I don't know for certain,' said Gandalf. 'There is only one [added: Power] in this world who knows all about the ring and its effects. But I don't think you need fear for him. Of course, if anyone possessed the ring for many years, it would probably take a long while for the effects to wear off. How long is not really known. He might live for ages. But not wearily, I think. He would, I now believe, just stop as he was when he parted with the ring; and would be happy, if he parted with it of his own accord and with good intent. Though as far as I know that has only happened once. I was not troubled about dear Bilbo any more, once he had let the ring go. It is for *you* that I feel responsible...'[5]

There is of course no reference here to Bilbo's 'two stories' of how he came by the Ring; nor does Saruman appear. Yet Gandalf's mention of the discussion of Rings at the White Council, and his suggestion that there are wizards who, unlike himself, 'go in for such things', prepares the place that Saruman would fill when he had arisen – although, characteristically, he did not arise in order to fill that place.

The new version introduced no changes into Gandalf's account of the Ruling Ring and its history (for the text as it had developed through the three preceding versions see VI.78, 258–61, 319–20): indeed almost all of this part of the chapter is constituted from pages taken out of the 'third phase' manuscript (see p. 18). Before the new version of the chapter was completed, however (see note 12), my father changed Gollum's original name from *Dígol* (through *Deagol*) to *Smeagol*, and introduced a rider telling the story of Deagol and his murder:

He had a friend called Deagol, of similar short, sharper-eyed but not so quick and strong. They were roaming together, when

24   THE TREASON OF ISENGARD

in the mud of a river-bank, under the twisted roots of an ancient thorn-tree,[6] Deagol found the Ring. Smeagol came up behind him, just as he was washing the mud off, and the Ring gleamed yellow.

'Give us that, Deagol my love,' said Smeagol over his friend's shoulder.

'Why?' said Deagol.

'Because it's my birthday...

The remainder of the inserted text is virtually word for word as in FR (p. 62). On this new story see pp. 27–8.

Very substantial rewriting begins again with Gandalf's discussion of Gollum's motives (FR pp. 63–6; for the previous versions see VI.79–80, 261–2, 320–1). Here there is more than one draft preceding the new manuscript B, and the relations between these texts are not entirely clear, though they differ chiefly only in the placing of certain elements. I give this passge in the form of B, with some variants from the drafts A recorded in the notes.

'Gollum!' said Frodo. 'Do you mean the very Gollum-creature that Bilbo met? Is that his history? How loathsome!'

'I think it is a sad story,' said the wizard, 'and it might have happened to others, even to some hobbits I have known.'

'I can't believe Gollum was connected with hobbits, however distantly,' said Frodo with some heat. 'What an abominable idea!'

'It is true all the same,' replied Gandalf. 'It is suggested even by Bilbo's own account; and partly explains the very curious events. There was a lot in the background of their minds and memories that was very similar: Bilbo and Gollum understood one another (if you think of it) better than hobbits have ever understood dwarves or goblins, or even elves. Think of the riddles they both knew, for one thing!'

'But why did Gollum start the Riddle-game, or think of giving up the Ring at all?' asked Frodo.[7]

'Because he was altogether miserable, and yet could not make up his wretched mind. Don't you realize that he had possessed the Ring for ages, and the torment was becoming unendurable? He was so wretched that he knew he was wretched, and had at last understood what caused it. There was nothing more to find out, nothing left but darkness, nothing to do but furtive eating and regretful remembering. Half his mind wanted above all to

THE FOURTH PHASE (1) 25

be rid of the Ring, even if the loss killed him. But he hated parting with it as much as keeping it. He wanted to hand it on to someone else, and to make him wretched too.'

'Then why didn't he give it to the Goblins?'

'Gollum would not have found that amusing! The Goblins were already beastly and miserable. And anyway he was afraid of them: naturally he had no fancy for an invisible goblin in the tunnels. But when Bilbo turned up half his mind saw that he had a marvellous chance; and the other half was angry and frightened, and was thinking how to trap and eat Bilbo. So he tried the Riddle-game, which might serve either purpose: it would decide the question for him, like tossing up. Very hobbit-like, I call that. But of course, if it had really come to the point of handing the Ring over, he would have immediately desired it terribly, and have hated Bilbo fiercely. It was lucky for Bilbo that things were arranged otherwise.'[8]

'But how was it that Gollum did not realize that he had got rid of it, if Bilbo had the Ring already?'

'Simply because he had only lost it for a few hours: not nearly long enough for him to feel any change in himself. And also he had not given it away of his own free will: that is an important point. All the same I have always thought that the strangest thing about Bilbo's whole adventure was his finding the Ring like that: just putting his hand on it in the dark. There was something mysterious in that; I think more than one power was at work. The Ring was trying to get back to its master. It had ruined Gollum, and could make no further use of him; he was too small and mean. It had already slipped from one owner's hand and betrayed him to death. It now left Gollum: and that would probably have proved Gollum's death, if the finder had not been the most unlikely creature imaginable: a Baggins all the way from the Shire! But behind all that there was something at work beyond any design of the Ringmaker. I can put it no plainer than by saying that *Bilbo was meant* to find the Ring, and *not* by its maker. In which case *you* were also meant to have it, and that may be an encouraging thought, or it may not.'

'It isn't,' said Frodo, 'though I am not sure that I understand you. But how have you learned all this about the Ring, and about Gollum? Do you really know it all, or are you guessing?'

'I have learned some things, and guessed others,' answered Gandalf. 'But I am not going to give you an account of the last few years just now. The story of Gilgalad and Isildur and the

26   THE TREASON OF ISENGARD

One Ring is well known to the learned in Lore. I knew it myself, of course, but I have consulted many other Lore-masters. Your ring is shown to be that One Ring by the fire-writing, quite apart from other evidence.'

'And when did you discover that?' asked Frodo interrupting.

'Just now in this room, of course,' answered Gandalf sharply. 'But I expected to find it. I have come back from many dark journeys to make that final test. It is the last proof, and all is now clear. Making out Gollum's part, and fitting it into the gap in the history, required some thought; but I guessed very near the truth. I know more of the minds and histories of the creatures of Middle-earth than you imagine, Frodo.'

'But your account does not quite agree with Bilbo's, as far as I can remember it.'

'Naturally. Bilbo had no idea of the nature of the Ring, and so could not guess what was behind Gollum's peculiar behaviour. But though I started from hints and guesses, I no longer need them. I am no longer guessing about Gollum. I know. I know because I have seen him.'[9]

'You have seen Gollum!' exclaimed Frodo in amazement.

'The obvious thing to try and do, surely,' said Gandalf.

'Then what happened after Bilbo escaped from him?' asked Frodo. 'Do you know that?'

'Not so clearly. What I have told you is what Gollum was willing to tell – though not, of course, in the way I have reported it. Gollum is a liar, and you have to sift his words. For instance, you may remember that he told Bilbo that he had been given the Ring as a birthday present long ago when such rings were less uncommon.[10] Very unlikely on the face of it: no kind of magic ring was ever common in his part of the world. Quite incredible, when one suspects what ring this one really was.[11] It was a lie, though with a grain of truth. I fancy he had made up his mind what to say, if necessary, so that the stranger would accept the Ring without suspicion, and think the gift natural. And that is another hobbit-like thought! Birthday present! It would have worked well with any hobbit. There was no need to tell the lie, of course, when he found the Ring had gone; but he had told that lie to himself so many times in the darkness, trying to forget Deagol,[12] that it slipped out, whenever he spoke of the Ring. He repeated it to me, but I laughed at him. He then told me more or less the true story, but with a lot of snivelling and snarling. He thought he was misunderstood and ill-treated...

THE FOURTH PHASE (1)   27

In the third version of this chapter Gandalf had said (VI.321): 'Very unlikely on the face of it: incredible when one suspects what kind of ring it really was. It was said merely to make Bilbo willing to accept it as a harmless kind of toy' (i.e., Gollum, speaking – according to Gandalf's elaborate theory – from that part of his mind that wished to get rid of the Ring, said off the top of his head that it had been a birthday present in order to get Bilbo to accept it more readily). While drafting a new version of this passage, my father was struck by a perturbing thought. He stopped, and across the manuscript he wrote: 'It must be [i.e. It must have been] a birthday present, as the birthday present is not mentioned by Gollum until after he finds the ring is *lost*'.[13] In other words, if the story of its being a birthday present was a fabrication pure and simple, why should Gollum only trot it out when there was no longer any use for it? Apparently in order to counter this, Gandalf's words were changed:

It was a lie, though with a grain of truth. But how hobbit-like, all that talk of birthday-presents! I fancy he had made up his mind what to say, if it came to the point of giving, so that Bilbo would accept the Ring without suspicion, and think it just a harmless toy. He repeated this nonsense to me, but I laughed at him.

The implication of this seems to be that Gollum brought out this story of the Ring having been a birthday present to him long ago only when he found that he had it no longer, because it had 'a grain of truth'; and it was because it had 'a grain of truth' that he had decided on this story. But there is no suggestion in the draft of what this grain of truth might be. Only with the fair copy B does it appear – and there only by implication: 'There was no need to tell the lie, of course, when he found the Ring had gone; but he had told that lie to himself so many times in the darkness, *trying to forget Deagol*, that it slipped out, whenever he spoke of the Ring.' This shows of course that the Deagol story (pp. 23–4) had already entered; but my father made the point clearer by pencilling on the fair copy after the words 'though with a grain of truth': *He murdered Deagol on his birthday.*

He was being driven to more and more intricate shifts to get round what had been said in *The Hobbit*. But it seems to me very likely that it was precisely while he was pondering this problem that the story of the murder of Deagol (and incidentally the changing of Gollum's true name to Smeagol) arose. That Gollum had *lied* about its being a birthday present was an obvious necessity, from the story of the Ring that had come into being; but Gandalf's theory in the third version that Gollum told this lie to Bilbo in order to get him to accept the Ring had a serious weakness: why did Gollum only do so (as the story was told in *The Hobbit*) *after* he found that he had lost it? The answer to

28   THE TREASON OF ISENGARD

this was that it was an invention of Gollum's that he had come partly to believe, quite independently of Bilbo's arrival; but why was that?

And this story of the murder of Deagol on Smeagol's birthday, the ground of Smeagol's 'lie with a grain of truth', became a permanent element in the tale of Gollum; surviving when, years later, the story of 'Riddles in the Dark' was recast and the very difficulty that (if I am right) had brought it into being was eliminated.

From 'He thought he was misunderstood and ill-treated' (p. 26) this fourth version of 'Ancient History' scarcely differs for a long stretch from the third, whose pages were largely retained;[14] and since the third version closely followed the second, this part of the conversation of Gandalf and Frodo preserves, apart from detail of expression, the text given in VI.263–5. But from 'The Wood-elves have him in prison, if he is still alive, as I expect; but they treat him with such kindness as they can find in their wise hearts' the new version reaches the form in FR (p. 69) with almost no difference to the end of the chapter. Gandalf's words about the fire that could melt and consume the Rings of Power (FR p. 70) remain however nearer to the earlier form:

It has been said that only dragon-fire can melt any of the Twenty Rings of Power; but there is not now any Dragon left on earth in whom the old Fire is hot enough to harm the Ruling Ring. I can think of only one way: one would have to find the Cracks of Doom in the depths of Orodruin, the Fire-Mountain, and cast the Ring in there, if he really wished to destroy it, or put it beyond all reach until the End.

The name *Orodruin* is met here for the first time.[15] In another point also the former version is retained: Gandalf still says when he goes to the window and draws aside the curtain (VI.322):

'In any case it is now too late. You would come to hate me and call me a thief; and our friendship would cease. Such is the power of the Ring. Keep it, and together we will shoulder the burden that is laid on us.'

Lastly, Gandalf does not in this version give Frodo a 'travelling name' ('When you go, go as Mr. Underhill', FR p. 72).

The subsequent history of this chapter, traced in detail, would itself almost constitute a book, for apart from the marvellous intricacies of the route by which the story of Gollum and the 'birthday present' was ultimately resolved, Gandalf's conversation with Frodo became the vehicle for the developing history of the Rings of Power, afterwards removed from this place, and the chapter could not be treated separately from 'The Council of Elrond'. But the great mass of this work, and probably all of it, belongs to a later time than we have

THE FOURTH PHASE (1)   29

reached; and in any case the attempt to trace in 'linear' fashion the history of the writing of *The Lord of the Rings* cannot at the same time take full account of the great constructions that were rising behind the onward movement of the tale. So far as the story of Bilbo and Gollum is concerned it seems that this fourth version of 'Ancient History', in which my father was still constrained within the words of the original story told in *The Hobbit*, remained for some time as the accepted form.

Chapter III: 'Three is Company'

The third version of this chapter, described in VI.323–5, was also revised at this time. The title was now changed from 'Delays are Dangerous' to 'Three is Company' (cf. the original title, 'Three's Company and Four's More', VI.49 and note 2); and the order of the opening passages was reversed, so that the chapter now begins as in FR with ' "You ought to go *quietly*, and you ought to go *soon*," said Gandalf', and his conversation with Frodo precedes the speculations in the *Ivy Bush* and *Green Dragon* (see VI.274 and note 1). This reorganisation and rewriting was very roughly done on the pages of the third phase manuscript and on inserted riders ('A'); the revised opening was then written out fair ('B'), as far as Gaffer Gamgee's conversation with the Black Rider in Bagshot Row, and the remainder of the existing text added to it, to form textually speaking a hybrid, just as in the case of the first two chapters.

The draft revision A of Gandalf's departure from Bag End takes this form:

> Gandalf stayed at Bag-End for over two months. But one evening, soon after Frodo's plan had been arranged, he suddenly announced that he was going off again next morning. 'I need to stretch my legs a bit, before our journey begins,' he said. 'Besides, I think I ought to go and look round, and see what news I can pick up down south on the borders, before we start.'
>
> He spoke lightly, but it seemed to Frodo that he looked rather grave and thoughtful. 'Has anything happened? Have you heard something?' he asked.
>
> 'Well, yes, to tell you the truth,' said the wizard, 'I did hear something today that made me a bit anxious. But I won't say anything, unless I find out more for certain. If I think it necessary for you to get off at once, I shall come back immediately. In the meanwhile stick to your plan...'

The remainder of his farewell words are as in FR (p. 76), except that he says 'I think you will need my company on the Road', not that

30 THE TREASON OF ISENGARD

'after all' Frodo 'may' need it. As written in the fair copy B the passage is the same as this, except that Gandalf no longer refers to 'our journey' – he says: 'I need to stretch my legs a bit. There are one or two things I must see to: I have been idle longer than I should'; and his last words are: 'I think after all you will need my company on the Road.'

Frodo's friends, who came to stay with him to help in the packing up of Bag End, are now (as also in the contemporary rewriting of 'Ancient History', p. 21) Hamilcar Bolger, Faramond Took,[16] and his closest friends Peregrin Boffin and Merry Brandybuck. It is now Hamilcar Bolger who goes off to Buckland with Merry in the third cart.[17] In the draft revision A 'Peregrin Boffin went back home to Overhill after lunch', whereas in B 'Faramond Took went home after lunch, but Peregrin and Sam remained behind', and Frodo 'took his own tea with Peregrin and Sam in the kitchen.' At the end of the meal 'Peregrin and Sam strapped up their three packs and piled them in the porch. Peregrin went out for a last stroll in the garden. Sam disappeared.'

Throughout these manuscripts 'Pippin' appears as a later correction of 'Folco'; and in the passage referred to above, naming Frodo's four friends who stayed at Bag End, 'Faramond Took' was changed subsequently to 'Folco Boffin', 'Peregrin Boffin' to 'Pippin Took', and 'Hamilcar Bolger' to 'Fredegar Bolger'. These, with Merry Brandybuck, are the four who are present on this occasion in FR (p. 76). But such corrections as these prove nothing as to date: they could have been entered on the manuscript at any subsequent time.

Nonetheless, it must have been at this stage, I think, that 'Peregrin Took' or 'Pippin' at last entered. Under Chapter V 'A Conspiracy Unmasked' below, it will be seen that in a rewritten section of the manuscript from this time (as distinct from mere emendation to the existing 'third phase' text) not only does 'Hamilcar' appear, as is to be expected, but 'Pippin' appears for the first time *as the text was written*. This rewritten section of 'A Conspiracy Unmasked' certainly belongs to the same time as the rewritten ('fourth phase') parts of 'Ancient History' and 'Three is Company'. The correction of 'Folco (Took)' to 'Pippin' in these manuscripts therefore does in fact belong to the same period; though they are carefully written texts, the final stage in the evolution of the 'younger hobbits' was taking place as my father wrote them; and though at the beginning of the B text of 'Three is Company' Frodo's friend was Peregrin Boffin, he may have already been Peregrin Took by the time he took his last stroll in the Bag End garden.

The question is not perhaps worth spending very long on, since it is now very largely one of name simply, but I have followed the tortuous trail too long to leave it without an attempt at analysis at the end. What happened, I think, was as follows. Folco Took of the 'third

THE FOURTH PHASE (1)

31

phase' (who had an interesting and complex genesis out of the original 'young hobbits', Frodo (Took) and Odo, see VI.323–4) was renamed Faramond Took (p. 15, note 1). At this time 'Peregrin Boffin', who had first entered as the 'explanation' of Trotter, became one of Frodo's younger friends. This is the situation in the rewritten or 'fourth phase' portions of Chapters II and III (pp. 21, 30). In Chapter III Faramond Took 'went home after lunch', and he is then out of the story. 'Peregrin' and Sam stayed on at Bag End, and it is clear that they are going to be Frodo's companions on the walk to Buckland.

'Peregrin' (Boffin) is thus stepping into the narrative place of Folco (briefly renamed Faramond) Took; or rather – since the narrative was now in a finished form – this *name* takes over the character. Just why Folco/Faramond Took would not do I cannot say for certain. It may have been simply a preference of names. But if Faramond Took is got rid of and Peregrin Boffin made the third member of the party walking to Buckland, there would be no Took at all: my father would have left himself with a Baggins, a Boffin, a Brandybuck, and a Gamgee. Perhaps this is why the Boffin was changed into a Took, and the Took into a Boffin: Peregrin Boffin became Peregrin (or Pippin) Took, and Faramond Took, reverting to his former name Folco, became Folco Boffin (who 'went home after lunch' in FR, p. 77). These corrections to the new text of Chapter III were evidently made before my father rewrote the ending of Chapter V, where 'Pippin' first appears in a text as written and not by later correction.

Thus it is that Peregrin Took of LR occupies the same *genealogical* place as did Frodo Took of the earliest phases (see VI.267, note 4): and thus 'Folco' of the 'third phase' manuscripts is corrected everywhere to 'Pippin'.

It would be legitimate, I think, to see in all this a single or particular hobbit-character, who appears under an array of names: Odo, Frodo, Folco, Faramond, Peregrin, Hamilcar, Fredegar, and the very ephemeral Olo (VI.299) – Tooks, Boffins, and Bolgers. Though no doubt a very 'typical' hobbit of the Shire, this 'character' is in relation to his companions very distinct: cheerful, nonchalant, irrepressible, commonsensical, limited, and extremely fond of his creature comforts. I will call this character 'X'. He begins as Odo Took, but becomes Odo Bolger. My father gets rid of him from the first journey (to Buckland), and as a result Frodo Took (Merry Brandybuck's first cousin), who had been potentially a very different character (see VI.70), becomes 'X', while retaining the name Frodo Took. Odo, however, reappears, because he has gone on ahead to Buckland with Merry Brandybuck while the others are walking; he may be called 'XX'. He will have a separate adventure, riding with Gandalf to Weathertop and ultimately turning up again at Rivendell, where (for a very brief time in the development of the narrative) he will rejoin 'X', now renamed 'Folco Took' (since Bingo Baggins has taken over the name Frodo).

32   THE TREASON OF ISENGARD

In the 'third phase' of the narrative, then, 'X' is Folco Took, Merry's cousin; and 'XX' is Odo Bolger. But now 'X' is renamed Faramond Took, and 'XX' is renamed Hamilcar Bolger. A new character called Peregrin Boffin appears: beginning as a much older figure, originally a hobbit of the Shire who became through his experiences a most unusual person, known as 'Trotter', he, or rather his name, survives to become one of Frodo's younger friends. 'Faramond Took' is pushed aside and left with scarcely any rôle at all, becoming the shadowy Folco Boffin; and 'Peregrin Boffin', becoming 'Peregrin Took' or 'Pippin', becomes 'X' – and Merry's first cousin.

Looking back to the beginning, therefore, 'Pippin' of LR will largely take over 'Odo's' remarks; but as I said (VI.70), 'the way in which this came about was strangely tortuous, and was by no means a simple substitution of one name for another.' For Pippin is Merry's first cousin, and is derived through Folco/Faramond from the original Frodo Took: he is not derived from Odo, who was moved sideways, so to speak, becoming Hamilcar (Fredegar). But Pippin *is* derived from Odo, in the sense that he like Odo is 'X'.

For the rest, Lobelia Sackville-Baggins' son, while keeping his name Cosimo, loses his pimples and gains 'sandy-haired' as his defining epithet. Gaffer Gamgee's observation on the subject of having Lobelia as his neighbour is recorded: ' "I can't abide changes at my time of life," said he (he was 99),[18] "and anyhow not changes for the worst." ' In FR the Gaffer's complaint was reported by Gandalf to the Council of Elrond (p. 276).

From the point where my father merely retained the manuscript of the 'third phase', and in subsequent chapters, 'Folco' was corrected to 'Pippin'.

Chapter IV: 'A Short Cut to Mushrooms'

In this case the third phase manuscript was retained intact (apart from 'Peregrin' or 'Pippin' for 'Folco' throughout), the final form having already been attained (see VI.325).

Chapter V: 'A Conspiracy Unmasked'
(with 'The Dream of the Tower')

A rough draft of a rewriting of the end of this chapter survives (for the previous forms of the passage see VI.104–5, 301–2, 326). Odo has become Hamilcar, and the conversation proceeds now almost exactly as in FR p. 118: that Hamilcar should stay behind was part of the original plan. Frodo no longer gives a letter to Odo/Hamilcar (VI.326), but says: 'It would not have been safe to leave a written message: the Riders might get here first, and search the house.' The

THE FOURTH PHASE (1)   33

only elements in FR that are still lacking are that Hamilcar's family came from Budgeford in Bridgefields,[19] and that 'he had even brought along some old clothes of Frodo's to help him in playing the part.' This rewriting stops before the account of Frodo's dream that night, of a sea of tangled trees and something snuffling among the roots (VI.302), but it is clear that at this stage it remained unchanged.

It is necessary here to turn aside for a moment from the end of 'A Conspiracy Unmasked' and to bring in a remarkable brief narrative of this time, extant in several texts, which may be called 'The Dream of the Tower'. In the narrative outline dated 'Autumn 1939' given on p. 9 Gandalf is 'besieged in the *Western Tower*. He cannot get away while they guard it with five Riders. But when Black Riders have located Frodo and found that he has gone off without Gandalf they ride away.' This is what Frodo saw in his dream.

My father was much exercised about the placing of it (see p. 11). In the Time-schemes A and B the date of Gandalf's escape from the Western Tower was first given as 24 September, and there is a suggestion that Frodo dreamt his dream of the event that night, when with the Elves in the Woody End. The date was then changed to the 25th, when Frodo was at Crickhollow, and so appears in schemes A, B, and C. Scheme D gives no date for Gandalf's escape, and places the 'Dream of the Tower' variously on the 24th, 25th, or 26th. For some reason, however, my father decided to place it after the event, on the night of the 29th, when Frodo was at Bree, and Gandalf was at Crickhollow.

The text of Frodo's dream at Bree is found in three forms, two preparatory drafts and a finished manuscript.[20] I give it here in the third form, since the only significant difference from the drafts is that in them the figure who summons the watchers from the Tower is seen by the dreamer ('another dark-robed figure appeared over the brow of the hill: it beckoned and gave a shrill call in a strange tongue').

The narrative begins almost exactly as in FR p. 189, with Frodo waking suddenly in the room at *The Prancing Pony*, seeing Trotter sitting alert in his chair, and falling asleep again.

Frodo soon went to sleep again; but now he passed at once into a dream. He found himself on a dark heath. Looking up, he saw before him a tall white tower, standing alone upon a high ridge. Beyond it the sky was pale, and far off there came a murmur like the voices of the Great Sea which he had never heard nor beheld, save in other dreams. In the topmost chamber of the tower there shone dimly a blue light.

Suddenly he found that he had drawn near and the tower loomed high above him. About its feet there was a wall of faintly shining stones, and outside the wall sat silent watchers:

34   THE TREASON OF ISENGARD

black-robed figures on black horses, gazing at the gate of the tower without moving, as if they had sat there for ever.

There came at last the soft fall of hoofs, climbing up the hill. The watchers all stirred and turned slowly towards the sound. They were looking towards Frodo. He did not dare to turn, but he knew that behind him another dark figure, taller and more terrible, had appeared: it beckoned, and called out in a strange tongue. The horsemen leaped to life. They raised their dark heads towards the lofty chamber, and their mocking laughter rang out cruel and cold; then they turned from the white wall and rode down the hill like the wind. The blue light went out.

It seemed to Frodo that the riders came straight towards him; but even as they passed over him and beat him to the ground, he thought in his heart: 'I am not here; they cannot hurt me. There is something that I must see.' He lifted his head and saw a white horse leap the wall and stride towards him. On it rode a grey-mantled figure: his white hair was streaming, and his cloak flew like wings behind him. As the grey rider bore down upon him he strove to see his face. The light grew in the sky, and suddenly there was a noise of thunder.

Frodo opened his eyes. Trotter had drawn the curtains and had pushed back the shutters with a clang. The first grey light of day was in the room. The vision of his dream faded quickly, but its mingled fear and hope remained with him all the day; and for long the far sound of the Sea came back to him whenever great danger was at hand.

As soon as Trotter had roused them all he led the way to their bedrooms.

The manuscript continues a little further, almost word for word as in FR, and ends with Butterbur's 'Guests unable to sleep in their beds, and good bolsters ruined and all! What are we coming to?'

Taking into account the words of the outline given on p. 9 that Gandalf, pursued by the Riders, tried to get round to the west of the Shire, and the mention of the sound of the Sea in the text, it is seen that Gandalf had fled to the Elf-towers[21] on the Tower Hills beyond the west marches of the Shire – those towers which, at the very beginning of the writing of *The Lord of the Rings*, Bingo said that he had once seen, shining white in the Moon: 'the tallest was furthest away, standing alone on a hill' (VI.93; cf. VI.312 and FR p. 16).

Turning back to 'A Conspiracy Unmasked': my father now rewrote the ending again, on the basis of the draft already referred to, and added it to the 'third phase' manuscript, rejecting the existing

THE FOURTH PHASE (1)   35

conclusion of the chapter.[22] In this new text he still kept the original dream, but now combined with it the 'Dream of the Tower', transferring it back from Frodo's night at Bree to his night at Crickhollow (see p. 33). Thus Frodo has the vision of Gandalf's escape from the Western Tower on the night of the event itself, the 25th of September. The new version reads thus, in part:

When at last he got to bed, Frodo could not sleep for some time. His legs ached. He was glad that he was riding in the morning. Eventually he fell into a vague dream, in which he seemed to be looking out of a high window over a dark sea of tangled trees. Down below among the roots there was the sound of creatures crawling and snuffling. He felt sure they would smell him out sooner or later.

Then he heard a noise in the distance. At first he thought it was a great wind coming over the leaves of the forest. Then he knew that it was not leaves, but the sound of the Sea far-off: a sound he had never heard in waking life, though it had often troubled other dreams. Suddenly he found he was out in the open. There were no trees after all. He was on a dark heath, and there was a strange salt smell in the air. Looking up he saw before him a tall white tower, standing alone on a high ridge. In its topmost chamber a blue light shone dimly.

As he drew nearer the tower loomed high above him. About its feet there was a wall of faintly gleaming stones, and outside the wall sat silent watchers: there seemed to be four blackrobed figures seated on black horses, gazing at the tower without moving, as if they had sat there for ever.

He heard the soft fall of hoofs climbing up the hill behind him. The watchers all stirred . . .

From this point the vision is told in practically the same words as in the previous text, and ends in the same way: 'A light grew in the sky, and there was a noise of thunder.' When Frodo had dreamt the dream at Bree, the light in the sky and the noise of thunder were associated with Trotter's opening the shutters with a clang and the light of morning entering the room.

In this text 'Pippin' is the name that was first written, not a subsequent correction of 'Folco'; see p. 30.

Later (see p. 139, note 36), when the story of Gandalf had been further changed, the description of the Western Tower and the siege of the Riders was largely, but not entirely, struck out on this manuscript: the opening was retained, as far as 'Looking up he saw before him a tall white tower, standing alone on a high ridge.' At the same time a brief new conclusion was added:

36　　　THE TREASON OF ISENGARD

A great desire came over him to climb the tower and see the Sea. He started to struggle up the ridge towards the tower; but suddenly a light came in the sky, and there was a noise of thunder.

Thus altered, this is the text of FR, pp. 118–19. And so the tall white tower of Frodo's dream at Crickhollow in the final tale remains from what was the precursor of Orthanc; and the thunder that he heard goes back to the interruption of his dream by Trotter's thrusting back the shutters at *The Prancing Pony*. But Frodo would still dream of Gandalf imprisoned in a tower: for as he slept in the house of Tom Bombadil he would see him standing on the pinnacle of Isengard.

Chapter VI: 'The Old Forest'

The existing 'third phase' manuscript of this chapter was retained, but with a good deal of correction, evidently deriving from different times. To this period belong the alteration of 'Odo' to 'Hamilcar' at the beginning of the chapter, and 'Folco' to 'Pippin'; I would ascribe to it also the attainment of the final form of the hobbits' descent out of the forest to the Withywindle (see VI.327), and the final ascription of the parts in the encounter with Old Man Willow, with Merry exchanging rôles with Frodo as the one trapped in the tree and the one pushed into the river (*ibid.*).

Chapter VII: 'In the House of Tom Bombadil'

In this chapter as in the last, the existing manuscript was retained intact. As the story stood in that text, Gandalf came to Crickhollow and routed the Riders on the night of Monday 26 September, the first night spent by the hobbits in the house of Tom Bombadil, and the account of the attack on Crickhollow was introduced as a short separate narrative in the body of Chapter VII (see VI.303–4, 328). But this had now been changed, and the attack by the Riders delayed by three days, with the postponement of Gandalf's coming to Bree. My father therefore wrote on the manuscript at this point: 'This did not occur till Sept. 29', i.e. the night passed by the hobbits at Bree (see the time-schemes tabulated on p. 12). The episode was now in the wrong chapter, and was struck from the text here.

It is often difficult or impossible to say with certainty when changes to the manuscripts that are unrelated to movements in the narrative structure (or to movements in names) were made. Thus the introduction of Frodo's dream of Gandalf on Orthanc is obviously later; but the striking out of 'I am Ab-Origine, that's what I am' (and the substitution of Tom's words in FR, p. 142: 'Don't you know my name

THE FOURTH PHASE (1)   37

yet?...'), and of 'He saw the Sun rise in the West and the Moon following, before the new order of days was made' (see VI.329) may well belong to this time.

Chapter VIII: 'Fog on the Barrow-downs'

The original manuscript was again retained, and most of the changes that were made to it were from a later time (notably those introducing Carn Dûm and Angmar, FR pp. 154, 157). The final page of the 'third phase' manuscript was however rejected and replaced by a new ending to the chapter, most of which is found also in a preparatory draft, marked 'Revised ending of VIII to fit revised plot (concerning Gandalf's delay and Trotter's knowledge of the name Baggins)'. Now Frodo says, 'Please note – all of you – that the name Baggins must *not* be mentioned again. I am Mr *Green*, if any name must be given.' In the narrative of the third phase, as in that of the second, Frodo took the name of 'Mr Hill of Faraway' (VI.280, 334). 'Green' as a pseudonym (for Odo) goes back to the original version (VI.135 etc.).

At this time Tom's words (VI.329) 'he [Butterbur] knows Tom Bombadil, and Tom's name will help you. Say "Tom sent us here", and he will treat you kindly' were rejected, and Tom's parting words in FR appear: 'Tom's country ends here: he will not pass the borders.' In this connection see the note given on p. 10 concerning the boundaries of Tom's domain: there my father was thinking of harmonising Gandalf's remark at the Council of Elrond that Bombadil never left his own ground with the story that he was known to Butterbur by supposing that Tom's 'boundaries' extended to Bree. But he concluded that Tom Bombadil was not in fact known to Butterbur, and the changes here reflect that decision.

NOTES

1 The texts in such a situation are often very tricky to interpret, for there are these possible ingredients or components: (1) a page from the 'third phase' manuscript corrected but retained; (2) a page from the 'third phase' manuscript rejected and replaced; (3) draft version(s) for replacement of rejected 'third phase' manuscript; (4) fair copy replacement of rejected 'third phase' manuscript (with or without preceding draft). A correction, say of a name, made in a case of (1) will stand on the same footing in the textual history as the name first written in a case of (3) or (4), but the latter provide more certain indication of the relative dating.

2 With Bilbo's remark 'I have thought of a nice ending for it: *and he lived happily ever after to the end of his days*' (FR p. 41) cf. the outline §1 on p. 5. With the passage that follows, in which Bilbo says of Frodo

THE TREASON OF ISENGARD

> He would come with me, of course, if I asked him. In fact he offered to once, just before the party. But he does not really want to, yet. I want to see the wild country again before I die, and the Mountains; but he is still in love with the Shire...

cf. the fragment of narrative given in note 8 to the preceding chapter (p. 15).

3 Cf. the outline §1 on p. 5: 'Says to Gandalf he sometimes feels it is like an eye looking at him.'

4 Gandalf's words 'He said and did things then that were unmistakeable signs of something wrong' refer of course to his parting conversation with Bilbo in this 'phase', given on pp. 19–20, where Bilbo's behaviour was still not violently out of character as it afterwards became.

5 This is the form of the text in B. The draft A has no reference to the discussion of Rings at the White Council.

6 At this stage the old story of how the Ring was found 'in the mud of the river-bank under the roots of a thorn tree' (VI.78) was retained.

7 In the later form of 'Riddles in the Dark' in *The Hobbit* there was no question of Gollum's giving up the Ring, of course: Bilbo's prize if he won the competition was to be shown the way out, and Gollum only went back to his island in the lake to get the Ring so that he might attack Bilbo invisibly.

8 This passage, from 'But of course...', was added to the text, but it takes up a draft passage against which my father had written 'Omit?':

> Yet I wonder what would have happened in the end, if he had been obliged to hand it over. I don't think he would have dared to cheat openly; but I am sure he would have tried to get the Ring back. He would have immediately desired it terribly, and have hated Bilbo fiercely. He would have tried to kill him. He would have followed him, visible or invisible, by sight or smell, till he got a chance.'

9 The draft text still retained the curious passage, going back through the third to the second version of the chapter (VI.263), in which Gandalf has Frodo quote the first riddle that Gollum asked, and then says, in this version: 'Roots and mountains: there's a good deal of Gollum's mind and history in that.'

10 This was said in the original story of Gollum in the first edition of *The Hobbit*: 'in the end Bilbo gathered that Gollum had had a ring – a wonderful, beautiful ring, a ring that he had been given for a birthday present, ages and ages before when such rings were less uncommon.'

11 Draft texts still retain the wording of the third version (VI.321): 'what *kind of ring* it really was.'

12 The words *trying to forget Deagol* are a part of the text B as

THE FOURTH PHASE (1)   39

written, and show that the passage (pp. 23–4) concerning the murder of Deagol was inserted before this version was completed.

13 In the original story in *The Hobbit* it was only when Gollum came back from his island in the lake, where he had gone to get the 'present', that Bilbo learnt – from Gollum's 'tremendous spluttering and whispering and croaking' – about the ring and that it had been a birthday present; see note 10.

14 The change noted in VI.320, whereby Gandalf ceases to be the one who actually tracked Gollum down, belongs to this 'fourth phase'.

15 Above -*ruin* was pencilled -*naur*, sc. *Orodnaur*.

16 In the draft revision A of this passage Faramond is called 'Faramond II and the heir apparent'; cf. VI.251, where Faramond's precursor Frodo Took is called 'Frodo the Second ... the heir and rather desperate hope of the Hole of Took, as the clan was called.'

17 In the draft revision A at this point 'Ham (that is Hamilcar)' was replaced by 'Freddy (that is Fredegar)', but Ham/Hamilcar was then restored. Cf. the note dated August 1939 given in VI.373: 'Odo > Fredegar Hamilcar Bolger'.

18 In the genealogy in LR, Appendix C, Gaffer Gamgee was 92, and he died at the age of 102.

19 Neither Budgeford nor Bridgefields appear on my father's original map of the Shire (frontispiece to Vol. VI). On my large map of the Shire made in 1943 (VI.107) both names were lightly pencilled in by him, Budgeford being the crossing of the Water by the road (pencilled in at the same time) to Scary. See note 22.

20 The second version stands as the opening of a chapter, numbered 'X' and without title (corresponding to the 'second opening' of Chapter XI 'A Knife in the Dark' in FR, after the 'Crickhollow episode'); the third likewise, but numbered 'XI' (because by then the 'Bree' chapter had been divided, see p. 40), and with an erased title 'The Way to Weathertop'.

21 In some rough chronological workings there is a reference to Gandalf's being besieged in 'the West Towers', which is what Trotter called the Elf-towers in VI.155, 159.

22 Hamilcar's family now comes from Bridgefields in the Eastfarthing. Budgeford was written in later, perhaps much later. See note 19.

III

THE FOURTH PHASE (2):
FROM BREE TO THE FORD OF RIVENDELL

Chapter IX: 'At the Sign of the Prancing Pony (i)
The Cow Jumped over the Moon'

The 'third phase' version of this chapter (VI.331 ff.) had been developed in two forms, in the first of which the story of the coming of Gandalf and Odo to Bree was told by Butterbur, while in the second (the 'red version' as my father called it) it was told by the narrator (VI.344–7); and in the second the coming of the four Riders to the west gate of Bree on the evening of Wednesday 28 September was described (VI.347–8). The already complex manuscript was then used for a rough, drastic recasting of the narrative, the 'blue version' (see VI.343): this belongs with the new plot, and all reference to a visit of Gandalf to Bree in the days immediately preceding Frodo's arrival is cut out. A 'blue' rider to the original 'third phase' manuscript is written on the back of a calendar page for September 1939.

So far as it went, this was effectively a draft ('A') for a new version of this always crucial chapter; and in this case my father set aside the now chaotic 'third phase' manuscript entirely (though taking from it the pages containing the text of *The Cat and the Fiddle*), and it got left behind in England many years later; the 'fourth phase' version is a new manuscript ('B'), and this went to Marquette. Notably, this bears a date on the first page: 'Revised Version Oct. 1939'.

It remained at this time a single, very long chapter, extending through FR Chapter 10 'Strider'; but my father decided (doubtless on account of its length) to divide it into two chapters, 'IX' and 'X', both called 'At the Sign of the Prancing Pony', but with sub-titles; and these names remained for a long time. This arrangement was apparently made soon after the new text was completed, and it is convenient to follow it here.

The new version, to the point where the hobbits returned from the common room of the inn after Frodo's 'accident', now reaches, except in a few features, the final form, and variation even from the precise wording of FR is infrequent. The most notable respect in which it differs is that at this stage my father preserved the account of the black horsemen who spoke to Harry Goatleaf the gatekeeper on the evening of the 28th of September:

THE FOURTH PHASE (2)   **41**

The fog that enveloped the Downs on Wednesday afternoon lay deep about Bree-hill. The four hobbits were just waking from their sleep beside the Standing Stone, when out of the mist four horsemen rode from the West and passed through the gates at dusk. ...

The episode closely follows that in the 'red version' of the 'third phase' (VI.347–8), but of course Harry Goatleaf no longer refers to 'a hobbit riding behind an old man on a white horse, last night', and his conversation with the Rider takes this form:

'We want news!' hissed a cold voice through the key-hole.

'What of?' he answered, shaking in his boots.

'News of hobbits, riding on ponies out of the Shire. Have they passed?'

Harry wished they had, for it might have satisfied these riders if he could have said *yes*. There was a threat in the cold voice; but he dared not risk a *yes* that was not true. 'No sir!' he said in a quavering voice. 'There's been no Shire-hobbits on ponies through Bree, and there isn't likely to be any.'

A hiss came through the key-hole, and Harry started back, feeling as if something icy cold had touched him. 'Yes, it is likely!' said the voice fiercely. 'Three, perhaps four. You will watch. We want Baggins. He is with them. You will watch. You will tell us and not lie! We shall come back.'[1]

This episode was struck from the text, but I cannot say when this was done.

The conversation between Frodo and Merry and the gatekeeper is as in FR. The gatekeeper still however calls out to 'Ned' (his brother, presumptively) to watch the gate a while, since he has 'business up at *The Pony*' (as in VI.349); then follows: 'He had been gone only a moment, and Ned had not yet come out, when a dark figure climbed in quickly over the gate and vanished in the dark in the direction of the inn.' The reference to Harry Goatleaf's visit to the inn was afterwards struck out, and does not appear in FR (see below).

There is now, as is to be expected, no reference to Tom Bombadil when the hobbits arrive at *The Prancing Pony*, and Frodo's pseudonym is 'Mr Green' (see p. 37); the reference in FR (p. 167) to the Underhills of Staddle is of course absent. Folco is still Folco, corrected to Pippin, which shows that this text was written before the revised ending of Chapter V (pp. 30, 35).[2] Frodo still noticed the gatekeeper among the company in the common room of the inn, wondering whether it was his night off duty, but this was struck out, and does not appear in FR. Folco/Pippin now tells the story of the collapse of the 'Town Burrow' in Michel Delving, though the fat

42 THE TREASON OF ISENGARD

Mayor is unnamed. Trotter is of course a Man, but the description of him is that of the old versions (VI.137, 334): he is still, as he was when he was a hobbit, 'queer-looking, brown-faced', with a short-stemmed pipe under his long nose, and nothing is said of his boots (FR p. 168).

When Bill Ferney and the Southerner left the common room, 'Harry the gatekeeper went out just behind them.' This, like the other references to the gatekeeper's presence at the inn noted above, was struck out. An isolated note of this time proposes: 'Cut out Harry – he is unnecessary': clearly referring to his visit to the inn after the arrival of the hobbits and his vaguely sinister association with Bill Ferney, not to his function as gatekeeper, which is certainly necessary. It is curious therefore that in the typescript that followed the present manuscript this last reference, though very clearly crossed out in the manuscript, was reinstated, and so appears in FR (p. 172), but quite anomalously, since all the references to his presence at the inn up to this point had been removed.

Chapter X: 'At the Sign of the Prancing Pony (ii)
All that is gold does not glitter'

In the 'blue version' recasting of the 'third phase' narrative, or 'A', the story of Trotter's 'eavesdropping' beside the Road reaches the final form, in association with the new ending to Chapter VIII (p. 37): he hears the hobbits talking with Bombadil, and Frodo declaring that he is to be called 'Mr Green' (for the previous story, in which Trotter overheard Gandalf and Odo talking, see VI.337). After Trotter's 'I should advise him and his friends to be more careful what they say and do' (FR p. 176) there follows in A:

'I have not "left my name behind", as you put it,' said Frodo stiffly. 'My reason for taking another here is my own affair. I do not see why my real name should interest anyone in Bree; and I have still to learn why it interests *you*. Mr Trotter may have an honest reason for spying and eavesdropping; but if so I should advise him to explain it!'

'That's the line to take!' laughed Trotter. 'But you wait till old Butterbur has had his private word with you – you'll soon find out how your real name could be guessed, and why it may be interesting in Bree. As for myself: I was looking for Mr Frodo Baggins, *because I had been told to look for him.* And I have already given you hints, which you have understood well enough, that I know about the secret you are carrying.'

'Don't be alarmed!' he cried, as Frodo half rose from his seat, and Sam scowled. 'I shall take more care of the secret than you do. But now I had better tell you some more about myself.'

THE FOURTH PHASE (2)   43

At that moment he was interrupted by a knock at the door. Mr Butterbur was there with a tray of candles...

Butterbur now has only news of the Black Riders to communicate. The story he tells is as before (VI.338–40), but the first Rider passed through Bree on the Tuesday, not the Monday, preceding, three not four of them came to the inn-door, and of course he does not refer to Gandalf and 'Baggins' (Odo) having gone off eastwards. The conversation continues:

' "Baggins!" said I. "If you are looking for hobbits of that name, you'd best look in the Shire. There are none in Bree. The last time one of that name came here was nigh on a score of years back.[3] Mr Bilbo Baggins he was, as disappeared out of Hobbiton: he went off East long enough ago."

'At that name he drew in his breath and sat up. Then he stooped at me again. "But there is also Frodo Baggins," said he,[4] in a whisper like a knife. "Is he here? Has he been? Do not lie to us!"

'I was all of a twitter, I can tell you; but I was angry as well. "*No* is the answer," said I; "and you'll get no lies here, so you'd best be civil. If you have any message for any party, you may leave it, and I'll look out for them." "The message is *wait*," said he. "We may return." And with that the three of them turned their horses and rode off into the fog. Now, Mr Green, what do you say to that?'

'But they asked for Baggins, you say, not Green,' said Frodo warily.

'Ah!' said the landlord with a knowing wink. 'But they wanted news of hobbits out of the Shire, and such a party doesn't come here often. It would be queer, if there were two different parties. And as for *Baggins*: I've heard that name before. Mr Bilbo was here more than once, in my dad's time and mine; and some funny tales have come out of the Shire since he went off: vanished with a bang while he was speaking, they say. Not that I believe all the tales that come out of the West – but here you go vanishing in the middle of a song by all accounts, right in my house. And when I have time to scratch my head and think, I remember noticing your friends call you Frodo, and I begin to wonder if Baggins should not come next. "Maybe those black men were right," I says to myself. Now the question is, what shall I say, if they come back? Maybe you want to see them, and more likely not. They mean no good to anyone, I'll wager. Now you and your friends *seem* all right in spite of your

44 THE TREASON OF ISENGARD

pranks, so I thought I had best tell you and find out what you wish.'

'They mean no good at all,' said Frodo. 'I did not know they had passed through Bree, or I should have stayed quiet in this room, and I wish I had. I ought to have guessed it, from the way the gatekeeper greeted us – and you, Mr Butterbur; but I hoped perhaps Gandalf had been here asking for us. I expect you know who I mean, the old wizard. We hoped to find him here or have news of him.'

'Gandalf!' said the landlord. 'Know him! I should think I do. He was here not so long back, in the summer. A good friend of mine is Gandalf, and many a good turn he has done me. If you had asked after him sooner I should have been happier. I will do what I can for any friends of his.'

'I am very grateful,' said Frodo, 'and so will he be. I am sorry I can't tell you the whole story, but I assure you we are up to no mischief. I *am* Frodo Baggins, as you guess, and these – er – Black Riders are hunting for me, and we are in danger. I should be thankful for any sort of help, though I don't want you to get into trouble on my account. I only hope these Riders won't come back.'

'I hope not indeed,' said the landlord with a shiver. 'But spooks or no spooks, they'll have to mend their manners at my door.'

The latter part of this version is in hasty pencil, and soon after this point it peters out without further significant development. Obviously Gandalf's letter will still come from Trotter, not from Butterbur.

As I have said, this revision belongs with the new conception of Gandalf's movements: he only got ahead of Frodo and his friends by racing on horseback to Weathertop while they were toiling through the Midgewater Marshes. In the outline given on p. 9 there is mention of a visit of Gandalf to Bree before Frodo set out, and before his captivity in the Western Tower; and Butterbur says in this draft that he saw him 'not so long back, in the summer' (cf. also note 1). This led, I think, to the bringing back of the story (present in one of the alternative versions of the original 'Bree' chapter, VI.156) that it was Butterbur and not Trotter who had the letter from Gandalf; and this in turn led to refinement of the scene at the inn where Trotter proves that he is a friend.

As in the draft A above (p. 42), in the new or 'fourth phase' manuscript B Trotter says: 'I was looking for Mr Frodo Baggins, *because I had been told to look for him*.' But an important change in the structure now enters. In A Trotter has just said 'But now I had

THE FOURTH PHASE (2)   45

better tell you some more about myself' when he is interrupted by Mr Butterbur's knock on the door – an interruption at this point that goes back through the earlier versions: see VI.338 ('third phase'), VI.150 (original text). In the new account, Trotter is not interrupted at this point. After saying that he will take more care of the secret than they do, the story now proceeds thus:

'...But now I had better tell you some more.' He leaned forward and looked at them. 'Black horsemen have passed through Bree,' he said in a low voice. 'On Tuesday morning one came up the Greenway; and two more appeared later. Yesterday evening in the fog three more rode through the West-gate just before it was closed. They questioned Harry the gatekeeper and frightened him badly. I heard them. They also went eastward.'

There follows a passage quite closely approaching that in FR (pp. 176–7, from 'There was a silence'), with Frodo's regret that he had gone to the common room of the inn, and Trotter's recounting that the landlord had prevented him from seeing the hobbits until it was too late. But to Frodo's remark that the Riders 'seem to have missed me for the present, and to have gone on ahead' Trotter replies:

'I should not be too sure of that. They are cunning, and they divide their forces. I have been watching them. Only six have passed through Bree. There may be others. There are others. I know them, and their proper number.' Trotter paused and shivered. 'Those that have passed on will probably return,' he went on. 'They have questioned folk in the village and outlying houses, as far as Combe [> Archet], trying to get news by bribes and threats – of a hobbit called Baggins. There were others beside Harry Goatleaf in the room tonight who were there for a purpose. There was Bill Ferney. He has a bad name in the Bree-land, and queer folk call at his house sometimes. You must have noticed him among the company: a swarthy sneering fellow. He was very close with one of the southern strangers, and they slipped out together just after your "accident". Harry is an old curmudgeon, and he is frightened; but he won't do anything, unless they go to him.[5] Ferney is a different matter – he would sell anything to anybody; or make mischief for the fun of it.'

From this point (Frodo's 'What will Ferney sell?') the text of FR is largely achieved, as far as Trotter's question: 'Will you have him?' Then follows:

46   THE TREASON OF ISENGARD

Frodo made no answer. He looked at Trotter: grim and wild and rough-clad. It was hard to know what to do, or to feel sure of his good will. He had been successful in one thing at any rate: he had made Frodo suspect everybody, even Mr Butterbur. And all his warnings could so well apply to himself. Bill Ferney, Trotter: which was the most likely to betray them? What if Trotter led them into the wild, to 'some dark place far from help'? Everything he had said was curiously double-edged. He had a dark look, and yet there was something in his face that was strangely attractive.

The silence grew, and still Frodo found no answer. 'There is one obvious question you have not put,' said Trotter quietly. 'You have not asked me: "Who told you to look out for us?" You might ask that before you decide to class me with Bill Ferney.'

'I am sorry,' stammered Frodo; but at that moment there came a knock at the door. Mr Butterbur was there with candles...

The interruption by Mr Butterbur takes place at structurally the same point as in FR (p. 178), though the conversation he interrupts is quite different. Trotter now withdrew into a dark corner of the room, and when Nob had gone off with the hot water to the bedrooms, the landlord began thus:

'I've been asked to look out for a party of hobbits, and for one by the name of Baggins in particular.'

'What has that got to do with me, then?' asked Frodo warily.

'Ah!' said the landlord with a knowing wink. 'You know best; but old Barnabas can add up two and two, if you give him time. Parties out of the Shire don't come here often nowadays, but I was told to look out for one at just about this time. It would be queer, if there was no connexion, if you follow me. And as for Baggins, I've heard that name before. Mr Bilbo was in this house more than once, and some funny stories have come out of the Shire since he went off: vanished with a bang, while he was speaking, they say. Not that I believe all the tales that come from the West – but here you go vanishing in the middle of a song by all accounts, right in my house. Maybe you did, and maybe there was some mistake, but it set me thinking. And when I have time to scratch my head, I remember noticing how your friends call you *Frodo*; so I begin to wonder if Baggins should not come after it.[6] For it was Frodo Baggins I was told to

THE FOURTH PHASE (2)   47

look for; and I was given a description that fits well enough, if I may say so.'

'Indeed! Let's hear it then!' said Frodo, a little impatient with the slow unravelling of Mr Butterbur's thoughts.

'*A round-bellied little fellow with red cheeks*,' answered the landlord with a grin. 'Begging your pardon; but he said it, not me.' Folco [> Pippin] chuckled, but Sam looked angry.

'*He* said it? And who was he?' asked Frodo quickly.

'Oh, that was old Gandalf, if you know who I mean. A wizard they say he is, but he is a right good friend of mine, whether or no. Many a good turn has he done me. "Barney," he says to me, it would be a matter of a month and more ago, in August,[7] if I recollect rightly, when he came in late one evening. Very tired he was, and uncommon thirsty. "Barney," he says, "I want you to do something for me." "You've only to name it," said I. "I want you to look out for some hobbits out of the Shire," said he. "There may be a couple, and there may be more. Nigh the end of September[8] it will be, if they come. I hope I shall be with them, and then you'll have no more to do than draw some of your best ale for us. But if I'm not with them, they may need help. One of them will be Frodo Baggins, if it is the right party: a great friend of mine, a round-bellied..." '

'All right!' said Frodo, laughing in spite of his impatience. 'Go on! We've heard that already.'

Mr Butterbur paused, put out of his stride. 'Where was I?' he said. 'Ah yes. "If this Frodo Baggins comes," said he, "give him this"; and he handed me a letter. "Keep it safe and secret, and keep it in your mind, if your head will hold anything so long," says he. "And don't you mention all this to anybody." I've kept that letter by me night and day, since he gave it to me.'

'A letter for me from Gandalf!' interrupted Frodo eagerly. 'Where is it?'

'There now!' cried Mr Butterbur triumphantly. 'You don't deny the name! Old Barney can put two and two together. But it's a pity you did not trust me from the beginning.' Out of an inner pocket he brought a sealed letter and handed it to Frodo.[9] On the outside it was inscribed: TO F.B. FROM G. ⚅

'There's another thing I ought to say,' Mr Butterbur began again. 'I guess you may be in trouble, seeing how Gandalf isn't here, and *they* have come, as he warned me.'

'What do you mean?' said Frodo.

'The black horsemen,' said Butterbur. ' "If you see horsemen

48   THE TREASON OF ISENGARD

in black," says Gandalf to me, "look out for trouble! And my friends will need all the help you can give." And they have come, sure enough: yesterday and the day before.[10] The dogs all yammered, and the geese screamed at them. Uncanny, I call it. They've been asking for news of a hobbit called Baggins, I hear. And that Ranger, Trotter, he has been asking questions, too. Tried to get in here, before you had had bite or sup, he did.'

'He did!' said Trotter suddenly, coming forward into the light. 'And a lot of trouble would have been saved, if you had let him in, Barnabas.'

The landlord jumped with surprise. 'You!' he cried. 'You're always popping up. What do *you* want?'

'He's here with my leave,' said Frodo. 'He's offering us his help.'

'Well, you know best, maybe,' said Mr Butterbur, looking doubtfully at Trotter. 'Of course, I don't know what's going on, or what these black fellows want with you. But they mean no good to you, I'll swear.'

'They mean no good to anyone,' answered Frodo. 'I am sorry I can't explain it all. I am tired and very worried, and it is a long tale. But tell Gandalf everything, if he turns up, and he will be very grateful, and he may tell you more than I can. But I ought at least to warn you what you are doing in helping me. The Black Riders are hunting me, and they are perilous. They are servants of the Necromancer.'

'Save us!' cried Mr Butterbur, turning pale. 'Uncanny I knew they were; but that is the worst bit of news that has come to Bree in my time!'

This version now attains the form in FR (p. 181) as far as Butterbur's departure to send Nob out to look for Merry with scarcely any deviation. Trotter speaks of 'the Shadow in the South', not 'in the East', and refers of course to 'Mr Green', not 'Mr Underhill'; and after Butterbur's remark that there are others in Bree quicker in the uptake than Nob is, he adds: 'Bill Ferney was here tonight, and he's an ugly customer.' – It will be seen that with the structural change in the ordering of the chapter (bringing the landlord to the hobbits' room at a later point) the information about the Black Riders (itself very brief) is now given by Trotter, while Butterbur himself is left with only a few words on the subject.[11] In previous versions his account of the coming of the Riders to the inn door was a chief element in the conversation; now there is no mention of it (though it reappears briefly in FR, p. 180).

In this version, the landlord before leaving the room asks if Trotter

THE FOURTH PHASE (2)

is going to stay there, to which Trotter replies: 'I am. You may need me before the morning.' 'All right, then,' said the landlord, 'if Mr Green is willing.' When Butterbur has gone:

'Well, now you ought to guess the answer to the question I spoke of before he came in,' said Trotter. 'But aren't you going to open the letter?'

Frodo looked carefully at the seal before he broke it. It seemed certainly to be Gandalf's. Inside, written in the wizard's thin long-legged script,[12] was the following message. Frodo read it aloud.[13]

The Prancing Pony, Bree; Tuesday, September 12th.[14] Dear F. I am starting back tomorrow, & should reach you in a day or two. But things have become very dangerous, and I may not get through in time. (He has found the Shire: the borders are watched, and so am I.) If I fail to come, I hope that will be sufficient warning to you, & you will have sense to leave Shire at once. If so, there is just a chance you will get through as far as Bree. Look out for horsemen in black. They are your worst enemies (save one): they are Ringwraiths. Do not use It again: not for any reason at all. Do not move in the dark. Try and find Trotter the ranger. He will be looking out for you: a lean, dark, weatherbeaten fellow, but one of my greatest friends. He knows our business. He will see you through, if any one can. Make for Rivendell as fast as possible. There I hope we may meet again. If not, Elrond will advise you. Yours ᛉᚠᚻᛗᚠᚱᚤ ·⊗·

PS. You can trust Barnabas Butterbur and Trotter. But make sure it is really Trotter. The real Trotter will have a sealed letter from me with these words in it

> *All that is gold does not glitter,*
> *all that is long does not last,*
> *All that is old does not wither,*
> *not all that is over is past.*

PPS. It would be worse than useless to try and go beyond Bree on your own. If Trotter does not turn up, you must try and get Butterbur to hide you somewhere, and hope that I shall come.

PPPS. I hope B. does not forget this! If he remembers to give it to you, tell him I am very grateful, & still more surprised. Fare well wherever you fare. ⊗

'Well, that is from Gandalf all right, quite apart from the

50 THE TREASON OF ISENGARD

hand and the signature,' said Frodo as he finished. 'What about your letter, Trotter?'

'Do you need it? I thought you had made up your mind about me already! If not, you ought not to have let me stay; and you certainly ought not to have read that aloud to me.'

'I haven't made up *my* mind,' said Sam suddenly. 'And I am not going to see Mr Frodo made fun of and put upon. Let's see that letter, or Sam Gamgee'll take a hand!'

'My good Sam,' said Trotter. 'I've got a weapon under my cloak, as well as you! And I don't mind telling you that if I was not the real Trotter, you would not have a chance, not all three of you together. But steady there!' he said, as Sam sprang up. 'I *have* got a letter, and here it is!'

Onto the table he tossed another sealed letter, outwardly exactly like the other. Sam and Folco [> Pippin] looked at it, as Frodo opened it. Inside there was a small paper in Gandalf's hand. It said:

> *All that is gold does not glitter;*
> *all that is long does not last;*
> *All that is old does not wither;*
> *not all that is over is past.*
> *This is to certify that the bearer is Aragorn son of Celegorn,*[15]
> *of the line of Isildur Elendil's son, known in Bree as Trotter;*
> *enemy of the Nine, and friend of Gandalf.* ᚷ ᚠ ᚼ ᛗ ᚠ ᚱ ᚦ ᛬ ⚭ ᛬

Frodo stared at the words in amazement. 'Of the line of Elendil!' he said, looking with awe at Trotter. 'Then It belongs to you as much as to me, or more!'

'It does not belong to either of us,' said Trotter; 'but you are to keep it for a while. For so it is ordained.'[16]

'Why didn't you show this to us sooner? It would have saved time, and prevented me, and Sam, from behaving absurdly.'

'Absurdly! Not at all. Sam is very sensible: he doubted me to the last, and I think he still does. Quite right, too! If you'd had more experience of your Enemy, you would not trust your own hands, except in broad daylight, once you knew that he was on your track. I had to make sure of *you*, too. That was one reason why I delayed. The Enemy has set snares for me before now. But I must admit that I tried to persuade you to take me as a friend, for my own sake without proofs. A hunted wanderer wearies sometimes of distrust, even while he is preaching it.[17] But there, I fear my looks are against me.'

THE FOURTH PHASE (2) 51

There follows the ill-judged intervention of Folco/Pippin – '*Handsome is as handsome does* we say in the Shire', which had remained unchanged from Odo's original remark in VI.155; then follows:

Folco [> Pippin] subsided; but Sam was not daunted, and he still eyed Trotter dubiously. 'You could make yourself look like you do, if you were play-acting,' he said. 'What *proof* have we had that you are the real article, I should like to know?'

Trotter laughed. 'Don't forget Butterbur's letter, Sam!' he said. 'Think it out! Butterbur is certainly the real Butterbur, unless the whole of Bree is bewitched. How could the words *all that is gold* appear in Butterbur's letter and in mine, unless Gandalf wrote them both? You may be sure Gandalf did not give a spy a chance of knowing that Butterbur's letter existed. Even if he did, a spy could not know the key-words, without reading the letter. How could that have been done without Butterbur's knowledge?'

Sam scratched his head long and thoughtfully. 'Ah!' he said at last. 'I dessay it would have been difficult. But how about this: you could have done in the real Trotter and stolen his letter, and then popped it out, like you did, after hearing Butterbur's and seeing how the land lay? You seem mighty unwilling to show it. What have you got to say to that?'

'I say you are a splendid fellow,' said Trotter. 'I see why Gandalf chose you to go with your master. You hang on tight. I am afraid my only answer to you, Sam, is this: if I had killed the real Trotter, I could kill you, and I should have killed you already without so much talk. If I was after the Ring, I could have it – now!' He stood up, and seemed suddenly to grow taller. In his face there gleamed a light, keen and commanding. They did not move. Even Sam sat still, staring dumbly at him.

'But I am the real Trotter, fortunately,' he said, looking down at them with a sudden kindly smile. 'I am Aragorn son of Celegorn, and if by life or death I can save you, I will.' There was a long silence.

At last Frodo spoke hesitatingly. 'Did those verses of Gandalf's apply to you, then?' he asked. 'I thought at first they were just nonsense.'

'Nonsense, if you will,' answered Trotter. 'Don't worry about them. They have served their turn.'

'If you want to know,' said Frodo, 'I believed in you before Butterbur came in. I was not trying to trust you, but struggling not to trust you, to follow your own teaching. You have

52   THE TREASON OF ISENGARD

frightened me several times tonight, but never in the way that servants of the Enemy would, or so I imagine. I think one of those would ... would, well, seem fairer and feel fouler. You ... well, it is the other way round with you.'

'I look foul and feel fair, is it?' laughed Trotter. 'We'll leave it at that, and say no more about round bellies!'

'I am glad you are to be our guide,' said Folco [> Pippin]. 'Now that we are beginning to understand the danger, we should be in despair without you. But somehow I feel more hopeful than ever.'

Sam said nothing.

Afterwards my father abandoned this spider's web of argumentation, arising from there being two letters from Gandalf, and handled the question of the verse of recognition *All that is gold does not glitter* and Aragorn's knowledge of it extremely adroitly by making Aragorn use the words himself (not having seen or heard Gandalf's one letter) à propos Frodo's remark (already present in this version) about 'foul and fair' (FR p. 184). But the complication of the two letters survived the crucial decision that Gandalf's letter to Frodo was written to be received by him before he left Bag End and failed in delivery through Butterbur's forgetfulness.

After 'Sam said nothing' this version is the same as FR (p. 184), with Trotter's words about the leaving of Bree and the making for Weathertop. But his answer to Frodo's question about Gandalf is much slighter:

Trotter looked grave. 'I don't know,' he said. 'To tell you the truth, I am very troubled about him – for the first time since I have known him. He meant to arrive here with you two days sooner than this. We should at least have had messages. Something has happened. I think it is something that he feared, or he would not have taken all these precautions with letters.'

From Frodo's question 'Do you think the Black Riders have anything to do with it?' the remainder of FR Chapter 10 was now attained except in a few minor particulars, the chief of which occurs in Merry's account of his experience. This story now returns to the original version (VI.161–2), according to which the Rider went eastwards through the village and stopped at Bill Ferney's house (whereas in the 'third phase' version, VI.353–4, it went in the other direction to the West-gate); but it differs from FR (p. 185) in that when Merry was about to bolt back to the inn 'another black shape rose up before me – coming down the Road from the other gate – and ... and I fell over.' In this version Trotter says: 'They may after all try some attack before

THE FOURTH PHASE (2) 53

we leave Bree. But it will be dark. In the light they need their horses.'[18]
For the subsequent history of this chapter see pp. 76–8.

Chapter XI: 'A Knife in the Dark'

This chapter was another of those that my father at this time reconstituted partly from the existing 'third phase' text (the latter part of Chapter X and the first part of Chapter XI, see VI.359) and partly from new manuscript pages, and as with the previous chapters in this form some rejected pages of the older version became separated and did not go to Marquette.

The new text opens with the attack on Crickhollow, which with the change in its date had been moved from its original place in Chapter VII (see p. 36). For the previous form of the episode see VI.328; this was almost identical to the original text, VI.303–4. To both of these my father pencilled in glimpses of the story that Odo left with Gandalf as he rode after the Black Riders – a story that seems only to have entered the 'third phase' narrative when the 'Bree' chapter was reached: see VI.336. But in the second version Crickhollow was not empty: a curtain moved in a window – for Odo had stayed behind.

I give first a preliminary draft of the attack on Crickhollow written for its new place in the story.

As they slept there in the inn of Bree, darkness lay on Buckland. Mist strayed in the dells and along the river-bank. The house at Crickhollow stood silent. Not long before, when evening had just fallen, there had been a light in a window. A horse came quickly up the lane, and halted. Up the path in haste a figure walked, wrapped in a great cloak, leading a white horse. He tapped on the door, and at once the light went out. The curtain at the window stirred, and soon after the door was opened and he passed quickly in. Even as the door closed a black shadow seemed to move under the trees and pass out through the gate without a sound.[19] Then darkness slowly deepened into night, a dead and misty night: no stars shone over Buckland.

There came the soft fall of hoofs, horses were drawing near, led slow and cautiously. The gate in the hedge opened, and up the path filed three shapes, hooded, swathed in black, and stooping low towards the ground. One went to the door, one to each corner of the house-end on either side; and there they stood, silent as the black shadows of stones, while time went slowly on, and the house and the trees about it seemed to be waiting breathlessly.

54   THE TREASON OF ISENGARD

There was a faint stir in the leaves, and a cock crowed. The cold hour before dawn had come.[20] Suddenly the figure by the door moved. In the dark, without star or moon, the blade that was drawn gleamed, as if a chill light had been unsheathed. There was a blow, soft but heavy, and the door shuddered.

'Open in the name of Sauron!' said a voice, cold and menacing. At a second blow the door yielded, and fell back with its lock broken and timbers burst. The black figures passed swiftly in.

At that moment, nearby among the trees a horn rang out. It rent the night like fire on a hill-top, echoing over the land. *Awake! Fear! Fire! Foes! Awake!* Someone was blowing the Horn-call of Buckland, which had not been sounded for a hundred years, not since the white wolves came in the Fell Winter when the Brandywine was frozen. Far away[21] answering horns were heard. Distant sounds of waking and alarm came through the night. The whole of Buckland was aroused.

The black shapes slipped swiftly from the house. In the lane the sound of hoofs broke out, and gathering to a gallop went racing into the darkness. Behind them a white horse ran. On it sat an old man clad in grey, with long silver hair and flowing beard. His horn still sounded over hill and dale. In his right hand a wand flared and flickered like a sheaf of lightning.[22] Behind him, clinging to his cloak, sat a hobbit. Gandalf and Hamilcar were riding to the North Gate, and the Black Riders fled before them. But they had found out what they wished to know: Crickhollow was empty and the Ring had gone.

The story here must be that Gandalf and Hamilcar left the house by the back door, as Fredegar Bolger did in FR (p. 188), but then waited among the trees surrounding the open space in which the house stood. A note added to the time-scheme B (p. 11) seems to fit this version: 'The Black Riders creep into Buckland, but too late to see Frodo depart. They track him to Crickhollow and guard it, and see Gandalf enter. But Gandalf (and Ham pretending to be Frodo) burst out on night of Sept. 29.'

Another short text, written on the same slip of paper and obviously at the same time as that just given, provided only the end of the episode; and in this text, which was later struck through, there is no mention of Gandalf:

Ham Bolger was blowing the Horn-call of Buckland, which had not been sounded for a hundred years... [*&c. as before*] The black shapes slipped swiftly from the house.

THE FOURTH PHASE (2)   55

In the lane the sound of hoofs broke out and gathering to a gallop raced off madly northwards into the dark. The black riders had fled, for their concern was not yet with the little folk of the Shire, but only with the Ring. And they had discovered what they wished to know: Crickhollow was empty and the Ring had gone.

This perhaps goes with the outline §4 on p. 9: 'Crickhollow scene – only Hamilcar there. He blows horn...'

The version of the story that appears in the 'fourth phase' manuscript changes again. It begins thus:

As they slept there in the inn at Bree, darkness lay on Buckland: mist strayed in the dells and along the river-bank. The house at Crickhollow stood silent. A curtain stirred in a window and for a moment a light gleamed out. At once a black shadow moved under the trees and passed out through the gate without a sound. The night deepened. There came the soft fall of hoofs...

The draft text given on p. 53 is then followed closely; but from 'The black figures passed swiftly in' there is a new story:

The black figures passed swiftly in. In a moment they came out again; one was carrying a small bundled figure in an old cloak: it did not struggle. Now they leaped upon their horses without caution; in the lane the noise of hoofs broke out, and gathering to a gallop went hammering away into the darkness.

At the same moment, [*struck out:* from the direction of the Ferry,] another horse came thundering along the lane. As it passed the gate a horn rang out.[23] It rent the night like fire on a hill-top... [*&c. as before*] Far away answering horns were heard; the alarm was spreading. Buckland was aroused.

But the Black Riders rode like a gale to the North Gate. Let the little people blow! Sauron would deal with them later. In the meanwhile they had earned his thanks: Baggins was caught like a fox in a hole. They rode down the watchmen, leaped the gate, and vanished.

And that is how Hamilcar Bolger first crossed the Brandywine Bridge.

This version evidently belongs with the story in the time-scheme D (p. 12), where on September 29 'the Riders attack Crickhollow and carry off Ham, pursued by Gandalf' – although there this took place at midnight, whereas here it was 'the cold hour before dawn'. Gandalf arrived just too late, and (and as will appear later) thought that it was

56   THE TREASON OF ISENGARD

Frodo who had been taken; but the further story of Hamilcar Bolger must be briefly postponed (see pp. 68 ff.).

Frodo's 'dream of the tower' had been removed from the night at Bree to the night at Crickhollow (see pp. 33–6), and his sleep at Bree is now described as it is in FR: 'his dreams were again troubled with the noise of wind and of galloping hoofs ... far off he heard a horn blowing wildly.'

New writing (i.e. replacement of the 'third phase' manuscript) continues as far as the departure of the hobbits with Trotter from Bree and their coming into open country. At this stage Folco was still Folco, not Pippin; but the text of FR (pp. 189–93) was reached in all but trifling details.[24] The later story of Merry's ponies now appears, changed from the earlier (VI.164) in which Tom Bombadil, when he found them, went to the inn at Bree to find out what had happened to the hobbits, and paid Mr Butterbur for the ponies; the relationship between Bombadil and Butterbur had been abandoned (pp. 10, 37).

From the point where the companions saw the houses and hobbit-holes of Staddle on their left (FR p. 193) the 'third phase' manuscript was retained, and lightly corrected, as far as the arrival of Trotter, Frodo, and Merry on the summit of Weathertop. As the manuscript stood at this stage the text of FR was very nearly attained, but some additions were later: such as the lights in the eastward sky seen from the Midgewater Marshes, the burnt turf and blackened stones on the summit of Weathertop, and the ring of ancient stonework about it; apparently the alteration of Trotter's remark that 'not all the rangers are to be trusted, nor all the birds and beasts', which goes back to the original form of the story (VI.167), to 'not all the birds are to be trusted, and there are other spies more evil than they are' was also a much later change. Strider's account in FR (p. 197) of the great watchtower on Weathertop and its ruin is not entered on the manuscript at all, and the text remains here unchanged from its earliest form (VI.169, 355). Sam's song of Gil-galad was written at this time, and entered into the manuscript.[25]

On the summit of Weathertop the old story underwent an important change. Gandalf's message on a paper that fluttered from the cairn of stones (VI.170, 355) has gone, and the text of FR (p. 199) is reached (without, as already noted, any mention of a fire: the stone on which the marks were found was not 'flatter than the others, and whiter, as if it had escaped the fire', but 'smaller than the others, and of different colour, as if it had been rubbed clean'). The scratches on the stone were X : IIII (the Old English G-rune still being used), interpreted to mean that Gandalf had been there on 4 October. The marks were however changed to read X : I.III, and a new passage was inserted (and subsequently rejected):

'But there's a dot between the first 1 and the next three,' said

THE FOURTH PHASE (2)   57

Sam poring over the stone. 'It doesn't say G.4, but G.1.3.'

'Quite right!' agreed Trotter. 'Then if Gandalf made these marks, it might mean that he was here from the first to the third; or perhaps that he and another were here on the third.'

This is odd, because Sam stayed down in the dell and did not go up to the summit of Weathertop; moreover this inserted discussion takes place at the summit, so that it is no help to suppose that Trotter brought the stone down with him to the dell. – Later, the marks were changed again to X:III.

To Frodo's 'It would be a great comfort to know that he was on the way to Rivendell' Trotter replies simply: 'It would indeed! But in any case, as he is not here himself, we must look after ourselves, and make our own way to Rivendell as best we can.' In answer to Merry's question 'How far is Rivendell?' Trotter at first replied very much as in the original version (VI.171), but distinguished between three weeks in fair weather and a month in foul weather from Brandywine Bridge to the Ford, and concludes: 'So we have at least twelve days' journey before us,[26] and very likely a fortnight or more.' This was rejected in the act of writing and the text of FR substituted, in which Trotter states the time it took from Weathertop to the Ford without computing it so elaborately: 'twelve days from here to the Ford of Bruinen, where the Road crosses the Loudwater[27] that runs out of Rivendell.'

In the 'third phase' the chapter ended with Trotter, Frodo, and Merry slipping down from the summit, and the next chapter began with 'Sam and Folco had not been idle' (in the dell). In the new version the chapter continues, and as in FR includes the attack by the Black Riders. The passage opens exactly as in FR (p. 201), and Gandalf's supplies of *cram*, bacon, and dried fruits (VI.357) have gone,[28] but Trotter has different things to report from his examination of the tracks in the dell, and he does not assert that Rangers had been there recently, and that it was they who had left the firewood.

'It is just as I feared,' he said when he came back. 'Sam and Folco [> Pippin] have trampled the soft ground, and the marks are spoilt or confused. There has been somebody here in *boots* lately, which means somebody who is not a Ranger, but that is all I can say for certain. But I don't quite like it: it looks as if there had been more than one pair of boots.' To each of the hobbits there came the thought of the cloaked and booted riders. If they had already found the dell, the sooner Trotter took them somewhere else the better. But Trotter was still considering the meaning of the footprints.

'There was also something even more strange,' he went on: 'I think there are hobbit-tracks, too: only I can't now be sure that

58   THE TREASON OF ISENGARD

there is a third set, different from Folco's [> Pippin's] and Sam's.'

'But there aren't any hobbits in this part of the world, are there?' said Merry.

'There are four here now,' answered Trotter, 'and one more can't be called impossible; but I have no idea what that would mean.'

'It might mean that these black fellows have got the poor wretch as a prisoner,' said Sam. He viewed the bare dell with great dislike...

Sam's remark is of course a mere surmise, and he speaks without any particular reference: boots and hobbit-tracks merely suggest the possibility that the Riders might have a hobbit with them. But though Trotter's remarks are inconclusive, and within the narrative intentionally so, it is obvious that the story of Hamilcar Bolger's ride with Gandalf is present here.

Merry's question to Trotter beginning 'Can the Riders *see*?' now takes the same form as in FR (p. 202), and Trotter's reply is similar but less elaborate.[29]

In this text, as noted above, Trotter does not say anything about its being a Rangers' camp in the dell, and the firewood is left unexplained. Where in FR he says simply: 'Let us take this wood that is set ready for the fire as a sign', here he adds: 'Whoever left it, brought it and put it here for a purpose; for there are no trees near. Either he meant to return, or thought that friends in need might follow him. There is little shelter or defence here, but fire will make up for both. Fire is our friend in the wilderness.'[30]

The passage in the previous version (VI.358) describing Trotter's tales as they sat by the fire in the dell was changed, presumably at this time, to its reduced form in FR (p. 203); and his story of Beren and Lúthien now appears in the form that it has in FR (pp. 205–6). The song itself is missing; but the final form was apparently achieved at this time, since it is found written out roughly but in finished composition among draft papers of this period.[31]

Chapter XII: 'Flight to the Ford'

This chapter was constituted from the existing text, with replacement of some pages; but in this case the whole manuscript was kept together. Folco is still Folco in the passages of new writing, but was corrected to Pippin or Peregrin throughout.

The River Hoarwell or Mitheithel, and the Last Bridge, have now emerged, and the Ettenmoors and Ettendales[32] of FR (the Dimrill-dale(s) of the 'third phase') are now the Entish Lands and Entish Dales

THE FOURTH PHASE (2)   59

(see p. 10 and note 14, and p. 14 and note 18). The 'Riven River' or 'Rivendell River' of the 'third phase' (VI.360) is now the Loudwater or Bruinen (note 27); and Trotter tells his companions that the Hoarwell joins the Loudwater away in the South: 'Some call it the Greyflood after that' (FR p. 212).

Trotter finds the elf-stone in the mud on the Last Bridge; but the passage in which he speaks of the country to the north of the Road remains virtually as it was in the earliest form of the story (VI.192–3; cf. FR p. 214): he does not say that he once dwelt in Rivendell, and the history of Angmar and the North Kingdom had not emerged (cf. pp. 37, 56).

The removal of the names 'Bert' and 'William' from the Stone Trolls was also a later decision; but it was now that Sam's 'Troll Song' was introduced (after some hesitation). My father's original intention had been to have Bingo sing it at *The Prancing Pony* (see VI.142, notes 11 and 12), and he had made a rough, uncompleted version for that occasion, developed and much changed from the original Leeds song *The Root of the Boot* of the 1920s (given in Vol.VI, see pp. 142–4).[33]

The 'Troll Song' is found here in three distinct and carefully written versions, beside much rough working; the third version was taken up into the manuscript. The 'Bree' version, which I did not print in Vol.VI, was already much closer to the first of these than to *The Root of the Boot*, from which my father rejected all such references as 'churchyard', 'aureole', 'wore black on a Sunday', etc. I give the first text here, in the form in which it was written out fair in ink; there are many pencilled variants, here ignored. For the development of the second and third versions see note 35.

In *The Root of the Boot* the Troll's opponent was named Tom, and his uncle John; in the 'Bree' version he was John, and his uncle Jim, with John changed back to Tom while the text was being worked on. In all three of the present texts the names are John and Jim, as they still were when my father sang the song to Mr and Mrs George Sayer at Malvern in 1952;[34] in FR they are Tom and his uncle Tim.

> *A troll sat alone on his seat of stone,*
> *And munched and mumbled a bare old bone;*
> *For many a year he had gnawed it near,*
> *And sat there hard and hungry.*
> *Tongue dry! Wrung dry!*
> *For many a year he had gnawed it near*
> *And sat there hard and hungry.*
>
> *Then up came John with his big boots on.*
> *Said he to the troll: 'Pray, what is yon?*
> *For it looks like the shin o' my nuncle Jim,*
> *As went to walk on the mountain.*
> *Huntin'! Countin'!*

THE TREASON OF ISENGARD

> It looks like the shin o' my nuncle Jim,
>   As went to walk on the mountain.'
>
> 'My lad,' said the troll, 'this bone I stole;
> But what be bones that lie in a hole?
>   Thy nuncle were dead as a lump o' lead,
>   Before I found his carkis.
>   Hark'ee! Mark'ee!
>   Thy nuncle were dead as a lump o' lead,
>   Before I found his carkis.'
>
> Said John: 'I doan't see why the likes o' thee
> Without axin' leave should go makin' free
>   With the leg or the shin o' my kith and my kin,
>   So hand the old bone over!
>   Rover! Trover!
>   So give me the shin o' my kith and my kin,
>   And hand the old bone over!'
>
> 'For a couple o' pins,' says the troll, and grins,
> 'I'll eat thee too, and gnaw thy shins.
>   A bit o' fresh meat will go down sweet,
>   And thee shall join thy nuncle!
>   Sunk well! Drunk well!
>   A bit o' fresh meat will go down sweet,
>   And thee shall join thy nuncle.'
>
> But just as he thought his dinner was caught,
> He found his hands had hold of naught;
>   But he caught a kick both hard and quick,
>   For John had slipped behind him.
>   Mind him! Blind him!
>   He caught a kick both hard and quick,
>   For John had slipped behind him.
>
> The troll tumbled down, and he cracked his crown;
> But John went hobbling back to town,
>   For that stony seat was too hard for feet,
>   And boot and toe were broken.
>   Token! Spoken!
>   That stony seat was too hard for feet,
>   And boot and toe were broken.
>
> There the troll lies, no more to rise,
> With his nose to earth and his seat to the skies;
>   But under the stone is a bare old bone
>   That was stole by a troll from its owner.
>   Donor! Boner!

THE FOURTH PHASE (2) 61

Under the stone lies a broken bone
That was stole by a troll from its owner.[35]

At the end of the recital Frodo says of Sam: 'First he was a conspirator, now he's a jester. He'll end up by becoming a wizard – or a toad!' – The stone that marked the place where the trolls' gold was hidden is still marked with Old English G and B runes in a circle, and the text remains as in the 'third phase' (VI.360).

Glorfindel now hails Trotter, not as in the previous version with *Ai, Du-finnion!* but with *Ai, dennad Torfir!* A short preparatory draft for the passage beginning with Glorfindel's greeting to Frodo (VI.361, FR p. 222) is found, as follows:

'Hail, and well met at last!' said the elf-lord to Frodo. 'I was sent from Rivendell to look for your coming. Gandalf feared that you might follow the Road to the Ford.'

'Gandalf has reached Rivendell then?' cried Frodo joyfully.

'More than five days ago,' answered Glorfindel. 'He rode out of the Entish Dales over the Hoarwell springs.'

'Out of the Entish Dales!' exclaimed Trotter.

'Yes,' said Glorfindel, 'and we thought you might come that way to avoid the peril of the Road. Some are seeking you in that region. I alone have come this way. I rode as far as the Bridge of

Here the text breaks off. That Glorfindel should have set out after Gandalf reached Rivendell is at variance with the time-schemes (p. 14) and this brief draft must have preceded them. Abandoned in mid-sentence, it was replaced by another very close to what Glorfindel says in FR: he had left Rivendell nine days before; Gandalf had not then come; and Elrond had sent out from Rivendell not on account of Gandalf but because he had had news from Gildor's people – 'some of our kindred journeying beyond the Branduin (which you have turned into Brandywine)'. This was taken up into the manuscript of the chapter (without the reference to the hobbits' name for the river: the moment was too urgent for such reflections).[36] It may be that this change in the story came about from the consideration that too little time was allowed for Gandalf's great detour northward through the Entish Dales.

In any case, the time-scheme D reflects the revised text: Glorfindel left Rivendell on 9 October and found Trotter and the hobbits nine days later, on the 18th, while Gandalf and Ham Bolger only reached Rivendell on that same day, having taken a full fortnight from Weathertop.

In the new version, Sam's protective fierceness when Frodo was attacked by pain and swayed is more bitterly expressed: ' "My master is sick and wounded, though perhaps Mr Trotter has not told you that," said Sam angrily.' Much later, the latter part of this was struck out.

62 THE TREASON OF ISENGARD

At the end of the chapter the three Riders who came out of the tree-hung cutting become, by correction to the existing manuscript, five, and the six who came from ambush away to the left become four. This change goes of course with the change of three Riders to five in the attack on Weathertop (see note 31).

NOTES

1 In the draft A there is also a rejected version of the words between the Rider and the gatekeeper:
'Have you seen Gandalf?' said the voice after a pause.
'No sir, not since midsummer,' said Harry.
'You will watch for him,' said the voice slowly. 'You will watch for hobbits. We want Baggins. He is with them....'

2 In the fair copy B of the end of Chapter V (pp. 34–5); in the draft A (p. 32) the name is still Folco.

3 'nigh on a score of years back' refers to Bilbo's passage through Bree after his Farewell Party, on his way to Rivendell. Butterbur had therefore seen Bilbo since he 'vanished with a bang while he was speaking', as the landlord goes on to say. See p. 83.

4 This development, showing the Riders to be well informed about the Bagginses of Bag End, was not retained.

5 On Trotter's references to Harry Goatleaf see pp. 41–2.

6 This speech of Butterbur's is largely derived from the draft text A (p. 43), where however it stands in a different context: there, it was on account of the questions of the Black Riders at the inn door, whereas here Butterbur has not mentioned the Riders.

7 'a month' was corrected to 'a fortnight', and at the same time 'in August' was struck out. The date on Gandalf's letter (p. 49) is 12 September, showing that these changes were made while the chapter was in progress.

8 'September' was corrected to 'this month'; see note 7.

9 The relations between the versions in respect of Gandalf's letter are:
'Third phase' of the 'Bree' chapter:
Butterbur tells Frodo of Gandalf's visit two days before, and of his message to hurry on after him (VI.338–9)
Trotter has the letter from Gandalf (VI.343)

Draft revision A of the 'third phase' version:
Butterbur has nothing to communicate from Gandalf, who has not recently been in Bree (p. 43)
Trotter has the letter from Gandalf (p. 44)

The present text:
Butterbur tells Frodo of Gandalf's visit to Bree (in August >) on 12 September (p. 47 and note 7)

THE FOURTH PHASE (2)   63

Butterbur has the letter from Gandalf (p. 47)

The Fellowship of the Ring:
Butterbur tells Frodo of Gandalf's visit at the end of June, leaving with the landlord a letter to be taken to the Shire, which was not done (p. 179).

10 'yesterday and the day before': i.e. Tuesday and Wednesday, 27 and 28 September. Similarly in A the first Rider passed through Bree on the Tuesday (p. 43), not as in the previous versions on the Monday (VI.151, 339). In FR (pp. 176, 180) the first appearance of the Black Riders in Bree was again on Monday the 26th.

11 This is in fact a reversion to the alternative text 'B' of the original 'Bree' chapter (see VI.159), where Butterbur does not encounter the Riders and has nothing to say about them.

12 'thin long-legged script': 'strong but graceful script' FR. In the earlier versions Gandalf's handwriting is 'trailing' (VI.154, 352).

13 There are two very rough draft versions of the letter. The first reads:

> *The Prancing Pony* Aug. 30. Tuesday. Dear F. I hope you will not need this. If you get this (I hope old Butterbur will not forget) things will be far from well. I hope to get back in time, but things have happened which make it doubtful. This is to say: look out for horsemen in black. Avoid them: they are our worst enemies (save one). Don't use It again, *not for any reason whatever*. Make for Rivendell as fast as you possibly can; but *don't move in the dark*. I hope, if you reach Bree, you will meet Trotter the Ranger: a dark rather lean weather-beaten fellow, but my great friend, and enemy of our enemies. He knows all our business. He has been watching the east borders of the Shire since April, but for the moment has disappeared. You can trust him: he will see you through if it can be done. I hope we may meet in Rivendell. If not Elrond will advise you. If I don't come I can only hope that will be sufficient warning for you, and that you (and Sam, too, at least) will leave the Shire as soon as possible.

> The other draft is the very close forerunner of the letter in the present manuscript, and scarcely differs from it, but it bears no date. – For previous forms of the letter see VI.154, 158, 352.

14 On the date 12 September (beside 30 August in the draft, note 13) see notes 7 and 8.

15 'Aragorn son of Celegorn' is certainly later than 'Aragorn son of Aramir' (p. 7). – The original form of the name of the third son of Fëanor was *Celegorm*, but this was changed to *Celegorn* in the course of the writing of the *Quenta Silmarillion* (V.226, 289). Later it became *Celegorm* again.

16 These words of Frodo and Aragorn were afterwards used in 'The Council of Elrond' (see p. 105, note 3).

64   THE TREASON OF ISENGARD

17   There is much initial drafting in exceedingly rough form for this
     part of the chapter. The first form of this passage was:
        The Enemy has set snares for me before now. Of course I did
        not really doubt you after seeing you with Tom Bombadil, and
        certainly not after hearing Frodo's song. Bilbo wrote that, and I
        don't see how servants of the Enemy could possibly have
        known it. But I had to teach you caution and convince you that
        I was personally to be trusted all the same – so that you should
        have no doubts or regrets later. Also a wanderer, an old ranger,
        had a desire to be taken as a friend for his own sake for once,
        and without proofs.
     For the origin of this speech of Trotter's see VI.155.
18   With 'In the light they need their horses' cf. Strider's words on
     Weathertop (FR p. 202): 'the black horses can see, and the Riders
     can use men and other creatures as spies'; for earlier forms of this
     see VI.178, 357, and p. 58 and note 29.
19   I take the significance of this to be that the one Rider who had
     stood sentinel under the trees went to fetch the other two.
20   These two sentences replaced, soon after the time of writing, 'A
     curtain in one of the windows moved' (cf. VI.328).
21   'Far away answering horns were heard': in all the variant forms
     of the 'Crickhollow episode' the reading is 'Far away' (adverbial).
     The reading of FR (p. 189), 'Far-away answering horns' (adjec-
     tival), which appears already in the first impression of the first
     edition, is I think an early error.
22   The expression *a sheaf of lightning*, going back to the earliest
     form of the episode (VI.304), seems not to be recorded. The
     Oxford English Dictionary gives a meaning of *sheaf* 'a cluster of
     jets of fire or water darting up together', with quotations from the
     nineteenth century, but I doubt that this is relevant. Conceivably
     my father had in mind a 'cluster' or 'bundle' of lightnings', like a
     'sheaf of arrows'.
23   These sentences (from 'At the same moment...') were a replace-
     ment, made as I think at or very soon after the time of
     composition, of 'Nearby among the trees a horn rang out.'
24   Some corrections made to attain it were put in subsequently, as is
     seen at once from the fact that in one of them 'Pippin' is the name
     written, not changed from 'Folco'; but I doubt that they were
     much later, and the question has here no importance.
25   The original workings of Sam's song of Gil-galad are extant, with
     the original form of the dialogue that followed his recital:
        The others turned in amazement, for the voice was Sam's.
        'Don't stop!' said Folco.
        'That's all I know, sir,' stammered Sam blushing. 'I learned it
        out of an old book up at Mr. Bilbo's, when I was a lad. I always
        was one for elves: but I never knew what that bit was about,

THE FOURTH PHASE (2)   65

until I heard Gandalf talking. Mr. Frodo'll remember that day.'
'I do,' said Frodo; 'and I know the book. I often wondered where it came from, though I never read it carefully.'
'It came from Rivendell,' said Trotter. 'That is part of
Here the text breaks up into a mass of rough variants, including 'It comes from "The Fall of Gilgalad", which is in an old tongue. Bilbo must have been translating it', and 'I know the book you mean (said Frodo). Bilbo wrote his poems in it. But I never thought of them as true.'

26   'at least twelve days' journey before us': i.e. 21 less 9 (2 from the Brandywine Bridge to Bree, 7 from Bree to Weathertop).

27   *Bruinen* occurs in the time-scheme D, p. 14; *Loudwater* is first met here (but is found also on one of the sketch-maps redrawn in VI.201).

28   In draft fragments there are many versions of the passage concerning the problem of provisions that now beset the travellers, and in these there are still several mentions of 'the additional supplies left by Gandalf.'

29   The passage in the final form 'but our shapes cast shadows in their minds ... they smell the blood of living things, desiring and hating it' is lacking. The final text is found in this manuscript, but whether added at this time or later I cannot say.

30   Aragorn's remark in FR about the Riders and fire ('Sauron can put fire to his evil uses ...') was added to the manuscript. – In a draft for the earlier passage where he examines the traces in the dell he says:
    'The wood is interesting. It is beech. There are no trees of that sort for many miles from this place, so the wood was brought from a distance. It must have been hidden here for a purpose: that is, either the campers meant to stay or to return, or they thought friends were likely to follow.'

31   Two differences from FR that remained in the 'third phase' were corrected on this manuscript: 'three tall figures' to 'five', and Frodo's cry to O *Elbereth! Gilthoniel!* (see VI.358).

32   The *Ettenmoors* and *Ettendales* of FR (pp. 212, 215) were written into this manuscript, but certainly at some later time – replacing *Entish Lands* and *Entish Dales* when the word *Ent* had acquired its special meaning. It may be that *Etten-* from Old English *eoten* 'giant, troll' (Grendel in *Beowulf* was an *eoten*), Middle English *eten*, was first devised on this manuscript, in the passage where Trotter says 'If we keep on as we are going we shall get up into the Entish Dales far north of Rivendell' (FR p. 215), for my father wrote here *Thirs* before he wrote *Ettendales*. He must have been thinking of using the Old English word *þyrs*, of the same general meaning as *ent*, *eoten*, Middle English *thirs* (and other forms). On the other hand a note on the First

66 THE TREASON OF ISENGARD

Map (see p. 306) seems also to show *Etten-* at the moment of its emergence.

33 There was also a fleeting idea that it would be Bilbo's song at Rivendell (see VI.412, note 6).

34 See Humphrey Carpenter, *Biography*, p. 213; *Letters of J. R. R. Tolkien* no. 134 (29 August 1952). The tape-recording of the 'Troll Song' made by Mr. Sayer on that occasion is heard on the Caedmon record (TC 1477) issued in 1975. The version sung by my father was the third of the present texts.

35 The second text is much closer to that in FR, but still distinct: in the first verse *And sat there hard and hungry* stands in place of *For meat was hard to come by*, in the third *Before I found his carkis* for *Afore I found his shin-bone*, and in the fifth *Thee'll be a nice change from thy nuncle!* for *I'll try my teeth on thee now*. In this text the fifth, sixth, and seventh lines of each verse were omitted, but were pencilled in later, mostly as they appear in FR.

The third text changed *And sat there hard and hungry* in the first verse to *And seen no man nor mortal* (with rhyming words *Ortal! Portal!*), which goes back to *The Root of the Boot* in *Songs for the Philologists* (VI.143), but this was corrected on the manuscript to the final line *For meat was hard to come by* (and was so sung by my father in 1952, see note 34). The third verse preserved *Afore I found his carkis* (with the last line *He's got no use for his carkis*), and the fifth preserved *Thee'll be a nice change from thy nuncle!*

36 But the information that the Baranduin was the Brandywine survived as a footnote at this point in FR (p. 222). – This is no doubt the first occurrence of *B(a)randuin* in the narrative, origin of the 'popular etymology' *Brandywine* among the hobbits. Both *Branduin* and *Baranduin* are given in an added entry in the *Etymologies* in Vol. V (stem BARÁN, p. 351). – As the passage appears in the manuscript, the name of the river was written *Branduin*, corrected to *Baranduin*, and (much later) to *Malevarn*.

IV

OF HAMILCAR, GANDALF, AND SARUMAN

On 5 August 1940 the Registrar of Oxford University wrote to my father enclosing examination scripts that had been received from an American candidate in the Honour School of English. These provided a good quantity of paper, and my father used it for the continuation of the interrupted story of the Mines of Moria and for revisions of the story already in existence; he was still using it when he came to the departure of the Company from Lothlórien.[1] In the Foreword to the Second Edition of *The Lord of the Rings* he said that he 'halted for a long while' by Balin's tomb in Moria; and that 'it was almost a year later' when he went on 'and so came to Lothlórien and the Great River late in 1941.' I have argued (VI.461) that in saying this he erred in his recollection, and that it was towards the end of 1939, not of 1940, that he reached Balin's tomb; and the use of this paper, received in August 1940, for the renewed advance in the narrative seems to support this view.[2] Of course it may be that he did not begin using it until significantly later, though that does not seem particularly likely.

At any rate, for the attempt to deduce a consecutive account of the writing of *The Lord of the Rings* this was a most fortunate chance, since the use of a readily recognisable paper the supply of which was limited makes it possible to gain a much clearer idea of the development that took place at this time than would otherwise be the case. I shall refer to this paper as 'the August 1940 examination script'.

It is not, to be sure, clear whether my father meant that he put the whole thing away for the better part of a year, or whether he distinguished between 'new narrative' – the onward movement of the story from the Chamber of Mazarbul – and the rewriting of existing chapters. Dates in the latter part of 1939 have appeared in the preceding chapters: the 'final decisions' of 8 October 1939 (p. 8), the 'New Plot' of Autumn 1939 (p. 9), and the date October 1939 of the 'fourth phase' version of the long 'Bree' chapter (p. 40). A 'New Plot', given in the present chapter, is dated August 1940. It may be much oversimplified to suppose that nothing at all was done between the last months of 1939 and the late summer of 1940, but at least it is convenient to present the material in this way, and in this chapter I collect together various texts that certainly belong to the latter time.

68   THE TREASON OF ISENGARD

In the 'fourth phase' version of 'A Knife in the Dark' the story of the attack on Crickhollow took this form (p. 55): the Black Riders carried Hamilcar Bolger out of the house as an inert bundle, and as they rode away 'another horse came thundering along the lane. As it passed the gate a horn rang out.' I noted that this story belongs with what is said in the time-scheme D (p. 12: Thursday 29 September: 'Riders attack Crickhollow and carry off Ham, pursued by Gandalf').

A very rough manuscript written on the August 1940 examination script described above gives a version of the event as recounted later at Rivendell by Gandalf and Hamilcar Bolger. This text takes up at the point where Frodo, leaving his bedroom at Rivendell, goes down and finds his friends in the porch (for the previous state of this part of the story see VI.365); but I do not think that anything has been lost before this point – it was a particular passage of the 'Many Meetings' chapter rewritten to introduce the new story.

There seemed to be three hobbits sitting there with Gandalf. 'Hurray!' cried one of them, springing up. 'Here comes our noble cousin!' It was Hamilcar Bolger.

'Ham!' cried Frodo, astounded. 'How did you come here? And why?'

'On horseback; and representing Mr. F. Baggins of Crickhollow, and late of Hobbiton,' answered Ham.

Merry laughed. 'Yes,' he said. 'We told him so, but he didn't believe it: we left poor old Ham in a dangerous post. As soon as the Black Riders had found Crickhollow, where Mr. Baggins was popularly supposed to be residing, they attacked it.'

'When did that happen?' asked Frodo.

'Before dawn on Friday morning,[3] four days nearly after you left,' said Ham. 'They got me' – he paused and shuddered – 'but Gandalf came in the nick of time.'

'Not quite the nick,' said Gandalf. 'A notch or two behind, I am afraid. Two of the Riders must have crept into Buckland secretly, while a third took the horses down the other side of the River inside the Shire. They stole the ferryboat from the Buckland shore on Thursday night, and got their horses over. I arrived too late, just as they reached the other side. Galeroc had to swim the river. Then I had a hard chase: but I caught them ten miles beyond the Bridge. I have one advantage: there is no horse in Mordor or in Rohan that is as swift as Galeroc.[4] When they heard his feet behind them they were terrified: they thought I was somewhere else, far away. I was terrified too, I may say: I thought it was Frodo they had got.'

'Yes!' said Hamilcar with a laugh. 'He did not know whether

OF HAMILCAR, GANDALF, AND SARUMAN 69

he was relieved or disgusted when he found it was only poor old Ham Bolger. I was too crushed to mind at the time: he bowled the Rider that was carrying me clean over; but I feel rather hurt now.'

'You are perfectly well now,' said Gandalf; 'and you have had a free ride all the way to Rivendell, which you would never have seen, if you had been left to your own sluggishness. Still, you have been useful in your way.' He turned to Frodo: 'It was from Ham that I heard you had gone into the Old Forest,' he said; 'and that filled me with fresh anxiety. I turned off the Road at once, and went immediately to visit Bombadil. That seems to have proved lucky; for I believe the three Riders reported that Gandalf and "Baggins" had ridden East. Their chieftain was at Amrath, far down the Greenway in the south, and the news must have reached him late on Friday. I fancy the Chief Rider was sorely puzzled when the advance guard reported that Baggins and the Ring had been in Bree the very night when they thought they had caught him in Crickhollow! Some Riders seem to have been sent straight across country to Weathertop. Five[5] came roaring along the Road. I was safe back at the *Pony* when they passed through Bree on Saturday night. They leaped the gates and went through like a howling wind. The Breelanders are still shivering and wondering what is happening to the world. I left Bree next morning, and rode day and night behind them, and we reached Weathertop on the evening of the third.'

'So Sam was right!' said Frodo. 'Yes, sir, seemingly,' said Sam, feeling rather pleased;[6] but Gandalf frowned at the interruption.

'We found two Riders already watching Weathertop,' he went on. 'Others soon gathered round, returning from the pursuit further east along the Road. Ham and I passed a very bad night besieged on the top of Weathertop. But they dared not attack me in the daylight. In the morning we slipped away northwards into the wilds. Several pursued us; two followed us right up the Hoarwell into the Entishlands. That is why they were not in full force when you arrived, and did not observe you at once.'

Here the text ends, but it is followed by another version of the last part, following on from 'we slipped away northwards into the wilds':

...not too secretly – I wanted to draw them off. But the Chief Rider was too cunning: only four came after us, and only two

70   THE TREASON OF ISENGARD

pursued us far; and they turned aside when we reached the Entishlands and went back towards the Ford, I fancy. Still, that is why they were not in full force when you arrived, and why they did not at once pursue [you] in the wild/Still, that is why they did not immediately hunt for you in the wilderness, or observe your arrival at Weathertop; and why they were not in full force for the attack on you.

Comparison of this account with the time-scheme D (pp. 12–13) will show that the narrative fits the scheme closely. In both, the Riders crossed the Brandywine by the Ferry on the night of Thursday 29 September; Gandalf rescued Ham from the Riders on Friday morning; two Riders (as the narrative was first written, see note 5) were sent direct to Weathertop, and (again as first written) seven rode through Bree, throwing down or leaping the gates, on the night of Saturday 1 October, while Gandalf and Ham were at *The Prancing Pony*; two Riders were already at Weathertop when Gandalf and Ham got there in the evening of Monday 3 October, after riding day and night; and Gandalf and Ham left Weathertop on the following morning.

Gandalf's horse is now named *Galeroc*, replacing earlier *Narothal* (VI.345); and the name *Amrath* appears, of the place where the chief of the Riders remained, 'far down the Greenway in the south.'[7]

This narrative seems to belong also with the 'fourth phase' version of 'A Knife in the Dark' (p. 55): the horse that came racing up the lane as the Riders rode off with Ham Bolger was bearing Gandalf from the Ferry, 'a notch or two behind' the nick of time, as he said at Rivendell. Yet there is a difficulty, or at any rate a difference; for the story of the attack on Crickhollow in this version, as in all those preceding it, described a long period ('time went slowly on') between the coming of the Riders into the garden of Crickhollow and the breaking into the house. If Gandalf came to Bucklebury Ferry just as the Riders with their horses reached the other side, and he at once put Galeroc to swim the river, he cannot have been more than a matter of minutes behind them.

A new narrative outline, written roughly and rapidly on two sides of a single sheet, is headed: '*New Plot*. Aug. 26–27, 1940'. This outline was subsequently altered and added to, but I give it here as first written. I have expanded contractions and in other small ways slightly edited the text to make it easier to follow.

The wizard Saramond the White [*written above at the same time:* Saramund the Grey] or Grey Saruman sends out a message that there is important news: Trotter hears that Black Riders are *out* and moving towards the Shire (for which they are asking). He sends word to Gandalf, who leaves Hobbiton at the end of June. He goes

OF HAMILCAR, GANDALF, AND SARUMAN 71

S.E. (leaving Trotter to keep an eye on the Shire-borders) towards Rohan (or Horserland).

Gandalf knows that 9 Black Riders (and especially their king) are too much for him alone. He wants the help of Saramund. So he goes to him where he lived on the borders of Rohan at Angrobel (or Irongarth).

Saramund betrays him – having fallen and gone over to Sauron: (*either*) he tells Gandalf false news of the Black Riders, and they pursue him to the top of a mountain; there he is left standing alone with a guard (wolves, orcs, etc. all about) while they ride off with mocking laugh; (*or else*) he is handed over to a giant Fangorn (Treebeard) who imprisons him?

Meanwhile the Black Riders attack the Shire, coming up the Greenway and driving a crowd of fugitives among which are one or two evil men, Sauronites.[8] The King of the Black Riders encamps at Amrath to guard Sarn Ford and Bridge.

6 Riders (D E F G H I) go ahead and invade the Shire. The vanguard Rider (D) reaches Bag-End on Sept. 23 (night). Two (D E) then trail Frodo etc. to the Ferry (Sept. 25). F G H I are on the main road. D E, foiled at the Ferry (Sept. 25), ride off to Brandywine Bridge and join F G H I (dawn on Sept. 26).

H I then ride along scouring both sides of the Road and reach Bree up and down Greenway [*sic*] on Tuesday Sept. 27.[9]

On night (cockcrow) of Sept. 26–27 D E F attack Crickhollow. There they carry off Ham. G was left guarding the Bridge but now comes with them.

H I go on through Bree asking for news, to make sure 'Baggins' has not escaped and got ahead. They get in touch with Bill Ferney.

D E F G with poor Ham now ride to Greenway (does Harry see them? Probably not). At Amrath they meet the King (A) and B C, on Wednesday 28th, leaving for the moment the Road deserted. The King is angry at this. He is suspicious of a plot since Ham has no Ring. D E are sent back to Bree, arriving late on Thursday 29th. (Meanwhile the hobbits have got to the Inn.) F G go back to the Shire.

D E get in touch with Bill Ferney, and hear of news at the Inn. [*Struck out at once:* They attack the Inn but fail (and get the idea that 'Green'[10] has gone off?)] They fear 'Trotter', but get Bill Ferney and the Southerner to burgle the Inn and try and get more news, especially of the Ring. (They are puzzled by two Bagginses.) The burglary fails; but they drive off all the ponies.

F G bring news to the King that Gandalf has escaped and is in the Shire (which he reached on Wednesday 28th [> Thursday 29th night], and visited Bag-End and the Gaffer).

D E return to the King and report (Sept. 30): he is puzzled by 'Green' and the Ring, by Baggins and Ham, and troubled by news of

THE TREASON OF ISENGARD

Gandalf behind. He does not kill Ham because he wants to find out more, and Sauron has ordered him to bring 'Baggins' to Mordor. HI return (Oct. 1) reporting nothing on the Road as far as Weathertop, and that Green and Trotter have left Bree and vanished. The King decides to pursue Green with all his forces, carrying Ham with him.

Gandalf goes to Crickhollow late on Thursday 29th and finds it deserted. Old cloak of Frodo dropped. Gandalf is terrified lest Frodo is captive. (? Does he visit Tom – if so make him arrive in the Shire on the 28th and visit Buckland on the 29th; if not, arrive in the Shire on the 29th, visit Buckland on the 30th.) Either visiting Tom or not, Gandalf reaches Bree on Saturday Oct. 1 (after the hobbits have gone). He rides after them. The Black Riders meanwhile have left Amrath and revisited Bree to get news of Green, and gone off along the Road on both sides. Gandalf crashes into D E who are carrying Ham and rescues him. He gallops to Weathertop, reaching it on Oct. 3. He sees Black Riders gather and goes off North (three Riders, D E F, pursue him). The rest patrol round and watch Weathertop.

Here we have the story of the capture of Hamilcar Bolger again, but with a significant difference. In Time-scheme D (p. 12), and in the story told by Gandalf at Rivendell (p. 68), the attack on Crickhollow took place on the night of Thursday–Friday 29–30 September; and the story there was that Gandalf arrived just as the Riders left, and he was able to catch them up ten miles east of the Brandywine Bridge. In the present outline, the attack on Crickhollow took place three nights earlier, on that of Monday–Tuesday 26–27 September (Frodo and the others having left on the Monday morning), and since Gandalf still arrives there late on the 29th (or the 30th) he finds the trail cold; but he also finds Frodo's cloak dropped on the step. He still rescues Ham, but not till his captors have passed Bree. It is curious therefore that (though he was uncertain about it) my father had not decisively rejected the visit to Tom Bombadil, since with this plot Gandalf could have had no notion that the hobbits had entered the Old Forest.

This is very probably the first appearance of Saruman (Saramond, Saramund), who steps into the narrative quite unheralded – but he enters at once as a Wizard whose aid Gandalf seeks, and who has 'fallen and gone over to Sauron'; moreover he dwells at *Angrobel* or 'Irongarth' (cf. *Isengard*) 'on the borders of Rohan'. But my father was still quite uncertain what happened to Gandalf, having rejected the story of the Western Tower: the possibilities suggested here show that the imprisonment in a tower had been for the moment abandoned. Giant Fangorn or Treebeard again appears as a hostile being (cf. p. 9).

I suspect that the primary question that my father was pondering here was that of the emergence of the Ringwraiths from Mordor, Gandalf's knowledge of this in the summer before Frodo left Bag End,

OF HAMILCAR, GANDALF, AND SARUMAN 73

and Trotter's message. It has been said already (p. 9) that 'It was a message of Trotter's in July (?) that took Gandalf away – fearing Black Riders', and again (p. 10) 'It was a message from Trotter that fetched Gandalf away in summer before Frodo left'. These notes indicate that Gandalf already had reason, when he left Hobbiton, to suspect the emergence of the Ringwraiths; but it is now told, at the beginning of the present outline, that the message from Trotter (itself emanating from Saruman) was an actual report that the Nine had left Mordor and were moving towards the Shire. This would raise the question: why, in that case, did Gandalf, before he went off, not urge Frodo to leave for Rivendell as soon as he could? Scribblings on the manuscript of this outline show my father concerned with the question: 'Both Gandalf and Trotter must go away *together* and not fear to be captured, or else Gandalf would have sent a message to Frodo to start, or Trotter would have.' Then follows a suggestion that Trotter 'got cut off from Gandalf, only arriving in Bree hard on the tracks of the Black Riders.' But this does not seem entirely to meet the difficulty. Later my father noted here: 'Leaves Butterbur a letter which he *forgets* to send to Frodo', and this is clearly where that essential idea arose.

In FR (p. 269) the problem is resolved by reverting to the story that when Gandalf left Hobbiton he had no definite knowledge, and by the introduction of Radagast. 'At the end of June I was in the Shire, but a cloud of anxiety was on my mind, and I rode to the southern borders of the little land; for I had a foreboding of some danger, still hidden from me but drawing near.' It was Radagast who told Gandalf that the Nine were abroad, whereupon Gandalf, at Bree, wrote the letter to Frodo which Butterbur forgot to send.

Another brief but distinctive narrative passage is clearly associated with this 'August 1940' outline. It was substituted in the manuscript of the 'fourth phase' version of Chapter IX ('At the Sign of the Prancing Pony (i)') for that in which the Black Riders spoke to Harry Goatleaf, the gatekeeper at Bree, on the evening of Wednesday the 28th of September (pp. 40–1), and was itself subsequently rejected.

The rain that swept over the Forest and the Downs on Tuesday was still falling long and grey on Bree when evening came. The lights were just being lit in Tom's house,[11] when the noise of horses approaching came down the Road from the west. Harry Goatleaf the gatekeeper peered out of his door and scowled at the rain. He had been thinking of going out to close the gate, when he caught the sound of the horsemen. Reluctantly he waited, wishing now that he had shut the gate earlier: he did not like the sound. Two horsemen had appeared in Bree late the day before[12] and wild stories were going about. People had been scared; some said the riders were uncanny: dogs yam-

74   THE TREASON OF ISENGARD

mered, and geese screamed at them. Yet they were asking for news of hobbits out of the Shire, especially for one called Baggins. Very queer.

Harry thought it even queerer a minute later. He went out, grumbling at the rain, and looking up the Road he thought he saw dark figures approaching swiftly, three or maybe four. But suddenly they turned left at the Cross Roads[13] just beyond the gate, and went off southwards and down the Greenway; all sound of their horses' feet died away on the grass-grown track.

'Queerer and queerer!' he thought. 'That way leads nowhere. Who would turn off on a wet night just in sight of the Inn at Bree?' He shivered suddenly all down his back. Locking the gate he hurried into his house and bolted the door.

Wednesday turned foggy after midday; but still the queer events went on. Out of the mists up the Greenway there straggled such a company as had not been seen in Bree for many a year: strange men from the South, haggard and wayworn, and bearing heavy burdens. Most of them had a hunted look and seemed too tired and scared to talk; but some were ill-favoured and rough-spoken. They made quite a stir in Bree.

The next day, Thursday, was clear and fine again, with a warm sun and a wind that veered from East towards the South. No traveller passed the western gate all day, but Harry kept on going to the gate, even after nightfall.

This would then join on to the next part of the text, 'It was dark, and white stars were shining, when Frodo and his companions came at last to the Greenway-crossing and drew near the village' (cf. VI.348).

With this compare the 'August 1940' outline (p. 71): 'DEFG with poor Ham now ride to Greenway (does Harry see them? Probably not).' I think it is clear that when Harry Goatleaf saw the dark figures mysteriously turn off down the Greenway at the crossroads in the rain at dusk, they had Hamilcar Bolger with them, bearing him to the King at Amrath. And with the description of the company that came up the Greenway on the Wednesday cf. an earlier passage in the same outline: 'Meanwhile the Black Riders attack the Shire, coming up the Greenway and driving a crowd of fugitives among which are one or two evil men, Sauronites.'

In the margin of the 'fourth phase' version of the attack on Crickhollow (p. 55) my father later noted:

Omit, or bring into line with old version (in middle of Chapter VII). Ham cannot be captured (Black Riders would obviously kill him). It probably spoils surprise to show what Gandalf is up to at this point. Gandalf can briefly explain that [? he was at] Crickhollow.

OF HAMILCAR, GANDALF, AND SARUMAN 75

There is a definitive tone about this that suggests that this is where the 'Odo-Hamilcar' adventure was finally abandoned; and if this is so it must be placed, of course, after the outline dated 'Aug. 26–27, 1940'. Presumably it was at this time that the 'fourth phase' version of the 'Crickhollow episode' was struck through.

Labelling this rejected form 'A', my father seems now to have tried out a version (labelled 'B') which follows his direction to 'bring (the story) into line with the old version (in middle of Chapter VII)' – i.e. the original form of the episode, which was inserted in the course of the 'second phase' into Chapter VII 'In the House of Tom Bombadil' (VI.303–4), at which stage the story was that the house at Crickhollow was empty when the Riders came, for no hobbit had been left behind there. In version 'B' there is no mention of Hamilcar Bolger at all. The 'man in grey', leading a white horse, comes up the path, looks in at the windows, and disappears round the corner of the house; then the Black Riders come; at first cockcrow they break in the door; and at that moment the horn call rings out, the Riders flee, with 'a cry like the cry of hunting beasts stricken unawares' (cf. VI.304), and Gandalf appears wielding horn and wand and thunders after them.

A page of notes is associated with these attempts to find the right form for the opening of 'A Knife in the Dark'. These begin:

> It will improve matters to cut out Ham Bolger. Version B will provide for that. (Gandalf arrives, takes Ham Bolger out of the house, and chases off the Black Riders.)

This is obscure, since there is no mention in the version labelled 'B' of Gandalf's entering the house, no mention of a light in the window, nor any suggestion that it was inhabited. But in any case it was clearly not my father's meaning when he wrote 'It will improve matters to cut out Ham Bolger' that he intended to cut him out of the narrative altogether: he meant only that Ham was to be excluded from further adventures after the 'Crickhollow episode' was ended. Conceivably, he had here a passing notion that Gandalf came to Crickhollow, entered secretly, told Ham Bolger to clear out, and proceeded to look after the Black Riders himself. Whatever the meaning, these notes continue:

> But better would be this:
> Gandalf is captured by [Saramund >] Saruman.
> Elves send word that he is missing, which reaches Rivendell Sat. 8th.[14] Glorfindel is sent out, and messengers sent to Eagles. The Eagles are told about Oct. 11. They fly all over the lands, and find Gandalf about Sat. 15. Bring ... to Rivendell Wed. 19th.
> The XIII and wood are Sam's discovery. Trotter says it is *a rangers' camp*.
> Weakness of this is that Black Riders are sure to make *some* attempt on Crickhollow. How was it foiled?

76   THE TREASON OF ISENGARD

Ham flies as shown overleaf.

Then Gandalf can come and find house deserted and only old cloak of Frodo's. He thinks Frodo [*struck out:* is capt(ured)]. He follows like thunder.

'Ham flies as shown overleaf' refers to a third version, labelled 'C', which (though at first differently ordered in the articulation of the narrative) scarcely differs from that in FR (with Ham opening the door of the house, seeing a black shape in the garden, and fleeing out of the back door and over the fields), apart of course from the fact that this is Hamilcar and not Fredegar, and apart from the notable words, afterwards lost, following 'Ham Bolger had not been idle': 'Terror will drive even a Bolger to action'. The hobbit-cloak let fall by one of the Riders as he fled reappears from the 'August 1940' outline (p. 72). At the head of this version my father noted:

> Gandalf *does not follow* [i.e. he does not follow the Black Riders from Crickhollow]. Either he comes later, Saturday Oct. 1 or [Sunday Oct.] 2 (and finds cloak), or else he is taken by eagles ... to Rivendell.

This no doubt preceded the notes given above. These are certainly the first references to Gandalf's escape from captivity by the aid of the Eagles; and the entry of Radagast is now on the threshold.[15]

The apparently irrelevant mention of Trotter's saying that 'it is a rangers' camp' is presumably associated with the idea that the Eagles found Gandalf and carried him to Rivendell – so that, with this story, he would never go to Weathertop at all. But what the significance of 'The XIII and wood are Sam's discovery' may be I cannot say. Sam's *interpretation* of the 'X:IIII' has appeared, but that was only a refinement of Trotter's view that they were marks made by Gandalf on the stone found on the summit of Weathertop and referred to the date: see pp. 56–7. I have noticed there that Sam's intervention does not fit the story, since there is never any suggestion that he was among those who went up to the high place where the stone was found; and also that 'X:IIII' was subsequently changed to 'X:III'. Conceivably, the passing idea here was that the 'X III', retained but given a different significance (a Rangers' mark?), was not found on the stone on the cairn, but on the firewood in the dell.

At this time Chapter X, 'At the Sign of the Prancing Pony (ii)', was once more heavily overhauled.[16] This revision was carried out in two stages, clearly not long separated. The completion of the revision was written on pages of the August 1940 examination script; and with this the chapter as it stands in FR was achieved in all points, save for a few minor additions and alterations that were certainly later.

By this time 'Pippin' was firmly established. In the first stage of revision Frodo's assumed name at Bree was still 'Green', but became

OF HAMILCAR, GANDALF, AND SARUMAN   77

'Underhill' in the second. Mr Butterbur is still Barnabas, not Barliman. His account of Frodo's distinguishing marks as received from Gandalf (in addition to his bring 'a round-bellied little fellow with red cheeks') at first gave him 'a white lock of hair by his left ear and a wart on his chin.' The second version made him 'broader than most and fairer than some', and still with a wart on his chin. The final description came in later.

The scribbled suggestion on the manuscript of the 'New Plot' (p. 73), 'Leaves Butterbur a letter which he *forgets* to send to Frodo', was now taken up, but it was not until the second stage of revision that the form of the episode in FR was reached. At first the preceding version was more largely retained, notably in the story of the two letters (pp. 49 ff.). The substance of Gandalf's letter to Frodo reaches the form in FR (with the date now Friday July 2nd), but there are differences in the postscripts:

> *PS. Look out for horsemen in black. Deadly enemies, especially after dark. Do not move by night. Do not use IT again, not for any reason whatever.*
>
> *PPS. Make sure it is the real Trotter. His true name is Aragorn son of Celegorn.*[17]
>> *All that is gold does not glitter,*
>> *not all those that wander are lost;*
>> *All that is old does not wither,*
>> *and fire may burn bright in the frost;*
>> *Not all that have fallen are vanquished,*
>> *not only the crowned is a king;*
>> *Let blade that was broken be brandished,*
>> *and Fire be the Doom of the Ring!*[18]
>
> *Aragorn would know that rhyme. Ask him what follows after All that is gold does not glitter.*
>
> *PPPS. I hope Butterbur sends this promptly. A worthy man, but his mind is like a lumber-room: things wanted always buried. If he forgets, I shall have words with him one day.*
>
> *The real Trotter will have a sealed letter (addressed to you) with these words inside: All that is gold does not glitter etc.*

At this stage Frodo still read Gandalf's letter aloud; and Trotter produced the second letter, which after the verse reads:

> *This is to witness that the bearer is Aragorn son of Celegorn* [> *Kelegorn*] *known as the Trotter. Who trusts Gandalf may trust him.*

As there is now no mention of Elendil, the passage that followed in the former version ('Then It belongs to you as much as to me, or more' etc., p. 50) was removed (see p. 105, note 3); and Trotter now says, after 'The Enemy has set traps for me before now', 'I was puzzled –

78   THE TREASON OF ISENGARD

because you did not produce your letter or ask for the pass-words. It was not till old Barnabas confessed that I understood.'

I do not think that it was long before my father abandoned the story of the second letter, and on pages of the August 1940 script the FR text was reached – with Gandalf's letter read silently, Trotter using the words *All that is gold does not glitter* quite independently, and drawing out the Sword that was Broken (see p. 116). The date of Gandalf's letter now becomes Wednesday June 30th, and (probably at this time) the verse was changed again:

> *All that is gold does not glitter,*
> *not all those that wander are lost;*
> *All that is old does not wither,*
> *and bright may be fire in the frost.*
> *The flame that was low may be woken;*
> *and sharp in the sheath is the sting;*
> *Forged may be blade that was broken;*
> *the crownless again may be king.*[19]

Gandalf's signature remains still in Old English runes.

Aragorn's account of his last meeting with Gandalf at Sarn Ford on the first of May (FR p. 184) now appears, and in the same words.[20] The story in the 'New Plot' (p. 70) that 'Trotter hears that Black Riders are *out* and moving towards the Shire.... He sends word to Gandalf, who leaves Hobbiton at the end of June' had presumably been abandoned, and the rôle of Radagast in telling Gandalf of the emergence of the Ringwraiths introduced (see pp. 82, 131).

The now chaotic text of the chapter, a mass of emendations, rejected pages, and inserted riders, was later replaced by a typescript fair copy: how much later I cannot say. Near the end of the chapter (FR p. 184) Trotter says (in the manuscript): 'Well, with Sam's permission we'll call that settled. Trotter shall be your guide. *And now I think it is time you went to bed and took what rest you can.* We shall have a rough road tomorrow....' In the typescript text that followed (the latter part of which was not typed by my father) the italicised words were omitted; but there is no suggestion in the manuscript that they should be, and indeed the words 'We shall have a rough road tomorrow' clearly depend on them. But the omission was never picked up, and the sentence does not appear in FR.

The series of rewritings of the beginning of Chapter XI, 'A Knife in the Dark', leading to the final elimination of Ham Bolger's ride with Gandalf, have been considered already (pp. 74–6). An associated revision belonging to this time removed the passage (pp. 57–8) in which Trotter thought that he found hobbit footprints in the dell below Weathertop that might be distinct from those of Pippin and Sam, and replaced it by a form very close to that in FR p. 201 (beginning

OF HAMILCAR, GANDALF, AND SARUMAN 79

'Rangers have been here lately. It is they who left the firewood behind'; cf. 'Trotter says it is *a rangers' camp*', p. 75).

NOTES

1 The candidate's name was Richard Creswell Rowland. The scripts had been sent from the United States. At first my father received only the scripts in the subjects that personally concerned him as an examiner, but subsequently most or all of the candidate's writing came to him. He used not only the blank verso sides of the paper, but also the blue covers of each booklet, where his writing becomes peculiarly hard to decipher.

2 A further argument in favour of this dating can now be adduced. In notes dated Autumn 1939 and October 8 1939 (pp. 8–9) Trotter has definitively ceased to be a hobbit and has become a man, Aragorn; but in the original 'Moria' chapter he was still a hobbit (or at any rate he certainly was in the original version of 'The Ring Goes South', with which 'The Mines of Moria' was continuous). See further p. 379.

3 'Before dawn on Friday morning' was an immediate change from 'Thursday night'; cf. p. 55.

4 I do not think that there is any suggestion here that Galeroc was a horse from Rohan: he is simply Gandalf's horse, and it is essential that he be extraordinarily swift.

5 In the preceding sentence 'Some Riders' (those sent to Weathertop) was first written 'Two Riders', and 'Five' here (those who rode along the Road to Bree) was written 'Seven', agreeing with the scheme D (p. 13). 'Two' was then changed to 'Four' and 'Seven' to 'Five'; finally 'Four' to 'Some'. – By *roaring along the Road* my father meant going at wild speed, with also a suggestion of the great noise of their passage.

6 This refers to the markings on the stone at Weathertop, which (by a change introduced into the 'fourth phase' version of 'A Knife in the Dark') Sam realised were to be read, not as G.4, but as G.1.3, and which Trotter in his turn thought might mean that Gandalf and another were at Weathertop on 3 October; see pp. 56–7.

7 With this cf. *Unfinished Tales* p. 348: 'The Black Captain established a camp at Andrath, where the Greenway passed in a defile between the Barrow-downs and the South Downs.' On the First Map (p. 305) *Andrath* (very probably first written *Amrath*, p. 298) is marked as a point beside the Greenway a little nearer to Bree than to Tharbad.

8 Cf. the end of the short text given on pp. 73–4.

9 The date Tuesday Sept. 27 was subsequently altered to 'late Monday 26th'; see p. 63, note 10, and note 12 to this chapter.

80   THE TREASON OF ISENGARD

10   Frodo's assumed name 'Green' (replacing 'Hill') has already appeared (pp. 37, 41, etc.).

11   Tuesday 27 September was the second night spent by the hobbits in the house of Tom Bombadil.

12   The riders H and I, according to the outline (p. 71), where their arrival in Bree was altered from Tuesday 27 September to Monday the 26th (note 9).

13   'turned *left* at the Cross Roads': i.e. from the point of view of the gatekeeper, who was looking out westwards.

14   Word reaches Rivendell that Gandalf is missing on Saturday 8 October: cf. the time-scheme D, p. 14.

15   Radagast has been named, but no more, in previous texts (VI.379, 397), and with no indication of what part my father was envisaging for him.

16   A development from this time in Chapter IX, 'At the Sign of the Prancing Pony (i)', has been given on pp. 73–4.

17   *Aragorn* was later changed here to *Elfstone, Erkenbrand*, again *Elfstone, Ingold*, and finally back to *Aragorn*, and in the passage 'I am Aragorn son of Kelegorn, and if by life or death I can save you, I will' the name was changed to *Elfstone son of Elfhelm*. But these changes were made after the second stage of revision had been completed. The renaming of Aragorn and its implications are discussed on pp. 277–8.

18   An earlier stage in the evolution of the verse, following from the original form in the 'fourth phase' version of the chapter (pp. 49–50), was:

> *All that is gold does not glitter;*
> *not all those that wander are lost.*
> *All that grows old does not wither;*
> *not every leaf falls in the frost.*
> *Not all that have fallen are vanquished;*
> *a king may yet be without crown,*
> *A blade that was broken be brandished;*
> *and towers that were strong may fall down.*

19   In all these versions of *All that is gold does not glitter*, including the original form on pp. 49–50, the verses are written in the manuscript as long lines (i.e. four lines not eight).

20   In FR Gandalf arrived at Bag End after his long absence on an evening of early April (pp. 54–5); 'two or three weeks' later he advised Frodo that he ought to leave soon (p. 74); and he 'stayed in the Shire for over two months' (p. 76) before he left at the end of June. There is no reference to his having left Hobbiton during this time.

V

BILBO'S SONG AT RIVENDELL:
ERRANTRY AND *EÄRENDILLINWË*

We come now again to Rivendell, and to Book II of *The Fellowship of the Ring*. In the 'third phase' the chapter which afterwards became 'Many Meetings' was numbered XII and entitled 'The Council of Elrond' (VI.362) – because at that stage my father thought that it would include not only Frodo's conversation with Gandalf when he awoke at Rivendell, the feast, and his meeting with Bilbo, but the deliberations of the Council also. Trotter was still at that time, of course, a hobbit. I have argued (VI.369) that this chapter (and the 'third phase' of writing) ended abruptly in the middle of Glóin's conversation with Frodo at the feast – at precisely the same point as did the original form of the story in the 'first phase'; and that the remainder of the chapter in this manuscript was added in later – when Trotter had become Aragorn. Simply for the purpose of this discussion I will call the first or 'third phase' part of the manuscript (VI.362–6) 'I', and the second part 'II'. Behind 'II' lie the rough draftings given in VI.391–4 (in which Trotter was still the hobbit Peregrin Boffin).

I have not been able to determine when 'II' was written, but it perhaps comes from the period of work represented by the notes and rewritings of the 'fourth phase' in the first three chapters of this book. Both 'I' and 'II' were subjected to emendation at different times: for one substantial passage of rewriting the August 1940 examination script was used, but many other minor alterations may be earlier or later. In view of these uncertainties I shall do no more here than look briefly through the chapter (now numbered XIII, since the 'Bree' chapter had been divided into two, IX and X) and show what seems to have been its form at the stage of development we have now reached.

Looking first at changes made to section 'I' of the manuscript, the passage in the third phase version (VI.362–3) beginning 'It is no small feat to have come so far and through such dangers, still bearing the Ring', in which Gandalf told of his captivity at the hands of Giant Treebeard and teased Frodo's curiosity about Trotter, was entirely rewritten. It now begins:

'We should never have done it without Trotter,' said Frodo.

82   THE TREASON OF ISENGARD

'But we needed you. I did not know what to do without you.'

'I was delayed,' said Gandalf; 'and that nearly proved our ruin. And yet I am not sure: it may have been better so. Knowing the peril I should not have dared to take such risks, and we might either have been trapped in the Shire, or if I had tried some long way round we might have been hunted down in some wild place far from all help. As it is we have escaped the pursuit – for the moment.'

To Frodo's astonished 'You?' when Gandalf said that he was held captive his reply now takes this form:

'Yes, I, Gandalf the Grey,' said the wizard solemnly. 'There are many powers greater than mine, for good or evil, in the world. I cannot stand alone against all the Black Riders.'[1]

'Then you knew of the Riders already – before I met them?'

The text is then as in FR, including Gandalf's words 'But I did not know that they had arisen again or I should have fled with you at once. I heard news of them only after I left you in June' (see p. 78). He says: 'There are few left in Middle-earth like Aragorn son of Kelegorn.[2] The race of the Kings from over the Sea is nearly at an end', and Frodo in reply says: 'Do you really mean that Trotter is of the race of Númenor?'[3] To Frodo's 'I thought he was only a Ranger' Gandalf replies 'indignantly':

'Only a Ranger! Many of the Rangers are of the same race, and the followers of Aragorn: all that he has left of the realm of his fathers. We may need his help before all is over. We have reached Rivendell; but the Ring is not yet at rest.'

From this point to the end of section 'I' of the manuscript the 'third phase' text was little changed, and the differences from FR noted in VI.363–6 were mostly still present. Gandalf's words 'And the Elves of Rivendell are descendants of his chief foes' (VI.364) were changed to 'And among the Elves of Rivendell are some descendants of his chief foes', and 'the Wise say that he [the Dark Lord] is doomed in the End, though that is far away' (ibid.) was removed. Also removed of course were the references to Odo's arrival, and when Frodo goes down with Sam to find his friends in the porch Odo's remarks are given to Pippin. The sentence describing Elrond's smile and laughter (VI.365) was struck out, and Glóin's wink (VI.366) also disappears: his reply to Frodo's question concerning his errand from the Lonely Mountain now takes the form it has in FR (p. 240).

In section 'II' of the manuscript (see p. 81), beginning at Frodo's question 'And what has become of Balin and Ori and Oin?', the text of

BILBO'S SONG AT RIVENDELL
83

FR (pp. 241 ff.) was very largely reached (apart from the absence of Arwen), and there are only a few particular points to notice.

When in the first draft (VI. 392) Bilbo said 'I shall have to get that fellow *Peregrin* to help me', he now says the same of *Aragorn*, changed in the act of writing to *Tarkil* (in FR, *the Dúnadan*). At this stage Aragorn's absence from the feast was still explained by his being much in demand in the kitchens.

I noted that in the original draft 'the entire passage (FR pp. 243–4) in which Bilbo tells [Frodo] of his journey to Dale, of his life in Rivendell, and his interest in the Ring – and the distressing incident when he asks to see it – is absent.' In this version Bilbo does give an account of his journey, but it was at first different from what he says in FR:

When he had left Hobbiton he had wandered off aimlessly along the Road, but somehow he had steered all the time for Rivendell.

'I got here in a month or two without much adventure,' he said, 'and I stayed at *The Pony* in Bree for a bit;[4] somehow I have never gone any further. I have almost finished my book. And I make up a few songs which they sing occasionally ...'

This was changed, probably soon, to the text of FR, in which Bilbo tells of his journey to Dale. The rest of the passage, in which Bilbo speaks of Gandalf and the Ring, was present in this version from the start, the only differences being that Bilbo names the Necromancer, not the Enemy, and where in FR he says that he could get little out of Gandalf concerning the Ring but that 'the Dúnadan has told me more', here he calls him *Tarkil*, and adds 'He was in the Gollum-hunt' (this being afterwards struck out).

The episode of Bilbo's asking to see the Ring is present as in FR, the only difference here being that where FR has 'When he had dressed, Frodo found that while he slept the Ring had been hung about his neck on a new chain, light but strong', this version has 'When he dressed Frodo had hung the Ring upon a chain about his neck under his tunic.'

When Aragorn joins Bilbo and Frodo, the conversation is as in FR, with *Tarkil* for *Dúnadan*, *the Dúnadan*; but Bilbo's reply to Frodo's 'What do you call him *Tarkil* for?' is different:

'Lots of us do here,' answered Bilbo, 'just to show off our knowledge of the old tongue, and to show our deep respect. It means Man of the West, out of Númenor, you know, or perhaps you don't. But that is another story. He can tell it you some other time. Just now I want his help. Look here, friend Tarkil, Elrond says this song of mine is to be finished before the end of the evening ...'

84   THE TREASON OF ISENGARD

This was changed to:

'He is often called that here,' answered Bilbo. 'It is a title of honour. The Elder Tongue is remembered in Rivendell; and I thought you knew enough at least to know *tarkil*: Man of Westernesse, Númenórean. But this isn't the time for lessons. Just now I want your Trotter's help in something urgent. Look here, friend Tarkil...'[5]

The passage leading up to Bilbo's song is much as in FR (pp. 245–6), but the sentence beginning 'Almost it seemed that the words took shape...' is absent, and where FR has 'the interwoven words in elven-tongues' ('in the Elven-tongue', First Edition) this text has 'the interwoven words in the high elven-tongue'.

The reception of the song moves close to the text of FR (p. 249), but with some differences. No Elf is individually named (*Lindir* in FR). From Bilbo's words about Men and Hobbits – 'They're as different as peas and apples' – this version has:

'No! – little peas and large peas!' said some. 'Their languages all taste much the same to us, anyway,' said others.

'I won't argue with you,' said Bilbo. 'I am sleepy after so much music and singing. I'll leave you to guess, if you want to.'

'Well, we guess that you thought of the first two lines, and Tarkil did all the rest for you,' they cried.

'Wrong! Not even warm; stone cold, in fact!' said Bilbo with a laugh. He got up and came towards Frodo.

'Well, that's over!' he said in a low voice. 'It went off better than I expected. I don't often get asked for a second hearing, for any reason. As a matter of fact quite a lot of it was Tarkil's.'

'I'm not going to try and guess,' said Frodo, smiling. 'I was half asleep when you began – it seemed to follow on from something I was dreaming about, and I didn't realize it was really you who were speaking until near the end.'

The chapter ends now as it does in FR, except that the old form of the chant to Elbereth remains (VI.394), and the passage following it, concerning Aragorn and Arwen, is of course absent.

★

No poem of my father's had so long and complex a history as that which he named *Errantry*. It issued ultimately in two entirely distinct poems, one of which was the song that Bilbo chanted at Rivendell; and this is a convenient place to set out fairly fully the nature of this divergence, this extraordinary shape-changing.

BILBO'S SONG AT RIVENDELL

My father described the origin and nature of *Erranty* in a letter written to Donald Swann on 14 October 1966. (*Errantry* had been published in *The Adventures of Tom Bombadil* in 1962, and it was set to music by Donald Swann in *The Road Goes Ever On*, 1967: see his remarks on the poem in his foreword to that book.) In this letter my father said:

> With regard to *Errantry*: I am most interested in your suggestion. I wonder if it is not too long for such an arrangement? I looked to see if it could be abbreviated; but its metrical scheme, with its trisyllabic near-rhymes, makes this very difficult. It is of course a piece of verbal acrobatics and metrical high-jinks; and was intended for recitation with great variations of speed. It needs a reciter or chanter capable of producing the words with great clarity, but in places with great rapidity. The 'stanzas' as printed indicate the speed-groups. In general these were meant to begin at speed and slow down. Except the last group, which was to begin slowly, and pick up at *errand too!* and end at high speed to match the beginning.[6] Also of course the reciter was supposed at once to begin repeating (at even higher speed) the beginning, unless somebody cried 'Once is enough'.[7]
>
> The piece has had a curious history. It was begun very many years ago, in an attempt to go on with the model that came unbidden into my mind: the first six lines, in which, I guess, *D'ye ken the rhyme to porringer* had a part.[8] Later I read it to an undergraduate club that used to hear its members read unpublished poems or short tales, and voted some of them into the minute book. They invented the name *Inklings*, and not I or Lewis, though we were among the few 'senior' members. (The club lasted the usual year or two of undergraduate societies; and the name became transferred to the circle of C. S. Lewis when only he and I were left of it.)[9] It was at this point that *Errantry* began its travels, starting with a typed copy, and continuing by oral memory and transmission, as I later discovered.

The earliest version that my father retained is a rough pencilled manuscript without title: there were certainly preliminary workings behind it, now lost, since this text was set down without hesitations or corrections, but it seems very probable that it was in fact the first complete text of the poem, possibly that from which he read it to the original 'Inklings' in the early 1930s. The page has many alterations and suggestions leading to the second version, but I give it here as it was first set down.

> There was a merry passenger,
> a messenger, an errander;
> he took a tiny porringer
> and oranges for provender;

86   THE TREASON OF ISENGARD

> he took a little grasshopper
> and harnessed her to carry him;
> he chased a little butterfly
> that fluttered by, to marry him.
> He made him wings of taffeta
> to laugh at her and catch her with;
> he made her shoes of beetle-skin
> with needles in to latch them with.
> They fell to bitter quarrelling,
> and sorrowing he fled away;
> and long he studied sorcery
> in Ossory a many day.
> He made a shield and morion
> of coral and of ivory;
> he made a spear of emerald
> and glimmered all in bravery;
> a sword he made of malachite
> and stalactite, and brandished it,
> he went and fought the dragon-fly
> called wag-on-high and vanquished it.
> He battled with the Dumbledores,
> and bumbles all, and honeybees,
> and won the golden honey-comb,
> and running home on sunny seas,
> in ship of leaves and gossamer
> with blossom for a canopy,
> he polished up and burnished up
> and furbished up his panoply.
> He tarried for a little while
> in little isles, and plundered them;
> and webs of all the attercops
> he shattered, cut, and sundered them.
> And coming home with honey-comb
> and money none – remembered it,
> his message and his errand too!
> His derring-do had hindered it.[10]

Among my father's papers are five further texts, all titled *Errantry*, before the poem's publication in *The Oxford Magazine*, Vol. LII no. 5, 9 November 1933, which I give here. In fact, the form published in 1933 was virtually achieved already in the second version, apart only from the beginning, which went through several stages of development: these are given at the end of the *Oxford Magazine* version.

> There was a merry passenger
> a messenger, a mariner:
> he built a gilded gondola

BILBO'S SONG AT RIVENDELL

to wander in, and had in her
a load of yellow oranges
and porridge for his provender;
he perfumed her with marjoram
and cardamom and lavender.

He called the winds of argosies
with cargoes in to carry him
across the rivers seventeen
that lay between to tarry him.

He landed all in loneliness
where stonily the pebbles on
the running river Derrilyn
goes merrily for ever on.
He wandered over meadow-land
to shadow-land and dreariness,
and under hill and over hill,
a rover still to weariness.

He sat and sang a melody
his errantry a-tarrying;
he begged a pretty butterfly
that fluttered by to marry him.
She laughed at him, deluded him,
eluded him unpitying;
so long he studied wizardry
and sigaldry and smithying.

He wove a tissue airy-thin
to snare her in; to follow in
he made a beetle-leather wing
and feather wing and swallow-wing.
He caught her in bewilderment
in filament of spider-thread;
he built a little bower-house,
a flower house, to hide her head;
he made her shoes of diamond
on fire and a-shimmering;
a boat he built her marvellous,
a carvel all a-glimmering;
he threaded gems in necklaces –
and recklessly she squandered them,
as fluttering, and wavering,
and quavering, they wandered on.

They fell to bitter quarrelling;
and sorrowing he sped away,

THE TREASON OF ISENGARD

on windy weather wearily
and drearily he fled away.

He passed the archipelagoes
where yellow grows the marigold,
where countless silver fountains are,
and mountains are of fairy-gold.
He took to war and foraying
a-harrying beyond the sea,
a-roaming over Belmarie
and Thellamie and Fantasie.

He made a shield and morion
of coral and of ivory,
a sword he made of emerald,
and terrible his rivalry
with all the knights of Aerie
and Faërie and Thellamie.
Of crystal was his habergeon,
his scabbard of chalcedony,
his javelins were of malachite
and stalactite – he brandished them,
and went and fought the dragon-flies
of Paradise, and vanquished them.

He battled with the Dumbledores,
the Bumbles, and the Honeybees,
and won the Golden Honeycomb;
and running home on sunny seas
in ship of leaves and gossamer
with blossom for a canopy,
he polished up, and furbished up,
and burnished up his panoply.

He tarried for a little while
in little isles, and plundered them;
and webs of all the Attercops
he shattered them and sundered them –
Then, coming home with honeycomb
and money none, to memory
his message came and errand too!
In derring-do and glamoury
he had forgot them, journeying,
and tourneying, a wanderer.

So now he must depart again
and start again his gondola,
for ever still a messenger,

BILBO'S SONG AT RIVENDELL

89

> a passenger, a tarrier,
> a-roving as a feather does,
> a weather-driven mariner.[11]

In the second version the poem began thus:

> There was a merry messenger,
> a passenger, an errander;
> he gathered yellow oranges
> in porringer for provender;
> he built a gilded gondola
> a-wandering to carry him
> across the rivers seventeen
> that lay between to tarry him.
>
> He landed there in loneliness
> in stoniness on shingle steep,
> and ventured into meadow-land
> and shadow-land, and dingle deep.
>
> He sat and sang a melody, &c.

The poem otherwise, as I have said, scarcely differs from the *Oxford Magazine* version; but the last four lines were:

> for ever still a-tarrying,
> a mariner, a messenger,
> a-roving as a feather does,
> a weather-driven passenger.[12]

The third version reached the opening of the published form, except that it began 'There was a merry *messenger*, a *passenger*, a mariner', and retained the lines

> He landed all in loneliness
> in stoniness on shingle steep,
> and wandered off to meadowland,
> to shadowland, to dingle deep.

The fourth version reached the published form except in this third verse, which now read:

> He landed all in loneliness
> where stonily on shingle go
> the running rivers Lerion
> and Derion in dingle low.
> He wandered over meadow-land
> to shadow-land and dreariness, &c.

Rayner Unwin mentioned in a letter to my father of 20 June 1952 that he had received an enquiry from someone unnamed about a poem

90 THE TREASON OF ISENGARD

called *Errantry*, 'which made such a deep impression on him that he is most anxious to trace it again.' To this my father replied (22 June 1952, *Letters* no. 133):

> As for 'Errantry': it is a most odd coincidence that you should ask about that. For only a few weeks ago I had a letter from a lady unknown to me making a similar enquiry. She said that a friend had recently written out for her from memory some verses that had so taken her fancy that she was determined to discover their origin. He had picked them up from his son-in-law who had learned them in Washington D.C. (!); but nothing was known about their source save a vague idea that they were connected with English universities. Being a determined person she apparently applied to various Vice-Chancellors, and Bowra[13] directed her to my door. I must say that I was interested in becoming 'folk-lore'. Also it was intriguing to get an oral version – which bore out my views on oral tradition (at any rate in early stages): sc. that the 'hard words' are well preserved,[14] and the more common words altered, but the metre is often disturbed.

In this letter he referred to two versions of *Errantry*, an 'A.V.' ('Authorised Version'), this being the *Oxford Magazine* text, and an 'R.V.' ('Revised Version'). The 'R.V.', in which substantial alterations were made to the 'A.V.', is the text published in *The Adventures of Tom Bombadil* ten years later. – He also said in this letter that the poem was

> in a metre I invented (depending on trisyllabic assonances or near-assonances, which is so difficult that except in this one example I have never been able to use it again – it just blew out in a single impulse).

On this Humphrey Carpenter remarked (*Letters* p. 443):

> It may appear at a first glance that Tolkien did write another poem in this metre, 'Eärendil was a mariner', which appears in Book II Chapter 1 of *The Lord of the Rings*. But this poem is arguably a development of 'Errantry' rather than a separate composition.

That this is true will be seen from the earlier forms of Bilbo's song at Rivendell.

*

There are no less than fifteen manuscript and typescript texts of the 'Rivendell version', and these may be divided into two groups: an earlier, in which the poem begins with the line *There was a merry messenger* (or in one case a variant of it), and a later, in which the poem begins *Earendel was a mariner* (the name being spelt thus in all texts). The textual history of the first group is very complex in detail,

BILBO'S SONG AT RIVENDELL   91

and difficult to unravel with certainty owing to the fact that my father
hesitated back and forth between competing readings in successive
texts.

In the earliest text of all the poem was still in the process of
emergence. The opening lines are here particularly interesting, for they
remain so close to the first verse of *Errantry* as to be scarcely more
than a variant:

> There was a merry messenger
> a passenger a mariner:
> he built a boat and gilded her,
> and silver oars he fashioned her;
> he perfumed her with marjoram
> and cardamon[15] and lavender,
> and laded her with oranges
> and porridge for his provender.

Eärendel is hardly present here! Yet this initial text at once moves
away from *Errantry*, and the new poem in its first 'phase' was already
quite largely achieved in this manuscript. It was followed, no doubt
immediately, by the version that I print below. It is indeed extremely
difficult and even unreal to delimit 'versions' in such cases, where my
father was refining and enlarging the poem in a continuous process;
but this second text was originally set down as if in a finished and final
form, and in this form I give it here.[16]

> There was a gallant passenger
> a messenger, a mariner:
> he built a boat and gilded her
> and silver oars he fashioned her;
> her sails he wove of gossamer
> and blossom of the cherry-tree,
> and lightly as a feather
> in the weather went she merrily.   8
>
> He floated from a haven fair
> of maiden-hair and everfern;
> the waterfalls he proudly rode
> where loudly flowed the Merryburn;
> and dancing on the foam he went
> on roving bent for ever on,
> from Evermorning journeying,
> while murmuring the River on   16
> to valleys in the gloaming ran;
> and slowly then on pillow cool
> he laid his head, and fast asleep
> he passed the Weepingwillow Pool.

THE TREASON OF ISENGARD

The windy reeds were whispering,
and mists were in the meadow-land,
and down the River hurried him
and carried him to Shadowland.   24

The Sea beside a stony shore
there lonely roared, and under Moon
a wind arose and wafted him
a castaway beyond the Moon.

He woke again forlorn afar
by shores that are without a name,
and by the Shrouded Island o'er
the Silent Water floating came.   32

He passed the archipelagoes
where yellow grows the marigold,
and landed on the Elven-strands
of silver sand and fallow gold,
beneath the Hill of Ilmarin
where glimmer in a valley sheer
the lights of Elven Tirion,
the city on the Shadowmere.   40

He tarried there his errantry,
and melodies they taught to him,
and lays of old, and marvels told,
and harps of gold they brought to him.
Of glamoury he tidings heard,
and binding words of sigaldry;
of wars they spoke with Enemies
that venom used and wizardry.   48

In panoply of Elvenkings,
in silver rings they armoured him;
his shield they writ with elven-runes,
that never wound did harm to him.
His bow was made of dragon-horn,
his arrows shorn of ebony,
of woven steel his habergeon,
his scabbard of chalcedony.   56
His sword was hewn of adamant,
and valiant the might of it;
his helm a shining emerald,
and terrible the light of it.

His boat anew for him they built
of timber felled in Elvenhome;
upon the mast a star was set,

BILBO'S SONG AT RIVENDELL

its spars were wet with silver foam;   64
and wings of swans they made for it,
and laid on it a mighty doom
to sail the seas of wind and come
where glimmering runs the gliding moon.[17]

From Evereven's lofty hills,
where softly spill the fountains tall,
he passed away, a wandering light
beyond the mighty Mountain-wall;   72
and unto Evernight he came,
and like a flaming star he fell:
his javelins of diamond
as fire into the darkness fell.
Ungoliant abiding there
in Spider-lair her thread entwined;
for endless years a gloom she spun
the Sun and Moon in web to wind.[18]   80

His sword was like a flashing light
as flashing bright he smote with it;
he shore away her poisoned neb, ꞌ
her noisome webs he broke with it.
Then shining as a risen star
from prison bars he sped away,
and borne upon a blowing wind
on flowing wings he fled away.   88

To Evernoon at last he came,
and passed the flame-encircled hill,
where wells of gold for Melineth
her never-resting workers build.
His eyes with fire ablaze were set,
his face was lit with levin-light;
and turning to his home afar,
a roaming star at even-light   96
on high above the mists he came,
a distant flame, a marineer
on winds unearthly swiftly borne,
uplifted o'er the Shadowmere.
He passed o'er Carakilian,
where Tirion the Hallowed stands;
the sea far under loudly roared
on cloudy shores in Shadowland.   104

And over Evermorn he passed,
and saw at last the haven fair,
far under by the Merry-burn

94 THE TREASON OF ISENGARD

in everfern and maidenhair.
But on him mighty doom was laid,
till moon should fade and all the stars,
to pass, and tarry never more
on hither shore where mortals are,   112
for ever still a passenger,
a messenger, to never rest,
to bear his burning lamp afar,
the Flammifer of Westernesse.

The chief changes introduced on this manuscript were in lines 14–17, altered to read:

on roving bent from hitherland,
from Evermorning journeying,
while murmuring the River ran
to valleys in the Gloaming fields

and in lines 93–6, which were rewritten and extended thus:

The seven-branchéd Levin-tree
on Heavenfield he shining saw
upflowering from its writhen root;
a living fruit of fire it bore.
The lightning in his face was lit,
ablaze were set his tresses wan,
his eyes with levin-beams were bright,
and gleaming white his vessel shone.

From World's End then he turned away
and yearned again to seek afar
his land beneath the morning light
and burning like a beacon star
(on high above the mists he came, &c.)

The *seven-branchéd Levin-tree* was first *everbranching*, and it bore *a living fruit of light*.

The third version was that in the text of 'Many Meetings' described at the beginning of this chapter. The pages in that manuscript (at Marquette) bearing the poem have been lost, but Taum Santoski has provided me with a transcription of the pages that he made before the loss occurred. This text was remarkably close to the second version (as emended) printed above. The opening now returns to *There was a merry messenger;*[19] *from Evermorning* in line 15 becomes *through Evermorning*; *the Weepingwillow Pool* in line 20 becomes *Pools* (a return to the earliest workings); and lines 67–8 become:

to sail the windy skies and come
behind the Sun and light of Moon.

BILBO'S SONG AT RIVENDELL

95

This, then, was the form at the time we have reached. It will be seen that in this poem the Merry Messenger, the Passenger, the Mariner, 'changes shape' and emerges as the figure of Eärendel (though he is not named). At the beginning he *dances on the foam* in his boat with *sails of gossamer and blossom of the cherry-tree*, and he still *passed the archipelagoes where yellow grows the marigold*, but he is drawn into the gravity of the myth and *mighty doom* is laid on him; the dance dies out of the verse, and he ends as the *Flammifer of Westernesse*. There is no question now of returning to the beginning, even though the fate of Eärendel remains that of the Merry Messenger: *for ever still a passenger, a messenger, to never rest...*

Many years later my father ingeniously related the two poems thus, in the Preface to *The Adventures of Tom Bombadil* – when the Eärendel version was of course that given in FR:

> [Errantry] was evidently made by Bilbo. This is indicated by its obvious relationship to the long poem recited by Bilbo, as his own composition, in the house of Elrond. In origin a 'nonsense rhyme', it is in the Rivendell version found transformed and applied, some-what incongruously, to the High-elvish and Númenorean legends of Eärendil. Probably because Bilbo invented its metrical devices and was proud of them. They do not appear in other pieces in the Red Book. The older form, here given, must belong to the early days after Bilbo's return from his journey. Though the influence of Elvish traditions is seen, they are not seriously treated, and the names used (*Derrilyn, Thellamie, Belmarie, Aerie*) are mere inventions in the Elvish style, and are not in fact Elvish at all.

Yet the places of Eärendel's journey in this first phase of the Rivendell version are not by any means entirely identifiable in terms of *The Silmarillion*. Was his journey to the Sea a journey down Sirion? Are *the Weepingwillow Pools* Nan-tathren, the Land of Willows? Or are they still 'mere inventions in the *Silmarillion* style'? And what of *the seven-branchéd Levin-tree on Heavenfield*, and *the wells of gold for Melineth* that *her never-resting workers build*? These certainly do not suggest 'mere invention' like *Thellamie* or *Derrilyn*.

Some names are in any case clear in their reference: as *Tirion* (in the *Quenta Silmarillion* still named *Tûn* or *Túna*, upon the hill of Kôr), *Carakilian* (in the *Quenta Silmarillion* in the form *Kalakilya*, the Pass of Light). *The Hill of Ilmarin* (a name not met before) is Taniquetil, and *the mighty Mountain-wall* is the Pelóri, the Mountains of Valinor. *The Shadowmere* perhaps looks back to the 'shadowy arm of water', the 'slender water fringed with white', which is described in the old tale of *The Coming of the Elves* (I.122). *The Shrouded Island* is perhaps the Lonely Isle: it was subsequently changed to *the Shrouded Islands*, but then became *the Lonely Island* before the line was lost. That Eärendel slew Ungoliant 'in the South' is recorded in the *Sketch*

96 THE TREASON OF ISENGARD

of the Mythology (IV.38), and in the *Quenta Noldorinwa* (IV.149, 152); cf. also the very early notes on Eärendel's voyages, II.254, 261.[20]

But the legend of Eärendel as found in the existing sources is not present here.[21] Indeed, it seems as if he arose unbidden and unlooked for as my father wrote this new version of the poem: for how could Eärendel be called *a merry messenger?* Years later, in the Preface to *The Adventures of Tom Bombadil* just cited, my father described the transformation as 'somewhat incongruous' – and he was then referring of course to the form of the poem in FR, where the transformation had gone far deeper than in the present version. Yet there was a 'congruity' that made this original transformation possible, and even natural. Behind both figures lay the sustaining idea of the wanderer, a restless spirit who seeks back to the places of his origin, but cannot escape the necessity of passing on. At this stage therefore we should not, I believe, try to determine where was Evernoon, or to give any other name to

> the haven fair,
> far under by the Merry-burn
> in everfern and maidenhair.

They belong to the same geography as *the archipelagoes where yellow grows the marigold.*

Following the third version, lost but happily not unknown, there are six further texts in the 'Merry Messenger' phase. Five of these are typescripts that can be readily placed in order. The sixth is a beautiful small manuscript, written on four slips of paper the last of which is the back of a letter addressed to my father and dated 13 December 1944. Precisely where the manuscript comes in this series is not perfectly clear, but it seems most likely to have preceded the first typescript.[22] Thus there was an interval of several years between the first three and the next six texts. Progressive emendation of these gave a final version in this 'phase':

> There was a merry messenger,
> a passenger, a mariner:
> he built a boat and gilded her,
> and silver oars he fashioned her;
> her sails he wove of gossamer
> and blossom of the cherry-tree
> and lightly as a feather in
> the weather went she merrily.   8
>
> He floated from a haven fair
> of maidenhair and ladyfern;
> the waterfalls he proudly rode
> where loudly flowed the Merryburn;
> and dancing on the foam he went

BILBO'S SONG AT RIVENDELL

on roving bent from Hitherland
through Evermorning journeying,
while murmuring the river ran   16
to valleys in the Gloaming-fields;
then slowly he on pillow cool
let fall his head, and fast asleep
he passed the Weeping-willow Pools.

The windy reeds were whispering,
and mists were in the meadowland,
and down the river hurried him,
and carried him to Shadowland.   24
He heard there moan in stony caves
the lonely waves; there roaring blows
the mighty wind of Tarmenel.
By paths that seldom mortal goes
his boat it wafted pitiless
with bitter breath across the grey
and long-forsaken seas distressed;
from East to West he passed away.   32

Through Evernight then borne afar
by waters dark beyond the Day
he saw the Lonely Island rise
where twilight lies upon the Bay
of Valinor, of Elvenhome,
and ever-foaming billows roll;
he landed on the elven-strands
of silver sand and yellow gold   40
beneath the Hill of Ilmarin,
where glimmer in a valley sheer
the lights of towering Tirion,
the city on the Shadowmere.

He tarried there from errantry,
and melodies they taught to him,
and lays of old and marvels told,
and harps of gold they brought to him.   48
Of glamoury he tidings heard,
and binding words of wizardry;
they spoke of wars with Enemies
that venom used and sigaldry.

In panoply of Elven-kings,
in silver rings they armoured him;
his shield they writ with elven-runes
that never wound did harm to him.   56
His bow was made of dragon-horn,

his arrows shorn of ebony,
of mithril was his habergeon,
his scabbard of chalcedony.
His sword of steel was valiant;
of adamant his helm was wrought,
an argent wing of swan his crest;
upon his breast an emerald.   64

His boat anew they built for him
of timber felled in Elvenhome;
upon the mast a star was set,
her spars were wet with driven foam;
and eagle-wings they made for her,
and laid on her a mighty doom,
to sail the windy skies and come
behind the Sun and light of Moon.   72

From Evereven's lofty hills,
where softly silver fountains fall,
he passed away a wandering light
beyond the mighty Mountain Wall.
From World's End then he turned away,
and yearned again to seek afar
his land beneath the morning-light;
and burning like a beacon-star   80
on high above the mists he came,
a distant flame, a mariner,
on winds unearthly swiftly borne,
uplifted o'er the Shadowmere.

He passed o'er Calacirian,
where Tirion the hallowed stands;
the Sea below him loudly roared
on cloudy shores in Shadowland;   88
and over Evermorn he passed
and saw at last the haven fair
far under by the Merryburn
in ladyfern and maidenhair.

But on him mighty doom was laid,
till Moon should fade, an orbéd star
to pass and tarry never more
on Hither Shores where mortals are;   96
for ever still a passenger,
a messenger, to never rest,
to bear the burning lamp afar,
the Flammifer of Westernesse.

BILBO'S SONG AT RIVENDELL
99

The major change in the poem, rendering it substantially shorter than before, had come about in two stages. By emendation to the second of these typescripts the original lines 25–8 (p. 92) became:

The Sea beside a stony shore
there lonely roared; and wrathful rose
a wind on high in Tarmenel,
by paths that seldom mortal goes
on flying wings it passed away,
and wafted him beyond the grey
and long-forsaken seas distressed
from East or West that sombre lay.

In this text the remainder of the poem was unaffected by any important changes, and remained close to the original form (with of course the alterations given on p. 94). In the last two of these typescripts, however, a new form of lines 25 ff. entered, as given above: *He heard there moan in stony caves*, &c.[23] Now *Evernight* is named at this point, and at the same time the entire section of the poem in the existing text from line 73 *and unto Evernight he came* to *From World's End then he turned away* (pp. 93–4) was eliminated, with the disappearance of Ungoliant and the mysterious scenes of Evernoon, the 'Tree of Lightning' with its seven branches and the *wells of gold for Melineth* in *the flame-encircled hill*.

*

While I certainly do not know this as a fact, I think that there is a strong presumption that there was a further long interval between the 'Merry Messenger' versions and the second group beginning *Eärendel was a mariner*.

The first text of this group, which I will for convenience call A, I give in full. It will be seen that while it advances far towards the poem in FR, much is retained from the preceding version, and notably the arming of Eärendel (*In panoply of Elven-kings*..., p. 97 lines 53 ff.) stands in its former place, during his sojourn in Tirion, and not as in FR at the beginning of his great voyage.

Eärendel was a mariner
that tarried in Arvernien;
he built a boat of timber felled
in Nimbrethil to journey in;
her sails he wove of silver fair
of silver were her lanterns made,
her prow he fashioned like a swan,
and light upon her banners laid.   8

Beneath the moon and under star
he wandered far from northern strands,

THE TREASON OF ISENGARD

bewildered on enchanted ways
beyond the days of mortal lands.
From gnashing of the Narrow Ice
where shadow lies on frozen hills,
from nether heat and burning waste
he turned in haste, and roving still   16
on starless waters far astray
at last he came to night of Naught,
and passed, and never sight he saw
of shining shore nor light he sought.
The winds of wrath came driving him,
and blindly in the foam he fled
from West to East, and errandless,
unheralded he homeward sped.   24

As bird then Elwing came to him,
and flame was in her carcanet,
more bright than light of diamond
was fire that on her heart was set.
The Silmaril she bound on him
and crowned him with a living light,
and dauntless then with burning brow
he turned his prow, and in the night   32
from otherworld beyond the Sea
there strong and free a storm arose,
a wind of power in Tarmenel;
by paths that seldom mortal goes
his boat it bore with mighty breath
as driving death across the grey
and long-forsaken seas distressed;
from East to West he passed away.   40

Through Evernight then borne afar
by waters dark beyond the Day,
he saw the Lonely Island rise,
where twilight lies upon the Bay
of Valinor, of Elvenhome,
and ever-foaming billows roll.
He landed on forbidden strands
of silver sand and yellow gold;   48
beneath the Hill of Ilmarin
a-glimmer in a valley sheer
the lamps of towering Tirion
were mirrored on the Shadowmere.

He tarried there from errantry
and melodies they taught to him,

BILBO'S SONG AT RIVENDELL

and lays of old and marvels told,
and harps of gold they brought to him.
In panoply of Elven-kings,
in serried rings they armoured him;
his shield they writ with elven-runes
that never wound did harm to him,
his bow was made of dragon-horn,
his arrows shorn of ebony,
of silver was his habergeon,
his scabbard of chalcedony;
his sword of steel was valiant,
of adamant his helmet tall,
an argent flame upon his crest,
upon his breast an emerald.

His boat anew they built for him
of mithril and of elven-glass;
the Silmaril was hanging bright
as lantern light on slender mast;
and eagle-wings they made for her,
and laid on her a mighty doom,
to sail the shoreless skies and come
behind the Sun and light of Moon.

From Evereven's lofty hills,
where softly silver fountains fall,
he rose on high, a wandering light
beyond the mighty Mountain Wall.
From World's End then he turned away,
and yearned again to seek afar
his land beneath the morning-light,
and burning like a beacon-star
on high above the mists he came,
a distant flame, a marineer,
on winds unearthly swiftly borne,
uplifted o'er the Shadowmere.

He passed o'er Calacirian
where Tirion the hallowed stands;
the sea below him loudly roared
on cloudy shores in Shadowland;
and over Middle-earth he passed,
and heard at last the weeping sore
of women and of Elven-maids
in Elder Days, in years of yore.

But on him mighty doom was laid,
till Moon should fade, an orbéd star,

102   THE TREASON OF ISENGARD

> to pass, and tarry never more
> on Hither Shores where mortals are;
> for ever still on errand, as
> a herald that should never rest,
> to bear his shining lamp afar,
> the Flammifer of Westernesse.   104

The next text (B) is a typescript of A, but introduces some minor changes that were retained in the FR version (*his boat it bore with biting breath / as might of death* 37–8, *the lamplit towers of Tirion* 51), and line 25 is here *Bird-Elwing thither came to him*. My father then used this typescript B as the vehicle for massive rewriting, including the movement of the 'arming of Eärendel' to its later place as the second stanza. A new typescript (C)[24] was made incorporating all this, and the form of the poem in FR was now virtually achieved; a very few further minor changes were made, and entered on this text.[25] Careful examination of these texts shows the development from A to the published form with perfect clarity.

But the history of this, perhaps the most protean, in its scale, of all my father's works, does not end here. It ends, in fact, in the most extraordinary way.

This text C was not the last, although the published form of the poem was achieved in it. Another typescript (D) was made, doubtless at the same time as C, and given the title *The Short Lay of Eärendel*. In this, a new element entered at the beginning of the fourth stanza (*There flying Elwing came to him*): the attack of the four surviving sons of Fëanor on the Havens of Sirion, Elwing's casting herself into the sea, bearing the Silmaril, and her transformation into a seabird, in which guise she flew to meet Eärendel returning (IV.152–3).

> In wrath the Fëanorians
> that swore the unforgotten oath
> brought war into Arvernien
> with burning and with broken troth;
> and Elwing from her fastness dim
> then cast her in the roaring seas,
> but like a bird was swiftly borne,
> uplifted o'er the roaring wave.
> Through hopeless night she came to him
> and flame was in the darkness lit,
> more bright than light of diamond
> the fire upon her carcanet.
> The Silmaril she bound on him (&c.)

There then followed a fine manuscript (E), with elaborate initials to the stanzas, and this was entitled *The Short Lay of Eärendel:*

BILBO'S SONG AT RIVENDELL

Eärendillinwë. In this text a rewriting of lines 5–8, which had been entered in the margin of D, appears:

> Her woven sails were white as snow,
> as flying foam her banner flowed;
> her prow was fashioned like a swan
> that white upon the Falas goes.

But my father abandoned E at the foot of the first page, the end of the third stanza, and the reason why he abandoned it was that he had already begun to rewrite in the margin both the lines just given and also the second stanza (*In panoply of ancient kings*). So he began once again, with a very similar and equally beautiful manuscript (F), bearing the same title; and this was completed. The revisions made to D and to E (so far as that went) were taken up; and this manuscript remained intact, without the smallest further change.

It was in fact the last, the ultimate development of the poem. The history I have attempted to convey is schematically thus:

A – B { – C (the form in FR achieved)
{ – D – E – F (the ultimate form of the poem)

I have studied all these texts at length and at different times, and it had always seemed strange to me that the chain of development led at last to a superb manuscript (F) without any disfigurement through later changes, but which was *not* the form found in FR. The solution was at last provided by the text C at Marquette, which showed that there were *two lines of development* from B.

What actually happened one can only surmise. I believe the most likely explanation to be that the texts D, E, F were mislaid, and that at the crucial time the version represented by C went to the publishers, as it should not have done. It looks also as if these lost texts did not turn up again until many years had passed, by which time my father no longer remembered the history. In what are obviously very late notes he went so far as to analyse their readings in relation to the published form, and was evidently as puzzled as I was: his analysis at that time contains demonstrably incorrect conclusions – because he assumed, as I did, that all these texts must have *preceded* the 'final form' in FR.

I give finally the *Eärendillinwë* in the form in which it should have been published.[26]

Stanza 1   Eärendil was a mariner
that tarried in Arvernien:
he built a boat of timber felled
in Nimbrethil to journey in.
Her sails he wove of silver fair,
with silver were her banners sewn;
her prow he fashioned like the swans
that white upon the Falas roam.

104   THE TREASON OF ISENGARD

Stanza 2   His coat that came from ancient kings
of chainéd rings was forged of old;
his shining shield all wounds defied,
with runes entwined of dwarven gold.
His bow was made of dragon-horn,
his arrows shorn of ebony,
of triple steel his habergeon,
his scabbard of chalcedony;
his sword was like a flame in sheath,
with gems was wreathed his helmet tall,
an eagle-plume upon his crest,
upon his breast an emerald.

Stanza 3   As in FR, but with *winds of fear* for *winds of wrath* in line
13 of the stanza.

Stanza 4   In might the Fëanorians
that swore the unforgotten oath
brought war into Arvernien
with burning and with broken troth;
and Elwing from her fastness dim
then cast her in the waters wide,
but like a mew was swiftly borne,
uplifted o'er the roaring tide.
Through hopeless night she came to him,
and flame was in the darkness lit,
more bright than light of diamond
the fire upon her carcanet.
The Silmaril she bound on him,
and crowned him with the living light,
and dauntless then with burning brow
he turned his prow at middle-night.
Beyond the world, beyond the Sea,
then strong and free a storm arose,
a wind of power in Tarmenel;
by paths that seldom mortal goes
from Middle-earth on mighty breath
as flying wraith across the grey
and long-forsaken seas distressed
from East to West he passed away.

Stanza 5   As in FR.

Stanza 6   As in FR, but with a difference in the twelfth line:[27]

for ever king on mountain sheer;

Stanza 7   A ship then new they built for him
of mithril and of elvenglass

BILBO'S SONG AT RIVENDELL   105

with crystal keel; no shaven oar
nor sail she bore, on silver mast
the Silmaril as lantern light
and banner bright with living flame
of fire unstained by Elbereth
herself was set, who thither came (&c. as in FR)

Stanza 8   As in FR.

Stanza 9   As in FR except at the end:

till end of Days on errand high,
a herald bright that never rests,
to bear his burning lamp afar,
the Flammifer of Westernesse.

Only one line survived now from *Errantry* (as published in 1933):
his scabbard of chalcedony.

NOTES

1   This suggests that the story of Gandalf's captivity found in the 'New Plot' of August 1940 was present (p. 71): 'Saramund betrays him ... he tells Gandalf false news of the Black Riders, and they pursue him to the top of a mountain...' The final story of what had happened to Gandalf (set to stand on the pinnacle of Orthanc) first appears in this period of the work (pp. 131 ff.).

2   Changed in pencil later to *Elfstone son of Elfhelm*; see p. 80 note 17. At one occurrence of Trotter in this passage, where Gandalf names him, this too was changed to *Elfstone*; at the other two *Trotter* was retained, since it is Frodo who is speaking.

3   In a preliminary draft for this passage Frodo says 'in wonder': 'Is he of that race?' Then follows:

'Didn't he tell you, and didn't you guess?' said Gandalf. 'He could have told you even more: he is Aragorn son of Kelegorn, descended through many fathers from Isildur the son of Elendil.'

'Then It belongs to him as much as to me or more!' said Frodo.

'It does not belong to either of you,' said Gandalf; 'but you, my good hobbit, are to keep it for a while. For so it is ordained.'

This was the second time that this dialogue had been used; it first occurred at Bree between Trotter and Frodo (p. 50), when Gandalf named Aragorn as a descendant of Elendil in his letter, but this had now been removed (p. 77). It was finally used in 'The Council of Elrond'.

106   THE TREASON OF ISENGARD

4   See p. 43 and note 3. The words 'I stayed at *The Pony* in Bree for
     a bit' were crossed out before the rest of the passage was changed,
     perhaps at the time of writing.
5   On *Tarkil* see p. 8. *Westernesse*: Númenor.
6   In the version of *Errantry* published in 1962 the last stanza began
     not as in the 1933 *Oxford Magazine* version but at *He tarried for
     a little while* (p. 88).
7   One of the early texts has the head-note: 'Elaboration of the
     well-known pastime of the never-ending Tale'; and at the end,
     after the last line *a weather-driven mariner*, returns to *He called
     the winds of argosies* in the second verse (p. 87), with the note: *da
     capo, ad lib, et ad naus.*
8   I cannot explain this reference.
9   See Humphrey Carpenter, *The Inklings*, pp. 56–7; also *Letters*
     no. 133 (to Rayner Unwin, 22 June 1952) and no. 298 (to W. L.
     White, 11 September 1967).
10   *morion*: helmet. *bravery*: splendour, finery. *dumbledore*:
     bumble-bee. *panoply*: suit of armour. *attercop*: spider (Old
     English *attor* 'poison'; cf. *cobweb*, 'cop-web'). Bilbo called the
     spiders in Mirkwood *Attercop*.
         On the back of the page, with every appearance of having been
     written at the same time, is a section of a dramatic dialogue in
     rhyming verse that preceded by more than twenty years the
     publication of *The Homecoming of Beorhtnoth Beorhthelm's
     Son* in *Essays and Studies*, 1953. The Englishmen who took the
     body of Beorhtnoth from the battlefield at Maldon are here called
     Pudda and Tibba. – *Panta* (Old English) is the river Blackwater.

Pudda   Come, hurry. There may be more. Let's get away
            Or have the pirate pack on us.
Tibba   Nay, nay.
            These are no Northmen. What should such come for?
            They are all in Ipswich drinking to Thor.
            These have got what they deserved, not what they
            sought.
Pudda   God help us, when Englishmen can be brought
            By any need to prowl like carrion-bird
            And plunder their own.
Tibba   There goes a third
            In the shadows yonder. He will not wait,
            That sort fight no odds, early or late,
            But sneak in when all's over. Up again!
            Steady once more.
Pudda   Say, Tibba, where's the wain?
            I wish we were at it! By the bridge you say –
            Well, we're nearer the bank. 'Tis more this way,
            If we're not to walk in Panta, and the tide's in.

BILBO'S SONG AT RIVENDELL

Tibba Right! here we are.
Pudda How did they win
Over the bridge, think you? There's little sign
Here of bitter fight. And yet here the brine
Should have been choked with 'em, but on the planks
There's only one lying.
Tibba Well, God have thanks.
We're over! Gently! Up now, up! That's right.
Get up beside. There's a cloth; none too white,
But cover him over, and think of a prayer. I'll drive.
Pudda Heaven grant us good journey, and that we arrive!
Where do we take him? How these wheels creak!
Tibba To Ely! Where else?
Pudda A long road!
Tibba For the weak.
A short road for the dead – and you can sleep.

This text is extremely rough, one would say in the first stage of composition, were there not another text still rougher, but in very much the same words (though with no ascription of the speeches to speakers), in the Bodleian Library, where it is preserved (I believe) with my father's pictures. This begins at *In the shadows yonder* and continues a few lines further. On it my father wrote: 'early version in rhyme of Beorhtnoth'.

11 *sigaldry*: sorcery (see note 14). *glamoury*: magic.

12 Preliminary lines of a new ending were written on the manuscript of the first version:

So now he must depart again
and start again his gondola,
a silly merry passenger,
a messenger, an errander,
a jolly, merry featherbrain,
a weathervane, a mariner.

Other differences in the second version from that published in 1933 were:

he wrought her raiment marvellous
and garments all a-glimmering

in the fifth verse; and 'He made a *sword* and morion' in the eighth (with *spear* for *sword* in the third line).

13 Maurice Bowra, at that time Vice-Chancellor of Oxford University.

14 In the letter to Donald Swann cited on p. 85 my father gave an example of this (Swann had himself known the poem by 'independent tradition' for many years before its publication in *The Adventures of Tom Bombadil*): 'A curious feature was the preservation of the word *sigaldry*, which I got from a 13th century text (and is last recorded in the Chester Play of the

108   THE TREASON OF ISENGARD

Crucifixion).' The word goes back to the second version of *Errantry*; it was used also in the *Lay of Leithian* line 2072, written in 1928 (*The Lays of Beleriand*, p. 228).

15   *cardamon* is so spelt, but *cardamom* in preliminary rough workings, as in the *Oxford Magazine* version of *Errantry*.

16   I ignore all variants (though a few, as *merry* written above *gallant* in line 1, *ladyfern* above *everfern* in line 10) may belong to the time of writing. A few inconsistencies of hyphenation are preserved. In the latter part of the poem the stanza-divisions are not perfectly clear. Line-numbers at intervals of 8 are marked on the original.

17   This verse is absent from the first text, but a space was left for it, with the note: 'They enchant his boat and give it wings'.

18   A four-line stanza follows here:

> She caught him in her stranglehold
> entangled all in ebon thread,
> and seven times with sting she smote
> his ringéd coat with venom dread.

But this was struck out, apparently at once, since the line-numbering does not take account of it. – *ebon*: old form for *ebony*; here meaning 'black, dark'.

19   In the second version (that printed here) *merry* was written as a variant to *gallant*; in the third *gallant* is a variant to *merry*.

20   The encounter of the Messenger with the Attercops in *Errantry* was a point of contact with the Eärendel legend.

21   The texts are found in II.252–77; IV.37–8, 41, 148–54; V.324–9.

22   The manuscript was perhaps a development from the third version parallel to the first typescript, for it takes up certain variants from the former (as *everfern* in line 10, *Gloaming-bree* (bree 'hill') in line 17), where the first typescript takes up others (*ladyfern*, *Gloaming-fields*).

23   An intermediate version of these lines was:

> He heard there moan in stony caves
> the lonely waves of Orfalas;
> the winds he heard of Tarmenel:
> by paths that seldom mortals pass
> they wafted him on flying wings
> a dying thing across the grey
> and long-forsaken seas distressed;
> from East to West he passed away.

24   This is the typescript of 'Many Meetings' that followed the version described at the beginning of this chapter.

25   These were made on B also, and so appear in the other line of development as well.

26   It could be argued of course that my father actually *rejected* all

BILBO'S SONG AT RIVENDELL

the subsequent development after the text C, deciding that that was the version desirable at all points; but this would seem to me to be wholly improbable and far-fetched.

27 This case is slightly different, in that it is the only point where text C does not reach the form in FR (*in Ilmarin on mountain sheer*), but has the line found also in D (followed by E and F), *for ever king on mountain sheer*. This must have been a final emendation in the 'first line' of development, and might of course have been made to the 'second line' as well if that had been available.

VI

THE COUNCIL OF ELROND (1)

The Second Version

A new version of this part of the narrative[1] is a characteristic 'fair copy': too close to the preceding text (VI.399 ff.) to justify the space needed to set it out, but constantly differing in the expression chosen. The chapter is numbered XIV (see p. 81), but has no title.

The story was still that Bilbo and Gandalf came to Frodo's room in the morning (VI.395); and those present at the Council were in no way changed (VI.400). Boromir still comes from 'the Land of Ond, far in the South'.[2] The first important change comes after Gandalf's speech, in which he 'made clear to those who did not already know it the tale of the Ring, and the reasons why the Dark Lord so greatly desired it.' Here, in the original version, Bilbo's story followed; but in this text the following passage enters:

When he told of Elendil and Gilgalad and of their march into the East, Elrond sighed. 'I remember well their array,' he said. 'It reminded me of the Great Wars and victories of Beleriand, so many fair captains and princes were there, and yet not so many or so fair as when Thangorodrim was broken [> taken].'

'You remember?' said Frodo, breaking silence in his astonishment, and gazing in wonder at Elrond. 'But I thought the fall of Gilgalad was many ages ago.'

'So it was,' said Elrond, looking gravely at Frodo; 'but my memory reaches back many ages. I was the minstrel and counsellor of Gilgalad. My father was Eärendel, who was born in Gondolin, seven years before it fell; and my mother was Elwing, daughter of [Dior, son of] Lúthien, daughter of Thingol, King of Doriath; and I have seen many ages in the West of the World. I knew Beleriand before it was broken in the great wars.'

This is the origin of the passage in FR p. 256; but it goes back to and follows quite closely part of an earlier and isolated writing, given in VI.215–16,[3] in which the story of Gil-galad and Elendil was told at much greater length by Elrond to Bingo, apparently in a personal

Second Version   THE COUNCIL OF ELROND (1)   **111**

conversation between them; and that text was in turn closely related to the conclusion of the second version of *The Fall of Númenor* (V.28–9).

The new text continues:

They passed then from the winning and losing of the Ring to Bilbo's story; and once more he told how he had found it in the cave of the Misty Mountains. Then Aragorn took up the tale, and spoke of the hunt for Gollum, in which he had aided Gandalf, and of his [> their] perilous journey through southern Mirkwood, and into Fangorn Forest, and over the Dead Marshes to the very borders of the land of Mordor. In this way the history was brought slowly down to the spring morning ... (&c. as VI.401).

In the first version Trotter was still the hobbit Peregrin, with his wooden shoes (VI.401 and note 20).

Gandalf in his reply to Elrond's question about Bombadil 'Do you know him, Gandalf?' now says:

'Yes. And I went to him at once, naturally, as soon as I found that the hobbits had gone into the Old Forest. I dare say he would have kept them longer in his house, if he had known that I was so near. But I am not sure – not sure that he did not know, and not sure that he would have behaved differently in any case. He is a very strange creature, and follows his own counsels: and they are not easy to fathom.'

It seems that when my father wrote this he cannot have had in mind the outline dated August 26–27 1940, in which Gandalf arrived at Crickhollow and found it deserted (p. 72), since Gandalf could only have learnt from Hamilcar Bolger that the other hobbits had gone into the Old Forest. On the other hand my father was still uncertain (p. 72), in that outline and with that plot, whether Gandalf had visited Bombadil or not. At any rate, by what looks to be an almost immediate change, the wizard's remarks were rewritten:

'I know of him, though we seldom meet. I am a rolling stone, and he is a gatherer of moss. Both have a work to do, but they do not help one another often. It might have been wiser to have sought his aid, but I do not think I should have gained much. He is a strange creature...'

It must have been at this point that my father finally decided that there had been no visit to Bombadil, and the story reverted to its earlier form (see VI.413 note 23).

The sentence in Gandalf's reply to Erestor 'I doubt whether Tom

112 THE TREASON OF ISENGARD

Bombadil alone, even on his own ground, could withstand that Power'[4] (VI.402) was soon rewritten thus (anticipating in part both Gandalf and Glorfindel in FR p. 279): 'Whether Bombadil alone, even on his own ground, could withstand that Power is beyond all guessing. I think not; and in the end, if all else is conquered, Tom will fall: last as he was first, and the Night will come. He would likely enough throw the Ring away, for such things have no part in his mind.'

Glóin's answer to Boromir's question concerning the Seven Rings remains almost exactly as it was (VI.403–4),[5] but Elrond's reply to the question about the Three Rings has certain changes: notably, he now states as a fact known to him what Gandalf (in 'Ancient History', VI.320) had asserted only as his belief: 'The Three Rings remain still. But wisely they have been taken over the Sea, and are not now in Middle-earth.' He continues:

From them the Elvenkings have derived much power, but they have not availed them in their strife with Sauron. For they can give no skill or knowledge that he did not himself already possess at their making. To each race the rings of the Lord bring such power as each desires and can best wield. The Elves desired not strength, or domination, or hoarded wealth, but subtlety of craft and lore and knowledge of the secrets of the world's being. These things they have gained, yet with sorrow. But all in their mind and heart which is derived from the rings will turn to their undoing, and become revealed to Sauron, if he regains the Ruling Ring, as was his purpose.'

The omission here of the words in the original text 'For they came from Sauron himself' does not, I think, show that the conception of the independence of the Three Rings of the Elves from Sauron had arisen, in view of the following words which were retained: 'For they can give no skill or knowledge that he did not himself already possess at their making'; moreover Boromir still in his question concerning them says that 'these too were made by Sauron in the elder days', and he is not contradicted. See further pp. 155–6.

The next text then follows the old very closely indeed (VI.404–7), until the point where Gandalf, in the afternoon following the Council, overtakes Frodo, Merry, and Faramond (still so called, with Peregrin written in later) walking in the woods; and here the new version diverges for a stretch, Gandalf's remarks about the composition of the Company being quite different – and not only because Trotter is now Aragorn: a doubt here appears about the inclusion of the two younger hobbits.

'... So be careful! You can't be too careful. As for the rest of the party, it is too soon to discuss that. But whether any of you go

Second Version THE COUNCIL OF ELROND (1) **113**

with Frodo or not, I shall make other arrangements for the supply of intelligence.'

'Ah! Now we know who really is important,' laughed Merry. 'Gandalf is never in doubt about that, and does not let anyone else forget it. So you are already making arrangements, are you?'

'Of course,' said Gandalf. 'There is a lot to do and think of. But in this matter both Elrond and Trotter will have much to say. And indeed Boromir, and Glóin, and Glorfindel, too. It concerns all the free folk left in the world.'

'Will Trotter come?' asked Frodo hopefully. 'Though he is only a Man, he would add to the brains of the expedition.'

'"Only a Man" is no way to speak of a *tarkil*, and least of all Aragorn son of Celegorn,' said Gandalf. 'He would add wit and valour to any expedition. But as I said, this is not the time and not the place to discuss it. Yet I will say just this in your ears.' His voice sank to a whisper. 'I think *I* shall have to come with you.'

So great was Frodo's delight at this announcement that Gandalf took off his hat and bowed. 'But I only said: I *think* I shall have to go, and perhaps for part of the way only. Don't count on anything,' he added. 'And now, if you want to talk about such things, you had better come back indoors.'

They walked back with him in silence; but as soon as they were over the threshold Frodo put the question that had been in his mind ever since the Council. 'How long shall I have here, Gandalf?' he asked.

'I don't know,' answered the wizard. 'But we shan't be able to make our plans and preparations very quickly. Scouts have already been sent out, and some may be away a long while. It is essential to find out as much as we can about the Black Riders.'

The new version then returns to the first and follows it very closely to the end of that text ('... waiting for him to set out', VI.409). But it then continues into 'The Ring Goes South' (VI.415) without break or heading, and again follows the old pretty closely for some distance – as far as Gandalf's words 'And the hunters will have to come all the way back to the Ford to pick up the trail – if we are careful, and lucky' (VI.416). There are a few differences to be noted. This version begins: 'When the hobbits had been some three weeks in the house of Elrond, and November was passing' (see VI.415 and note 2); the scouts who had gone north had been 'almost as far as Hoardale' (later > 'as far as the Hoardales'), where in the original text they had reached 'the

114   THE TREASON OF ISENGARD

Dimrill-dales' (see p. 10 and note 14); and it is said of the High Pass: 'where formerly the Goblins' door had been'. Very faint pencillings at the foot of the page give Elvish names of the places mentioned in the text, just as are found in the preceding version (see VI.432 note 4), but these are not the same. The note reads:

In Elvish *Annerchion* = Goblin Gate   *Ruinnel* = Redway
         Nenvithim = Hoardales   *Palath-ledin* = Gladden
                                              Field[s]
                                           Palath = Iris

But where in the first version Gandalf says: 'We had better get off as soon as possible now – and as quietly', and the story then passes almost at once to the day of departure, this text diverges to the first full and clear account of the selection of the Company of the Ring – who are still to be seven (see VI.409–10); and the selection now takes place at the same point in the narrative as it does in FR (pp. 288–9).

'... It is time we began to make preparations in earnest, and the first thing to do is to decide who is going. I have my own ideas, but I must consult Elrond.'

Both Elrond and the wizard were agreed that the party must not be too large, for their hope lay in speed and secrecy. 'Seven and no more should there be,' said Elrond. 'If Frodo is still willing, then Frodo as ring-bearer must be the first choice. And if Frodo goes, then Sam Gamgee must go too, because that was promised, and my heart tells me that their fates are woven together.'

'And if two hobbits go, then I must go,' said Gandalf, 'for my wits tell me that I shall be needed; and indeed *my* fate seems much entangled with hobbits.'

'That is three then,' said Elrond. 'If there are others, they should represent the other free folk of the world.'

'I will go on behalf of Men,' said Trotter. 'I claim some right to share in the adventures of the Ring; but I wish also to go out of friendship for Frodo, and therefore I will ask his leave to be his companion.'

'I could choose no one more gladly,' said Frodo. 'I had thought of begging what is freely offered.' He took Trotter's hand.

'Boromir will also come,' said Gandalf. 'He is resolved to return as soon as he can to his own land, to the siege and war[6] that he has told of. His way goes with ours. He is a valiant man.'

'For the Elves I will choose Galdor of Mirkwood,' said Elrond, 'and for the Dwarves Gimli son of Glóin. If they are

Second Version   THE COUNCIL OF ELROND (1)   **115**

willing to go with you, even as far as Moria, they will be a help to you. That is seven and the full tale.'

'What about Meriadoc and Faramond [> Peregrin]?' said Frodo, suddenly realizing that his friends were not included. 'Merry has come far with me, and it will grieve him to be left behind now.'

'Faramond [> Peregrin] would go with you out of love for you, if he were bidden,' said Gandalf; 'but his heart is not in such perilous adventures, much though he loves you. Merry will be grieved, it is true, but Elrond's decision is wise. He is merry in name, and merry in heart, but this quest is not for him, nor for any hobbit, unless fate and duty chooses him. But do not be distressed: I think there may be other work for him to do, and that he will not be left long idle.'

When the names and number of the adventurers had thus been decided, it was agreed that the day of departure should be the following Thursday, November the seventeenth. The next few days were busy with preparations, but Frodo spent as much time as he could alone with Bilbo. The weather had grown cold, and was now cheerless and grey, and they sat often together in Bilbo's own small room. Then Bilbo would read passages from his book (which seemed still very incomplete), or scraps of his verses, and take notes of Frodo's adventures.

On the morning of the last day, Bilbo pulled out from under his bed a wooden box, and lifted the lid, and fumbled inside. 'You have got a good sword of your own, I believe,' he said hesitatingly to Frodo; 'but I thought, perhaps, you would care to have this as well, or instead, don't you know.'

From this point the new text reaches virtually the final form in FR pp. 290–1,[7] as far as 'I should like to write the second book, if I am spared.' This was evidently where the chapter ended at this stage.

For a brief while my father evidently suspected that Meriadoc and Faramond/Peregrin would be superfluous in what he conceived to be the last stage of the Quest. – It is curious that Elrond, when declaring his choice of Galdor of Mirkwood and Gimli son of Glóin, here refers to Moria as if the passage of the Mines were already determined; but this cannot have been intentional.

Later pencilled changes made to the name *Ond* in this manuscript may be mentioned here. At the first occurrence *the Land of Ond* was struck out, and in the margin my father wrote *Minas-tir Minas-ond Minas-berel*, finally putting *the City of Minas-tirith*. This may be the place where *Minas Tirith* (which already existed in the *Quenta*

116   THE TREASON OF ISENGARD

Silmarillion, V.264, 269) first emerged in this application. At a subsequent occurrence *Ond* was changed to *Minas-berel* and then to *Minas Tirith*.

*

A very rough pencilled outline, written on the 'August 1940' examination script described on p. 67, brings in entirely new aspects of the discussion at the Council. At the head of the page stand these names:

Minas Giliath   Minas rhain[8] *Othrain* = ... *city*[9] *Minas tirith*
Then follows:

> At Council.
> Aragorn's ancestry.
> Glóin's quest – to ask after Bilbo. ? News of Balin. ??
> Boromir. Prophecies had been spoken. The Broken Sword should be reforged. Our wise men said the Broken Sword was in Rivendell.
> I have the Broken Sword, said Tarkil. My fathers were driven out of your city when Sauron raised a rebellion, and he that is now the Chief of the Nine drove us out.
> Minas Morgol.
> War between Ond and Wizard King.
> There Tarkil's sires had been King. Tarkil will come and help Ond. Tarkil's fathers had been driven out by the wizard that is now Chief of the Nine.
> Gandalf's story of Saruman and the eagle. Elrond explains that Eagles had been sent to look. This only if Gandalf goes straight to Rivendell. Otherwise how could the eagles find Gandalf?

The Broken Sword appears in the last revisions to the 'Prancing Pony' story (written on the same paper as this outline), where Trotter draws it out in the inn (p. 78).[10] – The meaning of the last two sentences of the outline is presumably that Gandalf went straight to Rivendell when he left Hobbiton in June, and there told Elrond that he intended to visit Saruman. Compare the notes given on p. 75: 'Gandalf is captured by Saruman. Elves send word that he is missing ... Glorfindel is sent out, and messengers sent to Eagles. ... They fly all over the lands, and find Gandalf...'

The Third Version

More is told of this story of 'Tarkil's sires' and Ond in a manuscript written on the same paper, which I give next, and which despite its being so rough and incomplete I will call 'the Third Version'. This text develops Glóin's story, and is followed by the account given by Galdor of Mirkwood of Gollum's escape, which here first enters.[11] In these

Third Version THE COUNCIL OF ELROND (1) 117

parts of the text there is a great advance towards FR (pp. 253–5, 268–9), where however the ordering of the speeches made at the Council is quite different. Finally we reach the story of the Númenórean kingdoms in Middle-earth, still in an extremely primitive form, and written in a fearsome scrawl; most unhappily a portion of this is lost.

There are a fair number of alterations in pencil, but I think that these belong to much the same time as the writing of the manuscript (which ends in pencil). I take these up silently where they are of slight significance, but in many cases I show them as such in the text.

Much was said of events in the world outside, especially in the South, and in the wide lands east of the Mountains. Of these things Frodo had already heard many rumours. But the tales of Glóin and of Boromir were new to him, and he listened attentively. It appeared that the hearts of the Dwarves of the Mountain were troubled.

'It is now many years ago,' said Glóin, 'that a shadow of disquiet fell upon our folk. Whence it came we did not at first know. Whispered words began to be spoken: it was said that we were hemmed in a narrow place, and that greater wealth and splendour were to be found in the wider world. Some spoke of Moria – the mighty works of our fathers of old, that we called in our ancient tongue Khazaddûm – and they said that we now had the power and numbers to return and there re-establish our halls in glory and command the lands both West and East of the Mountains. At the last, some score of years ago, Balin departed, though Dáin did not give leave willingly, and he took with him Óin and Ori and many of our folk, and they went away south. For a while we heard news, and it seemed good: messages reported that Moria had been re-entered, and great work begun there. Then all fell silent. There was peace under the Mountain again for a space, until rumour of the rings began to be heard.

'Messages came a year ago from Mordor far away; and they offered us rings of power such as the lord of Mordor could make – on condition of our friendship and aid. And they asked urgently concerning one Bilbo, whom it seemed they had learned was once our friend. They commanded us to obtain from him if we could, willing or unwilling, a certain ring that he had possessed. In exchange for this we were offered three such rings as our fathers had of old. Even for news of where he might be found we were promised lasting friendship and great reward.

'We knew well that the friendship of such messages was

118   THE TREASON OF ISENGARD

feigned and concealed a threat, for by that time many rumours of evil also reached us concerning Mordor. We have returned yet no answer; and I have come first from Dáin, to warn Bilbo that he is sought by the Dark Lord, and to learn (if may be) why this is so. Also we crave the counsel of Elrond, for the shadow grows. We perceive that messages have also been sent to King Brand in Dale, and that he is afraid to resist. Already there is war gathering on his southern borders. If we make no answer the Dark Lord will move other men to assail him and us.'

'You have done well to come,' said Elrond. 'You will hear today all that is necessary for the understanding of the Enemy's purposes, and why he seeks Bilbo. There is nought you can do other than to resist, whether with hope or without it. But as you will hear, your trouble is only part of ours [> the troubles of others]; and your hope will rise and fall with the fortunes of the Ring. Let us now hear the words of Galdor of Mirkwood, for they are yet known to few.'

Galdor spoke. 'I do not come,' he said, 'to add to all the accounts of gathering war and unrest, though Mirkwood is not spared, and the dark things that fled from it for a while are returning in such number that my people are hard put to it. But I am sent to bear tidings: they are not good, I fear; but how ill, others must judge. Smeagol that is now called Gollum has escaped.'

'What!' cried Trotter in surprise. 'I judge that to be ill news, and you may mark my words: we shall regret this. How came the Wood-elves to fail in their trust?'

'Not through lack of vigilance,' said Galdor; 'but perhaps through overmuch kindness, and certainly through aid from elsewhither. He was guarded day and night; but hoping for his cure we had not the heart to keep him ever in dungeons beneath the ground.'

'You were less tender to me,' said Glóin with a flash of his eye, as ancient memories of his prison in the halls of the Elven-king were aroused.

'Now, now!' said Gandalf. 'Don't interrupt! That was a regrettable misunderstanding.'

'In days of fair weather we led him through the woods,' Galdor went on; 'and there was a high tree, standing alone far from others, which he liked to climb. Often we let him climb in it till he felt the free wind; but we set a guard at the foot. One day he would not descend, and the guards having no mind to

Third Version THE COUNCIL OF ELROND (1) 119

climb after him (he could cling to branches with his feet as well as with his hands) sat by the tree into the twilight. It was on that very evening in summer under a clear moon that the Orcs came down upon us. We drove them off after some time; but when the battle was over, we found Gollum was gone, and the guards had vanished also. It seems clear that the attack was arranged for the rescue of Gollum, and that he knew of it beforehand; but in what way we cannot guess. We failed to recapture him. We came on his trail and that of some Orcs, and it seemed to plunge deep into Mirkwood going south and west; but ere long it escaped even our skill, nor dare we continue the hunt, for we were drawing near the Mountains of Mirkwood in the midst of the forest, and they are become evil, and we do not go that way.'

'Well, well!' said Gandalf. 'He has got away, and we have no time or chance now to go after him again. Evidently the Enemy wants him. What for, we may discover in good time, or in bad time.[12] I still had some hopes of curing him; but evidently he did not wish to be cured.'

'But now our tale goes far away and long ago,' said Elrond [> Gandalf]. [*Direction here for insertion of a rider which is not extant; but see p. 126.*] 'In the days that followed the Elder Days after the fall of Númenor the men of Westernesse came to the shores of the Great Lands, as is recorded still in history and legend [> in lore]. Of their kings Elendil was the chief, and his ships sailed up the great river which flows out of Wilderland [*in margin, struck out in pencil:* This river they name *Sirvinya*, New Sirion.] and finds the Western Sea in the Bay of [Ramathor Ramathir >] Belfalas. In the land about they made a realm [> In the land about its lower course he established a realm]; and the [> his] chief city was Osgiliath the Fort of Stars, through which the river flowed. But other strong places were set upon hills upon either side: Minas Ithil the Tower of the Moon in the West, and Minas Anor the Tower of the Sun in the East [> Minas Ithil the Tower of the Rising Moon in the East, and Minas Anor the Tower of the Setting Sun in the West].

'And these cities were governed by the sons of Elendil: Ilmandur [*struck out in pencil*], Isildur, and Anárion. But the sons of Elendil did not return from the war with Sauron, and only in Minas Ithil [> Anor] was the lordship of the West maintained. There ruled the son of Isildur [> Anárion] and his sons after him. But as the world worsened and decayed Osgiliath fell into ruin, and the servants of Sauron took Minas

120 THE TREASON OF ISENGARD

Anor [*not changed to* Ithil], and it became a place of dread, and
was called Minas Morgol, the

> The whole of the last paragraph was struck through in pencil. The
> last words stand at the foot of a page, and the following page is lost.
> This is a misfortune, since a part of the earliest form of the history is
> lost with it. The text when it takes up again is complex, and it is
> clearest to number it in sections from (i) to (iii). We are now in the
> middle of a speech by Boromir.

(i)

'... But of these words none of us could understand anything,
until we learnt after seeking far and wide that *Imlad-ril* [>
Imlad-rist] was the name of a far northern dale, called by men
[> men in the North] Rivendell, where Elrond the Half-elven
dwelt.'

'But the rest shall now be made clear to you,' said Trotter,
standing up. He drew forth his sword, and cast it upon a table
before Boromir: in two pieces. 'Here is the Sword that was
Broken, and I am the bearer.'

'But who are you, and what have you or it to do with Minas
Tirith?' asked Boromir.

'He is Aragorn son of Celegorn, descended in right line
[*added:* through many fathers] from Isildur of Minas Ithil, son
of Elendil,' said Elrond. 'He is *tarkil* and one of the few now left
of that people.'

> (At this point there is a mark of insertion for another passage, here
> identified as (iii), which is to replace what now follows, the continua-
> tion of passage (i).)

(ii)

'And the Men of Minas Tirith drove out my fathers,' said
Aragorn. 'Is not that remembered, Boromir? The men of that
town have never ceased to wage war on Sauron, but they have
listened not seldom to counsels that came from him. In the days
of Valandur they murmured against the Men of the West, and
rose against them, and when they came back from battle with
Sauron they refused them entry into the city.[13] Then Valandur
broke his sword before the city gates and went away north; and
for long the heirs of Elendil dwelt at Osforod the Northburg in
slowly waning glory and darkening days. But all the Northland

Third Version   THE COUNCIL OF ELROND (1)   121

has now long been waste; and all that are left of Elendil's folk
few.

'What do the men of Minas Tirith want with me – to return
to aid [them] in the war and then reject me at the gates again?'

This passage (ii) was struck through in pencil. Hurled onto the page,
this narrative is only one stage advanced from the highly provisional
outlines which my father made at various points as the work
proceeded. I think that this obscure story, with its notable suggestion
of a subject population that was not Númenórean (although the cities
were founded by Elendil), was rejected almost as soon as written; it
may be that it was the earliest form of the history of the Númenórean
realms in exile that my father conceived.

The passage to replace (ii) was scribbled very rapidly and in pencil;
it was not struck out.

(iii)

'Then it belongs to you as much as me, or more!' cried Frodo,
looking at Trotter in amazement.

'It does not belong to either of us,' said Trotter, 'but it is
ordained that you should keep it for a while.[14] Yes, I am the heir
of Elendil,' said he, turning again to Boromir; [*all the following
struck out at the time of writing:* 'for I have heard it said that
long ago you drove out the Men of the West from Minas Anor.
You have ever fought against Sauron, but not seldom you have
hearkened to counsels that came from him. Do you wish that I
should return to Minas Morgol or to Minas Tirith? For
Valandil son of Elendil was taken [?as child] For the Men of
Minas Ithil] 'For Valandil son of Isildur remained among the
Elves, and was saved, and he went at last with such of his
father's men as remained, and dwelt in the North in Osforod,
the Northburg, which is now waste, so that its very foundations
can scarce be seen beneath the turf. And our days have ever
waned and darkened through the years. But ever we have
wandered far and wide, yes, even to the borders of Mordor,
making secret war upon the Enemy. But the sword has never
been reforged. For it was Elendil's and broke under him as he
fell, and was brought away by his esquire and treasured. And
Elendil said: "This sword shall not be brandished again for
many years; but when a cry is heard in Minas Anor, and the
power of Sauron grows great in the Middle-earth, then let it be
whetted."'

122 THE TREASON OF ISENGARD

Finally, (ii) continues in pencil from the point reached ('...and then reject me at the gates again?'), and this was not struck out:

'They did not bid me to make any request,' said Boromir, 'and asked only for the meaning of the words. Yet we are sorely pressed, and if Minas Tirith falls and the land of Ond, a great region will fall under the Shadow.'

'I will come,' said Trotter. 'For the half-high have indeed set forth, and the spoken days are near.' Boromir looked at Frodo and nodded with sudden understanding.

The text ends here. In these earliest workings it is interesting to see that the Sword that was Broken existed before the story that it was broken beneath Elendil as he fell: indeed it is not clear that at first it was indeed Elendil's sword, nor how Valandur (whose sword it was) was related to him (though it seems plain that he was a direct descendant of Elendil: very possibly he was to be Isildur's son).

In the passage (iii) the final story of the Broken Sword is seen at the moment of its emergence. Valandil appears as the son of Isildur, and there is a glimpse of the later story that Valandil, the youngest son, remained on account of his youth in Imladris at the time of the War of the Last Alliance, that he received the sword of Elendil, and that he dwelt in Elendil's city of Annúminas.

As my father first wrote the present text he evidently meant (p. 119) that Ilmandur (probably the eldest son of Elendil) ruled Osgiliath, the name of his city being appropriate to his own name (*Ilmen*, region of the stars), as were the cities which they ruled to his brothers' names; but Ilmandur was removed and Osgiliath became Elendil's city – for in this text Elendil sailed up the Great River (which receives ephemerally the name *Sirvinya* 'New Sirion', displacing *Beleghir* 'Great River', VI.410) and established a realm in the land about its lower course. This is entirely at variance with the story found much earlier in Elrond's conversation with Bingo (see p. 110; VI.215–16), where Elrond told that Elendil was 'a king in Beleriand', that 'he made an alliance with the Elf-king of those lands, whose name is Gilgalad', and that their joined armies 'marched eastward, and crossed the Misty Mountains, and passed into the inner lands far from the memory of the Sea.'

That text was very closely related to the end of the second version of *The Fall of Númenor* (V.28–9), and used many of the same phrases. Subsequently a new ending to *The Fall of Númenor* was substituted; this has been given in V.33, but I cite it again here.

But there remains a legend of Beleriand. Now that land had been broken in the Great Battle with Morgoth; and at the fall of Númenor and the change of the fashion of the world it perished; for the sea covered all that was left save some of the mountains that

Third Version THE COUNCIL OF ELROND (1) 123

remained as islands, even up to the feet of Eredlindon. But that land where Lúthien had dwelt remained, and was called Lindon. A gulf of the sea came through it, and a gap was made in the Mountains through which the River Lhûn flowed out. But in the land that was left north and south of the gulf the Elves remained, and Gil-galad son of Felagund son of Finrod was their king. And they made Havens in the Gulf of Lhûn whence any of their people, or any other of the Elves that fled from the darkness and sorrow of Middle-earth, could sail into the True West and return no more. In Lindon Sauron had as yet no dominion. And it is said that the brethren Elendil and Valandil escaping from the fall of Númenor came at last to the mouths of the rivers that flowed into the Western Sea. And Elendil (that is Elf-friend), who had aforetime loved the folk of Eressëa, came to Lindon and dwelt there a while, and passed into Middle-earth and established a realm in the North. But Valandil sailed up the Great River Anduin and established another realm far to the South. But Sauron dwelt in Mordor the Black Country, and that was not very distant from Ondor the realm of Valandil; and Sauron made war against all Elves and all Men of Westernesse or others that aided them, and Valandil was hard pressed. Therefore Elendil and Gil-galad seeing that unless some stand were made Sauron would become lord of [?all] Middle-earth they took counsel together, and they made a great league. And Gil-galad and Elendil marched into the Middle-earth [?and gathered force of Men and Elves, and they assembled at Imladrist].

These three accounts can only be placed in this sequence:

(I) Elrond's account to Bingo (together with the original ending of the second version of *The Fall of Númenor*): Elendil in Beleriand.

(II) The present text (the 'third version' of 'The Council of Elrond'): Elendil comes up the Great River and founds a realm in the South.

(III) The revised ending of *The Fall of Númenor*, cited above: Elendil comes to Lindon; Valandil his brother comes up the Great River and founds the realm of Ondor in the South.

That (I) is the earliest is shown of course by the name Bingo; that (III) followed (II) is shown by the names *Anduin* and *Ondor*. But this is hard to understand: for the story seen emerging in (II), pp. 119–21 above – Isildur and Anárion the rulers of Minas Ithil and Minas Anor, and Valandil Isildur's son surviving and dwelling in the North – is the story that endured into *The Lord of the Rings*.

A single sheet of manuscript found in isolation bears on this question without aiding its solution; it is also of great interest in other respects.

124   THE TREASON OF ISENGARD

After the 'breaking of the North' in the Great Battle, the shape of the North-west of Middle-earth was changed. Nearly all Beleriand was drowned in the Sea. Taur na Fuin became an Island. The mountains of Eredwethion &c. became small isles (so also Himling). Eredlindon was now near the Sea (at widest 200 miles away). A great gulf of the Sea came in through Ossiriand and a gap made in the Mountains through which [the Branduinen flowed (later corrupted to Brandywine) >] the Lhûn flowed. In what was left between the Mountains and the Sea the Elves of Beleriand remained in North and South Lindon; and Havens of Escape were made in the Gulf. The lord was Gilgalad (son of [*struck out:* Fin...] Inglor?). Many of his people were Gnomes; some Doriath-Danians.

Between Eredlindon and Eredhithui [*written above:* Hithdilias] (Misty Mountains) many Elves dwelt, and especially at Imladrist (Rivendell) and Eregion (Hollin). In Hollin there was a colony of Gnomes, who would not depart. Down in Harfalas (or Falas) ...[15] the Black Mountains [Ered Myrn >] Eredvyrn (Mornvenniath) dwelt a powerful assembly of Ilkorins.

Elendil and Valandil kings of Númenórë sailed to the Middle-earth and came into the mouths of the Anduin (Great River) and the Branduinen and the Lhûn (Blue River).

Here the name *Anduin* shows that this text followed (II), the present version of 'The Council of Elrond'. Here, as in (III), Elendil has a brother Valandil (and they are called 'kings of Númenórë'),[16] and the meaning of the last sentence is presumably that, again as in (III), they came separately to Middle-earth and sailed up different rivers.

The simplest conclusion, indeed the only conclusion that seems available, is that my father for some time held different views of the coming of the Númenóreans, and pursued them independently.

Other features of this text must be briefly noticed. That it preceded (III) seems clear from its being at first the Branduinen (Brandywine), subsequently changed to the Lhûn, that flowed through the great gap in Eredlindon (the Blue Mountains), whereas in (III) Lhûn was written from the first. This indicates also that the text preceded that portion of the original map (Map I, p. 302) which shows these regions. On the other hand the statement that Eredlindon was now at no point further than 200 miles from the Sea agrees well with that map;[17] and we meet here an apparently unique reference to the isles of *Tol Fuin* and *Himling*, which are shown on it.[18]

The Misty Mountains receive for the first time Elvish names (*Eredhithui, Hithdilias*), as do the Black Mountains in the South, afterwards the White Mountains, (*Eredvyrn, Mornvenniath*); and the

Fourth Version   THE COUNCIL OF ELROND (1)   **125**

name *Eregion* of Hollin appears. The name of Gil-galad's father as first written cannot be interpreted; the fourth letter seems to be an *r*, but the name is certainly not *Finrod*. *Inglor*, though here marked with a query, agrees with (III), which has *Felagund*; in the texts that I have called (I) above he was a descendant of Fëanor.

I return now to the 'third version' of 'The Council of Elrond'.

The verse (if it was already a verse) that brought Boromir to Rivendell is lost in its earliest form with the lost page (p. 120), but from what follows it is plain that it referred to the Sword that was Broken, which was in *Imlad-ril*, and to 'the half-high', who will 'set forth' (cf. FR p. 259).

There are several interesting names in this text.

Khazaddûm (p. 117) is here first used – in the narrative – of Moria (see V.274, VI.466), but it appears in the original sketch of a page from the Book of Mazarbul: see VI.467 and the Appendix to this book, p. 458.

The city of *Osgiliath* on the Great River appears, with the fortresses of *Minas Anor* and *Minas Ithil* on either side of the river valley, though their positions were originally reversed, with Minas Ithil in the west becoming *Minas Tirith* and Minas Anor in the east becoming *Minas Morgol*.

The *Bay of Belfalas* (replacing at the time of writing *Ramathor*, *Ramathir*) here first appears (see VI.438–9). On the name *Sirvinya* 'New Sirion' of the Great River see p. 122.

Imlad-ril is no doubt the earliest form and first appearance of the Elvish name of Rivendell; *Imlad-rist* which here replaced it is the form found in the texts given on pp. 123–4. *Imladris* is found in the *Etymologies* (V.384, stem R I S).

With *Osforod* 'the Northburg' cf. the later *Fornost (Erain)*, 'Norbury (of the Kings)'.

At the end of the manuscript there are a few lines concerning Bombadil: ' "I knew of him," answered Gandalf. "Bombadil's one name. He has called himself by others, suiting himself to the times. Tombombadil's for the Shire-folk. We have seldom met." '

Pencilled scribbles beneath this, difficult to interpret, give other names of Bombadil: *Forn for the Dwarves*[19] (as in FR p. 278); *Yárë for the Elves*, and *Iaur* (see the *Etymologies*, V.399, stem Y A); *Erion* for the Gnomes; *Eldest for m[en]* (cf. FR p. 142: 'Eldest, that's what I am').

The Fourth Version

The next complete manuscript of the chapter is a formidably difficult document. It contains pages 'cannibalised' from the second version, with just such elements retained from them as were still suitable, and it

126   THE TREASON OF ISENGARD

also contains later writing at more than one stage in the evolution of
the Council, with further emendation on top of that clearly deriving
from different times. It is difficult to determine how this complex
evolved; but I think a good case can be made for the account of the
evolution that I give here, in which a 'fourth' and a 'fifth' version are
separated out.

On this view, my father now decided that the extremely difficult and
incomplete 'third version', introducing so much new material, called
for an ordered text in clear manuscript. The chapter (XIV) was now
titled 'The Council of Elrond', and it begins (on the 'August 1940'
examination script) with a revised version of the opening (see p. 110):
Frodo and Sam now meet Gandalf and Bilbo sitting 'on a seat cut in
the stone beside a turn in the path', as in FR (p. 252). But there is no
further development at this stage in the membership of the Council:
the Elf of Mirkwood is still Galdor. Boromir is now 'from the city of
Minas Tirith in the South'.

From the start of the Council itself, the 'third version', taking up at
the words 'Much was said of events in the world outside' (p. 117), was
for the most part closely followed, though with movement in detail
towards the expression in FR. Glóin is still followed by Galdor's news
of Gollum's escape and Gandalf's resigned observations on the matter.
But after 'And now our tale goes far away and long ago' Elrond here
adds:

'for all here should learn in full the tale of the Ring. I know,' he
added with a glance at Boromir, who seemed about to speak.
'You think that you should speak now in turn after Galdor. But
wait, and you will see that your words will come in more fitly
later.'

This passage may very well represent what was contained in the
missing rider referred to on p. 119.

Elrond's brief account of the foundation of the realm of Ond is not
changed from the 'third version' (as emended: see p. 119). Elendil still
established it, about the lower course of the Great River (here not
given any other name), and 'his chief city was Osgiliath, the Fortress of
Stars', while Isildur and Anárion governed Minas Ithil and Minas
Anor. But where the previous text has (as emended) 'But the sons of
Elendil did not return from the war with Sauron, and only in Minas
Anor was the lordship of the West maintained. There ruled the son of
Anárion and his sons after him' this fourth version greatly expands
Elrond's speech:

'...But Isildur, the elder, went with his father to the aid of
Gilgalad in the Last Alliance. Very mighty was that host.'
Elrond paused for a while, and sighed. 'I remember well the
splendour of their banners,' he said...

Fourth Version   THE COUNCIL OF ELROND (1)   **127**

Elrond's recollection of the mustering of the hosts of the Last Alliance, and Frodo's astonished interjection, now reach the form in FR (p. 256; for the earlier forms of the passage see p. 110); but after 'I have seen many ages in the West of the World, and many defeats, and many fruitless victories' the new text proceeds:

'... Such proved indeed the alliance of Gilgalad and Elendil.'

And thereupon Elrond passed to the tale of the assault upon Mordor that Frodo had heard already from Gandalf / yet not so fully or so clearly; and he spoke of the winning of the Ring [*changed perhaps at this time to:* But now all was set forth in full, and memories were unlocked that had long lain hidden. Great forces were gathered together, even of beasts and of birds; and of all living things some were in either host, save only the Elves. They alone were undivided, and followed Gilgalad.[20] Then Elrond spoke of the winning of the Ring], and the flight of Sauron, and the peace that came to the West of Middle-earth for a time.

'Yet,' said Elrond, 'Isildur, who took the Ring, and greatly diminished the power of Sauron, was slain, and he came never back to Minas Ithil, in the Land of Ond, nor did any of his folk return. Only in Minas Anor was the race of Westernesse maintained for a while.[21] But Gilgalad was lost, and Elendil was dead; and in spite of their victory, Sauron was not wholly destroyed, and the evil creatures that he had made or tamed were abroad, and they multiplied. And Men increased, and Elves were estranged from them; for the people of Númenor decayed, or turned to dark thoughts, and destroyed one another; and the world worsened. Osgiliath fell into ruin; and evil men took Minas Ithil, and it became a place of dread, and was called Minas-Morgol, the

It is at this point that the previous manuscript breaks off, through the loss of a leaf, and does not take up again till after Boromir has declared the 'dream-verse' of Minas Tirith, concerning which he came to Rivendell (p. 120).

Tower of Sorcery, and Minas Anor was renamed Minas Tirith the Tower of Guard. And these two cities stood opposed to one another, and were ever at war; and in the ruins of Osgiliath shadows walked. So it has been for many lives of men. For the men of Minas Tirith fight on, though the race of Elendil has long failed among them. But listen now to Boromir, who is come from Minas Tirith in the Land of Ond.'

128   THE TREASON OF ISENGARD

'Truly in that land,' said Boromir proudly, taking up the tale, 'we have never ceased to defend ourselves, and to dispute the passage of the River with all enemies from the East. By our valour some peace and freedom has been kept in the lands to the West behind us. But now we are pressed back, and are near to despair, for we are beset and the crossing of the River has been taken.[22] And those whom we defend shelter behind us, and give us much praise and little help.

'Now I am come on an errand over many dangerous leagues to Elrond. But I do not seek allies in war; for the might of Elrond is not in numbers, nor do the High-elves put forth their strength in armies. I come rather to ask for counsel and the unravelling of hard words. A dream came many months ago to the Lord of Minas Tirith in the midst of a troubled sleep; and afterward a like dream came to many others in the City, and even to me. Always in this dream there was the noise of running water upon one hand, and of a blowing fire upon the other; and in the midst was heard a voice, saying:

> *Seek for the Sword that was broken:*
> *in Imlad-rist it dwells,*
> *and there shall words be spoken*
> *stronger than Morgol-spells.*
> *And this shall be your token:*
> *when the half-high leave their land,*
> *then many bonds shall be broken,*
> *and Days of Fire at hand.*

Of these words none of us could understand anything,[23] until after long seeking we learned that *Imlad-rist* was the elvish name of a far northern dale, called by Men in the North *Rivendell*, where Elrond Halfelven dwelt.

The third version is then followed closely (pp. 120–1, passages (i) and (iii)) as far as 'but it has been ordained that you should have it for a while'; then follows in this fourth version:

'Yes, it is true,' he said, turning to Boromir with a smile. 'I do not look the part, maybe: I have had a hard life and a long, and the leagues that lie between here and Ond would go for little in the count of my wanderings. I have been in Minas Tirith, and walked in Osgiliath by night, and even to Minas Morgol I have been, and beyond.' He shuddered. 'But my home, such as I have, has been in the North; for Valandil son of Isildur was harboured by the Elves in this region after the death of his father;

Fourth Version   THE COUNCIL OF ELROND (1)   **129**

and he went at last with such of his folk as remained, and dwelt in Osforod the North-burg. But that is now waste, so that its very foundations can scarce be seen beneath the turf. And our days have ever waned and darkened through the years; and we are become a wandering folk, few and secret and sundered, pursued ever by the Enemy, and pursuing him. And the sword has never been reforged. For it was Elendil's, and broke beneath him in his fall; and it was brought away by his esquire and treasured. For Elendil said in his last hour: "This blade shall not be brandished again for many ages. And when a voice is heard in Minas Anor, and the shadow of Sauron grows great again in Middle-earth, let it then be remade." '

It seems to me extremely probable that it was here, very near the point where the draft third version ended, that my father abandoned in its turn this fourth version, or more accurately went back over what he had written, changing the sequence of the speeches at the Council and introducing much new material. He then continued to the end of the chapter; and this is the fifth version.

In the third and fourth versions, ending (on this view) at much the same place, the sequence had been the same:
(1) Glóin's account of the return to Moria and the messages from Mordor;
(2) Galdor's news of Gollum's escape;
(3) Elrond's story ('But now our tale goes far away and long ago...');
(4) Boromir and the 'dream-verse' of Minas Tirith;
(5) Aragorn produces the Sword of Elendil, and Elrond proclaims his ancestry; Frodo says 'Then it belongs to you as much as me, or more!'
(6) Aragorn speaks of Valandil son of Isildur and the life of his descendants in the North.

The differences between this structure and that of FR are essentially that in the final form the story of (Galdor) Legolas comes in much later, and that after Frodo's exclamation in (5) and Aragorn's reply Gandalf calls on Frodo to bring forth the Ring – whereupon Elrond says 'Behold Isildur's Bane!'; this in turn leads to Aragorn's account of himself, Aragorn being followed by Bilbo's story and then Frodo's.

A single page of rough drafting shows both developments: Frodo's bringing forth the Ring at this juncture and Elrond's naming it 'Isildur's Bane' (which would lead to the insertion of the name into the 'dream-verse', from which it was at first absent, p. 128), and also a scheme for a new sequence. In this, after Aragorn's explanation to Boromir of the Broken Sword (FR p. 260), there follows:
(1) Bilbo's story;

130   THE TREASON OF ISENGARD

(2) Gandalf's account of the Rings, and of the identification of Bilbo's Ring with Isildur's Bane;
(3) The story of the hunt for Gollum;
(4) Galdor's tidings of Gollum's escape;
(5) Frodo's story;
(6) 'Gandalf's captivity';
(7) 'Question about Tom Bombadil'.

Although in FR (2) was very greatly enlarged, and embraces Aragorn's story (3), this is essentially the final sequence, with the exception of (5): in FR Frodo follows Bilbo. An intervention, following Frodo's story, by the Elf from the Grey Havens (Galdor, not yet present) leads in FR to Gandalf's two long accounts (2) and (6), into which (4) comes as an interruption.

The sequence given above is found in the fifth version, to be given (in part) shortly; and the way in which the speeches at the Council were relinked to achieve the final sequence can be understood from a comparison of FR with the material presented here.

Gandalf's Tale

I think it very likely, indeed almost certain, that it was at this juncture, before he began on the fifth version of 'The Council of Elrond', that my father finally set down the full story of why Gandalf failed to return to Hobbiton before Frodo's departure. Only a few hints towards this had been put in writing. Saruman appeared for the first time in the outline dated 26–27 August 1940 (pp. 70–1), where the earliest ideas concerning him and his rôle emerge. He dwells at Angrobel or Irongarth, on the borders of Rohan; he 'sends out a message that there is important news' (that the Ringwraiths had come forth from Mordor); Gandalf wants his help against them; but Saruman has 'fallen and gone over to Sauron'. At that stage my father was still entirely uncertain what in fact happened to Gandalf – whether he was pursued by the Riders to the top of a mountain from which he could not escape, or whether he was handed over to Treebeard and imprisoned by him; and in that outline there is no mention of his escape from whatever durance he suffered. In the brief scheme given on p. 116, however, there is mention of 'Gandalf's story of Saruman and the eagle'; and the question is touched on there, how did the Eagles know where to seek for Gandalf? – unless he had gone at once to Rivendell when he left the Shire in June, and had told Elrond of his intention.

Now at last the final story emerges; and the earlier conception of the Western Tower, an Elf-tower of Emyn Beraid, in which Gandalf stood guarded by the Ringwraiths sitting motionless on their horses, as Frodo saw them in his dream (see pp. 33–6), changes into Orthanc,

Fourth Version THE COUNCIL OF ELROND (1) 131

Saruman's tower within the circuit of the 'Irongarth'; and Saruman is his captor.

This first draft, for which my father used the blue booklet-covers of the 'August 1940' examination script, was written in his most rapid handwriting, in which words were often reduced to mere marks or lines with slight undulations, and I have not been able to interpret it at every point. But this original text of Gandalf's story is of much interest, and I give it here in full so well as I can. It will be seen that while the texture of the narrative is thinner than in the final form (FR pp. 269 ff.), many essential features were already present. The pages of the manuscript are lettered from 'b' onwards, showing that the first page is lost.

'It has', said Gandalf, 'and I was about to give an account.[24] At the end of June a cloud of anxiety came upon my mind and I went through the Shire to its southern borders. I had long felt a foreboding of some danger that was still hidden from me. I passed down the Baranduin as far as Sarn Ford, and there I met a messenger. I found I knew him well, for he leapt from his horse when he saw me and hailed me: it was Radagast who dwelt once upon a time near the southern borders of Mirkwood.

Here my father broke off, and without striking out what he had written began again in the course of the second sentence.

and rode round the borders of the Shire, for I felt a foreboding of some danger that was still hidden from me. I found nothing, though I came upon many fugitives, and it seemed to me that on many a fear sat of which they could not speak. I came up from the South and along the Greenway, and not far from Bree I came upon a man sitting by the roadside. His [?dappled grey] horse was standing by. When he saw me he leaped to his feet and hailed me. It was Radagast my cousin,[25] who dwelt once upon a time near the southern borders of Mirkwood. I had lost sight of him for many years. "I am seeking you," he said. "But I am a stranger in these parts, and I heard a rumour that you were in a land called by a strange name: the Shire." "I was," said I, "and you are near. ... [?River] but [?far] to East. What do you want with me so urgently?" For he is never a great traveller.

'He then told me dread news and revealed to me what I had feared without knowing it. This is what he said. "The Nine Wraiths are released," he said. "The Enemy must have some great and urgent need, but what it is that should make him

132   THE TREASON OF ISENGARD

look to these desolate ... parts where men and wealth are scanty
I do not know." "What do you mean?" said I. "The Nine are
coming this way," he said. "Men and beasts are flying before
them. [*Added in pencil:* They have taken the guise of horsemen
clad in black as of old.]"

'Then my heart failed for a moment; for the Chief of the Nine
was of old the greatest of all the wizards of Men, and I have no
power to withstand the Nine Riders when he leads them.

' "Who sent you?" I asked. "It was Saruman the [Grey >]
White,"[26] he said, [*added in pencil:* "and he bids me say that
though the matter is too great for you he will help, but you must
seek his help at once, and this seemed good to me"] and then I
had a light of hope. For Saruman the [Grey >] White is as you
know the greatest among us, and was chief of the White
Council. Radagast the Grey [*in pencil* > Brown] is of course a
master of shapes and changes of hue,[27] and has much lore of
beast, bird, and herb; but Saruman has long studied the works
of the Enemy to defeat him, and the lore of rings was his
especial knowledge. The last of the 19 rings he had....[28]

' "I will go to Saruman," I said. "Then you must go now,"
said Radagast; "for the time is very short, and even if you set
out this hour you will hardly come to him before the Nine cross
the Seven Rivers.[29] I myself shall take my horse and ride away
now, since my errand is at an end." And with that he mounted
and rode off without another word – and that seemed to me
very strange. [*Marginal addition:* and would have ridden off
there and then. "Stay a moment, Radagast," I said. "We need
help of many kinds. Send out messages to all the birds and
beasts that are your friends. Tell them to bring news to Saruman
and Gandalf. Let any message go to Orthanc."][30] But I could
not follow him. I had ridden far and Galeroc[31] was weary. I
stayed the night in Bree and departed at dawn – and if I ever see
the [?innkeeper] again there will be no Butter left in Butterbur. I
will melt the fat from him....[32] But bless him, he is a worthy
man and seems to have shown a stout heart. I shall probably
relent. However, being in great need I trusted him to send the
message to Frodo, and went off at dawn; and I came at last to
the dwelling of Saruman the White. And that is in Isengard, in
the north of the Black Mountains in the South.[33] There there is
a circle of sheer-sided hills that enclose a vale, and in the midst
of the vale is a tower of stone that is called Orthanc. I came to
the great gate in the wall of rock and they said that Saruman

Fourth Version THE COUNCIL OF ELROND (1) 133

expected me;[34] and I rode in, and the gate closed behind, and a sudden fear came on me.

'Saruman was there but he had changed. He wore a ring on his finger. "So you have come, Gandalf," he said to me, and I seemed to see a deadly laughter in his eyes. "Yes, I have come for your aid, Saruman the White." But that title seemed to fill him with anger. "For aid?" he said coldly. "It is seldom heard that Gandalf the *Grey* sought for aid, one so cunning and so wise, wandering about the lands, and concerning himself in every business, be it his own or others".'

'"But now matters are afoot," I said, "that need all our strengths [?in union]. The Chief of the Nine is guised as a Rider in Black and his companions likewise. This Radagast told me."

'"Radagast the Brown," he said, and shook with laughter. "Radagast the Simple, Radagast the Fool. [*Added in pencil:* Yet he had just the wits to play the part that I set him.] He must have played his part well nonetheless. For here you are [*added in pencil:* and that is the purpose of the message]. And, Gandalf the Grey, here you will stay. For I am Saruman: Saruman the Wise, Saruman of many colours. For white cloth may be dyed, and the white page overwritten, and the white light broken." [*Pencilled in margin without direction for insertion:* And I looked then and saw that his robes were not white as had been his custom, but were of many hues, and with every movement he changed hue.]

'"In which case it is no longer white," I said. "For white may be blended of many colours, but many colours are not white." "You need not speak to me as to one of the fools that you make your friends," he said. "I have not brought you here to be instructed, but to give you a choice. A new power has arisen. Against it there is no hope. With it there is such hope as we never had before. The power is going to win. [*Added in margin without direction for insertion:* We fight against it in vain – and in any case foolishly; for we have looked always at it from the outside with hatred, and have not considered what are its further purposes. We have seen only the things done, often under necessity, or caused by resistance and foolish rebellion.] I shall grow as it grows, until all things are ours. In the end, I – or *we*, if you will join me – may in the end come to control that Power. Indeed why not? Could not we by this means accomplish all, and more than all, that we have striven for before with, the help of the weak Men and fugitive Elves?"

134 THE TREASON OF ISENGARD

' "Be brief!" I said. "Name your choice! It is this, is it not? To submit as you have to Sauron [*alternative reading:* To submit to you and to Sauron], or what?"

' "To stay here till the end," said he.

' "Till what end?"

' "Till the Lord has time to consider what fate for you would give him most pleasure."

'They took me,' said Gandalf, 'and placed me on the pinnacle of Orthanc, in the place where Saruman of old was wont to watch the stars. There is no descent but by a narrow stair. And the vale that was once fair was filled with wolves and orcs, for Saruman was there mustering a great force for the service of his new master.[35] I had no chance of escape, and my days were bitter. For I had but little room in which to walk to and fro, and brood on the coming of the Riders to the North. But there was always a hope that Frodo had set forth as I had bidden, and would reach Rivendell ere the inescapable pursuit began. But both my fear and my hope were cheated. For I made the mistake that others have made. I did not yet understand that in the Shire the power of Sauron would halt and fumble, and the hunt be at a loss. And my hope was founded on an innkeeper: one of the best in the world, but not made to be a tool in high matters.'

'Who sent the eagles?' said Frodo eagerly, for suddenly the strange dream that he had had came back to him.

Gandalf looked at him in surprise. 'I thought you asked what had happened to me,' he said. 'But you seem to know, and don't need ... the telling of my tale ...'

'Your words have recalled a dream,' said Frodo, 'that I thought only a dream and had forgotten.'

'Well,' said Gandalf, 'your dream was true.[36] Gandalf was caught like a fly in a spider's web; yet he is an old fly that has known many spiders. I was not content to send a message only to the Shire. At first I feared, as Saruman wished that I should, that Radagast had also fallen. But it is not so: he trusted Saruman, who had not revealed his purposes to him. And the very fact that Saruman had so successfully deceived Radagast proved the undoing of his scheme. For Radagast did as I bid.[37] And the Eagles of the Misty Mountains kept watch and they saw the mustering of orcs, and got news of the escape of Gollum, and they sent word to Orthanc of this to me. And so it was when the moon was still young on a night of autumn that Gwaewar the Windlord[38] chief of the eagles came to me; and I

Fourth Version   THE COUNCIL OF ELROND (1)   135

spoke to him and he bore me away before Saruman was aware, and the orcs and wolves that he released found me not.

' "How far can you bear me?" said I to Gwaewar.

' "Many leagues," he said; "but not to the ends of the earth. Had I known that you wished to fly I would have brought helpers. I was sent as the swiftest and as a bearer of [?tidings]."

' "Then I must have a steed," I said, "and a steed of surpassing swiftness; for I have never had such a need."

' "Then I will take you to Rohan," he said, "for that is not far off. For in Rohan [*added:* the ?Riddermark] the Rohiroth[39] the horse-masters dwell still, and there are no horses like the horses of that land."

' "But are they yet to be trusted?" "They pay tribute ... yearly in horses to Mordor," said Gwaewar, "but they are not yet under the yoke;[40] yet their doom is not far off, if Saruman is fallen."

'I reached Rohan ere dawn, and there I got a horse the like of which I have never seen.'

'He is indeed a fine steed,' said [Elrond >] Aragorn; 'and it grieves me that Sauron should have such tribute. For in the steeds of Rohan there is a strain that ... descended from the Elder Days.'

'One at least is saved,' said Gandalf; 'for there I got my grey horse, and I name him Greyfax. Not even the Chief of the Nine could go with such tireless speed; and by day his coat glistens like silver, and at night it is as unseen as a shadow. So swift was my going from Rohan that I reached the Shire within a week of the appointed day, and I came to his[41] home and found he was gone. I found in fact the Sackville-Bagginses there and was [?ordered off]. I went to the Gaffer's and he was hard to comfort; but I had need of comfort myself, for amidst his confused talk I gathered that the Riders had come even as you left; and I rode to Buckland and all was in uproar; but I found Crickhollow broken and empty, and on the threshold I picked up a cloak that was Frodo's.

'That was my worst moment. I rode then on the trail of the Black Riders like the wind, and I came behind them as they rode through Bree. They threw down the gates ... and passed by like a wind. The Breelanders I guess are quaking still, and expect the end of the world. This was on the night after you had left, I now know. Next day I rode on, and in two days I reached Weathertop, and there I found two of the Enemy already, but

136   THE TREASON OF ISENGARD

they drew off before my [?wrath]. But that night ... gathered, and I was besieged on the top, but I perceived they had not got you.

The text ends with the words: 'Fled at sunrise'. – With only slight prevision (as it appears), a massive new element and dimension had entered the history. There were of course certain essential features lacking. Most important, Saruman was not acting independently of the Dark Tower (see note 35); and while Gandalf's great ride from Rohan on 'Greyfax' now enters, there is no suggestion that the relations of Rohan with Mordor will have any especial significance in the story (though those relations are now differently conceived: see note 40) – and Gandalf's remark 'In Rohan I found evil already at work' (FR p. 275) is absent.

The story of Hamilcar Bolger's ride with Gandalf has finally gone (see p. 75), as has that of Gandalf's visit to Tom Bombadil (see p. 111).

A notable feature is the evolution of the 'colours' of the wizards, Gandalf, Saruman, and Radagast, which came to the final form in the course of the writing of this draft. Saruman is at first 'the Grey',[42] becoming at once 'the White', and Radagast immediately takes on the epithet 'Grey' (p. 132). But Gandalf then becomes 'the Grey',[43] and Saruman calls Radagast 'the Brown' in the text as written on p. 133.

NOTES

1   This text has been put together from pages used in a subsequent version that went to Marquette University and others that were left behind. Many changes were made to it afterwards, but in the citations that I make from it here I take account only of those that were made in ink and at or very near to the time of composition.

2   Elrond still says of Boromir that he 'brings tidings that must be considered', but as in the original version (VI.409) we are again not told what they were, and no explanation is given of his journey to Rivendell. Subsequently in this version, however, Gandalf says that Boromir 'is resolved to return as soon as he can to his own land, to the siege and war that he has told of.'

3   That my father had the earlier text before him is shown by the recurrence here of the casual error (which I did not observe in Vol. VI) 'Elwing daughter of Lúthien': Elwing was the daughter of Dior, son of Lúthien.

4   In the preceding sentence, 'In time the Lord of the Ring would find out its hiding-place', just as in the first version (VI.402 and note 25) Lord of the Rings was first written but changed at once to Lord of the Ring.

5   'Thráin father of Thrór' (VI.403 and note 28), contradicting The Hobbit, was repeated. See pp. 159–60.

THE COUNCIL OF ELROND (1)   137

6 See note 2.
7 That Bilbo gave Frodo Sting and his mailcoat appears in the original outline for 'The Council of Elrond', VI.397. Bilbo does not here, as he does in FR, produce the pieces of Frodo's sword, nor indeed refer to the fact of its having been broken, though the story of its being broken at the Ford of Bruinen goes back to the beginning (VI.197). – The coat of mail (which Bilbo still calls his 'elf-mail') is described as 'studded with pale pearls' ('white gems', FR); cf. the original text of *The Hobbit*, before it was changed to introduce 'mithril': 'It was of silvered steel, and ornamented with pearls' (VI.465, note 35).
8 See p. 287 note 3.
9 The illegible word probably begins with F and might be 'Fire'.
10 It is possible that the Sword that was Broken actually emerged from the verse 'All that is gold does not glitter': on this view, in the earliest form of the verse in which the Broken Sword is referred to (p. 80, note 18) the words *a king may yet be without crown, A blade that was broken be brandished* were no more than a further exemplification of the general moral.
11 Gollum's escape, though only now emerging, had been a necessity of the story ever since Gandalf told Bingo (VI.265) that 'the Wood-elves have him in prison', if Gollum was to reappear at the end, as had long been foreseen (see VI.380–1).
12 Afterwards it is Treebeard who says this (*The Two Towers* III.4, p. 75): 'There is something very big going on, that I can see, and what it is maybe I shall learn in good time, or in bad time.'
13 Cf. the outline given on p. 116: 'My [i.e. Aragorn's] fathers were driven out of your city when Sauron raised a rebellion', and 'There Tarkil's sires had been King'.
14 For previous uses of this dialogue in other contexts see pp. 50 and 105 note 3.
15 The illegible word is an abbreviation, perhaps 'bet.', which my father used elsewhere for 'between'; if this is what it is, he may have intended (the manuscript is very hasty) to write 'between the Black Mountains and the Sea'. *Harfalas* is not named here on the First Map (p. 309, map III).
16 Cf. p. 119: 'Of their kings [i.e. of the Men of Westernesse] Elendil was the chief'.
17 Text (III), the revised ending to *The Fall of Númenor*, says that 'the sea covered all that was left ... *even up to the feet of Eredlindon*' (pp. 122–3), but this can be accommodated to the map by supposing that it refers to the northern extent of the range (where it bent North-east).
18 In the Introduction to *Unfinished Tales* (p. 14) I said that 'though the fact is nowhere referred to it is clear that Himring's top rose above the waters that covered drowned Beleriand. Some way to

138 THE TREASON OF ISENGARD

the west of it was a larger island named *Tol Fuin*, which must be the highest part of *Taur-nu-Fuin*.' When I wrote that I did not know of the existence of this text. – The later form *Himring* had appeared already in the second text of the *Lhammas* (V.177, 189), and in the *Quenta Silmarillion* (V.263, 268); *Himling* here and on the map are surprising, but can have no significance for dating.

19 This is Old Norse *forn* 'ancient'.

20 Cf. *Of the Rings of Power*, in *The Silmarillion* p. 294: 'All living things were divided in that day, and some of every kind, even of beasts and birds, were found in either host, save the Elves only. They alone were undivided and followed Gil-galad.'

21 In this text there is no reference to the death of Anárion. It is made clear that he did not go to the War of the Last Alliance.

22 Contrast FR: 'But if the passages of the River should be won, what then?' In FR (pp. 258–9) Boromir describes the assault on Osgiliath: 'A power was there that we have not felt before. Some said that it could be seen, like a great black horseman, a dark shadow under the moon'; but 'still we fight on, holding all the west shores of Anduin'. An addition to the present text may belong to this time or later: 'Nine horsemen in black led the host of Minas Morgol that day and we could not withstand them.' See p. 151.

23 Here the 'third version' draft takes up again after the missing page (p. 120).

24 Cf. the next version (p. 149): ' "It has much to do with it," said Gandalf, "and if Elrond is willing I will give my account now." '

25 Cf. *The Hobbit*, Chapter VII 'Queer Lodgings': ' "I am a wizard," continued Gandalf. "I have heard of you, if you have not heard of me; but perhaps you have heard of my good cousin Radagast who lives near the Southern borders of Mirkwood?" ' – On Radagast's appearance in the story see p. 76 and note 15.

26 The change of *Grey* to *White* followed the same change in the next sentence, which was made in the act of writing; a little further on *Saruman the White* was written thus from the first.

27 Can this have been suggested by Beorn's acquaintance with Radagast? (see note 25).

28 I cannot make out the two concluding words, though the first might be 'gathered'. But whatever the words are, the meaning is clearly that Saruman had acquired the last of the Rings – and wore it on his finger, as appears subsequently in this text (cf. FR p. 271). – In the last text of 'Ancient History' that has been given Gandalf refers to the discussion of the Rings at the White Council, and to those who 'go in for such things'; see p. 22.

29 The *Seven Rivers*: see pp. 310–12.

30 It is seen subsequently (see note 37) that this addition was made

THE COUNCIL OF ELROND (1)   139

while the writing of this text was in progress; and it is seen from the addition that Radagast first entered the story as the means by which Gandalf was lured to Saruman's dwelling. The abrupt haste of Radagast's departure seemed to Gandalf 'very strange', and it is possible that when first drafting the story my father supposed that Radagast's part was not simply that of innocent emissary: later, at Isengard, Saruman says (p. 133) 'He must have played his part well nonetheless'. This is not in FR. When the addition here was made, Radagast became also the means by which the Eagles knew where to find Gandalf (see p. 130); and this development necessarily disposed of the idea that Radagast had been corrupted — but Gandalf's fear that he had been remains: 'At first I feared, as Saruman wished that I should, that Radagast had also fallen' (p. 134; this is preserved in FR, p. 274). — This is the first appearance of the name *Orthanc*, though its first actual use in the narrative is probably in the description of Isengard that immediately follows.

31   *Galeroc*: see pp. 68 and note 4, 70.

32   The illegible words are perhaps 'fingers and all' ('butterfingers').

33   The name *Isengard* first occurs here (cf. *Angrobel* or *Irongarth*, p. 71), and it is placed, not at the southern end of the Misty Mountains, but in the north of the Black Mountains.

34   This is the first description of Isengard. — There is a faint pencilled addition at this point: 'But something strange in their look and voices struck me; and I dismounted from my horse and left him without. And that was well, for' (here the addition breaks off). This was perhaps a thought, abandoned as soon as written, for some other story of Gandalf's escape, and his need for a horse to take him back to the Shire. The great speed of Galeroc had been emphasised earlier (p. 68: 'there is no horse in Mordor or in Rohan that is as swift as Galeroc').

35   Cf. FR pp. 273–4: 'for Saruman was mustering a great force on his own account, in rivalry of Sauron and not in his service yet.'

36   Before writing this passage about Frodo's dream (' "Who sent the eagles?"...) my father first put ' "And how did you get away?" said Frodo.' It was thus probably at this very point that he decided to introduce Frodo's vision of Gandalf on the pinnacle of Orthanc into his dream in the house of Tom Bombadil (FR p. 138; for previous narratives of his dream on that night see VI.118–20, 328). His vision of Gandalf imprisoned in the Western Tower had also of course to be removed (see p. 35).

37   It is seen from this passage that the addition discussed in note 30 was put in while the draft was in course of composition.

38   On the form *Gwaewar* (*Gwaihir* in LR) see V.301.

39   The name following *Rohan* is very unclear, but can scarcely be other than the first occurrence of *Riddermark*. *Rohiroth, Rochi-*

140　　THE TREASON OF ISENGARD

roth is found on the earliest rough map of the region, VI.439–40.

40　Cf. VI.422 (the earliest text of 'The Ring Goes South'): 'The Horse-kings have long been in the service of Sauron.'

41　'his', though Frodo has not been mentioned, because 'the appointed day' replaced 'Frodo's departure'.

42　In the plot dated 26–27 August 1940 (p. 70), where Saruman first appears, he was 'Saramond the White or Grey Saruman'.

43　He calls himself 'Gandalf the Grey' in the version of his conversation with Frodo at Rivendell cited on p. 82, but that is not earlier than the present text.

VII

THE COUNCIL OF ELROND (2)

The Fifth Version

A fifth version of 'The Council of Elrond' followed, and is conveniently placed here, though it is not necessarily the case that these revisions
proceeded in unbroken sequence while other writing remained at a
standstill. This version incorporated the changed sequence of speakers
(pp. 129–30) and Gandalf's story, and changed the history of Elendil
and his sons; but for this rewriting and reconstruction my father made
use of existing material, whence arises the extraordinarily complicated
state of the manuscript. Many emendations were made to this version
at different times. In this case they can be readily separated into two
groups, on the basis of a typescript that was made of the fifth version
after a certain amount of change had been carried out.

This typescript was very carefully and accurately made, with a
remarkably small number of errors, seeing that the typist seems not to
have been well acquainted with the story: the name *Saruman* was
typed *Samman* throughout (*ru* and *m* being very similar or identical in
my father's handwriting). Where my father missed a needed change (as
Galdor > *Legolas*) the typist dutifully set down the manuscript form.
These characteristics make the typescript a mirror of the state of the
manuscript when it was made. This is to be sure of only limited value
without knowledge of when that was; but I think that it belongs
clearly to this period.

In those parts of the fifth version that are cited here, I indicate only
those subsequent emendations to the manuscript (and only if of
significance) that appear in the typescript as typed.

Glóin's story was altered in the following way. In the third version,
retained in the fourth, he had said: 'At the last, some score of years
ago, Balin departed, though Dáin did not give leave willingly, and he
took with him Óin and Ori and many of our folk, and they went away
south' (p. 117). This was now replaced by the following, written on a
page of the 'August 1940' examination script.

'... For Moria was of old one of the wonders of the Northern
world. It is said that it was begun when the Elder Days were
young,[1] and Durin, father of my folk, was king; and with the
passing of the years and the labour of countless hands its mighty

142   THE TREASON OF ISENGARD

halls and streets, its shafts and endless galleries, pierced the mountains from east to west and delved immeasurably deep. But under the foundations of the hills things long buried were waked at last from sleep, as the world darkened, and days of dread and evil came. Long ago the dwarves fled from Moria and forsook there wealth uncounted; and my folk wandered over the earth until far in the North they made new homes. But we have ever remembered Moria with fear and hope; and it is said in our songs that it shall be re-opened and re-named ere the world ends. When again we were driven from the Lonely Mountain, Erebor,[2] in the days of the Dragon, Thrór returned thither. But he was slain by an Orc, and though that was revenged by Thorin and Dáin, and many goblins were slain in war, none of Thrór's folk, neither Thráin, nor Thorin his son, nor Dáin his sister-son, dared to pass its gates; until at last Balin listened to the whispers that I have spoken of, and resolved to depart. Though Dáin did not give leave willingly, he took with him Óin and Ori and many of our people, and they went away south. That was two score years ago.

This passage, of which only a trace remains in FR (pp. 253–4), reveals the development of new conceptions in the history of the Dwarves. In the original text of 'The Ring Goes South' (VI.429) Gandalf said that *the Goblins drove the Dwarves from Moria*, and most of those that escaped removed into the North. This must have been based on what was told in *The Hobbit*: in Chapter III Elrond had said that 'there are still forgotten treasures to be found in the deserted caverns of the mines of Moria, since the dwarf and goblin war', and in Chapter IV there was a reference to the goblins having 'spread in secret after the sack of the mines of Moria'. Presumably therefore what my father said in the first version of 'The Ring Goes South' was what he actually had in mind when he wrote those passages in *The Hobbit*: the Goblins drove the Dwarves out of Moria.
If this is so, it was only now that a new story emerged, in which the Dwarves left Moria for an entirely different reason. In the present passage the cause of their flight is indeed only hinted at most obliquely: 'they delved immeasurably deep', and 'under the foundations of the hills things long buried were waked at last from sleep'. With this compare LR Appendix A (III):

The Dwarves delved deep at that time.... Thus they roused from sleep a thing of terror that, flying from Thangorodrim, had lain hidden at the foundations of the earth since the coming of the Host of the West: a Balrog of Morgoth. Durin was slain by it, and the

Fifth Version   THE COUNCIL OF ELROND (2)   **143**

year after Náin I, his son; and then the glory of Moria passed, and its people were destroyed or fled far away.

On this question see further pp. 185–6.

Concomitantly with this, the 'dwarf and goblin war' took on a new interpretation and history (and this was why the word 'sack' in the sentence quoted from Chapter IV of *The Hobbit* above was changed in the third edition (1966) to 'battle'). It was the savage murder of Thrór, Thorin's grandfather, on his return to Moria, that led to the war of the Dwarves and the Orcs, ending in the fearsome victory of the Dwarves in the battle of Azanulbizar (Dimrill Dale), described in LR Appendix A (III). The passage in the present text, telling that Thrór 'was slain by an Orc, and though that was revenged by Thorin and Dáin, and many goblins were slain in war, none of Thrór's folk, neither Thráin, nor Thorin his son, nor Dáin his sister-son, dared to pass [Moria's] gates', suggests that the essentials of the later story were now already present. In the story told in LR Appendix A (III) Thorin played an important part in the battle, and from his prowess derived his name 'Oaken-shield'; and Dáin slew Azog, the slayer of Thrór, before the East Gate of Moria. This latter event was indeed derived from *The Hobbit*, where in Chapter XVII Gandalf said of Dáin that he slew the father of Bolg (leader of the Goblins in the Battle of Five Armies) in Moria.[3] It is further told in Appendix A (III) that after the death of Azog Dáin came down from the Gate 'grey in the face, as one who has felt great fear'; and that he said to Thráin, Thorin's father:

'You are the father of our Folk, and we have bled for you, and will again. But we will not enter Khazad-dûm. You will not enter Khazad-dûm. Only I have looked through the shadow of the Gate. Beyond the shadow it waits for you still: Durin's Bane. The world must change and some other power than ours must come before Durin's Folk walk again in Moria.'

It appears from *The Hobbit* Chapter XV that Dáin of the Iron Hills was Thorin Oakenshield's cousin (and from Chapter XVII that his father was called Náin). In the present text Dáin is called Thráin's sister-son. In the table given in LR Appendix A (III), however, he is not Thráin's sister-son: his father Náin was Thráin's first cousin, and thus Thorin Oakenshield and Dáin Ironfoot were second cousins.

After Elrond's words to Glóin 'You will learn that your trouble is only part of the trouble that we are here met to consider' (cf. p. 118), Galdor of Mirkwood no longer follows (see pp. 129–30), and the fifth version reads here:[4]

'For hearken all!' said Elrond in a clear voice. 'I have called you together to listen to the tale of the Ring. Some part of that

144 THE TREASON OF ISENGARD

tale is known to all, but the full tale to few. Other matters may be spoken of, but ere all is ended, it will be seen that all are bound up with the Ring, and all our plans and courses must wait upon our decision in this great matter. For, what shall we do with the Ring? That is the doom that we must deem ere we depart.

'Behold, the tale begins far away and long ago. In the Black Years that followed the Elder Days, after the fall of Númenor the Men of Westernesse returned to the shores of Middle-earth, as is recorded still in lore. Of their kings Elendil the Tall was their chief, and his sons were Isildur and Anárion, mighty lords of ships. They sailed first into the Gulf of Lindon, where the Elf-havens were and still are, and they were befriended by Gilgalad, King of the High-elves of that land. Elendil passed on into Middle-earth and established a realm in the North, about the rivers Lhûn and Branduin, and his chief city was called Tarkilmar [> Torfirion] (or Westermanton), that now is long desolate. But Isildur and Anárion sailed on southwards, and brought their ships up the Great River, Anduin,[5] that flows out of Wilderland and finds the Western Sea in the Bay of Belfalas. In the lands about its lower courses they established a realm where are now the countries of Rohan and Ondor.[6] Their chief city was Osgiliath, the Fortress of Stars, through the midst of which the river flowed. Other strong places they made: Minas Ithil, the Tower of the Rising Moon, to the eastward upon a spur of the Mountains of Shadow; and Minas Anor, the Tower of the Setting Sun, westward at the feet of the Black Mountains. But Sauron dwelt in Mordor, the Black Country, beyond the Mountains of Shadow, and his great fortress, the Dark Tower, was built above the valley of Gorgoroth; and he made war upon the Elves and the Men of Westernesse; and Minas Ithil was taken. Then Isildur sailed away and sought Elendil in the North; and Elendil and Gilgalad took counsel together, seeing that Sauron would soon become master of them all, if they did not unite. And they made a league, the Last Alliance, and marched into Middle-earth gathering great force of Elves and Men. Very mighty was that host.

It will be found that in this passage are the bones of a part of the narrative of the separate work *Of the Rings of Power and the Third Age*, which was published in *The Silmarillion* (see pp. 290–3). In the later development of 'The Council of Elrond' the chapter became the vehicle of a far fuller account of the early Númenórean kingdoms in

Fifth Version   THE COUNCIL OF ELROND (2)   **145**

Middle-earth, and much of this is now found not in *The Lord of the Rings* but in *Of the Rings of Power and the Third Age*.

Here the later story of Elendil enters (see pp. 122–4), in which Elendil remained in the North, whereas his sons sailed south down the coasts of Middle-earth and brought their ships up the Great River. Elendil's city in the North emerges, afterwards *Annúminas*, but here bearing the names *Tarkilmar* or *Westermanton*: on the western portion of the First Map (pp. 304–5) the Elvish name is *Torfirion*, to which *Tarkilmar* was changed on the present manuscript. In Mordor the valley of *Gorgoroth* appears, the name deriving from the *Ered Orgoroth (Gorgoroth)*, the Mountains of Terror south of Taur-na-Fuin in the Elder Days; and the *Mountains of Shadow* are the first mention of the later-named *Ephel Dúath*, the great chain fencing Mordor on the West and South.

From 'Very mighty was that host' my father returned to and retained the pages of the preceding (fourth) version, pp. 126–8. The result of this combination of the new passage just given with the text of the fourth version was to *repeat the taking of Minas Ithil*. In the original account (pp. 119–20) Elrond told that *after* the war with Sauron 'as the world worsened and decayed Osgiliath fell into ruin', and the servants of Sauron took the eastern city, so that 'it became a place of dread, and was called Minas Morgol'. In the fourth version (pp. 126–7) this was repeated more fully and plainly; and the structure of Elrond's story here can be summarised thus:

- Isildur went to the War of the Last Alliance
- Elrond recalls the mustering of the hosts
- He tells of the war
- Isildur's death; 'he came never back to Minas Ithil, nor did any of his folk return. Only in Minas Anor was the race of Westernesse maintained for a while'
- Despite the victory over Sauron, the world worsened; the Númenóreans decayed and were corrupted, 'Osgiliath fell into ruin; *and evil men took Minas Ithil*, and it became a place of dread, and was called Minas-Morgol'

But in the fifth version the structure of Elrond's story becomes:

- *Sauron captured Minas Ithil.* Thereupon Isildur departed and went north, *and there followed the War of the Last Alliance* (The story returns to the fourth version)
- Elrond recalls the mustering of the hosts (&c. as in the fourth version)

This is the form of the story in the typescript made from the fifth version. It is not clear to me whether my father fully intended this result. As the fifth version stands, Minas Ithil was captured by Sauron *before* the War of the Last Alliance, and indeed its capture was a prime cause of the making of the league; yet it is still said that Isildur 'came never back to Minas Ithil', and it is still told that *long after the war*

146   THE TREASON OF ISENGARD

'evil men took Minas Ithil'. This is of course perfectly explicable: when Sauron was cast down Minas Ithil was retaken from his servants, and only much later did the 'evil men' repossess it. But one might expect this to have been made explicit; and the impression remains of a 'doubled' account arising from the use of the fourth version material at this point.

However this may be, it is curious that the history of Minas Ithil never was made entirely explicit. In *Of the Rings of Power and the Third Age* nothing is said of its retaking after the war, nor indeed of its history until the time of the great plague that came upon Gondor in the seventeenth century of the Third Age, when 'Minas Ithil was emptied of its people' (*The Silmarillion* p. 296).

Various changes were made to the manuscript, which is common to both fourth and fifth versions, in this part of the chapter (extending as far as 'it has been ordained that you should have it for a while', p. 128). These changes were apparently made at different times; those that were taken up into the typescript (see p. 141) are given here.

Elrond now says that 'It was even at Imladris, here in Rivendell, that they were mustered'. *Ond* becomes *Ondor* (see note 6), and *Minas-Morgol* becomes *Minas-Morghul*. The sentence 'Only in Minas Anor was the race of Westernesse maintained for a while' was cut out, and the following inserted at this point: 'And Anárion was slain in battle in the valley of Gorgoroth' (see p. 127 and note 21). In the 'dream-verse' of Minas Tirith *Imlad-rist* was altered to *Imlad-ris*, and the second half of the verse was changed to read:

> *This sign shall there be then*
> *that Doom is near at hand:*
> *The Halfhigh shall you see then*
> *with Isildur's bane in hand.*

On *Isildur's bane* see pp. 129–30. At every occurrence of *Trotter* or *Aragorn* in this passage, and throughout the manuscript, the name *Elfstone* was written in, and is the name found in the typescript, and *Aragorn son of Kelegorn* becomes *Elfstone son of Elfhelm* (cf. p. 80 note 17, and for discussion of this question see pp. 277–8).

But at Aragorn's words 'it has been ordained that you should have it for a while' the new structure enters, with ' "Bring out the Ring, Frodo!" said Gandalf solemnly' (see pp. 129–30), and the text that follows in FR (pp. 260–1) is all but achieved. It is (significantly) not said that 'Boromir's eyes glinted as he gazed at the golden thing'; but Aragorn's explanation to him of the meaning of the 'Sword that was broken' in the 'dream-verse' is as in FR, with his reference to the prophecy that it should be re-made when Isildur's Bane was found, and he ends 'Do you wish for the house of Elendil to return to the land of Ond [> Ondor]?'[7] Bilbo in irritation at Boromir's doubtfulness of Aragorn 'bursts out' with the verse *All that is gold does not glitter*[8]

Fifth Version THE COUNCIL OF ELROND (2) 147

(' "I made that up for Tarkil [> Elfstone]," he whispered to Frodo with a grin, "when he first told me his long tale" '). But Aragorn's speech to Boromir (cf. pp. 121, 128) is still substantially different from that in FR, and lacks much that he afterwards said.

Aragorn [> Elfstone] smiled; then he turned again to Boromir. 'I do not look the part, truly,' he said; 'and I am but the heir of Elendil, not Elendil himself. I have had a hard life and a long; and the leagues that lie between here and Ond [> Ondor] are a small part in the count of my journeys. I have crossed many mountains, and many rivers, and trodden many plains, even into far regions where the stars are strange. I have been in Minas Tirith unknown,[9] and have walked in Osgiliath by night; and I have passed the gates of Minas-Morgol [> Minas-Morghul]; further have I dared even to the Dark Borders, and beyond. But my home, such as I have, is in the North. For Valandil, Isildur's son, was harboured by the Elves in this region when his father was lost; and he went at last with such of his folk as remained to him, and dwelt in Osforod [> Fornobel],[10] the North Burg. But that is now waste, and the foundations of its walls can scarce be seen beneath the turf.

'Our days have ever waned and darkened through the years, and we are dwindled to a wandering folk, few and secret and sundered, pursued ever by the Enemy. And the sword has never yet been re-forged, for Isildur's Bane was lost. But now it is found and the hour has come. I will return to Minas-Tirith.'

At the end of Aragorn's speech the fourth version of 'The Council of Elrond' ended (p. 129). The fifth version continues:

'And now,' said Elrond, 'the tale of the Ring comes down the years. It fell from Isildur's hand and was lost. And it shall now be told in how strange a manner it was found. Speak Bilbo! And if you have not yet cast your story into verse,' he added with a smile, 'you may tell it in plain words.'

To some of those present Bilbo's tale was new, and they listened with amazement while the old hobbit (not at all displeased) retold the story of his adventure with Gollum, not omitting a single riddle.

Then Gandalf spoke, and told of the White Council that had been held in that same year, and of the efforts that had been made to drive the Necromancer from Mirkwood, and how that had failed to check the growth of his power. For he had taken again his ancient name, and established a dominion over many

148   THE TREASON OF ISENGARD

men, and had re-entered Mordor. 'It was in that year,' said
Gandalf, 'that rumour first came to us that he was seeking
everywhere for the lost Ring; and we[11] gathered such lore as we
could from far and wide concerning its fashion and properties,
but we never thought that it would be found again to our great
peril.' Gandalf spoke then of the nature and powers of the One
Ring; and how it had at last become clear that the ring of
Gollum was indeed Isildur's Bane, the Ruling Ring.

He told how he had searched for Gollum; and then the story
was taken up first by Galdor [> Legolas] of the Wood-elves,[12]
and in the end by Aragorn [> Elfstone]. For in that chase he had
made a perilous journey following the trail from the deep places
of Mirkwood through Fangorn Forest and the Riddermark,
Rohan the land of Horsemen, and over the Dead Marsh
[> Marshes] to the very borders of the land of Mordor.

'And there I lost the trail,' he said, 'but after a long search I
came upon it again, returning again northwards. It was lurking by
a stagnant pool, upon the edge of the Dead Marsh [> Marshes],
that I caught Gollum; and he was covered with green slime.
I made him walk before me, for I would not touch him; and
I drove him towards Mirkwood. There I gave him over to
Gandalf and to the care of the Elves, and was glad to be rid of
his company, for he stank. But it is as well that he is in
safekeeping. We do not doubt that he has done great harm, and
that from him the Enemy has learned that the Ring is found; but
he might well do further ill. He did not return, I am sure, of his
own will from Mordor, but was sent forth from there to aid in
the design of Sauron.'

'Alas!' said Galdor [> Legolas] interrupting, 'but I have news
that must now be told. It is not good, I fear; but how ill, others
must judge. All that I have heard warns me that you may take it
amiss. Smeagol, who is now called Gollum, has escaped.'

'What!' cried Aragorn [> Elfstone] in angry surprise. 'Then
all my pains are brought to nothing! I judge that to be evil news
indeed. You may mark my words: we shall all rue this bitterly.
How came the Wood-elves to fail in their trust?'

Galdor's story, which was already close (see pp. 118–19) to that in
FR, now moves still closer in detail of expression. Gandalf's rather
resigned comments on Gollum's escape remain as they were; now
however he ends by saying: 'But now it is time that the tale came to
Frodo' (on the sequence here see p. 130). Frodo's story, and Bilbo's
remarks about it, are very much as in FR, where they come in at a

Fifth Version THE COUNCIL OF ELROND (2) **149**

different point, pp. 262–3: here his brief conversation with Bilbo forms the link to Gandalf's story, which is given a heading in the manuscript,

Gandalf's tale

'There are whole chapters of stuff before you ever got here!'

'Yes, it made quite a long tale,' answered Frodo; 'but the story doesn't seem complete to me. I still want to know a good deal.'

'And what question would you ask?' said Elrond, overhearing him.

'I should like to know what happened to Gandalf after he left me, if he is willing to tell me now. But perhaps it has nothing to do with our present business.'

'It has much to do with it,' said Gandalf, 'and if Elrond is willing I will give my account now. At the end of June a cloud of anxiety came upon my mind...

Gandalf's story in this version is still fairly close to the preliminary draft (pp. 131–5), but the writing is much developed towards the form in FR. A detailed comparison of the three would take a great deal of space, but I notice here all the chief features of difference.

Gandalf now calls Radagast his 'kinsman', not his 'cousin', and his dwelling is named (but by an addition to the manuscript: see p. 164) *Rhosgobel*; he still says that the Nine Wraiths 'have taken the guise of Riders in black, *as of old*' (this was a pencilled addition to the draft, p. 132); he does not name them *Nazgûl*. Gandalf says of the 'fell captain of the Nine' that he was 'a great king of old'; and of Saruman he says:

... For Saruman the White is, as some of you know, the greatest of my craft, and was the leader in the White Council. ... But Saruman long studied the arts of the Enemy, and was thus often able to defeat him; and the lore of rings was one of his chief studies. He knew much of the history [of the rings of power >] of the Nine Rings and the Seven, and somewhat even of the Three and the One; and it was at one time rumoured that he had come near the secret of their making.

Radagast tells Gandalf that 'even if you set out from this spot you will hardly reach him before the Nine have crossed the seventh river' (cf. p. 132). Gandalf's horse, formerly Galeroc, is not now named.

Isengard is still in the Black Mountains, but is now defined as being 'not far from the great vale that lies between them and the last hills of the Misty Mountains, in that region which is known to some as the

150 THE TREASON OF ISENGARD

Gap of Rohan' (which is here first named); and of Orthanc Gandalf now says that in the midst of the valley of Isengard 'is the tower of stone called Orthanc, for it was made by Saruman, and it is very great, and has many secrets, but it looks not to be a work of craft. It cannot be reached save by passing the circle of Isengard, and in that there is only one gate.' The implication of the word *for* in 'for it was made by Saruman' is that the tower was called *Orthanc* (Old English *orþanc* 'artifice, device, work of craft') because it was such (it was made by Saruman); yet it did not look to be.

Saruman says nothing of Gandalf's having concealed from him 'a matter of greatest import' (FR p. 272); and Gandalf still says as in the draft (p. 133): 'For white may be blended of many colours, but many colours are not white', not 'And he that breaks a thing to find out what it is has left the path of wisdom'.

Saruman's declamatory and visionary speech to Gandalf at this stage may be cited in full:

'He stood up then, and began to declaim as if he were speaking to many: "A new Power has arisen. Against it, there is no hope. With it, there is such hope as we never had before. None can now doubt its victory, which is near at hand. We fought it in vain – and foolishly. We knew much but not enough. We looked always at it from the outside and through a mist of old falsehood and hate; and we did not consider its high and ultimate purpose. We saw not the reasons, but only the things done, and some of those seemed evil; but they were done under necessity. There has been a conspiracy to hinder and frustrate knowledge, wisdom, and government. The Elder Days are gone. The Middle Days are passing. The Younger Days are beginning. The day of the Elves is over. But Our Days are begun! The Power grows, and I shall grow as it grows, until all things are ours. And listen, Gandalf my old friend," he said, coming near and speaking now suddenly in a soft voice. "In the end, I – or *we*, if you will join with me – we may come to control that Power. We can bide our time. We can keep our thoughts in our hearts. There need not be any real change of purpose – only of method. Why not use this new strength? By it we may well accomplish all and more than all that we have striven to do with the help of the weak and foolish. And we shall have time, more time. Of that I can assure you."[13]

'"I have heard this before, but in other places," I said. "I do not wish to hear it again. All that I wish to hear is the choice that I am offered. One half at least is already clear. I am to submit to you and to Sauron, or – what?"

Fifth Version   THE COUNCIL OF ELROND (2)   **151**

' "To stay here till the end," he said.

' "Till what end?"

' "Till the Power is complete, and the Lord has time to turn to lighter matters: such as the pleasure of devising a fitting end for Gandalf the Grey."

' "There is a chance that I may not prove one of the lighter matters," said I. I am not given to idle boasting; but I came near it then.'

At this point, separate from the text but I think belonging to the same time, my father wrote: 'I don't suppose my fate would have been much different if I had welcomed his advance; but I have no doubt that Saruman will prove a faithless ally; and less doubt that the Dark Lord knows it, well.' This was marked with a query; and it does not appear in the typescript text (see note 16). – Saruman is of course still 'mustering a great force for the service of his new master', as in the draft (p. 134 and note 35).

Frodo's interruption concerning his dream is now given in two forms, marked as alternatives. The first reads:

'I saw you!' said Frodo, 'walking backwards and forwards: the moon shone in your hair.'

Gandalf looked at him in amazement. 'Wake up, Frodo,' he said, 'you are dreaming.'

'I *was* dreaming,' said Frodo. 'Your words suddenly recalled a dream I had. I thought it was only a dream and had forgotten it. I think it was in Bombadil's house. I saw a shadow –'

'That's enough!' laughed Gandalf. 'It was a dream, but a true one, it seems. However, the story is mine, and you need not spoil the telling of it.'

This was rejected in favour of the second version, which begins in the same way and follows with the dialogue preserved in FR (p. 274).

The Eagles of the Misty Mountains are now said by Gandalf to have seen, not 'the Nine Riders going hither and thither in the lands', as in FR, but 'the Nine Riders driving back the men of Minas Tirith'. This goes with the addition to Boromir's speech given on p. 138, note 22, where he speaks of the nine horsemen in black who led the host of Minas Morgol when the crossing of the Anduin was taken. The Eagle who came to Orthanc is still *Gwaewar* (and also *Gwaiwar*), not *Gwaihir*, but he is now called 'swiftest of the Great Eagles', not 'chief of the eagles' as in the draft. In Gandalf's conversation with Gwaewar as they flew from Isengard Rohan was first called *the Horsermark*, changed at once to *the Riddermark*; the men of Rohan are still the *Rohiroth*. Gandalf still makes no reference to his having found 'evil already at work' in Rohan (see p. 136). Aragorn says of the horses of

152   THE TREASON OF ISENGARD

Rohan that 'in them is a strain that is descended from the days of Elendil', not 'from the Elder Days'; and of the horse that he got in Rohan Gandalf says: 'One at least is saved. He is a grey horse and was named Halbarad,[14] but I have called him [Greyfax *changed at once to*] Shadowfax. Not even the horses of the Nine are so tireless and swift. ...'

When Gandalf came to Crickhollow 'hope left me; till I found Hamilcar Bolger. He was still shaking like a leaf, but he had the wits to rouse all the Brandybucks.' This was changed at the time of writing to the reading of FR (p. 276): 'and I did not wait to gather news, or I might have been comforted.' His thought of Butterbur is expressed thus: ' "Butterbur they call him," thought I; "but he will be plain Bur when I leave him, or nothing at all: I will melt all the butter in him..." ' His account of his visit to Bree and his ride to Weathertop, and the siege of him there by the Riders, reached almost the final form (FR p. 277): his defence by fire ('such light and flame cannot have been seen on Weathertop since the war-beacons of old') now at last appears (see p. 56).

Lastly, Gandalf's journey from Weathertop to Rivendell, 'up the Hoarwell and through the Entish lands', took him ten days – 'I was only three days ahead of you at the end of the chase';[15] and he makes no further mention of Shadowfax (in FR he 'sent him back to his master', since he could not ride him on that journey).

At the end of Gandalf's tale there follows:

There was a silence. At last Elrond spoke again. 'This is grave news concerning Saruman,' he said. 'All trust is shaken in these days. But such falls and betrayals, alas! have happened before.[16] Of all the tales the tale of Frodo was most strange to me. I have known few hobbits save Bilbo here; and it seems to me now that he is perhaps not so alone and singular as I had thought. The world has changed much since I was last in the West. The Barrow-wights we knew of by many names;[17] and of the Old Forest, that was once both ancient and very great, many tales have been told; but never before have I heard tell of this strange Bombadil. Is that his only name? I would like to know more of him. Do you know him, Gandalf?'

'I knew *of* him,' answered the wizard. 'Bombadil is one name. He has called himself others, suiting himself to times and tongues. Tom-bombadil's for the Shirefolk; Erion is for Elves, Forn for the dwarves, and many names for men.[18] We have seldom met. I am a rolling-stone and he is a moss-gatherer. There is work for both, but they seldom help one another. It might have been wise to have sought his aid, but I do not think I

Fifth Version   THE COUNCIL OF ELROND (2)   153

should have gained much.[19] He is a strange creature, and follows his own counsels – if he has any: chance serves him better.'

'Could we not now send messages to him, and obtain his help?' asked Erestor. 'It seems that he has a power even over the Ring.'

'That is not quite the way of it,' said Gandalf. 'The Ring has no power over him, or for him: it cannot either cheat or serve him. He is his own master. But he has no power *over* it, and he cannot alter the Ring itself, nor break its power over others. And I think that the mastery of Bombadil is seen only on his own ground, from which he has never stepped within my memory.'[20]

The discussion of what to do with the Ring is much developed from the original form (VI.402–3), which had been little changed in the second version; but it remains far from the debate in FR (pp. 279–80). It is still Gandalf, not as in FR Glorfindel, who expounds the ultimate futility of entrusting the Ring to Bombadil, since he could not withstand the assault of the Dark Lord (cf. p. 112); but then follows in the new version:

'In any case,' said Glorfindel, 'his ground is far away; and the Ring has come from his house hither only at great hazard. It would have to pass through far greater peril to return. If the Ring is to be hidden, it is here in Rivendell that we must hide it – if Elrond has the might to withstand the coming of Sauron at the last, when all else is conquered.'

'I have not the might,' said Elrond.

'In that case,' said Glorfindel, 'there are but two things for us to attempt: we may send the Ring West over Sea; or we may destroy it.'[21]

'There is great peril in either course, but more hope in the former,' said Erestor: 'we must send the Ring West. For we cannot, as Gandalf has revealed, destroy it by our own skill; to destroy it we must send it to the Fire. But of all journeys that journey is the most perilous, and leads straight to the jaws of the Enemy.'

'I judge otherwise,' said Glorfindel. 'The peril of the road of flight is now the greater; for my heart tells me that Sauron will expect us to take the western way, when he hears what has befallen. Too often have we fled, and too seldom gone forward against him. As soon as news reached him that any from Rivendell were journeying westwards, he would pursue them

154   THE TREASON OF ISENGARD

swiftly, and he would send before us and destroy the Havens to prevent us. Let us hope, indeed, that he does not assail the Towers and the Havens in any case, so that hereafter the Elves may have no way of escape from the shadows of Middle-earth.'

'Then there are two courses,' said Erestor, 'and both are without hope. Who will read this riddle for us?'

'None here can do so,' said Elrond gravely. 'None can foretell what will betide if we take this road or that, whether good or ill – if that is what is meant. But it is not hard to choose which is now the right road. The Ring must be sent to the Fire. All else is but postponement of our task. In the One Ring is hidden much of the ancient power of Sauron before it was first broken. Even though he himself has not yet regained it, that power still lives [*struck out:* and works for him and towards him]. As long as the Ring remains on land or in the sea, he will not be overcome. He will have hope; and he will grow, and all men will be turned to him; and the fear lest the Ring come into his hand again will weigh on all hearts, and war will never cease.

'Yet it is even as Glorfindel says: the way of flight is now the more perilous. But on the other road, with speed and care travellers might go far unperceived. I do not say that there is great hope in this course; but there is in other courses less hope, and no lasting good.'

'I do not understand all this,' said Boromir. 'Though Saruman is a traitor, did he not have some glimpse of wisdom? Why should not the Elves and their friends use the Great Ring to defeat the Enemy? And I say that all men will *not* turn to him. The Men of Minas Tirith are valiant and they will *never* submit.'

'*Never* is a long word, Boromir,' replied Elrond.

From this point the conclusion of the chapter remains little changed from the second version, whose pages my father retained here, which is to say that it is little changed from the original text, VI.403 ff. Glóin's reply to Boromir's question about the Rings of the Dwarves now however takes this form (and appears thus in the typescript):

'I do not know,' answered Glóin. 'It was said in secret that Thrór, father of Thráin, father of Thorin who fell in battle, possessed one that had descended from his sires. Some said it was the last. But where it now is no dwarf knows. We think maybe it was taken from him, ere Gandalf found him in the dungeons of the Necromancer long ago, or maybe it was lost in

Fifth Version THE COUNCIL OF ELROND (2) 155

the mines of Moria. We guess that it was partly in hope to find the ring of Thráin that Balin went to Moria. For the messages of Sauron aroused old memories. But it is long since we heard any news: it is unlikely that he found any Ring.'

'It is indeed unlikely,' said Gandalf. 'Those who say that the last ring was taken from Thrór by the Necromancer speak truly.'

This passage was the product of emendation on the manuscript of the second version at different times, and in the result a strange confusion was produced.

In the earliest sketch for 'The Council of Elrond' (VI.398) Glóin said: 'Thráin of old had one that descended from his sires. We do not now know where it is. We think it was taken from him, ere you found him in the dungeons long ago (or maybe it was lost in Moria).' The same is said in the first full form of the chapter (VI.403), where however Glóin's words begin: 'It was said in secret that Thráin (father of Thrór father of Thorin who fell in battle) possessed one that had descended from his sires.' This was a contradiction of the text of *The Hobbit*, where Thrór was the father of Thráin, not his son; but it was repeated in the second version of 'The Council of Elrond' (p. 136 note 5). On this question see the Note at the end of this chapter, pp. 159–60.

In the present text the genealogy is corrected (Thrór – Thráin – Thorin), but it now becomes *Thrór* who was found in the dungeons of the Necromancer, and Gandalf says that the ring was taken there from *Thrór*; whereas in *The Hobbit* it was explicit that Thrór was killed by a goblin in Moria, and his son Thráin was captured by the Necromancer. On the other hand Glóin says here that the Dwarves believe that it was partly in hope to find the ring of *Thráin* that Balin went to Moria.[22]

In the original version of the chapter Elrond had said (VI.404) that 'The Three Rings remain still', and he continued:

'They have conferred great power on the Elves, but they have never yet availed them in their strife with Sauron. For they came from Sauron himself, and can give no skill or knowledge that he did not already possess at their making. And to each race the rings of the Lord bring such powers as each desires and is capable of wielding. The Elves desired not strength of domination or riches, but subtlety of craft and lore, and knowledge of the secrets of the world's being. These things they have gained, yet with sorrow. But they will turn to evil if Sauron regains the Ruling Ring; for then all that the Elves have devised or learned with the power of the rings will become his, as was his purpose.'

This was largely retained in the second version (p. 112), with the

156   THE TREASON OF ISENGARD

difference that Elrond now declared that the Three Rings had been taken over the Sea. In the fifth version he says:

'The Three Rings remain. But of them I am not permitted to speak. Certainly they cannot be used by us. From them the Elvenkings have derived much power, but they have not been used for war, either good or evil. For the Elves desire not strength, or domination, or hoarded wealth, but subtlety of craft and lore...'

and continues as in the second version. Thus, while in the second version the original words 'For they came from Sauron himself' were removed but 'they can give no skill or knowledge that he did not himself already possess at their making' were retained, in this text the latter words are also lost. Yet *Certainly they cannot be used by us* in the new version seems to me to imply that they were made by Sauron; and the argument that I suggested (p. 112) in connection with the second version, that when Boromir says that they were made by Sauron he is not contradicted, holds here with equal force.

There were no further changes of any moment[23] from the original text of the chapter (VI.405–7, scarcely altered in the second version); but the chapter now ends at virtually the same point as in FR ('A nice pickle we have landed ourselves in, Mr. Frodo!'), continuing only with the brief further passage that goes back to the original version (VI.407):

'When must I start, Master Elrond?' asked Frodo.

'First you shall rest and recover full strength,' answered Elrond, guessing his mind. 'Rivendell is a fair place, and we will not send you away until you know it better. And meanwhile we will make plans for your guidance, and do what we can to mislead the Enemy and discover what he is about.'

NOTES

1   Cf. VI.429 (the original text of 'The Ring Goes South'), where Gandalf said that the Mines of Moria 'were made by the Dwarves of Durin's clan many hundreds of years ago, when elves dwelt in Hollin'.

2   The first occurrence of the name *Erebor*, which in the narrative of LR is not found before Book V, Chapter IX of *The Return of the King*.

3   In the original edition of *The Hobbit* the goblin who slew Thrór in Moria was not named, as he is not in the present passage ('he was slain by an Orc'). In the third edition of 1966 the name *Azog* was introduced (from LR) in Chapter I as that of the slayer of

THE COUNCIL OF ELROND (2)   157

Thrór, and a footnote was added in Chapter XVII stating that Bolg, leader of the Goblins in the Battle of Five Armies, was the son of Azog.

4 The new passage was written in ink over pencil, but the underlying text, which has been deciphered by Taum Santoski, was little changed. The name *Anduin* was not present, though *Ond* was already *Ondor* (see notes 6 and 7); and the translated name of Elendil's city Tarkilmar was both *Westermanton* and *Aldemanton* (*Alde* probably signifying 'old', sc. 'the "town" of the ancient Men (of the West)').

5 This is the first occurrence of the name *Anduin*, as originally written, in the narrative texts of LR – as they are here presented, but it is not in the over-written pencilled text of the passage (note 4).

6 This is the first occurrence of *Ondor* for *Ond*, and is so written in both pencilled text and ink overlay (note 4).

7 It is curious that here, in a passage of new manuscript, and again a few lines below, the form should have been first written *Ond*, whereas on p. 144 it is *Ondor* (note 6).

8 The verse remains in the latest form that has been given (p. 78).

9 Aragorn had said in the fourth version (p. 128) that he had been in Minas Tirith, but the word 'unknown' here is possibly the first hint of the story of Aragorn's service in Minas Tirith under the name Thorongil (LR Appendix A (I, iv, *The Stewards*), Appendix B (years 2957–80)).

10 *Fornobel* is the name on the First Map (Map II, pp. 304–5).

11 Written above 'we' and probably at once, but struck out: 'Saruman our chief'.

12 It is not clear why Galdor/Legolas should have contributed to the story of Gollum at this point, but cf. 'Ancient History' (VI.320), where Gandalf says 'it was friends of mine who actually tracked him down, *with the help of the Wood-elves*'.

13 Various minor changes (mostly expansions) were made to the manuscript in Saruman's speech, and since these appear in the typescript (p. 141) I have included them in the text. – In speaking of 'more time' Saruman was referring to possession of the Ring. In a later change to the typescript he adds after 'more time': 'longer [> lasting] life'.

14 Afterwards *Halbarad* became the name of the Ranger who bore Aragorn's standard and died in the Battle of the Pelennor Fields.

15 That Gandalf should have taken only ten days from Weathertop to Rivendell does not agree with the dating. He left Weathertop early on 4 October, and if he reached Rivendell three days before Frodo he arrived on the 17th, i.e. just under a fortnight from Weathertop, not ten days. This is in fact what he says in the same passage in FR (p. 278): 'It took me nearly fourteen days from

158 THE TREASON OF ISENGARD

Weathertop ... I came to Rivendell only three days before the Ring.' But this does not agree with LR Appendix B (nor with the Time-scheme D on p. 14), where he arrived on the 18th, only two days before Frodo.

16 Struck out here: 'Sauron it would seem has gained an ally already faithless to himself; yet I do not doubt that he knows it and laughs'. This is very similar to the sentence doubtfully given to Gandalf on p. 151.

17 In a rejected draft of this passage Elrond goes on: 'There are others elsewhere, wherever the men of Númenor sought dark knowledge under the shadow of death in Middle-earth, and they are akin to the' [Ringwraiths]. Cf. VI.118–20, 401.

18 See p. 125. The reading given is the product of much changing on the manuscript. At first my father wrote: *Yárë's for the Elves, Erion is for Gnomes, Forn for the dwarves*; and names of Bombadil among Men, all struck out, were *Oreald*, *Orold* (Old English: 'very old'), and *Frumbarn* (Old English: 'first-born'). In FR (p. 278) Bombadil was called *Orald* 'by Northern Men'.

19 This passage in which Gandalf contrasts his nature with Bombadil's entered in the second version, p. 111, replacing the earlier story that Gandalf had visited him as a matter of course. Much further back, however, in an isolated draft for a passage in Gandalf's conversation with Bingo at Rivendell on his first waking (VI.213–14), he spoke of Bombadil in a way not unlike his words here (though his conclusion then was entirely different):

We have never had much to do with one another up till now. I don't think he quite approves of me somehow. He belongs to a much older generation, and my ways are not his. He keeps himself to himself and does not believe in travel. But I fancy somehow that we shall all need his help in the end – and that he may have to take an interest in things outside his own country.

20 Gandalf's account of Bombadil's power and its limitations goes back almost word for word to the original text of 'The Council of Elrond', VI.402.

21 This speech was first given to Erestor, as in the original version (VI.402). When my father gave it to Glorfindel instead, he followed it at first with the remainder of Erestor's original speech, in which he defined the opposing perils, and ended 'Who can read this riddle for us?' This speech was struck out as soon as written, and in its place Erestor was given the speech that follows in the text ('There is great peril in either course . . .'), in which he argues that the Ring must be sent to the Grey Havens and thence over the Sea.

22 The following seems a plausible explanation of this strange situation. My father added Glóin's surmise that Balin had hoped

THE COUNCIL OF ELROND (2)   159

to find the ring of *Thráin* in Moria to the existing (second) version while the statement 'It was said in secret that Thráin, father of Thrór, father of Thorin who fell in battle, possessed one' still stood. Subsequently he added in Gandalf's assurance that the last ring had indeed been taken from the captive dwarf in the dungeons of the Necromancer. Now since according to the story in *The Hobbit* it was the son (Thorin's father) whom Gandalf found in the dungeon, and the son had received the map of the Lonely Mountain from *his* father (Thorin's grandfather), he made it *Thrór* who was captured by the Necromancer – for the erroneous genealogy Thráin – Thrór – Thorin was still present. Finally he realised the error in relation to *The Hobbit*, and roughly changed Glóin's opening words to 'It was said in secret that *Thrór*, father of *Thráin* ... possessed one', without observing the effect on the rest of the passage; and in this form it was handed over to the typist.

In Glóin's story at the beginning of the chapter, p. 142, the correct genealogy is present.

23 A correction to the manuscript which is also found in the typescript as typed altered Elrond's reply to Boromir's question 'What then would happen, if the Ruling Ring were destroyed?' Instead of 'The Elves would not lose what they have already won; but the Three Rings would lose all power thereafter' his answer becomes: 'The Elves would not lose that knowledge which they have already won; but the Three Rings would lose all power thereafter, and many fair things would fade.'

Note on Thrór and Thráin

There is no question that the genealogy as first devised in *The Hobbit* was Thorin Oakenshield – Thrain – Thror (always without accents). At one point, however, Thror and Thrain were reversed in my father's typescript, and this survived into the first proof. Taum Santoski and John Rateliff have minutely examined the proofs and shown conclusively that instead of correcting this one error my father decided to extend Thorin – Thror – Thrain right through the book; but that having done so he then changed all the occurrences back to Thorin – Thrain – Thror. It is hard to believe that this extraordinary concern was unconnected with the words on 'Thror's Map' in *The Hobbit*: 'Here of old was *Thrain* King under the Mountain'; but the solution of this conundrum, if it can be found, belongs with the textual history of *The Hobbit*, and I shall not pursue it further. I mention it, of course, because in early manuscripts of *The Lord of the Rings* the genealogy reverts to Thorin – Thror – Thrain despite the publication of Thorin – Thrain – Thror in *The Hobbit*. The only solution I can propose for this is that having, for whatever reason, hesitated so long between the

160 THE TREASON OF ISENGARD

alternatives, when my father was drafting 'The Council of Elrond' Thorin – Thror – Thrain seemed as 'right' as Thorin – Thrain – Thror, and he did not check it with *The Hobbit*.

Years later, my father remarked in the prefatory note that appeared in the second (1951) edition:

> A final note may be added, on a point raised by several students of the lore of the period. On Thror's Map is written *Here of old was Thrain King under the Mountain*; yet Thrain was the son of Thror, the last King under the Mountain before the coming of the dragon. The Map, however, is not in error. Names are often repeated in dynasties, and the genealogies show that a distant ancestor of Thror was referred to, Thrain I, a fugitive from Moria, who first discovered the Lonely Mountain, Erebor, and ruled there for a while, before his people moved on to the remoter mountains of the North.

In the third edition of 1966 the opening of Thorin's story in Chapter I was changed to introduce Thrain I into the text. Until then it had read:

> 'Long ago in my grandfather's time some dwarves were driven out of the far North, and came with all their wealth and their tools to this Mountain on the map. There they mined and they tunnelled and they made huge halls and great workshops . . .'

The present text of *The Hobbit* reads here:

> 'Long ago in my grandfather Thror's time our family was driven out of the far North, and came back with all their wealth and their tools to this Mountain on the map. It had been discovered by my far ancestor, Thrain the Old, but now they mined and they tunnelled and they made huger halls and greater workshops . . .'

At the same time, in the next sentence, 'my grandfather was King under the Mountain' was changed to 'my grandfather was King under the Mountain again.'

The history of Thráin the First, fugitive from Moria, first King under the Mountain, and discoverer of the Arkenstone, was given in *The Lord of the Rings*, Appendix A (III), *Durin's Folk*; and doubtless the prefatory note in the 1951 edition and the passage in Appendix A were closely related. But this was the product of development in the history of the Dwarves that came in with *The Lord of the Rings* (and indeed the need to explain the words on the map 'Here of old was Thrain King under the Mountain' evidently played a part in that development). When *The Hobbit* was first published it was Thrain son of Thror – the only Thrain at that time conceived of – who discovered the Arkenstone.

VIII
THE RING GOES SOUTH

The intractable problems that had beset *The Lord of the Rings* thus far were now at last resolved. The identity of Trotter had been decisively established, and with the work done in successive versions of 'The Council of Elrond' his place and significance in the history of Middle-earth was already made firm – meagre though that history still was by comparison with the great structure that would afterwards be raised on these foundations. The hobbits were equally secure in number and in name, and the only Bolger who ever roved far afield would rove no more. Bombadil is to play no further part in the history of the Ring. Most intractable of all, the question of what had happened to Gandalf was now conclusively answered; and with that answer had arisen (as it would turn out) a new focal point in the history of the War of the Ring: the Treason of Isengard.

There still remained of older narrative writing the journey of the Company of the Ring from Rivendell to the Red Pass beneath Caradras, and the passage of the Mines of Moria as far as Balin's tomb. One major question remained, however, and a final decision must imperatively be made: who were the members of the Company to be?

Notes and drafts written on the 'August 1940' examination script show my father pondering this further. One manuscript page reads as follows:

Chapter XV. Cut out converse in garden.[1]
Begin by saying hobbits were displeased with Sam.
Tell them of the scouts going out.
Elrond then says *union of forces* is impossible. We cannot send or summon great force to aid Frodo. We must send out messages to all free folk to resist as long as possible, and that a new hope, though faint, is born. But with Frodo must go helpers, and they should represent all the Free Folk. Nine should be the number to set against the Nine Evil Servants. But we should support the war in Minas Tirith.

Galdor Legolas[2]

Hobbits	{ Frodo	1
	{ Sam (promised)	2
Wizard	Gandalf	3

162 THE TREASON OF ISENGARD

Elf   Legolas   4
Half-elf   Erestor   5

The road *should go to Minas Tirith*, therefore so far at least should go:

Men { Aragorn   6
     { Boromir   7
Dwarf   Gimli son of Glóin   8

Merry, Pippin. They insist on going. [*Struck out:* Pippin only if Erestor does not go.] Elrond says there may be work in the Shire, and it may prove ill if they all go.
Shall Pippin return to the Shire?
Then come preparations, and the scene with Bilbo and Frodo and giving of Sting &c.

Here the number of Nine members of the Company, expressly corresponding to the Nine Ringwraiths, is reached;[3] but even so there remains a doubt as to its composition where the hobbits are concerned (see p. 115), and my father's lingering feeling that one at least should return to the Shire at this stage was still a factor, especially since the inclusion of Erestor 'Half-elf'[4] took the number to eight. But this was the last moment of indecision. A short draft, written hastily in ink on the same paper, introduces the final complement of the Company of the Ring. On it my father pencilled: 'Sketch of reduction of the choosing of the Company'.[5]

In the end after the matter had been much debated by Elrond and Gandalf it was decided that the Nine of the Company of the Ring should be the four hobbits, aided by Gandalf; and that Legolas should represent the Elves, and Gimli son of Glóin the Dwarves. On behalf of Men Aragorn should go, and Boromir. For they were going to Minas Tirith, and Aragorn counselled that the Company should go that way, and even maybe go first to that city. Elrond was reluctant to send Merry and Pippin, but Gandalf [?supported].

My father now proceeded to a new text of 'The Ring Goes South'; and of preliminary work nothing survives, if any existed, apart from a few passages in rough drafting from the beginning of the chapter. The new version is a good clear manuscript in ink, using in part the 'August 1940' script that had been used for the drafting of major developments in 'The Council of Elrond'. The story now advanced confidently, and for long stretches scarcely differs from that in FR in the actual wording of the narrative and the speeches of the characters. There are a number of later emendations, a good many of which can be shown to come from a little later in the same period of composition. As written, the chapter had no title, various possibilities being pencilled in afterwards: although in the original text, when the chapter was continuous with 'The Council of Elrond', there was a sub-heading

THE RING GOES SOUTH

163

'The Ring Goes South' (VI.415), my father now tried also 'The Company of the Ring Departs' and 'The Ring Sets Out'.

Since the previous chapter now ended where it ends in FR, at the conclusion of the Council, the ensuing conversation among the hobbits, interrupted by Gandalf, was moved to the beginning of 'The Ring Goes South'. My father now took up his direction to 'cut out converse in garden' (see note 1), and the chapter begins exactly as in FR, with the hobbits talking in Bilbo's room later on the same day, and Gandalf looking in through the window. The new conversation almost reaches the form in FR (pp. 285–7), and only the following differences need be mentioned. Gandalf speaks of 'the Elves of Mirkwood', not of 'Thranduil's folk in Mirkwood', and he does not say that 'Aragorn has gone with Elrond's sons' (who had not yet emerged); and Bilbo's remarks about the season of their departure were first written:

'...you can't wait now till Spring, and you can't go till the scouts come back. So off you go nice and comfortable just when winter's beginning to bite.'

'Quite in the Gandalf manner,' said Pippin.

'Exactly,' said Gandalf.

This was replaced at once by Bilbo's verse (*When winter first begins to bite*) that he speaks here in FR. Lastly, Gandalf says: 'In this matter Elrond will have [the decision >] much to say, and your friend Trotter, Aragorn the tarkil, too' (FR: 'and your friend the Strider').

While still writing the opening of the chapter, my father hesitated about the structure. One possibility seems to have been to keep the new conversation in Bilbo's room but to put it back into the end of 'The Council of Elrond', ending at Sam's remark 'And where will they live? That's what I often wonder'; another, to cut out the conversation among the hobbits, and Gandalf's intervention at the window, almost in its entirety. He went so far as to provide a brief substitute passage; but decided against it.[6]

The chronology in FR, according to which the Company stayed more than two months in Rivendell and left on 25 December, had not yet entered. In the second version of 'The Council of Elrond', which continued for some distance into the narrative of 'The Ring Goes South', 'the hobbits had been some three weeks in the house of Elrond, and November was passing' when the scouts began to return; and at the Choosing of the Company the date of departure was settled for 'the following Thursday, November the seventeenth' (pp. 113, 115).[7] In the new text the same was said ('some three weeks ... November was passing'), but this was changed, probably at once, to 'The hobbits had been nearly a month in the house of Elrond, and November was half over, when the scouts began to return'; and subsequently (as in FR p. 290) Elrond says: 'In seven days the Company must depart.' No

164   THE TREASON OF ISENGARD

actual date for the leaving of Rivendell is now mentioned, but it had been postponed to nearer the end of the month (actually to 24 November, see p. 169).

The account of the journeys of the scouts moves on from the previous versions (VI.415–16 and VII.113–14), and largely attains the text in FR, apart from there being, as at the beginning of the chapter, no mention of Aragorn's having left Rivendell, nor of the sons of Elrond. Those scouts who went north had gone 'beyond the Hoarwell into the Entishlands', and those who went west had 'searched the lands far down the Greyflood, as far as Tharbad where the old North Road crossed the river by the ruined town'. This is where *Tharbad* first appears.[8] Those who had climbed the pass at the sources of the Gladden[9] had 'reached the old home of Radagast at Rhosgobel': this is where *Rhosgobel* is first named, and in the margin my father wrote 'Brownhay'.[10]

These last 'had returned up the Redway[11] and over the high pass that was called the Dimrill Stair'. The name 'Dimrill Stair' for the pass beneath Caradras has appeared in later emendations to the original version of 'The Ring Goes South' (VI.433–4, notes 14 and 21). In the present passage the name was not emended at any stage; but further on in the chapter, where in this text Gandalf says 'If we climb *the pass that is called the Dimrill Stair* ... we shall come down into the deep dale of the Dwarves', my father (much later) emended the manuscript to the reading of FR (p. 296): 'If we climb *the pass that is called the Redhorn Gate* ... we shall come down *by the Dimrill Stair* into the deep vale of the Dwarves' (and thus Robert Foster, in *The Complete Guide to Middle-earth*, defines *Dimrill Stair* as 'Path leading from Azanulbizar to the Redhorn Pass'). The name of the pass (called in this text the 'Dimrill Pass' as well as the 'Dimrill Stair') was changed also at other occurrences in this chapter, but at this place my father having missed it in the manuscript it was retained in the typescript that soon followed (note 6), and so survived into FR, p. 287: 'over the high pass that was called the Dimrill Stair' – an error that was never picked up.

The Choosing of the Company is found in this manuscript in two alternative versions. Though the essential content is the same in both, and both end with the inclusion of Merry and Pippin after Gandalf's advocacy, the one written first is rather nearer to the preceding version (pp. 113–15): the chief difference between them being that in the first the formation of the Company is seen as it takes place, whereas in the second (which is almost identical to the form in FR) the deliberations have been largely completed and Elrond announces the decision to the hobbits.[12]

There are several differences worth noticing in the first of these versions. After Gandalf's remark that his fate 'seems much entangled with hobbits' Elrond says: 'You will be needed many times before the journey's end, Gandalf; but maybe when there is most need you will

THE RING GOES SOUTH 165

not be there. This is your greatest peril, and I shall not have peace till I see you again.' The loss of Gandalf was of course foreseen (VI.443, 462). Aragorn, after saying to Frodo that since he himself is going to Minas Tirith their roads lie together for many hundreds of leagues, adds: 'Indeed it is my counsel that you should go first to that city'. And after saying that for the two unfilled places needed to make nine he may be able to find some 'of my own kindred and household' Elrond continues (but the passage was at once deleted): 'The elf-lords I may not send, for though their power is great it is not great enough. They cannot walk unhidden from wrath and spirit of evil, and news of the Company would reach Mordor by day or night.'

In these passages, and throughout the rest of the chapter (in intention), *Aragorn* was again changed to *Elfstone*, and *son of Kelegorn* to *son of Elfhelm* (see pp. 277–8), as also was *Trotter*, except where he is directly addressed thus by one of the hobbits.

The reforging of the Sword of Elendil now enters, and the description of it is at once precisely as in FR (p. 290), with the 'device of seven stars set between the crescent moon and the rayed sun', save that the reforged sword is given no name. This was added in somewhat later: 'And Elfstone gave it a new name and called it *Branding*' (see p. 274 and note 19).

For the next part of the chapter (Bilbo and Frodo during the last days at Rivendell) my father simply took over the actual manuscript pages of the second version of 'The Council of Elrond', from 'The weather had grown cold ... ' (p. 115); this passage was already close to the form in FR.[13] After 'I should like to write the second book, if I am spared' (which is where the second version of 'The Council of Elrond' ended) my father wrote on the manuscript 'Verses?', but Bilbo's song *I sit beside the fire and think* is not found in this manuscript. The original workings for the song are extant, however, and certainly belong to this time.[14]

The day of departure was 'a cold grey day near the end of November' (see p. 164). At first there were two ponies, as in the original version (VI.416), but 'Bill' bought in Bree, and greatly invigorated by his stay in Rivendell, was substituted as my father wrote.[15] The departure was at this time much more briefly treated than it is in FR: there is no blowing of Boromir's war-horn, no account of the arms borne by each member of the Company or of the clothing provided by Elrond, and no mention of Sam's checking through his belongings – so that the important minor element of his discovery that he has no rope is absent (cf. pp. 183, 280).

The story of the journey from Rivendell to Hollin is now very close to FR, but there are differences in geography and geographical names, which were evolving as the new version progressed. The journey had still taken 'some ten days' to the point where the weather changed (VI.418), whereas in FR it took a fortnight; and there was only one

166   THE TREASON OF ISENGARD

great peak, not three. An Elvish name for Hollin: '*Nan-eregdos* in the elfspeech' was added, apparently at the time of writing.[16] Gandalf estimates that they have come 'fifty leagues as the crow flies' ('five-and-forty leagues as the crow flies' FR, 'eighty leagues' in the original version). And where in the first version, in reply to the observation of Faramond (Pippin) that since the mountains are ahead they must have turned east, Gandalf said 'No, it is the mountains that have turned', he now replies, 'No, it is the mountains that have bent west' (FR: 'Beyond those peaks the range bends round south-west'). On this difficult question of geography see VI.440–1.

Gimli's speech about the Mountains is present, almost word for word as in FR, except that the three peaks not yet being devised his words 'we have wrought the image of those mountains into many works of metal and of stone, and into many songs and tales' seem to have a more general bearing. But he continues (as in FR): 'Only once before have I seen them from afar in waking life, but I know them and their names, for under them lies Khazad-dûm, the Dwarrowdelf, that is now called the Black [Gulf >] Pit,[17] Moria in the elvish tongue', and it seems that he is here speaking of certain notable and outstanding peaks, distinctive in the chain of the Misty Mountains, beneath which lay Moria. (The three great Mountains of Moria were in any case just about to enter, in Gimli's next speech.) Here he says, as in FR, 'Yonder stands Barazinbar, the Redhorn, cruel Caradhras', 'cruel' being altered at the moment of writing from 'the windy', and that from 'the tall', as also was *Caradhras* from *Caradras*.[18] And he speaks also of 'Azanulbizâr, the Dimrill-dale that elves call Nanduhirion'.[19]

Gandalf's reply, and Gimli's further words about the Mirrormere, are a difficult complex of rapid changes in the manuscript, when new elements are seen at the moment of emergence. With some slight doubt as to the precise sequence of correction, the passage seems to have developed thus:

'It is for Dimrill-dale that we are making,' said Gandalf. 'If we climb the pass that is called the Dimrill Stair under the red side of Caradhras, we shall come down into the deep dale of the Dwarves.[20] There the River [Redway rises in the black wat(er) Morthond Blackroot >] Morthond the cold rises in the Mirrormere.'

'Dark is the water of Kheledzâram,' said Gimli, 'and mirrors only the far sky and three white peaks; and cold is the water of Buzundush. My heart trembles at the thought that I may see them soon.'

Obviously, it was as my father began to write the words he intended: 'the River Redway rises in the black wat[er of the Mirrormere]' that he changed the name of the river to *Morthond*, 'Blackroot'; and I think

THE RING GOES SOUTH 167

that it was here also that the three peaks above Moria entered, mirrored in the water.[21] He then wrote a new passage, no doubt intended to supersede part of that just given, but struck it out, probably immediately:

There lies Kheledzâram, the Mirror-mere, deep and dark, in which can be seen only the far sky and three white peaks. From it issues Buzundush, the Blackroot River, Morthond cold and swift. My heart trembles at the thought that I may see them soon.'[22]

Gandalf replying said: '. . . we at least cannot stay in that valley. We must go down the Morthond into the woods of Lothlórien . . .' (FR: 'into the secret woods'). This is where, as it seems, the name *Lothlórien* first appears. And when Merry asked: 'Yes, and where then?' the wizard answered: 'To the end of the journey – in the end. It may be that you will pass through Fangorn, which some call the Topless Forest. But we must not look too far ahead. . . .' The reference to Fangorn was deleted.

Several versions of Legolas' words about the forgotten Elves of Hollin were written before the final form was achieved: the first reads:

'That is true,' said Legolas. 'But the Elves of this land were of a strange race, and the spirit that dwells here is alien to me, who am of the woodland folk. Here dwelt Noldor, the Elven-wise, and all the stones about cry to me with many voices: they built high towers to heaven, and delved deep to earth, and they are gone. They are gone. They sought the Havens long ago.'

The story of the great silence over all the land of Hollin, the flights of black crows, Pippin's disappointment at the news and Sam's failure to comprehend the geography, the mysterious passage of something against the stars, and the sight of Caradhras close before them on the third morning from Hollin, all this is told in words that remained virtually unchanged in FR, save for a few details. Trotter says that the crows are 'not natives to this place', but does not add that 'they are *crebain* out of Fangorn and Dunland'; and after saying that he has glimpsed many hawks flying high up, he says 'That would account for the silence of all the birds', this being struck out immediately (see VI.420 and note 17). Sam calls Caradhras 'this Ruddyhorn, or whatever its name is', as he did in the original version (VI.421), but *Ruddyhorn* was then to be its accepted English name (VI.419 and note 11).

As the Company walked on the ancient road from Hollin to the Pass, the moon rose over the mountains 'almost at the full'; as in the original version it is said that the light was unwelcome to Trotter and

168   THE TREASON OF ISENGARD

Gandalf, and 'they were relieved when at last late in the night the moon set and left them to the stars'. In the original text it was a crescent moon (VI.421 and note 19), and 'it stayed but a little while'; in FR the moon was full, and still low in the western sky when the shadow passed across the stars.

In the original version it was Trotter who favoured the passage of Moria, Gandalf who favoured the Pass, and what they said was coloured by their opinions. This was still the case when my father came to the new version, although what is said is virtually what is said in FR (p. 300):

'Winter is behind,' [Gandalf] said quietly to Trotter. 'The peaks away north are whiter than they were; snow is lying far down their shoulders.'

'And tonight,' said Trotter, 'we shall be on our way high up the Dimrill Stair. If we are not seen by watchers on that narrow path, and waylaid by some evil, the weather may prove as deadly an enemy as any. What do you think of our course now?'

Frodo overheard these words [&c. as in FR]

'I think no good of any part of our course from beginning to end, as you know well, Aragorn', answered Gandalf, his tone sharpened by anxiety. 'But we must go on. It is no good our delaying the passage of the mountains. Further south there are no passes, till one comes to the Gap of Rohan. I do not trust that way, since the fall of Saruman. Who knows which side now the marshals of the Horse-lords serve?'

'Who knows indeed!' said Trotter. 'But there is another way, and not by the pass beneath Caradhras: the dark and secret way that we have spoken of.'

'And I will not speak of it again. Not yet. Say nothing to the others, I beg. Nor you, Frodo,' said Gandalf, turning suddenly towards him. 'You have listened to our words, as is your right as Ring-bearer. But I will not say any more until it is plain that there is no other course.'

'We must decide before we go further,' said Gandalf.

'Then let us weigh the matter in our minds, while the others rest and sleep,' answered Trotter.

Since the speakers of the last two speeches are out of order with the preceding conversation, it was at this point that my father 'realised' that it was Trotter and not Gandalf who especially feared Moria, and at once changed the text of the passage accordingly.

Gandalf's words to the Company at the end of his discussion with Trotter, and the whole account of the snowstorm, are very much as in

THE RING GOES SOUTH   169

FR (pp. 300–2), though in the latter part of this chapter the actual wording underwent more development later to reach the FR text than had been the case till now. Boromir says that he was born in the Black Mountains (see VI.436, note 31); and the reference to Bilbo alone of hobbits remembering the Fell Winter of the year 1311 is absent. Another use of names from the legends of the Elder Days, immediately rejected, appears in Boromir's words about the snowstorm: 'I wonder if the Enemy has anything to do with it? They say in my land that he can govern the storms in [*struck out*: Mountains of Shadow Daedeloth Delduath] the Mountains of Shadow that lie on the confines of Mordor.'[23]

In Frodo's dream, as he fell into a snow-sleep, Bilbo's voice said: *Snowstorm on December the ninth* (in the original version 2 December, VI.424; in FR 12 January). The journey from Rivendell to Hollin had taken 'some ten days' (p. 165); and a chronological scheme that seems clearly to derive from this time and to fit this narrative gives the date of departure from Rivendell as the evening of Thursday 24 November. According to this scheme the Company reached Hollin on 6 December, the journey from Rivendell having thus taken eleven days (and twelve nights), and 'Snow on Caradras' is dated 9 December.

The liquor that Gandalf gives to the Company from his flask is still called 'one of Elrond's cordials', as in VI.424, and the name *miruvor* does not appear. Gandalf, as the flame sprang up from the wood, said: 'I have written *Gandalf is here* in signs that even the blind rocks could read', but he does not say, as he thrusts his staff into the faggot, *naur an edraith ammen!*[24]

The account of the descent remains distinctively different from the story in FR, and closer to the original (VI.426–7), despite the fact that Trotter was there still a hobbit, and Gimli and Legolas not present.

'The sooner we make a move and get down again the better,' said Gandalf. 'There is more snow still to come up here.'

Much as they all desired to get down again, it was easier said than done. Beyond their refuge the snow was already some feet deep, and in places was piled into great wind-drifts; and it was wet and soft. Gandalf could only get forward with great labour, and had only gone a few yards on the downward path when he was floundering in snow above his waist. Their plight looked desperate.

Boromir was the tallest of the Company, being above six feet and very broad-shouldered as well. 'I am going on down, if I can,' he said. 'As far as I can make out our course of last night, the path turns right round that shoulder of rock down there. And if I remember rightly, a furlong or so beyond the turn there was a flat space at the top of a long steep slope – very heavy

170 THE TREASON OF ISENGARD

going it was as we came up. From that point I might be able to get a view, and some idea of how the snow lies further down.'

He struggled slowly forward, plunging in snow that was everywhere above his knees, and in places rose almost shoulder-high. Often he seemed to be swimming or burrowing with his great arms rather than walking. At last he vanished from sight and passed round the turn. He was long gone, and they began to be anxious, fearing that he had been engulfed in some drift or snow-filled hollow, or had fallen over the hidden brink into the ravine.

When more than an hour had passed they heard him call. He had reappeared round the bend in the path and was labouring back towards them, 'I am weary,' he said; 'but I have brought back some hope. There is a deep wind-drift just round the turn, and I was nearly buried in it, but fortunately it is not wide. Beyond it the snow suddenly gets less. At the top of the slope it is barely a foot deep, and further down, white though it looks, it seems to be but a light coverlet: only a sprinkling in places.'

'It is the ill will of Caradras,' muttered Gimli. 'He does not love dwarves, or elves. He has cast his snow at us with special intent. That drift was devised to cut off our descent.'

'Then Caradras happily has forgotten that we have with us a mountaineer who knows his far kindred, the peaks of the Black Mountains,' said Gandalf. 'It was a good fortune that gave us Boromir as a member of our Company.'

'But how are *we* to get through this drift, even if we ever get as far as the turn?' asked Pippin, voicing the thoughts of all the hobbits.

'It is a pity,' said Legolas, 'that Gandalf cannot go before us with a bright flame, and melt us a path.'

'It is a pity that Elves cannot fly over mountains, and fetch the Sun to save them,' answered Gandalf. 'Even I need something to work on. I cannot burn snow. But I could turn Legolas into a flaming torch, if that will serve: he would burn bright while he lasted.'

'Spare me!' cried Legolas. 'I fear that a dragon is concealed in the shape of our wizard. Yet a tame dragon would be useful at this hour.'

'It will be a wild dragon, if you say any more,' said Gandalf.

'Well, well! *When heads are at a loss, bodies must serve*, as they say in my country,' said Boromir. 'I have some strength still left; and so has Aragorn. We must use that, while it lasts. I will

THE RING GOES SOUTH   171

carry one of the Little Folk, and he another. Two shall be set on the pony, and led by Gandalf.'

At once he set about unlading Bill. 'Aragorn and I will come back when we have got the Little Folk through,' he said. 'You, Legolas and Gimli, can wait here, or follow behind in our track, if you can.' He picked up Merry and set him on his shoulders. Trotter took Pippin. Frodo was mounted on the pony, with Sam clinging behind. They ploughed forward.

At last they reached and passed the turn, and came to the edge of the drift. Frodo marvelled at the strength of Boromir, seeing the passage that he had already forced through it with no better tool than his sword and his great arms.[25] Even now, burdened as he was with Merry clinging on his back, he was thrusting the snow forward and aside, and widening the passage for those who followed. Behind him Trotter was labouring. They were in the midst of the drift, and Boromir and Merry were almost through, when a rumbling stone fell from the slope above and, hurtling close to Frodo's head, thudded deep into the snow. But with the casting of that last stone the malice of the mountain seemed to be expended, as if it were satisfied that the invaders were in retreat and would not dare to return. There was no further mishap.

On the flat shelf above the steep slope they found, as Boromir had reported, that the snow was only shallow. There they waited, while Trotter and Boromir returned with the pony to fetch the packs and burdens and give some help to Legolas and the dwarf.

By the time they were all gathered together again morning was far advanced.

It was Gandalf's reply here ('It is a pity that Elves cannot fly over mountains, and fetch the Sun to save them') to Legolas' remark (originally Boromir's, VI.426) about melting a path that led to Legolas' saying in FR 'I go to find the Sun!', and was very probably (as I think) the source of the idea that the Elf, so far from being as helplessly marooned as Gimli, Gandalf, and the hobbits, could run upon the snow. It is noticeable that Gandalf's real ill-humour in the original version is here diminished, while in FR it has probably disappeared.

The remainder of the chapter is as in FR, but it ends thus:

The wind was blowing stiffly again over the pass that was hidden in cloud behind them; already a few flakes of snow were curling and drifting down. Caradras had defeated them. They

172   THE TREASON OF ISENGARD

turned their backs on the Dimrill Stair, and stumbled wearily down the slope.

NOTES

1 This refers to the story, first appearing in the original version of 'The Council of Elrond' (VI.407) and retained in the second (p. 112), that Gandalf came upon the hobbits walking in the woods in the afternoon following the Council.

2 This is probably the point at which my father determined on the change of *Galdor* to *Legolas* (see p. 141). Legolas Greenleaf the keen-eyed thus reappears after many years from the old tale of *The Fall of Gondolin* (II.189, etc.); he was of the House of the Tree in Gondolin, of which Galdor was the lord.

3 In fact, nine had been the original number, in the first sketch for 'The Council of Elrond' (VI.397): Frodo, Sam; Gandalf; Glorfindel; Trotter; Burin son of Balin; Merry, Folco, Odo. It is curious to see how close in its conception the complement of the Company was at the very beginning to the final form, though it was at once rejected.

4 On Erestor 'Half-elf' see VI.400 and note 17.

5 The word 'reduction' may however imply that the first of two alternative versions of the final 'Choosing of the Company' had already been written; see note 12.

6 This latter option survived into a typescript text made not long after (probably by myself), where the long and short openings of the chapter are set out one after the other as variants.

7 On the days of the week in relation to the dates see p. 14. Frodo's escape over the Ford of Bruinen took place on Thursday 20 October. If precisely three weeks are counted from that day we are brought to Thursday 10 November.

8 *Tharbad*: see the *Etymologies*, V.392, stem THAR; and see Map II on p. 305.

9 In the original form of the passage (VI.416) and in that in the second version of 'The Council of Elrond', as well as in the present text, my father wrote 'the *sources* of the Gladden'. This was obviously based on the Map of Wilderland in *The Hobbit*, where the Gladden, there of course unnamed, rises in several streams falling from the Misty Mountains (these are not shown on the First Map (Map II, p. 305), but the scale there is much smaller). In the typescript that followed the present text the typist put *source*, and my father corrected it to *sources*. I suspect therefore that *source* in FR is an error.

10 *Rhosgobel* has appeared previously, but as a subsequent addition

THE RING GOES SOUTH
173

to the fifth version of 'The Council of Elrond' (p. 149); the present passage is clearly where the name was devised. In *Brownhay* 'Brown' is evidently to be associated with Radagast 'the Brown', and 'hay' is the old word meaning 'hedge', as in the *High Hay, Ringhay* (= Crickhollow, VI.299). For the etymology of *Rhosgobel* see V.385, Noldorin *rhosc* 'brown' (stem RUSKĀ), and V.380, Noldorin *gobel* 'fenced homestead', as in *Tavrobel* (stem PEL(ES)).

11 *Redway*: original name of the Silverlode.

12 The brief account of the 'Choosing' given on p. 162 may be compared: 'In the end *after the matter had been much debated by Elrond and Gandalf* it was decided ... ' It is possible that this text followed the first and preceded the second of the alternative versions: my father referred to the second as the 'short version' (though it is not markedly shorter than the other), which may explain why he noted on the brief draft text that it was a sketch of a 'reduction' of the choosing of the Company. – As with the variant openings of the chapter (note 6) both alternatives were retained in the typescript.

13 A few minor changes were introduced (but not the mention of the lay of Beren and Lúthien heard by the hobbits in the Hall of Fire); Bilbo now refers to the fact that Frodo's sword had been broken (see p. 136, note 7), but does not produce the pieces (and the mailcoat remains 'elf-mail', not 'dwarf-mail').

14 In these workings the last verse (for which there is a preparatory note: 'He ends: but all the while he will think of Frodo') reads:

> But all the while I sit and think
> I listen for the door,
> and hope to hear the voices come
> I used to hear before.

This is the form of the verse in the typescript text, where the song first appears in the chapter.

15 A halfway stage is found in a draft for the passage: here there were still two pack-ponies, but one of them was the beast bought in Bree; this Sam addresses as 'Ferny', though it is also called 'Bill'. Cf. the note about Bill Ferny's pony given on p. 9: 'Does this remain at Rivendell? – Yes.'

16 *Eregion* was written in subsequently (this name appears in the isolated text given on p. 124). No Elvish name is given in the typescript.

17 This is the first occurrence of the name *Dwarrowdelf*. Cf. my father's letter to Stanley Unwin, 15 October 1937 (*Letters* no. 17): 'The real "historical" plural of *dwarf* ... is *dwarrows*, anyway: rather a nice word, but a bit too archaic. Still I rather wish I had used the word *dwarrow*.' – 'Black Gulf' as a translation of *Moria* is found several times in the original text of

174   THE TREASON OF ISENGARD

'The Ring Goes South', once as a correction of 'Black Pit' (VI.435, note 24).

18   This is the first occurrence of the Dwarvish name *Barazinbar*, concerning which my father wrote long after (in the notes referred to in VI.466, notes 36, 39) that Khuzdul *baraz* (BRZ) probably = 'red, or ruddy', and *inbar* (MBR) a horn, Sindarin *Caradhras* < *caran-rass* being a translation of the Dwarvish name. – Subsequently both *Caradhras* and *Caradras* occur as the manuscript was originally written, but the latter far more frequently.

19   On *Azanulbizâr* see VI.465, note 36. *Nanduhirion* here first occurs, but the form *Nanduhiriath* is found as an emendation to the text of the original version of the chapter, VI.433, note 13.

20   On *Dimrill Stair* as the name of the Redhorn Pass see p. 164.

21   The names of the other Mountains of Moria were not devised at once, however, since though entered on the manuscript they are still absent from the typescript, where my father inserted them in the same form. As first devised, the names of the other peaks were *Silverhorn*, *Celebras* (*Kelebras*) *the White* (in FR *Silvertine*, *Celebdil*), and *the Horn of Cloud*, *Fanuiras the Grey* (in FR *Cloudyhead*, *Fanuidhol*); the Dwarvish names were as in FR, *Baraz*, *Zirak*, *Shathûr* (but *Zirak* was momentarily *Zirik*). In the later notes referred to in note 18 my father said that since *Shathûr* was the basic Dwarvish name the element probably refers to 'cloud', and was probably a plural 'clouds'; *Bund(u)* in the fuller name *Bundu-shathûr* 'must therefore mean "head" or something similar. Possibly *bund* (BND) – *u* – *Shathûr* "head in/of clouds".' On *Zirak* and the longer form *Zirakzigil* see note 22.

22   When *Silverlode* superseded *Blackroot*, as it did before the original text of the 'Lothlórien' story was completed, the passage was changed to its form in FR: ' "Dark is the water of Kheled-zâram," said Gimli, "and cold are the springs of Kibil-nâla." ' The name *Kheledzâram* first appears in these variant passages; see VI.466, note 39, where I cited my father's much later note explaining the name as meaning 'glass-pool'. In the same notes he discussed the Dwarvish word for 'silver':

> *Zirak-zigil* should mean 'Silver-spike' (cf. 'Silvertine', and *Celebdil* < Sindarin *celeb* 'silver' + *till* 'tine, spike, point'). But 'silver' is evidently KBL in *Kibil-nâla* – KBL seems to have some connexion with Quenya *telep-* 'silver'. But all these peoples seem to have possessed various words for the precious metals, some referring to the material and its properties, some to their colour and other associations. So that *zirak* (ZRK) is probably another name for 'silver', or for its grey colour. *Zigil* is evidently a word for 'spike' (smaller and more slender than a 'horn'). Caradhras seems to have been a great mountain

THE RING GOES SOUTH   175

tapering upwards (like the Matterhorn), while Celebdil was simply crowned by a smaller pinnacle.

Still later pencilled notes reversed this explanation, suggesting that *zigil* (ZGL) meant 'silver' and *zirak* meant 'spike'. – Of *Kibil-nâla* my father noted that 'the meaning of *nâla* is not known. If it corresponds to *rant* [in *Celebrant*] and *lode* [in *Silverlode*], it should mean "path, course, rivercourse or bed".' He added later: 'It is probable that the Dwarves actually found silver in the river.'

23 *Deldúath*: 'Deadly Nightshade', Taur-na-Fuin; *Dor-Daedeloth*: 'Land of the Shadow of Dread', the realm of Morgoth. See references in the Index to Vol. V, entries *Deldúwath*, *Dor-Daideloth*.

24 Literally: 'fire be for saving of us'.

25 The passage that follows here must have been rejected as soon as written:

As he stepped forward Boromir suddenly stumbled on some hidden point of stone, and fell headlong. Trotter, who was just behind, was taken unawares and fell on top of him. Merry and Pippin were flung from their shoulders and vanished deep into the snow.

This, though changed to suit the altered story of the descent, was derived from the old version, VI.427.

IX

THE MINES OF MORIA (1):
THE LORD OF MORIA

It seems very probable, if not actually demonstrable, that a new version of the first part of the Moria story (corresponding to FR II Chapter 4, 'A Journey in the Dark') preceded the first draft of its continuation, and I therefore give the texts in their narrative sequence. The original draft of 'The Mines of Moria' (VI.445–60) had come to an end as the Company stood before the tomb of Balin, and at this time the narrative of *The Lord of the Rings* went no further – apart from a preliminary sketch of the further events in Moria, VI.442–3 and 462. This therefore is the last chapter for which formed narrative from an earlier phase of work existed.

In a manuscript that bears a distinct resemblance in style to that of the new version of 'The Ring Goes South' described in the last chapter, my father now rewrote the first part of the story of the journey through the Mines. As in the last chapter, there are a few pages of rough initial drafting for particular passages, but (unless more have been lost) the development of the new version was very largely achieved in the actual writing of this manuscript, which is a mass of (mostly small) corrections made at the time of composition. Of subsequent pencilled emendation there is not a great deal, for the text of FR II.4 was effectively reached here: for most of its length the only differences from the final form are extremely minor points of sentence structure and choice of words, with no significance for the narrative, and for substantial stretches the two texts are identical. There are however certain features where this is not the case.

The chapter, numbered XVI, was given a title, 'The Mines of Moria (i)'. Pencilled titles were written in beside this: 'The Lord of Moria' and 'The Tomb'; the latter was struck through, and the typescript that followed this manuscript was titled: 'The Mines of Moria (1): The Lord of Moria'. The original version had included the debate of the Company after the descent from the Pass of Cris-caron and the discussion of Moria in 'The Ring Goes South' (VI.428–30), and 'The Mines of Moria' had begun at 'Next day the weather changed again' (VI.445; FR p. 313). Now, of course, the new chapter XVI follows on from the end of the new chapter XV, and the division is as in FR.

Aragorn is called *Trotter* throughout, and throughout *Trotter* was changed later in pencil to *Elfstone* (see pp. 277–8).

THE LORD OF MORIA   177

In the debate of the Company Boromir's references to the geography of the southern lands are very curious (cf. FR p. 309):

> 'It is a name of ill-omen,' said Boromir. 'Nor do I see the need to go there. If we cannot cross the mountains, let us take the road to my land that I followed on my way hither: through Rohan and the country of Seven Streams. Or we could go on far into the South and come at length round the Black Mountains, and crossing the rivers Isen and Silverlode[1] enter Ond from the regions nigh the sea.'
>
> 'Things have changed since you came north, Boromir,' said Gandalf. 'Did you not hear what I told of Saruman? We must not come near Isengard or the Gap of Rohan. As for the even longer road, we cannot afford the time. . . .'

The remainder of Gandalf's reply is very much as in FR, except that he tells Boromir that 'you are free to leave us and return to Minas Tirith by any road you choose.'

The 'Seven Rivers' have been referred to in the first version of Gandalf's story to the Council of Elrond, where he reported Radagast's words to him (p. 132): 'even if you set out this hour you will hardly come to him [Saruman] before the Nine cross the Seven Rivers' (in the next version this becomes 'before the Nine have crossed the seventh river', p. 149).

Features of the geography much further to the South were already in being. Before the story had got very much further it is made plain that 'the Land of Seven Streams' lay 'between the mountains [i.e. the Black Mountains, the later White Mountains] and the sea' (see p. 272); yet Boromir's words here seem only to allow of a quite contrary interpretation of 'the country of Seven Streams'. The choices he proposes are essentially as in FR: through Rohan from the West (i.e. passing through the Gap of Rohan) and so to Minas Tirith, or going on South, crossing the Isen, and coming to Minas Tirith through the lands between the mountains and the sea; but they will traverse 'the country of Seven Streams' if they choose the *first* option, and pass north of the mountains. I cannot explain this, except on the assumption that it was a mere slip, or else on the assumption that the geography of these regions was still in a more fluid state than one would otherwise suppose.

The river Isen first appears here in the narrative,[2] and the 'Silverlode', which was afterwards the 'Blackroot', the two names being transposed (see p. 235). In this passage also are the first occurrences of an Elvish name for Sauron's dwelling in Southern Mirkwood, and of the name *Barad-dûr*:

> 'I alone of you have ever been in the dungeons of the Dark Lord;

178   THE TREASON OF ISENGARD

and only in his older and lesser dwelling at Dol-Dúgol in Southern Mirkwood. Those who pass the gates of Barad-dûr, the Dark Tower in the Land of Shadow, do not return.'

The confusion over Thrór and Thráin is no longer present: 'Yet it will not be the first time that I have been to Moria: I sought there long for Thráin son of Thrór after he was lost.' And Trotter utters his warning to Gandalf (on the change of rôles between Gandalf and Trotter in their willingness to consider the passage of Moria see p. 168).

The episode of the attack by the Wargs enters in this text, and reached virtually the final form outright, with relatively little correction in the course of composition;[3] and the account of the journey of the Company from the little hill where the attack took place to the arrival of Gandalf, Gimli, and Frodo at the top of the steps by the Stair Falls reaches the FR text in almost every point.[4] But Gandalf's words when they saw what had happened to the Gate-stream were much changed. At first he made no reference to the Door(s); then the following was substituted:

'That is where the Door stood once upon a time,' said Gandalf pointing across the water to the cliff opposite. But Frodo could see nothing that marked the spot, unless it was some bushes at the foot of the wall, and some rotting stems and branches that stood up from the water near its further side.

This was in turn rejected and replaced by:

'That is where the Doors stood once upon a time,' said Gandalf pointing across the water. 'There was the Elven-door at the end of the road from Hollin by which we have come, [*struck out:* and the Dwarven-door further south]. We must get across [*struck out:* to the Elven-door] as quickly as we can. This way is blocked....'

The idea that there were two distinct western entrances to Moria had appeared in the original version, where Gandalf said (VI.429): 'There were two secret gates on the western side, though the chief entrance was on the East.' Gandalf's words in the present passage in FR (p. 315): 'And there the Gate stood once upon a time, *the Elven Door* at the end of the road from Hollin by which we have come' derive from this, although in the context of FR, where there is no 'Dwarven Door', the 'Elven Door' is understood in relation to what Gandalf said subsequently: 'the West-door was made chiefly for [the Elves'] use in their traffic with the Lords of Moria' (an idea which in fact goes back to the original version, VI.448: 'the westgates were

THE LORD OF MORIA
179

made chiefly for their use in their traffic with the dwarves'). See further p. 191 and note 3.

The many references to the Moon in this part of the chapter were almost all removed by emendation to the typescript that followed this manuscript, and do not appear in FR. All references to the time of day, and the sunset, are here precisely as in FR to this point in the story, but after the words 'The day was drawing to its end' (FR p. 315) my father wrote: 'and the moon was already shining on the edge of the sunset', where FR has 'and cold stars were glinting in the sky high above the sunset'. As Pippin, the last in the Company (in FR Sam), stepped onto the dry ground after wading through the 'green and stagnant pool' (following the old version: in FR 'a narrow creek') at the northernmost end of the lake, and there was 'a swish, followed by a plop' in the distant water, 'at that moment shadows came over the last gleams of the sunset, and the rising moon was veiled in a passing cloud.' 'Rising' can only be a slip without significance; but here FR has: 'The dusk deepened, and the last gleams of the sunset were veiled in cloud.' The two great holly-trees beneath the cliff stood 'stiff, dark, and silent, throwing deep shadows in the moon', where FR has 'throwing deep night-shadows about their feet'. Thus in FR there is no reference to the moon until Gandalf passed his hands over the smooth space on the cliff-wall and 'The Moon now shone upon the grey face of the rock'.

After this point, other references to the Moon were similarly removed. When Gandalf's spells had no effect, it is said here that 'the moon shone pale, the wind blew cold, and the doors stood fast'; in FR 'the countless stars were kindled,' etc. When the doors at last opened, 'a shadowy stair could be seen climbing steeply up. The moonlight fell upon the lower steps, but beyond the darkness was deeper than night'; in FR the reference to the moonlight on the steps is absent. The tentacles of the Watcher in the Water 'came wriggling over the threshold, glistening in the moon', where FR (p. 322) has 'glistening in the starlight'. But inside Moria, when Gandalf stood in doubt before the archway opening into three passages, and said in the present text 'It is all night inside here; but outside the moon has long sunk and the night is getting old [> the moon is sinking and the dark hours are passing]', in FR he said 'outside the late Moon is riding westward and the middle-night has passed.'

My father had said that six nights before, the first night march of the Company from Hollin (p. 167), the Moon was 'almost at the full' ('at the full', FR); and on the previous night, when the Wargs attacked again, 'the night was old, and westward the waning moon was setting' (so also in FR). My father had forgotten this, and as he wrote the present version he evidently saw a young moon in the West ('shining on the edge of the sunset'). When he realised that the moon must now be almost into its last quarter and rising late he changed the text as

180   THE TREASON OF ISENGARD

described above; but surely the reference to the moon shining on the cliff-face should have been removed with all the others?[5]

A narrative element that came to nothing is seen in some rejected passages. While Gandalf was 'gazing at the blank wall of the cliff' (FR p. 317) it is said that Legolas (who in FR was 'pressed against the rock, as if listening') 'exploring southward along the lake-side was lost in the twilight'; and when the ripples on the water came closer to the shore 'the voice of Legolas was calling; his feet were running in haste towards them.' As Bill the pony dashed away into the darkness 'Legolas ran up breathless with his drawn knife in his hand; he was talking wildly in the elvish tongue' – but this was evidently rejected as soon as written in view of what is said subsequently, when Gandalf drove the Company into the doorway: 'Legolas at last came running up, gasping for breath' and sprang over the tentacles that were already fingering the cliff-wall; 'Gimli grasped him by the hand and dragged him inside.' It was at this point that my father abandoned the idea.[6]

As first written, the description of the design that Gandalf brought to light was scarcely developed from the original account (VI.449). Beneath the arch of interlacing letters 'in the elvish character' there were 'the outlines of an anvil and hammer surmounted by a crown and crescent moon. More clearly than all else there shone forth three stars with many rays.' It is now Gimli, not Gandalf, who says 'There are the emblems of Durin!', and Legolas says 'And there are the star-tokens of the High-elves!' Gandalf still says that 'they are made of some silver substance that is seen only when touched by one who knows certain words', but he adds: 'and I guess too that they shine only in the moonlight' (in the original text, when the story was that the sun was shining on the cliff-wall, he said 'at night under the moon they shine most bright'). His words were changed, apparently at once, to the text of FR: 'They are made of *ithildin*[7] that mirrors only the starlight and the moonlight, and sleeps until it is touched by one who speaks words now long forgotten in Middle-earth.'

The description of the design itself was changed to read:

... the outlines of an anvil and hammer surmounted by a crown with seven stars. Below were two trees bearing a crescent moon. More clearly than all else there shone forth in the middle of the door a single star with many rays.

'There are the emblems of Durin!' cried Gimli.

'And there is the Tree of the High-elves!' said Legolas.

'They are made of *ithildin*,' said Gandalf...

Gandalf's reference in FR to 'the Star of the House of Fëanor' is thus absent.

There is found in this manuscript, as an integral part of the text, the

THE LORD OF MORIA

181

earliest drawing of the arch and the signs beneath (reproduced on p. 182).[8] It will be seen that this drawing fits the *revised* description, in that the crown is accompanied by seven stars, there are two trees surmounted by crescent moons, and there is only one star in the centre, not three as in the first description. The natural assumption would be that the alteration of the description in the text, which stands on the page preceding the drawing, was made immediately; but in that case it is very puzzling that a little later in this version, when Gandalf uttered the word *Mellon*, 'the *three stars* shone out briefly, and faded again' (which was not corrected).

Taum Santoski has provided the explanation of this characteristic textual impasse. The fuzziness at the top of the trees is caused by heavy erasures; and he suggests that in the drawing as it was originally made, accompanying the first description in the text, there were three stars: the one in the centre was retained, but the two to either side were erased and replaced by trees. I have no doubt whatever that this is the correct solution. The revised description in the text thus fits the revised drawing; and at that time my further merely failed to notice the subsequent reference to the three stars when Gandalf spoke the word *Mellon*.

An erasure above the crown shows that there was originally a crescent moon here, as in the first form of the description. Taum Santoski has also been able to see that in a preliminary stage of the introduction of the two trees they were larger, and each had both a circle (whether a sun or a full moon) and a crescent above it.[9]

When Gandalf was striving to find the spell that would open the doors he said that he once knew 'every spell in all the tongues of Elf, Dwarf, or Goblin' (FR 'of Elves or Men or Orcs') that was ever so used; he did not say 'I shall not have to call on Gimli for words of the secret dwarf-tongue that they teach to none'; and he declared that 'the opening word was Elvish' (FR 'the opening words were Elvish') – anticipating the solution of the riddle. The words of the first spell that Gandalf tried remain exactly as in the original version (VI.451); but as already indicated the opening word is now *Mellon* as in FR, not the plural *Mellyn* as formerly.

When Frodo asked Gandalf what he thought of the monster in the water of the lake (FR p. 323) Gandalf at first replied: 'I do not know. I have never before seen or heard tell of such a creature'. This was struck out and replaced by the words in FR, 'but the arms were all guided by one purpose'. Possibly in relation to this, there is a pencilled note at this point in the manuscript: '? Insert words of Gimli saying that there were traditions among the Dwarves about strangling fingers in the dark.' -- 'Goblins' appear again, as in the old version, where FR has 'Orcs', in Gandalf's 'There are older and fouler things than goblins in the deep places of the world.'

In the account of the two long marches through Moria there are

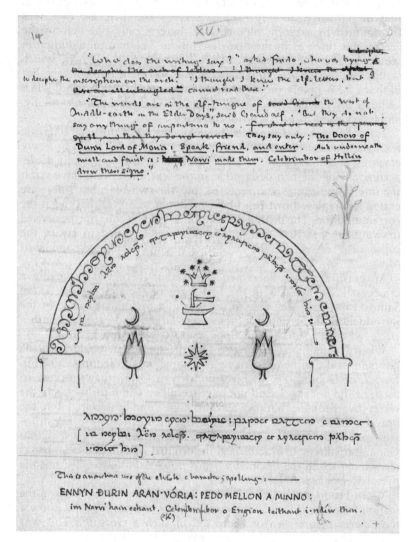

The West Gate of Moria:
the earliest drawing of the inscription and signs.

THE LORD OF MORIA   183

scarcely any differences to be remarked. It is 'the hobbits' (not Pippin) who dared not make the leap over the great fissure (FR p. 325); and Sam's mention of rope ('I knew I'd want it, if I hadn't got it!') is absent – just as the passage in which he goes through his belongings before leaving Rivendell and discovers that he has no rope ('Well, I'll want it. I can't get it now', FR p. 294) is absent from the preceding chapter (p. 165).[10]

When the Company came to the great hall in which they passed the second night (and which Gandalf declared, as in FR, was a good deal higher than 'the Dimrill Gate'), Gimli replied thus to Sam's question 'They didn't live down in these nasty darksome holes, surely?':

'They were not nasty holes, and even now they are not so, unless others than the dwarves here made them so. How would you have passed through, and breathed and lived, if it were not for the skill of the builders long ago? Though many shafts, I doubt not, are blocked and broken with the years, the air still flows and is for the most part good. And of old the halls and mines were not darksome

Here the text breaks off, all of Gimli's speech being struck through and replaced by his words in FR: 'These are not holes. This is the great realm and city of the Dwarrowdelf. And of old it was not darksome but full of light and splendour, as [I will sing you a song >] is still remembered in our songs.' There is an isolated draft for this rejected speech of Gimli's, in which it is completed: 'And of old they were not darksome: they were lit with many lights and sparkled with polished metals and with gems.'

Gimli's song here appears (in a rider to the manuscript) written out clear in its final form (but with *countless lamps* for *shining lamps* in the third verse, and *There ruby, beryl, opal pale* for *There beryl, pearl, and opal pale* in the fourth). A few pages of rough drafting are found (one of which begins with the draft of Gimli's words in praise of Moria just mentioned), but these do not carry the development of the song very far; more workings must have been lost. Only the verse beginning *The world was fair, the mountains tall* was achieved here, and there is little else save fragmentary and rejected lines. There is also drafting (no doubt the earliest) for a form in four-line stanzas with a rhyme scheme *aaba* and internal rhyme in the third line; of this three quatrains were completed:

> *The world was young, the mountains green,*
> *No mark upon the moon was seen,*
> *When Durin came and gave their name*
> *To lands where none before had been.*
>   *nameless lands had been.*

184   THE TREASON OF ISENGARD

The world was fair, the mountains tall,
With gold and silver gleamed his hall,
When Durin's throne of carven stone
Yet stood behind the guarded wall.

The world is dark, the mountains old,
In shadow lies the heapéd gold;
In Durin's halls no hammer falls,
The forges' fires are grey and cold.

Among many other half-formed lines or couplets are:

When Durin woke and gave to gold
its first and secret name of old

When Durin came to Azanûl
and found and named the nameless pool[11]

There are also the isolated words *Where Nenechui cold* > *Where cold Echuinen spills*. *Nen Echui* has occurred as the Noldorin name for *Cuiviénen*, the Waters of Awakening (V.366, 406); here my father was pondering its application to Mirrormere (for the much later Elvish name *Nen Cenedril* 'Lake Looking-glass' see VI.466, note 39).

On one of the pages of drafting for Gimli's song my father wrote: 'Gandalf on *Ithil Thilevril*[12] *Mithril*' (i.e. Gandalf is to speak on this subject). This is the first appearance of the name *Mithril*, replacing the passing *Thilevril, Ithil,* and the original *Erceleb* (see VI.458 and notes 34–5); and an isolated page of drafting shows my father developing Gandalf's account of it. This text begins with various forms of Gandalf's reply to Sam's question 'Are there piles of jewels and gold lying about here then?' Several answers to this question were tried. In one Gandalf said: 'There may be. . . . For the wealth of Durin was very great: not only in such things as were found in the Mines themselves. There was a great traffic to his gates from East and West.' In another he said: 'No. The dwarves carried much away; and though the dread of its dark mazes has protected Moria from Men and Elves it has not defended it from the goblins, who have often invaded it and plundered it.' Against these my father wrote: 'Mithril is now nearly all lost. Orcs plunder it and pay tribute to Sauron who is collecting it – we don't know why – for some secret purpose of his   weapons not for beauty.'[13]

The final version here, written in a rapid scrawl with pencilled additions and alterations, is as follows:

'No one knows,' said Gandalf. 'None have dared to seek for the armouries and treasure chambers down in the deep places since the dwarves fled. Unless it be plundering orcs. It is said that they were laid under spells and curses, when the dwarves fled.'

THE LORD OF MORIA

'They were,' said Gimli, 'but orcs have plundered often inside Moria nonetheless [*added:* and nought is left in the upper halls].'

'They came here because of Mithril,' said Gandalf. 'It was for that that Moria was of old chiefly renowned, and it was the foundation of the wealth and power of Durin: only in Moria was mithril found save rarely and scantily. Moria-silver or true-silver some have called it. Mithril was the Elvish name: the dwarves have a name which they will not tell. Its value was thrice that of gold, and now is beyond price. It was nearly as heavy as lead, malleable as copper, but the dwarves could by some secret of theirs make it as hard as [> harder than] steel. It surpassed common silver in all save beauty, and even in that it is its equal. [*Added:* It was used by the Elves who dearly loved it – among many other things they [?wrought] it to make *ithildin*. *Also perhaps to be placed here:* ... the dwarflords of Khazad-dûm were wealthier than any of the Kings of Men, and the traffic to the Gatés brought them jewels and treasure from many lands of East and West.] Bilbo had a corslet of mithril-rings that Thorin gave him. I wonder what he did with it. I never told him, but its worth was greater than the value of the Shire and everything in it.'[14]

[*Added:* Frodo laid his hand under his tunic, and felt the rings of the mail-shirt, and felt somewhat staggered to think he was walking about with the price [of the] Shire...]

The text of the passage that appears in the completed manuscript is very close to FR. It is still said that *mithril* was not found only in Moria: 'Here alone in the world, save rarely and scantily in far eastern mountains, was found Moria-silver.' The reference to Bilbo's having given his mailcoat to 'Michel Delving Museum' (not 'Mathom-house') appears.

But there is one important difference. It is said in this text: 'The dwarves tell no tale, but even as *mithril* was the foundation of their wealth so also it was their destruction: they delved too greedily and too deep, and disturbed that from which they fled.'[15] This is exactly as in FR, but without the last two words: *Durin's Bane.* In this connection also, where Gandalf says in FR: 'And since the dwarves fled, no one dares to seek the shafts and treasuries down in the deep places: they are drowned in water – or in a shadow of fear', my father first wrote in this manuscript: '...some are drowned in water, and some are full of the evil from which the dwarves fled and of which they will not speak.' This was changed to: '... they are drowned in water – or in shadow.'

The absence of the words 'Durin's Bane' does not of course prove that the conception of 'Durin's Bane' had not yet arisen; while a feeling that the words 'some are *full of the evil* from which the dwarves fled' are not really appropriate to the Balrog is too slight to build on. That there was a Balrog in Moria appears in the original sketch for the story given in VI.462. Even so, I think it probable that at this stage it was not the Balrog that had caused the flight of the Dwarves from the great Dwarrowdelf long before. The strongest evidence for this comes from the original version of the Lothlórien story, where it is at least strongly suggested (being represented as the opinion of the Lord and Lady of Lothlórien) that the Balrog had been sent from Mordor not long since (see further on this question p. 247 and note 11). Moreover, in the texts of the story of the Bridge of Khazad-dûm from this time Gimli does not cry out 'Durin's Bane!' (pp. 197, 202–3).

I think also that Gandalf is represented as not knowing himself what was the evil from which the Dwarves fled (it cannot be said, of course, what my father knew).[16]

There is nothing else to note in the remainder of the chapter except the Runic inscription on the tomb of Balin (on which see the Appendix on Runes, pp. 456–7). Gandalf's words about the inscription differ from what he says in FR: 'These are dwarf-runes, such as they use in the North. Here is written in the old tongue and the new: *Balin son of Fundin, Lord of Moria.*' In FR he says: 'These are Daeron's Runes, such as were used of old in Moria. Here is written in the tongues of Men and Dwarves...'

The inscription is written on a strip of blue paper,[17] and since that could not be reproduced in black and white there is here reproduced instead the version from the typescript that followed the manuscript, this being very closely similar to the first in its design and identical in all its forms.

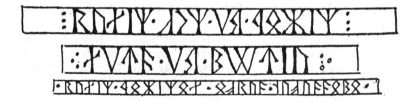

The inscription reads:

    BALIN SON OF FUNDIN
      LORD OF MORIA
   Balin Fundinul Uzbad Khazaddūmu

THE LORD OF MORIA 187

NOTES

1 *Silverlode* was changed in pencil to *Blackroot*; see p. 235. At the same time *Ond* was changed to *Ondor*.

2 On the First Map the name was first *Iren*, changed to *Isen*; see p. 298.

3 Gandalf's cry as he tossed the blazing brand into the air (FR p. 312) here takes the form: *Naur ad i gaurhoth!*

4 The references to the 'power that wished now to have a clear light in which things that moved in the wild could be seen from far away', and Gandalf's remark that 'here Aragorn cannot guide us; he has seldom walked in this country', are lacking; while a comment is made in this text on the fact of the land in which Gandalf sought for the Sirannon, the Gate-stream, being 'bleak and dry': 'not a flake of snow seemed to have fallen there.'

5 The change in the present text of 'outside the moon has long sunk' to 'outside the moon is sinking' implies the corrected view of the moon's phase, but none of the previous references were emended on the manuscript.

6 This is a convenient place to mention a textual detail. Gimli says that Dwarf-doors are invisible when shut, 'and their own makers cannot find them or open them, if their secret is forgotten.' *Makers* is certain (but could be misread), and seems altogether more appropriate and likely than *masters*. This, appearing in the first typescript of the chapter, was clearly an error, perpetuated in FR (p. 317).

7 The name *ithildin* was devised here. My father first wrote *starmoon or thilevril* (on *thilevril* see p. 184 and note 12).

8 This has been previously reproduced by Humphrey Carpenter, *Biography*, facing p. 179. – The writing on the arch, but nothing more, appears in the original version of the chapter, VI.450.

9 The trees in the design reproduced on p. 182 are of a highly stylized form seen frequently in my father's pictures (for example, the tree in the drawing of Lake-town in *The Hobbit*). These trees might be further formalized into geometrical shapes, or their surfaces cut into planes (so that they appear like rocks rising from trunks). The tree pencilled in above the arch, with distinct branches, single large leaves, and a crescent moon as its topmost growth, was the model for a second version of the design (also at Marquette University), which differs from the first only in the form of the trees. It may be that it was to this that the corrected text in the manuscript refers, since the trees are said to *bear* crecent moons. In a third version (in the Bodleian Library) the trees, much larger, still bear a crescent moon at the summit, but the branches also curl over into crescents (as in the final form). A fourth version (also in the Bodleian) differs from the final form

188 THE TREASON OF ISENGARD

only in that the branches pass behind and do not entwine the pillars.

It can be seen in the narrative passage above the first version of the design that the name *Narvi* was first spelt *Narf[i]*, as in the original text (VI.449). The stroke through the first *m* of *Celebrimbor* in the transcription of the *tengwar* at the bottom of the page removes an erroneous *m*; the stroke through the second removes a necessary *m*. – The second *tengwa* in the penultimate word of the inscription, transliterated as *i·ndíw*, is used in the words *ennyn* and *minno* to represent *nn*, not *nd*. Perhaps to be connected with this is the form of the eighth *tengwa* in *Celebrimbor*, which would naturally be interpreted as *mm*, not *mb*.

10   The origin of Gandalf's sword Glamdring is still referred to here, as in VI.454, since the passage where it occurs in FR (p. 293), the account of the arms borne by the members of the Company, had not yet been added to the previous chapter.

11   Cf. VI.466, note 36.

12   *Thilevril* was thus a rejected possibility for both *ithildin* and *mithril* (see note 7).

13   Another draft puts this slightly more fully: 'They give it in tribute to Sauron, who has long been gathering and hoarding all that he can find. It is not known why: not for beauty, but for some secret purpose in the making of weapons of war.'

14   This is the point (at least in terms of actual record) at which the connection was made between *mithril* or 'Moria-silver' and Bilbo's mailcoat, ultimately leading to an alteration in the text of *The Hobbit*, Chapter XIII: see VI.465–6, notes 35, 38. The mailcoat will no longer be called 'elf-mail' (see p. 173, note 13).

15   A final draft for this passage ends illegibly: 'The dwarves will not say what happened; but mithril is rich only far down and northward towards the roots of Caradras, and some ... [?think] they disturbed some [?guarding]'. – *Caradras* is spelt thus also in the text of the passage in the completed manuscript; see p. 174, note 18.

16   In the fifth version of 'The Council of Elrond' (p. 142) Glóin says that the Dwarves of Moria 'delved immeasurably deep', and 'under the foundations of the hills things long buried were waked at last from sleep'.

In FR there seems to be some ambiguity on the question of what Gandalf knew. He says that the Dwarves fled from Durin's Bane; but when the Balrog appeared, and Gimli cried out 'Durin's Bane!', he muttered: 'A Balrog! Now I understand.' (These words, like Gimli's cry, are lacking in the versions of the scene from this time, pp. 197, 202–3). What did Gandalf mean? That he understood now that the being that had entered the Chamber of Mazarbul and striven with him for the mastery

THE LORD OF MORIA   189

through the closed door was a Balrog? Or that he understood at last what it was that had destroyed Durin? Perhaps he meant both; for if he had known what Durin's Bane was, would he not have surmised, with horror, what was on the other side of the door? – 'I have never felt such a challenge', 'I have met my match, and have nearly been destroyed.'

17 The blue paper is from the cover of one of the booklets of the 'August 1940' examination script, which my father was still using for drafting. The strip was pasted onto the manuscript page, covering an earlier form of the Runic inscription; for this see the Appendix on Runes, p. 457.

X

THE MINES OF MORIA (2):
THE BRIDGE

We come at last to the point where my father took up the narrative again beside Balin's tomb in Moria. A sketch for the fight in the Chamber of Mazarbul was in existence (VI.443), going back to the time when he wrote the original text of 'Moria (i)', and this sketch he now for the most part followed closely. There was also a sketch from the same time (VI.462) of Gandalf's encounter on the bridge and his fall, when his opponent was to be a Black Rider.

The new chapter, numbered XVII, was entitled 'The Mines of Moria (ii)', and corresponds to Book II Chapter 5 in FR, 'The Bridge of Khazad-dûm'. The original manuscript is in pencil, ink, and ink over pencil, and was written on the same 'August 1940' examination script as was used for so much of the preceding work. It is a very rough draft indeed: parts of it would be quite beyond the limits of legibility were it not for clues provided by later texts. Some very minor editorial alteration is made here in respect of punctuation and the breaking of sentences, increasing the readability and comprehensibility of the text though disguising the furious haste in which it was written.

That this manuscript followed the new text of 'The Ring Goes South' is seen at once from the occurrence of the name *Blackroot* (the later *Silverlode*) in the Book of Mazarbul; for *Blackroot* replaced *Redway* as that text was being written (p. 166). For evidence that it followed the second version of 'Moria (i)' see note 3.

Two notes are written at the head of the first page: '2 West Gates' (see note 3), and 'No dates in Book'.

THE MINES OF MORIA (ii)

The Company of the Ring stood some time in silence beside the tomb of Balin. Frodo thought of Bilbo and his friendship with the dwarf, and Balin's visit to Bilbo long ago.

After a while they looked about the chamber to see if they could discover any tidings or signs of Balin's people. There was another door on the other side, under the shaft. By both doors they now saw that in the dust were lying many bones, and among them broken swords, and axe-heads, cloven shields and

THE BRIDGE 191

helms. Some of the swords were crooked: orc-weapons with black blades.

There were recesses and shelves cut in the wall, and in them were large iron-bound chests: all had been broken open and plundered; but beside the broken lid of one lay the tattered fragments of a book. It had been hewn with a sword and stabbed, and was so stained with dark marks like old blood that only little of it could be read. It only a cover [sic][1] and much was missing or in small pieces. Gandalf laid it carefully on the slab and pored over it; it was written in dwarvish and elvish script by many different hands.

'It is a record of the fortunes of Balin's folk,' said the wizard, 'and seems to begin with their coming to the Great Gate 20 years ago. Listen!

'*We drove out Orcs from ... first hall. We slew many under the bright sun in the Dale. Flói was killed by an arrow. He slew... We have occupied* [> *taken*] *the Twenty-first Hall of North-end* [added: *to dwell in*]. *There is there ... shaft is... Balin has set up his seat in the Chamber of Mazarbul ... gold ... Durin's axe. Balin is Lord of Moria ... We found true-silver... Well-forged ... (To)morrow Óin is ... seek* [> *Óin to seek*] *for the upper armouries and treasury of the Third Deep ... mithril.*

'There are one or two more rather ill-written and much-damaged pages of that sort. Then there must be a number missing, and some I cannot read. Let me see. No, it is burned and cut and stained. I can't read that. Wait! Ah, here is one more recent, well-written. Fifth year of their colony. Look – a large hasty hand and using *elvish* character!

'*Balin Lord of Moria fell in Dimrill Dale. He went alone to look in Mirror-mere. an orc shot him from behind a stone. We slew the orc, but many ... up from East up Blackroot...* Now two lines are gone. *We have barred the Gates.* No more is clear on that page. What is this? The last written page – rest seems blank [> stuck to the cover]. *We cannot get out. We cannot get out. The Pool is up to the Wall in the West. There lies the Watcher in the Water. It took Óin. We cannot get out.*

'*They have taken the Gates. Frár and Lóni and Náli*[2] *fell there ... noise in the Deeps.* Poor things. They could not get out by either Gate. It was perhaps well for us that the water had sunk somewhat, and that the Watcher was guarding the Dwarf-door not the Elfdoor we came by.[3] *The last thing written*,'

192   THE TREASON OF ISENGARD

said Gandalf, 'is a hasty scrawl in elf-letters. *They are coming.*'

He looked round. 'They seem to have made a last stand by both the doors of this chamber,' he said. 'But there were not many left by that time. So ended the attempt to re-take Moria. It was brave but foolish. The time is not yet. Their end must have been desperate. But I fear we must now say farewell to Balin son of Fundin: he was a noble dwarf. Here may he lie in the halls of his fathers. We will take this book, and look at it more carefully later. You had better keep it, Frodo, and give it to Bilbo. It will interest him though I fear it will grieve him.[4] I think I know where we are now. This must be the Chamber of Mazarbul and that hall the 21st Hall of the North-end. Then we ought to leave either by the south or the east arch in the hall, or possibly by this other eastward door here. I think we will return to the Hall. Come, let us go! The morning is passing.'

At that very moment there was a great sound, a great rolling *boom* that seemed to come from far below and to tremble in the stone at their feet. They sprang to the door in alarm. But even as they did so there was an echoing blast; a great horn was being blown in the hall, and answering horns and harsh cries were heard in the corridors; there was a hurrying sound of many feet.

'Fool that I have been!' cried Gandalf, 'to delay here. We are nicely trapped just as they were before. But I was not here then: we will see what—'

Boom came the shuddering noise again, and the walls shook.

'Slam the doors and wedge them!' shouted Trotter. 'And keep your packs on: we may get a chance to cut a way out.'

'No!' said Gandalf. 'Wedge them but keep them just ajar. We must not get shut in. We'll go by the further door if we get a chance.'

There was another harsh horn-call and shrill cries coming down the corridor. There was a ring and clatter as the Company drew their weapons. [*Added:* Glamdring and Sting were shining with whitish flames, glinting at the edges.] Boromir thrust wedges of broken blades and splinters of wooden chest under the bottom of the western door by which they had entered. Then Gandalf went and stood behind it. 'Who comes here to disturb the rest of Balin Lord of Moria?' he cried in a loud voice.

There was a rush of hoarse laughter like the fall of a slide of stones into a pit, but amid the clamour there was one deep voice. *Boom boom boom* went the noises in the deep. Swiftly

THE BRIDGE   193

Gandalf went to the opening and thrust forward his staff. There was a blinding flash that lit the chamber and the passage beyond. For an instant Gandalf looked out. Arrows whined and whistled down the corridor as he sprang back.

'There are goblins: very many of them,' he said. 'Evil they look and large: black Orcs.[5] They are for the moment hanging back, but there is something else there. A troll, I think, or more than one. There is no hope of escape that way.'

'And no hope at all if they come at the other door as well,' said Boromir.

'But there is no sound outside,' said Trotter, who was standing by the eastern entrance listening. 'The passage here goes down steps: it [?prob(ably)] does not give on to the hall at all. Our only chance is to gather here. Do what damage we can to the attackers and then fly down these steps. If only we could block the door as we went: but they both open inwards.'

Heavy feet were heard in the corridor. Boromir kicked the wedges away from the west door and heaved it to.[6] They retreated toward the still open eastern door, first Pippin and Merry, then Legolas, then Frodo with Sam at his side, then Boromir, Trotter, and last Gandalf. But they had no chance to fly yet. There was a heavy blow at the door, and it quivered; and immediately it began to move inwards grinding at the wedges and thrusting them back. An enormous arm and shoulder with dark green scaly skin (or clad in some horrible mesh) thrust through the widening gap. Then a great three-toed foot was thrust in also. There was dead silence outside.

Boromir leaped forward and hewed the arm with his sword[7] but it glanced aside and fell from his shaken hand: the blade was notched.

Frodo suddenly, and very unexpectedly, felt a great wrath leap up in his heart. 'The Shire,' he cried, and ran forward with Sting stabbing at the hideous foot. There was a bellow and the foot jerked back, nearly wrenching the blade from his hand: drops dripped from it and smoked on the stone.

'One for the Shire!' cried Trotter delightedly. 'You have a good blade, Frodo son of Drogo.' Sam looked as if for the first time he really liked Trotter. There was a crash and another crash: rocks were being heaved with huge strength against the door. It staggered back and the opening widened. Arrows came whistling in, but struck the north wall and fell to the ground. The horns rang again, there was a rush of feet, and orcs one

194   THE TREASON OF ISENGARD

after another leaped in. Then Legolas loosed his bow. Two fell pierced through the throat. The sword of Elendil struck down others.[8] Boromir laid about him and the orcs [?feared] his sword. One that dived under his arm was cloven ... by Gimli's axe. Thirteen orcs they slew and the others fled. 'Now is the time if ever,' said [Trotter >] Gandalf, '– before that Troll-chief or more of them return. Let us go!'

But even as they retreated once more a huge orc-chief, almost man-high, clad in black mail from head to foot, leaped through the door. Behind him but not yet daring to advance stood many followers. His eyes were like coals of fire. He wielded a great spear. Boromir who was at the rear turned, but with a thrust of his shield the orc put aside his stroke and with huge strength bore him back and flung him down. Then leaping with the speed of a snake he charged and smote with his spear straight at Frodo. The blow caught him on the right side. Frodo was hurled against the wall and pinned. Sam with a cry hewed at the spear and it broke. ... but even as the orc cast the shaft aside and drew his scimitar the sword of Elendil drove down upon his helm. There was a flash like flame and the helm burst. The orc-chieftain fell with cloven head. His followers who were ... by the now nearly open door yelled and fled in dismay. *Boom, boom* went the noises in the Deep. The great voice rolled out again.

'Now!' said Gandalf. 'Now is the last chance!' He picked up Frodo and sprang through the eastern door. The others followed. Trotter the last to leave pulled the door behind him. It had a great iron ring on either side, but no lock to be seen.

'I am all right,' gasped Frodo. 'Put me down!'

Gandalf nearly dropped him in amazement.

Without striking out this last passage my father at once went on to rewrite it:

'Now!' cried Gandalf. 'Now is the last chance!' Trotter picked up Frodo and sprang through the eastern door. Even in the heat of battle Gimli bowed to Balin's tomb. Boromir heaved the door to: it had a great iron ring on each side but the key was gone and the lock broken.

'I am all right,' gasped Frodo. 'Put me down!'

Trotter nearly dropped him in amazement. 'I thought you were dead,' he cried. 'Not yet,' said Gandalf turning round. 'But there is no time [*struck out:* to count (*sc.* wounds)].[9] Get away

THE BRIDGE   195

down these stairs, and look out! Wait a moment for me and then run: bear right and south.'

As they went down the dark stairs they saw the pale light gleam from the wizard's staff. He was still standing by the closed door. Frodo leaning on Sam halted a moment and peered back. Gandalf seemed to be thrusting the tip of his staff into the ancient keyhole.

Suddenly there was a flash more dazzling ... [than] any that they had ever conceived of. They all turned. There was a deafening crash. The swords in their hands leaped and wrenched in their fingers, and they stumbled and fell to their knees as the great blast passed down the stairway. Into the midst of them fell Gandalf.

'Well, that's that,' he said. 'It was all I could do. I expect I have buried Balin. But alas for my staff: we shall have to go by guess in the dark. Gimli and I will lead.'

They followed in amazement, and as they stumbled behind he gasped out some information. 'I have lost my staff, part of my beard, and an inch of eyebrows,' he said. 'But I have blasted the door and felled the roof against it, and if the Chamber of Mazarbul is not a heap of ruins behind it, then I am no wizard. All the power of my staff was expended [?in a flash]: it was shattered to bits.'

Here the text in ink stops for the moment. My father at once heavily rewrote the passage beginning 'Suddenly there was a flash ...' in pencil and then continued on in pencil from the point he had reached (cf. note 4). There is of course no question that the story was coming into being in these pages, and the handwriting is so fast as to be practically a code, while words are missed out or misrepresented, so that one must try to puzzle out not merely what my father did write, but what he intended.

Suddenly they heard him cry out strange words in tones of thunder, and there was a flash more dazzling ... [than] any that they had ever conceived of: it was as if lightning had passed just before their eyes and seared them. The swords in their hands leapt and wrenched in their fingers. There was a deafening crash, and they fell or stumbled to their knees as a rush of wind passed down the stairway. Into the midst of them fell Gandalf.

'Well, that's that,' he said. 'I have buried poor old Balin. It was all I could do. I nearly killed myself. [*Struck out as soon as written:* It will take me years to recover my strength and

196   THE TREASON OF ISENGARD

wizardry.] Go on, go on! Gimli, come in front with me. We must go in the dark. Haste now!'

They followed in amazement feeling the walls, and as they stumbled behind him he gasped out some information. 'I have lost part of my beard and an inch of my eyebrows', he said. 'But I have blasted the door and felled the roof against it, and if the Chamber of Mazarbul is not a heap of ruins behind it, then I am no wizard. But I have expended all my strength for the moment. I can give you no more light.'

The echoes of Gandalf's blast seemed to run to and fro, ... ing in the hollow places of stone above them. From behind they heard *boom, boom*, like the beating and throbbing of a drum. But there was no sound of feet. For an hour they [?hurried on guided by Gandalf's nose]; and still there was no sound of pursuit. Almost they began to hope that they would escape.

'But what about you, Frodo?' asked Gandalf, as they halted to take a gasping breath. 'That is really important.'

'I am bruised and in pain, but I am whole,' said Frodo, 'if that is what you mean.'

'I do indeed,' said Gandalf. 'I thought it was a heroic but dead hobbit that Aragorn picked up.'

'... it seems that hobbits or this hobbit is made of a stuff so tough that I have never met the like,' said Trotter. 'Had I known I would have spoken softer in the Inn at Bree. That spear thrust would have pierced through a boar.'

'Well, it has not pierced through me,' said Frodo, 'though I feel as if I had been caught between a hammer and anvil.' He said no more. His breath was difficult, and he thought explanations could wait.

From this point ('They now went on again', FR p. 342) the original text is very largely lost for some distance, because my father overwrote it (and largely erased it first) as part of a revised version, but something can be read at the end of this section:

There was no time to lose. Away beyond the pillars in the deep [?gloom] at the west end of the hall to the right there came cries and horn calls. And far off again they heard *boom, boom* and the ground trembled [?to the dreadful drum taps]. 'Now for the last race!' said Gandalf. 'Follow me!'

The remainder of the original text is in ink and is at first fairly legible, but towards the end becomes in places impossible to decipher,

THE BRIDGE 197

being written at great speed, with small words indicated by mere marks, word-endings omitted, and scarcely any punctuation.

He turned to the left and darted across the floor of the hall. It was longer than it looked. As they ran they heard behind the beat and echo of many feet running on the floor.[10] A shrill yell went up: they had been seen. There was a ring and clash of steel: an arrow whistled over Frodo's head.

Trotter laughed. 'They did not expect this,' he said. 'The fire has cut them off for the moment. We are on the wrong side!'

'Look out for the bridge!' cried Gandalf over his shoulder. 'It is dangerous and narrow.'

Suddenly Frodo saw before him a black gulf. Just before the end of the hall the floor vanished and fell into an abyss. The exit door could not be reached save by a narrow railless bridge of stone that spanned the chasm with a single curving leap of some fifty feet. Across it they could only pass in single file. They reached the chasm in a pack and halted at the bridge-end for a moment. More arrows whistled over them. One pierced Gandalf's hat and stuck there like a black feather. They looked back. Away beyond the fiery fissure Frodo saw the swarming black figures of many orcs. They brandished spears and scimitars which shone red as blood. *Boom, boom* rolled the drumbeats now advancing louder and louder and more and more menacing. Two great dark troll-figures could be seen [?towering] among the orcs. They strode forward to the fiery brink.

Legolas bent his bow. Then he let it fall. He gave a cry of dismay and terror. Two great dark troll-shapes had appeared; but it was not these that caused his cry.[11] The orc-ranks had opened as if they themselves were afraid. A figure strode to the fissure, no more than man-high yet terror seemed to go before it. They could see the furnace-fire of its yellow eyes from afar; its arms were very long; it had a red [?tongue]. Through the air it sprang over the fiery fissure. The flames leaped up to greet it and wreathed about it. Its streaming hair seemed to catch fire, and the sword that it held turned to flame. In its other hand it held a whip of many thongs.

'Ai, ai,' wailed Legolas. '[The Balrogs are >] A Balrog is come.'

'A Balrog,' said Gandalf. 'What evil fortune – and my power is nearly spent.'

The fiery figure ran across the floor. The orcs yelled and shot many arrows.

198   THE TREASON OF ISENGARD

'Over the Bridge,' cried Gandalf. 'Go on! Go on! This is a foe beyond any of you. I will hold the Bridge. Go on!'

When they gained the door they turned, in spite of his command. The troll-figures strode across the fire carrying orcs across. The Balrog rushed to the Bridge-foot. Legolas [?raised] his bow, and [an] arrow pierced his shoulder. The bow fell useless. Gandalf stood in the midst of the bridge. In his hand Glamdring gleamed. In his left he held up his staff. The Balrog advanced and stood gazing at him.

Suddenly with a spout of flame it sprang on the Bridge, but Gandalf stood firm. 'You cannot pass,' he said. 'Go back [*struck out probably as soon as written:* into the fiery depths. It is forbidden for any Balrog to come beneath the sky since Fionwë son of Manwë overthrew Thangorodrim]. I am the master of the White Fire. The red flame cannot come this way.' The creature made no reply, but standing up tall so that it loomed above the wizard it strode forward and smote him. A sheet of white flame sprang before him [?like a shield], and the Balrog fell backward, its sword shivered into molten pieces and flew, but Gandalf's staff snapped and fell from his hand. With a gasping hiss the Balrog sprang up; it seemed to be [?half blind], but it came on and grasped at the wizard. Glamdring shore off its empty right hand, but in that instant as he [?delivered the stroke] the Balrog [?struck with] its whip. The thongs lashed round the wizard's knees and he staggered.

Seizing Legolas' bow Gimli shot, [but] the arrow fell ... Trotter sprang back along the bridge with his sword. But at that moment a great troll came up from the other side and leaped on the bridge. There was a terrible crack and the bridge broke. All the western end fell. With a terrible cry the troll fell after it, and the Balrog [?tumbled] sideways with a yell and fell into the chasm. Before Trotter could reach the wizard the bridge broke before his feet, and with a great cry Gandalf fell into the darkness.[12]

Trotter [?recoiled]. The others were rooted with horror. He recalled them. 'At least we can obey his last command,' he said. They [?passed] by the door and stumbled wildly up the great stair beyond, and beyond [?up there] was a wide echoing passage. They stumbled along it. Frodo heard Sam at his side weeping as he ran, and then he [?realized] that he too was weeping. *Boom, boom, boom* rang the echo of ... behind them.

On they ran. The light grew. It shone through great shafts.

THE BRIDGE 199

They passed into a wide hall, clear-lit with high windows in the east. [?Through that] they ran, and suddenly before them the Great Gates with carven posts and mighty doors – cast back.

There were orcs at the door, but amazed to see that it was not friends that ran they fled in dismay, and the Company took no heed of them.

The original draft of the chapter ends here, and does not recount the coming of the Company into Dimrill Dale. There is a pencilled note written on the manuscript against the description of the Balrog: 'Alter description of Balrog. It seemed to be of man's shape, but its form could not be plainly discerned. It *felt* larger than it looked.' After the words 'Through the air it sprang over the fiery fissure' my father added: 'and a great shadow seemed to black out the light.' And at the end of the text – before he had finished it, for the concluding passage is written around the words – he wrote: 'No – Gandalf breaks the bridge and Balrog falls – but lassoos him.'

It will be seen that for much of its length this chapter was very fully formed from its first emergence; while scarcely a sentence remained unchanged into FR, and while many details of speech and event would be altered, there really was not very far to go. But in certain passages this earliest draft underwent substantial development in the narrative.

The first of these is the account of Gandalf's blocking of the east door out of the Chamber of Mazarbul (FR pp. 340–1), where there was as yet no suggestion that some greater power than any orc or troll had entered the chamber, and where the blasting of the door and felling of the roof was not caused by competing spells of great power, but was a deliberate act on Gandalf's part to preserve the Company from pursuit down the stair.

It cannot be said precisely how the story stood in the lost passage (p. 196), though from a word still decipherable here and there it can be seen that Gimli saw a red light ahead of them, and that Gandalf told them that they had reached the First Deep below the Gates and were come to the Second Hall. Clearly then the essential elements of the final narrative were already present.

The second passage in which the original draft would undergo major development is the narrative of the final attack on the fugitives and the battle on the Bridge of Khazad–dûm (FR pp. 343–5). That there was a bridge in Moria, that Gandalf would hold it alone against a single adversary of great power, and that both would fall into an abyss when the bridge broke beneath them, had been foreseen in the original sketch (VI.462); but the final form of the famous scene was not achieved at a stroke. Here, the trolls do not bring great slabs to serve as gangways over the fiery fissure, but carry orcs across (it may be noted incidentally that 'orcs', rather than 'goblins', becomes

200   THE TREASON OF ISENGARD

pervasive in this text: see note 5); the form of the Balrog is clearly perceived; there is no blast of Boromir's horn; Legolas is pierced in the shoulder by an arrow as he attempts to shoot; and Aragorn and Boromir do not remain with Gandalf at the end of the bridge. The physical contest between Gandalf and the Balrog is differently conceived: Gandalf's staff breaks at the moment when the Balrog's sword shivers into molten fragments in the 'sheet of white flame', and though the whip catches Gandalf round his knees it is not the cause of his fall. Here, it is the great troll leaping onto the bridge that causes it to break, carrying with it troll, Balrog, and wizard together. But even before he had finished the initial draft of the chapter my father saw 'what really happened': 'Gandalf breaks the bridge and the Balrog falls – but lassoos him'. He thereupon moved the 'sheet of white flame' and the snapping of Gandalf's staff from the initial clash between the adversaries to the point where Gandalf broke the bridge.

It is clear that my father turned at once to the making of a fair copy of the original draft text – that he did so at once, before continuing the story, is seen from the fact that Sam's wound in the affray in the Chamber of Mazarbul only appears in the new version but is present at the beginning of 'Lothlórien'.

The new version (a good clear manuscript in ink, with little hesitation in the course of composition and without a great deal of subsequent pencilled alteration) was still called 'The Mines of Moria, 2'; a subtitle was added in pencil, 'The Bridge'. For some distance the text proceeds as a characteristic polishing and slight elaboration of the draft, bringing it very close to FR, which I take here as the basis with which the present text is compared.

The Book of Mazarbul is not described as 'partly burned', and its pages are said to have been written 'in both dwarf-runes and elvish script', where in FR a distinction is made between the runes of Moria and of Dale. The text of the first page that Gandalf read out runs thus:

'*We drove out Orcs ... from guard* something *and first hall. We slew many under the bright sun in the Dale. Flói was killed by an arrow. He slew* ... then I can only read stray words for many lines. Then comes *We have taken the Twenty-first Hall of North-end to dwell in. There is* ... I cannot read what: a *shaft* is mentioned. Then *Balin has set up his seat in the Chamber of Mazarbul.*'

'The Chamber of Records,' said Gimli. 'I guess that is where we now stand.'

'Well, I can read no more for a long way, except the word *gold,*' said Gandalf; 'and, yes, *Durin's axe* and something *helm*. Then *Balin is Lord of Moria*. After some stars there comes *We found true-silver* and later the word *well-forged*; then some-

THE BRIDGE 201

thing, I have it! *Óin to seek for the upper armouries and treasury of the Third Deep and* ... but I can make out no more on the page but *mithril, west,* and *Balin.*'

This text corresponds almost exactly to the third drawing of the page (see the Appendix, p. 459).

The text of the second page that Gandalf read out, in 'a large bold hand writing in elvish script', now identified by Gimli as Ori's, scarcely differs from the text given on p. 191, except that after *We have barred the Gates* Gandalf can doubtfully read *horrible* and *suffer: all is.* Thus the passage giving the date (10 November) of Balin's death in Dimrill Dale is still absent. The earliest, or earliest extant, drawing of Ori's page was done at the same time as the third drawing of the first page (see the Appendix, p. 459), and obviously accompanies the present version of the narrative.

The text of the last page of the book remains exactly the same as that given on p. 191; and the earliest extant drawing (accompanying the third of the first page and the first of Ori's page) fits it exactly.

In this version Gandalf no longer makes any mention of the Watcher in the Water and the two Doors, but Gimli says: 'It was well for us that the pool had sunk a little, and that *we came to the Elven-door that was closed.* The Watcher was sleeping, or so it seems, down at the southern end of the pool.' The italicized words were struck out, probably at once, and so the conception of the two separate entrances into Moria from the West was finally abandoned. Gandalf still gives the Book of Mazarbul to Frodo, for him to give to Bilbo 'if you get a chance.'

In his last words before the attack on the Chamber of Mazarbul began Gandalf says that 'the Twenty-first Hall should be on the seventh level, that is five above the Gate level' (six in FR). He still says 'There are goblins ... They are evil and large: black Orcs', but the troll becomes 'a great cave-troll' as in FR, and its three-toed foot was changed on the manuscript to a toeless foot.[13] Sam now gets a wound in the affray, 'a cut on the arm', which as mentioned above appears in the original draft of 'Lothlórien' ('The cut in his arm was paining him', p. 220). A rider to the present text changed this to 'a glancing cut in his shoulder'. 'The sword of Elendil' still has no other name, *Branding* being substituted later in pencil (see p. 165, and p. 274 and note 19).

In the story of the flight of the Company from the Chamber of Mazarbul the new version followed the original draft fairly closely. As Frodo and Sam peered up the steps they heard Gandalf muttering, and the sound, they thought, of his staff tapping. The searing flash like lightning, the wrenching of their swords in their hands, and the great rush of wind down the stairs forcing them to their knees, were still present (the blasting of the Chamber remaining a deliberate act); and Gandalf still says 'I have lost part of my beard and an inch of my

202   THE TREASON OF ISENGARD

eyebrows'. The long descent in the dark down flights of stairs now enters, Gandalf feeling the ground with his staff 'like a blind man'; but at the words 'Almost they began to hope against hope that they would escape' (FR p. 341) this new version stops, and all this part of the story, from the killing of the orc-chieftain in the Chamber, was rejected.[14]

The development of the chapter from this point took much unravelling, but it seems clear that my father decided at this juncture that further drafting was required before the fair copy on which he was engaged could be continued. He therefore wrote now a new rough draft carrying the story from the flight of the Company from the Chamber of Mazarbul to their final escape out of Moria; and having done this, he returned to the fair copy and went on with it again, following the draft quite closely. I believe that all this was continuous work, that it can be shown that the story of the chapter 'The Bridge of Khazad-dûm' was brought almost to its final form before the story of Lothlórien was begun (see p. 204 and note 20). For clarity, in the remainder of this chapter I will call the new draft 'B' and the fair copy manuscript 'C', the original draft, which has been given in full, being 'A'.[15]

This new draft B for the latter part of the chapter was written very fast, mostly in soft pencil, and is hard to read, but for much of its length the final narrative was now almost achieved, with scarcely any differences of substance. Gandalf still says 'I nearly killed myself', and he does not say 'I have met my match, and have nearly been destroyed'; he knows 'one or two (shutting-spells) that will hold, though they don't stop the door being smashed if great strength comes'; and he says that the Orcs on the other side of the door 'seemed to be talking their horrible secret language, which I never knew more than a word or two of.' In the fair copy C these become: 'I ran up against something unexpected I haven't met before'; 'I know several that will hold'; and 'talking their hideous secret language.'

The overwriting of the erased passage in the primary text A (p. 196) forms a part of the new draft, and the new text (from 'They now went on again' to ' "Now for the last race!" cried Gandalf') is so close to the final form in FR (pp. 342–3) as to need no commentary.

In the last part of the chapter (from 'He turned left and sped across the smooth floor of the hall') the drafting of the new version is as rough as was the original text A that it replaced in this part, the language unpolished and the conclusion scarcely legible. The actual narrative of FR pp. 344–6 is present, however, except in these points. The Balrog when first seen beyond the fiery fissure is described as 'the shape of a man perhaps, and not much larger' (cf. pp. 197, 199). The fair copy C has here likewise 'and not much greater' (FR: 'of man-shape maybe, yet greater').[16] Gimli's cry of 'Durin's Bane!' and Gandalf's words 'Now I understand' were still absent from both B and C,

THE BRIDGE   203

Gimli's words (only) being added in pencil to the latter; on this matter see pp. 185–6 and note 16 to the last chapter.

Following Legolas' cry 'Ai! Ai! A Balrog is come!' it is told in B that 'he turned to fly and an arrow struck him in the shoulder. He stumbled and began to crawl on all fours along the Bridge.' That an arrow pierced Legolas in the shoulder is told in the original version of the story (p. 198). In B my father struck out the incident, then ticked it for retention; but it is absent from C. Boromir's horncall is absent from both texts, though my father added it in pencil to C, at first placing it after 'A Balrog is come!' but then deciding to put it in earlier, before 'Legolas turned and set an arrow to the string', so that it was the Orcs who were momentarily halted by the blast of the horn and not the Balrog. In neither text do Aragorn and Boromir remain at the bridge-foot, and thus it is said subsequently that Trotter 'ran back out to the bridge' and 'ran out onto the Bridge', i.e. from the doorway where he had been standing with the others.

In B it is said only that the Balrog 'stood facing him': in C 'the Balrog halted facing him, and the shadow about him reached out like great wings'.[17] Immediately afterwards, where in FR the Balrog 'drew itelf up to a great height, and its wings were spread from wall to wall', neither B nor C has the words 'to a great height' nor speaks of the 'wings'. Gandalf's words to the Balrog remain in B very close to the original draft (p. 198), with 'White Fire' for 'the White Fire'; in C this was changed in the act of writing: 'You cannot pass. I am the master of White Flame. [Neither Red Fire nor Black Shadow can >] The Red Fire cannot come this way. Go back to the Shadow!'

Both B and C continued a little way beyond the point where 'The Bridge of Khazad–dûm' ends in FR, the former giving first a description of Dimrill Dale and Mirrormere, which was omitted in C.

Northward it ran up into a glen of shadows between two great arms of the mountains, over which towered three white peaks. Before them (west) [*read* east][18] the mountains marched to a sudden end. To their right (south) they receded endlessly into the distance. Less than a mile away (and below them where they stood on the skirts of the mountains) lay a mere – just clear of the shadow, under the sunny sky. But its waters looked dark, a deep blue such as the night sky seen through a lighted window. Its surface was utterly still. About it lay a smooth sward, sloping swiftly down on all sides towards its bare unbroken brink. There lay the Mirror Mere. High on the shores above stood a rough broken column. Durin's Stone.

This passage was an overwriting in ink, but the pencilled text beneath, visible here and there, was written continuously with what precedes

204   THE TREASON OF ISENGARD

(the Company looking back at Moria Gate), and is certainly the most original form of the description of Mirrormere. Against it my father wrote *Not yet used*. He used it in fact in the original draft of 'Lothlórien' (p. 219): a clear demonstration that the new draft B of the latter part of the present chapter preceded work on 'Lothlórien' (see note 20).

B then continues to its conclusion thus:

'So we have passed through Moria,' said Trotter at last, passing his hand over his eyes. 'I know not what put the words into my mouth, but did I not say to Gandalf: If you pass the Gates of Moria, beware![19] Alas that I should have spoken true. No fortune could have been so ill as this: hardly ... had all perished. But now we must do as we can without our friend and guide. At least we may yet avenge him. Let us gird ourselves. It is better for us to strike hard than to mourn long.'

With slightly altered wording this was used as the conclusion of the chapter in the fair copy C also.[20]

Throughout C, *Trotter* (as he is named at every occurrence save once where Gandalf names him) was subsequently changed to *Elfstone* (see pp. 277–8).

                            NOTES

1   Though the words 'it only a cover' seem clear, my father cannot have intended 'it only had a cover', as the following text shows.

2   A dwarf *Frár*, companion of Glóin, appeared in the earliest drafts of 'The Council of Elrond' (VI.397, 412), where he was replaced by Burin son of Balin. The three Dwarf-names *Frár, Lóni, Náli*, retained in FR, were again taken from the Old Norse *Elder Edda* – whereas *Flói* (slain in the Dimrill Dale) was not.

3   On the conception of two distinct entrances to Moria from the West, which goes back to the original version of 'The Ring Goes South', see p. 178. The striking out (probably at once) of the reference in the previous chapter (*ibid.*) to 'The Dwarven-door further south' (i.e. south of the Elven-door at the end of the road from Hollin) could be taken as an indication that the present text in fact preceded the new version of 'Moria (i)'. On the other hand, if this were so, it is hard to see why my father should have put in the direction '2 West Gates' at the beginning of the present text (p. 190), seeing that the two entrances were already present in the oldest version of the story of Moria. It seems to me most probable that he wrote '2 West Gates' precisely because he had now changed his mind again; this detail being therefore actually evidence that the first writing of 'Moria (ii)' did follow the new

THE BRIDGE   205

version of 'Moria (i)'. – Further, in the fair copy text of the present chapter Gimli says (p. 201) that 'it was well for us that... we came to the Elven-door that was closed', though this was at once or soon rejected.

4   In FR Gandalf entrusted the book to Gimli, to give to Dáin. – The first page of the manuscript, which ends at approximately this point, was written in pencil, but from the beginning of Gandalf's reading from the book my father overwrote it in ink – and then, from this point, carried on the initial text in ink. Thus the original drafting of the words and phrases which Gandalf could interpret in the Book of Mazarbul is partly obliterated; but most of the underlying pencil can be made out, and it can be seen that the text given here (itself emended) did not greatly differ from what it superseded.

5   My father first wrote here: 'veritable Orcs'. Cf. the original sketch for the chapter given in VI.443: 'Gandalf says there are goblins – of very evil kind, larger than usual, real orcs', and my discussion of 'goblins' and 'orcs' in VI.437 note 35. In FR at this point Gandalf says: 'There are Orcs, very many of them. And some are large and evil: black Uruks of Mordor.'

6   In FR it was at this point that Boromir, closing the west door of the chamber, wedged it with broken sword-blades and splinters of wood. It is odd that in the present text it is said here that Boromir kicked the wedges away from the door and heaved it to, and yet immediately afterwards the door 'began to move inwards grinding at the wedges and thrusting them back.'

7   This sentence replaced: 'Gandalf leaped forward and hewed the arm with Glamdring.'

8   The reforging of the Sword of Elendil has been told in the new version of 'The Ring Goes South' (p. 165).

9   In a subsequent version of the passage Gandalf says 'There is no time for counting wounds.'

10 This sentence was first written: 'As they ran cries and the noise of many feet entered the far end behind them.'

11 This passage, with the two references to the appearance of the Trolls, is confused. Though all was written at the same time, phrases were added and rejected phrases were left standing, and my father's intention is in places impossible to determine.

12 Written in the margin at the time of composition: 'Go on... Do I fight in vain? Fly!' Cf. Trotter's words 'At least we can obey his last command' in the text immediately following.

13 The oddity of the original story (see p. 193 and note 6) in the matter of the wedging of the western door is now removed, for when Boromir had kicked away the wedges and heaved it to he then re-wedged it. All the passages concerned were corrected, probably at once, to give the story as it is in FR.

206 THE TREASON OF ISENGARD

14 The rejected part of the manuscript (a single sheet written on both sides) was found among my father's papers, the rest of it having gone to Marquette.

15 The sequence of development in this chapter can be expressed thus:

A → C (C interrupted); B → C (C continued).

16 In a pencilled addition in C to the scene of the Balrog's fall from the Bridge my father changed 'the stone upon which it stood' (the text of FR) to 'the stone upon which *the vast form* stood'.

17 The second *him* is Gandalf, not only from the syntax, but also because the Balrog is always referred to as *it*. FR has 'the shadow about it'.

18 See p. 237 note 5.

19 Aragorn's words to Gandalf *If you pass the doors of Moria, beware!* had entered in 'Moria (i)', p. 178.

20 With this revised wording the passage is found at the beginning of the first draft of 'Lothlórien' (p. 219). In the fair copy C of the present chapter my father subsequently struck it out, and wrote at the end of the text that precedes it: *End of Chapter*. It is clear from this that not only the draft B but also the fair copy of 'The Mines of Moria (ii): The Bridge' were completed before 'Lothlórien' was begun.

XI

THE STORY FORESEEN FROM MORIA

At about this time, and still using the reverse pages and blue covers of the same invaluable examination script, my father wrote a much more elaborate outline of the story to come than any he had yet done. When this was written in relation to the narrative that had been achieved cannot be precisely demonstrated, but far the most likely time, to judge from the beginning of the outline, would be when 'The Mines of Moria (ii)' was at least initially drafted (and probably actually completed in the fair copy) and 'Lothlórien' was immediately contemplated; and therefore I give it in this place.

It is particularly interesting to observe what elements in this new plot derive from earlier sketches, and how those ideas had evolved by this time, as the actual writing of the narrative drew nearer. These are: (1) an isolated page which I have tentatively dated to August 1939 (VI.380); (2) a page actually dated August 1939 (VI.381); (3) an outline set down at the time of the first drafting of 'The Council of Elrond' (VI.410–11).

The new text was written very quickly and roughly, mostly in pencil, and is in places hard to make out. I have expanded contractions and made a few other very small editorial clarifications. It will be seen that despite its fullness it does not at all represent a clearly defined, step-by-step sequence: ideas were emerging and evolving as my father wrote it.

Sketch of Plot

Reach Lothlórien Dec. 15.[1] Take refuge up Trees. Elves befriend them. Dec. 15, 16, 17 they journey to Angle between Anduin and Blackroot.[2] There they remain long. (While they are up trees orcs go by – also Gollum.)

At Angle they debate what is to be done. Frodo feels it is his duty to go straight to Fire Mountain. But Aragorn and Boromir wish to go to Minas Tirith, and if possible gather force. Frodo sees that that will not help. As Minas Tirith is still a long way from Fire Mountain and Sauron will only be the more warned. (Boromir is secretly planning to use the Ring, *since Gandalf is gone.*)

208   THE TREASON OF ISENGARD

Boromir takes Frodo apart and talks to him. Begs to see Ring again. Evil enters into his heart and he tries to daunt Frodo and then to take it by force. Frodo is obliged to slip it on to escape him. (What does he see then – cloud all round him getting nearer and many fell voices in air?)

Frodo seeing that evil has entered into the Company dare not stay and does not want to imperil hobbits or others. He flies. His loss is not discovered for some time because of Boromir's lies. (Boromir says he has climbed a tree and will be coming back soon?) The hunt eventually fails because Frodo went a long way invisible.

The search. Sam is lost. He tries to track Frodo and comes on Gollum. He follows Gollum and Gollum leads him to Frodo.

Frodo hears following feet. And flies. But Sam comes up too to his surprise. The two are too much for Gollum. Gollum is *daunted* by Frodo – who has a power over him as Ringbearer. (But use of Ring proves bad since it re-establishes power of Ring over Frodo after his cure. At end he cannot willingly part with it.)

Gollum pleads for forgiveness and feigns reform. They make him lead them through the Dead Marshes. (Green faces in the pools.) Lithlad Plain of Ash. The Searching Eye of Barad-dur (a single light in a high window).

★ At point where Sam, Frodo and Gollum meet return to others – for whose adventures see later. *But they should be told at this point.*

The Gap of Gorgoroth not far from Fire Mountain. There are Orc guard-towers on either side of Gorgoroth.[3] They see a host of evil led by Black Riders. Gollum betrays Frodo. He is beaten off, but escapes shrieking to the Black Riders. The Black Riders now have taken form of demonic eagles and fly before host, or [?take eagle-like] vulture birds as steeds.

Frodo toils up Mountain to find Crack.

Rumour of Battle had already reached Frodo, Sam and Gollum. (That is why the host of Mordor was riding out.)

While Frodo is toiling up Mountain he looks back and sees Battle gathering. He hears faint sound of horns in the hills. A great dust where the Horsemen are coming. Thunder from Baraddur and a black storm comes up on an East wind. Frodo wonders what is happening but has no hope that he himself can be saved. The Ringwraiths swoop back. They have heard Gollum's cries.

THE STORY FORESEEN FROM MORIA 209

Orodruin [*written above:* Mount Doom] has three great fissures North, West, South [> West, South, East] in its sides. They are very deep and at an unguessable depth a glow of fire is seen. Every now and again fire rolls out of mountain's heart down the terrific channels. The mountain towers above Frodo. He comes to a flat place on the mountain-side where the fissure is full of fire – Sauron's well of fire. The Vultures are coming. He *cannot* throw Ring in. The Vultures are coming. All goes dark in his eyes and he falls to his knees. At that moment Gollum comes up and wrestles with him, and takes Ring. Frodo falls flat.

Here perhaps Sam comes up, beats off a vulture and hurls himself and Gollum into the gulf?

Function for Sam? Is he to die? (He said there is something I have to do before [I die >] the end.)[4]

Sam could get hold of the Ring. Frodo betrayed by Gollum and taken by orcs (?) to Minas Morgol.[5] They take his ring and find it is no good; they put him in a dungeon, and threaten to send him to Baraddur.

How can Sam get hold of Ring? He keeps watch at night and hears Gollum muttering to himself, words of hatred for Frodo. He draws his sword and leaps on Gollum, [?dragging] him off. He tries to [*insert* utter] horrible words over Frodo – incantation of sleep. A spider charm, or does Gollum get spiders' help? There is a ravine, a spiders' glen, they have to pass at entrance to Gorgoroth. Gollum gets spiders to put spell of sleep on Frodo. Sam drives them off. But cannot wake him. He then gets idea of taking Ring. He sits beside Frodo. Gollum betrays Frodo to the Orc-guard. They are overwhelmed and Sam knocked silly with a club. He puts on Ring and follows Frodo. (A ring from Mazarbul would be useful.)[6]

Sam comes and *uses* Ring. Passes into Morgol and finds Frodo. Frodo feels hatred of Sam and sees him as an orc. But suddenly the orc speaks and holds out Ring and says: Take it. Then Frodo sees it is Sam. They creep out. Frodo is unable.... Sam dresses up like an orc.

They escape but *Gollum follows.*

It is *Sam* that wrestles with Gollum and [?throws] him finally in the gulf.

How are Sam and Frodo saved from the eruption?[7]

An additional passage, but contemporary with the rest, is marked for insertion to this part of the outline.

When Ring *melts* Dark Tower falls or is buried in ash. A great

210   THE TREASON OF ISENGARD

black cloud and shadow floats away east on a *rising west wind*.
(The smell and sound of the Sea?)

Eruption. The forces of Mordor flee and Horsemen of Rohan
pursue.

Frodo standing on side of Fire Mountain holds up sword. He
now commands Ringwraiths and bids them be gone. They fall
to earth and vanish like wisps of smoke with a terrible wail.

How is Frodo (and Sam) saved from Eruption?

Story turns for a while – after first meeting of Sam, Frodo and
Gollum – to others.

Owing to Boromir's treachery and Frodo's use of Ring the
hunt fails. Merry and Pippin are distracted by loss of Sam and
Frodo. They themselves get lost following echoes. They come to
Entwash and the Topless Forest,[8] and fall in with Treebeard
and his Three Giants.

Legolas and Gimli also get lost and get captured by Saruman.?

Boromir and Aragorn (who notes a change in Boromir – who
is keen to break off the chase and go home) reach Minas Tirith,
which is besieged by Sauron except at back. ? Siege is briefly
told from point of view of watchers on battlements. Evil has
now hold of Boromir who is jealous of Aragorn. The Lord of
Minas Tirith is slain[9] and they choose Aragorn. Boromir deserts
and sneaks off to Saruman, to get his help in becoming Lord of
Minas Tirith.

How does Gandalf reappear?

All this section, concerned with the 'western story', was struck out
and replaced, immediately, by a fuller and altered version, in which
the idea that Legolas and Gimli were captured by Saruman is rejected
and their new story is linked to the reappearance of Gandalf.

Story turns for a while to the others – ? after first meeting of
Sam, Frodo and Gollum.

(one chapter) Owing to Boromir's treachery and Frodo's use of
Ring the hunt fails. Aragorn is overwhelmed with grief, thinking
he has failed trust as Gandalf's successor. Merry and Pippin are
distracted by losing Sam and Frodo, and wandering far (deluded
by echoes) they also get lost. Merry and Pippin come up
Entwash into Fangorn and have adventure with Treebeard.
Treebeard turns out a decent giant. They tell him their tale. He
is very perturbed by news of Saruman, and more so by the fall of
Gandalf. He won't go near Mordor. He offers to carry them to
Rohan and perhaps Minas Tirith. They set off.

THE STORY FORESEEN FROM MORIA   211

(one chapter)   Boromir, Aragorn, and Legolas and Gimli.

Legolas feels the Company is broken up, and Gimli has no more heart. The four part. Aragorn and Boromir to Minas Tirith, Legolas and Gimli north. Legolas means to join Elves of Lothlórien for a while. Gimli means to go back up Anduin to Mirkwood and so home. They journey together. Legolas and Gimli both sing laments. Suddenly they meet Gandalf!

Gandalf's story. Overcame Balrog. The gulf was not deep (only a kind of moat and was full of silent water). He followed the channel and got down into the Deeps. ?? Clad himself in Mithril-mail and fought his way out slaying many trolls.

[?Does] Gandalf *shine* in the sun. He has a new power after overcoming of Balrog? *He is now clad in white.*

Gandalf is dreadfully downcast at the news of the loss of Frodo. He hastens south again with Legolas and Gimli.

(one chapter)   Inside Minas Tirith. Aragorn began to suspect Boromir at the time of the loss of Frodo. A sudden change seems to come over Boromir. He is anxious to go away home at once and not look for Frodo.

Minas Tirith is besieged by Sauron's forces that have crossed Anduin at Osgiliath, and by Saruman who is come up in rear. There seems no hope. Evil has now got complete hold of Boromir. The Lord of Minas Tirith is slain. They choose Aragorn as chief. Boromir is jealous and enraged – he deserts and sneaks off to Saruman, seeking his aid in getting lordship.

At this point the siege must be broken by Gandalf with Legolas and Gimli and by Treebeard. (But not too much fighting or it will spoil last battle of Gorgoroth.) Gandalf might simply walk through lines, or else have a contest with Saruman. Treebeard walks through. They see a huge tree walking over plain.

Saruman shuts himself up in Isengard.

Sally from Minas Tirith. Gandalf drives Black Riders back and takes crossing of Anduin at Osgiliath. Horsemen ride behind him to Gorgoroth. Hear a great wind and see flames out of Fire Mountain.

Somehow or other Frodo and Sam must be found in Gorgoroth. Possibly by Merry and Pippin. (If any one of the hobbits is *slain* it must be the cowardly Pippin doing something brave. For instance –

Here the outline breaks off, but after a large space continues again lower down on the same page, and now with numbered chapters,

212   THE TREASON OF ISENGARD

beginning at 'XXVI'. Since 'Moria (ii)' was XVII, my father envisaged eight further chapters to this point.

   After fall of Mordor. They return to Minas Tirith. Feast. Aragorn comes to meet them. Moon rises [?on] Minas Morgol. XXVI Aragorn looks out and sees moon rise over Minas Morgol. He remains behind – and becomes Lord of Minas *Ithil*. What about Boromir? Does he repent? [*Written later in margin:* No – slain by Aragorn.]
   Gandalf calls at Isengard (see addition). [*This addition is found on a separate slip:* On way home: they ride horses from Rohan. The[y] call at Isengard. Gandalf knocks. Saruman comes out very affable. 'Ah, my dear Gandalf. What a mess the world is in. Really we must consult together – such men as we are needed. Now what about our spheres of influence?'
   Gandalf looks at him. 'I am the White Wizard now,' he said – 'look at your many colours.' Saruman is [?clad] in a filthy mud colour. 'They seem to have run.' Gandalf takes his staff and breaks it over his knee. [?He gives a thin shriek.] 'Go, Saruman,' he said, 'and beg from the charitable for a day's digging.'
   Isengard is given to the Dwarves. Or to Radagast?]
   They ride home to Rivendell.
XXVII Song of the Banished Shadow.
   Rivendell.   Meeting with Bilbo.
XXVIII What happens to Shire?
   Last scene. *Sailing away of Elves* [*added faintly*: Bilbo with them] and the [*sic*]
XXIX Sam and Frodo go into a green land by the Sea?

Certain of these narrative ideas had appeared before, in the earlier plot-sketches referred to on p. 207, such as the siege of Minas Tirith, Frodo's separation from the Company and Sam's seeking for him, Gollum's seeming reform and guidance to the Mountain of Fire, the Searching Eye, the 'host of evil' led by Black Riders, Gollum's treachery, Frodo's inability to cast the Ring into the Fire, and the eruption of the Mountain. But now the structure becomes more solid and secure.
   To look through this new outline in sequence: the fact that nothing is told here about Lothlórien (though its people are mentioned – 'Elves befriend them', and later it is told that it was Legolas' intention 'to join Elves of Lothlórien for a while') suggests, not that the Lothlórien story had been written, but that my father was on the verge of writing it and had no need to set down much about it. If it had been written he would surely not have included it in the outline at all; and the words

THE STORY FORESEEN FROM MORIA   213

'While they are up trees orcs go by – also Gollum' look like the first written emergence of this element in the story. But the actual name *Lothlórien* has already made its appearance in the LR papers, in the new version of 'The Ring Goes South', p. 167.

The 'angle' between the river flowing down from Dimrill Dale (Redway, Blackroot, Silverlode) and the Great River (see the original rough sketch-map given in VI.439) is now called *Angle*. Here the Company 'remained long', but there is no indication whether Elves of Lothlórien were present. It is at Angle that a major feature of the structure of LR first enters. In an earlier outline (VI.410) Frodo becomes separated from the Company, involuntarily as it seems, through fear of Gollum; but now (being already determined to go directly to Mordor rather than by way of Minas Tirith) he is brought to the point of fleeing away alone through Boromir, who desires to appropriate the Ring for the purposes of Minas Tirith. Already my father foresaw that Boromir, speaking to Frodo apart, would ask to see the Ring again, that (as is implied) Frodo would refuse, and that Boromir would then try to take it by force and oblige Frodo to put it on in order to escape from him – explaining how it was that Frodo got clear away and could not be found despite the hunt for him. On the other hand, since all this takes place at Angle, there is *no journey down Anduin*, boats are never mentioned – and there is no mention even of Frodo's need to cross the river. The whole story of how Sam would come to accompany Frodo on his journey to the Fiery Mountain would be entirely changed (though not before it had been further developed from its form in this outline).

In the account of that journey several new names appear. *Lithlad* the Plain of Ash appears once in LR (*The Two Towers* IV.3, 'the mournful plains of Lithlad and of Gorgoroth'), though for some reason the name was not entered on either of the maps published in LR; it is found however on the First Map (p. 309) and subsequently. The plain of Lithlad lay south of Ered Lithui, the Ash Mountains, away to the east of Barad–dûr; there would thus seem no reason for Frodo and Sam ever to have come to it, as seems to be implied in this outline. The valley of Gorgoroth, above which was built the Dark Tower, appears in the fifth version of 'The Council of Elrond' (p. 144), and the Gap of Gorgoroth ('with Orc guard-towers on either side') in this outline is the first intimation of a pass between the mountain-walls fencing Mordor on north and west (afterwards Udûn, between the Morannon and the Isenmouthe).

The winged Nazgûl – Black Riders horsed now upon vultures – appear, but here in the rôle of leaders of the host of Mordor as it rides out to battle. Sam's part in the final events was still very shadowy and speculative, but already the idea enters that Gollum (whose inner motives seem to have been far less complex in respect of Frodo than they afterwards became) would betray Sam and Frodo to spiders in a

214   THE TREASON OF ISENGARD

ravine or glen 'at the entrance to Gorgoroth'. At this stage, as will be
seen later, the entry into Mordor by way of the Stairs of Cirith Ungol
did not exist, and when that name appears it will bear a different
geographical sense. The spiders seem to have arisen in the context of
explaining how Sam came to take the Ring from Frodo; and features
of the later story begin to take shape: Sam's rout of the spider(s),
Gollum's betrayal of the unconscious Frodo to the orcs, his capture
and imprisonment (but here in Minas Morgol), Sam's entry into the
fortress wearing the Ring, Frodo's sudden hatred of Sam whom he sees
as an orc, and their escape.

The Breaking of the Fellowship imposed on my father the need to
follow two distinct narrative paths, but he would still follow the
fortunes of Frodo and Sam somewhat further before returning to the
others (since the reunion of Sam and Frodo, involving Sam's first
falling in with Gollum, was much less swiftly achieved than it is in
FR).

The second narrative again takes a huge step forward here, but there
was still a great way to go. Most important, Merry and Pippin now
move into a central position in the story, and it is they (not as in a
former outline Frodo, VI.410) who encounter Treebeard – although
the entire narrative of the attack by Orcs on the camp beneath Amon
Hen, Boromir's death, the forced march across Rohan, and the battle
between the Rohirrim and the Orcs on the eaves of Fangorn is absent.
Merry and Pippin merely become lost as they seek for Frodo and Sam,
and wandering along the river Entwash (which here first appears)
come to the Forest of Fangorn without any relation to the larger story;
but through them Treebeard (now finally established as a 'decent' sort
of person, cf. p. 71) comes to play a part in the breaking of the siege of
Minas Tirith.

On the other hand, for Aragorn and Boromir my father had at this
time a plan almost wholly different from what would soon emerge.
Departing together to Minas Tirith, the original Company will be still
further fragmented, for Legolas and Gimli (escaping the fate of
capture by Saruman momentarily projected for them, p. 210) set off
north together. It is indeed Legolas and Gimli who fall in with Gandalf
returned, now clad in white and possessed of new powers, and with
him they turn back and hasten south; but there is no indication of
where they met him (save that it was south of Lothlórien), and in fact
no indication of geography for any of these events. Rohan plays no
part in the story at all (beyond the several mentions of the Horsemen
riding against Mordor), and the Siege of Minas Tirith is (mysteriously)
to be 'broken by Gandalf with Legolas and Gimli and by Treebeard.'
Boromir would play a shameful part, treacherously fleeing to Saruman
(a faint adumbration of Wormtongue?) in his hatred for Aragorn,
chosen to be successor to the slain lord of Minas Tirith. Isengard
remains inviolate, and the Ents do not appear[10] – yet the visit of

THE STORY FORESEEN FROM MORIA   215

Gandalf to Saruman in his fortress, and his humiliation, is present, placed here on the homeward journey.

Much of the narrative 'material', it may be said, was now assembled. But the structure of that narrative in the lands west of Anduin as my father now foresaw it would be wholly changed, and changed above all by the emergence of the Kingdom of Rohan into the full light of the story, and of its relations with Gondor and with Isengard.[11]

NOTES

1 'Reach Lothlórien Dec. 15': this date does not agree with the chronology, which is surprising. The time-scheme referred to on p. 169, which clearly accompanied this state of the narrative, continues on from 'December 9 Snow on Caradras' (a date that actually appears in the text) thus:
Dec. 10 Retreat. Wolves at night.
  11 Start for Moria. Reach Doors at sundown. Travel in Mines till midnight (15 miles).
  12 Well-chamber. All day in Moria (20 miles). Night in 21st Hall.
  13 *Mazarbul*. Battle of Bridge. Escape to Lothlórien.
This scheme was made when the 'Lothlórien' story was at any rate in progress, but the earliest sketch of the march of the Company from Dimrill Dale (p. 218) demands the date 13 December.

2 The name *Anduin*, thus written and not the result of subsequent correction, occurs in the fifth version of 'The Council of Elrond' (p. 157 note 5). The name *Blackroot* shows that this outline was written after the new version of 'The Ring Goes South' (see p. 166).

3 This sentence was put in as an afterthought at a different point in the manuscript, but it seems appropriate to insert it here.

4 Sam said this to Frodo after the night spent with the Elves in the Woody End (FR p. 96).

5 This part of the text was written in pencil, but these few lines were overwritten in ink later (apparently simply for clarity's sake), and the form as overwritten is actually *Morgul*; elsewhere in the outline, however, the form is *Morgol*.

6 The 'ring from Mazarbul' evidently refers back to what is said earlier: 'They take [Frodo's] ring and find it is no good.'

7 A scrap of torn paper found in isolation bears the following pencilled notes dashed down in haste:
Could Sam *steal the Ring* to save Frodo from danger?
The Black Riders capture Frodo and he is taken to Mordor – but he has no Ring and is put in prison.

216   THE TREASON OF ISENGARD

> Sam flees – but is pursued by Gollum.
> It is Sam and Gollum that wrestle on the Mountain.
> Frodo is saved by the fall of the Tower.

It seems very probable that these notes belong to the same time as the present outline. On the same scrap are notes referring to the Shire at the end of the story, when Frodo and Sam returning find that 'Cosimo [Sackville-Baggins] has industrialised it. Factories and smoke. The Sandymans have a biscuit factory. Iron is found.' The last words are: 'They go west and set sail to Greenland.' *Greenland* is clear, however improbable it may seem; but cf. the last words of the present outline (p. 212): 'Sam and Frodo go into a *green land* by the Sea'.

8   Fangorn is called 'the Topless Forest' in a rejected sentence in the new version of 'The Ring Goes South', p. 167.

9   In the outline given in VI.411 the King of Ond was Boromir's father.

10   Since in the sketch-plot given in VI.410 the 'tree-giants' assailed the besiegers of Ond, it may be that their presence was understood in this outline also; but this is not in any way suggested.

11   Looked at in terms of the movements of the principal persons, it seems that a crucial idea, though at once rejected, would turn out to have been the capture of Legolas and Gimli by Saruman (p. 210). My father remained convinced, perhaps, that Saruman did nonetheless play a part in the fragmentation of the Company of the Ring; and the aimless wanderings of Merry and Pippin along the Entwash that brought them to Treebeard's domain were transformed into the forced march of captives to Isengard – for Isengard was close to the Forest of Fangorn. Thus entered also the death of Boromir, and the withdrawal of Aragorn from immediate departure to Minas Tirith.

XII

LOTHLÓRIEN

In the first fully-written narrative, the two chapters 6 and 7 in Book II of FR ('Lothlórien' and 'The Mirror of Galadriel') are one, though here treated separately. This text is extremely complex in that, while it constitutes a nearly complete narrative, the form in which it exists is not the result of writing in a simple sequence; parts of it are later, with later names, and were written over a partly or wholly erased earlier form. Other parts were not rewritten and earlier names appear, sometimes corrected, sometimes not; and the original text was much emended throughout.

In fact, it seems to me certain that the whole text, including some scraps of initial drafting and outlining on isolated pages, belongs to the same time and the same impulse. The 'August 1940' examination script was once again used for the entire complex of papers. The manuscript varies greatly in difficulty, some sections being fairly clear and legible, others very much the reverse. In places words are so reduced and letter-shapes so transformed that one might well hit upon the right word but not know it, if there are insufficient clues from the context or from the later text. Word-endings are miswritten or omitted, successive forms of a sentence are left standing side by side, and punctuation is constantly lacking. This is a case where the actual appearance of the manuscript is exceedingly different from the printed interpretation of it.

No satisfactory presentation of such a text as this is really possible. If the earliest form of the story is given, and the later alterations ignored, then difficulties such as the following are encountered. In the passage where Legolas reports to the others his conversation with the Elves in the mallorn-tree (FR p. 357) the original narrative (in ink) had:

> Now they bid us to climb up, three in each of these trees that stand here near together. I will go first.

This was corrected (in pencil) to a form close to that of FR:

> Now they bid me to climb up with Frodo, of whom they seem to have heard. The rest they ask to wait a little, and to keep watch at the foot of the tree.

But the primary narrative then continues (in pencil) on the next sheet

218   THE TREASON OF ISENGARD

with this revised story, in which Legolas and Frodo are the first to ascend (with Sam behind). On the other hand, if all later alteration (which is in any case far from achieving an overall consistency) is admitted, the FR form is closely approached and the earlier stages ignored. I have adopted therefore the former method, and attempt to clarify complexities as they arise. The notes to this chapter form a commentary on the text and are integral to its presentation.

A few brief notes about the sojourn of the Company in Lothlórien begin the long preparatory synopsis given in the last chapter (p. 207). There is there no suggestion of Galadriel and Celeborn; and it is 'at Angle', between Blackroot and Anduin, that Boromir accosts Frodo and attempts to take the Ring. The first march from Moria is more fully sketched in the following notes.

> They pass into Dimrill Dale. It is a golden afternoon, but dark in the Dale.
> Mirrormere. Smooth sward. Deep blue like night sky.
> [*Notes scribbled in later:* Orcs won't come out by day. Frodo's wounds dressed by Trotter, so they discover the mithril-mail.]
> No time to stay. Gimli's regret. See the black springs of Morthond;[1] follow it.
> Make for Lothlórien. Legolas' description. The wood is in winter but still bears leaves that have turned golden. They do not fall till spring, when the green comes, and great yellow flowers. It was a garden of the Wood-elves long ago -- before the dwarves disturbed the evils beneath the mountains, he said (Gimli does not like that). They lived in houses in trees before the darkening world drove them underground.[2]
> In dusk Frodo again hears feet but cannot see anything following. They march on into the dusk.
> They take refuge in trees, and see Orcs march by beneath.
> Frodo long after sees a sloping back[ed] figure moving swiftly. It sniffs under the tree, stares up, and then disappears.

The passage of the Orcs beneath, and the coming of Gollum, were first referred to in the outline given on p. 207.

I turn now to the narrative. The chapter is numbered XVIII, and paginated continuously (with one gap), but it has no title. As I have said, I give (so far as possible) the most original form of the text, and do not, as a rule, indicate small subsequent emendations bringing it nearer to FR, though many or all of them may well belong to the same time.

'Alas, I fear we cannot wait here longer!' said Aragorn. He looked towards the mountains, and held up his sword. 'Farewell, Gandalf,' he cried. 'Did I not say to you: *if you pass*

LOTHLÓRIEN 219

the doors of Moria, beware? I know not what put the words into my mouth, but alas! that I spoke true. No fortune could have been more grievous. What hope have we without you?' He turned to the Company. 'We must do without hope!' he said. 'At least we may yet be avenged. Let us gird ourselves and weep no more. It is better to strike hard than to mourn long![3] Come! We have a long road and much to do!'

They rose and looked about them. Northward the Dale ran up into a glen of shadows between two great arms of the mountains, above which three tall white peaks towered.[4] Many torrents fell white over the steep sides into the valley. A mist of foam hung in the air.

To the west [*read* east][5] the mountains marched to a sudden end, and far lands could be descried beyond them vague and wide. To the south the mountains receded endlessly as far as sight could reach. Less than a mile away, and below them a little (for they stood still on the skirts of the mountains) lay a mere: it was long and oval, shaped like a great spear-head that thrust up deep into the northern glen. Its southern end was beyond the edge of the shadow, under the sunny sky. But its waters were dark: a deep blue like the night sky seen through a lighted window. Its face was still and unruffled. About it lay a smooth sward shelving on all sides down to its bare unbroken rim.[6]

'There lies Kheledzâram,[7] the Mirror-mere!' said Gimli sadly. 'I hoped to look on it in joy and linger here a while. I remember that he said: "May you have joy of the sight, but whatever you may do I cannot stay." Now it is I that must hasten away, and he that must stay.'

The Company went down the road, fading and broken, but still showing that here a great paved way had once wound up from the lowlands to the gate. It passed hard by the sward of Mirror-mere, and there not far from the road by the brink of the water there stood a single column, now broken at the top.

'That is Durin's Stone,' said Gimli. '[We >] I cannot pass without pausing there a minute, to look upon the wonder of the Dale.'

'Be swift then,' said Trotter, looking back towards the Gate. 'The sun sinks early. Orcs will not come out till it is dusk, but we must be far away ere night comes. The moon will appear for the last time tonight and it will be dark.'

'Come with me, Frodo,' said the dwarf, 'and any else who wish.' But only Sam and Legolas followed.[8] He ran down the

220   THE TREASON OF ISENGARD

sward and looked at the pillar. The runes upon it were worn
away. 'This stone marks the spot where Durin first looked in the
Mirror-mere,' said the dwarf. 'Let us look.' They stooped over
the water.

For a while they could see nothing. No shadow of themselves
fell on the mere. Slowly at the edges they saw the forms of the
encircling mountains revealed, mirrored in a profound blue, and
amidst it a space of sky. There like jewels in the deep shone
glinting stars, though the sunlight was in the sky above. No
shadow of themselves was seen.

'Fair Kheledzâram,' said Gimli. 'There lies the crown of
Durin till he wakes. Farewell.' He bowed and turned away, and
hastened back up the sward to the road again.

It wound now quickly down running away southwest [read
southeast][9] out from between the arms of the mountains. A
little below the Mere they came upon a deep well of dark water
almost black; from it a freshet fell over a stone lip and ran
gurgling away in a stony channel. 'This is the spring whence the
Blackroot rises,' said Gimli. 'Do not drink from it: it is icy cold.'

'Soon,' said Trotter, 'it will become a swift river, fed by many
other torrents from [?all the land]. Our road leads beside it. And
we must go swifter than it runs. There is our way.' Out on
before them they could see the Blackroot winding away in the
lower land, until it was lost in a distance that glowed like pale
gold on the edge of sight.

'There lie the woods of Lothlórien,' said Trotter. 'Their eaves
are yet many miles away (four leagues or more), but we must
reach them before night.'

[Now they went on silently][10] for some time, but every step
grew more painful for Frodo. In spite of the bright [?winter] sun
the air seemed biting after the warm dark of Moria. Sam at [his]
side was also failing. The cut in his arm was paining him.[11]
They lagged behind together. Trotter looked back anxiously.
'So much has happened,' he said, 'that I had forgotten you,
Frodo, and Sam. I am sorry: you are both hurt, and we have
done nothing to ease you or to find out how serious are your
hurts. What shall we do? There is nothing we can do in this
empty region, with the gate and our foes so near behind.'

'How far is there still to go?' said Frodo.

They have a first meal 2½ hours after noon. Beside a
beautiful little fall in the Blackroot, where another torrent
coming from west flowed out and they both fell over some green

LOTHLÓRIEN   221

stone. Trotter dresses Sam's wound. 'The cut is looking ill – but luckily is not (as orc-cuts may be) poisoned.' Trotter bathes it in the water and lays a leaf of *athelas* against it.

Then he turns attention to Frodo. Reluctantly he strips off his jacket and tunic, and suddenly the mithril-corslet shines and flashes in the sun. Trotter strips it from him and holds it up. Description of its radiance.

'This is a pretty hobbit-skin!' said Trotter. 'If it were known they wore such a hide, all the hunters of the world would be crowding to the Shire.'

'And all the hunters of the world [would] shoot in vain,' said Gimli, staring in amazement. 'Bilbo saved your life – it was a generous and timely gift.'

There was a great dark bruise on Frodo's side and breast, the rings driven through shirt into flesh... His left side also was bruised against the wall.

'Nothing is broken,' said Trotter.

The text now becomes for a space very ragged, the story being in its most primitive form of composition, and soon passes into a rough sketch of the narrative to come.

Kindle fire warm water bathed in *athelas*. Pads fastened under the mail, which is put on again.

They hurry on again. Sun sinks behind mountains. Shadows creep out down mountain side and over the land. Dusk is about them, but there is a glow on the land to the East. ... pale yellow in dusk.[12] They have come 12–14 miles from Gate and are nearly done. Legolas describes Lothlórien.

Near forest gate another small river comes in from right (west) across the path. The bridge is no longer there. They wade across and halt on other side with water as defence. Climb trees.

Orcs ... at night. But a pleasant [?adventure] with Wood-elves next day. They are escorted to Wood-elves' houses in trees in angle of Blackroot and Anduin by light marches (no orc comes). Several (2–3) pleasant days. 40 miles. Sorrow of whole world for news of fall of Gandalf. They are now nearly 100 leagues (300 miles) south of Rivendell.[13]

An isolated page of very rough drafting takes up with Frodo's reply to Gimli's question (' "What is it?" said the dwarf', FR p. 351):

'I don't know,' said Frodo. 'I thought I heard feet, and I thought I saw light – like eyes. I have done so often since we entered Moria.'

Gimli paused and stooped to the ground. 'I can hear nothing but

222   THE TREASON OF ISENGARD

the night-speech of plant and stone,' he said. 'Come, let us hurry! The others are out of sight already.'

The night wind blew chill up the valley to meet them. They passed many scattered trees, tall with pale stems. In front a great shadow loomed, and the endless rustle of leaves like poplars in the breeze.

'Lothlórien,' said Legolas. 'Lothlórien. We are come to the [?gates] of the golden wood. Alas that it is winter.'

Here the formed narrative takes up again.[14]

Under the night the trees stood tall before them, arched over the stream and road that ran suddenly beneath their spreading boughs. In the dim light of the stars their stems were grey, and their quivering leaves a hint of fallow gold.

'Lothlórien!' said Aragorn. 'Glad I am to hear the leaves! We are barely five leagues from the Gates, but we can go no further. Let us hope that there is some virtue of the Elves that will protect us this night – if Elves indeed dwell here still in the darkening world.'[15]

'It is long since any of my folk returned hither,' said Legolas; 'for we dwell now very far away; yet it is told that though some have gone for ever some abide still in Lothlórien, but they dwell deep in the wood many leagues from here.'[16]

'Then we must fend for ourselves tonight,' said Aragorn. 'Let us go on yet a little way until the wood is all about us, and then will turn aside from the road.'

A mile within the wood they came upon another stream flowing down swiftly from the tree-clad slopes that climbed back towards the Mountains. They heard it splashing over a fall away among the shadows on their right. Its dark hurrying waters ran across the path before them and joined the [Blackroot >] Morthond in a swirl of dim pools among the roots of trees.

'Here is the [Taiglin >] Linglor,' said Legolas. 'Of it the wood-elves made many songs, remembering the rainbow upon its singing falls and the golden flowers that floated in its foam. All is dark now, and the Bridge of Linglor that the elves made is broken down. But it is not deep. Let us wade across. There is healing in its [cold >] cool waters / But I will bathe my feet in it – for it is said that its waters are healing. On the further bank we can rest, and the sound of running water may bring us sleep.'[17]

They followed the elf, and one by one climbed down the steep bank and bathed their [feet][18] in the stream. For a moment

LOTHLÓRIEN 223

Frodo stood near the bank and let the cold water flow about his tired feet. It was cold but its very touch was clean, and as it mounted to his knees he felt that the stain of travel and the weariness of his limbs was washed away.

When all the Company had crossed they sat and rested and ate a little food, while Legolas told them tales of Lothlórien before the world was grey.

Here there is a space in the manuscript, with the words *insert song*. There are many pages of rough working for Legolas' song of Amroth and Nimrodel, leading to a version that (while certainly belonging to this time) is for much of its length very close to the form in FR (pp. 354–5). The name of the maiden is *Linglorel* (once *Inglorel*), becoming *Nimladel*, *Nimlorel* (see note 17), and in the final version found here *Nimlothel* (corrected to *Nimrodel*). Her lover was *Ammalas* (as he appears in the narrative that follows), and the form *Amroth* can be seen emerging as my father wrote the first line of the ninth verse: 'When Ammalas beheld the shore', with a rejected name *Amaldor* momentarily appearing before the line became 'When *Amroth* saw the fading shore'.

Associated with the texts of the song is a version of the words of Legolas that preceded it (FR p. 353):

'I will sing you a song,' he said. 'It is a fair song in the woodland tongue: but this is how it runs in the common speech, as some in Rivendell have turned it.' In a soft voice hardly to be heard amid the rustle of the leaves above he began.

This is apparently the first appearance of the term *Common Speech*. – The final version found here is virtually as that in FR through the first six verses (but with the name *Nimlothel*); then follows:

A wind awoke in Northern lands
and loud it blew and free,
and bore the ship from Elven-strands
across the shining sea.

Beyond the waves the shores were grey,
the mountains sinking low;
as salt as tears the driving spray
the wind a cry of woe.

When Amroth saw the fading shore
beyond the heaving swell
he cursed the faithless ship that bore
him far from Nimlothel.

An Elven-lord he was of old
before the birth of men

224   THE TREASON OF ISENGARD

> *when first the boughs were hung with gold*
> *in fair Lothlórien.*

A variant of this verse is given:

> *An Elven-lord he was of old*
> *when all the woods were young*
> *and in Lothlórien with gold*
> *the boughs of trees were hung.*

The eleventh verse, and the last verse, are as in FR, but the twelfth reads here:

> *The foam was in his flowing hair,*
> *a light about him shone;*
> *afar they saw the waves him bear*
> *as floats the northern swan.*

Pencilled suggestions in the margins, no doubt of this same time, move the verses a little further towards the final form; and at the end of the song my father noted: 'If all this is included, Legolas will have to say that it represents only a few of the verses of the original (e.g. the departure from Lórien is omitted).'

An outline for the next part of the story may be given here. It is very roughly written indeed, and I have made one or two obvious corrections.

> Legolas sings song of Linglorel.
> Legolas describes the houses of the Galadrim.
> Gimli says trees would be safer.
> Aragorn decides to climb for night.
> They find a group of great trees near the falls (to right). Legolas is about to climb one with many low boughs when a voice in elven-speech comes from above. He fears arrows. But after a converse in elven-speech reports that all is well. Warnings of things afoot have reached folk of Lórien from the Gladden Fields, when Elrond's messengers came East. They have set guards. (Saw many orcs passing west of Lórien towards Moria: put this in later, when Elves talk to Company.) [See pp. 227–8.]
> They did not challenge or shoot because they heard Legolas' voice – and after the sound of his song. They have a great platform in 2 trees by the falls.
> Legolas, Sam and Frodo go on platform with 3 elves. Others on another platform and Aragorn and Boromir in crotch of a large tree.
> Orcs come to Linglorel in night. The Elves do not shoot because they are in too great number: but one slips away to warn folk in wood and prepare an ambush.

LOTHLÓRIEN

After all is quiet again Frodo sees Gollum creep into wood. He looks up and begins to climb, but just as the Elves fit arrows to bow Frodo stays them. Gollum has a sense of danger and fades away.

Next day the Elves lead them to Angle.

After the song of Legolas the narrative continues:

His voice faltered and fell silent. 'I do not remember all the words,' he said. 'It is a fair song, and that is but the beginning; for it is long and sad. It tells how sorrow came upon Lothlórien, Lórien of the flowers, when the world darkened, and the dwarves awakened evil in the Mountains.'

'But the dwarves did not make the evil,' said Gimli.

'I said not so,' said Legolas sadly. 'Yet evil came. And it was told that Linglorel[19] was lost. For such was the name of that maiden, and they gave the same name to the mountain-stream that she loved: she sang beside the waterfalls playing upon a harp. There in spring when the wind is in the new leaves the echo of her voice may still be heard, they say. But the elves of her kindred departed, and she was lost in the passes of the mountains,[20] and none know where she now may be. It is said in the song that the elven ship waited in the havens long for her, but a wind arose in the night and bore him into the West; and when Ammalas[21] her lover saw that the land was far away he leaped into the sea, but whether he came ever back to the Hither Shores and found Linglorel is not told.

'It is said that Linglorel had a house built in branches of a tree; for that was the manner of the Elves of Lórien, and may be yet; and for that reason they are called Galadrim, the Tree-people.[22] Deep in the wood the trees are very tall and strong. And our people did not delve in the ground or build fastnesses before the Shadows [*read* Shadow] came.'

'Yet even so, in these latter days, a dwelling in the trees might be thought safer than sitting on the ground,' said Gimli. He looked across the water to the road that led back to Dimrill Dale, and then up into the roof of dark boughs above them.

'Your words bring good counsel, Gimli,' said Aragorn.[23] 'We have no time to build, but tonight we will become Galadrim and seek refuge in the tree-tops, if we can. We have sat here beside the road longer already than was wise.'

The Company now turned aside from the path, and went into the shadows of the deeper woods westward, away from the Blackroot. Not far from the falls of Linglorel they found a

226   THE TREASON OF ISENGARD

cluster of tall strong trees, some of which overhung the stream.[24]

'I will climb up,' said Legolas, 'for I am at home among trees, or in their branches; though these trees are of a kind strange to me. *Mallorn* is their name, those that bear the yellow blossom, but I have never climbed in one. I will see now what is their shape and growth.' He sprang lightly upward from the ground and caught a branch that grew from the tree-bole high above his head. Even as he swung a voice spoke from the shadows above them.

'*Daro!*'[25] it said, and Legolas dropped back again in surprise and fear. He shrank against the tree-bole. 'Stand still,' he whispered to the others, 'and do not speak!'

There was a sound of laughter above their heads and another clear voice spoke in the Elven-tongue. Frodo could catch little that was said, for the speech of the silvan folk east of the mountains, such as they used among themselves, was strange.[26] Legolas looked up and answered in the same tongue.

'Who are they and what do they say?' said [Pippin >] Merry.

'They're elves,' said Sam. 'Can't you hear the voices?'

'They say,' said Legolas, 'that you breathe so loud that they could shoot you in the dark. But that you need have no fear. They have been watching us for a long time. They heard my voice across the Linglorel and knew of what people I came, so that they did not oppose our crossing. And they have heard my song and heard the names of Linglorel and Ammalas. Now they bid us to climb up, three in each of these trees that stand here near together. I will go first.'

The last part of Legolas' remarks was changed in pencil to the text of FR: 'Now they bid me to climb up with Frodo, of whom they seem to have heard. The rest they ask to wait a little, and to keep watch at the foot of the tree.' The manuscript then continues for a short stretch in pencil, and clearly belongs with this alteration, since Legolas and Frodo are the first to ascend.

Out of the shadows there was let down a ladder of silver rope – very slender it looked, but proved strong enough to bear many men. Legolas climbed swiftly followed more slowly by Frodo, and behind came Sam trying not to breathe loud. The tree was very tall [*written above:* a mallorn], and its large bole was fair and round with a smooth silken bark. The branches grew out nearly straight at first and then swept upwards; but near the top of the main stem dwindled into a crown, and there they found a wooden platform [*added:* or 'flet' as such things were called in those days: the elves called it *talan*. It was] made of grey close-grained wood – the wood of the mallorn.

Three elves were seated on it. They were clad in grey, and could not be seen against the tree-stems unless they moved. One of them uncovered a small lamp that gave out a slender silver beam and held it up, looking at their faces. Then he shut out the light and spoke words of welcome in the Elven tongue. Frodo spoke haltingly in return.

'Welcome,' they said again in ordinary speech. Then one spoke slowly. 'We speak seldom any tongue but our own,' he said; 'for we dwell now in the heart of the woods and do not willingly have dealings with any other folk. Some only of us go abroad for the gathering of tidings and our protection. I am one. Hathaldir is my name. My brothers Orfin and Rhimbron speak your tongue but little. We have heard of your coming, for the messengers of Elrond passed through Lothlórien on their way home by the Dimrill Stair.[27] We had not heard of hobbits before, nor even seen one until now. You do not look evil, and you come with Legolas, who is of our northern kindred. We are willing to do as Elrond asked and befriend you. Though it is not our custom we will lead you through our land. But you must stay here tonight. How many are you?'[28]

'Eight,' said Legolas. 'Myself, four hobbits, two men (one is Aragorn, an elf-friend, beloved of Elrond), and a dwarf. [And we are yet weighed with sorrow, for our leader is lost. Gandalf the wizard was lost in Moria.]'[29]

'A dwarf!' said Hathaldir. 'I do not like that. We do not have dealings with dwarves since the evil days. We cannot allow him to pass.'

'But he is an elf-friend and known to Elrond,' said Frodo. 'Elrond chose him to be of our company; and he has been valiant and faithful.'

The Elves spoke together in soft voices, and questioned Legolas in their own tongue. 'Well then,' said Hathaldir. 'We will do this though it is against our liking. If Aragorn and Legolas will guard him and answer for him he shall go blindfold through Lothlórien.

'But now there is need of haste. Your company must not remain longer on the ground. We have been keeping watch on the rivers, ever since we saw a great troop of orcs going north

228   THE TREASON OF ISENGARD

along the skirts of the mountains towards Moria many days ago. Wolves were howling on the wood's border. If you have indeed come from Moria the peril cannot be far behind. Tomorrow you must go far. The hobbits shall climb up here and stay with us – we do not fear them! There is another [guard's nest > flet >] *talan* in the next tree. There the others must go. You Legolas must be our security. And call to us if aught is amiss. Have an eye on that dwarf!'

Legolas went down again bringing Hathaldir's message; and soon afterwards Merry and Pippin climbed up onto the high [?platform]. 'There,' said Merry, 'we have brought up your blankets for you. The rest of our baggage Aragorn has hidden in a deep drift of old leaves.'

'There was no need,' said Hathaldir. 'It is chill in the tree tops in winter, though the wind is southward; but we have drink and food to give you that will keep out night chills, and there are skins and wraps to spare with us.'

The hobbits accepted the second supper gladly, and soon, wrapped as warmly as they could, they tried to get to sleep. Weary as they were it was not easy for them, for hobbits do not like heights and do not sleep upstairs (even when they have any upstairs, which is rare). The flet was not at all to their liking. It had no kerb or rail, and only a wind screen on one side which could be moved and fixed in different places. 'I hope if I do get to sleep I shan't roll off,' said Pippin. 'Once I get to sleep, Mr Pippin,' said Sam, 'I shall go on sleeping whether I roll off or no.'

Frodo lay for a while and looked at the stars that glinted now and again through the thin roof of pale rustling leaves above him. Sam was snoring at his side before he himself, lulled by the wind in the leaves above and the sweet murmur of the falls of Nimrodel[30] below, fell into a sleep with the song of Legolas still running in his mind. Two of the elves sat with arms about their knees speaking in whispers; one had gone down to take up his post on one of the lower boughs.

Late in the night Frodo woke. The other hobbits were asleep. The elves were gone. The last thin rind of the waning moon was gleaming dimly in the leaves. The wind was still. A little way off he heard a harsh laugh and the tread of many feet. Then a ring of metal. The sounds died away southward going deeper into the wood.

The grey hood of one of the elves appeared suddenly above

LOTHLÓRIEN   229

the edge of the flet. He looked at the hobbits. 'What is it?' said
Frodo, sitting up.

'Yrch!' said the Elf in a hissing whisper, and cast onto the flet
the rope-ladder rolled up.

'Orcs,' said Frodo, 'what are they doing?' But the Elf was
gone.

There was no more sound; even the leaves were silent. Frodo
could not sleep. Thankful as he was that they had not been
caught upon the ground, he knew that the trees offered little
protection save concealment, if orcs discovered where they
were, and they have a scent keen as hounds. He drew out Sting
and saw it glow like a blue flame, and slowly fade.

[Before long Hathaldir came back to the flet and sat near the
edge with drawn bow and arrow in the string. Frodo rose and
crawled to the edge of the flet and peered over.][31] Nonetheless
the sense of immediate danger did not leave him. Rather it
deepened. He crawled to the edge of the flet and peered over. He
was almost sure he heard the soft sound of stealthy movement
in the leaves at the tree's foot far below. Not the elves, he feared,
for the woodland folk were altogether noiseless in their movements (so quiet and deft as to excite the admiration even of
hobbits). And there seemed to be a sniffing noise. Something
was scrabbling on the bark of the tree. He lay looking down
holding his breath. Something was climbing, and breathing with
a soft hissing sound. Then coming up close to the stem he saw
two pale eyes. They stopped and gazed upwards unwinking.
Suddenly they turned away and a shadowy figure slipped round
the trunk and vanished on the further side. Shortly afterwards
Hathaldir climbed up.

'There was something in this tree that I have never seen
before,' he said. 'Not an orch [sic]. But I did [not] shoot because
I was not sure, and we dare not risk battle. It fled as soon as I
touched the tree-stem. There was a strong company of orcs.
They crossed the Nimrodel (curse them for defiling our water)
and went on – though they seemed to pick up some scent, and
halted for a while searching on both sides of the path where you
sat last evening. We dare not risk a battle, three against a
hundred, and we did not shoot, but Orfin has gone back by
secret ways to our folk, and we shall not let them return out of
Lórien if we can help it. There will be many elves hidden
[?beside] Nimrodel ere another night is gone. But now we too
must take the road as soon as it is light.'

230 THE TREASON OF ISENGARD

Dawn came pale from the East. As the light grew it filtered through the golden leaves of the mallorn, and chill though the dawn-wind blew it seemed to be sunshine of an early summer morning. The pale blue sky peeped between the moving leaves. Climbing a slender branch up from the flet Frodo looked out and saw all the valley southward, eastward of the dark shadow of the mountains, lying like a sea of fallow gold tossing gently in the breeze.

[When they had eaten the sweet food of the elves, sparing their own dwindling stores,] The morning was still young and cold when / the Company set out again, guided by Hathaldir. Rhimbron remained on guard on the flet. Frodo looked back and caught a gleam of white among the grey tree-stems. 'Farewell Nimrodel!' said Legolas. 'Farewell,' said Frodo. It seemed to him that he had never heard a running water so musical: ever changing its note and yet playing ever the same endless music.

They went some way along the path on the east [read west][32] of the Blackroot, but soon Hathaldir turned aside into the trees and halted on the bank under their shadow. 'There is one of my people over there on the other side,' he said, 'though you may not see him. But I see the gleam of his hair in the shadow.' He gave a call like the low whistle of a bird, and from the tree-stems an elf stepped out, clad in grey, but with his hood thrown back. Skilfully Hathaldir flung over the stream to him a coil of stout grey rope. He caught it and fastened it to a tree-stem near the bank.

'The river has already a strong stream here,' said Hathaldir. 'It is not wide; but it is too deep to wade. And it is very cold. We do not set foot in Morthond unless we are compelled. This is how we cross! Follow me!' Securing his end of the rope to another tree, he stepped onto it and ran lightly across, as if he was on a firm path.

'I can walk this path,' said Legolas, 'but only with care, for we have not this skill in Mirkwood; but the rest cannot. Must they swim?'

'No,' said Hathaldir. 'We will cast two more ropes. Fasten them to the tree man-high and half-high, and then with care they can cross.' The Elves drew the strong grey ropes taut across the stream. Then first Aragorn crossed slowly, holding the upper rope. When it came to the hobbits' turn Pippin went first. He was light of foot and went across with fair speed, holding

LOTHLÓRIEN
231

only with one hand on the lower rope. Merry trying to rival him slipped for a moment and hung over the water. Sam shuffled across slowly and cautiously behind Frodo, looking down at the dark eddying water below his feet as if it was a chasm of many fathoms deep. Gimli and Boromir came last.

When they had all crossed Rhimbron[33] untied the ends of the ropes and cast two back. Then coiling up the other he returned to Nimrodel to keep watch in his post.

'Now,' said Hathaldir, 'you have entered the Gore, Nelen[34] we call it, which lies in the angle between Blackroot and Anduin the Great River. We do not allow strangers to walk here if we can prevent it, nor to go deep into the angle where [our dwellings are >] we live. As was agreed I shall here blindfold the eyes of Gimli the dwarf; the others shall walk free for a while until we get nearer to our hidden dwellings.'

This was not at all to Gimli's liking. 'The agreement was made without my consent,' he said. 'I will not walk blindfold like a prisoner or traitor. My folk have ever resisted the Enemy, nor had dealings with orcs or any of his servants. Neither have we done harm to the Elves. I am no more likely to betray your secrets than Legolas or any others of the Company.'

'You speak truly, I do not doubt,' said Hathaldir. 'Yet such is our law. I am not master of the law, and cannot set it aside at my own judgement. I have done all that I dared in letting you set foot in [Nelen >] the Gore.'

But Gimli was obstinate. He set his feet firmly apart and laid his hand upon the haft of his axe. 'I will go forward free, or I will go back north alone, though it be to perish in the wilderness,' he said.

'You cannot depart,' said Hathaldir grimly. 'You cannot cross Morthond, and behind you north are hidden defences and guards across the open arms of the Angle between the rivers. You will be slain before you get nigh them.' The other elf fitted an arrow to his bow as Gimli drew his axe from his belt.

'A plague on dwarves and their stiff necks!' muttered Legolas.

'Come!' said Aragorn. 'If I am to lead the Company you must all do as I bid. We will all be blindfold, even Legolas. That will be best, though it will make the journey slow and dull.'

Gimli laughed suddenly. 'A merry troop of fools we shall look!' he said. 'But I will be content, if only Legolas shares my blindness.'

This was little to Legolas' liking.

232   THE TREASON OF ISENGARD

'Come!' said Aragorn. 'Let us not cry "plague on your stiff neck" also. But you shall not be our hostage. We will all share the necessity alike.'

'I shall claim full amends for every fall and stubbed toe, if you do not lead us well,' said Gimli as they bound a cloth about his eyes.

'You will not have need,' said Halthadir. 'We shall lead you well, and our paths are smooth and green.'

'Alas! for the folly of these days,' said Legolas in his turn. 'Here all are enemies of the one Enemy, and yet I must walk blind, while the sun is shining in the woodland under leaves of gold!'

'Folly it may seem,' said Hathaldir. 'And in truth in nothing is the evil of the Enemy seen more clear than in the estrangements that divide us all. Yet so little faith and trust is left that we dare not endanger our dwellings. We live now in ever-growing peril, and our hands are more often set to bowstring than to harp. The rivers have long defended us, [but] they are no longer a sure guard. For the Shadow has crept northward all about our land. Some speak [?already] of departing, yet for that maybe it is already too late. The mountains to the west have an evil name for us. To the east the land is waste. It is rumoured that we cannot with safety go south of the mountains through Rohan, and that even if we did pass into the western lands the shores of the sea are no longer secure. It is still said that there are havens in the north beyond the land of the half-high,[35] but where that lies we do not know.'

'You might at least guess now,' said Pippin. 'The havens lie west of my land, the Shire.'

The elf looked at him with interest. 'Happy folk are hobbits,' he said, 'to dwell near Havens of Escape. Tell me about them, and what the sea is like, of which we sing, but scarce remember.'

'I do not know,' said Pippin. 'I have never seen it. I have never been out of my land before. And had I known what the world was like outside, I do not think I should have had the heart to leave it.'

'Yes, the word is full of peril, and dark places,' said Hathaldir. 'But still there is much that is very fair, and though love is now mingled with grief it is not the less deep. And some there are among us who sing that the Shadow will draw back again and peace shall be. Yet I do not believe that the world will be again as of old, or the light of the sun as it was before. For the

LOTHLÓRIEN   233

Elves I fear it will mean only a peace in which they may pass to
the Sea unhindered and leave the middle-earth for ever. Alas!
for Lothlórien. It would be a life far from the *mellyrn*. But if
there are mallorn-trees beyond the Sea none have reported it.'

As they spoke thus the Company went slowly along paths in
the wood. Hathaldir led them and the other elf walked behind.
Even as Hathaldir had said they found the ground beneath their
feet smooth and soft, and they walked slowly but without fear
of hurt or fall.[36] Before long they met many grey-clad elves
going northward to the outposts.[37] They brought news, some of
which Legolas interpreted. The orcs had been waylaid, and
many destroyed; the remainder had fled westward towards the
mountains, and were being pursued as far as the sources of
Nimrodel. The elves were hastening now to guard the north
borders against any new attack.

I interrupt the text here to introduce a page of fearsomely rough
notes which show my father thinking about the further course of the
story from approximately this point. They begin with references to
Cerin Amroth and to 'a green snowdrop', with the Elvish words *nifred*
and *nifredil*. It may well be that this is where the name *nifredil* arose
(both *nifred* 'pallor' and *nifredil* 'snowdrop' are given under the stem
NIK-W in the *Etymologies*, V.378). Then follows:

News. H[athaldir] says he has spoken much of Elves. What of
Men? The message spoke of 9. Gandalf. Consternation at news.

With this cf. p. 227 and note 29. My father was thinking of
postponing the revelation of Gandalf's fall to the halt at Cerin
Amroth, before he finally decided that it should not be spoken of until
they came to Caras Galadon.

There is then a sentence, placed within brackets, which is unhappily
– since it is probably the first reference my father ever made to
Galadriel – only in part decipherable: '[?Lord] of Galadrim [?and ?a]
Lady and . . . . . . [?went] to White Council.' The remaining notes are as
follows:

They climb Cerin Amroth. Frodo says [*read* sees] Anduin far
away a glimpse of Dol Dúgol.[38] H[athaldir] says it is reoccupied and
a cloud lowers there.

They journey to Nelennas.[39]

Lord and Lady clad in white, with *white hair*. Piercing eyes like a
lance in starlight.[40] Lord says he knows their quest but won't speak
of it.

They speak [of] Gandalf. Song of Elves.

Of the [?harbour] to Legolas and aid to Gimli. Beornings.[41]

Leave Lothlórien. Parting of ways at Stonehills.

234   THE TREASON OF ISENGARD

I return now to the draft text.

'Also,' said Hathaldir, 'they bring me a message from the
Lord of the Galadrim. You may all walk free. He has received
messages from Elrond, who begs for help and friendship to you
each and all.' He removed the bandage from Gimli's eyes. 'Your
pardon,' he said bowing. 'But now look on us nonetheless with
friendly eyes. Look and be glad, for you are the first dwarf to
behold the sun upon the trees of Nelen-Lórien since Durin's
day!'

As the bandage dropped from his eyes Frodo looked up. They
were standing in an open space. To the left stood a great mound
covered with a sward of grass, as green as if it were springtime.
Upon it as a double crown grew two circles of trees: the outer
had a bark of snowy white and were leafless but beautiful in
their slender and shapely nakedness; the inner were mallorn-
trees of great height, still arrayed in gold. High amid their
branches was a white flet. At their feet and all about the sides of
the hill the grass was studded with small golden starshaped
flowers, and among them nodding on slender stalks flowers of a
green so pale[42] that it gleamed white against the rich green of
the grass. Over all the sky was blue and the sun of afternoon
slanted among the tree-stems.

'You are come to Coron [*written above:* Kerin] Amroth.[43]
For this is the mound of Amroth, and here in happier days his
house was built. Here bloom the winter flowers in the unfading
grass: the yellow *elanor*[44] and the pale *nifredil*. Here we will rest
a while, and come to the houses of the Galadrim[45] at dusk.'

They cast themselves on the soft grass at the mound's foot;[46]
but after a while Hathaldir took Frodo and they went to the hill
top, and climbed up to the high flet. Frodo looked out East and
saw not far away the gleam of the Great River which was the
border of Lórien. Beyond the land seemed flat and empty, until
in the distance it rose again dark and drear. The sun that lay
upon all the lands between seemed not to lie upon it.

'There lies the fastness of Southern Mirkwood,' said Hathaldir. 'For the most part it is a forest of dark pine and close fir –
but amidst it stands the black hill Dol-Dúgol, where for long the
Necromancer had his [?fort]. We fear it is now rehabited and
threatens, for his power is now sevenfold. A dark cloud lies
often above it. [?? Fear of the time is] war upon our eastern
borders.'

LOTHLÓRIEN   235

The draft text continues ('The sun had sunk behind the mountains') without a break, whereas in FR a new chapter, 'The Mirror of Galadriel', now begins; and I also pause in the narrative here (it was not long before my father introduced this division). It will be noticed that towards the end of the earliest 'Lothlórien' material given thus far the narrative is less advanced towards the final form, and notably absent is Frodo's sight southward from Cerin Amroth of 'a hill of many mighty trees, or a city of green towers', Caras Galad(h)on (FR p. 366).

The next text of 'Lothlórien' is a good clear manuscript, thus titled, with a fair amount of alteration in the process of composition; but it cannot be entirely separated off from the initial drafting as a distinct 'phase' in the writing of the story, for it seems certain that at the beginning of the chapter the draft and the fair copy overlapped (see note 14). There seems nothing to show, however, that the rest of the new text actually overlapped with the drafts, and it is in any case most convenient to treat it separately.

The text of 'Lothlórien' in FR was now for the most part very closely approached, the chief differences of substance being the absence of all passages referring to or implying Aragorn's previous knowledge of Lothlórien,[47] and the meeting of the Company with the Elves coming up from the south shortly after their rest at noon on the first day of their journey from Nimrodel (see note 37). The original story was still followed in various minor points, as in its being Pippin and not Merry who speaks to Haldir (replacing Hathaldir of the draft text, see note 28) of the Havens (p. 232); Sam does not refer to his uncle Andy (FR p. 361), and it was still in his arm that he was wounded in Moria (p. 201).[48]

By an addition to the text that looks as if it belongs with the first writing of the manuscript the *Dimrill Stair* acquires its later meaning (see p. 164): ' "Yonder is the Dimrill Stair," said Aragorn pointing to the falls. "Down the deep-cloven way that climbs beside the torrent we should have come, if fortune had been kinder" ' (FR p. 347).

The Silverlode was at first named Blackroot or Morthond, but in the course of the writing of the manuscript the name became Silverlode (the Elvish name *Kelebrant* being added afterwards). The Company 'kept to the old path on the west side of the Blackroot' (FR p. 360; cf. note 32); but ten lines later Haldir says, in the text as written, 'Silverlode is already a strong stream here'. It was presumably at this juncture that my father decided on the transposition of the names of the northern and southern rivers (see note 36), a transposition that had already taken place in the initial drafting of 'Farewell to Lórien' (p. 279).

One of Haldir's brothers is still called *Orfin* as in the original draft; at one occurrence only, he is changed to *Orofin*, and in the drafting of

236   THE TREASON OF ISENGARD

'Farewell to Lórien' he is *Orofin* (p. 279; FR *Orophin*). The other, in the draft text *Rhimbron*, is now *Romrin*, becoming *Rhomrin* in the course of the writing of the manuscript.

The Elvish name for 'the Gore' is here *Narthas*, where the original text (p. 231) has *Nelen* (replacing *Nelennas*): 'you have entered Narthas or the Gore as you would say, for it is the land that lies like a spear-head[49] between the arms of Silverlode and Anduin the Great', and 'I have done much in letting you set foot in Narthas'. But Haldir here says also: 'The others may walk free for a while until we come nearer to *the Angle, Nelen, where we dwell*', where the original draft has 'until we get nearer to our hidden dwellings'; and when they come to Kerin Amroth (as it is now written) he tells Gimli that he is 'the first dwarf to behold the trees of *Nelen-Lórien* since Durin's Day!' – where the original draft has *Nelen-Lórien* likewise (p. 234).

This seems to show that in the first stage my father intended *Nelen*, *Nelen-Lórien*, 'the Gore', 'the Gore of Lórien', as the name for Lórien between the rivers, without devising an Elvish name for the southward region where the Elves of Lórien actually dwelt; while in the stage represented here *Narthas* 'the Gore' is the larger region, and *Nelen* 'the Angle' the smaller, the point of the triangle or tip of the spearhead. If this is so, when Hathaldir/Haldir first spoke of 'the trees of Nelen-Lórien' the name bore a different sense from what he intended by the same words in the present manuscript.[50]

In the first sentence of this chapter in this manuscript *Trotter* is so named, as he was throughout the preceding one (p. 204); this was changed at once to *Aragorn*, and he is *Aragorn* as far as the Company's coming to the eaves of the Golden Wood, where he becomes *Elfstone* in the text as written.[51] Subsequently *Aragorn*, so far as it went, was changed to *Ingold*, and *Elfstone* was likewise changed to *Ingold*; then *Ingold* was changed back to *Elfstone*.[52]

There remain to notice some remarkable pencilled notes that occur on pages of this manuscript. The first is written on the back of the page (which is marked as being an insertion into the text) that bears the Song of Nimrodel, and reads:

> Could not Balrog be Saruman? Make battle on Bridge be between Gandalf and Saruman? Then Gandalf ... clad in white.

The illegible words might conceivably be *comes out*. This was struck through; it had no further significance or repercussion, but remains as an extraordinary glimpse into reflections that lie beneath the written evidence of the history of *The Lord of the Rings* (and the thought, equally baldly expressed, would reappear: p. 422).

A second rejected note was written at some later time against Haldir's words 'they bring me a message from the Lord and Lady of the Galadrim':

> Lord? If Galadriel is alone and is wife of Elrond.

LOTHLÓRIEN 237

A third note, again struck through, is written on the back of an inserted page that carries a revision of the account of Frodo's perceptions of Lothlórien:

Elf-rings
.... [*illegible word or name*]
The power of the Elf-rings must *fade* if One Ring is *destroyed*.

NOTES

1 On 'the black springs of Morthond' see p. 166.

2 At this point, then, my father conceived of the Elves of Lothlórien as dwelling underground, like the Elves of Mirkwood. Cf. Legolas' later words on p. 225: 'It is said that Linglorel had a house built in branches of a tree; for that was the manner of the Elves of Lórien, and may be yet... And our people [i.e. the Elves of Mirkwood] did not delve in the ground or build fastnesses before the Shadow came.'

3 This passage was first used at the end of the preceding chapter, 'Moria (ii)': see p. 204 and note 20.

4 On the emergence of the three peaks (the Mountains of Moria) in the new version of 'The Ring Goes South' see p. 166.

5 The word *west* is perfectly clear, but can only be a slip; FR has of course *east*. The same slip occurs in the first emergence of this passage at the end of 'Moria (ii)' (p. 203), and it occurs again in the fair copy of 'Lothlórien'.

6 This passage, from 'Northward the Dale ran up into a glen of shadows', was first used at the end of 'Moria (ii)': see pp. 203–4.

7 For the first appearance of *Kheledzâram* see p. 166.

8 In FR Legolas did not go down with Gimli to look in Mirrormere.

9 The word *southwest* is clear (and occurs again in the fair copy of 'Lothlórien'), yet is obviously a slip; cf. note 5.

10 The words *Now they went on silently* were struck out emphatically, but they are obviously necessary.

11 It is not told in the original text of 'Moria (ii)' (p. 194) that Sam received any wound in the Chamber of Mazarbul; this story first appears in the fair copy of that chapter (see p. 201).

12 The text becomes illegible for a couple of lines, but elements of a description of the wood can be made out.

13 This passage possibly suggests that at this stage the Company did not encounter Elves on the first night. The 'several (2–3) pleasant days' are clearly the days of their journey through Lothlórien, not the days they spent at 'Angle' (cf. the plot outline, p. 207: 'Dec. 15, 16, 17 they journey to Angle between Anduin and Blackroot. There they remain long').

238   THE TREASON OF ISENGARD

That they were now nearly 300 miles south of Rivendell accords precisely with the First Map: see Map II on p. 305, where the distance from Rivendell to the confluence of Silverlode and Anduin on the original scale (squares of 2 cm. side, 2 cm. = 100 miles) is just under six centimetres measured in a straight line. Aragorn's reckoning, when they came to the eaves of the Golden Wood, that they had come 'barely five leagues from the Gates', does not accord with the First Map, but that map can scarcely be used as a check on such small distances.

14   It seems that my father began making a fair copy of the chapter when the draft narrative had gone no further than the point where Frodo and Sam began to lag behind as the Company went down from Dimrill Dale. When he came to this point he stopped writing out the new manuscript in ink, but continued on in pencil on the same paper, as far as Legolas' words 'Alas that it is winter!' He then overwrote this further passage in ink and erased the pencil; and then went back to further drafting on rough paper – which is why there is this gap in the initial narrative, and why it takes up again at the words 'Under the night the trees stood tall before them...' Overlapping of draft and fair copy, often writing the preliminary draft in pencil on the fair copy manuscript and then erasing it or overwriting it in ink, becomes a very frequent mode of composition in later chapters.

15   In FR these last words are given to Gimli, for Aragorn in the later story had of course good reason to know that Elves did indeed still dwell in Lothlórien.

16   In a preliminary draft of Legolas' words here they take this form:
So it is said amongst us in Mirkwood, though it is long since we came so far. But if so they dwell deep in the woods down in Angle, *Bennas* between Blackroot and Anduin.
The name *Bennas* occurs only here in narrative, but it is found in the *Etymologies*, V.352, under the root BEN 'corner, angle': Noldorin *bennas* 'angle'. The second element is Noldorin *nass* 'point; angle' (V.374–5).

17   The passage beginning 'A mile within the wood...' (of which the first germ is found on p. 221) appears also in a superseded draft:
A mile within the wood they came upon another stream flowing down swiftly from the tree-clad slopes that climbed back towards the Mountains to join the Blackroot (on their left), and over its dark hurrying waters there was now no bridge.
'Here is the Taiglin,' said Legolas. 'Let us wade over if we can. Then we shall have water behind us and on the east, and only on the west towards the Mountains shall we have much to fear.'
In the consecutive narrative at this point the name *Taiglin* (from

LOTHLÓRIEN 239

The Silmarillion: tributary of Sirion in Beleriand) underwent many changes, but it is clear that all these forms belong to the same time – i.e., the final name had been achieved before the first complete draft of the chapter was done (see note 30). *Taiglin* was at once replaced by *Linglor*, and then *Linglor* was changed to *Linglorel*, the form as first written shortly afterwards in the manuscript and as found in the rough workings for Legolas' song. This was succeeded by *Nimladel*, *Nimlorel*, and finally *Nimrodel*.

18 The word actually written was *waters*.

19 *Linglorel* was altered in pencil, first to *Nimlorel* and then to *Nimrodel* (see note 17). I do not further notice the changes in this case, but give the name in the form as it was first written.

20 *the mountains* changed to *the Black Mountains* (*the White Mountains* FR).

21 *Ammalas* changed in pencil to *Amroth*; see p. 223.

22 In a separate draft for this passage the reading here is: 'Hence the folk of Lórien were called *Galadrim*, the Tree-folk (*Ornelië*)'.

23 *Aragorn* was here changed later to *Elfstone*, and at some of the subsequent occurrences; see p. 236 and note 52.

24 Written in the margin here: 'Name of the tree is *mallorn*'. This is where my father first wrote the name; and it enters the narrative immediately below.

25 On *daro!* 'stop, halt' see the *Etymologies*, V.353, stem D A R.

26 A detached (earlier) draft describes the event differently:

Turning aside from the road they went into the shadows of the deeper wood westward of the river, and there not far from the falls of Linglorel they found a group of tall strong trees. Their lowest boughs were above the reach of Boromir's arms; but they had rope with them. Cast[ing] an end about a bough of the greatest of the trees Legolas ... up and climbed into the darkness.

He was not long aloft. 'The tree-branches form a great crown near the top,' he said, 'and there is a hollow where even Boromir might find some rest. But in the next tree I think I saw a sheltered platform. Maybe elves still come here.'

At that moment a clear voice above them spoke in the elven-tongue, but Legolas drew himself hastily [?close] to the tree-bole. 'Stand still', he said, 'and do not speak or move.' Then he called back into the shadows above, [?answering] in his [?own] tongue.

Frodo did not understand the words, for [the speech of the wood-elves east of the mountains differed much from] the language was the old tongue of the woods and not that of the western elves which was in those days used as a common speech among many folk.

240 THE TREASON OF ISENGARD

There is a marginal direction to alter the story to a form in which the voice from the tree speaks as Legolas jumps up. The passage which I have bracketed is not marked in any way in the manuscript, but is an example of my father's common practice when writing at speed of abandoning a sentence and rephrasing it without striking out the first version.

For a previous reference to the 'Common Speech' see p. 223; now it is further said that the Common Speech was the tongue of 'the western elves'.

27 The words *by the Dimrill Stair* still refer to the pass (later the Redhorn Pass or Redhorn Gate): see p. 164. FR has here (p. 357) *up the Dimrill Stair.*

28 In a rejected draft for this passage, in content otherwise very much the same as that given, none of the three Elves of Lórien speak any language but their own, and Legolas has to translate. The three Elves are here called *Rhimbron, [Rhimlath >] Rhimdir,* and *Haldir*: when this last name replaced *Hathaldir* it was thus a reversion. – *Hathaldir the Young* was the name of one of Barahir's companions on Dorthonion (V.282).

29 This passage was enclosed in square brackets in the manuscript, and subsequently struck out. It is explicit later (p. 247) that the loss of Gandalf was not spoken of at this time.

30 The name *Nimrodel* now appears in the text as written; see notes 17 and 19.

31 These two sentences are not marked off in any way in the manuscript, but were nonetheless obviously rejected at once. In the narrative that follows Hathaldir did not climb up to the flet until Gollum had disappeared (as in FR, p. 360); Frodo's peering over the edge is repeated; and 'Nonetheless the sense of immediate danger did not leave him' must follow on the fading of Sting at the end of the previous paragraph.

32 'They went back to the old path on the west side of the Silverlode', FR p. 360 (second edition: 'to the path that still went on along the west side of the Silverlode'). Since the Nimrodel flowed in from the right, and they had to cross it, the road or path from Moria was on the right (or west) of the Blackroot (Silverlode), which was on their left, as is expressly stated (see note 17); the word *east* here, though perfectly clear, is therefore a mere slip (cf. notes 5 and 9).

33 Earlier (p. 230) Rhimbron has remained at the flet, and the Company is guided by Hathaldir alone; now Rhimbron, like Rúmil in FR (pp. 360–1), comes with Hathaldir as far as the crossing of the river and then returns. It is seen from the manuscript that my father perceived here the need for Rhimbron's presence at the crossing.

LOTHLÓRIEN 241

34 A rejected form here was *Nelennas*; cf. *Bennas* 'Angle' in note 16, and stem N E L 'three' in the *Etymologies*, V.376. On *Nelennas* see note 39.

35 Contrast Hathaldir's words earlier (p. 227): 'We had not heard of hobbits before' (i.e. before they received tidings of the Company from the messengers of Elrond). At the corresponding point in FR (p. 357) Haldir said: 'We had not heard of – hobbits, of halflings, for many a long year, and did not know that any yet dwelt in Middle-earth.'

36 An isolated passage, dashed down on a sheet of the same paper as that used throughout and clearly belonging to the same time, shows the first beginning of the passage in FR p. 364, 'As soon as he set foot upon the far bank of Silverlode a strange feeling had come upon him...':

> As soon as they pass Silverlode into Angle Frodo has a curious sense of walking in an older world – unshadowed. Even though 'wolves howled on the wood's border' they had not entered. Evil had been heard of, Orcs had even set foot in the woods, but it had not yet stained or dimmed the air. There was some secret power of cleanness and beauty in Lórien. It was winter, but nothing was dead, only in a phase of beauty. He saw never a broken twig or disease or fungus. The fallen leaves faded to silver and there was no smell of decay.

A part of this appears a little later in FR, p. 365, where however the 'undecaying' nature of Lothlórien is expressed in terms less immediate: 'In winter here no heart could mourn for summer or for spring. No blemish or sickness or deformity could be seen in anything that grew upon the earth.' Cf. note 46.

Silverlode has here replaced *Blackroot*: see p. 235. On the same page as this passage are the following notes:

> Transpose names *Blackroot* and *Silverlode*. *Silverlode* dwarfish *Kibilnâla* elvish *Celeb(rind)rath*.

The meaning of this is seen from Boromir's words in the new version of 'Moria (i)', p. 177: 'Or we could go on far into the South and come at length round the Black Mountains, and crossing the rivers Isen and *Silverlode* enter Ond from the regions nigh the sea.' The two river-names being transposed, *Silverlode* in this speech of Boromir's in the earlier chapter was changed at this time to *Blackroot* (p. 187 note 1); and in the new version of 'The Ring Goes South' the Dwarvish name of the northern river was changed from *Buzundush* to *Kibil-nâla* (p. 167 and note 22).

In the original text of 'The Ring Goes South' occurs by later substitution the form *Celebrin* (VI.434 note 15). For *rath* in *Celeb(rind)rath* (and also *rant* in the later name *Celebrant*) see the *Etymologies*, V.383, stem R A T.

242   THE TREASON OF ISENGARD

37   The following passage was rewritten several times. In the original
     form this dialogue occurs:
          'What is this?' said one of the Elves, looking in wonder at
     Legolas. 'By his raiment of green and brown [?he is an] Elf of
     the North. Since when have we taken our kindred prisoner,
     Hathaldir?'
          'I am not a prisoner,' said Legolas. 'I am only showing the
     dwarf how to walk straight without the help of eyes.'
     Later, a passage was inserted making the blindfold march longer:
          All that day they marched on by gentle stages. Frodo could
     hear the wind rustling in the leaves and the river away to the
     right murmuring at times. He had felt the sun on his face when
     they passed across a glade, as he guessed. After a rest and food
     at noon, they went on again, turning it seemed away from the
     river. After a little while they heard voices about them. A great
     company of elves had come up silently, and were now speaking
     to Hathaldir.
     In the corresponding passage in FR (p. 364) they had passed a
     day and a night blindfold, and it was at noon on the second day
     that they met the Elves coming from the south and were released
     from their blindfolds.
38   *Dol Dúgol* occurs in 'Moria (i)', p. 178.
39   'They journey to Nelennas': at an earlier occurrence of *Nelennas*
     (see p. 231 and note 34) it was changed to *Nelen*, 'the Gore'.
     Since they are now deep in 'the Gore', *Nelennas* perhaps refers
     here to the city (Caras Galadon); see p. 261 note 1.
40   It is notable that the Lady of Lothlórien at first had white hair;
     this was still the case in the first actual narratives of the sojourn of
     the Company in Caras Galadon (pp. 246, 256).
41   For explanation of these references see p. 248 and note 15.
42   The actual text here is extremely confused, and I set it out as a
     characteristic, if extreme, example of my father's way of writing
     when actually composing new narrative (nothing is struck out
     except as indicated):
          ... the grass was studded with small golden [*struck out:*
     flowers] starshaped and slanting [?leaved] and starshaped and
     among them on slender nodding on slender stalks flowers of a
     green so pale...
43   In the *Etymologies*, V.365, stem KOR, both *coron* and *cerin*
     appear as Noldorin words, the latter being the equivalent of
     Quenya *korin* 'circular enclosure' (cf. the *korin* of elms in which
     Meril-i-Turinqi dwelt in *The Book of Lost Tales*, where the word
     is defined (I.16) as 'a great circular hedge, be it of stone or of
     thorn or even of trees, that encloses a green sward'). But the
     meaning of *cerin* in *Cerin Amroth* is certainly 'mound', and
     indeed long afterwards my father translated the word as 'circular

LOTHLÓRIEN   243

mound or artificial hill'. – *Amroth* has now replaced *Ammalas* in the text as written; see note 21.

44 This is the first appearance of the name *elanor*, which replaced at the time of writing another name, *yri* (see note 45).

45 After 'the houses of the Galadrim' my father wrote *Bair am Yru* (see note 44), but struck it out.

46 A page inserted into the manuscript (but obviously closely associated in time with the surrounding text) gives the primitive drafting for the passage in FR p. 365 beginning 'The others cast themselves down upon the fragrant grass' and continuing to Sam's words about the 'elvishness' of Lórien. The latter part of this is of an extreme roughness, but I give the rider in full as a further exemplification of the actual nature of much preliminary drafting:

> The others cast themselves down on the fragrant grass, but Frodo stood for a while lost in wonder. Again it seemed to him as if he had stepped through a high window that looked on a vanished world. It was a winter that did not mourn for summer or for spring, but reigned in its own season beautiful and eternal and perennial. He saw no sign of blemish or disease, sickness or deformity, in anything that grew upon the earth, nor did he see any such thing in [Nelen >] the heart of Lórien.
>
> Sam too stood by him with a puzzled expression rubbing his eyes as if he was not sure that he was awake. 'It's sunlight and bright day,' he muttered. 'I thought Elves were all for moon and stars, but this is more Elvish than anything in any tale.'
>
> and caught his breath for the sight was fair in itself but it had a quality different to any that he felt before [*variant:* had beside a beauty that the common speech could not name]. The shapes of all that he saw All that he saw was shapely but its shapes seemed at once clearcut and as if it had been but newly conceived and drawn with swift skill swift and [?living] and ancient as if [it] had endured for ever. The hues were green, gold and blue white but fresh as if he but that moment perceived them and gave them names.

47 Thus the entire passage (FR pp. 352–3) in which Boromir demurs at entering the Golden Wood and is rebuked by Aragorn is absent, as also is the conclusion of the chapter in FR, from 'At the hill's foot Frodo found Aragorn, standing still and silent . . .' (pp. 366–7).

This is a convenient point to mention a small textual corruption in the published form of this chapter (FR p. 359). In the fair copy manuscript Pippin says: 'I hope, if I do get to sleep in this bird-loft, that I shan't roll off'; but in the typescript that followed, not made by my father, *bird-loft* became *bed-loft*, and so remains.

244   THE TREASON OF ISENGARD

48   A few other details worth recording are collected here:
     wood-elves (p. 222) remains, where FR (p. 353) has *Silvan Elves*.
     the common speech (p. 223) remains, where FR (p. 353) has *the Westron Speech*.
     in ordinary speech (p. 227) becomes *in ordinary language*, changed later to *in the Common Tongue* (*in the Common Language* FR p. 357).
     Hathaldir's words about hobbits (p. 227) are scarcely changed: *We had not heard of – hobbits before, and never until now have we seen one*; see note 35.
     and that even if we did pass into the western lands the shores of the sea are no longer secure in the original draft (p. 232) becomes *and the mouths of the Great River are held by the Enemy* (*are watched by the Enemy*, FR p. 363).
     there are still havens to be found, far north and west, beyond the land of the half-high (cf. p. 232 and note 35), where FR (p. 363) has *havens of the High Elves ... beyond the land of the Halflings*.
     near Havens of Escape (p. 232) was at first retained, but changed at once to *near the shores of the Sea*, as in FR.

49   'Narthas or the Gore as you would say, *for* it is the land that lies like a spear-head': the word *for* (preserved in FR p. 361) is used because *gore*, Old English *gāra* (in modern use meaning a wedge-shaped piece of cloth, but in Old English an angular point of land) was related to *gār* 'spear', the connection lying in the shape of the spear-head.

50   Later, *Narthas* and *Nelen-Lórien* were changed to *the Naith* (*of Lórien*), though in 'the Angle, Nelen, where we dwell' *Nelen* was left to stand. – *Dol Dúgol*, retained from the original draft, with the reference to the Necromancer (p. 234), was later changed to *Dol Dûghul*.

51   This is to be connnected with the interruption in the writing of the fair copy manuscript (note 14).

52   In fact, there is a good deal of variation, since when making these name-changes my father worked through the manuscripts rapidly and missed occurrences. Thus in this manuscript, in addition to *Aragorn > Ingold > Elfstone* and *Elfstone > Ingold > Elfstone*, there is found also: *Aragorn > Elfstone*; *Elfstone > Ingold*; *Elfstone > Ingold > Aragorn*; *Elfstone > Aragorn*. This apparently patternless confusion can be explained: see pp. 277–8. The name *Ingold* for Aragorn has been met before, in later emendation to the text of Gandalf's letter at Bree (p. 80 and note 17).

XIII

GALADRIEL

I have divided the draft manuscript of the 'Lothlórien' story into two parts, although at this stage my father continued without break to the end of FR Book II Chapter 7, 'The Mirror of Galadriel'; and I return now to the point where I left it on p. 234. From the coming of the Company to Cerin Amroth the draft is in thick, soft pencil, and very difficult.

The sun had sunk behind the mountains, and the shadows were falling in the wood, when they went on again. Now their paths went deep into dense wood where already a grey dusk had gathered. It was nearly night under the trees when they came out suddenly under a pale evening sky pierced by a few early stars. There was a wide treeless space running in a vast circle before them. Beyond that was a deep grass-clad dike, and a high green wall beyond. [?Rising] ground inside the circle was [??thick with] mallorn-trees, the tallest they had yet seen in that land. The highest must have been nearly 200 feet high, and of great girth. They had no branches lower than 3 fathoms above their roots. In the upper branches amid the leaves hundreds of lights gold and white and pale green were shining.

'Welcome to Caras Galadon,' he said, 'the city of Nelennas which [?mayhap] in your tongue is called Angle.[1] But we must go round; the gates do not look north.'

There was a white paved road running round the circuit of the walls. On the south side there was a bridge over the dike leading to great gates set on the side where the ends of the wall overlapped. They passed within into deep shadow where the two green walls ended [?in a] lane. They saw no folk on guard,[2] but there were many soft voices overhead, and in the distance he [*sc.* Frodo] heard a voice falling clear out of the air above them.

The original pencilled text continues for some distance from this point, but my father partly overwrote it in ink, and (more largely) erased it wholly before the new text was set down in its place. Here and there bits of the original text were retained, and where it was not erased but overwritten a name or a phrase can be made out. There was

246   THE TREASON OF ISENGARD

no long interval between the two forms of the text; my father may in any
case have rewritten this section mainly because it was so nearly illegible.

They passed along many paths and climbed many flights of
steps, until they saw before them amid a wide lawn a fountain.
It sprang high in the air and fell in a wide basin of silver, from
which a white stream ran away down the hill. Hard by stood a
great tree. At its foot stood three tall elves. They were clad in
grey mail and from their shoulders hung long white cloaks.
'Here dwell Keleborn and Galadriel,[3] the Lord and Lady of the
Galadrim,' said Halldir.[4] 'It is their wish that you should go up
and speak to them.'

One of the elf-wardens then blew a clear note on a small
horn, and a ladder was let down. 'I will go first,' said Haldir.
'Let the chief hobbit go next, and with him Legolas. The others
may follow as they wish. It is a long climb, but you may rest
upon the way.'

As he passed upwards Frodo saw many smaller flets to this
side or that, some with rooms built on them; but about a
hundred feet above the ground they came to a flet that was very
wide – like the deck of a great ship. On it was built a house so
large that almost it might have been a hall of men upon the earth.
He entered behind Haldir, and saw that he was in a chamber of
oval shape, through the midst of which passed the bole of the
great tree. It was filled with a soft golden light. Many elves were
seated there. The roof was a pale gold, the walls of green and
silver. On two seats at the further end sat side by side the Lord
and Lady of Lothlórien. They looked tall even as they sat, and
their hair was white and long.[5] They said no word and moved
not, but their eyes were shining.

Haldir led Frodo and Legolas before them, and the Lord bade
them welcome, but the Lady Galadriel said no word, and
looked long into their faces.

'Sit now, Frodo of the Shire,' said Keleborn. 'We will await
the others.' Each of the companions he greeted courteously by
name as they entered. 'Welcome, Ingold son of Ingrim!'[6] he
said. 'Your name is known to me, though never in all your
wanderings have you sought my house. Welcome, Gimli son of
Glóin! It is almost out of mind since we saw one of Durin's folk
in Calas Galadon. But today our long law is broken: let it be a
sign that though the world is dark, better things shall come, and
friendship shall grow again between our peoples.'

GALADRIEL 247

When all the Company had come in and were seated before him, the Lord looked at them again. 'Is this all?' he asked. 'Your number should be nine. For so the secret messages from Rivendell have said. There is one absent whom I miss, and had hoped much to see. Tell me, where is Gandalf the grey?'[7]

'Alas!' said Ingold. 'Gandalf the grey went down into the shadows. He remains in Moria, for he fell there from the Bridge.'

At these words all the Elves cried aloud with grief and amazement. 'This is indeed evil tidings,' said Keleborn, 'the most evil that have here been spoken for years uncounted. Why has nothing been said to us of this before?' he asked, turning to Haldir.

'We did not speak of it to [your people >] Haldir,' said Frodo. 'We were weary and danger was too nigh, and afterwards we were overcome with wonder.[8] Almost we forgot our grief and dismay as we walked on the fair paths of Lothlórien. But it is true that Gandalf has perished. He was our guide, and led us through Moria; and when our escape seemed beyond hope he saved us, and fell.'

'Tell me the full tale,' said Keleborn.

Ingold then recounted all that had happened upon the pass of Caradras and afterwards; and he spoke of Balin and his book and the fight in the Chamber of Mazarbul, and the fire, and the narrow bridge, and the coming of the Balrog.

'A Balrog!' said Keleborn.[9] 'Not since the Elder Days have I heard that a Balrog was loose upon the world. Some we have thought are perhaps hidden in Mordor [?or] near the Mountain of Fire, but naught has been seen of them since the Great Battle and the fall of Thangorodrim.[10] I doubt much if this Balrog has lain hid in the Misty Mountains – and I fear rather that he was sent by Sauron from Orodruin, the Mountain of Fire.'

'None know,' said Galadriel, 'what may lie hid at the roots of the ancient hills. The dwarves had re-entered Moria and were searching again in dark places, and they may have stirred some evil.'[11]

There was a silence. At length Keleborn spoke again. 'I did not know,' he said, 'that your plight was so evil. I will do what I can to aid you, each according to his need, but especially that one of the little folk that bears the burden.'

'Your quest is known to me,' said Galadriel, [?seeing] Frodo's look, 'though we will not here speak more openly of it. I was at

248   THE TREASON OF ISENGARD

the White Council, and of all those there gathered none did I love more than Gandalf the Grey. Often have we met since and spoken of many things and purposes. The lord and lady of Lothlórien are accounted wise beyond the measure of the Elves of Middle-earth, and of all who have not passed beyond the Seas. For we have dwelt here since the Mountains were reared and the Sun was young.[12]

'Now we will give you counsel.[13] For not in doing or contriving nor in choosing this course or that is my skill, but in knowledge of what was and is, and in part of what shall be. And I say that your case is not yet without hope; yet but a little this way or that and it will fail miserably. But there is yet hope, if all the Company remains true.' She looked at each in turn, but none blenched. Only Sam blushed and hung his head before the Lady's glance left him. 'I felt as if I hadn't got nothing on,' he explained afterwards. 'I didn't like it – she seemed to be looking inside me, and asking me whether I would like to fly back to the Shire.' Each of them had had a similar experience, and had felt as if he had been presented with a choice between death and something which he desired greatly, peace, ease [*written above:* freedom], wealth, or lordship.

'I suppose it was just a test,' said Boromir. 'It felt almost like a temptation. Of course I put it away at once. The men of Minas Tirith at any rate are true.'[14] What he had been offered he did not say.

'Now is the time for any to depart or turn back who feels that he has done enough, and aided the Quest as much as he has the will or power to do. Legolas may abide here with my folk, as long as he desires, or he may return home if chance allows. Even Gimli the dwarf may stay here, though I think he would not long be content in my city in what will seem to him a life of idleness. If he wishes to go to his home, we will help him as much as we can; as far as the Gladden Fields and beyond. He might hope thus to find the country of the Beornings, where Grimbeorn Beorn's son the Old is a lord of many sturdy men. As yet no wolf or orc make headway in that land.'

'That I know well,' said Gimli. 'Were it not for the Beornings the passage from Dale to Rivendell would not be possible.[15] My father and I had the aid of Grimbeorn on our way west in the autumn.'

'You, Frodo,' said Keleborn, 'I cannot aid or counsel. But if you go on, do not despair – but beware even of your right hand

GALADRIEL   249

and of your left. There is also a danger that pursues you, which I do not see clearly or understand. You others of the little folk I could wish had never come so far. For now unless you will dwell here in exile while outside in the world many years run by, I see not what you can do save go forward. It would be vain to attempt to return home or to Rivendell alone.'

The whole of this passage, from 'Now is the time for any to depart', is marked off with directions 'To come in later' and 'At beginning of next chapter before they go'. At the top of the page, and no doubt written in after this decision was made, is the following:

'Now we have spoken long, and yet you have toiled and suffered much, and have travelled far,' said Keleborn. 'Even if your quest did not concern all free lands deeply, you should here have refuge for a while. In this city you may abide until you are healed and rested. We will not yet think of your further road.'

The character of the manuscript now changes again. Very roughly written in ink, it is evidently the continuation of the original pencilled text that was over-written or erased in the preceding section (see p. 245). At the top of the first page of this part are notes on the names of the Lord and Lady of Lothlórien. In pencilled text visible in the last section their original names *Tar* and *Finduilas* had changed to *Aran* and *Rhien* (note 3), and then to *Galdaran* and *Galdri(e)n* (note 9) – *Galadriel* on p. 246 belongs with the later, overwritten text. Their names now change further:

Galathir = *Galað-hîr* tree-lord
Galadhrien = *Galað-rhien* tree-lady

The name of the Lord does not appear in the concluding part of this chapter, but the name of the Lady is *Galadrien* (at the first occurrence only, *Galdrien*), with pencilled correction in some cases to *Galadriel*.

This is a convenient place to set out my father's original scheme for the next part of the story. This was written at furious speed but has fortunately proved almost entirely decipherable.

They dwell 15 days in Caras Galadon.

Elves sing for Gandalf. They watch weaving and making of the silver rope of the fibre under mallorn bark. The [?trimming] of arrows.

King Galdaran's mirror shown to Frodo. Mirror is of silver filled with fountain water in sun.

Sees Shire far away. Trees being felled and a tall building being made where the old mill was.[16] Gaffer Gamgee turned out. Open trouble, almost war, between Marish and Buckland on one hand – and the West. Cosimo Sackville-Baggins very rich, buying up land. (All / Some of this is future.)

250 THE TREASON OF ISENGARD

King Galdaran says the mirror shows past, present, and future, and skill needed to decide which.

Sees a grey figure like Gandalf [?going along] in twilight but it seems to be clad in white. Perhaps it is *Saruman*.

Sees a mountain spouting flame. Sees Gollum?

They depart. At departure Elves give them travel food. They describe the Stone hills, and bid them beware of Fangorn Forest upon the *Ogodrûth* or Entwash. He is an Ent or great giant.

It is seen that it was while my father was writing the 'Lothlórien' story *ab initio* that the Lady of Lothlórien emerged (p. 233); and it is also seen that the figure of Galadriel (Rhien, Galadrien) as a great power in Middle-earth was deepened and extended as he wrote. In this sketch of his ideas, written down after the story had reached Caras Galadon, as the name *Galdaran* shows (note 9), the Mirror belongs to the Lord (here called King).

It is also interesting to observe that the images of the violated Shire seen in the Mirror were to be Frodo's. The Stone hills mentioned at the end of this outline are mentioned also in the plot-notes given on p. 233, where the 'parting of the ways' is to take place 'at Stonehills'. The Entwash (though not the Elvish name *Ogodrûth*) has been named in the elaborate outline that followed the conclusion of the story of Moria (p. 210): 'Merry and Pippin come up Entwash into Fangorn and have adventure with Treebeard.' Here the name *Entwash* clearly implies that Treebeard is an *Ent*, and he is specifically so called (for the first time) in the outline just given; but since Treebeard was still only waiting in the wings as a potential ingredient in the narrative this may be only a slight shift in the development of the word. The Troll-lands north of Rivendell were the *Entish Lands* and *Entish Dales* (Old English *ent* 'giant'); and only when Treebeard and the other 'Ents' had been fully realised would the Troll-lands be renamed *Ettendales* and *Ettenmoors* (see p. 65 note 32).

I return now to the narrative, which as I have said recommences here in its primary form (and thus we meet again here the names *Gal(a)drien*, *Hathaldir*, and *Elfstone*, which had been superseded in the rewritten section of the draft text).

'Yet let not your hearts be troubled,' said the Lady Galdrien. 'Here you shall rest tonight and other nights to follow.'

That night they slept upon the ground, for they were safe within the walls of Caras Galadon. The Elves spread them a pavilion among the trees not far from the fountain, and there they slept until the light of day was broad.

All the while they remained in Lothlórien the sun shone and the weather was clear and cool like early spring rather than mid-winter. They did little but rest and walk among the trees,

GALADRIEL 251

and eat and drink the good things that the Elves set before them. They had little speech with any for few spoke any but the woodland tongue. Hathaldir had departed to the defences of the North. Legolas was away all day among the Elves. [*Marginal addition of the same time as the text:* Only Frodo and Elfstone went much among the Elves. They watched them at work weaving the ropes of silver fibre of mallorn bark, the [?trimming] of arrows, their broidery and carpentry.]

They spoke much of Gandalf, and ever as they themselves were healed of hurt and weariness the grief of their loss seemed more bitter. Even the Elves of Lothlórien seemed to feel the shadow of that fall. Often they heard near them the elves singing, and knew that they made songs and laments for the grey wanderer [*written above:* pilgrim], as they called him, *Mithrandir.*[17] But if Legolas was by he would not interpret, saying that it passed his skill. Very sweet and sad the voices sounded, and having words spoke of sorrow to their hearts though their minds understood them not.[18]

On the evening of the third day Frodo was walking in the cool twilight apart from the others. Suddenly he saw coming towards him the Lady Galadrien gleaming in white among the stems. She spoke no word but beckoned to him. Turning back she led him to the south side of the city, and passing through a gate in a green wall they came into an enclosure like a garden. No trees grew there and it was open to the sky, which was now pricked with many stars.[19] Down a flight of white steps they went into a green hollow through which ran a silver stream, flowing down from the fountain on the hill. There stood upon a pedestal carved like a tree a shallow bowl of silver and beside it a ewer. With water from the stream she filled the bowl, and breathed on it, and when the water was again still she spoke.

'Here is the mirror of Galadrien,' she said. 'Look therein!'

Sudden awe and fear came over Frodo. The air was still and the hollow dark, and the Elf-lady beside him tall and pale. 'What shall I look for, and what shall I see?' he asked.

'None can say,' she answered, 'who does not know all that is in your heart, in your memory, and your hope. For this mirror shows both the past and the present, and that which is called the future, in so far as it can be seen by any in Middle-earth.[20] But those are wise who can discern [to] which of [these] three [the] things that they see belong.'

Frodo at last stooped over the bowl. The water looked hard

252   THE TREASON OF ISENGARD

and black. Stars were shining in it. Then they went out. The dark veil was partly withdrawn, and a grey light shone; mountains were in the distance, a long road wound back out of sight. Far away a figure came slowly: very small at first, but slowly it drew near. Suddenly Frodo saw that it was like the figure of Gandalf. So clear was the vision that he almost called aloud the wizard's name. Then he saw that the figure was all clothed in white, not in grey, and had a white staff. It turned aside and went away round a turn of the road with head so bowed that he could see no face. Doubt came over him: was it a sight of Gandalf on one of his many journeys long ago, or was it Saruman?[21]

Many other visions passed over the water one after another. A city with high stone walls and seven towers, a great river flowing through a city of ruins, and then breathtaking and strange and yet known at once: a stony shore, and a dark sea into which a bloodred sun was sinking among black clouds, a ship darkly outlined was near the sun. He heard the faint sigh of waves upon the shore. Then ... nearly dark and he saw a small figure running – he knew that it was himself, and behind him [?stooped to the ground] came another black figure with long arms moving swiftly like a hunting dog.[22] He turned away in fear and would look no more.

'Judge not these visions,' said Galadrien, 'until they are shown true or false. But think not that by singing under the trees [?and alone], nor even by slender arrows from [?many] bows, do we defend Lothlórien from our encircling foes. I say to you, Frodo, that even as I speak I perceive the Dark Lord and know part of his mind – and ever he is groping to see my thought: but the door is closed.' She spread out her hands and held them as in denial towards the East.[23] A ray of the Evening Star shone clear in the sky, so clear that the pillar beneath the basin cast a faint shadow. Its ray lit the ring upon her finger and flashed. Frodo gazed at it stricken suddenly with awe. 'Yes,' she said, divining his thought. 'It is not permitted to speak of it, and Elrond [?said nought]. But verily it is in Lothlórien that one remains: the Ring of Earth, and I am its keeper.[24] He suspects but he knows not. See you not now why your coming is to us as the coming of Doom? For if you fail then we are laid bare to the Enemy. But if you succeed, then our power is minished and slowly Lothlórien will fade.'[25]

Frodo bent his head. 'And what do you wish?' he said at last.

GALADRIEL 253

'That what should[26] be shall be,' she said. 'And that you should do with all your might that which is your task. For the fate of Lothlórien you are not answerable; but only for the doing of your own task.'

Here the narrative ends (and on the last page of the manuscript my father wrote 'Chapter ends with Lady's words to Frodo' – meaning of course the whole story from Dimrill Dale), but the text continues at once with Sam's vision in the Mirror (see note 19), which my father did not at this stage integrate with what he had just written. What Sam saw in the water appeared already in the preliminary outline (p. 249), though there given to Frodo.

(Put in *Sam's* vision of the Shire before the ring scene.)

Sam saw trees being felled in the Shire. 'There's that Ted Sandyman,' he said, 'a-cutting down trees that .shouldn't be. Bless me, if he's not felling them on the avenue by the road to Bywater where they serve only for shade. I wish I could get at him. I'd fell *him*.' Then Sam saw a great red building with a tall [?smoke] chimney going up where the old mill had been. 'There's some devilry at work in the Shire,' he said. 'Elrond knew what was what, when he said Mr Brandybuck and Pippin should go back.'[27]

Suddenly Sam gave a cry and sprang away. 'I can't stay here,' he said wildly. 'I must go home. They're digging up Bagshot Row and there is the poor old gaffer going down the hill with his bits of stuff in a barrow. I must go home!'

'You cannot go home,' said the Lady. 'Your path lies before you. You should not have looked if you would let anything that you see turn you from your task. But I will say this for your hope: remember that the mirror shows many things, and not all that you see have yet been. Some of the things it shows come never to pass, unless one forsakes the path [?and] turns aside to prevent them.'

Sam sat on the grass and muttered. 'I wish I had never come here.'

'Will you now look, Frodo? said the Lady, 'or have you heard enough?'

'I will look,' said Frodo ... Fear was mingled with desire.

Here the manuscript ends, with the following notes scribbled at the foot of the page: 'Chapter ends with Lady's words to Frodo. Next Chapter begins with departure from Lothlórien on New Year's Day, midwinter day, just before the sun turned to the New Year and just after New Moon.'[28]

254   THE TREASON OF ISENGARD

On a separate slip, certainly of this time, is written (in ink over pencil) the passage in which Frodo sees the searching Eye in the Mirror (see note 23). This is almost word for word the same as in FR (pp. 379–80), except for these sentences: 'the black slit of its pupil opened on a pit of malice and despair. It was not still, but was roving in perpetual search. Frodo knew with certainty and horror...'

On the back of this slip is scribbled the original draft of the speeches of Galadriel and Frodo beside the Mirror in FR pp. 381–2:

> Frodo offers Galadriel the Ring. She *laughs*. Says he is revenged for her temptation. Confesses that the thought had occurred to her. But she will only retain the unsullied Ring. Too much evil lay in the Ruling Ring. It is not permitted to use anything that Sauron has made.
>
> Frodo asks why he cannot *see* the other rings. Have you tried? You can see a little already. You have penetrated my thought deeper than many of my own folk. Also you penetrated the disguise of the Ringwraiths. And did you not see the ring on my hand? Can you see my ring? she said, turning to Sam. No, Lady, he said. I have been wondering much at all your talk.

In this passage there emerges at last and clearly the fundamental conception that the Three Rings of the Elves were not made by Sauron: 'She will only retain the unsullied Ring. Too much evil lay in the Ruling Ring. It is not permitted to use anything that Sauron has made.'

With this compare the passage from the original version of 'The Council of Elrond' (VI.404) cited on p. 155: 'The Three Rings remain still. They have conferred great power on the Elves, but they have never yet availed them in their strife with Sauron. For they came from Sauron himself, and can give no skill or knowledge that he did not already possess at their making.' In the fifth version of that chapter (p. 156) Elrond's words become: 'The Three Rings remain. But of them I am not permitted to speak. Certainly they cannot be used by us. From them the Elvenkings have derived much power, but they have not been used for war, either good or evil.' I have argued in the same place that though no longer explicit the conception must still have been that the Three Rings came from Sauron, both because Boromir asserts this without being contradicted, and because it seems to be implied by 'Certainly they cannot be used by us.' If this is so, there is at least an apparent ambiguity: 'they cannot be used by us', but 'from them the Elvenkings have derived much power' – though in 'they cannot be used by us' Elrond is evidently speaking expressly of their use for war. But any ambiguity there might be is now swept away by Galadriel's assertion: *nothing* that was Sauron's can be made use of: from which it must follow that the Three Rings of the Elves were of other origin.

A page found wholly isolated from other manuscripts of *The Lord*

GALADRIEL
255

of the Rings carries more developed drafting for Galadriel's refusal of the Ring. This page had been used already for other writing, on the subject of the origin of the Rings of Power; but I have no doubt at all that the two elements (the one in places written over and intermingled with the other) belong to the same time. This other text consists of several distinct openings to a speech, each in turn abandoned – a speech that I think was intended for Elrond at the Council in Rivendell, since the following very faint pencilling can be made out on this page: ' "Nay," said Elrond, "that is not wholly true. The rings were made by the Elves of the West, and taken from them by the Enemy..." '

The first of these openings reads thus, printed exactly as it stands:

In Ancient Days, the Rings of Power were made long ago in the lands beyond the Sea. It is said that they were first contrived by Fëanor, the greatest of all the makers among the Elves. His purpose was not evil, yet in it was the Great Enemy But they were stolen by the Great Enemy and brought to Middle-earth. Three Rings he made, the Rings of Earth, Sea and Sky.

This was at once replaced by:

In Ancient Days, before he turned wholly to evil, Sauron the Great, who is now the Dark Lord that some call the Necromancer, made and contrived many things of wonder. He made Rings of Power

Then follows, written out anew, the opening sentence of the first version; and then:

In Ancient Days the Great Enemy came to the lands beyond the Sea; but his evil purpose was for a time hidden, even from the rulers of the world, and the Elves learned many things of him, for his knowledge was very great and his thoughts strange and wonderful.

In those days the Rings of Power were made. It is said that they were fashioned first by Fëanor the greatest of all the makers among the Elves of the West, whose skill surpassed that of all folk that are or have been. The skill was his but the thought was the Enemy's. Three Rings he made, the Rings of Earth, Sea and Sky. But secretly the Enemy made One Ring, the Ruling Ring, which controlled all the others. And when the Enemy fled across the Sea and came to Middle-earth, he stole the Rings and brought them away. And others he made like to them, and yet false.

And many others he made of lesser powers, and the elves wore them and became powerful and proud

Breaking off here, my father began once more: 'In Ancient Days the Great Enemy and Sauron his servant came'; and at this point, I think, he definitively abandoned the conception.

These extraordinary vestiges show him revolving the mode by

256   THE TREASON OF ISENGARD

which he should withdraw the Three Rings of the Elves from inherent evil and derivation from the Enemy. For a fleeting moment their making was set in the remote ages of Valinor and attributed to Fëanor, though inspired by Morgoth: cf. the *Quenta Silmarillion*, V.228, §49, 'Most fair of all was Morgoth to the Elves, and he aided them in many works, if they would let him.... the Gnomes took delight in the many things of hidden knowledge that he could reveal to them.' And Morgoth stole the Rings of Fëanor, as he stole the Silmarils.

The fair copy manuscript of 'Chapter XVIII, Lothlórien' (p. 235) continued on without break, following the primary draft, into the account of the arrival of the Company in Caras Galadon and the story of Galadriel's Mirror. My father's decision to divide the long chapter into two seems however to have been made at the point where Galadriel silently searched the minds of each member of the Company in turn;[29] and it had certainly been taken by an early stage in the writing of 'Farewell to Lórien' (p. 272). The new chapter (XIX) was given the title 'Galadriel', which I have adopted here; and it advances in a single stride almost to the text of FR for most of its length, though there remain some notable passages in which the final form in 'The Mirror of Galadriel' was not achieved.

When the Company came to the city of the Galadrim, Haldir said: 'Welcome to Caras Galadon, the city of Angle' (cf. p. 245 and note 1), which was changed in the act of writing to 'Welcome to Caras Galadon, the city of Lothlórien'; continuing 'where dwell the Lord Arafain and Galadriel the Lady of the Elves'. Since the present text is self-evidently the successor of the text (written over the original draft, see p. 245 and note 3) in which *Keleborn* and *Galadriel* first appear, *Arafain* must have been a fleeting substitution for *Keleborn*, which was immediately restored, and is the name as written throughout the remainder of the manuscript. The journey round the circuit of the walls of Caras Galadon seems to have been differently conceived from its representation in the earliest version, to judge by the little sketch inserted into the manuscript (see note 2), from which it appears that the Company, coming from the north, would pass down the western side – as they did in FR (p. 368). Here, on the other hand, the city climbed 'like a green cloud upon their right', and the gates of the city 'faced eastward'.

Both Galadriel and Keleborn still have long white hair (pp. 233, 246), though this was early changed to make Galadriel's hair golden. As in the rewritten portion of the first draft, 'Aragorn' is greeted by Keleborn as 'Ingold, son of Ingrim' (p. 246 and note 6), and Ingold is his name in the text as written at subsequent occurrences in the chapter.[30] Keleborn speaks the same words to him as in the first draft: 'Your name was known to me before, though never yet in all your wanderings have you sought my house'; and no greeting to Legolas is

GALADRIEL 257

yet reported, as it is in FR, where he is named 'son of Thranduil'.

In Keleborn's opening words to the Company he says here: 'Your number should be nine: so said the messages. Can we have mistaken them? They were faint and hard to read, for Elrond is far away, and darkness gathers between us: even in this year it has grown deeper.' Galadriel then intervenes: 'Nay, there was no mistake...' (see note 7). But most notably, it is here that the history and significance of the Balrog of Moria first appears (see pp. 185–6, and p. 247 and note 11). The passage in the present version is as follows:

Ingold then recounted all that had happened upon the pass of Caradras, and in the days that followed; and he spoke of Balin and his book, and the fight in the Chamber of Mazarbul, and the fire, and the narrow bridge, and the coming of the Balrog. 'At least, that name did Legolas give to it,' said Ingold. 'I do not know what it was, save that it was both dark and fiery, and was terrible and strong.'

'It was a Balrog,' said Legolas: 'of all elf-banes the most deadly, save the One who sits in the Dark Tower.'

'A Balrog!' said Keleborn. 'Your news becomes ever more grievous. Not since the Days of Flight have I heard that one of those fell things was loose. That one slept beneath Caradras we feared. The Dwarves have never told me the tale of those days, yet we believe that it was a Balrog that they aroused long ago when they probed too deep beneath the mountains.'

'Indeed I saw upon the bridge that which haunts our darkest dreams, I saw Durin's Bane,' said Gimli in a low voice, and terror was in his eyes.

'Alas!' said Keleborn. 'Had I known that the Dwarves had stirred up this evil in Moria again, I would have forbidden you to pass the northern borders, you and all that went with you....'

The remainder of this passage is virtually as in FR (p. 371). – Galadriel's words following 'But we will not here speak more openly of it' were at first retained exactly from the first draft (pp. 247–8), but were changed immediately to read thus:

'... The Lord and Lady of the Galadrim are accounted wise beyond the measure even of the Elves of Middle-earth, and of all who have not passed beyond the Seas. For we have dwelt here since the mountains were reared and the sun was young. Was it not I that summoned the White Council? And if my designs had not gone amiss, it would have been governed by Gandalf the

258   THE TREASON OF ISENGARD

Grey; and then mayhap things would have gone otherwise. But even now there is hope left. . . .'[31]

The account of the thoughts and sensations of the members of the Company as Galadriel looked at each in turn at first followed closely the text of the original draft (p. 248), but this was changed, probably at once, to the form in FR (pp. 372–3), with however these differences: whereas in the first version 'none blenched' beneath her gaze, and in FR 'none save Legolas and Aragorn could long endure her glance', here 'none of them could long endure her glance' (changed subsequently to 'none of the hobbits'); and their feelings are thus described: 'It seemed that each of them had had a similar experience, and had felt that he was offered a choice between a shadow full of fear and something he greatly desired, that lay clear before his mind lit with an alluring light.' Boromir's remarks on the subject and Ingold's reply here run:

'To me it seemed exceedingly strange,' said Boromir, 'and I do not feel too sure of this elvish lady. Maybe it was only a test, and she sought to read our thoughts for her amusement; but almost I should have said that she was tempting us, and offering us what she had the power to give. It need not be said that I refused to listen, since the gift was not offered to all alike. The Men of Minas-Tirith at least are true to their friends.' But what he thought the Lady had offered him Boromir did not tell.

'Well, whatever you may think of the Lady,' said Ingold, 'she was a friend of Gandalf, it seems. Though this was one of his secrets that he did not tell me. Tonight I shall sleep without fear for the first time since we left Rivendell . . .'

Nothing is said yet of Frodo's experience.[32]

A curious detail arises here, in that in the conversation of the Company in their pavilion near the fountain, before they began to discuss the encounter with Galadriel, 'they talked of their night before in the tree-tops'. At this stage in the evolution of the narrative they met the northbound Elves at Cerin Amroth, and had their blindfolds removed, on the same day as they left Nimrodel (see pp. 233, 235); the whole journey to Caras Galadon thus took a single day, and so it was indeed 'the night before' that they passed in the tree-tops. In FR (p. 364) the journey was extended, and they passed the first night after leaving Nimrodel in the woods: 'Then they rested and slept without fear upon the ground; for their guides would not permit them to unbind their eyes, and they could not climb.' In the light of this, the passage in FR (pp. 372–3) required revision that it did not receive: the words 'the travellers talked of their night before in the tree-tops' survive from the present version, as does Aragorn's 'But tonight I shall sleep without fear for the first time since I left Rivendell.'

GALADRIEL 259

The remainder of the chapter in this manuscript is very close indeed to FR. The Company 'remained many days in Lothlórien, so far as they could tell or remember', where FR has 'some days'; but the meeting with Galadriel was now on the last evening spent there, not 'on the evening of the third day' (p. 251).[33] At first my father followed the original draft of Galadriel's reply to Frodo's questions 'What shall we look for, and what shall we see?' (*ibid.*), then changed it to read: 'None can tell, who do not know fully the mind of the beholder. The Mirror will show things that were, and things that are, and things that yet may be. But which it is that he sees, even the wisest cannot always tell. Do you wish to look?' This was further developed to the text of FR in an inserted rider that I think belongs to the time of the writing of the manuscript.

On the back of this inserted page is the following, struck out:

In Ancient Days Sauron the Great contrived many things of wonder. For a time his purpose was not turned wholly to evil, or was concealed; and he went much among the Elves of Middle-earth and knew their secret counsels; and they learned many things of him, for his knowledge was very great. In those days the Rings of Power were made by elven-smiths, but Sauron was present at their making: his was the thought and theirs the skill; for these Rings (he said) would give the Elves of Middle-earth power and wisdom like that of the Elves of the West. [*Struck out as soon as written:* They made many rings, but One and Three and Seven and Nine were rings of special potency. The One only did Sauron take as his reward]; but he cheated them. [*Struck out as soon as written:* For knowing the secret of the rings he] The Elves made many rings at his bidding: Three, Seven and Nine of special potency, and others of lesser virtue. But knowing the secret of their making, secretly Sauron made One Ring, the Ruling Ring that governed all the rest, and their power was bound up with it, to last only so long as it too should last. And as soon as he had made it and set it upon his hand, the Elves found that he was master of all that they had wrought; and they were filled with fear and anger. Then Sauron sought to seize all the Rings, for he saw that the Elves would not lightly submit to him. But the Elves fled and hid themselves, and the Three Rings they saved; and these Sauron could not find because the Elves concealed them, and never again used them while Sauron's mastery endured. War and enmity has never ceased between Sauron and the Elves since those days.

It seems to have been on this page (in view of the rejected words 'The One only did Sauron take as his reward') that the final

260 THE TREASON OF ISENGARD

conception of the relation of the Rings of Power to Sauron emerged, at least in this essential: the Rings of Power were made by the Elven-smiths under the guidance of Sauron, but he made the One in secret to govern all the rest. (This idea had indeed been approached in one of the passages given on p. 255, but there it had been Fëanor himself who made the Rings of Power, and Morgoth who made the Ruling Ring in secret.) It is not said in the passage just cited that Sauron had no part in the making of the Three, which were unsullied by his hand, although this is very clearly implied in the original draft of Galadriel's refusal of Frodo's offer of the One (p. 254).

As with the earlier passages on this subject, I do not think it was written for inclusion in 'Galadriel', but its association with this chapter is again not accidental: for here the questions of the relation of the Three to the One, and the nature of the Three, were at last – through the showing forth of the Ring of Earth on Galadriel's finger – brought to the point where they must necessarily be answered. Ultimately, this passage foreshadows that in *Of the Rings of Power* in *The Silmarillion* (pp. 287–8); my father at this stage probably intended it for 'The Council of Elrond' (cf. p. 255).

Sam's visions in the Mirror, Galadriel's response to his outburst, and Frodo's visions of the wizard and of Bilbo proceed almost word for word as in FR; but the further scenes that appeared to Frodo follow the draft given in note 21, without the mysterious 'vast figure of a man' leaning on a tree. Gollum is no longer seen (p. 252); and the vision of the Eye reaches the form in FR, as does all that follows, with these differences. The white stone in Galadriel's ring is not mentioned; and as in the original text she still calls it 'the Ring of Earth.' In response to Frodo's offer to her of the One Ring Galadriel laughed 'with a sudden clear laugh of pure merriment': 'pure' was struck out early, and afterwards 'of merriment'. And as my father first wrote her words she said: 'And now at last it comes, the final probe.'[34]

A further text of this chapter may be mentioned here. This is an unfinished typescript of the fair copy manuscript just described. Some early emendations made to the manuscript were taken up, but there is no variation whatsoever in the phrasing (always a clear sign that a text was not made by my father). I have noticed (p. 256 and note 30) that in the manuscript Aragorn was 'Ingold' throughout, changed at one occurrence to 'Aragorn' and at another to 'Elfstone', but at the other three left unchanged. The typescript has 'Ingold' at all occurrences except at that where in the manuscript the name was changed to 'Elfstone'. From this I judge that it belongs to the period we have reached, i.e. before 'Aragorn' was restored (see pp. 277–8). But this typescript stops at the bottom of its sixth page, at the words *The air was cool and soft, as if it were* (FR p. 374); and the text is continued to the end of the chapter in a very carefully written manuscript that I

GALADRIEL
261

made when I was seventeen, beginning at the head of 'page 7' with the words that follow: *early spring, yet they felt about them the deep and thoughtful quiet of winter* (it is thus obvious that my manuscript simply took up from the point where the typescript stopped). The text in my copy shows no further development from my father's manuscript: thus Galadriel's ring remains the Ring of Earth, and she still laughs 'with a sudden clear laugh of merriment'. At the end of it I wrote the date: 4 August 1942.

Whatever the date of the typewritten part of this composite text, my continuation of it in manuscript was certainly made well after my father had completed work on the 'Lothlórien' story. He himself declared, many years later, that he reached Lothlórien and the Great River late in 1941, and it will be seen subsequently that he was writing 'The Breaking of the Fellowship' and 'The Departure of Boromir' in the middle of the winter of that year (p. 379).

NOTES

1 My father first wrote here 'Welcome to Nelennas', immediately striking out *Nelennas* and substituting *Caras Galadon* (which here first appears), and continuing 'the city of Nelennas which [?mayhap] in your tongue is called Angle'. This seems to show that *Nelennas* was very briefly the name of the city, as I have suggested (p. 242 note 39) is the case in the plot-notes given on p. 233: 'They journey to Nelennas'. But the alteration changes the meaning of *Nelennas* back to the 'Gore' or 'Angle', replacing *Nelen* (see p. 231 and note 34).

2 A little rough diagram set in the body of the text shows a circular figure shaped like one ring of a coil, with a very substantial overlap between the ends of the line: the external opening (the entrance into Caras Galadon through the walls) is on the left side of the figure, and the internal opening (the opening from the 'lane' into the city) is at the bottom (i.e. the walls overlap for a full quarter of the circuit or more).

There is no mention of how they passed through the gates (contrast FR p. 368). My father actually wrote here: 'They saw ... the elves on guard at the gate they saw no folk on guard', etc., striking no words out.

3 This is the first appearance of Celeborn and Galadriel. Just visible in the underlying pencilled text are other names: *Tar* and *Finduilas* struck out, and then *Aran* and *Rhien*. *Rhien* is perhaps to be equated with *Rían* (the name of Tuor's mother); cf. the *Etymologies*, V.383, stem RIG: '*Rhian* name of a woman, = "crown-gift", *ríg-anna*'. See notes 5 and 9.

262 THE TREASON OF ISENGARD

4 The first occurrence of *Halldir* (*sic*) for *Hathaldir*; a few lines further on the name is spelt *Haldir* and so remains. *Haldir* was the original name for this Elf; see p. 240 note 28. In the underlying text the superseded name *Hathaldir* can be seen.

5 This passage (from 'The roof was a pale gold') was retained (i.e. not overwritten in ink or erased) from the original pencilled text, and here reappear (after the words 'side by side') the names *Aran* and *Rhien* (see note 3), subsequently struck out. On the white hair of Galadriel cf. the plot-notes given on p. 233.

6 *Ingold son of Ingrim* for Aragorn replaced *Elfstone* (see p. 239 note 23), since that name can be made out in the pencilled text beneath. At his last appearance in this manuscript (p. 232) he was still *Aragorn*; and it is thus here that *Elfstone* first appears *ab initio* (as also does *Ingold* in the secondary text).

7 Written in here is the following, apparently of the same time but disconnected from the narrative:

'Nay, there was no mistake,' said Galadriel, speaking for the first time. Her voice was deeper but clear and musical / clear and musical but deep, and seemed to carry knowledge that was too deep for mirth.

This depends on something said by Keleborn, of which however there is no trace in this manuscript; see p. 257.

8 See p. 227 and note 29.

9 In the underlying pencilled text *Aran* was changed here, as my father wrote, to *Galdaran*; and at the head of the page are written the names *Galdaran* and *Galdrin* (perhaps miswritten for *Galdrien*, see pp. 249–50).

10 On the survival of Balrogs from the Elder Days see V.336, §16.

11 Parts of the underlying pencilled text of this passage can be made out, and the purport of Keleborn's words was very much the same – except that it was Keleborn (Galdaran) himself, not Galadriel, who raised a doubt:

'A Balrog,' said [Aran >] Galdaran. 'Of them I have not heard since the Elder Days ... had hidden in Mordor but of them naught has been seen since the fall of Thangorodrim. I doubt much if this Balrog has ... and I fear rather ... Orodruin in Mordor by Sauron. Yet who knows what lies hid at the roots of the ancient hills...'

At the bottom of the page is a variant, added to the revised text but belonging to the same time, in which it is Galadriel who expresses the opinion previously given to Keleborn, and more decisively:

'No Balrog has lain hid in the Misty Mountains since the fall of Thangorodrim,' said Galadriel. 'If truly one was there, as is told, then it is come from Orodruin, the Mountain of Fire, and was sent by the Lord whom we do not name in this land.'

GALADRIEL   263

In FR, of course, the view expressed here by Keleborn or Galadriel that the Balrog, sent from Mordor, had entered Moria not long since ('*it is come* from Orodruin') has no place. In LR the Balrog of Moria came from Thangorodrim at the end of the First Age, and 'had lain hidden at the foundations of the earth since the coming of the Host of the West' (see pp. 142–3).

I have suggested (p. 186) that although a Balrog appears in the original sketch of the Moria story, the connection with the flight of the Dwarves from Moria had not yet been made. The present passage is the chief evidence for this. It is true that in the version in the main text Galadriel is less positive than Keleborn, but in the subsequent variant she utters an emphatic denial that a Balrog could have 'lain hid in the Misty Mountains since the fall of Thangorodrim' (not that anybody present had suggested that it did). This must have been my father's view, since it would be strange indeed to introduce the Lord and Lady of Lothlórien, 'accounted wise beyond the measure of the Elves of Middle-earth', in the immediate expression of an erroneous opinion.

12   The phrases 'The lord and lady of Lothlórien are accounted wise *beyond the measure of the Elves of Middle-earth*' and 'For we have dwelt here *since the Mountains were reared and the Sun was young*' strongly suggest that my father conceived them to be Elves of Valinor, exiled Noldor who did not return at the end of the First Age. The Noldor came to Middle-earth in exile at the time of the making of the Sun and the Hiding of Valinor, when the Mountains of the West were 'raised to sheer and dreadful height' (V.242). Afterwards, when my father returned to *The Silmaril-lion* again, Galadriel entered the legends of the First Age as the daughter of Finarfin and sister of Finrod Felagund.

13   The first word in this sentence could be 'Nor' or 'Now', but must in fact be 'Now' since it is followed by 'we will', not 'will we'. But in FR Galadriel says 'I will not give you counsel', and her explanation of why she will not is almost word for word the same as what she says here. I think therefore that my father must have changed his mind concerning Galadriel's speech as he wrote, but failed to alter her opening words.

14   A scribble at the foot of the page advances Boromir's words towards the form in FR (p. 373): 'she was tempting me, and offered something that she had the power to give. It need not be said that I refused to listen.' Cf. p. 258.

15   A first suggestion of Keleborn's offer to Legolas and Gimli appears in the plot-notes on p. 233. The last two sentences of Keleborn's speech and the first part of Gimli's reply were subsequently used in Glóin's conversation with Frodo at Riven-dell (FR p. 241): 'Frodo learned that Grimbeorn the Old, son of Beorn, was now the lord of many sturdy men, and to their land

264   THE TREASON OF ISENGARD

between the Mountains and Mirkwood neither orc nor wolf dared to go. "Indeed," said Glóin, "if it were not for the Beornings the passage from Dale to Rivendell would long ago have become impossible." '

16 The biscuit factory of Sandyman & Son (p. 216).

17 This is the first appearance of the name *Mithrandir* (see V.345).

18 Scribbled notes at this point direct that Merry and Pippin should speak of Gandalf, and that they should speak of the 'temptation of Galadriel'; there is also a reference to the 'Song of Frodo and Sam' (FR pp. 374–5). A page of rough workings for the song is found with these papers, though without any narrative framework. The first and third verses were almost in final form; the second at this time read:

> *When morning on the Hill was bright*
> *across the stream he rode again;*
> *beside our hearth he sat that night*
> *and merry was the firelight then.*

The second verse in FR, *From Wilderland to Western shore*, was added in, apparently to stand between verses 2 and 3. The fourth verse ran:

> *A shining sword in deadly hand,*
> *a hooded pilgrim on the road,*
> *a mountain-fire above the land,*
> *a back that bent beneath the load.*

The fifth verse had virtually reached the form in FR; the sixth read:

> *Of Moria, of Khazaddûm*
> *all folk shall ever sadly tell*
> *and now shall name it Gandalf's tomb*
> *where hope into the Shadow fell.*

19 The meeting with Galadriel was altered at the time of writing to the form given. At first my father did not say that it was the *evening* of the third day, and when they came to 'a green hollow over which there was no roof or trees' the sun, which was in the south, looked down into it; cf. the outline given on p. 249; 'Mirror is of silver filled with fountain water in sun'.

A note in the margin directs that Sam should also be present, and another reads: 'Answer to remarks of Sam and Frodo that these elves seem simple woodland folk, skilled, but not specially magical' (cf. FR pp. 376–7).

20 At this point the following was entered disconnectedly in the manuscript: 'Frodo (Sam?) had been heard to say to Elfstone: Elves seem quiet, and ordinary. Have they magic as is reported?' Cf. note 19.

21 Against this passage my father wrote in the margin: *Bilbo*. In an isolated draft developing this passage the vision of Bilbo in his room at Rivendell (FR p. 379) is found almost as in the final

GALADRIEL 265

form. In this draft the vision of 'a fortress with high stone walls and seven towers' is followed by 'a vast figure of a man who seemed to be standing leaning on a tree that was only up to his breast'; this was placed in brackets. This is followed by 'a great river flowing through a populous city' (as in FR), and then by the vision of the Sea and the dark ship, as in the primary text.

22 Cf. the outline of the visions in the Mirror given on p. 250: 'Sees Gollum?'

23 It is notable that in this earliest form of the story the visions that Frodo sees in the Mirror have no reference to Sauron, yet Galadriel at once speaks of him, and the contest of their minds, introducing thus her revelation that she is the keeper of the Ring of Earth. In FR (p. 380) it is because Galadriel knows that Frodo has seen the Eye that she at once speaks to him of the Dark Lord, and the showing of her Ring is directly related to his vision: 'it cannot be hidden from the Ring-bearer, and one who has seen the Eye.'

24 For 'the Ring of Earth' see VI.260, 269, 319.

25 Cf. the isolated note concerning the fading of the power of the Elf-rings if the One Ring were destroyed, p. 237.

26 The word could be equally well read as 'shall' or 'should'; 'should' in the next manuscript of the chapter (and in FR).

27 Cf. pp. 115, 162. In FR Sam says here that 'Elrond knew what he was about when he wanted to send Mr. Merry back'; earlier (FR p. 289) Elrond had said that he had thought to send both Merry and Pippin back to the Shire, but after Gandalf's support for their inclusion in the Company he expressed doubt specifically concerning Pippin.

28 In the outline given on p. 249 'They dwell 15 days in Caras Galadon'. Starting from 15 December as the date of arrival in Lothlórien, even though that seems to be two days out (see p. 215 note 1), and seeing that in the original story it was only a single day's journey from the night spent on the flet near the falls of Nimrodel to the arrival in Caras Galadon at nightfall, the date of departure can be reckoned to be 1 January.

29 Up to this point the pagination is doubled, e.g. 'XVIII.34 / XIX.8'; from this point only that of 'XIX' is given.

30 At three occurrences *Ingold* was never changed; at one it was changed afterwards to *Elfstone*, and at one to *Aragorn*. See pp. 277–8.

31 An addition to the manuscript after the words 'For we have dwelt here since the mountains were reared and the sun was young' reads: 'And I have dwelt here with him since the days of dawn, when I passed over the seas with Melian of Valinor; and ever together we have fought the long defeat.' This was not taken up into the following typescript text (p. 260), though it was entered

266   THE TREASON OF ISENGARD

onto it in manuscript, and no doubt belongs to a later time. For the coming of Melian to Middle-earth in a very remote age of the world see IV.264, V.111.

32   There are pencilled additions to the manuscript after the words 'But what he thought the Lady had offered him Boromir did not tell': 'Here insert what Frodo thought?' and 'Neither did Frodo. Whether it had been a temptation, or a revealing to himself of the way of escape from his task that he had already secretly considered, he could not tell. But now that the thought had been made plain he could not forget it.' Against this my father wrote: '(rather so:) And as for Frodo, he would not speak, though Boromir pressed him with questions. "She held you long in her gaze, Ringbearer," he said. "Yes," said Frodo, "but I will say no more than this: to me no choice was given." He drooped and laid his head upon his knees.'

Frodo's reply to Boromir was then struck out, with the note: 'No! for this does not fit with the scene at the Mirror', and the following substituted: ' "Yes," said Frodo, "but whatever came into my mind then, I will keep there" ' (as in FR, p. 373).

None of this appears in the following typescript text (though the two latter versions were written onto it in turn), and as with the passage cited in note 31 must be accounted a later revision. But what is hinted at in the words 'the way of escape from his task that he had already secretly considered'? My father meant, I think, that Frodo, under Galadriel's gaze, pondered the thought of surrendering the Ruling Ring to her (cf. the passage cited on p. 254).

33   Of Frodo's song of Gandalf it is said: 'yet when he wished to repeat it to Sam only snatches remained that said little of what he had meant.' At this point there is a large space on the manuscript page and a pencilled note: 'Insert Frodo's Song?' The verses are found on a page of the familiar examination script, headed 'Frodo's Song', and were evidently written before this point in the manuscript was reached. For the earliest form of the song see note 18. The song has now 8 verses, since both *When morning on the Hill was bright* and *From Wilderland to Western shore* are included, and the last verse in FR *He stood upon the bridge alone* here appears as the penultimate (with the fourth line *the cloak of grey is cast aside*), the final verse being the same as in the earliest version, *Of Moria, of Khazad-dûm*.

34   '*Eärendil*, the Evening Star' is spelt thus, not *Eärendel* (see p. 290 note 22). – In Frodo's question 'why cannot I see all the others' (FR p. 381) 'I' should be italicized; and in Sam's reply to Galadriel's question at the end of the chapter 'Did you see my ring?' he should say 'I saw a star through your fingers', not 'finger'.

XIV

FAREWELL TO LÓRIEN

In the earliest materials for this chapter (without title) my father did not complete a continuous primary text, but (as it might be described) continually took two steps forward and one step back. He halted abruptly, even at mid-sentence, at certain points in the narrative, and returned to revise what he had written, often more than once; the result is a great deal of near-repetition and a very complex sequence. On the other hand, much (though by no means all) of this drafting is written in ink in a quick but clear and orderly hand on good paper (the 'August 1940' examination script being now virtually exhausted).

The reason for this situation is clear. The first consecutive text of the chapter, a well-written 'fair copy' manuscript, stands in very close relation to the draft materials. By this time it had become my father's method to begin making a fair copy before a new stretch of the narrative had proceeded very far: it has been seen in 'The Bridge of Khazad-dûm' (p. 202) and in 'Lothlórien' (pp. 221–2 and note 14) that drafting and fair copy to some extent overlapped. This was the case here also (thus the extracts from Keleborn's description of the Great River given on pp. 282–3 were drafts for the text found in the fair copy, and they immediately preceded that point in the writing of that text), but to a much more marked degree: for in this case, as I think, the fair copy was built up in stages, as the different sections of draft were completed.

Before turning to the original text, or texts, of this chapter, however, I give first some very difficult pencilled outlines, which I will call (a), (b) and (c). I take (a) to be the first since in it the name *Toll-ondren*, which occurs also in the others, is seen at the point of emergence. The pencil is now faint to the point of vanishing, and the first lines (as far as 'the Bridges of Osgiliath'), which were written before and apparently disconnectedly from the following portion, are partly illegible.

(a)

The travellers must choose which side of Anduin [?to be on] at [?Naith] Lórien. River is narrow but... at Stone Hills.[1] Not possible to cross without a boat until the Bridges of Osgiliath.

268   THE TREASON OF ISENGARD

Keleborn says they must [?journey] in the morning. Though his people do not often go outside borders he will send them by *boat* as far as [*struck out: Toll-ondu Toll-onnui*] *Toll-ondren* the Great Carrock.[2] The east bank is perilous to elves. River winds among the Border Hills [*struck out: Duil*] *Emyn Rain*.[3] There they must decide because the Wetwang *Palath Nenui*[4] lies before them and to reach Minas Tirith they must go west round and across [*added:* along hills and then across] Entwash. But to go the other way they must cross Dead Marshes.

(b)

This outline is also extremely faint. It takes up towards the end of the narrative in this chapter and extends beyond it, but was written at an early stage in the development of the story, since the presence of Elves accompanying the travellers is mentioned, and this element was soon abandoned.

This is the Naith or Angle.[5] Calendil or the Green Spit.
[*Struck out:* Nelen] Calennel[6]
We are come before you to make all ready, said the Lady Galadriel, and now at last we must bid you farewell. Here you are come at last to the end of our realm, to Calendil, the green-spit tongue. Green-tine.[7] Three boats await you with rowers.
They get into the boats. Elv[en] archers in one behind and before. Company 2 in first, Ingold, Boromir. Hobbits in middle. Legolas, Gimli behind.
Parting gifts.
Warning against Entwash (Ogodrûth) and Fangorn[8] – not necessary to Boromir and Ingold, but probably Gandalf did not tell them all.
Blessing of Galadriel on Frodo.
Song of Farewell of Elves.
Swift passing down the River.
Description of the [?Green Ravines].
Tollondren.
Scene with Boromir and loss of Frodo.
End of Chapter.

In this outline the names *Galadriel* and *Ingold* were written *ab initio*.

(c)

This third outline, again in very faint pencil, belongs with the others; a further section was added to it, but not I think after any significant interval.

FAREWELL TO LÓRIEN   269

Argument in pavilion at night.

They postpone decision until they reach Tolondren the Great Carrock.

They sail in [*number changed between* 2, 3, 4, *final figure probably* 3] boats. 1 filled with bowmen before and after.

Farewell of Galadriel.

They pass into the Rhain hills[9] where river winds in deep ravines.

A few arrows from East.

Elves give travellers special food and grey cloaks and hoods.

They say farewell at Tol Ondren and leave travellers [*struck out:* a boat > 2 small boats].

The Company lands and goes up into Rhain Hills for a safe place. The debate. Then comes Boromir's attempt at seizing Ring and Frodo's flight.

Arrows from East shore as they pass down river?

The Company lands on Tollondren. Then debate. Frodo (and Sam) want to go on with the Quest and get it over. Boromir against it (vehemently?). They beg Elves to wait while they decide. They cross to East bank and go up into Green Hills (or Emyn Rhain?) to look around.

The journey by boat down Anduin enters in outline (*a*) (see p. 213); in (*b*) the 'scene with Boromir and loss of Frodo' is removed from 'Angle' (see pp. 207–8, 213) and takes place after the journey down the river, while in (*c*) it occurs in the 'Rhain Hills'.

The geography of these regions was coming into being. My father knew at this stage that the Great River wound in ravines (the 'Green Ravines' doubtfully read in outline (*b*)?) through a range of hills (Stone Hills; Emyn Rhain, Rhain Hills, Border Hills; Green Hills – which were not merely alternative names, as will be seen in the next chapter); and that there was a great rock or tall island (the Great Carrock; *Tolondren*, variously spelt) in the midst of Anduin. This was associated with the hills, since the Company lands on the island and goes up into Emyn Rhain or into the Green Hills. In the added section of (*c*) they cross the river to do so. The Wetwang now appears, obviously if not explicitly associated with the confluence of Anduin and Entwash (or *Ogodrûth*), flowing out of Fangorn (p. 210).

I turn now to the earliest narrative texts of 'Farewell to Lórien', in which indications are found that the fair copy manuscript of 'Galadriel' was already in existence (notes 10 and 21). The opening portion of the chapter, in which the Company came before Keleborn and Galadriel on the eve of departure and then returned to their pavilion to debate their course, is extant in several different versions. The earliest of them begins clearly but soon descends to my father's roughest script; it was written in ink over a faint pencilled text some of which can be read (see note 12).

270   THE TREASON OF ISENGARD

(i)

That night[10] the Company was summoned again to the chamber of Keleborn, and the Lord and Lady of the Galadrim looked upon their faces. After a silence Keleborn spoke to them.

'Now is the time,' he said, 'when those who wish to continue the Quest must harden themselves to depart. And now is the time for those to say farewell to the Company who feel that they have gone as far as they have the strength to go. All that do not wish to go forward may remain here until there is a chance for them to return to their own homes.[11] For we stand now on the edge of doom; and ere long things will grow better, or will grow so evil that all must fight and fall where they stand. There will be no homes to seek, save the long home of those that go down in battle. Here you may abide the oncoming of the hour till the ways of the world lie open again, or we summon you to help us in the last stand of Lórien.'[12]

'They are all resolved to go forward,' said Galadriel.

'As for me,' said Boromir, 'my way home lies onward.'

'That is true,' said Keleborn. 'But are all the Company going with you to Minas Tirith?'

'We have not decided that yet,' said Ingold.

'But you must do so soon,' said Keleborn. 'For after you leave Lothlórien the River cannot easily be crossed again until you come to Ondor,[13] if indeed the passage of the river in the South is not held by the Enemy. Now the way to Minas Tirith lies on this side of the River, on the West bank, but the straight way of the Quest lies upon the other, upon the East bank. You should choose before you go.'

'If they take my advice it will be the west side,' said Boromir, 'but I am not the leader.'

'It shall be as you choose. But as you seem still in doubt, and do not maybe wish to hasten your choice, this is what I will do. It will speed your journey somewhat, and show you my good will – for I do not send my people often and only at [?great] need beyond my borders. I will furnish you with boats which we use upon the rivers. Some of my folk shall go with you as far as the Green Hills, where the river winds deep among [?wooded] slopes. But beyond the Toll-ondren, the isle that is there amid the river flood, they shall not go. Even so far there are perils for Elves upon the East bank; beyond that it is not safe for any to go by water.'

The words of Keleborn lightened their hearts a little that were

FAREWELL TO LÓRIEN

271

heavy with the thought of departure. They took leave of the Lord and Lady and went back to their pavilion. Legolas was with them. They debated long but they came to no decision. Ingold was evidently torn between two things. His own plan and desire was to have gone to Minas Tirith; but now that Gandalf was lost he felt that he could not abandon Frodo if he could not be persuaded to come. To the others there was little choice, for they knew nothing of the ... of the land in the South. Boromir said little but kept his eyes ever fixed on Frodo as if he waited for his decision. At length he spoke. 'If you are to *destroy the Ring*,' he said, 'then there is little use in arms, and Minas Tirith cannot help you greatly. But if you wish to *destroy the Lord*, then there is little use in going without force into his domain. That is how it seems to me.'

Here this text ends.

(ii)

The next version is a fair copy of (i) so far as it went, and follows it closely, improving the wording but introducing few significant changes; but it extends further into the chapter.

Keleborn now speaks with greater certainty of the crossings of Osgiliath: 'it is said that the Enemy holds the passages [> bridges].' Elves of Lórien shall go with the Company 'as far as the Green Hills where the river winds among deep ravines'; here *Rhain* is written in pencil over *Green*. 'There is a wooded island there, Toll-ondren, amid the branching waters. There at last in the midst of the stream you must decide your courses, left or right.' Above *(Toll-)ondren* is written in pencil *Galen?*, i.e. *Tol Galen*: another use of a name from the legends of the Elder Days (the Green Isle in the river Adurant in Ossiriand, home of Beren and Lúthien after their return, and a further instance of an island amid a river's 'branching waters' – from which indeed the *Adurant* took its name, V.268).

In the part of this version that extends beyond the point reached in (i) the text of FR (pp. 385–6) is closely approached. Boromir now breaks off at the words 'and no sense in throwing away...', finishing his sentence lamely after a pause with 'no sense in throwing lives away, I mean.' And as in FR Ingold was deep in his thoughts and made no sign at this, while Merry and Pippin were already asleep.

The passage describing the bringing of the Elvish cakes and Gimli's delight at discovering that they were not *cram* is at once almost exactly as in FR, the only difference being that the words 'But we call it *lembas* or waybread' do not appear. The description of the cloaks is however

272   THE TREASON OF ISENGARD

much briefer than in FR – and there is no mention of the leaf-shaped brooches that fastened them.

For each member of the Company they had provided a grey hood and cloak made according to his size of the light but warm silken stuff that the Galadrim used.

'There is no magic woven in these cloaks,' they said, 'but they should serve you well. They are light to wear, and at need warm enough and cool enough in turn...'

Later, my father would not have the Elves introduce the idea of 'magic' cloaks, and it is Pippin who uses the word, which the leader of the Elves finds hard to interpret. The remainder of the passage is as in FR, except just at the end: 'We have never before clad strangers in the garb of our own people, certainly never a dwarf.' With these words the second text stops abruptly.

(iii)

The next text, going back once more to the beginning of the chapter, carries the number XX, showing that the story of Galadriel's Mirror had been separated off, as XIX 'Galadriel', from XVIII 'Lothlórien' (see p. 256). This manuscript rapidly becomes very complex through a process of what might be called 'overlapping false starts'. The form in FR is now very closely approached as far as the point where Keleborn says 'I see that you have not decided this matter' (cf. FR p. 383). It is to be noted that *Ingold* was changed subsequently, at both occurrences in the opening dialogue, first to *Elfstone* and then to *Trotter* (see pp. 277–8). Keleborn now says: 'And are not the bridges of Osgiliath broken down, and the passages of the river held now by the Enemy since his late assault?'[14] But from the point mentioned the story is developed thus:

'I see that you have not decided this matter, nor yet made any plan,' said Keleborn. 'It is not my part to choose for you, but I will do what I can to help you. Are there any among you that can manage boats upon a strong river?'

Boromir laughed. 'I was born between the mountains and the sea, on the borders of the Land of Seven Streams,'[15] he said, 'and the Great River flows through Ondor.'

'I have journeyed by boat on many rivers,' said Ingold;[16] 'and Legolas here is from the elf-folk of Mirkwood who use both rafts and boats on the Forest River. One at least of the hobbits is of the riverside folk that live on the banks of Baranduin. The rest can at least sit still. They have all now passed through such

FAREWELL TO LÓRIEN 273

perils that I do not think a journey by boat would seem so terrible as once it might.'

'That is well,' said Keleborn. 'Then I will furnish you with two small boats. They must be small and light, for if you go far by river there are places where you will have to carry your craft: there are the falls of Rhain where the River runs out of the ravines in the Green Hills,[17] and other places where no boat can pass. [*The following struck out as soon as written:* This I will do to show you my good will. Two Elves shall guide you for a short way, but far abroad I cannot permit my folk to stray in these evil days. But when you leave the River, as you must whichever way you go at the last, I ask only that you should not destroy my boats save only to keep them from the orcs, and that you should draw them ashore and] In this way your journey will be made less toilsome for a while, though perhaps not less perilous. How far you can go by water who now can tell? And the gift of boats will not decide your purpose: it may postpone your choice, yet at the last you must leave the River and go either east or west.'

Ingold thanked Keleborn many times in the name of all the Company. The offer of the boats comforted him much, and indeed it cheered most of the travellers. Their hearts were heavy with the thought of leaving Lothlórien, but now for a while the toils of the road at least would be lessened, though the dangers doubtless would remain. Sam only felt a little alarm. In spite of all the perils he had now passed through

(iv)

Here the third text breaks off, and all from 'Are there any among you that can manage boats upon a strong river?' was rejected, and begun again; the narrative now becoming close to the form in FR: 'There are some at least among you that can handle boats: Legolas, whose folk go on rafts and boats on the Forest River; and Boromir of Ondor, and Ingold [> Elfstone] the traveller.' The Elves to accompany them down the River have now gone; and *the falls of Rhain* 'where the River runs out of the ravines in the Green Hills' become *the Falls of Rosfein* (with the same comment).

After Ingold (> Elfstone > Trotter) had thanked Keleborn, and after the account of the lightened hearts of all the travellers,[18] the new text continues with Keleborn's words 'All shall be prepared for you and await you before noon tomorrow at the haven' (FR p. 384); but whereas in texts (i) and (ii) – as in FR – Keleborn's offer of boats is followed by the withdrawal of the Company to their pavilion, and there is no mention of gifts, this new version has Galadriel say: 'Good night, fair guests! But before you go I have here parting gifts which I beg you to take, and remember the Galadrim and their Lord and Lady.' The outline *(b)* on p. 268, obviously earlier than the stage now reached since there is mention in it of Elves going with the Company in boats, placed the Parting Gifts at the time of the final departure down the River, and this must have been my father's original intention, which he now temporarily changed. In this version (iv) there now follows the recital of the gifts to each member of the Company.

Galadriel's gift to Ingold (the name not here changed) is the sheath that had been made to fit his sword, which is called *Branding*:[19] overlaid with silver and with runes of gold declaring the name of the sword and its owner. Nothing more is said, and there is no mention of the great green stone (FR p. 391). Boromir's belt of gold, the silver belts for Merry and Pippin, and the bow of the Galadrim given to Legolas, appear and are described in the same words as in FR. Galadriel's gift to Sam and her words to him are almost exactly as in FR. The box containing earth from her garden was 'unadorned save for a single flowering rune upon the lid' ('a single silver rune,' FR). On the manuscript page my father drew an Old English G-rune ('X') in the form of two flowering branches crossed one upon the other:[20]

The word 'flowering' was later crossed out, and another, purely formal elaboration of the rune was drawn at the head of the next page:

FAREWELL TO LÓRIEN   275

The gift to Gimli differs, however, from his gift in FR, and differs in the most remarkable way.

'And what gift would a dwarf ask of Elves?' said the Lady to Gimli.

'None, Lady,' answered Gimli. 'It is enough for me to have seen the Lady of the Galadrim and known her graciousness. I will treasure the memory of her words at our first meeting.'[21]

[*Rejected, but not struck out, as soon as written:* 'Hear, all you Elves!' said the Lady, turning to those about her. 'And say not that dwarves are all rough and ungracious, grasping at gifts and / I have heard it said that dwarves are openhanded – to receive, and count their words – when they give thanks'] 'It is well that those about me should hear your fair words,' said Galadriel, 'and may they never again say that dwarves are grasping and ungracious. Let this small token be given as a sign that goodwill may be remade between dwarves and elves, if better days should come.' She put her hand to her throat and unclasped a brooch, and gave it to Gimli. On it was an emerald of deep green set in gold. 'I will set it near my heart,' he said, bowing to the floor, 'and Elfstone shall be a name of honour in my [?kin] for ever, and like a leaf [?amid] ... gold.'

Once again the text was stopped short, before Frodo's gift was reached. Beneath the last words my father wrote: *Elfstone Elfhelm*, and then:

'Hail, Elfstone,' she said. 'It is a fair name that merits a gift to match.'

It was clearly at this point that 'the Elfstone' first emerged, as a green gem set in a brooch worn by Galadriel and given as a parting gift to Gimli; and it seems equally plain that my father immediately adopted it (or more accurately, re-adopted it) as the true name of Trotter. To this question I will return in a moment.

(v)

He now started again from Keleborn's words 'All shall be prepared for you and await you at the haven before noon tomorrow' (p. 273), and repeated what he had written of the gifts to Boromir, Merry, Pippin, and Sam, but omitting Ingold; and now Gimli's request and gift (a strand of Galadriel's hair) are told word for word as they appear in FR (pp. 392–3), the sole difference being that at the end, after 'and yet over you gold shall have no dominion', Galadriel said: 'Dark are the waters of Kheledzâram, yet there maybe you shall one

276   THE TREASON OF ISENGARD

day see a light.' The phial in which was caught the light of Eärendel's star,[22] her gift to Frodo, now appears, and this passage also is almost word for word as in FR.

It looks as if Ingold's gift was omitted inadvertently; or else my father may have briefly intended to make it the last. There are four versions describing it, the final one being a rider marked for insertion into the text at the beginning of the gift-giving.

It has been seen that the Elfstone was at first the gift to Gimli, and that Gimli in accepting it took it also as a name; but that the moment he had set this down my father wrote: ' "Hail, Elfstone," she said. "It is a fair name that merits a gift to match" '; and this is obviously addressed to Trotter. The variant versions of the description of Galadriel's gift to the leader of the Company are developed from this; and the pages on which they stand are covered with names: *Elfstone, Elfstone son of Elfhelm, Elfstan, Eledon, Aragorn, Eldakar, Eldamir, Qendemir*. There is no need to cite these successive variants except in their opening sentences, until the last, which I give in full.

(1) 'Eledon!' she said to Trotter. 'Elfstone you are named; it is a fair name, and my gift shall match it.' (She then gives him a green gem.)

(2) 'Elfstone,' she said. 'It is a fair name...' (as in 1, except that here she unclasps the gem from her throat).

(3) 'Here is the gift of Keleborn to the leader of the Company,' she said to Trotter...' (continuing as in the final version, 4).

(4) (The version inserted into the text)

'Here is the gift of Keleborn to the leader of your Company,' she said to Elfstone [> Trotter], and gave him a sheath that had been made to fit his sword. It was overlaid with a tracery of flowers and leaves wrought of silver and gold, and on it were set in runes formed of many gems the name Branding and the lineage of the sword. 'The blade that is drawn from this sheath shall not be stained or broken even in defeat,' she said. 'Elfstone is your name, Eldamir in the language of your fathers of old, and it is a fair name. I will add this gift of my own to match it.'[23] She put her hand to her throat and unclasped from a fine chain a gem that hung before her breast. It was a stone of clear green set in a band of silver. 'All growing things that you look at through this,' she said, 'you will see as they were in their youth and in their spring. It is a gift that blends joys and sorrow; yet many things that now appear loathly shall seem otherwise to you hereafter.'

The seeming conundrum presented by the bewildering movements in the names which replaced 'Aragorn' in this phase of the work must now be confronted.

FAREWELL TO LÓRIEN   277

For all the apparently contradictory changes, whereby *Aragorn* becomes *Elfstone* but *Elfstone* also becomes *Aragorn*, and *Elfstone* becomes *Ingold* but *Ingold* also becomes *Elfstone*, it is in fact perfectly clear that the first change was from *Aragorn* to *Elfstone*. This took place in the course of the writing of the original draft of the long 'Lothlórien' chapter (see p. 262 note 6) and in the fair copy (p. 236). That this is so is confirmed and explained by a note on the 'August 1940' examination script:

> NB. Since Aragorn [> Trotter] is a *man* and the common speech (especially of mortals) is represented by English, then he must not have an Elvish name. Change to *Elfstone* son of *Elfhelm*.

Beside this are written other names, *Elf-friend*, *Elfspear*, *Elfmere*. It was now that *Aragorn* (or *Trotter*) was changed to *Elfstone* in earlier chapters;[24] but at this stage the name 'Elf-*stone*' will not have had any particular significance or association.

That *Ingold* was a replacement of *Elfstone* is shown by its appearance *ab initio* (i.e. not as a correction of an earlier name) in the overwritten part of the original draft of the 'Lothlórien' story, where *Elfstone* can be read in the primary pencilled text beneath (p. 262 note 6). This change is the subject of another note written on the same paper as the first:

> Instead of Aragorn son of Kelegorn *and* instead of the later variant Elfstone son of Elfhelm use *Ingold son of Ingrim*; since Trotter is a *man* he should not have a Gnome-elvish name like Aragorn.[25] The *Ing-* element here can represent the 'West'.

Some texts, therefore, call him *Ingold* from the first; and at the same time *Ingold* replaced (in principle) *Elfstone* in texts already extant at this time.

When my father wrote the first version of the Parting Gifts passage (p. 275) the gift of Galadriel to Gimli of the green gem set in gold was totally unforeseen, as was Gimli's thereupon taking the name *Elfstone* to be 'a name of honour' in his kin. At that very moment a sudden new possibility and connection emerged. Trotter had been for a while *Elfstone* – a name chosen for linguistic reasons; that had been rejected and replaced by *Ingold*; but now it turned out that *Elfstone* was after all the right name. The Elfstone was the Lady's gift to him, not to Gimli; and in giving it to him she made a play on his name.

The next step, therefore, and principal cause of the apparent confusion, was a *reversion* from the short-lived *Ingold* to *Elfstone*, and the chain of changes now becomes:

> *Aragorn* (or *Trotter*) > *Elfstone* > *Ingold* > *Elfstone*

The further emendation of this new *Elfstone* to *Trotter* (pp. 272–3, 276) does not necessarily mean that *Elfstone* had been abandoned again as his real name, but rather that my father now wished to make

278   THE TREASON OF ISENGARD

his name *Trotter* for general use in the immediate narrative (thus he is *Trotter* throughout the fair copy manuscript of 'Farewell to Lórien', see p. 293). Ultimately *Aragorn* returned; and thus the circular series is completed:

Aragorn (or *Trotter*) > *Elfstone* > *Ingold* > *Elfstone* (> *Trotter*) > *Aragorn*

This series appears in more or less fragmentary form in the manuscripts (cf. p. 244 note 52) for various reasons, but largely because my father carried out the corrections to the extant texts at each stage rather haphazardly. In some cases only parts of the series are found because in these cases the succession of changes was already more or less advanced; in some cases the expected change is not made because the text was rejected before the occasion for it arose (note 16). Running through and crossing this is the name *Trotter*, which might be changed or retained according to my father's changing view of when it should be employed.

Afterwards, of course, when Galadriel gave Aragorn the Elfstone she *conferred* on him the name 'that was foretold' for him (FR p. 391); Aragorn became *Elessar, the Elfstone* in that hour. On the history and properties of the Elfstone or Elessar see *Unfinished Tales* pp. 248 ff.; cf. especially 'For it is said that those who looked through this stone saw things that were withered or burned healed again or as they were in the grace of their youth.' In FR nothing is said of the properties of the stone.

This text (v) continues — since the gift-giving took place on the last night, in the chamber of Keleborn and Galadriel — with a further version of the debate of the Company, and the gifts next morning of elven-cloaks and food for the journey. The text of FR is further approached in many details of wording; but of Trotter's thoughts on the question of what they should do now this is said:

Elfstone [> Trotter] was himself divided in mind. His own plan and desire had been to go with Boromir, and with his sword help to deliver Ondor. For he had believed that the message of the dreams was a summons, and that there in Minas Tirith he would become a great lord, and maybe would set up again the throne of Elendil's line, and defend the West against assault. But in Moria he had taken on himself Gandalf's burden...

The remainder of the debate is now virtually as in FR (p. 385), the only difference being that the sentence 'He [Boromir] had said something like this at the Council, but then he had accepted the correction of Elrond' is here absent. The passage concerning the cloaks remains the same as in the previous draft (p. 272), except that the

FAREWELL TO LÓRIEN 279

Elves now add that 'All who see you clad thus will know that you are friends of the Galadrim', and the words 'certainly never a dwarf' are omitted. Thus there is still no mention of the detail, afterwards important, that each cloak was fastened with a leaf-shaped brooch. But the sentence previously absent (p. 271), 'But we call it *lembas* or waybread', now appears.

(vi)

For the next part of the chapter, from 'After their morning meal they said farewell to the lawn by the fountain' (FR p. 386), the form of the text changes, though the actual writing was clearly continuous with what precedes. There was first a draft in very faint pencil which went as far as the Elves' warning about the handling of the boats, and then became an outline of the further course of the narrative:

> They were arranged thus. Elfstone and Frodo and Sam in one, Boromir and Merry and Pippin in another, and in a third Legolas and Gimli (... dwarf become more friendly).[26] The last boat being more lightly burdened with passengers took more of the packs. They are steered and driven by broad-bladed paddles. They practise on advice of Elves and though they will only be going downstream practise going up the Silverlode.
>
> Thus they meet the Lord and Lady in their *swan-shaped* barge. Curved neck, and jewelled eyes, and half-raised wings. They take a meal on the grass and then a last farewell. Here comes in advice of Keleborn and last farewell of Galadriel.
>
> Frodo looks back and sees in the westering sun upon the haven a tall, slender, and sad figure with an upraised hand. Last sight of the Ring of Earth. (He never saw it again?)
>
> Song of Galadriel.

On top of the pencilled draft my father wrote a new text in ink, so that virtually all – except the outline just given, which was left intact – was obliterated. He then continued this new text, which soon became very rough and petered out at Keleborn's invitation to eat with them. Since this was in turn overtaken by a further version which followed it closely so far as it went, nothing is lost by turning at once to that.

(vii)

This text is in soft pencil on large and now very battered sheets, but legible. The story as told in FR appears fully formed, even to much of its wording, and I shall not give it in full; there are however many interesting features of names and geography.

With Haldir, returned from the 'northern fences' and acting as guide to the Company from Caras Galadon, his brother Orofin came also. It

280 THE TREASON OF ISENGARD

is said that 'Haldir brought news': ' "There are strange things happening away back there," he said. "We do not know the meaning of them. But the Dimrill Dale is full of clouds of smoke and vapour..." ' (see note 11).

The Tongue is thus described (cf. FR p. 387):

The lawn ran out into a narrow tongue of green between bright margins: on the right and west glittered the narrower and swifter waters of the Silverlode, and on the left and east ran the broader greener waters of the Great River. On the far banks the woodlands still marched southwards as far as they could see, but beyond the Naith or Angle (as the elves called this green sward) and upon the east side of the Great River all the boughs were bare. No mallorn-trees grew there.[27]

On 'Naith or Angle' as a name of the Tongue see note 5. This sentence was corrected, probably at once, to: 'but beyond the Tongue (*Lamben* the elves called this green sward)'; then the words '*Lamben* the elves called this green sward' were in turn crossed out. On Elvish names of the Tongue see p. 268 and note 6.

The passage in FR concerning the ropes and Sam's interest in rope-making is wholly absent, just as his realisation too late that he has no rope before leaving Rivendell (p. 165) and his bemoaning that he has none in Moria (p. 183) are also lacking.[28] The old text reads here:

Three small grey boats had already been prepared for the travellers, and in these the elves stowed their goods.

'You must take care,' they said. 'The boats are light-built, and they will be more deeply laden than they should be, when you go aboard. It would be wise if you accustomed yourselves to getting in and out here, where there is a landing-place, before you set off downstream.'

In the first draft (vi) of this passage Trotter is here called *Elfstone*, and it is said that 'Trotter led them up the Silverlode'; in this second version (vii) he is *Eldamir* at both occurrences, replaced (at the time of writing) by *Trotter*. *Eldamir* ('Elfstone') appears in Galadriel's address to him at the time of her parting gifts (p. 276); as will be seen shortly, my father was on the point of removing the gift-giving from the evening before their departure to their final farewell on the Tongue, and this apart from any other consideration would probably explain his removing *Eldamir* at this point in the story.

A curious detail in the description of the swan-boat was subsequently removed:

Two elves, clad in white, steered it with black paddles so

FAREWELL TO LÓRIEN   283

and smoke over the cataracts of Rhosfein [*written above in pencil:* Dant-ruin] down into the Nindalf – the Wetwang as it is called in your speech. That is a wide region of sluggish fen, where the stream becomes tortuous and much divided; there the Entwash river flows in by many mouths from the West. Beyond, on this side of the Great River, lies Rohan. On the further side are the bleak hills of Sarn-gebir [*in version (i)* Sarn > Sern Gebir]. The wind blows from the East there, for they look out over the Dead Marshes and the Nomenlands [*in version (i)* the Nomenlands (of Uvanwaith)] to the passes of Mordor: Kirith Ungol.

This passage in its variant forms is the fullest account of the geography of these regions yet encountered, and I postpone discussion of it, in relation to the earliest map of *The Lord of the Rings*, to the next chapter.

Despite his direction to bring in the gift scene 'just before the drink of farewell' (p. 282) my father now changed his mind, and introduced the cup of parting here, in the same place as in FR (pp. 390–1), and in the same words, except that Galadriel first said 'though the hour of shadow has come in its appointed time', and then 'though shadows long foretold approach', before her words in FR were reached: 'though night must follow noon, and already our evening draweth nigh.' After 'Then she called to each in turn' my father directed: 'Here take in gift-scene (in short or longer form).' The 'short form' of the scene is found under the heading 'If the gift-scene is cut out, or down, it might run thus:'

To each of the guests she gave a small brooch shaped like a golden flower with three leaves of jewelled green. 'This shall be in remembrance of Lothlórien,' she said, 'and all elves that see these shall know that you are friends. For you two,' she said, turning to Frodo and Sam, 'I have also small gifts of my own in remembrance of our last meeting. To you, little gardener and lover of trees, I will give this, though it may seem little to look on. She beckoned to Sam and laid in his hand (... so to end of Sam ...)
    'And for you, Frodo, I have prepared this,' she said ...

(The last part of this text is written thus in the original.)

(viii)

The conclusion of the chapter in its earliest extant form is written in ink in clear script with little hesitation in the phrasing, and closely approaches FR (despite very many small differences in the actual words). The feeling of the Company as the River bore them away from Lórien is expressed thus (and is the first suggestion of the idea that

284   THE TREASON OF ISENGARD

Lórien existed in a mode of Time distinct from that of the world beyond its borders, unless it is present in Keleborn's words on p. 249):

Lórien was slipping backward like a green vessel masted with trees sailing to forgotten shores, while they were cast again on the grey never-halting water of time.

Galadriel's song heard in the distance as the boats slipped down Anduin is not recorded; indeed there is a clear suggestion that when he first wrote this concluding passage my father did not intend that it should be (although the words 'Song of Galadriel' in the outline on p. 279 perhaps suggest otherwise):

But she sang in [the ancient elvish tongue >] some ancient hidden tongue, and he heard not the words. [*Added:* The music was fair but it bore no heart's ease.] Then suddenly the river swept round a bend and the banks rose upon either side. They saw her never more. Turning now their faces to their journey they faced the sun . . .

The initial workings for Galadriel's songs were nonetheless found with the earliest manuscripts of this chapter, both her song upon the swan-boat (of which there is also a finished text) and *Namarië*. The completed form of the first reads:

I sang of leaves, of leaves of gold, and leaves of gold there grew:
Of wind I sang, a wind there came and in the branches blew.
Beyond the Sun, beyond the Moon, the foam was on the Sea,
And by the strand of Tirion there grew a golden Tree.
Beneath the stars of Evereve in Eldamar it shone,[35]
In Eldamar beside the walls of Elven Tirion.
But far away and far away beyond the Shadow-meres
Now long the golden leaves have grown upon the branching
     years.
And Lórien, O Lórien! the river flows away
And leaves are falling in the stream, and leaves are borne away;
O Lórien, too long I dwell upon this Hither Shore
And in a fading crown I twine the golden elanor.
But if a ship I now should sing, what ship would come to me,
What ship would bear me ever back across so wide a sea?

Pencilled changes bring the song in all points to the form in FR. My father was working at the same time on the Elvish song, which had reached this form:

> *Ai! laurie lantar lassi sūrinen*
> *inyalemīne rāmar aldaron*

FAREWELL TO LÓRIEN

inyali ettulielle turme mārien
anduniesse la mīruvōrion
Varda telūmen falmar kīrien
laurealassion ōmar mailinon.

Elentāri Vardan Oiolossëan
Tintallen māli rāmar ortelūmenen
arkandavā-le qantamalle tūlier
e falmalillon morne sindanōrie
no mīrinoite kallasilya Valimar.

I have mentioned earlier (p. 266) the very close relationship between the writing of the foregoing drafts and the writing of the fair copy manuscript; and the result of this mode of composition is that there is very little that need be said about the new text (numbered XX but without title: 'Farewell to Lórien' was pencilled in later).

In Keleborn's words to the Company on the last evening (see p. 273) he still speaks of 'the great falls of Rosfein, where the River runs out of the ravines among the Green Hills', but this was changed, before the manuscript was completed, to 'where the River thunders down from Sarn-gebir'. His parting advice at the Tongue on the following day naturally scarcely differs from the text (pp. 282–3) which was written for this place in the fair copy (note 34); but 'the cataracts of Rhosfein' become 'the cataracts of Dant-ruinel' (*Dant-ruin* is pencilled over *Rhosfein* in the draft text), and at the end of the passage Keleborn says, not 'to the passes of Mordor: Kirith Ungol', but 'to Kirith Ungol, and the gates of Mordor'.

Pencilled alterations to the passage in the fair copy manuscript changed *Tolondren* to *Eregon*, then to *Brandor*, then to *the Tindrock that we call Tol Brandor*; and *Dant-ruinel* to *Rauros* (with marginal notes *Rauros* = 'Rush-rain' or 'Roar-rain'). At this time *Rosfein* in Keleborn's earlier speech was changed to *Rauros*.[36]

The much fuller account in FR (p. 386) of the elven-cloaks provided for the members of the Company (see p. 272) was added in, probably not much later (see p. 343 and note 35), and the words of the Elves 'There is no magic woven in these cloaks' removed with the introduction of Merry's question (Pippin's in FR) 'Are these garments magical?' The leaf-brooches were a further and subsequent addition (see p. 398).

When Haldir reappeared to act as their guide from Caras Galadon (now without his brother Orofin) he said, just as in the draft for this passage, 'There are strange things happening away back there. We do not know what is the meaning of them' (see pp. 279–80). This was subsequently struck out on the fair copy, but then marked *Stet*; this was in turn struck out, and Haldir's words do not appear in the following text of the chapter or in FR (p. 387). It is very hard to see why my father removed them, and why he hesitated back and forth

286 THE TREASON OF ISENGARD

before finally doing so. Apparently as a comment on this, he pencilled a note on the manuscript: 'This won't do – if Lórien is timeless, for then *nothing* will have happened since they entered.' I can only interpret this to mean that within Lórien the Company existed in a different Time – with its mornings and evenings and passing days – while in the world outside Lórien no time passed: they had left that 'external' Time, and would return to it at the same moment as they left it. This question is further discussed later (pp. 367–9). But it does not seem to me to explain why only Haldir's opening words were removed. His announcement, which was allowed to stand, that the Dimrill Dale was full of smoke and that there were noises in the earth, merely explains what the 'strange things' were which the Elves did not understand; and these 'strange things' had obviously only begun *since* the Company entered the Golden Wood.

As in the draft (p. 281) the words of Galadriel's song on the swan-boat are not reported, but my father subsequently put a mark of insertion on the manuscript, with the word 'Song'. On the completed text of her song found with the draft papers and given on p. 284 he then wrote 'Galadriel's Song for XX.8', this being the number of the page in the present manuscript. Similarly there is no suggestion that Galadriel's parting song ('in some ancient tongue of the West, from beyond the margin of the world') should be given, though 'he heard not the words' was changed on the manuscript to 'he did not understand the words', as in FR; but here again my father subsequently pencilled a mark of insertion and the word 'Song' in the margin.

'They saw her never more' of the draft (p. 284) becomes now 'Never again did Frodo see the Lady Galadriel', where in FR it is said 'To that fair land Frodo never came again.'

The following outline is found on a small, isolated scrap of paper. The only evidence of date that I can see is the fact that 'Sam's casket' (i.e. his gift from Galadriel) is referred to, and it therefore followed the present chapter. But this seems as good a place as any to give it, in relation to the end of the major outline which I have called 'The Story Foreseen from Moria' on p. 212.

The Three Rings are to be *freed*, *not* destroyed by the destruction of the One. Sauron cannot arise again in person, only work through men. But Lórien is saved, and Rivendell, and the Havens – until they grow weary, and until Men (of the East) 'eat up the world'. Then Galadriel and Elrond will sail away. But Frodo saves the Rings.

Frodo saves the Shire; and Merry and Pippin become important.

Sackville-Bagginses are chucked out (become pot-boys at Bree).

Sam's casket restores Trees.

FAREWELL TO LÓRIEN   287

When old, Sam and Frodo set sail to island of West and [sic]   Bilbo finishes the story. Out of gratitude the Elves adopt them and give them an island.

At the head of the page is written: 'Saruman becomes a wandering conjuror and trickster'.

NOTES

1   The Stone Hills are named in the outlines given on pp. 233 and 250. The last word in the illegible phrase preceding 'at Stone Hills' might possibly be 'drop', which taken with the note in the outline on p. 233 that the 'parting of ways' would take place 'at Stonehills' might suggest that this was a first hint of the great falls in Anduin.

2   The word *Carrock* is very indistinct; it occurs again in outline *(c)*, but is there equally so. Yet I think that this is what it must certainly be, especially since it seems very suitable: for Tolondren was the origin of Tol Brandir, and thus the 'Great Carrock' would answer to Beorn's 'Little Carrock' or 'Lesser Carrock', itself also rising amid the waters of Anduin but far to the North; *ondren* being no doubt a derivative of the stem GOND 'stone' (*Etymologies*, V.359).

3   With the rejected word *Duil* cf. *Duil Rewinion*, name of the Hills of the Hunters (west of the river Narog) on the first *Silmarillion* map, IV.225. – *Emyn Rain* is subsequently spelt *Rhain* (see note 9); cf. the *Etymologies*, V.383, stem REG, Noldorin *rhein, rhain* 'border', also *Minas rhain* (Minas Tirith) p. 116.

4   This is the first occurrence of the *Wetwang*. The second word in the Elvish name *Palath Nenui* is slightly uncertain, but seems probable. Cf. the *Etymologies*, V.380, stem PAL, Noldorin *palath* 'surface'; also *palath* 'iris', VI.432, VII.101. *Palath Nen[ui]* occurs also on the First Map (see pp. 299, 308).

5   The word *Naith* 'Angle' (see the Etymologies, V.387, stem SNAS, Noldorin *naith* 'gore') seems in the context of this outline to be a name for the 'green spit' or 'Tongue' where the Company embarked from Lórien on their journey down Anduin (cf. also *Naith Lórien* in outline *(a)*); and subsequently (p. 280) this is expressly stated: 'The Naith or Angle (as the elves called this green sward)'.

The name *Angle* is variously used. In the earliest mention of the Lórien story, p. 207, the Company 'journey *to Angle* between Anduin and Blackroot. *There they remain long*'; and '*at Angle* they debate what is to be done.' Since this was written before the actual story of Lothlórien had been begun, the precise wording cannot perhaps be pressed; and in the original text of the first

288 THE TREASON OF ISENGARD

'Lothlórien' chapter the meaning seems entirely unambiguous. As soon as they had crossed the Blackroot Hathaldir told them that they had 'entered the Gore, Nelen we call it, which lies in the angle between Blackroot and Anduin' (p. 231), and he told Gimli (*ibid.*) that in the north there were 'hidden defences and guards *across the open arms of the Angle between the rivers*'. The other references in that text do not contradict the obvious conclusion from these two passages, that whatever the extent of the woods of Lothlórien may have been, the Angle or Gore (*Bennas, Nelen, Nelennas*) was 'the heart of Lórien' (see p. 243 note 46), Lórien-between-the-Rivers, the base of the triangle being the eaves of the forest in the North.

Thus 'Naith or Angle' in this outline, and again in the text of the present chapter, referring expressly to the 'Tongue' (the apex of the triangle), represents either a changed meaning of *Angle*, or else perhaps the use of the English word to signify both the large triangle ('Lórien-between-the-Rivers') and the very small triangle (the Tongue) that was the apex of the other.

On the other hand, in the fair copy manuscript of 'Lothlórien' the distinction is between *Narthas* 'the Gore', the larger region, and *Nelen* 'the Angle', the region in the south where the Elves dwelt (see p. 236). I doubt that any clearly correct and consecutive formulation can be reached amid such fluidity.

In FR (p. 361) 'the Naith of Lórien, or the Gore' is the large triangle, entered after passage of the Silverlode; and in the same passage Haldir speaks of the dwellings of the Elves *down in Egladil, in the Angle between the waters. Egladil* occurs once again in FR, p. 389: 'There in the last end of Egladil upon the green grass the parting feast was held.' Robert Foster, in *The Complete Guide to Middle-earth*, defines *Naith* as 'That part of Lórien between Celebrant and Anduin', adding: 'The Naith included Egladil but was of greater extent'; and he defines *Egladil* as 'The heart of Lórien, the area between Anduin and Celebrant near their confluence. Called in Westron the Angle.'

6   *Nelen* (with changed application) and *Calennel* were presumably other possible names, beside *Naith* (see note 5) and *Calendil*, of the 'green spit' or 'Tongue', for which in FR no Elvish name is given.

7   *Green-tine*: translation of *Calendil*; Old English *tind* (cf. the *Tindrock*, Tol Brandir), later *tine*, spike, prong, tooth of a fork; now probably known chiefly of the branches of a deer's horn. Cf. *Silvertine*, one of the Mountains of Moria (*Celebdil*).

8   Cf. the outline on p. 250: the Company is told to 'beware of Fangorn Forest upon the Ogodrûth or Entwash'.

9   In the original text of the chapter the word is clearly spelt *Rhain*, while *Rain* is clear in outline (*a*). In this outline (*c*) it seems to be

FAREWELL TO LÓRIEN   289

Rhein at the first occurrence, with *Rhain* written above, but *Rhan* at the second and third; but the writing is very unclear and I read *Rhain* here also.

10   The showing of the Mirror now took place on the last evening in Lothlórien: see p. 259. Very probably the fair copy manuscript of 'Galadriel' was now in existence.

11   Obviously written at the same time as the rest of the text on the page is a disconnected passage that seems best placed here:

> At present that is not possible. Westward the servants of Sauron are far abroad and are ... the land ... the Baranduin and the Greyflood. Northward there are strange things happening which we do [not] understand clearly. The Dimrill [Dale] is filled with ash and smoke, and the mountains are troubled. You, Gimli and Legolas, would find it hard to make your way back even with a great company.
>
> 'What of the Beornings?' said Gimli.
>
> 'I do not know,' said Keleborn. 'They are far away. But I do not think you could now reach them'

The illegible passage could possibly be read (assuming rejection of the word 'are') as 'and have taken over the land between the Baranduin and the Greyflood.' See further note 12. – A part of Keleborn's speech here was afterwards given to Haldir, returned from the northern borders of Lórien to guide the Company from Caras Galadon: pp. 280, 285–6.

12   With this speech of Keleborn's compare that in the last chapter (pp. 248–9) which was marked for transference to the beginning of this. That passage was indeed quite different, in that Keleborn seemed almost to assume that Gimli and Legolas at least would not continue the Quest, and offered them both the hospitality of Lórien, while also advising Gimli that he might be able to make his way back through the land of the Beornings. Now (quite closely approaching the text of FR, p. 383) he offers a generalised invitation to remain to any of the Company who wish. But from what can be read of the underlying pencilled text it is seen that my father at first retained the passage transferred from the previous chapter in much the same form. The passage given in note 11 shows a change of mind: Gimli and Legolas would stand little chance if they tried to return.

13   The form *Ondor* (as written *ab initio*) occurs in the fifth version of 'The Council of Elrond' (p. 144 and note 6).

14   In a rejected form of this passage Keleborn takes up Ingold's remark that he doubted whether even Gandalf had had any clear plan:

> 'Maybe,' said Keleborn. 'Yet he knew that he would have to choose between East and West ere long. For the Great River lies between Mordor and Minas Tirith, and he knew, as do you

290   THE TREASON OF ISENGARD

Men at least of this Company, that it cannot be crossed on foot, and that the bridges of Osgiliath are broken down or in the hands of the Enemy since the late assault.'

15 On 'the Land of Seven Streams' see p. 177 and pp. 310–12.

16 Here and again below ('Ingold thanked Keleborn many times') *Ingold* was not changed to *Elfstone* because the passage was rejected before my father decided to abandon the name *Ingold* (see pp. 277–8).

17 This is the first mention of the great falls in Anduin (apart from a very doubtful hint of their existence referred to in note 1).

18 As the text was written Sam's attitude to the boats was different from what it had been in the previous version (where he felt 'a little alarm') and from what it is in FR:

Even Sam felt no alarm. Not long ago crossing a river by a ferry had seemed to him an adventure, but since then he had made too many weary marches and passed through too many dangers to worry about a journey in a light boat and the peril of drowning.

This was subsequently changed to the passage in FR.

19 The name of the Sword of Elendil reforged, *Branding*, was first devised here, and then written into 'The Ring Goes South' at the time of the reforging in Rivendell: 'and Elfstone gave it a new name and called it *Branding*' (p. 165). *Branding* is obviously an 'English' name (Old English *brand* 'sword'), and consorts with the names *Ingold*, *Elfstone*: see my father's notes on this subject cited on p. 277.

20 The drawing, in pencil, is now very faint. I have reinforced the drawing on a photocopy, and the reproduction is based on this.

21 In the original account of the first meeting of the Company with the Lord and Lady of the Galadrim (pp. 246 ff.) Galadriel addresses no words to Gimli. These first appear in the fair copy manuscript of 'Galadriel', where she says just as in FR (p. 371) 'Dark is the water of Kheled-zâram, and cold are the springs of Kibil-nâla...': a further indication that that text was already in existence.

22 Although *Eärendil* appears in the fair copy manuscript of 'Galadriel' (p. 266 note 34), *Eärendel* is the spelling here, both in the draft and in the fair copy. In my copies of these chapters made in 1942 I wrote *Eärendil* in Chapter XIX and *Eärendel* in Chapter XX.

23 The meaning of Galadriel's words to Trotter is plainly that *Elfstone* was his real name. The fact that the final version of the passage begins ' "Here is the gift of Keleborn to the leader of your Company," she said to Elfstone' – before the green gem, the Elfstone, has been mentioned – is decisive.

24 This change has often been remarked in earlier parts of this book.

FAREWELL TO LÓRIEN

291

The first examples of *Aragorn* > *Elfstone* are p. 80 note 17 (at Bree) and pp. 146 ff. (the fifth version of 'The Council of Elrond'). It was carried through the fair copy manuscripts of 'The Ring Goes South' (p. 165; including *Trotter* > *Elfstone*), and of the two 'Moria' chapters (pp. 176, 204, the change here being always *Trotter* > *Elfstone*).

25 With the statement in both these notes that Trotter's real name must not be 'Elvish' or 'Gnome-elvish' ('like Aragorn') contrast LR Appendix F ('Of Men'): 'The Dúnedain alone of all races of Men knew and spoke an Elvish tongue; for their forefathers had learned the Sindarin tongue, and this they handed on to their children as a matter of lore, changing little with the passing of the years', together with the footnote to this passage: 'Most of the names of the other men and women of the Dúnedain [i.e. those whose names were not Quenya], such as *Aragorn, Denethor, Gilraen* are of Sindarin form . . .'

26 In the first draft following this outline it is said of Gimli and Legolas that they 'had grown more and more friendly during their stay in Lothlórien'; in the following version (vii) that they 'had grown strangely friendly of late'. In FR they 'had now become fast friends'. – The complement of each boat is now as in FR, and not as in outline *(b)* to this chapter (p. 268), although there already Legolas and Gimli were placed together in the third boat.

27 In the fair copy manuscript of 'Farewell to Lórien' the text here is:

> On the further shores the woodlands still marched on southwards, as far as eye could see; but beyond the Tongue and upon the east side of the River all the boughs were bare. No mallorn-trees grew there.

The intended meaning seems clear: on the west bank beyond the confluence of Silverlode and Anduin, and all along the east bank of Anduin, there was still forest, but the trees not being mallorns they were leafless. So Keleborn says that as they go down the River they will find that 'the trees will fail', and they will come to a barren country. In the following manuscript, which I made (undated, but clearly following on my copy of 'Galadriel' dated 4 August 1942, p. 261), the sentence reads 'all the *banks* were bare'. This, I think, must have been a mere error (as also was 'the eye could see' for 'eye could see', retained in FR), since (in relation to 'the woodlands still marched on southwards') it is obviously a less well-chosen and somewhat ambiguous word: 'bare banks' suggests treeless banks, not wooded banks in winter.

Probably in order to correct this, but without consulting the earlier manuscript and so not seeing that it was an error, my father at some stage changed 'further shores' to 'further western shores' on my copy, but this still gives a confused picture. The

292 THE TREASON OF ISENGARD

text in FR (p. 387) removes the reference to the west shores of Anduin altogether, but retains the 'bare banks', which must therefore be interpreted as 'wooded banks in winter'.

28 In the earliest draft for the scene in the first 'Lothlórien' chapter in which the Company encounters the Elvish scouts near the falls of Nimrodel (p. 239 note 26) the lowest boughs of the trees 'were above the reach of Boromir's arms; but they had rope with them. Casting an end about a bough of the greatest of the trees Legolas ... climbed into the darkness.'

29 There is no more than the briefest outline sketch of Galadriel's 'refusal in the garden' in the original 'Lothlórien' chapter (p. 254), whereas in the fair copy the scene is fully formed (p. 260).

30 This reference to the once far greater extent of the Forest of Lothlórien is not found in FR (see note 34). Perhaps to be compared is *Unfinished Tales*, p. 236: 'the Nandorin realm of Lórinand [Lórien] ... was peopled by those Elves who forsook the Great Journey of the Eldar from Cuiviénen and settled in the woods of the Vale of Anduin; and it extended into the forests on both sides of the Great River, including the region where afterwards was Dol Guldur.'

31 *Ingold* here can only have been a slip for *Elfstone*.

32 The *Seventh River* has been mentioned in the fifth version of 'The Council of Elrond', p. 149. See pp. 310–12.

33 *Tharbad* has been named in the second version of 'The Ring Goes South', p. 164 and note 8.

34 These passages were actually written when the fair copy had reached this point. In the fair copy a page ends with the words 'you will find that for a while the trees march on. For of old the Forest of Lórien'. It was at this point that my father wrote the first of these passages, which was in fact simply the top of the next page of the fair copy. Deciding however to cut out the reference to the once much greater extent of Lothlórien, he struck out these words at the bottom of the preceding page in the fair copy, and wrote the second draft given here.

35 In the original workings the fourth line was *And by the mere of Tirion there grew the golden tree*. Another version of the fifth line was *Beneath the Hill of Ilmarin lies Aelinuial* – Aelinuial 'Lakes of Twilight' being the name of the region of great pools at the confluence of the rivers Aros and Sirion in Beleriand; cf. *the Shadow-meres* in the seventh line. In Bilbo's song at Rivendell occur the lines

> *beneath the hill of Ilmarin*
> *where glimmer in a valley sheer*
> *the lights of Elven Tirion*
> *the city on the Shadowmere*

and also *From Evereven's lofty hills* (see pp. 93, 98; FR pp. 247–8).

FAREWELL TO LÓRIEN

293

36 Boromir's words 'I have not myself been there' (referring to Fangorn), p. 282, were changed to 'I have not myself ever crossed Rohan.'

Additional Notes on the name Elfstone

A puzzling detail in the fair copy manuscript of this chapter is that while Trotter is referred to as *Trotter* throughout the narrative (see pp. 277–8), on the two occasions where he is named by Keleborn the name is *Ingold*. According to the explanation advanced on pp. 277–8 he should now, if called by his true name, be *Elfstone*. Moreover when we come to the scene of the Parting Gifts in this manuscript Galadriel's words to Trotter remain exactly as in the draft text on p. 276 ('Elfstone is your name ... and it is a fair name. I will add this gift of my own to match it'). How then can Keleborn call him *Ingold*?

The answer, I feel sure, is (as I have suggested, p. 267) that the fair copy manuscript itself grew in close relation to the drafts, where the names were not stable; and that it was not carefully revised in this point. In the first case, near the beginning of the chapter, where in the draft text Keleborn names 'Boromir of Ondor and Ingold the traveller' among those of the Company accustomed to boats, *Ingold* was changed subsequently to *Elfstone* (p. 273), but in the fair copy 'Ingold the traveller' remained unchanged. In the second case also, towards the end of the chapter, where in the draft Keleborn says 'it may be that Ingold and Boromir know the lands well enough to need no counsel' – which can only have been a casual inadvertence, note 31 – *Ingold* was corrected to *Elfstone* in the draft but not in the fair copy.

Later, my father corrected the second *Ingold* on the fair copy to *Aragorn* but did not notice the first. Without knowledge of the earlier texts this hasty and incomplete revision of names can produce incomprehensible tangles later on, when amanuenses such as myself simply followed what they saw before them: so in the next text of this chapter, a manuscript that I made (note 27), I wrote *Ingold* at the first occurrence and *Aragorn* at the second.

Galadriel's words at the gift-giving, *Elfstone is your name, Eldamir in the language of your fathers of old, and it is a fair name*, were struck out on the fair copy, with the curious result that in the manuscript that I wrote in 1942 Galadriel says: 'The blade that is drawn from this sheath shall not be stained or broken even in defeat. I will add this gift of my own to match it.' Later on, my father wrote on his fair copy manuscript (but not on the one that I made), against the description of Galadriel's gift and her words concerning it (retained exactly from the draft on p. 276): *Make this the reason for his taking the name Elfstone*; and after the words 'yet many things that now appear loathly will appear otherwise to you hereafter' he wrote in: 'And

294   THE TREASON OF ISENGARD

[Eldamir >] Elessar shall be a name for you hereafter, Elfstone in [the tongues of common speech >] your speech. Long may it be remembered.'

XV

THE FIRST MAP
OF THE LORD OF THE RINGS

Of the various small-scale maps of the western regions of Middle-earth that my father made, one is very easily seen to be the earliest; and I have no doubt at all that this was not only the earliest of the maps that are extant, but was in fact the first one that he made (other than the hasty sketches of particular regions published in Vol. VI).

This 'First Map' is a strange, battered, fascinating, extremely complicated and highly characteristic document. To gain understanding of it, its construction must first be described. It consists of a number of pages glued together and on to backing sheets, with a substantial new section of the map glued over an earlier part, and small new sections on top of that. The glue that my father used to stick down the large new portion was strong, and the sheets cannot be separated; moreover through constant folding the paper has cracked and broken apart along the folds, which are distinct from the actual joins of the map-sections. It was thus difficult to work out how the whole was built up; but I am confident that the following account is correct. In this account I refer to the figure 'Construction of the Original Map of The Lord of the Rings' on p. 297. This is a diagram and not a map, but I have inserted a few major features (the sea-coast, Anduin, Mirkwood, the rough outlines of the mountainous regions) as a guide.

The original element in the map consisted of two pages glued together along their vertical edges, and is the big rectangle framed in the figure by a black and white line and lettered **A**. East of the vertical line of squares numbered 22 it extended for a further three lines, but these were left blank.

A new section (made up of three portions glued together) extended the original map to North and West. (I say 'new section', since the paper is slightly different, and it was obviously added to what was already in existence.) This section is marked **B** on the figure and framed in double lines. It extends north of what is shown on the figure by five more horizontal lines of squares (A–E, 1–17).

As already mentioned, a third section, marked **C** on the figure and framed in double lines (squares O–W, 9–19), was superimposed on a part of the original map 'A', obliterating almost all of its southern half.

296   THE TREASON OF ISENGARD

This new section 'C' extends further south than did 'A', by three horizontal lines of squares (U–W, 9–19). Fortunately, a good part of this section has no backing paper, and by shining a bright light through it it has been possible to make out certain names and geographical features on the 'lost', southern half of 'A'. This is a difficult and confusing operation, and the results are very incomplete, but they are quite sufficient to show the essentials of what lies beneath 'C'. All that I can make out after long peering is shown on the map numbered III^A (p. 308).

The small rectangle lettered D on the figure and framed in dots was replaced over and over again, and is by far the most complex part of the map, as the region covered is also crucial in the story: from the Gap of Rohan and Isengard to Rauros and the mouths of Entwash.

The original element in the First Map

The First Map was my father's working map for a good while, and thus as it stood when he left it – as it stands now – it represents an evolution, rather than a fixed state of the geography. Determination of the sequence in which the map was built up does not, of course, demonstrate that names or features on 'A' are necessarily earlier than names or features on 'B' or 'C', since when 'A' + 'B' + 'C' were in being the map was a single entity. There are, however, certain clues to relative dating. The earliest layer of names is recognisable from the style of lettering, and also to some extent from the fact that my father at that stage used red ink for certain names, chiefly in the case of alternatives (as for example *Loudwater* in black ink, *Bruinen* beside it in red). On the directly visible part of 'A', virtually all of which is shown on Map II (p. 305), all the names are 'original' with the exception of the following: *Torfirion (Westermanton)*; *North Downs, Fornobel (Northbury)*; *Forodwaith (Northerland)*; *Enedwaith (Middlemarch)*; *Caradras*; *Nimrodel, Silverlode*; *Mirkwood the Great, Southern Mirkwood, Rhovanion*; *Rhosgobel, Dol Dúghul* (but *Dol Dúgol* in red ink, struck out, on M 15–16 is original); *Bardings*; *Sea of Rhûnaer* and *Rhûn*. Notable is the case of *Silverlode*: here the original name was *Redway*, struck out and changed in the same script to *Blackroot*, and this change is very precisely documented in the second version of 'The Ring Goes South', p. 166.

In this 'original layer' of names are a few others which I have not included in the redrawn map (II) since I could not find room for them without unnecessarily confusing it, the scale being so small: these are *Chetwood, Midgewater, Forest River, Woodmen, Wood Elves, Dale*. F.I. (so written in the original) on the Road east of Bree stands for *Forsaken Inn*. On the *River Rushdown (Rhimdad)* cf. V.384, VI.205, where the form is *Rhimdath* (also *Rhibdath*).

Three of the original names were changed, and I have entered the

THE FIRST MAP

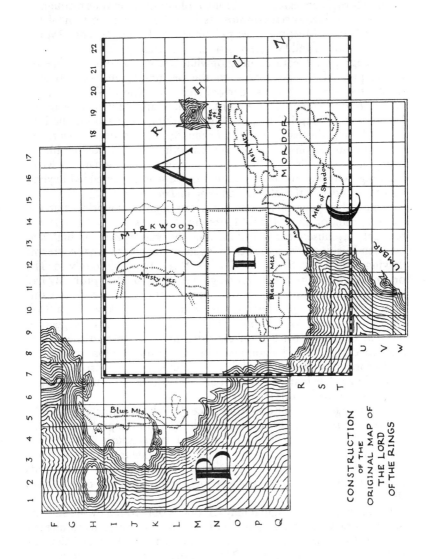

298   THE TREASON OF ISENGARD

later form. These are the river *Isen*, first written *Iren* on P 8 (Old English, 'iron', which varied with *Isen*); *Andrath* on L 8, where the original form is unclear since a broken fold of the map runs through it, but seems to have been *Amrath* (as in a draft for a portion of the chapter 'Many Meetings', see pp. 69–70 and note 7); and *Anduin* (M–N 13, Maps II and IV^A), first written *Andon* (see p. 299).

Of geographical features, most of what is represented on the directly visible part of 'A' goes back to the beginning, and of course a substantial part of that was derived from the Map of Wilderland in *The Hobbit*. Elements that are not 'original' are the highlands in the North-west of Map II (I 8–9, J 7–8); the markings representing the Iron Hills (though the name itself is original); the Sea of Rhûnaer, the mountainous region to the South-west of it, the river flowing into it from the Iron Hills, and the lower course of the (unnamed) River Running, which as the map was first made scarcely extended beyond the eastern edge of the Wilderland Map in *The Hobbit*.

Some other geographical features are slightly doubtful, but the western arm of the Misty Mountains across squares I 10–11 was probably a subsequent addition, and the vast region of highland between Mirkwood and the Sea of Rhûnaer, together with the streams flowing from it into the Dead Marshes (N 16), almost certainly so. The original siting of the name *Dol Dúgol* (M 15; see p. 296) probably had nothing to do with these highlands (at the first occurrence of the name on p. 178 Gandalf speaks of Sauron's 'older and lesser dwelling at Dol-Dúgol in Southern Mirkwood'): faint traces of green colour suggest to me that originally Mirkwood extended much further to the South-east, covering L 15 and a good part of M–N 15–16, and that this region of the forest was erased. The hills that emerge onto N 15 from the area which I have left blank on Map II are also additional: this region will be discussed later in this chapter.

The river Isen is a bit doubtful, since though the name as originally written (*R. Iren*, see above) clearly belongs with the primary layer of names, the coastline as drawn had no river-mouth opposite the off-shore island on P 7, and a pencilled indentation was made subsequently. The same is true of the unnamed river (afterwards Lefnui) to the south of Isen, whose mouth was drawn in on R 8 (Map III).

On the part of the original map 'A' that is obliterated by the sticking on of portion 'C' some names and features can be seen, as already described (p. 296; Map III^A). It is clear that at that stage relatively little was entered on the map. Those in black ink can be readily seen, and I do not think that there were any others beyond *Land of Mor-dor*, *Minas Morgol* (with *Ithil* in red ink), *Osgiliath*, *Minas Tirith* (with *Anor* in red ink), *Blackroot > Silverlode* (see under Map II on p. 306), *Tolfalas*, *Bay of Belfalas*, and *Ethir-andon* (as it seems to have been written, before being changed to *-anduin*, as on the northern part

THE FIRST MAP

of 'A'). *Dead Marshes* is in red ink; other names seem to have been entered in red chalk (*Land of Ond*) or pencil. The actual sites of Minas Morgol and the Dark Tower cannot be seen, nor can the last two letters of *Palath Nen[ui]* (on which see p. 268 and note 4); and the mountain-chains are extremely hard to make out. The bits of the mountains of Mordor in the North-west that I have been able to distinguish with certainty suggest however a disposition essentially the same as that in 'C'. The occurrence of *Dol [?Amroth]* at this stage is notable.

It is thus clear that, whenever the First Map was actually begun, it had reached the stage seen in the original 'layer' of portion 'A' before the time we have now reached in the texts, and also that much of that layer belongs to this period of the work: many of these original names on the map emerge first in the texts given in this book – for example *Sarn Ford* (p. 9), *Entish Land* (p. 10), *Mitheithel* (p. 14), *Bruinen* (p. 14), *Minas Tirith* (p. 115), *Minas Morgol* (p. 116), *Minas Anor, Minas Ithil* (p. 119), *Bay of Belfalas* (p. 119), *Tharbad* (p. 164), etc. *Andon (Ethir-andon)* was a form preceding *Anduin* which never occurred in the texts: *Anduin* appears in the fifth version of 'The Council of Elrond' where the name *Sirvinya* 'New Sirion' appears in the third (pp. 119, 144).

The 1943 Map

In 1943 (see *Letters* nos. 74 and 98) I made a large elaborate map in pencil and coloured chalks, companion to a similar one of the Shire (see VI.107, 200). It was the First Map that I had in front of me when I made it. My map is thus of historical value in showing what the state of the First Map was at that time – especially in respect of names, for though I was as faithful to the courses of rivers and coasts as I have attempted to be 45 years later, I used pictorial forms for the mountains and hills, which are less precise.[1]

The redrawn maps in this book

In *Unfinished Tales* I referred (pp. 13–14) to my father's maps of *The Lord of the Rings* as 'sketch-maps'; but this was an ill-chosen word, and in respect of the First Map a serious misnomer. All parts of the First Map were made with great care and delicacy until a late stage of correction, and it has an exceedingly 'Elvish' and archaic air. The difficulties of interpretation do not arise from any roughness in the original execution, but in part from subsequent alteration in very small space, and in part from its present condition: it is wrinkled, creased, and broken from constant use, so that connections are lost,

300   THE TREASON OF ISENGARD

and many names and markings added in pencil are so blurred and faint as to be almost invisible. My father made a good deal of use of pencil and coloured chalks: mountain-chains are shaded in grey, rivers (for the most part) represented in blue chalk, marshland and woodland in shades of green (Mirkwood is conveyed by little curved marks in green chalk, suggestive of treetops); and this colouring is rubbed and faded (it is often very difficult to be sure of the courses of rivers). In regions where the development of the story caused substantial alteration in the geography, notably where the hills and mountains were much changed and overlaid by new representations, there are so many lines and strokes and dots that it is impossible to feel certain what my father intended, or even to make out what there is on the paper.[2]

Inevitably, the attempt to redraw the map involves more than merely copying (and since it must be represented in black and white, different symbolisation, notably of wooded regions, must to some extent be used, or else dispensed with); to redraw is in such a case to interpret. My redrawings are therefore to an extent simpler, less subtle, and more decisive in detail, than the original, and of course uniform in appearance, since they have all been made at one time and with the same pens. These maps are therefore quite insufficient in themselves as a substitute for the original, and the discussion of the redrawn maps is an integral part of my attempt to present this remarkable document.

The major question to resolve, however, arose from the fact that this map was a continuous development, evolving in terms of, and reacting upon, the narrative it accompanied. To redraw it involved a decision on what to include and what to exclude. But to attempt to limit its content to the names and features that might be supposed to have been present at a particular time (in terms of the narrative) would involve a host of complexities and dubious or arbitrary decisions. It was clearly far better to represent the map in a developed form; and except in the case of Map III[A] (where a large part of the original map 'A' was early abandoned) and of maps IV[A–E] (where there are six successive and distinct versions) I have therefore taken my 1943 map as a conveniently fixed and definite terminus, though not without a number of exceptions. It is to be understood throughout the following discussion that everything on my redrawn versions in this book appears in that form on the 1943 map unless something is said to the contrary. Many of the subsequent alterations made to the First Map or to the 1943 map or to both are however mentioned.

The map-squares of the original are of 2 centimetre side (on my 1943 map the squares were enlarged to 4 centimetres). No scale is given; but a later and much rougher map, also ruled in squares of this size, gives 2 centimetres = 100 miles, and this was clearly the scale of the First Map also.

THE FIRST MAP   301

Maps I and I^A

Map I, with the extreme North and North-east on I^A, gives virtually the whole of the added portion 'B' (see the figure on p. 297): thus 'B' extends from A to H, 1–17, and from I to Q, 1–6 and a portion of 7. The section marked off on the right-hand side of Map I is the left-hand side of the original portion 'A', and this is duplicated on Map II.

This portion 'B' received no emendation whatsoever after its first drawing except in one minor point. The great highlands (afterwards called the Hills of Evendim) between the river Lune and the North Downs certainly belong with the rest of 'B', and were extended into square J 7 of 'A', already in existence; and the North Downs were entered on 'A' at the same time (for the place-names see under Map II).

This is the only map that shows the far northern coast, and the vast bay shaped like a human head and face (E–G 7–9, on map I^A). In view of Appendix A (I. iii) to *The Lord of the Rings*, where there is a reference to 'the great cape of Forochel that shuts off to the north-west the immense bay of that name', it is clear that this bay is 'the Icebay of Forochel' (see *Unfinished Tales* p. 13 and footnote) – although on a subsequent map my father's the much smaller southern bay (H 6–7) is very clearly labelled and limited 'the Icebay of Forochel', as it is on my map published with *The Lord of the Rings*[3]. No names are given in this region on the First Map, but subsequently my father pencilled in *North Sea* across G 4–5, and this I entered on my 1943 map, though inadvertently omitted on Map I.

On the islands of *Tol Fuin* and *Himling* see p. 124 and note 18. – The 'sea-lines' are not present in the original, but they are marked on parts 'A' and 'C' and I have therefore extended them throughout. – I cannot explain the wavy line that extends roughly parallel to the coast from H 4 to K 3[4].

It will be seen on Map I that the distinction between the North and South Havens (here *Forlorn* and *Harlorn* for later *Forlond* and *Harlond*), situated in bays of the Gulf of Lune, and *Mithlond*, the Grey Havens, at the head of the gulf, was already present (but see p. 423).

With this first representation of Ered Luin, the Blue Mountains, in the context of *The Lord of the Rings* cf. the revision of the end of *The Fall of Númenor* cited on pp. 122–3. Very notable is the appearance of *Belegost* (L 5), which is marked on the 1943 map also, but on no subsequent one. The Dwarf-cities of the Blue Mountains were not originally marked on the second *Silmarillion map* (V.409, 411), but were put in roughly later: Belegost being situated on the eastern side of the mountains somewhat north of Mount Dolmed and the pass by which the Dwarf-road crossed them. Cf. *Unfinished Tales* p. 235:

There were and always remained some Dwarves on the eastern side of Ered Lindon, where the very ancient mansions of Nogrod and

302   THE TREASON OF ISENGARD

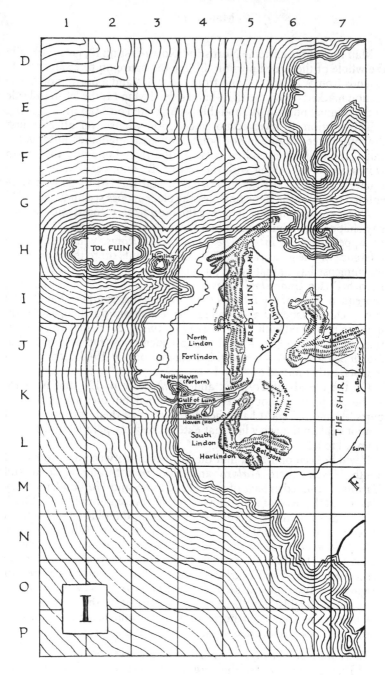

THE FIRST MAP

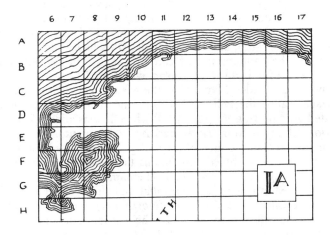

304   THE TREASON OF ISENGARD

Belegost had been – not far from Nenuial; but they had transferred most of their strength to Khazad-dûm.

The White Towers on the Tower Hills are represented by three dots in a line (K 6). – The letter F on square M 7 of Map I and the letters ITH on square H 11 of Map I^A belong to *Forodwaith*, on which see under Map II.

Map II

This redrawing, as will be seen by comparison with the diagram on p. 297, covers almost all the still directly visible part of 'A', the only areas not included being the almost blank squares I–T 20 eastwards and Q–T 7–8 in the South-west, which is mostly sea (and is shown on Map III). It also covers the two top lines of squares of the superimposed portion 'C' (O–P 9–19), and the rectangle 'D', which is here left blank apart from the continuation of certain names. On the left Map II overlaps with Map I and at the bottom with Map III.

I have noted under Map I that the eastern end of the highlands afterwards called the Hills of Evendim and the North Downs were extended onto portion 'A' (I 8–9, J 7–8) when 'B' was added. The names *Torfirion* (changed from *Tarkilmar*) or *Westermanton* occur in the fifth version of 'The Council of Elrond', p. 144; on the First Map my father afterwards scribbled *Annúminas* here, but *Torfirion (Westermanton)* appears on my 1943 map. The name originally written here on the First Map was in fact *Fornobel*, but this seems to have been changed at once, and *Fornobel (Northbury)* written against the habitation on the North Downs. The earlier name for this was *Osforod, the Northburg* (pp. 120–1, 129), but *Fornobel* appears by emendation in the fifth version of 'The Council of Elrond' (p. 147). Here my father scribbled in the later name *Fornost*, but the 1943 map still has *Fornobel (Northbury)*.

Most of the names and features on the 'A' part of Map II are original, and have been commented on already (p. 296). On the significance of *Greyflood or Seventh River* see pp. 310–12. *Gwathlo* is certainly an original name, though it has not appeared in any text.

The various additions made to 'A' (listed on p. 296) were made in the same spidery lettering and very fine lines characteristic of the superimposed section 'C'. The name *Enedwaith (Middlemarch)* was written across 'A' and 'C' after 'C' had been stuck on, and *Forod-(waith) (Northerland)* belongs with it (though *-waith* was a further and rougher addition). *Enedwaith* here denotes a much greater region than it afterwards became (the lands between Greyflood and Isen): the original conception, it is seen, was of a great 'triad', *Forodwaith* or *Northerland*, bounded on the South-east by the Greyflood, *Enedwaith* or *Middlemarch* between Greyflood and Anduin, and *Haradwaith* or

THE FIRST MAP

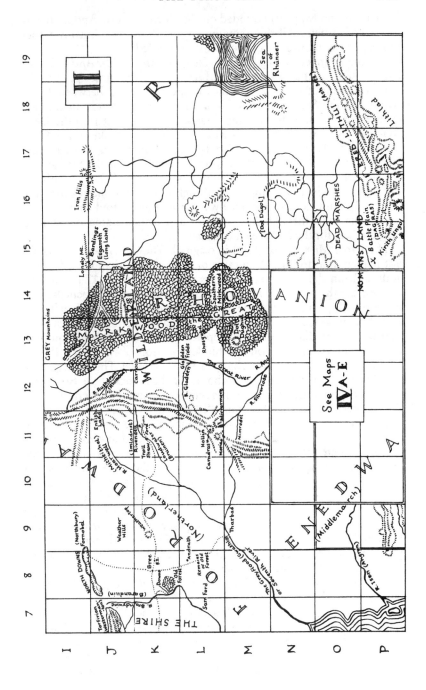

306   THE TREASON OF ISENGARD

Sutherland (on Map III) bounded on the North-west by Anduin (or by the river Harnen). All this remains on the 1943 map, but my father wrote on that map against Forodwaith: *(or Eriador)*.

On the changed names *Iren* > *Isen*, *Amrath* (?) > *Andrath* (not entered at all on the 1943 map), and *Andon* > *Anduin*, see p. 298.

I have mentioned (p. 298) that the great highland between Mirkwood and the Sea of Rhûnaer was almost certainly not an original element of 'A', and the streams flowing down from it into the Dead Marshes (N 16) were continued with the same pen-strokes onto 'C' (O 16), which had already been added. (Of this highland region there is no trace on my 1943 map: all this area is a pure blank, though the streams on N 16 are shown.) Within the outline of these highlands pencilled markings showing lines of high hills or mountains are now extremely faint, and disrupted by a large cracked fold that extends across the map through line M; and a pencilled name on M 16 is illegible save for the initial element *East*. . . .

The name *Mirrormere* (L 11) is original. The Misty Mountains are not named, nor are the Mountains of Moria other than *Caradras* (an addition); on the 1943 map appears also *Kelebras* (p. 174 note 21), but not the third peak (*Fanuiras*). Afterwards my father pencilled on the First Map the final names *Celebdil* and *Fanuidol* (so spelt). As already mentioned (p. 296) *Silverlode* was a correction (in the style of portion 'C') of *Blackroot*, itself replacing *Redway*; and the southern river *Blackroot* appears on the hidden portion of 'A' (Map III^A) – where however it also was changed to *Silverlode*! The change here should have been the other way about: for the names of the two rivers were transposed, the northern 'Blackroot' becoming 'Silverlode', and the southern 'Silverlode' becoming 'Blackroot' (see p. 177 and note 1, and p. 241 note 36). But there is no doubt that the first name written against the southern river was *Blackroot*, and that this was then changed to *Silverlode*. Subsequently my father struck out *Silverlode* and wrote *stet* against *Blackroot*: I suppose therefore that this was either a passing hesitation, when he thought for a moment of going back on his previous decision to change the names, or else a mere slip.

Entish Land (J 11) is original, but is absent from the 1943 map; a later note against this on the First Map says: 'Alter *Entish Lands* to [*Trollfells* > *Bergrisland* >] *Ettenmoor*'. This would seem to be the place where *Ettenmoor(s)* was first devised, but see p. 65 note 32. *Bergrisland* is from Old Norse *berg-risi* 'hill-giant'.

On the two sites of *Dol Dúgol (Dol Dúghul)* see p. 298. For the emergence of the name *Rhosgobel* see p. 164.

Against *Lonely Mt.* is pencilled *Dolereb*, and also *Erebor* with a query (neither of these names appear on the 1943 map). *Erebor* first occurs in the fifth version of 'The Council of Elrond', p. 142 and note 2. The Grey Mountains and the Iron Hills were originally marked only as names, but my father afterwards drew in the latter, and also rather

THE FIRST MAP

vague pencillings to show a mountainous region to west and south-west of the Sea of Rhûnaer; these features are shown on the 1943 map, as also are the river flowing from the Iron Hills and the eastward extension of the River Running to join it (K 16–17), though on the 1943 map the River Running is very much the major stream and that from the Iron Hills a slender tributary. *Rhûn* was an addition in the 'C' style. The name *Rhûnaer* (i.e. 'Eastern Sea'), also an addition to 'A' (as was the Sea itself), is unclear on the First Map on account of a crack in the paper, but is confirmed by its appearance on the 1943 map and on a later map of my father's, where, though the Sea itself is not included, there is a direction that the River Running flows into the *Sea of Rhûnaer*. On the map published in *The Lord of the Rings*, it is the *Sea of Rhûn*, and there are three references to the *Sea of Rhûn* in Appendix A (see also p. 333 in the next chapter). The forest bordering the Sea of Rhûnaer (L 19) extends on the First Map round the north-eastern point of the Sea and down its eastern shore (L–M 20), and against it my father pencilled *Neldoreth*; no name for the forest is marked on the 1943 map, which ends at the same point eastwards as does Map II in this book.[5] The island in the Sea is coloured green on the First Map, and on the 1943 map is marked as wooded.

The name *Bardings* on J 15 was a pencilled addition that appears on the 1943 map; the pencilled addition of *Eotheod* on I 12, however, does not (on the regions where the Éothéod dwelt, at first between the Carrock and the Gladden Fields and afterwards in the region of the source-streams of Anduin, Greylin and Langwell, see *Unfinished Tales* pp. 288, 295).

For features marked on the south-east corner of Map II, O–P 15–19, see under Map III.

Maps III^A and III

The line of squares P 7–19 overlaps with Map II. Map III contains no portion of the original map 'A' except for the two lines of squares on the left, P–T 7–8, where the river (afterwards Lefnui) on Q 8–9, P 9 seems certainly a later addition. Map III^A shows the names and geographical features of the original map 'A' that I can make out through the overlay (pp. 298–9). Granting the difficulty of seeing what was there, it is clear, I think, that when this part of 'A' was made the story itself had not advanced into these regions, and only a few names and features were entered. Comparison of Maps III^A and III will show that in the second version Ethir Anduin was moved south and east, becoming a vast delta, and the course of Anduin was entirely changed, flowing in a great eastward bend between Nindalf and the Mouths, whereas originally its course was almost in a straight line south-south-west. Concomitantly with this, Minas Tirith and Osgiliath were moved

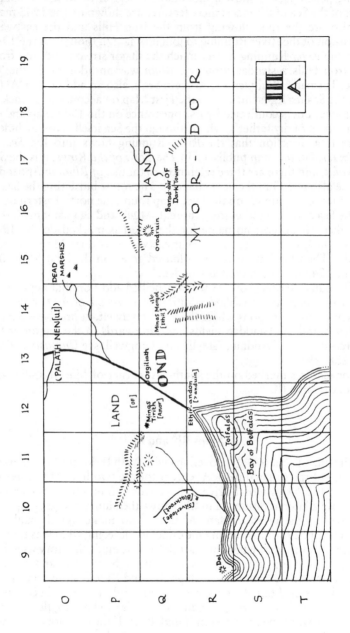

THE FIRST MAP 309

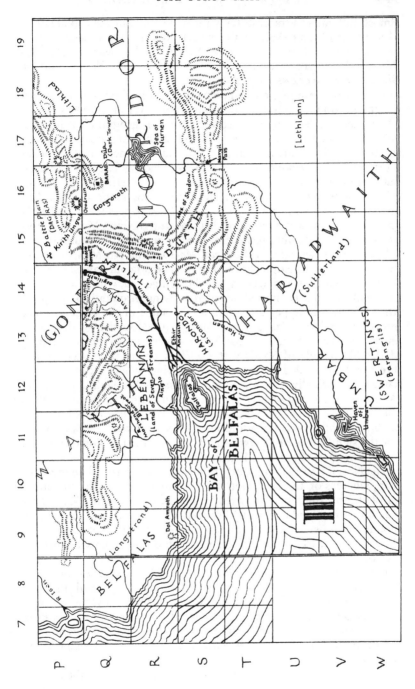

310   THE TREASON OF ISENGARD

almost 200 miles to the east. Only the name and not the actual site of Minas Morgol can be seen on the underlying map, but it seems to have been a good deal further to the east of Osgiliath than was subsequently the case.[6] On other features of Map III[A] see pp. 298–9, and on *Blackroot > Silverlode* see p. 306.

Turning to the superimposed portion 'C' of the First Map (of which the uppermost horizontal line of squares O 9–19 is found on Map II), as I have said the lettering and representation of geographical features were here done with an exceptionally fine pen-nib; at the same time it is scarcely possible to distinguish earlier and later elements by this means – for example, *Harondor (S. Gondor)* is obviously later than *Ondor*, but there is nothing in the appearance of the lettering to show this. (*Ondor* here replaces *Ond* of the underlying map; for the first appearance of *Ondor* in the *Lord of the Rings* papers see p. 144.) My 1943 map is however effectively identical with the First Map in almost every feature, and only a few points need to be specially noticed here.

I postpone discussion of the *Dead Marshes* and *No Man's Land* to the notes on the development of Map IV. The original name *Dagras* of the Battle Plain was replaced in pencil by *Dagorlad*, which appears on the 1943 map but is omitted on the redrawing through lack of space. *Kirith Ungol* still appears in 1943 as the name of the chief entrance into Mordor, but I placed *Minas Morgul* (Q 15) further to the north, and so further north than Minas Tirith – very near to the northern tip of the Mountains of Shadow (P 15). This change complied with a direction by pencilled arrow on the First Map (where incidentally the name was originally spelt *Minas Morgol*, as on the overlaid portion of 'A' beneath). Among several changes that my father made to the 1943 map in these regions he replaced Minas Morgul in its original position on Q 15. Another was the addition of *Ephel* to *Duath* on both maps. For the significance of the two small circles on either side of the *n* of *Kirith Ungol* on P 15 see p. 349 note 41.

The *Nargil Pass* (S 17) is clearly represented and lettered on the 1943 map, whereas on the First Map it was scribbled in very hastily and is hardly legible (but apparently reads *Narghil Pass*). *Mount Mindolluin* was similarly added in roughly between Minas Tirith and the original mountain shown in the north-east corner of Q 13, but is carefully shown on mine (see note 1); the name is left off the redrawing through lack of space.

On the 1943 map only, my father moved *Dol Amroth* from R 9 to R 11 (south of the mouth of the river Morthond); on both maps he changed *Belfalas* to *Anfalas*; on the First Map only, he changed *Anarion* on Q 14 to *Anórien*, and altered *Land of Seven Streams* to *Land of Five Streams*; and on the 1943 map he struck out *Anarion* and *Lebennin (Land of Seven Streams)* and re-entered *Lebennin* in the place of *Anarion* on Q 14.

This question of the southern rivers is very curious. In the original

THE FIRST MAP   311

draft of Gandalf's story of his adventures to the Council of Elrond (p. 132) Radagast told him that he would scarcely come to Saruman's abode 'before the Nine cross the Seven Rivers', which in the next version (p. 149) becomes 'before the Nine have crossed the seventh river'. In 'the Lord of Moria' (p. 177) Boromir advises that the Company should 'take the road to my land that I followed on my way hither: *through Rohan and the country of Seven Streams*. Or we could go on far into the South and come at length round the Black Mountains, and crossing the rivers Isen and Silverlode [> Blackroot] enter Ond from the regions nigh the sea.' I have remarked there that this can only mean that the Company would pass through 'the country of Seven Streams' if they went to Minas Tirith by way of Rohan, north of the Black Mountains. On the other hand, in 'Farewell to Lórien' (p. 282) Boromir on his journey to Rivendell 'went round by the south about the Black Mountains and up the Greyflood – or the Seventh River as we call it.' And earlier in the same chapter (p. 272) he says that he was born 'between the mountains and the sea, on the borders of the Land of Seven Streams.'

The naming of Greyflood *the Seventh River* is an original element of the oldest portion 'A' of the First Map, and is surely to be associated with *the Land of Seven Streams*, especially in view of the change in the drafts of Gandalf's tale to the Council of Elrond, cited above, from 'the Seven Rivers' to 'the seventh river'. But what then were these rivers? I am certain that there is no river save Blackroot (with a tributary) west of Ethir Anduin on the hidden part of 'A' (Map III^A). Even if Anduin itself is counted, and the tributary of Blackroot, and if the unnamed river (later Lefnui) is supposed a very early addition, Isen is the fifth and Greyflood the sixth. I have not been able to find any solution to this puzzle.

With the replacement portion 'C' the nature of the puzzle changes. *Lebennin (Land of Seven Streams)* is a small region, and it is notable that seven rivers are indeed shown here (Map III, Q–R 11–14): Morthond and an unnamed tributary; Ringlo and an unnamed tributary; an unnamed river that enters Anduin above the Mouths; and an unnamed river entering Anduin further up its course (R 14), formed of two tributaries one of which flows from Minas Tirith.[7] But Greyflood, some 450 miles to the north-west of the most westerly of these seven streams, remains *the Seventh River*.[8] A further twist to the problem arises from the fact that *Lebennin* does not in any case mean 'Seven Streams', but 'Five Streams'. The original Quenya word for 'five' was *lemin* (I.246); and in the *Etymologies* (V.368) are found the Quenya word *lempe* 'five' and the Noldorin word *lheben* (cf. Q. *lepse*, N. *lhebed*, 'finger'). *Ossiriand* was the Land of Seven Rivers (cf. the *Etymologies*, V.379, Quenya *otso*, Noldorin *odog* 'seven'). As noted above, my father afterwards changed 'Seven' to 'Five' on the First Map, and in *The Lord of the Rings* the name *Lebennin* means 'Five

312   THE TREASON OF ISENGARD

Streams': cf. *The Return of the King* V.1 (p. 22), 'fair Lebennin with its five swift streams'.

A later map of my father's does not solve these problems, but carries a note that is very interesting in this connection. When this map was made *Lebennin* had been moved to its final position. The note reads:

Rivers of Gondor
Anduin
   From East
Ithilduin or *Duin Morghul*
Poros   Boundary
   From West
Ereg   First
Sirith   The 5 rivers
Lameduin (of Lamedon) with tributaries   of Lebennin
   Serni (E.) and *Kelos* (W.)
Ringlo, *Kiril*, *Morthond* and *Calenhir* that
   all flow into Cobas Haven
Lhefneg   Fifth
In counting only the mouths are counted: *Ereg* 1, *Sirith* 2, *Lameduin* 3, *Morthond* 4, *Lhefneg* 5, *Isen* 6, *Gwathlo* 7

Thus in relation to the final geography of the region:
- *Ereg* (the unnamed river on the First Map flowing into Anduin on R 14) became *Erui*.
- *Sirith* (the unnamed river on the First Map flowing into Anduin on R 13) remained.
- *Lameduin* here has tributaries *Serni* and *Kelos*, which evidently constitute Lameduin from their confluence. On the First Map Lameduin is *Ringlo*, with unnamed tributaries. In the final form Lameduin became *Gilrain*, with its tributary *Serni*, while *Kelos* was transferred to become a tributary of Sirith.[9]
- Of the four rivers *Ringlo*, *Kiril*, *Morthond*, and *Calenhir* 'that all flow into Cobas Haven' the first three only are named on this map; but though the *Calenhir* is not, it is shown as an unnamed river, most westerly of the four, flowing eastwards from Pinnath Gelin. These four rivers join together not far from the coast, and flow (as *Morthond*, according to the list of river-mouths above) into the sea in the bay north of Dol Amroth, which is named *Cobas Haven*.[10] In the final geography this configuration remains, although *Calenhir* is lost.
- *Lhefneg* became *Lefnui*.
- *Isen* remained.
- *Gwathlo* or *Greyflood* is on this map given an alternative name *Odotheg*, changed to *Odothui* (i.e. 'seventh').

For the first appearance in the texts of the *Mountains of Shadow*

THE FIRST MAP

313

and the *Valley of Gorgoroth* see p. 144; cf. also the *Gap of Gorgoroth*, p. 208. *Kirith Ungol* ('the passes of Mordor') appears in 'Farewell to Lórien', p. 283. For *Lithlad* ('Plain of Ash') see pp. 208, 213, and for the first occurrence of *Orodruin* p. 28. *Lothlann* (U 17–18) was apparently an original name on portion 'C' of the First Map, but it was struck out; whether it appeared on the 1943 map cannot be said, for the bottom right-hand corner of that map was torn off. *Lothlann* ('wide and empty') derives from *The Silmarillion*: see the Index to Vol. V.

On *Haradwaith (Sutherland)* see pp. 304, 306. The name *Swertings* appears in *The Two Towers*, IV.3 (p. 255), where Sam speaks of 'the big folk down away in the Sunlands. Swertings we call 'em in our tales.' *Barangils* is found later as a name in Gondor for the men of the Harad.

Maps IV^A to IVE

We come now to what is by far the most complex part of the First Map, the rectangle of fifteen squares (N–P 10–14) lettered 'D' on the figure on p. 297, and left blank on Map II. This section was redrawn and replaced many times.

IV^A

In Map IV^A the uppermost line of squares N 10–14 is part of the original 'A' portion of the First Map, whereas lines O and P are part of the superimposed portion 'C'; but I believe that most of the features and names shown on the line N were added in after portion 'C' had been glued on, and that there is no need to trouble with this distinction. The little that can be seen (and very little seems to have been marked in) on lines O and P of the original 'A' portion is shown on Map III^A, where the line of Anduin below Palath Nenui (Wetwang) was entirely different (see p. 307).

The vertical line of squares N–P 15 on the right-hand side of Map IV^A is repeated from Map II, and is merely added to make the conjunction easier to follow (it includes also the remainder of the name *Border Hills*, which was later struck out). The shaded area on N–P 10–11 is invisible owing to a later pasted overlay (see under Map IV^D below).

I think it is certain that the hills marked *Green Hills* and those marked *Emyn Rhain (Border Hills)* were put in at the same time, at the making of portion 'C'; but I do not think that they were named at once. This matter is rather complex, but it reveals, as I believe, an interesting aspect of the relation between my father's narrative writing and his maps. I set out first the various statements made in the earliest texts of the chapter 'Farewell to Lórien' about the country through which the Anduin flowed south of Lothlórien.

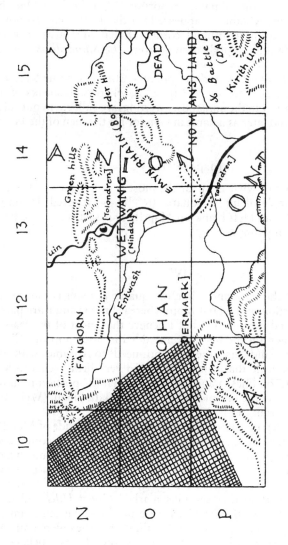

THE FIRST MAP

315

(i) The River *winds among the Border Hills, Emyn Rain*. They must decide their course there, *because the Wetwang lies before them* (p. 268).

(ii) They pass into *the Rhain Hills where the River winds in deep ravines* (p. 269).

(iii) The Company lands (on Tolondren, the island in Anduin) and *goes up into the Rhain Hills* (p. 269).

(iv) The Company lands on Tolondren. . . . They cross to the East bank and *go up into the Green Hills (or Emyn Rhain?)* (p. 269).

(v) Elves of Lórien shall go with the Company *as far as the Green Hills where the River winds among deep ravines* (with *Rhain* written above *Green*) (p. 271).

(vi) Keleborn speaks of *the falls of Rhain where the River runs out of the ravines in the Green Hills* (p. 273).

(vii) Keleborn says that the River will pass through *a bare and barren country before it flows into the sluggish region of Nindalf*, where the Entwash flows in. *Beyond that are Emyn Rhain the Border Hills* . . . The Company should leave the River *where the isle of Tolondren stands in the stream above the falls of Rosfein* and cross the Entwash above the marshes (pp. 281–2).

(Here the Border Hills are displaced southwards, *beyond* Tolondren and the Nindalf. Keleborn's words were rewritten to say:)

(viii) the River will pass through *a bare and barren country, winding among the Border Hills before it falls down into the sluggish region of Nindalf* (p. 281).

There is clearly a doubt or confusion here as to the Green Hills and the Border Hills, and different views of how the Border Hills relate to Tolondren, the falls, and the Nindalf or Wetwang. I do not think that any definite conclusion can be drawn from these texts taken by themselves, but from the Map IV^A I believe that the development can be tolerably well understood.

The line of hills extending on either side of Anduin (N 12–14), and the hills rising to east and south-east of these (N–O 14–15), were drawn in at the same time and in the same style, characteristic of portion 'C', with outlining in short strokes. The lettering, I feel sure, was put in subsequently. My belief is that these ranges were a datum already provided, illustrating my father's words in his letter to Naomi Mitchison of 25 April 1954 (*Letters* no. 144): 'I wisely started with a map, *and made the story fit*'; and that the confusing statements in the earliest 'Farewell to Lórien' papers show him moving towards a satisfactory relation between the evolving narrative, his vision of the lands about Anduin in these regions, and what was drawn on the map (i.e. these ranges of hills).

316   THE TREASON OF ISENGARD

At one stage he decided that the hills should be the Green Hills and the Border Hills respectively. He wrote in these names, and at the same time extended the latter (more roughly, and with dotted outlines) southwest, so as to embrace both sides of Anduin (O 14, P 13–14). This perhaps illustrates Keleborn's words in extract (vii) above, where the Border Hills are south of Tolondren and the Nindalf. But in the margin of the First Map he noted: 'Place [?Tolondren a little more south] and *combine Green Hills with Border Hills*, and make Nindalf or Wetwang all round mouths of Entwash.' The last remark probably refers to the curious feature seen on Map IV^A, that the Wetwang lies distinctly northward of the mouths; that concerning Tolondren is no doubt reflected in the striking out of the name on N 13 and its reintroduction in a more southerly position (P 13, at the confluence with Anduin of a stream flowing in from the Black Mountains), where it was again struck out. This bit of the map had clearly become in need of redrawing.

It may be noted incidentally that the stream from the Black Mountains rises in an oval lake on P 11; and it seems perfectly clear that the Morthond rises in this lake also: see Map III, Q 11.

Map IV^B

What now happened to the geography is clear. In the extract (viii) above Keleborn says that the River will pass through 'a bare and barren country, winding among the Border Hills before it falls down into the sluggish region of Nindalf.' In the draft (ii) given on p. 282 he says that 'the trees will fail, and you will come to a barren country. There the river flows in stony vales among high moors, until it comes to the tall island of Tolondren' (largely preserved in FR, p. 389). Thus the *Brown Lands* emerge, in place of the original Green Hills, on Map IV^B, which is a detached slip of 9 squares that was never pasted in. Here Tolondren (but no longer so named) is definitively in the more southerly position, and in relation to this the course of Entwash is greatly changed, bending in a great southward sweep, *so that the Wetwang is still south of Tolondren and the falls* (here called *Dant Ruinel*, this name being struck out: *Rauros* was later added in pencil).[11] In fact, the new course of Entwash partly takes over that of the unnamed river in IV^A, flowing in from the Black Mountains (P 12–13). The southwestward extension of the Emyn Rhain, lightly entered on IV^A, is now called *Sarn Gebir* and strongly reinforced (cf. Keleborn's reference to 'the bleak hills of Sarn-gebir', p. 283), but this was done very coarsely, clearly after the little slip was first drawn; on account of the heavy lines marking these hills other markings are difficult to interpret, but it can be seen that there is now a large lake (coloured blue), and a large island in the lake named the *Isle of*

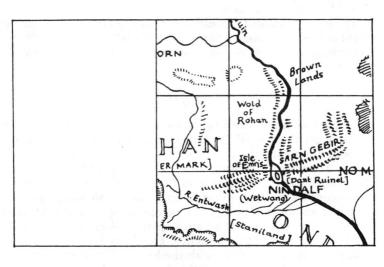

IV B

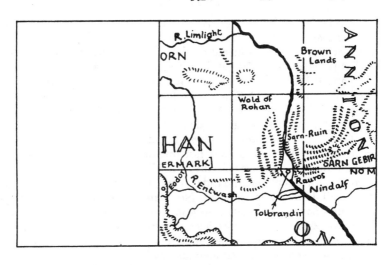

IV C

318   THE TREASON OF ISENGARD

Emris,[12] while on either shore are dark spots, no doubt representing Amon Hen and Amon Lhaw.

The name *[Staniland]* beneath *Ond(or)* was entered in pencil. The Wold of Rohan is coloured green, as are the hills on N 12–13. The river Limlight now appears (N 12–13), though the name was only pencilled in later.

Map IV^C

This is another detached slip showing the same 9 squares and not differing greatly from IV^B, save in the representation of Sarn Gebir to the west of Anduin, where the line of hills now runs North-South. The names *Tolbrandir*,[13] *Rauros*, and *River Limlight* were now entered (the latter two added in pencil on IV^B), and the rapids, called *Sarn-Ruin*, north of the lake. In pencil the names *Westemnet*, *Eastemnet*, and the *Entwade*, not included in the redrawing, were added. *G* was written before *Ondor*, and an arrow moved *Wold of Rohan* to N 12, north of the hills (again coloured green) on N 12–13. The name *(Rhov)annion* is spelt thus, with doubled *n*. The name *Eodor* was entered in pencil on P 12, but struck through, and (apparently) moved westwards onto P 11 (the six squares N–P 10–11 at this time existing in the form they have on Map IV^A, where however much is obliterated by later overlay).

Maps IV^D and IVE

Map IV^D is a section of twelve squares (N–P 10–13) which was glued onto the map when it was in the state represented by Map IV^A, but here the glue has only adhered on the left-hand side, and thus much of IV^A is revealed. The vertical line of squares N–P 14 was cut off from IV^C, and IV^D was drawn to join (more or less) with this strip. Then, the four squares O–P 10–11 were overlaid by yet another superimposed section (IVE), and here the corresponding part of IV^D is totally hidden.

On IV^D pencilled changes made to IV^C were now included: *Gondor* for *Ondor*, the *Entwade*, *Eastemnet* and *Westemnet*, and the movement of the *Wold of Rohan* northwards. The two great loops in Anduin on N 13 (afterwards called the North and South Undeeps: see *Unfinished Tales* p. 260 and Index, entry *Undeeps*) appear,[14] while the course of Limlight is changed. No name is given to the rapids in Anduin – *Sarn* is not written to join with *Ruin* on the strip cut from IV^C; *Sarn Gebir* was written here subsequently in pencil. The names *Anarion* on Q 14 (Map III) and *Ithilien* opposite on the eastern bank of Anduin were entered at the same time as *Anarion* on P 13 here. On the First Map my father changed *Anarion* to *Anórien* on Q 14; on my 1943 map he changed *Anarion* to *Anórien* on P 13, whereas on Q 14 he changed *Anarion* to *Lebennin* (p. 310). On the western side of the

THE FIRST MAP 319

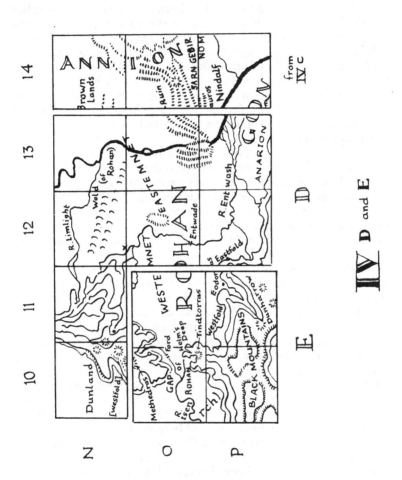

320 THE TREASON OF ISENGARD

Misty Mountains *Dunland* was entered (N 10), and against the vale to the south was written *Westfold*, which was struck through.

It seems that when map IVE was glued on much of the adjoining region on IV^D was rather coarsely overdrawn, and this is a very difficult part to interpret and to represent; but as this part of the geography has not yet been reached in the texts I shall not consider it here. The westward extension of the Black Mountains on P 8–9 (Map III) belongs with this.[15] Map IVE is the first representation of Isengard and the Gap of Rohan that can be reached, IV^A and IV^D being invisible. Here appear *Helm's Deep*, *Tindtorras* (earlier name for *Thrihyrne*), the *Ford of Isen*, *Dunharrow*, and *Methedras*. *Eodoras* appears on P 11 (see above under Map IV^C); *Eastfold* appears to be represented by a dot, which may however be no more than a mark on the paper; and *Westfold* is pencilled in along the northern foothills of the Black Mountains. The letters *rch* on O–P 10 continue the name *Middlemarch* (see Map II).

On IV^{D-E} (but not on the 1943 map) certain roads or tracks are shown which I have not inserted on the redrawing. At about 12 miles NNW of Eodoras there is a road-meeting: one road goes to the Ford of Isen, keeping near to the foothills but running across the outer limits of the Westfold Vale; another goes north-east to the Entwade and then north along the east bank of Entwash, passing between the river and the downs; and a third runs south-east and east to Minas Tirith, crossing the streams that flow down into Entwash.

The 1943 map is here anomalous and I cannot relate it to the series of replacements made to the First Map. My map was obviously made when the First Map had reached its present state (i.e. when IV^D had been stuck on, and IVE on top of a part of that), for it agrees in every feature and name in its representation of the Gap of Rohan and Helm's Deep; Dunland, Methedras, Tindtorras, Dunharrow, etc. all appear. On the other hand, the courses of Anduin and Limlight on N 12–13 are very distinctly as on Map IV^C. Seeing that the course of the Entwash in the square below (O 12) is carefully represented in the later form of IV^D, this is inexplicable, except on the assumption that the courses of Anduin and Limlight on N 12–13 (introducing the Undeeps) were changed after the 1943 map had been made; but I cannot detect any sign of alteration or erasure on IV^D. On the 1943 map the rapids in Anduin are named *Sarn Ruin*, and the hills *Sarn Gebir*.

My father afterwards changed *Black Mountains* to *White Mountains* on the 1943 map (only).

No Man's Land and the Dead Marshes

In 'Farewell to Lórien' (p. 281) Keleborn says that beyond the Wetwang are *the Nomenlands, dreary Uvanwaith that lies before the passes of Mordor*; and in a subsequent draft of the passage (p. 283) he

THE FIRST MAP   321

speaks of the bleak hills of Sarn-gebir, where the wind blows from the East, *for they look out over the Dead Marshes and the Nomenlands to the passes of Mordor: Kirith Ungol*. With the later names *Emyn Muil* and *Cirith Gorgor*, this was retained in FR (p. 390): 'On the further side are the bleak hills of the Emyn Muil. The wind blows from the East there, for they look out over the Dead Marshes and the Noman-lands to Cirith Gorgor and the black gates of Mordor.' This is the land described in *The Two Towers*, IV.2 (p. 238):

> The air was now clearer and colder, and though still far off, the walls of Mordor were no longer a cloudy menace on the edge of sight, but as grim black towers they frowned across a dismal waste. The marshes were at an end, dying away into dead peats and wide flats of dry cracked mud. The land ahead rose in long shallow slopes, barren and pitiless, towards the desert that lay at Sauron's gate.

And when Sam and Frodo at last approached the Black Gate (*ibid.* p. 239):

> Frodo looked round in horror. Dreadful as the Dead Marshes had been, and the arid moors of the Noman-lands [*First Edition*: of Nomen's land], more loathsome far was the country that the crawling day now slowly unveiled to his shrinking eyes.

It will be seen that when the mouths of Entwash and the Wetwang were moved south (Maps IV^B, IV^C) 'No Man's Land' lay between the Wetwang and the Dead Marshes. My 1943 map is in complete agreement with this. On my father's later maps, when the geographical relations in this region had shifted somewhat, the Wetwang and the Dead Marshes are continuous, and no map later than that of 1943 shows *No Man's Land* (*Noman-lands, Nomenlands, Nomen's Land*). From these passages in *The Two Towers*, however, it is plain that this region of 'long shallow slopes, barren and pitiless', of 'arid moors', that succeeded the marshes still lay between Frodo and Sam and the pass into Mordor (see the large-scale map of Gondor and Mordor accompanying *The Return of the King*).

After this demanding journey across the First Map we can return to the lands themselves, and in the next chapter follow the fortunes of (unexpectedly, as it may seem) Sam and Frodo.

NOTES

1 A note of my father's about this map is extant:
> This map was made before the story was complete. It is incomplete and much is missed out.
> Chief errors are in Gondor and Mordor. The White Moun-

322   THE TREASON OF ISENGARD

tains are not in accord with the story. Lebennin should be Belfalas. Mindolluin should be immediately behind Minas Tirith, and the distance across the vale of Anduin *much* reduced, so that Minas Tirith is close to Osgiliath and Osgiliath closer to Minas Morgul. Kirith Ungol is misplaced.

2   The style in which natural features were represented varied. In particular, my father when drawing the Black Mountains surrounded them with a fine continuous line (whereas for the Mountains of Shadow and Ered Lithui he used small strokes to define the foothills), and this can be very confusing in relation to the similar lines representing streams falling from the mountains (see note 7). To make my redrawing as clear as possible, I have substituted lines of dots or small strokes in representing the foothills of the Black Mountains (see note 15).

3   On the revised map first published in *Unfinished Tales* an arrow directs that the name *Icebay of Forochel* applies to the great bay of which the southern bay is only a small part.

4   In the absence of 'sea-lines' the inner line could itself be taken to be the coast; but on my 1943 map the coastline follows the outer line on the First Map (and neither the inner wavy line nor the small circular area are present). This no doubt followed my father's instruction.

5   For another use of *Neldoreth*, from the legends of the First Age, in *The Lord of the Rings* see VI.384.

6   The three cities were still relatively far apart on the redrawn portion 'C' of the First Map, repeated on the 1943 map; see note 1.

7   That this river flowed from Minas Tirith is not perfectly clear on the First Map, owing to a difficulty in distinguishing between the fine lines that mark the outer contours of the mountains and those that mark streams (see note 2); but on my 1943 map it is shown very clearly as flowing out of the city (and I have so redrawn it on Map III).

8   This is still the case not only on the 1943 map but also on a later map of my father's (p. 312).

9   This is a convenient place to notice that the redrawn version of the LR map first published in *Unfinished Tales* contains an error, in that I showed Sirith as the western arm and Celos, its tributary, as the eastern, whereas it should be the reverse (as it is on the large-scale map of Mordor, Gondor, and Rohan in *The Return of the King*).

10   *Cobas Haven*: cf. *Kópas Alqaluntë* in *The Book of Lost Tales* (I.257 and Index). In the *Etymologies* (V.364–5) Quenya *kópa* 'harbour, bay' was given under the stem KOP, but this entry was replaced by a stem KHOP, whence Quenya *hópa*, Noldorin *hobas*, as in *Alfobas = Alqualondë*.

THE FIRST MAP

11   For *Dant-ruin, Dant-ruinel,* and *Rauros* see pp. 283, 285.

12   This name can in fact only be made out in the light of the appearance of the *Isle of Emris* in a time-scheme of this period (see p. 367), where it was changed to *Eregon,* and that to *Tolbrandir.* On the fair copy manuscript of 'Farewell to Lórien' *Tolondren* was changed to *Eregon* (p. 285).

13   For earlier forms *Brandor, Tol Brandor* see p. 285.

14   The divided course of Anduin on O 13 is very clear on the map.

15   I have represented the extension of the Black Mountains on P 8–9 with dots and strokes to make it consistent with the representation of mountains elsewhere on Map III (see note 2); in the original the contours are shown by continuous lines, as on Map IVE.

XVI

THE STORY FORESEEN FROM
LÓRIEN

(i)

The Scattering of the Company

It seems certain that *before* my father wrote the conclusion of 'Farewell to Lórien' – that is, from the point where the Company returned to the hythe and departed down the Great River – he began to write a new and very substantial outline of the way ahead. The opening pages of this outline are complex, and at the beginning the text was much altered, though it is clear that my father was changing the embryonic story as he wrote and that the layers of the text belong together. The notes are here again an essential part of the elucidation.

At the head of the text he wrote, in a second stage, 'XXI', then changed it to 'XX continued' and after the opening words 'The Company sets off from Tongue' wrote in 'XXI'. On the arrangement of chapters in this outline see pp. 329–30.[1]

The Company sets off from Tongue.
They are attacked with arrows.[2]

They come to [*struck out:* Stony] Stoneait [*struck out:* Tolharn] Tollernen[3] [*added:* sheersided except on North where there [is] a little shingle beach. It rises to a high brown hill, higher than the low brown hills on either bank. They land and camp on the island]. Debate whether to go East or West. Frodo feels it in his heart that he should go East and crosses over with Sam to east shore and climbs a hill, and looks out south-east towards the Gates of Mordor. He tells Sam that he wishes to be alone for a while and bids him go back [and] guard the boat on which they had crossed from the Island. Meanwhile Boromir taking another boat crossed over. He hides his boat in bushes. [*This passage changed to read:* Debate whether to go East or West. Frodo feels it in his heart that he should go East and climbs the tall hill in the midst of the island. Sam goes with him but near the top Frodo says to him that he is going to sit on hill top alone and bids him wait for him. Frodo sits alone and looks

THE STORY FORESEEN FROM LÓRIEN   325

out towards Mordor over Sarn Gebir and Nomen's land.[4] Meanwhile Boromir has crept away from Company and climbed hill from west side.]

As Frodo is sitting alone on hill top, Boromir comes suddenly up and stands looking at him. Frodo is suddenly aware as if some unfriendly thing is looking at him behind. He turns and sees only Boromir smiling with a friendly face.

'I feared for you,' said Boromir, 'with only little Sam. It is ill to be alone on the east side of the River.[5] Also my heart is heavy, and I wished to talk a while with you. Where there are so many all speech becomes a debate without end in the conflict of doubting wills.'

'My heart too is heavy,' said Frodo, 'for I feel that here doubts must be resolved; and I foresee the breaking up of our fair company, and that is a grief to me.'

'Many griefs have we had,' said Boromir, and fell silent. There was no sound; only the cold rustle of the chill East wind in the withered heather. Frodo shivered.

Suddenly Boromir spoke again.

'It is a small thing that lies so heavy on our hearts, and confuses our purposes,' said Boromir. [Here include conversation written above and bring down to Boromir's attempt to seize the Ring.]

This last sentence was written continuously with the preceding text. The conversation referred to is found on two pages of the 'August 1940' examination paper, written in pencil so faint and rapid that my father went over it more clearly in ink, although, so far as the underlying text can be made out, he followed it almost exactly. This obviously preceded the new outline into which it is inserted, and was a development from the scene in the previous Plot ('The Story Foreseen from Moria') given on p. 208, where the debate, Boromir's intervention, and Frodo's flight wearing the Ring all take place 'at Angle': here the scene is set 'at the Stone Hills, whence Eredwethion[6] can be glimpsed' (these words being visible in the underlying text also). In the notes given on p. 233 the 'parting of the ways' took place 'at Stonehills'; in the outlines for 'Farewell to Lórien' (pp. 268–9) the debate and the 'scene with Boromir' follow the landing on Tolondren and the ascent into the Green Hills, or the Emyn Rhain.

Conversation of Boromir and Frodo at the Stone Hills, whence Eredwethion can be glimpsed like a smudge of grey, and behind it a vague cloud lit beneath occasionally by a fitful glow.

326 THE TREASON OF ISENGARD

'It is a small thing from which we suffer so much woe,' said Boromir. 'I have seen it but once for an instant, in the house of Elrond. Could I not have a sight of it again?'

Frodo looked up. His heart went suddenly cold. He caught a curious gleam in Boromir's eye, though his face otherwise was friendly and smiling as of old.

'It is best to let it lie hid,' he answered.

'As you will. I care not,' said Boromir. 'Yet I will confess that it is of the Ring that I wish to speak. (Yet hidden or revealed I would wish now to speak to you of the Ring?) . . . [sic]

Boromir says that Elrond etc. are all foolish. 'It is mad not to use the power and methods of the Enemy: ruthless, fearless. Many elves, half-elves, and wizards might be corrupted by it – but not so a true Man. Those who deal in magic will use it for hidden Power. Each to his kind. You, Frodo, for instance, being a hobbit and desiring peace: you use it for invisibility. Look what a warrior could do! Think what I – or Aragorn, if you will – could do! How he would fare among the enemy and drive the Black Riders! It would give power of command.

'And yet Elrond tells us not only to throw it away and destroy it – that is understandable (though not to my mind wise since I have pondered on it by night on our journey). But what a way – walk into the enemy's net and offer him every chance of re-capturing it!'

Frodo is obdurate.

'Come at least to Minas-tirith!' said Boromir. He laid his hand on Frodo's shoulder in friendly fashion, but Frodo felt his arm tremble as if with suppressed excitement. Frodo stepped away and stood further off.

'Why are you so unfriendly?' said Boromir. 'I am a valiant man and true,' he said. 'And I give you my *word* that I would not keep it – would not, that is I should say, if you would lend it to me. Just to make trial!'

'No! No!' said Frodo. [*Added:* 'It is mine alone by fate to bear.']

Boromir gets more angry, and so more incautious (or actually evil purpose now only begins to grow in him). 'You are *foolish!*' he cried. 'Doing yourself to death and ruining our cause. Yet the Ring is not yours, save by chance. It might as well have been Aragorn's – or mine. Give it to me! Then you will be rid of it, and of all responsibility. You would be free' (cunningly) 'You can lay the blame on me, if you will, saying that I was too strong

THE STORY FORESEEN FROM LÓRIEN   327

and took it by force. For I *am* too strong for you, Frodo,' he said. And now an ugly look had come suddenly over his fair and pleasant face. He got to his feet and sprang at Frodo.

Frodo could do nothing else. He slipped the Ring on, and vanished among the rocks. Boromir cursed, and groped among the rocks. Then suddenly the fit left him, and he wept.

'What folly possessed me!' he said. 'Come back, Frodo!' he called. 'Frodo! Evil came into my heart, but I have put it away.'

But Frodo was now frightened, and he hid until Boromir went back to camp. Standing on rocks he saw nothing about him but a grey formless mist, and far away (yet black and clear and hard) the Mountains of Mordor: the fire seemed very red. Fell voices in air. Feels Eye searching, and though it does not find him, he feels its attention is suddenly arrested (by himself).[7]

Here the inserted text ends and the new Plot continues:

Then Frodo took counsel with himself, and he perceived that the evil of the Ring was already at work even among the Company. (Also its evil was again on him, since he had put it on again.) He said to himself: this is laid on me. I am the Ringbearer and none can help me. I will not emperil the other hobbits or any of my companions. I will depart alone.

He slips away unseen and coming to the boats takes one and crosses over to the East.

Boromir is now himself frightened and though (half) repenting his own greed for the Ring the curse has not wholly left him. He ponders what tale he shall tell to the others. Hastening back to the River he comes upon Sam, who anxious at Frodo's long absence is coming to the hill-top to find him.

'Where is my master?' says Sam.

'I left him on the hill-top,' said Boromir, but something wild and odd in his face caused Sam sudden fear. 'What have you done with him?' 'I have done nothing,' said Boromir. 'It is what he has done himself: he has put on the ring and vanished!'

'Thank goodness the island is not large,' said Sam in great alarm, but he thought also to himself: 'And what made him do that, I should like to know. What mischief has this great fool been up to?' Without another word to Boromir he ran back to the camp to find Trotter. 'Master Frodo has disappeared!' he cried.

Consternation. The hunt. Some scour the island. But Sam discovers the fact that a boat is missing. Has Frodo gone East or

328 THE TREASON OF ISENGARD

West? Trotter decides that they cannot hope to recapture Frodo against his will, but they must *follow* him if they can. Which way?

[Or make Island inaccessible: steep shores. Black birds circle high above its tall cliffs and central summit. Distant noise of the falls of Dantruinel.[8] They camp on *west* shore. Hence when Frodo is lost they all go after him. Thus Pippin and Merry get separated.[9] Sam sits alone and so discovers missing boat. He takes another and goes after Frodo.] [*Against this bracketed passage is written* Yes.]

It is clear that my father at once accepted his suggestion in this last passage that the Company camped on the west bank, not on the island in the river, because that passage contains the words 'Sam ... discovers missing boat. He takes another and goes after Frodo', and this, as will be seen in a moment, is a necessary element in the story that follows.

Boromir is for West. In any case he says he is afraid – the Ring will fall now almost certainly into the Enemy's hands. 'This madness was set [in] him for that purpose.'[10] He wishes to get now to Minas-Tirith as quick as possible. Sam goes West [*read* East], others East [*read* West].

Sam picks up trail of Frodo.[11] How? He finds boat knocking against the bank.[12] A little further he finds a scrap of grey stuff on a bramble – a great bramble tract has to be crossed. Very soon Sam discovered that he was lost in a pathless listening land. But he felt sure his master would steer towards the Fiery Mt. Away on his right the falls roared. He climbed down into the Wetwang. Daylight fell. Slept in tree. Heard Gollum at foot and tried to track *him*, thinking he was after Frodo. But Sam is not clever enough for Gollum, who is soon aware of him and turns and discovers him. He confesses to Gollum that he is trying to find Frodo.

Gollum laughs. 'Then his luck is better than he deserves, yes,' said Gollum, 'for Gollum has been following him: Gollum can see footprints where he can't see nothings, no!'

Gollum was so intent on the trail – muttering to himself 'Footsteps, Gollum sees them, and he smells them: Gollum is wary' – that he did not seem aware of Sam's (relatively) clumsy efforts at stalking the stalker.[13]

It was near the evening of the second day when Frodo, every sense keyed up, became suddenly aware of footfalls. He puts on the ring, but Gollum comes up and circles near. To Frodo's

THE STORY FORESEEN FROM LÓRIEN   329

great surprise Sam appears. To the equal surprise of Sam and Gollum Frodo suddenly takes off ring and stands before them.

Gollum is the most surprised: for between Frodo and Sam he is overmatched. He cringes: for as Ringbearer Frodo has a power over him (though he is really an object of great hatred). Gollum pleads for forgiveness, and promises help, and having nowhere else to turn Frodo accepts. Gollum says he will lead them over the Dead Marshes to Kirith Ungol.[14] (Chuckling to himself to think that that is just the way he would wish them to go.)

Here ends Chapter.

At this stage my father was following the previous Plot (p. 208): 'At point where Sam, Frodo and Gollum meet return to others – for whose adventures see later. But they should be told at this point.' He now decided, I think, that not even so much of the story of Frodo and Sam east of Anduin should yet be told, and he bracketed all that follows from 'Sam picks up trail of Frodo', writing against it 'Put in later chapter. XXIV' (subsequently altering XXIV to XXV: see p. 330).[15] At the same time he struck out 'Here ends Chapter' and went on with the story of the other members of the Company.

Dismay of the hunt at finding no trace of Frodo. Boromir, Legolas, Gimli, Trotter return to camp, only to find now that Sam also is missing, and Pippin and Merry as well.

Trotter is overwhelmed with grief, thinking that he has failed in his charge as Gandalf's successor. He imagines that the hobbits are all together; and waits in camp until the morning.[16]

In the morning no sign is found of them. The Company is now broken. Trotter sees nothing for it but to go south to Minas-Tirith with Boromir. But Legolas and Gimli have no further heart for the Quest, and feel that already too many leagues are between them and their homes. They go north again: Legolas meaning to join the Elves of Lothlórien for a while, Gimli hoping to get back to the Mountain.[17]

Here ends Chapter XX.

('Chapter XX' was subsequently changed to 'XXI', and the numbers of the chapter synopses that follow were also altered, as will be explained in a moment.)

XXI   What happened to Gimli and Legolas. They meet Gandalf?

XXII   What happened to Merry and Pippin. They are lost – led astray by echoes – in the hunt, and wander away up

330 THE TREASON OF ISENGARD

the Entwash River and come to Fangorn. Here they meet with Giant Fangorn or Tree-beard. He takes them to Minas Tirith.

XXIII What happened in Minas Tirith. Siege by Sauron and Saruman. Treachery of Boromir. Sudden arrival of Gandalf – now become *a white wizard*. Treebeard raises the siege. Enemy driven over the Anduin. Horsemen of Rohan come to assistance.

XXIV What happened to Frodo and Sam.

Comparison with the previous Plot (pp. 210–11) will show that these synopses repeat, much more briefly, what was set out there, and show no further development. At this juncture my father made various alterations of chapter-structure in the plot-sketch. At the beginning, as already noted (p. 324), he indicated that 'The Company sets off from Tongue' should form the conclusion of Chapter XX ('Farewell to Lórien'), while all that follows should constitute XXI (apart from the story of Sam's tracking of Frodo and the encounter with Gollum, which would be placed in a later chapter, as already decided: p. 329). The brief synopses just given were now renumbered and slightly reordered: XXII (Merry and Pippin); XXIII (Gimli and Legolas); XXIV (Minas Tirith); XXV (Frodo and Sam).[18]

(ii) *Mordor*

While my father seems never to have doubted that after the breaking of the Company the 'western' stories must be followed, the 'eastern' story of Frodo and Sam was bursting into life and expression; and he now at once went on with the outline of that story from the point where he had left it (p. 329), noting: 'XXV: continuation after part above.'

They sleep in pairs, so that one is always awake with Gollum.[19]

Gollum all the while is scheming to betray Frodo. He leads them cleverly over the Dead Marshes. There are dead green faces in the stagnant pools; and the dry reeds hiss like snakes. Frodo feels the strength of the searching eye as they proceed.

At night Sam keeps watch, only pretending to be asleep. He hears Gollum muttering to himself, words of hatred for Frodo and lust for the Ring.

The three companions now approach Kirith Ungol, the dreadful ravine which leads into Gorgoroth. Kirith Ungol means Spider Glen: there dwelt great spiders, greater than those

THE STORY FORESEEN FROM LÓRIEN   331

of Mirkwood, such as were once of old in the land of Elves and Men in the West that is now under sea, such as Beren fought in the dark cañons of the Mountains of Terror above Doriath. Already Gollum knew these creatures well. He slips away. The spiders come and weave their nets over Frodo while Sam sleeps: sting Frodo. Sam wakes, and sees Frodo lying pale as death – greenish: reminding him of the faces in the pools of the marshes. He cannot rouse or wake him.[20]

The idea suddenly comes to Sam to carry on the work, and he felt for the Ring. He could not unclasp it, nor cut the chain, but he drew the chain over Frodo's head. As he did so he fancied he felt a tremor (sigh or shudder) pass through the body; but when he paused he could not feel any heart-beat. Sam put the Ring round his own neck.

[Suddenly the Orc-guard of the Pass, guided by Gollum, comes upon them. Sam takes Galadriel's present to Frodo – the phial of light. Sam slips on the Ring, and attempts to fight unseen to defend Frodo's body; but gets knocked down and nearly trampled to death. The Orcs rejoicing pick up Frodo and bear him away, after searching in vain (but only a short while) for 'the other hobbit' reported by Gollum.]

This last paragraph, which I have bracketed, was struck through with a direction to replace it by the following much longer passage on a separate page. It is clear, however, that this replacement was not written significantly later.[21]

Then he sat and made a *Lament for Frodo*. After that he put away his tears and thought what he could do. He could not leave his dear master lying in the wild for the fell beasts and carrion birds; and he thought he would try and build a cairn of stones about him. 'The silver mail of mithril rings shall be his winding-sheet,' he said. 'But I will lay the phial of Lady Galadriel upon his breast, and Sting shall be at his side.'

He laid Frodo upon his back and crossed his arms on his breast and set Sting at his side. And as he drew out the phial it blazed with light. It lit Frodo's face and it looked now pale but beautiful, fair with [an] elvish beauty as of one long past the shadows. 'Farewell, Frodo,' said Sam; and his tears fell on Frodo's hands.

[But] at that moment there was a sound of strong footfalls climbing towards the rock shelf. Harsh calls and cries echoed in the rocks. Orcs were coming, evidently guided to the spot.

332   THE TREASON OF ISENGARD

'Curse that Gollum,' said Sam. 'I might have known we had not seen the last of him. These are some of his friends.'

Sam had no time to lose. Certainly no time to hide or cover his master's body. Not knowing what else to do he slipped on the Ring, and then he took also the phial so that the foul Orcs should not get it, and girded Sting about his own waist. And waited. He had not long to wait.

In the gloom first came Gollum sniffing out the scent, and behind him came the black orcs: fifty or more it seemed. With a cry they rushed upon Frodo. Sam tried to put up a fight unseen, but even as he was about to draw Sting he was run down and trampled by the rush of the Orcs. All the breath was knocked out of his body. [Added in pencil: Courage failed him.] In great glee the Orcs seized Frodo and lifted him.

'There was another, yes,' whined Gollum. 'Where is he, then?' said the Orcs. 'Somewheres nigh. Gollum feels him, Gollum sniffs him.'

'Well, you find him, sniveller,' said the Orc-chief. 'He can't go far without getting into trouble. We've got what we want. Ringbearer! Ringbearer!' They shouted in joy. 'Make haste. Make haste. Send one swift to Baraddur to the Great One. But we cannot wait here – we must [get] back to our guard post. Bear the prisoner to Minas Morgul.' [Added in pencil: Gollum runs behind wailing that the Precious is not there.]

Here the replacement text ends.

Even as they do so, Frodo seems to awake, and gives a loud cry, but they gag him. Sam is torn between joy at learning he is alive and horror at seeing him carried off by Orcs. Sam tries to follow, but they go very speedily. The Ring seems to grow in power in this region: he sees clearly in the dark, and seems to understand the orcs' speech. [He fears what may happen if he meets a Ringwraith – the Ring does not confer courage: poor Sam trembles all the time.][22] Sam gathers that they are going to Minas Morgul: since they are not allowed to leave their post – but a messenger has at once been despatched to announce to the Dark Lord the capture of Ringbearer, and to bring back his orders.[23] 'The Mighty One has great business afoot,' says one. 'All that has gone before is but a skirmish compared with the war that is about to be kindled. Fine days, fine days! Blood on blade and fire on hill, smoke in sky and tears on earth. Merry weather, my friends, to bring in a real New Year!'

THE STORY FORESEEN FROM LÓRIEN   333

The Orcs go so fast that Sam soon gets weary and falls
behind; but he plods on behind in the direction of Minas
Morgul, remembering as much as he could of the maps. The
path led up into the mountains – the north horn of the Mountains of Shadow that sundered the ashen vale of Gorgoroth
from the valley of the Great River. Sam looking out saw all
the plain alive with armies, horse and foot, black plumes, red
and black banners. Countless hosts of the wild peoples of Rhûn,
and the evil folk of Harad, were pouring out of Kirith Ungol to
war. Smoke and dust afar off suggested that away in the East
more were coming. [In truth they were – far beyond Sam's
eyesight the armies rode and marched: the Dark Lord had
determined to strike. From beyond the Inland Sea of Rhûn[24] up
the rivers east of Mirkwood, round the towers of Dol Dúghul
they poured through fen and forest to the banks of the Great
River. Lothlórien was lapped in flame. From the Misty Mountains, from Moria – Khazaddûm and many hidden caves poured
the orcs to meet them; from Harad and from Mordor they came
against Ondor, and sought the walls of Minas-Tirith; and out
from Isengard, seeing the war-beacons afar off blazing in
Mordor, came the traitor Saruman with many wolves.][25]
Sam comes so close behind that he sees from below the
orc-host entering the gates of the City[26] [*struck out:* – and they
have not time to despoil Frodo].
At last Sam saw before him the walled city that had once been
the City of the Sun [> Moon]: Minas Anor [> Ithil] in the days
of old (Elendil).[27] Amidst it stood a tall tower – from afar off it
looked beautiful. But Sam passed into the city and saw that all
was defiled: and on every stone and corner were carved figures
and faces and signs of horror. Such a dread ran through all the
streets that he could hardly drag his legs or force himself along.
'Where in all this devilish hole have they put my poor master,'
thought Sam. He feels drawn to the Tall Tower. He wanders up
a seemingly endless winding stair, windowless; shrinks into
foul-smelling recess[es] when snarling Orcs go up or down. At
the top are four locked doors, North, South, East, West. Which
is it? And anyway how can he get in: all are locked.
Suddenly Sam took courage and did a thing of daring – the
longing for his master was stronger than all other thoughts.
He sat on the ground and began to sing. 'Troll-song' – or
some other Hobbit song – or possibly part of the Elves' song
O Elbereth. (Yes).

334 THE TREASON OF ISENGARD

Cries of anger are heard and guards come from stairs above and from below. 'Stop his mouth – the foul hound' cry the Orcs. 'Would that the message would return from the Great One, and we could begin our Questioning [or take him to Baraddur. He he! They have a pretty way there. There is One who will soon find out where the little cheat has hid his Ring.]28 Stop his mouth.' 'Careful!' cried the captain, 'do not use too much strength ere word comes from the Great One.' By this trick Sam found the door, for an Orc unlocked the East door and went inside with a whip. 'Hold your foul tongue,' he said, as Sam heard the whip crack.

Swift as lightning Sam slipped inside. He longed to stab the Orc but wisely restrained himself. In the light of [the torch >] the small East window he saw Frodo lying on the bare stone – his arms over his face [?guarding] from the whip blow. Muttering the orc went out and closed the door.

Frodo groaned and turned over uncovering his face – still pale from the poison. 'Why do dreams cheat me?' he said. 'I thought I heard a voice singing the song of Elbereth!'

'You were not dreaming!' said Sam. 'It is me, master.' He drew off the Ring.

But Frodo felt a great hatred well up in his heart. Before him there stood a small orc, bowlegged, leering at him out of a gloating face. It reminded him faintly of some one he had once known and loved – or hated. He stood up. 'Thief!' he cried. 'Give it to me.'

Sam was greatly taken aback: and stepped away, so sudden and grim was his master's face. 'The poor dear is still mithered,'29 he thought.

'Surely, Master Frodo. I have come behind as quick as I could just for to give it you.' And with that he gave the ring into Frodo's snatching hand, and took the chain from about his neck. [Only for two days had he been Ringbearer, yet he felt a curious regret as it left him.]30

'Sam!' cried Frodo. 'Sam! my dear old Sam. How did you come here? I thought' – and then he leant upon Sam and wept long. 'I thought,' he said again at last. 'Well never mind. I thought I was lost and that they had taken the Ring and all was in ruin. How did you get it – tell me.'

'Not by thieving,' said Sam with an effort at a smile. 'Or not exactly. I took it when I thought you were gone, Master. Yes, I thought you were dead for certain away back in that Kirith

THE STORY FORESEEN FROM LÓRIEN 335

place, with those crawling horrors. That was a black hour, Master Frodo, but it seemed to me that Sam had got to carry on – if he could.' Then he told the tale of the attack and how he had followed. 'And it is in a place called Minas Morgul that we are,' he said, 'and not for a small mercy in the Dark Tower itself, leastways not yet. But Minas whatever it be: we have got to get out quick. And how, I don't see.'

They talked it over long in whispering voices. 'The Ring won't cover two,' said Sam; 'and I think you won't want to part from it again. Anyhow the Ring is yours, master,' said Sam. 'Once out of here you can get away fairly easy, so long as none of the Ring-wraiths or Black Riders turn up, or something worse. There is some nasty eyes in this town, or the pricking of my skin is merely the shivers of a cold coming on. My advice to you is to leg it as quick as may be.'

'And you?' said Frodo.

'O, me,' said Sam. 'That can't be helped. I may find a way out, or I may not. Anyway I have done the job I came to do.'

'Not yet, I think,' said Frodo. 'Not yet. I do not think that we part here, dear friend.'

'Well then, master, tell me how.'

'Let me think,' said Frodo. 'I have a plan,' he said at last. 'A risk, but it may work. Have you still got your sword?'

'I have,' said Sam, 'and Sting too, and your glass of light. I was a-going to lay them by you under the stones,' he stammered, 'when the murdering Orcs came on us. I thought you were dead – until you cried out as they gripped you.'

Frodo smiled and took back his treasures. He drew Sting half from its sheath and the pale blue light of it flickered from the blade. 'Not surprising,' he said, 'that Sting should shine in Minas Morgul! Well now, Sam, get away over there – where you will be behind the door when it opens. Draw your sword. I will lie on the floor as I was. Then you can start your song again – and that should bring in an orc soon enough. Let us hope it is not many more than one.'

'But the whips, master, the murdering hounds will fetch you one for me, and I cannot abide it.'

'You won't have to abide it if you are quick with your sword,' said Frodo. 'But you need not worry! They have not had time to search me – not that Orcs dare touch the Ring that is for none less than servants of the Ring or for Sauron himself. They made sure that I had no sword and flung me on the floor. So I have

336   THE TREASON OF ISENGARD

still my mithril-coat. That lash you heard as you came in was
laid well across my side and back – but I don't think you would
find any weal.'

Sam was much relieved. 'Very well, what's the idea, Mr.
Frodo?' he asked.

'You must do your best to kill the Orc that comes in,' said
Frodo. 'If there is more than one I must leap up and help, and
maybe we shall have to try and fight our way out. But to get
someone to come in seems our only way of getting out.'

Frodo now began again to sing O Elbereth (a few lines). With
an oath the door was flung open and in strode the orc-captain,
cracking his lash. 'Lie quiet, you dog,' he shouted, and raised his
whip. But even as he did so, Sam leapt from behind the door and
stabbed at his throat. He fell with a gurgle. Frodo sprang up,
pushed the door gently to, and crouched waiting for any other
orc that might come. The sound of harsh voices far off up the
further stairs came to them, but no other sounds.

'Now's our chance,' said Frodo. 'Get into his gear as quick as
you can.' Swiftly they stripped the orc, peeling off his coat of
black scale-like mail, unbuckling his sword, and unslinging the
small round shield at his back. The black iron cap was too large
for Sam (for orcs have large heads for their size), but he slipped
on the mail. It hung a little loose and long. He cast the black
hooded cloak about him, took the whip and scimitar, and slung
the red shield. Then they dragged the body behind the door and
crept out. Frodo went first.

It was dark outside when the door was shut again. Frodo
took out the glass of light. They hurried down the stairs.
Halfway down they met someone coming up with a torch.
Frodo slipped on his Ring and drew aside; but Sam went on to
meet the goblin. They brushed into one another and the goblin
spoke in his harsh tongue; but Sam answered only with an
angry snarl. That seemed satisfactory. Sam was evidently
mistaken for someone important. The goblin drew aside to let
him pass, and they hastened on. [*Struck out:* They did not guess
that it was the messenger returning from Baraddur!]

Now they issued from the Loathly Tower. Evening was
falling: away in the West over the valley of the Anduin there
was some light. Far away loomed the Black Mountains and the
tower of Minas Tirith, had they known. But in the East the sky
was dark, with black and lowering clouds that seemed almost to
rest upon the land. An uneasy twilight lay in the shadowy

THE STORY FORESEEN FROM LÓRIEN 337

streets. Shrill cries came as it were from underground, strange shapes flitted by or peered out of alley[s] and holes in the [?gaping] houses; there were [??dispirited] voices and faint echoes of monotonous and unhappy song. All the carven faces leered, and their eyes glowed with a fire at great depth.

The hobbits shuddered as they hurried on. Feet seemed to follow them, and they turned many corners, but they never threw them off. Rustling and pattering on the stones they came doggedly after them.

They came to the gates. The main gates were closed; but a small door was still open. Sentinels stood on either side, and at the opening stood an armed warder, gazing out into the gathering dusk. The Orcs were waiting for the messenger from Baraddur.

'Stay here,' whispered Frodo, drawing Sam into a shadow of a pillar just before the gate. 'While I wear the Ring I can understand much of their speech, or of the thought behind it – I don't know which. If I cry out come at a run, and get through the door if you can.'

[*The following was struck out probably as soon as written:* He went forward. The guard at the open door was grumbling. 'One would have thought we had caught no more than a stray elf,' he said. 'Is [?the] Ringbearer [*written above:* Thief] of no matter to them at the Dark Tower now? One would have thought He would have sent a Rider at least. Not even the war that is now set afoot can surely have lessened the worth of the One Treasure.'

Suddenly Frodo stabbed with Sting. The warder fell. But Frodo leant against the door lest a guard should thrust it to and called out. The sentinels sprang up. Sam came running, but at first they took him for a goblin running up to help. He smote one down before they were aware of his enmity and sprang through the door]

'Nay,' said Sam, 'that won't do. If we have a fight at the gate it won't be much use getting through. We'll have the whole wasps' nest a-buzzing after us before we have gone many yards: and they know these nasty mountains as well as I mind me of Bagend. Swagger is the only hope, Mr. Frodo, begging your pardon.'

'Very well, my good Sam,' said Frodo, 'try swagger.'

Feeling as little like 'swagger' as ever in his life, Sam walked as unconcernedly as he could manage into the shadow of the

338 THE TREASON OF ISENGARD

dark gateway. The sentinels on either side looked at him and did not move. He came beside the warder and looked out. The warder started and looked at him angrily.

Frodo came behind warily. He saw the orc's hand go to the hilt of his scimitar. 'Who are you and who do you think you are pushing,' said he. 'Am I in charge of the gate or not?' Sam tried the trick again. He snarled angrily and stepped out of the gate. But the trick did not work so well a second time. The warder sprang after him and grabbed at his cloak. 'Closing time is [? by *read* past by?] half an hour,' he said, 'and you know that. No one but the Lord's messengers are allowed in or out, and you know that well enough. If I have any more trouble I shall report you to the Captain [*struck out:* of Morgul].' Sam prepared to give battle. He turned to face the warder gripping his hilt and swung round his shield. It was a red shield, and in the midst was painted a single black eye. The warder fell back nimbly. 'Your pardon,' he said, 'O Captain of Morgul. I did not recognize you. I only did my duty as I thought.' Sam, guessing something of what had occurred, snarled again and waved his hand as if in dismissal and walked away down the path into the dusk. The warder stared after him shaking his head. He stood blocking the door so that Frodo could not pass.

Sam had now disappeared on the downward track, and still Frodo waited hoping for a chance to slip out without a fight, before the door was closed. Suddenly there was a loud boom. Dong Dong Dong. A big bell was ringing in the Loathly Tower: the alarm was sounded. Frodo heard distant cries. Soon he could hear voices calling: 'Close the gates. Bar the door. Watch the walls. The Bearer has escaped from the Tower.'

The warder seized the door and began to close it. Feet came running. Frodo took the only chance. Stooping he seized the warder's legs and threw him down and sprang out. As he ran he heard loud shouts and oaths. 'But the Captain is lying dead and stripped in the Tower, I tell you,' he heard. 'Take that for a fool. You have let the bearer escape. Take that for a fool.' There was a blow and a cry. Orcs came pouring out of the gate, and still the bell tolled.

Suddenly dark overhead a black shape appeared flying low out of the east: a great bird it seemed, like an eagle or more like a vulture. The orcs halted chattering shrilly: but Frodo did not wait. He guessed that some urgent message concerning himself had come from the Dark Tower.

THE STORY FORESEEN FROM LÓRIEN 339

Here the text in ink ends, but is followed by a few pencilled notes:

Finds Sam
They escape – and as they are actually making *towards* Mordor this delays hunt which goes towards the Anduin North and West.

End of Chapter XXV
Gorgoroth
How Frodo came to the Fiery Mountain. See sketch (b) (c).

This last is a reference to the pages of the previous Plot, in this book pp. 208–9, from 'The Gap of Gorgoroth not far from Fire Mountain' to 'hurls himself and Gollum into the gulf?'

All this story of the escape from Minas Morgul was developed from the brief words of the earlier Plot (p. 209):

> Sam ... passes into Morgol and finds Frodo. Frodo feels hatred of Sam and sees him as an orc. But suddenly the orc speaks and holds out Ring and says: Take it. Then Frodo sees it is Sam. They creep out. ... Sam dresses up like an orc.

There can be no doubt whatsoever that the text just given, beginning as an outline in the present tense and sliding almost imperceptibly into full narrative, was the actual emergence on paper of what ultimately became 'The Tower of Cirith Ungol' in *The Return of the King* (VI.1). It was written very fast (though surprisingly legibly), with virtually no correction made on grounds of suitability of phrasing, and gives an impression of uninterrupted composition, perhaps even at one sitting. Being written at this stage,[31] its relation to the ultimate form of the story in 'The Tower of Cirith Ungol' is much more remote than has been the case anywhere else, and although certain new elements (not present in the previous Plot) now enter and would be preserved – notably Sam's song, instrumental in his discovery of where Frodo was – the story would be radically refashioned in every point, in geography, in motives, in the structure of events, so as to become almost a new conception.

Some further development seems in fact to have taken place quite soon. Found with this text are some other papers, themselves all of the same time, but entirely distinct in appearance and mode of writing. Here the story of Frodo and Sam is roughly outlined further, and the escape from Minas Morgul is reconsidered and rewritten. I think that this further material belongs in fact to the same or much the same time as the primary text. There are various pointers to this. The suggestion found here that 'it could be Merry and Pippin that had adventure in Minas Morgul if Treebeard is cut out' shows that the fully formed narrative had not at any rate advanced beyond the Breaking of the Fellowship; and the chapter is still referred to as 'XXV', which carries

340   THE TREASON OF ISENGARD

the same implication (i.e. my father was still assuming the chapters 'XXI–XXIV' as outlined on pp. 329–30 and had not yet embarked on the writing of the 'western' adventures).

The text is written fairly legibly in ink, but towards the end becomes a pencilled scribble, here and there formidably difficult to make out.

Ch. XXV

Minas Morgul must be made more horrible. The usual 'goblin' stuff is not good enough here.

The Gate shaped like a gaping mouth with teeth and a window like an eye on each side. As Sam passes through he feels a horrible shudder.[32] There are two silent shapes sitting on either side as sentinels.

Substitute something of the following sort for p. [337].

The main outer gates were now closed. But a small door in the middle of one was open. (It faced south.) The tunnelled Gate-house was dark as night and the pale skylight showed up as a small patch at the end of a tunnel. As Sam and Frodo crept closer they saw or guessed the great ominous shape of the Sentinels on either side: still sitting soundless and unmoved: but from them there seemed to issue a nameless threat.

'Stay here!' whispered Frodo drawing Sam into the shadow of a wall not far from the gate. 'While I wear the Ring, I can understand much of the speech of the enemies, or of the thought behind their speech: I don't know which. I will go forward, and try and find out something. If I call out, come at a run: and get through the door if you can.'

'Nay!' said Sam, 'that won't do. If we have a fight at the gate, we might as well or better stay inside. We'd have the whole wasps' nest, orcs and bogeys and all, buzzing after us, before we'd gone a dozen yards: and they know these horrible mountains as well as I mind me of Bag-End. Swagger is the only hope, Mr. Frodo, begging your pardon.'

'Very well, my good Sam,' said Frodo, 'try swagger!'

Feeling as little like 'swagger' as ever in his life, Sam walked forward, as bold and unconcerned as he could manage to look, all shaking at the knees as he was, and with a queer tightening of his breath. Each step forward became more difficult. It was as if some will denying the passage was drawn like invisible ropes across his path. He felt the pressure of unseen eyes. It seemed an age before he passed under the gloom of the gate's arch, and he felt tired as if he had been swimming against a strong tide. The

THE STORY FORESEEN FROM LÓRIEN   341

Sentinels sat there: dark and still. They did not move their clawlike hands laid on their knees, they did not move their shrouded heads [*struck out:* staring stiffly] in which no faces could be seen; but Sam felt a sudden prickle in his skin, he sensed that they were alive and suddenly alert. As he came between them he seemed to shrink [and] shrivel, naked as an insect crawling to its hole under the eyes of gigantic birds. He came to the open door: just outside the path ran to a flight of stairs leading to the downward road. Only one step and he would be out – but he could not pass: it was as if the air before him had become stiff. He had to summon up his strength and his will. Like lead he lifted his foot and forced it slowly bit by bit over the threshold, on either side he felt the darkness leer and grin at him. Slowly he pressed his foot down, down. It touched the step outside: and then something seemed to snap. He stood fixed. He thought he heard a cry, but whether just beside him, or far away in some remote watchful tower he could not tell. There was a sudden clash of iron. An Orc ran out from the guard-room.

Frodo creeping warily behind was now also under the archway. He heard the guard cry out in harsh tones. 'Ho there: who are you, and what do you think you are doing?' He laid hold of Sam's cloak. Sam snarled angrily, but the trick did not work so well a second time. The guard held him. 'Closing-time is past, half an hour ago,' he growled. 'No one but the Lord's messengers are allowed in or out, and you know that. The door awaits the bringer of word from Baraddur, but it is not for any other.'

Of all this Sam understood only that he was forbidden to pass. He could not move forward: so he stepped suddenly back stepping on the feet of the Orc behind. Frodo saw the guard's hand go to the hilt of his scimitar. 'Hey, who are you stamping on?' said he. Sam prepared for battle. He turned, etc. as before.

[*Struck out:* An alternative would be to make the gate impassable. The alarm is sounded. The City is aroused. The Vulture (Black Rider) arrives in the main square. Frodo at once knows that Ring is useless. He feels almost discovered. Messenger says Ring is still in the town: he feels it.]

Alternative account.

Make light fade in the window as Sam and Frodo talk in the

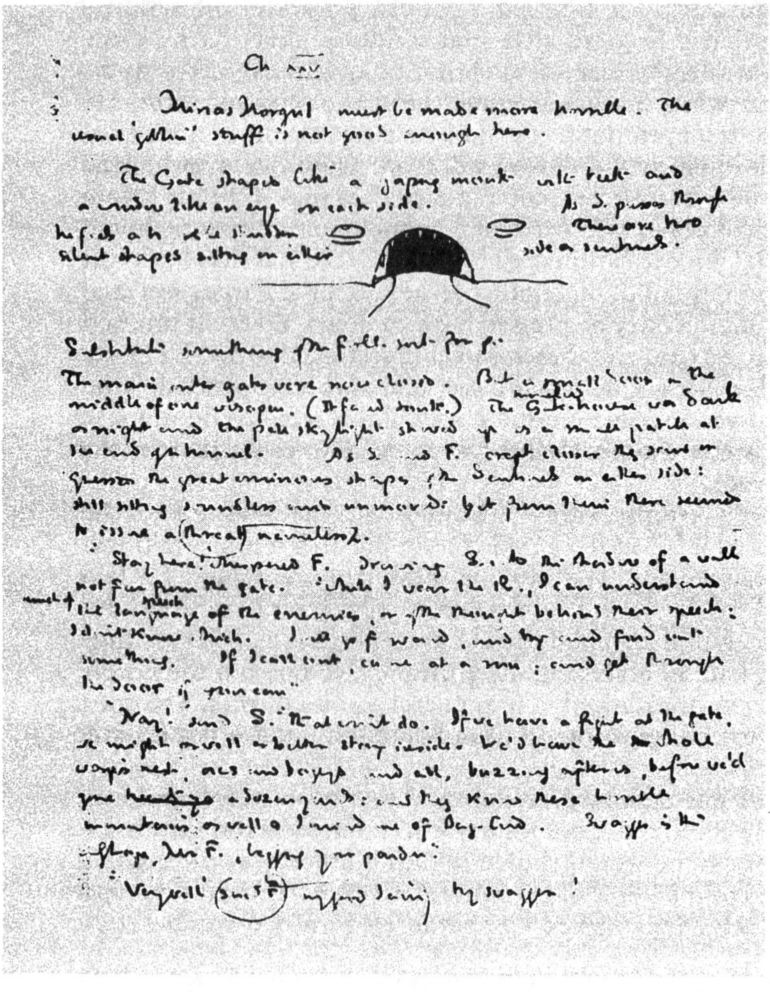

Sketch for the Gate of Minas Morgul.

THE STORY FORESEEN FROM LÓRIEN   343

Loathly Tower. They try the trick of getting an orc to open the door as twilight deepens. *No dressing up.* They creep out into the town. Something warns Frodo *not* to use the Ring. The elf-hoods prove better in the City of Sorcery than the Ring – the two hobbits (aided by some grace of Galadriel that went with the garments) pass along the streets like mist. The gate is closed – the sentinels described: three a side.[33]

The walls are high and if it were possible to get onto them unseen – it is not: the few ascents are guarded – they could not get down. They are trapped.

A cry from a watch tower. The waning moon rises in East. A dark shape flying out of the East, a black speck against clouds. Vulture bearing a Ringwraith settles in main square. The Ringwraith has come to take Frodo back to the Dark Tower. At that moment *boom*, the alarm is sounded from Loathly Tower. Ringwraith says Ring has not left City: he feels it. Hunt in town. Hairbreadth escape of hobbits. In spite of the Ringwraith a host of orcs assemble to scour mountains (? Frodo and Sam trap two orcs in an alley and take their cloaks and gear. ?) Pass out in rear of the company. Describe the reluctant feeling, and moveless sentinels. Even as they pass the sentinels stir: and give a fell, horrible, far-off cry. The moon is suddenly clouded. A fierce cold wind from East. Rain? The hobbits fling themselves flat among the rocks. Orcs pass over them. Hunt misses them because they go *towards* Mordor. The hunt goes West and North.

Now go on to describe the journey to Fiery Mountain. Footsteps come after them. Gollum has picked up trail.

Frodo and Sam journey by night down the slopes of Duath out into the dreadful waste of Gorgoroth.[34]

[The grey cloaks of Lothlórien must be made more magical and efficacious. 'Are these garments magical?' asks Frodo. 'We do not know what you mean by magical,' said they. 'They have virtues: for they are elvish.' They were green and grey: their property is to blend perfectly with all *natural* surroundings: leaves, boughs, grass, water, stone. Unless a full light of sun was on them, and the wearer was moving or set against the sky, they were not invisible, but *unnoticeable*.][35]

Far away they saw the underside of the Mountains stained red with the glow of Amarthon [*written above*: Dolamarth]: Mount Doom: the Mountain of Fire.[36] There is a constant rumble of thunder. Frodo feels the Eye. They come down a long

344   THE TREASON OF ISENGARD

ravine opening onto Gorgoroth beyond the south-east end of Kirith Ungol: it is end of road from Barad-dûr to Morgul.[37] Great hideous cavern[38] pillars. They peer [?out ?about] in the grey day over Gorgoroth. Mount Doom is smoking and burning to left. Black cloud lies over Baraddur. Millions of birds – [?led by vultures]: plain seems crawling with insects – a great host assembled – all sweeping out towards Kirith. By evening all plain is silent and empty. Cinders fall on plain. Moon rises late. Very dark. They begin the perilous crossing. Rustle of following feet. Journey all night.

Distances are rather too large – it would be eased if Orcs took Frodo to [?East] Guard Tower of R... – Loath and Grim [written above: Fell and Dire]. They could then see easier the host and would not have to cross Kirith Ungol.[39]

[Struck out: It could be Merry and Pippin that had adventure in Minas Morgul if Treebeard is cut out.][40]

From Dire-castle Gorgos (and Nargos) it would be only 70 miles. They could creep round edge of Eredlithui.[41]

Sam must fall out somehow. Stumble and break leg: thinks it is a crack in ground – really Gollum. [?Makes ?Make] Frodo go on alone.

Frodo toils up Mount Doom. Earth quakes, the ground is hot. There is a narrow path winding up. Three fissures. Near summit there is Sauron's Fire-well. An opening in side of mountain leads into a chamber the floor of which is split asunder by a cleft.[42]

Frodo turns and looks North-west, sees the dust of battle. Faint sound of horn. This is Windbeam the Horn of Elendil blown only in extremity.[43]

Birds circle over. Feet behind.

It is then at night before ascent of Mount Doom that Frodo sees the lone eye, like a window that does not move and yet searches in Baraddur.

Description of Baraddur seen afar.

I give here the latter part of a time-scheme of this period which covers the events of this outline plot. For the chronological structure in this scheme see p. 367 ('scheme I').

Dec. 25   Reach Tolbrandir in evening.
    26   Flight of Frodo.
Jan. 3   Gollum slips away.
      5   Frodo, Sam [struck out: and Gollum] reach Kirith Ungol.
      6   Frodo captured.
      8   Sam rescues Frodo in [Minas Morgul >] Gorgos.

THE STORY FORESEEN FROM LÓRIEN   345

  9   Sam and Frodo journey in Duath.
10   Sam and Frodo see host in Gorgoroth and lie hid.
       [*These two entries changed to read:* Jan. 9, 10, 11 Sam
       and Frodo journey in Eredlithui (see hosts going to war).]
12, 13   Ascent of Mount Doom.
14   [?Horns] ... Fall of Mordor.
15   Victory and return to Minas Tirith.
       [*Added:* Jan. 25 Reach Minas Tirith. Jan. 26 Great Feast.]

Notable points in this time-scheme are the corroboration of the statement in the text that Sam had been Ringbearer for two days (see p. 334 and note 30); the change in the place of Frodo's imprisonment from Minas Morgul to Gorgos (see p. 344 and notes 39, 41); and the mention of the great feast that followed the victory (cf. p. 212).

NOTES

1   On the back of the first page of this outline are some rough workings for revision of *The Lay of Aotrou and Itroun*, which was completed in its original form in 1930. This stray page perhaps shows my father turning to it again at this time. It was ultimately published in greatly revised form, to which these workings were moving, in 1945.

2   Cf. the outline *(c)* for 'Farewell to Lórien', p. 269: 'Arrows from East shore as they pass down river?'

3   *Tolharn* and *Tollernen* were passing replacements of *Tolondren*. Subsequently *Stoneait* (*ait* 'islet', = *eyot*) and *Tollernen* were struck out in pencil (all other changes in the opening section being made in ink) and replaced by *Eregon* (= *Stone pinnacle*). On *Eregon* see p. 323 note 12.

4   Sarn Gebir and Nomen's land (Nomenlands) emerged in the course of the writing of 'Farewell to Lórien' (pp. 281, 283).

5   *It is ill to be alone on the east side of the River*: this was left unchanged when the text immediately preceding was altered to the story that Frodo and Sam did not cross to the east bank but climbed the hill on the island where they camped. – In the outline *(c)* to 'Farewell to Lórien' (p. 269) it is told that 'They' crossed to the east bank and went up into the hills 'to look around', where 'They' may be the whole Company or Frodo and Sam only.

6   *Eredwethion* 'Mountains of Shadow' is derived from *The Silmarillion*.

7   With this scene compare the previous Plot (p. 208):
      Boromir takes Frodo apart and talks to him. Begs to see Ring again. Evil enters into his heart and he tries to daunt Frodo and

346   THE TREASON OF ISENGARD

then to take it by force. Frodo is obliged to slip it on to escape
him. (What does he see then – cloud all round him getting
nearer and many fell voices in air?)

In that Plot there is no mention of the Eye – but cf. the much
earlier outline dated August 1939 (VI.381): 'Horrible feeling of
an Eye searching for him'.

8   On the name *Dantruinel* for Rauros see pp. 285, 316.

9   It seems very likely that the reason for shifting the place where the
Company camped to the west bank of the river and making the
island inaccessible was to allow Merry and Pippin to become
separated and lost – a development that had already been
conceived in the previous Plot (see note 16).

10   I take these words, set in inverted commas, to be Boromir's,
referring deceitfully to Frodo's having put on the Ring.

11   The account of Sam's tracking of Frodo that follows is developed
from that in the previous Plot (p. 208):

> The search. Sam is lost. He tries to track Frodo and comes on
> Gollum. He follows Gollum and Gollum leads him to Frodo.
>
> Frodo hears following feet. And flies. But Sam comes up
> too to his surprise. The two are too much for Gollum. Gollum
> is *daunted* by Frodo – who has a power over him as Ring-
> bearer....
>
> Gollum pleads for forgiveness and feigns reform. They make
> him lead them through the Dead Marshes.

12   Sam is now on the east side of Anduin, and the boat 'knocking
against the bank' is the boat in which Frodo has crossed.

13   This paragraph ('Gollum was so intent on the trail...') evidently
replaced the story that preceded, although that was not struck
out.

14   Kirith Ungol was at this time the name of the great pass leading
into Mordor in the North-west (pp. 283, 285, and Map III on
p. 309).

15   At some time later my father struck it all out and wrote in pencil:

> Steep place where Frodo has to climb a precipice. Sam goes first
> so that if Frodo falls he will knock Sam down first. They see
> Gollum come down by moonlight *like a fly*.

This is where the story in *The Two Towers* (IV.1, 'The Taming of
Smeagol', p. 219) first appears.

16   Cf. the previous Plot, p. 210. It is seen from the synopsis that
immediately follows (pp. 329–30) of the chapter telling what
happened to Merry and Pippin that my father had still no idea
that anything more untoward had happened to them.

17   This passage remains virtually unchanged in substance from the
previous Plot (p. 211).

18   At a later stage my father pencilled in various developments to
Chapters XXII and XXIII (as renumbered). The synopsis of the

THE STORY FORESEEN FROM LÓRIEN   347

former he altered thus: 'Black orcs of Misty Mountains capture Merry and Pippin, bear them to Isengard. But the orcs are attacked by the Rohiroth on borders of Fangorn, and in the confusion Merry and Pippin escape unnoticed.' Also added here was 'Trotter is led astray by [?finding] orc-prints. He follows the orcs believing Frodo, Sam, etc. captured. He meets Gandalf.' To 'What happened to Gimli and Legolas' he added: 'Went with Trotter to rescue Merry and Pippin.'

19 Noted beside this sentence: S G – F asleep. F G – S asleep. S F – G asleep.

20 The origin of this passage is seen in the earlier Plot (p. 209): 'There is a ravine, a spiders' glen, they have to pass at entrance to Gorgoroth. Gollum gets spiders to put spell of sleep on Frodo. Sam drives them off. But cannot wake him.' Kirith Ungol was not yet its name when that was written: there is mention in that outline of the Gap of Gorgoroth, clearly the pass leading into Mordor (pp. 208, 213), but the words 'a ravine they have to pass' perhaps suggest that the 'spiders' glen' led off the Gap. In the present Plot, however, Kirith Ungol, ravine of spiders, is the pass itself.

21 It was no doubt put in when the story had gone somewhat past this point, since it is avowedly narrative in form and not outline (present tense).

22 This sentence is enclosed in square brackets in the original.

23 At the top of the page is written: 'All Sauron's folk, however, know that if Ringbearer is taken he is to be guarded as their life, but otherwise to be untouched and undespoiled, and brought intact to the Lord.' This was struck out.

24 On the Sea of Rhûn or Rhûnaer see p. 307.

25 This passage is enclosed in square brackets in the original.

26 For the site of Minas Morgul see Map III on p. 309. The Orcs appear to have come from there, in view of 'Sam gathers that they are going to Minas Morgul: since they are not allowed to leave their post'; and 'the path led up into the mountains' suggests that the way to Minas Morgul was by a track leading upwards out of Kirith Ungol; hence Sam sees 'from below' the Orcs entering the City.

27 Unless my father had decided to restore the original conception of Minas *Anor* in the East becoming Minas Morgul, and Minas *Ithil* in the West becoming Minas Tirith, which seems exceedingly improbable, this can only be a momentary confusion. But it occurs again: p. 366 note 19.

28 This passage is enclosed in square brackets in the original.

29 *mithered*: 'confused, bewildered'. My father often used this English dialect word, though as I recollect always in the form *moithered*; but *mithered* is recorded from Staffordshire and

348 THE TREASON OF ISENGARD

Warwickshire and the neighbouring counties of the English midlands.

30 This sentence is enclosed in square brackets in the original. Two days seems a very long time to have elapsed since Sam took the Ring from Frodo in Kirith Ungol, and is by no means suggested in the narrative; on the other hand, on Map III (p. 309) Minas Morgul was at least 30 miles from the eastern edge of the Mountains of Shadow at Kirith Ungol. See also the time scheme on pp. 344–5.

31 It should be emphasized that the fact of its being written at this stage in the history of *The Lord of the Rings*, and not later, is clear and certain.

32 This refers of course to Sam's entry into Minas Morgul, alone.

33 Cf. 'The Tower of Cirith Ungol' in *The Return of the King*, p. 178: 'They were like great figures seated upon thrones. Each had three joined bodies, and three heads facing outward, and inward, and across the gateway. The heads had vulture-faces, and on their great knees were laid clawlike hands.' – A little diagrammatic sketch is included in the manuscript at this point:

34 *Duath* (replacing *Eredwethion*, p. 325) is the name of the Mountains of Shadow on the First Map and on my map made in 1943; my father added *Ephel* before *Duath* on both maps subsequently (pp. 309–10). – The sentence was changed in pencil to read: 'Frodo and Sam journey by night among the slopes and ravines N. of Duath towards the dreadful waste of Gorgoroth.'

35 The brackets are in the original. This notable passage is the origin of the much enlarged description of the cloaks of Lothlórien which first appears as an addition to the fair copy of 'Farewell to Lórien' (p. 285), though expressed in a wholly different way. The question 'Are these garments magical?', here asked by Frodo, was then given to Merry, and finally (FR p. 386) to Pippin ('Are these magic cloaks?').

36 The first devising of an elvish name for Mount Doom (later *Amon Amarth*).

37 My father first wrote here: 'They come down a long ravine opening on Kirith Un(gol)', striking out this name at once and writing instead 'opening onto Gorgoroth', etc. It is hard to be sure, but it seems likely that he saw a path climbing up to Minas Morgul out of Kirith Ungol (the pass into Mordor), by which Frodo was taken, and another more southerly approach, a road running westwards from the Dark Tower and climbing to Minas

THE STORY FORESEEN FROM LÓRIEN 349

Morgul by the 'long ravine' down which Sam and Frodo made their escape (see Map III, p. 309).

38 This word is clearly written *cavern*, not *carven*.

39 This short paragraph is very hard to read and not easy to interpret, but at least it is clear that here is the first suggestion of a doubt that it was to Minas Morgul that Frodo was taken. The word I have given as *East* begins *Ea* but does not look at all like *East*; yet that seems appropriate to the sense (see further note 41). The name of the tower might be *Rame* or *Raine*, among other possibilities. The words 'They would not have to cross Kirith Ungol' are at first sight puzzling, since it has just been said that they emerged from the long ravine 'beyond the south-east end of Kirith Ungol'; but I think that my father meant that they would not have to cross the open plain between the Mountains of Shadow and the Ash Mountains (Ered Lithui), whether this be called Kirith Ungol or Gorgoroth at that point.

40 See p. 339; and for an earlier suggestion that Merry and Pippin might find themselves in Mordor see p. 211.

41 On the First Map there are two small circles on either side of Kirith Ungol (on my redrawing, square P 15 on Map II, p.305). These reappear on my 1943 map as two small towers. On neither map are they named; but it seems clear that they represent a western and an eastern guard tower – presumably the Nargos and Gorgos named here (cf. 'There are Orc guard-towers on either side of Gorgoroth', p. 208). The words 'From Dire-castle Gorgos (and Nargos) it would be only 70 miles' mean, I think, 'From the eastern tower Gorgos (and for the matter of that from the western tower Nargos also) it was only 70 miles to Mount Doom.'

42 The three fissures and Sauron's well of fire appear in the earlier Plot (p. 209), but this is the first glimpse of the Sammath Naur.

43 *Windbeam*: if this name occurs elsewhere in my father's writings I have not found it, except in the Last Letter of Father Christmas, where he calls it the Great Horn, and says that he has not had to blow it for over four hundred years (cf. 'only in extremity' here) and that its sound carries as far as the North Wind blows. (Cf. Old English *bēme (bēam)* 'trumpet'.)

XVII

THE GREAT RIVER

It has been seen (pp. 324, 330) that having written an outline of the story from the departure from Lórien to the 'Scattering of the Company' at 'Tollernen' my father decided that the first element in the outline, 'The Company sets off from Tongue', should in fact form the conclusion to Chapter XX ('Farewell to Lórien'), and XXI should take up with 'They are attacked with arrows'.

As I have mentioned (p. 283), the original draft for the last section of 'Farewell to Lórien' (i.e. 'The Company sets off from Tongue') was written in ink in a clear script with little hesitation. That draft section ends with the words 'End of Ch. XX', showing that the chapter-arrangement just referred to had already been devised. The character-istic very pale ink used for this section was also used for the text 'The Story Foreseen from Lórien' and for the first part of the new chapter XXI: the three texts have a strong general likeness, and were obviously written at the same time.

The draft of the last section of 'Farewell to Lórien' ends halfway down a page, and is followed by 'XXI: The Scattering of the Company'; at this stage my father assumed that the narrative outlined on pp. 324–8, 329 (i.e. excluding the story of Sam's tracking of Frodo) would constitute a single chapter. For the journey down the River to 'Tollernen' he had set down no more in the way of event than 'They are attacked with arrows.' I give now the opening draft of the new chapter as it was first written.[1]

Sam woke him. He was lying in a bed of blankets and furs under tall grey-stemmed trees near the river bank. The grey of morning was dim among the bare branches. Gimli was busy with a small fire near at hand. He had slept the first night of their river journey away. They started again before the day was broad. Not that most of the Company were eager to hurry southwards: they were content that the decision which they must make when they came to Rauros and the Isle of Eregon[2] lay yet some days ahead, and still less did they wish to run swiftly into the perils that certainly lay beyond, whatever course they took, but Trotter felt that the time was urgent and that willing or not they should hasten forward.

THE GREAT RIVER   351

As the second day of their voyage wore on the lands changed slowly: trees thinned and then failed: on the East bank to their left, long formless slopes stretched up and away towards the sky; brown they looked as if a fire had passed over them, leaving no living thing of green; an unfriendly waste without even a withered tree or a bold stone to break the emptiness. They were come to the Brown Lands, the Withered Wold that lay in a vast desolation between Dol Dúghul in Southern Mirkwood and the hills of Sarn-Gebir: what pestilence of war or fell deed of the Lord of Mordor had so blasted all that region they did not know.[3] Upon the west bank to their right the land was treeless and quite flat, but green: there were forests of reeds of great height in places that shut out the view as the little boats went rustling by along their fluttering borders: the great withered flowering heads bent in the light cold airs hissing softly and waving like funeral plumes. Here and there in open spaces they could see across the wide rolling meads hills far away, or on the edge of sight a dark line where still the southernmost phalanx of the Misty Mountains marched.

'You are looking out across the great pastures of Rohan, the Riddermark, land of the Horsemasters,' said Trotter; 'but in these evil days they do not dwell nigh the river or ride often to its shores. Anduin is wide, yet the orc-bows will with ease shoot an arrow across the stream.'

The hobbits looked from bank to bank uneasily. If before the trees had seemed hostile, as if harbouring secret dangers, now they felt that they were too naked: afloat in little open boats in the midst of wide bare land, on a river that was the boundary of war. As they went on the feeling of insecurity grew upon them. The river broadened and grew shallow: bleak stony beaches lay upon the east, there were gravel shoals in the water and they had to steer carefully. The Brownlands rose into bleak wolds over which flowed a chill air from the East. Upon the other side the meads had become low rolling downs of grey grass, a land of fen and tussock. They shivered thinking of the lawns and fountains, the clear sun and gentle rain of Lothlórien: there was little speech and no laughter among them. Each was busy with his own thoughts. Sam had long since made up his mind that though boats were maybe not as dangerous as he had been brought up to believe, they were far more uncomfortable. He was cramped and miserable, having nothing to do but stare at the winter lands crawling by and the dark grey water, for the

352   THE TREASON OF ISENGARD

Company used the paddles mainly for steering, and in any case they would not have trusted Sam with a paddle. Merry and Pippin in the middle boat were ill at ease. [*Added and then struck out:* Merry was at the stern, facing Sam and steering.] Boromir sat muttering to himself, sometimes biting his nails as if some restlessness or doubt consumed him. Often Pippin who sat in the prow, looking back, caught a queer gleam in his eye when he peered forward gazing at the boat in front where Frodo sat.

So the time passed until the end of the sixth [> seventh] day. The banks were still bare, but on both sides on the slopes above them bushes were scattered, behind and further south ridges with twisted fir-trees could be glimpsed: they were drawing near the grey hill country of Sarn-Gebir: the southern border of Wilderland, beyond which lay the Nomanland and the foul marshes that lay for many leagues before the passes of Mordor. High in the air there were flocks of dark birds. Trotter looked at them with disquiet.

'I fear we have been too slow and overbold,' he said. 'Maybe we have come too far by day, and ere this we should have taken to journeying between dusk and dawn and lain hidden in the day.'

He stayed his boat with his paddle, and when the others came up he spoke to them, counselling that they should go on into the night, and put off their rest until night was old and dawn was at hand. 'And if we make another two or three leagues,' said he, 'we shall come, if I am right in my memories, to Sarn Gebir, where the river begins to run in deep channels: there maybe we shall find better shelter and more secrecy.'

Already twilight was about them. The hobbits at any rate had been hoping soon for the warmth of a fire to their cold feet, and the feel of solid earth beneath them. But there seemed no place in that houseless country which invited them to halt; and a cold drowsiness was on them, numbing thought. They made no answer, yes or no. Trotter drove his paddle in the water and led them on again. [*Added:* The stars leapt out above. The sky [was] clear and cold. It was nearly night when][4] Just ahead there loomed up rocks in the midst of the stream, nearer to the west bank. To the east there was a wider channel, and that way they turned: but they found the current swift. In the dusk they could see pale foam and water beating against the rocks upon the right hand.

'This is an evil time of day to pass through such a dangerous

THE GREAT RIVER

353

reach,' said Boromir. 'Hey Trotter,' he cried, cupping his hands and calling above the noise of the waters to the boat ahead – it was already too dark to see whether it was far or near. 'Hey!' he called. 'Not this way tonight!'

'No indeed,' said Trotter, and they saw that he had turned his boat and had come back almost alongside without their seeing him. 'No: I did not know we had come so far yet: the Anduin flows faster than I reckoned. The rapids of Pensarn[5] are ahead. They are not very long nor very fierce, yet too dangerous to venture on in the dark for those who know the Great River little or only from tales. See,' he said, 'the current has flung us right over to the east shore: in a little we shall be on the shoals. Let us turn and go back to the western side, above the rocks.'

Even as he spoke there was a twanging, and arrows whistled over and among them. One smote Frodo between the shoulders but fell back, foiled by the hidden coat of mail; another passed through Trotter's hair; and a third stood fast in the gunwale of the middle boat close by Merry's hand.

'To the west bank!' shouted Boromir and Trotter together. They leaned forward straining at the paddles – even Sam now took a hand, but it was not so easy. The current was flowing strong. Each one expected at any minute to feel the sting of a blackfeathered orc-arrow. But it was now grown very dark, dark even for the keen night-eyes of goblins; goblins were on the bank, they did not doubt. When they had come into midstream as far as they could judge, and out of the swirl of waters running into the narrow channel, Legolas laid down his paddle, and lifting the bow he had brought from Lórien strung it, and turned, peering back into the gloom. Across the water there came shrill cries; but he could see nothing. The enemy were shooting wildly now and few arrows came near the boats: it was grown very dark: there was not even a grey glimmer on the face of the river, only here and there the broken twinkle reflecting a misty star.

As he gazed into the blackness away east the clouds broke and the white rind of the new moon appeared riding slowly up the sky; [but its faint light did little to illumine the further shore.][6] Sam looked up at it in wonder.[7] Even as he did so a dark shape, like a cloud yet not a cloud, low and ominous, for a moment shut off the thin crescent and winged its way towards them, until it appeared as a great winged shape black against the dark heaven.[8] Fierce voices greeted it from across the water.

354   THE TREASON OF ISENGARD

Frodo felt a sudden chill about his heart, and a cold like the
memory of an old wound in his shoulder: he crouched down in
the boat.

Suddenly the great bow of Legolas sang. He heard an arrow
whistle / whine. He looked up. The winged shape swerved: there
was a harsh croaking cry and it seemed to fall, vanishing down
into the darkness of the eastern shore; the sky seemed clean
again. They heard a tumult as of many voices murmuring and
lamenting [*written above:* cursing], and then silence. No more
arrows came towards them.

'Praised be the bow of Galadriel and the keen eye of Legolas!'
said Gimli. 'That was a mighty shot in the dark.'

'But what it hit who can say,' said Boromir.

'I cannot,' said Gimli. 'Yet I liked that shape as little as the
shadow of the Balrog of Moria.'

'It was not a Balrog,' said Frodo, still shivering. 'I think it
was...' He did not finish.

'You think what?' asked Boromir quickly.

'I do not know,' said Frodo. 'Whatever it was its fall seems to
have dismayed the enemy.'

'So it seems,' said Trotter. 'Yet where they are, and how
many, or what they will do next, we do not know. This night
must be watchful!'

At last the boats were brought to the western bank again.
Here they moored them close inshore. They did not lie on the
land that night, but remained in the boats with weapons close to
hand. One sat alert and vigilant watching either bank while the
other [? *read* others] dozed uneasily.

Sam[9] looked at the moon again, slipping down now swiftly to
the horizon. 'It is very strange,' he murmured drowzily. 'The
moon I suppose does not change his courses in Wilderland?
Then I must be wrong in my reckoning. If you remember, the
old moon was at its end as we lay on the flet up in that tree.[10]
Well now I can't remember how long we were in that country: it
was certainly three nights, and I seem to remember a good many
more – but I am certain sure it was not a month. Yet here we
are: seven days from Lórien and up pops a New Moon. Why,
anyone would think we had come straight from Nimrodel
without stopping a night or seeing Caras Galadon. Funny it
seems.'

'And that Sam is probably about the truth of it,' said Trotter.

THE GREAT RIVER   355

'Whether we were in the past or the future or in a time that does not pass, I cannot say: but not I think till Silverlode bore us back to Anduin did we return to the stream of time that flows through mortal lands to the Great Sea. At least, so I guess: but maybe I dream and talk nonsense. Yet do either of you remember seeing any moon in Lórien, old or young? I remember only stars by night and sun by day.'[11]

The text, becoming ragged at the end, now peters out in pencilled notes for its continuation:

In morning Trotter and Legolas go forward to find path. They lie hid among rocks all day and at evening laboriously cart their boats to end of the rapids. (Hear the sound as they pass.) No sign on far shore. Below rapids stream is soon quiet and deep again – but less broad. They creep along the west bank by night. They pass into the gullies of Sarn Gebir. Pinewoods. About dawn on 10th day come to Eregon [*later* > Tol Brandor *or* -ir] and hear roar and [?foam] of Rauros. Inaccessible isle high peak many birds.[12]

In the journey down Anduin at this stage the chronology differed by one day from that in FR, for the attack at the head of the rapids took place at the end of the seventh day (p. 352), not of the eighth (FR pp. 400–1), and much detail remained to be changed or added: notably the incident of Gollum, the 'log with eyes', was absent. This story was written on a separate sheet while the drafting of the chapter was still in progress, and was immediately achieved in the final form at almost all points. Some of the Company were sleeping that night on the eyot and some in the boats; and after Frodo had seen Gollum's eyes and had put his hand on the hilt of Sting the original text continues:

Immediately they [the eyes] went out, and there was a soft splash and a dark shape shot away downstream into the night. Nothing else occurred, until the first grey of dawn peeped in the East. Trotter awoke on the eyot and came down to the boats. But Frodo now knew that Sam had not been deceived; and also that he must warn Trotter.
    'So you know about our little footpad, do you? . . .

Primary drafting from the point reached (the discussion of Time in Lórien) is of an extreme roughness, some of it scribbled faintly between the lines of the candidates' writing on examination scripts, and it is not entirely complete and consecutive. In this case the fair copy manuscript, following immediately on the primary drafting, is

356   THE TREASON OF ISENGARD

the first complete text, and it is most convenient to turn now to this manuscript.

In this version Chapter XXI bore a succession of titles, all of them pencilled in subsequently: 'Southward'; 'The Company is Scattered'; 'Sarn Gebir'; 'Breaking of the Fellowship'; and finally 'The Great River' – this last not struck out, and obviously arising when my father had decided that his original ideas for XXI had so expanded as to require two chapters to fulfil the narrative. As usual, in point of expression the fair copy advances very largely to the form in FR, although a good deal of change in respect of the actual narrative had still to come.

To the original opening of the chapter (p. 350) my father made the following alteration and addition on the manuscript of the draft:

Sam woke him. He was lying in a bed of blankets and furs under tall grey-stemmed trees near the bank of the Great River, in a corner of quiet woodland where a small stream (the Limlight) flowed in from the western mountains.

This is the first mention of the Limlight in the texts. In the fair copy the chapter opens:

Frodo was roused by Sam. He found that he was lying, well wrapped, under tall grey-skinned trees in a quiet corner of the woodlands. [Beside them a stream ran down from the western mountains far away and joined the Great River close by their camp] on the western bank of the Great River Anduin.

The sentence I have bracketed was struck out as soon as written. That their first night camp on the journey down the River was beside the inflow of Limlight agrees with maps IV^B and IV^C (p. 317), where the Limlight, here first shown, joins Anduin not far south of Silverlode (see Map II, square M 12); on map IV^D the confluence is much further south (p. 319).

Where the draft has 'Rauros and the Isle of Eregon' (p. 350) the new text has 'Rauros and the Isle' (changed later to 'the Tindrock Isle', as in FR). Trotter's policy of letting them drift with the stream as they wished appears; but the chronology remains here as in the draft: 'Nonetheless they saw no sign of any[13] enemy that day. The dull grey hours passed without event. As this second day of their voyage wore on, the lands changed slowly...' The 'Withered Wold' of the draft becomes 'the withered wolds' (and was then struck out). The flight of the black swans is still absent.

Trotter now speaks of the latitude and climate, the Bay of Belfalas, and their distance from the Shire – but here he first said 'I doubt if you are much more than sixty leagues south of the Sarn Ford at the southern end of your Shire', this being changed at once to the reading

THE GREAT RIVER 357

of FR; and he says that 'ere long we shall come to the mouth of the Limlight' (see above),[14] defining the Limlight, as in FR, as the north boundary of Rohan. But he says here 'Of old all that lay between Limlight and Entwash belonged to the Horsemasters' (FR: 'all that lay between Limlight and the White Mountains belonged to the Rohirrim').

In the next part of the chapter (after the episode of Gollum in the river) the story advances to the form in FR, but it was still at the end of the seventh day of the journey, not of the eighth, that they came to the rapids, and there is no mention at this point of the weather, or of the New Moon, which in FR (p. 400) was first seen on the seventh night. Though the bird-haunted cliffs of Sarn Gebir and the flocks of birds circling high above are described in the same words as in FR (p. 401) there is no mention of the eagle seen far off in the western sky. Following the mention of the birds, the new version continues thus:

Trotter had glanced often at them doubtfully, wondering if Gollum had been up to some mischief. But now it was dark: the East was overcast, but in the West many stars were shining.

After they had been paddling for about an hour, Trotter told Sam to lie forward in the boat and keep a sharp look-out ahead. 'We shall soon come to the gates of Sarn-Gebir,' he said; 'and the river is difficult and dangerous there, if I remember rightly. It runs in deep swift channels under overhanging cliffs, and there are many rocks and eyots in the stream. But I do not know these reaches, for I have never journeyed by water in these parts before. We must halt early tonight, if we can, and go on by daylight.'

It was close on midnight, and they had been drifting for a while, resting after a long spell of paddling, when suddenly Sam cried out.

After Boromir's shouted remonstrance ('This is a bad time of day to shoot the rapids!') Trotter, struggling to back and turn his boat, said to Frodo: 'I am out of my reckoning. I didn't know we had come so far. We must have passed the gates of Sarn-Gebir in the dark. The Rapids of Pensarn must be just ahead' (the last two sentences were crossed out, probably immediately). There is no indication here of what 'the gates of Sarn-Gebir' might be (see p. 359).

The attack by Orcs from the east bank, and the struggle to get the boats back to the west bank, follows the draft pretty closely, with some changed or added detail: an arrow passed through Trotter's hood, not his hair; Frodo 'lurched forward with a cry'. The weather is changed from the obscure statements in the draft (note 6): the clouds in the east mentioned earlier had now almost entirely covered the sky,

358   THE TREASON OF ISENGARD

and so 'it was very dark, dark even for the night-eyes of orcs' as they paddled the boats back. The same is said of the New Moon 'riding slowly up the sky' in 'a sudden break in the cloud-cover away in the East' as in the draft (see note 7); here it is seen 'passing behind dark isles of cloud and out into black pools of night.' In FR (p. 401) it had set hours before.

Sam's remarks about Time in Lothlórien remain almost exactly as in the draft (p. 354), as does Trotter's reply (in FR given to Frodo), except that he now says (as does Frodo in FR): 'In that land, maybe, we were in some time that elsewhere has long gone by.' Then Frodo speaks:

'The power of the Lady was on us,' said Frodo. 'There are days and nights and seasons in Lothlórien; but while she holds the ring, the world grows no older in her realm.'
'That should not have been said,' muttered Trotter, half rising and looking towards the other boats; 'not outside Lórien, not even to me.'[15]

The warm and foggy morning that succeeded the night of the attack and the argument between Aragorn and Boromir about the course to follow were roughly sketched in initial drafting, where the conversation proceeds thus:

'I do not see why we should pass the rapids or follow this cursed River any further,' said Boromir. 'If Pensarn lies before us, then we can abandon these cockles and strike westward, and so come round the east shoulders of Sarn-Gebir and cross the Entwash into my own land of Ondor.'
'We can, if we make for Minas Tirith,' said Trotter. 'But that is not yet agreed. And even so such a course is perhaps more perilous than it seems. The land is flat and shelterless south and east [read west] of Sarn-Gebir, and the [?first] ford over Entwash is a great way west.[16] Since the Enemy took ... Osgiliath that land may be full of foes: what do we know of events of late in Rohan or in Ondor?'
'Yet here the Enemy marches all along the east bank,' said Boromir. 'And when you come to Rauros what will you do? You must then either turn back hitherward, or cross the hills of Gebir and land in the marshes, and still have the Entwash to cross.'
'The River is at least a path that cannot be missed. In the vale of Entwash fog is a mortal peril. I would not abandon the boats until we must,' said Trotter. 'And I have a fancy that in some

THE GREAT RIVER   359

high place above the Falls we may be able to see some sign that shall direct us.'

That a 'high place' would be the scene of a decisive moment in the unfolding of the story had already been conceived: the summit of the island in the River whence Frodo looked out (p. 324); but there is no suggestion in Trotter's words here that this 'high place' would be an ancient post of the men of Ondor.

In the fair copy manuscript Boromir objects: 'But the Enemy holds the eastern bank. And even if you pass the gates of Gebir, and come unmolested to the Tindrock, what will you do then? Climb down from the hills and land in the marshes?' Here, the 'gates of Gebir' are the later Gates of Argonath; thus the earlier references (p. 357), where Trotter places the 'gates' before the rapids, had already been rejected.

Of Trotter's reply to Boromir's scoffing question there are three forms: a draft text in pencil taking up at this point, and two versions in the fair copy manuscript. The first version in the manuscript has Trotter reply:

'Say rather, climb down from the hills to Rauros-foot and then take boat again, and hope to slip unseen up the mouths of Entwash – if we go to Minas Tirith. Do you choose to forget the ancient path, Boromir, and the high seat upon Tol-Brandir, that were made in the days of Valandil?[17] I at least have a mind to stand in that high place before I decide my course. There maybe we shall see some sign that will direct us.'

This version of Trotter's reply was struck out, and the pencilled draft (which continues on for some distance) seems to have been written at this point. This draft begins:

'No,' said Trotter. 'Do you choose to forget, Boromir, the North Stair, and the high seat upon Tol-Brandir that were made in the days of Isildur? I at least have a mind to stand in that high place again before I decide my course. There maybe we shall see some sign that will guide us. Thence we [may] perhaps descend by the ancient way to Rauros-foot and take again to the water; and those who make for Minas Tirith may slip unseen up the mouths of Entwash.'

Finally, the second version written in the manuscript is as in FR (p. 406), but still with 'in the days of Isildur' for 'in the days of the great kings', and the high seat is still upon the isle – which is here *Tol-Brandor* for *Tol-Brandir* of the previous versions. The isle therefore was not inaccessible; and this is puzzling, for the inaccessibility of Tol Brandir is found both in the outline given on p. 328 and in the preliminary draft material for the present chapter (p. 355).

360 THE TREASON OF ISENGARD

Trotter's words before he and Legolas set off into the fog to find a path take this form (and are very similar in the draft):

'No road was ever made along this bank by the men of Ondor: for even in their great days their realm did not reach beyond Sarn-Gebir, and the high seat upon the Tindrock was their northmost watchtower. Yet there must be some path, or the remains of one; for light boats used to journey out of Wilderland down to Osgiliath; and still did so, until Sauron returned to Mordor.'

'But he has returned,' said Boromir; 'and if you go forward, you are likely to meet some peril, whether you find a path or no.'

The story of the exploration made by Trotter and Legolas, their return, the portage of the boats and baggage, and the departure of the Company next morning, reaches in the fair copy virtually the text of FR, with *Pensarn* for *Sarn Gebir* as the name of the rapids and the *Gates of Sarn-Gebir* for the *Gates of Argonath*. From painfully difficult writing the original description of the Pillars of the Kings can be extracted out of the initial drafting, of which I give the following as an example:

The great pillars seemed to rise up like giants before him as the river whirled him like a leaf towards them. Then he saw that [they] were carved, or had been carved many ages ago, and still preserved through the suns and rains of many forgotten years the likenesses that had been hewn upon them. Upon great pedestals founded in the deep water stood two great kings of stone gazing through blurred eyes northwards. The left hand of each was raised beside his head palm outwards in gesture of [?warning] and refusal: in each right hand there was a sword. On each head there was a crumbling crown and helm. There was still a power in these silent wardens of a long-vanished kingdom.

In the fair copy the text of FR was almost reached, through a good deal of correction as the manuscript was being written.

Trotter's words as they passed through the chasm ('"Fear not!" said a strange voice behind him...') are exactly as in FR (p. 409), except in two notable respects: 'In the stern sat Elfstone son of Elfhelm' – a decisive demonstration of the correctness of the view (p. 277) that *Elfstone* had reappeared and supplanted *Ingold*; and 'Under their shadow nought has Eldamir son of Eldakar son of Valandil to fear.'[18] It seems very improbable indeed that some other Valandil is meant

THE GREAT RIVER   361

and not the son of Isildur: only shortly before Valandil has been named in a draft ('in the days of Valandil', p. 359 and note 17, where the text immediately replacing this has 'in the days of Isildur'), and in the corresponding passage to the present in FR Aragorn calls himself 'son of Arathorn of the House of Valandil Isildur's son'. But if this Valandil is the son of Isildur, then at this stage Trotter/Elfstone/ Aragorn was the great-grandson of Isildur; and what then are we to make of the Pillars of the Kings, carved *many ages ago*, preserved through the suns and rains of *many forgotten years*, the silent wardens of *a long-vanished kingdom*? How can Frodo's amazement at the Council of Elrond that Elrond should remember the array of the Last Alliance ('But I thought the fall of Gilgalad was *many ages ago*', p. 110) be reconciled to a matter of four generations of mortal Men? And Gandalf had said to Frodo at Rivendell (p. 105 note 3) that 'he is Aragorn son of Kelegorn, *descended through many fathers* from Isildur the son of Elendil.' For the moment, at any rate, I can cast no light on this.[19]

After the description of the Pillars of the Kings there is no further initial drafting, and the earliest, or earliest extant, text is the fair copy manuscript, in which the conclusion of the chapter 'The Great River' in FR is very closely approached. Trotter, so called throughout the chapter until he becomes 'Elfstone son of Elfhelm' when they pass the Pillars of the Kings, is called 'Elfstone' when he points to Tol Brandir at the far end of the lake (which is not named): see p. 370. And after 'Behold Tol Brandir!' he says no more than 'Ere the shade of night falls we shall come thither. I hear the endless voice of Rauros calling.' The journey had taken nine days; in FR 'the tenth day of their journey was over.'

In the foregoing account I have attempted to discern the form of the fair copy manuscript as my father first set it down; but the text was heavily worked on, and certainty in distinguishing immediate from subsequent corrections is not possible without close examination of the original papers. This manuscript, as emended and added to, reached in fact almost the form of the final text; yet an object of this history is to try to determine the mode and pace in which the whole structure came into being. Since some error is inevitable, I have erred by assuming, if uncertain, a correction to be 'later' rather than 'immediate'; but that a good deal of the development took place during this present phase of writing is clear. In particular, it is clear that the entire section of the narrative from the end of the Gollum episode to the escape of the Company from the rapids had been rewritten before my father reached 'The Departure of Boromir', because an outline for the opening of that chapter (p. 380) refers to Trotter's having seen an eagle far off from the river 'above the rapids of Sarn Ruin',[20] and this element (previously absent, p. 357) is

362 THE TREASON OF ISENGARD

inseparable from the whole complex of revision at this point in the present chapter.

This revision was carried out on inserted slips, one of which is an Oxford University committee report dated 10 March 1941. This slip provides of course only a *terminus a quo*, and proves no more than that my father was revising this chapter during or after March 1941; while a similar slip, dated 19 February 1941, used for initial drafting at a later point in Chapter XXI (i.e. in the part corresponding to 'The Breaking of the Fellowship' in FR), proves no more. It might be argued that he would scarcely have preserved such reports of committee meetings for use long after, and that these revisions therefore belong to 1941, but this is much too flimsy to support any view of the external dating. See further p. 379.

The next version of the chapter was a manuscript made by myself, presumptively after 4 August 1942, the date that I wrote at the end of my copy of '[The Mirror of] Galadriel' (p. 261). I think that this copy of mine provides exact evidence of the state of this chapter when my father moved on from it to new regions of the story, and I shall now therefore turn to it, noticing first certain names (in the form in which I wrote them, of course, and before subsequent emendation by my father).

Sarn-Gebir remains in my copy, for later *Emyn Muil*; the *Gates of Gebir* or the *Gates of Sarn-Gebir* for the *(Gates of) Argonath*;[21] and *Ondor* for *Gondor*. *Trotter* remains *Trotter*, because my father had not emended it on his manuscript, until the end of the chapter, where the Company passes beneath the Pillars of the Kings, and he is called in the first manuscript 'Elfstone son of Elfhelm': this my father had changed to 'Aragorn son of Arathorn', and my copy follows. On the other hand he did not correct 'Under their shadow nought has Eldamir son of Eldakar son of Valandil to fear', and my copy retains it. This might be thought to be a mere inconsistency of correction on his part; but this is evidently not the case, since on *both* manuscripts he added a further step in the genealogy: 'Eldamir *son of Valatar* son of Eldakar son of Valandil.' Since he did not strike out 'Eldamir son of Eldakar son of Valandil' on my copy, but on the contrary accepted the genealogy and slightly enlarged it, it must be presumed that *Eldamir* beside *Aragorn* was intentional; cf. FR (p. 409): 'Under their shadow Elessar, the Elfstone son of Arathorn ... has nought to dread!', and cf. *Eldamir* > *Elessar*, p. 294. My father's retention of the genealogy, with the addition of Valatar, is also remarkable in that it shows him still accepting the brief span of generations separating Aragorn from Isildur.

By the criterion of presence or absence in my copy of the chapter the flight of the black swans was added early. The chronology remained as it was, the attack at the rapids taking place on the night of the seventh

THE GREAT RIVER

363

day; and the references to the New Moon in FR pp. 400–1 are still absent. The New Moon still first appears in the course of the attack, but changed in that the clouds through which it broke were now in the South, and the Moon rode 'across' not 'up' the sky (see pp. 353, 358).

The conversation concerning Time in Lothlórien (p. 358) was developed in several competing and overlapping riders, and when I came to make my copy my father evidently instructed me to set the passage out in variant forms. The opening speeches (Sam's and Trotter's – the latter given in FR to Frodo) remained effectively unchanged – Sam's now ending: 'Why, anyone would think we had come straight on, and never passed no time in the Elvish land at all.'[22] The conversation that follows contains two pairs of alternatives, which I here mark with numbers: 1 to 1 or 2 to 2 being alternatives, and (within 2) 3 to 3 or 4 to 4 being alternatives.

1 'The power of the Lady was on us,' said Frodo. 'I do not think that there was no time in her land. There are days and nights and seasons in Lothlórien; and under the Sun all things must wear to an end sooner or later. But slowly indeed does the world wear away in Caras Galadon, where the Lady Galadriel wields the Elven Ring.'[1]

2 Legolas stirred in his boat. 'Nay, I think that neither of you understand the matter aright,' he said. 'For the Elves the world moves, and it moves both very swift and very slow. Swift, because they themselves change little, and all else fleets by: it is a grief to them. Slow, because they do[23] not count the running years, not for themselves. The passing seasons are but ripples ever repeated in the flowing/endless stream. Yet beneath the Sun all things must wear to an end at last.'

3 'But Lórien is not as other realms of Elves and Men,' said Frodo. 'The Power of the Lady was upon us. Slow for us there might time have passed, while the world hastened. Or in a little while we could savour much, while the world tarried. The latter was her will. Rich were the hours and slow the wearing of the world in Caras Galadon, where the Lady Galadriel wields the Elven Ring.'[3]

4 'But Lothlórien is not as other realms of Elves and Men,' said Frodo. 'Rich are the hours, and slow the wearing of the world in Caras Galadon. Wherefore all things there are both unstained and young, and yet aged beyond our count of time. Blended is the might of Youth and Eld in the land of Lórien, where Galadriel wields the Elven Ring.'[4, 2]

'That should not have been said,' muttered Trotter, half rising

364 THE TREASON OF ISENGARD

and looking towards the other boats; 'not outside Lórien, not even to me.'

The night passed silently ...

At the end of the chapter the lake remains nameless in my copy, first *Kerin-muil* and then *Nen-uinel* being added to both manuscripts; but an addition to my father's manuscript in which Aragorn speaks of Amon Hen and Amon Lhaw was made before my copy was written. This addition is precisely as in FR p. 410, except that both manuscripts have 'In the days of Isildur' for 'In the days of the great kings', and both add after Amon Lhaw '[Larmindon]' and after Amon Hen '[Tirmindon]'.

The original drafting shows that my father included all the narrative to the end of 'The Fellowship of the Ring' as Chapter XXI, and the fair copy manuscript likewise; but it is convenient to interrupt it at the point where the break (present in my copy) between XXI 'The Great River' and XXII 'The Breaking of the Fellowship' was subsequently made.

NOTES

1 Like the companion texts, the last section of 'Farewell to Lórien' and 'The Story Foreseen from Lórien', this was written very legibly for one of my father's initial drafts, and with remarkably little hesitation. I take up small changes made at the time of composition into the text given.

2 This is the first occurrence of *Rauros* in a text *ab initio*. For *Eregon* see p. 345 note 3.

3 I have attempted to set out the evolution of the Brown Lands in relation to the First Map on pp. 313–16. In this passage appears the description of them that survived with very little change into FR (p. 396).

4 It looks as if this addition were made immediately. See note 6.

5 My father wrote here first *Sarn*, then *Pen*, striking them out in turn before arriving at *Pensarn* (cf. the *Etymologies*, stems PEN, SAR, V.380, 385).

6 The brackets are in the original. – The weather described is obscure. Nothing is in fact said in this earliest form of the narrative about the weather during the journey down Anduin until the evening of the seventh day, when the weather was clear and cold, and starlit (but this was an addition); now, not much

THE GREAT RIVER   365

later, it was very dark, though the water reflected here and there a misty star. Then, 'as Legolas gazed into the blackness away east the clouds broke.'

7 'Sam looked up at it in wonder': as well he might, seeing 'the white rind of the new moon' rising in the East and 'riding up the sky'. This is strangely paralleled in VI.325, where the moon on the night spent by the hobbits with the Elves in the Woody End was described thus: 'Above the mists away in the East the thin silver rind of the New Moon appeared, and rising swift and clear out of the shadow it swung gleaming in the sky.' In FR (pp. 400–1) the new moon is seen glimmering in the western sky on the evening before the Orc-attack, and on the evening of the attack 'the thin crescent of the Moon had fallen early into the pale sunset.'

As the text was written it was Trotter who 'looked up at it in wonder'. This was changed first to Merry, then to Sam; see note 9.

8 The dark shape 'like a cloud yet not a cloud' that momentarily cut off the moon's light is surely reminiscent of the shadow that passed over the stars as the Company journeyed on from Hollin in 'The Ring Goes South' (VI.421–2), and which Gandalf unconvincingly suggested might be no more than a wisp of cloud. Then too Frodo shivered, as here he 'felt a sudden chill'. As I noted (VI.434), the former incident was retained in FR but never explained: the Winged Nazgûl had not yet crossed the Anduin. But it seems likely to me that the shadow that passed across the stars near Hollin was in fact the first precocious appearance of a Winged Nazgûl.

9 Sam is again (see note 7) changed from Merry, and Merry from Trotter. In fact, the speech was given to Sam before its end was reached, as is seen from ' "And that Sam is probably about the truth of it," said Trotter'; and the transition from one speaker to another is seen in the transition from the very un-Samlike 'The moon I suppose does not change his courses in Wilderland?' to 'up pops a New Moon'.

10 Cf. the original draft of 'Lothlórien', p. 228: 'The last thin rind of the waning moon was gleaming dimly in the leaves.'

11 Cf. the comment on Time in Lórien written on the fair copy manuscript of 'Farewell to Lórien', p. 286; and see further on this matter the 'Note on Time in Lórien' that follows.

12 On the emergence of the idea of the inaccessibility of the island see p. 328.

13 *any enemy* is the correct reading, not *an enemy* (FR p. 396).

14 Sixty leagues (180 miles) south of Sarn Ford agrees well with the more southerly confluence of Limlight and Anduin on Map IV^D (p. 319).

366   THE TREASON OF ISENGARD

15 Aragorn says this ('not even to me') also in FR (p. 405); but at this stage he had no previous knowledge of Lórien, and presumably had no knowledge until this moment of Galadriel's Ring.

16 No doubt the first reference to the Entwade, which was pencilled in on map IV^C and entered on IV^D (pp. 318–19).

17 Valandil is named as the son of Isildur in texts of 'The Council of Elrond' (pp. 121, 128, 147).

18 For an earlier occurrence of *Eldakar* see p. 276. An isolated scrap (in fact the back of an envelope) has this note:

> *Trotter's names*
> Elessar
> Eldamir (= Elfstone) son of Eldakar (= Elfhelm). Or Eldavel = Elfwold.

On the same envelope is written, in almost identical words, the passage concerning Frodo's thoughts under Galadriel's scrutiny that was added to the fair copy manuscript of 'Galadriel' (p. 266 note 32: 'Neither did Frodo...').

19 On the back of the preceding page in the fair copy manuscript my father scribbled down a first version of Trotter's words (in which no genealogy appears), and it is curious that he wrote here: 'How my heart yearns for Minas Ithil...', changing *Ithil*, probably at once, to *Anor*: see p. 333 and note 27. – Also noted down here in extreme haste are thoughts for the story immediately to come:

> Frodo on Tol Brandir.
> [?Strong] sight. Sees Minas Tirith and Minas Morgul opposed. Sees Mordor. Sees Gandalf. Suddenly feels the *Eye* and wrenches off the ring and finds himself crying Wait, wait!

20 A passing name for the rapids, replacing *Pensarn*, was *Ruinel*. *Sarn-Ruin* is the name on map IV^C, p. 317. Cf. *Dant-ruin*, *Dant-ruinel*, earlier names of Rauros (p. 285).

21 A passing form which my father entered on both manuscripts before *Argonath* was reached was *Sern Aranath*.

22 When the chronology was changed, with the attack at the head of the rapids taking place on the eighth night, and the New Moon seen far away in the West on the seventh and eighth evenings, Sam's words were expanded (and entered on both manuscripts), though subsequently largely rejected:

> Yesterday evening I saw it, as thin as a nail-paring, and this evening it wasn't much bigger. Now that's just as it should be, if we'd only been in the Elvish land for about a day, or more than a month. Why, anyone would think that time slowed down in there!

23 The phrase as my father wrote it was 'because they *need* not count the running years', but in copying I missed out the word *need*. Looking through my copy, but without consulting his own manuscript, he wrote in *do*; and *do* survives in FR (p. 405).

THE GREAT RIVER 367

Note on Time in Lórien

The narrative passages that introduce this question are found on pp. 285–6, 354–5, 358, 363, and in note 22 above. This note is primarily concerned with the various time-schemes that bear on it, but for their understanding it is necessary to consider the chronology a little more widely.

The first time-scheme to be considered here I will call 'I'; for previous references to it see pp. 169, 215 note 1, and 344–5. In its 'Lothlórien' section it obviously belongs with the first drafting of the story, and preceded the emergence of the idea that there was a different Time in the Golden Wood. Here the dates are:

Nov. 24	Leave Rivendell
Dec. 6	Hollin (Full Moon)
9	Snow on Caradras
11	Reach Moria
13	Escape to Lothlórien (Moon's last quarter)
14	Go to Caras Galadon
15	Night at Caras Galadon
16	Mirror of Galadrien
17–21	Stay in Caras Galadon (Dec. 21 New Moon)

This stands at the foot of a page, but a second page, though in pencil and not in ink, was clearly continuous:

Dec. 22–31 Remain at Caras Galadon, leave with the New Year (Dec. 28 Moon's first quarter)

Jan. 1–4 No notes against these dates except Jan. 4 Full Moon.

On the departure of the Company from Lórien on New Year's Day see p. 253 and note 28. But at this point, it seems, the idea of the disparity of time entered; for after Jan. 4 my father wrote: 'Dec. 15 onwards time at Caras does not count, therefore they leave on morning of Dec. 15' (cf. p. 286: 'if Lórien is timeless ... *nothing* will have happened since they entered'). The rest of the scheme is based on this chronology (and has been given on pp. 344–5).

At first the journey down the Great River was only to take two days: 'Dec. 17 Reach Tolondren. Dec. 18 Flight of Frodo. Dec. 19 Frodo meets Sam and Gollum.' This was struck out, with the note: 'Take ten days to reach [Emris > Eregon >] Tolbrandir' (on Emris see pp. 316–18 and note 12). The New Moon that caused Sam to raise the question of Time in Lórien was still on Dec. 21; and they reached Tolbrandir in the evening of Dec. 25.

Another scheme ('II') takes up at Dec. 22, but this is based on a later date of departure from Rivendell: Dec. 25, as in FR. The chronology of FR from Rivendell to Lothlórien was not yet reached, however, for two reasons: first, that the journey to Hollin still took eleven days and not fourteen (pp. 165, 169); and second, that in FR there are two

368   THE TREASON OF ISENGARD

Yule-days after Foreyule (December) 30 as against Dec. 31 in scheme II. Thus II is two days in advance of FR. The numerical dates in II, when the Company left Rivendell on Dec. 25, soon become identical to those in I, when they left on Nov. 24, simply because November has 30 days but December has 31; thus in I they crossed the Silverlode by the rope-bridge and entered the Gore on Dec. 14, and in II on Jan. 14. At this point the scheme in II reads:

Jan. 14   Over Silverlode
   Time ceases
Jan. 15   Leave Lórien

Scheme II continues for some way on this basis before petering out. These therefore are the relations between the former chronology (I), the new (II), and FR:

	I	II	FR
Leave Rivendell	Nov. 24	Dec. 25	Dec. 25
Hollin	Dec. 6	Jan. 6	Jan. 8
Snow on Caradras	Dec. 9	Jan. 9	Jan. 11
Reach Moria	Dec. 11	Jan. 11	Jan. 13
Escape from Moria	Dec. 13	Jan. 13	Jan. 15
Cross Silverlode	Dec. 14	Jan. 14	Jan. 16
Leave Lórien	[Jan. 1 >] Dec. 15	Jan. 15	Feb. 16
Reach Tol Brandir	Dec. 25	Jan. 25	Feb. 25
Flight of Frodo	Dec. 26	Jan. 26	Feb. 26

In II the New Moon was on Jan. 21, just as in I it was on Dec. 21, and against this date in II is also: 'Battle with Orcs?' This was the seventh day of the voyage down Anduin, as in the texts. But it is odd that in both I and II the journey took eleven days, whereas in the texts it took nine (pp. 361–2).

At the foot of the page carrying scheme II my father wrote: 'Does Time cease at Lórien or go on faster? So that it might be Spring or nearly so.' With this cf. p. 363: 'The Power of the Lady was upon us. Slow for us there might time have passed, while the world hastened. Or in a little while we could savour much, while the world tarried. *The latter was her will.*'

Another chronology of far greater elaboration, made after the changes introduced in October 1944 (see p. 406), was still based on the conception that 'exterior' Time ceased in Lórien, for it begins:

Thurs. Jan. 19   Fifth day of voyage
Fri.   20   Sixth day
Sat.   21   Seventh day. Sam observes New Moon and is puzzled.

THE GREAT RIVER   369

Lastly, another later scheme of dates begins:

> They spend what seems many days in Lórien, but it is about the same time and date when they leave. [*Added:* In fact, one day later, time moving about 20 times slower (20 days = 1).]

Here the Company again leaves Lórien on Jan. 15, but the chronology of the journey approaches that of FR: 'Sam sees New Moon low in West after sunset' on Jan. 21, but as in FR the attack by Orcs takes place on the night of the eighth day, here Jan. 22; and Tol Brandir is reached at dusk on Jan. 24. Here this scheme ends; but across the page my father afterwards wrote these separate notes:

> Why have any difference of time? Shift the dates a month forward.
> If Lórien time is not different, then no need for Sam to see the Moon.
> Better to have *no* time difference.

A passage in the first manuscript of 'The White Rider' (p. 431) may be mentioned here: Gandalf tells that after his rescue by Gwaihir from the peak above Moria he came to Lothlórien and 'tarried there in the long time which in that land counts for but a brief hour of the world'.

Phases of the Moon
Either while the making of Time-scheme I was in progress or at some later point my father wrote at the head of the first page of it: *Moons are after 1941–2 + 6 days.* He changed this to *+ 5 days,* and added: *thus Full Moon Jan. 2 is Jan. 7.* The phases of the Moon were entered on scheme I in red pencil, and it is very hard to know whether they belong with its making or were put in later. Many of these dates were much changed, but no discernible relation with the phases of 1941–2 emerges, the dates in the scheme varying between two to six days later. The phases as entered, also in red pencil, on scheme II, when the departure from Rivendell took place on Dec. 25, are however regularly five days later than those of 1941–2, beginning with New Moon on Dec. 23, and then First Quarter on Dec. 30, Full Moon Jan. 7, Last Quarter Jan. 15, New Moon Jan. 21 (against which is written the time: 9.32), First Quarter Jan. 29 (time 6.35), Full Moon Feb. 6. It is possible, therefore, though far from certain, that it was only with scheme II and the decision to postpone the departure from Rivendell by a month that my father decided to pattern the phases precisely on those of 1941–2.

It will be seen shortly (p. 379) that my father was working on 'The Departure of Boromir' in the winter of 1941–2. The postponement of the departure from Rivendell is first seen in an outline for the story following the ride of Gandalf and his companions from Fangorn to Eodoras (p. 434 and note 1; see also pp. 422–3).

XVIII

THE BREAKING OF THE FELLOWSHIP

In the latter part of the original chapter 'XXI' initial drafting and 'fair copy' were a continuous process. Up to the point where Sam broke in on the discussion among the Company beside the river with 'Begging your pardons, but I don't think you understand Mr. Frodo at all' (FR p. 419), the drafting is very rough indeed, with separate passages written in slips and not forming a consecutive narrative, while the 'fair copy' is itself a mass of correction and rewriting in the act of composition. Some passages gave my father great difficulty and he experimented with their ordering and phraseology in many forms. But from that point, and evidently made after the 'fair copy' had reached it, there is a clear primary draft, in which the story just as it is in FR (pp. 419–23) 'wrote itself', on the basis of a preliminary outline; and the fair copy from here onwards can be properly so called. In this manuscript the text of FR was effectively reached throughout, but the division of 'XXI' into two, with a new chapter 'XXII The Breaking of the Fellowship', was not made until after the text had been completed.

At first Trotter is 'Elfstone', not corrected, in both draft and fair copy (see p. 361), but soon becomes 'Trotter', and is then so named throughout.

The draft text begins:

That night they went ashore, and camped upon a green sward beneath the slopes of [*added:* Amon Hen] the western hill. They set a watch, but they saw no sign of any enemy or spy. If Gollum had contrived to follow them, he remained unseen. 'I do not think he would dare the passage of the Gates,' said Elfstone. 'But he may have travelled far over the hills, while we were delayed at Pensarn. By now he knows the country well, and he will guess too much of our divided purposes.[1] For we have with us what he long possessed and it draws him ever towards us. "If they turned west at Pensarn," he will say, "then for a time I can do no more. Sooner or later I shall know, and then Gollum can find a way, even to the walls of Minas-Tirith. But if they did not turn west there is but one end to the river-road: Tol Brandir and Rauros, and the North Stair. There they must go West or East. I will watch upon the East." Likely enough he spied us with his

THE BREAKING OF THE FELLOWSHIP 371

fell eyes far off from the eastern beaches or from some post among the hills.'
The day came like fire and smoke ...

Amon Hen looks as if it were added immediately, and is probably the first occurrence of the name. An addition to the draft text introduces the nocturnal conversation between Trotter and Frodo and the drawing of Sting to see what its blade would show – a sign that the attack by Orcs had now entered; but here it is Frodo who feels 'some shadow or threat', and it is Frodo who says 'I thought as much. Orcs are near. But how came they across the river? Never have I heard that they came into this region before', with an authoritative tone more characteristic of Trotter. In the fair copy Trotter's surmises about Gollum's intentions were lost, and the opening of the chapter 'The Breaking of the Fellowship' in FR was attained, except that the green lawn beneath Amon Hen was named *Kelufain*, subsequently changed to *Calenbel*.[2]

The description of Tol Brandir as Frodo saw it that morning, already in the primary draft very close to the final form (FR p. 412), with its sides springing sheer out of the running water (where 'no landing place could be seen'), shows that the idea of its inaccessibility was present (see p. 359). The conversation before Frodo departed from the Company alone was very largely achieved at once, but in the fair copy Trotter says: 'My own heart desires to go to Minas-Tirith, but that is for myself and apart from your Quest', this being rejected, probably immediately; and in both texts, in very similar words, he says: 'Very well, Frodo son of Drogo. You shall be alone. But do not let your thoughts be too dark. For after you have chosen you shall not be alone. I will not leave you, should you decide to go to the gates of Baraddur; and there are others of the same mind, I think.' To this Frodo replied, in the fair copy: 'I know, and it does not aid my choice [> it does not help me at all].' The primary draft continues:

The others remained behind near the shore, but Frodo got up and walked away. Sam watched his master with great concern. Then the Company turned again to debating what they could do to aid the Quest, hopeless as it seemed [*struck out:* and whether it were wise to try and end it swiftly or to delay]. Boromir spoke strongly, urging ever the wisdom of strong wills, and weapons, and great plans he drew for alliances, and victories to be, and the overthrow of Mordor.[3]

Sam slipped away unnoticed. 'If orcs are anywhere nigh,' he muttered, 'I am not going to let Mr. Frodo wander about alone. In his frame o' mind he would not see an elephant coming, or he might walk off the edge of a precipice.'

372　　　THE TREASON OF ISENGARD

In the meanwhile aimlessly wandering Frodo found that his feet had led him up the slopes of the hill.

The idea that Sam left the Company at this point was evidently very soon abandoned.

The encounter with Boromir on Amon Hen was now developed from the form it had reached in the outline given on pp. 325–7, and with much difficulty the text of FR was achieved. I give here so much as I can puzzle out of the form in which my father first wrote down what Frodo saw when he looked out from Amon Hen wearing the Ring (for the brief suggestions in previous outlines see p. 327 and note 7 and p. 366 note 19): his writing here is at its most difficult, the marks very weak and the pen seeming to float or glide on the paper.

Northward he looked, and the Great River lay like a ribbon beneath him, and the Misty Mountains small and hard as broken teeth. Eastward into wide uncharted lands he looked. West he gazed and saw little horsemen galloping like the wind upon wide green plains, and beyond was the dark tower of [Isengard >] Orthanc in the ring of Isengard.

Southward he looked ..... Ethir Anduin the mighty delta of the Great River, and myriads of seabirds [like a dust of white specks] whirling ... like a white dust, and beneath them a green and silver sea rippling in endless moving lines.

But everywhere he looked he saw signs of war. The Misty Mountains were like anthills to his sight: orcs were [?pouring] out from countless [?holes]. Under the boughs of Mirkwood there was deadly strife. The land of the Beornings was aflame. A cloud was over Dimrilldale / Moria gates. Smoke rose upon the borders of Lórien. [Dol Dúghul] Horsemen galloping wildly on the grass of Rohan, wolves poured forth from Isengard. From the grey southward Havens [or Haven] an endless column of armed men came. Out of the wild East men were moving in endless [?shining] swordmen, [?spearmen], bowmen upon horse; chariots and wains: whole peoples. All the power of the Dark Lord was in motion.

Then as he came back south he saw Minas Tirith. Far and beautiful it was, white-walled, many-towered, high upon its mountain seat strong in the sun: its battlements glittered with steel and its turrets were bright with many banners. .... was Minas Morgul .... its dark walls carven with ... shapes, its great tower like a tooth, its banners black, its gates like evil mouths, and to eastward the Shadow of Death the hopeless

THE BREAKING OF THE FELLOWSHIP   373

[?gates] of Gorgoroth. Then he saw the . . . . Mount [Doom >] Dûm: the Hill of Fire and . . . . Baraddur.

Then suddenly his gaze halted. The [?mists cleared] and he cried aloud in fear. There was an eye in Baraddur. It did not sleep. And suddenly it had become aware of . . . . There was a fierce eagerness . . . [?will] . . . It leapt towards him, almost like a finger he felt it [?feeling] for him. In a minute it would nail him down, know just exactly [?to an inch] where he was. Amon Lhaw it touched, it glanced at Tol Brandir – he cast himself from the seat, [?crouching, covering] his head with his grey hood. He was crying out but whether he was saying Never will it get me, never, or Verily I come, I come to you, he could not say. [?Probably] both.

Then as a flash from some other point of power there came . . . another thought. Take it off. Take it off. O foolish! Take it off. The two powers strove in him: for a moment perfectly balanced between their . . . points he writhed. Suddenly he was aware of himself.

In the complete manuscript that followed the draft, with much further correction and experimentation of phrase as he wrote, my father reached the final form; but the opening description of Frodo in the high seat (for which there is no earlier drafting) in this manuscript is of much interest. As first written, with a good deal of correction in the process, the passage read:

At first he could see little: he seemed to be in a world of mist in which there were only shadows. The Ring was on him. [Then the virtue (*written above:* power) of Amon Hen worked upon him] Then here and there the mists gave way and he saw many things: small and clear as if they were beneath him on a table and yet remote: the world seemed to have shrunk. [*Added:* He heard no sound, seeing only bright images that moved and changed.][4] He looked South and saw below his very feet the Great River curve and bend like a toppling wave and plunge over the falls of Rauros into a foaming pit: the fume rose like smoke and fell like rain lit by a glimmering rainbow of many colours. More remote still beyond the roaring pools were fens and black mountains, many streams winding like shining ribbons. Then the vision changed: nothing but water was below him, a wide rippling plain of silver, and an endless murmur of distant waves upon a shore he could not see.

374 THE TREASON OF ISENGARD

He looked West and saw horsemen galloping like the wind: their

On beyond the falls his eye wandered, here crossing reed-grown fens, there marking the winding ribbons of swift streams leaping down from small hard black mo(untains).

At this point my father rejected the entire passage from the words 'Then the virtue (power) of Amon Hen worked upon him' and began again:

At first he could see little: he seemed to be in a world of mist in which there were only shadows. The Ring was on him. [*Struck out at once*: But also he sat now upon the seat of Sight which the Men of Númenor had made.] Then here and there the mists gave way and he saw many visions ...

The new text then reaches the form in FR (p. 416); Frodo is sitting on 'the seat of Seeing, upon Amon Hen, the Hill of the Eye of the Men of Númenor.'

Frodo 'seemed to be in a world of mist in which there were only shadows. *The Ring was on him. Then the power of Amon Hen worked upon him*': and the mists began to break. Still clearer is the next stage of revision: '... *The Ring was on him. But also* he sat now upon the seat of Sight which the Men of Númenor had made. Then here and there the mists gave way ...' Only one interpretation seems possible: the wearing of the Ring *inhibited his sight* − he was in a world of mists and shadows; but nonetheless he was sitting on the Seat of Seeing on the Hill of the Eye, and 'the power of Amon Hen worked upon him.' On the other hand, in the last outline written before this point in the narrative was actually reached, the idea of the 'Seat of Seeing' had not emerged (p. 327): Frodo was 'standing on rocks' in the Stone Hills when Boromir attempted to take the Ring. It is said there that from this place the range of the Mountains of Shadow could be glimpsed 'like a smudge of grey, and behind it a vague cloud lit beneath occasionally by a fitful glow'; but when Frodo put on the Ring 'he saw nothing about him but a grey formless mist, and far away (*yet black and clear and hard*) the Mountains of Mordor: *the fire seemed very red*.' In its origin, then, the peculiar clarity of Frodo's vision on this occasion derived solely from the wearing of the Ring. This question is discussed further on pp. 380–1.

When Frodo came down from the summit of Amon Hen, and putting on the Ring again 'vanished and passed down the hill like a rustle of the wind', the primary draft continues: 'The power of the Ring upon him had been renewed; and maybe it aided his choice, drawing him to Mordor, drawing him to the Shadow, alone.'

There exists a rough outline for the last part of the chapter, where

THE BREAKING OF THE FELLOWSHIP 375

the story turns from Frodo to the Company, sitting where he left them beside the river. This was written in faint pencil, subsequently inked over.

Frodo does not come back in an hour. The hour wears on to two, and the sun is at noon. Trotter gets anxious. He saw Boromir go off, and return. 'Have you seen Frodo?' 'No,' said Boromir, lying with a half truth. 'I looked for him and could not see him.' [*Added:* ? 'Yes,' said Boromir, 'but he ran from me and I could not find him.'] Trotter decides they must search and blames himself for allowing Frodo to go alone. Boromir comes back ?

Great agitation, and before Trotter can control them they all run off into the woods. Trotter sends Boromir after Merry and Pippin. He runs himself toward the Hill of Amon Hen followed by Sam. But suddenly Sam stops and claps his head. 'You're a fool, Sam Gamgee. You know quite well what was in Mr. Frodo's mind. He knew he had to go East – that old Gandalf intended it. But he was afraid, and still more afraid of taking anyone with him. ..... He's run away, that's it – and .... boat.'[5] Sam dashed down the path. The green camp-ground was empty. As he raced across it he gasped. A boat was grinding on the shingle – seemingly all by itself was slipping into the water. It was floating away. With a cry Sam raced to the water-edge and sprang after it. He missed it by a yard and fell into deep water. He went under with a gurgle.

Conversation of Sam and Frodo. They go off together.

At this stage my father was not intending to end the chapter here, and this sketch continues into the story of what became the first chapter of *The Two Towers*, III.1 'The Departure of Boromir'; but I postpone the remainder of it to the next chapter in this book.

The discussion among the members of the Company during Frodo's absence took draft after draft to achieve,[6] and though the actual content of what was said does not greatly differ from the form in FR (pp. 418–19) it was at first given in part to different speakers (thus in the earlier form it is Trotter who emphasizes, as does Gimli in FR, that on no member of the Company save Frodo was obligation laid).

Notably, there appear in these drafts the phrases found in FR: 'the Lord Denethor and all his men cannot hope to do what Elrond declared to be beyond his power', and 'Boromir will return to Minas Tirith. His father and people need him.' This is where the name *Denethor* first emerged, with only the slightest initial hesitation: my father wrote a B, or perhaps an R, then *Denethor*.[7] That Boromir was

376   THE TREASON OF ISENGARD

the son of Denethor is clear, and is explicit in the outline given at the beginning of the next chapter; in any case he was named long before as the son of the King of Ond (VI.411).

As I have said, from the point where Sam intervened in the discussion the conclusion of *The Fellowship of the Ring* was virtually achieved at its first drafting and with very little hesitation, and there are only two matters to notice. One concerns the return of Boromir to the Company, where at first he replied to Trotter's question quite differently (cf. the outline on p. 375):

'He has not returned then?' asked Boromir in return.
'No.'
'That's strange. To say the truth I felt anxious about him, and went to seek him.'
'Did you find him?'
Boromir hesitated for an instant. 'I could not see him,' he answered, with half the truth. 'I called him and he did not come.'
'How long ago was that?'
'An hour maybe. Maybe more: I have wandered since. I do not know! I do not know!' He put his head in his hands and said no more.
Trotter looked wonderingly at him.

This was rejected at once and replaced by his account as it stands in FR. – The other passage is that describing Sam's headlong descent down the slopes of Amon Hen:

He came to the edge of the open camping-place[8] by the shore where the boats were drawn up out of the water. No one was there. There seemed to be cries and faint hornblasts in the woods behind, but he did not heed them.

Before this was written, my father had already sketched out, in the continuation of the outline of which I have given the first part on p. 375, the story of the Orc-attack and Boromir's death (p. 378). He had now abandoned important elements in his former vision of the course of the story after the disintegration of the Company: the journey of Merry and Pippin up the Entwash, and the evil dealings of Boromir in Ondor (pp. 211–12, 330). So far as written record goes, it was only now that he perceived that Boromir would never return to Minas Tirith.

THE BREAKING OF THE FELLOWSHIP 377

NOTES

1   I think that Trotter's meaning was: 'he will guess, too, much of our divided purposes.'
2   The fair copy in fact followed the draft in the opening sentences, and the paragraph with which 'The Breaking of the Fellowship' opens in FR, describing the green lawn (*Parth Galen*), was added. As the manuscript was written, the green lawn was not named. See note 8, and p. 382.
3   This sentence was subsequently marked: 'Put this into his talk with Frodo' (cf. FR p. 414).
4   The sentence a little later in this passage, 'an *endless murmur* of distant waves upon a shore he could not see', was not changed when this was added.
5   Written transversely across this part of the text, before the underlying pencil was inked over, and extremely difficult to read, is the following:
    A good arrangement would be for Frodo running down hill to run [?into] orcs attacking Merry and Pippin and Boromir. Boromir is aware of his presence. When Boromir falls Frodo escapes [to *or* (in) the] boat – because Frodo would not leave Merry and Pippin in hands of orcs.
    I do not understand the implication of the last sentence.
6   One of these drafts is written on an Oxford University committee report dated 19 February 1941: see p. 362.
7   In the First Age *Denethor* led the Green-elves over Eredlindon into Ossiriand. On the name see V.188.
8   Replaced in pencil in the fair copy manuscript by 'the lawn of Kelufain': see note 2.

XIX

THE DEPARTURE OF BOROMIR

I mentioned in the last chapter that the outline for the end of the story of 'The Breaking of the Fellowship' (p. 375) in fact continues on into the narrative of the first chapter ('The Departure of Boromir') in *The Two Towers* (henceforward abbreviated as TT).

Horns and sudden cries in the woods. Trotter on the hill becomes aware of trouble. He races down. He finds Boromir under the trees lying dying. 'I tried to take the Ring,' said Boromir. 'I am sorry. I have made what amends I could.' There are at least 20 orcs lying dead near him. Boromir is pierced with arrows and sword-cuts. 'They have gone. The orcs have got them. I do not think they are dead. Go back to Minas Tirith, Elfstone, and help my people. I have done all I could.' He dies. Thus died the heir of the Lord of Minas Tirith. Trotter at a loss. He is found standing perplexed and grief-stricken by Legolas and Gimli (who have driven off a smaller company). Trotter is perplexed. Was Frodo one of the hobbits? In any case ought he to follow and try to rescue? Or go to Minas Tirith? He cannot go in any case without burying Boromir. With help of Legolas and Gimli he carries Boromir's body on a bier of branches and sets it in a boat, and sends it over Rauros.

Trotter now finds that one boat is missing. No orc-prints at camp. Whether hobbit-marks are old or new cannot be made out. But Sam is missing. Trotter sees that either Frodo and Sam, and Merry and Pippin, were together, or Frodo (and Sam?) have gone off. Now little or no hope of finding Frodo in latter case. He with Gimli and Legolas decide to follow Merry and Pippin. 'On Amon Hen I said I might see a sign to guide us! We have found a confusion – but our paths at least are set for us. Come, we will rescue our companions or else we will die after slaying all the orcs we can.'

An addition to this text, certainly of much the same time, reads:

Trotter sees by the shape and arms of the dead orcs that they are northern orcs of the Misty Mountains – from Moria? In fact

THE DEPARTURE OF BOROMIR   379

they are orcs of Moria that escaped the elves, + others who are servants of *Saruman*. They report to Saruman that Gandalf is dead. Their mission is to capture hobbits *including Frodo* and take them to Isengard. (Saruman is playing a double game and wants the Ring.)

At the bottom of the page is written:

Does Trotter have any vision on Amon Hen? If he does, let him see (1) an Eagle coming down. (2) old man, like Frodo [sees] in mirror. (3) orcs creeping under trees.

While working on the book my father would sometimes 'doodle' by writing, often in careful or even elaborate script, names or phrases from a newspaper that lay beside him or on which his paper rested. On the back of the sheet carrying this outline – an examination script, like most of the paper he used – he wrote out many such odds and ends, as 'Chinese bombers', 'North Sea convoy'; and among them are 'Muar River' and 'Japanese attack in Malaya'. It is out of the question, I think, that these writings on the verso should come from a different time from the text on the recto. It is certain, therefore, that the time was now the winter of 1941–2.[1]

This obviously agrees with my father's statement in the Foreword to the Second Edition of *The Lord of the Rings* that he 'came to Lothlórien and the Great River late in 1941.' He said that 'almost a year' had passed since he halted by Balin's tomb in Moria; but I have argued (VI.461), I think with good reason, that he stopped in fact at the end of 1939. To maintain this view it must be supposed of course that something like two years (1940–1) passed between the halt in Moria and the point we have now reached; but further evidence on the subject seems to be lacking.

There are two preliminary versions of 'Trotter upon Amon Hen', the first proceeding directly from the suggestions at the end of the outline just given.

Trotter sped up the hill. Every now and again he bent to the ground. Hobbits go light, and their footprints are not easy even for a ranger to pick up. [Most of the path was stony, or covered with old leaves still lying thick; but in one place a small spring crossed it, and here Trotter stooping saw tracks in the moist earth, and beyond on the stones faint traces. 'I guessed right', he said. 'When he came to the top he saw . . .][2] But not far from the top a small spring crossed the path and in the wet earth he saw what he was looking for. Quickly he ran forward across the flagstones and up the steps. 'He has been here,' he said to

380   THE TREASON OF ISENGARD

himself. 'Not so long ago his wet feet came this way, [and up the steps.] He climbed to the seat. I wonder what he saw?'

Trotter stood up and looked round. The sun seemed to be darkened, or else the eastern clouds were spreading. He could see nothing in that direction. As his glance swept round it stopped. Under the trees he saw orcs crawling stealthily: but how near to Amon Hen he could not guess. Then suddenly far away he saw an eagle, as he had seen it before above Sarn Ruin.[3] It was high in the air, and the land below was dim. Slowly it circled. It was descending. Suddenly it swooped and fell out of the sky and passed below his [?view].

As Trotter gazed the vision changed. Down a long path came an old man, very bent, leaning on a staff. Grey and ragged he seemed, but when the wind tossed his cloak there came a gleam of white, as if beneath his rags he was clad in shining garments. Then the vision faded. There was nothing more to be seen.

At the end of the text, and I think immediately, my father wrote: 'The second vision on Amon Hen is inartistic. Let Trotter be stopped by noise of orcs, and let him see nothing.'

The second version continues on into Trotter's leaping descent from the summit, his discovery of Boromir, and his words with him before he died. Though written here in the roughest fashion the text was scarcely changed afterwards, except in one respect: here (following the instruction at the end of the first version) Trotter does not go up to the high seat at all:

Trotter hesitated. He himself desired to [sit in the Seat of Seeing >] go to the high seat, but time was pressing. As he stood there his quick ears caught sounds in the woodlands below and to his left, away west of the River and camping-place. He stiffened: there were cries, and among them he feared that he could distinguish the harsh voices of orcs; faintly and desperately a horn was blowing.

In the first version the power of the Seat of Seeing upon Amon Hen 'works upon' Trotter indeed, but the visions he sees are isolated scenes, more akin in their nature perhaps to those in the water of Galadriel's Mirror than to the vast panorama of lands and war vouchsafed to Frodo. In the second draft he does not ascend to the high seat, and therefore sees nothing. In the fair copy manuscript that immediately followed he does go up, as in TT, but again sees nothing, save the eagle descending out of the sky: 'the sun seemed darkened, and the world dim and remote.' Why should this be? The utter

THE DEPARTURE OF BOROMIR
381

unlikeness of the experiences of Frodo and of Aragorn in the Seat of Seeing is not explained. I have said (p. 374) that as my father first drafted the account of Frodo's vision it is explicit that it was 'the power of Amon Hen', and not the wearing of the Ring, that accorded it to him; and the first version of Aragorn's ascent to the summit shows this still more clearly (by the very fact that he also saw visions there). The final text of Frodo's vision is less explicit, and if this is associated with the fact that in the final form Aragorn does go up but sees nothing it may suggest a more complex relation between the power of Amon Hen and the power of the Ring, a relation which is not uncovered.

As I have said, the second of the original drafts for 'Trotter on Amon Hen'[4] continues to the death of Boromir, and there are a few details worth mentioning: it is not said (nor is it in the fair copy) that the glade where Boromir died was a mile or more from the camping-place (TT pp. 15, 18); Trotter says 'Thus passes the heir of Denethor, Lord of the T[ower]' ('Lord of the Tower of Guard' in the fair copy, as in TT); and very oddly, Boromir says 'Farewell, Ingold' – which can surely be no more than an unwitting reversion to the former name, instead of 'Elfstone'. In the fair copy, where he is otherwise called 'Trotter' throughout, Boromir says 'Farewell, Aragorn'; and this was probably the first time that the name 'Aragorn' was used again (apart, of course, from later correction at earlier points) after its abandonment.

A full and tolerably legible draft takes up just a little further on, from the coming of Legolas and Gimli to the glade, and there are only very minor differences from TT (pp. 16–17) as far as 'The River of Ondor will take care that no enemy dishonours his bones' (here given to Legolas). At this point in the draft manuscript there is a little hasty sketch, reproduced on p. 383, which indicates a difference (though immediately rejected) from the later story: Legolas alone returned to the camping-place. In the sketch are seen the rill that flowed through the greensward there, and the two remaining boats (the third having been taken by Frodo) moored at the water's edge, with Tol Brandir, and Amon Lhaw beyond; X marks the battle where Boromir died. At the shore is the boat brought back by Legolas, marking the place where Boromir's body was set aboard it.

In the draft text there is no mention of finding the hobbits' 'leaf-bladed' knives (cf. VI.128, FR p. 157), nor of Legolas' search for arrows among the slain; the first is absent from the fair copy also. Then follows:

'These are not orcs of Mordor,' said Trotter. 'Some are from the Misty Mountains, if I know anything of orcs and their [gear >] kinds; maybe they have come all the way from Moria. But

382   THE TREASON OF ISENGARD

what are these? Their gear is not all of goblin-make.' There were several orcs of large stature, armed with short swords, not the curved scimitars usual with goblins, and with great bows greater than their custom. Upon their shields they bore a device Trotter had not seen before: a small white hand in the centre of the black field. Upon the front of their caps was set a rune ᚻ fashioned of some white metal.[5]

'S is for Sauron,' said Gimli. 'That is easy to read.'

'Nay,' said Legolas. 'Sauron does not use the Runes.'

'Neither does he use his right name or permit it to be spelt or spoken,' said Trotter. 'And he does not use white. The orcs of his immediate service bear the sign of the single eye.' He stood for a moment in thought. 'S is for Saruman, I guess,' he said at last. 'There is evil afoot at Isengard, and the West is no longer safe. What is more: I guess that some of our pursuers escaped the vigilance of Lórien or avoided that land, passing through the foothills, and that Saruman also knows now of our journey, and maybe of Gandalf's fall. Whether he is merely working under the command of Mordor, or playing some hand of his own, I cannot guess.'

'Well, we have no time to ponder riddles,' said Gimli.

With this compare the passage added to the outline on pp. 378–9. – Both Legolas and Gimli now went back to the green lawn of the camping-place, which is here named *Kelufain*, corrected to *Forfain*, and that in turn to *Calen-bel* (all these changes being made at the moment of writing),[6] but they returned together in a single boat. Thus whereas in TT, where they brought both the remaining boats, the three companions in the one towed out the other bearing Boromir, and after passing Parth Galen cast it loose, here Legolas took the funeral boat to Calen-bel while Trotter and Gimli returned there on foot. At Calen-bel, 'All three now embarked in the remaining boat, and drew the funeral boat out into the running river.' In the fair copy the final story entered as my father wrote the text.

Apart from this, the account of Boromir's departure is almost word for word as in TT, save that his hair is called 'gold-brown' (so also in the fair copy, changed to 'long brown'; 'dark' in TT), and that it ends:

But in Ondor it was long recorded in song that the elven-boat rode the falls and the foaming pit, and bore him down through Osgiliath, and past the many mouths of Anduin, and out into the Great Sea; and the voices of a thousand seabirds lamented him upon the beaches of Belfalas.

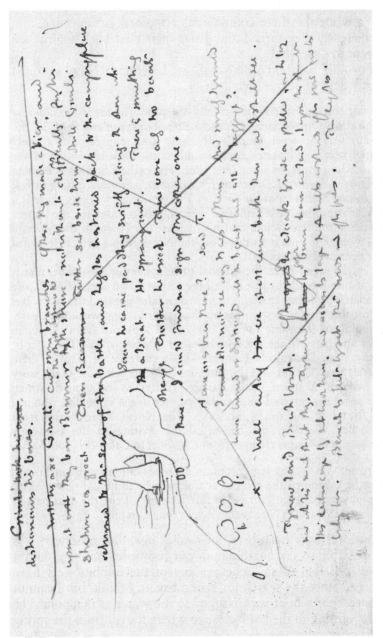

Sketch-plan of the scene of the Breaking of the Fellowship.

384   THE TREASON OF ISENGARD

There is no suggestion however that any lament was sung for him by his companions; the draft reads here simply:

For a while the three companions remained gazing after him, then silently they turned and drove their boat back against the current to Calen-bel.
    'Boromir has taken his road,' said Trotter. 'Now we must swiftly determine our own course....'

The fair copy manuscript is virtually the same. The earliest extant text of the lament for Boromir (*Through Rohan over fen and field*, TT pp. 19–20) was however found with these draft papers, and a finely written text was inserted into the fair copy, with re-writing of the surrounding prose, at some later time. The earliest version is entitled [*Song >*] *Lament of Denethor for Boromir*, and only differs in few and minor points from the form in TT;[7] of rough working there is a page bearing the most primitive sketching of phrases for the lament (including the East Wind, that blows 'past the Tower of the Moon'), and another of rough working for the North Wind (which seems to have been swiftly achieved).
    It might seem, from the original title *Lament of Denethor*, that it was at first intended to be indeed the father's own song of grief, and not merely in form: to be brought in at a later point in the story. But against this are the first words on the page of rough working, clearly belonging to the same time: ' "They shall look out from the white tower and listen to the sea," said Trotter in a low voice.' The song is, in any case, Denethor's Lament. The occurrence of 'Trotter' here suggests that it belongs to this time, for before much more of the story was written 'Aragorn' would replace 'Trotter' as the name by which he is generally referred to. Another pointer in the same direction is a line found in the rough working: 'The North Wind blows from Calen-Bel', since in the course of the writing of the fair copy manuscript the name changes from *Calen-bel* to *Calembel* (note 6).[8]

    Trotter was at first less certain in his observations and conclusions when he examined the ground at Calen-bel; and he did not think to examine the baggage (nor yet in the fair copy). I cite the next part of the draft text, which here becomes very rough, in full:

'No orcs have been here,' he said at last. 'But otherwise it is not possible to say anything: all our footprints are here, and it is not possible to say whether any of the hobbits' feet have returned since the search for Frodo began. I think, but I cannot be sure, that a boat was dragged to the water at this point,' he said, pointing to the bank close to where the rill from the spring trickled into the river.

THE DEPARTURE OF BOROMIR   385

'How then do you read the riddle?' asked Gimli.

'I think that Frodo returned from the hill-top wearing the Ring,' said Trotter. 'He may have met Sam, but I think not: Frodo was probably wearing the Ring. I think Sam guessed Frodo's mind: he knew it better from love than we from wisdom; and caught him before he went.'

'But that was ill done, to go and leave us without a word, even if he had seen the orcs and was afraid,' said Gimli.[9]

'No, I think not,' said Trotter. 'I think Sam was right. He did not wish us to go to death in Mordor, and saw no other way to prevent that but by going alone and secretly. No, I think not,' said Trotter. 'He had a   Something happened on the hill to make him fly. I do not know all, but I know this. Boromir tried to take the Ring by force.'

Exclamation of horror from Legolas and Gimli.

'Think not ill of him,' said Trotter. 'He paid manfully and confessed.'

Then follows in pencil:

Don't let Trotter tell of Boromir's misdeed?

They draw up boat. Set out west after orcs. Trotter's plan is to descend from Sarn Gebir into Rohan and try and learn of orcs and *borrow horses*.

Legolas sees Eagle from escarpment, descending.

They meet an old man coming up hill to meet them. Don't recognize him, though there is something familiar. Suspect he is Saruman?

The final story of the reappearance of Gandalf moves a step closer. In the 'Plot' written before Lothlórien was reached (p. 211) it was Gimli and Legolas, on their way back North, who fell in with Gandalf, Aragorn having gone with Boromir to Minas Tirith; and Gandalf then 'hastens south' with them. This was still the story in the subsequent outline (p. 329). Now, the death of Boromir having entered, Trotter, Gimli and Legolas are as in the final story on the trail of Merry and Pippin when they encounter Gandalf returned; but they are to meet him before their journey through Rohan has begun, before they have set foot in the grasslands. The descending eagle that Legolas saw from the escarpment of Sarn Gebir was bearing Gandalf (see p. 396); and it is clear that the eagle that Trotter saw descending to earth as he looked out from the summit of Amon Hen in the original draft (p. 380) was the first appearance of this idea.[10]

386   THE TREASON OF ISENGARD

In the fair copy the suggestion in this outline that Trotter should not tell Gimli and Legolas what Boromir had done was taken up:

'... Something occurred after he left us to make his mind up: he must suddenly have overcome his fear and doubt. I do not think that it was a meeting with orcs.' What he thought it was Trotter did not say. The last words of Boromir he kept ever secret.

This was changed, probably at once, to the dialogue in TT (p. 21), but it is still said of Trotter that 'the last words of Boromir he kept ever secret' ('he long kept secret', TT).

The draft text becomes formed narrative again with words of Trotter's that in TT are given to Legolas: ' "One thing at least is clear," said Trotter. "Frodo is no longer on this side of the River. Only he could or would have taken the boat. As for Sam, he must be either with Merry or Pippin or Frodo, or dead. He would have returned here otherwise ere now." ' Gimli's words that follow, and Trotter's, expounding his decision to follow the Orcs, are much as in TT; and I give the remainder of the draft, which at the end peters out, in full:

They drew up the last boat and carried it to the trees, and laid beside it such of their goods as they did not need and could not carry. Then they struck west. Dusk was already falling.

'Go warily,' said Gimli. 'We are assuming that all the orcs made off after they had slain Boromir and captured Merry and Pippin. But those that attacked Boromir were not the only ones. Legolas and I met some away southwards on the west slopes of Amon Hen. We slew many, creeping on them among the trees: the cloaks of Lórien seem to deceive their sight. But many more may still linger.'

'We have not time for wariness. We will follow the trail from the glade. Well is it that Orcs do not walk like hobbits! No folk, even Men of the cities, make such a trampling, and they slash and hack and beat down growing things as they pass, as if the breaking of things delighted them.

'It is plain to see which way they went – west near to the shore, but not on it, keeping to the trees.'[11]

'But orcs go swiftly,' said Gimli. 'We shall have to run!'

'If my guess is right,' said Trotter, 'and they make for Isengard, they will descend from the hills into Rohan. [Struck out: There they will not dare to journey save by night – and I wonder indeed how they cross] Mayhap we can get horses in Rohan,' said Trotter. 'If my guess is right and the orcs are making for Isengard, they will

THE DEPARTURE OF BOROMIR 387

I interrupt the narrative here because, although my father had no thought of halting, initial drafting from this point is lost (p. 390).

The draft that takes up with the coming of Legolas and Gimli to the glade (p. 381) is numbered on each page 'XXIII', and 'XXIII' continues on through the story of the chase across Rohan; the fair copy likewise begins 'XXIII' at 'Trotter sped on up the hill', with the title 'The Riders of Rohan', though another title apparently underlies this. Although all these were pencilled additions to the manuscripts in ink, I think it very probable that by this time the chapter-divisions of LR had been introduced: XXI 'The Great River' ending after the passage of the Pillars of the Kings and XXII 'The Breaking of the Fellowship' ending at the departure of Frodo and Sam, with XXIII extending all the way from Trotter's ascent of Amon Hen into whatever adventures might befall the three companions from their setting out from Calembel on the trail of the Orcs.

NOTES

1 The Japanese invaded Thailand and N.E. Malaya on 7–8 December 1941. The crossing of the Muar River was on 16 January 1942. This information has been kindly provided by Mr. F. R. Williamson. – Further evidence is provided by the use of the Moon's phases of 1941–2; see p. 369.

2 This passage was placed within square brackets in the original, as also was 'and up the steps' immediately following.

3 On the eagle seen far off on the evening before the Company came to the rapids of Sarn Ruin see pp. 361–2.

4 At the top of the page carrying this text are written many experimental Elvish names: *Llawhen, Amon Tirlaw, Lhawdir, Lasthen, Henlas, Hendlas*, all being struck out save the first and last. I am at a loss to account for these satisfactorily. Since both *Amon Hen* and *Amon Lhaw* appear in primary drafting and outlines that obviously preceded this text, it is perhaps possible that the names already stood on the page before my father used it for the account of Trotter on Amon Hen. If this were so, it might be – since all of them are compounds of elements one of which refers to hearing (*l(h)aw, las(t)*) and the other to sight (*hen(d), tir*) – that they were devised before the eastern and western hills were distinguished as the Hill of Hearing and the Hill of Sight.

5 The Old English S-rune is found also in the fair copy manuscript, but there with the vertical strokes strongly curved, the upper

388　　　THE TREASON OF ISENGARD

curve open to the left, the lower to the right. In that text the caps of the Orcs become 'leathern caps' ('iron helms' TT).

6 The name *Kelufain* for the green lawn below Amon Hen was added to the fair copy of 'The Breaking of the Fellowship', and in one instance changed to *Calenbel* (p. 371 and note 2). In the fair copy of the present chapter the name was *Calenbel* at the first occurrence but subsequently *Calembel* (and once *Cálembel*).

7 The differences are:
Verse 1: line 1　*Through the mountain-pass, through Rohan* >
　　Over mountains tall, through Rohan
　　　　　5　*over many streams*
Verse 2: 2　*brings*
　　　　　4　*Why tarries Boromir the fair? For Boromir I grieve.*
Verse 3: 4　*Where now is Boromir the bold?*
　　　　　5　*I heard his horn.*

In every case these readings were replaced in careful script by those in TT. At first only the third verse had the concluding couplet beginning O *Boromir!*; but against this my father wrote: 'Omit? Or put extra couplet onto the other stanzas?' and then provided them, as in the final form. Certain other changes were put in later: see note 8.

8 The text of the Lament inserted into the fair copy is the final form, though here written in short lines. An accompanying page gives 'Alternatives to Song of Boromir', which were not used. These change verse 1 line 3 *tonight?* to *this morn?*, line 4 becoming *Have you seen Boromir the fair or heard his blowing horn?*; and verse 2 line 3 *at eve?* to *tonight?*, line 4 becoming *Where tarries Boromir the tall by moon or by starlight?* Another variant given here was to change verse 2 line 3 *at eve?* to *at morn?*, line 4 becoming *Where dwells now Boromir the fair? What valleys hear his horn?* These changes were pencilled also onto the first text of the song. – In LR *Calembel* is a town in Lamedon ('The Passing of the Grey Company', at end).

9 Cf. the passage given on p. 377 note 5.

10 Both sightings of the eagles survived in TT: Aragorn on Amon Hen still sees one descending, and Legolas sees one from the western escarpment of the Emyn Muil (see pp. 396–7).

11 Though no speaker is named, this speech ('We have not time for wariness') is certainly Trotter's.

XX

THE RIDERS OF ROHAN

A single page of extremely rough notes, headed 'Sketch' and 'XXIII' was written in pencil, and partly inked over.

Dusk. Night. Track less easy to follow. Sarn-Gebir runs North-South.[1] They press on through night. Dawn on ridge – then .... the escarpment. Legolas sees eagle far away. (Fangorn.)[2] Rich vegetation.

They see Black Mountains, 100 miles south. Entwash winding. Find orc trail going up river. Meeting with Rohiroth. They ride to Fangorn and hear news of battle and destruction of orcs and mysterious old man who had discomfited orcs. They hear that *no* captives were rescued. Despair. Old man appears.

[*Added:* XXV and later.] They think he is Saruman. Revelation of Gandalf, and his account of how he escaped. He has become a *white* wizard. 'I forgot most of what I knew.[3] I was badly burned or *well* burned.' They go to Minas Tirith and enter in.

Rest of war in which Gandalf and / on his eagle in white leads assault must be told later – partly a dream of Frodo, partly seen by him (and Sam), and partly heard from orcs. (? Frodo looks out of Tower, while prisoner.)

Minas Tirith defeats Haradwaith. They cross at Osgiliath [*written above:* Elostirion], defeat orcs and Nazgûl. Overthrow Minas Morghul, and drive forward to *Dagorlad* (Battle Plain). They get news that Ringbearer is captured.

Now Treebeard.

Then Frodo again.

In those passages where the original text was inked over the underlying pencil can be largely made out, and it is seen that *Haradwaith* was present: this appears on the First Map, translated *Sutherland*, as the name of the great region south of Mordor and east of the Bay of Belfalas (Map III, p. 309).[4] On the other hand *Nazgûl*, here first met with, was not, and nor was *Dagorlad* (the pencilled text had only Battle Plain); the First Map had *Dagras*, changed to *Dagorlad* (p. 310). *Elostirion* above *Osgiliath* was also an addition when the text was inked over; on this new name see p. 423. – There are other notes on the page which do not relate directly to the foregoing consecutive sketch, but which may be given here.

390 THE TREASON OF ISENGARD

(1) Greyfax [> Shadowfax]. Halbarad. Horse of Gandalf reappears – sent for from Rivendell. Arrives later. It is 500–600 miles from Rivendell and would take Shadowfax 10–14 days.

The name *Halbarad* was added at the same time as *Greyfax* > *Shadowfax*, and these changes look as if they were made at once. In Gandalf's tale in the fifth version of 'The Council of Elrond' the horse that Gandalf got in Rohan was likewise named *Halbarad* and *Greyfax*, and there *Greyfax* was certainly changed to *Shadowfax* in the act of writing. In that text there is no mention of what happened to Shadowfax after Gandalf reached Rivendell (see p. 152); but an isolated slip of paper has a note on this (together with a passage of initial drafting for 'The King of the Golden Hall'): 'Some account of "Shadowfax" in the house of Elrond must be given and what arrangements were made about him. Or did he just run off after Gandalf got to Rivendell? How did Gandalf summon him?'

(2) Rohiroth are relations of Woodmen and Beornings, old Men of the North. But they speak Gnomish – tongue of Númenor and Ondor, as well as [?common] tongue.
(3) Trotter should *know* Eomer.
(4) Marhad Marhath is 2nd Master. [*Written in margin:* Marhad Marhath Marhelm Marhun Marhyse Marulf][5]
(5) Eowyn Elfsheen daughter of Eomund?

On the back of this page is very rough drafting for the conversation with Eomer (p. 400), but there is also here the note: *Eowyn Elfsheen daughter of Theoden.*

The original manuscript of 'The Riders of Rohan' is a difficult and chaotic document, and its textual history was hard to ascertain. In this chapter (numbered throughout 'XXIII' and without new title, see p. 387), as in those that follow, my father adopted the practice, occasionally found earlier, of *erasing* his primary draft, or substantial portions of it, and writing a new version on the pages where it had stood. In this case the original drafting from the point reached on p. 386 ('If my guess is right and the orcs are making for Isengard, they will') is lost for a long stretch through erasure and the re-use of the pages, though here and there bits of it can be read. The original draft, which I will call 'A', emerges however at the point in the narrative (corresponding to TT p. 29) where Aragorn, Legolas and Gimli approached the low downs to the east of the river Entwash, and continues through the story of the encounter with the Riders; at which point my father abandoned it, realizing that the story as he was telling it was 'not what really happened' (see the letter cited on p. 411). It was now that he returned to the beginning, and began a new text ('B') using the erased pages of A up to the point mentioned. It seems clear

THE RIDERS OF ROHAN 391

that what survives of A survives because it was written largely in ink
and not in pencil. The structure of the manuscript is thus:

A erased   B written on erased A

A not erased; ends because abandoned

                                          B continued independently

The textual history of the writing of the chapter is of course simply A
followed by B.

Both ways of presenting the material have their disadvantages, but
after much experimentation it seems to me best to look first at what
remains of A. This I give in full, excepting only one passage.

[Their elven-cloaks faded against the] background, and even in
the clear cool sunlight few but elvish eyes would have seen them
until close at hand as they passed, running or striding tirelessly
with a brief pause every three hours or so.

That evening they reached the low downs. A narrow strip
of moist green land some ten miles wide lay between them and
the river winding in dim thickets of sedge and reed. Here the
Entwash and the line of downs bent due north,[6] and the orc-trail
was plain to see under the lee of the hills. 'These tracks were
made today,' said Trotter. 'The sun was already high before our
enemy passed. We might perhaps have glimpsed them far ahead,
if there had been any rising ground to give us a long view.'

'Yet all the while they draw nearer to the mountains and the
forest, where our hope of aiding our friends will fail,' said
Gimli. Spurred by this thought the companions sped onward
again through the dusk, and far into the night. They were
already half-way along the downs before Trotter called a halt.
The waxing moon was shining bright. 'Look!' he said. 'Even
orcs must pause at times.' Before them lay a wide trampled
circle, and the marks of many small fires could be seen under the
shelter of a low hillock. 'They halted here about noon, I guess,'
said Trotter. 'How long they waited cannot be told, but they are
not now many hours ahead. Would that we need not stay; but
we have covered many a long league since we last slept, and we
shall all need our strength maybe tomorrow, if we come up with
our enemies at last.'

Before dawn the companions took up the hunt again. As soon
as the sun rose and the light grew they climbed the downs and
looked out. Already the dark slopes of the forest of Fangorn
could be seen, and behind, glimmering, the white head of
Methen Amon, the last great peak of the Misty Mountains.[7]
Out of the forest flowed the river to meet them. Legolas looked

392 THE TREASON OF ISENGARD

round, turning his gaze through west to south. There his keen elf-eyes saw as a shadow on the distant green a dark moving blur.

'There are folk behind as well as in front,' he said, pointing away over the river. Trotter bent his ear to the earth, and there was a silence in the empty fields, only the airs moving in the grass could be heard. 'Riders,' said Trotter rising: 'many horsemen in haste. We cannot escape in this wild bare land. Most likely it is a host of the Rohiroth that have crossed the great ford at Entwade.[8] But what part the Horsemasters are minded to play and which side they serve I do not know. We can but hope for the best.'

The companions hastened on to the end of the downs. Behind them now they could hear the beat of many hooves. Wrapping their cloaks about them they sat upon a green bank close to the orc-trail and waited. The horsemen grew ever nearer, riding like the wind. The cries of clear strong voices came down the following breeze. Suddenly they swept up with a noise like thunder: a long line riding free many abreast, but following the orc-trail, or so it seemed, for the leaders rode bent low, scanning the ground even as they raced. Their horses were of great stature...

The account of the Riders and their horses, though rougher in expression, is very much as that in TT pp. 33–4, and the description in this original draft of the wheeling horses suddenly halting was never changed – except in the point that 'fifty lances were at rest pointing towards the strangers', where TT has 'a thicket of spears' (Legolas had counted one hundred and five Riders, p. 32).[9] – The conclusion of the primary draft, the conversation between Eomer and Aragorn in its earliest form, ran thus:

'Who are you, and what are you doing in this land?' said the rider, using the common speech of the West, in manner and tone like Boromir and the men of Minas Tirith.

[*Rejected immediately:* 'I am Aragorn Elessar (*written above:* Elfstone) son of Arathorn.][10] 'I am called Trotter. I come out of the North,' he replied, 'and with me are Legolas [*added:* Greenleaf] the Elf and Gimli Glóin's son the Dwarf of Dale. We are hunting orcs. They have taken captive other companions of ours.'

The rider lowered his spear-point and leaped from his horse, and standing surveyed Trotter keenly and not without wonder. At length he spoke again. 'At first I thought you were orcs,' he

THE RIDERS OF ROHAN

said, 'but that is not so. Indeed you know little about them, if you go hunting them in this fashion. They are swift and well-armed, and there are very many, it is said. You would be likely to change from hunter to quarry, if you ever caught up with them. But there is something strange about you, Master Trotter.' He bent his clear bright eyes again upon the ranger. 'That is no name for a man that you give. And strange is your raiment – almost it seems as if you had sprung out of the grass. How did you escape our sight?'

'Give me your name, master of horses, and maybe I will give you mine, and other news,' answered Trotter.

'As for that,' said the rider, 'I am Eomer son of Eomund, Third Master of the Riddermark. Eowin the Second Master is ahead.'

'And I am Aragorn Elfstone son of Arathorn Tarkil, the heir of Isildur Elendil's son of Ondor,' said Trotter. 'There are not many among mortal men who know more of orcs. But he that lacks a horse must go on foot, and when need presses no more friends may a man take with him than he has at hand. Yet I am not unarmed.' He cast back his cloak: the elven-sheath glittered and the bright blade of Branding shone like a sudden flame as he swept it out. 'Elendil!' cried Trotter. 'See the sword that was broken and is now remade. As for our raiment, we have passed through Lothlórien,' he said, 'and the favour of the Lady of the Galadrim goes with us. Yet great is our need, as is the need of all the enemies of Sauron in these days. Whom do you serve? Will you not help us? But choose swiftly: both our hunts are delayed.'

'I serve the Father and Master of the Riddermark,' said Eomer. 'There is trouble upon all our borders, and even now within them. Fear which was once a stranger walks among us. Yet we do not serve Sauron. Tribute he seeks to lay on us. But we – we desire only to be free, and to serve no foreign lord. Guests we will welcome, but the unbidden robber will find us swift and hard. Tell me [?briefly] what brings you here.'

Then Trotter in few words told him of the assault on Calenbel and the fall of Boromir. Dismay was plain to see on Eomer's face and many of his men at that news. It seemed that between Rohan and Ondor there was great friendship. Wonder too was in the eyes of the riders when they learned that Aragorn and his two companions had come all the way from Tolbrandir since the evening of the third day back on foot.

394 THE TREASON OF ISENGARD

'It seems that the name of Trotter was not so ill given,' said Eomer. 'That you speak the truth, if not all the truth, is plain. The men of Rohan speak no lies, but they are not easily deceived. But enough – there is now more need of speed than before. We were hastening only to aid of Eowin, since news came back that the orc-host was large and outnumbered the pursuers, but twenty-five that we first sent. But if there are captives to rescue we must ride faster. There is one spare horse that you can have, Aragorn. The others must make shift to ride behind my two esquires.'

Aragorn leapt upon the back of the great grey horse that was given to him.

Here the primary draft A ends, and as my father broke off he noted:

This complicates things. Trotter etc. should meet Eomer *returning* from battle north of the Downs near forest .... and Eomer should [?deny] any captives.

Trotter learns war has broken out with Saruman [?even] since Gandalf's escape.[11]

From 'Aragorn and his two companions had come all the way from Tolbrandir since the evening of the third day back' the chronology at this stage can be deduced:

Day 1 Death of Boromir. Leave Calenbel; night in Sarn Gebir.
Day 2 First day in plains of Rohan.
Day 3 Second day in plains of Rohan; reach downs in evening.
Day 4 In morning go on to northern end of downs; encounter with Riders.

Despite the radical alteration in the story that now entered (the Riders were returning from battle with the Orcs, not on their way to it) this chronology was retained for a long time.

We come now to the second version 'B'. This text was much worked on subsequently, but I mostly cite it as it was first written, unless a change seems to have been immediate. It was now that my father began to use 'Aragorn' again in place of 'Trotter' as the ordinary name in narrative, though at first he still now and then wrote 'Trotter' out of habit before changing it immediately to 'Aragorn'.

At the point where in TT 'The Departure of Boromir' ends and 'The Riders of Rohan' begins the text reads thus:

'We have no time now for wariness,' said Aragorn. 'Dusk will soon be about us. We must trust to the shadows and our cloaks, and hope for a change of luck.' He hastened forward, hardly pausing in his stride to scan the trail; for it needed little of his skill to find.

THE RIDERS OF ROHAN   395

'It is well that the orcs do not walk with the care of their captives,' said Legolas, as he leaped lightly behind. 'At least such an enemy is easy to follow. No other folk make such a trampling. Why do they slash and beat down all the growing things as they pass? Does it please them to break plants and saplings that are not even in their way?'

'It seems so,' answered [Trotter >] Aragorn; 'but they go with a great speed for all that. And they do not tire.'

'In both we may prove their equals,' said Gimli. 'But on foot we cannot hope to overtake their start, unless they are hindered.'

'I know it,' said Aragorn; 'yet follow we must, as best we can. And may be that better fortune awaits us if we come down into Rohan. But I do not know what has happened in that land in late years, nor of what mind the Horse-Masters may now be between the traitor Saruman and the threat of Sauron. They have long been friends with the people of Ondor and the lords of Minas Tirith, though they are not akin to them. After the fall of Isildur they came out of the North beyond Mirkwood, and their kinship is rather with the Brandings, the Men of Dale, and with the Beornings of the woods, among whom still may be seen many Men, tall and fair, like the Riders of Rohan. At the least they will not love the Orcs or aid them willingly.'[12]

Dusk deepened. Mist lay behind them among the trees below...

Here in TT the chapter 'The Riders of Rohan' begins, and this earliest extant text is already very close to it in the story of the night spent scrambling on the ridges and in the gullies of *Sern-gebir* (as the name is written at this point) and the discovery of the slain Orcs. The Rohirrim are still the *Rohiroth*, Gondor is *Ondor*, and the White Mountains are the Black Mountains (described in precisely the same words as in TT p. 24, and as there distant 'thirty leagues or more').

Aragorn's verse took this form:

(Aragorn sings a stave)
Ondor! Ondor! Between the Mountains and the Sea
Wind blows, moon rides, and the light upon the Silver Tree
Falls like rain there in gardens of the King of old.
O white walls, towers fair, and many-footed throne of gold!
O Ondor, Ondor! Shall Men behold the Silver Tree
Or West Wind blow again between the Mountain[s] and the Sea?

It can be made out from the erased primary text A that this verse was not present, but only Aragorn's words that precede it. In this earliest form *many-footed throne of gold* was changed, probably very soon, to

396　　THE TREASON OF ISENGARD

wingéd crown and throne of gold as in TT. These are the first references to the Winged Crown and the White Tree of Gondor.[13]

Then follows (as originally written):

The ridge fell steeply before their feet: twenty fathoms or more it stood above the wide shelf below. Then came the edge of a sheer cliff: the East Wall of Rohan. So ended Sarn Gebir, and the green fields of the Horsemasters rolled against its feet like a grassy sea. Out of the high land fell many freshets and threadlike waterfalls, springing down to feed the wandering Entwash, and carving the grey rock of the escarpment into countless crannies and narrow clefts. For a breathing space the three companions stood, rejoicing in the passing of night, feeling the first warmth of the mounting sun pierce the chill of their limbs.

'Now let us go!' said Aragorn, drawing his eyes of longing away from the south, and looking out west and north to the way that he must go.

'See!' cried Legolas, pointing to the pale sky above the blur where the Forest of Fangorn lay far across the plains. 'See! The eagle is come again. Look! He is high, but he is coming swiftly down. Down he comes! Look!'

'Not even my eyes can see him, my good Legolas,' said Aragorn. 'He must be away upon the very confines of the forest. But I can see something nearer at hand and more urgent...'

On previous references to the descending eagle see p. 385. Subsequently my father pencilled in against this passage:

Eagle should be flying *from* Sarn Gebir, bearing Gandalf from Tolbrandir where he resisted the Eye and saved Frodo? If so substitute the following:

'Look!' said Legolas, pointing up in the pale sky above them. 'There is the eagle again. He is very high. He seems to be flying from Sarn Gebir now back northward. He is going back northward. Look!'

'No, not even my eyes can see him, my good Legolas,' said Aragorn. 'He must be far aloft indeed. I wonder what is his errand, if he is the same bird that we have seen before. But look! I can see something'

This is virtually the text of TT (p. 25); and it is curious to see what its meaning was when it was first written – that Gandalf was passing high above their heads. The eagle was flying to Fangorn (and therefore north-west rather than north), whereas in TT Gandalf explains later to

THE RIDERS OF ROHAN   397

Legolas (pp. 98–9) that he had sent the eagle, Gwaihir the Windlord, 'to watch the River and gather tidings': Gwaihir had told him of the captivity of Merry and Pippin.[14] Against the suggestion here that the eagle was carrying Gandalf from Tol Brandir 'where he resisted the Eye and saved Frodo' my father wrote N O in large letters; cf. TT p. 99: 'I sat in a high place, and I strove with the Dark Tower; and the Shadow passed.' Nonetheless he preserved the new text.

In TT (pp. 25–6) the three companions followed the Orc-trail north along the escarpment to the ravine where a path descended like a stair, and followed the trail down into the plain. In the present text the story is different:

> ...a rough path descended like a broad steep stair into the plain. At the top of the ravine Aragorn stopped. There was a shallow pool like a great basin, over the worn lip of which the water spilled: lying at the edge of the basin something glistening caught his eye. He lifted it out and held it up in the light. It looked like the new-opened leaf of a beech-tree, fair and untimely in the winter morning.
>
> 'The brooch of an elven-cloak!' cried Legolas and Gimli together, and each with his hand felt for the clasp at his own throat; but none of their brooches were missing.
>
> 'Not lightly do the leaves of Lórien fall,' said Aragorn solemnly. 'This clasp did not betray its owner, nor stray by chance. It was cast away: maybe to mark the point where the captors turned from the hills.'
>
> 'It may have been stolen by an orc and dropped,' said Gimli.
>
> 'True enough,' said Legolas, 'but even so it tells us that one at least of our Company was carried off as Boromir said.'
>
> 'It may tell no more than that one of our Company was plundered,' answered Gimli.
>
> Aragorn turned the brooch over. The underside of the leaf was of silver. 'It is freshly marked,' he said. 'With some pin or sharp point it has been scored.[15] See! A hand has scratched on it M K P.'
>
> The others looked at the faint letters eagerly. 'They were both alive then so far,' said Gimli. 'That is heartening. We do not pursue in vain. And one at least had a hand free: that is strange and perhaps hopeful.'
>
> 'But the Ringbearer was not here,' said Aragorn. 'At least so we may guess. If I have learned anything of these strange hobbits, I would swear that otherwise either Merry or Pippin

398   THE TREASON OF ISENGARD

would have put F first, and F alone if time allowed no more. But the choice is made. We cannot turn back.'

The three companions climbed down the ravine. At its foot they came with a strange suddenness upon the grass of Rohan.

I think that it was here, arising out of this moment in the narrative, that the leaf-brooches of Lórien were conceived; they were then written into the fair copy manuscript of 'Farewell to Lórien' (p. 285). But it is strange that Aragorn should speak as though the brooch was at last a clear if not altogether final evidence that Frodo was not a captive of the Orcs, for in drafting for 'The Departure of Boromir' (p. 386) he had said: 'One thing at least is clear. Frodo is no longer on this side of the River. Only he could or would have taken the boat'; and that he should feel that this evidence called for some reinforcement of the decision to pursue the Orcs. – The postponement of the discovery of Pippin's brooch to its place in TT (p. 26) was introduced not long afterwards in a rider; see p. 408.

The entire account in TT from the debate at nightfall of the first day in the plains of Rohan (27 February: the second day of the chase) to their setting off again on the following morning (pp. 27–9) is lacking here. The text reads thus:

... No longer could any sight of them be seen in the level plains.

When night was already far advanced the hunters rested for a while, somewhat less than three hours. Then again they went on, all the next day with scarcely a pause. Often they thanked the folk of Lórien for the gift of *lembas*; for they could eat and find new strength even as they ran.

As the third day [*i.e. of the chase*] wore on they came to long treeless slopes, where the ground was harder and drier and the grass shorter: the land rose, now sinking now swelling up, towards a line of low, smooth downs ahead. To their left the river Entwash wound, a silver thread in the green floor. The dwellings of the Rohiroth were for the most part far away [south >] to the west[16] across the river, under the wooded eaves of the Black Mountains, which were now hidden in mist and cloud. Yet Aragorn wondered often that they saw no sign of beast or man, for the Horsemasters had formerly kept many studs and herds in this eastern region (Eastemnet),[17] and wandered much, living often in camp or tent, even in the winter-time. But all the land was now empty, and there was a silence upon it that did not seem to be the quiet of peace. Through the wide solitude the hunters passed. Their elven-cloaks faded against the background of the green fields ...

THE RIDERS OF ROHAN
399

It is at this point that the original text A emerges (p. 391). The new version B, still replacing it but no longer destroying it, advances far towards the final text, and for long stretches is almost identical. The original time-scheme, as set out on p. 394, was retained: the three companions still came to the downs at the end of the third day of the chase (i.e. the second day in the plains of Rohan); Aragorn still asserted that the tracks which they found there had been made that day; and they still went on far into the night, not stopping until they were halfway along the downs, where they found the orc-encampment. In this version, in fact, the Orcs were less far ahead than they were in A: ' "They halted here in the early evening, I guess," said Aragorn.' It was at this point that Aragorn lay on the ground for a long time motionless (cf. TT pp. 28–9; but here it was by moonlight, in the night following 'Day 3' of the chase, not at dawn of 'Day 3' and still far east of the downs).

'The rumour of the earth is dim and confused,' he said. 'Many feet I heard, far away; but it seemed to me also that there were horses, horses galloping, and yet all were going away from us. I wonder what is happening in this land. All seems strange. I distrust the very moonlight. Only the stars are left to steer by, and they are faint and far away. I am weary, as a Ranger should never be on a fresh trail; yet we must go on, we must go on.'

In this version they seem not to have slept at all that night: 'when dawn came they had almost reached the end of the downs'; and 'as the sun rose upon the fourth day of the pursuit, and the light grew, they climbed the last height, a rounded hill standing alone at the north end of the downs' – where in TT (p. 31) they spent the night of the fourth day.[18]

The coming of the Rohiroth now reaches the text of TT,[19] and the only difference to mention is that Legolas, seeing them far away, said: 'There are one hundred save three'; this almost certainly indicates, I think, that three Riders had been lost from an *éored* of 100 horse. But 'one hundred save three' was changed to 'one hundred and five' before the end of the chapter was reached, for Eomer subsequently tells Aragorn that they had lost fifteen men in the battle. (On the constitution of an *éored* see *Unfinished Tales* p. 315.)

The first part of Aragorn's conversation with Eomer in B is actually a third version, for it is written over erased pencil drafting, as far as the point where Gimli explains to Eomer the meaning of the word 'hobbits' (TT p. 37); and here the final form is reached apart from one or two details: *Branding* as the name of Aragorn's sword, *Masters* for *Marshals* of the Mark. It is here that *Theoden son of Thengel* first appears: if some other names preceded these they are lost in the

400 THE TREASON OF ISENGARD

underlying erased text. Theoden is not here called 'King', but 'the First Master'.

For the next portion of the chapter there is some extremely rough drafting, scarcely more than notes, preliminary to the writing of B. In these my father did not see Gandalf as a well-known figure in Rohan, and he still thought that there was another troop of Riders in that region (detached from Eomer's host?):

> The old man who said he had escaped from Orthanc on an eagle! And demanded a horse and got it! Some said he was a wizard. And Shadowfax ... [?came back] only a day ago.
>
> Eomer says some orcs fled towards Wold. Aragorn may meet other Riders: Marhath the Fourth Master [see p. 390] is there with a few men. Aragorn wishes to go on. Eomer gives him token to show Marhath. Aragorn pledges his word to return to Theoden and vindicate Eomer. Farewell.

In the part of the B-text developed from these notes the hobbits are called the 'Half-high', not as in TT the 'Halflings': in Gimli's reference to 'the words that troubled Minas Tirith' he says 'They spoke of the Half-high', as in the form of the verse in the fifth version of 'The Council of Elrond' (p. 146).[20] Aragorn's reply to the scoffing question of Eothain 'Are we walking in legends or on the green earth under the daylight?' here takes the form: 'One may do both; and the latter is not always the safer' (added to the manuscript: 'But the green earth is a legend seen under the light of day'). Eomer's remarks about Gandalf, which were achieved in this form through a mass of small changes, now read thus:

'Gandalf?' said Eomer. 'We have heard of him. An old man of that name used to appear at times in our land. None knew whence he came or where he went. His coming was ever the herald of strange events. Indeed since his last coming all things have gone amiss. Our trouble with Saruman began from that time. Until then we had counted Saruman our friend, but Gandalf said that evil was afoot in Isengard. Indeed he declared that he had been a prisoner in Orthanc and had escaped. Riding on an eagle! Nonetheless he asked us for a horse! What arts he used I cannot guess, but Theoden gave him one of the *mearas*: the steeds that only the First Master of the Mark may ride; for it is said that [they are descended from the horses which the Men of Westernesse brought over the Great Seas >] their sires came out of the Lost Land over the Great Sea when the Kings of Men came out of the Deeps to Gondor. Shadowfax was the name of that horse. We wondered if evil had befallen the old man; for seven nights ago Shadowfax returned.'[21]

THE RIDERS OF ROHAN 401

'But Gandalf left Shadowfax far in the North at Rivendell,' said Aragorn. 'Or so I thought.[22] But, alas, however that may be, Gandalf is gone down into the shadows.' Aragorn now told briefly the story of their journey from Moria. To his account of Lórien Eomer listened with amazement. At last Aragorn spoke of the assault of the orcs on Calen-bel, and the fall of Boromir.

Only shortly before in this text the name was still *Ondor*. In view of the fact that it is *Ondor* in the draft and fair copy of 'Treebeard', it may be that the alteration of the sentence about the *mearas*, in which the form *Gondor* appears, was made later. On the actual date of the change *Ondor* > *Gondor* see p. 423.

In the remainder of the conversation with Eomer there are only these differences from the text of TT (pp. 38–41) to notice. There is no suggestion yet of Wormtongue: Eomer does not speak of 'some, close to the king's ear, that speak craven counsels'. He says that there has been war with Saruman 'since the summer' ('for many months', TT); and he remarks of Saruman himself that 'He walks about like an old man, indeed there are some that say Gandalf was only old Saruman in disguise: certainly they are much alike to look on.'[23] In his account of his own present expedition Eomer does not refer to his going without Theoden's leave:

'... I do not know how it all will end. There is battle even now away upon the Westemnet under the shadow of Isengard. Hardly could we be spared. But scouts warned us [> Theoden] of the orc-host coming down out of the East Wall three nights ago: among them they reported some that bore the badges of Saruman. We overtook them yesterday at nightfall, only a little way from the edges of the Forest. We surrounded them, and gave battle at dawn. We lost fifteen of my *eored* and twelve horses, alas!'

On the chronology see the *Note on Chronology* at the end of this chapter. Eomer tells of the Orcs that came in from the East across the Great River, and the Isengard Orcs that came out of the Forest. The story of the finding of Pippin's brooch was still in its former place (p. 397), as is seen from Aragorn's words here: 'Yet our friends are not behind. We had a clear token that they were with the Orcs when they descended into the plain.'[24]

At the end of the conversation Eomer says:

'... But it is hard to be sure of anything among so many marvels. One may pardon Eothain, my squire. The world is all turned strange. Old men upon eagles; and raiment that deceives the eye; and Elves with bows, and folk that have spoken with the

402   THE TREASON OF ISENGARD

Lady of the Wood, and yet live; and the Sword comes back to war that was broken ere the Fathers of the Fathers rode into the Mark! How shall a man judge what to do in such times. It is against our law to let strangers wander free in our land, and doubly so at this time of peril. I beg you to come back honourably with me, and you will not.'

Aragorn in his reply tells (as in TT p. 41) that he had been in Rohan, and had spoken with Eomund father of Eomer, and with Theoden, 'and with Thengel that was Master before him.' 'None of them would have desired to force a man to abandon friends whom the orcs had seized, while hope or even doubt remained.' Eomer relents. He requests that Aragorn return with the horses over the Entwade to '...torras where Theoden now sits.' This name was changed at once or very soon to *Meodarn*, *Meduarn* ('Mead-hall'), and then to '*Winseld* ['Wine-hall'], the high house in Eodor.' *Eodor* (singular, 'fence, enclosure, dwelling') is seen on Map IV^C (p. 317); *Eodoras* (plural) on Map IV^{D-E} (p. 319). Eothain's surliness at the loan of the horses is not present. The horses were first given names in Modern English, that for Aragorn being 'Windmane' and that for Legolas 'Whitelock'; these were changed to the Old English names found in TT, *Hasofel* ('Grey-coat', cf. *Hasupada*, note 21) and *Arod* ('Swift').

In the last part of the chapter, after the Riders had gone, the story is for most of its length at once almost as in the final text; but Aragorn's words about Fangorn, the earliest account of it that my father wrote,[25] took this form:

'I do not know what fables men have made out of old knowledge,' said Aragorn. 'And of the truth little is now known, even to Keleborn. But I have heard tell that in Fangorn, clinging here on the east side of the last slopes of the Misty Mountains, the ancient trees have taken refuge that once marched dark and proud over the wide lands, before even the first Elves awoke in the world. Between the Baranduin and the Barrowdowns is another forest of old trees; but it is not as great as Fangorn. Some say that both are but the last strongholds of one mighty wood, more vast than Mirkwood the Great, that held under its dominion all the countries through which now flow the Greyflood and the Baranduin; others say that Fangorn is not akin to the Old Forest, and that its secret is of other kind.'

This was rejected at once and replaced by a shorter passage, close to Aragorn's words in TT (p. 45), though Elrond is not here cited as his authority: 'Some say the two are akin, the last strongholds of the

THE RIDERS OF ROHAN   403

mighty woods of the Elder days, in which the Elves strayed, when they first awoke.'

At the end of the chapter, when Gimli was watchman and all was silent, save that the tree rustled and that 'the horses, picketed a little way off, stirred now and again,' the old man appeared; and his apparition and disappearance are told in precisely the same words as in TT, except that he was 'clad in rags', not in a great cloak, and his hat was 'battered', not 'wide-brimmed'. But the chapter ended altogether differently.

There was no trace of him to be found near at hand; and they did not dare to wander far – the moon was hidden in cloud, and the night was very dark. [*Struck out:* The horses remained quiet, and seemed to feel nothing amiss.] ? The horses were restive, straining at their tether-ropes, showing the whites of their eyes. It was a little while before Legolas could quiet them.

For some time the companions discussed this strange event. 'It was Saruman, of that I feel certain,' said Gimli. 'You remember the words of Eomer. He will come back, or bring more trouble upon us. I wish that the morning were not so far off.'

'Well, in the meantime there is nothing we can do,' said Aragorn, 'nothing but to get what rest we can, while we are still allowed to rest. I will watch now for a while, Gimli.'

The night passed slowly, but nothing further happened, in any of their two-hour watches. The old man did not appear again.

While this is no more than a guess, I suspect that when my father wrote this he thought that it was Gandalf, and not Saruman, who stood so briefly in the light of the fire (cf. the outline given on p. 389).[26]

NOTES

1 *Sarn-Gebir runs North-South:* see Map IV[C], pp. 317–18.

2 This means that the eagle was seen in the direction of Fangorn; see p. 396.

3 *I forgot most of what I knew:* cf. TT p. 98.

4 *Haradwaith* is here the name of a people: see p. 434, and cf. *Enedwaith*, rendered 'Middlemarch' on the First Map (Map II, p. 305), but afterwards (while remaining the name of a region) 'Middle-folk.'

5 On *Mar-* and *Eo-* names in Rohan see *Unfinished Tales* p. 311 note 6 and p. 315 note 36. – Names in *Eo-* are not written with an accent at this period.

404   THE TREASON OF ISENGARD

6   None of the successive variants of this section of the First Map illustrate this.

7   *Methen Amon*: earliest name of *Methedras* – which appears on the First Map (Map IVE, p. 319). For *Methen* see the *Etymologies*, V.373, stem MET: Noldorin *methen* 'end'; and see note 18.

8   This is the first occurrence of the name *Entwade* in the texts: see p. 366, note 16.

9   Aragorn does not (of course) cry out: 'What news from the North, Riders of Rohan?'; it is said only that he 'hailed them in a loud voice.'

10 This is the first occurrence of the name *Arathorn* of Aragorn's father, replacing earlier *Kelegorn* (cf. also *Eldakar* p. 360, *Valatar* p. 362).

11 Gandalf's escape from Orthanc.

12 This passage is found later in TT (p. 33). The reference there to Eorl the Young is here absent; and the *Brandings* of Dale (named from King Brand son of Bain son of Bard) are in TT the *Bardings* (which was added to the First Map, p. 307). See note 19.

13 In a design of my father's for the cover of *The Return of the King* the throne is shown with four feet. This design, in white, gold and green on a black ground shows (as he noted) 'the empty throne awaiting return of the King' with outstretching wings; the Winged Crown; the white-flowering Tree, with seven stars; and dimly seen beyond in the darkness a vision of the fall of Sauron. This design, in simplified form, was used for the cover of the India paper edition of *The Lord of the Rings* published by George Allen and Unwin in 1969.

14 Yet Gandalf had himself been in, or over, those regions, it seems: 'No, I did not find them. There was a darkness over the valleys of the Emyn Muil, and I did not know of their captivity, until the eagle told me.'

15 Altered later to: 'It has been scored with the pin, which is broken off.' – An error in the text of TT may be mentioned here. Aragorn did not say (p. 26) that Pippin was smaller than *the other*' – he would not refer to Merry in such a remote tone – but 'smaller than *the others*', i.e. Merry and Frodo and Sam.

16 *to the west*: subsequently changed back to *to the south*.

17 This is the first occurrence in the texts of the name *Eastemnet*, which is found on the First Map (Map IV^D, p. 319). *Westemnet* occurs later in this text (p. 401).

18 Here, as they looked about them, they saw to their right 'the windy uplands of the Wold of Rohan', and beyond Fangorn the last great peak of the Misty Mountains (first named *Methen Amon*, p. 391 and note 7), *Methendol*, immediately changed to *Methedras*.

19 The passage in which Aragorn tells Gimli what he knows of the

THE RIDERS OF ROHAN   405

Riders of Rohan (TT p. 33), which had first appeared much earlier in B (p. 395), was transferred subsequently to the place that it occupies in TT on an inserted rider. This retains almost exactly the form in which it was first written, without mention of Eorl the Young, but with *Bardings* for *Brandings*.

20 In the preliminary drafting the Old English form is used: *Halfheah* (*Halfheh*, *Healfheh*).

21 A pencilled rider was inserted into the manuscript later as a substitute for this speech: here the origin of the *mearas* remains the same, but in other respects the text of TT is largely reached: Gandalf (not yet called Greyhame) is murmured by some in Rohan to be a bringer of ill, Theoden is called King, and his anger against Gandalf for taking Shadowfax and the horse's wildness after his return appear. By an addition to the rider Eomer says: 'We know that name, or *Gondelf* as we have it.' *Gondelf* is an 'Anglo-Saxonising' of Norse *Gandalf(r)*. At the foot of the page is written the Old English word *Hasupada* ('Grey-coat'), and it appears from a subsequent typescript text of the chapter that this refers to Gandalf ('Greyhame'): ' "Gandalf!" said Eomer. "We know that name, and the wandering *witega* that claims it. *Hasupada* we call him mostly in our tongue" ' (Old English *witega* 'wise man, one who has knowledge').

22 On Shadowfax at Rivendell and after see pp. 390 and 438 note 2.

23 Eomer calls Saruman 'a wizard of great power', changed to 'a wizard and man of craft', and that to 'a wizard and very crafty'. Against the word *wizard* is pencilled *wicca* (Old English, 'wizard', surviving at any rate until recently as *witch*, masculine, not distinct in form from *witch* deriving from the Old English feminine *wicce*).

24 These words are in themselves ambiguous, but what my father intended is shown, I think, by the fact that he afterwards corrected them on the manuscript to 'We had a clear token that one at least was still with the orcs not far from the East Wall.' The original story was still present when he wrote the outline for the next chapter.

25 If the very early images, when Treebeard was a Giant and his forest correspondingly gigantic (VI.382–4, 410), are excepted.

26 Other supports, admittedly slight, for this idea are the statements that the old man was 'clad in rags' (cf. Trotter's vision on Amon Hen, p. 380); that he had a 'battered hat' (cf. Frodo's song in Lórien, FR p. 375: *an old man in a battered hat*); and that 'the horses remained quiet, and seemed to feel nothing amiss.' – It is curious that Aragorn's words in TT, p. 46 (when the old man was certainly Saruman, TT p. 102) 'I marked also that this old man had a hat not a hood' were an addition to the text made long after.

406   THE TREASON OF ISENGARD

Note on the Chronology

'The Riders of Rohan' is unusual in that the narrative underwent an important change in structure long after it was to all intents and purposes completed.

I set out below the relations between the time-scheme in the second text (B) and that in *The Two Towers*. 'Day 1' is the day of Boromir's death.

	Text B		*The Two Towers*
Day 1	Orcs descend into plains of Rohan at night.	(Feb. 26)	The same
Day 2	Aragorn &c. descend into Rohan in the morning. First day in the plains.	(Feb. 27)	The same
Day 3	Second day in the plains. Aragorn &c. reach the downs in the evening and go on through the night. – Riders overtake Orcs at nightfall.	(Feb. 28)	Aragorn &c. approach downs in the evening and halt for the night. – Riders overtake Orcs at nightfall.
Day 4	Battle of Riders and Orcs at dawn. – Aragorn &c. reach northmost hill of the downs at dawn. Encounter with Riders returning in the morning.	(Feb. 29)	Battle of Riders and Orcs at dawn. – Aragorn &c. reach downs towards noon. Night spent on northmost hill of the downs.
Day 5		(Feb. 30)	Aragorn &c. encounter Riders returning in the morning.

In B, Aragorn, Legolas and Gimli took two days and two nights after their descent from the 'East Wall' to reach the isolated hill at the northern end of the downs where they met the Riders; in TT they took three days and two nights to reach that place, and passed the third night there. In B, they encountered the Riders returning in the morning after the battle at dawn; in TT the meeting was on the following day: the Riders had passed a whole further day and night by the eaves of Fangorn before setting off south again.

This change in the chronology, with very substantial rewriting and reordering (TT pp. 27 ff.) of the existing chapter, was introduced in October 1944. On 12 October my father wrote a letter to me in South Africa in which he said (*Letters* no. 84):

I began trying to write again (I would, on the brink of term!) on

THE RIDERS OF ROHAN   407

Tuesday, but I struck a most awkward error (one or two days) in the synchronization, v. important at this stage, of movements of Frodo and the others, which has cost labour and thought and will require tiresome small alterations in many chapters ...

Four days later he wrote again (*Letters* no. 85):

I have been struggling with the dislocated chronology of the Ring, which has proved most vexatious ... I think I have solved it all at last by small map alterations, and by inserting an extra day's Entmoot, and extra days *into Trotter's chase* and Frodo's journey ...

(On the extra day of the Entmoot see p. 419.)

In one point however the text of TT retains an uncorrected vestige of the original story. Éomer tells Aragorn (p. 39) that 'scouts warned me of the orc-host coming down out of the East Wall *three nights ago,*' just as he does in the B text (p. 401). But in B this was said on the morning of Day 4, and the reference is to the night of Day 1; in TT it was said on the morning of Day 5. It was therefore not three nights ago, but four, that the Orcs came down from the Emyn Muil.

In *The Tale of Years* in Appendix B to LR the dates are:

Feb. 26 Éomer hears of the descent of the Orc-band from the Emyn Muil.

Feb. 27 Éomer sets out from Eastfold about midnight to pursue the Orcs.

Feb. 28 Éomer overtakes the Orcs.

Feb. 29 The Rohirrim attack at sunrise and destroy the Orcs.

Feb. 30 Éomer returning to Edoras meets Aragorn.

Thus Éomer's 'three nights ago' in TT cannot be explained by taking it to refer, not to the descent of the Orcs into Rohan, but to his receiving news of it.

XXI

THE URUK-HAI

For this chapter there exists, first, a brief outline as follows:

Some want to go North. Some say ought to go straight to Mordor. The great orcs were ordered to go to Isengard.

They carry prisoners. Neither of them are the One. They haven't got it. Kill 'em. But they're hobbits. Saruman said bring any *hobbit*, *alive*. Curse Saruman. Who does he think he is? A good master and lord. Man's flesh to eat.

Fight breaks out. Slain orc falls on top of Pippin with blade drawn. Pippin manages to cut wrist bands. Ties cord loosely again.

Isengarders win. Mordor orcs are killed. They start on. [?Leader] called Uglúk [?leaves them]. They rouse Merry, give him drink; cut ankle bonds and drive hobbits with whips. Dark night. Pippin manages to unclasp brooch unseen.

They get into plain. Merry and Pippin made to run till they faint and fall. Orcs carry them.

Pippin awakes to hear horsemen. Night.... Terror of orcs. They run at great speed. Uglúk refuses to let hobbits be slain or cast aside. Horsemen ride up. Uglúk steals off [?from his friends seizing] hobbits. But a horseman rides after him. Pippin pulls Merry down flat and covers him with cloak, the horseman rides past and spears Uglúk. Merry and Pippin fly into forest.

'Uglúk' is here of course the Mordor Orc subsequently called Grishnákh. It is seen that Pippin still drops his brooch before the descent into the plain (p. 401 and note 24).

For almost half of this chapter there is no initial drafting extant, and this is largely because my father again, as in the previous chapter, wrote a new version in ink over erased drafting in pencil; in addition, it seems that some initial drafting on separate pages has been lost. As far, then, as ' "Very well," said Uglúk' (TT p. 54) the earliest extant text is this second version or fair copy, in which the story as told in TT was reached almost down to the last detail, with relatively very little subsequent correction and addition. The manuscript begins without title, but my father clearly saw it as a new chapter, 'XXIV'.[1] A title, 'An Orc-raid', was written in later.

The later story of Pippin's casting aside his brooch after the descent into the plain had now entered. The Orc-names are all present:

THE URUK-HAI   409

Lugbúrz, Uruk-hai; *Uglúk* (leader of the Isengarders), *Grishnák* (so spelt), *Lugdush*. Uglúk does not use the word *Halflings* (TT p. 48), but calls them *hobbits*; he says 'We are the servants of *the old Uthwit* and the White Hand' (cf. TT p. 49), this being Old English *ūþwita* 'sage, philosopher, one of great learning'; and he calls the descent into the plain of Rohan 'the Ladder' (changed to 'the Stair': TT p. 50). Grishnák does not name the Nazgûl (TT p. 49), but says 'The winged one awaits us northward on the east bank'.

At the point where Pippin is given the orc-draught my father wrote a brief outline in the body of the text:

> Uglúk smears Merry's wound. He cries out. Orcs jeer. But torment not the object. Merry recovers.
>
> Orcs become aware of pursuit by horsemen. Merry and Pippin do not know about horsemen; but perceive that orcs are afraid.
>
> Grishnák brings a small company of Mordor-orcs from the East. Uglúk evidently does not like it. He asks why the Nazgûl has not come to help them. The Nazgûl is not yet permitted to cross River: Sauron is keeping them for the War – and for another purpose.
>
> Grishnák brings a small company of Mordor-orcs from the East. what a mess you have got into! They fly to the Forest.
>
> When surrounded Grishnák searches Merry and Pippin and drags them out of ring of horsemen. He is slain, and Merry and Pippin passed over. They run into forest.
>
> Adventure with Treebeard.

From the point where Uglúk sends the 'Northerners' running off towards the Forest (TT p. 54) initial drafting is extant, except for a further passage where my father reverted to the method of erasing it and writing a new version above. This draft text, dashed down in faint pencil and extremely difficult to make out, is astonishingly close to the final form. I give a brief passage in exemplification (TT p. 56), where the draft text is not in fact so close to the final form as it is in some others:

The Forest was drawing near. Already they had passed a few isolated trees. The land was beginning to slope upward, ever more steeply. But this did not stay the orcs, now desperately putting on their last spurt. Looking to one side Pippin saw that riders coming in the East were already level with them, galloping over the plain, the sunset touching their spears and helmets and their pale flowing hair. They were hemming in the orcs driving them along the line of the river. He wondered very much what sort of folk they were. He wished he had learned more in Rivendell, looked at more maps – but then the journey was all in more competent hands, he had not reckoned on being cut off

410 THE TREASON OF ISENGARD

from Gandalf and Trotter – and even Frodo. All he could remember about them was that he [*read* they] had given Gandalf a horse. That [?sounded] well.

If the original drafting where it is extant is characteristic of the parts where it is not, as seems very probable, it can be said this chapter was achieved with far greater facility than any previous part of the story of *The Lord of the Rings*.

The second version of the latter part of the chapter only differs in very minor touches here and there from the final form.[2] The watchfires of the Riders were a later addition to the text; Grishnákh (now so spelt) had evidently had personal experience of Gollum, for he says 'That's what he meanss, iss it?' (cf. TT p. 59); and at the point where the chapter ends in TT this text has only:

There he was slain at last by Eomer the Third Master of Rohan, who dismounted and fought him sword to sword. So ended the raid, and no news of it came ever back either to Mordor or to Isengard.[3]

Neither in the draft nor in the second text did my father stop at this point, but continued on into the following chapter in *The Two Towers*, 'Treebeard'.

NOTES

1   The manuscript is paginated 'XXIV', as also is the draft (with numbers written at the same time as the text).

2   The Orc-names *Snaga* and *Mauhúr* appear already in the preliminary draft.

3   The expansion of the end of the chapter came in with the chronological revision made in October 1944 (see pp. 406–7). In notes on the subject my father said that 'at end of "Uruk-hai" the fight should be made to take longer – chase of stray fugitives, etc.', and that something should be said of the burning of the corpses.

XXII

TREEBEARD

Of 'Giant Treebeard' there have been many mentions in the outlines scattered through the early texts of *The Lord of the Rings*, but there was nothing in any of them to prepare for the reality when he should finally appear. My father said years later (*Letters* no. 180, 14 January 1956):

> I have long ceased to *invent* ... : I wait till I seem to know what really happened. Or till it writes itself. Thus, though I knew for years that Frodo would run into a tree-adventure somewhere far down the Great River, I have no recollection of inventing Ents. I came at last to the point, and wrote the 'Treebeard' chapter without any recollection of previous thought: just as it now is.

This testimony is fully borne out by the original text. 'Treebeard' did indeed very largely 'write itself'.

First, however, there is a page of pencilled notes of much interest but with various puzzling features. I give here this text exactly as it stands, and postpone discussion of it till the end.

> Did first lord of the Elves make Tree-folk in order to or through trying to understand trees?
>
> Gimli and Legolas to go with Trotter and Boromir. It must be Merry and Pippin who find Gandalf.
>
> Notes for *Treebeard*.
>
> In some ways rather stupid. Are the Tree-folk ('Lone-walkers') *hnau* that have gone tree-like, or trees that have become *hnau*?[1] Treebeard might be 'moveless' – but here are some notes [?or] first [?suggestions].
>
> There are very few left. Not enough room. 'Time was when a fellow could walk and sing all day and hear no more than the echo of his voice in the mountains.'
>
> Difference between *trolls* – stone inhabited by goblin-spirit, *stone-giants*, and the 'tree-folk'. [*Added in ink:* Ents.]
>
> Treebeard is anxious for news. He never hears much. But he smells things in the air. Prefers breath from South and West of the Sea. Too much East wind these days. He is bothered about Saruman: a machine-minded man. Fondest of Gandalf. Very upset at news of his fall. Only one of the wizards who understood trees.

412   THE TREASON OF ISENGARD

Tells how the Horsemasters have ridden away south leaving land empty.

There are only three of us left: myself and Skinbark and Leaflock [*written above in ink:* Fangorn   Fladrib > Fladrif   Finglas]. Saruman has got hold of Skinbark. He went off to Isengard some time ago. Leaflock has gone 'tree-ish'. He seldom comes into the hills: has taken to standing half-asleep all through the summer with the deep grass of the meadows round his knees. Covered with leaves he is. Wakes up a bit in winter. May be somewhere about.

Treebeard offers to take them across Rohan to or towards Minas Tirith. Treebeard smells war.

They see a battle of Wolfriders (Saruman) and the Horsemasters – wild flowing hair and little bows.

How do they meet Gandalf? It should really be *Sam* or Frodo who saw vision in the Mirror of Galadriel.

A possible return of Gandalf would be as an old bent beggar with a battered hat coming to gates of Minas Tirith. He is let in. After, at siege's darkest hour when outer walls have fallen, he throws off cloak and stands up – *white*. He leads sortie. Or he comes with horses of Rohan riding on [*struck out:* Arfaxed] Shadowfax.

Another possibility. Cut out rescue of Frodo by Sam. Let Sam get lost and meet Gandalf, and have adventures getting into Minas Tirith. (But it was Frodo saw vision of Gandalf. Also Sam saw vision of Frodo lying under dark cliff, pale, and of himself on a winding stair.)

The winding stair must be cut in rocks and go up from Gorgoroth to watch-tower. Cut out Minas Morgul.

More roughly scribbled notes were added:

Trotter sends Legolas and Gimli with Boromir to Minas Tirith. He himself wanders looking for the hobbits. He meets Gandalf. He is tempted but forsakes his ambition.

What are Treebeard and Ents to do about Saruman. Seek help of Rohiroth?

It is evident that this page does not belong to the time we have reached in the narrative texts, but to some earlier stage, before the death of Boromir had entered the story. To suppose otherwise would depend, of course, on the assumption that the words 'Gimli and Legolas to go with Trotter and Boromir. It must be Merry and Pippin who find Gandalf' already stood on this page which my father used afterwards for notes on the Ents; but there is nothing in the appearance of the page to suggest it. '*It must be Merry and Pippin* who find Gandalf' suggests the rejection of some earlier idea, and 'How do they meet Gandalf?' later in these notes obviously relates to this. Moreover the notes at the end, in which Boromir is still thought of as going to

TREEBEARD 413

Minas Tirith, seem certainly to have been set down after the main text had been written.

In the outline which I have called 'The Story Foreseen from Moria' it was Merry and Pippin who were to encounter Treebeard but Gimli and Legolas who were to meet Gandalf returned (pp. 210–11); and this was repeated in the outline 'The Story Foreseen from Lórien' (pp. 329–30). The reference to the cutting-out of Minas Morgul and the substitution of a watchtower (see on this question p. 344 and note 39) is a reference to the story of Sam and Frodo in 'The Story Foreseen from Lórien'. The death of Boromir entered in an outline for the end of 'The Breaking of the Fellowship', and 'The Departure of Boromir' (pp. 375, 378). On the face of it, then, these notes belong to the time of work on 'The Great River' and 'The Breaking of the Fellowship', and show my father pondering the way ahead after the Company should have been brought to its dismemberment above the falls of Rauros.

The note 'It should really be *Sam* or Frodo who saw vision in the Mirror of Galadriel' – at first sight incomprehensible, since there has never been a suggestion that it was anybody else who looked in the Mirror – is I think to be explained in this way: it would have been clearer if my father had written 'It really *should* be Sam or Frodo...', i.e. the story of the Mirror has been written of Sam and Frodo, and so it should be; it should not be changed. What is the purport of this? I think that my father was changing direction as he wrote – already doubting the rightness of the decision to make it Merry and Pippin who met Gandalf returned; and this seems to have been largely on account of the visions in the Mirror. Hence his suggestion (implying the rejection of the whole story of Sam and Frodo in Mordor as projected in 'The Story Foreseen from Lórien') that Sam should be the one who met Gandalf. Nonetheless he was unwilling to alter the visions seen by Frodo and Sam in the Mirror, to make it Sam who saw Gandalf walking down the long grey road (for that was not 'what really happened'). In the event, of course, Gandalf reappeared to members of the Company who had never looked into the Mirror of Galadriel. Possibly to be connected with this is the vision of Gandalf vouchsafed to Trotter on Amon Hen (pp. 379–80).

The word *Ents* added in ink to the note on the difference between 'trolls' and 'tree-folk' (with its striking definition of 'trolls') was perhaps the first use of it in the new and very particular sense; for its former use in *Entish Lands, Entish Dales* see p. 16 note 14 and p. 65 note 32, and cf. also *Letters* no. 157, 27 November 1954:

> As usually with me they [the Ents] grew rather out of their name, than the other way about. I always felt that something ought to be done about the peculiar Anglo-Saxon word *ent* for a 'giant' or mighty person of long ago – to whom all old works were ascribed.

The textual situation in this chapter is essentially very similar to that

414   THE TREASON OF ISENGARD

in the last, in that there is initial drafting for part of the chapter, but in the rest of it the draft text was erased and the 'fair copy' written over it; and here again, and even more so, the first draft is for the most part extraordinarily close to the final form. My father's words in the letter cited on p. 411, 'just as it now is', must be modified, however, in respect of certain passages where the narrative leaves the immediate experience of Merry and Pippin and touches on wider themes.

The separation of 'Treebeard' as 'Chapter XXV' from XXIV ('The Uruk-hai') was carried out in the course of the writing of the fair copy.

Taking first the part of the chapter for which the original setting down of the story is available, this runs from the beginning of the chapter in TT to 'they were twisted round, gently but irresistibly' (p. 66), and then from ' "There is quite a lot going on," said Merry' (p. 69) to Treebeard's denunciation of Saruman (p. 77). The draft, written so fast as to touch on total illegibility if the later text did not generally provide sufficient clues, remained in all essentials of description into TT, and for long stretches the vocabulary and phrasing underwent only the most minor forms of change. As in the last chapter I give a single brief passage to exemplify this (TT p. 73):

No trees grew there. Treebeard strode up with scarcely any slackening of his pace. Then they saw a wide opening. On either side two trees grew like living gate-posts, but there was no gate save their crossing and interwoven branches; and as the Ent approached the trees raised up their boughs and all their leaves rustled and whispered. For they were evergreen trees, and their leaves were dark and polished like the leaves of the holm-oak.

Beyond the trees there was a wide level space, as though the floor of a great hall had been hewn out of the side of the hill. On either side the walls sloped upward until they were fifty feet in height or more and at their feet grew trees: two long lines of trees increasing in size. At the far end the rock wall was sheer, but in it was cut a shallow bay with an arched roof: the only roof save the branches of the trees which overshadowed all the ground save for a broad aisle / path in the middle. A little stream that escaped from the Entwash spring high above and left the main water fell tinkling down the sheer face of the rear wall, pouring like a clear curtain of silver drops in front of the arched bay. It was gathered again in [a] green rock basin, and thence flowed out down the open aisle / path and on to rejoin the Entwash in its journey through the Forest.

All the tiny meticulous changes of word and rhythm that differentiate this from the text of TT were introduced in the writing of the fair copy manuscript.

TREEBEARD 415

There are some small particular points worthy of mention in this first part of the chapter. In the fair copy corresponding to TT pp. 66–7 (the passage is lacking in independent draft) Treebeard's height was changed from ten feet to twelve, and then to fourteen; he says that if he had not seen the hobbits before he heard them 'I should have just batted you with my club'; and his ejaculation 'Root and twig!' replaced 'Crack my timbers!'[2]

When Merry (Pippin in the draft) suggested that Treebeard must be getting tired of holding them up (TT p. 69), he replied, both in draft and fair copy: 'Hm, *tired? Tired?* What is that. Ah yes, I remember. No, I am not tired'; and later he says when they come to the Ent-house that perhaps they are 'what you call "tired"'.

The first major development from the original text comes with Treebeard's long brooding discourse on Lórien and Fangorn, as he carried Merry and Pippin through the woods (TT pp. 70–2). At first he said:

'... Neither this country nor anything else outside the Golden Wood is what it was when Keleborn was young. *Tauretavárea tumbalemorna Tumbaletaurea landataváre.*[3] That is what they used to say. But we have changed many things.' (He means they have weeded out rotten-hearted trees such as are in the Old Forest.)

This was changed immediately to:

'... Things have changed, but it is still true in places.'

'What do you mean? What is true?' said Pippin.

'I am not sure I know, and I am sure I could not explain to you. But there are no longer any evil trees here (none that are evil according to their kind and light). ...'

Treebeard's remarks about trees awakening, 'getting Entish', and then showing in some cases that they have 'bad hearts', are very much as in TT; but to Pippin's question 'Like the Old Forest, do you mean?' he replies:

'Aye, aye, something like, but not as bad as that. That was already a very bad region even in the days when there was all one wood from here to Lune, and we were called the East End. But something was queer (went wrong) away there: some old sorcery in the Dark Days, I expect. Ah, no: the first woods were more like Lórien, only thicker, stronger, younger. Those were days! Time was when one could walk and sing all day and hear no more than the echo of his own voice in the mountains. And the scent. I used to spend weeks [?months] just breathing.'

416 THE TREASON OF ISENGARD

In the fair copy this was greatly expanded, but by no means to the text of TT. Here Treebeard begins as in the original draft (with *Mountains of Lune* for *Lune*) as far as 'this was just the East End', but then continues:

'... Things went wrong there in the Dark [> Elder] Days; some old sorcery, I expect [> some old shadow of the Great Dark lay there]. They say that even the Men that came out of the Sea were caught in it, and some of them fell into the Shadow. But that is only a rumour to me. Anyway they have no treeherds there, no one to care for them: it is a long, long time since the Ents walked away from the banks of the Baranduin.'

'What about Tom Bombadil, though?' asked Pippin. 'He lives on the Downs close by. He seems to understand trees.'

'What about whom?' said Treebeard. '*Tombombadil? Tombombadil?* So that is what you call him. Oh, he has got a *very* long name. He understands trees, right enough; but he is not an Ent. He is no herdsman. He laughs and does not interfere. He never made anything go wrong, but he never cured anything, either. Why, why, it is all the difference between walking in the fields and trying to keep a garden; between, between passing the time of a day to a sheep on the hillside, or even maybe sitting down and studying sheep till you know what they feel about grass, and being a shepherd. Sheep get like shepherd, and shepherd like sheep, it is said, very slowly. But it is quicker and closer with Ents and trees. Like some Men and their horses and dogs, only quicker and closer even than that. For Ents are more like Elves: less interested in themselves than Men are, better at getting inside; and Ents are more like Men, more changeable than Elves are, quicker at catching the outside; only they do both things better than either: they are steadier, and keep at it. [*Added:* Elves began it of course: waking trees up and teaching them to talk. They always wished to talk to everything. But then the Darkness came, and they passed away over the Sea, or fled into far valleys and hid themselves. The Ents have gone on tree-herding.] Some of my trees can walk, many can talk to me.

'But it was not so, of course, in the beginning. We were like your Tombombadil when we were young. The first woods were more like the woods of Lórien....'

Most of this passage, including all reference to Bombadil, was bracketed for omission,[4] and my father then struck it all out and substituted a new version on a separate page. It is clear that all this revision belongs to the time of the writing of the fair copy

TREEBEARD

417

manuscript.[5] In this new version the text of TT is all but reached; but Treebeard says this of the Old Forest:

'...I do not doubt that there is some shadow of the Great Darkness lying there still away North; and bad memories are handed down; for that Forest is old, though none of the trees are really old there, not what I call old. But there are hollow dales in this land where [the shadow >] the Darkness has never been lifted....'

Treebeard's song (*In the willow-meads of Tasarinan*) was set down in the draft manuscript in a faint scribble that nonetheless reached without hesitation almost the final form.[6]

When in the draft Treebeard reaches the Ent-house (TT p. 73) he makes no remark about the distance they have come, and in the fair copy he says: 'I have brought you three times twelve leagues or thereabouts, if measurements of that kind hold good in the country of Fangorn', where 'three' was changed to 'seven' before the words were rejected and replaced by his computation in 'Ent-strides'. In the draft he says that the place is named *Fonthill*, changed to *Funtial*, then back to *Fonthill*,[7] and finally 'Part of the name of this place could be called *Wellandhouse* in your language' (*Wellinghall* in the fair copy).

Treebeard *stooped* and lifted the two great vessels onto the table (this my father wrote in the fair copy also before at once striking it out); and he said before he lowered himself onto the bed ('with only the slightest bend at the waist') 'I think better flat'.

The next major development in the evolution of the text comes at this point, when Merry and Pippin tell Treebeard their story. Here the draft reads:

They followed no order for Treebeard would often stop them, and go back again or jump forward. He was only interested in parts of the tale: in their account of the Old Forest, in Rivendell, in Lothlórien, and especially in anything to do with Gandalf, most of all in Saruman. The hobbits were sorry that they could not remember more clearly Gandalf's account of that wizard. Treebeard kept reverting to him.

'Saruman has been here some time, a long time you would call it. Too long I should now say. Very quiet he was to begin with: no trouble to any of us. I used to talk to him. Very eager to listen he was in those days, ready to learn about old days. Many a thing I have told him that he would never have known or guessed otherwise. Never. He never repaid me – never told me anything. And he got more like that: his face more like windows in a stone wall, windows with blinds (shutters inside).

418   THE TREASON OF ISENGARD

'But now I understand. So he's thinking of becoming a Power, is he. I have not troubled myself with the great wars: Elves are not my business, nor Men; and it is with them that wizards are mostly concerned. They are always worrying about the future. I don't like worrying about the future. But I shall have to begin, I see. Mordor seemed a long way, but these orcs! And if Saruman has started taking them up, I have got trouble right on my borders. Cutting down trees. Machines, great fires. I won't stand it. Trees that were my friends. Trees I had known from nut and acorn. Cut down and left sometimes. Orc-work.

'I have been thinking I should have to do something. But I see it will be better sooner than later. Men are better than orcs, especially if the Dark Lord doesn't get at them. But the Rohiroth and the folk of Ondor if Saruman attacks at the back will soon be in a [?lonely].... We shall have [?hordes] from the East and ... [?swarm] of orcs all over us. I shall be [?eaten] up – and there will be nowhere to go. The flood will rise into the pines in the mountains. I don't think the Elves would find room for me in a ship. I could not go over sea. I should wither away from my own soil.

'If you'll come with me we'll go to Isengard! You'll be helping your own friends.'

With the further words '[?Of] the Ents and Entwives' the initial draft peters out here; but in these last hastily jotted lines we see the emergence of a major new idea and new direction. The rôle that Treebeard was to play in the raising of the siege of Minas Tirith (pp. 211, 330, and cf. p. 412) is gone, and all is suddenly clear: Treebeard's part is to attack *Saruman*, who dwells on his very borders.

There is very little further initial drafting for this chapter extant; almost all is lost erased beneath the fair copy text. Rough workings for the Song of the Ent and the Entwife are found (see p. 421); and there is also a little scrap which shows my father's first thoughts for the march on Isengard:

Ents excited. To Isengard!
Hobbits see trees behind. Is Forest moving?
Orc woodcutters come on the Ents. Horrible surprise to find wood alive. They are destroyed. Ents take shields. They go on to Isengard. End of Ch. XXV.

But it seems to me most unlikely that those parts of the original drafting that are lost were any less close to the fair copy than are those that survive.[8] The text of the fair copy manuscript in the latter part of the chapter was retained in TT (pp. 75–90) without the smallest

TREEBEARD

419

deviation of expression almost throughout its length: Treebeard's thoughts of Saruman and his becoming 'hot', his story of the Entwives, the Entmoot, the time spent with Bregalad, the march of the Ents and Pippin's awareness of the moving groves of trees behind them, to the last words: ' "Night lies over Isengard," said Treebeard.'

Exceptions to this are very few.[9] Against the passage in which Treebeard condemns Saruman this note (it is scarcely in Treebeard's style) is written in the margin (and subsequently struck through): 'It is not perhaps mere chance that *Orthanc* which in Elvish means "a spike of rock" is in the tongue of Rohan "a machine".' With this cf. 'The Road to Isengard' (TT p. 160): 'This was Orthanc, the citadel of Saruman, the name of which had (by design or chance) a twofold meaning; for in the Elvish speech *orthanc* signifies Mount Fang, but in the language of the Mark of old the Cunning Mind.'

The alteration to the text made in 1944, extending the Entmoot by an extra day, has appeared already: see p. 407. Until this change was made the Entmoot ended on the afternoon of the second day (cf. TT pp. 87–8):

Most of the time they sat silent under the shelter of the bank; for the wind was colder, and the clouds closer and greyer; there was little sunshine. There was a feeling of expectancy in the air. They could see that Bregalad was listening, although to them, down in the dell of his Ent-house, the sound of the Ent-voices was faint.

The afternoon came, and the sun, going west towards the mountains, sent out long yellow beams . . .

At the same time as this was rewritten, my father replaced the Entish words (first appearing in the fair copy manuscript) of the song sung by the Ents as they marched from the Moot past Bregalad's house, but not to the text in TT p. 88.[10]

NOTES

1　The word *hnau* is taken from C. S. Lewis, *Out of the Silent Planet*: on Earth there is only one kind of *hnau*, Men, but on Malacandra there are three totally distinct races that are *hnau*.

2　A pencilled note on the fair copy says that 'Crack my timbers' had been 'queried by Charles Williams'. The same change was made at a later point in the chapter (TT p. 75).

3　This was changed to the form in TT already on the draft manuscript, but with *lómeamor* for *lómeanor*, and this remained uncorrected on the fair copy.

4　It would be interesting to know why Treebeard's knowledge of and estimate of Tom Bombadil was removed. Conceivably, my

420 THE TREASON OF ISENGARD

father felt that the contrast between Bombadil and the Ents developed here confused the conflict between the Ents and the Entwives; or, it may be, it was precisely this passage that gave rise to the idea of that conflict.

5 This is seen from the fact that the new version was still numbered in 'Chapter XXIV', i.e. 'Treebeard' had not yet been separated off as a new chapter, as was done in the course of the writing of the fair copy (p. 414). Moreover, when later the hobbits told Treebeard their story he was 'enormously interested in everything', and 'everything' included Tom Bombadil.

6 The names in the draft have these differences from those in TT: *Dorthonion* is *Orod Thuin* (preceded by *Orod Thon*), which remained in the fair copy and following typescript, changed later to *Orod-na-Thôn* (see the *Etymologies*, V.392); and for *Aldalómë* appears another name that I cannot certainly read: *His..eluinalda*.

7 The name *Fonthill* is specifically derived from Fonthill in Wiltshire, as is seen from *Funtial*, which is the form of the place-name found in a tenth-century charter. The first element of the name is probably Old English *funta* 'spring', and the second the Celtic word *ial* 'fertile upland region'; but my father no doubt intended it to be taken as if from Old English *hyll* 'hill'.

8 This is supported by the bits of text where the erased draft can to some extent be made out, and by a piece of independent draft revision of a part of the 'Saruman' passage. − The name *Dernslade* (*slade* 'valley, dell, dingle') can be seen in the draft where the fair copy has *Derndingle*.

9 In addition to those mentioned in the text, it may be noted that Treebeard's answer to Pippin's question about the small number of the Ents: 'Have a great many died?' is here briefer: ' "Oh no!" said Treebeard. "But there were only a few to begin with, and we have not much increased. There have been no Entings..."'

Among names, *Angrenost* (Isengard) now appears; a blank was left for the Elvish name of the Valley of Saruman, *Nan Gurunír* being added in; and Gondor remains *Ondor* (see p. 401).

10 The original form of the Entish words was thus:
Ta-rúta dūm-da dūm-da dūm / ta-rāra dūm-da dūm-da būm /
Da-dūda rūm-ta rūm-ta rūm / ta-dāda rūm-ta rūm-ta dūm /
The Ents were coming: ever nearer and louder rose their song.
Ta-būmda romba būmda-romba banda-romba būm-ta būm /
Da-dūra dāra lamba būm / ta-lamba dāra rūm-ta rūm!
Ta-būm-da-dom / ta-rūm-ta-rom / ta-būm-ta lamba dūm-da-dom //
ta-būm / ta-rūm / ta-būm-ta lamba dūm //
This was changed in 1944 to:
A! rundamāra-nundarūn tahōra-mundakumbalūn,

TREEBEARD   421

tarūna-rūna-rūnarūn tahōra-kumbakumbanūn.
The Ents were coming: ever nearer and louder rose their song:
Tarundaromba-rundaromba mandaromba-mundamūn,
tahūrahāra-lambanūn talambatāra-mundarūn,
   tamunda-rom, tarunda-rom, tamunda-lamba-munda-
   tom.

The Song of the Ent and the Entwife

Rough workings and a first completed draft are extant; in this, verses
1 and 3 are as in the final form.

2   When Spring is in the sprouting corn and flames of green arise,
   When blossom like a living snow upon the orchard lies,
   When earth is warm, and wet with rain, and its smell is in the air,
   I'll linger here, and will not come, because my land is fair.

4   When Summer warms the hanging fruit and burns the berry brown,
   When straw is long and ear is white and harvest comes to town,
   When honey spills and apple swells and days are wealthiest,
   I'll linger here, and will not come, because my land is best.

5   When winter comes and boughs are bare and all the grass is grey,
   When   and starless night o'ertakes the sunless day,
   When storm is wild and trees are felled, then in the bitter rain
   I'll look for thee, and call to thee, I'll come to thee again.

The blank space in this verse is left thus in the original. Verse 6 differs
from the final form only in the first line, with repeated *When Winter*
comes, when Winter comes; and the concluding lines differ only in *the*
roads that lead for *the road that leads*. A preliminary version of the
ending is found, written as prose, thus:

> I'll come back to thee and look for thee again, I'll come to thee and
> comfort thee, and find thee in the rain. We'll walk the land together
> and gather seed and set, and journey to an island where both can
> live again.

XXIII
NOTES ON VARIOUS TOPICS

There are three isolated pages of notes, heterogeneous in content and obviously even on the same page written at different times, but each of which has links to the others. Some of the notes may well be earlier than the time we have reached,[1] others later, but rather than split them up and try to fit them in uncertainly elsewhere it seems best to give them together.

The page that I give first begins with the note 'Wizards = Angels', and this same note is found on the other two pages also. I take it to be the first appearance in written record of this conception, i.e. that the Istari or Wizards were *angeloi*, 'messengers', emissaries from the Lords of the West: see *Unfinished Tales* pp. 388 ff., and especially my father's long discussion in *Letters* no. 156 (4 November 1954). Then follows:

> Gandalf to reappear again. How did he escape? This might never be fully explained. He passed through fire – and became *the* White Wizard. 'I forgot much that I knew, and learned again much that I had forgotten.' *He has thus acquired something of the awe and terrible power of the Ring-wraiths*, only on the good side. Evil things fly from him if he is revealed – when he shines. But he does not as a rule reveal himself.
>
> He should have a trial of strength with Saruman. Could the Balrog of the Bridge be in fact Saruman?
>
> Or better? as in older sketch   Saruman is very affable.

With this compare the initial sketch for 'The Riders of Rohan', p. 389. The extraordinary idea that the Balrog of Moria might be Saruman has appeared in a note written on the back of a page of the fair copy manuscript of 'Lothlórien', p. 236: 'Could not Balrog be Saruman? Make battle on Bridge be between Gandalf and Saruman?' The reference to the 'older sketch' – 'Saruman is very affable' – is to 'The Story Foreseen from Moria', p. 212, where on the homeward journey 'They call at Isengard. Gandalf knocks. Saruman comes out very affable', etc.

The next note on this page records my father's decision to move the whole chronology of the Quest forward by a month:

> Time Scheme. Too much takes place in *winter*. They should

NOTES ON VARIOUS TOPICS 423

remain longer at Rivendell. This would have additional advantage of allowing Elrond's scouts and messengers far longer *time*. He should discover Black Riders have gone back. Frodo should not start until say Dec. 24th.

It seems likely that 24 December was chosen as being 'numerically' one month later than the existing date, 24 November (p. 169); and that it was changed to 25 December to make the new dates agree 'numerically' with the existing time-structure (since November has 30 days but December 31): see p. 368. I do not understand the statement here that 'he [Elrond] should discover Black Riders have gone back', since the final text of 'The Ring Goes South' had been reached in Gandalf's words 'It is rash to be too sure, yet I think that we may hope now that the Ringwraiths were scattered, and have been obliged to return as best they could to their Master in Mordor, empty and shapeless.'

Another note on this page, not written at the same time, refers to 'Chapter XXIV: Open with conversation of Goblins and their quarrel. How are Merry and Pippin armed?' And the last reads: '*Sarn-gebir* = Grailaw or Graidon Hills'. Both these names mean 'Grey Hill(s)': Old English *hlāw* 'hill', Northern English and Scottish *law*, and Old English *dūn*, Modern English *down*.

The second page contains exact repetitions of notes found on the other pages or in outlines already given, and need not be cited. On the third page the following (only) was written in ink, and seems to be the primary element on the page:

Feb. 9 1942 Geography
Ondor > *Gondor*
Osgiliath > *Elostirion*. *Ostirion* = fort. *Lorn* = haven. *Londe* = gulf.

On the date see p. 379, where I have noted that on the back of an outline for 'The Departure of Boromir' is a clear indication that it was written in the winter of 1941–2. The precise date given here for the change of *Ondor* to *Gondor* is notable; in the fair copy of 'Treebeard' the form was still *Ondor* (see p. 401).

Elostirion was written above *Osgiliath* in the outline for 'The Riders of Rohan' given on p. 389. This change was of course impermanent, but the name *Elostirion* became that of the tallest of the White Towers on Emyn Beraid, in which the *palantír* was set (*Of the Rings of Power*, in *The Silmarillion*, p. 292).[2] – With *lorn* 'haven' cf. *Forlorn* 'North Haven' and *Harlorn* 'South Haven' on the First Map (pp. 301–2), for later *Forlond*, *Harlond*; but on that map appears also *Mithlond*, the Grey Havens (where however it is possible that *Mithlond* actually meant 'Grey Gulf').

The other notes on this page are heterogeneous and not necessarily

424   THE TREASON OF ISENGARD

of the same time. The heading 'Geography' was extended to 'Geography and Language'. Some of these notes are concerned to find a new name for Sarn Gebir: rejected names are *Sern Lamrach*; *Tarn Felin*; *Trandóran*, before (added much later to the page) *Emyn Muil* is reached (for *Muil* see the *Etymologies*, V.374, stem MUY). There are also the English names *Graydon Hills* and *Grailaws*, as on the first page of these notes, and *Hazowland*.[3]

Another group of notes reads:

Language of Shire = modern English
Language of Dale = Norse (used by Dwarves of that region)
Language of Rohan = Old English
'Modern English' is *lingua franca* spoken by all people (except a few secluded folk like Lórien) – but little and ill by orcs.

NOTES

1   It is to be remembered that statements such as 'Gandalf to reappear again' do not by any means imply that this is where the idea first arose: often they are to be taken as reassertions of existing but as yet unachieved ideas.

2   An altogether isolated and undateable note on a slip of paper also evinces dissatisfaction with the name *Osgiliath*. The reverse of the slip carries notes on unconnected matters which my father dated '1940', which may or may not be significant. At the present time, at any rate, I can cast no light on the purport of this note:

    Lord of Rings
      Osgiliath won't do. Name should = New building   'Newbold'
      Town built again   *echain Ostechain*

The word 'building' is very unclear, but is assured by 'Newbold', a common English village name meaning 'New building', from Old English *bold* (also *boðl*, *botl*) closely associated with *byldan*, Modern English *build*. I will add here, incidentally and irrelevantly, that another derivative from the same source is *Nobottle* (Northamptonshire), which my father allowed me to add to my map of the Shire made in 1943 (VI.107, item V) and which remains in that published in *The Lord of the Rings*, although at that time I was under the impression that the name meant that the village was so poor and remote that it did not even possess an inn.

3   *Hazowland* is clearly from the Old English poetic word *hasu* (inflected *hasw-*) 'grey, ashen'; cf. *Hasupada* 'Greycoat', name of Gandalf in Rohan (p. 405 note 21), and *Hasofel* (*Hasufel*) of the same meaning, the horse lent to Aragorn by Eomer.

XXIV

THE WHITE RIDER

For the greater part of this chapter the evolution can be traced very clearly. Initial drafting not erased or overwritten, more developed but discontinuous drafting, and a 'fair copy' that itself underwent constant correction in the act of composition, were a continuous process, and the history of almost every sentence can be followed until near the end of the chapter. This was numbered 'XXVI' from an early stage; a title was added to the 'fair copy' later, first *Sceadufax* in Old English spelling, then 'The White Rider'. The process of composition here was continuous and all of the same time, so that 'first draft', 'second draft', 'fair copy', 'corrections to fair copy' cannot be treated as distinct entities, each complete before the next stage.

An example of this overlapping is seen at once. In the original form of the opening, to Gimli's insistence that the old man who stood by the fire in the night was Saruman, Aragorn replies: 'I wonder. The horses showed no signs of fear.' In the 'fair copy' (more accurately, the first coherent manuscript) this became: ' "I wonder," said Aragorn. "What did he seem to be? An old man? It is strange enough in itself: that an old man should be walking alone by the eaves of Fangorn. Yet the horses showed no signs of fear." ' This obviously belongs with the sentence struck out at the end of 'The Riders of Rohan': 'The horses remained quiet, and seemed to feel nothing amiss', and suggests to my mind that my father believed the old man to be Gandalf (see p. 403 and note 26). Yet in the most 'primitive' drafting further on in the chapter the old man in the night certainly was Saruman (see further pp. 427–8).

The later chronology of the chase across Rohan not being present, of course (see p. 406), Aragorn remarks that the footprints by the riverside 'are a day old'; Gandalf says that the hobbits 'climbed up here yesterday', and that he himself had seen Treebeard 'three days ago': in TT all these are made one day earlier, on account of the extra day added in 1944. At one point, however, the need for correction escaped my father's notice: Legolas' words that the last time he saw the eagle was 'three days ago, above the Emyn Muil' (TT p. 98). This should have been changed to 'four days ago': see the table on p. 406, and cf. *The Tale of Years* in LR: 'February 27   Aragorn reaches the west-cliff at sunrise', and (February having 30 days) 'March 1   Aragorn meets Gandalf the White'.

426 THE TREASON OF ISENGARD

The story of the first meeting with Gandalf was sketched out in every essential point in the earliest draft. When the three companions saw the old man walking through the wood below them, Gimli's horror of Saruman was at first expressed in more murderous fashion: 'Shoot, Legolas! Draw your bow! Shoot! It is Saruman, or worse. Do not let him speak or bewitch us!' This was retained in the fair copy; and when subsequently it was softened to a demand that Legolas only prepare to shoot, Gimli's following words were retained: 'Why are you waiting? What is the matter with you?' In the earliest draft the wizard wore an 'old hat'; this became a 'battered hat', then a 'wide-brimmed hat' (see p. 403).[1]

The opening of their long conversation proceeds thus in the earliest draft (cf. TT pp. 98–9):

'... At the turn of the Tide. The great storm is coming, but the Tide has turned even at this moment. I have passed through fire and ruin and I have been badly burned, or well burned. But come, tell me now of yourselves. I have seen much in deep places and in high since we parted; I have forgotten much that I knew, and learned again much that I had forgotten.[2] [Some things I can see far off and some close at hand; but not all can I see. *Changed at once to:*] Many things I can see far off but many that are close at hand I cannot see.'

'What do you wish to know?' said Aragorn. 'All that has happened would be a long tale. Will you not first tell us tidings of Merry and Pippin? Did you find them, and are they safe?'

'No, I did not find them,' said Gandalf.[3] 'I was busy with perilous matters, and did not know of their captivity until the eagle told me.'

'The eagle!' said Legolas. 'We have seen an eagle high and far off: the last time was three days ago, above Sarn Gebir.'

'Yes,' said Gandalf, 'that was Gwaewar the Windlord who rescued me from Orthanc. I sent him before me to gather tidings, and to watch the River. His sight is keen, but he cannot see all that passes in wood and valley. But there are some things that I can see unaided. This I may tell you: the Ring has passed beyond my help or the help of any of our original Company. Very nearly it was revealed to the Enemy, but not quite. I had some part in that. For I sat upon the mountains beneath the snows of Methedras and I strove with the Dark Tower, and the shadow passed. Then I was weary: very weary.'

The story that Gandalf was on Tol Brandir when Frodo sat on Amon Hen, and that he was borne across Rohan by the eagle (see p. 396), has

THE WHITE RIDER   429

'Safe? Yes, as far as the Ents go. But there is [?terrible] hurry.'
Gandalf tells them about Ents. Says it was well that Merry and
Pippin [?came there]. They did right to follow. Yet to meet the Ents
is not their task. Too late anyway. He looks at sun. 'We have spent
all the time allowed to a meeting of parted friends. We must go. We
are needed South.'

In a more developed draft Aragorn's response to Gandalf's naming
'the Ents' (TT p. 102) reads:

> 'The Ents!' exclaimed Aragorn. 'Then there is truth in the ancient
> legends, [and the names that they use in Rohan have a meaning! The
> Entwash and the Entmark (for that is how they call the Forest)]

Above *Entmark* is written *Entwood*. – These remarks about the names
containing *Ent* were bracketed for rejection at once, since the text
continues: 'about the dwellers in the deep forest, and the giant
Shepherds of the Trees', as in TT. In one of many draftings for
Legolas' words at this point he says: 'I thought that [Fangorn] was the
name of the Forest. A strange name for a wood, now I consider it.'
   The words 'he is the oldest living thing that still walks beneath the
sun upon this Middle-earth' appear in the draft, written just so,
without any hesitation in reaching them. Of his seeing Treebeard in
the woods Gandalf says:

> '. . . I passed him in the forest three days ago; and I do not doubt that
> he saw me, since the eyes of Treebeard miss little [*written in margin:*
> and he saw me, indeed he called my name]; but I did not speak, for I
> had much to think about, and I did not then know that Merry and
> Pippin had been carried off.'

The text of TT is reached in the fair copy. He says in the draft that
'something is going to happen which has not happened since the Elves
awoke'; in the fair copy this becomes 'since the Elves first woke',
changed to 'since the Elves were born' ('since the Elder Days', TT
p. 103). But when Legolas says 'What is going to happen?' Gandalf
replies: 'I do not know. Merry and Pippin do perhaps, by now; but I
do not.'
   To his words to Aragorn, urging him not to regret his choice 'in the
valley of Sarn Gebir', he adds (both in draft and fair copy):

> '. . . Also I say to you that your coming to Minas Tirith will now be
> very different from what would have been, had you come there
> alone reporting that Boromir son of the Lord Denethor had fallen,
> while you lived. . . .'

In the draft text he tells Aragorn that he must go now to Winseld,
changed to Eodoras (see p. 402): 'The light of Branding must now be
uncovered. There is battle in Rohan and they are hard put to it in the

430   THE TREASON OF ISENGARD

West, even as the great [?flood] of war comes up from the East.' In the fair copy this becomes: 'There is war in Rohan and it goes ill for the horsemasters': thus again (see p. 401) there is no suggestion of Wormtongue (cf. TT p. 104: 'There is war in Rohan, *and worse evil: it goes ill with Théoden*').

The textual development of the last part of this chapter and its relation to the beginning of the next is complex and doubtful, the manuscript material being very hard to interpret, and I shall not go into the question in any detail. But it is clear that at least half of 'The King of the Golden Hall' had been written before the conclusion of 'The White Rider' approached at all the form it has in *The Two Towers*; for as will be seen (p. 446) Aragorn tells Theoden in Eodoras that Gandalf *had not told them* 'what befell him in Moria'.

How my father ended 'The White Rider' at this stage is not entirely clear to me, but it seems probable that he stopped at Gandalf's words of the Balrog (TT p. 105): 'Name him not!': 'and for a moment it seemed that a cloud of pain passed over his face, and he sat silent, looking old as death.' He would then have begun a new chapter (XXVII) at 'Gandalf now wrapped himself again in his old tattered cloak. They descended quickly from the high shelf...' (TT p. 107).

I cannot say at what precise point my father decided that Gandalf should in fact tell something at least of what had happened to him after his fall from the Bridge of Khazad-dûm, but it must have been in the course of the writing of 'The King of the Golden Hall'. In what is apparently the earliest draft (but written over erased pencil) of Gandalf's story of his escape from Moria[4] the four companions are already riding south from Fangorn when he tells it:

> On the way they ask Gandalf how he escaped. He refuses the full tale – but tells how he passed through fire (and water?) and came to the 'bottom of the world', and there finally overthrew the Balrog, who fled. Gandalf followed up a secret way to Durin's Tower on the summit of the mountains (?of Caradras). There they had a battle – those who beheld it afar thought it was a thunderstorm with lightning. A great rain came down. The Balrog was destroyed, and the tower crumbled and stones blocked the door of the secret way. Gandalf was left on the mountain-top. The eagle Gwaihir rescued him. He went then to Lothlórien. Galadriel arrayed him in white garments before he left. While Gandalf was on mountain top he saw many things – a vision of Mordor etc.

This is the first appearance of the form *Gwaihir* (here apparently first written *Gwaehir*) for earlier *Gwaewar*, which was still the name in the earlier part of this chapter.

A very rough and unfinished draft for the final form and placing of Gandalf's story ('Long I fell, and he fell with me...', TT p. 105) is

THE WHITE RIDER   431

found. Here Gandalf describes the Balrog, his fire quenched, thus: 'he was a thing of slime, strong as a strangling snake, sleek as ice, pliant as a thong, unbreakable as steel.' Of the 'dark things unguessed' that gnaw the world 'below the deepest delvings of the dwarves' he says: 'Sauron alone may know of them, or one older than he.' And after his words 'I will bring no report to stain the light of day' the text continues:

> '...Little had I guessed the abyss that was spanned by Durin's Bridge.'
> 'Did you not?' said Gimli. 'I could have told you had there been time. No plummet ever found the bottom – indeed none that was ever cast therein was ever recovered.'[5]

The form of Gandalf's story in TT is almost reached in the 'fair copy' manuscript, but there remain some differences. He tells that clutching at the Balrog's heel 'I set my teeth in it like a hunting hound, and tasted venom'; and that Durin's Tower was 'carved in the living rock in the very pinnacle of red Caradras.' This was subsequently changed to 'the living rock [of] Zirakinbar,[6] the pinnacle of the Silverhorn. There upon Kelebras was a lonely window in the snow...' On these names see pp. 174–5, notes 18, 21–2.

Gandalf does not say, as in TT (p. 106), 'Naked I was sent back – for a brief time, until my task is done', but simply 'Naked I returned, and naked I lay upon the mountain-top.'[7] And of his coming thence to Caras Galadon, borne by Gwaihir, he says that he 'found you three days gone', and that he 'tarried there in the long time which in that land counts for but a brief hour of the world' ('in the ageless time of that land', TT): see pp. 368–9.

At this time the messages that he bore from Galadriel to Aragorn and Legolas were very different:

> *Elfstone, Elfstone, bearer of my green stone,*
> *In the south under snow a green stone thou shalt see.*
> *Look well, Elfstone! In the shadow of the dark throne*
> *Then the hour is at hand that long hath awaited thee.*
>
> *Greenleaf, Greenleaf, bearer of the elven-bow,*
> *Far beyond Mirkwood many trees on earth grow.*
> *Thy last shaft when thou hast shot, under strange trees*
> *shalt thou go!*

The dialogue that follows, between Gimli, Legolas, and Gandalf, is however precisely the same as in TT, p. 107. On the significance of the verse addressed to Aragorn see p. 448.

With the addition of Gandalf's story to this chapter, what was originally the opening of 'The King of the Golden Hall' (from 'Gandalf now wrapped himself again in his old tattered cloak', see p. 430) was

432   THE TREASON OF ISENGARD

incorporated into 'The White Rider', which now ended at Gandalf's words 'Show no weapon, speak no haughty word, I counsel you all, until we are come before Theoden's seat' (TT p. 111). The final form of the story of the departure from Fangorn, the summoning of the horses, the great ride south across the plains with the sight at sunset of smoke rising far off in the Gap of Rohan, and the distant view of Eodoras at sunrise (TT pp. 107–11, where it constitutes the end of the one chapter and the beginning of the next), was achieved almost down to the last detail in the fair copy manuscript.[8] By this time my father had changed the ending of 'The Riders of Rohan' (p. 403) to the form it has in TT, pp. 45–6 ('The horses were gone. They had dragged their pickets and disappeared'), and had changed the beginning of 'The White Rider' similarly to its form in TT, p. 91 (' "Did you hear them, Legolas? Did they sound to you like beasts in terror?" "No," said Legolas. "I heard them clearly. ...I should have guessed that they were beasts wild with some sudden gladness"').

NOTES

1   A little slip of paper used to draft the moment of recognition of Mithrandir (TT p. 98) was a page from an engagement calendar 'for the week ending Saturday February 22'. February 22 fell on a Saturday in 1941, not in 1942.

2   The forerunner of this phrase appeared in the outline given on p. 389, as also did 'I was badly burned or *well* burned'; cf. also the notes given on p. 422. Gandalf's suggestion that he now 'is' Saruman, in the sense that he is 'Saruman as he should have been', is lacking, but appears in the fair copy as first written.

3   Gandalf's words that follow in TT: 'There was a darkness over the valleys of the Emyn Muil' are absent in the draft, but are found in the fair copy (with *Sarn Gebir* for *the Emyn Muil*).

4   For the earliest notes on Gandalf's escape from Moria see VI.462 and p. 211 in this book.

5   It is interesting to look back to my father's original ideas about the chasm in the passages referred to in note 4: 'probably fall is not as deep as it seemed ... eventually following the subterranean stream in the gulf he found a way out', and 'The gulf was not deep (only a kind of moat and was full of silent water). He followed the channel and got down into the Deeps.'

6   This form *Zirakinbar*, preceding *Zirakzigil*, is found also in an entirely isolated note: '*Barazinbar, Zirakinbar, Udushinbar*', together with a reference to 'Silverhorn and the Horn of Cloud'.

7   Cf. *Letters* no. 156 (4 November 1954): ' "Naked I was sent back – for a brief time, until my task is done." Sent back by whom, and whence? Not by the "gods" whose business is only with this embodied world and its time; for he passed "out of thought and

THE WHITE RIDER   433

time". Naked is alas! unclear. It was meant just literally, "unclothed like a child" (not discarnate), and so ready to receive the white robes of the highest. Galadriel's power is not divine, and his healing in Lórien is meant to be no more than physical healing and refreshment.'

8   Initial drafting is very largely lost through overwriting. – The only points of any significance in which the text of the fair copy differs from that of TT, other than names, are that Theoden is the 'Master of Rohan' and 'lord of the Mark' where in TT he is called 'King' (see p. 444); that Gandalf says to Shadowfax 'Far let us ride now together, ere we part again!' where in TT he says 'and part not in this world again!'; and that 'the mountains of the South' (the Black Mountains) are 'black-tipped and streaked with white', whereas in TT, where they are the White Mountains, they are 'white-tipped and streaked with black': cf. the earlier description in 'The Riders of Rohan' (TT p. 24), where the original text was retained (p. 395), 'rising into peaks of jet, tipped with glimmering snows'.

Among names, *Sarn Gebir* (for *Emyn Muil*), *Winseld, Eodoras* are still present. At the end of the chapter, in Gandalf's phrase 'the Horse-masters do not sleep' (TT p. 111), the form *Rohir* (not *Rohiroth*) was written above.

XXV

THE STORY FORESEEN FROM
FANGORN

In this chapter I give two outlines of great interest, for in them my father discussed the structural problems of the story that he foresaw at this time. The first one given here was evidently written when 'The White Rider' had been completed in its earlier form (i.e. without Gandalf's story of the Balrog, see p. 430); the ride across Rohan and the distant sight of Eodoras in the morning may or may not have existed yet, but the question is immaterial.

XXVII
Gandalf, Aragorn, Legolas, Gimli reach Eodoras on the morning of Jan. 31.[1] (That aft[ernoon] Merry and Pippin go with Ents to Isengard.)

They enter Theoden's halls. Theoden greets Gandalf dubiously – as herald of trouble. Shadowfax had been reported coming from the West through the Gap and fleeing away north.[2] They feared Gandalf would return. Then Eomer had come riding back, with strange news concerning Gandalf's fall. 'That,' said Theoden, 'was too much to hope, it seems; for now Gandalf returns and worse tidings follow.'

Against this paragraph was written in the margin, at the same time as the text, 'A messenger from Minas Tirith is present.'

There is a battle on the borders of the West Emnet. An invasion of Orcs of Saruman had been driven back (not without loss to the Rohiroth) to the banks of the Isen River. But news came that orcs were pouring out of Isengard, and that men of the Middlemarch[3] (whom Saruman had long subjected) were coming up. 'We cannot hope long to hold the river,' said Theoden. 'Eomer has gone thither with what men could still be spared. And now as we are beset in the West, there comes dire news indeed. The whole of Rhûn the Great, the endless East, is in motion. Under the command of the Dark Lord of Mordor they move from the far North even to the South. Minas Tirith is beset. The fierce dark men of the South, the Haradwaith

THE STORY FORESEEN FROM FANGORN 435

(Harwan Silharrows Men of Sunharrowland Men of Harrow-land) have come in many ships and fill the Bay of Belfalas, and [have] taken the isle of Tolfalas. They have passed up the Anduin in many galleys, and out of Mordor others have crossed at Elostirion.[4] A tide of war rolls beneath the very walls of Minas Tirith. They have sent us urgent prayer for help. And we cannot give it. Yet if Minas Tirith falls then the dark tide will sweep over us from the East.

Against this passage concerning Minas Tirith was written in the margin, at the same time as the text, 'Not yet have they heard of Boromir's fall.' Later, the whole passage from 'And now as we are beset in the West' to this point was closed off in pencil with the note 'Place after return victorious from Isengard.' Theoden continues:

You come at the end of the days of Rohan. Not long now shall the hall (which Brego son of Brytta [*changed later in pencil to* Eorl son of Eofor] built)[5] stand. Fire shall eat up the high seat. What can you say?'

Gandalf speaks words of comfort. All that can be done is to do one deed at a time and go forward and not look back. Let us assail Saruman and then if fortune is with us turn and face East. There is a hope. Something may happen in West (he does not openly name Ents).

Gandalf begs for the gift of Shadowfax.

Theoden says Yes – that will at least ensure Gandalf's escape, when all else fall. Gandalf does not lose temper. He says there will be no escape for anyone. But he wishes for *gift*, as he will take Shadowfax into great peril: silver against black.

The ceremony of gift. Gandalf casts aside grey robe and becomes White Rider. He bids Theoden arm, old as he is, and follow with all left who can bear arms. The rest shall pack and prepare to flee to the mountains.

They ride off without rest. Meet messengers reporting death of the Second Master and the forces of Rohan hemmed almost in, while the forces of Saruman are continually strengthened.

Gandalf spurs Shadowfax and spurs into the setting sun.

By his help and Aragorn the Isengarders are driven back. The camp of the Rohiroth. *But Isengarders are across the river.*

In the morning they awake and look out in wonder. A *wood* stood where none had been, between the Isengarders and the West. There is clamour and confusion. Vast columns of vapour are seen rising from Isengard, and the rumour of strange noises

436 THE TREASON OF ISENGARD

and rumblings. The Isengarders are driven into the river. Those who cross are suddenly assailed by the trees which seem to come to life. Only a few escape fleeing southward to the Black Mountains.

The victorious forces under Eomer and Gandalf ride to the gates of Isengard. They find it a pile of rubble, blocked with a huge wall of stone. On the top of the pile sit Merry and Pippin!

Meeting of Treebeard and Gandalf.

How did the Ents overcome Isengard? They open[ed] sluice gates at North end and blocked the outlet near the Great Gate. First they watched all the night seeing more and more orcs etc. pour out of Isengard. Then they simply broke a way in at North end and spied and found Saruman was left nearly all alone in his tower. They broke the door and stairway to the tower and then withdrew. At North end they let in the River Isen but blocked its outflow. Soon all the floor of the circle was flooded to many feet deep. Then while some kept guard the rest fell on the rear of the battle.

Here comes scene of Saruman being let out of his tower and trying to speak in friendly fashion to Gandalf. 'Ah, my dear Gandalf! I am so pleased to see you; we at least (we wizards) understand one another. These people all seem so unnecessarily angry.[6] What a mess the world is in. Really you and I must consult together – such men as we are needed. Now what about our spheres of influence?'

Gandalf looks at him and laughs. 'Yes, I understand you well enough, Saruman. Give me your staff,' he said in a voice of terrible command. He took it and broke it. 'I am the White Wizard now,' he said. 'Behold you are clad in many colours!' They turn his coat inside out. Gandalf gives him a rough staff. [*Added subsequently:* Saruman is to go without a staff, and have no wooden thing to lean on by decree of Treebeard.] 'Go Saruman!' he said, 'and beg from the charitable for a day's digging.'[7] [*Added subsequently:* Or put this toward end of story – in meanwhile give Saruman over to the guard of the Ents. *Further addition:* Yes.]

[*Written in margin at the same time as the text:* Better: the ring of Isengard is broken by Ents, but Saruman shuts himself up in Orthanc and cannot be assailed *yet* for there is no time.]

Another way of telling the story would be to carry on from end of Chapter XXVI and relate the coming of Ents to

THE STORY FORESEEN FROM FANGORN   437

Isengard.[8] How they resolved not to break in at first, but came behind the orc-army. Let Merry and Pippin see the orcs driving the men of Rohan back over the River. Ents camp behind them. Then relate the battle from Merry and Pippin's point of view – distant vision of the white rider on a shining horse. They recognize the sword and voice of Aragorn, but do not know who the White Rider is. Gandalf and Treebeard meet after the battle – and then comes the storming of Isengard by Gandalf and the Ents.

Return to Eodoras. Funeral of —— the Second Master[9] [*Added above:* Háma and Theodred]. Feast in Winseld.[10] Eowyn sister of Eomer waits on the guests. Description of her, and of her love for Aragorn.

News comes at the feast or next morning of the siege of Minas Tirith by the Haradwaith.[11] [*Added subsequently:* brought by a dark Gondorian like Boromir.[12] Theoden answers that he does not owe fealty – only to heirs of Elendil. But he will come.] The horsemen of Rohan ride East, with Gandalf, Aragorn, Gimli, Legolas, Merry and Pippin. Gandalf as the White Rider. [*Added subsequently:* Eowyn goes as Amazon.] Vision of Minas Tirith from afar.

In the part of this outline that concerns the immediate story to come, and with which this book ends, it will be seen that while Theoden is unwelcoming and scarcely well-disposed towards Gandalf, he is nothing more than that: of the ugly state of affairs at Eodoras that came in with Wormtongue there is no trace – no hint of the subjugation of Theoden's mind and will, of the disgracing of Eomer, of Gandalf's triumphant display of his power in the hall of Winseld. Eowyn, Eomer's sister, appears, and her love for Aragorn, but not until the funeral feast held in Winseld after the victory.

Judging by the opening of the second outline, this also belongs to about this time.

Order of Tale.
Bring each party to crisis. Ents break off with 'Night lies over Isengard'. End XXVI with far vision of Winseld's golden roof (and sight of the smoke).[13] (Possibly they see men in strange armour riding also from East to Eodoras.)

Now return to Frodo and Sam. Meeting with Gollum. Betrayal by him. Capture of Frodo on *west* side of Kirith Ungol. Frodo imprisoned in tower[14] – because (a) no ring is on him, (b) Sauron is busy with war and it takes time for message to reach him.

438   THE TREASON OF ISENGARD

Then return to Gandalf and battle of Isen, feast of victory, relief
of Minas Tirith, and march of the army of Gandalf towards
Dagorlad and gates of Kirith Ungol.
Then return to Frodo. Make him look out onto impenetrable
night. Then use phial which has escaped (clutched in his hand or
wrapped in rag). By its light he sees the forces of deliverance
approach and the dark host go out to meet them.[15] Grieves for
Sam – or thinks he has betrayed him too.

The orc-guards come on him and take phial and shutter
windows, and he lies in dark and despair.

Where put parley of Sauron and Gandalf? If after capture of
Frodo readers will know that Frodo [*written above:* Sauron] has
not Ring. [*Added subsequently in two stages:* No, not if you
break off with Frodo carried off by Orcs and before Sam rescues
him. / Even if Sam's taking of Ring is told,[16] you can make Sam
fly among the rocks with Gollum (and orcs) on his trail and his
escape seem unlikely.]

Possibly best as originally planned – [?all account] of Gandalf
as far as Kirith Ungol – and then return to Sam and Frodo.
Sam rescues Frodo and while battle is joined at mouth of
Gorgoroth they fly towards Orodruin.

NOTES

1 The later date of the departure of the Company from Rivendell,
   25 December, had now entered (see pp. 422–3): thus 'Day 1' (the
   day of Boromir's death) in the table on p. 406 was January 26
   (see the table on p. 368), and Aragorn, Legolas and Gimli
   encountered Gandalf in Fangorn on January 30 ('Day 5').
2 In the fifth version of 'The Council of Elrond' (p. 152) Gandalf
   does not say what happened to Shadowfax, but the isolated note
   given on p. 390 says that 'some account of Shadowfax in the
   house of Elrond must be given.' This note asks also, however, 'Or
   did he just run off after Gandalf got to Rivendell?', and 'How did
   Gandalf summon him?' In preliminary notes for 'The Riders of
   Rohan' (p. 390) it is said that 'the horse of Gandalf reappears –
   sent for from Rivendell'; and in the text of that chapter (pp.
   400–1) Eomer tells Aragorn that he had returned seven days
   before, to which Aragorn replies: 'But Gandalf left Shadowfax
   far in the North at Rivendell. Or so I thought.' In the present
   passage Shadowfax had recently come out of the West through

THE STORY FORESEEN FROM FANGORN 439

the Gap of Rohan and then gone away north: which surely suggests that he had come from Rivendell and was going north to Fangorn in obedience to a summons from Gandalf mysteriously conveyed to him.

The earliest extant account of Gandalf's summons to Shadowfax with his three great whistles, and his coming across the plain to the eaves of Fangorn with Arod and Hasofel returning, is already exactly as in TT (see p. 432); and this seems to fit the story in the present text, for Gandalf says to Shadowfax 'It is a long way from Rivendell, my friend; but you are wise and swift, and come at need,' and he says to Legolas 'I bent my thought upon him, bidding him to make haste; for yesterday he was far away in the south of this land.' (On the other hand, Legolas says 'I have not seen his like before', which does not suggest that Shadowfax had been at Rivendell when the Company was there.)

The story in the published LR is extremely difficult to understand. In 'The Council of Elrond' (FR p. 278) Gandalf says: 'It took me nearly fourteen days from Weathertop, for I could not ride among the rocks of the troll-fells, and Shadowfax departed. *I sent him back to his master...*' This was about October 4. The next we hear is in 'The Riders of Rohan', where Eomer still tells Aragorn that Shadowfax had returned 'seven nights ago' (but 'now the horse is wild and will let no man handle him'), to which Aragorn replies: 'Then Shadowfax has found his way alone from the far North; for it was there that he and Gandalf parted.' But it was now February 30, so that on his return nearly five months had elapsed since Gandalf dismissed him at Weathertop! And then, at the end of 'The White Rider' (TT p. 108), there is the passage already cited: 'It is a long way from Rivendell, my friend; but you are wise and swift and come at need.' It is hard to resist the conclusion that the alteration in Gandalf's story to the Council of Elrond was not carried through.

3 *Middlemarch:* Enedwaith, between Greyflood and Anduin; see Maps II and III, pp. 305, 309.

4 Cf. the outline given on p. 389: 'Minas Tirith defeats Haradwaith.' – All these names (*Harwan, Silharrows; Harrowland, Sunharrowland*) are derived from the Old English *Sigelhearwan* 'Ethiopians'. My father's article in two parts entitled *Sigelwara land (Medium Ævum* 1 and 3, Dec.1932 and June 1934) studied the etymology and meaning of the name *Sigelhearwan*, and concluded that while the meaning of the first element *Sigel* was certainly 'Sun', that of the second element *hearwan* was not discoverable: 'a symbol ... of that large part of ancient English language and lore which has now vanished beyond recall, *swa hit no wære* [as if it had never been].' With these names cf. *Sunlands, Swertings,* p. 313. – *Tolfalas* appears on the original element of

440 THE TREASON OF ISENGARD

the First Map (see p. 298, and Map III^A on p. 308). – On *Elostirion* for Osgiliath see p. 423.

5 In LR the father of Eorl was Léod, and Brego was Eorl's son; Brytta was the eleventh King of the Mark, some two and a half centuries after Brego (see LR Appendix A (II)).

6 These remarks of Saruman's, from 'we at least...', were bracketed at the time of writing.

7 This sketch of the 'affable' Saruman and Gandalf's breaking of his staff is derived very closely from 'The Story Foreseen from Moria', p. 212; cf. also p. 422.

8 Chapter XXVI is 'The White Rider'.

9 The Second Master was first called *Marhath* (p. 390; this name was then given to the Fourth Master, p. 400), then *Eowin* (pp. 393–4).

10 For the name of the Golden Hall see p. 402.

11 Thus the passage on pp. 434–5 (in which Theoden in his initial conversation with Gandalf speaks of the attack by the Haradwaith on Minas Tirith) bracketed with the note that it should be placed after the victorious return to Eodoras has already been moved.

12 I have not found an explanation of the conception underlying this. Possibly to be compared are Gandalf's words in *The Return of the King*, Ch. 1 'Minas Tirith', p. 31: 'by some chance the blood of Westernesse runs nearly true in him; as it does in his other son, Faramir, *and yet did not in Boromir* whom he loved best.' But this was written several years later.

13 The smoke seen rising at sunset of the day before in the direction of the Gap of Rohan (p. 432).

14 On the taking of Frodo to a guard-tower (not to Minas Morgul) see p. 344 and note 39, and p. 412.

15 The light of the Phial of Galadriel must be conceived here to be of huge power, a veritable star in the darkness.

16 I do not follow the thought here: for Sam's taking of the Ring must in any case be told before Frodo is carried off by the Orcs.

XXVI

THE KING OF THE GOLDEN HALL

The textual history of this chapter is much the same as that of 'The White Rider': the first coherent and legible manuscript is also in a sense the first extant text of the chapter, because the rough drafts were set down, section by section, as the main manuscript proceeded. In other words, that manuscript was the vehicle of the development of the narrative, and the distinction between 'draft' and 'fair copy' is not at all a distinction between two separate manuscript entities, the one completed as a whole before the other was begun. For almost all of the last third of the chapter, however, there is no independent drafting, for the initial conception in pencil was overwritten in ink.

A substantial part of the chapter was in being in some form before Gandalf's story of the Balrog was added to 'The White Rider' (see p. 430), and the point of separation of 'The King of the Golden Hall' (not so named) from 'The White Rider' was twice changed.[1]

In the earliest stage of the narrative, abandoned before it had gone far, Gandalf (with Gimli) left Aragorn and Legolas before they came to Eodoras:

'Eodoras those courts are called,' said Gandalf, 'and Winseld is that golden hall. There dwells Theoden[2] son of Thengel, lord of the mark of Rohan. We are come with the rising of the day. Now the road lies plain to see before you. Make what speed you may!'

Then suddenly he spoke to Shadowfax, and like an arrow from the bow the great horse sprang forward. Even as they gazed, he was gone: a flash of silver, a wind in the grass, a vision that fled and faded from their sight.

Swiftly they urged their horses in pursuit, but if they had walked upon their feet they would have had as much chance of overtaking him. They had gone only a small part of the way when Legolas exclaimed: 'That was a mighty leap! Shadowfax has sprung across the mountain stream and already he has passed up the hill and vanished from my sight.'

The morning was bright and clear about them, and birds were singing, when Aragorn and Legolas came to the stream; running swiftly down into the plain it bent across their path, turning east

442   THE TREASON OF ISENGARD

to feed the Entwash away to the left in its marshy bed. Here there were many willow-trees, already in this southern land blushing red at the tips of twigs in presage of spring. They found a ford, much trampled upon either bank with the passage of horses, and passed over, and so at length they too rode up along the green road to Eodoras.

At the foot of the hill they passed between seven high green mounds. Already they were starred with small pale flowers, and in the shelter of their western flanks the grass was white with nodding flowers (blossoms) like tiny snowdrops. 'See, Legolas!' said Aragorn, 'we are passing the mounds where the sires of Theoden sleep.' 'Yes,' said Legolas. 'Seven mounds there be, and seven long lives of men it is, since the Rohiroth came hither from the North. Two hundred times and more have the red leaves fallen in Mirkwood in my home since then,[3] and little change does it seem to us. But to them it seems so long ago, that their dwelling in the North is but a memory of song, and their speech is already sundered from their northern kin.'

The companions entered the gates. Horsemen guarded them, and led them to the hall. They dismounted and walked in up the echoing hall. There they saw Theoden the old. Beside him sat Gandalf, and at his feet Gimli the dwarf.

At the foot of the page, where this draft ends, is the note: '? News of the attack on Minas Tirith by Haradwaith in ships'; see pp. 434–5, 437.

It would be interesting to know what thought lay behind this story of the 'divided entry' into Eodoras; but whatever it was, the arrival there and even the entry into Winseld was accomplished, as it appears, without any ceremony, interrogation, or laying aside of arms. There is no suggestion of hostility or even suspicion towards the strangers, and this accords with the first outline given in the last chapter (see p. 437). It will be seen in what follows that the entire conception of the situation at Eodoras arose during the writing of 'The King of the Golden Hall'.

While the story of the divided entry of the four companions was still maintained, however, a strongly 'Beowulfian' reception of Aragorn and Legolas at the gates was at once introduced, in a revised draft.[4]

...they came at last to the wide windswept walls and the gates of Eodoras. There sat men in bright mail upon proud steeds, who spoke to them in a strange tongue.

'Abidath cuman uncuthe! [*Rejected at the time of writing:* Hwæt sindon ge, lathe oththe leofe, the thus seldlice gewerede ridan cwomon to thisse burge gatum? No her inn gan moton ne

THE KING OF THE GOLDEN HALL 443

wædla ne wæpned mon, nefne we his naman witen. Nu ge feorran-cumene gecythath us on ofste: hu hatton ge? hwæt sindon eower ærende to Theoden urum hlaforde?'⁵ Aragorn understood these words] asking their names and errand. These words Aragorn understood and answered. 'Aragorn son of Arathorn am I,' he said, 'and with me is Legolas of Mirkwood. These names maybe ye have already heard, and our coming is awaited? But we ask now to see Theoden your lord; for we come in friendship and it may be that our coming

Here this draft tails off. It does not seem that the story that Gandalf with Gimli went ahead on Shadowfax and entered Eodoras first was taken any further. It is curious, however, that when the story was changed my father seems to have forgotten Gimli: he is not named in the encounter with the guard at the gates, there is no mention of his surrendering his axe at the doors of the house, and my father even wrote 'Now the three companions went forward' up Theoden's hall. These references were added in to the 'fair copy' manuscript, and 'three' changed to 'four'; and Gimli appears as the text was written when he strode forward, and was restrained by Gandalf, at Wormtongue's words about Lothlórien (TT p. 118). I do not think that this can have any narrative significance; but it was certainly an odd lapse, and not easy to explain.⁶

The story of the arrival at Eodoras was now revised again. Gandalf is present when the travellers are challenged at the gates, and the guards, crying *Abidath cuman uncuthe*, are rebuked by him for using the tongue of Rohan.⁷ The flowers on the mounds (still seven) become *nifredil*, the flowers of Lórien (see note 4, and pp. 233–4); and Aragorn utters the verse *Where now the horse and the rider?*,⁸ referring to 'Eorl the Old', changed at once to 'Eorl the Young', 'who rode down out of the North', and to 'his steed Felaróf, father of horses' (TT p. 112). But at this stage Wormtongue had still not emerged, and the suspicion and hostility of the guards evidently proceeded from Theoden's unfortified dislike and distrust of Gandalf;⁹ moreover Eomer had not returned to Eodoras since Aragorn, Legolas and Gimli parted from him:

'...Has not Eomer then returned and given warning of our coming?'

'Nay,' said the guard. 'He has not passed these gates. He was turned aside by messengers from Theoden, and went away west to the war without staying. But maybe, if what you say is true, Theoden will have knowledge of it. I will go to my lord and learn his will. But what names shall I report? ...'

With this cf. TT p. 113. – In the original draft for the scene in which

444   THE TREASON OF ISENGARD

the travellers must lay aside their weapons before entering Theoden's house there is a brief description of it:

Before Theoden's hall there was a portico, with pillars made of mighty trees hewn in the upland forests and carved with interlacing figures gilded and painted. The doors also were of wood, carven in the likeness of many beasts and birds with jewelled eyes and golden claws.

It is curious that in the 'fair copy' manuscript, and thence in the final text, there is no description at all of the exterior of the house, and I think that it may have got lost in the complexities of redrafting and reordering of the material.[10]

As they stood in the darkness by the doors of the hall and saw on one of the hangings the figure of the young man on a white horse (TT p. 116) Aragorn said: 'Behold Eorl the Young! Thus he rode out of the North to the Battle of the Field of Gorgoroth.' A very difficult draft preceding this has 'the Battle of Gorgoroth where Sauron was [?overthrown],' making it clear that at this stage my father conceived that Eorl came south to the great battle in which Gil-galad and Elendil were slain and Isildur took the Ring.[11]

In the encounter with Theoden the manuscript evidence is not very easy to interpret, but it seems certain that it was at this point that Wormtongue entered the story; for what is obviously the very earliest description of Theoden, written in the faintest scribble, reads thus:

At the far end of the hall beyond the hearth and facing the doors was a dais with three steps, and in the midst of the dais was a great chair. In the chair sat a man so bent with age that he seemed almost a dwarf. His white hair was [?braided] upon his [?shoulders], his long beard was laid upon his knees. But his eyes burned with a keen light that glinted from afar off. Behind his chair stood two fair women. At his feet upon the steps sat a wizened [*struck out:* old] figure of a man with a pale wise face. There was a silence.

In the 'fair copy' the text moves close to that of TT (pp. 116–17), and now appears the 'thin golden circlet' worn by Theoden (who is subsequently called 'King' in this manuscript); but he bears on his forehead 'a large green stone' (not the 'single white diamond' of TT: see p. 448), and there were still 'two fair women' standing behind his chair.

But though Wormtongue was present he did not, as the scene was first drafted, intervene, and it is Theoden who speaks of the death of the Second Master of the Mark, here called *Eofored*,[12] on the west marches of Rohan, and it is Theoden who names Gandalf *Láthspell*,

THE KING OF THE GOLDEN HALL 445

Ill-news. Gandalf responds, as in TT, by speaking of the different ways in which a man may come with evil tidings, and it is again Theoden, not Wormtongue, who retorts 'Verily he may, or he may be of a third kind', and who decries the idea that Gandalf had ever brought aid to Rohan: 'Last time it seemed to me that you asked my aid rather, and to get you from my land I astonished all men and myself also by lending you Shadowfax.'[13] At this stage Eomer's story remains as it was: 'Eomer has ridden away thither [to the west marches] with all but the last handful of my horsemen.'

At this point, however, before the conversation had proceeded any further, 'the pale man sitting upon the steps of the dais' began to play a part; for he now took over those parts of Theoden's remarks that are given to him in TT. Yet it is interesting to observe that my father did not introduce him into Theoden's household with the conscious intent that he should play the rôle that he did in fact come to play: for he still says, as Theoden had done, 'Now Eomer has ridden away thither with all but our last handful of horsemen.'[14]

After Gandalf's triumph over Wormtongue (who is not yet given any other name) Theoden is assisted down the hall by the two women, and he says to them: 'Go, Idis, and you too Eowyn sister-daughter!'[15] As they went, the younger of them looked back: 'very fair and slender she seemed. Her face was filled with gentle pity, and her eyes shone with unshed tears. So Aragorn saw her for the first time in the light of day, and after she was gone he stood still, looking at the dark doors and taking little heed of other things.'

Looking out from the porch of his house with Gandalf Theoden says: 'Not long now shall stand the high hall which Brego son of Brytta built' (cf. p. 435 and note 5; TT p. 120 'Brego son of Eorl'); and Gandalf tells him, as in TT, to send for Eomer. It was at this point in the writing of the chapter that there entered the story of the imprisonment of Eomer by the instigation of Wormtongue, who now receives his true name: *Frána* (*Gríma* did not replace this till much later).

In TT when Gandalf spoke to Theoden (p. 121) 'his voice was low and secret, and none save the king heard what he said.' In the early form of the chapter, however, this was not so:

His voice was low and secret, and yet to those beside him keen and clear. Of Sauron he told, and the lady Galadriel, and of Elrond in Rivendell far away, of the Council and the setting forth of the Company of Nine, and all the perils of their road. 'Four only have come thus far,' he said. 'One is lost, Boromir prince of Gondor. Two were captured, but are free. And two have gone upon a dark Quest. Look eastward, Theoden! Into the heart of menace they have gone: two small folk, such as you

446   THE TREASON OF ISENGARD

in Rohan deem but the matter of children's tales. Yet doom hangs upon them. Our hope is with them – hope, if we can but stand meanwhile!'

There are several drafts for this passage preceding that in the fair copy just given, and in one of these occurs the following:

Of the Council and the setting forth of the Company of Nine. So he came at last to the Mines of Moria and the Battle upon the Bridge.

'Then it was not wholly false, the rumour that Eomer brought,' said Theoden.

'No indeed,' said Aragorn, 'for he did but repeat what I said to him. And until this time yestermorning we thought that Gandalf had fallen. Even now he has not said what befell him in Moria. We would gladly hear.'

'Nay,' said Gandalf. 'The sun is riding towards noon.'

This is clear evidence that my father had reached this point, at least, in 'The King of the Golden Hall' *before* he wrote the conclusion of 'The White Rider' in its later form: see p. 430.

The passage just given is followed by a brief outline:

Eomer returns. *Wes thu Theoden hal.* He rejoices to see Theoden so much better; but begs pardon – save only for his advice to ride west. Says how the day's delay has grieved him.

Gandalf continues tale and holds out a *hope* (of Frodo in the East). But they must ride west.

Theoden bids them stay and rest. But Gandalf won't stay except for food ... Theoden has to take heart and send every man west. He himself is to lead his folk out of Eodoras into the secret refuge[?s] in the mountains – more defensible if all goes ill.

Eomer asks that Wormtongue should go west too. Shadowfax. They set out. Gandalf fleets ahead.

As already mentioned, in the last third of the chapter, from the point where Legolas gazes far off and believes that he can see 'a glint of white' and 'a tiny tongue of flame' (TT p. 121), there is little further independent drafting, the manuscript in ink being written over the original pencilled text. But it is clear that the story as known from *The Two Towers* of the unmasking of Wormtongue, the rehabilitation of Eomer, the meal before departure, the gift of Shadowfax, was achieved almost unhesitatingly.[16] In an important respect, however, my father at first conceived things differently.

In this first version of 'The King of the Golden Hall' the Second Master of the Mark, slain in fighting at the River Isen, is Eofored, and

THE KING OF THE GOLDEN HALL 447

he is not Theoden's son (p. 444 and note 12).[17] On the other hand, in addition to Eowyn (Eomer's sister, p. 437; addressed by Theoden as 'sister-daughter', p. 445), there is another lady in close association with Theoden, Idis – his daughter. All through this part of the chapter she is present, yet never once does she speak. When Gandalf asks Theoden who shall rule his people in his place when he departs to the war, he replies that Eowyn 'shall be lady in my stead'; and Gandalf says 'That is a good choice.' There is no mention of Idis here; yet she was still present, for at the meal before the riding of the host 'there also waiting upon the king were the ladies, Idis his daughter, and Eowyn sister of Eomer.' It was Eowyn who brought the wine, and Idis is again not mentioned; yet Háma still says, in response to Theoden's words that Eomer is the last of the House of Eorl (TT p. 128): 'I said not Eomer. He is not the last. There are Idis your daughter, and Eowyn his sister. They are wise and high-hearted.' But it was at this point that the brief existence of Idis came to an end; for the next words that my father wrote were: 'All love *her*. Let *her* be as lord to the Eorlingas, while we are gone.' All references to Idis were then removed from the manuscript.

I cannot say what function in the narrative my father had in mind for Idis (and it is notable that in the original outline, p. 437, only Eowyn sister of Eomer is mentioned as waiting on the guests at the feast in Winseld after the victory); still less why the daughter of the King (and older than Eowyn, p. 445) should be so silent and so overshadowed by the niece.

The significance of the meeting of Aragorn and Eowyn, on the other hand, was destined to survive, though fundamentally transformed. In this first version, in a passage already cited (p. 445), after she had gone 'he stood still, looking at the dark doors and taking little heed of other things'; at the meal before the departure 'Aragorn was silent, but his eyes followed Eowyn' (struck out); and when she brought the wine to the guests 'Long she looked upon Aragorn, and long he looked upon her' – for which was substituted: 'As she stood before Aragorn she paused suddenly and looked upon him, as if only now had she seen him clearly. He looked down upon her fair face, and their eyes met. For a moment they stood thus, and their hands met as he took the cup from her. "Hail Aragorn son of Arathorn!" she said.' With this contrast the passage that appears in its place in TT (p. 127). And after Theoden's words 'But in [Dunberg >] Dunharrow the people may long defend themselves, and if the battle go ill thither will come all who escape' (TT p. 128) Aragorn says: 'If I live, I will come, Lady Eowyn, and then maybe we will ride together.' Then Eowyn 'smiled and bent her head gravely.'

There is an isolated list of matters 'to be explained before the end', which in view of the first item seems to have been written just about this time. Only one other item is relevant here, but I give the whole list:

448 THE TREASON OF ISENGARD

Gandalf's escape – put this at the end of XXVI [i.e. 'The White Rider']
What happens to Bill (the pony)? [*Added*: Goes back to Bree and is found by Sam who rides him home.]
Bill Ferney.
Bree and Merry's ponies.
Barnabas Butterbur [*added*: and the ponies).
Galadriel.
Ents. Treebeard. Entwives.
Aragorn weds Eowyn sister of Eomer (who becomes Lord of Rohan) and becomes King of Gondor.
Feast in Gondor. Home Journey. They pass by round Lórien.[18]

But the story of Aragorn and Eowyn would in the event, of course, be quite otherwise; and in another short group of notes, isolated and undateable, this marital alliance of Rohan and Gondor was rejected (and no other was foreseen):

? Cut out the love-story of Aragorn and Eowyn. Aragorn is too old and lordly and grim. Make Eowyn the twin-sister of Eomund, a stern amazon woman.
If so, alter the message of Galadriel (XXVI.17).
Probably Eowyn should die to avenge or save Theoden.

But my father added in a hasty scribble the possibility that Aragorn did indeed love Eowyn, and never wedded after her death.

The reference 'XXVI.17' is to the page in the 'fair copy' manuscript of 'The White Rider' where appears Galadriel's message to Aragorn delivered to him by Gandalf (p. 431):

Elfstone, Elfstone, bearer of my green stone,
In the south under snow a green stone thou shalt see.
Look well, Elfstone! In the shadow of the dark throne
Then the hour is at hand that long hath awaited thee.

The green stone in the south was borne on Theoden's brow (p. 444), beneath his white hair, and it was Eowyn who would stand in the shadow of the dark throne within his hall.

NOTES

1 Beginning originally at 'Gandalf now wrapped himself again in his old tattered cloak' (p. 430; TT p. 107), the opening of 'The King of the Golden Hall' was then moved to 'The morning was bright and clear about them' (pp. 431–2; TT p. 111). The second rearrangement, giving the form in TT, was made after 'The King of the Golden Hall' was completed.

THE KING OF THE GOLDEN HALL 449

2 Names in *Theod-*, like names in *Eo-* (p. 403 note 5), are not written with an accent at this time.

3 In TT there are sixteen barrows at the foot of the hill of Edoras, and it is 500 years since Eorl the Young came out of the North. See note 11.

4 The flowers on the burial mounds, 'like tiny snowdrops' in the first draft, became in the second 'tiny flowers star-shaped and frail'. And in the second Legolas says: 'Seven mounds I see, and seven long lives of men it is, since the golden hall was built. [*Struck out at once:* And many more lives still since the Rohiroth first passed into this land.]' It seems curious that such awareness of the history of the Riders of Rohan should be attributed to Legolas.

5 'Stay, strangers unknown! Who are ye, friends or foes, that have come thus strangely clad riding to the gates of this town? None may here enter in, neither beggarman nor warrior, if we know not his name. Now, ye comers from afar, declare to us in haste: what are ye called? What is your errand to Theoden our lord?' – My father first used the Old English letter 'thorn' but changed to 'th' as he wrote.

The passage in *Beowulf* (lines 237–57) in which Beowulf and his companions are accosted by the watchman on the coast of Denmark is very distinctly echoed, as it is also in the passage in Modern English in TT, p. 113 ('Who are you that come heedless over the plain . . .').

6 Conceivably there was some confusion arising from the initial idea that Gandalf with Gimli entered Eodoras in advance of Aragorn and Legolas: Gandalf was introduced into the scenes at the gates and the doors, but Gimli, who would play little explicit part in them, was neglected. 'The *three* companions went forward' is certainly very surprising, since here the scene seems to be expressly visualised without Gimli; but this may have been a mere slip, deriving from the frequent use of 'the three companions' (Aragorn, Legolas, and Gimli) in preceding chapters.

7 One of the guards replies that 'None are welcome here in days of war save only those that come from [*struck out: Gemenburg*] *Heatorras Giemen Minas Tirith*', with *Mundbeorg* written in the margin. These Old English words are *gēmen, gīemen* 'care, heed, watch'; *Hēatorras* 'high towers'; and *Mundbeorg* 'protection-hill', distinct from *Mundburg* in LR. *Mundbeorg* occurs in another draft: 'And I am Aragorn son of Arathorn ... and it is to Mundbeorg that I journey as to my home' (cf. TT p. 113, 'it is to Mundburg that he goes').

8 An echo of the Old English poem known as *The Wanderer*, line 92: *Hwær cwom mearg? Hwær cwom mago?*

9 It is perhaps possible that the 'Beowulfian' reception at the gates

450   THE TREASON OF ISENGARD

played some part in the increased hostility of Theoden before ever Wormtongue entered the story.

10   Two small details in the scene before the doors may be mentioned. The guards, turning their sword-hilts towards the strangers, cried *Cumath her wilcuman!* This was later changed to *Wesath hale, feorran cumene*, which appears in TT (p. 114) translated, 'Hail, comers from afar!' And Gandalf speaks to Aragorn with an asperity that was afterwards softened (TT p. 115): 'Needless is Theoden's demand, but needless also is your refusal, Aragorn.'

11   In LR the time-span was of course vastly greater: according to the Tale of Years Eorl the Young won the victory of the Field of Celebrant and the Rohirrim settled in Calenardhon (Rohan as a province of Gondor) in the year 2510 of the Third Age, which was that number of years after the overthrow of Sauron by Gilgalad and Elendil. With the statement here cf. the genealogy that Aragorn gives of himself at the passage of the Pillars of the Kings, in which he is only separated from Isildur by three (subsequently four) generations (pp. 360–1).

It is difficult to explain the name 'Battle of the Field of Gorgoroth': on the First Map the Battle Plain (*Dagras*, later *Dagorlad*) is placed where it remained, outside the mountain-fences of Mordor and separated from Gorgoroth by the great pass, then named Kirith Ungol (Map III, p. 309).

12   Eofored is not named as Theoden's son. In the outline for this chapter the Second Master seems to have been slain in the final battle of the River Isen, and his funeral feast was held after the return to Eodoras (pp. 435, 437). His death has now been moved back to the fighting before Gandalf's arrival.

13   Theoden here says that 'only a few days ago men reported to me that Shadowfax had come back out of the West; but none could lay hands on him, for he went away swiftly northwards.' See p. 434 and note 2. This then became 'men reported that Shadowfax had been seen again, running wild through the land'; and finally, as in TT, 'I heard that Shadowfax had come back riderless'.

14   Wormtongue still says that 'to the wonder of us all my lord *lent to you* Shadowfax'. This was subsequently changed to his words in TT: 'my lord bade you choose any horse you would and be gone; and to the wonder of us all you took Shadowfax in your insolence.'

15   In the draft for this passage the reading is 'Go [*struck out:* Eowyn and you too Ælflæd Flæd] Idis and you too Eowyn'. Cf. the Old English poetic word *ides* 'woman, lady'. In early notes Eowyn is 'daughter of Theoden' and 'daughter of Eomund' (p. 390).

16   Even to the names of Theoden's sword, *Herugrim*, and his horse, *Snowmane*: only in the case of Dunharrow was there an earlier

form, *Dunberg*. *Dunharrow* is so named on Map IVE, p. 319.

17 In LR the genealogy is:

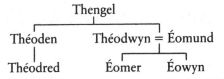

Near the end of the chapter 'Theodred' appears: ' "Behold I go forth," said Theoden. "[*Struck out at once:* Theodred my son] I have no son. I name Eomer my sister-son to be my heir" ' (cf. TT p. 127). On the other hand, in a second version of this passage, Theoden says: 'I have no child. Theodred my brother's son is slain.'

18 To this last item in the list the following was added at some later time:

No. They learn (in Rivendell?) that Nazgûl razed Lórien and Keleborn fled with a remnant to Mirkwood. Galadriel was lost or was hidden. Or shall Lórien be left slowly to fade? Yes. Galadriel parts with Keleborn who elects to stay in the world and [?woods]. She is seen by Frodo in old age, when he and Sam see Galadriel and Bilbo (and Elrond? No – he has one [*written above*: 3?] [*struck out*: age] life of men still to rule in Rivendell).

APPENDIX ON RUNES

It is notable that all references to runes in *The Lord of the Rings* were associated with Gandalf until my father came to the words graved on Balin's tomb in Moria. In *The Hobbit* runic writing is almost entirely associated with Dwarves (who are said, in Chapter III 'A Short Rest', to have invented the runic Moon-letters), but runes had been an element in Middle-earth from a very early stage.* In his letter to G. E. Selby of 14 December 1937, cited in the Foreword to Vol. VI *The Return of the Shadow*, my father said that he preferred his own mythology 'with its consistent nomenclature and organized history' to *The Hobbit*, and spoke with humorous disparagement of 'this rabble of Eddaic-named dwarves out of Völuspá, new-fangled hobbits and gollums (invented in an idle hour) and *Anglo-Saxon runes*.' As will be seen, when he wrote these last words he was thinking of his own runic alphabets, already at that time highly developed, and not in any way particularly associated with the Dwarves, if associated with them at all. It is conceivable, I think, that it was nonetheless Thror's Map, bearing runic writing of great importance in the story of *The Hobbit*, that brought that close association into being (although the Dwarves always remained the inheritors and not the first devisers of the *Angerthas*).

There seems to be relatively little extant writing concerning the runes from the period we have reached in this book, but my father's linguistic papers and work on scripts and alphabets were left in so chaotic a state that it is often impossible to be sure even of a broad and relative dating. A central problem lies, as always in this context, in the existence of two sets of variables. The richly divergent development of scripts, as of speech-sounds, among different peoples was a datum from the start; but the detail of those divergences was subject to unceasing modification in the mind of their deviser. When the papers (almost always undated and often without consecutive pagination) are so disordered that material which may well be separated by decades is jumbled together, the risk is great of false conjunctions and false constructions.

---

*The earliest runic document relating to Middle-earth that I know of is a little slip of paper in my father's early handwriting, headed *Gondolinic Runes*. This gives an alphabet in which the values of the runes are almost totally different from the *Angerthas*, but in which the principles of phonetic organisation in relation to letter-shape are strongly evident.

APPENDIX ON RUNES

453

I give here first two brief texts that seem to me to come most likely from the period shortly before the beginning of *The Lord of the Rings* – more or less contemporary with the *Quenta Silmarillion* and the *Lhammas* given in Vol. V, *The Lost Road and Other Writings*. Both are clear manuscripts in ink, and to both of them my father later added in pencil; I give these additions, though I suspect that they were substantially later. It will be seen that these additions concern the especial importance of Runic writing among the Dwarves, of which no mention is made in these texts as written.

(i)

The Elvish Alphabets

These have three main forms: the alphabets of Rúmil, of Fëanor, and [of] Dairon; also called the Valinorian, Túnian, and Beleriandic letters.

The first two are of Noldorin origin and ultimately related; the last is distinct and of Ilkorin origin.

The oldest is the *Alphabet of Rúmil.* This is a final cursive elaboration of the oldest letters of the Noldor in Valinor. Only the completion and arrangement of this system was actually due to Rúmil of Túna; its author or authors are now forgotten. Though originating in Túna it is called 'Valinorian' because it was mainly used for writing of Qenya, and was later ousted from use among the Noldor by the alphabet of Fëanor. It is said still to be used by the Lindar of Valinor; but is not in general use among the Qendi.*

The *Alphabet of Fëanor* was partly derived from this, and partly devised afresh to fit a different system of writing (from left to right). Its actual author – in all forms except the later modifications to fit the changed conditions of Noldorin after the Exile, which were made after his death – was Fëanor. He constructed it both as a general phonetic alphabet, and devised special arrangements to fit the characteristics of Qenya, Noldorin, and Telerin. This alphabet is the one generally used for Qenya, and for all purposes by the surviving Qendi.

The so-called *Alphabet of Dairon* was in origin a 'runic' script devised for inscriptions, especially on wood, that originated among the Ilkorins. It is usually said to have arisen in Doriath, and it certainly there developed most completely, even

---

* With this passage cf. the *Lhammas* in Vol. V, pp. 173–4.

454 THE TREASON OF ISENGARD

producing a written form. But probably its actual invention was due to the Danian elves of Ossiriand (who were ultimately of Noldorin race).* The name 'alphabet of Dairon' is due to the preservation in this script of some fragments of the songs of Dairon, the ill-fated minstrel of King Thingol of Doriath, in the works on the ancient Beleriandic languages by Pengolod the Wise of Gondolin. The Noldor did not use this script much, even in Beleriand, though Pengolod cites cases of inscriptions at Nargothrond and Sirion's mouth that are in Noldorin tongue. [*Added in pencil:* But this runic alphabet spread eastward from Ossiriand to the Dwarves, and was largely used by them.]

(ii)

The 'Alphabet of Dairon'

The Ilkorins of Beleriand devised an alphabet of 'runes', or angular letters used in inscriptions. This became widespread in Beleriand, already before the exile of the Noldor of Valinor, and showed various divergences in forms and uses at different times and places. Its chief elaboration took place in Doriath, where a written form was developed. Owing to the ruin of Beleriand, before the departure of the Noldor to Eressëa, no actual inscription or book in this script is now preserved. Knowledge of it [*changed in pencil to:* no actual Elvish inscription or book in this script was preserved. Knowledge of its use by the Elves] is now preserved only in books in Eressëa – in the works of Pengolod of Gondolin upon the Beleriandic languages, and other similar writings. Pengolod copied and gave extracts from various inscriptions and books that were still extant in his day. Of the books, or written form, his principal source was some fragments of the songs of King Thingol's minstrel Dairon. From this fact is derived the [*struck out:* erroneous] name: Alphabet of Dairon.

The origin of the script is probably to be placed in Ossiriand among the Danian elves, many of whom were incorporated in Doriath after the coming of Morgoth and the fall of their king, Denethor.† The Danian elves were ultimately of Noldorin race, and inventions of this sort were a special aptitude of the

* On the Danian elves or *Danas* see especially V.176, 188–9.
† See the *Quenta Silmarillion* in Vol. V, p. 263.

APPENDIX ON RUNES   455

Noldor.* Moreover a related alphabet was early in use among the eastern branch of the Danians, beyond the Blue Mountains, whence it also spread to Men in those regions, becoming the foundation of the Taliskan *skirditaila* or 'runic series'. [*Added in pencil:* Related alphabets were (> A related alphabet was) also borrowed (from both Men and Elves) by the Dwarves; the western Dwarves early borrowed and adapted the full inscriptional 'Alphabet of Dairon', and most of the inscriptions in this form that survived the Great War in Eriador and elsewhere are of Dwarvish origin, though their language is seldom the secret tongue of the Dwarves.]

This alphabet was not much used by the exiled Noldor, but in certain cases, in the absence of parchment or for carving on wood, or where as at Sirion's mouth they were mingled with Ilkorins, they employed these letters during their exile, and modified their forms or applications to fit their own language. Pengolod gives some examples of this Noldorin usage. [*Added in pencil:* The greatest elaboration was reached in Eregion and Moria, where during the Second Age Elves and Dwarves lived in harmony. This later form was called the 'Runes of Moria', because it remained long in use among the Dwarves, and most of the inscriptions employing it survived in the halls and chambers of Moria.]

With this view of the origin of the name *Alphabet of Dairon* cf. *The Lord of the Rings* Appendix E (II): 'Their richest and most ordered form was known as the Alphabet of Daeron, since in Elvish tradition it was said to have been devised by Daeron, the minstrel and loremaster of King Thingol of Doriath.'

The reference to Taliska (for which see V.179, 191, 196: 'the language of the three houses of Bëor, of Haleth, and of Hador') is very interesting as adumbrating a relationship between the runes of Beleriand and the ancient Germanic runes; cf. V.279 on the 'Indo-European' word *widris* 'wisdom' in the ancient tongue of the people of Bëor. It seems clear that the second element of Taliskan *skirditaila* 'runic series' is to be understood as an ancestral cognate of the word seen in Old English *tæl* (with a sense 'number, reckoning, series'; Old Norse *tal*, etc., and cf. Modern English *tale, tell*); the first element may perhaps be connected with the Germanic stem *sker-*, seen in Old Norse *skera* 'cut, carve', Old English *sceran* (Modern English *shear*, cf. ultimately related *shard, potsherd*).

Detailed exposition from this time of the ancient Elvish runes seems

---

* Cf. the *Ainulindalë* in Vol. V, p. 162.

456   THE TREASON OF ISENGARD

to be restricted to a series of five manuscript pages – which are indeed extremely informative. In style and bearing they seem to me to belong with substantial work on Noldorin phonology that certainly comes from the time not long preceding the start of *The Lord of the Rings*. Since it would be extremely difficult to print these pages as part of the text, and since they would be unclear in facsimile reproduction (and require a lot of unnecessary explanation and annotation), I have rewritten and redrawn them as a series of plates, numbered I to IV, at the end of this Appendix. I have attempted to remain very faithful to the originals, and have only edited them in a few minor points that in no way alter their purport; I have not attempted to smooth away the various inconsistencies of presentation. There are a very few pencilled changes that are ignored. At the head of the first sheet my father wrote: 'All this has been revised and rewritten. See Appendices to *Lord of the Rings*.'

On plate V I reproduce a separate manuscript leaf entitled 'Dwarf-runes for writing English (phonetic)', which I shall refer to in this Appendix as 'E'. This is obviously quite distinct from the other pages, but it will be found that it agrees well on the whole with 'the later Noldorin use' on plate II (referred to subsequently as 'N'), though there is some difference in the application of signs, notably in the nasals and in those representing English *š* (*sh*), *ž* (as in *vision*), *tš* (*ch*), and *dž* (*j* as twice in *judge*), which are either used for different sounds in N or not found there. As will be seen shortly, this page evidently dates from the time of my father's return to the Moria story, as described in this book. Curiously, *kw* (*qu*) is absent from E, and the rune ⱴ for *kw* in the Doriath and Noldorin usage is there given to *tš* (*ch*). In E, also, *h* is represented by ⟨, but by ⟩ in the others.

At the bottom of plate V I have transcribed the runic inscription on Balin's tomb from the end of the original first 'Moria' chapter in Vol. VI (see p. 460 and note 40). As noted there, it was at that point that my father decided to use the Runes of Beleriand in preference to Old English runes, for he first wrote the inscription in the latter but at once wrote it in the former as well – in two forms, which I have marked (i) and (ii). The words *Runes of Dwarves* on the same page (VI.460) no doubt have some significance in this connection; cf. also Gandalf's words in the second version of the chapter ('The Lord of Moria', p. 186): 'These are dwarf-runes, such as they use in the North.' – On the name *Burin* of Balin's father see VI.444.

Version (i) of the tomb-inscription agrees with E (and with N) in every point save one: the use of the rune ⟩ for *s* in *son* instead of ⋋. In E ⟩ is used for the vowel [ʌ] (as in English *cup*); while in N it is used for *h*.

Version (ii) agrees with (i) in the *s*-rune, but reverses ō and ŏ in *lord* and *Moria*, and for *l* in *lord* substitutes ⱴ for ⱡ: the former is found

APPENDIX ON RUNES   457

in the Doriath and Noldorin use. Here the rune ᛖ is used for the vowel in *son*, where (i) has the unphonetic ∨ (*o*). In E this rune has the value *ai*, in N the value *ae* (later changed in pencil to *ai* in a reversal of the values *ai* and *ae*).

The next (third) version of the tomb-inscription, at the end of the second version ('The Lord of Moria') of the chapter, is hidden by a fourth version pasted over it; but Taum Santoski has been able to read the underlying inscription by lighting the page from the back. With *Fundin* for *Burin* (see VI.444) the runic writing thus recovered is almost as in version (i), with the same use of > for *s*; but very curiously this same rune is used for *o* in both occurrences of the word *of*, although ∨ for *o* appears in *son*, *lord*, and *Moria*. In addition, the Dwarvish words *Balin Fundinul Uzbad Khazaddûmu* are added beneath, the rune for *z* being apparently ᛉ, which is *s* in all the alphabets given here.

The fourth version of the inscription, that pasted over the third, and the fifth, at the end of the typescript text that followed, are identical in all forms; the latter is reproduced on p. 186. So far as the brief text goes, agreement with E is here complete, with *s* represented by ᛉ, *z* represented by ᛉ, and > used for the vowel [ʌ], which here appears in the word *son*, treated phonetically.

On plate VI I have redrawn the runic writing from the two earliest illustrations of a burnt and blackened page from the Book of Mazarbul. These redrawings are intended to show the runes and their relative placing and nothing more. The earliest form (i) is found on the back of the last page of the original 'Moria' chapter (see VI.460, 467). This is the merest sketch, an indication of what might be done in this direction: it was made very hastily, scribbled down, with little attempt at verisimilitude, the illegible parts of the page being represented by rough scribbled strokes (and the number of missing lines in my redrawing is approximate and impressionistic). The right-hand bottom corner is shown as a triangular detached piece, on which only the word *Kazaddûm* is written. The second form (ii) is a much more developed representation of the slashed and discoloured leaf, done in pencil and coloured chalks; here again the bottom corner is shown as torn right off. (The evolution of this page is emblematic in miniature of my father's mode of work: the evolution of the details of shape is progressive and continuous. In this second version there are two holes on the right hand side of the page and a bite out of the top; in the third and fourth versions these remain, but the bottom corner is added back, with a triangular indentation above, continuing into the page as a black line. In the final form, reproduced in *Pictures by J. R. R. Tolkien* no. 23, the central hole is enlarged and moved to the left, but the black line remains where the bottom corner was originally shown as torn off and separate.)

458 THE TREASON OF ISENGARD

The words of the original sketch have been given in VI.467, but I repeat them here in phonetic form:

1	Wē drouv aut *the* orks fro[m] .... gard
2	... [f]irst hōl. Wī slū meni ʌndr *the* brait sʌn
3	in *the* deil. Flōi woz kild bai ʌn arou ....
4	Wī did ....
9	Wī ha[v] okjupaid *the* twentifʌrst hōl ov
10	norþ end. Ðer ǒr iz ....
11	.... šaft iz ....
12	[B]alin haz set ʌp hiz tšēr in *the* tšeimbr ov Mazar
13	bul ....Balin iz lord ov
14	Moria ....
18	Balin ....
20	Kazaddūm

Here there is close but not complete agreement with E. The *s*-rune is *ʎ* not *>*, the latter being used for [ʌ], as in E; but there is divergence in the *w*-rune, which is here *ʋ*, to which E gives the value *dž* (*j*) and N the value *gw*. The short single vertical used in E as abbreviation for *the* when in the upper position and as a sign for the vowel [ə] when in the lower position is here used for *the* in the lower position, but in the upper position for *h* (in *have, has, his*): in both occurrences of the word *hall* the stroke stands in the lower position, but this may have been no more than an inadvertence, for the runes in this sketch were pencilled very rapidly and several were written erroneously and then corrected. The rune for the initial consonants [š] in *shaft* and [tš] in *chair, chamber* also differ in their values from those ascribed to them in E. The use of the *m*-rune for *v* in *we have occupied* (line 9) can only be a slip. Lastly, the vowel [ʌ] is employed not only in *under, sun, up* but also in *an (arrow)* and in *first* (at the second occurrence).

Comparison with E will show that the second version of the page from the Book of Mazarbul agrees with it in every point and detail. The different form of the *l*-rune in *Flōi* (line 4), with the crossing stroke falling, not rising, to the right, is probably merely accidental (in the third version the shape is normal at this point).

To this version my father appended a phonetic transcription. In this he interpreted *oukn* in line 6 as *?broken*, *it* at the end of line 10 as *?its*, and the word before *helm* in line 17 as *(?sil)vr*, though the last rune is very clearly *n*, not *r* (in the third version an *r*-rune is written here).

The sequence of development in this much-considered passage was very probably as follows. The original form of the text that Gandalf first read out from the Book of Mazarbul seems to have been that of the earliest drawing of the page itself (plate VI, i). Closely related to it is the form in the original pencilled narrative of the scene, which can be largely made out beneath the text written over it in ink (see pp. 191

APPENDIX ON RUNES 459

and 205 note 4). Both forms had *the Orcs* for *Orcs* and Balin's *chair* for Balin's *seat*; but the original narrative text had *we have found truesilver, well-forged*, and *(To)morrow Óin is ... lead ... seek for the upp(er) armoury of the Third Deep*, all of which is absent from the first drawing of the page.

The overwritten text in the first narrative, which is given on p. 191, is effectively the same as the text in the second drawing of the page (plate VI, ii).

The third drawing of the page (which is otherwise very similar to the second, and employs exactly the same runic system) corresponds to the text of the fair copy manuscript of 'The Mines of Moria (ii)' given on pp. 200–1.

It is plain therefore that the first three drawings of this page from the Book of Mazarbul all belong to the same time, and relate step by step to the rewriting of this passage through the original draft and first fair copy of the narrative chapter; and that the runic alphabet set out in E, 'Dwarfrunes for writing English' (plate V), belongs to this time also. But when the fourth version of this page was done the runic values had changed.

The first drawings of the other two pages from the Book of Mazarbul (that written by Ori in Elvish script and the last page of the book, in runes) belong with and were done at the same time as the third drawing of the first page; for the texts see pp. 200–1.

Runes of Beleriand

The oldest signs seem to have been the following:-
Series (1) ᛈ . ᛒ . ᛟ . ᛥ . ᚹ . ᚱ . ᛉ . ᛯ .
     (2) ᚠ . ᚡ . ᚾ . ᚿ . ᛏ . ᛐ . ᛒ . ᛙ . ᛉ .
     (3) ᚲ . ᚳ . ᚴ . ᛃ . ᚼ . K . ᛪ . ⁂ .
     (4) miscellaneous. I . X . ᚻ . ᚥ . V . ᛯ .

The distribution of these signs among the required values differed considerably at different times and in different places, but all varieties agreed on taking Series 1 generally as <u>labials</u> and Series 2 as <u>dentals</u>, while the principles were also usually observed that reversal represented a spirant (ᛈ p ᛟ f) and addition voicing (ᚠ t ᚡ d ᚾ d̶).

The chief divergence occurred in the invention and application of later signs. As usual in runes there were no horizontal bars in the original runic form; but it may be noted that most of the runes consisted of a single vertical with a side appendage which was never attached to the bottom (except as a reduplication of one already at the top). Later elaborations developed inverted forms as ᛚ ᛒ and here the application was variable.

The original Doriath order of letters in transcription (phonetic) was as follows: (1) a. i. u. e. o. (2) p. t. k. (3) b. d. g. (4) f. þ. s. χ (h). (5) ƀ. ð. ʒ. l. r. z. (6) m. n. ŋ. ng. (7) j. w. In this order it was borrowed in Ossiriand, and so in E. Danian and Taliska.

The runes associated with these values were usually:-

This series was altered by the intrusion of signs for kw etc. (inverted p or k runes being used: ᛒ or ᛚ); and the use of signs for vocalic and consonantal diphthongs; also a differentiation was made between n and ng, h and χ, and between ē/e, ō/o (the other long vowels being distinguished

APPENDIX ON RUNES

II

later).

The special <u>Doriath</u> long series thus became as follows:—

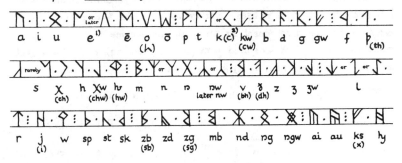

(The values in brackets are normal transcriptions).

Notes. 1) o+o V+V > W; therefore M taken as ∧+∧ = long ē. But also ∧ = inverted V = o; therefore ʞ was also used as o. 2) Normally a spirant is a reverse; therefore when > was invented as differentiation of Y = χ and h, also < as variant of Y = k,c arose.

The later Noldorin use.

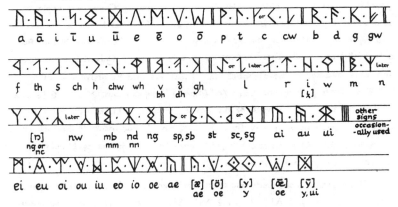

The order was variable. The above order was usual. The only vowel diphthongs ever counted as fixed letters were ai, au, ui : the rest were only occasionally used instead of writing with two letters (aj, uj, aw, ow, ei, ej

462   THE TREASON OF ISENGARD

III

and so on), which was frequently done even with ai, au, ui.

Since later in Noldorin mb, nd became m(m), n(n) confusion arose with ꞵ ꜷ, and both tended to be used indiscriminately, while ✳ dropped out of use except for occasional employment as nn. ng also became ꞑ, so two developments occurred : (a) ꭥ was used = ꞑ (transcription ng), and X was used for ꞑk (transcription nc); or (b) ꭥ was dropped and only X used.

The written form, or 'Alphabet of [Pengolod >] Dairon'

ꞑ.I.O.Λ.V .   ꞅ.H.ꟺ.M.Ϣ.   m.ꞟ.ꭆ.   P.Γ.Ρ.Ⴑ.
   u   ω ɰ
a i u e o á í ú é ó⁽¹⁾ ai au ui   p t c⁽²⁾ cw

ꞧ.ꞙ.ꝅ.Ⴑ .   ꝗ.Ɬ.ɗ.ꓒ or'.ꞅ.ꞎ or ꓶ.Φ.   ꓮ.ꞝ.ꓘ.C.S.Ȝ or Z.
b d g gw ſ th s h ch chw wh v dh gh⁽³⁾ ' l lh

Τ.Ψ.I or ꝉ.Q.   B.Y.X or X.Λ(Λ).   ꓱ.ꓘ.✳.Ⴆ.ꞗ.ꓯ.
r rh i(=ı)⁽⁴⁾ w m n ng nw mb⁽³⁾ nd⁽³⁾ ng sp st sg
              mm nn (sb) (sc)

Notes. (1) These letters (á í ú é ó) originally longs were variously employed in representations of later Noldorin. (2) Originally C was also employed as a variant; but later it was used as a sign of hiatus between vowels, and especially initially to represent vocalic beginning after loss of ꓮ (gh from g by mutation). (3) These letters though only employed regularly in Old Noldorin were retained in the alphabet and sometimes in orthography — as Zꞑꓱ = lamb pronounced lăm (< *lambē) 'tongue'; but X and ꭥ became used as mere variant shapes of the same letter. (4) Originally Ψ was used as a variant of Y = n (and ꝓ of Λ = nw); but later Ψ became used as the sign for initial voiceless r (rh), when the two forms of Ⴑ became differentiated (as S = l Ȝ or Z = lh).

Other vocalic signs were also often employed but not reckoned as separate letters. Thus Λ ei = ΛI; Λ eo = ΛV; ꓯ or ꓴ oe = VΛ; and the modifications : ꓦ ꟺ = oe monophthong [ö], Θ, ω = y.

The signs ꓯ z, Ⴆ zd. ꝓ ngw were no longer retained in the alphabet. Similarly ꝅ (x, ks, hs), H or ꞟ = ly were only used in representing foreign words

APPENDIX ON RUNES

IV

The smaller and more cursive letters were as follows.

pennas na·ngoeloeidh

Eredwethion

THE TREASON OF ISENGARD

464

V

Dwarf runes for writing English (phonetic)

(runic chart)

p	b	f	v	m	mb	w	hv (wh)

t	d	þ	ð	n	nd	r	l	s	z

tš (ch)	dž (j)	š (sh)	ž	ñ	ndž	j (y)	hy

k	g	χ (ch)	ʒ (gh)	ɲ	ng	h

ps	ts	dz	ks (x)	gz (x)	bs, bz

General nasal sign ^ as R̂ = ᚦ mb but on P̂ = mp

a	e	i	o	u	ʌ	ə		ā	ē	ī	ō	ū

ö ø	y (ü)	æ

ai	au	oi	ou	ei	eu	ui	iu

the _ı of ᚱ and ʃ

The earliest forms of the inscription on Balin's tomb in Moria

(i)

ᚱᚢᛏᛁᛉ ∘ ᚦᚢᛉ ∘ ᚢᛉ ⠆ ᚱᛟᛏᛁᛉ ⠇ ᛏᚢᛏᚠ ∘ ᚢᛉ ⠆ ᛒᚹᛏᛁᚢ

(ii)

ᚱᚢᛏᛁᛉ ∘ ᚦᛗᛁᛉ ∘ ᚢᛉ ᚱᛟᛏᛁᛉ ⠇ ᛁᚹᛏᚠ ∘ ᚢᛉ ᛒᚢᛏᛁᚢ

APPENDIX ON RUNES

(i)

'Page of Balin's Book'

VI

(ii)

'One page of the Book of Moria'

INDEX

As in the Index to *The Return of the Shadow*, I have slightly reduced the number of page-references in the case of names that occur very frequently by using the word *passim* to mean that the name is missing only from a single page here and there in a long series otherwise unbroken.

The very large number of names occurring in this book that were soon rejected and replaced are nearly all given separate cross-references to a primary name; exceptions are cases where such a name falls in immediate proximity to the primary name (thus whereas *Dolamarth* is entered separately from *Amon Amarth*, *Amarthon* is not), and certain purely experimental names (such as the rejected names for *Amon Hen/Amon Lhaw*). Names in *Errantry* are all entered under *Errantry*.

Names appearing on the redrawn maps, on the reproductions of pages from texts of *The Lord of the Rings*, and on the manuscript pages at the end of the *Appendix on Runes*, are not indexed.

Adurant, River   In Ossiriand. 271
Aelinuial   'Lakes of Twilight'. 292
Ainulindalë   The Music of the Ainur. 455
Aldalómë   Fangorn. 420
Aldemanton   See *Westermanton*.
All that is gold does not glitter   49–50, 52, 77–8, 80, 137, 146
Alphabets   453–5
Alqualondë   322; Noldorin *Alfobas* 322
Amaldor, Ammalas   See *Amroth*.
Amon Amarth   Mount Doom. 348. Earlier names *Amarthon, Dolamarth* 343
Amon Hen   214, 318, 364, 370–6, 378–81, 385–8, 405, 413, 426–7; *Tirmindon* 364. Rejected names for Amon Hen/Amon Lhaw 387. Visions on Amon Hen 372–4, 379–81
Amon Lhaw   318, 364, 373, 381, 387; *Larmindon* 364
Amrath   See *Andrath*.
Amroth   223, 234, 239, 243. Earlier names *Ammalas* 223, 225–6, 239, 243; *Amaldor* 223
Anárion   119, 123, 126, 138, 144, 146; realm of 282; name of region 310, 318
Ancient Days   255, 259
Andon   See *Anduin*.

INDEX   467

Andrath Place near the Greenway. 79, 298, 306. Earlier form *Amrath* 69–72, 74, 79, 298, 306

Anduin 123–4, 138, 144, 151, 157, 207, 211, 213, 215, 218, 221, 231, 233, 236–8, 267, 269, 284, 287–8, 290–2, 295, 298–9, 304, 306–7, 311–13, 315–16, 318, 320, 323, 329–30, 339, 346, 351, 353, 355–6, 364–5, 368, 427, 435, 439; *Mouths* 307, 311, 382; *Vale (valley) of Anduin* 292, 322, 336. Earlier names *Beleghir* 122; *Sirvinya* 119, 122, 125, 299; *Andon* 298–9, 306. See *Ethir Anduin, Great River.*

Anfalas 310

Angerthas 452. See *Runes.*

Angle (of Lothlórien) 207, 213, 218, 221, 225, 231, 236–8, 241, 244–5, 256, 261, 268–9, 280–1, 287–8, 325. The meaning of *Angle* discussed 287–8; see *(The) Gore.*

Angmar 37, 59

Angrenost Isengard. 420. Earlier name *Angrobel* 'Irongarth' 71–2, 130, 139

Angrobel See *Angrenost.*

Annerchion 'Goblin Gate'. 114

Annúminas 122, 145, 304. See *Tarkilmar, Torfirion, Westermanton.*

Anórien 310, 318

Aotrou and Itroun, Lay of 345

Arafain See *Keleborn.*

Aragorn 6–7, 9, 15, 50–2, 63, 65, 77–84, 105, 111–13, 116, 120, 129–30, 135, 137, 146–8, 151, 157, 162–5, 168, 170–1, 176, 187, 196, 200, 203, 206–7, 210–12, 214, 216, 218, 222, 224–5, 227–8, 230–2, 235–6, 238–9, 243–4, 256, 258, 260, 262, 265, 276–8, 291, 293, 326, 358, 361–2, 364, 366, 381, 384–5, 390, 392–404, 406–7, 424–31, 434–5, 437–9, 441–50. His ancestry and history 6–8, 116, 120–1, 147, 360–2; weds Éowyn 448; King of Gondor 448. See *Elfstone, Ingold, Tarkil, Trotter.*

Aramir See *Arathorn.*

Aran See *Keleborn.*

Arathorn Father of Aragorn. 361–2, 392–3, 404, 443, 447, 449. Original name *Aramir* 7, 63; and see *Elfhelm, Ingrim, Kelegorn.*

Archet In the Bree-land. 45

Arfaxed See *Shadowfax.*

Argonath, Gates of 359–60, 362. Earlier names *Gates of (Sarn) Gebir* 359–60, 362; *Sern Aranath* 366. *Pillars of the Kings* 360–2, 387, 450

Arkenstone, The 160

Arod 'Swift', Legolas' horse of Rohan. 402, 439. Earlier name *Whitelock* 402

Aros, River In Beleriand. 292

Arvernien Coastlands west of Sirion. 99, 102–4

Arwen 83–4

468   THE TREASON OF ISENGARD

Ash Mountains   See *Ered Lithui.*

Athelas   Healing plant. 221

Attercops   Spiders (in the poem *Errantry*). 86, 88, 108; (in *The Hobbit*) 106

Azanulbizar   Dimrill Dale. 143, 164, 166, 174; *Azanûl* 184

Azog   Orc, slayer of Thrór. 143, 156–7

Bag End   8, 16, 20–1, 29–31, 52, 62, 71–2, 80, 337, 340

Baggins   (family name) 13, 25, 31, 37, 41, 43, 45–6, 48, 55, 62, 69, 71–2, 74

Baggins, Bilbo   5–8, 10, 15–16, 19–27, 29, 37–9, 43, 46, 62, 64–6, 81, 83–4, 95, 106, 110–11, 115–18, 126, 129–30, 137, 146–9, 152, 162–3, 165, 169, 173, 185, 188, 190, 192, 201, 212, 221, 260, 264, 287, 292, 451. His book(s) 5, 65, 83, 115; wrote *The Cat and the Fiddle* 64; his song at Rivendell 90 ff., 292; his mailcoat (*elf-mail, dwarf-mail*, etc.) 19, 137, 173, 185, 188, 218, 221, 331, 336, 353

Baggins, Bingo   31, 34, 59, 110, 122–3, 137, 158

Baggins, Drogo   193, 371

Baggins, Frodo   6–11, 13–16, 20–52 *passim*, 54, 56–7, 61–5, 68–9, 71–4, 76–7, 80–4, 105, 110, 112–15, 117, 122, 126–7, 129–30, 132, 134–5, 137, 139–40, 146–9, 151–2, 156–7, 161–2, 165, 168–9, 171–3, 178, 181, 185, 190, 192–8, 201, 207–54 *passim*, 258–60, 263–6, 268–9, 271, 275–6, 281, 283, 286–7, 321, 324–58 *passim*, 361, 363, 365–8, 371–81, 384–7, 389, 396, 398, 404–5, 407, 409, 411–13, 423, 426–8, 437–8, 440, 446, 451. His sword 10, 16, 115, 137, 173. See *Baggins, Dream of the Tower.*

Bagshot Row   29, 253

Bain   Son of Bard, King in Dale. 404

Bair am Yru   Dwellings of the Galadrim. 243

Balin   82, 116–17, 141–2, 155, 158, 172, 190–2, 195, 200–1, 204, 247, 257, 456–9; *Balin Lord of Moria* 186, 191–2, 200, 458; his tomb 67, 161, 176, 190, 194, 379; inscription on the tomb 186, 452, 456–7

Balrog(s)   (almost all references are to the Balrog of Moria) 142, 186, 188–9, 197–200, 202–3, 206, 211, 236, 247, 257, 262–3, 354, 422, 430–1, 434, 441; the Balrog described 197, 199, 202

Barad-dûr   177–8, 208–9, 213, 332, 334, 336–7, 341, 344, 371, 373. See *Dark Tower, (The) Eye*

Barahir   240

Baranduin   66, 131, 272, 289, 402, 416; *Baranduinen* 124; *Branduin* 61, 66, 144. Ephemeral name *Malevarn* 66. See *Brandywine.*

Barangils   Men of the Harad, Southrons. 313

Barazinbar   Caradras. 166, 174, 432; *Baraz* 174

Bard   King in Dale. 404

INDEX   469

Bardings Men of Dale. 296, 307, 404–5. See *Brandings*.

Barrow-downs (including references to *the Downs*) 11, 41, 73, 79, 402, 416

Barrows 16; hobbits' swords from 16, 381

Barrow-wights 152

Battles Great Battle (at the end of the Elder Days) 122, 124, 247. *Battle of Five Armies* 22, 143, 157. Last battle of the War of the Ring 208; *last battle of Gorgoroth* 211. At end of the last Alliance: *Battle of (the Field of) Gorgoroth* 444, 450; *Battle Plain* 310, 389, 450 (see *Dagorlad*).

Beleghir See *Anduin*.

Belegost Dwarf-city in Eredlindon. 301, 304

Beleriand 110, 122–4, 137, 239, 292, 454; *Beleriandic letters* 453, *languages* 454; runes of Beleriand 455–6

Belfalas 310, 322, 382. *Bay of Belfalas* 119, 125, 144, 298–9, 356, 389, 435. Earlier name *Bay of Ramathor, Ramathir* 119, 125

Bennas The Angle of Lothlórien. 238, 241, 288

Bëor (house of, people of) 455

Beorhtnoth 106–7

Beorn 138, 248, 263, 287

Beornings 233, 248, 264, 289, 372, 390, 395

Beowulf 65, 442, 449

Beren 58, 173, 271, 331

Bergrisland See *Ettendales*.

Bilbo Baggins See under *Baggins*.

Bill the pony See *Ferney, Bill*.

Black Gate See *Morannon*.

Black Gulf, Black Pit See *Moria*.

Black Mountains (including references to *the mountains*) 124, 132, 137, 139, 144, 149, 169–70, 177, 225, 239, 241, 272, 282, 311, 316, 320, 322–3, 336, (373–4), 389, 395, 398, 433, 435, 446; *Mountains of the South* 453; Elvish names *Ered Myrn, Eredvyrn, Mornvenniath* 124. Replaced by *White Mountains*.

Black Riders (also *Riders, black horsemen*, etc.) 6–7, 9, 11–14, 16–17, 29, 32–6, 40–1, 43–5, 47–9, 52–5, 57–8, 62–5, 68–79, 82, 105, 113, 130, 132–5, 138, 149, 151–2, 190, 208, 211–13, 215, 326, 335, 337, 341, 423; borne upon vultures, see *Vultures*. *King, Captain, Chief, of the Riders (the Nine)* 9, 13, (33–4), 69–72, 74, 116, 132–3, 135, 149; *Black Captain* 79. See *Nazgûl, (The) Nine, Ringwraiths, Wizards*.

Blackroot, River (1) Earlier name of Silverlode, replacing *Redway*. 166–7, 174, 190–1, 207, 213, 215, 218, 220–2, 225, 230–1, 235, 237–8, 240–1, 287–8, 296, 306. (2) River of Gondor. 177, 187, 241, 298, 306, 310–11. On the transposition of the names see 235, 241; and see *Buzundush, Celebrant, Morthond*.

Blackwater, River In Essex. 106; Old English *Panta* 106

470 THE TREASON OF ISENGARD

Black Years 144

Blue Mountains 124, 301, 455; *the Mountains* 123–4; *Mountains of Lune* 416. See *Eredlindon, Eredluin*.

Bodleian Library 107, 187

Boffin (family) 31

Boffin, Folco 30–2

Boffin, Peregrin (1) Trotter. 7–8, 15, 19, 21, 31–2, 81, 83, 111. (2) Friend of Frodo Baggins. 8–9, 11–12, 16, 21, 30–2; called *Perry* 8, 11–12

Bolg Orc, son of Azog. 143, 157

Bolger (family) 31, 76, 161; ~ *Olo* 31; ~ *Odovacar* 20; ~ *Rollo* 20

Bolger, Fredegar (also *Freddy*) 8, 30–2, 39, 54, 76

Bolger, Hamilcar (also *Ham*) 8–9, 11–14, 21, 30–3, 36, 39, 54–6, 58, 61, 68–72, 74–6, 78, 111, 136, 152

Bolger, Odo 6–8, 31–2, 36–7, 39–40, 42–3, 51, 53, 75, 82, 172; originally *Odo Took* 31

Bombadil See *Tom Bombadil*.

Book of Lost Tales 242, 322; individual tales 95, 172

Border Hills 268–9, 281, 313, 315–16. See *Emyn Rhain*.

Boromir 110, 112–14, 116–17, 120–2, 125–9, 136, 138, 146–7, 151, 154, 159, 162, 165, 169–71, 175, 177, 192–4, 200, 203–18 *passim*, 224, 231, 239, 241, 243, 248, 254, 258, 263, 266, 268–75, 278–9, 281–2, 292–3, 311, 324–30, 345–6, 352–4, 357–60, 371–88 *passim*, 392–4, 397, 401, 406, 411–13, 429, 435, 437–8, 440, 445; Lament for Boromir 384, 388

Bowra, Maurice 90, 107

Brand King in Dale. 118, 404

Branding Aragorn's sword. 165, 201, 274, 276, 290, 393, 399, 429, (437). See *Elendil, Sword that was Broken*.

Brandings Men of Dale. 395, 404–5. See *Bardings*.

Brandor See *Tol Brandir*.

Branduin See *Baranduin*.

Brandybuck (family) 31, 152

Brandybuck, Meriadoc (also *Merry*) 6, 8, 21, 30–2, 36, 41, 48, 52, 56–8, 68, 112–13, 115, 162, 164, 167, 171–2, 175, 193, 210–11, 214, 216, 226, 228, 231, 235, 250, 253, 264–5, 271, (272), 274–5, 279, 285–6, 328–30, 339, 344, 346–9, 352–3, 365, 375–8, 385–6, 397, 404, 408–9, 411–15, 417, 423, 426–7, 429, 434, 436–7, 448; his ponies 56, 71, 448

Brandywine Bridge (including references to *the Bridge*) 12–13, 55, 57, 65, 68, 71–2

Brandywine, River (including references to *the River*) 13, 54, 61, 66, 68, 70, 124. See *Baranduin*.

Bree 7, 9–13, 33, 35–7, 40–5, 48–53, 55–6, 59, 62–3, 65, 69–74, 76, 79, 83, 105–6, 130, 132, 135, 152, 165, 173, 196, 244, 286, 291, 296, 448; *Bree-hill* 41; *Bree-land* 45; *Breelanders* 69, 135

INDEX
471

Bregalad Quickbeam the Ent. 419

Brego Builder of the Golden Hall. Son of Brytta 435, 445; in LR son of Eorl the Young 440, 445

Bridgefields In the Eastfarthing. 33, 39

Broken Sword, The See *Sword that was Broken.*

Brownhay Rhosgobel, home of Radagast. 164, 173

Brown Lands 316, 351, 364. See *Withered Wold.*

Bruinen, River 17, 59, 65, 296, 299; *Ford of Bruinen* (including references to *the Ford*) 13–14, 16, 57, 61, 70, 113, 137, 172. See *Loudwater.*

Brytta Father of Brego. 435, 445; in LR eleventh King of Rohan 440

Buckland 6, 11, 13, 30–1, 53–5, 68, 72, 135, 249; *Horn-call of Buckland* 54

Bucklebury Ferry (including references to *the Ferry*) 13, 55, 70–1

Budgeford In the Eastfarthing. 33, 39

Bundu-shathûr One of the Mountains of Moria (Cloudyhead). 174; *Shathûr* 174. Earlier name *Udushinbar* 432

Burin (1) Son of Balin. 172, 204. (2) Father of Balin. 456–7

Butterbur, Barnabas 10, 34, 37, 40, 42–9, 51–2, 56, 62–3, 73, 77–8, 132, (134), 152, 448; *Barney* 47; later name *Barliman* 77

Buzundush Dwarvish name of the Blackroot river (= Silverlode). 166–7, 241

Bywater 253

Calacirian The Pass of Light. 98, 101; *Carakilian* 93, 95; *Kalakilya* 95

Calenardhon Rohan as a province of Gondor. 450

Calembel (1) Town in Lamedon. 388. (2) See *Calenbel.*

Calenbel Lawn beneath Amon Hen (afterwards *Parth Galen*). 371, 382, 384, 388, 393–4, 401; *Calembel* 384, 387–8. Earlier names *Kelufain* 371, 377, 382, 388; *Forfain* 382

Calendil, Calennel See *(The) Tongue.*

Calenhir, River In Gondor. 312

Caradras 161, 164, 166, 169–71, 174, 188, 215, 247, 257, 296, 306, 367–8, 430; *Caradhras* 166–8, 174. See *Barazinbar, Redhorn, Ruddyhorn.*

Carakilian See *Calacirian.*

Caras Galadon 233, 235, 242, 245–6, 249–50, 256, 258, 261, 265, 279, 285, 289, 354, 363, 367, 431; *Caras Galadhon* 235; *Caras* 367

Carn Dûm 37

Carpenter, Humphrey Biography 66, 187; in *Letters* 90; *The Inklings* 106

Carrock Beorn's 'carrock' 287, 307; *the Great Carrock* (Tolondren) 268–9, 287

472   THE TREASON OF ISENGARD

Cat and the Fiddle, The 40, (64)
Celebdil Silvertine. 174–5, 288, 306. Earlier name *Celebras, Kelebras (the White)* 174, 306, 431
Celeborn See *Keleborn.*
Celebrant, Kelebrant 175, 235, 241, 288; *Field of Celebrant* 450. Earlier names *Celebrin, Celeb(rind)rath* 241. See *Silverlode* (2), *Kibil-nâla.*
Celebras, Kelebras See *Celebdil.*
Celebrimbor 188
Celebrin, Cele(rind)rath See *Celebrant.*
Celegorn (1) Son of Fëanor; also *Celegorm.* 63. (2) Father of Aragorn; see *Kelegorn.*
Celos, River See *Kelos.*
Celtic 420
Cerin (Kerin) Amroth 233–6, 242, 245, 258; *Coron Amroth* 234
Cheerless Lands East of Weathertop. 14
Chetwood 11, 296
Chronology (1) Within the narrative. 10–15, 33, 36, 47, 49, 55–6, 61–3, 68–72, 77–80, 113, 115, 157–8, 163–5, 169, 172, 207, 215, 237, 253, 265, 344–5, 355–7, 361–2, 366–9, 393–4, 398–9, 401, 406–7, 419, 422–3, 425, 434, 438, 450. (2) Years of Middle-earth. 9. (3) Of composition (external dating). 8–9, 40, 67, 70, 79, 96, 261, 362, 379, 406–7, 419–20, 423, 425
Cirith Gorgor 321
Cirith Ungol, Stairs of (later sense) 214; see *Kirith Ungol.*
Cloudyhead Fanuidhol. 174. Earlier name *Horn of Cloud* 174, 432
Cobas Haven Bay north of Dol Amroth. 312, 322
Combe In the Bree-land. 45
Common Speech 223, 239–40, 244, 277, 294, 392; *Common Tongue* 244, 390; *Common Language* 244; *lingua franca* 424; *ordinary speech, language* 227, 244
Company (of the Ring), The 67, 112–14, 161–72 *passim*, 176–80, 183, 188, 190, 192, 199, 201–2, 204, 208, 211–16, 218–19, 223–5, 227, 230–41 *passim*, 245, 247–8, 256–9, 265, 269–93 *passim*, 311, 315, 324–5, 327–30, 345–6, 350, 352, 355, 360–2, 365, 367–72, 375–6, 387, 397, 413, 426–7, 438–9, 445–6. Choosing of the Company 112–15, 161–5, 172–3
Council of Elrond 10, 14, 32, 37, 81, 110, 112–13, 116–17, 126, 129–30, 163, 172, 177, 255, 278, 311, 361, 439, 445–6
Crack(s) of Doom 6, 28, 208
Cram 57, 271
Crebain Crows seen over Hollin. 167
Crickhollow 8–13, 16, 33, 35–6, 53–6, 64, 68–72, 74–6, 111, 135, 152, 173
Cris-caron Pass beneath Caradras. 176

INDEX 473

Cuiviénen The Waters of Awakening. 184, 292

Daedeloth (1) See *Ephel Dúath*. (2) *Dor-Daedeloth*, realm of Morgoth. 175

Daeron See *Dairon*.

Dagorlad Battle Plain. 310, 389, 438, 450. Earlier name *Dagras* 310, 389, 450

Dáin (Ironfoot) 117–18, 141–3, 205; *Dáin of the Iron Hills* 143

Dairon Minstrel of Doriath. 454; runic alphabet, songs of 453–5. Later form *Daeron* 186, 455 (runes of).

Dale 83, 118, 248, 264, 296, 392, 404; runes of 200; Men of 395; language of, = Norse, 424.

Danians, Danian Elves Green-elves. 124, 454–5; *Danas* 454

Dant-ruin Falls in Anduin. 283, 285, 323, 366; *Dant-ruinel* 285, 316, 323, 328, 346, 366. See *Rhain Hills, Rhosfein, Rauros*.

Dark Days, Darkness See *Great Dark(ness)*.

Dark Lord 6–7, 10, 82, 110, 118, 151, 153, 177, 252, 255, 265, 332–3, 372, 418, 427, 434. See *(The) Lord*.

Dark Tower 136, 144, 178, 209, 213, 257, 299, 335, 337–8, 343, 348, 397, 426–8; *the Tower* 216. See *Barad-dûr, (The) Eye*.

Days of Flight 257

Dead Marshes 10, 111, 148, 208, 268, 283, 298–9, 306, 310, 321, 329–30, 346, (352); *Dead Marsh* 148

Deagol (1) Gollum. 23; earlier form *Dígol* 23. (2) Gollum's friend. 23–4, 26–8, 38–9

Deldúath (1) See *Ephel Dúath*. (2) Taur-na-Fuin. 175

Denethor (1) King of the Green-elves. 377, 454. (2) Lord of Minas Tirith. 291, 375–6, 381, 429; *Lament of Denethor* 384

Derndingle Place of the Entmoot. 420. Ealier name *Dernslade* 420

Dígol See *Deagol*.

Dimrill Dale (1) Original sense, troll-country north of Rivendell. 10, 16, 58, 114; see *Entish Land(s)*. (2) Later sense (including references to *the Dale*) 10, 16, 143, 166, 191, 199–201, 203–4, 213, 215, 218–19, 225, 237–8, 253, 280, 286, 289, 372. See *Nanduhirion*.

Dimrill Gate East Gate of Moria. 183

Dimrill Stair (1) The pass beneath Caradras. 164, 166, 168, 171, 174, 224, 240; *Dimrill Pass* 164, *the Pass* 167–8. (2) Later sense, path from Dimrill Dale to the Pass. 164, 235

Dior Thingol's Heir. 110, 136

Distances 57, 65, 165–6, 215, 220–1, 238, 282, 311, 344, 348–9, 356, 365, 389–90, 395, 417

Dolamarth See *Amon Amarth*.

Dol Amroth 299, 310, 312

Dolereb See *Erebor*.

474 THE TREASON OF ISENGARD

Dol Dúgol Dwelling of the Necromancer in Southern Mirkwood (see 298). 178, 233–4, 242, 244, 296, 298, 306. Replaced by *Dol Dúghul* 244, 296, 306, 333, 351, 372; and that by *Dol Guldur* 292

Dol Guldur See *Dol Dúgol*.

Dolmed, Mount In the Blue Mountains. 301

Doriath 110, 124, 331, 453–5; runes of Doriath 456–7

Dorthonion 240, 420. See *Orod-na-Thôn*.

Downs East of Entwash. 320, 391–2, 394, 398–9, 406. See *Barrow-downs*.

Dragon(s) 28, 170; referring to Smaug 22, 142, 160; *dragon-fire* 28

Dream of the Tower, Frodo's 11, 33–6, 56, 130. See *Western Tower*.

Duath See *Ephel Dúath*.

Du-finnion Trotter. 61

Duil Rewinion Hills of the Hunters. 287

Duin Morghul Stream in the Morgul Vale (in LR *Morgulduin*). 312. Also named *Ithilduin* 312

Dúnadan, The (of Aragorn). 83. *Dúnedain* 291. See *Tarkil*.

Dunharrow 320, 447, 450–1. Earlier name *Dunberg* 447, 451

Dunland 167, 320

Durin 141–2, 180, 183–5, 189, 220, 234; *Durin's folk, clan* 143, 156, 246; ~ *axe* 191, 200; ~ *crown* 220; ~ *stone* 203, 219; ~ *tower* 430–1; ~ *bridge* 431

Durin's Bane 143, 185–6, 188–9, 202, 257

Dwarrowdelf Moria. 166, 173, 183, 186

Dwarves At Bag End 20–1; of the Blue Mountains 301; of the Lonely Mountain 117, 142, 155, 160, 424; of Moria 142, 156, 164, 166, 175, 179, 181, 183–6, 188, 218, 225, 247, 263, 304, 431, 455; other references 24, 114, 125, 142–3, 152, 158, 160, 162, 170, 181, 212, 227, 231, 257, 275. War of the Dwarves and the Orcs (Goblins) 142–3; *Western Dwarves* 455; *Dwarf-cities, Dwarf-road* 301; *Dwarf-door* (of Moria) 191, *Dwarf-doors* 187; language 117, 181, 185–6, 455; runes of the Dwarves 186, 200, 452–9. See *Seven Rings*.

Dwarvish 174, 191, 241, 455, 457; *dwarfish* 241; *dwarven* 104, the *Dwarven-door* of Moria 178, 204

Eagle(s) 75–6, 116, 130, 134, 139, 151, 389, 400–1; eagle seen far off 357, 361, 379–80, 385, 387–9, 396–7, 403, 425–6. See *Gwaewar*.

Eärendel 91, 95–6, 99, 102, 108, 110, 266, 290; *Eärendil* 95, 103, 266, 290; *Eärendel's star* 276, the *Evening Star* 266; the *Short Lay of Eärendel: Eärendillinwë* 102–3 (development of the 'Rivendell version' of *Errantry*, 90–105).

Eastemnet 318, 398, 404

INDEX   475

East End   Fangorn. 415–16
Eastfarthing   39
Eastfold   320, 407
East Road   See *(The) Road.*
East Wall   (of Rohan) 396, 401, 405–7; *west-cliff* 425; descent into the plain: *the Ladder, the Stair* 409. See *Sarn Gebir* (1).
Echuinen   See *Nen Echui.*
Edoras   See *Eodoras.*
Egladil   In Lothlórien. 281, 288
elanor   Golden flower of Lothlórien. 234, 243, 284
Eldakar   'Elfhelm' (366), father of Eldamir ('Elfstone'). 276, 360, 362, 366, 404; grandfather of Eldamir 362
Elbereth   Varda. 65, 105; songs to Elbereth 84, 333–4, 336
Eldamar   Elvenhome. 284
Eldamir   Elfstone (Aragorn). 276, 280, 293–4, 360, 362, 366. Transient names: *Eldavel* 366, *Eledon* 276, *Quendemir* 276
Eldar   292
Elder Days   101, 112, 119, 135, 141, 144–5, 150, 152, 169, 247, 262, 271, 403, 416, 429
Elder Edda   204; *Eddaic* 452; *Völuspá* 452
Elder Tongue   Quenya. 84; *old tongue* 83
Eldest   See *Tom Bombadil.*
Elendil   8, 10, 50, 77, 105, 110, 119–24, 126–7, 129, 137, 141, 144–7, 152, 157, 278, 333, 361, 393, 437, 444, 450. Horn of Elendil (*Windbeam*) 344, 349; Sword of Elendil 121–2, 129, 165, 194, 201, 205, 290; see *Branding, Sword that was Broken.*
Elentári   'Queen of Stars', Varda. 285
Elessar   (The) Elfstone. 278, 294, 362, 366, 392
Elf-   *Elf-door*, see *Moria*; *Elf-friend* 123 (Elendil), 227, 277 (Aragorn), 227 (Gimli); *Elf-havens*, see *Grey Havens*; *Elf-king* 122 (Gil-galad); *Elf-letters* 192; *Elf-lords* (of Rivendell) 165; *Elf-rings*, see *Three Rings*; *Elf-speech* 166; *Elf-towers*, see *White Towers*; other compounds 257, 272, 343, 392
Elfhelm   Father of Elfstone (Aragorn). 80, 105, 146, 165, 275–7, 360–2, 366. See *Eldakar.*
Elfstone   (1) The elfstone on the Last Bridge. 59. (2) The Elfstone of Galadriel. 274–8, 290, 431; *Elfstone, Elfstone, bearer of my green stone* 431, 448. (3) Name of Aragorn (see 277–8). 80, 105, 146–8, 165, 176, 204, 236, 239, 244, 250–1, 260, 262, 264–5, 272–3, 275–81, 290–3, 360–2, 366, 370, 378, 381, 392–3, 431, 448; *Elfstan* 276. Transient names: *Erkenbrand* 80; *Elf-friend, Elfmere, Elfspear* 277; *Elfwold* 366. See *Eldamir, Elessar.* (4) As name of Gimli. 275–7
Elostirion   (1) See *Osgiliath.* (2) White Tower on Emyn Beraid. 423
Elrond   6, 10, 13–15, 49, 61, 63, 82–3, 95, 110–23 *passim*, 126–30, 135–6, 138, 142–3, 145–7, 149, 152–65 *passim*, 169, 173, 224,

476   THE TREASON OF ISENGARD

227, 234, 236, 241, 252–5, 257, 265, 278, 286, 326, 361, 375, 390, 402, 423, 438, 445, 451. *Sons of Elrond* 163–4. See *Council of Elrond, Half-elven.*

Elven-   Elven-door, see *Moria*; *Elven-lord* 223–4 (*Amroth*); *Elven-kings* 92, 97, 101, 112, 156, 254, the *Elven-king* (in Mirkwood) 118; *Elven-smiths* 259–60; *Elven-speech, Elven-tongue* 84, 224, 226–7, 239; *Elven-wise* (Noldor) 167. Other compounds 92, 97, 101, 104, 223, 225, 278, 281, 285, 382, 391, 393, 397–8

Elvenhome   92, 97–8, 100. See *Eldamar.*

Elves   Of Gildor's company 10–11, 13, 33, 61, 75, 116, 215, 333, 365; of Hollin 124, 156, 167, 178, 455; of Lindon 123–4; of Lórien (general references, and see *Wood-elves*) 167, 207, 211–13, 222, 225, 237–9, 251, 264, 275, 288, 329, 379; of Mirkwood (and see *Wood-elves*) 148, 163, 237, 242; of Rivendell 14, 82, 84, 124, 128, 147
    Other references: 24, 64, 114, 121, 123, 125, 127, 133, 138, 144, 150, 152, 154, 158, 162, 166, 170–1, 181, 184–5, 212, 231, 233, 243, 248, 255–7, 259, 263, 275, 281, 283, 287, 292, 326, 331, 363, 402–3, 416, 418, 429, 454–5; and the Rings 112, 154–6, 159, 254–6, 259–60; *Western Elves* 239–40, *Elves of the West* 255, 259; *first lord of the Elves* 411

Elvish   (of language and writing) 8, 17, 114, 125, 128, 145, 166, 173, 177, 180–1, 184–5, 191, 200–1, 233, 236, 241, 250, 277, 280, 284, 287–8, 291, 348, 387, 419–20, 454–5, 459; and see under *Elf-, Elven-*. Elvish cited 169, 187, 284–5, 415; Elvish words not given separate entries 114, 173, 181, 188, 226, 233, 238–9, 241–3, 261, 287, 311, 322, 404, 419, 423–4
    (with other reference) 95, 243, 258, 271, 292, 299, 331, 343, 363, 366, 391, 455; *Elvishness* 243

Elwing   100, 102, 104, 110, 136; *Bird-Elwing* 102

Ely   107

Emris, Isle of   Early name of Tol Brandir. 318, 323, 367

Emyn Beraid   The Tower Hills. 130, 423

Emyn Muil   321, 362, 388, 404, 407, 424–5, 432–3. See *Sarn Gebir* (1).

Emyn Rhain (Rain)   The Border Hills. 268–9, 281, 287–8, 313, 315–16, 325; *Rhain Hills* 269, 271, 315

End, The   28, 82

Enedwaith   'Middlemarch'. 296, 304, 403, 439; 'Middle-folk' 403

Enemy, The   50, 52, 64, 77, 83, 118–19, 121, 129, 131–2, 147–9, 153–4, 156, 169, 231–2, 244, 252, 255–6, 270–2, 290, 326, 328, 358–9, 426

Ent-house   415, 417, 419; *Entmoot* 407, 419; *Ent-strides* 417; *Ent-voices* 419

Entish Land(s)   10, 13, 16, 58, 65, 69–70, 152, 164, 250, 299, 306, 413; *Entish Dale(s)* 10, 13, 16–17, 58, 61, 65, 250, 413. Earlier

INDEX

477

names *Hoardale(s)* 10, 16, 114, *Nen fimred* 10, *Nenvithim* 114, *Wolfdale* 10; and see *Dimrill Dale, Ettendales.*

Entmark, Entwood Fangorn. 429

Ents 16, 65, 214, 250, 411–14, 416, 418–21, 428–9, 434–7, 448; *Entwives* 418–20, 448; *Entings* 420; *Song of the Ent and the Entwife* 418, 421; *Entish* 415; 419–21 (marching song). Called *Lone-walkers* 411, *Shepherds of the Trees* 429, *Tree-folk* 411, 413, *treeherds* 416; cf. *tree-giants* 216

Entwade 318, 320, (358), 366, 392, 402, 404

Entwash, River (including references to *the River*) 210, 214, 216, 250, 268–9, 281–3, 288, 315–16, 320, 330, 357–8, 376, 389–92, 396, 398, 409, 414, 429, 442; *mouths* 296, 321, 359; *vale of Entwash* 358. See *Ogodrûth.*

Eodoras 320, 369, 402, 429–34, 437, 440–3, 446, 449–50; earlier from *Eodor* (singular) 318, 402, later form *Edoras* 407, 449

Eofor Father of Eorl the Young. 435. See *Léod.*

Eofored Second Master of the Mark. 444, 446, 450

Éomer Third Master of the Mark. 390, 392–4, 399–403, 405, 407, 410, 424, 434, 436–9, 443, 445–8, 451; *Lord of Rohan* 448

Éomund Father of Éomer and Éowyn. 390, 393, 402, 448, 450–1

éored Body of cavalry in Rohan. 399, 401

Eorl the Young 404–5, 435, 440, 443–5, 449–50; *Eorl the Old* 443; *House of Eorl* 447; *Eorlingas* 447

Éothéod Original name of the Riders of Rohan. 307

Éothain Éomer's esquire. 400–2

Éowin Second Master of the Mark. 393–4, 440

Éowyn Sister of Éomer. 390, 437, 445, 447–8, 450–1; 'Elfsheen' 390

Ephel Dúath 145, 310, 348; earlier *Duath* 310, 343, 345, 348. Transient names *Deldúath, Daedeloth* 169

Erebor The Lonely Mountain. 142, 156, 160, 306. Earlier name *Dolereb* 306

Erceleb See *Mithril.*

Eredhithui The Misty Mountains. 124. Another proposed name *Hithdilias* 124

Eredlindon The Blue Mountains. 123–4, 137, 301, 377. See *Ered Luin.*

Ered Lithui The Ash Mountains. 213, 322, 344–5, 349

Ered Luin The Blue Mountains. 301. See *Eredlindon.*

Ered Myrn See *Black Mountains.*

Ered Orgoroth (Gorgoroth) 145. See *Mountains of Terror.*

Eredvyrn See *Black Mountains.*

Eredwethion Mountains of Shadow. (1) In the Elder Days. 124. (2) Mountains fencing Mordor on the West. 325, 345, 348, 374; replaced by *(Ephel) Duath.*

Ereg, River See *Erui.*

478 THE TREASON OF ISENGARD

Eregion Hollin. 22, 124–5, 173, 455. Earlier name *Nan-eregdos* 166

Eregon, Isle of 'Stone Pinnacle', early name of Tol Brandir. 285, 323, 345, 350, 355–6, 364, 367

Eressëa The Lonely Isle. 123, 454

Erestor 'Half-elf' Kinsman of Elrond. 111, 153–4, 158, 162, 172

Eriador 306, 455

Erion See *Tom Bombadil.*

Erkenbrand See *Elfstone.*

Errantry 84–91, 95, 105–6, 108; metre and nature described 85, 90. See *Eärendel.* Names in *Errantry: Aerie* 88, 95; *Belmarie* 88, 95; *Derion* 89; *Derrilyn* 87, 95; *Faërie* 88; *Fantasie* 88; *Lerion* 89; *Ossory* 86; *Thellamie* 88, 95

Erui, River In Gondor. 312. Earlier form *Ereg* 312

Ethiopians 439

Ethir Anduin 298, 307, 311, 372. Earlier form *Ethir-andon* 298–9

Ettendales 58, 65, 250; *Ettenmoor(s)* 58, 65, 250, 306. Earlier name *Bergrisland* 306. See *Entish Land(s).*

Etymologies In Vol. V. 8, 66, 125, 172, 233, 238–42, 261, 287, 311, 322, 364, 404, 420, 424

Evendim, Hills of 301, 304

Evening Star 252; *Eärendil the Evening Star* 266

Evereven 93, 98, 101, 292, *Evereve* 284; *Evermorning* 91, 94, 97, *Evermorn* 93, 98; *Evernight* 93, 97, 99–100; *Evernoon* 93, 96, 99

Exile, The (of the Noldor) 453–5

Eye, The (in the Dark Tower) 208, 212, 254, 260, 327, 330, 343–4, 346, 366, 373, 396

Falas 103; = *Harfalas* 124

Falls of Rhain, Falls of Rosfein See *Rhain Hills, Rosfein.*

Fangorn (1) Treebeard. 71–2, 390, 412, 428. (2) Fangorn Forest (including references to *the Forest*) 10, 16, 111, 148, 167, 210, 214, 216, 250, 268–9, 282, 288, 293, 330, 347, 369, 389, 391, 394, 396, 401–4, 406, 408–9, 414–15, 417–18, 425, 427–30, 432, 438–9. Called *the Topless Forest* 167, 210, 216; and see *East End, Entmark, Entwood.* Moving trees 418–19, 435–6

Fanuidhol Cloudyhead. 174; *Fanuidol* 306. Earlier name *Fanuiras (the Grey)* 174, 306

Faramir 440

Faraway See *Hill of Faraway.*

Father Christmas Letters 349

Fëanor 125, 255–6, 260, 453. Son(s) of Fëanor 63, 102; House of 180; Alphabet of 453; Rings of 255–6. *Fëanorians* 102, 104

Feast after the final victory 212, 345, 448

Felagund See *Finrod* (2).

Felaróf Eorl's horse. 443

Fellowship, Breaking of the 214, 339

INDEX

479

Fell Winter   54, 169

Ferney, Bill   42, 45–6, 48, 52, 71, 173, 448; his pony, called *Bill*, 9, 165, 171, 173, 180, 448, called *Ferny* 173

Fiery Mountain   6, 213, (250), 328, 339, 343; *Fire Mountain* 28, 207–8, 210–11, 339; *Mountain of Fire* 212, 247, 262, 343; *the Mountain* 216; *Hill of Fire* 373; *the Fire* 153–4, 212. See *Orodruin*.

Finarfin   263

Finduilas   See *Galadriel*.

Finglas   Ent ('Leaflock'). 412

Finrod   (1) Third son of Finwë, later *Finarfin*. 123, 125. (2) *Finrod Felagund*, son of Finarfin. 263; *Felagund* 123, 125; *Inglor* 124–5

Fionwë   Son of Manwë. 198

Fire-well, Sauron's   344; *Sauron's well of fire* 209, 349

First Age   263, 322, 377

First Map   See *Maps*.

Fladrif   Ent ('Skinbark'). 412; earlier *Fladrib* 412

Flói   Companion of Balin in Moria. 191, 200, 204, 458

Fonthill, Funtial   See *Wellinghall*.

Ford of Bruinen   See *Bruinen*.

Ford of Isen   See *Isen*.

Forest River   272–3, 296

Forfain   See *Calenbel*.

Forlond   The North Haven in the Gulf of Lune. 301, 423; earlier form *Forlorn* 301, 423

Forn   See *Tom Bombadil*.

Fornobel   See *Fornost*.

Fornost (Erain)   Norbury (of the Kings). 125, 304. Earlier names *Osforod, the Northburg* 120–1, 125, 129, 147, 304; *Fornobel, the North Burg* or *Northbury* 147, 157, 296, 304

Forochel, Icebay of   301, 322; *Cape of Forochel* 301

Forodwaith   'Northerland'. 296, 304, 306

Forsaken Inn   East of Bree. 296

Foster, Robert   The Complete Guide to Middle-earth. 164, 288

Frána   Wormtongue. 445. (Replaced by *Gríma*.)

Frár   (1) Companion of Glóin at Rivendell. 204. (2) Companion of Balin in Moria. 191, 204

Free Folk   161

Frodo Baggins   See under *Baggins*.

Frumbarn   See *Tom Bombadil*.

Fundin   Father of Balin. 186, 192, 457

Galadriel   218, 233, 236, 246–7, 249–50, 254–86 *passim*, 293, 331, 343, 354, 363, 366, 380, 412–13, 430–1, 433, 440, 445, 448, 451; *The Lady* (also *The Lady of Lothlórien, of the Galadrim*) 233, 236, 246, 248–50, 253–4, 256–8, 263, 266, 270–1, 274–5,

480 THE TREASON OF ISENGARD

277, 279, 290, 358, 363, 368, 393, 402 (*Lady of the Wood*).
Galadriel's Ring, see *Ring of Earth*; her parting gifts 268, 274–8,
280, 282–3, 293 (and see *Elfstone* (2)); her phial, or 'glass of
light' 276, 331–2, 335–6, 438, 440; her songs 279, 281, 284,
286; as wife of Elrond 236. See *(The) Mirror*.
    Earlier names *Finduilas* 249, 261; *Rhien* 249–50, 261–2;
Galdrin 262, *Galdrien* 249–50, 262, *Galadhrien* 249, *Galadrien*
249–50, 252, 367
Galadrim 'Tree-people'. 224–5, 233–4, 236, 239, 243, 246, 256–7,
270, 272, 274–5, 279, 290, 393. Earlier name *Ornelië* ('Tree-
folk') 239
Galathir, Galdaran See *Keleborn*.
Galdor (1) A lord of Gondolin. 172. (2) Elf of Mirkwood (replaced
by *Legolas*). 114–16, 118, 126, 129–30, 141, 143, 148, 157,
161, 172. (3) Elf of the Grey Havens. 130
Galdrien See *Galadriel*.
Galeroc Gandalf's horse. 68, 70, 79, 132, 139, 149. See *Narothal*.
Gamgee, Gaffer 9, 11, 29, 32, 39, 71, 135, 249, 253
Gamgee, Sam 6, 8, 30–1, 42, 47, 50–2, 56–9, 61, 63–4, 69, 75–6,
78–9, 82, 114, 126, 161, 163, 165, 167, 171–3, 179, 183–4,
193–5, 198, 200–1, 208–16, 218–21, 224, 226, 228, 231, 235,
237–8, 243, 248, 253–4, 260, 264–6, 269, 273–5, 279–80, 283,
286–7, 290, 313, 321, 324–57 *passim*, 363–72 *passim*, 375–6,
378, 385–7, 389, 404, 412–13, 427, 437–8, 440, 448, 451. His
songs 56, 59–61, 64, 331, 333–4, 339; his uncle Andy 235
Gandalf 5–16, 19–44, 47–58, 61–3, 65, 68–83, 105, 110–16,
118–19, 125–7, 129–43, 146–73 *passim*, 177–207 *passim*,
210–12, 214–15, 218–19, 227, 233, 236, 244, 247–52, 257–8,
264–6, 268, 271, 278, 289, 298, 311, 329–30, 347, 361, 365–7,
369, 375, 379, (380), 382, 385, 389–90, 394, 396–7, 400–1,
403–5, 409, 411–13, 417, 422–50, 452, 456, 458
    Names in Rohan: *Gondelf* 405, *Hasupada* 402, 405, 424,
Láthspell 444; called *the Grey* (75), 82, 133, etc. (see especially
136), *Greyhame* 405; clad in white 211, 214, 236, 250, 252, 380,
412, 430, 433, *Gandalf the White* 425, *the White Rider* 435, 437;
see *Saruman, White Wizard, Mithrandir*.
    Letters from Gandalf cited 49–50, 63, 77; his tale to the
Council of Elrond 130–6, 149–52
Gap of Rohan 150, 168, 177, 296, 320, 432, 434, 439–40
Gate-stream Sirannon. 178, 187
Gates of Moria See *Moria*.
Germanic 455
Gildor 61; see *Elves*.
Gil-galad 10, 25, 56, 64, 110, 122–5, 126–7, 138, 144, 361, 444,
450. Descendant of Fëanor 125; son of Inglor Felagund 123–4.
The Fall of Gil-galad 65

INDEX

481

Gilraen   Mother of Aragorn. 291

Gilrain, River   In Gondor. 312. See *Lameduin*.

Gilthoniel   Varda. 65

Gimli   114–15, 162, 166, 169–71, 174, 178, 180–1, 183–5, 186–8, 194–203 *passim*, 205, 210–11, 214–25 *passim*, 231–4, 236–8, 246, 248, 257, 263, 268, 271, 275–7, 279, 288–9, 291, 329–30, 347, 350, 354, 375, 378, 381–2, 385–7, 390–2, 395, 397, 399–400, 403–4, 406, 411–13, 425–8, 431, 434, 437–8, 441–3, 449. His song in Moria 183–4; called *elf-friend* 227. See *Elf-stone* (4).

Gladden Fields   114, 224, 248, 307. See *Palath-ledin*.

Gladden River   164, 172

Glamdring   Gandalf's sword. 188, 192, 198, 205

Gloaming-fields   94, 97, 108; *Gloaming-bree* 108

Glóin   81–2, 112–18, 126, 129, 141, 143, 154–5, 158–9, 162, 188, 204, 246, (248), 263–4, 392

Glorfindel   14, 61, 75, 112–13, 116, 153–4, 158, 172

Gnomes   124–5, 158, 256. *Gnomish* 390; *Gnome-elvish* 277, 291

Goatleaf, Harry   Gatekeeper at Bree. 40–2, 44–5, 62, 71, 73–4, 80; Ned his brother (?) 41

Goblins   24–5, 114, 142–3, 155–7, 181, 184, 193, 199, 201, 205, 336–7, 340, 353, 382, 423; *goblin-spirit* 411. On Goblins and Orcs see 199–200, 205. *Goblin Gate* 114 (see *Annerchion*), *Goblins' door* 114. See *Dwarves, Orcs*.

Gods   432. See *Rulers of the World*.

Golden Hall   440–1, 449; described 444. See *Winseld*.

Golden Wood   222, 236, 238, 243, 286, 367, 415

Gollum   7, 9–10, 15, 23–9, 38–9, 83, 111, 116, 118–19, 126, 129–30, 134, 137, 147–8, 157, 208–18 *passim*, 225, (229), 240, 250, (252), 260, 265, 328–32, 339, 343–4, 346–7, 355, 357, 361, 367, 370–1, 410, 437–8. See *Deagol* (1), *Smeagol*.

Gondelf   See *Gandalf*.

Gondolin   110, 172, 454; *Gondolinic Runes* 452

Gondor   146, 215, 312–13, 318, 321–2, 362, 395–6, 400–1, 420, 423, 445, 448, 450; *Gondorian* 437; *South Gondor (Harondor)* 310. See *Ond, Ondor*.

Gore, The   (of Lothlórien) 231, 236, 242, 244, 261, 288, 368. See *Angle; Bennas, Naith, Narthas, Nelen, Nelennas*.

Gorgoroth   208–9, 211, 213–14, 330, 339, 343–5, 347–9, 373, 412, 450; *Gap of Gorgoroth* 208, 213, 313, 339, 347; *mouth of* 438; *valley (vale, plain) of* 144–6, 213, 313, 333; Orc guard-towers 208, 213, (310), 344, 349, 412–13, 437, 440 (see *Gorgos, Nargos*). See *Battles*.

Gorgos   'Dire-castle', eastern guard tower in Kirith Ungol. 344–5, 349. See *Nargos*.

Graidon Hills, Grailaws   See *Sarn Gebir* (1).

482 THE TREASON OF ISENGARD

Great Battle See *Battles.*

Great Dark(ness) 416–17; *the Darkness* 416–17; *the Dark Days* 415–16

Great Journey (of the Eldar) 292

Great Lands 119

Great River (including many references to *the River*) 67, 119, 122–6, 128, 138, 144–5, 213, 231, 234, 244, 261, 267–73, 280–3, 285, 289, 291–2, 315–16, 324–5, 327, 333, 345–6, 350–3, 355–60, 367, 370, 372–3, 379–81, 384, 386, 397–8, 401, 411, 426–7. See *Anduin.*

Great Sea(s) 33, 355, 382, 400; *the Sea(s)* 5, 15, 34–6, 82, 92–3, 95, 98–100, 104, 112, 122–4, 137, 153, 156, 158, 177, 210, 212, 216, 232–3, 244, 248, 252, 255, 257, 265, 272, 284, 295, 311–12, 331–3, 384, 395, 411, 416, 418; *Western Sea* 119, 123, 144

Great War The War of the Ring. 455; *Great Wars* (of the Elder Days) 110

Green, Mr. Frodo's assumed name at Bree. 37, 41–3, 48–9, 71–2, 76, 80. See *Hill of Faraway, Underhill.*

Green Dragon The inn at Bywater. 29

Green-elves 377. See *Danians.*

Green Hills (about the middle course of Anduin) 269–71, 273, 285, 313, 315–16, 325; *Green Ravines* (?) 268–9

Green Isle See *Tol Galen.*

Greenland 216; *a green land* 212, 216

Green Spit See *(The) Tongue.*

green stone of Galadriel, see *Elfstone* (2); of Théoden, 431, 444, 448

Green-tine See *(The) Tongue.*

Greenway 45, 69–71, 74, 79, 131; *Greenway-crossing, Cross Roads* 74, 80; *the old North Road* 164

Grendel (in Beowulf) 65

Greyfax See *Shadowfax.*

Greyflood, River 59, 164, 282, 289, 304, 311–12, 402, 439. Called *the Seventh River* 149, 177, 282, 292, 304, 311. See *Gwathlo, Odothui, Seven Rivers.*

Grey Havens 130, 158, 301, 423; *Havens in the Gulf of Lhûn* 123; *Havens of the High-elves* 244, *Elf-havens* 144; *Havens of Escape* 124, 232, 244; *(the) Havens* 154, 167, 232, 235, 244, 286. See *Mithlond.*

Greylin, River A source-stream of Anduin. 307

Grey Mountains 306

Gríma Wormtongue. 445. See *Frána.*

Grimbeorn the Old Son of Beorn. 248, 263

Grishnákh Orc of Mordor. 408, 410; earlier form *Grishnak* 409

INDEX
483

Gwaewar (the Windlord) 134–5, 139, 151, 426–7, 430; *Gwaiwar* 151. Later name *Gwaihir* 139, 151, 369, 397, 427, 430; *Gwaehir* 430–1

Gwathlo, River The Greyflood. 304, 312

Hador (house of) 455
Halbarad (1) See *Shadowfax*. (2) Ranger, bearer of Aragorn's standard. 157
Haldir Elf of Lórien, guide of the Company. 235–6, 240–1, 246–7, 256, 262, 279–80, 285–6, 288–9; *Halldir* 246, 262. Earlier name *Hathaldir* 227–36, 240–2, 244, 250–1, 262, 288; origin-ally *Haldir* 240, 262
Haleth (house of) 455
Half-elven 120, 128 (Elrond); *Half-elf* 162, 172 (Erestor); *Half-elves* 326
Half-high Hobbits. 122, 125, 128, 146, 232, 244, 400; Old English *Halfheah* etc. 465
Halflings Hobbits. 241, 244, 400, 409
Hall of Fire In Elrond's house. 173
Háma Rider of Rohan. 437, 447
Harad The South. 313, 333
Haradwaith 'Sutherland'. 304, 313, 389; people of the Harad 389, 403, 434, 437, 439–40, 442. See *Harrowland*.
Harfalas Southern coastal regions. 124, 137; *Falas* 124
Harlond The South Haven in the Gulf of Lune. 301, 423; earlier form *Harlorn* 301, 423
Harnen, River 306
Harondor South Gondor. 310
Harrowland, Men of Haradwaith. 435, 439. Other names *Harwan, Silharrows, Men of Sunharrowland* 435, 439
Hasofel 'Greycoat', Aragorn's horse of Rohan. 402, 424, 439; *Hasufel* 424. Earlier name *Windmane* 402
Hasupada 'Greycoat', see *Gandalf*.
Harwan See *Harrowland*.
Hathaldir (1) Hathaldir the Young, companion of Barahir. 240. (2) See *Haldir*.
Havens (1) Havens of Sirion. 102 (and see *Sirion*). (2) North and South Havens in the Gulf of Lune, see *Forlond, Harlond*. (3) See *Grey Havens*. (4) Haven(s) in the South 372
Hazowland See *Sarn Gebir* (1).
Heavenfield 94–5
Helm's Deep 320
Herugrim Théoden's sword. 450
High-elves 128, 144, 180, 244; *high elven-tongue* 84; *High-elvish* 95

484 THE TREASON OF ISENGARD

High Hay The Hedge of Buckland. 10, 173

High Pass Over the Misty Mountains. 114

Hildi 'The Followers', Men. 8

Hill of Faraway, Mr. Frodo's assumed name at Bree. 37, 80. See *Green, Underhill.*

Hill of Hearing Amon Lhaw. 387

Hill of Sight Amon Hen. 387; *Hill of the Eye* 374

Hills of the Hunters See *Duil Rewinion.*

Himling (Hill of) Remaining as an island. 124, 138, 301; *Himring* 137–8

Hithdilias See *Eredhithui.*

Hitherland 94, 97. *Hither Shore(s)* 94, 98, 102, 225, 284

hnau See 411, 419.

Hoardale(s) See *Entish Land(s).*

Hoarwell, River 10, 14, 16–17, 58–9, 69, 152, 164; *Hoarwell springs* 61. See *Mitheithel.*

Hobbiton 6–8, 10–13, 43, 68, 70, 73, 78, 80, 83, 116, 130; the mill 249, 253; the Hill 264, 266

Hobbits (general references) 24–6, 31, 84, 114–15, 228–9, 232, 241, 244, 326, 379, 386, 397. See *Half-high, Halflings.*

Hobbit, The 27, 29, 38–9, 137–8, 142–3, 155–6, 159–60, 172, 187–8, 298, 452

Hollin 124–5, 156, 165–6, 167, 169, 178–9, 204, 365, 367–8. See *Eregion.*

Homecoming of Beorhtnoth, The Early version in rhyme. 106–7

Horn of Cloud See *Cloudyhead.*

Horsemasters 135, 351, 357, 392, 395–6, 398, 412, 430, 433. *Horse-kings* 140; *Horse-lords* 168; *Horsemen (of Rohan)* 148, 208, 210–11, 214, 330, 372, 374, 408–9, 437, 442

Horserland Rohan, 71; *Horsermark* 151

Host of the West 142, 263

Iaur See *Tom Bombadil.*

Icebay of Forochel See *Forochel.*

Idis Théoden's daughter. 445, 447, 450. Suggested name *Ælflæd* 450

Ilkorins 124, 453–5; *Ilkorin* (adjective) 453

Ilmandur Eldest (?) son of Elendil. 119, 122

Ilmarin, Hill of Taniquetil. 92, 95, 97, 100, 109, 292

Ilmen Region of the stars. 122

Imladris Rivendell. 122, 125, 146. Earlier forms *Imladril* 120, 125; *Imladrist* 120, 123–5, 128, 146

Indo-European 455

Inglor Felagund. See *Finrod* (2), *Gil-galad.*

Inglorel See *Nimrodel.*

Ingold Name for a time replacing Aragorn, Elfstone (see 277–8). 80,

INDEX

485

236, 244, 246–7, 256–8, 260, 262, 265, 268, 270–8, 281, 289–90, 292–3, 360, 381

Ingrim   Father of Ingold. 246, 256, 262, 277
Inklings, The   85
Ipswich   106
Iren, River   See *Isen.*
Irongarth   See *Isengard.*
Iron Hills   143, 298, 306–7
Isen, River   177, 187, 241, 298, 304, 306, 311–12, 434, 436–8, 446, 450; *Ford of Isen* 320; *Battle of Isen* 438, 450. Earlier form *Iren* 187, 298, 306
Isengard   36, 72, 132, 139, 149–51, 161, 177, 211–12, 214–16, 296, 320, 333, 347, 372, 379, 382, 386, 390, 400–1, 408, 410, 412, 418–20, 422, 434–7; its original site 132, 139, 149; *Great Gate* 436. Earlier name *Irongarth* (Angrobel) 71–2, 130–1, 139. See *Angrenost.*
Isengarders   408, 435–6
Isenmouthe   213
Isildur   25, 50, 105, 119–21, 123, 126–9, 144–5, 147, 359, 361–2, 364, 366, 393, 395, 444, 450
Isildur's Bane   129–30, 146–8
I sit beside the fire and think   165, 173
Istari   Wizards. 422
Ithil   See *Mithril.*
Ithildin   'Starmoon'. 180, 185, 187–8. Earlier name *Thilevril* 187
Ithilduin   See *Duin Morghul.*
Ithilien   318
Ivy Bush   Inn on the Bywater road. 29

Kalakilya   See *Calacirian.*
Keleborn   246–9, 256–7, 262–3, 267–85 *passim*, 289–91, 293, 315–16, 320, 402, 415, 451; *Celeborn* 218, 261; *The Lord* (also *The Lord of Lothlórien, of the Galadrim*) 233–4, 236, 246–9, 256–7, 263, 270–1, 274, 279, 290. Other names: *Tar* 249, 261; *Aran* 249, 261–2; *(King) Galdaran* 249–50, 262 (*King Galdaran's Mirror* 249–50); *Galathir* 249, *Arafain* 256
Kelebrant   See *Celebrant.*
Kelebras   See *Celebdil.*
Kelegorn   Father of Aragorn. 50–1, 63, 77, 80, 82, 105, 113, 120, 146, 165, 277, 361, 404, 451. See *Arathorn.*
Kelos, River   In Gondor. 312; *Celos* 322
Kelufain   See *Calenbel.*
Kerin Amroth   See *Cerin Amroth.*
Kerin Muil   See *Nen-uinel.*
Khazad-dûm   117, 125, 143, 166, 185–6, 199, 264, 266, 304, 333, 430, 457; *Kazaddūm* 457–8; the Bridge in Khazad-dûm 186,

486   THE TREASON OF ISENGARD

190, 197–200, 203, 206, 215, 236, 247, 257, 266, 422, 430, 446 (*Durin's Bridge* 431). See *Dwarrowdelf, Moria.*
Kheled-zâram   Mirrormere. 166–7, 174, 219–20, 237, 275, 290
Khuzdul   174
Kibil-nâla   Silverlode. 174–5, 241, 290
Kings from over the Sea   82; *Kings of Men* 185, 400
Kiril, River   In Gondor. 312
Kirith Ungol   The great pass into Mordor (see 333, 344). (214), 283, 285, 310, 313, 321–2, 329–30, 333–4, 344, 346–9, 437–8, 450; *Kirith* 344; *gates of* 438; translated '*Spider Glen*' 330. See *Cirith Ungol.*
Kôpas Alqaluntë   322
Kôr   95

Lake-town   187
Lamben   See *(The) Tongue.*
Lamedon   Region of Gondor. 312, 388
Lameduin, River   In Gondor. (Afterwards *Gilrain.*) 312
Land of Five Streams   310–11. See *Lebennin.*
Land of Seven Streams   See *Lebennin, Seven Rivers.*
Land of Shadow   Mordor. 178
Langwell, River   A source-stream of Anduin. 307
Larmindon   See *Amon Lhaw.*
Last Alliance   122, (123), 126–7, 138, 144–5, 361. See *Battles.*
Last Bridge   See *Mitheithel.*
Láthspell   'Ill-news'. See *Gandalf.*
Lay of Leithian   108
Leaflock   Ent. 412. See *Finglas.*
Lebennin   'Land of Five/Seven Streams'. 310–12, 318, 322
Leeds, University of   59
Lefnui, River   In Gondor. 298, 307, 311–12; earlier *Lhefneg* 'fifth' 312
Legolas   (1) Legolas Greenleaf of Gondolin. 172. (2) Elf of Mirkwood. 129, 141, 148, 157, 161–2, 167, 169–72, 180, 193–4, 197–8, 200, 203, 210–33 *passim*, 237–40, 242, 246, 248, 251, 256–8, 263, 268, 271–4, 279, 289, 291–2, 329–30, 347, 353–5, 360, 363, 365, 378, 381–2, 385–90, 392, 395–7, 399, 402–3, 406, 411–13, 425–9, 431–2, 434, 437–9, 441–3, 446, 449; called *Greenleaf* 392, 431
Lembas   'waybread'. 271, 279, 398
Léod   Father of Eorl the Young. 440. See *Eofor.*
Letters of J. R. R. Tolkien, The   66, 90, 106, 173, 299, 315, 406–7, 410, 413, 422, 432; other letters 85, 89, 107, 452
Levin-tree   94–5; *Tree of Lightning* 99
Lewis, C. S.   85; 419 (*Out of the Silent Planet*).
Lhammas, The   138, 453

INDEX
487

Lhefneg, River See *Lefnui.*

Lhûn 'Blue River' (124). 123–4, 144; written *Lune* 301, 415–16. *Gulf of Lhûn* 123–4; written *Lune* 301. *Mountains of Lune* 416. See *Lindon.*

Limlight, River 318, 320, 356–7, 365

Lindar The First Kindred of the Elves. 453

Lindir Elf of Rivendell. 84

Lindon 123; *North and South Lindon* 124 (*Forlindon* and *Harlindon* on the First Map, 302). *Gulf of Lindon* 144

Linglor, Linglorel See *Nimrodel.*

Lithlad 'Plain of Ash'. 208, 213, 313

Little Folk Hobbits. 171, 247, 249

Lofar Dwarf who remained at Bag End. 21

Lonely Isle, Lonely Island 95, 97, 100. See *Eressëa.*

Lonely Mountain (also *the Mountain*) 82, 117, 142, 159–60, 306, 329; *King under the Mountain* 160. See *Erebor.*

Lóni Companion of Balin in Moria. 191, 204

Lords of the West 422

Lord, The Sauron. 112, 134, 151, 155, 262, 271, 338, 341, 347; *Lord of the Ring(s)* 136; *Lord of Mordor* 117, 351, 434; *Great One* 332, 334, *Mighty One* 332. See *Dark Lord.*

Loremasters 26

Lórien See *Lothlórien. Nelen-Lórien* 234, 236, 244; (?) *Naith-Lórien* 267, 287; (the ancient) *Forest of Lórien* 281–2, 292

Lórinand Lórien. 292

Lost Land Númenor. 400

Lothlann (1) Great plain north of the Marches of Maidros in the Elder Days. 313. (2) Region south of Mordor. 313

Lothlórien (including references to *Lórien*) 67, 167, 186, 207, 211–12, 214–15, 218, 220–5, 229, 233–7, 239–43, 246–53, 256, 259, 261, 263, 270–1, 273, 281–92 *passim*, 313, 315, 333, 343, 351, 353–5, 358, 363–9, 372, 379, 382, 385–6, 393, 397–8, 401, 405, 415–17, 424, 427, 430, 433, 443, 448, 451. References to Time in Lothlórien 249, 284–6, 354–5, 358, 363, 366–9, 431. Cloaks of Lothlórien 269, 271–2, 278–9, 285, 343, 348, 386, 391, 393–4, 397–8, (401), 408; leaf-brooches 272, 279, 283, 285, 397–8, 401, 408; making of rope 249, 251, 280

Loudwater, River 57, 59, 65, 296. See *Bruinen.*

Lugbúrz The Dark Tower. 409

Lugdush Orc of Isengard. 409

Lune See *Lhûn.*

Lúthien 58, 110, 123, 136, 173, 271

Maggot, Farmer 10

Malacandra In C. S. Lewis, *Out of the Silent Planet.* 419

488   THE TREASON OF ISENGARD

Maldon, Battle of 106

Malevarn See *Baranduin.*

mallorn, mallorn-trees 217, (218), 226–7, 230, 233–4, 239, 245, 249, 251, 280, 291; plural *mellyrn* 233; *mallorn bark* 249, 251

Manwë 198

Maps In *The Hobbit*: Thrór's Map 159–60, 452; Wilderland 172, 298. Maps of LR: Shire maps 39, 299, 424; the First Map 65–6, 137, 145, 157, 172, 187, 213, 238, 287, 295–323, 348–9, 364, 389, 404, 423, 440, 450, described 295–6, 299–300; 1943 map 299–301, 304, 306–7, 310, 313, 318, 320–2, 348–9; later maps 301, 307, 312, 321–2; published maps 213, 301, 307, 321–2, 424. First *Silmarillion* map 287, second 301

Marhath (Marhad) Second Master of the Mark. 390, 440; Fourth Master 400, 440. Other unused names in *Mar-* 390

Marish, The 249

Mark, The Rohan. 399–400, 402, 419, 433, 441; *Lord of the Mark* 433, 441; *King of the Mark* 440. See *Riddermark.*

Marquette University 18, 40, 53, 94, 103, 136, 187, 206

Marshals of the Mark 399

Masters of the Mark 399. *First Master* (Théoden) 400; *Second Master*: Marhath 390, Éowin 393, unnamed 435, 437, 450, Eofored 444, 446, 450; *Third Master* (Éomer) 393, 410; *Fourth Master* (Marhath) 400, 440. *Master of Rohan* (Théoden) 433. See *Mark, Riddermark.*

Matterhorn 175

Mauhur Orc of Isengard. 410

Mazarbul Book of Mazarbul 125, 190–2, 200–1, 205, (247, 257), 457–9. *Chamber of Mazarbul* 67, 188, 190, 192, 195–6, 199–202, 209, 215, 237, 247, 257, 458; *Chamber of Records* 200

Mearas Noblest horses of Rohan. 400–1, 405

Meduarn, Meodarn See *Winseld.*

Melian 265–6

Melineth 93, 95, 99

Men Men of the North 6, 120, 128, 158, 390, 395; of the East 286, 372, 455; of the South 372, 434; of the West, see *Númenórean(s)*, *Westernesse.* Other references 84, 113–14, 125, 127, 133, 144, 152, 158, 162, 181, 184, 186, 286, 291, 326, 331, 363, 386 (*Men of the cities*), 395, 416, 418–19, 455

Meriadoc Brandybuck, Merry See under *Brandybuck.*

Meril-i-Turinqi The Lady of Tol Eressëa. 242

Merryburn 91, 93, 96, 98

Methedras 320, 404, 426–7. Earlier names *Methen Amon* 391, 404; *Methendol* 404

Michel Delving 41, 185; *the Town Burrow* 41; *the Museum, Mathom-house* 185

Middle Days 150

INDEX

Middle-earth 26, 82, 101, 104, 112, 117, 123–4, 127, 129, 144–5, 154, 158, 161, 180, 241, 248, 250–1, 255, 257, 259, 263, 266, 295, 429, 452; *the Middle-earth* 121, 123–4, 233

Middle English 65

Middlemarch 296, 304, 320, 403, 439; *men of the Middlemarch* 434. See *Enedwaith*.

Midgewater Marshes 11, 44, 56, 296

Minas Anor 119–21, 123, 125–7, 129, 144–6, 298–9, 333 (error for *Ithil*), 347, 366; *Tower of the Sun* 119, *of the Setting Sun* 119, 144; *City of the Sun* 333

Minas Ithil 119–20, 123, 125–7, 144–5, 212, 298–9, 333, 347, 366 (error for *Anor*); *Tower of the Moon* 119, 384, *of the Rising Moon* 119, 144; *City of the Moon* 333; *Lord of Minas Ithil* (Aragorn) 212

Minas Morgol 116, 120–1, 125, 127–8, 138, 145–7, 151, 209, 212, 214–5, 298–9, 310, 339; *Minas Morghul* 146–7, 389; *Minas Morgul* (also *Morgul*) 215, 310, 322, 332–3, 335, 338–40, 344–5, 347–9, 366, 372, 412–13, 440; the City described 333, 337.

City of Sorcery 343, *Tower of Sorcery* 127; *the Tall Tower* 333, *the Loathly Tower* 336, 338, 343, and cf. 372; *Captain of Morgul* 338; *Morgul-spells* 128; *the Gate* 337–8, 340–1, 343, 372, *the Sentinels* 337–8, 340–1, 343, 348

Minas Tirith 115–16, 120–2, 125–9, 147, 151, 154, 157, 161–2, 165, 177, 207, 210–14, 216, 248, 258, 268, 270–1, 278, 281–2, 287, 289, 298–9, 307, 310–11, 320, 322, 326, 328–30, 333, 336, 345, 347, 358–9, 366, 370–2, 375–6, 378, 385, 389, 392, 400, 412–13, 418, 429, 434–5, 437–40, 442, 449. Early names *Minas-berel* 115–16, *Minas-ond* 115, *Minas Giliath* 116, *Minas rhain* 116, 287, *Othrain* 116

Tower of Guard 127, 381; *the white tower* 384; *Lord of Minas Tirith* 128, 210–11, 214, 378, *Lords of* 395; earliest history of 116, 119–21, 127; prophecies in, prophetic verse 116, 120, 122, 125, 127–9, 146, 400. See *Mundbeorg*.

Mindolluin, Mount 310, 322

Mirkwood 106, 114–16, 118–19, 126, 131, 138, 143, 147–8, 163, 211, 230, 237–8, 264, 272, 295–6, 298, 306, 331, 333, 372, 395, 402, 431, 442–3, 451; called *the Great* 296, 402; *Southern Mirkwood* 111, 177–8, 234, 296, 298, 351. See *Mountains of Mirkwood*.

Mirrormere 166–7, 184, 191, 203–4, 218–20, 237, 306. See *Nen Cenedril, Nen Echui*

Mirror, The Of King Galdaran 249–50; of Galadriel (Galadrien) 251, 253–4, 256, 259–60, 264–6, 272, 289, 367, 379–80, 412–13

miruvor Cordial of Elrond. 169

490   THE TREASON OF ISENGARD

Misty Mountains (including references to *the Mountains*) 10, 16, 111, 117, 122, 124, 134, 139, 142, 149, 151, 166, 168, 172, 177, 203, 218–20, 222, 225–6, 228, 230, 232–3, 235, 238–9, 247, 257, 262–4, 289, 298, 306, 320, 333, 347, 351, 356, 372, 378, 391, 402, 404, 419, 426–7. See *Eredhithui*.

Mitheithel, River 14, 17, 58, 299; *Bridge of Mitheithel, Last Bridge* 14, 17, 58–9, 61. See *Hoarwell*.

Mithlond The Grey Havens (see 423). 301, 423

Mithrandir Gandalf. 251, 264, 432

Mithril 98, 101, 104, 137, 184–5, 188, 191, 200–1; *mithril-coat, -corslet, -mail, -rings* 185, 211, 218, 221, 331, 336; called *Moria-silver* 185, 188, *true-silver* 185, 191, 200, 459. Early names *Erceleb* 184, *Ithil* 184, *Thilevril* 184, 188

Moon, The 37, 92–4, 98, 101, 212, 284; in design on the West Gate of Moria 180–1, 187; phases of the Moon 167–8, 179–80, 187, 219, 228, 253, 343–4, 353–4, 357–8, 363, 365–9, 391; phases those of 1941–2, 369, 387; runic Moon-letters 452

Morannon 213; *the Black Gate* 321

Mordor 10, 68, 72–3, 111, 117–18, 121, 123, 127, 129–30, 135–6, 139, 144–5, 148, 165, 169, 186, 205, 210, 212–15, 247, 262–3, 289, 298, 310, 322, 325, 333, 339, 343, 345, 347–9, 351, 360, 366, 371, 374, 381–2, 385, 389, 408–10, 413, 418, 423, 427, 430, 434–5, 450; *the Black Country* 123, 144; *passes of Mordor* 281, 283, 285, 313, 320–1, 352, *gates of Mordor* 285, 321, 324; the host of Mordor riding out 208, 212–13, 345. See *(The) Lord, Mountains of Mordor*.

Morgoth 122, 142, 175, 256, 260, 454

Moria (including references to *the Mines of Moria, the Mines*) 5, 10, 16, 67, 115, 117, 125, 129, 141–3, 155–6, 158, 160–1, 166–8, 173, 175, 178–9, 181, 183–6, 188, 190, 192, 199–202, 204, 206, 215, 218–21, 224, 227–8, 235, 240, 247, 250, 257, 263–4, 266, 278, 280, 333, 354, 367–9, 378–9, 381, 401, 422, 430, 432, 446, 452, 455–8. *Black Gulf, Black Pit* 166, 173. *Lords of Moria* 178; *Runes of Moria* 200, 455. See *Balin*; *Khazad-dûm*; *Mithril*; *Mountains of Moria*.

Gates (Doors) of Moria: 184–5, 204, 206, 219, 372. In the West: 178, 181, 215; two entrances, the Elven-door and the Dwarven-door 178, 190–1, 201, 204–5. In the East: 143, 178, 191, 199, 201, 204, 219–22, 238, 372; *Dimrill Gate* 183; *Great Gate(s)* 191, 199. Design on the West Gate 180–1, 187–8. For the Bridge in Moria see *Khazad-dûm*. *Deep(s) of Moria* 191–2, 194, 211, 432; *Third Deep* 191, 201, 459

Mornvenniath See *Black Mountains*.

Morthond, River Blackroot. (1) Earlier name of Silverlode. 166–7, 218, 222, 230–1, 235, 237. (2) River of Gondor. 310–12, 316. See *Blackroot*.

INDEX

491

Mountain of Fire   See *Fiery Mountain*.

Mountains of Lune   See *Lhûn*.

Mountains of Mirkwood   119

Mountains of Mordor   299, 327, 374; *mountain-fences of Mordor* 450

Mountains of Moria   166–7, 174, (203, 219), 237, 288, 306

Mountains of Shadow   West-fences of Mordor. (Including references to *the Mountains*) 144–5, 169, 310, 312, 322, 333, 337, 343, 348–9, 374. See *Eredwethion* (2).

Mountains of Terror   North of Doriath. 145, 331. See *Ered Orgoroth*.

Mountains of the South   See *Black Mountains*.

Mountains of the West   The Mountains of Valinor. 263

Mountains of Valinor   See *Valinor*.

Mount Doom   209, 343–5, 348–9, 373; spelt *Mount Dûm* 373. See *Amon Amarth*.

Mount Fang   Orthanc. 419

Mundbeorg   Name in Rohan of Minas Tirith (in LR *Mundburg*). 449. Other suggested names *Heatorras, G(i)emenburg* 449

Náin   (1) Náin I, son of Durin. 143. (2) Father of Dáin. 143

Naith (of Lórien)   Of varying application (see 287–8). 244, 267–8, 280, 287–8

Náli   Companion of Balin in Moria. 191, 204

Namárië   284–5

Nandorin   Green-elven. 292

Nanduhirion   Dimrill Dale. 166, 174; earlier form *Nanduhiriath* 174

Nan-eregdos   See *Eregion*.

Nan Gurunír   Valley of Saruman. 420

Nan Tathren   Land of Willows. 95. Cf. *Weepingwillow Pool(s)* 91, 94–5, 97. See *Tasarinan*.

Narghil (Nargil) Pass   In the southern mountains of Mordor. 310

Nargos   Western guard-tower in Kirith Ungol. 344, 349. See *Gorgos*.

Nargothrond   454

Narog, River   287

Narothal   Gandalf's horse. 70. See *Galeroc*.

Narrow Ice   100

Narthas   The Gore of Lórien. 236, 244, 288

Narvi   Dwarf of Moria. 188; *Narfi* 188

Nazgûl   149, 213, 365, 389, 409, 451. See *Black Riders, the Nine, Ringwraiths, Vultures*.

Necromancer, The   48, 83, 147, 154–5, 159, 234, 244, 255

Neldoreth   (1) The northern forest of Doriath. 322. (2) Forest bordering the Sea of Rhûnaer. 307

Nelen, Nelen-Lórien   The Gore of Lórien (and other applications). 231, 234, 236, 242–4, 261, 268, 288

492   THE TREASON OF ISENGARD

Nelennas   The Gore of Lórien. 236, 241–2, 245, 261, 288; name of Caras Galadon (?) 233, 242, 261

Nen Cenedril   Mirrormere. 184

Nen Echui   (1) Cuiviénen. 184. (2) Mirrormere. 184; also *Echuinen* 184

Nen fimred   See *Entish Land(s)*.

Nenuial   Lake beneath the Hills of Evendim. 301

Nen-uinel   The great lake in Anduin north of Tol Brandir (in LR *Nen Hithoel*). 364; unnamed 361; another name *Kerin-muil* 364

Nenvithim   See *Entish Land(s)*.

nifredil   Pale green flower of Lothlórien. 233–4; flowers on the burial mounds at Eodoras 443

Nimbrethil   Birchwoods in Arvernien. 99, 103

Nimladel, Nimlorel, Nimlothel   See *Nimrodel*.

Nimrodel (references both to the Elf of Lórien and to the stream) 223, 228–31, 233, 235, 239–40, 258, 265, 292, 296, 354. Earlier names *Inglorel* 223, *Linglor* 222, 239; *Linglorel* 223–6, 237, 239; *Nimladel* 223, 239; *Nimlorel* 223, 239; *Nimlothel* 223; and see *Taiglin*. First mention of the stream, unnamed, 221; the bridge 221–2

Nindalf   The Wetwang. 281, 283, 307, 315–16. Earlier name *Palath Nenui* 268, 287, 299, 313

Nine Rings (of Men)   149, 259

Nine, The   (Riders, Ringwraiths) 50, 73, 116, 131–2, 135, 149, 151–2, 161–2, 177, 311. *Chief of the Nine*, see *Black Riders*.

Nob   Servant at *The Prancing Pony*. 46, 48

Nobottle   Village in the Westfarthing. 424

Nogrod   Dwarf-city in Eredlindon. 301

Noldor   167 (the Elven-wise), 263, 453–5

Noldorin   (of language and writing) 173, 184, 238, 242, 287, 311, 322, 404, 453–7; with other reference 454

Nomenlands   Also *Nomen's Land*, *Noman-land(s)*, *No Man's Land*. 281, 283, 310, 320–1, 325, 345, 352. See *Úvanwaith*.

Norbury of the Kings; *North Burg*, *Northbury*   See *Fornost*.

North Downs   296, 301, 304

Northerland   296, 304. See *Forodwaith*.

North Haven   301, 423. See *Forlond*.

North Kingdom   Arnor. 59; *Northland* 120

Northmen   Vikings. 106

North Road   164. See *Greenway*.

North Sea   (of Middle-earth) 301

North Stair   Portage-way beside Rauros. 359, 370

Númenor   82–3, 106, 119, 122–3, 144; *Númenórë* 124; Men of Númenor in Middle-earth 127, 158, 374; tongue of Númenor 390; *The Fall of Númenor* (title) 111, 122–3, 137, 301. See *Lost Land*, *Westernesse*.

INDEX

493

Númenóreans 84, 95, 121, 124, 145; *Men of the West* 83, 120–1, 157, *Men that came out of the Sea* 416. Númenórean kingdoms in Middle-earth 117, 121, 144

Odothui Seventh River (Greyflood); changed from *Odotheg.* 312. See *Greyflood.*
Ogodrûth, River Entwash. 250, 268–9, 288
Óin Companion of Balin in Moria. 82, 117, 141–2, 191, 201, 459
Oiolossë Taniquetil. 285
Old English 16, 56, 61, 65, 78, 106, 150, 158, 244, 250, 274, 288, 290, 298, 349, 387, 402, 405, 409, 420, 423–5, 439, 442–3, 446, 449–50, 455–6; *Anglo-Saxon* 405, 413, 452
Old Forest 6, 10, 36, 69, 72–3, 111, 152, 402, 415, 417
Old Man Willow 36
Old Norse 138, 204, 306, 405, 424, 455
Ond Original name of Gondor. 110, 115–16, 122, 126–8, 146–7, 157, 177, 187, 216, 241, 299, 310–11; *King of Ond* 216, 376
Ondor Replaced *Ond.* 123, 144, 146–7, 157, 187, 270, 272–3, 278, 289, 293, 310, 318, 333, 358–60, 362, 376, 381–2, 390, 393, 395, 401, 418, 420, 423; *Ondor! Ondor! Between the Mountains and the Sea* 395; tongue of Ondor 390; throne of Ondor 395–6, 404; name changed to *Gondor* 423. See *Staniland.*
Orald, Oreald, Orold See *Tom Bombadil.*
Orcs (in many instances used attributively, as *orc-arrow, -chieftain, -draught, -prints, -trail, -work,* etc.) 71, 119, 134–5, 142–3, 156, 181, 184–5, 191, 193–4, 197–203, 205, 207–9, 213–14, 218–19, 221, 224, 227, 229, 231, 233, 241, 248, 264, 273, 281, 331–41, 343–4, 347, 349, 351, 353, 357–8, 365, 368–9, 371–2, 376–402 *passim,* 405–10, 418, 424, 427, 434, 437–8, 440, 458–9; *orch,* plural *yrch,* 229
    With reference to place of origin (Isengard, Mordor, Moria) 378–9, 381–2, 401, 408–9, 434; and see *Isengarders. Black Orcs* 193, 347; *great Orcs* 408; language 181, 202, 336, 424. See *Dwarves, Goblins.*
Orfalas 108
Orfin See *Orofin.*
Ori Companion of Balin in Moria. 82, 117, 141–2, 201, 459
Ornelië See *Galadrim.*
Orod-na-Thôn Dorthonion. 420. Earlier *Orod Thon, Orod Thuin* 420
Orodruin 28, 39, 209, 247, 262–3, 313, 438; *Orodnaur* 39. See *Fiery Mountain.*
Orofin Elf of Lórien, companion of Hathaldir (Haldir). 235, 279, 285; earlier form *Orfin* 227, 229, 235–6; in LR *Orophin,* 236. Earlier names of this Elf *Rhimdir, Rhimlath* 240

494   THE TREASON OF ISENGARD

Orthanc   36, 105, 130, 132–4, 139, 150–1, 372, 400, 404, 419, 426, 436; on the name see 419.
Osforod   See *Fornost*.
Osgiliath   119, 122, 125–8, 138, 144–5, 147, 211, 267, 271–2, 290, 298, 307, 310, 322, 358, 360, 382, 389, 423–4, 440; 'Fort(ress) of Stars' 119, 126, 144. *Bridges of Osgiliath* 267, 271–2, 290. Name changed to *Elostirion* 389, 423, 435, 440; and to *Ostechain* 424
Ossiriand   124, 271, 311, 377, 454
Ostechain   See *Osgiliath*.
Othrain   See *Minas Tirith*.
Overhill   Village in the Westfarthing. 30
Oxford   *Oxford English Dictionary* 64; *Oxford Magazine* 86, 89–90, 106, 108; *Oxford University* 67, 107, 362, 377

palantír   423
Palath-ledin   The Gladden Fields. 114
Palath Nenui   See *Nindalf*.
Parth Galen   Lawn beneath Amon Hen. 377, 382. See *Calenbel*.
Party, The   5, 8, 15, 21, 38, 62
Pelennor Fields, Battle of the   157
Pelóri   The Mountains of Valinor. 95
Pengolod of Gondolin   454–5
Pensarn   The rapids in Anduin. 353, 357–8, 360, 364, 366, 370. Replaced by *Ruinel* 366. See *Sarn Ruin, Sarn Gebir* (2).
Peregrin Took, Pippin   See under *Took*.
Pictures by J. R. R. Tolkien   457
Pillars of the Kings   See *Argonath*.
Pinnath Gelin   Hills in the west of Gondor. 312
Poros, River   'Boundary'. 312
Prancing Pony, The   (including references to *The Pony* and *the inn*) 11, 13, 16, 33, 36, 40–5, 48–9, 52–3, 55–6, 59, 62–3, 69–71, 74, 83, 106, 116, 196
Precious, The   The Ring. 332
Pudda   Precursor of Torhthelm (Totta) in *The Homecoming of Beorhtnoth*. 106–7

Qendemir   See *Eldamir*.
Qendi   453
Quenta   *Quenta Noldorinwa* 96. *Quenta Silmarillion* 63, 95, 115–16, 138, 256, 453–4. See *(The) Silmarillion*.
Quenya   174, 242, 291, 311, 322; *Qenya* 453. See *Elder Tongue*.
Quest, The   115, 248–9, 269–70, 289, 329, 371, 422, 445

INDEX

495

Radagast 73, 76, 78, 80, 131–4, 136, 138–9, 149, 164, 173, 177, 212, 311; *the Grey* 132, 136, *the Brown* 132–3, 136, 173

Ramathor, Ramathir See *Belfalas.*

Ranger(s) 6–7, 10, 48–9, 56–8, 63–4, 75–6, 79, 82, 157, 379, 393, 399

Rateliff, John 159

Rauros 'Rush-rain' or 'Roar-rain' (285). 285, 296, 316, 318, 346, 350, 355–6, 358–9, 361, 364, 370, 373, 378, 413. For earlier names see *Rhain Hills, Rhosfein, Dant-ruin.*

Red Book (of Westmarch) 95

Red Fire The fire of the Balrog. 203; *the red flame* 198

Redhorn Caradras. 166. *Redhorn Gate* 164, 240; *Redhorn Pass* 164, 174, 240; *Red Pass* 161

Redway, River Original name of the river flowing out of Dimrill Dale. 114, 164, 166, 173, 190, 213, 296, 306; see *Blackroot, Siverlode.* Elvish name *Ruinnel* 114

Rhain Hills See *Emyn Rhain. Falls of Rhain* 273, 315; see *Rhosfein.*

Rhibdath, River See *Rushdown.*

Rhien See *Galadriel.*

Rhimbron Elf of Lórien, companion of Hathaldir (Haldir). 227, 230–1, 236, 240. Replaced by *Rhomrin, Romrin* 236, and finally *Rúmil* 240

Rhimdad, Rhimdath, River See *Rushdown.*

Rhimdir, Rhimlath See *Orofin.*

Rhomrin See *Rhimbron.*

Rhosfein, Rosfein, Falls of In Anduin. *(Rosfein)* 273, (281), 282, 285, 315; *cataracts of Rhosfein* 283, 285. See *Dant-ruin, Rhain Hills, Rauros.*

Rhosgobel Home of Radagast in Mirkwood. 149, 164, 172–3, 296, 306. See *Brownhay.*

Rhovanion Wilderland. 296; *Rhovannion* 318

Rhûn The East. 296, 307, 333; *Rhûn the Great* 434. *Sea of Rhûn* 307, 333, 347

Rhûnaer, Sea of 296, 298, 306–7, 347. On *Rhûn* and *Rhûnaer* see 307

Rían Mother of Tuor. 261

Riddermark, The 135, 139, 148, 151, 351, 393. See *Horserland, (The) Mark, Rohan.*

Riddle-game 24–5, 38, 147

Riders (1) See *Black Riders.* (2) Riders of Rohan. 390, 392–5, 399–400, 402, 404–6, 409–10, 449

Ringbearer 114, 168, 208, 265–6, 327, 329, 332, 334, 337, 345–7, 389, 397; *the Bearer* 338

Ringhay Crickhollow. 173

Ringlo, River In Gondor. 311–12

Ringmaker, The 25

496   THE TREASON OF ISENGARD

Ring of Earth   Galadriel's Ring. 252, 255, 260–1, 265, 279; other references 254, 266, 358, 363, 366. *Ring of Sea* 255. *Ring of Sky* 255.

Rings   22–3, 26, 38, 112, 117, 130, 132, 138, 149, 155, 255, 259; *Rings of Fëanor* 255–6; *Saruman's Ring* 133, 138; 'ring from Mazarbul' 209, 215

Rings of Power   22, 28, 117, 149, 255, 259–60; *the Great Rings* 22. Of the *Rings of Power* in *The Silmarillion* 138, 144–6, 260. See *Three Rings, Seven Rings, Nine Rings.*

Ring, The   5–6, 8, 13, 19–28, 38, 49–51, 54–5, 63, 69, 71, 77, 81–3, 105, 110–12, 114, 117–18, 121, 126–7, 129–30, 143–4, 146–8, 153–4, 157–8, 161–2, 207–18 *passim*, 254–5, 269, 271, 325–48 *passim*, 366, 370, 372–4, 378–80, 385, 426–7, 437–8, 444. The Ring confers understanding of Orc-speech 332, 337, 340; the Ring worn on Amon Hen 373–4, 381; *the Ring* as title of the work 407

Ring, The One   26, 148–9, 154, 237, 255, 259–60, 265, 286; *the One Treasure* 337, *the Great Ring* 154. See *Ruling Ring.*

Ringwraiths   (also *Wraiths*) 14, 49, 72–3, 78, 130–1, 149, 158, 162, 208, 210, 254, 332, 335, 343, 422–3. Borne upon vultures, see *Vultures; the Winged Messenger* 428. See *Black Riders, Nazgûl, (The) Nine.*

Rivendell   5–10, 13–14, 18, 31, 49, 57, 59, 61–3, 65–6, 68–70, 72–3, 75–6, 80–4, 95, 116, 120, 124–5, 127–8, 130, 134, 136, 140, 146, 152–3, 156–8, 161, 164–5, 169, 173, 183, 212, 221, 223, 238, 247–50, 255, 258, 263–4, 280, 286, 290, 292, 311, 361, 367–9, 390, 401, 405, 409, 417, 423, 438–9, 445, 451. See *Imladris.*

Riven River, Rivendell River   59

Road Goes Ever On, The   85

Road, The   7, 14, 29–30, 42, 52, 57, 59, 61, 69, 71–4, 79, 83, 296; *East Road* 9, 13, 17

Rohan   68, 71–2, 79, 130, 135–6, 139, 144, 148, 151–2, 177, 210, 212, 214–15, 232, 282–3, 293, 311, 322, 330, 351, 357–8, 372, 385–8, 390, 393–412 *passim*, 419, 424, 426, 429–30, 433–5, 437, 441, 443–6, 448–50. *Master of Rohan* 386; tongue of Rohan 419, 424, 442–3. See *Horseland, (The) Mark, (The) Riddermark; Gap of Rohan, Wold of Rohan.*

Rohiroth   Earlier form for *Rohirrim*. 135, 139, 151, 347, 389–90, 392, 395, 398–9, 412, 418, 433–5, 442, 449; *Rochiroth* 139; *Rohir* 433. See *Horsemasters, Riders* (2).

Rohirrim   214, 357, 395, 407, 450

Romrin   See *Rhimbron.*

Root of the Boot, The   The original 'Troll Song'. 59, 66

Rosfein   See *Rhosfein.*

Ruddyhorn   Caradras. 167

INDEX

497

Ruinel   See *Pensarn*.

Ruinnel   See *Redway*.

Rulers of the World   The Valar. 255. *The Gods* 432.

Ruling Ring, The   23, 28, 112, 148, 155, 159, 254, 259–60, 266

Rúmil   (1) See *Rhimbron*. (2) The alphabet of Rúmil of Túna. 453

Runes   47, 49–50, 56, 61, 78, 92, 97, 101, 104, 186, 189, 200, 220, 274, 276, 382, 387, 452–9

Running, River   298, 307

Rushdown, River   Tributary of Anduin. 296. Elvish names *Rhibdath, Rhimdad, Rhimdath* 296

Sackville-Bagginses   6, 8, 21, 135, 286; *Lobelia* 32; *Cosimo* 32, 216, 249

Sam Gamgee   See under *Gamgee*.

Sammath Naur   The Chambers of Fire in Orodruin. 349

Sandymans (of Hobbiton)   216, 264; *Ted Sandyman* 253

Santoski, T. J. R.   94, 157, 159, 181, 457

Sarn Ford   9, 16, 71, 78, 131, 299, 356, 365

Sarn Gebir   (1) The highlands afterwards called *Emyn Muil*. 283, 285, 316, 318, 320–1, 325, 345, 351–2, 355, 357–8, 360, 362, 385, 389, 394, 396, 403, 423, 429, 432–3; *hills of Gebir* 358; *Sern Gebir* 283, 395; and see *East Wall*. *Gates of (Sarn) Gebir* 357 (of obscure meaning), 359–60, 362 (= *Gates of Argonath*, q.v.), *the Gates* 370. Proposed names *Graidon Hills, Grailaws* 423–4; *Hazowland* 424; *Sern Lamrach, Tarn Felin, Trandóran* 424. (2) The rapids in Anduin. 318, 360. See *Pensarn, Sarn Ruin*.

Sarn Ruin   The rapids in Anduin. 318, 320, 361, 366, 380, 387, 428. See *Pensarn, Sarn Gebir* (2).

Saruman   23, 70, 72–3, 75, 116, 130–41, *passim*, 149–52, 154, 157, 168, 177, 210–12, 214–16, 236, 250, 252, 287, 311, 330, 333, 379, 382, 385, 389, 394–5, 400–1, 403, 405, 408, 411–12, 414, 417–20, 422, 426–8, 432, 434–6, 440; earlier forms *Saramond, Saramund* 70–2, 75, 105, 140; called *the Grey* 70, 132, 136, 138–9, *the White* 70, 132–3, 136, 138–9, 149; proposed identification with the Balrog of Moria 236, 422; his ring 133, 138; confusion with Gandalf 389, 401, 403, 405, 425, 428

Sauron   54–5, 65, 71–2, 112, 116, 119–21, 123, 126–7, 129–30, 134–5, 137, 140, 144–6, 148, 150, 153–6, 158, 177, 184, 188, 207, 209–11, 247, 254–5, 259–60, 262, 265, 286, 289, 298, 321, 330, 335, 344, 347, 349, 360, 382, 393, 395, 404, 409, 431, 437–8, 444–5, 450; *Sauronites* 71, 74; Sauron's well of fire 209, 344, 349. See *Dark Lord, (The) Lord*.

Sayer, George   59, 66

Scary   Village in the Eastfarthing. 39

Sea of Rhûn, Sea of Rhûnaer   See *Rhûn, Rhûnaer*.

Sea(s), The   See *Great Sea(s)*.

498 THE TREASON OF ISENGARD

Seat of Sight On Amon Hen. 374. *Seat of Seeing* 374, 380–1

Second Age 455

Sern Aranath See *Argonath.*

Serni, River In Gondor. 312

Sern Lamrach See *Sarn Gebir* (1).

Seven Rings (of the Dwarves) 112, 149, 259; other references to the Rings of the Dwarves 117, 154–5, 158–9

Seven Rivers 132, 138, 177, 311. *Country, Land, of Seven Streams,* region between the Black Mountains and the Sea, 177, 272, 310–11. *Land of Seven Rivers,* Ossiriand, 311

Seventh River See *Greyflood.*

Shadowfax 152, 390, 400–1, 405, 412, 433–5, 438–9, 441, 443, 445–6, 450; Old English *Sceadufax* 425; his return from the North 438–9. Earlier names: *Arfaxed* 412; *Greyfax* 135–6, 152, 390; *Halbarad* 152, 390

Shadowland 87, 89, 92–3, 97–8, 101. *Shadowmere* 92–3, 95, 97–8, 100–1, 292; *Shadow-meres* 284, 292

Shadow, The 48, 118, 122, 129, 203, 225, 232, 237, 264, 374, 397, 416–17, 426; *Song of the Banished Shadow* 212

Shathûr See *Bundu-Shathûr.*

Shepherds of the Trees See *Ents.*

Shire, The 6–7, 9–11, 13, 16, 25, 31–2, 34, 38, 41, 43, 46–7, 49, 51, 55, 63, 68, 70–4, 78, 80, 82, 130–1, 134–5, 139, 162, 185, 193, 212, 216, 221, 232, 246, 248–50, 253, 265, 286, 356, 424. *Shire Reckoning* 9; *Shire-folk* 125, 152; language 424; maps of, see *Maps.*

Short Lay of Eärendel See *Eärendel.*

Shrouded Island(s), The 92, 95

Sigelwara land (J. R. R. Tolkien, article in *Medium Ævum*) 439

Silent Water, The 92

Silharrows See *Harrowland.*

Silmarillion, The 95, 138, 144, 146, 239, 260, 263, 313, 345. See *Maps, Quenta.*

Silmaril, The 100–2, 104–5; *Silmarils* 256

Silvan Elves 244; *silvan folk* 226. See *Wood-elves.*

Silverhorn See *Silvertine.*

Silverlode, River (1) Earlier name of Blackroot, q.v. 177, 187, 241, 298, 306, 310–11. (2) Celebrant. 173–5, 190, 213, 235–6, 238, 240–1, 279–80, 288, 291, 296, 306, 355–6, 368

Silvertine Celebdil. 174, 288. Earlier name *Silverhorn* 174, 431–2

Sindarin 174, 291

Sirannon 187. See *Gate-stream.*

Sirion 95, 239, 292; *Havens of Sirion* 102; *Sirion's mouth* 454–5. *New Sirion,* see *Sirvinya.*

Sirith, River In Gondor. 312, 322

Sirvinya 'New Sirion'. See *Anduin.*

INDEX

499

Sketch of the Mythology 95–6

Skinbark Ent. 412. See *Fladrif.*

Smeagol Gollum. 23–4, 27–8, 118, 148

Snaga Orc scout. 410. (See LR Appendix F, III.409.)

Snowmane Théoden's horse. 450

Song of Frodo and Sam Lament for Gandalf. 264, 266

Song of the Banished Shadow See *(The) Shadow.*

Song of the Ent and the Entwife See *Ents.*

Songs of the Philologists 66

South Downs 79

Southerner (at Bree) 42, 45, 71. Men from the South at Bree 71, 74

South Haven 301, 423. See *Harlond.*

Spiders of Kirith Ungol 209, 213–14, 330–1, (335), 347

Staddle In the Bree-land. 41, 56

Stair Falls Falls in the Gate-stream of Moria. 178

Standing Stone On the Barrow-downs. 41

Staniland Ondor. 318

Starmoon 187. See *Ithildin.*

Stars On West Door of Moria 180–1 (cf. 404); *Star of the House of Fëanor* 180

Sting 10, 16, (115), 137, 162, 192–3, 229, 240, 331–2, 335, 337, 355, 371

Stoneait See *Tolondren.*

Stone-giants 411. See *Trolls.*

Stone Hills 233, 250, 267, 269, 287, 325, 374

Strider 56, 64, 163

Sumharrowland See *Harrowland.*

Sunlands 313, 439

Sun, The 37, 93–4, 98, 101, 170–1, 232, 248, 257, 263, 265, 284, 363, 429, 439

Sutherland 306, 313, 389. See *Haradwaith.*

Swann, Donald 85, 107

Swertings Men of the South. 313, 439

Sword that was Broken, the Broken Sword 77–8, 80, 116, 120–2, 125, 128–9, 137, 146–7, 393, 402. See *Elendil.*

Taiglin, River (1) In Beleriand. 238. (2) Earliest name of Nimrodel. 222, 238–9

talan Flet, platform in mallorn-tree. 227–8

Taliska Language of the Fathers of Men. 455; *Taliskan* 455

Taniquetil 95

Tar See *Keleborn.*

Tarkil Númenórean. 8, 83–4, 106, 113, 116, 120, 137, 147, 163 (of Aragorn); 393 (of Arathorn).

Tarkilmar Earliest name of Annúminas. 144–5, 157, 304. See *Torfirion, Westermanton.*

500 THE TREASON OF ISENGARD

Tarmenel 'High Heaven'. 97, 99–100, 104, 108
Tarn Felin See *Sarn Gebir* (1).
Tasarinan Land of Willows, *Nan Tathren*. 417
Taur-na-Fuin 124, 145, 175; *Taur-nu-Fuin* 138. See *Tol Fuin*.
Tavrobel 173
Telerin (language) 453
Tengwar 188
Thangorodrim 110, 142, 198, 247, 262–3
Tharbad 79, 164, 172, 282, 292, 299
Thengel Father of Théoden. 399, 402, 441, 451; called *Master* (i.e. of Rohan) 402
Théoden 390, 399–402, 405, 430, 432–5; 437, 440–51. *Father and Master of the Riddermark* 393, *First Master* 400; first named as *King* 444
Théodred In LR Théoden's son; see 437, 451.
Théodwyn Théoden's sister. 451
The world was young, the mountains green 183–4
Thilevril See *Ithildin, Mithril*.
Thingol 110, 454–5
Third Age 9, 146, 450
Thor 106
Thorin (Oakenshield) 142–3, 154–5, 159–60, 185
Thorongil Aragorn's name in Gondor. 157
Thráin (1) Thráin the Old, Thráin I. 160. (2) Son (or father) of Thrór (see 159–60). 136, 142–3, 154–5, 158–60, 178
Thranduil King of the Elves of Mirkwood. 163, 257
Three Rings (of the Elves) 112, 149, 155–6, 159, 254–6, 259–60, 286; *Elf-rings* 237, 265; Galadriel's Ring, see *Ring of Earth*.
Thrihyrne The three peaks above Helm's Deep. 320. Earlier name *Tindtorras* 320
Throne of Gondor 395–6, 404
Thrór Father (or son) of Thráin (see 159–60). 136, 142–3, 154–7, 159–60, 178; Thrór's Map, see *Maps*.
Tibba Precursor of Tídwald (Tída) in *The Homecoming of Beorhtnoth*. 106–7
Tindrock, The Tol Brandir. 285, 288, 356, 359–60; high seat upon, 360
Tindtorras See *Thrihyrne*.
Tintallë 'The Kindler', Varda. 285
Tirion 92–3, 95, 97–8, 100–2, 284, 292. See *Tûn*.
Tirmindon See *Amon Hen*.
Tol Brandir 287–8, 318, 323, 344, 355, 359, 361, 366–71, 373, 381, 393–4, 396–7, 426; high seat upon, 359. For earlier names see *Tolondren*; also *Brandor* 285, 323; *Tol Brandor* 285, 323, 355, 359. See *(The) Tindrock*.
Tolfalas Island in the Bay of Belfalas. 298, 435, 439

INDEX 501

Tol Fuin Island off the North-west coast, once Taur-na-Fuin. 124, 138, 301

Tol Galen (1) The Green Isle in Ossiriand. 271. (2) See *Tolondren*.

Tolharn, Tollernen See *Tolondren*.

Tolondren Early name for Tol Brandir (also *Tol Ondren, Tollondren*; original forms *Toll-ondu, Toll-onnui*, 268). 267–71, 282, 285, 287, 315–16, 323, 325, 345, 367. Other early names: *Tol Galen* 271; *Tolharn* 324, 345; *Tollernen* 324, 345, 350; *Stoneait* 324, 345; and see *Carrock, Emris, Eregon, Tol Brandir*.

Tom Bombadil (including references to *Tom* and *Bombadil*) 7, 10–13, 16, 36–7, 41–2, 56, 64, 69, 72–3, 80, 111–12, 125, 130, 136, 139, 151–3, 158, 161, 416, 419–20; '*Ab-Origine*' 36. Other names: *Eldest* 125; *Erion* 125, 152, 158; *Forn* 125, 138, 152, 158; *Frumbarn* 158; *Iaur* 125, *Yárë* 125, 158; *Orald, Oreald, Orold* 158. *The Adventures of Tom Bombadil* 85, 90, 95–6, 107

Tongue, The (in Lothlórien) (268), 280–1, 285, 287–8, 291, 324, 330, 350. Other names: *Calendil, Calennel* 268, 288; *Green Spit* 268, 287–8; *Green-tine* 268, 288; *Lamben* 280; *Angle, Naith* used in this sense 268, 280, 287–8, also *Nelen* 268, 288

Tooks 7, 31; *the Hole of Took* (clan-name) 39

Took, Adelard 20. See *Uffo Took*.

Took, Faramond 6, 8, 15, 21, 30–2, 39, 112, 115, 166; nicknamed *Far* 8. See especially 30–2.

Took, Folco 6–9, 15–16, 21, 30–2, 35–6, 41, 47, 50–2, 56–8, 62, 64, 172. See especially 30–2.

Took, Frodo 31–2, 39

Took, Peregrin (also *Pippin*) 30–2, 35–6, 41, 47, 50–2, 56–8, 64, 76, 78, 82, 112, 115, 162, 164, 166–7, 170–1, 175, 179, 183, 193, 210–11, 214, 216, 226, 228, 230, 232, 235, 243, 250, 253, 264–5, 271–2, 274–5, 279, 285–6, 328–30, 339, 344, 346–9, 352, 375–8, 385–6, 397–8, 401, 404, 408–9, 411–17, 419–20, 423, 426–7, 429, 434, 436–7

Took, Odo See *Bolger, Odo*.

Took, Uffo 20. (Replaced by *Adelard Took*.)

Topless Forest, The See *Fangorn*.

Torfir Trotter. 61

Torfirion Early name for Annúminas; replaced *Tarkilmar*. 144–5, 296, 304. See *Westermanton*.

Tower Hills 34, 304. See *Emyn Beraid, White Towers*.

Tower of Guard See *Minas Tirith*.

Trandóran See *Sarn Gebir* (1).

Treebeard 6–7, 9, 71–2, 81, 130, 210–11, 214, 216, 250, 330, 339, 344, 389, 405, 409, 411–20, 425, 427–9, 436–7, 448. References to Treebeard as a *giant* 9, 71–2, 81, 210, 330, 405, 411; *and his Three Giants* 210. *King of the Treebeards* 428; *oldest living thing* 429. Treebeard's song 417, 420. See *Fangorn*.

502   THE TREASON OF ISENGARD

Tree-folk   See *Ents*; *Galadrim*.
Trolls   10, 14, 59–61, 193–4, 197–9, 201, 205, 211, 411, 413; *Troll-ridge* 14, *Troll-lands* 250, *Troll-fells* 306, 439; *cave-troll* 201; *Troll Song* 59–61, 66, 333. *Stone-gaints* 411
Trotter   6–10, 13–15, 19, 21, 31–7, 39, 42, 44–6, 48–52, 56–9, 61–5, 70–84 *passim*, 105, 111–14, 116, 118, 120–2, 146, 161, 163, 165, 167–9, 171–2, 175–6, 178, 192–4, 197–8, 203–5, 218–21, 236, 272–3, 275–8, 280, 290–1, 293, 327–9, 347, 350–63, 365–6, 370–1, 375–95 *passim*, 407, 409, 411–13
Tûn, Túna   95; *Rúmil of Túna* 453; *Túnian letters* 453. See *Tirion*.
Tuor   15, 261
Túrin   6, 15

Udûn   Between the Morannon and the Isenmouthe. 213
Udushinbar   See *Bundu-Shathûr*.
Uglúk   (1) In the rôle of Grishnákh. (2) Leader of the Isengarders in the Orc-raid. 408–9
Undeeps, The   In Anduin. 318, 320
Underhill, Mr.   Frodo's assumed name at Bree. 28, 48, 77. See *Green, Hill of Faraway*. *The Underhills of Staddle* 41
Unfinished Tales   79, 137, 278, 292, 299, 301, 307, 318, 322, 399, 403, 422
Ungoliant   93, 95, 99
Unwin, Rayner   89
Uruk-hai   409; *Uruks* 205
Uthwit, The old   Saruman. 409
Úvanwaith   The Nomenlands. 281, 283, 320

Valandil   (1) Brother of Elendil. 123–4. (2) Son of Elendil. 121. (3) Son of Isildur. 121–3, 128–9, 147, 359–62, 366
Valandur   Son of Isildur (?). 120, 122
Valatar   Father of Eldamir (Elfstone). 362, 404
Valimar   City of the Valar in Valinor. 285
Valinor   256, 263, 265, 453–4; *Bay of* 97, 100; *Mountains of Valinor* 95, *Mountains of the West* 263, *the Mountains* 248, 257, 263, 265; *Hiding of* 263; *Valinorian letters* 453
Varda   285
Völuspá   See *Elder Edda*.
Vultures   Steeds of the Winged Nazgûl. 208–9, 213, 338, 341, 343–4, 353–4

Water, The   39
Wargs   178–9, (215)
Watcher in the Water, The   179, (181), 191, 201
Weathertop   7, 10–15, 31, 44, 52, 56–7, 61–2, 64–5, 69–70, 72, 76, 78–9, 135, 152, 157–8, 439

INDEX   503

Wellinghall   Treebeard's house. 417. Earlier names *Fonthill, Funtial*
  417, 420; *Wellandhouse* 417
Westemnet   318, 401, 404, 434
Westermanton   Annúminas. 144–5, 157, 296, 304. Also *Aldemanton* 157; and see *Tarkilmar, Torfirion.*
Westernesse   (1) Númenor. *Men of, race of, Westernesse* 84, 106,
  119, 123, 127, 137, 144–6, 400, 440. (2) The West Lands (see
  the map in IV.249). The *Flammifer of Westernesse* 94–5, 98,
  102, 105
Western Sea   See *Great Sea(s). Western Shore* 264, 266
Western Tower   The tower in which Gandalf was besieged. (Includ-
  ing references to *The Tower)* 9, 11–12, 33, 35, 44, 72, 130, 139;
  White Tower 12. See *Dream of the Tower, White Towers.*
Westfold   320 (in the Misty Mountains); *Westfold Vale* 320
Westron   244, 288
West, The   In various applications (West over Sea, Númenor, the
  West of Middle-earth, of the Shire). 110, 123 *(the True West),*
  127, 152–3, 249, 255, 259, 263, 277–8, 286–7, 331, 392. *Host
  of the West* 142, 263; *Lords of the West* 422; for *Men of the West*
  see *Númenórean(s).*
West Towers   39. See *White Towers.*
Wetwang   268–9, 281, 283, 287, 313, 315–16, 320–1, 328. See
  Nindalf.
When winter first begins to bite   163
Where now the horse and the rider?   443, 449
White Council   22–3, 38, 132, 138, 147, 149, 233, 248, 257
White Fire   Gandalf's fire opposed to the Red Fire of the Balrog. 198,
  203; *White Flame* 203
White Hand   Emblem of Saruman. 382, 409
Whitelock   See *Arod.*
White Mountains   Later name of the Black Mountains. 124, 177,
  239, 320–1, 357, 395, 433
White Rider, The   See *Gandalf.*
White Towers   304, 423; *the Towers* 154; *West Towers* 39; *Elf-
  towers* 34, 39, 130. See *Western Tower.*
White Tree of Gondor   396, 404; *Silver Tree* 395
White Wizard   212, 330, 389, 422, 436
Wilderland   119, 144, 264, 266, 352, 354, 360, 365. Map of
  Wilderland, see *Maps.*
Williams, Charles   419
Windbeam   See *Elendil.*
Windmane   See *Hasofel.*
Winged Crown of Gondor   396, 404
Winseld   The Golden Hall in Eodoras. 402, 429, 433, 437, 441–2,
  447. Earlier names *Meduarn, Meodarn* 402
Wise, The   82

504 THE TREASON OF ISENGARD

Withered Wold   The Brown Lands. 351, 356
Withywindle, River   36
Wizard(s)   (not including references expressly to Gandalf) 22–3, 72, 136, 326, 411, 418, 422, 436; referring to the King of the Ringwraiths 9, 132, *the Wizard King* 116
Wold of Rohan   318, 400, 404
Wolfdale   See *Entish Land(s)*.
Wolfriders   412
Wood-elves   (both of Mirkwood and of Lothlórien) 28, 118, 137, 148, 157, 218, 221–2, 239, 244, 296; woodland folk 167, 229; language 223, 227, 239–40, 251. See *Silvan Elves*.
Woodhall   11
Woodmen   (of Western Mirkwood) 296, 390
Woody End   11, 33, 215, 365
World's End   94, 98–9, 101; *margin of the world* 286
Wormtongue   214, 401, 430, 437, 443–6, 450. See *Frána*.
Wraiths   See *Ringwraiths*.

Yárë   See *Tom Bombadil*.
Younger Days   150
Yrch   See *Orcs*.
Yule-days   368; *Foreyule* 368

Zirakzigil   One of the Mountains of Moria (Silvertine). 174–5, 432; *Zirak* 174 (and *Zirik*). Earlier name *Zirakinbar* 431–2

'That's that!' said Sam. Which we expected. But I don't like it. I suppose we've caught exactly where he wanted to bring us. Well, let's get on as we can. The more we advance now... I said whistle if there wasn't plenty of getting out of the tunnel, it was pure wickedness of some sort, and what's more it'll soon be done.

Likely enough, said Frodo. But we carried it at even, got even so far without him. So if we can manage our errand, then Gollum and all his wickedness will be part of the plan.

So far, you say, said Sam. How far? Where are we now?

A bend at the end, the main range of Ephel-dúath... Igners, said Frodo. Look! The road speeds on, now it's on its way out on up, dark on top... sheer. Beyond and ahead there was an ominous glow in the sky; and like a great notch in the mountain wall... a cleft was outlined against it.

On their right the wall of rock fell away and beyond... indeed that it had no brink. Looking down Frodo saw with... darkness of... the spread... much wider head of Morghul dale. Down in the depths on the third gleam... the road that led over the Morghul pass for Last. On their left sharp, jagged pinnacles stood up like towers crowned by the ... bluffs, and between them were deep dark crevices and clefts. But the things... on the left side of it... and there how... high... no one saw black... must end like a shadow... a... cleft.

'I don't like the look of that,' said Sam. '... that... unguarded too. D'you remember he never would say if... there or no. D'you think he's gone to fetch him — or something?

No, I don't think so, said Frodo. The chap is no good, of course, but I don't think that he's gone to fetch orcs... unless he is... he is no slave of the Dark Lord. I suppose not, said Sam. No... I suppose... the whole time it has been the ring for poor Smeagol own. That's been his scheme. But how coming up here will help him, I can't guess. He will soon learn.

Frodo went forward now — the last lap — and he exerted all his strength. He felt that if once he could get to the saddle of the pass and look over into the Nameless Land he would have accomplished something. Sam followed. He sensed evil all round him. He knew that they had walked into some trap, but what? He had sheathed his sword, but now he drew it in readiness... He halted for a moment... and stooped to pick up his staff with his left hand.

SVELAS CIRIO

THE WAR OF THE RING

THE HISTORY OF THE LORD OF THE RINGS, PART THREE

J. R. R. TOLKIEN

The War of the Ring

The History of
The Lord of the Rings
PART THREE

Christopher Tolkien

CONTENTS

Foreword   *page* ix

PART ONE: THE FALL OF SARUMAN

I	THE DESTRUCTION OF ISENGARD *(Chronology)*	3
II	HELM'S DEEP	8
III	THE ROAD TO ISENGARD	25
IV	FLOTSAM AND JETSAM	47
V	THE VOICE OF SARUMAN	61
VI	THE PALANTÍR	68

PART TWO: THE RING GOES EAST

I	THE TAMING OF SMÉAGOL	85
II	THE PASSAGE OF THE MARSHES	104
III	THE BLACK GATE IS CLOSED	121
IV	OF HERBS AND STEWED RABBIT	131
V	FARAMIR	144
VI	THE FORBIDDEN POOL	171
VII	JOURNEY TO THE CROSS-ROADS	175
VIII	KIRITH UNGOL	183

PART THREE: MINAS TIRITH

I	ADDENDUM TO 'THE TREASON OF ISENGARD'	229

vi THE WAR OF THE RING

II BOOK FIVE BEGUN AND ABANDONED
 (i) Minas Tirith 231
 (ii) The Muster of Rohan 235
 (iii) Sketches for Book Five 252

III MINAS TIRITH 274

IV MANY ROADS LEAD EASTWARD (1) 296

V MANY ROADS LEAD EASTWARD (2) 312

VI THE SIEGE OF GONDOR 323

VII THE RIDE OF THE ROHIRRIM 343

VIII THE STORY FORESEEN FROM FORANNEST 359

IX THE BATTLE OF THE PELENNOR FIELDS 365

X THE PYRE OF DENETHOR 374

XI THE HOUSES OF HEALING 384

XII THE LAST DEBATE 397

XIII THE BLACK GATE OPENS 430

XIV THE SECOND MAP 433

Index 440

ILLUSTRATIONS

Shelob's Lair	first frontispiece
Dunharrow	second frontispiece
Orthanc '2', '3' and '4'	*page* 33
Orthanc '5'	34
A page from the first manuscript of 'The Taming of Sméagol'	90
Two early sketches of Kirith Ungol	108
Third sketch of Kirith Ungol	114
Frodo's journey to the Morannon (map)	117
Minas Morghul and the Cross-roads (map)	181
Plan of Shelob's Lair (1)	201
Kirith Ungol	204
Plan of Shelob's Lair (2)	225
Dunharrow	239
Harrowdale (map)	258
The earliest sketch of Minas Tirith	261
The White Mountains and South Gondor (map)	269
Minas Tirith and Mindolluin (map)	280
Plan of Minas Tirith	290
Starkhorn, Dwimorberg and Irensaga	314
The Second Map (West)	434
The Second Map (East)	435

Note:
Owing to the limitations of printing on 'India' paper, it has been necessary to reproduce in black and white the originally coloured frontispiece illustrations.

FOREWORD

The title of this book comes from the same source as *The Treason of Isengard*, a set of six titles, one for each 'Book' of *The Lord of the Rings*, suggested by my father in a letter to Rayner Unwin of March 1953 (*The Letters of J. R. R. Tolkien* no. 136). *The War of the Ring* was that proposed for Book V, and I have adopted it for this book since the history of the writing of Book V constitutes nearly half of it, while the first part concerns the victory of Helm's Deep and the destruction of Isengard. The second part describes the writing of Frodo's journey to Kirith Ungol, and this I have called 'The Ring Goes East', which was the title proposed by my father for Book IV.

In the Foreword to *The Return of the Shadow* I explained that a substantial collection of manuscripts was left behind in England when the bulk of the papers went to Marquette University in 1958, these manuscripts consisting for the most part of outlines and the earliest narrative drafts; and I suggested that this was a consequence of the papers being dispersed, some in one place and some in another, at that time. But the manuscript materials for *The Return of the King* were evidently preserved with the main body of the papers, for nothing of Books V and VI was left behind beyond some narrative outlines and the first draft of the chapter 'Minas Tirith'. For my account of Book V therefore I have been almost wholly dependent on the provision from Marquette of great quantities of manuscript in reproduction, without which the latter part of *The War of the Ring* could not have been written at all. For this most generous assistance I express my gratitude to all concerned in it, and most especially to Mr Taum Santoski, who has been primarily responsible for the work involved. In addition he has advised me on many particular points which can be best decided by close examination of the original papers, and he has spent much time in trying to decipher those manuscripts in which my father wrote a text in ink on top of another in pencil. I thank also Miss Tracy J. Muench and Miss Elizabeth A. Budde for their part in the work of reproducing the material, and Mr Charles B. Elston for making it possible for me to include in this book several

X   THE WAR OF THE RING

illustrations from manuscripts at Marquette: the pages carrying sketches of Dunharrow, of the mountains at the head of Harrowdale, and of Kirith Ungol, the plan of Minas Tirith, and the full-page drawing of Orthanc (5).

This book follows the plan and presentation of its predecessors, references to previous volumes in 'The History of Middle-earth' being generally given in Roman numerals (thus 'VII' refers to *The Treason of Isengard*), FR, TT, and RK being used as abbreviations for *The Fellowship of the Ring*, *The Two Towers*, and *The Return of the King*, and page-references being made throughout to the three-volume hardback edition of *The Lord of the Rings* (LR). In several parts of the book the textual history is exceedingly complex. Since the story of the evolution of *The Lord of the Rings* can of course only be discovered by the correct ordering and interpretation of the manuscripts, and must be recounted in those terms, the textual history cannot be much simplified; and I have made much use of identifying letters for the manuscripts in order to clarify my account and to try to avoid ambiguities. In Books IV and V problems of chronological synchronisation became acute: a severe tension is sometimes perceptible between narrative certainties and the demands of an entirely coherent chronological structure (and the attempt to right dislocation in time could very well lead to dislocation in geography). Chronology is so important in this part of *The Lord of the Rings* that I could not neglect it, but I have put almost all of my complicated and often inconclusive discussion into 'Notes on the Chronology' at the end of chapters.

In this book I have used accents throughout in the names of the Rohirrim (*Théoden*, *Éomer*, &c.).

Mr Charles Noad has again read the proofs independently and checked the very large number of citations, including those to other passages within the book, with a strictness and care that I seem altogether unable to attain. In addition I have adopted several of his suggestions for improvement in clarity and consistency in my account. I am much indebted to him for this generous and substantial work.

I am very grateful for communications from Mr Alan Stokes and Mr Neil Gaiman, who have explained my father's reference in his remarks about the origins of the poem *Errantry* (*The Treason of Isengard* p. 85): 'It was begun very many years ago, in an attempt to go on with the model that came unbidden into my mind: the first six lines, in which, I guess, *D'ye ken the*

FOREWORD

rhyme to porringer had a part.' The reference is to a Jacobite song attacking William of Orange as usurper of the English crown from his father-in-law, James II, and threatening to hang him. The first verse of this song runs thus in the version given by Iona and Peter Opie in *The Oxford Dictionary of Nursery Rhymes* (no. 422):

> *What is the rhyme for porringer?*
> *What is the rhyme for porringer?*
> *The king he had a daughter fair*
> *And gave the Prince of Orange her.*

The verse is known in several forms (in one of which the opening line is *Ken ye the rhyme to porringer?* and the last *And he gave her to an Oranger*). This then is the unlikely origin of the provender of the Merry Messenger:

> *There was a merry passenger,*
> *a messenger, an errander;*
> *he took a tiny porringer*
> *and oranges for provender.*

PART ONE

THE FALL OF SARUMAN

I

THE DESTRUCTION OF ISENGARD

(Chronology)

The writing of the story from 'The King of the Golden Hall' to the end
of the first book of *The Two Towers* was an extremely complex
process. The 'Isengard story' was not conceived and set down as a
series of clearly marked 'chapters', each one brought to a developed
state before the next was embarked on, but evolved as a whole, and
disturbances of the structure that entered as it evolved led to disloca-
tions all through the narrative. With my father's method of composition at this time – passages of very rough and piecemeal drafting being
built into a completed manuscript that was in turn heavily overhauled,
the whole complex advancing and changing at the same time – the
textual confusion in this part of *The Lord of the Rings* is only
penetrable with great difficulty, and to set it out as a clear sequence
impossible.

The essential cause of this situation was the question of chronology;
and I think that the best way to approach the writing of this part of the
narrative is to try to set out first the problems that my father was
contending with, and to refer back to this discussion when citing the
actual texts.

The story had certain fixed narrative 'moments' and relations.
Pippin and Merry had encountered Treebeard in the forest of Fangorn
and been taken to his 'Ent-house' of Wellinghall for the night. On that
same day Aragorn, Gimli and Legolas had encountered Éomer and his
company returning from battle with the Orcs, and they themselves
passed the night beside the battlefield. For these purposes this may be
called 'Day 1', since earlier events have here no relevance; the actual
date according to the chronology of this period in the writing of *The
Lord of the Rings* was Sunday January 29 (see VII.368, 406).

On Day 2, January 30, the Entmoot took place; and on that day
Aragorn and his companions met Gandalf returned, and together they
set out on their great ride to Eodoras. As they rode south in the
evening Legolas saw far off towards the Gap of Rohan a great smoke
rising, and he asked Gandalf what it might be: to which Gandalf
replied 'Battle and war!' (at the end of the chapter 'The White Rider').

They rode all night, and reached Eodoras in the early morning of
Day 3, January 31. While they spoke with Théoden and Wormtongue
in the Golden Hall at Eodoras the Entmoot was still rumbling on far

4   THE WAR OF THE RING

away in Fangorn. In the afternoon of Day 3 Théoden with Gandalf and his companions and a host of the Rohirrim set out west from Eodoras across the plains of Rohan towards the Fords of Isen; and on that same afternoon the Entmoot ended,[1] and the Ents began their march on Isengard, which they reached after nightfall.

It is here that the chronological problems appear. There were – or would be, as the story evolved – the following elements (some of them foreseen in some form in the outline that I called 'The Story Foreseen from Fangorn', VII.435–6) to be brought into a coherent time-pattern. The Ents would attack Isengard, and drown it by diverting the course of the river Isen. A great force would leave Isengard; the Riders at the Fords of Isen would be driven back over the river. The Rohirrim coming from Eodoras would see a great darkness in the direction of the Wizard's Vale, and they would meet a lone horseman returning from the battle at the Fords; Gandalf would fleet away westwards on Shadowfax. Théoden and his host, with Aragorn, Gimli and Legolas, would take refuge in a deep gorge in the southern mountains, and a great battle there would turn to victory after certain defeat with the coming of the 'moving trees', and the return of Gandalf and the lord of the Rohirrim whose stronghold it was. Finally, Gandalf, with Théoden, Aragorn, Gimli, Legolas and a company of the Riders would leave the refuge and ride to Isengard, now drowned and in ruins, and meet Merry and Pippin sitting on a pile of rubble at the gates.

I

In the original opening of 'Helm's Deep', as will be seen at the beginning of the next chapter, the cavalcade from Eodoras saw 'a great fume and vapour' rising over Nan Gurunír, the Wizard's Vale,[2] and met the lone horseman returning from the Fords of Isen, *on the same day* (Day 3, January 31) as they left the Golden Hall. The horseman (Ceorl) told them that the Riders had been driven back over the Isen with great loss on the previous day (Day 2, January 30); and it must have been 'the smoke of battle' that Legolas saw in the evening rising from the Gap of Rohan as they rode south from Fangorn – it cannot of course have been the steam rising from the drowning of Isengard by the Ents (see above). In this original story Théoden and his men, with Aragorn, Gimli and Legolas, took refuge in Helm's Deep (not yet so named) that same night (Day 3).

A chronological dislocation seems to have been already present in this: for the events of Days 1–3 as set out above were fixed in relation to each other, and the Ents must arrive at Isengard after nightfall of Day 3 (January 31); yet according to the original opening of 'Helm's Deep' the host from Eodoras sees the 'great fume and vapour' rising over Nan Gurunír (unquestionably caused by the drowning of Isengard) in the evening of that same day.

THE DESTRUCTION OF ISENGARD

II

This time-scheme was duly changed: Théoden and his host camped in the plain on the first night out from Eodoras (Day 3, January 31), and it was in the morning of the second day of the ride (Day 4, February 1) that they saw the great cloud over Nan Gurunír:

> As they rode they saw a great spire of smoke and vapour, rising up out of the deep shadow of Nan Gurunír; as it mounted it caught the light of the sun and spread in glowing banks that drifted on the wind over the plains towards them.
>
> 'What do you think of that, Gandalf?' said Théoden. 'One would say that all the Wizard's Vale was burning.'
>
> 'There is ever a fume above that valley in these days,' said Háma; 'but I never saw anything like that before.'

It is now in the evening of this second day of their ride that they met the horseman Ceorl coming from the Fords, and on the night of this day that the battle of the Hornburg took place. The chronology was now therefore:

> *(Day 3) January 31*   Gandalf, Théoden and the Rohirrim depart from Eodoras and camp for the night in the plains. Ents reach Isengard after nightfall and after the departure of the Orc-host begin the drowning of the Circle of Isengard.
>
> *(Day 4) February 1*   The host from Eodoras sees in the morning the steams rising from the drowning of Isengard; in the evening they meet Ceorl and learn of the defeat at the Fords of Isen on the previous day; and reach Helm's Deep after nightfall. Battle of the Hornburg.

It seems impossible to avoid the conclusion that the end of the chapter 'The White Rider' (Legolas' sight of the smoke in the Gap of Rohan on Day 2, January 30) escaped revision when the date of the (Second) Battle of the Fords of Isen was changed to January 31.

III

In the original form of what became the opening of 'The Road to Isengard' Gandalf and Théoden, with Aragorn, Gimli and Legolas and a party of Riders, set out from Helm's Deep shortly after the end of the battle of the Hornburg, without any rest; this was on Day 5, February 2, and *they reached Isengard not long after noon on the same day.* As they approached Nan Gurunír

> they saw rising up out of deep shadows a vast spire of smoke and vapour; as it mounted it caught the light of the sun, and spread in glowing billows in the sky, and the wind bore them over the plain.
>
> 'What do you think of that, Gandalf?' said Théoden. 'One would say that all the Wizard's Vale was burning.'

6   THE WAR OF THE RING

'There is ever a fume above that valley in these days,' said Éomer; 'but I have never seen anything like this before. These are steams, rather than smokes. Some devilry Saruman is brewing to greet us.'

This dialogue was lifted straight from its earlier place at the beginning of the 'Helm's Deep' story (see II above) – with substitution of Éomer for Háma, slain at the Hornburg, and in 'Helm's Deep' a different passage was inserted, as found in TT pp. 131–2, in which what is seen in the North-west is 'a shadow that crept down slowly from the Wizard's Vale', and there is no mention of fume or steam.

The reason for these changes was again chronological: the host on its way from Eodoras is not to see great steams rising from Isengard on Day 4, but the 'veiling shadow' of the Huorns as they came down into the Wizard's Vale. Thus:

> *(Day 4) February 1*   The host from Eodoras sees in the morning the shade of the moving trees far off in the North-west; the drowning of Isengard was not begun till night. At night Battle of the Hornburg.
>
> *(Day 5) February 2*   In the morning Théoden and Gandalf and their company ride to Isengard, and find it drowned.

IV

The chronology was then changed to that of 'The Road to Isengard' in TT, whereby Théoden and Gandalf and their company do not leave Helm's Deep until much later on Day 5, pass the night camped below Nan Gurunír, and do not reach Isengard until midday on Day 6 (February 3). This chronology is set out in a time-scheme (additions of mine in brackets):

> [Day 3] January 31   Ents arrive at Isengard, night. Break in.
>
> [Day 4] February 1   Dawn, they go away north to make dams. All that day Merry and Pippin alone until dusk. Gandalf arrives at Isengard at nightfall, and meets Treebeard. Drowning of Isengard begins late at night. [Battle of the Hornburg.]
>
> [Day 5] February 2   Isengard steams all day and column of smoke arises in evening. [Gandalf, Théoden, &c. see this from their camp below Nan Gurunír.] Huorns return in night to Isengard.
>
> [Day 6] February 3   Morning, Treebeard returns to Gates. Sets Merry and Pippin to watch. Wormtongue comes. [Gandalf, Théoden, &c. arrive shortly after noon.]

This is the chronology of LR, as set out in *The Tale of Years*, though the actual dates are of course different (in LR March 2 = January 31 in this scheme).

*

THE DESTRUCTION OF ISENGARD

This, I believe, is how the chronology evolved; but as will be seen in the following chapters, earlier time-schemes appear in the drafts for passages far on in the actual narrative, because as I have said all this part of LR was written as a whole. Thus for example in the first draft of Merry's story of the destruction and drowning of Isengard (in TT in the chapter 'Flotsam and Jetsam') the chronology belongs with the scheme described in II above, and against it my father noted: 'Drowning must not begin until night of Hornburg battle.'

Despite the way in which this part of the story was written, I think that it will in fact be clearest to break my account into chapters corresponding to those in *The Two Towers*; this inevitably entails a certain amount of advance and retreat in terms of the actual sequence of composition, but I hope that this preliminary account will clarify the shifting chronological basis in the different texts.

NOTES

1 The extra day of the Entmoot (TT pp. 87–8) was not added until much later: VII.407, 419.

2 *Nan Gurunír*, the Valley of Saruman, was added in to a blank space left for the name in the manuscript of 'Treebeard' (VII.420 note 9).

II

HELM'S DEEP

A first draft of this story, abandoned after it had proceeded for some distance, differs so essentially from its form in *The Two Towers* that I give it here in full. This text bears the chapter number XXVIII, without title. For the chronology see p. 4, § I.

There was a much-ridden way, northwestward along the foothills of the Black Mountains. Up and down over the rolling green country it ran, crossing small swift streams by many fords. Far ahead and to the right the shadow of the Misty Mountains drew nearer. Beneath the distant peak of Methedras in dark shadow lay the deep vale of Nan Gurunír; a great fume and vapour rose there and drifted towards them over the plain.[1] Halting seldom they rode on into the evening. The sun went down before them. Darkness grew behind.

Their spears were tipped with fiery red as the last shafts of light stained the clouds above Tindtorras;[2] the three peaks stood black against the sunset upon the northmost arm of the Black Mountains. In that last red light men in the van saw a horseman riding back towards them. As he drew near, the host halted, awaiting him.

He came, a weary man with dinted helm, and cloven shield. Slowly he climbed from his horse, and stood there a while, panting. At length he spoke. 'Is Éomer here?' he asked. 'You come at last, but too late and too few. Things have gone evilly, since Théodred fell.[3] We were driven back over the bend of the Isen with great loss yesterday; many perished at the crossing. Then at night fresh forces came over the river against our camp. All Isengard must be emptied; and the Wizard has armed the wild hill-men and the scattered folk of Westfold,[4] and these also he loosed upon us. We were overmastered. The shieldwall was broken. Trumbold [> Herulf > Heorulf][5] the Westmarcher has drawn off those he could gather towards his fastness under Tindtorras. Others are scattered. Where is Éomer? Tell him there is no hope ahead: he should return to Eodoras, before the wolves of Saruman come there!'

Théoden rode up. 'Come, stand before me, Ceorl!' he said. 'I

HELM'S DEEP

9

am here. The last host of the Eorlingas has ridden forth. It will not return unfought.'

The man's face lightened with wonder and joy. He drew himself up. Then he knelt offering his notched sword to the King. 'Command me, lord,' he cried, 'and pardon me! I did not know, I thought—'

'You thought I remained in Eodoras, bent like an old tree under winter snow. So it was when you went. But a wind has shaken off somewhat the cold burden,' said Théoden. 'Give this man a fresh horse. Let us ride to the aid of Trumbold [> Heorulf]!'

Forward they rode again, urging on their horses. Suddenly Gandalf spoke to Shadowfax, and like an arrow from the bow the great horse sprang away. Even as they looked, he was gone: a flash of silver in the sunset, a wind in the grass, a shadow that fled and faded from sight. For a while Snowmane and the horses of the King's guard strained in pursuit, but if they had walked they would have had as much chance of overtaking him.

'What does that mean?' said Háma to a comrade. 'Ever he comes and goes unlooked-for.'

'Wormtongue, were he here, would not find it hard to explain,' said the other.

'True,' said Háma, 'but for myself I will wait till we see him again.'

'If ever we do,' said the other.

It was night and the host was still riding swiftly, when cries and hornblasts were heard from the scouts that rode ahead. Arrows whistled overhead. They were crossing a wide vale, a bay in the mountains. On the further side the Tindtorras were hidden in darkness. Some miles ahead still lay the opening of the great cleft in the hills which men of that land called *Heorulf's Clough*:[6] steep and narrow it wound inward under the Tindtorras, and where it issued in the vale, upon an outjutting heel of rock, was built the fastness of Heorulf's Hold.[7]

The scouts rode back and reported that woltriders were abroad in the vale, and that a host of orcs and wild men, very great indeed, was hastening southward over the plain to gain the gates of the Nerwet.[8]

'We have found some of our men slain as they fled,' said one of the scouts; 'and scattered companies we have met, going this

10   THE WAR OF THE RING

way and that, leaderless; but many are making for Herulf's Hold, and say that Herulf is already there.'

'We had best not give battle in the dark, nor await the day here in the open, not knowing the number of the coming host,' said Éomer, who had ridden up to the King's side. 'What is your counsel, Aragorn?'

'To drive through such enemies as are before us, and encamp before the Nerwet Gate to defend if may be, while the men who have fought rest behind our shield.'

'Let it be so!' said Théoden. 'We will go thither in many [separate comp]anies: let a man who is nightsighted and knows [well the land] go at the head of each.'[9]

At this point my father stopped, and returned to 'It was night and the host was still riding swiftly . . .' In the passage just given is the first appearance of Helm's Deep ('Heorulf's Clough') and the Hornburg ('Heorulf's Hold') on its 'outjutting heel of rock'; Heorulf being the precursor of Erkenbrand of Westfold.

Night had fallen, and still the host was riding swiftly on. They had turned northward, and were bearing towards the fords of the Isen, when cries and hornblasts were heard from their scouts that went in front. Arrows whistled over them. At this time they were at the outer end of a wide vale, a bay in the mountains of the south. On its further western side the Tindtorras were hidden in darkness; beneath their feet [> the peaks], some miles away, lay the opening of the great cleft in the hills which men of that land called Heorulf's Clough [> lay the green coomb out of which opened a great cleft in the hills. Men of that land called it Helm's Deep],[10] after some hero of ancient wars who had made his refuge there. Ever steeper and narrower it wound inward under the Tindtorras, till the crowhaunted cliffs on either side towered far above and shut out the light. Where it issued in the vale, upon [added: the Stanrock,] an outjutting heel of land, was built the fastness of Heorulf's Hoe[11] (Hold?). Stanrock. [> was built the fastness of Helmsgate. There Heorulf the Marcher had his hold.]

A scout now rode back and reported that wolfriders were abroad in the valley, and that a host of orcs and wild men, very great indeed, was hurrying southward over the plain towards Heorulf's Hold.

'We have found many of our own folk lying slain as they fled thither,' said the scout. 'And we have met scattered companies,

HELM'S DEEP 11

going this way and that, leaderless. Some are making for the Clough [> Helmsgate], but it seems that Nothelm [> Heorulf] is not there. His plan was changed, and men do not know whither he has gone. Some say that Wormtongue was seen today [> Some say that Wormtongue was seen in the evening going north, and in the dusk an old man on a great horse rode the same way].'

'Well, if Nothelm be in the Hold or not, [> 'It will go ill with Wormtongue, if Gandalf overtakes him,' said Théoden. 'Nonetheless I miss now both counsellors, old and new. Yet it seems to me that whether Heorulf be in his Hold or no,] in this need we have no better choice than to go thither ourselves,' said Théoden. 'What is your counsel?' he said, turning to Éomer who had now ridden up to the King's side.

'We should be ill advised to give battle in the dark,' said Éomer, 'or to await the day here in the open, not knowing the number of the oncoming host. Let us drive through such foes as are between us and Herulf's Clough [> the fastness], and encamp before the Hold [> its gate]. Then if we cannot break out, we may retreat to the Hold. There are caves in the gorge [> Helm's Deep] behind where hundreds may hide, and secret ways lead up thence, I am told, onto the hills.'

'Trust not to them!' said Aragorn. 'Saruman has long spied out this land. Still, in such a place our defence might last long.'

'Let us go then,' said Théoden. 'We will ride thither in many separate companies. A man who is nightsighted and knows well the land shall go at the head of each.'

I interrupt the text here to discuss some aspects of this story. The names present an apparently impenetrable confusion, but I think that the development was more or less as follows. My father was uncertain whether 'Heorulf' ('Herulf') was the present lord of the 'Hold' or the hero after whom the 'Clough' was named. When he wrote, in the passage just given, 'which men of that land called Heorulf's Clough, after some hero of ancient wars who had made his refuge there' he had decided on the latter, and therefore the name of the present 'Westmarcher' (precursor of Erkenbrand) was changed, becoming *Nothelm*. Then, changing again, *Nothelm* reverted to *Heorulf*, while the gorge was named after *Helm*: *Helmshaugh* (note 10), then *Helm's Deep*. The fastness (*Heorulf's Hoe* or *Hold*) standing on the *Stanrock* is now called *Helmsgate*, which in LR refers to the entrance to Helm's Deep across which the Deeping Wall was built.

The image of the great gorge and the fortress built on the jutting

12   THE WAR OF THE RING

heel or 'hoe' arose, I believe, as my father wrote this first draft of the new chapter. In the outline 'The Story Foreseen from Fangorn' (VII.435) Gandalf's sudden galloping off on Shadowfax is present, and 'by his help and Aragorn the Isengarders are driven back'; there is no suggestion of any gorge or hold in the hills to the south. So again in the present narrative he says nothing before he rides off; whereas in TT he tells Théoden not to go the Fords of Isen but to ride to Helm's Deep. Thus in the original story it was not until 'cries and hornblasts were heard from their scouts that went in front' and 'arrows whistled over them' that the leaders of the host decided to make for the Hold; in TT (where the actual wording of the passage is scarcely changed) the host was 'in the low valley before the mouth of the Coomb' when these things happened.

The present text agrees well with the First Map (redrawn section IVE, VII.319). At this time the host was 'at the outer end of a wide vale, a bay in the mountains of the south'; and 'Heorulf's Clough' lay somewhere near the western end of this 'bay'. The First Map is in fact less clear at this point than my redrawing makes it, but the map that I made in 1943, which was closely based on the First Map (see VII.299), shows Helm's Deep very clearly as running in towards the Tindtorras (Thrihyrne) from a point well to the north and west of the 'bay in the mountains' – the Westfold Vale, in the present text not yet named (see note 4).[12]

On the page of the completed manuscript in which the final form of this passage (TT p. 133) was reached the text reads thus: 'Still some miles away, on the far side of the Westfold Vale, a great bay in the mountains, lay a green coomb out of which a gorge opened in the hills.' There is no question that this is correct, and that this was what my father intended: the great bay in the mountains was of course the Westfold Vale. In the typescript based on this, however, the sentence became, for some obscure reason (there is no ambiguity in the manuscript): 'Still some miles away, on the far side of the Westfold Vale, lay a green coomb, a great bay in the mountains, out of which a gorge opened in the hills.' This error is perpetuated in *The Two Towers*.

In this original narrative it was on the night of the day of departure from Eodoras that the host came to the hold in the hills; subsequently[13] it was on the night of the second day (for the chronology see pp. 4–5, §§ I–II). In the later story it is said (TT p. 131) that 'Forty leagues and more it was, as a bird flies, from Edoras to the fords of the Isen', and this agrees very well with the First Map, where the distance is almost 2.5 cm., or 125 miles (= just over 40 leagues). It may have been a closer look at the map that led to the extension of the ride across the plain by a further day. On the other hand, there was also an evident difficulty with the chronology as it now stood: see p. 4, § I.

The original draft continues:

HELM'S DEEP

Aragorn and Legolas rode with Éomer's *éored*. That company needed no guide more keen of sight than Legolas, or a man who knew the land, far and wide about, better than Éomer himself. Slowly, and as silently as they might, they went through the night, turning back from the plain, and climbing westward into the dim folds about the mountains' feet. They came upon few of the enemy, except here and there a roving band of orcs who fled ere the riders could slay many; but ever the rumour of war grew behind them. Soon they could hear harsh singing, and if they turned and looked back they could see, winding up from the low country, red torches, countless points of fiery light. A very wood of trees must have been felled to furnish them. Every now and then a brighter blaze leaped up.

'It is a great host,' said Aragorn, 'and follows us close.'

'They bring fire,' said Éomer, 'and are burning as they come all that they can kindle: rick and cot and tree. We shall have a great debt to pay them.'

'The reckoning is not far off,' said Aragorn. 'Shall we soon find ground where we can turn and stand?'

'Yes,' said Éomer. 'Across the wide mouth of the coomb, at some distance from Helmsgate there is a fall in the ground, so sharp and sheer that to those approaching it seems as if they came upon a wall. This we call [Stanshelf Stanscylf >][14] Helm's dike. In places it is twenty feet high, and on the top it has been crowned with a rampart of great stones, piled in ancient days. There we will stand. Thither the other companies will also come. There are three ways that lead up through breaches in the cliff:[15] these we must hold strongly.'

It was dark, starless and moonless, when they came to [the Stanshelf >] Helm's dike. Éomer led them up by a broad sloping path that climbed through a deep notch in the cliff and came out upon the new level some way behind the rampart. They were unchallenged. No one was there before them, friend or foe.[16] At once Éomer set guards upon the [breaches >] Inlets. Ere long other companies arrived, creeping up the valley from various directions. There were wide grass-slopes between the rampart and the Stanrock. There they set their horses under such guards as could be spared from the manning of the wall.

Gimli stood leaning against a great stone at a high point of the [Stanshelf >] dike not far from the inlet by which they had entered. Legolas was on the stone above fingering his bow and peering into the blackness.

14   THE WAR OF THE RING

'This is more to my liking,' said the dwarf, stamping his feet on the ground. 'Ever my heart lightens as we draw near the mountains. There is good rock here. This country has hard bones. I feel it under my feet. Give me a year and a hundred of my kin and we could make this a place that armies would break against like water.'

'I doubt it not,' said Legolas. 'But you're a dwarf, and dwarves are strange folk. I like it not, and shall like it no more by the light of day. But you comfort me, Gimli, and I am glad to have you stand by me with your stout legs and hard axe.'

Shapes loomed up beside them. It was Éomer and Aragorn walking together along the line of the rampart. 'I am anxious,' said Éomer. 'Most have now arrived; but one company is still lacking, and also the King and his guard.'

'If you will give me some hardy men, I will take Gimli and Legolas here, and go a little down the valley and look for tidings,' said Aragorn.

'And find more than you are looking for,' said Gimli.

'That is likely,' said Éomer. 'We will wait a while.'

A slow time passed, when suddenly at no great distance down the valley a clamour broke out. Horns sounded. 'There are some of our folk come into an ambush, or taken in the rear,' cried Éomer. 'Théoden will be there. Wait here, I will hold the men back to the wall, and choose some to go forth. I will be back swiftly.'

Horns sounded again, and in the still darkness they could hear the clash of weapons. In brief while Éomer returned with twenty men.

'This errand I will take,' said Aragorn. 'You are needed on the wall. Come, Legolas! Your eyes will serve us.' He sped down the slope.

'Where Legolas goes, I go,' said Gimli, and ran after them.

The watchers on the wall saw nothing for a while, then suddenly there were louder cries, and wilder yells. A clear voice rang, echoing in the hills. *Elendil!* It seemed that far below in the shadows a white flame flashed.

'Branding goes to war at last,' said Éomer.

A horseman appeared before the main breach, and was admitted. 'Where is Théoden King?' asked Éomer.

'Among his guard,' said the man. 'But many are unhorsed. We rode into an ambush, and orcs sprang out of the ground

HELM'S DEEP

15

among us, hamstringing many of our steeds. Snowmane and the King escaped; for that horse is nightsighted, and sprang over the heads of the orcs. But Théoden dismounted and fought among his guard. Herugrim sang a song that has long been silent. Aragorn is with them, and he sends word that a great host of orcs is on his heels. Man the wall! He will come in by the main breach if he can.'

The noise of battle drew nearer. Those on the rampart could do nothing to aid. They had not many archers among them, and these could not shoot in the darkness while their friends were still in front. One by one men of the missing company came in, till all but five were mustered. Last came the King's guard on foot, with the King in their midst, leading Snowmane.

'Hasten, Lord!' cried Éomer.

At that moment there was a wild cry. Orcs were attacking the [breaches >] inlets on either hand, and before the King had been brought in to safety out of the darkness there sprang a host of dark shapes driving towards the great breach. A white fire shone. There in their path could be seen for a moment Aragorn son of Arathorn: on his one side was Gimli, on the other Legolas.

'Back now, my comrades!' cried Aragorn. 'I will follow.' Even as Gimli and Legolas ran back towards the rampart, he leaped forward. Before the flame of Branding the orcs fled. Then slowly Aragorn retreated walking backward. Even as he did so step by step one great orc came forward, while others stalked behind him. As Aragorn turned at last to run up the inlet, the orc sprang after him: but an arrow whined and he fell sprawling and lay still. For some time no others dared to draw near. 'Sure is the shaft of the elven bow, and keen are the eyes of Legolas!' said Aragorn as he joined the elf and they ran together to the rampart.

Thus at last the King's host was brought within the fastness, and turned to bay before the mouth of Helm's Deep. The night was not yet old, and many hours of darkness and peril yet remained. Théoden was unhurt; but he grieved for the loss of so many of the horses of his guard, and he looked upon Snowmane bleeding at the shoulder: a glancing arrow had struck him. 'Fair is the riding forth, friend,' he said; 'but often the road is bitter.'

'Grieve not for Snowmane, lord,' said Aragorn. 'The hurt is light. I will tend it, with such skill as I have, while the enemy still

16   THE WAR OF THE RING

holds off. They have suffered losses more grievous than ours, and will suffer more if they dare to assail this place.'

Here the original draft ends as formed narrative, but continues as an outline, verging on narrative. This was written over a faint pencilled text that seems to have been much the same.

There is an attack. Endless numbers. Grappling hooks, ladders, piled slain. Riders block breaches with stones from high places, and with bodies. Orcs keep on getting in. Riders lose few men, most at breaches. Orcs once got near the horses. Late in the night the (waning?) moon shone fitfully, and the defenders see a boiling throng beneath the wall. Slowly the dead were piling up.

Wild men in steel mesh forced the north breach, and turning south began to drive men from the rampart. Orcs clamber over. Dawn sees the Men of Rohan giving way all along. The horses are taken away to Helm's Deep, with the King. They make a shieldwall and retreat slowly up towards the Stanrock.

The sun comes out, and then all stare: defenders and attackers. A mile or so below the Dike, from North to South in a great crescent, they beheld a marvel. Men rubbed their eyes thinking that they dreamed or were dizzy with wounds and weariness. Where all had been upland and grass-clad slopes, there stood now a wood of great trees. Like beeches they were, robed in withered leaves, and like ancient oaks with tangled boughs, and gnarled pines stood dark among them. The orcs gave back. The Wild Men wavered crying in terrified voices, for they came from the woods under the west sides of the Misty Mountains.

At that moment from the Stanrock a trumpet sounded. Forth rode Théoden with his guard, and a company (of Heorulf's men?). They charged down crashing into the Wild Men and driving them back in ruin over the cliff.

'Wizardry is abroad!' said [?men]. 'What can this betoken?'

'Wizardry maybe,' said Éomer. 'But it seems not to be any device of our enemies. See how dismayed they are.'

A few lines of very rapid and partly illegible notes follow:

Their horses were often nightsighted; but the men were not so nightsighted as the orcs. Rohan at a disadvantage in dark. As soon as it grows light they are able to fight. The orcs are no match for the horsemen on the slopes before the Stanrock. Sorties from Helm's Deep and Stanrock. Orcs dive back over wall. It is then that the Wood is seen.

HELM'S DEEP

17

Orcs trapped. Trees grab them. And the wood is full of Herulf's folk. Gandalf has collected the wanderers. [?About] 500. Hardly any of the attackers escape. So hopelessness turns to victory. Meanwhile Herulf told by Gandalf to hold the .... rode ....
another force sent .... Eodoras. This is now caught between Herulf and the victorious forces of the King. In a battle on the plain .... terror struck by Aragorn and Gandalf. The host not wishing to rest rides down the fleeing remnant [?back towards] Isengard.

The sentence beginning 'Meanwhile Herulf told by Gandalf to hold the' might possibly, but very doubtfully indeed, be completed: 'eastern rode [*for* road] has resisted another force sent towards Eodoras.'

This then was the original story of Helm's Deep, to become far more complex in its development with the emergence of a much more elaborate system of fortification across the mouth of the Deep (the description and narrative in *The Two Towers* can be followed, incidentally, very precisely in my father's drawing, 'Helm's Deep and the Hornburg', in *Pictures by J. R. R. Tolkien*, no. 26). In this earliest account the 'fastness' consisted only of the sudden natural fall in the land across the mouth of the coomb, fortified with a parapet of great stones; in this there were three 'breaches', a word that my father changed to 'inlets', perhaps to suggest that they had been deliberately made. The nature of the 'hold' of Heorulf on the Stanrock is not indicated; and all the battle of Helm's Deep took place along the line of Helm's Dike.

An isolated scrap of drafting that was not finally used evidently belongs with the original story and may be included here:

Aragorn was away behind the defences tending the wound in Snowmane's shoulder, and speaking gentle words to the horse. As the fragrance of *athelas* rose in the air, his mind went back to the defence on Weathertop, and to the escape from Moria. 'It is a long journey,' he said to himself. 'From one hopeless corner we escape but to find another more desperate. Yet alas, Frodo, I would be happier in heart if you were with us in this grim place. Where now do you wander?'

Written on this same page is an outline in which the radical alteration of the story of the assault first enters.

When Éomer and Aragorn reach Dike they are challenged. Heorulf has left watchers on Dike. They report that the fort of Helm's Gate is manned – mainly older men, and most of the folk of the Westmarch have taken refuge in the Deep. Great store of food and fodder is in the caves.

18   THE WAR OF THE RING

Then follows story as told above until rescue of King.[17]

Éomer and Aragorn decide that they cannot hold Dike in dark (without archers). The Dike is over a mile – 2 miles? – long. The main host and King go to Stanrock. The horses are led to the Deep. Aragorn and Éomer with a few men (their horses ready in rear) hold the inlets as long as they dare. These they block with stones rolled from the rampart.

The assault on the inlets. Soon drives in as the Orcs clamber up rampart in between. Ladders? Wild men drive in from North Inlet. The defenders flee. Tremendous assault upon the mouth of the Deep where a high stone wall was built. [*Added here but at the same time:* breastwork crowned with stones. Here G[imli] speaks his words. *Reduce description of Helm's Dike* – it is *not* fortified.] Orcs boil round foot of the Stanrock. Then describe the assault as above.[18] Orcs piling up over the wall. Wild men climb on the goblins' dead bodies. Moon ... men fighting on the wall top.[19] Disadvantage of the Riders. The wall taken and Rohan driven back into the gorge. Dawn. Éomer and Aragorn go to the Stanrock to stand by the King in the Tower.

They see in the sunlight the wonder of the Wood.

Charge of Théoden (Éomer left, Aragorn right). [? With day fortunes change.] Men issue on horses. But the host is vast, only it is disconcerted by the Wood. Almost [? the watchers could] believe it had moved up the valley as the battle raged.

Trees should come right up to Dike. In the midst out rides Gandalf from the wood. And rides through the orcs as if they were rats and crows.

My father •began a new text of the chapter before important elements in the story and in the physical setting had been clarified, and as a result this (the first completed manuscript) is an extremely complicated document. It was only after he had begun it that he extended the ride from Eodoras by a further day, and described the great storm coming up out of the East (TT pp. 131–2); and when he began it he had not yet realised that Helm's Dike was not the scene of the great assault: 'what really happened' was that the men manning the Dike were driven in, and the defence of the redoubt was at the line of a great wall further up at the mouth of the gorge – the 'Deeping Wall' – and the Hornburg. At this point in the manuscript the story can be seen changing as my father wrote: in Éomer's reply to Aragorn's question 'Shall we soon find ground where we can turn and stand?' (p. 13) he begins as before with an account of the fortification of the Dike ('crowned with a rampart of great stones, piled in ancient

HELM'S DEEP   19

days'), but by the end of his reply he is saying that the Dike cannot be held:

'... But we cannot long defend it, for we have not enough strength. It is near two miles from end to end, and is pierced by two wide breaches. We shall not be able to stand at bay till we get to the Stanrock, and come behind the wall that guards the entrance to the Deep. That is high and strong, for Heorulf had it repaired and raised not long ago.'

Immediately after this the Deeping Stream entered, and the two breaches in the Dike were reduced to one: there 'a stream flows down out of the Deep, and beside it the road runs from Helm's Gate to the valley.'[20] At this stage, however, the final story was still not reached, but follows the outline just given (p. 18):

The King and the main part of his host now rode on to man the Stanrock and Heorulf's wall. But the Westmarchers would not yet abandon the dike while any hope remained of Heorulf's return. Éomer and Aragorn and a few picked men stayed with them guarding the breach; for it seemed to Éomer that they might do great harm to the advance-guard of the enemy and then escape swiftly ere the main strength of the orcs and wild men forced the passage.

The story from this point was built up in a textually extremely complex series of short drafts leading to more finished forms, while earlier portions of the chapter were changed to accommodate the evolving conception of the redoubt as the scene of the battle. To follow this evolution in all its detail would require a very great deal of space, and I record only certain rejected narrative ideas and other particular points of interest.

Before the story (TT pp. 138–40) of the sortie of Éomer and Aragorn from the postern gate emerged, the repulse of the attack on the great gates of the Hornburg was differently conceived:

Now with a great cry a company of the wild men moved forward, among them they bore the trunk of a great tree. The orcs crowded about them. The tree was swung by many strong hands, and smote the timbers with a boom. At that moment there was a sudden call. Among the boulders upon the flat and narrow rim beneath the fastness and the brink a few brave men had lain hidden. Aragorn was their leader. 'Up now, up now,' he shouted. 'Out Branding, out!' A blade flashed like white fire. 'Elendil, Elendil!' he shouted, and his voice echoed in the cliffs.

20   THE WAR OF THE RING

'See, see!' said Éomer. 'Branding has gone to war at last. Why am I not there? We were to have drawn blades together.'

None could withstand the onset of Aragorn, or the terror of his sword. The orcs fled, the hill-men were hewn down, or fled leaving their ram upon the ground. The rock was cleared. Then Aragorn and his men turned to run back within the gates while there was yet time. His men had passed within, when again the lightning flashed. Thunder crashed. From among the fallen at the top of the causeway three huge orcs sprang up – the white hand could be seen on their shields. Men shouted warning from the gates, and Aragorn for an instant turned. At that moment the foremost of the orcs hurled a stone: it struck him on the helm and he stumbled, falling to his knee. The thunder rolled. Before he could get up and back the three orcs were upon him.

Here this story was overtaken by that of the sortie from the postern. In the final manuscript form of this, Aragorn, looking at the gates, added after the words (TT p. 139) 'Their great hinges and iron bars were wrenched and bent; many of their timbers were cracked': 'The doors will not withstand another such battering.' These words were left out of the typescript that followed, but there is nothing in the manuscript to suggest that they should be, and it seems clear that their omission was an error (especially since they give point to Éomer's reply: 'Yet we cannot stay here beyond the walls to defend them').

Gimli's cry as he sprang on the Orcs who had fallen on Éomer: *Baruk Khazâd! Khazâd ai-mênu!* appears in this form from the first writing of the scene. Years later, after the publication of LR, my father began on an analysis of all fragments of other languages (Quenya, Sindarin, Khuzdul, the Black Speech) found in the book, but unhappily before he had reached the end of FR the notes, at the outset full and elaborate, had diminished to largely uninterpretable jottings. *Baruk* he here translated as 'axes', without further comment; *ai-mênu* is analysed as *aya, mēnu*, but the meanings are not clearly legible: most probably *aya* 'upon', *mēnu* 'acc. pl. you'.

A curious point arises in Gimli's remark after his rescue of Éomer during the sortie from the postern gate (TT p. 140): 'Till now I have hewn naught but wood since I left Moria.' This is clearly inconsistent with Legolas' words in 'The Departure of Boromir', when he and Gimli came upon Aragorn beside Boromir's body near Parth Galen: 'We have hunted and slain many Orcs in the woods'; compare also the draft of a later passage (VII.386) where, when Aragorn, Legolas and Gimli set out in pursuit of the Orcs, Gimli says: '... those that attacked Boromir were not the only ones. Legolas and I met some away southwards on the west slopes of Amon Hen. *We slew many*, creeping on them among the trees ...' I do not think that any

HELM'S DEEP

21

'explanation' of this will serve: it is simply an inconsistency never observed.[21]

The 'wild hill-men' at the assault on Helm's Deep came from 'Westfold', valleys on the western side of the Misty Mountains (see p. 8 and note 4), and this application of 'Westfold' survived until a late stage of revision of the manuscript: it was still present in drafting for what became 'The Road to Isengard'.[22] Until the change in application was made, the Westfold Vale was called 'the Westmarch Vale'.

In this connection there are two notable passages. The dialogue between Aragorn and Éomer and Gamling the Westmarcher on the Deeping Wall, hearing the cries of the wild men below (TT p. 142), takes this form in a rejected draft:

'I hear them,' said Éomer; 'but they are only as the scream of birds and the bellowing of beasts to my ears.'

'Yet among them are many that cry in the tongue of Westfold [*later* > in the Dunland tongue],' said Aragorn; 'and that is a speech of men, and once was accounted good to hear.'

'True words you speak,' said Gamling, who had climbed now on the wall. 'I know that tongue. It is ancient, and once was spoken in many valleys of the Mark. But now it is used in deadly hate. They shout rejoicing in our doom. "The king, the king!" they cry. "We will take their king! Death to the Forgoil! Death to the Strawheads! Death to the robbers of the North." Such names they have for us. Not in half a thousand years have they forgot their grievance, that the lords of Gondor gave the Mark to Eorl the Young as a reward for his service to Elendil and Isildur, while they held back. It is this old hatred that Saruman has inflamed. ...'

With this compare the passage in drafting of 'The King of the Golden Hall' (VII.444) where Aragorn, seeing on one of the hangings in the Golden Hall the figure of the young man on a white horse, said: 'Behold Eorl the Young! Thus he rode out of the North to the Battle of the Field of Gorgoroth' – the battle in which Sauron was overthrown by Gil-galad and Elendil.[23] On the enormously much briefer time-span that my father conceived at this time see VII.450 note 11.

An extremely rapid initial sketch for the parley between Aragorn, standing above the gates of the Hornburg, and the enemy below shows an entirely different conception from that in TT (p. 145):

Aragorn and the Captain of Westfold.
Westfolder says if the King is yielded all may go alive. Where to? To Isengard. Then the Westmarch is to be given back to us, and all the .... land.

22   THE WAR OF THE RING

Who says so? Saruman. That is indeed a good warrant.
Aragorn rebukes Westfolder for [??aiding] Orcs. Westfolder is humbled.
Orc captain jeers. Needs must accept the terms when no others will serve. We are the Uruk-hai, we slay!
Orcs shoot an arrow at Aragorn as they retreat. But the Westfold Captain hews down the archer.

On the back of the page in which the new story of the assault entered (p. 17) my father wrote the following names: *Rohirwaith Rochirchoth Rohirhoth Rochann Rohann Rohirrim*; and also *Éomeark Éomearc*. I do not know whether *Rochann, Rohann* is to be associated with the use of *Rohan* on pp. 16, 18 apparently as a term for the Riders.[24]

In a draft for the passage describing the charge from the Hornburg the King rode with Aragorn at his right hand and Háma at his left. For Háma's death before the gates of the Hornburg see p. 41 note 8.

Lastly, at the end of the chapter, Legolas, seeing the strange Wood beyond Helm's Dike, said: 'This is wizardry indeed! "Greenleaf, Greenleaf, when thy last shaft is shot, under strange trees shalt thou go." Come! I would look on this forest, ere the spell changes.' The words he cited were from the riddling verse addressed to him by Galadriel and borne by Gandalf ('The White Rider', VII.431):

Greenleaf, Greenleaf, bearer of the elven-bow,
Far beyond Mirkwood many trees on earth grow.
Thy last shaft when thou hast shot, under strange trees
                                          shalt thou go!

His words were not corrected on the manuscript, and survived into the typescript that followed (see p. 420).

NOTES

1   For the subsequent history of this passage see pp. 4–6.
2   *Tindtorras*: earlier name for the *Thrihyrne*; see VII.320.
3   In the first version of 'The King of the Golden Hall' the Second Master of the Mark was Eofored, and when Théodred appears he is not Théoden's son (see VII.446–7 and note 17). The 'First Battle of the Fords of Isen', in which Théodred fell, was now present (VII.444 and note 12), and in a contemporary time-scheme is dated January 25, the day before the death of Boromir and the Breaking of the Fellowship (in LR February 25 and 26).
4   On the First Map (redrawn section IV^D, VII.319) *Westfold* was written against a vale on the western side of the Misty Mountains, south of *Dunland* (though afterwards struck out in this position and reinserted along the northern foothills of the Black Mountains west of Eodoras). It cannot be said whether *Dunland*

HELM'S DEEP

23

and *Westfold* originally stood together on the map as names of distinct regions, or whether *Dunland* was only entered when *Westfold* was removed.

5   The change from *Trumbold* to *Herulf*, *Heorulf* (afterwards Erkenbrand) was made while this initial drafting was in progress.

6   My father first wrote *Dimgræf*, but changed it as he wrote to *Heorulf's Clough*; above this he wrote *the Dimhale* (*hale* representing Old English *halh*, *healh*, 'corner, nook of land'), and after it *Herelaf's Clough*, this being struck out. In the margin he wrote *Nerwet* (Old English, 'narrow place'); and at the head of the page *Neolnearu* and *Neolnerwet* (Old English *neowol*, *nēol* 'deep, profound'), also *the Clough*, *the Long Clough*, and *Theostercloh* (Old English *þēostor* 'dark'). *Clough* is from Old English *clōh* 'steep-sided valley or ravine'.

7   Following this my father wrote, but struck out, '*Dimhale's Door*, by some called *Herulf's Hold (Burg)*'; and in the margin he wrote *Dimgraf's gate*, and *Dimmhealh* (see note 6).

8   *Nerwet*: see note 6.

9   The words enclosed in square brackets are lost (but are obtained from the following draft) through a square having been cut out of the page: possibly there was a small sketch-map here of 'Heorulf's Clough' and the 'Hold'.

10   Before *Helm's Deep* my father first wrote *Helmshaugh*, *haugh* being the Northern English and Scottish development of Old English *halh* (note 6).

11   *Heorulf's Hoe*: *Hoe* is from Old English *hōh* 'heel' (used in place-names in various senses, such as 'the end of a ridge where the ground begins to fall steeply').

12   The map redrawn on p. 269 is anomalous in this respect as in many others.

13   The extension of the ride across the plain by a day, and the shift in the date of the (second) battle of the Fords of Isen to January 31, entered in revision to the completed manuscript of 'Helm's Deep': see p. 18.

14   *Stanscylf*, beside *Stanshelf*, has the Old English form *scylf* (*sc* = *sh*).

15   *the cliff*: i.e. the Stanshelf, the great natural fall in the ground, constituting a rampart.

16   Cf. the two versions of the scout's report: 'many are making for Herulf's Hold, and say that Herulf is already there' (p. 10); 'some are making for the Clough, but it seems that Nothelm [> Heorulf] is not there' (p. 11).

17   In the first draft the fastness was deserted when the host from Eodoras arrived (p. 13). 'Then follows story as told above until rescue of King' refers to the story in the first draft given on pp. 13–16.

24   THE WAR OF THE RING

18 This presumably refers to the outline given on p. 16, where the assault was at the line of Helm's Dike, unless some other early account of the assault has been lost.

19 A scrap of drafting has the phrase 'Fitful late moon saw men fighting on the top of the wall'; but the illegible word here is not *saw*, though that may have been intended.

20 It is subsequently said (but rejected) of the Deeping Stream in this manuscript that 'far to the north it joined the Isen River and made the western border of the Mark.'

21 The second of these passages (VII.386) was lost in TT (p. 22). In the fair copy manuscript of 'The Departure of Boromir' as originally written Legolas in the first passage (TT p. 16) said only: 'Alas! We came when we heard the horn, but we are too late. Are you much hurt?'; the fuller form of his opening words on seeing Aragorn, in which he mentions the hunting and slaying of Orcs with Gimli in the woods, was added later (both to the manuscript and the following typescript). It is therefore possible that my father had now rejected the idea that appears in the second passage ('We slew many'), and did not reinstate it again until after the writing of 'Helm's Deep'. But this seems unlikely, and in any case does not alter the fact of the inconsistency in the published work. This inconsistency may have been observed before, but it was pointed out to me by Mr. Ralph L. McKnight, Jr.

22 Another notable instance of the overlapping in this part of the story is found in the name *Erkenbrand*. This appears in late stages of the revision of the completed manuscript of 'Helm's Deep', but it was a replacement of *Erkenwald* (itself replacing *Heorulf*); and *Erkenwald* is still the name of the Lord of Westfold in drafting for what became the chapter 'Flotsam and Jetsam'. See p. 40 note 2.

23 In TT (p. 142) Gamling says: 'Not in half a thousand years have they forgotten their grievance that the lords of Gondor gave the Mark to Eorl the Young *and made alliance with him.*'

24 In addition, the form *Rohir* is found in this chapter; this has occurred in the manuscript of 'The White Rider' (VII.433 note 8). *Rohirrim* is found in the completed manuscript of 'Helm's Deep', but it was not yet established, for *Rohir* appears in the final fair copy manuscript of 'The Road to Isengard' (p. 40), and much later, in 'Faramir' ('The Window on the West'), both *Rohir* and *Rohiroth* are used (pp. 155–6).

III

THE ROAD TO ISENGARD

This chapter was at first continuous with 'Helm's Deep', and when the division was made it received the title 'To Isengard' (Chapter XXIX). The preparatory drafting was here much more voluminous than that of 'Helm's Deep', because the first form of the story had reached a developed form and a clear manuscript before it was rejected. The interpretation of the very confused papers for this chapter is particularly difficult, since it is necessary to distinguish between drafts (often closely similar) for passages in the first version and drafts for passages in the second.

The essential differences in the original version from the form in *The Two Towers* are these: Gandalf and Théoden and their companions left Helm's Deep shortly after the end of the battle (see p. 5, § III); they did not see the Ents as they left the mysterious wood, and they did not go down to the Fords of Isen; but they encountered, and spoke with, Bregalad the Ent, bearing a message from Treebeard, in the course of their ride to Isengard, which they reached on the same day. In this chapter I shall give those parts of the original version that are significantly different from the later form, citing them from the completed manuscript of that version but with certain passages from the initial drafts given in the notes.[1]

First, however, there is an outline that my father evidently set down before he began work on the chapter. This was written in the rapid and often barely legible soft pencil that was usual for these preliminary sketches, but in this case a good deal of the outline was inked over.

Meeting of the chieftains. Éomer and Gimli return from Deep. (Both wounded and are tended by Aragorn?) Gandalf explains that he had ridden ranged about gathering scattered men. The coming of the King had diverted Isengard from Eodoras. But he [Gandalf] had sent some men back to defend it against marauders. Erkenbrand[2] had been [?ambushed] and the few horses remaining after the disaster at Isenford had been lost. He had [?perforce retreated] into hills.

They ask Gandalf about the Trees. The answer lies in Isengard, he said. We go now thither speedily – such as will.

Aragorn, Éomer, Gimli, Legolas, King Théoden and his company and [?a force] .... to Isengard. Erkenbrand. Gamling. Repair of Hornburg.

26   THE WAR OF THE RING

They pass down a great .... aisle among the trees that [?seems now to have opened]. No orcs to be seen. Strange murmurs and noises and half-voices among the trees. [*Added:* Gandalf discusses his tactics. Gimli describes the caves. *Here the overwriting in ink begins:*]

The sun shines in the plain. They see a tall giant figure striding towards them. The Riders draw swords, and are astonished. The figure greets Gandalf.

I am Bregalad the Quickbeam, he said. I come from Treebeard.

What does he wish? said Gandalf.

He wishes you to hasten. He wants to know what he is to do with Saruman!

Hm! said Gandalf. That is a problem. Tell him I am coming!

What was that, said Théoden. And who is Treebeard?

He was an Ent, said Gandalf. And so is Treebeard.

They hasten and enter Nan Gurunír. There they find a heap of ruins. The great walls of Isengard were burst and flung down in confusion. Only the tower of Orthanc stood alone in the midst of desolation, from which a great smoke went up. The great arch still stands, but a pile of rubble stands before it. On the top of the pile sat — Merry and Pippin, having lunch.[3] They jumped up, and as Pippin had his mouth full, Merry spoke.

'Welcome, lords, to Isengard!' he said. 'We are the door-wardens: Meriadoc son of Caradoc of Buckland is my name; and my companion is Peregrin son of Paladin of Tuckborough.[4] Far in the North is our home. The lord Saruman is within, but [alas, he is indisposed and unable to receive guests. >] at the moment he is closeted with one Wormtongue discussing urgent business.'

'It is possible that we could help in the debate,' laughed Gandalf. 'But where is Treebeard? I have no time to jest with young hobbits.'

'So we find you at last,' said Aragorn. 'You have given us a long journey.'

'How long have you been at Isengard?' said Gimli.

'Less than a day,' said Pippin.[5]

I turn now to the first version of the story, that is the first completed and coherent manuscript. In this, Théoden's words with Gandalf about riding to Isengard (TT p. 149) have a different outcome:

THE ROAD TO ISENGARD 27

'Nonetheless to Isengard I go,' said Gandalf. 'Let those who are weary rest. For soon there will be other work to do. I shall not stay long. My way lies eastward. Look for me in Eodoras, ere the moon is full!'

'Nay,' said Théoden. 'In the dark hour before dawn I doubted. But we will not part now. I will ride with you, if that is your counsel. And now I will send out messengers with tidings of victory through all the vales of the Mark; and they shall summon all men, old and young, to meet me at Eodoras, ere the moon wanes.'

'Good!' said Gandalf. 'Then in one hour we ride again. ...'[6]

After a brief hour of rest and the breaking of their fast, those who were to ride to Isengard made ready to depart.[7]

The account of the treatment of the men of Dunland and the burials (TT p. 150) reaches the final form,[8] but the description of the departure of the trees in the night and of the valley after they had gone, told in almost the same words as in TT,[9] first entered at this point, whereas in TT it is postponed till much later in the chapter (p. 158). The passage of the wood, and Gimli's description to Legolas of the Caves of Helm's Deep, reach in the completed manuscript of the first version almost exactly the form in TT (pp. 152–3), but with a slight structural difference, in that here the company had already left the trees and come to the road-parting when this conversation took place:

They passed through the wood and found that they had come to the bottom of the coomb, where the road from Helm's Deep branched, going one way to Eodoras and the other to the fords of the Isen. Legolas looked back with regret.

'Those are the strangest trees that ever I saw,' he said ...

Thus at the end of their talk together the old version again differs:

'You have my promise,' said Legolas. 'But now we must leave all that behind. How far is it to Isengard, Gandalf?'

'It is about twelve [*later* > fourteen > eleven] leagues from the bottom of Deeping Coomb to the outer wall of Isengard,'[10] said the wizard, turning round.

'And what shall we see there?' asked Gimli. 'You may know, but I cannot guess.'

'I do not know myself for certain,' answered Gandalf. 'Things may have changed again, since I was there last night. But we

28   THE WAR OF THE RING

shall all know before long. If we are eager for the answer to riddles, let us quicken the pace!'

[*Added:* 'Lead us!' said Théoden. 'But do not let Shadowfax set a pace we cannot keep!'

The company rode forward now with all the speed they could, over the wide grasses of the Westemnet.]

Thus the Caves of Helm's Deep do not receive from Gandalf here the name 'the Glittering Caves of Aglarond', which was only added to the typescript text at a later stage (see p. 77).

The first version of the story now becomes decisively different from that in *The Two Towers* (pp. 154 ff.).

The sun shone upon the vale about them. After the storm the morning was fresh, and a breeze was now flowing from the west between the mountains. The swelling grass-lands rose and fell, with long ridges and shallow dales like a wide green sea. Upon their left long slopes ran swiftly down to the Isen River, a grey ribbon that bent westward, winding away out of sight through the great Gap of Rohan to the distant shores of Belfalas.[11] Below them now lay the fords of Isen, where the river spread in stony shoals between long grassy terraces. They did not go that way. Gandalf led them due north, and they passed by, riding along the high ground on the east of the river; yet as they rode other eyes were turned towards the stony fords and the battlefield where so many good men of the Mark had fallen.[12] They saw crows wheeling and crying in the air, and borne upon the wind they heard the howling of wolves. The carrion-birds were gathered at the fords, and even the bright day had not driven them from their business.

'Alas!' cried Théoden. 'Shall we leave the steeds and riders of the Mark to be picked and torn by fowl and wolf? Let us turn aside!'

'There is no need, lord,' said Gandalf. 'The task would take us long, were it still left to do; but it is not. No horse or rider of your folk lies there unburied. Their graves are deep and their mounds are high; and long may they watch the fords! My friends have laboured there.[13] It is with the orcs, their masters, that the wolves and carrion-birds hold their feast: such is the friendship of their kind.'

'You accomplished much in an evening and a night, Gandalf my friend,' said Théoden.

THE ROAD TO ISENGARD
29

'With the help of Shadowfax – and others,' answered Gandalf. 'And this I can report for your comfort: the losses in the battles of the ford were less grievous than we thought at first. Many men were scattered but not slain. Some I guided to join Erkenwald, and some I gathered again and sent back to Eodoras. I found that all the strength of Saruman was hurrying to Helm's Deep; for the great force that had been ordered to go straight to Eodoras was turned aside and joined to those that had pursued Erkenwald. When it was known that you, Théoden King, were in the field, and Éomer beside you, a mad eagerness came upon them. To take you and slay Éomer was what Saruman most desired. Nonetheless I feared that wolf-riders and cruel plunderers might be sent swiftly to Eodoras and do great harm there, since it was unmanned. But now I think you need not fear; you will find the Golden Hall to welcome your return.'

They had been riding for about an hour since they left the Coomb, and already the dark mountainous arms of Nan Gurunír were opening wide before them. It seemed filled with smoke. Out of it the river flowed, now near upon their left. Suddenly they were aware of a strange figure striding south along the stream towards them.

This last paragraph was replaced by the following:

They had been riding for almost an hour [> It was close on noon. They had been riding for two hours][14] since they left the Coomb, and now the mountainous arms of Nan Gurunír began to stretch towards them. There seemed to be a mist about the hills, and they saw rising up out of deep shadows a vast spire of smoke and vapour; as it mounted it caught the light of the sun, and spread in glowing billows in the sky, and the wind bore them over the plain.

'What do you think of that, Gandalf?' said Théoden. 'One would say that all the Wizard's Vale was burning.'

'There is ever a fume above that valley in these days,' said Éomer; 'but I have never seen anything like this before. These are steams, rather than smokes. Some devilry Saruman is brewing to greet us.'

'Maybe,' said Gandalf. 'If so, we shall soon learn what it is.'[15]

Out of the steaming vale the river Isen flowed, now close upon their left hand. As they were gazing north, they were suddenly aware of a strange figure striding south along the east

30   THE WAR OF THE RING

bank of the stream. It went at great speed, walking stilted like a
wading heron, and yet the long paces were as quick, rather, as
the beat of wings; and as it approached they saw that it was very
tall, a troll in height, or a young tree.

Many of the horsemen cried aloud in wonder, and some drew
their swords. But Gandalf raised his hand.

'Let us wait,' he said. 'Here is a messenger for me.'

'A strange one to my eyes,' said Théoden. 'What kind of
creature may it be?'

'It is long since you listened to tales by the fireside,' answered
Gandalf; 'and in that rather than in white hairs you show your
age, without increase in wisdom.[16] There are children in your
land that out of the twisted threads of many stories could have
picked the answer to your question at a glance. Here comes an
Ent, an Ent out of Fangorn, that your tongue calls the Entwood
– did you think the name was given only in idle fancy?[17] Nay,
Théoden, it is otherwise: to them you are but the passing tale:
all the years from Eorl the Young to Théoden the Old are of
little count to them.'

Théoden was silent, and all the company halted, watching the
strange figure with wondering eyes as it came quickly on to meet
them. Man or troll, he was ten or twelve feet high, strong but
slim, clad in glistening close-fitting grey and dappled brown, or
else his smooth skin was like the rind of a fair rowan-tree. He
had no weapon, and as he came his long shapely arms and
many-fingered hands were raised in sign of peace. Now he stood
before them, a few paces off, and his clear eyes, deep grey with
glints of green, looked solemnly from face to face of the men
that were gathered round him.[18] Then he spoke slowly, and his
voice was resonant and musical.

'Is this the company of Théoden, master of the green fields of
Men?' he said. 'Is Gandalf here? I seek Gandalf, the white rider.'

'I am here,' said Gandalf. 'What do you wish?'

'I am Bregalad Quickbeam,' answered the Ent. 'I come from
Treebeard. He is eager for news of the battle, and he is anxious
concerning the Huorns.[19] Also he is troubled in his mind about
Saruman, and hopes that Gandalf will come soon to deal with
him. [*Added:* There is no sign or sound from the tower.]'

Gandalf was silent for a moment, stroking his beard thoughtfully. 'Deal with him,' he said. 'That may have many meanings
[> That may have more meanings than one].[20] But how it will
go, I cannot tell till I come. Tell Treebeard that I am on the way,

THE ROAD TO ISENGARD

31

and will hasten. And in the meanwhile, Bregalad, tell him not to be troubled about the Huorns. They have done their task, and taken no hurt. They will return.'

'That is good news,' said the Ent. 'May we soon meet again!' He raised his hand, and turned, and strode off back up the river, so swiftly that before the king's company had recovered from their wonder he was already far away.

The riders now went at greater speed. At last they rode up into the long valley of Nan Gurunír. The land rose steeply, and the long arms of the Misty Mountains, reaching towards the plains, rose upon either side: steep, stony ridges, bare of trees. The valley was sheltered, open only to the sunlit South, and watered by the young river winding in its midst. Fed by many springs and lesser streams among the rain-washed hills, it flowed and bubbled in its bed, already a swift strong water before it found the plain; and all about it once had lain a pleasant fertile land.[21]

The description of Nan Gurunír as it was now is almost as in TT (p. 159), but after the words 'many doubted in their hearts, wondering to what dismal end their journey led' there follows:

Soon they came upon a wide stone-bridge that with a single arch spanned the river, and crossing it they found a road that with a wide northward sweep brought them to the great highway to the fords: stone-paved it was, well-made and well-tended, and no blade of grass was seen in any joint or crack. Not far before them now they knew that the gates of Isengard must stand; and their hearts were heavy, but their eyes could not pierce the mists.

Thus the black pillar surmounted by the White Hand is absent. Being on the east side of Isen they cross the river by a bridge, and come to 'the great highway to the fords'. In TT they followed that road on the west side of Isen up from the fords, and it was at this point that the road became 'a wide street, paved with great flat stones'.[22]

Already in preliminary drafting the description of the Circle of Isengard reached almost its form in TT (pp. 159–60),[23] but that of the tower of Orthanc underwent many changes, which can be related to a series of contemporary illustrations. These descriptions, for clarity in my account, I label A, B, C, D.

The description in the preliminary draft is as follows:

(A)   And in the centre from which all the chained paths ran was a tower, a pinnacle of stone. The base of it, and that two hundred

32 THE WAR OF THE RING

feet in height, was a great cone of rock left by the ancient builders and smoothers of the plain, but now upon it rose a tower of masonry, tier on tier, course on course, each drum smaller than the last. It ended short and flat, so that at the top there was a wide space fifty feet across, reached by a stair that came up the middle.

This description fits the picture captioned 'Orthanc (1)' that was reproduced as frontispiece to Vol. VII, *The Treason of Isengard*,[24] except in one respect: in the text there was 'a wide space fifty feet across' at the top, whereas in the picture the tower is surmounted by three pinnacles or horns (see under 'C' below).

In the completed manuscript of the first version the description begins in the same way,[25] but after 'left by the ancient builders and smoothers of the plain' it continues:

(B) ... a tower of masonry marvellously tall and slender, like a stone horn, that at the tip branched into three tines; and between the tines there was a narrow space where a man could stand a thousand feet above the vale.

This accompanies the drawing labelled 'Orthanc (2)', reproduced on p. 33, where the basal cone is black, and steeper than in 'Orthanc (1)', and the tower much more slender. Against this second description of the tower my father subsequently wrote:

(C) Or – if first picture [i.e. 'Orthanc (1)'] is adopted (but with cone-like rock as in second picture) [i.e. 'Orthanc (2)']:
[a tower of masonry] marvellously tall and strong. Seven round tiers it had, dwindling in girth and height, and at the top were three black horns of stone upon a narrow space where a man could stand a thousand feet above the plain.

This precisely fits 'Orthanc (1)'. It seems likely then that that picture was made after the first description 'A' was written, since it differs from 'A' in that the tower possess three horns at the summit.

The accounts 'B' and 'C' were rejected together and replaced in the manuscript by the following (all this work obviously belonging to the same period):

(D) And in the centre, from which all the chained paths ran, there stood an island in a pool, a great cone of rock, two hundred feet in height, left by the ancient builders and smoothers [> levellers] of the plain, black and smooth and exceeding hard. A yawning chasm clove it from tip to middle into two great fangs and over the chasm was a mighty arch of masonry, and upon the arch a tower was founded, marvellously tall and strong. Seven round tiers it had, dwindling in girth and height, and at the top were three black horns of stone upon a narrow space, where a man could stand a thousand feet above the plain.

This conception is illustrated in the drawings 'Orthanc (3)' and '(4)' on the same page as 'Orthanc (2)' and reproduced below (the distinction between the two enters into successive descriptions of the tower in 'The Voice of Saruman', pp. 61–2). On the back of the page bearing 'Orthanc (1)' my father wrote: 'This is wrong. The rock should be steeper and *cloven*, and the tower should be founded over an *arch* (with greater "horns" at top), as is shown in small sketch (3).' He also wrote here: 'Omit the water-course', but struck this out. A stream or 'moat' surrounding the basal cone is seen in 'Orthanc (1)'. In description 'D' the tower stands on 'an island in a pool' ('in the lake', see note 25).

Finally, a rider was inserted into the first manuscript bearing the definitive description as found in TT (p. 160): 'A peak and isle of rock it was, black, and gleaming hard; four mighty piers of many-sided stone were welded into one, but near the summit they opened into

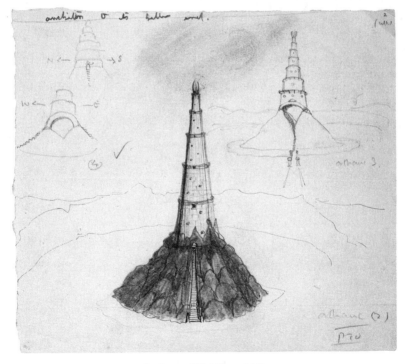

Orthanc '2', '3' and '4'

Orthanc '5'

THE ROAD TO ISENGARD   35

gaping horns, their pinnacles sharp as the points of spears, keen-edged as knives'. The only difference here from the final text is that my father first wrote that the top of Orthanc was three hundred feet above the plain; but this was changed, perhaps at once, to five hundred as in TT. On this rider he wrote: 'to fit Picture (5)', which is reproduced on p. 34. Here the conception is radically changed, and the 'horns', now four, are no longer a device surmounting the tower of diminishing cylindrical tiers but are integral to the marvellous structure of Orthanc.[26]

The successive versions of the description of the tower differ in the statements made about the name *Orthanc* (the earliest statement on the subject appears in a rejected note to the manuscript of 'Treebeard', VII.419: 'It is not perhaps mere chance that *Orthanc* which in Elvish means "a spike of rock" is in the tongue of Rohan "a machine".'). The preliminary draft, following description 'A', has:

> This was Orthanc, the citadel of Saruman, the name of which had double meaning (by design or chance); for in the tongue of the Mark *Orthanc* signified cunning craft, invention, (machine such as those have who fashion machines), but in the elvish speech it means the stony heart, [?tormented] hill.

The original text of the first completed manuscript, following description 'B', has:

> ... for in the language of the Mark *orthanc* signified 'cunning craft', but in the elvish speech it means 'Stone Fang'.

To this 'Cloven-hill' was added subsequently – when the conception of the great cleft in the basal cone arose. Following the description ('D') of that conception the statement about the meaning of the name is the final form: 'for in the elvish speech *orthanc* signifies Mount Fang, but in the language of the Mark of old the Cunning Mind.' It may be therefore that the translation 'Mount Fang' actually arose in association with the description of the cone as cloven 'into two great fangs'.

From here on the text of TT was reached at almost all points in the manuscript of this version to the end of the chapter,[27] but there are some interesting points in the preliminary drafting.

Gandalf's reply to the opening address of Merry (who declares himself 'Meriadoc, Caradoc's son of Buckland'), ending 'or doubtless he would hasten hither to welcome such honourable guests', originally took this form:

> 'Doubtless he would,' laughed Gandalf. 'But what he would say to find two young hobbits mocking him before his gates I do not know. Doubtless it was he that ordered you to guard his doors and watch for their arrival.'

36   THE WAR OF THE RING

Pippin's first observation and its effect on the Riders went thus:

'... Here we are sitting on the field of victory amid the plundered ruins of an arsenal and you wonder where we came by this and that.'
All those of the Riders that were near laughed, and none more loudly than Théoden.

Théoden's loud laughter remained into the completed manuscript, but then his gravity (at least of bearing) was restored and it was removed.
The dialogue concerning hobbits went like this in the draft:

'... This day is fated to be filled with marvels: for here I see alive yet others of the folk of story: the half-high.'
'Hobbits, if you please, lord,' said Pippin.
'Hobbits,' said Théoden. '*Hoppettan*?[28] I will try to remember. No tale that I have heard does them justice.'

In the completed manuscript Théoden said: 'Hobbits? It is a strange name, but I will not forget it.' In the preliminary draft he said subsequently: 'all that is told among us is that away in the North over many hills and rivers (over the sea say some) dwell the half-high folk, [*holbylta(n)*>] *holbytlan* that dwell in holes in sand-dunes...' This is where the word *Holbytla* arose.[29] The manuscript follows this, and Théoden does not say, as he does in TT, 'Your tongue is strangely changed.'
A wholly different and much longer lecture on the subject of tobacco was delivered by Merry in the first of several drafts of this passage:

'For one thing,' said Théoden, 'it was not told that they spouted smoke from their lips.'
'Maybe not. We only learned the pleasure of it a few generations back. It is said that Elias Tobiasson of Mugworth[30] brought the weed back to Manorhall in the South Farthing. He was a much travelled hobbit. He planted it in his garden and dried the leaves after a fashion he had learned in some far country. We never knew where, for he was no good at geography and never could remember names; but from the tale of leagues that he reckoned on his fingers people calculated that it was far South, 1200 miles or more from Manor Hall. [*Here is written* Longbottom.]'
'In the far South it is said that men drink smoke, and wizards I have heard do so. But always I had thought it was part of their

THE ROAD TO ISENGARD 37

incantations or a process aiding in the weaving of their deep thoughts.'[31]

'My lord,' said Merry, 'it is rest and pleasure and the crown of the feast. And glad I am that wizards know it. Among the wreckage floating on the water that drowned Isengard we found two kegs, and opening them what should we discover but some of the finest leaf that ever I fingered or set nose to. Good enough is the Manorhall leaf – but this is...[32] It smells like the stuff Gandalf would smoke at times when he returned from journeys. Though often he was glad enough to come down to Manorhall.'

At this time, and still in the same context (conversation at the Gate of Isengard), my father developed Merry's disquisition through three further drafts to a form approaching §2 *Concerning Pipe-weed* in the Prologue to LR. In the next stage, his account to Théoden of the history of tobacco in the Shire[33] proceeds thus:

'It is said that the art was learned of travelling dwarves, and that for some time folk used to smoke various herbs, some fairer and some fouler. But it was Tobias Smygrave[34] of Longbottom in the Southfarthing that first grew the true pipe-weed in his garden in the year 902, and the best Home-grown comes still from that part. How old Tobias came by the plant is not known for certain, for he never told, and the Smygraves own all [> most (of)] the crops to this day.'

'In the far East uncouth men drink smoke, or so I have heard,' said Théoden. 'And it is said that wizards do so also. But I supposed that this was but part of their secret lore, and a device to aid the weaving of their thoughts.'

'Maybe it does, lord,' said Merry, 'but even wizards use it for no better reason than common folk. It is rest and pleasure and the crown of the feast. ...'

The remainder of this draft is as the first, except that Merry here says 'Good enough is Longbottom leaf, but this far surpasses it' (see note 32), and he says that Gandalf 'did not disdain Longbottom if he stayed until his own store was short. Before Saruman took to making worse things with greater labour, he must once have had some wisdom.'

In the next version the context has probably changed to the conversation between the hobbits and Aragorn, Gimli and Legolas after Gandalf and Théoden had gone (see p. 49 and note 8). Here Tobias (not Tobold) Hornblower appears,[35] the date of his first growing of the plant in his gardens becomes 953 ('according to our

38   THE WAR OF THE RING

reckoning'), and Merry says that 'some think that he got it in Bree': to which Aragorn replies:

'True enough, I guess. Bree-folk smoked long before Shire-folk, and the reason is not far to seek. Rangers come there, as you may remember, unless you have already forgotten Trotter the ranger. And it was Rangers, as they call them in Bree, and neither wizard nor dwarf who brought the art to the North, and found plants that would thrive in sheltered places. For the plant does not belong there. It is said that far away in the East and South it grows wild, and is larger and richer in leaf; but some hold that it was brought over the sea. I expect Saruman got his leaf by trade; for he had little knowledge or care for growing things. Though in old days the warm valley of Nan Gurunír could have been made to grow a good crop.'

Finally, and still in the same context, the passage was developed to a form that my father evidently felt had outgrown its place, for he marked it 'Put into Foreword'.[36] Here the date of the first growing of pipe-weed at Longbottom by 'Old Toby' (still standing for Tobias) becomes 'about the year 1050', 'in the time of Isengrim Took the First';[37] and Merry now says of Old Toby:

'... He knew a great deal about herbs, but he was no traveller. It is said he went often to Bree, but he certainly never went further from the Shire than that. Some think he got the plant in Bree; and I have heard it said that Bree-folk claim to have found its uses long before Shire-folk. Certainly it grows well now on the south side of Bree-hill. And it was probably from Bree that the art spread in the last couple of hundred years, among dwarves and such folk as ever come westward nowadays.'

'Meaning Rangers,' said Aragorn smiling. 'They go to Bree as you may remember. And if you really want to know the truth I will tell it you. It was the folk that Bree-folk call Rangers who brought the plant from the South. For it does not belong natively to Bree and the Shire, and only flourishes so far north in warm and sheltered places. Green [Fuilas > Marlas > Romloth >] Galenas we called that kind. But it had long run wild and unheeded. This credit is certainly due to hobbits: they first put it into pipes. Not even the wizards thought of that before them, though one at least that I know took up the notion, and is now as skilful in that art as in all other things he puts his mind to.'

'More than one,' said Merry. 'Saruman likely enough got the idea from Gandalf: his greatest skill seems to have been in

THE ROAD TO ISENGARD

picking other people's brains. But I am glad of it, in this case. Among the wreckage floating on the water ...'

This version concludes with Merry's saying 'Longbottom Leaf is good enough, but this is better. I wonder where it came from. Do you think Saruman grew it?' And Aragorn replies: 'I expect so. Before he took to making worse things with greater labour, he must have had some wisdom. And this warm valley would grow a good crop, if properly tended.'

The decision to remove most of this to the Foreword had already been taken when the first completed manuscript was written, for here Merry says no more than the few words that Gandalf allows him in TT (p. 163) – with Tobias for Tobold and the date 1050.

Lastly, the conversation near the end of the chapter in the manuscript (there is no initial drafting for this) brings in the meeting with Bregalad on the journey to Isengard, and runs thus:

'It is past noon,' said Gandalf, 'and we at least have not yet eaten. Yet I wish to see Treebeard as soon as may be. If Bregalad took my message, Treebeard has forgotten it in his labours. Unless, as does not seem to be beyond belief, he left us some word with these door-wardens, which their noon-meal has driven from their minds.'

'Bless me! yes, of course,' said Pippin, tapping his forehead. ' "One thing drives out another," as Butterbur would say. Of course. He said: Greet the Lord of Rohan, fittingly. Tell him that Saruman is locked in Orthanc, and say that I am busy near the north gate.[38] If he and Gandalf will forgive me, and will ride there to find me, I will welcome them.'

'Then why did you not say so before?' said Gandalf.

'Because Gimli interrupted my fitting words,' answered Merry. 'And after that it appeared that hobbits had become the chief wonder and matter of debate.'

The chapter did not at this time end with Pippin's 'A fine old fellow. Very polite', but went on with 'Gandalf and the King's company rode away, turning east to make the circuit of the ruined Ring of Isengard', which in TT is the opening of 'Flotsam and Jetsam'.

Further abundant drafting, again discontinuous and closely related to the finished text, exists for the second stage in the development of the chapter. Here can be seen the new or altered elements in the narrative as they arose – the postponed departure from Helm's Deep, the Ents at the edge of the Huorn wood[39] that displaced the meeting with Bregalad, the passage of the Fords, the dry river, the burial

40   THE WAR OF THE RING

mound, the Isen suddenly running again in the night. At first, though the time of departure had been changed to the evening, the encounter with Bregalad was still present – but ends differently: for despite Gandalf's message to Treebeard, 'to the surprise of all he [Bregalad] raised his hand and strode off, not back northward but towards the Coomb, where the wood now stood as dark as a great fold of night.' The scene at the Fords likewise evolved in stages: at first there was no mention of the burial mound, then there were two, one on either bank of the Isen, and finally the island or eyot in the middle of the river appeared.[40] The passage describing the departure of the Huorns from the Deeping Coomb and the Death Down (see p. 27) was first moved to stand (apparently) after Gandalf's reply to Legolas' question concerning the Orcs: 'That, I think, no one will ever know' (TT p. 151), for an isolated draft of it begins: 'And that proved true. For in the deep of the night, after the departure of the king, men heard a great noise of wind in the valley ...'[41]

The second main manuscript of the chapter was a fair copy that remained so, being only lightly emended after its first writing. A few details still survived from the first stage: Merry's father Caradoc; Tobias Hornblower and the year 1050; *Eodoras*; and the form *Rohir*, not *Rohirrim* (the two latter being changed later on the manuscript). The assembly at Eodoras is still to be, as in the first version (p. 27), 'before the waning of the moon' (changed later to 'at the last quarter of the moon').

Lastly, in the account of the burials after the Battle of the Hornburg, there were not only the two mounds raised over the fallen Riders: following the words 'and those of Westfold upon the other' (TT p. 150) there stands in the manuscript 'But the men of Dunland were set apart in a mound below the Dike' (a statement that goes back through the first complete manuscript to the original draft of the passage, see note 8). This sentence was inadvertently omitted in the following typescript (not made by my father), and the error was never observed.

NOTES

1   A short section of initial drafting was written on the back of a letter to my father bearing the date 31 July 1942.

2   One would expect *Erkenwald*: see p. 24, note 22. In the first occurrence here my father in fact wrote *Erkenw* before changing it to *Erkenbrand*. It may be that he was for a time undecided between the two names, and that there was not a simple succession *Erkenwald* > *Erkenbrand*.

3   Cf. the outline 'The Story Foreseen from Fangorn', VII.436: 'The

THE ROAD TO ISENGARD

victorious forces under Éomer and Gandalf ride to the gates of Isengard. They find it a pile of rubble, blocked with a huge wall of stone. On the top of the pile sit Merry and Pippin!'

4 *Caradoc Brandybuck*: see VI.251 and note 4. This is the first appearance of Pippin's father Paladin Took: see VI.386.

5 *Less than a day*: this must imply the shortest possible time-scheme (see Chapter I):

Day 3 (January 31) Ents break into Isengard at night and divert the Isen; Théoden to Helm's Deep, Battle of the Hornburg.

Day 4 (February 1) Théoden, Gandalf, &c. to Isengard.

6 This conversation is found in no less than seven separate forms for the first version of the story alone. In one of these Théoden says to Gandalf: 'But would you assault the stronghold of Saruman with a handful of tired men?', and Gandalf replies: 'No. You do not fully understand the victory we have won, Lord of the Mark. The hosts of Isengard are no more. The West is saved. I do not go to an assault. I have business to settle, ere we turn back – to graver matters, and maybe to harder fortune.' — In different versions Gandalf advises Théoden to order an assembly at Eodoras 'on the second day from now' and 'at the full moon four days from now.'

7 In TT the company did not leave for Isengard until the late afternoon, and on the way they camped for the night below Nan Gurunír; see pp. 5–6, §§ III–IV.

8 In preliminary drafting for this passage the bodies of the Orcs were burned; the men of Dunland were still the men of Westfold; it was Gamling who addressed them, not Erkenbrand ('Help now to repair the evil in which you have joined ...'); the dead of this people were buried in a separate mound below the Dike (a statement that was retained in both the finished manuscripts of the chapter, though lost in TT: see p. 40); the slain Riders were buried in a single mound (not two); and Háma, whose death before the Gates of the Hornburg here first appears (see p. 22), was buried among them, yet he gave his name to the mound: 'the [*Hamanlow* >] *Hamelow* it was called in after years' (i.e. Old Engish *Hāman hlāw*, the Mound of Háma). In TT (p. 150) Háma was laid in a grave alone under the shadow of the Hornburg.

9 The Death Down, where the bodies of the Orcs were buried, was first called the Barren Hill ('for no grass would grow there').

10 See note 14.

11 See the First Map (redrawn map III, VII.309), where the Isen flows into the Great Sea in the region then named Belfalas.

12 In the draft for this passage the battlefield 'was but a mile or two away'. — In TT the company crossed the Fords of Isen (by moonlight) in order to follow the 'ancient highway that ran down from Isengard to the crossings'.

THE WAR OF THE RING

42

13 That the slain Riders had been buried by Ents is stated subsequently: see pp. 47, 49, 54. Contrast TT (p. 157): 'More [Riders] were scattered than were slain; I gathered together all that I could find. . . . Some I set to make this burial.'

14 In this version the company was riding fast, but even so my father seems to have been working on the basis of a much shorter distance from Helm's Deep to Isengard: contrast TT (p. 156): 'They had ridden for some four hours from the branching of the roads when they drew near to the Fords.' In a chronology written at this time, when the story was that Gandalf and Théoden and their company left Helm's Deep very soon after the end of the Battle of the Hornburg (see p. 5, § III), he said that they left about 9 a.m. Changing this to the story that they stopped for the night on the way (p. 6, § IV), he said that they left at 3.30 p.m., and noted: 'It is forty miles and they arrive about 12.30 p.m. on *next day*, Feb. 3.' This is followed by notes of distances that are in close agreement with the First Map (see p. 78 note 2), but 'Isengard Gates to mouth of Deeping Coomb' is given as 33 > 41 > 45 miles (cf. p. 27, where Gandalf's estimate was changed from 12 to 14 to 11 leagues).

As well as I have been able to interpret the First Map here I make the distance 1 cm. or 50 miles, and my map made in 1943 agrees. Section IVE of the First Map (VII.319) is stuck onto a portion of IV^D that is totally hidden, and it is possible that at this stage the Gap of Rohan was less wide. In any case, considerations of distance as well as of chronology evidently dictated the change whereby Gandalf and Théoden did not reach Isengard till the following day.

15 On the removal of this dialogue from the (revised) opening of 'Helm's Deep' and the chronological considerations that led my father to do so see pp. 5–6, §§ II–III.

16 This extremely squashing (and revealing) remark of Gandalf's to the King of Rohan was subsequently very firmly struck through on the manuscript.

17 Cf. Aragorn's words (at once rejected) in a draft for 'The White Rider', VII.429: 'The Ents! Then there is truth in the ancient legends, *and the names that they use in Rohan have a meaning!*'

18 In the original draft for this passage 'the strange figure came quickly on to meet them until it was about fifty [*written above:* a hundred] yards away. Then it stopped and lifting its grey arms and long hands to its mouth it called in a loud voice like a [?ringing] trumpet. "Is Gandalf with this company?" The words were clear for all to hear.'

19 The page of the manuscript that includes this passage was replaced by another, which introduced little significant change; but in the rejected page Bregalad and Gandalf speak of 'the trees',

THE ROAD TO ISENGARD

43

and only in the replacement do they call them 'the Huorns'. Several other terms in fact preceded *Huorns*: see pp. 47, 50, 52.

20 In the rejected page referred to in note 19 Bregalad said that Treebeard 'wishes to know what to do with Saruman', at which Gandalf 'laughed softly, and then was silent, stroking his beard thoughtfully. "Hm," he mused, "hm – yes, that will be a problem."' Cf. the outline for the chapter (p. 26).

21 The original drafting for the description of Nan Gurunír reads thus:

> On either side the last long arms of the Misty Mountains reached out down into the plain, bare and broken ridges half-hidden now in smoke. And now they came upon a strange thing. It seemed to them that ruinous rocks lay ahead, out of which in a new-riven channel came the river, flowing where they stood back into its old course; yet higher up the valley the former bed was dry.
>
> 'Yes, I knew it,' said Gandalf. 'Therefore I drew you this way. We may cross with no difficulty to the Gates of Isengard. As some of you who have journeyed here may know, of old the Isen flowed down, fed by many mountain-springs and streams, until it was already a swift and powerful water ere it left Nan Gurunír – it swept past the walls of Isengard upon the East. That river you claimed as your boundary, but Saruman did not agree. But things have changed. Come and see!'

This was not used at all in the completed text of the first version of the story. It was not the first appearance of the diversion of the Isen: cf. 'The Story Foreseen from Fangorn', VII.436: 'At North end [of Isengard] they let in the River Isen but blocked its outflow. Soon all the floor of the circle was flooded to many feet deep.'

In the passage just cited the meaning must be that the Isen had not been sent back into its former course after the drowning of the Circle of Isengard, but continued to flow in its new channel. Gandalf's words 'I knew it. Therefore I drew you this way. We may cross with no difficulty to the Gates of Isengard' must mean that that is why he had led the company along the east bank of the Isen from the Fords (p. 28), for thus they would only have to cross the dry former bed of the river, to the east of its new course.

22 Later, in 'Flotsam and Jetsam', Merry told (TT p. 171) that when the great host left Isengard 'some went off down the highway to the Fords, and some turned away and went eastward. A bridge has been built down there, about a mile away, where the river runs in a very deep channel.' See p. 56.

23 Differences from the final form were that a part of the Circle of Isengard on the western side was formed of the mountain-wall itself (this was taken up from the draft but rejected from the

44   THE WAR OF THE RING

completed manuscript in the act of writing); there were two
entrances, there being in addition to the great southern arch 'a
small gate at the north, near the mountains' feet'; the circle was
'almost two miles from rim to rim' ('a mile', TT); 'through it by
many carven channels water flowed, entering as a stream from
the mountains beneath the northern gate, and watering all the
hidden land'; and the windows in the walls of the circle are
described (in the preliminary drafting only) as 'countless dark
windows and deep, square-cut, menacing'.

24   This picture was drawn on the back of a page of the examination
     script of the poet John Heath-Stubbs, who took the final
     examinations in English at Oxford in 1942.

25   The opening of the description is confused. Apparently my father
     at first followed the draft 'A' very closely, writing: 'And in the
     centre ... was a tower, a pinnacle of stone. The base of it, and
     that two hundred feet in height, was a great cone of rock ...', but
     altered this at once to 'was an isle of stone, two hundred feet in
     height, a great cone of rock ...' Subsequently he changed 'was an
     isle of stone' to 'there stood an island in the lake.' See the
     description 'D' in the text.

26   On the back of this drawing my father wrote: 'This picture
     should be combined with old one': i.e. for a final version, which
     was never made, features of 'Orthanc (1)' should be incor-
     porated. — 'Picture 5' went to Marquette with the second
     completed manuscript of the chapter, whereas the others re-
     mained in England. — The conception of 'Orthanc (5)' is seen
     also in *Pictures by J. R. R. Tolkien*, no. 27, viewed from the side
     in which were the stairway and the door.

27   In a draft of the paragraph beginning 'A strong place and
     wonderful was Isengard' (TT p. 160) these words were followed
     by 'or *Ang(ren)ost* in elvish speech'. *Angrenost* has appeared
     before (VII.420); the variant *Angost* occurs subsequently (p. 72).

28   Perhaps *Hoppettan* was Théoden's turning of *Hobbits* into the
     sounds and grammatical inflexion of the language of the Mark –
     or else he was merely struck by the resemblance to the (Old
     English) verb *hoppettan* 'to hop, leap, jump for joy'.

29   *Holbytla* 'Hole-builder' has the consonants *lt* (*Holbylta*) re-
     versed, as in the closely related Old English *botl*, *boðl* beside *bold*
     'building' (see my note on Nobottle in the Shire, VII.424).

30   This name can be read either as *Mugworth* or as *Mugwort*, but
     the latter (a plant-name, and one of the family names in Bree)
     seems very unlikely as the name of a place. *Mugworth* is not
     recorded as a village name in England.

31   This passage about tobacco was dashed down in a single spurt
     without any corrections, and there is no indication that these

THE ROAD TO ISENGARD   45

sentences were spoken by Théoden; but that they were so is seen from the following draft.

32 The illegible word might possibly be 'grand'.

33 A pencilled note suggests that this should be 'a conversation at [the] feast'. See pp. 72–3.

34 *Smygrave*: with the first element cf. *Smial* (Old English *smygel*). The second element is probably Old English *græf*.

35 With the later change of *Tobias* to *Tobold* Hornblower cf. *Barliman* for earlier *Barnabas* Butterbur.

36 Cf. my father's letter to me of 6 May 1944 (*Letters* no. 66), referring to Faramir, then newly arrived on the scene: 'if he goes on much more a lot of him will have to be removed to the appendices – where already some fascinating material on the hobbit Tobacco industry and the Languages of the West have gone.'

37 *Isengrim Took the First* and the date 1050: in the Prologue to LR *in the days of Isengrim Took the Second* and the date 1070. See the original genealogical table of the Tooks in VI.316–17, according to which Isengrim the First would have been 400 years old at the time of Bilbo's Farewell Party. Since the Shire Reckoning date 1418 (as in LR) has already appeared for the year of Frodo's departure from Bag End (VII.9), Isengrim the First (afterwards Isengrim II) was born in S.R. 1001. According to the genealogical tree of the Tooks in LR Appendix C the dates of this Isengrim were S.R. 1020–1122. — The varieties of pipe-weed from the Southfarthing are here given as *Longbottom-leaf, Old Toby*, and *Hornpipe Shag*.

38 On the north gate of Isengard see note 23.

39 In the draft of this scene the three Ents who came out from the trees were not wholly indifferent to the company: 'Silently they stood, some twenty paces off, regarding the riders with solemn eyes.' But this was changed immediately.

In a draft for the passage that follows (TT p. 155), in which Théoden reflects on the Ents and the narrow horizons of the people of Rohan, it is Gandalf who speaks the thought that the war will bring about the disappearance of much that was beautiful in Middle-earth:

'You should be glad, Théoden King,' said Gandalf. 'For not only your little life of men is now endangered, but the life of those things also which you have deemed the matter of song and legend. Some we may save by our efforts, but however the fortune of war goes, it may soon come to pass that much that is fair and wonderful shall pass for ever out of Middle Earth. The evil that Sauron works and has worked (and has had much help of men in it) may be stayed or ended, but it cannot be wholly cured, nor made as if it had not been.'

46 THE WAR OF THE RING

40 The *Fords of Isen* in the plural appears earlier, however (pp. 10, 27–8, 31).

41 For another proposed placing of the description of the passing of the Huorns see p. 70.

IV

FLOTSAM AND JETSAM

The first completed manuscript of 'The Road to Isengard' was originally continuous with Chapter XXVIII 'The Battle of Helm's Deep' (the original title), but I think that the division was introduced at a fairly early stage, with a new chapter numbered XXIX beginning with the meeting of Gandalf and Théoden beside the Deeping Stream after the Battle of the Hornburg. The first completed manuscript of XXIX, of which the original title was 'To Isengard', ran on without break through the later 'Flotsam and Jetsam' and 'The Voice of Saruman', but a division between XXIX and XXX ('Flotsam and Jetsam') was made before it was completed: XXX then included the later 'Voice of Saruman' as well. A very rough and difficult outline for this part of the story in fact begins at the end of 'The Road to Isengard', and the chapter was then expressly to end with the return to Eodoras.

Gandalf asks where Treebeard is?
(Guarding Orthanc, says Merry. Some Ents still demolishing.)
He takes Théoden off.
Aragorn takes the hobbits aside and they sit and eat and chat on the stone heaps. Aragorn smokes. Talk about wizards and tobacco.
Aragorn and Gimli are told about Orc-raid and Treebeard. Merry gives up hope of describing them; says you will see them soon. How shall I describe them to Bilbo? (This was when he first tried to collect his ideas.)
Describes destruction of Isengard. Saruman not strong or brave. Merry tells all he knows about the battles of Ford. How trees dogged orcs.
Treebeard knocks on gates of Isengard. Arrows no good.[1] Saruman flies to Orthanc and sends up fires from floor of plain. Scorched Ents go mad. But Treebeard stops them. They let in Isen River by North Gate[2] and flood the bowl. Terrific fume and steam. Terrible noises, drowned wolves and slaves and smiths. The Ents pull the wall to pieces. They send Galbedirs (Talking Trees) to help Gandalf. They bury dead at Fords.
Gandalf's speech with Saruman. He rides over flooded causeway. Saruman looks out of window above door. Asks how he

48   THE WAR OF THE RING

dares to come without permission. Gandalf says he thought that as far as Saruman was concerned he was still a lodger in Orthanc.[3]

'Guests that leave from the roof have not always a claim to come in by the door.' Saruman refuses to repent or submit.

Gandalf gives Treebeard task of [?caring] for him. 'I do not doubt there are delved ways under Orthanc. But every time water subsides let it in again, till all these underground places are submerged. Then make a low bank and plant trees round it. Guard Orthanc with Ents.'

Théoden thinks a Nazgûl may carry him off. 'Let him!' says Gandalf. 'If Saruman thinks of that last treachery ... cannot pity him for the terrible fate that awaits him. Mordor can have no love [for] him. Indeed what he will do

Say that this must be clear to Saruman himself. Would it not be more dramatic to [?make] Saruman offer help: Gandalf says no – he knows that if Mordor wins he is done for now. Even the evidence that he had made war on us won't help him. Sauron knows that he did so only for [his] own ends. But if we win – with his belated help he hopes to re-establish himself and escape punishment. Gandalf demands his staff of office. He refuses; then Gandalf orders him to be shut up, as above.[4]

They rest the night in the ruins and ride back to Eodoras.

Feast on evening of their return and coming of the messenger – that ominous dark-visaged man[5] should end this chapter.

Another outline (in ink over pencil, but the underlying text though briefer was not greatly different) reads as follows:

Treebeard (and Merry and Pippin) relate events – their arrival at Isengard. They saw Saruman send out all his forces to overwhelm the Riders at Isenford. As soon as Isengard was well-nigh empty, the Ents attacked. Merry and Pippin tell of the terrifying anger and strength of the Ents. Saruman really had little power beyond *cunning*, persuasive words – when he had no slaves at hand to do his will and work his machines or light his fires he could do little himself. All his studies had been given to trying to discover how rings were made. He let his wolves out – but they were useless. A few of the Ents were scorched with fire – then they went mad. They drowned Isengard, by letting in River and blocking the outlet.

All the day they were destroying and making havoc of the outer walls and all within. Only Orthanc resisted them. Then

FLOTSAM AND JETSAM

49

just ere nightfall Gandalf came riding up like the wind.[6] He told them of King Théoden's danger. A considerable force of walking trees had already stalked after the orcs the night before. The Ents now sent a much great[er] force and commanded them all to gather at the mouth of the Coomb and let no *orc* come out alive. A few Ents had gone to Isenford, and buried the dead men of the Mark.

In the margin against the last sentences of this outline is written: 'Shall there be *more* real Ents?' Notably, a sentence in the underlying pencilled text reads: 'The Ents sent a force of walking trees (with split trunks). They crept on in darkness following the victorious orcs.'

There is not a great deal to notice in the scanty initial drafting or in the first completed manuscript as far as the beginning of Merry's story of the attack on Isengard (TT p. 170). The meal provided by the hobbits was not eaten in the guard-house by the gates: Merry and Pippin went off to get the food and returned with it, Pippin explaining that 'There is a door not far inside the old tunnel that leads down into some well-stocked stores' (cf. the outline, p. 47: they sit and eat 'on the stone heaps'). Of Ents, where in TT (p. 167) Pippin says: 'Oh, well, you have seen some at a distance, already', here he says 'Oh well, you have seen Quickbeam' – this being of course a reference to the earlier version of 'The Road to Isengard', where Gandalf and Théoden and their company met Bregalad on their ride from Helm's Deep.[7] And he says also, as in the outline on p. 47: 'But I wish Bilbo could have seen Treebeard: how we shall manage to describe him to the old hobbit, if ever we get back, I can't think.'

In a draft for the discussion of pipes (TT pp. 167–8) Aragorn leapt down from the stone heap and went to the saddle-bags that lay nearby. 'From them he drew out an old cloak, and a worn purse of soft hide. Coming back he wrapped himself in the cloak, and opened the purse, and drew out a blackened pipe of clay.' Before Pippin produced his spare pipe, Merry said: 'There are none to be found. Orcs don't smoke, and Saruman did not give his leaf to his slaves.' And when Pippin said 'Look! Trotter the Ranger has come back!' Aragorn replied: 'He has never been away. I am Trotter and Aragorn, and belong both to Gondor and the North.'[8]

A few other details in the opening of the chapter may be noted. There is no mention of Aragorn's returning of the hobbits' knives,[9] or of Pippin's brooch (TT p. 169). After Merry's story of Grishnákh[10] Aragorn spoke at greater length about Sauron and Saruman:

'All this about the orcs of Lugburz (Mordor, I suppose, from the Red Eye) makes me uneasy,' said Aragorn. 'The Dark Lord already knew too much, and Grishnákh clearly got some

50 THE WAR OF THE RING

message across the River after the quarrel. [But still there are some hopeful points. Saruman is in a cleft stick of his own cutting. Gandalf ought not to have much difficulty in convincing him that a victory for Mordor would not be pleasant for him, now. Indeed' (and here Aragorn lowered his voice) 'I do not see what can save him, except the Ring itself. It is well that he has no idea where it is. And we should do best never to mention it aloud: I do not know what powers Saruman in his tower may have, nor what means of communication with the East there may be.] From your tale it is plain that he thought one of you was possibly the Ringbearer; and Sauron must therefore have the same doubt. If so, it will hasten his attack westward: Isengard has fallen none too soon. But there are some hopeful points. All this doubt may help poor Frodo and Sam. But at any rate Saruman is in a cleft stick of his own cutting.

The part of this text (rather more confused in the manuscript than I have represented it) enclosed in square brackets, was rejected immediately and replaced by what follows ('From your tale it is plain ...'); this was rejected later, leaving only the last sentence. — Lastly, Pippin chants, in addition to *Though Isengard be strong and barred* [*sic*], the Entish *Ta-rūta, dūm-da, dūm-da dūm! ta-rāra dūmda dūmda-būm!* (see VII.420).

In the original draft Merry's story (TT pp. 170 ff.) was at first very different from what it became, and I give this text (written in ink over very faint pencil) in part. Of the opening of his story my father noted on the manuscript that he should know less: 'His account of the war is too detailed.'

'... We came down over the last ridge into Nan Gurunír after night had fallen. It was then that I first got an inkling that the forest was moving behind – or a lot of it was: all the Galbedirs [> Lamorni > Ornómar] were coming, as the Ents call them in their short language (which seems to be an oldfashioned Elvish): Talking Trees, that is, that they have trained and made half-entish.[11] All this must have been happening while you were riding south.[12] As far as I can make out, from Treebeard and Gandalf, the war seems to have gone like this: Saruman opened the game some weeks ago, and sent raiders into the west of Rohan. The Rohan-men sent out strong forces, and they retreated over the fords of Isen, and the Riders rather rashly pursued them right up to the bottom of Nan Gurunír. There

FLOTSAM AND JETSAM

they were ambushed by a host of Saruman's folk and one of the chieftains of Rohan seems to have been killed. That must be a good many days ago.[13] Then more Rohan-men arrived coming from Westfold[14] away south, and the Riders still remained on both sides of the River keeping the Isengarders from breaking out of the valley. Up to then Saruman was only fencing; then he struck. Men came up from the land away west, old enemies of Rohan, and the Riders were driven over the Fords. The next stage we were just in time to see.

'As we crept down into Nan-Gurunír – and there was no sign or challenge. [*sic*] Those Ents and their flocks can creep if they wish. You stand still, looking at the weather and listening to the rustling of the leaves, maybe, and then suddenly you find you are in the middle of a wood, with trees all round you. "Creepy" is the word for it! It was very dark, a cloudy night. The moon got up late – and long before it rose there was a deep and sombre forest all round the upper half of Isengard Ring without a sign of challenge. There was a light gleaming from one of the windows in the tower, that was all. Treebeard and some of the elder Ents crept on, right round to within sight of the gates. We were with him. I was sitting on Treebeard's shoulder and could feel a trembling tenseness in him, but even when roused the Ents can be very cautious and patient: they stood still as statues, listening and breathing. Then all at once there was a great stir. Trumpets blared, and all the Ring echoed. We thought that we had been spotted, and battle was going to begin. But nothing of the kind. It seems that news had come in that the Riders had been defeated and driven over the Fords, but were still trying to hold out on the east bank. Saruman sent out his whole forces: he pretty well emptied Isengard. Gandalf says that he was probably in a great taking, thinking that the Ring might have gone to Eodoras, and meant to blot out Théoden and all his folk, before they had time to do anything about it. But there were one or two bits of essential information he lacked: the return of Gandalf, and the rising of the Ents. He thought the one was finished for good, and the others no good, old slow-witted back-numbers. Two very bad mistakes. Anyway that is what he did. I saw them go – endless lines of Orcs, and squadrons / troops of them mounted on great wolves (a Saruman notion?), and whole regiments of men, too. Many of them carried torches, and by the flame I could see their faces. Some were just Men, rather tall, dark-haired, not particularly evil-looking.'

52 THE WAR OF THE RING

'Those would be Dunlanders,' said Aragorn. 'An upland folk from the west of the Misty Mountains, remnants of the old peoples that once dwelt in Rohan and all about the Black Mountains, south and north.'

The following dialogue, concerning the 'goblin-men' reminiscent of the squint-eyed Southerner at Bree, and Merry's estimate of the forces that left Isengard that night, is much the same as in TT (p. 171), except that Aragorn says that they had had many of the goblin-men to deal with at the Hornburg 'last night' (see note 7), and that there is here no mention of the bridge over the Isen over which a part of the host had passed. Then follows:

'... I thought it looked black for the Riddermark. But it seems in the end the only way in which Saruman could have been overcome. One wonders how much Gandalf knew, guessed, or planned. But Treebeard anyway let them go. He said that his concern was Isengard. "Stone – that we can fight," he said.

'But he sent off a whole wood of the Ornómi[15] down the valley after the army, as soon as the gates of Isengard were shut again. I don't know, of course, much of what happened away south down there; but you will tell us later.'

'I can tell you now briefly,' said Aragorn. 'The Saruman army came down on both sides of the Isen and overwhelmed the men of Rohan, and most of the survivors scattered. A strong force under Erkenwald of Westfold[16] fled south towards the Black Mountains. We met a survivor of the battles of the fords yesterday evening, and were just in time to take refuge in Helm's Deep, a gorge in the hills, before the whole pack came on us.'

'I don't know how you survived,' said Merry. 'But you helped us. As soon as all the army had gone, the fun began here. Treebeard went up and began hammering on the gates. ...'

Merry's account of the Ents' destruction of the gates of Isengard was already in this preliminary draft very close to that in TT (p. 172), but his estimate of Saruman was expressed more largely and with a degree of scornful and rather jaunty assurance that his experience of the master of Orthanc scarcely justified; and Aragorn does not here interrupt him with a more cautious view of Saruman's innate power (indeed the hypnotic potency of the wizard's voice only emerged, or was at any rate only fully realised, when the meeting with him came to be written).

FLOTSAM AND JETSAM

53

'I don't know what Saruman thought was happening. But all that I have seen since leads me to think that either he was never really a first-class wizard (not up to his reputation, which was partly due to Isengard, and that was not his making to begin with), or he had been deteriorating – relying on wheels and what not, and not on wisdom. And he does not seem to have much heart in any sense: certainly he had been going back in plain courage. The old fool had really become dependent on all his organized slaves. He had a daunting way with him: power of dominating minds and bewildering or persuading them was his chief asset all along, I fancy. But without his armies to do as he commanded, he was just a cunning old man, very slippery, but with no grit. And the old fool had sent all his armies off! ...'

Merry's account (given to Pippin in TT) of Saruman's flight into Orthanc chased by Bregalad, the spouting of fires and gases from vents in the plain of Isengard ('as soon as Saruman got back into his control-room he got some of his machinery working'), the scorching of some of the Ents and the quelling of their fury by Treebeard, is present in the draft in all essentials, though more briefly told (and the horrible fate of the Ent Beechbone does not yet appear). The time-scheme was still at the stage described in § II on p. 5, with the drowning of Isengard beginning later in the same night (31 January) as the Ents came there,[17] and so the story is much condensed in the draft text by comparison with that in TT. Gandalf came to Isengard 'yesterday at nightfall' (i.e. 1 February, the night of the Battle of the Hornburg); and where in TT (p. 175) Pippin says that he was surprised at the meeting of Gandalf and Treebeard 'because neither of them seemed surprised at all', here Merry says:

'... I do not know who was most surprised at their meeting, Gandalf or Treebeard. Gandalf, I think, for once. For from a look he gave us when we first met I have a fancy Treebeard had spotted Gandalf in Fangorn; but would not say anything even to comfort us. He has very much to heart the elvish saw of Gildor's: Do not meddle in the affairs of wizards; for they are subtle and quick to wrath.'[18]

'But Gandalf knew Treebeard was on the move,' said Gimli. 'He knew there was going to be an explosion.'

'But not even Gandalf could guess what that was going to be like,' said [Merry >] Pippin. 'It has never happened before. And even wizards know little about Ents. But talking about surprise – we were the surprised ones: coming on top of the astonishing rage of the Ents, Gandalf's arrival was like a thunderclap. We

54   THE WAR OF THE RING

had very little to do, except try and trot round after Treebeard (when he was too busy to carry us) and see the fun. We had a high time for a moment, when we got left alone, and came in front of a rush of some terrified wolves, and we had a brush with two or three stray orcs. [But when Gandalf arrived, I just stood staring with my mouth open, and then I sat down and laughed. >] But when Gandalf's horse came striding up the road, like a flash of silver in the dusk, well, I just gásped, and then I sat down and laughed, and then I wept. And did he say *pleased to see you again*? No, indeed. He said "Get up, you tom-fool of a Took. Where in the name of wonder in all this mess is Treebeard? Hurry, hurry, hurry, my lad! Don't let your toes grow whiskers." But later he was a bit gentler, after he had seen the old Ent: he seemed very pleased and relieved. He gave us a few minutes of concentrated news, a pat on the head, a sort of hasty blessing, and vanished away south again. We got some more news out of Treebeard after he had gone. But there must be much more to tell. We should have been far more worried and anxious about you, I expect, only it was difficult what with Treebeard and Gandalf to really believe you would come to grief.'

'Yet we nearly did,' said Aragorn. 'Gandalf's plans are risky, and they lead often to a knife-edge. There is great wisdom, forethought and courage in them – but no certainty. You have to do your part as it comes to you; or they would not work.'

'After that, said Merry, 'the Ents just went on and carefully and neatly finished the drowning of Isengard. I don't know what else, do you?'

'Yes,' said Aragorn, 'some went to the Fords to bury the men of Rohan who had fallen there; and to gather all the – what did you say they were called – the Ornómi, the moving woods, to the Deeping Coomb. Aye, that was a wonder and a victory as great as the one here. No orc is left. It was a long night, but the dawn was fair.'

'Well, let us hope that it is the beginning of better things,' said Gimli. 'Gandalf said the tide was turning.'

'Yes,' said Aragorn, 'but he also said that the great storm was coming.'

'Oh,' said Merry, 'I forgot. Not long before Gandalf, about sunset, a tired horse came up the valley with a pack of wolf-riders round it.[19] The Ents soon settled them, though one of Quickbeam's folk, a rowan-ent, got a bad axe-stroke, and

FLOTSAM AND JETSAM

55

that enraged the Ents mightily. On the horse there was a queer twisted sort of man: I disliked him at sight. It says a great deal about Treebeard and Ents generally, if you think about it – in spite of their rage, and the battle, and the wounding of Bregalad's friend Carandrian, that the fellow was not killed out of hand. He was miserable in his fear and amazement. He said he was a man called Frána, and was sent with urgent messages from Théoden and Gandalf to Saruman, and had been captured by orcs on the way (I caught him squinting at Treebeard to see how it went, especially the mention of Gandalf). Treebeard looked at him in his long slow way for many minutes. Then he said: "Hoom, ha, well, you can go to Saruman! I guess somehow that you know pretty well how to find him, though things have changed a little here. But false or true, you will do little harm now."

'We told Gandalf about it. He laughed, and said: "Well, I fancy of all the surprised people he had the worst shock. Poor Wormtongue! He chose badly. Just for a little I feel hardhearted enough to let those two stay and live together. They will be small comfort to each other. And if Wormtongue comes out of Orthanc alive, it will be more than he deserves."'

Against this passage my father wrote: 'No, Wormtongue must come after Gandalf'; and at the foot of the page: 'Shall Wormtongue actually murder Saruman?'

'Well,' he continued. 'Our job was to get rooms ready and prepare stuff for your entertainment. All yesterday and most of last night we worked. Indeed, say what you like, we did not knock off till close on noon this morning. And I don't know if we should even then, only Pippin found two tubs floating on the water'

Here this draft breaks off. The first completed manuscript, from the point where Merry's story begins, was based fairly closely on the draft text (pp. 50–5) in its narrative, but moved far towards the text of TT in expression. The passage about the 'Talking Trees' (p. 50) was developed thus:

'... The Ornómi were coming. That is what the Ents call them in their "short language", which seems to be an old-fashioned Elvish: *trees with voices* it means, and there is a great host of them deep in Fangorn, trees that the Ents have trained so long that they have become half entish, though far wilder, of course, and crueller.'

56   THE WAR OF THE RING

This was rejected, probably at once, and a passage for the most part very close to that in TT (p. 170) substituted. *Ornómi* was here replaced by *Huorns* in the act of writing and is the point where that name arose. Merry is now uncertain about their nature: 'I cannot make out whether they are trees that have become Entish, or Ents that have become tree-like, or both.'

At first Merry was still going to give a summary and commentary on the course of the war:

'... It seems that news had come in that the [Rohir >] Horsemen had been defeated and driven back across the Isen, but some were still trying to hold out on the eastern bank. We got this out of some of Saruman's men that the Ents captured and questioned. Saruman thought that no more was left of the King's forces, except what he would keep by him to guard his town and hall. He decided to finish off the Rohir with a decisive blow.'

But it must have been at this point that my father noted on the draft (p. 50) that Merry should be much less well-informed on these matters, and the passage just given was rejected and the text of TT (p. 171) substituted: 'I don't know much about this war ...'

Merry now tells (as he does not in the draft, p. 51) that when the great host left Isengard 'some went off down the main road to the fords, but still more turned off towards the bridge and the east side of the river'. This was changed in a hasty pencilled emendation to 'turned off towards where I believe Saruman has recently made a bridge'. See p. 31 and note 22.

Aragorn's brief account of what had happened southwards was still retained from the draft (p. 52), and here he adds the surmise (in the draft Gandalf's, reported by Merry, p. 51) about Saruman's purposes: '... the whole pack came howling after us. They had learned that the King was in the field, so none of them went to Eodoras. Saruman wanted the King and Éomer, his heir, dead or alive. He was afraid that the Ring might get into their hands after the battle from which you escaped.' He also gives the information that the force that fled south from the Fords to the Black Mountains numbered about a thousand men. With this passage cf. Gandalf's remarks to Théoden as they rode to Isengard (p. 29).

Merry's rather overconfident assessment of Saruman was reduced, in stages, virtually to its compass in TT, and Aragorn's intervention now appears, very much as in TT (p. 172), with his emphasis on the peril of private conversation with the master of Orthanc.

In this version a new time-scheme had entered, as is seen from the story of the drowning of Isengard:

FLOTSAM AND JETSAM

57

'... They calmly settled down to carry out a plan that Treebeard had made in his old head all along: they drowned Isengard. Day was dawning by that time. They set a watch on the tower, and the rest just faded away in the grey light. Merry and I were left alone most of that day, wandering and prying about. The Ents went north up the valley. They dug great trenches under the shadow of the Huorns, and made great pools and dams, and when all was ready, last night, about midnight, they poured in all the Isen, and every other stream they could tap, through a gap by the north-gate, down into the ring. ...'

'Yes, we saw the great vapour from the south this morning as we rode from Helm's Deep,' said Aragorn. ...

'By morning there was a fog about a mile thick,' said Merry. '... Treebeard stopped the inflow some hours ago, and sent the stream back into its old course. Look, the water is sinking again already. There must be some outlets from the caverns underneath. But Gandalf came before the drowning began. He may have guessed or been told by Treebeard what was afoot, but he did not see it happen. When he arrived the digging and damming was not quite finished, but old Treebeard had returned, and was resting. He was only about fifty yards away, soothing his arrow-smarts by pulling down a bit more of the southern wall in a leisurely fashion. ...'

This is still not quite the final time-scheme for the story of the destruction of Isengard (see pp. 5–6, §§ III–IV), because the party from Helm's Deep still reached Isengard in a single day (2 February); so here Pippin tells that it was 'last night' (1 February) that the drowning began, and Aragorn says that they had seen the great cloud of steam as they rode up from Helm's Deep 'this morning'.

All the last part of what would become the chapter 'Flotsam and Jetsam' was discarded from this manuscript and replaced by new pages, in which the text of TT (pp. 174–7, describing the day spent by Merry and Pippin alone while the Ents prepared the diversion of the Isen, Gandalf's coming, and the filling of the Ring of Isengard by moonlight) was reached save for the choice of a different word here and there. But the time-scheme of the rejected pages was still present, with the extra day still not inserted and the time during which the waters of Isen flowed into the Ring correspondingly shorter.[20] On this account the last part of the hobbits' story still differs from that in TT, and Merry ends thus:

'... By morning there was a fog about a mile high, but it was beginning to rise and sail away out of the valley. And the lake

58   THE WAR OF THE RING

was overflowing, too, and pouring out through the ruined gate, bringing masses of wreckage and jamming it near the outlet of the old tunnel. Then the Ents stopped the inflow, and sent the Isen back into its old course. Since then the water has been sinking again. There must be outlets somewhere from the caves underneath, or else they are not all filled up yet. There is not much more to tell. Our part, Pippin's and mine, was chiefly that of onlookers: rather frightened at times. We were all alone while the drowning was going on, and we had one or two bad moments. Some terrified wolves were driven from their dens by the flood, and came howling out. We fled, but they passed by. And every now and then some stray orc would bolt out of the shadows and run shrieking off, slashing and gnashing as he went. The Huorns were waiting. There were many of them still in the valley until the day came. I don't know where they have all gone. It seems very quiet now after such a night. I could sleep.'

But the coming of Wormtongue is now placed according to the direction on the draft text ('Wormtongue must come after Gandalf', p. 55): he came 'early this morning', and the story of his arrival is now much as in TT, though briefer. Aragorn's curiosity about tobacco from the Southfarthing turning up in Isengard appears (see note 8), and Pippin reports the same date on the barrels as in TT: 'the 1417 crop'.

After 'it is not a very cheerful sight', with which the later chapter 'Flotsam and Jetsam' ends, this text goes straight on to 'They passed through the ruined tunnel', with which 'The Voice of Saruman' begins.

NOTES

1 *Arrows no good*: i.e., against Ents.
2 On the North Gate of Isengard see p. 43 note 23.
3 *He was still a lodger in Orthanc*: i.e., Gandalf had never 'officially' left after his enforced residence in the tower.
4 This paragraph was enclosed in square brackets and marked with a query.
5 *That ominous dark-visaged man*: cf. 'The Story Foreseen from Fangorn' (VII.437): 'Return to Eodoras. ... News comes at the feast or next morning of the siege of Minas Tirith by the Haradwaith, brought by a dark Gondorian like Boromir.'
6 The time-scheme here is that described on p. 5, § II.
7 In that version Théoden and Gandalf and their company left Helm's Deep in the morning and reached Isengard on the same day, and so here in answer to Pippin's question (TT p. 168)

FLOTSAM AND JETSAM

'What is today?' Aragorn replies 'The second of February in the Shire-reckoning' (see p. 5, § III). Pippin then calculates on his fingers that it was 'only a week ago' that he 'woke up in the dark and found himself all strung-up in an orc-camp' (i.e. from the night of Thursday 26 January to Thursday 2 February). And again, when Pippin asks when it was that Aragorn, Gimli and Legolas 'caught a glimpse of the old villain, or so Gandalf hints' (as Gimli said) at the edge of Fangorn (TT p. 169), Aragorn replies: 'Four nights ago, the twenty-ninth.'

These dates were changed on the manuscript to 'The third of February', 'only eight days ago', and 'Five nights ago': see p. 6, § IV.

8 In an earlier version of this Aragorn's reply (here assembled from scarcely differing variants) was different:

'For a spell,' said Aragorn, with a glint of a smile. 'This is good leaf. I wonder if it grew in this valley. If so, Saruman must have had some wisdom before he took to making worse things with greater labour. He had little knowledge of herbs, and no love for growing things, but he had plenty of skilled servants. Nan Gurunír is warm and sheltered and would grow a good crop, if it were properly tended.'

With this cf. the passages given on pp. 37–9. — The decision, or perception, that the tobacco had not in fact been grown in Nan Gurunír, but that Saruman had obtained it from the Shire, appears in a rider pinned to the first complete manuscript, in which Merry tells Gimli that it is Longbottom-leaf, with the Hornblower brandmarks on the barrels (TT p. 167).

9 The finding of the hobbits' leaf-bladed knives and their sheaths at the site of the battle beneath Amon Hen (TT p. 17) is absent from the draft and the fair copy manuscript of 'The Departure of Boromir' (VII.381).

10 *Grishnákh* was changed on the manuscript at each occurrence to *Grishnák*, a reversion to the original form (VII.409–10). — On the back of this page is a reference that shows it was written during or more probably after June 1942.

11 This is the reverse of what Merry says in TT (p. 170): 'I think they are Ents that have become almost like trees, at least to look at.'

12 Merry was a day out: the march of the Ents on Isengard was in the evening of 31 January, and Aragorn, Gimli and Legolas had reached Eodoras early that morning (see pp. 3–4).

13 The death of Théodred in the First Battle of the Fords of Isen on 25 January (see p. 22 note 3).

14 *Westfold*: see p. 21.

15 *Ornómi*: in the underlying pencilled text the name *Galbedirs* can be read. At the earlier occurrence in this draft (p. 50) *Galbedirs*

60   THE WAR OF THE RING

was changed first to *Lamorni* and then to *Ornómar* – all these
names having the same meaning.

16 *Erkenwald of Westfold*: see p. 24 note 22.

17 Thus Merry says that '*by morning* there was a fog a mile thick',
Aragorn says 'we could see the great vapour from the south *as we
rode towards the Fords*' (i.e. as the host rode from Eodoras on
1 February), and my father wrote in the margin of the text:
'Drowning must not begin until night of Hornburg battle'.

18 In the first complete manuscript this becomes: ' "Don't be hasty"
is his motto, and also that saying Sam says he picked up from the
Elves: he was fond of whispering it to me when Gandalf was
peppery: "Do not meddle in the affairs of wizards ..." ' For its
original appearance see 'Three is Company', FR p. 93. In TT
(p. 196) Merry quotes it to Pippin à propos Pippin's interest in
the *palantír*.

19 Cf. 'Helm's Deep' in TT (p. 134): 'Some say also that Wormtongue was seen earlier, going northward with a company of
Orcs.' But in the present passage in TT (p. 178) Wormtongue
arrived alone.

20 In the time-scheme followed here it lasted from midnight on
1 February till the morning of 2 February; in the final story it
lasted till the night of 2 February (TT p. 177: 'The Ents stopped
the inflow in the night'), = 4 March.

V

THE VOICE OF SARUMAN

Book III Chapter 10 'The Voice of Saruman' in *The Two Towers* is in the first completed manuscript simply the further extension of Chapter XXX (see p. 47). The opening of this part of the narrative is here almost as in the final form (see note 8), but the conversation with Gandalf is much briefer; after Merry's 'Still, we feel less ill-disposed towards Saruman than we did' it continues:

'Indeed!' said Gandalf. 'Well, I am going to pay him a farewell visit. Perhaps you would like to come?'

'I should,' said Gimli. 'I should like to see him, and learn if he really looks like you.'

'You may not see him close enough for that,' laughed Gandalf. '[He has long been a shy bird, and late events may not have >] He may be shy of showing himself. But I have had all the Ents removed from sight, so perhaps we shall persuade him.'

They came now to the foot of Orthanc.

In TT Gandalf's last remarks were developed to: 'And how will you learn that, Master Dwarf? Saruman could look like me in your eyes, if it suited his purpose with you. And are you yet wise enough to detect all his counterfeits? Well, we shall see, perhaps. He may be shy of showing himself before many different eyes together. . . .'

The description of Orthanc in this text at first ran like this:

... A few scorings, and small sharp splinters near the base, were all the marks it showed of the fury of the Ents. In the middle from two sides, north and south, long flights of broad stairs, built of some other stone, dark red in hue, climbed up to the great chasm in the crown of the rock. There they met, and there was a narrow platform beneath the centre of the great arch that spanned the cleft; from it stairs branched again, running up west and east to dark doors on either side, opening in the shadow of the arch's feet.

This is the general conception described in version 'D' of the passage in 'The Road to Isengard' (p. 32), and precisely illustrated in the

62 THE WAR OF THE RING

drawing 'Orthanc (3)' reproduced on p. 33. But the text just given was replaced at the time of writing by the following:

... the fury of the Ents. On two sides, west and east, long flights of broad stairs, cut in the black stone by some unknown art, climbed up to the feet of the vast arch that spanned the chasm in the hill. At the head of each stair was a great door, and above it a window opening upon a balcony with parapet of stone.

This is the rather simpler conception illustrated in the drawing 'Orthanc (4)' reproduced on p. 33. At a later stage this was rejected and replaced on a slip inserted into the manuscript by the description in TT, where of course the conception of Orthanc had been totally changed (pp. 33–5, and the drawing reproduced on p. 34).

The description of Orthanc was followed immediately by 'Gandalf led the way up the western stair. With him went Théoden and Éomer, and the five companions.' There is thus no discussion here of who shall go up, or how close they shall stand.

From this point initial drafting (inked over very faint pencil, which is effectively illegible) exists for the interview with Saruman, and this was pretty closely followed in the first completed manuscript. Saruman's voice was at this stage differently described, and this was at first repeated in the manuscript: 'The window closed. They waited. Suddenly another voice spoke, low, melodious, and yet it seemed unpleasant [> unpleasing: its tone was scornful].'[1] This was changed, probably at once, to: 'low, melodious, and persuasive; yet now its tone was of one who, in spite of a gentle nature, is aggrieved.' All else that is said of that voice in TT (p. 183) is here absent; and the description of Saruman is briefer: 'His face was long with a high forehead; he had deep darkling eyes; his hair and beard were white, smudged with darker strands. "Like and unlike", muttered Gimli.'

With the opening of the conversation at this stage (cited here from the completed manuscript rather than from the draft text) cf. the original outline on pp. 47–8.

'Well?' said Saruman. 'You have a voice of brass, Gandalf. You disturb my repose. You have come to my private door without leave. What is your excuse?'

'Without leave?' said Gandalf. 'I had the leave of such gatekeepers as I found. But am I not a lodger in this inn? My host at least has never shown me the door, since he first admitted me!'

'Guests that leave by the roof have no claim to re-enter by the door at their will,' said Saruman.

THE VOICE OF SARUMAN

63

'Guests that are penned on the house-top against their will have a right to knock and ask for an apology,' answered Gandalf.[2] 'What have you to say, now?'

'Nothing. Certainly not in your present company. In any case I have little to add to my words at our last meeting.'

'Have you nothing to withdraw?'

Saruman paused. 'Withdraw?' he said slowly. 'If in my eagerness and disappointment I said anything unfriendly to yourself, consider it withdrawn. I should probably have put matters right long ago. You were not friendly yourself, and persisted in misunderstanding me and my intentions, or pretending to do so. But I repeat: I bore you no ill-will personally; and even now, when your – your associates have done me so much injury, I should be ready to forgive you, if you would dissociate yourself from such people. I have for the moment less power to help you than I had; but I still think you would find my friendship more profitable in the end than theirs. We are after all both members of an ancient and noble profession: we should understand one another. If you really wish to consult me, I am willing to receive you. Will you come up?'

This passage, whose original germ is seen in the outlines given in VII.212, 436, was developed into that in TT pp. 186–7. The draft text[3] goes on at once to 'Gandalf laughed. "Understand one another? ..."', and there is nothing said about the effect of Saruman's words on the bystanders; but in the manuscript his speech was changed, apparently at once, to a form somewhat nearer to that in TT (with 'a high and ancient order' for 'an ancient and noble profession'), and this was followed by the passage (TT p. 187) in which the voice of Saruman 'seemed like the gentle remonstrance of a kindly king with an errant but beloved minister'. But here the words 'So great was the power that Saruman exerted *in this last effort* that none that stood within hearing were unmoved' are absent; for of all that precedes this in TT, his long opening trial of Théoden's mind and will, with the interventions of Gimli and Éomer, there is no hint or suggestion in either draft or finished text. The interview is conducted exclusively between the two wizards.

For the remainder of the dialogue between them I give here the original draft:[4]

Gandalf laughed. 'Understand one another? I don't know. But I understand you at any rate, Saruman – well enough. No! I do not think I will come up. You have an excellent adviser with you, adequate for your understanding. Wormtongue has cun-

64 THE WAR OF THE RING

ning enough for two. But it had occurred to me that since Isengard is rather a ramshackle place, rather old-fashioned and in need of renovation and alteration, you might like to leave – to take a holiday, say. If so, will you not come down?'

A quick cunning look passed over Saruman's face; before he could conceal it, they had a glimpse of mingled fear and relief / hope. cunning. They saw through the mask the face of a trapped man, that feared both to stay and to leave his refuge. He hesitated. 'To be torn by the savage wood-demons?' he said. 'No, no.'

'O do not fear for your skin,' said Gandalf. 'I do not wish to kill you – as you would know, if you really understood me. And no one will hurt you, if I say no. I am giving you a last chance. You can leave Orthanc – free, if you choose.'

'Hm,' said Saruman. 'That sounds well. More like the old Gandalf. But why should I wish to leave Orthanc? And what precisely is "free"?'

'The reasons for leaving lie all around,' said Gandalf. 'And free means not a prisoner. But you will surrender to me the key of Orthanc – and your staff: pledges for your conduct. To be returned, if I think fit, later.'

Saruman's face was for a moment clouded with anger. Then he laughed. 'Later!' he said. 'Yes – when you also have the keys of Baraddur, I suppose; and the crowns of seven kings, and the staffs of the five wizards,[5] and have purchased yourself a pair of boots many sizes larger than those you have now. A modest plan. But I must beg leave to be excused from assisting. Let us end this chatter. If you wish to deal with me, deal with me! Speak sense – and do not come here with a horde of savages, and these boorish men, and foolish children that dangle at your tail.'

He left the balcony. He had hardly turned away, when a heavy thing came hurtling down from above. It glanced off the parapet, narrowly missed Gandalf, and splintered [struck out: into fragments] on the rock beside the stair. It seemed to have been a large ball of dark shining crystal.

'The treacherous rogue,' cried Éomer, but Gandalf was unmoved. 'Not Saruman this time,' he said. 'It came from a window above. That was a parting shot from Master Worm-tongue, I fancy. I caught the flash of a hand. And ill-aimed. Which do you think it was meant for, me or Saruman?' 'I think maybe the aim was ill because he could not make up his mind

THE VOICE OF SARUMAN

which he hated most' (? said Gimli). 'I think so too,' said Gandalf. 'There will be pleasant words in the Tower when we are gone.'

'And we had better go quickly out of stone's throw at least,' said Éomer.

'It is plain to me that Saruman has not yet given up hope [*added:* in his own devices],' said Gandalf. 'Well, he must nurse his hope in Orthanc.'

Here this draft stops, the ending being very ragged. It is notable that in this text there is no mention of Gandalf's summons to Saruman to return to the balcony when he turned away, and so the breaking of his staff does not appear (in the original sketches of the scene in the outlines referred to above, where Saruman was not in his tower, Gandalf took his staff from him and broke it with his hands).[6]

Since there is no evidence at all that the conception of the *palantír* had arisen at any earlier stage or in any earlier writing, this must be presumed to be its first appearance, but the draft does not make it clear whether my father perceived its nature at the moment of its introduction as Wormtongue's missile – Gandalf does not say what he thought of it, nor hint that it might be a device of importance to Saruman. In his letter to W. H. Auden of 7 June 1955 my father said (immediately following the passage from that letter cited at the beginning of *The Return of the Shadow*): 'I knew nothing of the *Palantíri*, though the moment the Orthanc-stone was cast from the window, I recognized it, and knew the meaning of the 'rhyme of lore' that had been running in my mind: *seven stars and seven stones and one white tree*.'[7] On the other hand, in this initial version of the scene he saw the ball of crystal as shattered by the impact, and still in the finished manuscript immediately following this draft he wrote that the ball 'splintered on the rock beside the stair. It seemed *from the fragments*', before breaking off at this point and writing that it smote the stair, and that it was the stair that cracked and splintered while the globe was unharmed. What further significance for the story could it have had if it were immediately destroyed?

The completed text develops the dialogue of Gandalf and Saruman a good way towards the form in TT, though much still remains from the original draft. But there now enters, almost in the final form, Gandalf's summons to Saruman to come back, his final admonition to him, and the breaking of his staff. The crystal ball now rolled down the steps, and it was 'dark but shining with a heart of fire'. In reply to Aragorn's suggestion that Wormtongue could not make up his mind whom he hated most Gandalf says: 'Yes, that may be so. There will be some debate in the Tower, when we are gone! We will take the ball. I

66   THE WAR OF THE RING

fancy that it is not a thing that Saruman would have chosen to cast away.'

Pippin's running down the stair to pick up the globe, and Gandalf's hasty taking of it and wrapping it in the folds of his cloak, were later additions (see p. 79 note 12). Yet that the globe was to be important is now plain. The scene ends thus in this version:

'Yet there may be other things to cast,' said Gimli. 'If that is the end of the debate, let us go out of stone's throw, at least.'

'It is the end,' said Gandalf. 'I must find Treebeard and tell him how things have gone.'

'He will have guessed, surely?' said Merry. 'Were they likely to end any other way?'

'Not likely,' answered Gandalf. 'But I had reasons for trying. I do not wish for mastery. Saruman has been given a last choice, and a fair one. He has chosen to withhold Orthanc at least from us, for that is his last asset. He knows that we have no power to destroy it from without, or to enter it against his will; yet it might have been useful to us. But things have not gone badly. Set a thief to hinder a thief! [*Struck out:* And malice blinds the wits.] I fancy that, if we could have come in, we should have found few treasures in Orthanc more precious than the thing which the fool Wormtongue tossed down to us!'

A shrill shriek, suddenly cut off, came from an open window high above. 'I thought so,' said Gandalf. 'Now let us go!'

The end of the chapter in TT, the meeting of Legolas and Gimli with Treebeard, his parting from Merry and Pippin, and the verse in which the Hobbits are entered into 'the Long Lists', is present in this first completed text all but word for word, save only at the very end, where his last words are brief:

'Leave it to Ents,' said Treebeard. 'Until seven times the years in which he tormented us have passed, we shall not tire of watching over him.'[8]

NOTES

1   The draft has: 'low, rather melodious, and yet unpleasant: it spoke contemptuously.'

2   Though this exchange was subsequently lost, the reference to Gandalf's manner of departure from Orthanc on the previous occasion was brought in at a later point (TT p. 187): 'When last I visited you, you were the jailor of Mordor, and there I was to be

THE VOICE OF SARUMAN   67

sent. Nay, the guest who has escaped from the roof will think twice before he comes back in by the door.'

3 The draft of Saruman's speech is very close to that cited from the completed manuscript, but after 'We should understand one another' Saruman says 'Building not breaking is *our* work.'

4 Not strictly the original draft, since as already noted it is inked over a faint and illegible pencilled text.

5 The first reference to the Five Wizards.

6 In drafting for the end of the chapter Gandalf's reply to Treebeard's 'So Saruman would not leave? I did not think he would' (TT p. 192) runs thus: 'No, he is still nursing what hope he has. He is of course pretending that he loves me and would help me (if I were reasonable – which means if I would serve him, and help him to power without [?bounds]). But he is determined to wait – sitting among the ruins of his old plans to see what comes. In that mood, and with the Key of Orthanc *and his staff* he must not be allowed to escape.'

7 The need that the *palantír* would come to fulfil had already been felt, as is seen from Aragorn's (rejected) remarks on p. 50: 'And we should do best never to mention it [the Ring] aloud: I do not know what powers Saruman in his tower may have, nor *what means of communication with the East there may be.*'

8 The meeting of Treebeard with Legolas and Gimli and his parting from Merry and Pippin was very largely achieved in preliminary drafting, but was placed at a different point, since it begins: 'The afternoon was half gone and the sun going behind the western arm of the valley when Gandalf and the King returned. With them came Treebeard. Gimli and Legolas gazed at him in wonder. "Here are my companions that I have spoken of to you," said Gandalf. The old Ent looked at them long and searchingly', &c. This was how the part of the narrative afterwards constituting 'The Voice of Saruman' originally began.

VI

THE PALANTÍR

Drafts and outlines for the opening of this chapter show my father very uncertain of the immediate course of events when the company left Isengard. These pages are extremely difficult to interpret and to place in sequence, but I take the one that I give now to be that first written, since it treats as the actual event what would become merely the abandoned plan ('When we came, we meant to go straight from Isengard back to the king's house at Edoras over the plains', TT p. 194).

The sun was sinking behind the long western arm of the mountains when Gandalf and his companions, and the King with his riders, set out from Isengard.

Ents in a solemn row stood like statues at the gate, with their long arms uplifted; but they made no sound. Merry and Pippin looked back as they passed down hill and turned into the road that led to the bridge.[1] Sunlight was shining in the sky, but long shadows reached out over Isengard. Treebeard stood there still, like a dark tree in the shade; the other Ents were gone, back to the sources of the stream.

By Gandalf's advice the company crossed the bridge and then struck away from the river, southward and east, making straight across the rolling plains of Rohan back to Eodoras: a journey of some forty-eight leagues.[2] They were to ride more with secrecy than speed, by dusk and night, hoping to reach the king's house by nightfall of the second day. By that time many of the king's men who had fought at the Fords and at Helm's Deep would be gathering at Eodoras.

'We have gained the first victory,' said Gandalf, 'yet that has some danger. There was a bond between Isengard and Mordor. Of what sort and how they exchanged their news I have not discovered. But the eyes of the Dark Tower will look now in this direction, I think.

'There is no one of this company, I think, whose name (and deeds) is not noted now in the dark mind of Sauron. We should walk in shadow, if we walk abroad at all – until we are ready. Therefore, though it may add to the miles, I counsel you go now

THE PALANTÍR 69

by night, and go south so that day does not find us in the open plain. After that we may ride with many men, or ride maybe [??back to the] Deeping Coomb that would be better by ways among the foothills of your own mountains Théoden, and come thus down to Eodoras ... long ravines about Dunharrow.

The last few lines are a ragged scrawl, across which my father wrote (at the same time) 'They meet Huorns returning'. Since against the statement that 'they passed down hill and turned into the road that led to the bridge' he noted in the margin 'No they rode south to the Fords', and against 'the company crossed the bridge and then struck away from the river' he wrote 'No, they go south', it seems clear that it was as he was writing this first draft of the opening that he realised that the company did not in fact make straight for Eodoras but went first to Helm's Deep – and therefore abandoned this text.[3]

In a rejected speech of Aragorn's (p. 67 note 7) there was a suggestion that he had given some thought to the matter, but there is here the first clear expression of the idea that there must have been some means by which news was rapidly exchanged between Orthanc and Barad-dûr. Why Gandalf was so certain of this is not made plain,[4] and one might wonder whether the idea did not arise from the *palantír* rather than the other way about.

On the reverse of this page is an outline that one would naturally suppose to have been written continuously with the text on the other side. That it followed the abandoned narrative draft is obvious from the fact that here the company did not head straight for Eodoras but rode down from Isengard to the Fords. The writing is here exceptionally difficult, not only extremely rapid but with letters idiosyncratically formed.

This was the Orthan[c] Stone [*written above: Orthancstone Orthankstone Orþancstán*] which kept watch on movements in neighbourhood but its range was limited to some 100 leagues?[5] It will help to keep watch on Orthanc from afar.

Night comes swiftly. They come to the Fords and note the river is failing and running dry again.[6] The starry night. They cross and pass the mounds.

They halt under stars and see the great black shadow passing between [?them] and stars. Nazgûl.

Gandalf takes out dark globe and looks at it. Good, he said. It shows little by night. That is a comfort. All they could see [?was] stars and [?far away] small batlike shapes wheeling. At the edge was a river in the moon. The moon is already visible in Osgiliath said Gandalf. That seems the edge of sight.[7]

70   THE WAR OF THE RING

As they draw near Helm's Deep a shadow comes up like a
mist. Suddenly they hear a rustling whisper and on both sides
of them so that they are in a lane .... Shadows pass away
northward. Huorns. Insert now page 3 of Ch.XXIX.

Next day they ride with many men in the Westfold Vale and
.... by [?paths winding] among the mountains. They strike the
Dunharrow ravine on the second day. And find folk streaming
back to Eodoras. Aragorn rides with Éowyn.[8]

Gandalf looks at the Dark Crystal on the terrace before
King's House. They see quite clearly Orthanc – Ents [?moving]
..... water   all very [?small] and clear. Horsemen riding over
plain from west and north. Strange [?figures of various kind].
And from Minas Tirith. It only shows *lights and men*   [?no
country].

The reference to 'page 3 of Chapter XXIX' is to the first completed
version of 'The Road to Isengard', where the description of the
departure of the Huorn wood from the Deeping Coomb was placed
before Théoden and Gandalf and their company left for Isengard, and
so before they passed through the wood (p. 27). It is clear from the
passage of the Huorns at this point in the story that the final time-
scheme had not yet been reached (see pp. 5–6, §§ III–IV): Théoden
and Gandalf and their company still reached Isengard on the day
(2 February) following the Battle of the Hornburg and did not spend
the night of 2 February encamped below Nan Gurunír (where
in TT, p. 158, they heard the Huorns passing, and after which the
passage about the departure of the wood from the Deeping Coomb,
and the Death Down, finally found its place).

In this outline there is nothing to suggest that the 'dark globe' was
the means of communication between Orthanc and Barad-dûr –
indeed, rather the reverse, since when Gandalf looks into it somewhere
near the Fords of Isen the range of its sight does not extend beyond
Osgiliath (although his words 'It shows little by night. That is a
comfort' suggest that he had feared that it might make them visible to
a hostile eye). On the other hand, in the preceding narrative draft
Gandalf is seen to be much concerned with that question of communication: 'There was a bond between Isengard and Mordor. Of
what sort ... I have not discovered.' It seems hard to believe that even
though Gandalf had not yet put two and two together my father had
failed to do so. A possible explanation is that when he wrote this
outline he did indeed already know the significance of the Dark
Crystal, but that Gandalf had not yet fathomed the full extent of its
range and powers, or did not yet know how to make use of them. Or it
may be truer to say simply that in these notes we see the formative
moment in which the significance of the Seeing Stone was at the point

THE PALANTÍR

71

of emergence: the fateful 'device' – devised long before – which in the final story would prove to have been of vast though hidden import-ance in the War of the Ring.[9]

A little scribbled note in isolation may be cited here:

The black-red ball shows movements. They see the lines of war advancing. [?Ships are seen] and Théoden's men in Helm's Deep and assembling in Rohan.

The context of this is altogether obscure: for who is seeing these things?

Another text – a brief and tantalising set of notes scrawled down very rapidly in faint soft pencil, vestiges of fugitive thoughts – shows further debate on the meaning of the Orthanc-stone. I cannot see any clear indication of where it would be placed in the narrative, or even of where it stands in the sequence of these preliminary papers;[10] but from various points it seems to have preceded the text that follows it here.

I said that Isengard was overthrown, and the Stone was going on a journey, said Gandalf. And that I would [look >] speak to it again later when I could, but [?at the] moment I was in a hurry.

auctor (No I think the dark globe to be in contact with Mordor is too like the rings)

Gandalf discovers that the Orthanc-stone is a far-seer. But he could not make out [how] to use it. It seemed capricious. It seems still to be looking in the directions in which it was last used, he said.

Hence, vision of the [*added:* 7] Nazgûl above the battlements. He was looking towards Mordor.

Can one see back. Possibly said Gandalf. It is perilous but I have a mind to use it.

He stands back. He has been seen [?bending over it].?

No, he said, this is an ancient stone set in an upper chamber of the tower long long ago before the Dark Tower was strong. It was used by the [?wardens] of Gondor. One also must have been in the Hornburg, and in Minas Tirith, and in Minas Morghul, and in Osgiliath. (Five).

They saw the Hornburg. They saw Minas Tirith. They saw Nazgûl above the battlements of Osgiliath. So Saruman learned some of his news he said.

The bracketing of the words 'No I think the dark globe to be in contact with Mordor is too like the rings' and the marginal *auctor* (meaning that this was my father's thought, not Gandalf's) were

72   THE WAR OF THE RING

added in ink. The implication of these words must be that Gandalf, in the opening sentences of this text, was speaking to a person in Mordor: and if that person was none other than Sauron himself, there is a delightful glimpse of Gandalf telling the Dark Lord that he was busy. — That here only five of the Seeing Stones are named (given a habitation) does not mean of course that at this stage there were only five, but that these were the five Stones of the southern kingdom (Gondor). In subsequent enumerations there were five Stones in Gondor, where in LR there were four.

Lastly, there is a brief outline, ending in a ragged scrawl, that seems to have preceded the first continuous drafting of the chapter in formed narrative.

Conversation with Saruman begins about 3.15 and ends about 4.30 (that is about sunset). Dark comes about 5.30. Gandalf leads them south in the dark – because now they must be more secret than ever. (Wonders what the connexion was between Saruman and Sauron.)

They pass out of Nan Gurunír at about 9 p.m. Camp under shadow of the last western hill. Dolbaran. They will ride fast on morrow. Two men are sent ahead to warn men that king is returning to Helm's Deep and that a strong force should be ready to ride with him. No men more than two or three are to ride openly on the plain. The king will go by mountain paths to Dunharrow.

Then episode of Pippin and Stone.

Gandalf says this is how Saruman fell. He studied such matters. The old far-seers of the Men of Númenor who made Amon Hen and Amon Lhaw One in Hornburg, Osgiliath, Minas Tirith, Minas Morghul, Isengard [Angrenost >] Angost.[11] That is how Saruman got news – though Hornburg and Minas Tirith were 'dark', their balls lost or destroyed. But he tried to peep at Barad-dur and got caught.

Nazgúl.

Feb. 4 They ride to Fords mid-morning (11 a.m.), rest an hour, and reach Deeping Coomb road-fork at 3 p.m. Helm's Deep at about 4. They rest, gather men, and ride by hill-paths lost to sight. Hobbits are given ponies – and Gimli!

Feb. 5, 6 Journey.

Feb. 7 Dunharrow. Joy of people. Éowyn comes forth. The King rides down the mountain valley with Éowyn and Éomund [*read* Éomer] on either side, Gandalf, Legolas, Aragorn beside them. The hobbits and Gimli ...

[?Regency.] Feast.   Tobacco.   Messenger.

THE PALANTÍR 73

In the previous text (p. 71) it is not actually stated that the Seeing Stones of Gondor 'answered' or corresponded one to another, but the idea was at the moment of emergence, as is seen from my father's passing doubt whether 'the dark globe to be in contact with Mordor is too like the rings', while 'Can one see back' seems clearly to refer to reciprocal vision between one Stone and another rather than to vision of past time. In the present outline this conception is fully present and accepted, and with it the central idea that it was through his knowledge of these matters that Saruman was corrupted, being snared by his use of the Stone of Orthanc to look towards Barad-dûr.

The 'episode of Pippin and the Stone' has arisen (though so far as the evidence goes it had not yet been committed to paper in any form); and the various elements were now coming to interlock in a beautifully articulated conception. The original idea (p. 69) that when Gandalf looked into the dark globe he saw 'small batlike shapes wheeling' will be retained but become Pippin's vision, and the explanation of why it should be that vision and no other (cf. 'It seems still to be looking in the directions in which it was last used', p. 71) will be found in the constant intercourse of Saruman and Sauron by means of the Seeing Stones (itself answering the question of the method of communication between Isengard and the Dark Tower), so that 'the Orthanc-stone [became] so bent towards Barad-dûr that, if any save a will of adamant now looks into it, it will bear his mind and sight swiftly thither' (TT p. 204).

The final time-scheme had now entered (see p. 6, § IV): Théoden and Gandalf and their company came to Isengard on 3 February and left that evening, two nights after the Battle of the Hornburg. It is remarkable that even when the plot had advanced to this stage, with the 'episode of Pippin and the Stone', and the first appearance of a Nazgûl west of Anduin, blacking out the stars (already present in the outline on p. 69), Gandalf was not impelled to ride on ahead in haste to Minas Tirith, but is present at the feast in Eodoras – that feast, often foreseen, which would never in the event take place. For the significance of the reference to tobacco here see p. 37 and note 33. But pencilled notes added to this outline later show the story of Gandalf's sudden departure: 'Feb. 4   Gandalf and Pippin reach Deeping Coomb before dawn', and 'Feb. 4–5   Gandalf rides all night and all day Feb. 5 reaching Minas Tirith at sunset on Feb. 5'.

There are no other writings extant before we come to a first draft of the chapter – which extends however only so far as the conclusion of Gandalf's words with Pippin after his vision in the Seeing Stone (TT p. 199).[12] This was written very fast and apparently set down without any preliminary workings, but the final text of the chapter to this point was achieved at once in all essentials – there are of course countless differences in the expression and a few in very small points of narrative detail, and many of these differences survived into the first

74 THE WAR OF THE RING

completed manuscript of the chapter.[13] The chief difference from the final text comes as Gandalf knelt by Pippin's body (TT p. 198): 'He removed the ball and wrapped it in a cloth again. "Take this and guard it, Aragorn," he said. "And do not uncover it or handle it yourself, I beg." Then he took Pippin's hand and bent over his face ...' Thus Gandalf hands the globe to Aragorn simply as a bearer whom he can trust, in contrast to the story in TT (pp. 199–200), where the charging of Aragorn with the Orthanc-stone takes place at a different point and is given much greater significance through Aragorn's claiming it by right. But Pippin's account of what happened to him when he looked into the globe and '*he* came' was achieved at once in this draft.

From this point there is very little further preliminary drafting, and for almost all the rest of the chapter the earliest available text is that of the first completed manuscript, much of which is written over erased pencil. This manuscript was later given the chapter-number XXXI, and the title 'The Orthanc-stone The Palantir', this being written over an erased title of which only 'The' can be read.

As this manuscript was first written Gandalf in his concluding words to Pippin said a good deal more than he does in TT (p. 199). Some of this was moved to his conversation with Théoden and Aragorn after he had carried Pippin back to his bed: that Pippin had saved him from the dangerous blunder of using the Stone himself, and of Sauron's delusion that the Stone, and the hobbit, were in Orthanc. But here Gandalf goes on:

'Very odd, very odd how things work out! But I begin now to wonder a little.' He stroked his beard. 'Was this ball really thrown to slay me after all? Or to slay me if it might, and do something else if it missed? Was it thrown without Saruman's knowledge? Hm! Things may have been meant to go much as they have gone – except that you looked in, not me! Hm! Well. They have gone so, and not otherwise; and it is so that we have to deal with.

'But come! This must change our plans. We are being careless and leisurely.

Against the paragraph beginning 'Very odd, very odd how things work out!' my father wrote in the margin: 'No! because if Saruman had wished to warn Mordor of the ruin of Isengard and the presence of Gandalf and hobbits he had only to use Glass in normal fashion and inform Sauron direct. ? But he may have wished (a) to kill Gandalf, (b) to get *rid* of the link. Sauron may have been *pressing* him to come to the stone?' He evidently decided that these were unprofitable speculations, and abandoning the direction Gandalf's words had taken returned to an earlier point in his final address to Pippin.

THE PALANTÍR

75

The text in this first manuscript then (with rewriting of some passages, obviously belonging to the same time) all but reaches that of TT (pp. 199–203) as far as Gandalf's opening remarks to Pippin about the Seeing Stones as they rode towards the Deeping Coomb. Only two matters need be noted. When Gandalf gives the Stone to Aragorn (cf. p. 74) he says here: 'It is a dangerous charge, but I can trust you even against yourself', and Aragorn replies only: 'I know the danger. I will not uncover it, or handle it.' Secondly, there is a curious series of shifts in the precise wording of Gandalf's remarks about his failure to understand immediately the nature of the ball thrown down from Orthanc. At first he said: 'I said nothing, because I knew nothing. I guessed only. I know now.' In the first rewriting of this passage he said: 'I ought to have been quicker, but my mind was bent on Saruman. And I did not guess *the full nature of the stone* – not until now. But now I know the link between Isengard and Mordor, which has long puzzled me.' This was again rewritten at this stage to read: 'And I did not guess *the nature of the stone, till I saw it in his* [Pippin's] *hands*. Not until now was I sure.' In further revision of the passage carried out much later it became: 'I did not guess the nature of the stone, *until it was too late*. Only now am I sure of it.' In the final form (TT p. 200) this was changed once more: 'I did not at once guess the nature of the stone. Then I was weary, and *as I lay pondering it, sleep overcame me*. Now I know!' There is, to be sure, among all these formulations no great difference in the actual meaning, but it was evidently a detail that concerned my father: just how much did Gandalf surmise about the *palantír* before Pippin's experience brought certainty, and how soon?

An element of ambiguity does in fact remain in LR. Already in the first manuscript of 'The Voice of Saruman' Gandalf had said: 'I fancy that, if we could have come in, we should have found few treasures in Orthanc more precious than the thing which the fool Wormtongue tossed down to us!' The nature of Wormtongue's missile cannot have been fully apparent to my father himself at that stage: it was in that manuscript, only a few lines above, that he changed, as he wrote, the initial story of the globe's having smashed into fragments on the rock (p. 65). But even when he had fully established the nature of the *palantír* he retained those words of Gandalf (TT p. 190) at the moment when it bursts upon the story – *although*, as Gandalf said at Dol Baran, 'I did not at once guess the nature of the Stone'. But then why was he so emphatic, as he stood beneath the tower, that 'we could have found few treasures in Orthanc more precious' – even before Wormtongue's shriek gave reinforcement to his opinion? Perhaps we should suppose simply that this much at least was immediately clear to him, that a great ball of dark crystal in Orthanc was most unlikely to have been nothing but an elegant adornment of Saruman's study.

At the words 'Hobbits, I suppose, have forgotten them' (the Rhymes

76 THE WAR OF THE RING

of Lore), following Gandalf's recital of the words of the Rhyme *Tall ships and tall kings / Three times three* (TT p. 202), a brief passage of original drafting, written out separately in ink and so not lost in erasure of pencil as elsewhere, takes up: the first framing of Gandalf's declaration of the history of the Seeing Stones, here called *Palantirs*, a word that so far as record goes now first appears.

They [the Rhymes of Lore] are all treasured in Rivendell. Treebeard remembers most / some of them: Long [Rolls >] Lists and that sort of thing. But hobbits I suppose have forgotten nearly all, even those that they ever knew.

And what is that one about: the seven stones and seven stars?

About the Palantirs of the Men of Old, said Gandalf. I was thinking of them.

Why, what are they?

The Orthanc stone was one, said Gandalf.

Then it was not made, Pippin hesitated, by the Enemy, he asked [?at a rush].

No, said Gandalf. Nor by Saruman; it is beyond his art, and beyond Sauron's too maybe. No, there was no evil in it. It has been corrupted, as have so many of the things that remain. Alas poor Saruman, it was his downfall, so I now perceive. Dangerous to us all are devices made by a knowledge and art deeper than we possess ourselves. I did not know that any Palantir had survived the decay of Gondor and the Elendilions until now.

Seven they set up. At Minas Anor that is now Minas Tirith there was one, and one at Minas Ithil, and others at Aglarond the Caves of Splendour which men call Helm's Deep, and at Orthanc. Others were far away, I know not where, maybe at Fornost, and at Mithlond [*struck out:* where Cirdan harboured the ... ships ...] (in) the Gulf of Lune where the grey ships lie. But the chief and master .... [?of (the) stones] was at Osgiliath before it was ruined.

In this passage are the first occurrences of *Aglarond* (see p. 28) and of *Fornost*, which on the First Map was named *Fornobel*, and still so on my map made in 1943, VII.304. Here also is the first appearance of *Cirdan* in the manuscripts of *The Lord of the Rings*.

In the first complete manuscript this was developed towards the form in TT. Gandalf now tells that 'The *palantirs* came from beyond Westernesse, from Eldamar. The Noldor made them: Fëanor himself maybe wrought them, in days so long ago that the time cannot be measured in years.' He speaks of Saruman as he does in the final text; but here he ends: 'No word did he ever speak of it to any of the

THE PALANTÍR

Council. It was not known that any of the *palantirs* had escaped the ruin of Gondor. Their very existence was preserved only in a Rhyme of Lore among Aragorn's people.' This was changed to: 'It was not known to us that any of the *palantirs* had escaped the ruin of Gondor. Outside the Council it was not among elves and men even remembered that such things had ever been, save only in a Rhyme of Lore preserved among Aragorn's people.'[14]

The remainder of the chapter in the first manuscript reaches the final form in all but a few respects. There were still five *palantirs* anciently in Gondor, one being still that of Aglarond (translated, as in the draft, 'Caves of Splendour', but changed to 'Glittering Caves').[15] Of the other two, Gandalf still says that they were far away, 'I do not know where, for no rhyme says. Maybe they were at Fornost, and with Kirdan at Mith[l]ond[16] in the Gulf of Lune where the grey ships lie.'

In answer to Pippin's question concerning the coming of the Nazgûl (TT p. 204) Gandalf here says only: 'It could have taken you away to the Dark Tower', and goes on at once: 'But now Saruman is come to the last pinch of the vice that he has put his hand in.' He says that 'It may be that he [Sauron] will learn that I was there and stood upon the stairs of Orthanc – with hobbits at my tail. That is what I fear.'[17] And at the end of the chapter he tells Pippin: 'You may see the first glimmer of dawn upon the golden roof of the house of Eorl. At sunset on the day after you shall see the shadow of Mount Tor-dilluin fall upon the white walls of the tower of Denethor.'[18]

★

In his foreword to the Second Edition of *The Lord of the Rings* my father said that in 1942 he 'wrote the first drafts of the matter that now stands as Book III, and the beginnings of Chapters 1 and 3 of Book V ['Minas Tirith' and 'The Muster of Rohan']; and there as the beacons flared in Anórien and Théoden came to Harrowdale I stopped. Foresight had failed and there was no time for thought.'[19] It seems to have been about the end of 1942 or soon after that he stopped; for in a letter to Stanley Unwin of 7 December 1942 (*Letters* no. 47) he said that the book had reached Chapter XXXI 'and will require at least six more to finish (these are already sketched).' This chapter was undoubtedly 'The Palantír' (not 'Flotsam and Jetsam', *Letters* p. 437, note to letter 47).

In the foreword to the Second Edition he went on: 'It was during 1944 that ... I forced myself to tackle the journey of Frodo to Mordor', and this new beginning can be very precisely dated; for on 3 April 1944 he said in a letter to me (*Letters* no. 58):

I have begun to nibble at Hobbit again. I have started to do some (painful) work on the chapter which picks up the adventures of

78   THE WAR OF THE RING

Frodo and Sam again; and to get myself attuned have been copying and polishing the last written chapter (Orthanc-Stone).

Two days later, on 5 April 1944 (*Letters* no. 59) he wrote to me:

I have seriously embarked on an effort to finish my book, & have been sitting up rather late: a lot of re-reading and research required. And it is a painful sticky business getting into swing again. I have gone back to Sam and Frodo, and am trying to work out their adventures. A few pages for a lot of sweat: but at the moment they are just meeting Gollum on a precipice.

The 'copying and polishing' of 'The Orthanc-Stone' that my father did at this time is the second, very finely written manuscript of the chapter. Well over a year had passed since the first manuscript of the chapter was written, but not unnaturally no changes of significance were made in the new text: thus Aragorn's reception of the *palantír* remains in the simple form it had (p. 75); Gandalf does not refer to the possibility that Wormtongue might have recognised Aragorn on the stairs of Orthanc (note 17); Aglarond was still one of the ancient sites of the *palantíri* of Gondor, and Gandalf still says that he does not know where the others had been 'for no rhyme says', but maybe in Fornost and with Cirdan at the Grey Havens.[20]

NOTES

1   On 'the road that led to the bridge' see p. 31, where coming in the other direction the company had crossed the bridge and 'found a road that with a wide northward sweep brought them to the great highway to the fords.'

2   In the notes on distances referred to on p. 42 note 14 *Eodoras to Isenford* is given as 125 miles, which agrees well with the First Map (VII.319) and with the statement in TT ('Helm's Deep', p. 131) that it was 'forty leagues and more': see p. 12. *Eodoras to Isengard* is given in these notes as 140 miles (46·6 leagues), which again agrees closely with the First Map (about 2·8 cm.). *Eodoras to Helm's Deep or mouth of Coomb* is 110 miles; in my redrawing this distance is 100 miles (2 cm.), but the map is here very difficult to interpret and I have probably not placed Helm's Deep at precisely the point my father intended: on my map made in 1943 the distance as the crow flies is 110 miles. – The idea that after the visit to Isengard Théoden and his companions returned to Eodoras goes back to the outline 'The Story Foreseen from Fangorn', VII.437.

3   There is a second draft of the opening, which need not be given in full. Here it is noted how they rode: 'Gandalf took Merry behind him, and Aragorn took Pippin; Gimli rode as before with Éomer,

THE PALANTÍR

79

and Legolas was upon Arod at his side'; but this was immediately changed to 'Legolas and Gimli rode together again.' After a further hesitation, whether the company went down to the Fords or passed over the bridge below Isengard and went east, this draft ends:

> Gandalf's plan had at first been to ride straight to Eodoras from Isengard. But he said 'Victory has its dangers', and Théoden had best ride with secrecy now, and with many men. They would return to the Deeping Coomb and send on a messenger, bidding the men who were labouring there to hasten their work and be prepared to ride on the morrow by hill-paths. So now the company rode at a gentle [pace]

4 Cf. *Unfinished Tales* p. 405: 'It needed the demonstration on Dol Baran of the effects of the Orthanc-stone on Peregrin to reveal suddenly that the "link" between Isengard and Barad-dûr (seen to exist after it was discovered that forces of Isengard had been joined with others directed by Sauron in the attack on the Fellowship at Parth Galen) was in fact the Orthanc-stone – and one other *palantír*.'

5 The distance from Orthanc to Barad-dûr on the First Map is 12·3 cm., = 615 miles or 205 leagues. – This is a convenient place to notice that in my redrawing of section IVE of the First Map (VII.319) what I have represented as a small circle on the western side of the Wizard's Vale seems not to be so, but is rather an alteration in the line marking the edge of the vale. At the upper end of the vale is a minute circle that must represent Isengard.

6 The story here was that the Ents (who at the beginning of the draft on p. 68 are said to have gone back to the sources of the stream, leaving Treebeard alone at the gate of Isengard) had at once obeyed Gandalf's parting request to Treebeard (TT p. 192) that the waters of Isen be again poured into the Ring.

7 From Isenford to Osgiliath on the First Map is 8·6 cm., = 430 miles or 143 leagues.

8 Cf. VII.447: 'If I live, I will come, Lady Éowyn, and then maybe we will ride together.'

9 Cf. Gandalf's words in *The Two Towers*, p. 203: 'Alas for Saruman! It was his downfall, as I now perceive'; and in *The Return of the King*, p. 133: 'Thus the will of Sauron entered into Minas Tirith.'

10 It is written in fact on the back of one of the pages of the initial continuous drafting of the chapter (p. 73), but seems entirely unconnected with it.

11 *Angost* was a passing substitution for *Angrenost*: see p. 44 note 27.

12 One of the pages of this draft carries also drafting of the passage in 'The Voice of Saruman' in which Gandalf, seeing Pippin

80   THE WAR OF THE RING

carrying the *palantír*, cries out 'Here, my lad, I'll take that! I did not ask you to handle it.' See p. 66.

13   I mention the following as examples of such differences in the detail of this part of the story. In Gandalf's talk with Merry as they rode from Isengard (TT p. 194), after saying that he had not yet fathomed what the link was between Saruman and Sauron and that 'Rohan will be ever in his thought', he used again the words found in the soon abandoned draft for the opening of the chapter (p. 68): 'There is no one of this company, be sure, whose name and deeds are not noted now in the mind of Sauron'; but my father bracketed this, with the marginal note: 'No: Gandalf's return hidden.' In the night halt beneath Dolbaran (so written, as also in the outline on p. 72) Merry and Pippin lay not far from Gandalf; when Pippin got up from his bed 'the two guards sitting on their horses had their backs to the camp'; Pippin saw a glitter from Gandalf's eyes as he slept 'Under his long dark lashes' ('long lashes' TT); the *palantír* lay beside the wizard's left hand.

14   This was preserved in the First Edition of *The Two Towers*.

15   As in TT, Gandalf guesses that the *palantír* of Barad-dûr was the Ithil-stone.

16   *Mithond* must be a mere slip, though it was left uncorrected. It is curious that in the next manuscript, made in 1944 (pp. 77–8), the form in this passage was *Mithrond*, corrected to *Mithlond*.

17   In TT 'That is what I fear' refers to additional sentences inserted after 'with hobbits at my tail': 'Or that an heir of Elendil lives and stood beside me. If Wormtongue was not deceived by the armour of Rohan, he would remember Aragorn and the title that he claimed.' But this insertion was made long after (on 'the armour of Rohan' borne by Aragorn see TT p. 127, and in this book p. 304 and p. 317 with note 9).

18   *Tor-dilluin* was emended to *Mindolluin*. The mountain was added roughly to the First Map and not named, but carefully shown on the 1943 map (VII.310). – With Gandalf's forecast that they will come to Minas Tirith at sunset cf. p. 73 (Gandalf reaches Minas Tirith at sunset on February 5).

19   Cf. my father's letter to Caroline Everett, 24 June 1957 (*Letters* no. 199):

I was in fact longest held up – by exterior circumstances as well as interior – at the point now represented by the last words of Book iii (reached about 1942 or 3). After that Chapter 1 of Book v remained very long as a mere opening (as far as the arrival in Gondor); Chapter 2 [The Passing of the Grey Company] did not exist; and Chapter 3, Muster of Rohan, had got no further than the arrival at Harrowdale. Chapter 1 of Book iv [The Taming of Sméagol] had hardly got beyond Sam's opening words (Vol. II p. 209). Some parts of the

THE PALANTÍR

adventures of Frodo and Sam on the confines of Mordor and in it had been written (but were eventually abandoned).

The last sentence evidently refers to the text that I called 'The Story Foreseen from Lórien', in VII.324 ff.

In fact, there is very clear evidence that my father erred in his recollection that the abandoned beginnings of Chapters 1 and 3 of Book V belonged to the time that we have now reached (i.e. the end of Book III); see pp. 231 ff., where the question is discussed in detail.

20   The text has *Mithrond* here, corrected to *Mithlond*: see note 16. – I collect a few further details from this second manuscript. *Palantirs* became *Palantíri* in the course of writing it. – Osgiliath is named *Elostirion* (*Elostirion* being roughly substituted for *Osgiliath* in the first manuscript, but very probably at this time). This change was introduced in a note dated February 9 1942 (VII.423), and appears in the outline 'The Story Foreseen from Fangorn' (VII.435). *Osgiliath* in the drafting and first manuscript of 'The Palantír' was thus a reversion, and *Elostirion* in 1944 another. Finally *Elostirion* was afterwards corrected back to *Osgiliath* on the 1944 manuscript.

Lastly, there was much hesitation about the phase of the moon on the night of the camp below Dol Baran. In the original draft no more was said than that 'The moon was shining' when Pippin got up from his bed. In the first manuscript 'The moon had risen far away but could not yet be seen; a pale sheen was in the sky above the bushes and the eastern rim of the dell'; with this compare perhaps the early notes given on p. 69, where Gandalf looks into the Seeing Stone and says 'The moon is already visible in Osgiliath.' This was changed to 'The moon was shining cold and white into the dell and the shadows of the bushes were black'; but on both the first and second manuscripts my father then shifted back and forth between the two statements, until he finally decided on the latter, which is the reading of TT (p. 196).

On the first manuscript he noted in the margin the following times (which show a much more rapid journey from Isengard than in the outline on p. 72): 'Sunset about 5 p.m. They camped about 6 p.m. This [i.e. Pippin's looking into the *palantír*] happened about 11 p.m. Moon rose 6.34 p.m.' According to the elaborate time-scheme that was made after the introduction of changes in October 1944 (VII.368), the New Moon had been on 21 January, the First Quarter on 29 January, and Full Moon was on 6 February, three nights after the camp beneath Dol Baran.

PART TWO

THE RING GOES EAST

I

THE TAMING OF SMÉAGOL

In his letter of June 1957 cited in note 19 to the last chapter (p. 80) my father said that at the time of this long break in the writing of *The Lord of the Rings* 'Chapter 1 of Book iv had hardly got beyond Sam's opening words (Vol. II p. 209)'. That beginning of a new story of Sam and Frodo in Mordor,[1] for so long set aside, can I think be identified: it consists of a brief narrative opening that soon breaks down into outline form ('A'), and a portion of formed narrative ('B') that ends at Sam's words (TT p. 210) 'a bit of plain bread, and a mug aye half a mug of beer would go down proper'. The original draft A went thus:

'Well Master this is a nasty place and no mistake,' said Sam to Frodo. They had been wandering for days in the hard barren heights of Sarn Gebir. Now at last on the fifth evening since their flight[2] they stood on the edge of a grey cliff. A chill east wind blew. Far below the land lay green at the feet of the cliff, and away S.W. [*read* S.E.] a pall of grey cloud or shadow hung shutting out the remoter view.

'It seems we have come the wrong way altogether,' went on Sam. 'That's where we want to get, or we don't want to but we mean to. And the quicker the better, if we must do it. But we can't get down, and if we do get down there is all that nasty green marsh. Phew, can you smell it.' He sniffed the wind: cold as it was it seemed heavy with a stench of cold decay and rottenness.

'We are above the Dead Marshes that lie between Anduin and the pass into Mordor,' said Frodo. 'We have come the wrong way – [we >] I should have left the Company long before and come down from the North, east of Sarn Gebir and over the hard of Battle Plain. But it would take us weeks on foot to work back northward over these hills. I don't know what is to be done. What food have we?'

A couple of weeks with care.

Let us sleep.

Suspicion of Gollum that night.   They work northward.

Next day footfalls on the rock. Frodo sends Sam ahead and hides behind a rock *using ring*.[3] Gollum appears. Frodo over-

86   THE WAR OF THE RING

come with sudden fear flies, but Gollum pursues. They come to a cliff rather lower and less sheer than that behind. In dread of Gollum they begin to climb down.

Here my father abandoned this draft, and (as I think) followed at once with a new opening (B), in which the text of TT is closely approached at almost all points (but the hills are still named *Sarn Gebir*, and the time is 'the [*struck out:* fourth or] fifth evening since they had fled from the Company'). With Sam's longing for bread and beer this manuscript ends, not at the foot of a page; and it is, I feel sure, the abandoned opening of the chapter to which my father referred.[4] When it was written, in relation to the work on Book III, there seems no way of telling.[5]

'A few pages for a lot of sweat,' my father said in his letter of 5 April 1944 (see p. 78), in which he told me of his turning again to the adventures of Sam and Frodo; and 45 years later one can feel it, reading these pages in which he struggled (in increasingly impossible handwriting) to discover just how Sam and Frodo did in the end get down out of the twisted hills into the horrible lands below.

When he took the chapter up again in 1944, he did not rewrite the original opening (which survives with little change into TT), but taking a new sheet began: 'The sun was caught into clouds and night came suddenly' (cf. TT p. 210). This text, which I will call 'C', soon degenerates into a terrible scrawl and at the end becomes in part altogether illegible.

The sun was caught into clouds and night came suddenly. They slept in turns, as best they could, in a hollow of the rocks, sheltered from the easterly wind.

'Did you see them again, Mr Frodo?' asked Sam, as they sat, stiff and chilled, munching wafers of *lembas* in the cold grey of early morning.

'Yes, once,' said Frodo. 'But I heard the snuffling several times, and it came nearer than it has before.'

'Ah!' said Sam. 'Growing bolder, it seems. I heard him, too, though I saw no eyes. He's after us still: can't shake him off nohow. Curse the slinking varmint. Gollum! I'd give him *gollum* if I could get my hands on his neck. As if we hadn't enough trouble in front, without him hanging on behind.'

'If only I dared use the Ring,' muttered Frodo, 'maybe I could catch him then.'

'Don't you do that, master!' said Sam. 'Not out up here! He'd see you – not meaning Gollum either. I feel all naked on the east side, if you understand me, stuck up here on the skyline with

THE TAMING OF SMÉAGOL   87

nought but a big flat bog between us and that shadow over yonder.'[6] He looked hurriedly over his shoulder towards the East. 'We've got to get down off it,' he said, 'and today we're going to get down off it somehow.'

But that day too wore towards its end, and found them still scrambling along the ridge. Often they heard the following footsteps, and yet however quick they turned they could not catch sight of the pursuer. Once or twice they lay in wait behind a boulder. But after a moment the *flip-flap* of the footsteps would halt, and all went silent: only the wind sighing over stones seemed to remind them of faint breathing through sharp teeth.

Toward evening Frodo and Sam were brought to a halt. They came to a place where they had at last only two choices: to go back or to climb down. They were on the outer eastward ridge of the Emyn Muil,[7] that fell away sheerly on their right. For many miles it had been falling lower towards the wet lands beyond; here after tending northwards it reared suddenly up again many fathoms in a single leap and went on again on a high level far above their heads. They were at the foot of a cliff facing S.W., cut down as if with a knife-stroke. There was no going further that way. But they were also at the top of another cliff facing east.

Frodo looked over the edge. 'It's easier to get down than up,' he said.

'Yes, you can always jump or fall, even if you can't fly,' said Sam.

'But look, Sam!' said Frodo. 'Either the ridge has sunk or the lands at its feet have swelled up – we are not nearly so high up as we were yesterday: about 30 fathoms,[8] not much more.'

'And that's enough,' said Sam. 'Ugh! How I do hate looking down from a height, and that's not so bad as climbing.'

'But here I almost think we could climb,' said Frodo. 'The rock is different here.' The cliff was indeed no longer sheer, but sloped somewhat backward, and the rock was of such a kind that great flat slabs seemed to have split away and fallen. It looked rather as if they were sitting on the eaves of a great roof of thin stone-shingles or tiles that had tipped over leaving their rough edges upwards.

'Well,' said Sam, standing up and tightening his belt. 'What about trying it? It'll give that flapping footpad something to think about anyway.'

88   THE WAR OF THE RING

'If we are going to try today we had better try at once,' said Frodo. 'It's getting dark early. I think there's a storm coming.'

The dark smudge of the mountains in the East was lost in a deeper blackness, that was already sending out great arms towards them. There was a distant rumble of thunder. 'There's no shelter at all down there,' said Frodo. 'Still, come on!' He stepped towards the brink.

'Nay, Mr Frodo, me first!' cried Sam.

'Why so eager?' said Frodo. 'Do you want to show me the way?'

'Not me,' said Sam. 'But it's only sense. Have the one most like to slip lowest. I don't want to slip, but I don't want to slip and come down atop of you and knock you off.'

'But [>I'd] do the same to you.'

'Then you'll have something soft to fall on,' said Sam, throwing his legs over the edge, and turning his face to the wall. His toes found a ledge and he grunted. 'Now where do we put our hands next?' he muttered.

'There's a much wider ledge about twice your height below you,' said Frodo from above, 'if you can slide down to it.' 'If!' said Sam. 'And what then?' 'Come, I'll get alongside and try it, and then we need not quarrel about first or second.' Frodo slid quickly down till he stood splayed against the cliff a yard or two to the right of Sam. But he could find no handhold between the cliff-top and the narrow ledge at his toes, and though the slope lean[t] forwards[9] he had not the skill nor the head to make the passage to the wider foothold below.

From about this point the text becomes increasingly rough and increasingly difficult to read: I reproduce a leaf of the manuscript on p. 90 (for the text of this leaf as best as I can interpret it see p. 91).

'Hm!' grunted Sam. 'Here we are side by side, like flies on a fly-paper.'

'But we can at least still get back,' said Frodo. 'At least I can. There's a hold just above my head.'

'Then you'd best get back,' said Sam. 'I can't manage this, and my toes are aching cruel already.'

Frodo hauled himself back with some difficulty, but he found that he could not help Sam. When he leaned down as far as he dared Sam's upstretched hand was just out of reach.

'Lor, this is a pickle I am in,' said poor Sam, and his voice

THE TAMING OF SMÉAGOL

89

began to quaver. The eastern sky grew black as night. The thunder rolled nearer.

'Hold up, Sam,' said Frodo. 'Just wait till I get my belt off.' He lowered it buckle first. 'Can you grasp it?'

'Aye,' said Sam. 'A bit lower till I get my two hands on it.'

'But now I haven't enough to hold myself, and anyway I can't lean back or get my foot against a stop,' said Frodo. 'You'll just pull me over, or pull the belt out of my hands. O for a rope.'

'Rope,' said Sam. 'I just deserve to hang here all night, I do. You're nobbut a ninnyhammer Sam Gamgee: that's what the Gaffer said to me many a time, that being a word of his. Rope. There is one of those grey ropes in my pack. You know, that one we got with the boats in Lórien. I took a fancy to it and stowed it away.'

'But the pack's on your back,' said Frodo, 'and I can't reach it, and you can't toss it up.'

'It did ought to be but it ain't,' said Sam. 'You've got my pack,' said Sam.

[?'How's that?'] . . . . .

'Now do make haste, Mr Frodo, or my toes'll break,' said Sam. 'The rope's my only chance.' It did not take Frodo long to tip up the pack, and there indeed at the bottom was a long coil of silk[en] grey rope. In a moment Sam [?tied] an end round his waist and ... clutched ... above his head [?with].[10] Frodo ran back from the brink and braced his foot against a crevice. Half hauled, half scrambling Sam came puffing and blowing up the few feet of cliff that had baffled him. He sat down and stroked his toes.

'Numbpate and Ninnyhammer,' he repeated. 'How long's that rope, I wonder.' Frodo wound it [?round his] elbows. '10, 20, 30, 40, 50, 60, 70, 80 hobbit-ells,' he said. 'Who'd have thought it.'

'Ah, who would,' said Sam. 'A bit thin, but it seems mighty tough. Soft to the hand as milk. 80 ells.[11] Well, *one* of us can get down, seemingly, or near enough, if your guess weren't far out.'

'That would not be much good,' said Frodo. 'You down and me up, or the other way. Is there nothing to make an end fast to up here?'

'What,' said Sam, 'and leave all handy for that Gollum!'

'Well,' said Frodo after some thought. 'I am going down with the rope on, and you're going to hold on to the end up here. But I am only going to use the rope for a precaution. I am going to

A page from the first manuscript of 'The Taming of Sméagol'

THE TAMING OF SMÉAGOL

91

see if I can find a way down that I can use without a rope. Then I climb up with your help, and then you go down with the rope and I follow. How's that?'

Sam scratched his head. 'I don't like it, Mr Frodo,' he said, 'but it seems the only thing to do. Pity we didn't think out this rock-climbing business before we started. I'll have to stand down there [?staring] and waiting to catch you. Do you be careful.'

Frodo went to the edge again. A few yards from the brink he thought he saw a better point for a descent. 'I am going to try here,' he said. 'Get a purchase somewhere Sam for your foot, but don't let the rope [?saw] over a [?sharp ... edge]. It may be elf-spun, but I shouldn't try it too far.' He stepped over the brink ... There was a ledge for his feet before he had gone his full height down: it sloped gently downward to the right. 'Don't pull on the rope unless I shout,' he said, and he had disappeared.

*The rope lay slack for a long while as Sam stared at it. Suddenly it drew taut, and nearly caught him at unawares. He braced his feet, and wondering [*read* wondered] what had happened and whether his master was now dangling in mid-air at the far rope's end, but not [*read* no] cry came, and the rope went slack again. After a long while as it seemed he thought he heard a faint hail. He listened, it came again, and cautiously he crawled to the brink taking in the slack as he went. The darkness was drawing nearer – and it seemed dim below; but in his grey cloak Frodo if he was there was quite invisible. But something white fluttered and the shout came up clear now. 'It's all right, not too difficult at all except in one place. I'm down. [?I've] 3 ells of rope to spare. Slowly [?to take] my weight ... I'm coming up and shall use the rope.'

In about 10 mins. he reappeared over the edge and threw himself down by Sam. 'That's that,' he said. 'I'll be glad of a short rest. Down you go now' – he described the route as best he could and direct[ed] Sam to hail when he came to the bad place. 'I slipped there,' he said, 'and [?should have gone] but for the rope, a little over halfway down, quite a drop [?start to finish]. But I think I can just ... you.[12] Pay it out slowly and take the weight off on any ledge you come on. Good luck.'

---

* At this point the text of the manuscript page reproduced on p. 90 begins, and continues to the end of the second paragraph.

92   THE WAR OF THE RING

With a grim face Sam went to the edge, [?turned], and found the first ledge. 'Good luck,' said Frodo.

... [?time to time] the rope went slack as Sam found some ledge to rest ..., but for the most part his weight was taken by the rope. It was ..... minutes before Frodo heard his call.

First he lowered his pack by the rope, then he cast it loose. He was left alone at the top. At that moment there was a great clap of dry thunder overhead and the sky grew dark. The storm was coming up the Emyn Muil on its way to Rohan and to the Hornburg far away where the riders were at bay.[13] He heard Sam cry from below, but could not make out the words, nor see Sam's pointing hands. But something made him look back. There not far away on a rock behind and overlooking him was a black figure [?whose glimmer(ing)] eyes like distant lamps were fixed on him. Unreasoning fear seized him for a moment – for after all it was Gollum there, it was not a whole ...., and he had Sting at his belt and mithril beneath his jacket: but he did not stop to think of these things. He stepped over the edge, which for the moment frightened him less, and began to climb down. Haste seemed to aid him, and all went well until he came to the bad place.

Perhaps my father was at just about this point when he wrote on 5 April 1944, in the letter cited on p. 78, that 'at the moment they are just meeting Gollum on a precipice'. — From here to the end of the draft there are so many 'bad places' and even sheer drops that I shall not attempt to represent the text as it stands. There follows an account of Frodo's descent: how he slipped again, and slithered down the cliff-face clinging with his fingers till he came up with a jolt, nearly losing his balance, on a wide ledge — 'and after that he was soon down.' There came then the great storm of wind and thunder, with a torrent of rain lashing down; and looking up 'they could see two tiny points of light at the cliff edge before the curtain of rain blotted them out. "Thank goodness you've done it," said Sam. "I near swallowed my heart when you slipped. Did you see him? I thought so, when you started to climb so quick." "I did," said Frodo. "But I think we've set him a bit of a puzzle for those [?soft padding] feet of his. But let's look about here. Is there no shelter from the storm?" '

They looked for shelter, and found some fallen rocks lying against the foot of the cliff, but the ground was wet and soggy; they themselves were not drenched through apparently on account of the elven-cloaks (this passage is very largely illegible). The storm passed on over the Emyn Muil and stars came out; 'far away the sun had set behind Isengard'. The draft ends with Sam's saying: 'It's no good

THE TAMING OF SMÉAGOL

93

going that way [i.e. towards the marshes] in the dark and at night. Even on this trip we've had better camping-places: but here we'd best stay.'

There was very evidently great need for a better text: my father himself would have had difficulty with this, when the precise thought behind the words had dimmed. He began again therefore at the beginning of the chapter, giving it now its title and number (XXXII) and the completed manuscript ('D') that evolved from this new start was the only one that he made (i.e., subsequent texts are typescripts). The opening of the chapter (text B), which went back to the time before the long break during 1943–4 (p. 86), was written out again, and effectively reached the form in TT (but when the story opens it was still 'the fifth evening' since they had fled from the Company, not as in TT the third: see the Note on Chronology at the end of this chapter).

When my father came to the point where his new draft (C) took up the tale ('The sun was caught into clouds and night came suddenly', p. 86), beyond rounding out the expression and making it less staccato he did not at first change any feature of the story until the beginning of the attempt to climb down – apart from introducing the point that on the last day in the Emyn Muil Sam and Frodo had been making their way along at some distance from the outer precipice, perhaps to explain why it was that they had not observed that the cliff was now less high and no longer sheer; but the long gully or ravine by which in TT they made their way to the precipice when their way forward was blocked was not yet present. The fir-trees in the gully would have a narrative function in the final form of the story, in that 'old broken stumps straggled on almost to the cliff's brink' (TT p. 212): for Sam would brace his foot against one of those stumps, and tie the rope to it (TT pp. 215–16), in contrast to text C, p. 89 ('Is there nothing to make an end fast to up here?' ... 'I am going down with the rope on, and you're going to hold on to the end up here').

My father at first retained the story in C (p. 88) that Frodo followed Sam over the edge and that they both stood splayed against the rock-face together, until Frodo climbed back up again. But as he wrote he changed this: before Frodo had time to say anything to Sam,

The next moment he gave a sharp cry and slithered downwards. He came up with a jolt to his toes on a broader ledge a few feet lower down. Fortunately the rockface leant well forwards, and he did not lose his balance. He could just reach the ledge he had left with his fingers.

'Well, that's another step down,' he said. 'But what next?'

'I don't know,' said Frodo peering over. 'The light's getting so dim. You started off a bit too quick, before we'd had a good

94 THE WAR OF THE RING

look. But the ledge you're on gets much broader to the right. If you could edge along that way, you'd have room enough, I think, to stoop and get your hands down and try for the next ledge below.'

Sam shuffled a little, and then stood still, breathing hard. 'No, I can't do it,' he panted. 'I'm going giddy. Can't I get back? My toes are hurting cruelly already.'

Frodo leaned over as far as he dared, but he could not help. Sam's fingers were well out of his reach.

'What's to be done?' said Sam, and his voice quavered. 'Here am I stuck like a fly on a fly-paper, only flies can't fall off, and I can.' The eastern sky was growing black as night, and the thunder rolled nearer.

'Hold on, Sam!' said Frodo. 'Half a moment, till I get my belt off.'

Having thus got rid of the unnecessary incident of Frodo's going down to the first ledge with Sam and then climbing back again, the new text then follows the former (C) – the failure of the experiment with the belt, Sam's sudden recollection of the rope, and his telling Frodo that they are wearing each other's packs – as far as 'He sat down well away from the edge and rubbed his feet' (p. 89; he felt 'as if he had been rescued from deep waters or a fathomless mine').

'Numbpate and Ninnyhammer!' he muttered.

'Well, now you're back,' said Frodo, laughing with relief, 'you can explain this business about the packs.'

'Easy,' said Sam. 'We got up in the dim light this morning and you just picked mine up. I noticed it and was going to speak up, when I noticed that yours was a tidier sight heavier than mine. I reckoned you'd been carrying more than your share of tackle and what not ever since I set off in such a hurry, so I thought I'd take a turn. And I thought less said less argument.'

'Well meant cheek,' said Frodo; 'but you've been rewarded for the well meaning anyway.' They sat for a while and the gloom grew greater.

'Numbpate,' said Sam suddenly, slapping his forehead. 'How long's that rope, I wonder.'

Here my father abandoned this story, feeling perhaps that it was all becoming too complicated, and rejecting these new pages he returned again, not to the beginning of the chapter, but to the beginning of the draft C, that is to say to the point where Frodo and Sam awoke on their last morning in the Emyn Muil (p. 86), with Frodo now saying, in

THE TAMING OF SMÉAGOL   95

answer to Sam's question 'Did you see them again, Mr Frodo?', 'No, I have heard nothing for three nights now.' From this point the final story was built up in the completed manuscript D. Some of it was written out first on independent draft pages,[14] but some of the pencilled drafting was overwritten in ink and included in the manuscript. It is plain, however, that the final story now evolved confidently and clearly, and since there is very little of significant difference to the narrative to be observed in those parts of the initial drafting that I have been able to read, I doubt that there is any more in those that I have not.

My father now saw at last how Sam and Frodo did manage the descent from the Emyn Muil, and he resolved their difficulty about leaving the rope hanging from the cliff-top for Gollum to use by simply not introducing the question into their calculations until they had both reached the bottom. In this text the further course of the storm was described thus:

The skirts of the storm were lifting, ragged and wet, and the main battle had passed – hastening with wind and thunder over the Emyn Muil, over Anduin, over the fields of Rohan, on to the Hornburg where the King Théoden stood at bay that night, and the Tindtorras now stood dark against the last lurid glow.

At a later stage (see the Note on Chronology at the end of this chapter) the following was substituted:

The skirts of the storm were lifting, ragged and wet, and the main battle had passed to spread its great wings over the Emyn Muil, upon which the dark thought of Sauron brooded for a while. Thence it turned, smiting the vale of Anduin with hail and lightning, and rolled on slowly through the night, mile by mile over Gondor and the fields of Rohan, until far away the Riders on the plain saw its black shadow moving behind the sun, as they rode with war into the West.

Sam's uncle, the Gaffer's eldest brother, owner of the rope-walk 'over by Tighfield', now appears (cf. VII.235), but he was at first called Obadiah Gamgee, not Andy.

The earlier drafts did not reach the point of Gollum's descent of the cliff-face, and it may be that my father had foreseen it long since. On the manuscript of the outline 'The Story Foreseen from Lórien' he struck out his first ideas for the encounter of Frodo and Sam with Gollum, and wrote: 'Steep place where Frodo has to climb a precipice. Sam goes first so that if Frodo falls he will knock Sam down first. They see Gollum come down by moonlight *like a fly*' (see VII.329 and note 15). But there is no way of knowing when he wrote this, whether when

96   THE WAR OF THE RING

he first began writing 'The Taming of Sméagol', or when he took it up
again in April 1944.

In initial drafting the discussion between Sam and Frodo after
Gollum's capture, in which Frodo heard 'a voice out of the past', went
like this:

> 'No,' said Frodo. 'We must kill him right out, Sam, if we do
> anything. But we can't do that, not as things are. It's against the
> rules. He's done us no harm.'
> 'But he means to / meant to, I'll take my word,' said Sam.
> 'I daresay,' said Frodo. 'But that's another matter.' Then he
> seemed to hear a voice out of the past saying to him: *Even Gollum I
> fancy may have his uses before all's over.* 'Yes, yes, may be,' he
> answered. 'But anyway I can't touch the creature. I wish he could be
> cured. He's so horribly wretched.'
> Sam stared at his master, who seemed to be talking to someone
> else not there.

At this stage in the evolution of the chapter 'Ancient History', at the
point in his conversation with Gandalf at Bag End which Frodo
was remembering, the text of the 'second phase' version (given in
VI.264–5) had been little changed. The actual reading of the 'current'
('fourth phase') text of 'Ancient History' (cf. VII.28) is:

> '... What a pity Bilbo did not stab that vile creature, before he left
> him!'
> 'What nonsense you do talk sometimes, Frodo!' said Gandalf.
> 'Pity! Pity would have prevented him, if he had thought of it. But he
> could not kill him anyway. It was against the Rules. ...'
> 'Of course, of course! What a thing to say. Bilbo could not do
> anything of the kind, then. But I am frightened. And I cannot feel
> any pity for Gollum. Do you mean to say that you, and the Elves, let
> him live on after all those horrible deeds? Now at any rate he is
> worse than a goblin, and just an enemy.'
> 'Yes, he deserved to die,' said Gandalf, 'and I don't think he can
> be cured before he dies. Yet even Gollum might prove useful for
> good before the end. Anyway we did not kill him: he was very old
> and very wretched. The Wood-elves have him in prison ...'

It is not often that the precise moment at which my father returned
to and changed a passage much earlier in *The Lord of the Rings* can be
determined, but it can be done here. When he came to write the
passage in the manuscript (D) of 'The Taming of Sméagol', Frodo's
recollection of his conversation with Gandalf began at an earlier point
than it had in the draft cited above:

> It seemed to Frodo then that he heard quite plainly but far off
> voices out of the past.

THE TAMING OF SMÉAGOL   97

What a pity Bilbo did not stab the vile creature, before he left him!
Pity! Pity would have prevented him. He could not kill him. It was against the Rules.
I do not feel any pity for Gollum. He deserves death.

It was at this point that my father perceived that Gandalf had said rather more to Frodo, and on another page of drafting for 'The Taming of Sméagol' he wrote:

Deserved it! I daresay he did / does, said Gandalf. Many that live do deserve death. And some that die deserve life. Can you give it to them? Then be not eager to deal out death even in the name of justice. For even the very wise cannot see all ends. I do not much hope that Gollum can be cured

This was then (as I judge) written into the manuscript of 'The Taming of Sméagol', in a slightly different form:

Deserves death! I daresay he does. Many that live deserve death. And some that die deserve life. Can you give that to them? Then be not too eager to deal out death in the name of justice, fearing for your own safety. Even the very wise cannot see all ends. Maybe the Enemy will get him. Maybe not. Even Gollum may do some good, willy nilly, before the end.

It was certainly at this time that my father changed the passage in 'Ancient History'. Omitting the words 'fearing for your own safety', he joined the new passage into that given on p. 96: '... Even the wise cannot see all ends. I do not much hope that Gollum can be cured before he dies. Yet even Gollum might prove useful for good before the end.' The two passages, that in 'The Shadow of the Past' (FR p. 69) and that in 'The Taming of Sméagol' (TT. p. 221), remain different in detail of wording, perhaps not intentionally at all points.

Lastly, there is an interesting difference between the passage in which Gollum makes his promise to Frodo as it was at this time and as it stands in TT. When Gollum said 'Sméagol will swear on the precious', there followed both in initial drafting and in the manuscript:

Frodo stepped back. 'On the precious!' he said. 'Oh, yes! And what will he swear?'
'To be very, very good,' said Gollum. Then crawling to Frodo's feet ...

This was changed at once, again both in draft and manuscript, to:

Frodo stepped back. 'On the precious?' he asked, puzzled for a moment: he had thought that *precious* was Gollum's self that he

98   THE WAR OF THE RING

talked to. 'Ah! On the precious!' he said, with the disconcerting
frankness that had already startled Sam [*draft text:* that surprised
and alarmed Sam, and still more Gollum].
    '*One Ring to rule them all and in the Darkness bind them.*
Would you commit your promises to that, Sméagol? ...' (&c. as in
TT, pp. 224–5]
The final text of this passage was not substituted till much later.[15]

NOTES

1 For the earliest ideas for this part of the narrative, when Sam
   crossed the Anduin alone and tracked Frodo together with
   Gollum, see the outline 'The Story Foreseen from Lórien',
   VII.328–9.
2 See the Note on Chronology following these Notes.
3 In 'The Story Foreseen from Lórien', VII.328, Frodo put on the
   Ring to escape from Gollum.
4 An argument against this is that in the 1957 letter my father gave
   the page-reference II.209, whereas this text extends to II.210. But
   there are various ways of explaining this, and the evidence of the
   manuscripts seems to me to count more heavily.
5 Together with these earliest manuscripts of 'The Taming of
   Sméagol' was found a slip bearing the following pencilled notes,
   which may very well not have been written all at one time (I have
   added the numbers)
   (1) Account of Rings in Ch. II ['Ancient History'] needs altering
        a little. It was *Elves* who made the rings, which Sauron *stole.*
        He only made the One Ring. The *Three* were never in his
        possession and were unsullied.
   (2) Tom could have got rid of the Ring all along [?without
        further] .... – if asked!
   (3) The Company must carry *ropes* – either from Rivendell or
        from Lórien.
   (4) *Emyn Muil* = Sarn Gebir as a knot or range of stony hills.
        [*Sern Erain* >] *Sarn Aran* the King Stones = the Gates of
        Sarn Gebir.
   With (1) cf. VI.404; VII.254–5 and 259–60. In (2), most
   frustratingly, I have not been able to form any guess even at the
   altogether illegible word. (3) seems quite likely to have arisen
   while my father was pondering the descent from Sarn Gebir
   (Emyn Muil). On the absence of the mentions in LR of Sam's
   having no rope, and the absence of the passage concerning ropes
   at the leaving of Lothlórien, see VII.165, 183, 280. As regards
   (4), in the long-abandoned opening of the chapter the hills were

THE TAMING OF SMÉAGOL 99

still called *Sarn Gebir*, but when my father took it up again in 1944 they had become the *Emyn Muil* (note 7). Many ephemeral names to replace *Sarn Gebir* are found in notes given in VII.424. *Sern Aranath* replaced *the Gates of Sarn Gebir* on the manuscripts of 'The Great River' (VII.362 and note 21).

6 · This sentence, little changed, is given to Frodo in TT (p. 211).

7 The first occurrence of *Emyn Muil* as written in a text *ab initio*. See note 5.

8 30 fathoms: 180 feet.

9 *leant forwards*: i.e. sloped down outwards from the vertical, what my father earlier in this account called 'backward': 'The cliff was indeed no longer sheer, but sloped somewhat backward.'

10 In the following text the corresponding passage has: 'He cast the end to Sam, who tied it about his waist, and grasped the line above his head with both hands.' In the present text the sentence seems to have been left unfinished and in the air.

11 These figures were much changed. At first, as shown in any case by *hobbit-ells*, my father did not intend the 'English ell' of 45 inches, for by that measure 80 ells is 300 feet or 50 fathoms, getting on for double the height of the cliff as Frodo had reckoned it: whereas Sam thought that the rope of 80 ells would only be 'near enough' to Frodo's guess of 30 fathoms or 180 feet. My father seems first to have changed '80' to '77', and in the margin he wrote '2 feet' and '154'. He then changed '2 feet' to '2½ feet', by which measure 77 ells would give 192½ feet. At some point he struck out *hobbit-* in *hobbit-ells*; and finally he substituted 50 ells for the length of the rope. He had then evidently decided on the measure of 1 ell = 45 inches, according to which 50 ells would be equivalent to 187½ feet, just a little longer than the height of the cliff as Frodo had estimated it. This was the measure in TT, where the cliff was about 18 fathoms, and the rope about 30 ells; taking these figures as exact, there would be 4½ feet of rope to spare ('there was still a good bight in Frodo's hands, when Sam came to the bottom', TT p. 216).

12 The meaning is presumably 'I think I can just hold you', but *hold* is certainly not the word written.

13 See the Note on Chronology below.

14 My father now introduced a further obstacle to the sleuth by using the same piece of paper to write, one on top of the other, drafts for wholly different portions of the narrative.

15 In these texts the word *precious* when referring to the Ring is not capitalised, but capitals were introduced in subsequent typescripts before the passage was changed to the final form.

100   THE WAR OF THE RING

Note on the Chronology

In this chapter the narrative opens on *the fifth evening* since Frodo and Sam had fled from the Company. That night also they passed in the Emyn Muil, and it was at dusk on the following day (therefore 'the sixth evening') that they made their descent. Since the date of the Breaking of the Fellowship and the flight of Frodo and Sam was 26 January (for the chronology at this period see pp. 3–4, and VII.368, 406), this should mean that the chapter opens on the evening of the 30th, and that they climbed down from the hills on the evening of the 31st. On the other hand, the great storm is described (p. 95) as 'hastening with wind and thunder over the Emyn Muil, over Anduin, over the fields of Rohan, on to the Hornburg where the King Théoden stood at bay that night'. But the Battle of the Hornburg was fought on the night of 1 February (pp. 5–6).

Two brief time-schemes, which I will call Scheme 'A' and Scheme 'B', bear on the question of the chronology of Frodo's wandering in the Emyn Muil relative to events in the lands west of Anduin. Scheme 'B', which begins at this point, is perfectly explicit:

> *Thursday Jan. 26 to Wednesday Feb. 1*   Frodo and Sam in Emyn Muil (Sarn Gebir).
>
> *Night Feb. 1–2*   Frodo and Sam meet Gollum. (Storm that reached Helm's Deep about midnight on Feb.1–2 passed over Emyn Muil earlier in the night.)

Scheme 'A', also beginning here, has:

> *Jan. 31*   Cold night
>
> *Feb. 1*   Descend, dusk (5.30). Meet Gollum about 10 p.m. Journey in gully till daybreak.

According to these, it would have been on the *sixth* evening since the flight of Frodo and Sam, not the fifth, that the chapter opens.

Since Vol. VII *The Treason of Isengard* was completed I have found two manuscript pages that are very clearly notes on chronological alterations needed that my father made in October 1944, some four and a half months after he had reached the end of *The Two Towers* (see VII.406–7). On 12 October (*Letters* no. 84) he wrote to me that he had 'struck a most awkward error (one or two days) in the synchronization', which would 'require tiresome small alterations in many chapters'; and on 16 October (*Letters* no. 85) he wrote that he had devised a solution 'by inserting an extra day's Entmoot, and extra days into Trotter's chase and Frodo's journey …'

These notes refer chapter by chapter to the changes that would have to be made (but not to all). Some of them have been encountered already: the complex alterations to 'The Riders of Rohan' in VII.406; the additional day of the Entmoot in VII.419; and the changes in 'The White Rider' in VII.425. Nothing further need be said of these. But in a note on 'The Taming of Sméagol' the question of the storm is raised;

THE TAMING OF SMÉAGOL

and here my father directed that the reference to Théoden and the Hornburg should be cut out, because it 'won't fit'. He noted that the thunderstorm over the Emyn Muil was at about five o'clock in the evening of 31 January, while the thunder in the Battle of the Hornburg was about midnight of 1 February, and that 31 hours to travel a distance of some 350 miles was too slow; but no solution was proposed.

I have referred (VII.368) to an elaborate time-scheme that was made after the changes of October 1944 had been introduced. This, being a major working chronology, is in places fearsomely difficult to interpret, on account of later alterations and overwritings in ink over the original pencil. It is arranged in columns, describing 'synoptically', and fairly fully, the movements of all the major actors in the story on each day. It begins on the fifth day of the voyage down Anduin and ends at the beginning of the ascent to the pass of Kirith Ungol; and I would guess that it belongs with the work on chronology in October 1944, rather than later. On this scheme, which I will call 'S', my father afterwards wrote 'Old Timatal stuff' (Icelandic *tímatál* 'chronology').

In this scheme S the death of Boromir and the Breaking of the Fellowship was put back by a day, to Wednesday 25 January.

Jan. 25 Company broken up. Death of Boromir. ... Frodo and Sam cross river eastward and fly into E. of Emyn Muil.

Jan. 26 Frodo and Sam wandering in Emyn Muil (1st evening since flight).

Jan. 27 In Emyn Muil (2nd evening).

Jan. 28 In Emyn Muil (3rd evening).

Jan. 29 In Emyn Muil (4th evening).

Jan. 30 On brink of Emyn Muil. Spend cold night under a rock (5th evening).

Jan. 31 Descent from Emyn Muil at nightfall. Meet Gollum about 10 p.m.

Journey in the gully (Jan.31/Feb.1).

Here therefore the opening of the story in 'The Taming of Sméagol' was on the evening of Jan. 30, and that was explicitly the sixth evening since the flight; but my father was for some reason not counting the first evening in the Emyn Muil (Jan. 25), and so he called that of Jan. 30 the fifth. Perhaps it was the same counting that explains the discrepancy between Scheme B and the text of the chapter (p. 100). And it may well be in any case that the records of these complicated manoeuvres are insufficient, or that there are clues which I have failed to perceive.

In Scheme B, as in the completed manuscript of the chapter (p. 95), it is explicit that the storm over the Emyn Muil reached the Hornburg later that same night; it was moving fast ('hastening with wind and thunder'). In Scheme S, however, this is not so; for (just as in the note

102   THE WAR OF THE RING

of October 1944 referred to above) the descent of Frodo and Sam
from the Emyn Muil was at nightfall of Jan. 31, but the Battle of the
Hornburg began on the night of Feb. 1. S as written had no mention of
the great storm, but my father added in against Jan. 31 'Thunder at
nightfall', and then subsequently 'It crawls west', with a line apparently directing to Feb. 1. The storm over Rohan, slowly overtaking the
Riders as they rode west across the plains on their second day out of
Edoras (at the beginning of the chapter 'Helm's Deep') and bursting
over the Hornburg in the middle of the night, was already present
when my father came to write 'The Taming of Smeagol'. The storm
over the Emyn Muil moving westwards, if not actually conceived for
the purpose, obviously had the desirable effect of drawing the now
sundered stories, east and west of Anduin, together. The revised
passage about the storm in 'The Taming of Sméagol' given on p. 95
was clearly intended to allow for another day in the storm's progress,
and implies that Frodo and Sam climbed down out of the hills on the
day *before* the Battle of the Hornburg, as in S; and this resolves the
problem of time and distance stated in the note of October 1944 by
asserting that the great storm did not 'hasten', but 'rolled on slowly
through the night.'

But in *The Tale of Years* the relative dating is entirely different:

Scheme S

Frodo enters Emyn Muil	(25 Jan.)	*Day 1*
In Emyn Muil	(26 Jan.)	*Day 2*
In Emyn Muil	(27 Jan.)	*Day 3*
In Emyn Muil	(28 Jan.)	*Day 4*
In Emyn Muil	(29 Jan.)	*Day 5*
In Emyn Muil	(30 Jan.)	*Day 6*
Descent from Emyn Muil	(31 Jan.)	*Day 7*
Battle of the Hornburg	(1 Feb.)	*Day 8*

The Tale of Years

Frodo enters Emyn Muil	(26 Feb.)	*Day 1*
In Emyn Muil	(27 Feb.)	*Day 2*
In Emyn Muil	(28 Feb.)	*Day 3*
Descent from Emyn Muil	(29 Feb.)	*Day 4*
	(30 Feb.)	*Day 5*
	(1 Mar.)	*Day 6*
	(2 Mar.)	*Day 7*
Battle of the Hornburg	(3 Mar.)	*Day 8*

Thus in the final chronology the Battle of the Hornburg took place
four nights after the descent of Frodo and Sam and the meeting with
Gollum. Yet the revised description of the westward course of the
storm in 'The Taming of Sméagol' (p. 95) survived into the proof stage

of *The Lord of the Rings*. On the proof my father noted against the passage: 'Chronology wrong. The storm of Frodo was 3 days before Théoden's ride' (i.e. 29 February and 2 March, the day on which Théoden rode from Edoras). The passage as it stands in TT, pp. 215–16, was substituted at the eleventh hour: giving the great storm a more widely curving path, and suggesting, perhaps, a reinforcement of its power and magnitude as it passed slowly over Ered Nimrais.

II

THE PASSAGE OF THE MARSHES

The writing of this chapter can again be closely dated from the letters that my father wrote to me in South Africa in 1944. On the 13th of April (*Letters* no. 60) he said that on the previous day he had read his 'recent chapter' ('The Taming of Sméagol') to C. S. Lewis and Charles Williams, and that he had begun another. On the 18th April (*Letters* no. 61) he wrote: 'I hope to see C.S.L. and Charles W. tomorrow morning and read my next chapter – on the passage of the Dead Marshes and the approach to the Gates of Mordor, which I have now practically finished.'[1] And on the 23rd of April (*Letters* no. 62) he wrote: 'I read my second chapter, Passage of the Dead Marshes, to Lewis and Williams on Wed. morning [19 April]. It was approved. I have now nearly done a third: Gates of the Land of Shadow. But this story takes me in charge, and I have already taken three chapters over what was meant to be one!' The completed manuscript of 'The Passage of the Marshes' was indeed first entitled 'Kirith Ungol' (that being still the name of the main pass into Mordor) – for he began writing the manuscript before he had by any means finished the initial drafting of the chapter.

Essential ideas for this part of the narrative had in fact emerged a long time before, in the outline 'The Story Foreseen from Lórien' (VII.329–30) – when he estimated that the chapter would be numbered XXV, eight less than the event had proved. In that outline he wrote:

Gollum pleads for forgiveness, and promises help, and having nowhere else to turn Frodo accepts. Gollum says he will lead them over the Dead Marshes to Kirith Ungol. (Chuckling to himself to think that that is just the way he would wish them to go.) ...

They sleep in pairs, so that one is always awake with Gollum.

Gollum all the while is scheming to betray Frodo. He leads them cleverly over the Dead Marshes. There are dead green faces in the stagnant pools; and the dry reeds hiss like snakes. Frodo feels the strength of the searching eye as they proceed.

At night Sam keeps watch, only pretending to be asleep. He hears Gollum muttering to himself, words of hatred for Frodo and lust for the Ring.

The three companions now approach Kirith Ungol, the dreadful ravine which leads into Gorgoroth. Kirith Ungol means Spider Glen: there dwelt great spiders ...

THE PASSAGE OF THE MARSHES   105

A single page of notes shows my father's thoughts as he embarked at last on the writing of this story. These notes were not written as a continuous outline and not all were written at the same time, but I give them in the sequence in which they stand on the page.

Food problem. Gollum chokes at *lembas* (but it does him good?). Goes off and comes back with grimy fingers [?and face]. Once he heard him crunching in dark.

Next chapter

Gollum takes them down into the water gully and then turns away eastward. It leads to a hard point in the midst of the Marshes. Over Dead Marshes. Dead faces. In some of the pools if you looked in you saw your own face all green and dead and corrupted. To Kirith Ungol.
Change in Gollum as they draw near
Gollum sleeps quite unconcerned – quietly at first; but as they draw near to Mordor he seems to get nightmares. Sam hears him beginning to hold colloquies with himself. It is a sort of good Smeagol angry with a bad Gollum. The latter [?grows] – filled with hatred of the Ring-bearer, in longing to be Ring-master himself.
Laid up [?in] rock near gates see great movements in and out. Explanation of why they had escaped the war-movement.
They lie up in day in beds of reeds
Feeling of weight. Ring feels heavier and heavier on Frodo's neck as Mordor approaches. He feels the Eye.

Another page, written at any rate before 'The Passage of the Marshes' had proceeded very far, outlines the story thus:

They come to a point where the gully falls into the marshes. Brief description of these (which take about 3 to 4 days to cross). Pools where there are faces some horrible, some fair – but all corrupted. Gollum says it is said that they are memories (?) of those who fell in ages past in the Battle before Ennyn Dûr the Gates of Mordor in the Great Battle. In the moon if you looked in some pools you saw your own face fouled and corrupt and dead. Describe the pools as they get nearer to Mordor as like green pools and rivers fouled by modern chemical works.
They lie up in foothills and see armed men and orcs passing in. Soon all is clear. Sauron is gathering his power and hiding it in Mordor in readiness. (Swart men, and wild men with long braided hair out of East; Orcs of the Eye etc.)

106   THE WAR OF THE RING

On the far (East) Horn of the Gates is a tall white tower. Minas Ithil now Minas Morghul which guards the pass. It was originally built by the men of Gondor to prevent Sauron breaking out and was manned by the guards of Minas Ithil,[2] but it fell soon into his hands. It now prevented any coming in. It was manned by orcs and evil spirits. It had been called [Neleg Thilim >] Neleglos [the Gleaming >] the White Tooth.[3]

This last passage is accompanied by a little sketch, reproduced on p. 108 (no. I). Until now, the pass and chief entry into Mordor had been named *Kirith Ungol* (cf. the citation from 'The Story Foreseen from Lórien' on p. 104). When contemplating the story ahead as he drafted 'The Passage of the Marshes' my father saw that this was not so: Kirith Ungol was a distinct way through the mountains – and (plainly enough) it is this path that Sam and Frodo are going to take. Concomitantly with this, he was proposing to change the site of Minas Morgul as he had long conceived it, and as it appears on the First Map (see Map III, VII.309).[4] There, the pass of Kirith Ungol was guarded by two towers, one on either side (see VII.349, note 41), and Minas Morgul was away to the west, on the other side of the mountains (i.e. on the western side of the northern extremity of the Dúath, the Mountains of Shadow); whereas now Minas Morgul is to be the tower that guards the pass.[5] A virtually identical sketch to this, in faint pencil, is found on a page of drafting for 'The Black Gate is Closed'. It clearly does not belong with that, however (the later text is written across it), but with the present passage; and accompanying this pencilled version of the sketch is this note:

It is better for the later story that Minas Ithil (Morghul) should be actually at the Gates of Mordor on its East side.

The scene is thus depicted from the North.

On a page used also for drafting of 'The Passage of the Marshes' there is another sketch of the tower and the pass (also reproduced on p. 108, no. II), very similar except in one important respect: whereas in Sketch I the cleft of Kirith Ungol is placed immediately below Minas Morgul (which thus stands on a high ridge or 'horn' *between* the 'cleft' and the 'pass'), in Sketch II Kirith Ungol lies on the far side of the pass from the tower. The scene is again depicted from the North, for the accompanying text reads: 'Kirith Ungol is *not* the main entrance but a narrow cleft to [S(outh) >] West.' I think it almost certain that Sketch II represents a further stage in the development of the conception, not its first appearance.

Most of 'The Passage of the Marshes' is extant in preliminary drafting (and most of it in excruciatingly difficult handwriting); in this

THE PASSAGE OF THE MARSHES 107

chapter my father made no use of his method of writing a text in pencil and then setting down a more finished version in ink on top of it. The narrative in the draft is not perfectly continuous, and it is clear that (as commonly) he built up the completed manuscript – the only one made of this chapter – in stages. The initial drafting is mostly extremely rough, written at great speed, and in places the completed manuscript (while perfectly legible – it was the text from which my father read the chapter to Lewis and Williams on April the 19th) is itself really the primary composition, constantly corrected and changed in the act of writing. Nonetheless the story of the passage of the Dead Marshes as it appears in *The Two Towers* seems to have been achieved almost to the form of every sentence (apart from certain substantial alterations made very much later) in that week of April 1944.

Only in one respect did the initial drafting differ significantly from the story as it appears in the manuscript. This was primarily a matter of the narrative structure, but I give most of the passage in question, so well as I can make it out, as exemplification. It takes up from Gollum's words 'Snakes, worms in pools. Lots of things in the pools. No birds' (TT p. 234).

So passed the third day of their travelling with Gollum.[6]

All the night they went on with brief halts. Now it was really perilous at least for the hobbits. They went slowly keeping close in line and following every move of Gollum's attentively. The pools grew larger and more ominous and the places where feet could tread without sinking into [?chilly] gurgling mires more and more difficult to find. There were no more reeds and grasses.

Later in the night, after midnight, there came a change. A light breeze got up and grew to a cold wind: it came from the North and though it had a bitter tang it seemed kindly to them, for it bore at last a hint of untainted airs and drove the reeking mists into banks with dark channels in between. The cloudy sky was torn and tattered and the moon nearly full rode among the [?wrack]. Gollum cowered and muttered but the hobbits looked up hopefully. A great dark shadow came out of Mordor like a huge bird crossed the moon and went away west. Just the same feeling came on them as at the ..... they cast themselves down in the mire. But the shadow passed quickly. Gollum lay like one stunned and they had to rouse him. He would say only Wraiths wraiths [?under] the moon. The precious the precious is their master. They see everything everywhere. He sees. After that [?even] Frodo sensed a change in Gollum once more. He was [?even] more fawning [and] friendly but he talked more often in

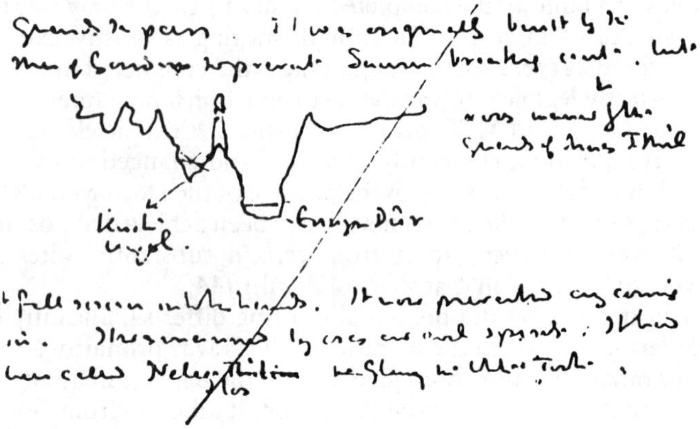

I

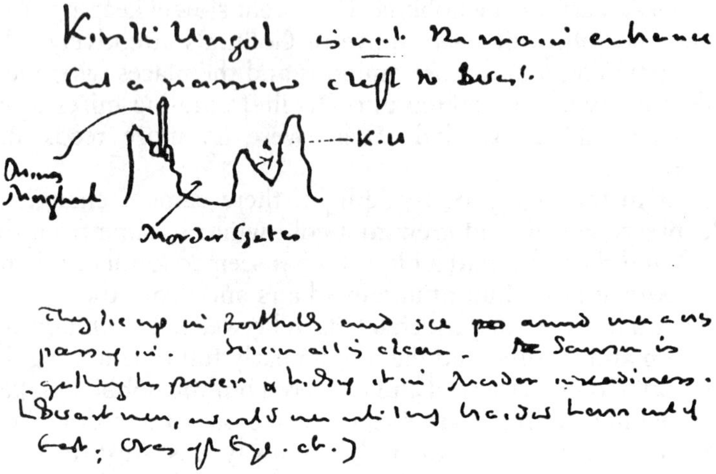

II

Two early sketches of Kirith Ungol

THE PASSAGE OF THE MARSHES 109

[his] old manner. They had great difficulty in making him go on while the moon

The last passage was then rewritten ('After that Sam thought he sensed a change in Gollum again' ...) and the draft continues with a description of Frodo's weariness and slowness and the weight of the Ring that approaches the text in TT (p. 238). Then follows:

He now really felt it as a weight: and he was getting conscious of the Eye: it was that as much as the weight that made him cower and stoop as he walked. He felt like someone hidden in a room (?garden) when his deadly enemy comes in: knowing that he is there though he cannot yet see him the enemy stands at gaze to espy all comers with his deadly eye. Any movement is fraught with peril.[7] Gollum probably felt something of the same sort. After the passing of the shadow of the Nazgûl that flew to Isengard it was difficult to get him to move if there was light. As long as the moon lasted he would only creep forwards on his hands cowering and whimpering. He was not much use as a guide and Sam took to trying to find a path for himself. In doing so he stumbled forward and came down on his hands in sticky mire with his face bending over a dark pool that seemed like some glazed but grimed window in the moonlight. Wrenching his hands out of the bog he sprang back with a cry. There are dead faces ..... dead faces in the pool he cried, dead faces!

Gollum laughed. The Dead Marshes, yes, yess. That is their name. Should not look in when the White Eye is up.[8] What are they, who are they, asked Sam shuddering and turning to Frodo who came up behind him. I don't know said Frodo. No don't master said Sam, they're horrible. Nonetheless Frodo crawled cautiously to the edge and looked. He saw pale faces – deep under water they looked: some grim some hideous, some noble and fair: but all horrible, corrupted, sickly, rotting .... Frodo crawled back and hid his eyes. I don't know who they are but I thought I saw Men and Elves and Orcs, all dead and rotten. Yes yes, said Gollum cackling. All dead and rotten. The Dead Marshes. Men and Elves and Orcs. There was a great Battle here long long ago, precious, yes, when Smeagol was young and happy long ago:[9] before the precious came, yes, yes. They fought on the plain over there. The Dead Marshes have grown greater.

But are they really there? Smeagol doesn't know, said Gollum. You can't reach them. I we tried, yes we tried, precious,

110   THE WAR OF THE RING

once: but you can't touch them. Only shapes to see perhaps, not to touch, no precious! Sam looked darkly at him and shuddered, thinking he guessed why Smeagol had tried to reach them.

The moon was now sinking west into cloud that lay above far Rohan beyond Anduin. They went on and Gollum again took the lead by [read but] Sam and Frodo found that he [read they] could not keep their [?fascinated] eyes from straying whenever they passed some pool of black water. If they did so they caught glimpses of the pallid dead faces. At last they came to a place where Gollum halted, a wide pool ...... barred their way.

The pools lit by *will o' the wisp* fire reveal dead faces. The moon shows their own.[10]

.... The moon came out of its cloud. They looked in. But they saw no faces out of the vanished past. They saw *their own*. ..... Sam Gollum and Frodo looking up with dead eyes and livid rotting flesh at them.

Let's get out of this foul place!

Long way to go yet said Gollum. Must get to somewhere to lie up before day.

This section of drafting peters out here. In the manuscript the text becomes that of TT at almost all points: the sequence of the story has been reconstructed, so that the change in the weather and the flight of the Nazgûl follows the passage of the pools of the dead faces; and there is no further hint of the idea (going back to the preliminary notes, p. 105) that the beholder's own face was mirrored as dead when the moonlight shone on the pools.

It is notable that in the draft the Nazgûl is said to have been flying to Isengard. In the manuscript as first written this was not said: '... a vast shape winged and ominous: it scudded across the moon, and with a deadly cry went away westward, outrunning the moon in its fell speed. ... But the shadow passed quickly, and behind it the wind roared away, leaving the Dead Marshes bare and bleak.' After the last sentence, however, my father added, probably not long after, 'The Nazgûl had gone, flying to Isengard with the speed of the wrath of Sauron.' The rewriting of the passage, so that the Nazgûl returns and, flying lower above them, sweeps back to Mordor, was done at a later time (see the Note on Chronology at the end of this chapter); but the words in TT (p. 237) 'with a deadly cry *went away westward*' are in fact a vestige of the original conception.

Among various other differences and developments the following seem the most worth remarking.

In the original draft, and at first in the manuscript, Gollum's 'song' (TT pp. 227–8) was wholly different after the first line:

THE PASSAGE OF THE MARSHES 111

The cold hard lands	*Our heart is set*
To feet and hands	*On water wet*
they are unkind.	*in some deep pool.*
There wind is shrill,	*O how we wish*
The stones are chill;	*To taste of fish*
there's nought to find.	*so sweet and cool!*

There was no reference to 'Baggins' and the fish-riddle.

The story that they slept the whole of the day after they had come down from the Emyn Muil was not present at first. In the preliminary draft of the opening of the chapter Sam, after testing that Gollum was really asleep by saying *fissh* in his ear, did not fall asleep:

> Time seemed to drag; but after an hour or two Gollum sat up suddenly wide awake as if he had been called. He stretched, yawned, got up and began to climb out of the gully. 'Hi, where are you off to?' cried Sam. 'Smeagol's very hungry,' said Gollum. 'Be back soon.'

In the manuscript the final story appears, to the extent that Sam does fall asleep; but when he wakes 'the sky above was full of bright daylight.' This however was changed immediately: Sam and Frodo slept the whole day away, not waking until after sunset, and Gollum's departure to find something to eat is postponed to the evening.[11]

There can be no doubt that the geography of the region in which the Dead Marshes lay had now been substantially changed. It is said in TT (p. 232):

> The hobbits were now wholly in the hands of Gollum. They did not know, and could not guess in that misty light, that they were in fact only just within the northern borders of the marshes, the main expanse of which lay south of them. They could, if they had known the lands, with some delay have retraced their steps a little, and then turning east have come round over hard roads to the bare plain of Dagorlad.

This passage appears in the manuscript, and is found embryonically in the original draft, of which, though partly illegible, enough can be made out to see that the new conception was present: 'They were in fact just within the north-west bounds of the Dead Marshes', and '[they could] have come round the eastern side to the hard of Battle Plain.' The First Map (Maps II and IV^c, VII.305, 317) and the large map based on it that I made in 1943 are entirely at variance with this: for in that conception the No Man's Land lay between Sarn Gebir (Emyn Muil) and the pass into Mordor. There could be no reason for one journeying in those hills to enter the Dead Marshes if he were making for the pass (Kirith Ungol on those maps); nor, if he were at the edge of the marshes, would he by any means come to Dagorlad if

112   THE WAR OF THE RING

instead of going through them he went round to their east. Essentially what has happened is that the Dead Marshes have been moved south-west, so that they lie between the Emyn Muil and the Gates of Mordor – into the region marked 'No Man's Land' on the First Map – and so become continuous with the Wetwang or Nindalf (see VII.320–1 and below); this is the geography seen on the large-scale map of Gondor and Mordor accompanying *The Return of the King*.[12]

In reply to Frodo's question whether they must cross the Dead Marshes, Gollum answered in the original draft (cf. TT p. 233): '"No need. Back a little, and round a little" – his skinny arm waved away north and east – "and you can come dry-foot to the Plain. Dagorlad that is, where the Battle was fought and He lost the precious, yess" – he added this in a sort of whisper to himself.' The manuscript here has the text of TT; but subsequently, in Gollum's explanation of the dead faces in the marshes (TT p. 235), he says: 'There was a great Battle long ago, yes, so they told him when Smeagol was young, long ago, before the Precious came. They took It from the Lord then, Elves and Men took It. It was a great battle. They fought on the plain for days and months and years at the Gates of Mornennyn [> Morannon]' (for the original draft of this see p. 109). Gollum's reference to the story of the taking of the Ring from Sauron was removed much later.

The account of the morning after the night of the dead faces in the pools and the flight of the Nazgûl, and of the lands through which they passed after leaving the marshes, was different in important respects from that in TT, pp. 238–9. The manuscript reads (following an initial draft):

> When day came at last, the hobbits were surprised to see how close the ominous mountains had drawn: the outer buttresses and the broken hills at their feet were now no more than a dozen miles away. Frodo and Sam looked round in horror: dreadful as the Marshes had been in their decay their end was more loathsome still. Even to the mere of the dead faces some haggard phantom of green spring would come ... (&c. as in TT p. 239)

The extended and altered passage that replaces this in TT, introduced at a later stage, was due to considerations of geography and chronology. With this new passage two more nights are added to the journey (see the Note on Chronology at the end of this chapter and the map on p. 117), and during this stage of it they pass through a country seen from the end of the marshes as 'long shallow slopes, barren and pitiless', and described subsequently as 'the arid moors of the Nomanlands'. Here this name reappears from Celeborn's words to the Company in 'Farewell to Lórien' (FR p. 390) and the old maps: see VII.320–1 and above.

THE PASSAGE OF THE MARSHES   113

An isolated page carries two distinct elements, though very probably both were set down at the same time. The change of the name of the Gates of Mordor in the act of writing from *Ennyn Dûr* (the name on Sketch I, p. 108) first to *Morennyn* and then to *Mornennyn* shows that this page preceded the point in the writing of the manuscript text where Gollum speaks of the dead faces in the pools, for there *Mornennyn* appears (p. 112), but it is convenient to give it here since it concerns the narrative of the end of the chapter (and the beginning of the next).

The famous pass of [Ennyn (Dûr) > Morennyn >] Mornennyn the Gates of Mordor was guarded by two towers: the Teeth of Mordor [Nelig Morn Mel >] Nelig Myrn. Built by Gondorians long ago: now ceaselessly manned. Owing to ceaseless passage of arms they dare not try to enter so they turn W. and South. Gollum tells them of Kirith Ungol beneath shadow [of] M. Morgul. It is a high pass. He does not tell them of the Spiders. They creep in to M[inas] M[orgul].

This text is accompanied by a further sketch of the site of Kirith Ungol, reproduced on p. 114. It is clear from this that the transference of Minas Morgul to become the fortress guarding the Black Gates was a passing idea now abandoned; and it was no doubt at this very point (Minas Morgul being restored to its old position in the Mountains of Shadow a good way south of the Black Gates) that the southward journey along the western side of the mountains entered the narrative. But it is also clear that the Tower of Kirith Ungol had not yet emerged: the cleft of the spiders passes beneath Minas Morgul, on the south side (on the assumption that the scene is depicted from the West); and the original story in the outline 'The Story Foreseen from Lórien' is again present, that Frodo and Sam entered Minas Morgul (but there is here no mention of Frodo's capture).

In the text accompanying Sketch I on p. 108 it is Minas Morghul, above the Black Gates, that was called 'the White Tooth', *Neleglos*; now there emerge (or perhaps re-emerge, from the original two towers guarding the pass, see p. 106) the Teeth of Mordor, *Nelig Myrn*.

It will be seen subsequently (p. 122) that at this stage 'the Gates of Mordor', 'the Black Gates' (*Ennyn Dûr, Mornennyn*) were specifically names of the pass, not of any barrier built across it.

The other brief text on this page places Sam's overhearing of Gollum's disputation with himself (foreseen already in the preliminary notes to the chapter, p. 105) at this point in the narrative (though it seems that at this stage my father envisaged them passing a night, not a day, before the Black Gates).

The night watching the [Ennyn D(ûr) >] Mornennyn. It is Frodo's turn to watch. Sam sleeps and suddenly awakes thinking he has

Third sketch of Kirith Ungol

THE PASSAGE OF THE MARSHES 115

heard his master calling. But he sees Frodo has fallen asleep. Gollum is sitting by him, gazing at him. Sam hears him arguing with himself: Smeagol versus 'another'. Pale light and a green light alternate in his eyes. But it is not *hunger* or desire to *eat* Frodo that he is battling with: it is the call of the Ring. His long hand keeps on going out and paw[ing] towards Frodo and then is pulled back. Sam rouses Frodo.

The actually reported 'colloquy' of Gollum was developed in stages. His references to 'She' ('She might help'), and Sam's passing reflection on who that might be, were added subsequently, doubtless when that part of the story was reached. A change made much later altered what the 'two Gollums' said about Bilbo and the 'birthday present'; roughly in the initial draft, and then in the manuscript and subsequent typescripts, the passage read:

'Oh no, not if it doesn't please us. Still he's a Baggins, my precious, yes a Baggins. A Baggins stole it.'
'No, not steal: it was a present.'
'Yes, steal. We never gave it, no never. He found it and he said nothing, nothing. We hates Baggins.'

Lastly, in the manuscript and following typescripts the chapter ended at the words: 'In the falling dusk they scrambled out of the pit and slowly threaded their way through the dead land' (TT p. 242). All that follows in TT, describing the menace of a Ringwraith passing overhead unseen at dusk and again an hour after midnight, and the prostration of Gollum, was added to the typescripts at a later stage (see the Note on Chronology below).

NOTES

1 My father went on to speak of a letter he had written adjudicating a dispute in an army mess concerning the pronunciation of the name of the poet Cowper (*Letters* no. 61). A draft for this letter is found on a page of drafting for the passage describing the change in the weather over the marshes, TT pp. 236–7.
2 This, I believe, is the first appearance of the conception that the fortresses on the confines of Mordor had been built looking inwards and not outwards.
3 Cf. the *Etymologies* (V.376), stem NÉL-EK 'tooth'.
4 My father had in fact moved Minas Morgul further north from its position as originally shown on the First Map (east of Osgiliath), and placed it not far from the northern tip of the Mountains of Shadow (see VII.310). With this cf. 'The Story Foreseen from Lórien', where Minas Morgul was said to be reached by a path that 'led up into the mountains – the north horn of the Mountains of Shadow that sundered the ashen vale of

116   THE WAR OF THE RING

Gorgoroth from the valley of the Great River' (VII.333). But Minas Morgul was still on the western side of the mountains (i.e. on the other side of the mountains to the Pass of Kirith Ungol).

5   In notes at the end of 'The Story Foreseen from Lórien' my father had suggested that Frodo should be taken as captive to one of the guard-towers of the pass, and in a time-scheme of that period he changed 'Sam rescues Frodo in Minas Morgul' to 'Sam rescues Frodo in Gorgos' (see VII.344); and again (VII.412): 'The winding stair must be cut in rocks and go up from Gorgoroth to watch-tower. Cut out Minas Morgul.' Now, as it appears, these conceptions were to be fused: Frodo was again to be taken to Minas Morgul, but Minas Morgul was itself the watch-tower above the pass.

6   *the third day:* see the Note on Chronology below.

7   This passage was developed in the manuscript thus, before being changed to the text of TT (p. 238):

> Frodo knew just where the present habitation and heart of that will now was. He could have walked, or flown straight there. He was facing it: and its potency beat upon his brow if he raised it for a moment. He felt like someone who, covered only by a grey garment, has strayed into a garden, when his enemy enters. The enemy knows he is there, even if he cannot yet see him, and he stands at gaze, silent, patient, deadly, sweeping all corners with the hatred of his eye. Any movement is fraught with peril.

8   *when the White Eye is up:* throughout this part of the story Gollum's names for the Sun and Moon were originally the Yellow Eye and the White Eye, not the Yellow Face and the White Face. — TT has here, as does the manuscript, 'when the candles are lit': see note 10.

9   Cf. Gollum's words in TT (p. 235): 'There was a great battle long ago, yes, so they told him when Sméagol was young'. His words in the present draft ('a great battle here long long ago when Sméagol was young') might suggest the far shorter time-span (see p. 21, and VII.450 note 11); but the manuscript had from the first 'so they said when Smeagol was young'.

10   This was no doubt the point at which the idea of the marsh-lights entered (*ignis fatuus, will-o'-the-wisp, jack-o'-lantern*). In TT, as in the manuscript, Gollum calls them 'candles of corpses', and in time-schemes of this period my father referred to the 'episode of the corpse-candles'. *Corpse-candle* is defined in the Oxford Dictionary as 'a lambent flame seen in a churchyard or over a grave, and superstitiously believed to appear as an omen of death, or to indicate the route of a coming funeral.'

11   In the conversation between Frodo and Sam that follows (TT

THE PASSAGE OF THE MARSHES 117

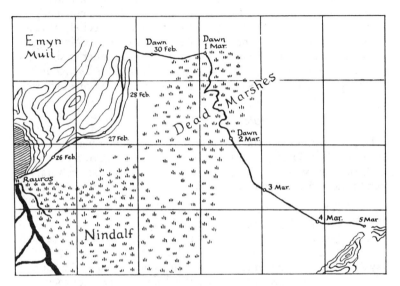

Frodo's journey to the Morannon

118 THE WAR OF THE RING

p. 231), in Frodo's words 'If we can nurse our limbs to bring us to Mount Doom' the name is spelt thus in the preliminary draft, but the manuscript has 'Mount Dûm': this spelling is found also in the preliminary draft of Frodo's vision on Amon Hen, VII.373.

12   The large-scale map of Gondor and Mordor was closely based on a map of my father's. This included the track of Frodo's journey from Rauros to the Morannon, and I have redrawn this section from the original (p. 117). My father's map is in some respects hard to interpret, for it was made roughly and hastily in point of its actual execution, the 'contour-lines' being very impressionistic, while the Nindalf and the Dead Marshes are shown merely by rough pencil hatching, for which I have substituted conventional reed-tufts; but I have attempted to redraw it as precisely as I can. The features of the uppermost line of squares were only roughed in on the original, above the top of the map, in order to show the track of the journey, and my version published in *The Return of the King* excluded this element. The squares are of one inch side, = 25 miles.

Note on the Chronology

As the story stood when the manuscript of this chapter was completed but before those changes were made to it that belong to a later stage the chronology was as follows (proceeding from the date February 1, when Frodo and Sam climbed down out of the Emyn Muil, p. 100):

	Feb. 1–2 Night. They advance along the gully. *(Journey 1)*
(Day 1)	Feb. 2 They sleep in the gully all day.
	Feb. 2–3 Night. They continue along the gully and come to its end towards daybreak. *(Journey 2)*
(Day 2)	Feb. 3 They enter the marshes and continue the journey by day ('So passed the third day of their journey with Gollum', manuscript text and TT p. 234). *(Journey 3)*
	Feb. 3–4 Night. They see the dead faces in the pools. 'It was late in the night when they reached firmer ground again', manuscript text and TT p. 236; followed by change in the weather and flight of the Nazgûl. *(Journey 4)*
(Day 3)	Feb. 4 When day came 'the outer buttresses and broken hills' at the feet of the mountains were 'no more than a dozen miles away' (p. 112). They were among the slag-mounds and poisonous pits. Day spent hiding in a hole. At dusk they went on (night of Feb. 4–5). *(Journey 5)*
(Day 4)	Feb. 5 (Beginning of the next chapter) They reach the Black Gate at dawn.

Both of the brief time-schemes of which the beginnings are given on p. 100 express precisely this chronology. Scheme B was written, apparently, when the story had already reached the departure from

THE PASSAGE OF THE MARSHES   119

Henneth Annûn, but A accompanied the writing of the present chapter and scarcely extends beyond it. Notably, in A the actual journeys they made are numbered (as I have numbered them in the chronology set out above), and it may well be that '3' against February 3 explains the statement cited above: 'So passed the third day of their journey with Gollum' – for it was the third journey, but not the third day.

Both schemes refer to the flight of the Nazgûl. In B, under February 3, 'Nazgûl passes over marshes and goes to Isengard', with a subsequent addition 'reaching there about midnight'. This is hard to understand, since already in the completed manuscript 'it was *late in the night* when they reached firmer ground again', and that was before the change in the weather and the flight of the Nazgûl. In A it is said that 'Nazgûl goes over at early morning before daybreak' (of February 4), agreeing with the text of the chapter; but Théoden and Gandalf and their company left Isengard on the evening of February 3, and camped below Dol Baran (over which the Nazgûl passed) that night, so that this offers equal difficulty.

In his notes of October 1944 (see p. 100) my father commented, under the heading 'Passage of the Marshes', that 'the Nazgûl over marshes cannot be the same as passed over Dolbaran', and directed that the relevant passage in that chapter, and also that at the end of 'The Palantír', should be changed. It must have been at this time, then, that the description of the Nazgûl's flight over the marshes was altered – it wheeled round and returned to Mordor (p. 110); while at the same time, in 'The Palantír', Gandalf's original words to Pippin 'It could have taken you away to the Dark Tower' (p. 77) were extended by Pippin's further question 'But it was not coming for me, was it?' and Gandalf's reply: 'Of course not. It is 200 leagues or more in straight flight from Baraddur to Orthanc, and even a Nazgûl would take some hours to fly between them, or so I guess – I do not know. But Saruman certainly looked in the Stone since the orc-raid, and more of his secret thought, I do not doubt, has been read than he intended. A messenger has been sent to find out what he is doing. ...'

Scheme S (in which the dates of Frodo's journey are a day earlier than in A and B, see p. 101) has the following chronology:

(Day 2)   Feb. 2   Journey in the marshes by day.
           Feb. 2–3 Night. 'Episode of corpse-candles' (see note 10).
(Day 3)   Feb. 3   Reach slag-mounds at dawn. Day spent hiding in a hole, going on at nightfall. Gandalf, Théoden, etc. leave Isengard at sunset and camp at Dolbaran.
(Day 4)   Feb. 4   Reach the Black Gate at daybreak and hide all day. Gandalf and Pippin sight Edoras at dawn.

In the notes accompanying the changes made in October 1944 my father also directed that 'the first Nazgûl' should pass over Frodo and his companions at dusk (5 p.m.) on the evening of February 3 'just

120   THE WAR OF THE RING

about when they start from the slag-mounds', and reach Dol Baran about 11 p.m. 'The second Nazgûl, sent after Pippin used the Stone', despatched from Mordor about one o'clock in the morning of the night of Feb. 3–4, should pass over Frodo at the end of the chapter 'Passage of the Marshes' before they reach the Morannon. This Nazgûl would pass over Edoras on February 4, about six hours later. 'But both may pass high up and only give them faint uneasiness.'

Scheme S is confused on the subject of the flights of the Nazgûl, offering different formulations, but in the result it agrees well with the notes just cited; here however the second Nazgûl leaves Mordor 'at 11 p.m.' or 'about midnight', and it 'scouts around the plain and passes over Edoras at ? 8 a.m.' These movements fit very well with the added conclusion to 'The Passage of the Marshes' (TT pp. 242–3; see p. 115), which I presume was introduced at this time. Thus the unseen Ringwraith that passed overhead soon after they left the hole amid the slag-heaps, 'going maybe on some swift errand from Barad-dûr', was the one that passed over Dol Baran six hours later (on its way to Orthanc to 'find out what Saruman was doing'); and that which passed over an hour after midnight, 'rushing with terrible speed into the West', was the one sent in response to Pippin's looking into the *palantír*.

In the final chronology as set out in *The Tale of Years* two days were added to the journey to the Morannon, during which Frodo and his companions passed through 'the arid moors of the Noman-lands' (see p. 112):

(Day 2)   Mar. 1   Frodo begins the passage of the Dead Marshes at dawn.

                Mar. 1–2 Night.   Frodo comes to the end of the Marshes late at night.

(Day 3)   Mar. 2–3 Night.   Frodo journeys in the Noman-lands.

(Day 4)   Mar. 3–4 Night.   Frodo journeys in the Noman-lands. Battle of the Hornburg.

(Day 5)   Mar. 4   Dawn, Frodo reaches the slag-mounds (and leaves at dusk). Théoden and Gandalf set out from Helm's Deep for Isengard.

(Day 6)   Mar. 5   Daybreak, Frodo in sight of the Morannon. Théoden reaches Isengard at noon. Parley with Saruman in Orthanc. Winged Nazgûl passes over the camp at Dol Baran.

Thus according to the final chronology neither of the unseen Nazgûl that passed over high up at the end of the chapter 'The Passage of the Marshes' (at dusk on March 4, and again an hour after midnight) can have been the one that wheeled over Dol Baran on the night of March 5, nor the one that passed over Edoras on the morning of March 6. A rigorous chronology led to this disappointing conclusion.

III

THE BLACK GATE IS CLOSED

I have already quoted (p. 104) my father's letter of 23 April 1944 in which he said that he had 'nearly done' the chapter which he called 'Gates of the Land of Shadow'. Since in the first fair-copy manuscript of this chapter the text goes on without a break through what was subsequently called 'Of Herbs and Stewed Rabbit', he had probably at that date got well beyond the point where 'The Black Gate is Closed' ends in TT (at Frodo's decision to take the southward road); and this is borne out by what he said on the 26th (continuation of a letter begun on 24 April, *Letters* no. 63): 'At this point I require to know how much later the moon gets up each night when nearing full, and how to stew a rabbit!'

Here I restrict my account to the portion of the new chapter that corresponds to 'The Black Gate is Closed'. This was a part of the narrative that largely 'wrote itself', and there is not a great deal to record of its development; it was achieved, also, in a much more orderly fashion than had been the case for a long time. Here there is a continuous, and for most of its length readily legible, initial draft, which extends in fact to the point where 'The Black Gate is Closed' ends in TT, and then becomes a brief outline that brings Frodo, Sam and Gollum to the Cross-roads and up the Stairs of Kirith Ungol – showing that at that time my father had no notion of what would befall them on the southward road. He headed this draft 'Kirith Ungol' (the original title of 'The Passage of the Marshes', p. 104), sure that he could get them there within the compass of this new chapter (but 'Kirith Ungol' now bore a different significance from what it had when he gave it to the previous chapter, see p. 106).

The draft was followed by a fair copy manuscript (in this chapter called 'the manuscript', as distinguished from 'the draft') which, as already noticed, extends without break through 'Of Herbs and Stewed Rabbit', and here again the first title given to it was 'Kirith Ungol', changed to 'The Gates of the Land of Shadow' (the title my father used in his letter of 23 April), and then to 'Kirith Gorgor: The Black gate is Closed'. At some stage, for some reason, he made a further manuscript of the chapter (ending it at the point where it ends in TT) in his most beautiful script, and this was copied in the first typescript. The chapter number is XXXIV.

In the (first) manuscript the text as it stands in TT was achieved in almost all points without much hesitation in the writing; but there was

122   THE WAR OF THE RING

much further shifting in the names that occur in this region. The opening passage concerning the defences of Mordor and their history differed in some respects from the form in TT (p. 244). The words following 'But the strength of Gondor failed, and men slept': *and for long years the towers stood empty*, are lacking.[1] The paragraph beginning 'Across the mouth of the pass, from cliff to cliff, the Dark Lord had built a rampart of stone. In it there was a single gate of iron, and upon its battlement sentinels paced unceasingly' was first written thus, both in draft and manuscript:

> No rampart, or wall, or bars of stone or iron were laid across the Morannon;[2] for the rock on either side was bored and tunnelled into a hundred caves and maggot-holes. A host of orcs lurked there ... (&c. as in TT)

This was changed in the manuscript as soon as written to the text of TT, introducing the rampart of stone and the single gate of iron; and it is thus seen that up to this point the 'Black Gate(s)' was the name of the pass itself.[3] So also at the beginning of the passage, where TT has 'between these arms there was a deep defile. This was Cirith Gorgor, the Haunted Pass, the entrance to the land of the Enemy', both draft and manuscript have 'between these arms there was a long defile. *This was the Morannon*, the Black Gate, the entrance to the land of the Enemy.' When the rampart and iron gate had been introduced this was changed in the manuscript to 'This was Kirith Gorgor, the Dreadful Pass, the entrance to the land of the Enemy.'[4]

The Mountains of Shadow were still in the draft named the *Dúath*, as on the First Map (Map III, VII.309); in the manuscript the name is *Hebel Dúath*, later changed to *Ephel Dúath* (see VII.310).[5] The 'Teeth of Mordor' are named in the draft *Nelig Morn* (cf. *Nelig Morn* > *Nelig Myrn*, p. 113);[6] in the manuscript they are *Naglath Morn*, which was subsequently struck out and not replaced.

It is convenient to notice here a few other points concerning names in this chapter. The name *Elostirion* for Osgiliath, used in the fine manuscript of 'The Palantír' made earlier in April (p. 78 and note 20), was retained in the draft[7] and in the following manuscript of 'The Black Gate is Closed', with *Osgiliath* later substituted in the latter (TT p. 249). The name of Sauron's stronghold in Mirkwood remains *Dol Dúghol*, the change to *Dol Guldur* being made at a very late stage.[8]

A curious vestige is seen in the name *Goodchild* pencilled above *Gamgee* in Sam's remark 'It's beyond any Gamgee to guess what he'll do next' (TT p. 247). In his letter to me of 31 May 1944 (*Letters* no. 72) my father said:

> Sam by the way is an abbreviation not of *Samuel* but of Samwise (the Old E. for Half-wit), as is his father's name the Gaffer (Ham)

THE BLACK GATE IS CLOSED
123

for O.E. Hamfast or Stayathome. Hobbits of that class have very Saxon names as a rule – and I am not really satisfied with the surname Gamgee and shd. change it to Goodchild if I thought you would let me.

I replied that I would never wish to see *Gamgee* changed to *Goodchild*, and urged (entirely missing the point) that the name *Gamgee* was for me the essential expression of 'the hobbit peasantry' in their 'slightly comical' aspect, deeply important to the whole work. I mention this to explain my father's subsequent remarks on the subject (28 July 1944, *Letters*, no. 76):

> As to Sam Gamgee, I quite agree with what you say, and I wouldn't dream of altering his name without your approval; but the object of the alteration was precisely to bring out the comicness, peasantry, and if you will the Englishry of this jewel among the hobbits. Had I thought it out at the beginning, I should have given all the hobbits very English names to match the shire. ... I doubt if it's English [i.e. the name Gamgee]. ... However, I daresay all your imagination of the character is now bound up with the name.

And so Sam Gamgee remained.

Turning now to the narrative itself, there are only certain details to mention. The distance from the hollow in which Frodo and his companions lay to the nearer of the Towers of the Teeth was in the initial drafting and in both manuscripts estimated at about a mile as the crow flies (a furlong in TT, p. 245). The description of the three roads leading to the Black Gate (TT p.247) was present in all essentials from the outset (they were in fact marked in by dotted lines on the First Map, though not included on my redrawing),[9] as were Frodo's stern words to Gollum (TT p. 248), and the conversation about the southward road; but Gollum's remembered tales of his youth and his account of Minas Morgul (TT pp. 249–50) differed from the final form in these respects. When Frodo said: 'It was Isildur who cut off the finger of the Enemy', Gollum replied: 'The tales did not say that'; then Frodo said: 'No, it had not happened then' (becoming in the second manuscript 'No, it had not happened when your tales were made').[10] Secondly, Gollum's reference to 'the Silent Watchers' in Minas Morgul (TT p. 250) was added to the manuscript, which as written had only: 'Nothing moves on the road that they don't know about. The things inside know.' Thirdly, after Gollum's explanation of why Sauron did not fear attack by way of Minas Morgul (his speech beginning 'No, no, indeed. Hobbits must see, must try to understand'), Sam says:

> 'I daresay, but even so we can't walk up along your climbing road and pass the time of day with the folk at the gates and ask if

124   THE WAR OF THE RING

we're all right for the Dark Tower. Stands to reason,' said Sam. 'We might as well do it here, and save ourselves a long tramp.'

Thus his jibe at Gollum ('Have you been talking to Him lately? Or just hobnobbing with Orcs?'), and Gollum's reply ('Not nice hobbit, not sensible ...') are lacking. With the expanded text (written into the manuscript later) there enters the second reference to 'the Silent Watchers' (and Sam's sarcasm 'Or are they too silent to answer?').

The brief text given on p. 113 and reproduced with the accompanying sketch on p. 114, in which Kirith Ungol is 'beneath the shadow of Minas Morgul', and in which Frodo and Sam actually enter Minas Morgul, shows that only a short time before the point we have reached the later story and geography had not emerged. But the conception of the entrances into Mordor was changing very rapidly, and the original draft of 'The Black Gate is Closed' shows a major further shift. The conversation following Sam's remarks about the futility of going on a long tramp south only to find themselves faced with the same impossibility of entering unseen (TT p. 251) ran thus in the draft:

'Don't joke about it,' said Gollum. 'Be sensible hobbits. It is not sensible to try to get in to Mordor at all, not sensible. But if master says I will go or I must go then he must try some way. But he must not go to the terrible city. That is where Smeagol helps. He found it, he knows it – if it is still there.'

'What did you find?' said Frodo.

'A stair and path leading up into the mountains south of the pass,' said Gollum, 'and then a tunnel, and then more stairs and then a cleft high above the main pass: and it was that way Smeagol got out of Mordor long ago. But it may [?have vanished] ...'

'Isn't it guarded?' said Sam incredulously, and he thought he caught a sudden gleam in Gollum's eye.

'Yes perhaps,' said he, 'but we must try. No other way,' and he would say no more. The name of this perilous place and high pass he could not or would not tell. Its name was Kirith Ungol, but that the hobbits did not know, nor the meaning of that dreadful name.

As the following manuscript was first written this was not significantly changed (the path and stair are still 'south of the pass'); the passage in which Frodo intervenes and challenges Gollum's story that he had escaped from Mordor, citing Aragorn's view of the matter, was added in a rider to the manuscript later.[11]

Thus Kirith Ungol is now not the pass guarded by Minas Morgul, as in the text given on p. 113, but a climbing stair high above it; it is

THE BLACK GATE IS CLOSED   125

however very difficult to say how my father saw the further course of the story at this time. In the text on p. 113 Frodo and Sam 'creep into Minas Morgul', which suggests that the story of Frodo's capture in 'The Story Foreseen from Lórien' had been temporarily abandoned – though it is not clear why they should be obliged to enter 'the terrible city'. With the new geography, however, it seems that they are going to avoid Minas Morgul, passing through the mountains high above it. Does it follow that the Tower of Kirith Ungol had already been conceived?

There is nothing in draft or manuscript to show that it had – but that proves little in itself, since in all texts from the original draft Gollum refuses to say clearly whether Kirith Ungol is guarded (cf. 'The Stairs of Cirith Ungol', TT p. 319: 'It was a black tower poised above the outer pass. ... "I don't like the look of that!" said Sam. "So this secret way of yours is guarded after all," he growled, turning to Gollum'). The gleam in Gollum's eye that Sam caught when he asked him if it were guarded certainly means that Gollum knew that it was, but does not at all imply that it was guarded by a tower. I feel sure that Gollum was thinking of the spiders (at this stage in the evolution of the story). The only other evidence is found in the outline which ends the original draft of 'The Black Gate is Closed':

Frodo makes up his mind. He agrees to take the south way.

As soon as dusk falls they start. Needing speed they use the road though fearful of meeting soldiers on it hurrying to the muster of the Dark Lord. Gollum says it is twenty leagues perhaps to the Cross Roads in the wood. They made all the speed they could. The land climbs a little. They see Anduin below them gleaming in the moon. Good [?water]. At last late on the third [day of their daylight journey >] night of journey from Morannon they reach the crossroads and pass out of the wood.

See the moon shining on Minas Ithil Minas Morghul.

Pass up first stair safely. But tunnel is black with webs [of] spiders. ... force way and get up second stair. They [??had] reach[ed] Kirith Ungol. Spiders are aroused and hunt them. They are exhausted.

This does not of course imply that the spiders were the only danger they faced in taking the way of Kirith Ungol, but possibly suggests it.

However this may be, and leaving open the question of whether at this stage my father had already decided that Kirith Ungol was guarded by its own tower, it would be interesting to know whether that decision had been taken when he introduced into the manuscript Gollum's references to 'the Silent Watchers'. The Watchers, called 'the

126   THE WAR OF THE RING

Sentinels', had already appeared in 'The Story Foreseen from Lórien' (see VII.340–3 and note 33); there of course they were the sentinels of Minas Morgul. Here too Gollum is speaking of Minas Morgul (at this point in the chapter he has not even mentioned the existence of Kirith Ungol). It would seem rather odd that my father should bring in these references to the Silent Watchers of Minas Morgul if he had already decided that the actual encounter with Silent Watchers should be at the Tower of Kirith Ungol; and one might suspect therefore that when he wrote them into the text the idea of that tower had not yet arisen. But this is the merest conjecture.[12]

The passage telling where Gandalf was when Frodo and his companions lay hidden in the hollow before the Black Gate underwent many changes. The original draft reads:

Aragorn perhaps could have told them, Gandalf could have warned them, but Gandalf was ? flying over the green [?plain] of Rohan upon Shadowfax   climbing the road to the guarded gates of Minas Tirith and Aragorn was marching at the head of many men to war.

This seems to express two distinct answers to the question, where was Gandalf? — In the manuscript this becomes:

Aragorn could perhaps have told them that name and its significance; Gandalf would have warned them. But they were alone; and Aragorn was far away, a captain of men mustering for a desperate war, and Gandalf stood upon the white walls of Minas Tirith deep in troubled thought. It was of them chiefly that he thought: and over the long leagues his mind sought for them.

In the second manuscript, taking up a revision made to the first, Gandalf is again riding over the plains:

... But they were alone, and Aragorn was far away, a captain of men mustering for a desperate war, and Gandalf was flying upon Shadowfax over the fields of Rohan swifter than the wind to the white walls of Minas Tirith gleaming from afar. Yet as he rode, it was chiefly of them that he thought, of Frodo and Sam, and over the long leagues his mind sought for them.

This was changed afterwards to the text of TT (p. 252):

... and Gandalf stood amid the ruin of Isengard and strove with Saruman, delayed by treason. Yet even as he spoke his last words to Saruman, and the *palantír* crashed in fire upon the

THE BLACK GATE IS CLOSED 127

steps of Orthanc, his thought was ever upon Frodo and Samwise, over the long leagues his mind sought for them in hope and pity.

On the significance of these variations see the Note on Chronology at the end of this chapter.

The distant flight of the Nazgûl (TT p. 253) and the arrival of the southern men observed and reported on by Gollum differ already in the draft text in no essential points from the final text (except that it is Gollum who calls them *Swertings*); but Sam's verse of the Oliphaunt was not present. It is found in abundant rough workings and a preliminary text before being incorporated in the manuscript; my father also copied it out for me in a letter written on 30 April 1944 (*Letters* no. 64), when the story had reached the end of what became 'Of Herbs and Stewed Rabbit', saying: 'A large elephant of prehistoric size, a war-elephant of the Swertings, is loose, and Sam has gratified a life-long wish to see an Oliphaunt, an animal about which there was a hobbit nursery-rhyme (though it was commonly supposed to be mythical).'[13]

NOTES

1 In a very rough initial sketching of the opening of the chapter, preceding the continuous draft, the reading is: 'They were built by the Men of Gondor long ages after the fall of the first Dark Tower and Sauron's flight, lest he should seek to [?retake] his old realm.' This was repeated in the draft text of the chapter ('after the felling of the first Dark fortress'), but changed immediately to 'after the overthrow of Sauron and his flight'.

2 The earliest sketch of the opening passage, referred to in note 1, has a name that ends in -*y*; it could be interpreted as *Mornennyn* with the final -*n* omitted, but is written thus at both occurrences. For *Mornennyn*, replacing *Ennyn Dûr*, see pp. 112–13.

3 The Old English word *geat* 'gate' is found in a number of English place-names in the sense 'pass, gap in the hills', as *Wingate* (pass through which the wind drives), *Yatesbury*.

4 It seems in fact that my father did not immediately transfer the name *Morannon* to the actual 'Black Gate' built by Sauron, but retained it for a time as the name of the pass: so later in the manuscript text (TT p. 247) Frodo 'stood gazing out towards the dark cliffs of the Morannon' (changed subsequently to *Kirith Gorgor*).

5 Here appear also the plain of *Lithlad* (see VII.208, 213) and 'the bitter inland sea of *Nûrnen*', shown on the First Map (Map III, VII.309).

128   THE WAR OF THE RING

6   In the text given on p. 113 and reproduced on p. 114 *Nelig Myrn* replaced *Nelig Morn* at the time of writing; yet it seems obvious that that text was written during the original composition of 'The Passage of the Marshes'.

7   The draft text has in fact *Osgiliath* at one occurrence, in the first description of the southward road (TT p. 247): 'It journeyed on into the narrow plain between the Great River and the mountains, and so on to Osgiliath and on again to the coasts, and the far southern lands'. But *Elostirion* is the name in this same text in the passage corresponding to TT p. 249.

8   The name *Amon Hen* was changed at its first occurrence in the manuscript (TT p. 247) to *Amon Henn*, but not at the second (TT p. 252). On the second manuscript the name was written *Amon Henn* at both occurrences.

9   The southward road is shown running a little to the east of Anduin as far as the bottom of square Q 14 on Map III, VII.309. The eastward road runs along the northern edges of Ered Lithui as far as the middle of square O 17 on Map II, VII.305. The northward road divides at ʌhe bottom of square O 15 on Map II, the westward arm running to the hills on the left side of O 15, and the northward arm bending north-east along the western edge of the Dead Marshes and then turning west to end on the left side of N 15.

    The passage describing the southward road was several times changed in respect of its distance from the hollow where Frodo, Sam and Gollum hid. In the original draft it was 'not more than a furlong or so'; in the first manuscript the distance was changed through 'a couple of furlongs', 'fifty paces', and 'a furlong', the final reading (preserved in the second manuscript) being '[it] passed along the valley at the foot of the hillside where the hobbits lay and not many feet below them.' For one, rather surprising, reason for this hesitation see pp. 172–3.

    In the First Edition the description of the topography differed from that in the Second Edition (TT p. 247), and read:

> The hollow in which they had taken refuge was delved in the side of a low hill and lay at some little height above the level of the plain. A long trench-like valley ran between it and the outer buttresses of the mountain-wall. In the morning-light the roads that converged upon the Gate of Mordor could now be clearly seen, pale and dusty; one winding back northwards; another dwindling eastwards into the mists that clung about the feet of Ered Lithui; and another that, bending sharply, ran close under the western watch-tower, and then passed along the valley at the foot of the hillside where the hobbits lay and not many feet

THE BLACK GATE IS CLOSED   129

below them. Soon it turned, skirting the shoulders of the mountains ...

This is the text of the second manuscript.

10 Frodo's meaning must be that these particular tales known to Gollum, concerning the cities of the Númenóreans, originated in the time before the Last Alliance and the overthrow of Sauron.

11 As the rider was first written there was this difference from the text of TT (p. 251):

> For one thing he noted Gollum used *I*, as he had hardly done since he was frightened out of his old bad wits away back under the cliff of Emyn Muil.

This was changed to: '... Gollum used *I*, and that seemed usually to be a sign, on its rare appearances, that Smeagol was (for the moment) on top', and then to the final text.

12 Even if this was so, it cannot be supposed that my father still thought that Frodo and Sam would enter Minas Morgul, and encounter the Silent Watchers there. The outline with which the draft text ends (p. 125) would obviously have said so if that had been in his mind. Moreover, not long after, in his letter of 30 April 1944 (*Letters* no. 64), he said that 'in the chapter next to be done they will get to Kirith Ungol and *Frodo will be caught*.'

13 It is hard to be sure, but it seems from the manuscript evidence that originally Sam's word was *oliphant*, and that *oliphaunt* was used only in the rhyme. — The form is mediaeval French and English *olifa(u)nt*. There are no differences in the texts, except that in the draft version and in the form cited in my father's letter line 11 reads 'I've stumped' for 'I stump', and in line 15 'Biggest of all' is written 'Biggest of All'.

Note on the Chronology

Where was Gandalf when Frodo, in hiding before the Morannon, was thinking of him? Four versions of the passage in question (TT p. 252) have been given on pp. 126–7. The original draft (1) seems to leave it open whether Gandalf was riding across Rohan or was almost at the end of his journey, climbing the road to the gates of Minas Tirith; in the following manuscript (2) he was standing on the walls of Minas Tirith; in the second manuscript (3) he was again riding across Rohan; and finally (4), as in TT, he was standing on the steps of Orthanc.

These versions reflect, of course, the difficulty my father encountered in bringing the different threads of the narrative into chronological harmony. According to the 'received chronology' at this time, the day in question here (spent by Frodo, Sam and Gollum in hiding before the Morannon) was 5 February (see p. 118); while Gandalf, Théoden and their companions left Isengard in the evening of 3 February (pp. 6, 73), camping at Dol Baran that night – the great

130   THE WAR OF THE RING

ride of Gandalf with Pippin therefore began during the night of
3–4 February.

At the end of the fine manuscript of 'The Palantír' that my father
had made at the beginning of April 1944 (p. 78) Gandalf had said to
Pippin as they passed near the mouth of the Deeping Coomb,
following the first manuscript of the chapter: 'You may see the first
glimmer of dawn upon the golden roof of the House of Eorl. At sunset
on the day after you shall see the purple shadow of Mount Mindolluin
fall upon the walls of the tower of Denethor.' This was said, according
to the chronology at the time, in the small hours of the night of
3–4 February; and Gandalf was therefore forecasting that they would
reach Minas Tirith at sunset on the fifth.

This is the chronology underlying the words of the original draft
(version 1). Subsequent shifting in the dates, so that Gandalf and
Pippin reached Minas Tirith later and Frodo reached the Morannon
earlier, meant that Gandalf was less far advanced in his journey, but
his ride across Rohan still coincided with Frodo at the Morannon
(version 3). None of the time-schemes, however, allows Gandalf to
have actually reached Minas Tirith at that time, and I cannot explain
version 2.

The final version 4 of this passage, as found in TT, reflects of course
the final chronology, according to which Frodo was in hiding before
the Black Gate on the same day (5 March) as Gandalf spoke with
Saruman on the steps of Orthanc.

IV

OF HERBS AND STEWED RABBIT

For this chapter, written as a continuation of 'The Black Gate is Closed' and only separated from it and numbered 'XXXV' after its completion, there exists a good deal of (discontinuous) initial drafting, some of it illegible, and a completed manuscript, some of which is itself the primary composition. As in the last chapter I distinguish the texts as 'draft' and 'manuscript' (in this case no other manuscript was made, see p. 121).

On 26 April 1944, in a letter to me already cited (p. 121), my father said that on the previous day he had 'struggled with a recalcitrant passage in "The Ring"', and then went on to say that 'at this point I require to know how much later the moon gets up each night when nearing full, and how to stew a rabbit!' From drafts and manuscript it is easy to see what this recalcitrant passage was: the southward journey as far as the point where Sam's thoughts turned to the possibility of finding food more appetizing than the waybread of the Elves (TT p. 260).

The original draft begins thus:

They rested for the few hours of daylight that were left, ate a little and drank sparingly, though they had hope of water soon in the streams that flowed down into Anduin from Hebel Dúath. As the dusk deepened they set out. The moon did not rise till late and it grew soon dark. After a few miles over broken slopes and difficult [?country] they took to the southward road, for they needed speed. Ever they listened with straining ears for sounds of foot or hoof upon the road ahead and behind ...

After the description of the road, kept in repair below the Morannon but further south encroached upon by the wild, the opening draft peters out, and at this point, probably, my father began the writing of the manuscript. Here the single red light in the Towers of the Teeth appears, but they passed out of sight of it after only a few miles, 'turning away southward round a great dark shoulder of the lower mountains', whereas in TT this took place 'when night was growing old and they were already weary'.[1] In this text they came to the less barren lands, with thickets of trees on the slopes, during that first night, and the shrubs which in TT the hobbits did not know (being strange to them) were here 'unrecognizable in the dark'. After a short

132   THE WAR OF THE RING

rest about midnight Gollum led them down onto the southward road, the description of which follows.

The precise sequence of composition as between drafts and manuscript is hard to work out, but I think that it was probably at this point that my father wrote a very brief outline for the story to come, together with notes on names. Frustratingly, his writing here has in places resisted all attempts to puzzle it out.

After so much labour and peril the days they spent on it seemed almost a rest. In Gollum's reckoning it was some 20 [*changed from some other figure*] leagues from the Morannon to the outer wards of Minas Morghul, maybe more. Gollum finds food. Night of Full Moon, they see a white ... far away up in the dark shadow of the hills to left, at head of a wide [?re-entrant, *sc. valley*], Minas Morghul.[2] Next night they come to the cross roads. An[d] a great [?stone] figure ... [3] back to Elostirion ... [*Struck out:* Sarnel Ubed.[4] Ennyn. Aran] Taur Toralt [*struck out*: Sarn Torath.] Annon Torath. Aranath. reminding Frodo of the Kings at Sern Aranath. or Sairn Ubed.

But his head was struck off and in mockery some orcs? had set ... a clay ball with ... The red eye was ... [?painted over].[5]

For *Sern Aranath* as the name of the Pillars of the Kings see VII.366 note 21; and cf. TT p. 311 (at the end of 'Journey to the Cross-roads'): 'The brief glow fell upon a huge sitting figure, still and solemn as the great stone kings of Argonath.' It is not clear to me whether *Sairn Ubed* is an alternative to *Sern Aranath*. On this same page, later but not much later, my father made further notes on names (see p. 137), and among these appears the following:

The two King Stones   Sern Ubed (denial)
                       Sern Aranath

The word *denial* makes one think of the description of the Pillars of the Kings in 'The Great River' (FR p. 409), where in the earliest draft of that passage (VII.360) 'the left hand of each was raised beside his head palm outwards in gesture of warning and *refusal*.'[6]

It is plain from this text that at this time the emergence of Faramir and the Window on the West was totally unforeseen, while on the other hand the broken statue at the Cross-roads was already present.

The next step in the development of the 'recalcitrant passage' is seen, I think, in what follows the description of the southward road in the manuscript:

After the labours and perils they had just endured the days that they spent upon the road seemed almost pleasant, though fear was about them and darkness lay before them. The weather

OF HERBS AND STEWED RABBIT 133

now was good, though the wind blowing from the north-west over the Misty Mountains far away had a sharp tooth. They passed on into the northern marches of that land that men once called Ithilien, a fair country of climbing woods and swift falling streams. In Gollum's reckoning it was some thirty leagues from the Morannon to the crossing of the ways above Elostirion, and he hoped to cover that distance in three journeys. But maybe the distance was greater or they went slower than he hoped, for at the end of the third night they had not come there.

This passage was rejected at once, but before this was done 'thirty leagues' was changed to 'twenty', and it was perhaps at this time that a sentence was added earlier, following 'But they were not going quick enough for Gollum' (TT p. 256): 'In his reckoning it was twenty leagues from the Morannon to the crossing of the ways above Osgiliath,[7] and he hoped to cover that distance in three journeys' (where TT has 'nearly thirty leagues' and 'four journeys').

My father now, if my analysis of the sequence is correct, decided that he was treating the journey from the Morannon to the Cross-roads too cursorily; and his next step, on the same page of the manuscript, was to return to the first night (which was that of 5 February):

All that night they plodded on, and all the next. The road drew ever nearer to the course of the Great River and further from the shadow of Hebel Dúath on their left. That second night the moon was full. Not long before the dawn they saw it sinking round and yellow far beyond the great vale below them. Here and there a white gleam showed where Anduin rolled, a mighty stream swollen with the waters of Emyn Muil and of slow-winding Entwash. Far far away, pale ghosts above the mists, the peaks of the Black Mountains were caught by the beaming moon. There glimmered through the night the snows on Mount Mindolluin; but though Frodo's eyes stared out into the west wondering where in the vastness of the land his old companions might now be, he did not know that under

This passage was in its turn struck out. The last words stand at the foot of a page.[8]

It was now, as it seems, that my father decided to introduce the episode of the rabbits caught by Gollum (developing it from the passage where it first appears, given in note 6).

All that night they plodded on. At the first sign of day they halted, and lay beneath a bank in a brake of old brown bracken

134   THE WAR OF THE RING

overshadowed by dark pinetrees. Water flowed down not far away, cold out of the hills, and good to drink.

Sam had been giving some earnest thought to food as they marched. Now that the despair of the impassable Gate was behind him, he did not feel so inclined as his master to take no thought for their livelihood beyond the end of their errand; and anyway it seemed wiser to him to save the elvish bread for worse times ahead. Two days or more had gone since he reckoned that they had a bare supply for three weeks.[9] 'If we reach the Fire in that time we'll be lucky at this rate,' he thought. 'And we may be wanting to come back. We may.' Besides at the end of [?their] long night march he felt more hungry than usual.

With all this in his mind he turned to look for Gollum. Gollum was crawling away through the bracken. 'Hi!' said Sam. 'Where are you going? Hunting? Now look here, my friend, you don't like our food, but if you could find something fit for a hobbit to eat I'd be grateful.'

Yes, yess.

Gollum brings back 2 rabbits. Angry at fire (a) fear (b) rage at nice juicy rabbits being spoiled. Pacified by Frodo (promise of fish?).

Night of full moon and vision of Anduin.

Third night. They do not reach the cross ways. [?Trying] to hasten they journey by day through wood. They come to cross ways and peer at it out of thicket.

The headless king with a mocking head made by orcs and scrawls on it.

That night they turn left. Vision of Minas Morghul in the moon high up in re-entrant.[10]

Here this text ends, and was followed by another draft, beginning precisely as does that just given, in which the story of Sam's cooking was developed almost to the final form. On one of the pages of this text my father pencilled a note: 'Describe baytrees and spicy herbs as they march.' It was thus the cooking of the rabbits that led to the account of the shrubs and herbs of Ithilien (TT p. 258) – 'which is proving a lovely land', as he said in his letter of 30 April 1944 (*Letters* no. 64).

He now returned again to the fair copy manuscript, and without changing, then or later, the opening of the chapter he wrote the story almost as it stands in TT, pp. 258 ff. (from 'So they passed into the northern marches of that land that Men once called Ithilien'). At this stage, therefore, the chronology of the journey was thus:

OF HERBS AND STEWED RABBIT   135

Feb. 5   Left the Morannon at dusk, and came into a less barren
country of heathland. Took to the southward road about midnight (p. 132).
Feb. 6   Halted at dawn. Description of Ithilien and its herbs and
flowers. Sam's cooking, and the coming of the men of Gondor.

With the introduction of a long rider to the following typescript text
an extra day and night were inserted into the journey between the
Morannon and the place of Sam's cooking (see the Note on Chronology at the end of this chapter). At dawn of this added day they found
themselves in a less barren country of heathland, and they passed the
day hidden in deep heather (TT p. 257); at dusk they set out again,
and only now took to the southward road.

At the end of the episode of 'Stewed Rabbit' there is a brief sketch in
the manuscript of the story to come, written in pencil so rapid that I
cannot make all of it out; but it can be seen that Sam finds that Gollum
is not there; he puts out the fire and runs down to wash the pans; he
hears voices, and suddenly sees a couple of men chasing Gollum.
Gollum eludes their grasp and vanishes into a tangled thicket. They go
on up the hill, and Sam hears them laugh. 'Not an orc,' says one. Sam
creeps back to Frodo, who has also heard voices and hidden himself,
and they see many men creeping up towards the road.

Another page found separately seems quite likely to be the continuation of this outline, and is equally hard to read. There is to be a
description of men like Boromir, dressed in lighter and darker green,
armed with knives; the hobbits wonder who they are – they are
certainly not scouts of Sauron. The fight on the road between the men
of Harad and the men of Minas Tirith is mentioned; then follows:

A slain Tirith-man falls over bank and crashes down on them.
Frodo goes to him and he cries *orch* and tries to ... but falls
dead crying 'Gondor!' The Harad-men drive the Gondorians
[?down] hill. The hobbits creep away through thickets. At last
they climb tree. See Gondorians fight and win finally. At dusk
Gollum climbs up to them. He curses Sam for [?bringing
enemies]. They dare not go back to road, but wander on
through the wild glades of Ithilien that night. See Full Moon.
Meet no more folk.

Strike the road to Osgiliath far down, and have to go back
long [?detour] East. Deep Ilex woods. Gollum goes [?on] by
day. Evening of third day they reach Cross ways. See broken
statue.[11]

The story of the ambush[12] of the Southron men thus seems at this
stage to have had no sequel. But from the point where this outline
begins (when Sam calls to Gollum that there is some rabbit left if he
wants to change his mind, but finds that he has disappeared, TT

136   THE WAR OF THE RING

p. 264) the final form of the story, partly extant in rough drafting, was achieved without hesitation – with, however, one major difference: the leader of the Gondorians was *not* Faramir, brother of Boromir. At this time he was Falborn son of Anborn (and remained so in the manuscript). Mablung and Damrod, the two men who were left to guard Frodo and Sam,[13] told them that Falborn was a kinsman of Boromir, and that 'he and they were Rangers of Ithilien, for they were descended from folk who lived in Ithilien at one time, before it was overrun' (cf. TT p. 267).

For the rest, Falborn's conversation with Frodo and Sam proceeds almost exactly as does that with Faramir in TT.[14] Mablung and Damrod used 'sometimes the Common Speech, but after the manner of older days, sometimes some other language of their own', but the description of this other tongue (TT p. 267) was added to the typescript that followed the manuscript at some later time. Their account of the Southrons scarcely differs from the final form, but where Mablung in TT (p. 268) speaks of 'These cursed Southrons', in the manuscript he says 'These cursed Barangils, for so we name them' (subsequently changed to the later reading). The name *Barangils* is written on the First Map beside *Swertings* (see Map III, VII.309).

The account of the Oliphaunt was never changed, save only in the name by which the great beasts were known in Gondor (*Mûmak* in TT). In the original draft Mablung[15] cried *Andabund!*, and this was the form first written in the manuscript also. This was changed to *Andrabonn*,[16] then to *Múmund*. These were immediate changes, for a few lines later appears 'the *Múmund* of Harad was indeed a beast of vast bulk', where drafting for the passage has *Múmar*. Soon after, the form *Mâmuk* was introduced in both passages: this was the form my father used in his letter to me of 6 May 1944 (*Letters* no. 66).

Lastly, in the manuscript Damrod cries 'May the gods turn him aside', where in TT he names the Valar; *gods* was preceded by a rejected word that I cannot interpret.

On 30 April 1944 (*Letters* no. 64) my father described to me the course of the story that I had not read:

['The Ring'] is growing and sprouting again ... and opening out in unexpected ways. So far in the new chapters Frodo and Sam have traversed Sarn Gebir,[17] climbed down the cliff, encountered and temporarily tamed Gollum. They have with his guidance crossed the Dead Marshes and the slag-heaps of Mordor, lain in hiding outside the main gates and found them impassable, and set out for a more secret entrance near Minas Morghul (formerly M. Ithil). It will turn out to be the deadly Kirith Ungol and Gollum will play false. But at the moment they are in Ithilien (which is proving a lovely land); there has been a lot of bother about stewed rabbit; and they have been captured by Gondorians, and witnessed them ambushing a

OF HERBS AND STEWED RABBIT   137

Swerting army (dark men of the South) marching to Mordor's aid. A large elephant of prehistoric size, a war-elephant of the Swertings, is loose, and Sam has gratified a life-long wish to see an Oliphaunt ... In the chapter next to be done they will get to Kirith Ungol and Frodo will be caught. ... On the whole Sam is behaving well, and living up to repute. He treats Gollum rather like Ariel to Caliban.

Since it was not until a week later that he referred to the sudden and totally unexpected appearance of Faramir on the scene, it seems to me that when he wrote this letter he had not progressed much if at all beyond the end of the Oliphaunt episode; for in the manuscript of the chapter that became 'Of Herbs and Stewed Rabbit' the leader of the Gondorians is Falborn, not Faramir, and there is as yet no indication that he will play any further part (cf. the outline on p. 135).[18]

This chapter (including what became 'The Black Gate is Closed') was read to C. S. Lewis on the first of May 1944 (*Letters* no. 65).

This is a convenient place to set down the notes on names added later to the page transcribed on p. 132:
Change *Black Mountains* to the *White Mountains. Hebel* [*Orolos>*] *Uilos Nimr*[?*ais*]
Alter the *Morannon* to *Kirith Naglath* Cleft of the Teeth
Gorgor
The two King Stones   *Sern Ubed* (denial)
                        Sern Aranath
Rohar?
To these pencilled notes my father added in ink:
Not *Hebel* but *Ephel. Et-pele* > *Eppele. Ephel-duath. Ephel* [*Nimras* >] *Nimrais. Ered Nimrath.*
With *Kirith Naglath* cf. *Naglath Morn*, p. 122; and on the reference to *Sern Ubed* and *Sern Aranath* see p. 132. On the change of the Black Mountains to the White see VII.433.

NOTES

1   In the manuscript as in the draft, 'The moon was not due until late that night'; in TT 'the moon was now three nights from the full, but it did not climb over the mountains till nearly midnight.'
2   That the illegible word is *re-entrant* seems assured by the recurrence of this word in perfectly clear form and in the same context in the text given on p. 134. In the present text at this point there is drawn a wavy line; this clearly indicates the line of the mountains pierced by a very wide valley running up into a point.

138   THE WAR OF THE RING

3   The illegible word is certainly not *pointing*. It begins with an *f* or a *g* and probably ends in *ing*, but does not suggest either *facing* or *gazing*.

4   The word *Ubed*, occurring twice here and again in the further notes on names on this page (where it is translated 'denial'), is written at all occurrences in precisely the same way, and I do not feel at all certain of the third letter.

5   Before the words 'The red eye' were written my father drew an Old English S-rune (cf. VII.382), but struck it out.

6   The remainder of this page carries disjointed passages: as elsewhere my father probably had it beside him and used it for jotting down narrative 'moments' as they came into his mind. The first reads:

> that great mountain's side was built Minas Tirith, the Tower of Guard, where Gandalf walked now deep in thought.

On this see note 8. Then follows:

> For a third night they went on. They had good water in plenty, and Gollum was better fed. Already he was less famished to look at. At early morning when they lay hidden for rest, and at evening when they set out again, he would slip away and return licking his lips. Sometimes in the long night he would take out something ..... and would crunch it as he walked.
>
> ..... and lay under a deep bank in tall bracken under the shadow of pine trees. Water flowed not far away, cold, good to drink. Gollum slipped away, and returned shortly, licking his lips; but he brought with him also a present for the hobbits. Two rabbits he had caught.

With Sam's having no objection to rabbit but a distaste for what Gollum brought, and a reference to his prudent wish, in contrast to Frodo's indifference, to save the elvish waybread for worse times ahead, these exceedingly difficult 'extracts' come to an end. It was clearly here that the episode of the stewed rabbit entered; but it seems scarcely possible to define how my father related it to the whole sequence of the journey from the Black Gate.

7   On the continued hesitation between *Elostirion* and *Osgiliath* at this time see p. 122 and note 7.

8   The last sentence is in fact, and rather oddly, completed by the first passage given in note 6, thus:

> There glimmered through the night the snows on Mount Mindolluin; but though Frodo's eyes stared out into the west wondering where in the vastness of the land his old companions might now be, he did not know that under / that great mountain's side was built Minas Tirith, the Tower of Guard, where Gandalf walked now deep in thought.

See the Note on Chronology below.

9   This sentence replaced a form of it in which Sam's reckoning had

OF HERBS AND STEWED RABBIT   139

been that they had 'a bare ten days' supply of waybread: that left eight.' In the manuscript of 'The Passage of the Marshes', corresponding to that in TT p. 231, Sam said 'I reckon we've got enough to last, say, 10 days now'. This was changed to 'three weeks or so', no doubt at the same time as the sentence in the present text was rewritten.

In TT (p. 260) it is said at this point that 'Six days or more had passed' since Sam made his reckoning of the remaining *lembas*, whereas here it is 'Two days or more'. Three days had in fact passed, the 3rd, 4th and 5th of February (p. 118). In TT the length of the journey had been increased, both by the two extra days during which they crossed the Noman-lands (pp. 112, 120), and by an extra day added to the journey from the Morannon to the place of the stewed rabbit episode (p. 135).

10   *re-entrant*: see note 2.

11   The brief remainder of this outline is illegible because my father wrote across it notes in ink on another subject (see p. 145).

12   It is not clear that it was first conceived as an ambush, which perhaps only arose when the story came to be written – and it was then that my father added to the manuscript at an earlier point 'They had come to the end of a long cutting, deep, and sheer-sided in the middle, by which the road clove its way through a stony ridge' (TT p. 258).

13   In a pencilled draft so faint and rapid as to be largely illegible another name is found instead of Mablung, and several names preceded Damrod, but I cannot certainly interpret any of them.

14   Rivendell is still *Imladrist* and the Halflings are still the *Halfhigh* (see VII.146). Boromir is called 'Highwarden of the White Tower, and our captain general', as in TT (p. 266).

15   Damrod in TT; the speeches of Damrod and Mablung were shifted about between the two.

16   Cf. the *Etymologies*, V.372, stem MBUD 'project': * *andambundā* 'long-snouted', Quenya *andamunda* 'elephant', Noldorin *andabon, annabon.*

17   *Sarn Gebir*: an interesting instance of the former name reappearing mistakenly – unless my father used *Sarn Gebir* deliberately, remembering that I had not read any of Book IV, in which the name *Emyn Muil* was first used. Cf. however p. 165 note 7.

18   It is clear that in the manuscript the chapter halted at Sam's words (TT p. 270) 'Well, if that's over, I'll have a bit of sleep.' The following brief dialogue between Sam and Mablung (with the hint that the hobbits will not be allowed to continue their journey unhindered: 'I do not think the Captain will leave you here, Master Samwise') was written in the manuscript as the beginning of the next chapter ('Faramir'), and only subsequently joined to

140   THE WAR OF THE RING

the preceding one and made its conclusion; and by then Falborn had become Faramir.

Note on the Chronology

The brief time-scheme B has the following chronology (see pp. 118, 135):

(Day 3)   Feb. 4   Frodo, Sam and Gollum come to the Barren Lands and Slag-mounds. Stay there during day and sleep. At night they go on 12 miles and come before the Morannon on Feb. 5.

(Day 4)   Feb. 5   Frodo, Sam and Gollum remain hidden all day. Pass southward to Ithilien at dusk.

(Day 5)   Feb. 6   Full Moon. Stewed rabbit. Frodo and Sam taken by Faramir. Spend night at Henneth Annûn.

There are two other schemes ('C' and 'D'), the one obviously written shortly after the other, both of which begin at February 4. As originally written, both maintain the chronology of B, but both give some information about other events as well, and in this they differ. Scheme C reads thus:

(Day 3)   Feb. 4   Gandalf and Pippin pass Fords and reach mouth of Coomb about 2.30 a.m. [*Added:* and rides on till daybreak and then rests in hiding. Rides again at night.]
           Théoden sets out from Dolbaran and reaches Helm's Deep soon after dawn.
           Frodo comes to the Barren Lands and Slag-mounds and stays there during day.

(Day 4)   Feb. 5   Théoden leaves Helm's Deep on return journey. Aragorn rides on ahead with Gimli and Legolas.
           Gandalf abandons secrecy and after short rest rides all day to Minas Tirith. He and Pippin reach Minas Tirith at sunset.
           At dawn on Feb. 5 Frodo comes before the Morannon. Frodo, Sam and Gollum lie hid all day and go south towards Ithilien at nightfall.

(Day 5)   Feb. 6   Frodo and Sam in Ithilien. They are taken by Faramir. Battle with the Southrons. Frodo spends night at Henneth Annûn.

Scheme D, certainly following C, runs as follows (as originally written):

(Day 3)   Feb. 4   Gandalf and Pippin begin their ride to Minas Tirith (pass Fords and reach mouth of Deeping Coomb about 2 a.m.). At dawn come to Edoras (7.30). Gandalf fearing

OF HERBS AND STEWED RABBIT 141

Nazgûl rests all day. Orders assembly to go to Dunharrow. Nazgûl passes over Rohan again.

(Day 4)   Feb. 5   Gandalf rides all night of 4–5 and passes into Anórien. Pippin sees the beacons blaze up on the mountains. They see messengers riding West.

Aragorn (with Legolas and Gimli) rides fast by night (4–5) to Dunharrow via Edoras, reaches Edoras at morning and passes up Harrowdale. Théoden with Éomer and many men goes by mountain-roads through south [*sic*] skirts of mountains to Dunharrow, riding slowly.

Frodo at dawn comes before the Morannon. At nightfall Frodo with Sam and Gollum turns south to Ithilien.

(Day 5)   Feb. 6   Full Moon (rises about 9.20 p.m. and sets about 6.30 a.m. on Feb. 7). Gandalf rides all night of 5–6 and sights Minas Tirith at dawn on 6th.

Théoden comes out of west into Harrowdale some miles above Dunharrow, and comes to Dunharrow before nightfall. Finds the muster already beginning.

Frodo and Sam in Ithilien; taken by Faramir; battle with Southrons; night at Henneth Annûn.

On the statement in scheme D that Théoden came down into Harrowdale *some miles above Dunharrow* see p. 259. The full moon of February 6 is the full moon of February 1, 1942, as explained in VII.369.

It will be seen that in their dating these time-schemes proceed from the schemes A and B (see p. 118), in which the day passed by Frodo among the slag-mounds was February 4, and in which he came before the Morannon at dawn on February 5. While these schemes obviously belong to 1944, and were made when Book IV was largely or entirely written (pp. 182, 226), it seems clear that they *preceded* the chronological problems that my father referred to in his letters of 12 and 16 October 1944 (see p. 100): for in the second of these he mentioned that he had made a small alteration in Frodo's journey, 'two days from Morannon to Ithilien', and this change is not present in these schemes, C and D.

Scheme D was revised at that time to provide the extra day in the journey from the Morannon to Ithilien, and this was done by revising the dates backwards: thus Frodo now comes before the Morannon on February 4, and on February 5 'lies in heather on the borders of Ithilien' (see p. 135 and TT p. 257); thus the episode of the stewed rabbit still takes place on February 6. Since this scheme only begins on February 4 it is not shown how the earlier arrival before the Morannon was achieved.

It is clear therefore that scheme S was devised following the chronological modifications of 12–16 October 1944; for in S the extra

142   THE WAR OF THE RING

day in the journey from the Morannon was present from its making, and the date of the extra day was February 5 (as in Scheme D revised), because in this scheme the date of the Breaking of the Fellowship was put back from January 26 to January 25 (see pp. 101, 119). The chronology in S I take therefore to represent the structure when my father wrote on 16 October 'I think I have solved it all at last':

(Day 3)   Feb. 3   Frodo etc. reach slag-mounds at dawn, and stay in a hole all day, going on at nightfall. Nazgûl passes high up on way to Isengard about 5 p.m. Another one hour after midnight.
          Gandalf and company leave Isengard and camp at Dolbaran. Episode of the Orthanc-stone. Nazgûl passes over about 11 p.m.
(Day 4)   Feb. 4   Frodo etc. reach dell in sight of Morannon at daybreak, and lie hid there all day. See the Harad-men march in. At dusk they start southward journey.
          Gandalf and Pippin ride east. Sight Edoras at dawn. Nazgûl passes over Edoras about 8 a.m.
(Day 5)   Feb. 5   Frodo etc. reach borderlands and lie in heather sleeping all day. At night go on into Ithilien.
          Gandalf passes into Anórien.
(Day 6)   Feb. 6   Frodo etc. camp in Ithilien. Episode of Stewed Rabbit. Frodo captured by Faramir and taken to Henneth Annûn.
          [Gandalf and Pippin reach Minas Tirith.]

The original entries concerning Gandalf on February 5 and 6 in this scheme cannot be read after the words 'Gandalf passes into Anórien', because they were afterwards overwritten, but it is clear that as in scheme D he reached Minas Tirith at dawn on February 6.

In this chapter relation to the movements of other members of the original Company arises in the rejected passage given on p. 133, interrupted in the manuscript but concluded as shown in note 8. In this passage, written before the episode of the stewed rabbit and the coming of the men of Gondor had entered the story, Frodo was walking southward through Ithilien, and in the late night of February 6–7 (the second of this journey) he saw the full moon sinking in the West. In its light he glimpsed from far off the snows on Mount Mindolluin; and at that same time Gandalf was walking 'deep in thought' below that mountain in Minas Tirith. When the story was entirely changed by the entry of Faramir it was from Henneth Annûn, before dawn on the 7th, that Frodo saw the setting of the full moon of that night, and in the original draft of 'The Forbidden Pool' appears his sad speculation on the fate of his former companions 'in the vastness of the nightlands' (TT p. 293). When that was written the

OF HERBS AND STEWED RABBIT

143

story was still that Gandalf and Pippin had already reached Minas Tirith.

In the final chronology the relations were altered. Pippin riding with Gandalf on Shadowfax caught as he fell asleep on the night of March 7–8 'a glimpse of high white peaks, glimmering like floating isles above the clouds as they caught the light of the westering moon. He wondered where Frodo was, and if he was already in Mordor, or if he was dead; and he did not know that Frodo from far away looked on that same moon as it set beyond Gondor ere the coming of the day' (*The Return of the King* p. 20). That was still the night that Frodo passed in Henneth Annûn; but now Gandalf did not ride up to the wall of the Pelennor until dawn of the ninth of March.

V

FARAMIR

On the 26th of April 1944 my father said (*Letters* no. 63) that he needed to know how to stew a rabbit; on the 30th (no. 64) he wrote that 'A large elephant of prehistoric size, a war-elephant of the Swertings, is loose' (but made no mention of anything further); on the 4th of May (no. 65), having read a chapter to C. S. Lewis on the 1st, he was 'busy now with the next'; and on the 11th (no. 67) he said that he had read his 'fourth new chapter ("Faramir")' to Lewis and Williams three days before.[1] It seems, then, that what was afterwards called 'The Window on the West' was achieved in not much more than a week. That must have been a time of intense and concentrated work, for the volume of writing that went into this chapter, the redrafting and reshaping, is remarkable. It is also very complex, and it has taken me a lot longer than a week to determine how the chapter evolved and to try to describe it here. In what follows I trace the development fairly closely, since in 'Faramir' there are bearings on other parts of *The Lord of the Rings* and much of special interest in Faramir's discourse on ancient history, most notably in his remarks on the languages of Gondor and the Common Speech (entirely lost in *The Two Towers*).

The various draft-sequences that constitute the history of the chapter are so confusing that I shall try to make my account clearer by using letters to distinguish them when it seems helpful. There was only one manuscript made, titled 'XXXVI. Faramir':[2] this is a good clear text, not extensively emended later, and in it the final form was achieved, with however certain important exceptions. It must have been from this text (referred to in this chapter as 'the completed manuscript', or simply 'the manuscript') that my father read 'Faramir' to Lewis and Williams on 8 May 1944. At this time the chapter began at ' "Sleep while you may," said Mablung': see p. 139 note 18.

The original draft for the end of what became 'Of Herbs and Stewed Rabbit', which I will call '**A**', continued on from Sam's 'If that's over I'll have a bit o' sleep' (TT p. 270) thus:

He turned and spoke in Frodo's ear. 'I could almost sleep on my legs, Mr Frodo,' he said. 'And you've not had much yourself. But these men are friends, it seems: they seem to come from Boromir's country all right. Though they don't quite trust us, I can't see any cause to doubt them. And we're done anyway if they turn nasty, so we'd best rest.'

FARAMIR

'Sleep if thou wilt,' said Mablung. 'We will guard thee and thy master until Falborn comes. Falborn will return hither, if he has saved his life. But when he cometh we must move swiftly. All this tumult will not go unmarked, and ere night is old we shall have many pursuers. We shall need all speed to gain the river first.'

It seemed to Sam only a few minutes before he woke and found that Falborn had returned and several men with him. They were talking nearby. Frodo was awake and among them. They were debating what to do about the hobbits.

Sam sat up and listened and he understood that Frodo had failed to satisfy the leader of the men of Gondor on some points: which part he had to play in the company sent from Rivendell, why they had left Boromir, and where he was now going. To the meaning of Isildur's Bane he kept on returning, but Frodo would not tell the story of the Ring.

'But the words said *with Isildur's Bane in hand*,' said Falborn.[3] 'If you are the Half-high then you should have that thing in hand, whatever it be. Have you it not? Or is it hidden because you choose to hide it?'

'Were Boromir here he would answer your questions,' said Frodo. 'And since Boromir was many days ago at Rauros on the way to your city, if you return swiftly you will learn the answer. My part in this company was known to him and to all and to the Lord Elrond indeed. The errand given to me brings me into this land, and it is not [?wise] that any enemy of the Dark Lord should hinder it.'

'I see there is more in this than I first perceived,' said Falborn. 'But I too am under command: to slay or take prisoner as [?reason justifies] all found in Ithilien. There is no cause to slay thee.'

Here this barely legible draft ends. At the end of it is written in pencil: *Death of Boromir known*. This is probably to be associated with the following notes written across the outline given on p. 135 (see note 11 to the last chapter):

Is Boromir known to be dead?
Only by a vision of the boat with a light about it floating down the river and a voice. And by some things of his drifting?
This is Feb. 6. Gandalf only arrives at sunset on Feb. 5 and the Rangers must have left Tirith long before that. Hardly time for messenger from Edoras to Minas Tirith (250 miles).

146

THE WAR OF THE RING

..... Jan. 31 morning to [Feb. 4 >] night Feb. 3. 3½ days.
Rangers must have left on night of Feb. 3rd.
NO.

On the date 6 February see pp. 140–2. 31 January was the day on which Gandalf came with Aragorn, Legolas and Gimli to Edoras and left with Théoden, riding west across the plains (see pp. 3–5). My father was evidently calculating that a man riding 70 miles a day could have brought the news of Boromir's death by word of mouth to Minas Tirith before Falborn and his men left the city to cross the river into Ithilien, but decided that this was not what had happened.

A new draft text ('B'), at the outset clearly written, was now begun, opening with Mablung's words 'Sleep, if thou wilt,'[4] and continuing as in the original draft A (p. 145): there is thus still no suggestion at this point that the hobbits will not be allowed to go on their way (see note 18 to the last chapter), and the leader of the men of Gondor is still Falborn. A was followed closely in this new text (which was a good deal emended subsequently) almost to its end,[5] but at the point where Frodo says 'But those who claim to oppose the Dark Lord would do well not to hinder it' the dialogue moves to the same point in TT (p. 272): 'Frodo spoke proudly, whatever he felt, and Sam very much approved of it; but it did not appease Falborn', and continues almost as in the final form, through the wary conversation about Boromir, as far as Frodo's 'though surely there are many perils in the world.' At Falborn's reply 'Many indeed, and treachery not the least' Sam does not in this text intervene, and Falborn continues: 'But thou askest how do we know that our captain is dead. We do not know it for a certainty, but yet we do not doubt it.' And he asks Frodo whether he remembers anything of special mark that Boromir bore with him among his gear, and Frodo fears a trap and reflects on his danger just as in TT (pp. 273–4). Then follows:

'I remember that he bore a horn,' he said at last.

'Thou rememberest well, as one who hath verily seen him,' said Falborn. 'Then maybe thou canst see it in thy mind's eye: a great horn of the wild ox of the [Eastern wilderness >] East, bound with silver, and written with his name, [struck out: worn upon a silver chain]. That horn the waters of Anduin brought unto us maybe [> more than] seven nights now gone. An ill token we thought it, and boding little joy to Denethor father of Boromir; for the horn was cloven in twain as by sword or axe. The halves of it came severally to shore ...'

Falborn's account of how the pieces of the horn were found now follows as in TT (p. 276),[6] ending 'But murder will out, 'tis said'; then he continues:

FARAMIR

147

'Dost thou not know of the cleaving of the horn, or who cast it over Rauros – to drown it for ever in the eddies of the fall, doubtless?'

'No,' said Frodo, 'I do not know. But none of our Company has the will for such a deed, and none the strength unless it were Aragorn. But though it may be a token of ill, a cloven horn does not prove the wearer's death.'

At this stage, therefore, Boromir's death was a supposition in Minas Tirith depending solely on the finding of the pieces of his horn in the river. But now there follows (and at this point my father's handwriting speeded up markedly and becomes very difficult, often a sign that a new conception had entered that would entail the rewriting and rejection of what had preceded, so that what follows slips back, as it were, into a more 'primitive' stage of composition):

'No. But the finding of the horn followed another and stranger thing,' said Falborn. 'And that sad chance befell me, and others beside [*changed to:* 'No,' said Falborn. 'But the finding of the horn followed another and stranger thing that befell me, and others beside]. I sat at night beside the waters of Anduin, just ere the first quarter of the moon, in the grey dark watching the ever moving stream and the sad reeds rustling. ...'

The account of the boat bearing the body of Boromir is for most of its length very close indeed to that in TT (p. 274), and it is here, most curiously, that Falborn becomes Boromir's brother, though he does not change his name: 'It was Boromir my brother, dead.' It is as if he slipped without conscious decision into the rôle that had been preparing for him. What else could he be, this captain of Gondor so concerned with Frodo's story and the fate of Boromir? Foreshortening the actual development, my father wrote in his letter of 6 May 1944 (*Letters* no. 66):

A new character has come on the scene (I am sure I did not invent him, I did not even want him, though I like him, but there he came walking into the woods of Ithilien): Faramir, the brother of Boromir ...

Falborn's story is different in its ending from the final form:

'... The boat turned into the stream and passed into the night. Others saw it, some near at hand, others from far off. But none dare touch it, nor maybe would even the evil hands of those that hold Osgiliath dare to hinder it.

148　　　THE WAR OF THE RING

'[?This] I thought was a vision though one of evil boding, and even when I heard the tale of others we doubted, Denethor my father and I, if it were more, though it boded evil. But none can doubt the horn. It lies now cloven in twain upon the lap of Denethor. And messengers ride far and wide to learn news of Boromir.'

'Alas,' said Frodo. 'For now I do not on my side doubt your tale. The golden belt was given him in Lórien by the Lady Galadriel. It was she who clothed us as you see us. This brooch is of the same workmanship' – he touched the [?enamelled] leaf that caught his cloak about his neck. Falborn looked at it curiously. 'Yes,' he said, 'it is work of the same [?manner].'

'Yet even so,' said Frodo, 'I think it can have been but a vision that you saw. How could a boat have ridden the falls of Rauros and the [?boiling] floods, and naught have been spilled but the horn, and founder not with its burden of water?'

'I know not,' said Falborn, 'but whence came the boat?'

'From Lórien, it was an elven-boat,' said Frodo.

'Well,' said Falborn, 'if thou wilt have dealings with the mistress of magic that ....eth [added: dwells] in the Golden Wood then they [sic] must look for strange things and evil things to follow.'

This was too much for Sam's patience. He stood up and walked into the debate. 'Not evil from Lórien,' he said. 'Begging your pardon, Mr Frodo,' he said, 'but I have been listening to a deal of this talk. Let's come to the point before all the Orcs of Mordor come down on us. Now look here, Falborn of Gondor if that is your name' – the men looked in amazement (not in merriment) at the small ... hobbit planted firmly on his feet before the seated figure of the captain. 'What are you getting at? If you think we murdered your brother and then ran away, say so. And say what you mean to do about it.'

'I was in mind to say so,' answered Falborn. 'Were I as hasty as thou I would have slain thee long ago. But we have taken but a few minutes in speech to learn what sort ye be. I am about to depart at once. Ye will come with me. And in that count yourselves fortunate!'

Here this second draft B ends,[7] and my father now proceeded to a third version ('C'), beginning at the same point as did draft B (p. 146) with Mablung's words 'Sleep, if you will', and extending no further into the chapter, but C is written on odd bits of paper, much of it very roughly, is not continuous, and contains some sections of the narrative

FARAMIR

149

in divergent forms. It seems clear therefore that these pages accompanied the commencement of the completed manuscript.

This third drafting C, in which *Falborn* has become *Faramir*,[8] largely retains the structure of B, while at the same time moving in detail of expression a good way towards the form of the opening dialogue between Faramir and Frodo in TT (pp. 271–6). There were various intricate shiftings and displacements and new conjunctions within the matter of this dialogue before my father was satisfied with its structure, and these I largely pass over. The essential differences from the final form are that Sam's indignation does not explode at Faramir's words 'and treachery not the least', but as in the second draft B at his disparaging remark about Lórien; and that Faramir's tale of how he heard far off, 'as if it were but an echo in the mind', the blowing of Boromir's horn had not entered.

There are a number of particular points to notice. At the beginning of his interrogation of Frodo ('which now looked unpleasantly like the trial of a prisoner') Faramir no longer cites the words of the verse as *with Isildur's Bane in hand* (see p. 145 and note 3), but as *Isildur's Bane upholding*,[9] and continues – in the completed manuscript as well as the draft – 'If you be the Halfling that was named, then doubtless you held it before the eyes of all the Council of which you speak, and Boromir saw it.' In TT (p. 271), when the concluding words of the verse were *For Isildur's Bane shall waken, / And the Halfling forth shall stand*, Faramir says: 'But it was at the coming of the Halfling that Isildur's Bane should waken ... If then you are the Halfling that was named, doubtless you brought this thing, whatever it may be, to the Council of which you speak, and there Boromir saw it.'

When Frodo says that if any could claim Isildur's Bane it would be Aragorn, Faramir replies, both in the draft and in the manuscript: 'Why so, and not Boromir, prince of the city that Elendil and his sons founded?', where in TT (p. 271) he speaks of 'the sons of Elendil' as the founders. The story that Elendil remained in the North and there founded his realm, while his sons Isildur and Anárion founded the cities of the South, appears in the fifth version of the 'Council of Elrond' (VII.144); and this may suggest that that version of 'The Council of Elrond' was written later than I have supposed.

As already mentioned, the sound of Boromir's horn blowing far off was not yet present in this third drafting C; and Faramir still relates the finding of the pieces of the horn before he tells of the funeral boat passing down Anduin. In answer to Frodo's objection that 'a cloven horn does not prove the wearer's death' (p. 147) there now follows: ' "No," said Faramir. "But the finding of the shards of the horn followed another and stranger thing that befell me, as if it were sent to confirm it beyond hope." ' Thus the words '(that befell me) and others beside' in B are omitted; but in this tale of the boat that bore Boromir's corpse Faramir still declares that he was not the only one to see it:

150　　　THE WAR OF THE RING

'Others too saw it, a grey shadow of a vessel from afar.' In yet another revision of this passage before the final form was reached he ends: 'A vision out of the borders of dream I thought it. But I do not doubt that Boromir is dead, whether his body of a truth has passed down the River to the Sea, or lies now somewhere under the heedless skies.'

The remote sound of Boromir's horn blowing only entered in the manuscript, and Faramir there says that he heard it 'eight days ere I set out on this venture, eleven days ago at about this hour of the day', where TT (p. 274) has the same, but with 'five' for 'eight'.[10] As my father wrote this passage in the manuscript he went on, after 'as it might be only an echo in the mind': 'And others heard it, for we have many men that wander far upon our borders, south and west and north, even to the fields of Rohan.' This was apparently struck out immediately.

To Sam's indignant and courageous confrontation of this great man from Minas Tirith Faramir's response in this draft was gentle:

'... Say what you think, and say what you mean to do.'

'I was about to do so,' said Faramir smiling, and now less stern. 'Were I as hasty as you I might have slain you long ago. I have spared the short part of [?an hour] in spite of peril to judge you more justly. [?Now] if you wish to learn what I think: I doubted you, naturally, as I should. But if I am a judge of the words and deeds of men I may perhaps make a guess at hobbits. I doubted but you were friends or allies of the orcs, and though the likes of you could not have slain my brother, you might have helped or fled with some picking.'

Here this third phase of drafting (C) ends.[11] — It is curious that in the completed manuscript Sam's intervention has entirely disappeared: the dialogue between Faramir and Frodo in the passage where it originally took place now reaches the form in TT (p. 275) and Faramir no longer expresses so conventional a view of the Lady of the Golden Wood (cf. p. 148).

It is plain, I think, that at this point, at Frodo's words 'Go back Faramir, valiant captain, and defend your city while you may, and let me go alone where my doom takes me', the writing of the manuscript was halted, and that at that time nothing further had been written: in other words, this chapter, in terms of composition, falls into two parts, all up to this point (apart from the absence of Sam's outburst) having been brought virtually to the final form before the story proceeded.

Very rough and here and there altogether illegible outline sketches show my father's preliminary thoughts for its continuation. One of these, impossibly difficult to read, begins at the point where the draft C ends, with Faramir still speaking to Sam: 'But you have not the

FARAMIR   151

manners of orcs, nor their speech, and indeed Frodo your master has an air that I cannot ..., an elvish air maybe.' In this text Faramir shows no hesitation about his course and does not postpone his decision, but concludes sternly: 'You shall be well treated. But make no doubt of it. Until my father Denethor releases you, you are prisoners of Gondor. Do not try to escape, if you do not wish to be slain' (cf. the passage given in note 7). Then follows:

> In a few minutes they were on their way again down the slopes. Hobbits [?tired]. Mablung carries Sam. They get to the fenced camp in a dense wood of trees, 10 miles away. They had not gone far before Sam suddenly said to Frodo: 'Gollum! Well thank heavens we've lost him!' But Frodo not so sure. 'We have still to get into Mordor,' he said, 'and we do not know the way.' Gollum rescues them

The last three words are very unclear, but I have no doubt that this is what they are – though what story lay behind them will never be known.

Another short text reads as follows:

> Faramir says he no longer doubts. If he is any judge of men. But he says that much [more] lies upon it than at first he thought. 'I should' he said 'take you back to Minas Tirith, and if things went ill my life would be forfeit. But I will not decide yet. Yet we must move at once.' He gave some orders and the men broke up into small groups and faded away into the trees. Mablung and Damrod remained. 'Now you will come with me,' he said. 'You cannot go along the road if you meant to. And you cannot go far for you are weary. So are we. We go to a secret camp 10 miles away. Come with us. Before morn we will decide.'
>
> They .... Faramir spoke. 'You do not deal openly. You were not friendly with Boromir. I see S.G. thinks ill of him. Now I loved him, yet I knew him well. Isildur's Bane. I say that this lay between you in some way. Heirlooms do not breed peace among companions. Ancient tales.'
>
> 'And ancient tales teach us not to blab,' said Frodo.
>
> 'But you must know that much is known in Minas Tirith that is not spoken aloud. Therefore I dismissed my men. Gandalf was here. We the rulers know that I[sildur] carried off the Ruling Ring. Now this is a terrible matter. I can well guess that Boromir, proud, ever anxious for the glory of Minas Tirith (and his own renown) might wish to seize it. I guess that you have the Ring, though how it could ...

152   THE WAR OF THE RING

The rest of the sentence is illegible. The brief sketch ends with Faramir's words 'I would not touch it if it lay by the highway' and his expression of his love for and desires for Minas Tirith (TT p. 280); the last words are 'I could advise you if you would tell me more.' It is a pity that the passage about the Ring is so brief and elliptical; but the implication must surely be that the rulers of the city knew that Isildur carried off the Ruling Ring because Gandalf had told them. This, of course, was not at all the way in which the story would unfold when it came to be written down.

Another page of even more hasty and staccato sketching takes up from the point reached in the first, and may be its continuation (cf. TT p. 280, where Faramir's words 'it may be that I can advise you ... and even aid you' are followed by 'Frodo made no answer').

Frodo does not say more. Something holds him back. Wisdom? Memory of Boromir? Fear of the power and treachery of what he carried – in spite of liking Faramir. They speak of other things. Reasons of decline of Gondor. Rohan (alter Boromir's words saying he did not go there).[12] Gondor gets like Rohan, loving war as game: so Boromir. Sam says little. Delighted that Gollum seems forgotten. Faramir falls silent. Sam speaks of elvish power, boats, ropes, cloaks. Suddenly aware that Gollum is padding behind. But when they halt he sheers off.

Faramir in accord with law makes them be blindfold as they reach secret stronghold. They talk. Faramir warns him, warns against Gollum. Frodo reveals that he has to go to Mordor. Speaks of Minas Ithil. Moonrise. Faramir bids farewell in morning. Frodo promises to come back to Minas Tirith and surrender to him if he returns.

At this stage, before the chapter proceeded further, Sam's intervention in the initial interrogation of Frodo by Faramir was reintroduced, at an earlier place in the dialogue (at 'and treachery not the least'), and inserted into the manuscript on a rider.[13]

The latter part of the chapter is extant in continuous and for the most part clearly written drafting, with a good deal of my father's characteristic 'over-lapping' – when the narrative takes a wrong direction or is in some respect unsatisfactory, collapses into a scrawl, and is replaced by a new page beginning at an earlier point (thus producing sections of near repetition). This drafting led to the finished manuscript, in which there were still important differences from the text in *The Two Towers*: it will be seen that at this time there was much development still to come in the past history of Rohan and Gondor.

FARAMIR   153

The new draft ('D') begins (as also does the recommencement of the manuscript, closely based on D) ' "I do not doubt you any more," said Faramir.'[14] The narrative from this point (TT p. 276), as far as Sam's glimpse of Gollum as they walked through the woodland (TT p. 281), already in the draft very largely achieved the final text; but there are some interesting differences.[15]

It is here that the Stewards of Gondor first appear, and the passage concerning them (TT p. 278) was written in the draft text virtually without hesitation or correction, although there is no preliminary material extant. It is notable that from his first appearance in 'The Breaking of the Fellowship' (VII.375–6) Denethor has never been called King: he is the Lord Denethor, Denethor Lord of the Tower of Guard. It seems more than likely, therefore, that this cardinal element in the history and government of Gondor was already of long standing, though never until now emerging into the narrative. The line of Denethor is traced in the draft to *Máraher* the good steward, changed probably at once to *Mardil* (the name in the manuscript); but the last king of the line of Anárion, in whose stead Mardil ruled when he went away to war, was not Eärnur. Both in draft and manuscript he is named *King Elessar*.

Gandalf's recital of his names, as reported by Faramir (who calls him in the draft 'the Grey Wanderer': 'the Grey Pilgrim' in the manuscript), was intricately changed in its initial composition, but apparently developed thus:

[*Added:* Mithrandir among the Elves. Sharkûn to the Dwarves.]
[The name of my youth in the West is forgotten >] [Olórion >]
Olórin I was in my youth that is forgotten; [*struck out:* Shorab *or* Shorob in the East,] [Forlong >] Fornold in the South, Gandalf in the North. To the East I go not. [*Struck out:* Not everywhere]

The passage was then written out again in the draft, in the same form as it has in TT, but with the names *Sharkûn* and *Fornold*, this latter being subsequently changed to *Incânus*. In the manuscript *Sharkûn* (for later *Tharkûn*) remains. — Here the name *Olórin* first appears, changed from *Olórion*. On Gandalf's names 'in the South', *Forlong* changed to *Fornold*, I can cast no light; I do not know whether it is relevant that in Appendix F to LR the name of Forlong, Lord of Lossarnach (who died in the Battle of the Pelennor Fields), is said to be among the names in Gondor that 'were of forgotten origin, and descended doubtless from days before the ships of the Númenoreans sailed the Sea.'

Faramir's words about Gandalf's eagerness for stories of Isildur were much changed: 'he was eager for stories of Isildur, though of him we had less to tell, [for Isildur was of the North in Fornost, and the realm of Gondor held from Anárion. > for to Gondor no sure tale

154   THE WAR OF THE RING

had ever come concerning his end, only rumour that he perished in the River being shot by orc-arrows. >] for nought was ever known for certain of his end.' For the first occurrence of the name *Fornost* in the texts, replacing *Fornobel*, see p. 76.

A last point here is that (both in draft and manuscript) Faramir says: 'Isildur took somewhat from the hand of the Unnamed, ere he went away from the battle', where in TT (p. 279) he says 'went away from Gondor'. Cf. 'The Council of Elrond' in FR (p. 265), where Gandalf says: 'For Isildur did not march away straight from the war in Mordor, as some have told the tale', and Boromir interrupts: 'Some in the North, maybe. All know in Gondor that he went first to Minas Anor and dwelt a while with his nephew Meneldil, instructing him, before he committed to him the rule of the South Kingdom.' Cf. also the beginning of 'The Disaster of the Gladden Fields' in *Unfinished Tales*.

At the point where Sam, listening to but not entering the conversation, and observing that Gollum was never mentioned, sees him slipping behind a tree, the draft text (which, since it was soon replaced by another, I will call 'D 1') continues thus:

He opened his mouth to speak, but did not. He could not be sure, and 'why should I mention the old villain anyway, until I'm obliged,' he thought.

After a while Frodo and Faramir began to speak again, for Frodo was eager to learn news of Gondor and its folk and of the lands about them, and what hope they had in their long war.

'It is long since we had any hope,' said Faramir.

These last words appear much later in TT (p. 286). Thus the entire story in TT pp. 281–6 is lacking at this stage: the blindfolding, the coming to Henneth Annûn, the account of the cave, the report of Anborn about the 'black squirrel' in the woods, the evening meal, and Frodo's stories of their journey (although the fact that Frodo and Sam would be blindfolded before they came to the 'secret stronghold' was known to my father: see the outline on p. 152). All this is found in the completed manuscript in virtually the final form.

Faramir's account of the history of Gondor and the coming of the Horsemasters (TT pp. 286–7) was developed in two stages before it was written in the manuscript. Already in the first version (D 1) Faramir speaks very much as in TT of the evils and follies of the Númenóreans in the Great Lands,[16] and of their obsession with death. But after 'Childless lords sat musing in hollow halls, or in high cold towers asked questions of the stars' he continues:

'... But we were more fortunate than other cities, recruiting our strength from the sturdy folk of the sea-coasts, and the

FARAMIR

155

hardy people of the White Mountains[17] — where lingered once many remnants of races long forgot. And then there came the men out of the North, the [Horse-marshals >] Rohir. And we ceded them the fields of [Rohan >] Elenarda [*written above:* Kalen(arda)] that are since called Rohan,[18] for we could not resist their rude strength, and they became our allies and have ever proved true, and they learn of our lore and speak our speech. Yet they hold by their old ways and their own speech among themselves. And we love them for they remind us of the youth of men as they were in the old tales of the wars of the Elves in Beleriand. Indeed I think that in [?that] way we are remotely akin, and that they are come of that old stock, the first to come out of the East from which the Fathers of the Fathers of Men were come, Beren and Barahir and Huor and Húrin and Tuor and Túrin, aye and Earendel himself the half-elven, first king of Westernesse. So does some kinship in tongue and heart still tell. But they never crossed the Sea or went into the West and so must ever remain [?alien]. Yet we intermarry, and if they have become somewhat like us and cannot be called wild men, we have become like them and are no longer Númenóreans. For now we love war and valour as things good in themselves, and esteem warriors above all others. Such is the need of our days. ...'

In this notable passage are adumbrated new elements of ancient history that were no doubt long preparing before they appeared in any narrative text, though Eorl the Young had entered in 'The King of the Golden Hall', riding out of the North to 'the Battle of the Field of Gorgoroth' in which Sauron was overthrown (see VII.444 and note 11). That 'between Rohan and Ondor there was great friendship' appeared in the initial draft of 'The Riders of Rohan' (VII.393), and in the outline 'The Story Foreseen from Fangorn' (VII.437), after 'News comes ... of the siege of Minas Tirith by the Haradwaith', was added: 'Théoden answers that he does not owe fealty — only to heirs of Elendil.'

The mention of Earendel as the 'first king of Westernesse' is strange indeed, but I think probably not significant, a passing inadvertence: see further p. 158 and note 26.

This draft D 1 continues on for some way, written fast, and I will return to it; but it is convenient now to turn to the draft that replaced it ('D 2'), and which takes up with Sam's decision to say nothing about Gollum:

'... why should I remind them of the old villain, if they choose to forget him? I wish I could.'

156   THE WAR OF THE RING

After a while Frodo and Faramir began to talk again, and Frodo asked many questions concerning Gondor and its people and the lands about them, and what hope they had in their long war. He was interested in such matters, but also he wished to discover, if he could, how much Faramir knew of old lore, and how he knew it. He remembered now that at the Council Boromir had shown much knowledge of these things [*struck out:* naming the number of the rings of].

The last part of this was changed to read:

He was interested in such matters, but also he thought of Bilbo. 'He'll want accounts of all these things,' he thought. 'It is long since I made any note in my diary: tonight perhaps, as we rest.' Then he smiled at himself: 'But he lives in the House of Elrond and can have more for the asking than all that is remembered in Gondor! O but well, he'll like it best from a hobbit, personal recollections. He will, if ever I see him again, alas!'

All this was struck from the page subsequently, when the later structure of the narrative was imposed; but the text as written continues (cf. p. 154): '"What hope have we?" said Faramir. "It is long since we had any hope. ...", and then proceeds to develop Faramir's discussion of Gondor and Rohan to a form much closer to that in *The Two Towers*, though still with important differences.

Where in the first version D 1 (p. 154) he said: 'But we were more fortunate than other cities, recruiting our strength from the sturdy folk of the sea-coasts, and the hardy people of the White Mountains', he now says: 'But we were wiser and more fortunate than some; wiser, for we recruited the strength of our people from the sturdy folk of the sea-coasts and the hardy mountaineers of Hebel Nimrath;[19] more fortunate in our foes that became our friends.'[20] Faramir still gives no indication of when the Horsemen came out of the North: 'For on a time there came men out of the North and assailed our borders, men of fierce valour, but not servants of the Dark Lord, not the wild hordes of the East, or the cruel hosts of the South. Out of the North came the Rohiroth,[21] the Eorlingas, and at the last we ceded to them the fields of Kalinarda[22] that are since called Rohan; for long these had been sparsely peopled, and we could not resist the strength of these golden-haired horsemen. And they became our vassals or indeed our allies ...' He continues very much as in TT (p. 287). In the completed manuscript Faramir gives this indication of the date of their coming: 'On a time in the days of Mardil's son there came men out of the North ...' But of course this conveys very little.

Of the origin of the Rohiroth this draft D 2 gives the following

FARAMIR   157

version. The passage was heavily emended, and I show the significant alterations:

'... Indeed, it is said by the loremasters among us that they are somewhat our kin in blood and in speech, being descended [from those of the Three Houses of Men who went not over sea into the West >] from those same Three Houses of Men as were the Númenóreans, from Beor and Hador and Haleth, but from such as went not over sea into the West at the calling of the Powers. Thus they have to us a kinship, [such as the Exiled Elves that linger still in the West (of such indeed is the Lady of the Golden Wood) and returned not to Elvenhome have to those who departed. But they have never returned. >] such as the High Elves that do here and there abide still in the West of these lands have to those who lingered and went never to Elvenhome. Such is the kinship of the Lady of the Golden Wood to the folk she rules.[23] And so, as the Elves are divided into three: the High Elves, and the Middle Elves, [the Lingerers the Elves of the Woods >] their kindred that lingered on the shores, and the Wild Elves [the Refusers >] of the woods and mountains, so we divide Men, calling them the High or the Men of [Light >] the West, which are the Númenóreans, and the Middle or the Men of Shadow, such as the Rohiroth and other of their kindred in Dale and Mirkwood, and the Wild Men, or the Men of the Darkness. And of the truth of this their likeness of tongue and heart still speaks. Nonetheless those of Númenor passed over the Sea indeed, even if they after forfeited their kingdom and returned, and so they became a people apart and should remain so. Yet if the Rohir became in some ways more like to us, enhanced in art and gentleness, we too have become more like to them, and do not now rightly claim the title High. We are become Middle Men, of the Shadow, but with memory of other things. ...'

This was very largely retained, as emended, in the manuscript, but with these chief differences: 'they are come from those same Three Houses of Men as were the Númenóreans, from Hador the Golden-haired, the Elf-friend maybe, but from such of their sons as went not over the Sea into the West, refusing the call';[24] there is no mention of the Lady of the Golden Wood; and 'the Middle People or the Men of the Shadows, such as the Rohiroth and others of their kindred in Dale and the upper waters of Anduin'.

The threefold division of the Elves here (lost in *The Two Towers*) is that introduced into the *Quenta Silmarillion* after the return of the

158 THE WAR OF THE RING

manuscript from the publishers at the end of 1937 (see *The Lost Road* pp. 200, 219): the Elves of Valinor; the *Lembi* or Lingerers; and the *Avari*, the Unwilling.

The draft D 1, left on p. 155, continues through Faramir's reply to Sam's remark about the Elves, and this is of great interest. Though a good deal was retained in TT (pp. 287–8) I give it here in full. At the end the writing becomes very fast and the draft ends in scrawled notes. Passages in square brackets are thus bracketed in the original.

'You don't say much in all your tales about the Elves, sir,' said Sam, suddenly plucking up courage: he was rather in awe of Faramir since his encounter on his master's behalf.

'No, Master Samwise,' said Faramir, 'and there you touch upon another point in which we have changed, becoming more as other men. For (as you may know, if Mithrandir was your guest; and you have spoken with Elrond) the Númenóreans were elf-friends, and came of those men who aided the Gnomes in the first wars, and were rewarded by the gift of the kingdom in the midst of the Sea, within sight of Elvenhome whither the High Elves withdrew [*written above:* where the High Elves dwelt]. But in the Great Lands[25] men and elves were estranged, by the arts of the Enemy [who had suborned most men (save only the Fathers of the Númenóreans) to his service] and by the slow changes of time in which each kind walked further down their sundered roads. Men fear and misdoubt the Elves, distinguishing not between the High-elves (that here and there remain) and those that like themselves never went over the Sea. And Elves mistrust men, who so often have served the Enemy. And we grow like other men, like the men even of Rohan who see them not if they pass (or persuade themselves that they do not see), and who speak of the Golden Wood in dread. Yet there are Elf-friends among us in Gondor still, more than among any other people; for though the blood of Númenor is now run thin in Gondor, still it flows there, indeed even Elvish blood maybe: for our kings of old were half-elven, even our first king Elros son of Earendel and brother of Elrond.[26] And 'tis said that Elendil's house was a younger branch of Elros. Some there are of Gondor who have dealings with the Elves, some even still fare to the Golden Wood (though often they return not). One great advantage we have: we speak an elvish speech, or one so near akin that we can in part understand them and they us.'

'But you speak the ordinary language,' exclaimed Sam. 'Like us, or a bit old-fashioned like, if you'll pardon me saying so.'

FARAMIR

159

'Yes,' said Faramir, 'we do, for that is our language. The Common Tongue, as some call it, is derived from the Númenórean, being a changed form of that speech of men which the fathers used, Beren and Túrin and Earendel and those others. [Hence its remote kinship with the tongues of Rohan and of Dale and of Westfold and Dunland and other places.] This language it is that has spread through the western world among all that are of good will, and among others also. But the lords of Númenor spoke the Gnomish tongue of the Noldor to whom they were allied, and that tongue, changed somewhat and mingled, still lives among us, though we do not commonly speak it. So it is that our earliest names were in the High Elvish Quendian, such as Elendil, Isildur, and the rest, but the names we have given to places, and still give to women and men, are of Elvish sort. Often we give them out of the old tales: so is Denethor, and Mablung, and many others.'

Here the draft D 1 peters out, and I return to D 2, left on p. 157, at the same point ('You don't say much in all your tales about the Elves, sir'). In his reply to Sam Faramir here says of the Elf-friends of the ancient wars of Beleriand that they 'were rewarded (such as would take it) by the gift of the Kingdom in the midst of the Sea, within sight of Elvenhome, which they had leave to visit.'[27] And he continues: 'But in the Great Lands Men and Elves were estranged in the days of Darkness ...' He no longer speaks of the men of Rohan being unable to see the Elves, or pretending to themselves that they do not see them if they do, but as in TT says only that they shun them; and he declares, again as in TT, that he would not himself go to Lothlórien, judging it 'perilous now for mortal men, at least to seek the Elder People wilfully.' But his answer to Sam's 'But you speak the ordinary language! Same as us, though a bit old-fashioned like' was substantially changed:

'Of course we do,' said Faramir. 'For that is our own tongue which we perhaps preserve better than you do far in the North. The Common Tongue, as some call it, is derived from the Númenóreans,[28] being but a form changed by time of that speech which the Fathers of the Three Houses [struck out: Hador and Haleth and Beor] spoke of old. This language it is that has spread through the western world amongst all folk and creatures that use words, to some only a second tongue for use in intercourse with strangers, to some the only tongue they know. But this is not an Elvish speech in my meaning. All speech of men in this world is Elvish in descent; but only if one go back

160   THE WAR OF THE RING

to the beginnings. What I meant was so: [the lords >] many men of the Three Houses long ago gave up man-speech and spoke the tongue of their friends the Noldor or Gnomes:[29] a high-elvish tongue [*struck out:* akin to but changed from the Ancient Elvish of Elvenhome]. And always the lords of Númenor knew that tongue and used it among themselves. And so still do we among ourselves, those who have the blood of Númenor still in our veins, though mayhap we have changed it somewhat mingling it like our blood with other strains. Thus it is that all our names of town and field, hill and river are in that tongue, and the names of our women and of our men. [*Struck out:* Only in the oldest days did we use the High Ancient Elven for such purposes: of that sort are Elendil and Isildur.] Indeed many of these we still take from tales of the old days: such are Mablung and Damrod, and mine own,[30] and my father's Denethor, and many others.'

'Well sir, I am glad you don't think ill of Elves at any rate,' said Sam. 'Wonderful folk, I think, sir. And the Lady of Lórien, Galadriel, you should see her, indeed you should, sir. I am only a hobbit, if you understand me, and gardening's my job at home ...'

This draft D 2 continues on through Sam's speech (essentially as in TT p. 288), his blurting out that Boromir always sought the Ring, and Faramir's response; but now in its turn it becomes quickly rougher and less formed (for its continuation beyond this point see p. 163) and was replaced by new drafting ('D 3') beginning at 'Indeed many of these we still take from tales of the ancient days ...'

In the text of the completed manuscript the draft D 2 just given was repeated with scarcely any change until towards the end. Faramir now says of the Elvish tongue spoken by the lords of Gondor that 'we can in part understand Elves [*struck out:* and they us] even when they speak to one another secretly', but all that he says in D 2 of the Common Tongue is repeated exactly as far as: 'All speech of men in this world is Elvish in descent; but only if one goes back to the beginnings.' The following sentence in D 2 ('What I meant was so: many men of the Three Houses long ago gave up man-speech and spoke the tongue of their friends the Noldor or Gnomes') was at first taken up in the manuscript, but struck out in the act of writing and replaced by the following (thus eliminating the reference to the abandonment of their own speech by the men of the Three Houses, see note 29):

'... What I meant was so: many men of the Three Houses long ago learned the High-elven tongues, as they were spoken

FARAMIR

161

[in Beleriand >] in Gondolin or by the Sons of Fëanor. And always the Lords of Númenor knew these tongues, and used the Gnomish speech among themselves. And so still do we, the rulers of Minas Tirith, in whom the blood of Númenor still flows ...'[31]

And Faramir, giving examples of names taken 'from tales of the Elder Days', adds Díriel to those he gave before.

Among occasional previous references to the Common Speech only once is its nature defined, and there in a wholly different way. This is in an early draft for a passage in the chapter 'Lothlórien' (VII.239 note 26), where it is said that Frodo did not understand the speech of the Elves of Lórien 'for the language was the old tongue of the woods and not that of the western elves which was in those days used as a common speech among many folk.'

With the present passage, in its various forms, concerning the Common Speech and the knowledge of the High-elven tongue of the Noldor among the lords of Gondor may be compared what is said in Appendix F to *The Lord of the Rings*:

The *Westron* was a Mannish speech, though enriched and softened under Elvish influence. It was in origin the language of those whom the Eldar called the *Atani* or *Edain*, 'Fathers of Men', being especially the people of the Three Houses of the Elf-friends who came west into Beleriand in the First Age, and aided the Eldar in the War of the Great Jewels against the Dark Power of the North. ...

The *Dúnedain* alone of all races of Men knew and spoke an Elvish tongue; for their forefathers had learned the Sindarin tongue, and this they handed on to their children as a matter of lore, changing little with the passing of the years. And their men of wisdom learned also the High-elven Quenya and esteemed it above all other tongues, and in it they made names for many places of fame and reverence, and for many men of royalty and great renown.

But the native speech of the Númenoreans remained for the most part their ancestral Mannish tongue, the Adûnaic, and to this in the latter days of their pride their kings and lords returned, abandoning the Elven-speech, save only those few that held still to their ancient friendship with the Eldar.

There follows an account of the spread of Adûnaic along the coasts before the Fall of Númenor, becoming a Common Speech in those regions, and of the use of it by the Elf-friends who survived the Downfall 'in their dealing with other folk and in the government of their wide realms', enriching it with many Elvish words.

In the days of the Númenorean kings this ennobled Westron speech spread far and wide, even among their enemies; and it

162 THE WAR OF THE RING

became used more and more by the Dúnedain themselves, so that at the time of the War of the Ring the Elven-tongue was known to only a small part of the peoples of Gondor, and spoken daily by fewer.

This much more complex conception seems nonetheless not radically different as regards the nature and origin of the Common Speech from that which Faramir presents here: for in both accounts, early and late, the Common Speech was directly descended from the ancestral tongue of the 'Fathers of Men'. It is thus curious to see that by later pencilled correction to the manuscript this was changed, Faramir now saying:

'Of course we do ... For that is also our own tongue, which we ourselves made, and here preserve better perhaps than do you far in the North. The Common Tongue, as some call it, is derived from the Númenóreans; for the Númenóreans coming to the shores of these lands took the rude tongue of the men that they here found and whom they ruled, and they enriched it, and it spread hence through the Western world ...'

And at the end of Faramir's discourse on linguistic history, after his examples of Gnomish names in Gondor, he now adds: 'But in intercourse with other folk we use the Common Speech which we made for that purpose.'

Here the idea that the Common Speech was derived from 'that speech which the Fathers of the Three Houses spoke of old' is denied.

In his letter of 6 May 1944 my father continued from the passage cited on p. 147:

(A new character has come on the scene ... Faramir, the brother of Boromir) – and he is holding up the 'catastrophe' by a lot of stuff about the history of Gondor and Rohan (with some very sound reflections no doubt on martial glory and true glory): but if he goes on much more a lot of him will have to be removed to the appendices – where already some fascinating material on the hobbit Tobacco industry[32] and the Languages of the West have gone.

The passage on linguistic history in the present chapter (with the emendations just given concerning the nature of the Common Speech) survived into subsequent typescripts, and was only removed at a later time; thus the excluded material on 'the Languages of the West' to which my father referred in this letter was not the account given by Faramir.

As already remarked (p. 160), a new 'overlapping' draft D 3 takes up at the end of Faramir's exposition, and in this Sam shows himself as more impressed by what he has been told than in the previous version, and has more to say about Elves before he gets on to the subject of Galadriel. This passage was retained and slightly extended in the

FARAMIR

163

manuscript (in which form I cite it here), and it survived in the following typescripts until it was removed from the chapter together with the account of languages that preceded it.

Sam looked at Faramir wide-eyed and almost with awe. To have an elvish name, and even a possible claim to Elvish blood however remote, seemed to him royalty indeed. 'Well Captain, your lordship, I should say, it is good to hear you speak so fair of Elves, sir. I wish I had an elvish name. Wonderful folk they are, aren't they? Think of the things they can make and the things they say! You don't find out their worth or their meaning all at once, as it were: it comes out afterwards, unexpected like. Just a bit of well-made rope in a boat, and there it is: one day it's just what you want, and it unknots itself when you ask it and jumps to your hand. And the boat: I agree with your lordship; I think it rode the falls and took no harm. Of course it would, if that was needed. It was an Elven-boat, sir; though I sat in one for many a day, and never noticed nothing special.'[33]

'I think you are right, Master Samwise,' said Faramir smiling; 'though some would say the White Lady had enchanted you.'

'And she did, sir!' said Sam. 'The Lady of Lórien! Galadriel! you should see her, indeed you should, sir. I am only a hobbit, and gardening's my job at home ...'[34]

I have mentioned (p. 160) that the Draft D 2, now become very ragged, continued on through Sam's description to Faramir of Galadriel, and his blurting out the truth, so long and so carefully concealed by Frodo, that 'Boromir wanted the Ring!'[35] In this draft, where in TT 'Frodo and Sam sprang from their stools and set themselves side by side with their backs to the wall, fumbling for their sword-hilts', and 'all the men in the cave stopped talking', all that is said is: 'Frodo and Sam sprang side by side, fumbling for their swords.' Faramir sat down and began to laugh, and then became suddenly grave. It is clear that he sat on the ground, where they were, in the woods. The last words of this draft before it was abandoned, barely legible, are:

'Do not fear. I do not wish to see or touch it – my only fear is lest I see it and be tempted. But now indeed it becomes my duty to aid you with all that I have. If this is the counsel of Mithrandir, that this [?dreadful] Thing should be sent [?a-wandering] in the borders of Mordor in the keeping of two hobbits, then he is desperate indeed and at his wits' end. Come, let us get to cover as quick as we may.'

164   THE WAR OF THE RING

It has been seen (pp. 154, 163) that in the drafting (D 1–2) for the latter part of this chapter the entire story of the coming to Henneth Annûn was absent, and the entire conversation that in TT took place there after the evening meal here took place as they walked through the woods. When we come to the third overlapping portion of the draft (D 3), however, at the dénouement, the revelation of the Ring, they are in the cave, and all is as in TT. It is clear therefore that it was only when he had come to the very end of the chapter that my father realised that the long conversation with Faramir had been interrupted by their coming to the refuge; and perhaps it was only now that he perceived what that refuge was: the Window of the Sunset, Henneth Annûn. Drafting for the new passage (TT pp. 281–6, from 'So they passed on, until the woodlands grew thinner ...') is found separately, with very little significant divergence from the finished form. There is no mention of Anborn and the sighting of Gollum in the woods at dusk: this first appears in the completed manuscript;[36] and Faramir says to Frodo and Sam before the meal: 'Do as we do, I pray. So do we always, look towards Númenor that was, and to Elvenhome beyond, and to that which is beyond Elvenhome, Valinor the Blessed Realm.'[37]

On the page of this drafting where appear Faramir's words 'This is the Window of the West' (changed to 'Window of the Sunset') my father wrote many names and forms before achieving *Henneth Annûn: Nargalad, Anngalad, Carangalad; Henneth Carandûn, Henneth Malthen; Henlo Naur, Henlo n'Annun; Henuil n'Annun.*

NOTES

1 The 'new chapters' were: (1) 'The Taming of Smeagol'; (2) 'The Passage of the Marshes'; (3) 'The Black Gate is Closed' (including 'Of Herbs and Stewed Rabbit'); (4) 'Faramir'. See note 2.

2 Since 'The Taming of Smeagol' was Chapter XXXII, 'The Passage of the Marshes' XXXIII, and 'The Black Gate is Closed' XXXIV, 'Faramir', the 'fourth new chapter', should be XXXV. Its actual number XXXVI implies that 'Of Herbs and Stewed Rabbit' had already been separated off as XXXV – but then of couse 'Faramir' became the fifth new chapter. Perhaps the actual number XXXVI was written in subsequently. See further p. 171.

3 This refers to the form of the 'dream-verse of Minas Tirith' in which the second half ran thus (see VII.146):
> *This sign shall there be then*
> *that Doom is near at hand:*
> *The Halfhigh shall you see then*
> *with Isildur's bane in hand.*

4 Throughout this draft Falborn addresses Frodo as 'thou', but this usage was emended throughout and does not appear in the following text.

FARAMIR

165

5   The men of Gondor were in this draft B 'sitting in a ring, in the middle of which were Falborn and Frodo. It seemed that there was a debate going on.' – Frodo refers to 'Elrond of Imlad-rist': cf. p. 139 note 14.

6   In a rejected version of this 'the other half was found further down the river above Osgiliath by other watchers.'

7   On the same page are written other passages that were presumably potential ingredients in Sam's remonstration to Falborn:

> It's a pity the folks against Mordor fall out so easy. I should have thought it as plain as a pikestaff.

> Boromir was on his way to Minas Tirith. We decided not to go that way and went on our own road. Boromir was not dead when we left, but orcs knew of our journey: they attacked us above the rapids beyond Sarn Gebir. What's in it?
>
> I daresay now we made a mistake. I don't know the lie of the lands; but maybe we'd have got there quicker through Minas Tirith. But here we would have come. And if you drag us back there'll be some that do not like it. Boromir would not. Nor Aragorn.

With *Sarn Gebir* here for *Emyn Muil* cf. p. 136 and note 17. – Another passage here, in part totally illegible, is a draft for a more substantial conclusion to the interrogation of Frodo by Falborn: harshly uncomprehending in tone compared to the later Faramir, and suggesting that no further conversation between them had been thought of at this stage.

> 'Thou'rt commanded to go – somewhere. But I too am under command: to slay all that roam in Ithilien unanswerable, or at least to take them prisoner to Minas Tirith. I see no cause to slay you, or at least too great doubt. But to Minas Tirith ye shall go. And if Boromir is there it will ... with you. If Boromir's death be proved it will interest Denethor to speak with those who saw him last before he died. If he [?cometh] doubtless ye will be glad – maybe not. Of your own errand ..... [*the following sentences are effectively illegible*] ..... Maybe if you would say more of the truth and reveal your errand we would help you and not hinder. But if you will not speak I have no choice in my doubt.'
>
> 'Maybe you would, and maybe not,' said Frodo. 'But it is not a matter to speak of to such as you are – not were the walls of [?Mordor] a thousand miles away, whereas they be but a few leagues.'

Also here are inconclusive rewritings of the second part of the 'dream-verse of Minas Tirith'.

8   *Falborn* was emended to *Faramir* (but not consistently) on the

166   THE WAR OF THE RING

second draft B, where also many other changes leading to the third version C were entered.

9   This line does not appear in the rewritings of the verse referred to at the end of note 7, but *A sign shall be upholden* is found there. It may be that no such form of the verse was ever actually written. The manuscript at first followed the draft, but was then changed to 'But the words said that the Halfling would hold up Isildur's Bane'. *Halfling* for *Half-high* entered by emendation to the second draft B: 'If you be the Half-high' > 'If you be the Halfling'.

10   The date of Boromir's death was 26 January (and in one of the time-schemes the hour of his death is stated to be 'noon'); it was now 6 February, eleven days later. (In the margin of the manuscript my father wrote 'twelve' beside 'eleven', which however was not struck out. This presumably depends on the chronology in time-scheme 'S', in which Boromir died on 25 January: see pp. 101, 142.) In *The Tale of Years* the corresponding dates are 26 February and 7 March, also eleven days later (February having 30 days). In the notes given on p. 146 Faramir and his men left Minas Tirith on 3 February, thus three days before; and both in the draft and in the manuscript he tells Frodo that no members of the Company had reached the city when he left it three days before (where TT has six days, p. 272). In *The Tale of Years* he left on 1 March, thus six days before.

11   A further isolated scrap of drafting may be noticed. It represents presumably unused words of Frodo's when he spoke to Faramir about the boats of Lothlórien: 'These boats are crafty and unlike those of other folk. They will not sink, not though they will be laden more than is their wont when you are all aboard. But they are wayward, and if mishandled' (the sentence ends here).

12   This apparently refers to a passage in 'Farewell to Lórien'. In the fair copy manuscript of that chapter Boromir's original words 'I have not myself been there' (referring to Fangorn) had become 'I have not myself ever crossed Rohan' (VII.282, 293 note 36). This was now changed on that manuscript to 'I have myself been seldom in Rohan, and have never crossed it northwards' (cf. FR p. 390).

13   Rough drafting for this new placing of Sam's intervention is found. In this, rather oddly, Faramir's reply continues on into his astute guessing about Frodo's relationship with Boromir and about Isildur's Bane, and Frodo's quickly smothered desire to 'tell all to this kindly but just man'. In TT this passage, in much more developed form, does not arise until after they have begun their journey to Henneth Annûn. However, this was clearly no more than a sketching of new elements in the dialogue; it was not a

FARAMIR   167

draft for the overhaul of all that had been achieved in the chapter thus far.

14 Cf. the beginning of the sketch given on p. 151. — The passage that precedes this in TT p. 276, from 'For me there is no comfort in our speech together' to 'But whatever befell on the North March, you, Frodo, I doubt no longer' (in which Faramir suggests that some of the Company are still alive, since who else can have arrayed Boromir in the funeral boat), did not enter till later (it was added to the first typescript of the chapter).

15 Various elements are lacking in the draft but are present in the manuscript: such are 'He wished this thing brought to Minas Tirith' (TT p. 278); and the passage concerning Gandalf (p. 279), from 'Are you sure of this' to 'He got leave of Denethor, how I do not know, to look at the secrets of our treasury' — where the draft text reads: '... so much lore be taken from the world. He had leave to look at the secrets of our treasury ...' The draft text has a few features lost in the manuscript: thus after 'There is a something, I know not what, an elvish air maybe, about you' (TT p. 276) it continues: 'And that is not what I should look for, if old tales and rumours from afar told the whole truth concerning the little people.' This was rejected and replaced by: 'Some power greater than the stature of your kind', also rejected. And after 'unlike they were, and yet also much akin' (TT p. 280) the draft goes on: 'Faramir was doubtless of a different temper, but Frodo feared the power and treachery of the thing he bore: the greater and wiser the stronger the lure and the worse the fall.' With this cf. the sketch given on p. 152.

16 *Great Lands*: this survival of old usage remains at this place in *The Two Towers* (p. 286), its only occurrence in *The Lord of the Rings*. At a subsequent occurrence of *Great Lands* in this chapter (p. 158) TT has *Middle-earth* (p. 288), suggesting that its appearance in the first passage was an oversight.

17 *White Mountains: White* was added, but almost certainly as the text was in progress. Cf. the notes given on p. 137: 'Change *Black Mountains* to the *White Mountains*'.

18 The writing of the name *Elenarda* is perfectly clear and unambiguous, and it was not struck out when *Kalen(arda)* was written above it (but see p. 156 and note 22). It is strange to find it applied to Rohan; for this old mythological word derives from the conception of the three 'airs' in the cosmology expounded in the *Ambarkanta*. There it is translated 'Stellar Kingdom', and is another name for the middle region of *Ilmen*, in which move the Sun, the Moon, and the stars (see IV.240–3, 253). — On the name Rohir in the preceding sentence see p. 22 and note 24.

19 *Hebel Nimrath* was the name of the White Mountains written in

168   THE WAR OF THE RING

the manuscript, subsequently changed to *Ered Nimras*. With these names cf. those given in the notes on p. 137.

20 In the manuscript Faramir says, as in TT (p. 286), 'But the stewards were wiser and more fortunate.' The Stewards of Gondor, ruling in Minas Tirith after the death of the last and childless king of the line of Anárion, have appeared already in the earlier part of the dialogue of Frodo and Faramir (p. 153). In the manuscript Faramir's balance of phrases ('wiser and more fortunate; wiser ..., more fortunate ...') was preserved ('more fortunate, for our most dangerous foes became our friends'); by alteration of the text here at a later time this was lost in TT.

21 *Rohiroth*: see p. 22. In the first of these drafts (D 1) the form is *Rohir* (note 18); in the present draft (D 2) both *Rohir* and *Rohiroth* are found in close proximity. In the manuscript the form is *Rohiroth*.

22 In the manuscript my father wrote *Kalin*, striking it out at once and writing *Calenardan*, then altering this to *Calenardhon*, all these changes being made in the act of writing. See note 18.

23 The difference between these formulations is evidently that in the rejected version the relationship is between the Noldor (such as Galadriel) who remained after the overthrow of Morgoth and those who departed and went to Tol Eressëa; whereas in the second version the relationship is between the Noldor who remained and the Elves who never went to Valinor (such as the Elves of Lothlórien). — Cf. the passage in the chapter 'Galadriel' in VII.248, with note 12.

24 In TT (p. 287) the reading is '*not* from Hador the Goldenhaired, the Elf-friend, maybe ...' This *not* was inserted by my father on a late typescript of the chapter; it was put in very hurriedly, and it seems to me possible that he read the sentence differently from his original meaning — which was certainly 'They may be descended from Hador indeed, *but if so*, then of course from those of Hador's descendants who did not pass over the Sea.' — In the manuscript 'such of their sons' was later emended to 'such of his people', and this seems to have been misinterpreted by the typist as 'such of his sons and people'.

It may be noted here that at the same time as this correction to the manuscript the words 'they became a people apart and should remain so' were changed to 'and should have remained so'.

25 *Great Lands*: here TT has *Middle-earth*; see note 16.

26 This sentence was apparently evolved thus: 'even Earendel our first king and Elros brother [*sc*. of Elrond]' > 'even our first king Elros son of Earendel and brother of Elrond'. See p. 155.

27 It was explicit from the beginning that the Númenóreans were expressly forbidden by the Gods to sail westward beyond the Lonely Isle (see the original outline and the original versions of

FARAMIR 169

The Fall of Númenor in *The Lost Road*, pp. 11, 14, 26). *Elvenhome* here means the Lonely Isle: for that isle lay in the Bay of Elvenhome (cf. *The Lost Road* p. 103: 'the Isle of Eressëa in Elvenhome'); and this is the meaning also in the same passage in TT (p. 288), where the words 'within sight of Elvenhome' are retained — cf. the passage in the *Akallabêth* (*The Silmarillion*, pp. 262–3) where the remote vision from Númenor of Avallónë, haven of Eressëa, is described. This is made certain, apart from any other considerations, by the passage given on p. 164.

28   The word *Númenórean(s)* is variously marked, with an accent on the first syllable or on the third, or no accent. Here the word is written *Númenóreans*, and I have extended this throughout.

29   Cf. the later *Annals of Beleriand* in *The Lost Road*, p. 131: 'the folk of Hádor abandoned their own tongue and spoke with the speech of the Gnomes'; also the *Lhammas* § 10, *ibid.* p. 179.

30   The name *Faramir* does not appear in any earlier writing.

31   By later pencilled correction of the manuscript Faramir's words were changed so that the reference is only to Noldorin: 'many men of the Three Houses long ago learned the High-elven tongue of the Noldor, as it was spoken in Gondolin or by the Sons of Fëanor. And always the Lords of Númenor knew that tongue, and used it among themselves.'

32   On the removal of the history of Pipe-weed from the text see pp. 36–9.

33   With these remarks of Sam's cf. the initial sketch given on p. 152: 'Sam speaks of elvish power, boats, ropes, cloaks.' This was written before the entry of Faramir's account of language (the cause of its loss from the chapter in *The Two Towers*).

34   In neither of the draft versions of Sam's words about Galadriel does Faramir interject: 'Then she must be lovely indeed. Perilously fair', leading (in the manuscript, and in TT) to Sam's consideration of the justice of the word *perilous* as applied to Galadriel; but in both drafts Sam nonetheless says 'I don't know about perilous', and makes the same observations. At this stage he was referring back to Faramir's earlier 'I deem it perilous now for mortal men, at least to seek the Elder People wilfully' (p. 159).

35   In this draft (D 2) Sam's gaffe is preceded by the same words as in TT (p. 289), but he ends: 'and it's my opinion as soon as he first heard of it he wanted the Ring.' Thus he does not refer to Lórien as the place where Boromir (in the words of the final draft, D 3) 'first saw himself clear, and saw what I saw sooner'.

36   The man who saw Gollum was first named *Falborn* in the manuscript, later altered to *Anborn* (this change was actually made in the course of the initial drafting of 'The Forbidden Pool'). In draft and manuscript of 'Of Herbs and Stewed Rabbit'

170   THE WAR OF THE RING

(p. 136) Anborn was the father of Falborn leader of the men of Gondor in Ithilien, who became Faramir.

37 On *Elvenhome* here (Tol Eressëa) see note 27. The manuscript has the final text (TT p. 285): '... towards Númenor that was, and beyond to Elvenhome that is, and to that which is beyond Elvenhome and will ever be.' Cf. *Letters* no. 211, footnote to p. 281, where the words 'that which is beyond Elvenhome and ever will be' [*sic*] are interpreted as 'is beyond the mortal lands, beyond the memory of unfallen Bliss, beyond the physical world.'

VI

THE FORBIDDEN POOL

The 'fourth new chapter ("Faramir")' had been read to C. S. Lewis and Charles Williams on 8 May 1944 (see p. 144) – 'fourth', because 'The Black Gate is Closed' and 'Of Herbs and Stewed Rabbit' had not yet been separated (see p. 164, notes 1 and 2). On 11 May my father wrote (*Letters* no. 67) that another chapter was in progress, 'leading to disaster at Kirith Ungol where Frodo is captured. Story then switches back to Gondor, & runs fairly swiftly (I hope) to denouement.' On the following day (*Letters* no. 68) he said that 'we are now in sight of Minas Morghul'; and he also quoted Faramir's words to Frodo: 'When you return to the lands of the living,[1] and we re-tell our tales, sitting by a wall in the sun, laughing at old grief, you shall tell me then.' In *The Two Towers* these words stand just before the end of 'The Forbidden Pool'. On the morning of 15 May 1944 (*Letters* no. 69) he read his '6th new chapter "Journey to the Cross Roads"' to C. S. Lewis.

Initial drafting for what became 'The Forbidden Pool' runs on continuously into what became 'Journey to the Cross-Roads', and in the completed fair copy manuscript likewise the two chapters are one, titled 'XXXVII. Journey to the Cross Roads'; the latter title and chapter-break were inserted into the manuscript later, when the first part became 'The Forbidden Pool'.[2] Since my father would not have called his 'new chapter' 'Journey to the Cross Roads' if Frodo, Sam and Gollum did not get there in the course of it, I conclude that this was where they were, beside the broken statue in the ring of trees, when he read his '6th new chapter' to Lewis on the 15th of May (by this time, presumably, he had divided 'Of Herbs and Stewed Rabbit' from 'The Black Gate is Closed', so making 'Faramir' the fifth). In his letter recording this (no. 69) he went on: 'So far it has gone well: but I am now coming to the nub, when the threads must be gathered and the times synchronized and the narrative interwoven; while the whole thing has grown so large in significance that the sketches of concluding chapters (written ages ago) are quite inadequate, being on a more "juvenile" level.'

This part of the story unfolded, once my father began to write it, virtually without any hestitation between rival courses; there is however a little sketch that he wrote for it, exceedingly hard to make out, when all was not yet plain.

172   THE WAR OF THE RING

They are roused late at night. Moonset over Mindolluin. Sam grumbles at being waked only to see moonlight.

They see Gollum fishing below the pool.

Faramir says he must shoot to kill, or Frodo must help to capture him.

Frodo and some men go out. Frodo calls Gollum and Gollum is caught still clutching a fish.

Faramir warns Frodo against Gollum.

[*Struck out:* Frodo tells him] No it is Gollum.

Frodo begs for his life. It is granted if Frodo will induce Gollum to come and .....[3]

Gollum is caught by guards and brought in.

He [?feigns] great delight at Frodo. Nice fish. Begs him not to delay but start in morning.

They go back to sleep till morning.

They go on through woods by day. No orcs. Farewell. They are out of reckoning, and take long[?er than]

Here these notes end. The sentences 'Frodo and some men go out. Frodo calls Gollum and Gollum is caught still clutching a fish' are marked with a line in the margin, which probably implies that this is the version to be followed, rather than 'Gollum is caught by guards and brought in. He feigns great delight at Frodo.' I cannot explain the rejected words 'Frodo tells him', followed by 'No it is Gollum'.

Drafting for the chapter (much of it in handwriting so difficult that were it not generally already close to the final form parts of it would be virtually uninterpretable) suggests extremely fluent composition, and there is very little to say of it. New elements entered in successive pages of drafting, but the fair copy manuscript, from which the chapter was read to C. S. Lewis on 15 May, reached the text of *The Two Towers* in all but a few minor points.

Minor in itself, but very notable, is what Faramir says of the Moon. In TT (p. 293) he says: 'Fair Ithil, as he goes from Middle-earth, glances upon the white locks of old Mindolluin'; but in the original draft of the passage he said: 'Fair Ithil touches with *her* fingers the white locks of old Mindolluin', and still in the manuscript, where the text is otherwise that of TT, he said: 'as *she* goes from Middle-earth ...'[4]

In the original draft of Frodo's reply to Far⌐mir's question concerning Gollum ('Why does he so?', TT p. 294) he says, in support of his suggestion that Gollum does not realise that men are concealed there, that 'He has night-eyes, but he is nearsighted and I doubt if he could see us up here.' In a second draft of the passage the last phrase became '... and sees to no great distance clearly'; in the manuscript, '... and distant things are dim to him.' Against this, in the second of these

THE FORBIDDEN POOL   173

drafts, my father wrote (at the same time): 'Make it *not* Gollum who looked out at Morannon – or make it 100 yards' (with '200 yards' written above). But the reference to Gollum's nearsightedness was struck from the typescripts and does not appear in TT, and Gollum remained the one who looked out from the hollow before the Black Gate and saw the 'very cruel wicked Men'·coming up the road from the south. My father hesitated much over the distance from the hollow to the road, and this was clearly one of the reasons for it; see p. 128 note 9. — The 'froglike figure' that climbed out of the water as Frodo and Faramir looked down on the pool was a subsequent change from 'spidery figure'.

In very rough and rapid initial drafting for the concluding part of the chapter in TT (pp. 300–2) Frodo says no more of the way past Minas Morghul than that Gollum had said that there was such a way, 'up in a high pass in the mountains'. Then follows Faramir's declaration of the name Kirith Ungol, as in TT. In the fair copy manuscript my father first wrote here:

'I do not know clearly,' said Frodo, 'but it climbs, I think, up into the mountains on the southern side of that vale in the mountains on the northern side of which the old city stands. It goes up to a high cleft and so down to – that which is beyond.'

This was subsequently changed to the text of TT. On the earlier idea that Kirith Ungol was on the south side of the valley see p. 113.

At the end of this initial draft my father briefly outlined the further course of the story: the blindfolding of the hobbits and Gollum, the report of the scouts on the strange silence and emptiness in the land, Faramir's advice to go by day through the woods 'skirting the last fall of the land before the river vale', and his farewell. At the foot of this page is a pencilled note only a part of which can I make out:

K[irith] U[ngol] must not be mentioned before Frodo ... to tell Faramir of Gollum.
Yes he found the ring many many years ago, said Frodo. He is the means by which all this great matter has been set going.

Two sentences follow in which I can make out nothing at all, except perhaps 'where the ring had been'. But in any case this was evidently a very short-lived idea.

NOTES

1 The original draft of the passage in 'The Forbidden Pool' was almost as in TT: 'If ever you return to the lands of the living ...'
2 A subsequent tentative arrangement was to put 'The Forbidden Pool' with 'Faramir', calling the first part 'Faramir (1): The

174   THE WAR OF THE RING

Window of the West' (not 'on the West'), and the second 'Faramir (2): The Forbidden Pool'.

3 The illegible end of this sentence looks in fact more like 'visit them' than anything else. If so, the meaning is presumably 'if Frodo can induce Gollum to leave the pool and come up with him to Faramir's presence'; the word is oddly chosen, but these notes were written at great speed.

4 *she* was corrected to *he* on the first typescript. Cf. the *Quenta Silmarillion* in *The Lost Road*, p. 241 §78: 'Varda commanded the Moon to rise only after the Sun had left heaven, but he travels with uncertain pace, and still pursueth her ...'

    Another matter concerning the Moon may be mentioned. At the beginning of the chapter, when Faramir waking Frodo says 'the full moon is setting', my father changed this on the manuscript to 'rising'; when they came out from the stairway in the rock the words 'Far off in the West the full moon was sinking' were changed to 'Behind him the round moon, full and majestic, rose out of the shadow of the East'; and Faramir's 'Moonset over Gondor' was changed to 'Moonrise over Gondor'. This would of course make it very much earlier in the night. But all these alterations were returned to the original readings, presumably at once, since subsequently 'It was now dark and the falls were pale and grey, reflecting only the lingering moonlight of the western sky' (TT p. 295) was not changed.

VII

JOURNEY TO THE CROSS-ROADS

I have recounted the original relationship of 'The Forbidden Pool' and 'Journey to the Cross-roads'[1] at the beginning of the last chapter. Preliminary drafting for this second part of the original single chapter runs continuously, in excruciatingly difficult handwriting, as far as the coming of Frodo and his companions to the ridge covered with whortleberry and gorse-bushes so tall that they could walk upright beneath them (TT p. 307).[2] The story to this point differed from that in *The Two Towers*. The journey took a day less: they came to the road from Osgiliath at dusk of the day on which they left Henneth Annûn in the morning; and their taking refuge in the great holm-oak was described at much greater length (cf. TT pp. 306–7, from 'Gollum reluctantly agreed to this'):

Gollum agreed to this, and the travellers turned back from the road, but Gollum would not rest on the ground in the open woodland. After some search he chose a large dark ilex with great branches springing together high up from a great bole like a [?giant] pillar. It grew at the foot of a small bank [?leaning] a little westward. From the bank Gollum leaped with ease upon the trunk, climbing like a cat and scrambling up into the branches. The hobbits climbed only with the help of Sam's rope and in that task Gollum would not help, he would not lay a finger on the elven rope. The great branches springing almost from the same point made a wide bowl and here they [?managed] to find some sort of comfort. It grew deep dark under the great canopy of the tree. They could not see the sky or any star.

'We could sleep snug and safe here, if it wasn't for this dratted Gollum,' thought Sam. Whether he was really as forgiving as he claimed or not, Gollum at least had no fear of his companions, and curled up like some tree-animal and soon went to sleep, or seemed to. But the hobbits did not trust it – neither of them (certainly not Sam) were likely to forget Faramir's warning. They took [it] in turn to watch and had about 3 hours' sleep each. All the while Gollum did not stir. Whether the 'nice fish' had given him strength to last for a bit or whatnot else, he did not go out to hunt.

176   THE WAR OF THE RING

Shortly before midnight he woke up suddenly and they saw his pale eyes unlidded staring in the darkness.

At the point where this opening draft ended my father wrote *Thunder*. But at this stage there is no suggestion in the text of any change in the weather or in the feeling of the air. Other points worth mentioning are that the staves given to Frodo and Sam by Faramir had 'carven heads like a shepherd's crook'; that the tree of which they were made was first named *melinon* (the last two letters are not perfectly clear), then *lebendron*, and finally *lebethras*, all these changes being made in the act of writing;[3] and that though Faramir warns them against drinking of any water that flows from the valley of Morghul he does not name it *Imlad Morghul* (but the name occurs soon after: p. 223, note 25).

A second draft takes up at the beginning of the passage just given ('Gollum agreed to this'), and the episode of the oak-tree was rewritten. In this text appears the first reference to an approaching change in the weather.

They were steadily climbing. Looking back they could see now the roof of the forests they had left, lying like a huge dense shadow spread under the sky. The air seemed heavy, no longer fresh and clear, and the stars were blurred, and when towards the end of the night the moon climbed slowly above Ephel Dúath[4] it was ringed about with a sickly yellow glare. They went on until the sky above the approaching mountains began to grow pale. Gollum seemed to know well enough where he was. He stood for a moment nose upward sniffing. Then beckoning to them he hurried forward. Following him wearily they began to climb a great hogback of land. ...

After the description of the great gorse-bushes and their hiding in a brake of tangled thorns and briars there follows (cf. TT p. 308):

There they lay glad to be at rest, too tired as yet to eat, and watched the slow growth of day. As the light grew the mountains of Ephel-dúath seemed to frown and lower at them across the tumbled lands between. They looked even nearer than they were, black below where night lingered, with jagged tips and edges lined in threatening shapes against the opening sky.

Away a little northward of where the hobbits lay they seemed to recede eastwards and fall back in a great re-entrant, the nearer shoulder of which thrusting forward hid the view in that direction. Below out of the great shadow they could see the road

JOURNEY TO THE CROSS-ROADS 177

from the River for a short stretch as it bent away north-east to join the southward road that still lay further off [?buried] in the crumpled land.

'Which way do we go from here?' said Frodo.

'Must we think of it yet?' said Sam. 'Surely we're not going to move for hours and hours?'

'No surely not,' said Gollum. 'But we must move sometime. ..... back to the Cross-roads that we told the hobbits about.'

'When shall we get there?'

'We doesn't know,' said Gollum. 'Before night is over perhaps, perhaps not.'

At this point the second draft breaks down into an outline of the story to come, and the handwriting becomes in places altogether inscrutable.

Gollum away a large part of the day. Reach Cross-roads in fact owing to difficult country not until evening. Start at dusk about 5.30 and do not reach Cross-roads and headless statue until morning [*sic*]. Gollum in a great state of fright. Weather changed. Sky above Ephel Dúath absolute black. Clouds or smoke? drifting on an East wind. Rumbles? Sun hidden. In this darkness they get out of the wood and see Minas Morghul. It shines amid a deep gloom as if by an evil moon – though there is no moon.

Horror of hobbits. Weight of Ring. .... vale of Morghul. Where road went away to the north shoulder and bases of the fortress they turned aside and climbed away southward to other side of V [*i.e.* Vale of Morghul]. Frodo and Sam .... see a track. They are already some way up and the gates of Minas Morghul frown at them when there is a great roll and rumble. Blast of Thunder .... rain. Out of gates comes host led by B[lack] R[ider].

It was in this text that the idea of the great cloud spreading out of Mordor emerged. In a third section of drafting my father returned to the point where the second had become a sketch, following Gollum's words about the Cross-roads: 'The sun that had risen with a red glare behind the Ephel-dúath passed into dark clouds moving slowly from the East. It was a gloomy morning. The hobbits took some food and settled to rest ...'

After Gollum's reappearance from his long absence that day this draft too turns to outline:

178   THE WAR OF THE RING

When he returns he says they ought to start. Hobbits think
something has worried him (or ?). They are suspicious but
have to agree. The [early evening >] afternoon is threatening
and overcast. At evening they come to the Cross-roads in a
wood. Sun goes down bloodred in the west over Osgiliath.
Terrible darkness begins.

The completed fair copy manuscript did not in this case reach the
form of the story in *The Two Towers*, for Frodo and his companions
still only took two days from Henneth Annûn to the Cross-roads, and
a major later change was the lengthening of their journey by a further
day. This was achieved by the insertion of the following passage into a
typescript of the chapter, following the words (TT p. 305) 'The birds
seemed all to have flown away or to have fallen dumb':

Darkness came early to the silent woods, and before the fall
of night they halted, weary, for they had walked seven leagues
or more from Henneth Annûn. Frodo lay and slept away the
night on the deep mould beneath an ancient tree. Sam beside
him was more uneasy: he woke many times, but there was never
a sign of Gollum, who had slipped off as soon as the others had
settled to rest. Whether he had slept by himself in some hole
nearby, or had wandered restlessly prowling through the night,
he did not say; but he returned with the first glimmer of light,
and roused his companions.

'Must get up, yes they must!' he said. 'Long ways to go still,
south and east. Hobbits must make haste!'

That day passed much the same as the day before had done,
except that the silence seemed deeper; the air grew heavy, and it
began to be stifling under the trees. It felt as if thunder was
brewing. Gollum often paused, sniffing the air, and then he
would mutter to himself and urge them to greater speed.

(As the third stage of their day's march drew on ...)

This was retained almost exactly in TT. In the manuscript the text
passes at once from 'The birds seemed all to have flown away or to
have fallen dumb' to 'As the third stage of their day's march drew on',
and thus in this narrative (as in the original draft, p. 175) they came
to the Cross-roads at sunset of the second day. They had come to
Henneth Annûn at sunset on 6 February (pp. 135, 141); they left on
the morning of the 7th, and coming to the Osgiliath road at dusk of
that day passed the first part of the night in the great oak-tree; they
went on again 'a little before midnight', and passed most of the
daylight hours of 8 February hiding in the thorn-brake before going on

JOURNEY TO THE CROSS-ROADS 179

to the Cross-roads (see further the Note on Chronology at the end of this chapter).

Thus the phrase 'As the third stage of their day's march drew on' referred, when it was written, to the statement then immediately preceding: 'Twice that day they rested and took a little of the food provided by Faramir'; as it stands in TT its reference is less clear.

In this inserted passage occurs the first reference in TT to the heaviness in the air and the feeling of thunder. In the manuscript as in the draft (p. 176) the first reference to the change in the weather does not appear until they set out again and began to climb eastwards, after spending the first part of the night (the second night in TT) in the oak-tree; at this point in TT, by a later change, 'There seemed to be *a great blackness* looming slowly out of the East, eating up the faint blurred stars.' On the following morning, as they lay hidden under the thorns, the manuscript retained the story in the draft: the hobbits 'watched the slow growth of day', and saw the mountain-tops outlined against the sunrise; and here again this was afterwards changed to the reading of TT (p. 308): the hobbits 'watched *for* the slow growth of day. *But no day came*, only a dead brown twilight. In the East there was a dull red glare under the lowering cloud: *it was not the red of dawn*.' Where the manuscript, again following the draft (p. 177), has 'The sun that had risen with a red flare behind Ephel-dúath passed soon into dark clouds moving slowly from the East. It was going to be a gloomy day, if no worse' TT has 'The red glare over Mordor died away. The twilight deepened as great vapours rose in the East and crawled above them.' On the other hand, the further references in this chapter to the darkness (and to the deep rumbling sounds) were already present in the original version, and at the end it is said, almost as in TT (p. 311): 'There, far away, the sun was sinking, finding at last the hem of the great slow-rolling pall of cloud, and falling in an ominous fire towards the yet unsullied sea.'[5]

Comparing the text as it stands in the manuscript with that in TT one might well suppose at first sight that all these careful alterations show my father at a later time (when he had reached Book V) developing the original idea of a great thunderstorm arising in the mountains into that of the 'Dawnless Day', an emanation of the power of Mordor that obliterated the sunrise and turned day into night, that stroke of Sauron's that preceded his great assault. But it is clear that this is not so. That conception was already present. In fact, the essential reason for these changes was chronological, and they are to be associated with the extra day of the journey from Henneth Annûn. The slow approach of the great cloud out of the East had to be advanced at each succeeding stage of the journey to the Cross-roads (see the Note on Chronology at the end of this chapter). It is also true, however, that the rewriting of these passages intensified the Darkness and made it more potent and sinister.

180 THE WAR OF THE RING

Lastly, another later alteration to the text in the manuscript was the sentence (TT p. 306) 'and the sound of the water seemed cold and cruel: the voice of Morgulduin, the polluted stream that flowed from the Valley of the Wraiths.'

On p. 181 is reproduced a plan of the Cross-roads and Minas Morghul.[6]

NOTES

1 My father wrote the word 'Cross-roads' very variously, but in this chapter I spell it thus throughout, as in TT.

2 Cf. *Unfinished Tales*, p. 99 and note 15.

3 In the fair copy manuscript it was still said that the heads of the staves were in the form of a shepherd's crook, though this was subsequently rejected (see p. 207), but the name of the tree was *lebethron* as first written.

4 In the first draft the form was still *Hebel Dúath*. On this change see p. 137. — This reference to the moon climbing above Ephel Dúath 'towards the end of night' is curious, in view of the opening of 'The Forbidden Pool', where towards the end of the previous night the full moon was setting in the West. The original draft here is even odder:

> The moon rose at last out of [?high] shadows ahead of them. It hardly showed yet any ... of its full light, but already away behind the mountains and the hollow land and the empty wastes day was beginning to grow pale.
>
> 'There comes White Face,' said Gollum. 'We doesn't like it. And Yellow Face is coming soon, sss. Two faces in sky together at once, not a good sign. And we've got some way to go.'

My father was certainly, as he wrote to me on 14 May 1944 (*Letters* no. 69), having 'trouble with the moon'.

In the manuscript the moon is still climbing above Ephel Dúath late in the night; only by a later change does it become 'the sinking moon' that 'escaped from the pursuing cloud' (TT p. 307).

5 The words in TT 'beyond sad Gondor now overwhelmed in shade' were a later addition.

6 At the head of the first stair there is evidently a track and not a tunnel, and therefore the later conception of the ascent to the pass is present (pp. 198–200).

Note on the Chronology

The time-schemes referred to as Scheme C and Scheme D (pp. 140–1) both cover this part of the narrative. Scheme C reads as follows (for comparison with the citations from *The Tale of Years* that follow I have added 'Day 1' etc. in both cases).

JOURNEY TO THE CROSS-ROADS 181

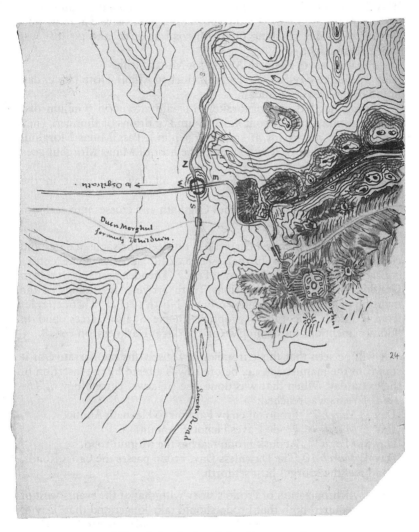

Minas Morghul and the Cross-roads

182

THE WAR OF THE RING

[Day 1] *Monday Feb. 6*   Frodo and Sam in Ithilien. They are taken by Faramir. Battle with the Southrons. Frodo spends night at Henneth Annûn.

[Day 2] *Tuesday Feb. 7*   Gollum captured in the Pool of Annûn in the early hours (5.30–6). Frodo Sam & Gollum leave Faramir, and journey all day reaching Osgiliath road at dusk, and go *east* just before midnight.

Faramir leaves Henneth Annûn for Minas Tirith.

[Day 3] *Wednesday Feb. 8*   Faramir rides to Minas Tirith late in day and brings news to Gandalf.

Frodo lies hid in thornbrake until late afternoon (Gollum disappears and returns about 4.30). Sound of drums or thunder. They reach the Cross-roads at sunset (5.5 p.m.). Pass Minas Morghul, and begin ascent of Kirith Ungol. The host of Minas Morghul goes out to war.

[Day 4] *Thursday Feb. 9*   Frodo etc. all day and night in the Mountains of Shadow.

Host of Minas Morghul reaches Osgiliath and crosses into realm of Gondor.

Here this scheme ends. Scheme D is precisely the same in dates and content, but continues further (see p. 226) and has some entries concerning Théoden's movements: Feb. 7 'Théoden prepares to ride to Gondor. Messengers from Minas Tirith arrive. Also tidings of the invasion of North Rohan and war in the North'; Feb. 8 'Théoden rides from Edoras'. The fully 'synoptic' scheme S also agrees, and in addition mentions the coming on of 'the Great Darkness' on Feb. 8.

It will be seen that this chronology precisely fits the narrative as it stands in the manuscript, i.e. before it was altered by the insertion of the extra day. When that was done, the (relative) chronology of *The Tale of Years* was reached:

[Day 1] *March 7*   Frodo taken by Faramir to Henneth Annûn.

[Day 2] *March 8*   Frodo leaves Henneth Annûn.

[Day 3] *March 9*   At dusk Frodo reaches the Morgul-road.

[Day 4] *March 10*   The Dawnless Day. Frodo passes the Cross Roads, and sees the Morgul-host set forth.

The synchronization of Frodo's story with that of the events west of Anduin required both that Frodo should take longer and that 'Day 4' should be the Dawnless Day. Thus in the original story Frodo and Sam see the red sunrise from their hiding in the thornbrake on 'Day 3'; in the final form they are hiding in the thornbrake on 'Day 4', and there is no sunrise, but a red glare over Mordor that 'was not the red of dawn'.

VIII
KIRITH UNGOL

In this chapter I shall describe the writing of the three last chapters of *The Two Towers*: 'The Stairs of Kirith Ungol', 'Shelob's Lair', and 'The Choices of Master Samwise'. As will be seen, this is dictated by the way in which my father developed the narrative.

This is the last part of *The Lord of the Rings* for which precise dating is possible, for when the doors of the Tower of Kirith Ungol slammed in Sam's face my father halted again for a long time, and when I returned to England in 1945 the constant correspondence between us naturally ceased. He wrote on 12 May 1944 (*Letters* no. 68) that 'we are now in sight of Minas Morghul'; and a good part of the work studied in this chapter must have been done during the following ten days, for on 21 May (*Letters* no. 70) he said:

> I have taken advantage of a bitter cold grey week ... to write: but struck a sticky patch. All that I had sketched or written before proved of little use, as times, motives, etc., have all changed. However at last with v. great labour, and some neglect of other duties, I have now written or nearly written all the matter up to the capture of Frodo in the high pass on the very brink of Mordor. Now I must go back to the other folk and try and bring things to the final crash with some speed. Do you think *Shelob* is a good name for a monstrous spider creature? It is of course only 'she + lob' (= spider), but written as one, it seems to be quite noisome.

Adding to this letter on the following day, Monday 22 May, he said:

> It was a wretched cold day yesterday (Sunday). I worked very hard at my chapter – it is most exhausting work; especially as the climax approaches and one has to keep the pitch up: no easy level will do; and there are all sorts of minor problems of plot and mechanism. I wrote and tore up and rewrote most of it a good many times; but I was rewarded this morning, as both C.S.L. and C.W. thought it an admirable performance, and the latest chapters the best so far. Gollum continues to develop into a most intriguing character.

At first sight the references in this letter seem inconsistent: in the past week he had written all or nearly all the story up to the capture of Frodo; he had just spent a day working hard 'at my chapter' (in the singular); and that morning he had read 'it' to Lewis and Williams. There are various ways of explaining this: my guess is that he had at

184   THE WAR OF THE RING

this time got the whole story in draft, which he was still working on, and which he thought of as a 'chapter'; but what he read to Lewis and Williams was 'The Stairs of Kirith Ungol'. That this last is certainly the case is seen from his letter of 31 May 1944 (*Letters* no. 72):

> The rest of my time ... has been occupied by the desperate attempt to bring 'The Ring' to a suitable pause, the capture of Frodo by the Orcs in the passes of Mordor, before I am obliged to break off by examining. By sitting up all hours, I managed it: and read the last 2 chapters (*Shelob's Lair* and *The Choices of Master Samwise*) to C.S.L. on Monday morning.

It had indeed been a great labour. The elements were present: the climb to the high pass, the spider's lair, the webs in the tunnel, the use of the phial of Galadriel, the disappearance of Gollum, his treachery, the attack of the spider, the tower guarding the pass, the coming of the Orcs; but they long defied a satisfactory articulation. Perhaps in no part of *The Lord of the Rings* can the work behind the finished text be more clearly discerned than here.

Already when drafting the chapter 'The Black Gate is Closed' my father had sketched out his idea of the approach to Kirith Ungol (p. 124): there Gollum tells Frodo and Sam of 'A stair and path leading up into the mountains south of the pass, and then a tunnel, and then more stairs and then a cleft high above the main pass'. And in the outline that ends the original draft of that chapter (p. 125) it is foreseen that after leaving the Cross-roads they will see the moon shining on Minas Morghul; they will pass up the first stair, force their way through the tunnel 'black with webs of spiders', and get up the second stair which will bring them to Kirith Ungol; but 'Spiders are aroused and hunt them. They are exhausted.' Whether at that stage Kirith Ungol was guarded by a tower is not clear (see pp. 125–6).

But long before this, my father had written an account of the entry of Frodo and Sam into Mordor, which beginning as outline soon became narrative ('The Story Foreseen from Lórien', in *The Treason of Isengard*, pp. 330 ff.).[1] That story was very largely concerned with Sam's rescue of Frodo from Minas Morghul, which does not concern us here; but the first part of it is very relevant, for my father had it before him in May 1944, and I cite a portion of it again here (taking up the various additions made to the text that were certainly present when he now turned to it).

> The three companions now approach Kirith Ungol, the dreadful ravine which leads into Gorgoroth.[2] Kirith Ungol means Spider Glen: there dwelt great spiders, greater than those of Mirkwood, such as were once of old in the land of Elves and Men in the West that is now under sea, such as Beren fought in the dark cañons of the Mountains of Terror above Doriath. Already Gollum knew these

KIRITH UNGOL   185

creatures well. He slips away. The spiders come and weave their nets over Frodo while Sam sleeps: sting Frodo. Sam wakes, and sees Frodo lying pale as death – greenish: reminding him of the faces in the pools of the marshes. He cannot rouse or wake him.

The idea suddenly comes to Sam to carry on the work, and he felt for the Ring. He could not unclasp it, nor cut the chain, but he drew the chain over Frodo's head. As he did so he fancied he felt a tremor (sigh or shudder) pass through the body; but when he paused he could not feel any heart-beat. Sam put the Ring round his own neck.

Then he sat and made a *Lament for Frodo*. After that he put away his tears and thought what he could do. He could not leave his dear master lying in the wild for the fell beasts and carrion birds; and he thought he would try and build a cairn of stones about him. 'The silver mail of mithril rings shall be his winding-sheet,' he said. 'But I will lay the phial of Lady Galadriel upon his breast, and Sting shall be at his side.'

He laid Frodo upon his back and crossed his arms on his breast and set Sting at his side. And as he drew out the phial it blazed with light. It lit Frodo's face and it looked now pale but beautiful, fair with an elvish beauty as of one long past the shadows. 'Farewell, Frodo,' said Sam; and his tears fell on Frodo's hands.

But at that moment there was a sound of strong footfalls climbing towards the rock shelf. Harsh calls and cries echoed in the rocks. Orcs were coming, evidently guided to the spot.

'Curse that Gollum,' said Sam. 'I might have known we had not seen the last of him. These are some of his friends.'

Sam had no time to lose. Certainly no time to hide or cover his master's body. Not knowing what else to do he slipped on the Ring, and then he took also the phial so that the foul Orcs should not get it, and girded Sting about his own waist. And waited. He had not long to wait.

In the gloom first came Gollum sniffing out the scent, and behind him came the black orcs: fifty or more it seemed. With a cry they rushed upon Frodo. Sam tried to put up a fight unseen, but even as he was about to draw Sting he was run down and trampled by the rush of the Orcs. All the breath was knocked out of his body. Courage failed him. In great glee the Orcs seized Frodo and lifted him.

'There was another, yes,' whined Gollum. 'Where is he, then?' said the Orcs. 'Somewheres nigh. Gollum feels him, Gollum sniffs him.'

'Well, you find him, sniveller,' said the Orc-chief. 'He can't go far without getting into trouble. We've got what we want. Ringbearer! Ringbearer!' They shouted in joy. 'Make haste. Make haste. Send one swift to Barradur to the Great One. But we cannot wait here – we must get back to our guard post. Bear the prisoner to Minas

186   THE WAR OF THE RING

Morgul.' (Gollum runs behind wailing that the Precious is not there.)

Even as they do so, Frodo seems to awake, and gives a loud cry, but they gag him. Sam is torn between joy at learning he is alive and horror at seeing him carried off by Orcs. Sam tries to follow, but they go very speedily. The Ring seems to grow in power in this region: he sees clearly in the dark, and seems to understand the orcs' speech. He fears what may happen if he meets a Ringwraith – the Ring does not confer courage: poor Sam trembles all the time. Sam gathers that they are going to Minas Morgul ...

Sam follows the Orcs as they march off to Minas Morgul, and sees them entering the city; then he follows them in.

My father now wrote a new outline, and it is clear that he wrote it before he had proceeded far with the story that constitutes the chapter 'The Stairs of Kirith Ungol'. The original draft of 'Journey to the Cross-roads' in fact continued straight on into what would become the next chapter, but soon became no more than a sketch. Frodo's sudden crazed dash towards the bridge (TT p. 313) was absent; after scarcely legible words corresponding to the later 'Frodo felt his senses reeling and his mind darkening' follows:

Gollum again drew him away. Not that way ..... he hissed ..... but the sound seemed to tear the air like a whistle. Not that way. He drew them aside and [?shrinking] after him they left the road and began to climb up into the darkness on the northern side of the valley, ... their eyes away from the city on their right, but always looking back again.

It is here that the placing of the high pass (Kirith Ungol) on the north side of the Morghul Vale first appears. Then follows:

They came to a .... and steps and laboured on. As they rose above the exhalations of the valley their track became easier and the [or their] steps less heavy and slow. But at last they could go no further. They were in a narrow place where the path or road – if it were one – was no more than a wide ledge winding along the face of the mountain shoulder. Before them it seemed to vanish into the shadow or into the very rock itself.

They halted and at that moment a great red flash lit up the valley. In that place of shadow and pale phosphorescent light it seemed unbearable, suddenly fierce and cruel. Two peaks with notches between sprang suddenly [?black] into view against the [?sudden] fire behind. At the same moment a great [?crack] of thunder ....

KIRITH UNGOL 187

There follows an illegible sentence that seems to refer to the great screeching cry, and the text ends with a reference to the coming forth of the host of Morghul.

At this point the new outline for the whole 'Kirith Ungol' story begins. Written at great speed and in pencil, it is often exceedingly difficult to make out, and in one passage very hard to follow.

Description of the endless long black lines. *Rider ahead*. He halts and sweeps glance round valley. Frodo's temptation to put on Ring. At last the host [?passes] away.

The [?storm] is bursting – they are going to Osgiliath and the crossing of the River he said. Will Faramir be across? Will army slay them?

[*Added:* long [?journey] up. Frodo uses phial.]

They pass into the tunnel. Halfway through they find it blocked with webs. Gollum refuses to say what they are. Frodo goes ahead and hews a path with Sting. Sam helps.

At other end after long struggle in dark he finds a *stair*. They can no longer see into valley, as sheer walls of rock are on either side. The stair goes up, up endlessly. [?Occasional] webs across path.

Gollum hangs back. They begin to have suspicion of him. Description of the spiders? There dwelt great creatures in spider form such as lived once of old in the Land of the Elves in the West that is now under the Sea, such as Beren fought in the dark ravines of the Mountains of Terror above Doriath. All light they snared and wove into impenetrable webs. Pale-fleshed, many-eyed, venomous they were, older and more horrible than the black creatures of Mirkwood. Already Gollum had met them: he knew them well. But thought to use them for his purposes.

They come out at last to the head of the stair. The road opens a little. There is still an ominous glare. They see the road [?clearly] .. through a [?narrow] cleft and now the right wall sinks and they look down into a vast darkness, the great cleft which was the head of Morghul Vale. On the left sharp jagged pinnacles full of black crevices. And high upon one tip a small black tower.[3]

What is that tower? said Frodo full of suspicion. Is there a guard? Then they found Gollum had slipped away and vanished.

Frodo is full of fear. But Sam says Well we're up this .... near very top of mountains. Further than we ever hoped to get. Let's go on and get it over.

188   THE WAR OF THE RING

Frodo goes forward and Sam follows. Sam is suddenly lassooed and falls back. He calls out but Frodo does not come. He struggles up and falls again – something is round his feet. Slashes himself free in a fury of rage. Frodo master he cries, and then sees the great spider that has attacked him. He lunges forward but the creature makes off. Then he sees that there [are] a great number about – issuing out of the crevices, but they are all hurrying forward along the road, taking no further notice of him.

Lines are drawn on the manuscript here, and though the immediately preceding passage was not struck out it was obviously rejected at this point. Its meaning is not immediately plain: does 'him' in 'the great spider that has attacked him' refer to Sam or to Frodo? On general grounds it might seem at first sight more likely to be Frodo: in both the earlier outlines it was Frodo who was the victim, and so also in the version that replaced this. That Frodo would be the victim here also cannot indeed be doubted; but it seems to me certain that 'him' is in fact Sam – precisely because he escaped (and the words 'lassooed' and 'slashes himself free' clearly refer to attack by a spider). Sam had to be delayed in some way so that he was not at hand when the attack on Frodo took place. The first idea was that one of the spiders went for Sam too, but unsuccessfully; my father then saw at once that it was not a spider that came on him from behind, but Gollum. What idea lay behind the statement that the other spiders were all hurrying forward along the path and taking no further notice of Sam is not clear, but presumably they were going after Frodo (instigated by Gollum?).

Returning to the beginning of the last paragraph, the outline continues:

Sam suddenly sees the spiders coming out of crevices. He can't see Frodo and calls out in warning, but at that moment he is seized from behind. He can't draw sword. Gollum trips him and he falls. Gollum tries to get at Sam's sword. Sam has long fight and eventually gets hand on his stave and deals Gollum a blow. Gollum wriggles aside and only gets a whack across his hands. He lets go. Sam is aiming another blow at him when he springs away and going like lightning disappears into a crevice. Sam rushes forward to find Frodo. He is too late. There are great spiders round him. Sam draws sword and fights but they don't seem to [?heed] it. Then he found Sting lying by Frodo's outstretched arm. (2 or 3 dead spiders by him.)

He seizes Sting and drives off the spiders. Frodo lying as if dead. Spiders have stung him. He is pale as death. Sam uses

KIRITH UNGOL   189

phial. Reminds Sam of his vision in the mirror of Galadriel.[4] All efforts to rouse his master fail. He can hear or feel no heart beat. He is dead. Sam [?falls] first into senseless rage against Gollum [?beating] the stones and shouting at him to come out and fight. Then into a black despair of grief. How long he sat there he never knew. He came out of this black trance to find Frodo still just as he had left him, but now greenish in hue, a horrible dead look with a ....[5]

Sam remembers he himself had said that he had a job to do. Wonders if it has come to him now. He takes the phial and Sting and buckles belt. Sam the two-sworded he says grimly. Prays for strength to fight and avenge Frodo. At that moment he would have marched straight to death, straight to the very Eye of Baraddur.

Two additions were made at the time of writing to the text on this page, the first directed to this point by an arrow: 'Lament see 5c'. This is a reference to the previous outline story, where the words 'Then he sat and made a *Lament for Frodo*' (p. 185) appear on a page numbered '5 continued'. The other addition is conveniently given here, since it is needed to explain the narrative immediately following:

Orcs have *captured* Gollum – all his little plan of getting Frodo tied up by spiders has gone [?wrong]. They are driving Gollum.

The text continues:

Noise of [?approaching] Orc-laughter. Down out of a cleft Gollum leading comes a band of black orcs. Desperate Sam draws off the ring from Frodo's neck and takes it. He could not unclasp it or cut the chain so he slipped it over Frodo's neck and put it on. As he did so he stumbled forward, it was as if a great stone had been suddenly strung about his neck. At that moment up come orcs. Sam slips on Ring.

Frodo cries – or is Sam's motive simply that [?wishing] to bury Frodo: he won't see Frodo's body carried off. Also wanting to get at Gollum.

To clarify the syntax of the sentence beginning 'Frodo cries' the word *wishing* (?) might be read as *wishes* (sc. 'he wishes'), or *of* might be understood before *wishing*; but even so my father's thought is most elliptically expressed and difficult to follow. However, since immediately beneath these last two sentences he drew lines on the manuscript, implying that the story just sketched was about to be modified, I think that an interpretation on these lines may be correct. 'Frodo cries' is to be understood in relation to the earlier outline

190 THE WAR OF THE RING

(p. 186): when the Orcs take Frodo he 'seems to awake, and gives a loud cry'. The following words ('or is Sam's motive...') show my father breaking off altogether, and questioning the rightness of what he had just outlined: perhaps this story of Sam's taking the Ring from Frodo because of the approaching Orcs was wrong. Perhaps Sam's only 'motive' (meaning his only purpose, or desire) at this juncture was not to leave Frodo simply lying where he fell (cf. the previous outline, p. 185: 'He could not leave his dear master lying in the wild for the fell beasts and carrion birds; and he thought he would try and build a cairn of stones about him') – and his desire to take revenge on Gollum. I think that some such interpretation is borne out by the revised story that immediately follows.

Make Sam *sit* long by Frodo all through night. Hold phial up and see him elvish-fair. Torn by not knowing what to do. He lays Frodo out, and folds his hands. Mithril coat. Phial in his hand. Sting at side.

Tries to go on and finish job. Can't force himself to. How to die [?soon]. Thinks of jumping over brink. But might as well try to do *something*. Crack of Doom? Reluctantly as it seems a theft in a way he takes Ring. Goes forward on the path in a violent sorrow and despair. [*In margin:* Red dawn.] But cannot drag himself away from Frodo. Turns back – resolved to lie down by Frodo till death comes. Then he sees Gollum come and paw him. He gives a start and runs back. But orcs come out and Gollum bolts. Orcs pick up Frodo and carry him off. Sam plods after them. *Sam puts on ring!* It seems to have grown in might and power. It weighs down his hand. But he can see with terrible clearness – even *through* the rocks. He can see every crevice filled with spiders. He can understand orc speech. But the ring does *not* confer courage on Sam.

It seems they had been warned for *special vigilance*. Some spy of more than usual importance could try to get in somehow. If any were caught messenger to be [?sent]. *Phial taken.* Sam follows up a long stair to the tower. He can see all plain below. The Black Gate and Ithilien and Gorgoroth and Mt. Doom.

Here this outline ends. As revised in the course of its composition, the story now stood thus in its essential structure:

- They enter a tunnel, which halfway through is blocked with webs. Frodo shears the webs with Sting.
- At the end of the tunnel they come to a long stair. (Description of the spiders, which are well known to Gollum.)

KIRITH UNGOL 191

- At the top of the stair they see the tower; and find that Gollum has disappeared.
- Frodo goes ahead; Sam behind sees spiders coming and cries out to Frodo, but at that moment is grappled by Gollum from behind. Sam fights him off, and Gollum escapes.
- Sam finds Frodo dead, as he thinks, stung by spiders. He seizes Sting and drives them off; he sits by Frodo all night; puts the phial in his hand and Sting beside him.
- He thinks that he must himself attempt Frodo's task, takes the Ring and sets off.
- But he cannot do this, and turns back; he sees Gollum come out and paw at Frodo, but as he runs back Orcs come and Gollum flees.
- The Orcs pick up Frodo and carry him off.
- Sam puts on the Ring, and follows the Orcs up a stair to the tower.

Comparison of this outline with the old one shows that the new narrative was a development from it, and by no means an entirely fresh start; here and there even the wording was preserved. The single Great Spider had not yet emerged. But (considered simply as a step-by-step structure) it was already transformed, partly through the wholly different conception of the pass of Kirith Ungol, partly through the changed view of Gollum's rôle; and even as the new outline was set on paper his rôle was changed further. At first the Orcs were guided to the spot by Gollum, though he was forced to do so, his own nefarious plan being entirely based on the spiders; but by the time my father had reached the end of it he had decided that Gollum had in fact no traffic whatsoever with the Orcs.

The idea that the tunnel was barred by great webs is present, but since Frodo was able to cut a way through with Sting their presence does not affect the actual evolution of the plot. The words 'Gollum refuses to say what they are' suggest that they entered the story as the explanation of what Gollum's 'little plan' had actually been: and that, I take it, was that Frodo and Sam should be entrapped in the tunnel and so delivered to the spiders. But he had not envisaged that Frodo's elvish blade would be able to cut the strands.

The important element now enters that Frodo went ahead when they issued from the tunnel (and thus Sam had become separated from him when he was attacked by the spiders), although no explanation of this is given.

A very notable feature of this outline is that Sam's clarity of vision when he wears the Ring is not merely retained from the old plot ('The Ring seems to grow in power in this region: he sees clearly in the dark', p. 186), but is greatly increased: he can even see *through* the rocks; in TT (p. 343), on the other hand, 'all things about him now were not

192   THE WAR OF THE RING

dark but vague; while he himself was there in a grey hazy world, alone, like a small black solid rock'. On this question see VII.373–4, 380–1; and for the further development of this element (the effect of the Ring on Sam's senses) see pp. 212, 214.

The fair copy manuscript was built up in stages. From the beginning of the chapter 'The Stairs of Kirith Ungol', as far as 'Frodo felt his senses reeling, his limbs weakening' (cf. TT p. 313), it was developed from the original draft (p. 186) and virtually attained the form in TT; but from this point my father briefly returned to his frustrating practice of erasing his pencilled draft and writing the fair copy on the pages where it had stood. This only extends for a couple of pages, however, and some words and phrases escaped erasure; while on the third page the draft was not erased but overwritten, and here much of the original text can be read. This carries the narrative to the point (TT p. 317) where the host out of Minas Morghul had disappeared down the westward road and Sam urged Frodo to rouse himself; and there is no reason whatever to think that the lost pages of the draft were other than a more roughly expressed version of the final narrative.[6]

But from this point (where the pencilled draft reads: 'Frodo rose, grasping his staff in one hand and the phial in the other. Then he saw that a faint light was welling through his fingers and he thrust it in his bosom') the original narrative diverged, and was followed in the fair copy manuscript (where it was subsequently replaced by the later story). This first form of the fully-written story may be called 'Version 1'. The textual situation at this point is odd and perplexing, but it is sufficient to say here that the opening of this section (of no great length) is lost, both in draft and fair copy, and the story only takes up again with the strange smell that the hobbits could not identify (cf. 'Shelob's Lair' in TT, p. 326).[7]

I feel certain that the lost lines carried an account of the climbing of *the first stair*, leading to an opening in the rock which was *the mouth of the tunnel*, from which the strange smell came (whereas in TT the text at this point tells how after the passage of the ledge the path came to 'a narrow opening in the rock' which was the entry to the high-walled *first stair*). My father still had in mind the series described in the draft text of 'The Black Gate is Closed' (p. 124), where Gollum says 'a *stair* and path, and *then a tunnel*, and *then more stairs* and then a cleft high above the main pass', and again in the following outline (p. 125), where they 'pass up *first stair* safely. But *tunnel* is black with webs of spiders. ... force way and get up *second stair*.' And again, in the original draft for 'The Stairs of Kirith Ungol' (p. 186), when they began to climb up from the valley they came to 'steps'. Further evidence in support of this will appear shortly.

After the obliterated lines the original story continues thus.

... a strange odour came out of it – not the odour of decay in

KIRITH UNGOL

193

the valley below, an odour that the hobbits did not recognize, a repellent taint on the air.[8]

Resigning themselves to fear they passed inside. It was altogether lightless. After some little time Sam suddenly tumbled into Gollum ahead of him and Frodo against Sam. 'What's up now?' said Sam. 'Brought us to a dead end, have you?' 'Dead end – that's good,' he muttered. 'It about describes it.' 'What's up, you old villain?' Gollum did not answer him.

Sam pushed him aside and thrust forward, only to meet something that yielded but would not give way, soft, unseen and strong as if the darkness could be felt. 'Something's across the path,' he said. 'Some trap or something. What's to be done? If this old villain knows about it, as I bet he does, why won't he speak?'

'Because he doesn't know,' hissed Gollum. 'He's thinking. We didn't expect to find this here, did we precious? No, of course not. We wants to get out, of course we does, yes, yes.'

'Stand back,' said Frodo, and then suddenly drawing his hand from his bosom he held aloft the phial of Galadriel. For a moment it flickered, like a star struggling through the mists of Earth, then as fear left him it began to burn[9] with dazzling silver light, as if Earendel himself had come down from the sunset paths with the Silmaril upon his brow. Gollum cowered away from the light, which for some reason seemed to fill him with fear.

Frodo drew his sword, and Sting leapt out. The bright rays of the star-glass sparkled upon the blade, but on its edges ran an ominous blue fire – to which at that time Frodo nor Sam gave heed.

'Version 1' in the fair copy manuscript stops here, at the foot of a page, the remainder having been taken out of it when rejected and replaced.[10] The next page of 'Version 1' is preserved, however; it was separated from the other 'Kirith Ungol' papers many years ago, and is now in the Bodleian Library at Oxford, among other illustrations to *The Lord of the Rings* – for the verso of the page, in addition to text, bears a picture of the ascent to Kirith Ungol. This was reproduced in *Pictures by J. R. R. Tolkien* (no. 28, 'Shelob's Lair'), and is reproduced again in this book (first frontispiece). That the recto of the page is the continuation of the text from the point reached is assured both by the page-number '[6]', following '[5]' in the fair copy manuscript, and by internal association, notably Sam's words when he sees that they are confronted by spiders' webs: 'Why didn't you speak, Gollum?' (cf. his

194 THE WAR OF THE RING

words on the preceding page: 'Something's across the path... If this old villain knows about it, as I bet he does, why won't he speak?'). The recto reads thus:

Before them was a greyness which the light did not penetrate. Dull and heavy it *absorbed* the light. Across the whole width of the tunnel from floor to floor and side to side were .... [11] webs. Orderly as the webs of spiders, but far greater: each thread as thick as a great cord.

Sam laughed grimly when he saw them. 'Cobwebs,' he said. 'Is that all! Why didn't you speak, Gollum? But I might have guessed for myself! Cobwebs! Mighty big ones, but we'll get at them.' He drew his sword and hewed, but the thread that he struck did not break, it yielded and then sprang back like a bowstring, turning the blade and tossing his sword and arm backward. Three times Sam struck, and at last one thread snapped, twisting and curling, whipping about like a snapped harpstring. As an end lashed Sam's hand and stung like a whip. [*sic*] He cried out and stood back. 'It'd take weeks this way,' he said. 'Let me try Bilbo's sword,' said Frodo. 'I will go ahead now: *hold my star-glass behind me.*' Frodo drew Sting[12] and made a great sweeping stroke and sprang back to avoid the lashing of the threads.

The sharp elven-blade blue-edged sparkling shore through the netted ropes and that web was destroyed. But there were others behind. Slowly Frodo hewed his way through them until at last they came to a clear way again. Sam came behind holding up the light and pushing Gollum – strangely reluctant – before him. Gollum kept on trying to wriggle away and turn back.[13]

At length they came to more webs, and when they had cut through these the tunnel came to an end.

The rock wall opened out and sprang high and the second stair was before them: walls on either side towering up to a great height – how high they could not guess, for the sky was hardly less black than the walls – and could only be discerned by an occasional glow and flicker of red on the underside of the clouds. The stair seemed endless, up, up, up. Their knees cracked. Here and there was a web across the way. They were in the very heart of the mountains. Up, up.

At last they got to the stair-head. The road opened out. Then all their suspicions of Gollum came to a head. He sprang unexpectedly out of Sam's reach forward, and thrusting Frodo

KIRITH UNGOL 195

aside ran out emitting a shrill sort of whistling cry, such as they had never heard him make before.

'Come here! you wretch,' cried Sam darting after him. Gollum turned once with his eyes glittering, and then vanished quite suddenly into the gloom, and no sign of him could they find.[14]

The verso of the page, numbered '[7]', carrying the picture of the ascent to the pass,[15] has the following text.

'That's that!' said Sam. 'What I expected. But I don't like it. I suppose now we are just exactly where he wanted to bring us. Well, let's get moving away as quick as we can. The treacherous worm! That last whistle of his wasn't pure joy at getting out of the tunnel, it was pure wickedness of some sort. And what sort we'll soon know.'

'Likely enough,' said Frodo. 'But we could not have got even so far without him. So if we ever manage our errand, then Gollum and all his wickedness will be part of the plan.'

'So far, you say,' said Sam. 'How far? Where are we now?'

'About at the crest of the main range of Ephel-dúath, I guess,' said Frodo. 'Look!' The road opened out now: it still went on up, but no longer sheerly. Beyond and ahead there was an ominous glare in the sky, and like a great notch in the mountain wall a cleft was outlined against it — so [here is a small sketch]. On their right the wall of rock fell away and the road widened till it had no brink. Looking down Frodo saw nothing but the vast darkness of the great ravine which was the head of Morghul dale. Down in its depths was the faint glimmer of the wraith-road that led over the Morghul pass from the city. On their left sharp jagged pinnacles stood up like towers carved by the biting years, and between them were many dark crevices and clefts. But high up on the left side of the cleft to which their road led (Kirith Ungol) was a small black tower, and in it a window showed a red light.

'I don't like the look of that,' said Sam. 'This upper pass is guarded too. D'you remember he never would say if it was or no. D'you think he's gone to fetch them – orcs or something?'

'No, I don't think so,' said Frodo. 'He is up to no good, of course, but I don't think that he's gone to fetch orcs. Whatever it is, it is no slave of the Dark Lord's.' 'I suppose not,' said Sam. 'No, I suppose the whole time it has been the ring for poor

196   THE WAR OF THE RING

Smeagol's own. That's been his scheme. But how coming up here will help him, I can't guess.' He was soon to learn.

Frodo went forward now – the last lap – and he exerted all his strength. He felt that if once he could get to the saddle of the pass and look over into the Nameless Land he would have accomplished something. Sam followed. He sensed evil all round him. He knew that they had walked into some trap, but what? He had sheathed his sword, but now he drew it in readiness. He halted for a moment, and stooped to pick up his staff with his left hand

Here the text on the 'Bodleian page' ends, but the further continuation of this extraordinarily dismembered text is found among the papers that failed to go to Marquette.[16] The next page is duly numbered '[8]' and '[9]', and continues as before in ink over pencilled drafting.

– it had a comfortable feel to his hand. As he stood up again, he saw issuing out of a crevice at the left the most monstrous and loathly form that he had ever beheld – beyond his imagination.[17] Spider-like it was in shape, but huge as a wild beast, and more terrible because of the malice and evil purpose in its eyes. These were many, clustered in its small head, and each of them held a baleful light. On great bent legs it walked – the hairs of them stuck out like steel spines, and at each end there was a claw. The round swollen body behind its narrow neck was dark blotched with paler livid marks, but underneath its belly was pale and faintly luminous as its eyes. It stank. It moved with a sudden horrible speed running on its arms, and springing. Sam saw at once that he [*sic*] was hunting his master – now a little ahead in the gloom and apparently unaware of his peril. He whipped out his sword and yelled. 'Look out! Mr Frodo! Look out! I'm —' But he did not finish. A long clammy hand went over his mouth and another caught his neck, while something wrapped itself about his legs. Taken off his guard he fell backwards in the arms of his attacker.

'Got you!' hissed Gollum in his ear. 'At last my precious one, we've got him yes, the nasty hobbit. We takes this one. She'll get the other. O yes. Ungoliant will get him.[18] Not Smeagol. He won't hurt master, not at all. He promised. But he's got you, you nasty dirty little thing!'

KIRITH UNGOL   197

The description of the fight is closely similar to that in TT (p. 335), with some difference in the detail of the wrestling.[19] After the second blow, falling across Gollum's back, the text continues:

But it was enough for Gollum! Grabbing from behind was an old game for him – and had never before failed him. But everything had gone wrong with his beautiful plan, since the unexpected web in the path. Here now he was faced by a furious enemy, little less than his own size, with a stout staff. This was not for him. He had no time even to grab at the sword lying on the ground. He squealed as the staff came down once more,[20] and sprang aside onto all fours, and then leaped away like a cat in one big bound. Then with astonishing speed he ran back and vanished into the tunnel. Sweeping up his sword Sam went after him – for the moment forgetful of all else, but the red light of fury in his brain. But Gollum had gone before he could reach him. Then as the dark hole and the stench smote him, like a terrible clap of thunder the thought of Frodo came back to Sam's mind. He span round, and rushed on up the road calling. He was too late. So far Gollum's plot had succeeded.

Frodo was lying on the ground and the monster was bending over him, so intent upon her victim that she seemed not to heed anything else until Sam was close at hand. It was not a brave deed Sam then did, for he gave no thought to it. Frodo was already bound in great cords round and round from ankle to breast, and with her great forelegs she was beginning to half lift, half drag him, but still his arms were free: one hand was on his breast, one lay spread wide, limp upon the stone, and the staff of Faramir broken under him.

At the point where Sam sees that Frodo is bound with cords the underlying pencilled draft stops; the legible fair copy in ink written over it continues, but at the same point declines very rapidly into the handwriting characteristic of initial drafting, decipherable only with labour and in this case often not at all.[21] This continues to the end of the page ('9' in the Version I text, the last page in this numeration), with Sam's attack on 'Ungoliant'. Many words and even whole sentences are totally illegible, but enough can be made out to see that in this earliest form of the story it was Sam's slash with Sting across Ungoliant's belly that caused her to leap back: there is no suggestion of the great wound she suffered when she drove her whole bulk down onto the point of the sword (TT p. 338). When she sprang back 'Sam stood reeling, his legs astride his master, but she a few paces off eyed him: and the green venom that was her blood slowly suffused the pale

198   THE WAR OF THE RING

light of her eyes. Sting held before him, Sam now .... and ere she attacked again he found his master's hand in his bosom. It was cold and limp, and quickly but gently he took from it the glass of Galadriel. And held it up.'

This rough drafting continues on other pages (not numbered on from '9', though that proves little); but I doubt that much more of it, if any, was written at this juncture (see p. 209). The question is not of much importance in the study of the evolution of the story, and in any case it is more convenient to pause here in the original draft.

The fact that my father had overwritten legibly in ink the original draft as far as the stinging of Frodo by Ungoliant suggests confidence in the story, while the sudden change from 'fair copy' to 'preliminary draft' at this point suggests that he now realised that important changes were required. The immediate reason for this may well have been that he observed what he had just written, as it were inadvertently: 'Then with astonishing speed [Gollum] ran back and vanished *into the tunnel*. ... Then as the dark hole and the stench smote him ... the thought of Frodo came back to Sam's mind. He span round, and rushed on up the road calling.' But in this version the far end of the tunnel was immediately succeeded by the agonisingly long second stair, and it was only after they reached the head of it that Gollum ran off (p. 194). The picture of the ascent to the pass contained in this text (see p. 193) shows with perfect clarity the *first stair* climbing up to the tunnel, and the *second* stair climbing away beyond it.[22] It is obviously out of the question that my father imagined that Gollum fled all the way down the second stair with Sam in pursuit, and that Sam then climbed up again! I think that the developing narrative was forcing a new topography to appear even as he wrote (see below).

There seem in fact to have been several interrelated questions. One was this of topography: the relation of the stairs and the tunnel. Another was the time and place of Gollum's disappearance. In the outline (p. 187) he is found to have vanished when they come to the head of the second stair; and in the present version he ran off with a strange whistling cry when they came to that place. And another was the question of Gollum's plan and its miscarriage. My father had written (p. 197): 'But everything had gone wrong with his beautiful plan, *since the unexpected web in the path*.' It certainly seems to be the case in this version that Gollum was very put out when they encountered it in the tunnel: 'We didn't expect to find this here, did we precious? No, of course not' (p. 193); and after the first webs had been cut through Gollum was 'strangely reluctant' to go on, and 'kept on trying to wriggle away and turn back.'

Leaving the 'Version I' text, now reduced to very rough drafting, at some point not determined, my father scribbled on a little bit of paper:

KIRITH UNGOL   199

Must be stair — stair — tunnel. Tunnel is Ungoliante's lair. The tunnel has unseen passages off. One goes right up to dungeons of tower. But orcs don't use it much because of Ungoliant. She has a great hole in the midst of path. Plan fails because she has made a *web* across path and is daunted by the phial-light. Stench out of *hole* which phial prevents Frodo and Sam falling into. Gollum disappears and they think he may have fallen in hole. They cut their way out of web at far end. Ungoliant comes out of tunnel.

Thus the series 'first stair — tunnel — second stair' inherent in the Version 1 story is changed. The reason for this was, I think, as follows. The arrangement 'stair — tunnel — stair' arose when there were many spiders in the pass; in the outline the tunnel seems only one part of their territory, and there are webs also across the second stair (p. 187) — the impression is given that all the cliffs and crags bordering the path are alive with them. But with the reduction of the spider-horde to one Great Spider, whose lair is very clearly in the tunnel (where the great webs were), her attack on the hobbits at the head of the second stair, high above the tunnel, becomes unsatisfactory. It was therefore not long after the emergence in Version 1 of Ungoliant as the sole breeder of the terror of Kirith Ungol that this version collapsed, and my father abandoned the writing of it in fair copy manuscript. Associated with this would have been the decision that Gollum deserted Frodo and Sam while they were still in the tunnel.

The plot outlined in the brief text just given is not very clear; but at this same time, perhaps on the same day, my father wrote the fuller note, together with a plan of the tunnels, that is reproduced on p. 201. This also is in the Bodleian Library (see p. 193). The title *Plan of Shelob's Lair* was written onto the page subsequently, since the name of the Spider in the text is Ungoliant(e); cf. note 15.

This text reads:

Must be Stair — Stair — Tunnel. Tunnel is Ungoliante's Lair.

This tunnel is of orc-make (?) and has the usual branching passages. One goes right up into the dungeons of the Tower — but orcs don't use it much because of Ungoliante.[23] Ungoliante has made a hole and a trap in the middle of the floor of the main path.

Gollum's plan was to get Frodo into trap. He hoped to get Ring, and leave the rest to Ungoliant. Plan failed because Ungoliant was suspicious of him —? he had come nosing up as far as the tunnel the day before? — and she had put a web on near (west) side of hole. When Frodo held up the phial she was daunted for [a] moment and retreated to her lair. But when the

200   THE WAR OF THE RING

hobbits issued from tunnel she came out by side paths and crept
round them.

Phial prevents F. and S. falling into the hole; but a horrible
stench comes out of it. Gollum disappears and they fear he has
fallen in the hole. But they do not go back — (a) they see tower
with a light on cliffs at head of pass and (b) while they are
wondering about this and suspect betrayal the attack is made:
Ungoliant going for Frodo, while Gollum grapples Sam from
behind. Ungol[iant] specially wants the star-glass? (Frodo had
hidden it again when he came out of tunnel).

Web at end of tunnel?

The plan of the tunnel was mostly drawn in pencil and then
overdrawn in black ink. The word pencilled against the minor tunnel
to the north of the main passage seems to read 'Bypas[s]'. The
pencilled circle in the main passage is marked 'Trap', and the large
black circle 'Ungoliant's lair'. Of the two southward tunnels that leave
the main one near its eastern end, the westerly one is marked
'Underground way to Tower', and the broad tunnel (drawn with
several lines) that leaves this one eastwards will be the way by which
Ungoliant emerged to the attack. The last tunnel branching southwards from the main one was added in blue ball-point pen, and is
marked 'orc-path'.[24]

Since my father is seen in these notes actually setting down his
decision that the second stair preceded the tunnel, it was presumably
at this juncture that (leaving aside the question of how far the further
story had progressed at this time) he turned back to the point where
the faulty conception entered the narrative (see p. 192); and indeed on
the back of the first of these notes is found drafting for the new version
of the story dependent on the decision (cf. TT p. 317):

Following him they came to the climbing ledge. Not daring to look
down to their right they passed along it. At last it came to a rounded
angle where the mountain-side swelled out again before them. There
the path suddenly entered into a dark opening in the rock, and there
before them was the first stair that Gollum had spoken of.

Then follows the description of the first stair. Thus the 'opening in the
rock' was neatly transformed from the mouth of the tunnel into the
beginning of the stair (p. 192).

Continuous drafting is found for the revised narrative ('Version 2'),
and the story as told in TT was very largely achieved already in the
draft as far as the events in the tunnel: the climbs up the Straight Stair
and the Winding Stair, the hobbits' rest beside the path, their talk of
the need to find water[25] leading to the conversation about tales
(written down *ab initio* in a form closely similar to that in TT), their

KIRITH UNGOL

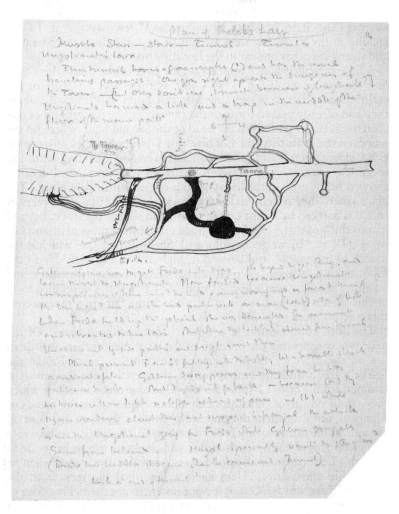

Plan of Shelob's Lair (1)

202   THE WAR OF THE RING

realisation that Gollum had disappeared, his return, finding them
asleep (with the description of his 'interior debate', looking back up
towards the pass and shaking his head, his appearance as of 'an old
weary hobbit who had lived beyond his time and lost all his friends
and kin: a starved old thing sad and pitiable'), and Sam's unhappy
mistaking of his gesture towards Frodo (TT pp. 317–25, where the
chapter 'The Stairs of Cirith Ungol' ends). A few passages in TT are
lacking in the draft, but they are not of importance to the narrative
and in any case they appear in the fair copy manuscript.

A little pencilled sketch appears on the page of the draft where they
first see the tower (TT p. 319) – just as there was a picture of the
earlier conception of Kirith Ungol at this point in Version 1 (where
they had already passed through the tunnel). In the foreground of this
sketch is seen the path from the head of the Second Stair, where (in the
words of the draft text) the hobbits 'saw jagged pinnacles of stone on
either side: columns and spikes torn and carven in the biting years and
forgotten winters, and between them great crevices and fissures
showed black even in the heavy gloom of that unfriendly place.' The
place where they rested ('in a dark crevice between two great piers of
rock') is marked by a spot on the right hand side of the track. Beyond
is seen the 'great grey wall, a last huge upthrusting mass of mountain-
stone' (TT p. 326, at the beginning of 'Shelob's Lair'), in which is the
mouth of the tunnel, and beyond it, high above, the 'cleft ... in the
topmost ridge, narrow, deep-cloven between two black shoulders; and
on either shoulder was a horn of stone' (TT p. 319). A developed form
of this sketch is found at the same place in the fair copy manuscript;
this is reproduced on p. 204.[26]

The draft continues on into 'Shelob's Lair' without break. Of the
narrative constituting the opening of the later chapter there is little to
say. In the draft the Elvish name of the tunnel is *Terch Ungol* 'the
Spider's Lair'; and the description of the stench from the tunnel is
retained from Version 1 (pp. 192–3): 'Out of it came an odour which
they could not place: not the sickly odour of decay by the meads of
Morghul, but a repellent noisome stuffy smell: a repellent evil taint on
the air.' In the fair copy my father first put *Te*, changing it as he wrote
to *Torech Ungol* 'the Spider's Hole', and changing this as he wrote to
'Shelob's Lair' (the name *Shelob* having been already devised when he
wrote this manuscript). Here he first described the reek from the
tunnel in these words: 'Out of it came a stench: not the sickly odour of
decay from the meads of Morghul, but a choking rankness, noisome, a
reek as of piled and hoarded filth beyond reckoning, tainting even the
open air with evil.' But he queried in the margin whether this
description was not too strong: if the stench had been so unendurably
horrible even from outside 'would they ever have gone in?'; and
replaced it immediately with the description in TT (p. 326). He
hesitated too about the width of the tunnel.

KIRITH UNGOL

203

The new story in the draft version reaches the final form in their realisation that there were side tunnels, and in the things that brushed against them as they walked, until they passed the wide opening on the left from which the stench and the intense feeling of evil came. From this point the draft text reads:

... a sense of evil so strong that for a moment he grew faint. Sam also lurched. 'There's something in there,' he says. 'It smells like a death-house. Pooh.' Putting out their remaining strength and resolution they went on. Presently they came to what almost seemed a fork in the tunnel: at least in the absolute gloom they were in doubt.

'Which way's Gollum gone,' said Sam, 'I wonder.'

'Smeagol!' said Frodo. 'Smeagol!' But his voice fell back dead from his lips. There was no answer, not even an echo. 'He's really gone this time, I fancy.'

'Now we are just exactly where he wanted to bring us, I fancy. But just what he means to do in this black hole I can't guess.' He had not to wait long for the answer.

'What about that star-glass?' said Sam. 'Did not the Lady say it would be a light in dark places? And we need some to be sure now.'

'I have not used it,' said Frodo, 'because of Gollum. I think it would have driven him away, and also because it would be so bright. But here we seem to have come to a desperate pass.' Slowly he drew his hand from his bosom and held aloft the phial of Galadriel. For a moment it flickered like a star struggling through the mists of Earth, then as fear left them it began to burn into a dazzling brilliant silver light, as if Earendel himself had come down from the sunset paths with the last Silmaril upon his brow. The darkness receded from it and it shone in a globe of space enclosed with utter blackness. But before them within the radius of its light were two openings. Now their doubt was resolved, for the one to the left turned quickly away, while the one to the right went straight on only a little narrower than the tunnel behind.

At that moment some prescience of malice or of some evil regard made them both turn. Their hearts stood still. [There was a shrill whistling cry of Gollum?] Not far behind, ... by the noisome opening perhaps, were eyes: two great clusters of eyes. Whether they shone of their own light or whether the radiance of the star-glass was reflected in their thousand facets .....
Monstrous and abominable and fell they were: bestial yet filled

L.C.11.C.(cont)   (8

Dimly could be seen discerned tall piers and jagged pinnacle of
stone on either side, and between them great crevices and fissures blacker
than the general night, —— where the forgotten winters in the Dark Years
had gnawed and carved the sunless stone. And now the red light in
the sky seemed stronger, though whether a dreadful morning was indeed
coming to this place of shadows they could not tell, or whether only they saw
the flame of some great violence of Sauron in the torment of Gorgoroth
beyond. Still far ahead, and still high above, Frodo looking up saw,
as he guessed, the very crown of this bitter road. Against the sullen redness
of the eastern sky a cleft in the topmost ridge, narrow, deep-cloven between
two black shoulders and on either shoulder was a horn of stone.

He paused and looked more attentively.
The horn upon the left was tall and slender;
and in it burned a red light, or the red light behind it
shone through a hole. He saw now: it was a black
tower poised above the outer pass. He touched
Sam's arm and pointed.

'I don't like the look of that!' said Sam. 'So,
this secret way of yours is guarded after all,' he
growled, turning to Gollum. 'And you knew all along,
I suppose?'
'All ways are watched, yes,' said Gollum. 'Of course they are. But this
Hobbits must try some way. This may be the least watched.
Perhaps they've all gone away to big battle — perhaps!'

'Perhaps!' grunted Sam. 'Well, it still seems a long way off and a
long way up, before we get there. And there's still the tunnel. I think you
ought to rest now, Mr. Frodo. I don't know what time of day
or night it is, but we've kept going now for hours and hours.'

'Yes, we must rest,' said Frodo. 'Let us find some corner out of the wind, if
we can, and gather our strength — for the last lap.' For so he felt it. The
terrors of the land beyond, and the deed to be done there seemed remote,
too far to trouble him. All his mind was bent on getting through,
or over this impenetrable wall and guard. If once he could do that impossible
thing, then somehow the errand would be accomplished, or so it seemed
still faltering in the strong shadows ...

In a dark crevice between two great piers of rock they sat down.
Frodo and Sam a little way within, and Gollum crouched upon the
ground at the opening. Then the Hobbits took what they supposed
would be their last meal before they went, said Sam, into the Nameless Land,
maybe their last meal they would ever eat. Some of the food of Gondor they
ate, and wafers of the waybread of the Elves, and they drank a little.

Kirith Ungol

KIRITH UNGOL   205

with a malice and purpose and even with a hideous glee and
delight such as no beast's eyes can show. An evil mind gloated
behind that baleful light.

At this point my father stopped, and noted that the eyes must come
first, and then the star-glass (necessarily implying that the eyes of the
Spider shone with their own light). An outline follows:

The creature backs away. They retreat up the tunnel. Frodo
holds glass aloft and ..... [27] and each time the eyes halt.
Then filled with a sudden resolve he drew Sting. It sparkled,
and calling to Sam he strode back towards the eyes. They ...
[?turned] retreated and disappeared. Sam full of admiration.
'Now let's run for it!' he said. They ran, and suddenly [?crashed]
into [?greyness] which rebounded and turned them back. Sam
cannot break the threads. Frodo gives him Sting. And Sam hews
while Frodo stands guard.

The web gives way. They rush out and find web was over
the mouth of the tunnel. They are in the last gully and the
horn-pass ... before them.

'That's the top,' said Sam. 'And we've come out of it. Our
luck's in still. On we go now, and take the last bit while the luck
lasts.'

Frodo ran forward placing his star-glass in his bosom, no
thought for anything but escape. Sam follows with Sting drawn
– constantly turning to watch the mouth of the tunnel –
thinking too little of the craft of Ungoliant. She had many exits
from her lair.

Frodo was gaining on him. He tried to run, and then some
way ahead he saw issuing out of a shadow in the wall of the
ravine the most monstrous and loathsome shape. Beyond the
imagination of his worst dreams.

This account agrees well with the plan reproduced on p. 201: they
had passed the wide opening on the left which led to the lair of
Ungoliant, and the fork in the tunnel, where 'the one to the left turned
quickly away, while the one to the right went straight on only a little
narrower than the tunnel behind', can be readily identified. But the
story has shifted radically from the outline accompanying the plan
(pp. 199–200), which apparently never received narrative form, where
the story ran thus:

–   Ungoliant had stretched a web on the west side of the trap (hole) in
    the main tunnel. The stench arose from the hole.

206   THE WAR OF THE RING

- Frodo held up the phial (cutting of the webs is not mentioned) and Ungoliant retreated to her lair.
- By the light of the phial they avoided the hole. Gollum disappeared, and they feared he had fallen into it.
- They left the tunnel, whereupon Ungoliant, having come round ahead of them by a side path, attacked Frodo, and Gollum grappled Sam from behind.

In the very similar short version of this plot (p. 199) it is said in addition that 'They cut their way out of web at far end.'

The story in the present draft has moved much nearer to the final form: they passed the opening to the lair, whence the stench came, and there is no mention of the 'trap' or 'hole' in the floor of the main passage; and they came to the fork in the tunnel.[28] But in this version the phial of Galadriel is used at this juncture, in order to show them which tunnel to take; and turning round on account of a sense of approaching evil the light of the phial is reflected in the eyes of the Spider. My father's direction at this point that the eyes must come before the star-glass clearly means that the eyes, shining with their own light, appeared in the tunnel, and that only then did the thought of the star-glass arise. The remainder of the episode is now essentially as in the final form – except that as they run from the tunnel Sam has Sting and Frodo has the phial of Galadriel.

The fair copy manuscript when it reached this point still did not attain the final story in all respects, and this section of it was subsequently rejected and replaced. In the first stage, the idea in the draft that the phial was used simply to illuminate the tunnel (with Frodo's explanation that he had not used it before for fear it would drive Gollum away) was abandoned, and as in TT it was the sound only of the Spider's approach, the 'gurgling, bubbling noise' and the 'long venomous hiss', that inspired Sam to think of it (thus reversing the decision that the eyes must come first and then the star-glass); the light of the phial illumined the eyes (although 'behind the glitter a pale deadly fire began steadily *to glow within*, a flame kindled in some deep pit of evil thought'). But at this stage the idea that the light did, if only incidentally, show the way to take, was retained: 'And now the way was clear before them, for the light revealed two archways; and the one to the left was not the path, for it narrowed quickly again and turned aside, but that to the right was the true way and went straight onward as before.'[29]

The pursuit of the 'eyes', and the rout of the Spider when Frodo confronted her with the phial in his left hand and the blue-flickering[30] blade of Sting in his right, is in the final form, but my father still followed the draft in making it Sam who cut the web at the far end of

KIRITH UNGOL   207

the tunnel with Sting. The text here reads thus, from Sam's 'Gollum! May the curse of Faramir bite him' (cf. TT p. 331):[31]

'That will not help us,' said Frodo. 'Come! I will hold up the light while my strength lasts. Take my sword. It is an elven blade. See what it may do. Give me yours.'

Sam obeyed and took Sting in his hand, a thrill running through his hand as he grasped its fair hilt, the sword of his master, of Bilbo, the sword that Elrond had declared to come out of the great wars before the Dark Years when the walls of Gondolin still stood.[32] Turning he made a great sweeping stroke and then sprang back to avoid the lashing [?threads]. Blue-edged, glinting in the radiance of the star, the elven blade shore through the netted ropes. In three swift blows the web was shattered and the trap was broken. The air of the mountains flowed in like a river.

'It's clear,' Sam cried. 'It's clear. I can see the [?night] light in the sky.'

No! Make Sam hold light and so *Frodo goes out first*, and so as he has the light Shelob attacks Frodo.

Sam sweeps up Frodo's sword from ground.

He drops the Phial in struggle with Gollum.

Cut out the staffs.

This is followed by a suggestion, not entirely legible, that the staffs should 'hang on *thongs*', and another that Frodo should tap the walls of the tunnel with the staffs. My father was apparently concerned here with the problem arising from having only two hands. No doubt it was at this time that the reading of the fair copy manuscript of 'Journey to the Cross-roads', where the heads of the staves were still in the form of a shepherd's crook (p. 176 and note 3), was changed to that of TT (p. 303): 'staves ... with carven heads through which ran plaited leathern thongs'. The text continues:

When Sam cannot hew web, Frodo says: 'I do not feel the eyes any longer. For the moment their regard has moved. You take the light. Do not be afraid. Hold it up. I will see what the elven-sword may do.'

Frodo hews the webs asunder. And so the trap as it was planned was frustrated. For though once long ago he [Gollum] had seen it, the nature of that sword he did not know, and of the Phial of Galadriel he had never heard.[33]

They rush out. Sam comes behind and suddenly they are aware (a) of red window (b) of the blue light of Sting. 'Orcs',

208   THE WAR OF THE RING

said Sam, and closing his hand about the phial hid it beneath his cloak again. A sudden madness (?) on Frodo. He sees the red cleft the goal of all his effort before him. No great distance, half a mile. Gain it in a rush. Run! ..... Sam, he said. The door, the path. Now for it, before any can stay us.

Sam tries to keep up. Then the spider attacks, and Gollum.

And so this extraordinarily resistant narrative was at last shaped at almost all points to my father's satisfaction: 'a sticky patch' he described it, achieved with 'very great labour'; and further drafting led to the final text of 'Shelob's Lair' in the fair copy manuscript. Yet even now he seems not to have been entirely confident of the rightness of the story, for the manuscript carries also a second text of the episode in the tunnel (marked 'other version'), and it seems beyond question that this was written *after* the other.[34] It takes up after the words 'a gurgling, bubbling noise, and a long venomous hiss' (TT p. 328).

They wheeled round, but at first they saw nothing. Still as stones they stood waiting, for they did not know what. Then, not far down the tunnel, just at the opening where they had reeled and stumbled, they saw a gleam. Very slowly it advanced. There were eyes in the darkness. Two great clusters of eyes. They were growing larger and brighter as very slowly they advanced. They burned steadily with a fell light of their own, kindled in some deep pit of evil thought. Monstrous and abominable they were, bestial and yet filled with purpose, and with hideous delight: beyond all hope of escape their prey was trapped.

Frodo and Sam backed away, their gaze held by the dreadful stare of those cold eyes, and as they backed so the eyes came on, unhurried, gloating. Suddenly both together, as if released simultaneously from the same spell, the hobbits turned and fled blindly up the tunnel. [*Struck out:* The left-hand opening was blocked with some unseen barrier; wildly they groped and found the right-hand opening, and again they ran.] But as they ran they looked back, and saw with horror the eyes come leaping up behind.

Then there came a breath of air: cold and thin. The opening, the upper gate, the end of the tunnel – at last: it was just ahead. Desperately they threw themselves forward, and then staggered backwards. The passage was blocked by some unseen barrier: soft, strong, impenetrable. Again they flung themselves upon it. It yielded a little and then like taut cords hurled them back once more. The eyes were nearer now, halted, quietly watching them,

KIRITH UNGOL 209

gloating, glittering with cruel amusement. The stench of death was like a cloud about them.

'Stand!' said Frodo. 'It's no use struggling. We're caught.' He turned to face the eyes, and as he did so, he drew his sword. Sting flashed out, and about the edges of the sharp elven-blade a blue fire flickered.

Sam, sick, desperate, but angry more than all, groped for the hilts of his own short sword, carried so far and to so little purpose all the way from the Barrowdowns. 'I wish old Bombadil was near.' he muttered. 'Trapped in the end! Gollum – may the curse of Faramir bite him.' Darkness was about him and a blackness in his heart. And then suddenly even in those last moments before the evil thing made its final spring he saw a light, a light in the darkness of his mind...

The text continues as in the other version (TT p. 329), but without the sentences 'The bubbling hiss drew nearer, and there was a creaking as of some great jointed thing that moved with slow purpose in the dark. A reek came on before it'; and it ends at *A light when all other lights go out!* There is then a direction to 'proceed' as in the other version.

This also was a good story. There is here a formally simpler disposition of the elements: for Frodo and Sam are caught directly between the monster and the trap – trapped indeed 'beyond all hope of escape',[35] and are saved in the very last nick of time by the Phial of Galadriel.

The Choices of Master Samwise

I left 'Version 1', the original narrative in which there was no encounter with the Spider in the tunnel, and the attack on Frodo took place at the head of the Second Stair (above the tunnel), at the point where my father abandoned that version as a 'fair copy' manuscript and the text precipitously collapsed into fearfully difficult drafting: see pp. 197–8.

It is difficult to be sure of the precise development from this point, because this very rough drafting runs on continuously to the end of the story in *The Two Towers*, being indeed the original setting down of the narrative of 'The Choices of Master Samwise', and yet it cannot have been an uninterrupted continuation of Version 1. The last page that was certainly a part of Version 1 ends with a near-illegible initial account of Sam's attack on Ungoliant and his holding up the phial that he took from Frodo's body (p. 198). The conclusion of the encounter with Ungoliant may belong to Version 1, but not much more, for when Sam, arising from his long trance of despair, composes Frodo's

210   THE WAR OF THE RING

body he says: 'He lent me Sting and that I'll take'. This of course
depends on the developed story (Version 2) in which Frodo gave Sting
to Sam for an attack on the web at the end of the tunnel while he
himself held the phial (see pp. 205–7).

From the point where Sam holds up the phial against Ungoliant the
draft continues:

'Galadriel!' he cried. 'Elbereth! Now come, you filthy thing.
Now at last we know what holds this path. But we are going on.
Come on, let's settle before we go.' As if his wrath and courage
set its potency in motion, the glass blazed like a torch – like [a]
flash not of lightning but of some searing star cleaving the dark
air with intolerable radiance white and terrible. No such light of
heaven had ever burned in her face before.[36]

The account of Ungoliant's retreat is largely illegible, but phrases
can be read: 'She seemed ... to crumple like a vast bag', 'her legs
sagged, and slowly, painfully, she backed from the light away in the
opening in the wall', 'gathering her strength she turned and with a
last ..... jump and a foul but already pitiable ... [37] she slipped into
the hole.'

The declaration that whatever might have been the fate of Ungoliant
thereafter 'this tale does not tell' appears in the draft, as does (in very
rough form) the passage that follows in TT (pp. 339–40) to the point
where Sam composes Frodo's body. Here the draft text reads:

He laid his master upon his back, and folded his cold hands.
'Let the silver mail of mithril be his winding sheet,' he said.[38]
'He lent me Sting and that I'll take, but a sword shall be at his
side.' And the phial he put into his right hand and hid it in his
bosom. 'It's too good for me,' he said, 'and She gave it to him to
be a light in dark places.' There were no stones for a cairn, but
he rolled the only two he could find of a wieldy size one to
Frodo's head and another to his feet. And then he stood and
held up the star-glass. It burned gently now with a quiet
radiance as of the evening star in summer, and in its light
Frodo's hue ..... [?pale] but fair, and an elvish beauty was in
his face, as of one that is long past the shadows.

And then he strove to take farewell. But he could not. Still he
held Frodo's hand and could not let it go.

An arrow directs that the placing of the phial in Frodo's hand and
Sam's words 'It's too good for me ...' should follow '... as of one
long past the shadows'.

KIRITH UNGOL 211

The account of Sam's agonized debate was not different from its form in *The Two Towers* (pp. 341–2) in the progression of his thoughts, and his parting words and the taking of the Ring are virtually in the final form; but he does not take the phial, which in this version of the story remains hidden in Frodo's hand. From this point I give the original draft in full.

At last with a great effort he stood up and turned away and seeing nothing but a grey mist stumbled forward towards the pass now straight ahead. But still his master drew him: Sam's mind was not at peace, not really made up. (He was acting as best he could reason but against his whole nature.) He hadn't gone far when he looked back and through his tears saw the little dark patch in the ravine where all his life had fallen in ruin. Again he turned and went on, and now he was come almost to the V [*i.e. the Cleft*]. So the very gate of parting. Now he must look back for the very last time. He did so.

'No I can't do it,' he said. 'I can't. I'd go to the Dark Tower to find him, but I can't go and leave him. I can't finish this tale. It's for other folk. My chapter's ended.' He began to stumble back. And then suddenly to his wrath and horror he thought he saw a slinking thing creep out of the shadow and go up to Frodo and start pawing him.[39] Anger obliterating all other thoughts blazed up again. 'Gollum! After his precious – thinks his plot has worked after all. The dirty –' He began to run silently. There wasn't more than 20 [?yards] to cover. He got his sword out. Gollum! He ground his teeth.

But suddenly Gollum paused [and] looked round, not at Sam, and with all his speed bolted diving back towards the wall and to [the] same opening out of which Ungoliant had come.

Sam realized that Gollum had not fled from him or even noticed him. Almost at once he saw the reason. Orcs! Orcs were coming out of the tunnel. He halted in his tracks. A new choice was on him and a quick one this time. Then from behind also he heard orc-voices. Out of some path leading down from the tower orcs were coming. He was between them. No going back now – Sam would never reach the Pass of Kirith Ungol now. He gripped on Sting. A brief thought passed through his mind. How many would he kill before they got him? Would any song ever mention it? How Samwise fell in the High Pass – made a wall of bodies for his master's body. No, no song, for the Ring would be captured and all songs cease for ever [in] an age of Darkness ... The Ring. With a sudden thought and impulse

212 THE WAR OF THE RING

he *put it on!* [*Added:* His hand hangs weighed down and useless.] At first he noticed nothing – except that he seemed to see much clearer. Things seemed hard and black and heavy, and the voices loud. The orc-bands had sighted one another and were shouting. But he seemed to hear both sides as if they were speaking close to him. And he understood them. Why, they were speaking plain language. Maybe they were, or maybe the Ring which had power over all Sauron's servants and was grown in power as the place of its forging was approached brought the thought of their minds in plain speech direct to Sam.

'Hola! Gazmog,' said the foremost of the orcs coming out of the tunnel.

'Ho you Zaglûn. So you've come at last. Have you heard them? Did you see it?'

'See what? We've just come through the tunnel of She-lob.[40] What should we see or hear?'

'Shouting and crying out here and lights. Some mischief afoot. But we're on guard in the tower and not supposed to leave. We waited but you didn't come. Hurry now for we must get back. There's only Naglur-Danlo and old Nûzu up here and he's in a taking.'

Then suddenly the orcs from the tower saw Frodo and while Sam still hesitated they swept past him with a howl and rushed forward. (Sting must be sheathed.) One thing the Ring did not confer was courage – rather the reverse, at any rate on Sam. He did not now [?rush] in – or make a hill of bodies round his master. There were about three dozen of them in all, and they were talking fast and excitedly. Sam hesitated. If he drew Sting they'd see that. They wouldn't ....: Orcs never did – but 36! They [?*read* They'd] see where he was.

No – above won't do, he must see Orcs from a greater distance and *follow them.* The cleft must be no great distance, 100 yards? from Frodo's body and that 20–30 yards from tunnel. *Cut out Gollum.*

Sam sees orcs coming *down* from tower as he turns back [for the] last time. They seem from afar to spot the little shape of Frodo and give a yell. It is answered by a yell – other orcs are coming out of the tunnel! Then put in the part about his thoughts of *song* as he runs back. Puts on ring and cannot wield sword.[41] Changes it to left hand [*broken staff* (Sam's broke on Gollum)].[42] By that time orcs have picked up Frodo and are off

KIRITH UNGOL 213

to tunnel. Sam follows. Ring confers language knowledge – not courage.

Sam follows and hears conversation as they go through tunnel. Orcs discuss Frodo. Special vigilance ordered. What is it? Leader [B......] Zaglûn says[43] orders are for messages [or messengers] to go to Morgul *and* direct to Lugburz. They [?groan]. Talk of Shelob and the worm (= Gollum).

Big things are on. Only preliminary strokes. News. Osgiliath taken and ford. Army has also left North Gate. [?Other crossing] away up north somewhere and into the north part of the Horseboys' land – no opposition there. We'll be at the Mouths of Anduin in a week and at the Gulf of Lûne before the summer's out – and then nowhere to escape. How we'll make 'em sweat! We haven't begun yet. Big stuff's coming.

Big stick if you don't hurry.

Prisoner is to be stripped naked. Teeth and nails? No. Is he half elf and man – [?there's] a fair blend of folly and mischief. Quick end better. Quick!

They round a corner. Sam sees red light in an arch. Underground door to tower. Horrified to see that tunnel deceived him: they're further ahead than he thought. He runs forward but the iron door closes with a clang. He is outside in the darkness.

Now go back to Gandalf.

[*Added:* Make most of goblin conversation await the rescue chapter?]

In the next stage of development my father returned to the words 'At last with a great effort he stood up and turned away and seeing nothing but a grey mist stumbled forward towards the pass now straight ahead' (p. 211), and now continued thus (cf. TT pp. 342–3):

He had not far to go. The tunnel was some fifty yards behind; the cleft a couple of hundred yards or less. There was a path visible in the dusk running now quickly up, with the cliff on one side, and on the other a low wall of rock rising steadily to another cliff. Soon there were broad shallow steps. Now the orc-tower was right above him, frowning black, and in it the red eye glowed. Now he was passing up the steps and the cleft was before him.

'I have made up my mind,' he kept saying to himself. But he had not. What he did, though he had long to think it out, was altogether against the grain. To stick by his master was his true

214   THE WAR OF THE RING

nature. 'Have I got it wrong,' he muttered. 'Was there something else to do?' As the sheer sides of the cleft closed about him
and before he reached the summit, before he looked upon the
descending path beyond, he turned, torn intolerably within. He
looked back. He could still see like a small blot in the gathering
gloom the mouth of the tunnel; and he thought he could see or
guess where Frodo lay, almost he fancied there was a light or a
glimmer of it down there. Through tears he saw that lonely,
stony high place where all his life had fallen into ruin.

What was the 'light, or a glimmer of it' (meaning, I suppose, 'a light,
or the glimmer of a light') that Sam saw? It survives in TT (p. 343):
'He fancied there was a glimmer on the ground down there, or perhaps
it was some trick of his tears'. Can the original meaning have been that
there was a faint shining from the Phial of Galadriel, very probably at
this stage (see pp. 210–11) still left clasped in Frodo's hand?
   From ' "No I can't do it," he said' (p. 211) my father repeated the
original text almost exactly, but excising the return of Gollum. When
he came to Sam's putting on the Ring he wrote: 'The Ring. With a
sudden impulse he drew it out and *put it on*. The weight of it weighed
down his hand. For a moment he noticed no change, and then he
seemed to see clearer.' But at this point he stopped, marked what he
had written with an X, and wrote: 'No! hear[d] clearer, crack of stone,
cry of bird, voices, Shelob bubbling wretchedly deep in the rocks.
Voices in the dungeons of the tower. But all was not dark but hazy,
and himself like a black solid rock and the Ring like hot gold. Difficult
to believe in his invisibility.' The account of Sam's understanding of
what the Orcs said here takes this form: 'Did the Ring give power of
tongues or did it give him comprehension of all that had been under its
power [*written above:* Sauron's servants], so that he heard direct?
Certainly the voices seemed close in his ears and it was very difficult to
judge their distance.' With a reference to the Ring's increasing power
in that region and its not conferring courage on its wearer this draft
ends, followed by an outline of the salient points in what Sam heard:

   Why such a long delay of Orcs to come? Terrified of Shelob. They
   know another spy is about. Leader says orders are for messengers to
   go to Morgul and direct to Baraddur Lugburz. Orcs [?groan]. Talk
   of Shelob and the Spider's worm [who] has been here before. News
   of war.

In further drafting the coming of the Orc-bands is described thus:

Then suddenly he heard cries and voices. He stood still.
Orc-voices: he had heard them in Moria and Lórien and on the
Great River and would never forget them. Wheeling about he

KIRITH UNGOL
215

saw small red lights, torches perhaps, issuing from the tunnel away below. And only a few yards below him, out of the very cliff as it seemed, through some gap or gate near the tower's foot he had not noticed as he passed debating on the road, there were more lights. Orc-bands. They were come at last to hunt. The red eye had not been wholly blind.

And a noise of feet and shouts came also through the cleft. Orcs were coming up to the pass out of Mordor too.

This conception of three Orc-bands converging survived into the fair copy manuscript, where however it was removed at once, or soon, for there is no further reference to it; here 'orcs were coming up to the pass out of the land beyond', while 'only a few yards off' lights and 'black orc-shapes' were coming through 'some gap or gate at the tower's foot'. In the event (TT p. 343) the Orcs of the tower appeared from the far side of the Cleft.

The draft continues:

Fear overwhelmed him. How could he escape? So now *his* chapter would be ended. It had not had above a page longer than Frodo's. How could he save the Ring? The Ring. He was not aware of any thought or decision: he simply found himself drawing out the chain and taking the Ring in his hand. The orcs coming towards him grew louder. Then he *put it on*.[44]

The achievement of the conversation between the leaders of the two Orc-bands in the tunnel took a good deal of work, extending into the fair copy, and to detail all the rearrangements, shifts of speakers, and so on would require a great deal of space. But there is one draft that deserves quotation in full, for very little of it survived. Here the two Orcs, and especially he of Minas Morghul, are greatly concerned with the precise timing of the various communications that had passed.

In the darkness [*of the tunnel*] he seemed now more at home; but he could not overcome his weariness. He could see the light of torches a little way ahead, but he could not gain on them. Goblins go fast in tunnels, especially those which they have themselves made, and all the many passages in this region of the mountains were their work, even the main tunnel and the great deep pit where Shelob housed. In the Dark Years they had been made, until Shelob came and made her lair there, and to escape her they had bored new passages, too narrow for her [as she slowly grew >] growth, that crossed and recrossed the straight way.[45]

216   THE WAR OF THE RING

Sam heard the clamour of their many voices flat and hard in
the dead air, and somewhere he heard two voices louder than
the rest. The leaders of the two parties seemed to be wrangling
as they went.

'Can't you stop your rabble's racket?' said one. 'I don't care
what happens to them, but I don't want Shelob down on me and
my lads.'

'Yours are making more than half the noise,' said the other.
'But let the lads play. No need to worry about Shelob for a bit.
She's sat on a pin or something, and none of us will weep.
Didn't you see the signs then? A claw cut off, filthy gore all the
way to that cursed crack (if we've stopped it once we've stopped
it a hundred times). Let the lads play. We've struck a bit of luck
at last: we've got something He wants.'

'Yes, *we*, Shagrat.[46] *We*, mark you. But why we're going to
your miserable tower I don't know. We found the spy, my lot
were there first. He should be ours. He should be taken back to
Dushgoi.'[47]

'Now, now, still at it. I've said before all there is to be said,
but if you must have more arguments, they're here: I've got ten
more swords than you, and thirty more just up yonder at call.
See? Anyway orders are orders, and I've mine.'

'And I've mine.'

'Yes, and I know them, for I was told 'em by Lugburz, see?
Yagûl[48] *from Dushgoi will patrol until he meets your guard, or
as far as Ungol top: he will report to you before returning to
report to Dushgoi.* Your report was *nothing*. Very useful. You
can take it back to Dushgoi as soon as you like.'

'I will, but I don't like [to] just yet. I found the spy, and I must
know more before I go. The Lords of Dushgoi have some secret
of quick messages and they will get the news to Lugburz quicker
than anyone you can send direct.'

'I know all that, and I'm not stopping you taking news to
them. I know all the messages. They trust me in Lugburz, He
knows a good orc when he sees one. This is what happened:
message from Dushgoi to Lugburz: *Watchers uneasy. Fear
elvish agent passed up the Stair. Guard pass.* Message from
Lugburz to Ungol: *Dushgoi uneasy. Redouble vigilance. Make
contact. Send report by Dushgoi and direct.* And there you are.'

'No, I'm not there, not yet. I'm going to take a report back,
my own report, Master Shagrat, and I want to know this first.
When did you get this message? We set out as soon as possible

KIRITH UNGOL   217

after the forces left, and we see no sign of you till we're right
through the Tunnel – a filthy place and inside *your* area. Then
we see you just starting. Now I guess you got that message early
today, this morning probably, and you've been drinking since to
give you the guts to look at the hole. That's what you think of
orders that don't suit you.'

'I've no need to account for myself to you Dushgoi horseboys,
Master Yagûl. But if you're so curious to know: the message
from Dushgoi was sent out late: things seem a bit slack with the
Lord away. Lugburz did not get it till *last night*, mark you, nor
me till this afternoon. By which time messages were hardly
needed. I'd had my lads out some time. There were very odd
things happening. Lights in the tunnel, lights outside, shouting
and whatnot. But Shelob was about. My lads saw her, and her
worm.'

'What's that?'

The remainder of this text is very rough working for what follows
from this point in TT (pp. 348–50). In a following draft Yagool (as he
is spelt) says of Frodo: 'What is it, d'you think? Elvish I thought by his
nasty smooth peaky face. But undersized.' Here the conversation
moves closer to the form in TT, and the long discussion between
Yagool and Shagrat about the messages is greatly reduced, though the
messages are still given, in very much the same form; but that from
Minas Morghul begins *Nazgûl of Dushgoi to Lugburz*. In another
brief passage of drafting this dialogue occurs:

'I tell you, nearly two days ago the Night Watcher smelt
something, but will you believe me it was nearly another day
before they started to send a message to Lugburz.'

'How do they do that?' said Shagrat. 'I've often wondered.'

'I don't know and I don't want to ...'

The manuscript of 'The Choices of Master Samwise'[49] was in
almost all respects very close to the chapter in *The Two Towers*.
Various points in which it differed as first written have been noticed,
but there remain a few others. The following account of Shelob was
rejected as soon as written and replaced by that in TT (p. 337):

Shelob was not as dragons are, no softer spot had she save
only in her eyes; not as the lesser breeds of Mirkwood was their
dam, and her age-old hide, knobbed and pitted with corruption
but ever thickened with layer on layer within, could not be
pierced by any blade of Middle-earth, not though elf or dwarf

218

THE WAR OF THE RING

should make it and all runes were written upon it, not though the hand of [*struck out:* Fingon wielded it whose] Beren or of Túrin wielded it.

Shagrat's reply to Yagûl's opening sally ('Tired of lurking up there, thinking of coming down to fight?') took this form:

'Tired! You've said it. Waiting for nothing, except to be made into Shelob's meat. But we've got orders, too. Old Shagram's in a fine taking. Your lot's to blame. These Dushgoi bogey-men: sending messages to Lugburz.'

This was rejected as soon as written, replaced by 'Orders to you. I'm in command of this Pass. So speak civil', and with it went the last appearance of the name *Dushgoi* of Minas Morghul. Who 'old Shagram' was is not clear, but he is evidently 'old Nûzu' of the original draft (p. 212), also reported to be 'in a taking', apparently because the garrison of the Tower of Kirith Ungol had been depleted. Possibly he was the actual captain of the Tower, until this point, when Shagrat asserts that he himself is the commander of the pass; but Shagrat's words in the draft cited on p. 216, 'They trust me in Lugburz, He knows a good orc when he sees one' suggest that he was so already.

Lastly, the words of Sam's Elvish invocation (TT p. 339) in his fight with the Spider take in a draft for this passage the same form as they did in the original verse chanted in Rivendell (VI.394), and this form was retained in the manuscript as written, the only difference being *lír* for *dir* in the third line:[50]

O Elbereth Gilthoniel
sir evrin pennar óriel
lír avos-eithen míriel

This was changed on the manuscript to give this text:

O Elbereth Gilthoniel
silevrin pennar óriel
hír avas-eithen míriel
a tíro'men Gilthoniel!

★

It was a long time before my father returned to Frodo and Sam. In October 1944 he briefly took up again the stories 'west of Anduin' from where he had left them nearly two years earlier, but soon abandoned them (see pp. 233–5).

On 29 November 1944 (*Letters* no. 91), when he was sending me the typescripts of 'Shelob's Lair' and 'The Choices of Master Samwise', he said that he had 'got the hero into such a fix that not even an author will be able to extricate him without labour and difficulty.' He had by this time conceived the structure of *The Lord of the Rings* as

KIRITH UNGOL   219

five 'Books', of which four were written (cf. also his letter to Stanley
Unwin of March 1945, *Letters* no. 98); and in this same letter of
November 1944 he forecast what was still to come:

> Book Five and Last opens with the ride of Gandalf to Minas Tirith,
> with which The Palantir, last chapter of Book Three closed. Some of
> this is written or sketched.[51] Then should follow the raising of the
> siege of Minas Tirith by the onset of the Riders of Rohan, in which
> King Theoden falls; the driving back of the enemy, by Gandalf and
> Aragorn, to the Black Gate; the parley in which Sauron shows
> various tokens (such as the mithril coat) to prove that he has
> captured Frodo, but Gandalf refuses to treat (a horrible dilemma, all
> the same, even for a wizard). Then we shift back to Frodo, and his
> rescue by Sam. From a high place they see all Sauron's vast reserves
> loosed through the Black Gate, and then hurry on to Mount Doom
> through a deserted Mordor. With the destruction of the Ring, the
> exact manner of which is not certain – all these last bits were written
> ages ago, but no longer fit in detail, nor in elevation (for the whole
> thing has become much larger and loftier) – Baraddur crashes, and
> the forces of Gandalf sweep into Mordor. Frodo and Sam, fighting
> with the last Nazgul on an island of rock surrounded by the fire of
> the erupting Mount Doom, are rescued by Gandalf's eagle; and
> then the clearing up of all loose threads, down even to Bill Ferny's
> pony,[52] must take place. A lot of this work will be done in a final
> chapter where Sam is found reading out of an enormous book to his
> children, and answering all their questions about what happened to
> everybody (that will link up with his discourse on the nature of
> stories in the Stairs of Kirith Ungol). But the final scene will be the
> passage of Bilbo and Elrond and Galadriel through the woods of the
> Shire on their way to the Grey Havens. Frodo will join them and
> pass over the Sea (linking with the vision he had of a far green
> country in the house of Tom Bombadil). So ends the Middle Age
> and the Dominion of Men begins, and Aragorn far away on the
> throne of Gondor labours to bring some order and to preserve some
> memory of old among the welter of men that Sauron has poured
> into the West. But Elrond has gone, and all the High Elves. What
> happens to the Ents I don't yet know. It will probably work out very
> differently from this plan when it really gets written, as the thing
> seems to write itself once I get going, as if the truth comes out then,
> only imperfectly glimpsed in the preliminary sketch.

From a letter to Stanley Unwin written on 21 July 1946 (*Letters* no.
105), now more than two years since the doors of the underground
entrance to the Tower of Kirith Ungol were slammed in Sam's face,
and getting on for two since 'the beacons flared in Anórien and
Théoden came to Harrowdale', it is clear that he had done no more.
He was then hopeful that he would soon be able to begin writing

220   THE WAR OF THE RING

again; and in another letter to Stanley Unwin of 7 December 1946 (*Letters* no. 107) he was 'on the last chapters'.

NOTES

1   This text went back in turn to an earlier outline, 'The Story Foreseen from Moria', VII.209.
2   At that time *Kirith Ungol* was the name of the main pass into Mordor.
3   The first mention of the Tower of Kirith Ungol.
4   As I have noted in VII.260, Sam's visions in the Mirror of Galadriel were already in the fair copy manuscript of 'Galadriel' almost exactly as in FR (p. 377); the actual words used in the manuscript of this vision were: 'and now he thought he saw Frodo lying fast asleep under a great dark cliff: his face was pale.' When my father wrote this the words of the outline 'The Story Foreseen from Moria' (VII.209) had already been written: 'Gollum gets spiders to put spell of sleep on Frodo. Sam drives them off. But cannot wake him.'
5   The illegible word might possibly be 'grin'.
6   The fair copy manuscript, with some correction and addition from the time of composition, reaches the text of TT, pp. 312–17, in all respects save one: the passage describing Frodo's dash towards the bridge is still absent. The manuscript reads here:

> ... Frodo felt his senses reeling and his limbs weakening.
> Sam took his master's arm. 'Hold up, Mr Frodo!' he whispered, but his breath seemed to tear the air like a whistle. 'Not that way! Gollum says not that way – thank goodness! I agree with him for once.'
> Frodo took a grip on himself and wrenched his eyes away.

The reading of TT, introduced later, thus in part returns to the outline given on p. 186.
7   In general I do not go into the detail of textual problems, but this is a very unusual case, and the reconstruction of the evolution of the story to some degree depends on the view taken of it; I therefore give here some account of it.

Page 4 of the manuscript, on which the pencilled draft though overwritten can mostly be read, ends with the words: 'Then he saw that a faint light was welling through his fingers and he thrust it in his bosom.' Page 5 was likewise originally a page of rough, continuous, pencil drafting. The top of this page, some 14 lines or so, was erased, and the *later* narrative was written in this space (ending at 'and there it suddenly entered a narrow opening in the rock. They had come to the first stair that Gollum had

KIRITH UNGOL   221

spoken of', TT p. 317). Towards the end of this short section, however, the erasure was not complete, and the following can be read: 'not the odour of decay in the valley below ..... that the hobbits could recognize, a'. Thus the original narrative was here entirely different, for within a short space they are already at the mouth of the tunnel.

The strange thing is that from this point the original pencilled draft (continuing with 'repellent evil taint on the air'), not erased any further but overwritten, was *overwritten with the earlier narrative* ('Version 1'). Thus as the text in ink stands on this page it reads:

> ... and there it suddenly entered a narrow opening in the rock. They had come to the first stair that Gollum had spoken of [TT p. 317].
> repellent evil taint on the air.

The text following on from 'that Gollum had spoken of' is found on another sheet. The only explanation that I can see is that my father for some reason left the first (approximately) fourteen lines in pencil, and only began to overwrite it in ink at an arbitrary point ('repellent evil taint on the air'). The first part of the page thus fell victim to erasure and re-use when the later story had come into being, but from the point where it had been overwritten in ink the earlier story (Version 1) could not be so used, and was merely struck out.

8   This version of the sentence is found in isolation on a slip, slightly different from and beginning slightly earlier than the form of it that can be read in the pencilled draft (see note 7).

9   With 'then as fear left him it began to burn' cf. the derived passage in 'Shelob's Lair', TT p. 329: 'then as its power waxed, and hope grew in Frodo's mind, it began to burn'; cf. also 'As if his indomitable spirit had set its potency in motion, the glass blazed suddenly' (TT p. 339).

10 This much of 'Version 1' (struck through) was preserved in the manuscript because the page carried a portion of the later story also, as explained in note 7.

11 The Bodleian page '6/7', like page '5', is written in ink over the underlying pencilled draft. At this point there is an adjective, describing the webs and ending in *-ing*, which my father could not read; he therefore merely let the pencilled word stand, without writing anything on top of it.

12 The words *hold my star-glass behind me* are underlined in the original – possibly because my father was emphasising to himself that Frodo had actually given the phial to Sam, though whereas in TT (p. 334) Sam did not give it back to Frodo, later in this version (p. 198) he takes it from Frodo's hand during his fight with Ungoliant.

THE WAR OF THE RING

Frodo drew Sting: on the previous page '5' of the manuscript Frodo had already drawn Sting (p. 193), but this, I feel certain, is no more than an oversight, and does not call into question the succession of the two pages.

13 In the margin is written here: 'Dis. into a side hole?', where 'Dis.' obviously stands for 'Disappears'. This was added later, when my father was pondering the idea that Gollum in fact disappeared while they were still in the tunnel.

14 At the foot of the page is written in pencil: 'Make Gollum come reluctantly back.' This clearly belongs with the underlying pencilled draft; when over-writing the draft in ink my father put a query against these words.

15 The caption of the picture, *Shelob's Lair*, was added afterwards; at this time the name of the Great Spider was Ungoliant (p. 196).

16 At the time of writing, page 4/5 of 'Version 1' is in the United States, page 6/7 in England, and page 8/9 in France.

17 This is the first appearance of the one Great Spider (as opposed to many spiders).

18 On the name *Ungoliant(e)*, derived from *The Silmarillion*, see the *Etymologies*, V.396.

19 When Sam twisted round as Gollum seized him from behind, in TT Gollum's hold on Sam's mouth slipped, whereas in Version 1 it was his hold with his left hand on Sam's neck that slipped (down to his waist). Thus it is not said in Version 1 that 'all the while Gollum's other hand was tightening on Sam's throat'. When Sam hurled himself backwards and landed on Gollum 'a sharp hiss came out of him, and for a breathless second his left arm that was about Sam's waist relaxed' (in TT 'for a second his hand upon Sam's throat loosened'). Sam's second blow, falling across Gollum's back, did not break the staff, and the third blow aimed, by Sam was with the staff, not with his sword.

20 Sam's staff was not broken at the second blow, as it was in TT; see notes 19 and 42.

21 The handwriting is so difficult that my father pencilled in glosses here and there where he had evidently been puzzled by what he had written not long before. – It is often the case with a very difficult preliminary draft, which can really only be deciphered by recourse to the following text, that some particularly puzzling word or phrase cannot be solved in this way: another expression appears in its place; and in such cases one may often suspect that my father could not make it out himself. Cf. note 11.

22 On the right is seen the 'Wraith-road' from Minas Morghul rising to the main pass in this region (p. 195).

23 The brackets round this sentence, seen in the reproduction, were put in subsequently, and probably the question mark also. On the tunnel being the work of Orcs see p. 215.

KIRITH UNGOL   223

24   I cannot read the word at the bottom of the plan of the tunnels, also in blue ball-point pen, though possibly it also reads 'orc-path'.

25   Here appears the name Imlad Morghul (see p. 176).

26   On lines 3–4 of the page reproduced on p. 204 are the words 'where forgotten winters in the Dark Years had gnawed and carved the sunless stone.' In TT (p. 319) the words *in the Dark Years* are absent. Seven lines from the bottom of the page the text reads: 'or so it seemed to him in feeling not in reason', with pencilled correction to the reading of TT: 'or so it seemed to him in that dark hour of weariness, still labouring in the stony shadows under Kirith Ungol.'

27   The illegible words look most like 'flies back'. If this is what they are, the meaning must be very elliptically expressed: Frodo flees and the eyes pursue, but every time he turns round holding up the phial the eyes halt.

28   A trace of a stage in which the 'trap' or 'hole' in the floor of the tunnel was present as well as the branching ways is found on a slip carrying very disjointed drafting:

Suddenly a thought came into Frodo's mind. Gollum, he had been ahead: where was he? Had he fallen into that awful lurking hole? 'Gollum! I wonder whether he's all right,' he muttered. 'Smeagol!'

Groping in the dark they found that the opening or arch to the left was blocked a few feet inside, or so it seemed: they could not push their way in, it was

he called or tried to call Smeagol! But his voice cracked and

They tried first the opening to the left, but quickly it grew narrower and turned away mounting by long shallow steps towards the mountain wall. 'It can't be this way,' said Frodo. 'We must try the other.'

'We'll take the broader way,' said Frodo. 'Any passage that turns sideways .....'

29   Frodo's cry here has the form *Alla Earendel Elenion Ankalima*, and *Alla* remained through the following texts, only being changed to *Aiya* after the book was in type.

30   The word *flicked* in TT p. 330 ('but at its edge a blue fire flicked') is an error for *flickered* which was missed in the proof.

31   Perhaps for no other reason than that this section of the manuscript had become very ragged through emendation, and would have to be replaced, it had well before this point degenerated into rough pencil, at the end becoming an outline very hard to read.

32   The reference is to *The Hobbit*, Chapter III 'A Short Rest', where Elrond, speaking of the swords Glamdring and Orcrist taken from the trolls' hoard, says (in the text of the original edition):

224   THE WAR OF THE RING

'They are old swords, very old swords of the elves that are now called Gnomes. They were made in Gondolin for the Goblin-wars.'

33   This sentence ('For though once long ago he had seen it ...') was at first retained in the final fair copy manuscript, with the addition: 'neither did he understand his master.'

34   It is clearly written in the 'fair copy' style, but with some repetition and other features pointing to immediate composition, and it was corrected subsequently in pencil; I cite it here as corrected.

35   These words are used also in the story in *The Two Towers* (p. 330), but there only Shelob knows of the web at the end of the tunnel.

36   If this part of the draft did in fact belong with Version 1 there had been no encounter with the Spider in the tunnel, so that when this scene (surviving of course in TT, p. 339) was first written this was the first time that she had been confronted with the light of Earendel's star in the Phial of Galadriel.

37   The words 'foul but already pitiable' are read from a subsequent gloss of my father's. He gave up on the next word and wrote a query about it; it may perhaps be 'scuttle'. The words 'but already pitiable' are notable. In TT there is no trace of the thought that Shelob, entirely hateful and evil, denier of light and life, could ever be 'pitiable' even when defeated and hideously wounded.

38   This goes back to the original outline 'The Story Foreseen from Lórien' (p. 185), as does Sam's thought of building a cairn of stones, and the phrase later in this passage 'an elvish beauty as of one that is long past the shadows', which survives in TT.

39   Cf. the initial outline, p. 190: 'Turns back – resolved to lie down by Frodo till death comes. Then he sees Gollum come and paw him. He gives a start and runs back. But orcs come out and Gollum bolts.'

40   The first occurrence of the name *Shelob* (see p. 183).

41   Cf. the sentence added earlier in this draft at the point where Sam puts on the Ring: 'His hand hangs weighed down and useless.'

42   In the original account of Sam's fight with Gollum his staff was not broken (notes 19 and 20); this was where, and why, that element entered the story. The words 'The staff cracked and broke' were added to the fair copy (TT p. 335).

43   This is obscure. A proper name beginning with B, possibly *Ballung* or something similar, is followed by a sign that might represent 'and' or 'or'; but 'and' would mean that *Leader* and *says* were miswritten for *Leaders* and *say*, and though in this exceedingly rapid script words are frequently defective or mis-written the sentence reappears (p. 214), and there the words are

again *Leader* and *says*. Perhaps my father intended 'or' and was merely hesitating between two possible names for the Orc.

44 On this page of drafting is a hasty pencilled sketch of the final approach to the Cleft, and a little plan of the tunnel. In the first of these the place where Frodo lay is marked by an X on the path, and just to the left of it in the cliff-wall is the opening from which Shelob came. Another entry is seen in the distance at the top of the steps leading to the summit of the pass, at the foot of the cliff on which the Tower stands.

The plan of the tunnel is reproduced here. It will be seen that it differs from the elaborate earlier plan reproduced on p. 201 in that only one passage is shown leading to the left off the main tunnel at the eastern end, curving round and leading to the Tower.

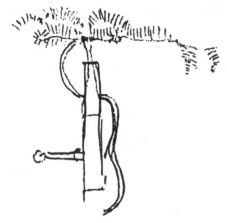

45 With this account of the origin of the tunnels cf. the outline accompanying the plan (p. 199): 'This tunnel is of orc-make (?) and has the usual branching passages.' It survived into the fair copy, where it was subsequently replaced by that in TT (p. 346).

46 The names of the leaders of the Orc-bands were rather bewilderingly changed in the drafts (and some transient forms cannot be read). At first (p. 212) they were *Gazmog* (of the Tower) and *Zaglûn* (of Minas Morghul), and in another brief draft of their genial greetings they become *Yagûl* and *Uftak Zaglûn* – so written: *Zaglûn* may have been intended to replace *Uftak*, but on the other hand the double-barrelled Orc-name *Naglur-Danlo* is found (p. 212). The name *Ufthak* was subsequently given to the Orc found (and left where he was) by Shagrat and his friends in Shelob's larder, 'wide awake and glaring' (TT p. 350). In the present text the names were at first *Yagûl* (of the Tower) and *Shagrat* (of Minas Morghul), but were reversed in the course of

226   THE WAR OF THE RING

writing (and in a following draft the names became reversed again at one point, though not I think intentionally). At this point, where the Orc from Morghul is speaking, my father first wrote *Shag*[*rat*], changed it to *Yagûl*, and then again changed it to *Shagrat*. See note 48. — *Yagûl* was replaced by *Gorbag* in the course of writing the fair copy.

47 *Dushgoi*: Orc name for Minas Morghul.
48 The text actually has *Shagrat* here, but this should have been changed to *Yagûl* (see note 46).
49 The story of the ascent of the Pass of Kirith Ungol was early divided into three chapters, with the titles which were never changed; the numbers being XXXVIII, XXXIX, and XL. See my father's letters cited on pp. 183–4.
50 After the verse my father wrote: 'such words in the Noldorin tongue as his waking mind knew not', striking this out at once.
51 This was work done in October 1944: see pp. 233–4.
52 Cf. VII.448.

Note on the Chronology

Time-scheme D continues somewhat further than does C (see p. 182):

Friday Feb. 10 Frodo and Sam come to Shelob's lair early in the morning. They get out in the late afternoon – nearly at top of the pass. Frodo is captured and carried to orc-tower at night.
Saturday Feb. 11 Attack at dawn on besieged Minas Tirith. Riders of Rohan suddenly arrive and charge, overthrowing the leaguer. Fall of Théoden. Host of Mordor flung into River.
Sunday Feb. 12 Gandalf (Éomer and Aragorn and Faramir) advance into Ithilien.

Time-scheme S goes no further than February 8.

Pencilled entries were added to February 11 in Scheme D: 'Sam at the Iron Door early hours of Feb. 11. Sam gets into orc-tower. Rescues Frodo. They fly and descend into Mordor'; and 'Ships of Harad burnt'.

PART THREE

MINAS TIRITH

I

ADDENDUM TO
'THE TREASON OF ISENGARD'

After the publication of 'The Treason of Isengard' I came upon the following manuscript page. It had ended up in a bundle of much later writings concerned with the events of Books V and VI, and when going through these papers I had failed to see its significance. It is in fact the concluding page of the first of the two outlines that I gave under the heading 'The Story Foreseen from Fangorn' in VII.434 ff.; and since it represents my father's earliest recorded conception of the events of Book V this seems the best place to give it. I repeat first the conclusion of the part printed in Vol. VII (p. 437):

> News comes at the feast [at Eodoras] or next morning of the siege of Minas Tirith by the Haradwaith. ... The horsemen of Rohan ride East, with Gandalf, Aragorn, Gimli, Legolas, Merry and Pippin. Gandalf as the White Rider. ... Vision of Minas Tirith from afar.

The text begins in the same pale ink as was used for the earlier part of the outline but soon turns to pencil. At the head of the page is written (later, in a different ink): 'Homeric catalogue. Forlong the Fat. The folk of Lebennin' (see p. 287).

Battle before walls. Sorties from city. Aragorn puts the Haradwaith to flight. Aragorn enters into Minas Tirith and becomes their chief. Recollection of the boding words (as spoken by Boromir).

The forces of Minas Tirith and Rohan under Aragorn and Gandalf cross the Anduin and retake Elostirion. The Nazgûl. How Gandalf drove them back. Wherever the shadow of the Nazgûl fell there was a blind darkness. Men fell flat, or fled. But about Gandalf there was always a light – and where he rode the shadow retreated.

The forces of West worst Minas Morghul [*written above:* Morgol] and drive back the enemy to the Field of Nomen's Land before Kirith Ungol. Here comes the embassy of Sauron. He sends to say that [*Here the ink text ends and is followed by pencil, the word* that *crossed out*] to Gandalf and Aragorn that he has got Frodo the Ringbearer captive. (Dismay of Aragorn.)

230   THE WAR OF THE RING

Sauron's messenger declares that Frodo has begged for deliverance at any price. Sauron's price is the immediate withdrawal of all forces west of Anduin – and eventual surrender of all land up to west of Misty Mountains (as far as Isen). As token Sauron's messenger shows Sting (or some other object taken – the phial?) taken when Frodo was prisoner – this would have to be something Sam overlooked [*written in margin:* mithril coat]. But Gandalf utterly rejects the terms.

'Keep your captive until the battle is over, Sauron! For verily if the day goes to me and we do not then find him unharmed, it shall go very ill with you. Not you alone have power. To me also a power is given of retribution, and to you it will seem very terrible. But if the day is yours then you must do with us all that remain alive as you will. So indeed you would do in any case, whatever oath or treaty you might now make.'

Gandalf explains that Frodo is probably *not* captive – for at any rate Sauron has not got the Ring. Otherwise he would not seek to parley.

The story must return to Sam and Frodo at the moment when Gandalf and Aragorn ride past Minas Morghul.   ?   And go down to moment when Ring is destroyed.

Then just as Gandalf rejects parley there is a great spout of flame, and the forces of Sauron fly. Aragorn and Gandalf and their host pour into Gorgoroth.

Part of Battle could be seen by Frodo from [?his] tower while a prisoner.

With the last part of this text compare the second part of the outline 'The Story Foreseen from Fangorn', VII.438.

II
BOOK FIVE BEGUN AND ABANDONED

(i) Minas Tirith

My father recorded years later (see p. 77 and note 19) that before the long gap in the writing of *The Lord of the Rings* in 1943–4 he had written the beginnings of Book V Chapters 1 and 3 ('Minas Tirith' and 'The Muster of Rohan'); but 'there as the beacons flared in Anórien and Théoden came to Harrowdale I stopped'. A preliminary question is whether the abandoned opening of 'Minas Tirith' still exists and can be identified.

What is certainly the earliest of several 'beginnings' ('**A**') consists first of a few lines clearly written in ink:

Pippin looked out from Gandalf's arms. Though he was awake now he felt that he was still in a swift-moving dream. Still the world of grey and green rushed by and the sun rose and sank and the wind sang in his ears. He tried to reckon the time, but he could not be sure.

From this point the text is continued in a rapid pencilled scribble:

Two days ago it was that he saw the sun glinting on the roof of the king's great house, and then he had slept, dimly aware of the bustle and a coming and going about him. Coming of Nazgûl. Then more darkness and wind, and then again. Yes, this must be the third riding. The stars seemed to be fleeing overhead.

He stirred. Where are we, he said.

Passing [?through] the land of Anórien, which is [?a realm] of Gondor, said Gandalf. Now we have turned southward. Dawn is at hand. Open your eyes.

Beacons. Messengers riding West.

Description of Minas Tirith and its immense concentric walls.

They come to presence of Denethor and hear news which Gandalf supplements.

Gandalf remains hidden [?communing] with himself. Pippin on the battlements. The allies come in. Faramir returns. War and siege. Gondor defeated. Ships of Harad. New force from North. Episode of the Palantír and Gandalf.

No sign of Riders.

232   THE WAR OF THE RING

This pencilled continuation was obviously written all at one time, and it was written therefore *after* May 1944, when Faramir, whose return to Minas Tirith is mentioned here, entered the story of *The Lord of the Rings*: it is new work on the story after Book IV had been completed. That the brief initial passage in ink ('Pippin looked out from Gandalf's arms ...') should be separated from its pencilled continuation by a long interval seems to me so unlikely as to be out of the question. Far more probably my father abandoned it because he had changed his mind about Gandalf's riding by day, and (as he often did in such cases) then sketched out the changed conception very rapidly (see the Note on Chronology at the end of this chapter).

This was followed by a further draft of the opening ('**B**'), a single page roughly written in ink that went no further than the errand-riders racing from Gondor to Edoras. I give this brief text in full, ignoring a few subsequent changes in pencil.

Pippin looked out from the shelter of Gandalf's cloak. He was awake now, though he had been sleeping, but he felt that he was still in a swift-moving dream. Still the dark world seemed to be rushing by, and a wind sang loudly in his ears. He could see nothing but the wheeling stars, and away to the right vast shadows against the sky, where the mountains of the south marched by. Sleepily he tried to reckon the time, but he could not be sure of his memory. This was the beginning of the second night of riding since he had seen the pale gleam of gold in the chill dawn and had come to the great empty house upon the hill in Edoras. There he had slept only dimly aware of much coming and going and of the great outcry when the winged flier had passed over. And since then riding, riding in the night.

A pale light came in the sky, a blaze of yellow fire was lit behind dark barriers. For a moment he was afraid, wondering what dreadful thing lay ahead; he rubbed his eyes, and then he saw it was the moon rising full out of the eastern shadows. So they had ... for four hours since dusk![1]

'Where are we, Gandalf?' he asked.

'Anórien the realm of Gondor is still fleeting by,' said Gandalf.

'What is that?' said Pippin, suddenly clutching at Gandalf's cloak. 'Fire! I thought for a moment it might be a dragon. I feel that anything might happen in this land. Look there is another!'

'On, Shadowfax!' cried Gandalf. 'We must not rest this night. Those are the beacons of Gondor calling for aid. War is kindled. See, there is the light on Amon Thorn, and a flame on Elenach;

BOOK FIVE BEGUN AND ABANDONED 233

and look there they go speeding west, Nardol, Penannon, Orodras, and Mindor Uilas on the borders of Rohan. Haste!'

And Shadowfax leaped forward, and as he sprang forward he neighed pricking his ears. Neighing of horses answered and like shadows flying on a wild wind riders went by them thundering west in the gloom.

'Those are post riders,' said Gandalf, 'riding from message post to message post – bearing tidings and summons. The message will reach Edoras by nightfall tonight.'[2]

This text was followed by another single page ('C'). This was typed by my father in the 'midget type' which he used in his letters to me from 7 July 1944 (see the beginning of no. 75 in *Letters*) and frequently until October of that year; and thus this one sheet carries the story as far as the point where Shadowfax passes through the narrow gate in the Pelennor wall (RK p. 21) – the text stopping just before the name *Pelennor* would appear (see p. 277). The final text was now very closely approached. The names of all the beacons (now seven, not six) are here in the final form: Amon Dîn, Eilenach, Nardol, Erelas, Minrimmon, Calenhad, and Halifirien on the borders of Rohan. There are however a few differences. Gandalf here tells Pippin that the message-posts were at distances of 'every fifty miles or so, where errand-riders were always in readiness to carry messages to Rohan or elsewhere' (in RK, p. 20, no distance is mentioned, and Belfalas is named as another destination of such errands). The passage in which Pippin, falling asleep, thinks of Frodo runs thus:

He wondered where Frodo was and if he was already in Mordor, little thinking that Frodo on that same night saw from afar the white snows under the moon; but the red flames of the beacons he did not see, for the mists of the Great River covered all the land between.

On this see the Note on Chronology at the end of this chapter.[3] — The leader of the men at the Pelennor wall is here named Cranthir, not Ingold.

The next stage in the evolution of 'Minas Tirith' was a complete, or nearly complete, draft text; that the page 'C' preceded it and was not an abortive start to a typescript of it is certain (e.g., the leader of the men at the wall is now Ingold).

My father here set a most curious puzzle. The datum is that (as he said) he abandoned 'Minas Tirith' about the end of 1942, as 'the beacons flared in Anórien': the story only went 'as far as the arrival in Gondor'. A single typescript page ('C') does precisely that, and when I first studied these papers I felt certain that it was the 'abandoned

234   THE WAR OF THE RING

opening'; but it is clear and obvious that 'C' was developed from 'B'
and that from 'A', and in 'A' there is a reference to Faramir, who only
entered the story in 1944. Moreover 'C' was typed with a special type
which my father seems only to have begun using in 1944. The
emphatically underlined words in A '*Beacons. Messengers* riding
West' certainly suggest that this is where those ideas actually arose;
but how could they have done so, since 'the beacons flared in Anórien'
already in the original opening of 1942? I was therefore forced to the
conclusion that that was lost.

But this conclusion is wrong; and there is very clear evidence that
my father erred in his recollection. The solution lies in a passage from
his letter of Thursday 12 October 1944, which I have cited before
(p. 100), but not in full:

> I began trying to write again (I would, on the brink of term!) on
> Tuesday, but I struck a most awkward error (one or two days) in the
> synchronization, v. important at this stage, of movements of Frodo
> and the others, which has cost labour and thought and will require
> tiresome small alterations in many chapters; *but at any rate I have
> actually begun Book Five* (and last: about 10 chapters per 'book').

I had taken (in view of what he said years later) the words that I have
italicised to mean that my father had begun 'Minas Tirith' anew, and
supposed that in this brief reference he simply passed over the fact that
the beginning of the chapter (and the beginning of 'The Muster of
Rohan') was long since in existence – or else that the earlier beginning
had now been rejected and set aside. But the words are much more
naturally taken to mean what they say: 'I have actually begun Book
Five' – on 10 October 1944, *ab initio*; and if they are so taken the entire
problem disappears. The abandoned opening is not lost, and it is indeed
the curious isolated page 'C' in 'midget type'; but it was written in
1944, not 1942. The page 'A', preceding 'B' and 'C', is indeed where
the ideas of the beacons and the westbound errand-riders first emerged
– and since it was written in 1944 the appearance of Faramir represents no difficulty. Thus in his letter of 29 November 1944 cited on
p. 219 my father could say that 'Book Five and Last opens with the
ride of Gandalf to Minas Tirith ... *Some of this is written or
sketched*': it had been 'written or sketched' in the previous month.

The reason for this error, made many years later, is easy to see: for
there was indeed a long hiatus in the writing of 'Minas Tirith' (and
'The Muster of Rohan'). But it fell not in the long halt of 1943–4,
between Book III and Book IV; it fell in the long halt between October
1944 and the summer of 1946 (see pp. 219–20), after Book IV was
completed. That this is so is strongly supported by the time-schemes.
I have argued (p. 141) that the schemes C and D preceded the
chronological problems that emerged in October 1944, while scheme
S represents their resolution. All three, however, deal both with Frodo

BOOK FIVE BEGUN AND ABANDONED   235

and Sam on the one hand and the events in Rohan and Gondor on the other; and it seems therefore very probable that they are all to be associated with the new narrative opening at that time. It was precisely because my father was now, in the latter part of 1944, returning 'west of Anduin' for the first time since he finished 'The Palantír' that the need for all this chronological synchronisation arose. See further the Note on Chronology at the end of this chapter.

The first full draft of 'Minas Tirith' belongs of course to the final period in the writing of *The Lord of the Rings*. This text was left behind in England; but apart from this, almost all manuscript material from the final period (Books V and VI), including outlines and initial draftings, went to Marquette University in the original consignment of papers.

(ii) *The Muster of Rohan*

The original draft for the opening of 'The Muster of Rohan', here called 'A', is a rapidly pencilled text in my father's most difficult script, some of which has defied repeated attempts to decipher it; I give it here as best I can. The opening paragraph was rejected as soon as written, but it was not struck through. It may be mentioned before giving the text that it had long been known that Théoden would return from Isengard through the mountains to Dunharrow: see the outlines given on pp. 70, 72 (written before Gandalf's sudden departure for Minas Tirith on Shadowfax had entered). In LR the journey of Théoden, Aragorn and their company from Dol Baran is described in 'The Passing of the Grey Company', but that had not yet been written.

Morning was come again, but dim still lay the deep dale about them. Dark and shadowy the great woods of fir climbed upon the steep sides of the ... hills. Long now it seemed to the travellers since they had ridden from Isengard, longer even than [?the] time of their weary journey.[4]

Day again was fading. Dim lay the high dale about them. Night had already come beneath the great woods of murmuring firs that clothed the steep mountain-sides. But now the travellers rode down a steep track and passing out of the scented sighing gloom of the pines they [?followed a] ... ... they found themselves at the ... where it passed into a wider vale. The long vale of Harrowdale. Dark on the right loomed the vast tangled mass of Dunharrow, its great peak now lost to sight, for they were crawling at its feet. Lights twinkled before them on the other side of the valley, across the river Snowborn[5] white and fuming on its stones. They were come at last at the end of many days to the old mountain homes of folk forgotten – to the Hold

236   THE WAR OF THE RING

of Dunharrow. Long it seemed since they rode from Isengard.
[?It was] ... days since they rode from Isengard, but it seemed
..., with little else but weary riding. So King Théoden came
back to his people.

As dusk fell they came to the river and the old stone bridges
that [?were there]. There they sounded a horn. Horns answered
gladly from above. Now they climbed up a winding path which
brought them slowly up to a wide upland field set back into the
side of the great [?bones of Dunharrow. Treeclad walls half
embraced it].[6] The Snowborn issued and fell down with a
waterfall. The rock behind was full of caves that had been bored
and cut with great labour in the rock walls. Legend said that
here was a dwelling and a [?holy] place of forgotten men in the
Dark Years – [?before ever] the ships came to Belfalas or
Gondor was built. What had become of them? Vanished, gone
away, to mingle with the people of Dunland or the folk of
Lebennin by the sea. Here the Eorlingas had made a stronghold,
but they were not a mountain folk, and as the days grew better
while Sauron was far away they passed down the vale and built
Edoras at the north of Harrowdale. But ever they kept the Hold
of Dunharrow as a refuge. There still dwelt some folk reckoned
as Rohir, and the same in speech, but dark with grey eyes. The
blood of the forgotten men ran in their veins.

Now all [?about] the vale on [?flat] sides of the Snowborn
they saw ... and ... of men, fires kindled. The [?upland plain]
was filled [?too]. Trumpets rang, glad was the cry of men to
welcome Théoden.

Éowyn comes forth and greets Théoden and Aragorn.

Gandalf's message tells her to hold assembly at Dunharrow.

This is not the House of Eorl. But [?that is guarded]. Here
we will [?hold] the feast of victory so long delayed, and the
[ale >] ... ale[7] of Háma and all who fell.

The torchlit stone hall.

Merry sat beside Théoden as was promised.[8]

Éowyn brings in the cup for the drinking.

Even as Théoden drains it the messenger comes.

Aragorn had already arrived and greets King Théoden[9] side
by side with Éowyn.

Halbarad sister-son of Denethor.[10] He asks for ten thousand
spears at once.

Men are [?gathering] in the East beyond the Inland Sea of
Nurnen, and far north. Eventually they may assail the East

BOOK FIVE BEGUN AND ABANDONED   237

Emnet, but that would not come yet. Now Orcs have passed south through Nargil pass in the Southland beyond [?River] Harnen.[11]

I postpone discussion of this earliest conception of Harrowdale and the Hold of Dunharrow to the end of the next version. This, which I will call 'B', began as a fully articulated narrative in ink and in clear script, but swiftly collapsed. The opening passage was much corrected both at the time of writing and subsequently; I give it here as it seems to have stood when my father abandoned it.

Day was fading. The high valley grew dim about them. Night had already come beneath the murmuring firwood that clothed the steep mountain-sides. Their path turning a sharp shoulder of rock plunged down into the sighing gloom under dark trees. At last they came out again and saw that it was evening, and their journey was nearly at an end. They had come down to the edge of the mountain-stream, which all day they had followed as far below it clove its deep path between the tree-clad walls. And now through a narrow gate between the mountains it passed out, and flowed into a wider vale.

'At last!' said Éomer. 'We are come

Here my father stopped. Perhaps at once, he added in pencil 'to Harrowdale', then struck out Éomer's words and continued the text in pencil, which soon becomes difficult to read, and finally as nearly impossible as text A.

They followed it, and saw the Snowborn white and fuming upon its stones rush down upon its swift journey to Edoras at the mountains' feet. To their right, now dark and swathed in cloud, loomed the vast tumbled mass of great Dunharrow, but his/its tall peak and cap of snow they could not see, for they were crawling under the shadow of his knees. Across the dale before them lights were twinkling.

'Long now it seems since we rode from Isengard about this hour of the day,' said Théoden. 'We have journeyed by dusk and night and by day among the hills, and I have lost count of time. But was not the moon full last night?'

'Yes,' said Aragorn. '[Five >] Four days have we passed on the road, and now six remain before the day that you appointed for the assembly at Edoras.'

'Then here at Dunharrow maybe we can rest a while,' said the King.

They came now [?under] dusk over a stone bridge across the

238   THE WAR OF THE RING

river; and when the head of [?his] long line had passed it a man
sounded a loud call upon [a] horn. It echoed in the valley, and
horn[s] answered it from far above. Lights sprang out and men
rode forward to meet them. King Théoden was welcomed back
with joy, and he rode on with Éomer and Aragorn and his
company up the steep winding path that led to the Hold of
Dunharrow on the mountain's knee. No foe could climb that
way while any defended it from above. [Looking back] Merry
was riding now on a pony furnished for him at Helm's Deep.
With him [?went] Legolas and Gimli. They looked back and
long after they had climbed high they could descry in the grey
dusk below the long winding line of the Riders of Rohan still
crossing by the bridge. Many men had followed Théoden from
Westfold.

So at last they came to the Hold – the mountain homes of
long forgotten folk. Dim legends only now remembered them.
Here they had dwelt [and had made a dark temple   a temple
and holy place in the Dark Years] in fear under the shadow of
the Dark Years, before ever a ship came to Belfalas or Gondor
of the Kings was built. That was in the first [?reign] of Sauron
the [?Great] when Baraddur first was founded, but they had ...
[?him] and built a refuge ...... [?that no enemy] could take.
There was a wide upland [field > ?slope] set back into the
mountain – the lap of Dunharrow. Arms of the mountain
embraced [it] except only for a space upon the west. Here the
[?green bay] fell over a sheer brink down into Harrowdale. A
winding path led up. Behind the sheer walls of the vale were
..... caves – made by ancient art. [?Water fell in a fall over the
.... and flowed ... the midst ...]

When the men of Gondor came [?there] the men of this place
lived for a while [?owning] no lord of Gondor. But what became
of them no legend knew. They had vanished and gone far away.

As my father wrote the end of this text he drew two little sketches of
the Hold of Dunharrow, and this page is reproduced on p. 239 (see
also note 6). These sketches show his earliest imagining of the Hold
very clearly: a natural 'amphitheatre' with caves in the further rock-
wall, and a stream (in text A stated to be the Snowbourn) falling
down from the heights behind and over the central door, thence
crossing the open space ('the lap of Dunharrow') and falling again
over the lower cliff up which the path climbs. It is less easy to be sure
of the situation of the Hold in relation to Harrowdale. When Théoden
and his company enter the dale 'the vast tumbled mass of great

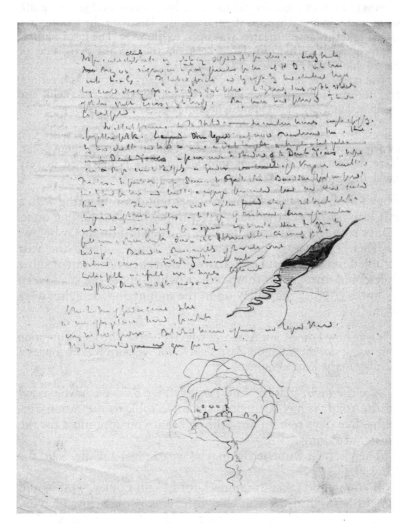

Dunharrow

240 THE WAR OF THE RING

Dunharrow' is on their right; Dunharrow is the name of the mountain (on the First Map, IVE, VII.319, 'Dunharrow' is written against the mountain at the head of the great valley extending south-west from Edoras). They crossed the Snowbourn by a stone bridge; the path, steep and winding, then led them up to the Hold 'on the mountain's knee'; and the 'amphitheatre' was open to the west. The most natural interpretation is that the Hold was on the far (eastern) side of Harrowdale, and near the head of the valley.

The references in A to the Hold having been preserved as a refuge, and to 'the torchlit stone hall' in which the feast was held, are explained and expanded in subsequent texts.

Text B was followed, no doubt immediately, by a third version ('C'), clearly written in ink, which however again stops at the same point. Here the entry of the Riders into Harrowdale is described in very much the same way as it is in B:

They followed it [the mountain-stream] and saw it spring with a last leap into the Snowbourn River that white and fuming on its stones rushed down upon its swift journey to Edoras far below. To their right, dark and swathed in cloud, loomed the vast tumbled mass of great Dunharrow, but its peak and cap of snow they could not see, for they were crawling under the shadow of its knees. Across the valley upon the mountain-side lights were twinkling.

It was now Éomer, not Aragorn, who replied to Théoden's question 'But was it not the full moon last night?'; for Aragorn was no longer a member of the King's company.

'No, the night before,' said Éomer. 'Five days we have passed on the road: it has been slow since we took to the mountain-paths; five days remain until the day that you appointed for the muster at Edoras.'

'Then here at Dunharrow maybe we can rest a while,' said the King.

'If you would take my counsel, lord,' said Éomer, 'you would remain here until the war that threatens is over, lost or won. [*Struck out at once:* You have ridden far and taxed your strength in the war with Saruman. Victory will have little joy for me, or for your people, unless we can lay our swords at your feet.]'

'We will speak of that later,' said Théoden.

They rode on. Merry looked about him. He was tired, for he was riding himself now, on a sturdy hill-pony furnished for him

BOOK FIVE BEGUN AND ABANDONED 241

at Helm's Deep; but he had enjoyed the journey among the passes and high dales, the tall pine-woods, and the bright waterfalls. He loved mountains, and the desire to see and know them had moved him strongly when he and his friends had plotted to go with Frodo, far away in the Shire.

He rode with the King's company, and often he had jogged along beside Théoden himself, telling him of the Shire, and the doings of hobbit-folk. They had got on well together, although much of Merry's language was hard for Théoden to understand. But all the same, and in spite of the honour, he was lonely, especially at the day's end. Aragorn had ridden on far ahead with the swifter riders, taking Legolas and Gimli; and he missed Pippin deeply. The fellowship seemed now altogether scattered.

They came now in the dusk to a stone bridge across the Snowbourn ...

It would be interesting to know why (at this stage in the development of the narrative, when they would all meet again at Dunharrow) Aragorn with Legolas and Gimli and others went on ahead (see note 9), but no explanation is given.

Text C now follows B very closely, and is largely identical with it. The mention of Legolas and Gimli riding with Merry is of course removed. Of the ancient men of Dunharrow it is said that 'their name was lost', and that here they 'had their refuge and hidden fane'; 'those were the days when Sauron first was lord, and Baraddur was founded; but they had not served him, making here a refuge that no foe could take.' The 'wide upland slope' is again named 'the Lap of Dunharrow', and it is again said to open on the west; 'There there was a sheer brink that fell some hundreds of feet down to the Snowbourn. Up this the winding path climbed. Inside the amphitheatre (?) was clasped by sheer walls of rock rising at the back to a great precipice; and the walls'

Here text C stops; there is thus no mention here of the falling stream referred to in A (where it is actually the Snowbourn) and B and shown on one of the accompanying sketches, nor of the relations of the men of Dunharrow with the men of Gondor.

A fourth text ('D') followed, in which the actual words of the opening of 'The Muster of Rohan' in RK were quite closely approached for the most part, but this extends no further than a single page, ending with Merry's 'listening to the noise of water, the murmur of dark trees, the crack of stone, and the vast waiting silence that brooded behind all sound.' The most notable feature of this brief text is the following passage:

242   THE WAR OF THE RING

To their right, dark and swathed in cloud, loomed the vast tumbled mass of [*struck out immediately:* great Du] mighty Starkhorn, [*struck out:* the grim mountain,] but its gnarled and jagged peak they could not see, for they were crawling under the shadow of its knees. Across the valley upon the lap of the great mountain lights were twinkling.

At this point, it is clear, the great mountain 'Dunharrow' became the Starkhorn, and though the text does not extend far enough to make the matter certain the last sentence of this extract suggests strongly (especially from the use of the word 'lap') that the Hold of Dunharrow, in which lights were twinkling, was situated on the lower slopes of the Starkhorn.

The next stage seems to have been two pages of notes in very rapid pencil ('E'), some but not all of which my father overwrote clearly in ink, and against some names and words putting queries.

When the Eorlingas came first to Dun Harrow they had found only one old man living in a cave, speaking in a strange tongue. None could understand him. Often he spoke and seemed to desire to tell them something, but he died before any could read his words. Where were all the rest of his folk?

Aragorn and Éowyn meet the King. They say that Riders are mustering at Dun Harrow – Gandalf's command: he had passed by Edoras some days ago. Many have already come in – and many strange folk. I do not .... understand how, but a summons went forth long ago. Rangers have come and Dunlanders and messengers from the Woodmen of Mirkwood.

They say that but for the shadow of the new war they would make a feast of victory. Even so they will feast and rejoice because of the King's return.

Torchlit stone hall.

Merry sat beside Théoden as promised.

The following was overwritten in ink, apparently only to clarify the pencilled text (parts of which can be made out), not to alter or expand it. Several of the names have queries against them in the ink overwriting, and some of the pencilled words my father could not interpret.

Éowyn bears wine to him, bidding him drink and be glad.

Even as Théoden drinks the cup, the messenger of Minas Tirith arrives. ? Barahir   ? Halbarad.

BOOK FIVE BEGUN AND ABANDONED   243

He asks for ten thousand spears at once! The Swertings have come. The forces of Sauron have crossed the Nargul ? Pass and raised the men of Harad and of ? Umbor. A fleet has put out from the Havens of Umbor – once Gondor's, but long lost – and sailed up the Anduin and reached Anárion, at the same time more enemies have crossed the river and taken the fords of Osgiliath again – won back hardly in the winter. [*In margin, ink over pencil:*] Swertings are only just moving, and a few preliminary ravages of Lebennin. Spies report a great fleet ? [*concluding pencilled words were illegible*]

Théoden replies that that is more than he could have mustered in a ? [*pencilled word was illegible*] at his height, and before the war with Saruman.

Éowyn says that women must ride now, as they did in a like evil time in the days of Brego son of [*mark showing name omitted*] Eorl's son, when the wild men of the East came from the Inland Sea into the Eastemnet.

[*Pencilled text struck through and not overwritten:*] Théoden decides to pass over the [*struck out:* Rath] Scada pass to the vale of Blackroot into Lebennin and fall on enemy in rear.

[*Ink over pencil:*] Aragorn [*in margin:* Éomer?] begs leave to take a force over the Scāda Pass and fall on the enemy's rear. 'I will go with you in my brother's stead' said Éowyn [*added:* to King Théoden].

[*Ink text original:*] As had been promised him at Isengard, Merry sat beside [*written above:* near] the King himself. On either side of the King were Éowyn and Éomer, and Aragorn beside Éowyn. Merry sat with Legolas and Gimli not far from the fire and spoke together – while all about rolled the speech of Rohan.

[*Ink over pencil:*] They had been bidden to the King's table but said that the lords would wish to talk high matters, and they wished to talk together. ? Legolas ? [*in margin:* No, King surely?] tells history of Dunharrow: how the men of Dunharrow lived in the valley; how Dunharrow was furnished; how the Kings of the Mark had once dwelt here – and still returned once a year in autumn. But Théoden had not kept this custom for several years. The Feast-hall had been long silent [*pencilled text:* But Théoden had not done so for many years].

Éowyn brings wine.

[*Ink text original:*] Remembering his promise at Isengard, Théoden summoned Merry and set him at his left hand at the

244   THE WAR OF THE RING

high table upon the stone dais. On the King's right sat Éowyn[12] and Éomer, and at the table's end Aragorn. Legolas and Gimli sat beside Merry. The three companions spoke much together in soft voices, while all about them the speech of Rohan rolled loud and clear.

These notes – very much a record of 'thinking with the pen' – have several curious features. The conception of the Hold of Dunharrow as a great redoubt of the Kings of the Mark, with a hall of feasting in its caverns (whence came the lights twinkling on the mountain-side), reappears from text A, and the last survivor of the ancient people of Harrowdale emerges.

Aragorn (with Gimli and Legolas) has ridden on ahead to Dunharrow, as in text C (p. 241); and in these notes is the first mention of the coming south of a body of Rangers. Éowyn's reference to the assault on Rohan long before, when in the days of Brego 'the wild men of the East came from the Inland Sea into the Eastemnet', is a sign that the history of Rohan had been evolving unseen. In LR (Appendix A (II), 'The Kings of the Mark') Eorl the Young fell in battle with the Easterlings in the Wold of Rohan, and his son Brego, builder of the Golden Hall, drove them out. In the outline 'The Story Foreseen from Fangorn' (VII.435) and in drafting for 'The King of the Golden Hall' (VII.445) Brego, builder of the hall, was the son of Brytta. In the present notes Brego is the grandson of Eorl, and a blank is left for the name of his father.

Among other names that appear here, I cannot certainly explain the queries that my father set against the first occurrence of *Umbor* and against *Nargul (Pass)*.[13] For *Anárion* as the name of a region of Gondor see VII.309–10, 318–19; *Anárion* on both the First Map and my 1943 map is given not only to *Anórien* (north of Minas Tirith) but also to the region south of Minas Tirith. For the former, *Anórien* appears already in the draft A of the opening of 'Minas Tirith', p. 231. The *Scāda Pass* leading over the mountains into the Blackroot Vale is not named on any map.[14] It is here that the possibility first appears that Aragorn (or Éomer) will lead some part of the forces mustering at Dunharrow across the mountains, rather than ride to Minas Tirith along their northern skirts, in view of the news brought by the messenger from Gondor (see further pp. 252–3). The name proposed here for the messenger, *Halbarad* (beside *Barahir*), has appeared already in the original draft A of 'The Muster of Rohan': see p. 236 and note 10.

A new version of the narrative ('F') was now begun, clearly written at the outset but soon collapsing into a scrawl; in this the story extends rather further. In the opening passage of this text lights still twinkle across the valley 'on the lap of the great mountain'; Éomer still

BOOK FIVE BEGUN AND ABANDONED   245

informs Théoden that the moon was full two nights before, that they
have passed five days on the journey, and that five remain to the
muster at Edoras; and the Riders still cross the Snowbourn by a stone
bridge (not as in RK by a ford), here described as 'a bare arch, wide
and low, without kerb or parapet'. The horns blown from far above
answering the blast blown as the King's company passed over the
bridge now become 'a great chorus of trumpets from high above' that
'sounded in some hollow place that gathered them into one great voice
and sent it forth rolling and beating on the walls of stone.' When this
was written, as will be seen shortly, the 'hollow place' was the interior
of the Hold of Dunharrow – in the sense that my father originally
intended by that name: the rock-ringed recess or 'amphitheatre' and
the great caverns in the cliff; but the description survived into RK
(with the addition of the words 'as it seemed' after 'some hollow
place'), when the Hold of Dunharrow was used to refer to the
Firienfeld, the wide upland reached by the twisting road, where the
upper camps were set. There is no mention (at this point) of Gandalf's
passage through Edoras, nor of the great encampment of Riders in
Harrowdale (cf. RK pp. 66–7, and see note 16); after the words 'So
the King of the Mark came out of the west to Dunharrow in the hills'
the text continues at once with 'Leading up from the valley there was a
road made by hands in years beyond the reach of song.'

The description of the climbing road here reached virtually its form
in RK, and now appear the Púkel-men described word for word as in
RK apparently without any previous sketching. But they were called
by the Riders of Rohan *Hoker-men* (Old English *hocor* 'mockery,
derision, scorn') – changed subsequently to *Pookel-men*.[15]

I give the remainder of this text in full.

After a time he [Merry] looked back and found that he had
mounted some hundreds of feet above the valley, but still far
below he could dimly see a winding line of riders crossing the
bridge. Many men had followed Théoden from Westfold to the
muster of Rohan.[16]

At last they came to a sharp brink and the road passed
between walls of rock and led them out onto a wide upland: the
Lap of Starkhorn men called it, [rising gently beyond the sheer
wall of the valley towards a great northern buttress of the
mountain >] a green mountain-field of grass and heath above
the sheer wall of the valley that stretched back to the feet of a
high northern buttress of the mountain. When it reached this at
one place it entered in, forming a great recess, clasped by walls
of rock that rose at the back to a lofty precipice. More than a
half-circle this was in shape, [and its entrance looked west, a
gap some fifty yards wide between sharp pinnacles of stone >]

246   THE WAR OF THE RING

its entrance a narrow gap between sharp pinnacles of rock that opened to the west. Two long lines of unshaped stones marched from the brink of the cliff [up to the slope to the Hold-gate >] towards it, and [in the middle of the Hold one tall pointed stone stood alone >] in the middle of its rock-ringed floor under the shadow of the mountain one tall menhir stood alone. [Beyond it in the eastern wall >] At the back under the eastern precipice a huge door opened, carved with signs and figures worn by time that none could read. Many other lesser doors there were at either side, and peeping holes far up in the surrounding walls.

This was the Hold of Dunharrow: the work of long-forgotten men.[17] No song or legend remembered them, and their name was lost. For what purpose they had made this place, a town, or secret temple, or a tomb of hidden kings, no one could say. Here they had dwelt under the shadow of the Dark Years, before ever ship came to the mouths of Anduin or Gondor of the Kings was built; and now they had vanished, and only the old Hocker-men [later > Pookel-men] were left, still sitting at the turnings of the road.

As the King climbed out upon [the Lap of Starkhorn >] the mountain's lap, and Snowmane paced forward up the long avenue of stones, riders came down to meet him, and again the trumpets sang. [Struck out: Now Merry saw that they were blown inside Dunharrow, and understood the great echo that they made.][18]

He looked about and marvelled, for there were many lights on either side of the road. Tents and booths clustered thick on the slopes and the smokes of little fires curled up in the dim air. Then again the trumpets rang, echoing in the hollow of the Hold, and riders came forth to meet him [Théoden] as Snowmane paced forward up the long avenue of stones.

As they drew near Merry saw to his delight that Aragorn rode at their head, and beside him was a woman with long braided hair, yet she was clad as a warrior of the Mark, and girt with a sword.

Very glad was the meeting of the lady Éowyn with Théoden the King and with Éomer her brother; but Merry did not wait for leave, while they spoke together he rode forward.

'Trotter, Trotter,' he cried. 'I am glad to see you again. Is Pippin here? or Legolas and Gimli?'

'Not Pippin,' said Aragorn. 'Gandalf has not been here [later > to Dunharrow], but Legolas and Gimli are here. You may

BOOK FIVE BEGUN AND ABANDONED 247

find them in Dunharrow [*later* > the Hold] if you like to go and look, but don't wander in through the doors if they are not in the open. Without a guide you will get lost in that place, and we might spend days looking for you.' Merry rode on up the line of stones and Aragorn turned back to the King.

'Is there any news, Aragorn?' said Théoden. 'Only this,' said Aragorn. 'The men of Rohan are mustering here as you see. The Hold is full and the fields round about will soon be covered over. This is Gandalf's doing. It seems that he passed by Edoras going East many days ago and gave word that no great gathering of men should be held on the edge of the plain, but that all should come to meet you here. Many have already come, and with them many strange folk not of Rohan. For in some manner the rumour of war has long been abroad and men from far away say that they have had summons / a word that all who hate Mordor should come to Edoras, or to Minas Tirith. There are Dunlanders here, and some even of the Woodmen from the borders of Mirkwood, and wandering folk of the empty lands; and even some of the Rangers of the North, last remnant of Elendil's race: my own folk: they have come seeking me.'

'And you, Éowyn, how has it fared with you?'

'Well, Théoden King,' she answered. 'It was a long weary road for the people to take from their homes, and there were many hard words but no evil deeds. Then hardly had we come to Dunharrow and ordered ourselves when tidings came of your victory, and the fall of Isengard. There was great rejoicing, though I thought the tale had grown as it travelled along the road, until Aragorn came back as he promised.[19] But all have missed you, lord, especially in the hour of victory. It is overshadowed now by new fear, yet not dimmed altogether. Tonight all are preparing the feast. For you do not come unexpected. Aragorn named the very hour at which we might look for you. And behold you come.' She clasped his hand. 'Now I will admit, Théoden, brother of my mother, that it is beyond any hope I had when you rode away. This is a glad hour. Hail, Lord of the Mark, may I never again be taken from your side while you live still and rule the Eorlingas. Father you are to me since Éothain my father fell at Osgiliath far away.[20] Come now – all is prepared for you. And though Dunharrow is a dark place, full of sad shadow, tonight it shall be filled with lights.'

So they passed on, through the pinnacles of the gate, and

248   THE WAR OF THE RING

beside the Middle-stone, and dismounting before the dark
portal they went in. Night gathered outside.

Far within Dunharrow there was a great cavern enlarged by
many hands [*added later:* at different ages] until it ran back
deep into the mountain, a great hall with pillars of living stone.
At the far end it rose by [?steep short steps] to a platform of
rock that rose far up above the light of torch. There was no
hearth and no louvre for the smoke that could be seen; but fires
of pinewood were lit all down the centre between the pillars,
and the air was full of the scent of burning pinewood, but the
smoke rose and escaped through fissures or channels that could
not be seen. Torches blazed on wall and pillar. Three thousand
men could stand there when the hall was cleared; but at the
feast when all the benches and tables were arranged five
hundred sat that night at the King's feast.

Here this text ends, and was followed, no doubt at once, by a
second version ('G') of the latter part of F, beginning at the description
of the Hold of Dunharrow (p. 245) and ending at the same point
('some five hundred sat that night at the King's feast').

While the description of the Hold was repeated virtually unchanged
from F (as emended) – the 'Hoker-men' or 'Hocker-men' become
'Pookel-men' – the story that follows was rearranged and expanded.
Merry does not now have any speech with Aragorn when he appears
with Éowyn, and it is Éowyn that Théoden first addresses; in her reply
she says:

There were hard words, for it is long since war has driven us
from the quiet life of the green hills and the fields; but there have
been no evil deeds. We had scarcely come to Dunharrow and all
was still in turmoil, when tidings came of your victory at Helm's
Deep. There was great rejoicing, and many at once went back to
the lowlands, caring nothing for rumours of greater perils to
come. I hindered as many as I could, for I thought that the tale
had grown as it travelled – until Aragorn returned, yesterday
morning, even as he said. Then we learned of the fall of Isengard
and many other strange happenings. And we missed you, lord,
desiring to make merry. ...

The remainder of her words are as in F, but she does not now mention
her father. When she has finished speaking the text continues:

Now they rode on. Aragorn was beside the King, and Éowyn
rode beside her brother exchanging many glad words. Merry

BOOK FIVE BEGUN AND ABANDONED 249

jogged along behind, feeling forlorn: Aragorn had smiled at him, but he had no chance to get a word with him, or find out what had become of Legolas or Gimli, or Pippin.

'Have you gathered any tidings by the way, Aragorn?' asked the King. 'Which way did you ride?'

'Along the skirts of the hills,' said Aragorn. 'Being few we did not take to the mountain-paths, but came to Edoras and then up the Harrowdale. No enemy has been to Edoras or harmed your house. A few men have been left to hold the walls, and send word if any evil thing is seen in the plains. But the men of Rohan are mustering here, as you see. The Hold is full, and the uplands round about are covered with the camps of men. This is Gandalf's doing. We found that he had passed by Edoras before us, riding East, and had given orders in your name that no great gathering should be held on the edge of the plains, but that all men should come to meet you here. Most were willing enough. The dark shadow that we saw flying to Isengard was seen there also; and it, or another like it, has been seen twice again, darkening the stars. They say that men cower with fear as it passes, men who have never feared any enemy before.

'Not all your folk that can come have assembled yet, for the Last Quarter of the Moon was the day set; but most have already arrived. And with them have come also strange folk that are not of Rohan. For in some manner, the rumour of war seems to have gone far abroad long days ago, and men in distant countries have heard the word go forth that all who hate Mordor should come to Edoras or Minas Tirith. There are tall warriors of Dunland, some that fought against you, and some that never listened to Saruman, hating the Orcs far more than the Rohir! There are even Woodmen from the borders of Mirkwood, and wanderers of the empty lands. Last and fewest, but to me not least, there have come seven Rangers out of the North, my own folk, remnant of Elendil's race: they have sought me here.'

'How many spears and horses can we muster, if sudden need should come?' asked Théoden.

'Somewhat short of ten thousand,' answered Aragorn: 'but in that count I reckon only men well-horsed, fully armed, and with gear and provision to ride to battle far away, if needs be. As many again there are of men on foot or with ponies, with sword and shield, or bowmen and light-armed men of the dales: a good force to defend strong places, if war should come to the

250   THE WAR OF THE RING

land of Rohan itself. If your Riders leave the land, then, lord, I should gather all your home-keeping men in one or at most two strong places.'

'It is my purpose to hold the Hornburg and Dunharrow,' said Théoden. 'I have left Erkenbrand and three hundred good men in Helm's Deep, together with many stout country folk, and yeomen of Westfold; and men skilled in the mountains are to keep watch on the tracks and passes that lead from there to here. The guard at Edoras I shall strengthen, commanding them to hold it as long as they may, and defend the mouth of Harrowdale. But here, where now the most part of my people who are willing to leave their homesteads and seek refuge is now gathered, I will leave the main host of my men that do not ride away. Not while any crumb of food remains will any foe overtake us here.'

'Not without wings,' said Aragorn.

So at length they passed the pinnacles of the gate, and the tall Middle Stone, and dismounted before the dark portals of Dunharrow. The king entered, and they followed him. Night drew down outside.

The description of the great hall in Dunharrow was scarcely changed from that in the text F (p. 248). The platform of stone at the far end was 'reached by seven shallow steps'; and 'two thousand men, maybe, could have stood in that place' when no tables and benches were set out.

It is interesting to observe that the picture in crayon of 'Dunharrow' in *Pictures by J.R.R. Tolkien* (1979), no. 29, reproduced as second frontispiece, represents this original conception: the dark cleft to which the double line of standing stones leads is (as I think) the 'gate of the Hold', the 'Hold' itself, the 'recess' or 'amphitheatre' with doors and windows in the cliff at the rear, being in this picture invisible.

Lastly, there is a typescript ('H') typed in the same 'midget type' as was used for the text 'C' of 'Minas Tirith' (see p. 233); this is only a little longer than the other, and the two texts are so closely similar in every respect that I think it certain that they come from the same time – i.e., this typescript of the present chapter belongs with all this original material for the opening of 'The Muster of Rohan', composed before my father again abandoned work on *The Lord of the Rings* towards the end of 1944.

It is therefore remarkable that in this typescript (which in other respects closely followed the previous version F, pp. 244–6) my father had already abandoned an essential element in the conception

BOOK FIVE BEGUN AND ABANDONED 251

he had devised. No lights now twinkled on the far side of the valley as the King and his company came into Harrowdale; and after the description of the Pukelmen (so spelt) at the turns of the climbing road the text reads thus:

At last the king's company came to a sharp brink, and the road passed between walls of rock and led out onto a wide upland. The Firienfeld men called it, a green mountain-field of grass and heath high above the sheer wall of the valley. Beyond it was a dark wood that climbed steeply on the sides of a great round hill; its bare black head rose above the trees far above and on it stood a single pinnacle of ruined stone. Two long lines of unshaped stones marched from the brink of the cliff towards it and vanished in the gloom of the trees. Those who followed that road came in the sighing darkness of the Firienholt to a huge doorway in the side of the black hill of Firien;[21] signs and figures were above it, worn by time, that none could read. Within were vast caverns, so men said, though in living memory none had ever dared to enter. Such was the dark Dunharrow, the work of long-forgotten men.

Then follows the passage cited from text F on p. 246 ('No song or legend remembered them ...'), which was little further changed in RK (p. 68); and the typescript breaks off at the words 'As the king climbed out upon the upland field'.

What was the thought that lay behind this change, whereby 'dark Dunharrow' was now set within 'the black hill of Firien', a pinnacle of stone on its bare head, and became, so far from a place of feasting for the lords of Rohan, a place of fear that no man dared to enter? Perhaps my father felt that there was too much likeness between Dunharrow as first conceived and Helm's Deep: 'There are caves in Helm's Deep where hundreds may lie hid' (TT p. 134), 'Behind us in the caves of the Deep are three parts of the folk of Westfold ... great store of food, and many beasts and their fodder, have also been gathered there' (TT p. 136). Perhaps also the idea that Aragorn would pass over the mountains by the Scāda Pass, as proposed in the notes E (p. 243), had already led to a new idea, that his road would lead *through* Dunharrow (cf. the outline V in the next section, p. 262). However this may be, I believe that it was here that my father laid aside *The Lord of the Rings*, at least in the actual written evolution of the narrative, until a further year and a half had passed.

There remains a further difference to notice in this last text from the preceding versions. To Théoden's question 'Was it not the full moon last night?' Éomer now replies: 'Nay, lord, the full moon will rise

252 THE WAR OF THE RING

tonight four hours after dark. Tomorrow ere evening you shall come to Edoras and keep tryst with your Riders.'

(iii) Sketches for Book Five

I give here first (the most convenient place for it) a brief text of especial interest that stands quite apart from the outlines that follow, those being of much larger narrative purview and concerned to work out a coherent chronology for the extremely complex story to come. This text is found on a single page torn into halves and preserved separately among the manuscripts of 'The Siege of Gondor' at Marquette University – the reason for this being that my father later used the reverse of one half of the torn sheet to draft a revision of the opening of that chapter; but the original text belongs with the initial work on Book V studied here, and represents in fact a very early stage in that work. It is written in rapid pencil and is in places very difficult to make out, but the first part of it (as far as 'Muster in Minas Tirith') was overwritten clearly in ink, and so far as I can see my father scarcely altered the underlying text, his sole purpose being clarification. The whole page was struck through. At the head is written in pencil '250 miles', which probably refers to the distance from Edoras to Minas Tirith.

Evil counsels for evil days.

Éomer rides away and the king laments – for the snow is still deep and the wind over the Scāda has been the death of many a man.

Now it is to be told that King Théoden rested a day in Dunharrow and rode then to Eodoras and passed thence with five ? thousand riders, fully armed and horsed, and took the road to Minas Tirith. Others were to follow.

In ? five days they came within sight of Minas Tirith (Feb. 15 ?).

Merry's first sight of Minas Tirith from afar.

The plain below the hill covered with camps.

It would be better geographically if the main attack were made to come from the direction of Kirith Ungol – and the Swertings only a diversion, which nearly turns the scale.

Muster in Minas Tirith. [*Here the overwriting in ink ends.*]

People come from Belfalas and Dol Amroth and from the Five Streams of Lebennin in [?Anárion].[22] [?There came] Inram the tall from the vale of ....[23] and Nosdiligand[24] and the people of the Delta and Benrodir prince of [?Anárion], and the remnants of the folk of [?Ithilien] across the [??vale], and .....

BOOK FIVE BEGUN AND ABANDONED   253

from Rhovanion ..... men of the East,[25] and Rangers from the empty North, and even some of the folk of Dunland. [*Written against this passage in the margin*: King of Rohan   Men of Rohan come *after* the assembly. Only Aragorn rode .. to it.]

And the counsel of Denethor was to retake the Fords [*of Osgiliath*] and drive back the Orcs. So they sounded their trumpets and flew the red banner from the tower and rode to meet the enemy. And the enemy could not withstand the swords of Gondor, and before the sword of Elendil they fled like ... But Gandalf stood on the hill and [?watched afar]. Then comes the fleet of the Swertings [> Harns] up from the Delta and the Swertings come up through Ithilien.

They watch for the men of Rohan who [?are late]. Men of Rohan camp nearby and charge in the morning. Then the Nazgûl come

Here the text stops abruptly. In its opening ('Éomer rides away ...') it is closely associated with a passage in the notes E in the preceding section, where is found the only other reference to the Scāda Pass, leading over the mountains to the Blackroot Vale on their southern side (see pp. 243–4): 'Aragorn [*in margin*: Éomer?] begs leave to take a force over the Scāda Pass and fall on the enemy's rear.' Thus the present text, where it is Éomer who takes this road, preceded – in this opening passage – the definitive emergence of the story that it was Aragorn who 'went with his rangers over the mountains' (see outline III on p. 260) or 'passed into the mountains with his Rangers' (see outline V on p. 262). On the other hand, in this earliest form of the 'catalogue'[26] of the peoples of Southern Gondor mustering in Minas Tirith mention is also made of men of Rhovanion, and Dunlanders, and 'Rangers from the empty North' coming into the city; whereas in the notes E (p. 242) it is to Dunharrow, not to Minas Tirith, that 'Rangers have come and Dunlanders and messengers from the Wood-men of Mirkwood' (and similarly in Aragorn's account to Théoden at Dunharrow in the text F, p. 247: 'There are Dunlanders here, and some even of the Woodmen from the borders of Mirkwood ...').

The present text seems then evidence of a fleeting stage in which certain important narrative ideas had emerged, but when their poten-tial significance for the whole structure of Book V had not yet been realised. From the host mustering at Dunharrow, intending to ride to Minas Tirith by the Anórien road, a detachment is separated and passes over the mountains in order to come down swiftly into Southern Gondor (and this is above all on account of news of the great fleet approaching from the South, whose coming had long been foreseen, and which seems to have been originally the chief menace in the assault on Minas Tirith: see VII.435, 437). And Rangers

254 THE WAR OF THE RING

come out of the North. These elements were of course essential to the story of 'the Grey Company' and all that flowed from it. But those who leave the main host of the Rohirrim are here led by Éomer, not Aragorn; and the Rangers come not to Dunharrow, but to Minas Tirith.

But if this is so, the stage was certainly fleeting. Apparently, even as he wrote this brief text my father began to move in a new direction. The Orcs before the city 'fled before the sword of Elendil' – and that can only mean that it was Aragorn who came over the mountains and so reached Minas Tirith before the main host out of Rohan. The marginal note ('Men of Rohan come *after* the assembly. Only Aragorn rode ... to it', where the illegible word might be 'in' but does not look like it) was obviously written concurrently with the passage that it adjoins, since in the sketch of the war that then follows the Men of Rohan are obviously *not* present at the 'assembly' at Minas Tirith.

In the conclusion of the text there seems to be no suggestion that the city was laid under siege. Of course it is very easy to misinterpret these allusive and elliptical outlines, in which my father would pick out salient 'moments' and pass over others equally essential to the narrative in silence; but although 'the siege of Minas Tirith by the Haradwaith' is mentioned in 'The Story Foreseen from Fangorn' (VII.437) I think that no siege is mentioned here because none existed, or at any rate not in a form significant for the narrative. The force of his remark 'It would be better geographically if the main attack were made to come from the direction of Kirith Ungol – and the Swertings only a diversion, which nearly turns the scale' must surely be that he had supposed hitherto that in the strategy of the Enemy the attack from the South was to be the major blow against the city. In the sketch of events given here the attack out of Mordor is repulsed with rapid victory by the forces riding out of Minas Tirith (which included Aragorn); but Gandalf 'stood on the hill' (of the city) and (if I read the words aright) 'watched afar': '*then* comes the fleet of the Harns up from the Delta and the Swertings come up through Ithilien' – and 'nearly turn the scale'. And so here, where (so far as record goes) the charge of the Rohirrim in the morning first appeared, it is against the attack from the South that the horsemen ride. If the city had been in anything like a state of siege, it was surely besieged no longer when they came.

Of the names that appear in this text, *Eodoras* can be no more than a casual reversion to the earlier form. On *Anárion* (?) see note 22. The reference to 'the Five Streams of Lebennin' is remarkable, since in the first full text of the chapter 'Minas Tirith', deriving from the period of renewed work on Book V in 1946, Lebennin is still 'the Land of Seven Rivers' (see p. 278). So far as I know, neither *Harns* (presumably = Haradwaith, Haradrim), nor the names of the rulers in Southern Gondor, Inram the tall of the Morthond Vale (? – see note 23),

BOOK FIVE BEGUN AND ABANDONED   255

Benrodir prince of Anárion (?), Nosdiligand of the people of the Delta, ever appear again.

There are half a dozen outlines sketching out the content of 'Book Five and Last' – at this stage my father was determined that *The Lord of the Rings* should extend to one further 'part' only: as he wrote to Stanley Unwin in March 1945 (*Letters* no. 98): 'It is divided into Five Parts, of 10–12 chapters each (!). Four are completed and the last begun.' It is not easy to determine the order in which these outlines were written down, and though the sequence in which I give them seems to me probable other arrangements are possible. There is however fairly clear evidence that all belong with the abandoned openings of 'Minas Tirith' and 'The Muster of Rohan' in October 1944.

The outline that I give first, numbering it 'I', obviously belongs to the earlier time, in view of the date of Gandalf's arrival at Minas Tirith: 'Feb 5 or 6' (see the Note on Chronology at the end of this chapter); and the date February 8 of Théoden's arrival at Dunharrow appears to agree with the third version C and the fifth version F of the opening of 'The Muster of Rohan' (*ibid.*). A part of this text, all of it originally written in pencil, was overwritten in ink, but the part that was not is here and there altogether illegible.

(I)   Book V

Gandalf comes with Pippin to Minas Tirith. Feb 5 or 6 [*later* > 6].

Faramir. The allies come in. Urgent messages are sent to Théoden.

(Messages[27] must bid Rohirrim assemble at Edoras as soon as may be after the Full Moon of Feb. 6. Théoden reaches Dunharrow Feb. 8. Edoras Feb. 10 ...)[28]

Denethor only willing to hold his walls. Knowing war drawing near he has long sent out summons to allies. They are coming in. But the messengers to Théoden, his chief ally, have not returned yet. Gandalf tells of Théoden's war. Gandalf and Pippin on battlements. See shadow as Nazgûl sweep over river. Faramir comes on night of Feb. [7 >]8. At same time [> Next day] comes news of war at Osgiliath. Orcs led by Nazgûl have crossed river. Fleet from Umbar is approaching mouths of Anduin.

Faramir supports Gandalf's policy of attack by sortie *on the plain*. The first battle. The mountaineers drive the orcs back and burn ships. But orcs [?win through]. Nazgûl. Minas Tirith forces driven back. Still Gandalf .... [?on] the battlements.

Théoden leaves Edoras Feb. 11 with Éomer and Éowyn. Ents drive off the attack in north of Rohan. They drive back orcs out of west [?Anórien] and [*struck out:* Feb. 15 Last Quarter.] Reach battle Feb. 15.[29] Siege relieved by the Rohirrim and the allies of Lebennin. Gandalf comes forth and the enemy driven off. Théoden

256　　　THE WAR OF THE RING

slain and Éowyn slays the King of the Nazgûl and is mortally wounded. They lie in state in the white tower.[30] Gandalf ..... [?Aragorn]. Cross the River at Osgiliath. Elves and Ents drive Orcs back. They reach Minas Morgul and press on to Dagorlad. Parley with Sauron.

Another outline, 'II', gives a brief, and increasingly brief, pencilled synopsis of each of the ten chapters that were to constitute Book V and complete *The Lord of the Rings*.

(II)　　　　　　　　　　　　Bk. V

1.　Gandalf goes to Minas Tirith. Mustering of forces. War breaks out. Gondor driven back. No sign of Riders.

2.　Théoden comes to Dunharrow. Beacons. Messengers arrive from Minas Tirith. Also from far afield reporting orcs across the river in Wold.

Théoden rides on the evening of Feb. 8.[31] Éowyn goes with him. Gamling is left in command in Westfold. The old seneschal of Edoras in Eastfold (Dunharrow).

Aragorn and Éomer ride to beat off orcs. They come back and rejoin main body reporting that Ents and Lórien Elves have driven back the north thrust. They ride to Minas Tirith.

3.　Charge of the Riders of Rohan breaks siege. Death of Théoden and Éowyn in killing the Nazgûl King. Gondor destroys ships of Harad and crosses into Ithilien.

4.　Sack of Minas Morgul. Victorious Gandalf [?pursues] on to Dagorlad. Elves of Lórien and Ents come from North. Parley with Mor..[32] Sauron's messenger.

5.　Frodo from high tower sees the coming of the hosts of the West and the great assembly of secret army of Sauron.[33]

Rescue of Frodo by Sam.

[?This army] goes out, as he and Sam pass into Gorgor all is still and empty and the noise of the war is far away.

Gandalf is ambushed in Kirith Ungol and comes to edge of defeat.

6.　Destruction of the Ring. Fall of Baraddur. Allies enter Mordor. Rescue of Frodo by Eagle.

7.　Return to Gondor. Crowning of Aragorn. Funeral of Théoden and Éowyn.

The Hobbits depart north. [*Struck out:* Pass Lórien and]
Fall of Sauron.
Galadriel's land ruined.[34]

8.　Rivendell.

9.　Shire.

10.　Epilogue. Sam's book.

There is no clear indication in this synopsis or in synopsis I that

BOOK FIVE BEGUN AND ABANDONED 257

Aragorn entered Gondor by a different route (indeed in II, § 2 the reverse seems to be implied).

This page carries also two notes deriving from the same time as the synopsis by chapters. One of these reads:

> Gandalf keeps back, not to reveal himself. As the siege grows and the armies of Gondor are pressed back he looks in the Palantír. He catches sight of Frodo in tower and then Sauron cuts in. Gandalf gives a great shout and hurls the Stone from the battlements. It slays ? a captain. Gandalf is now revealed. He rides forth. Nazgûl come. [?Host] comes out of Dagorlad.

Above the third sentence is written: 'Sauron holding the coat'. – With this note cf. the words 'Episode of the Palantír and Gandalf' in outline A for 'Minas Tirith', p. 231. This is the original germ of the story of Denethor and the Palantír of the White Tower, and also perhaps of that of the revelation of Aragorn to Sauron in the Hornburg.

The second of these notes is as follows:

> The Firien (Firgen) [added: or the Halifirien] is a hill surrounded by a dark pinewood (the Firienholt). In it is a great cave, the Dunharrow. No one has ever been in the cave. It is said to be a *haliern*,[35] and to contain some ancient relic of old days before the Dark. ?
>
> It is 22 miles up Harrowdale from Edoras.

This statement clearly agrees with the idea of Dunharrow that entered in the typescript H (p. 251), where the hill, clothed in a dark wood but with bare head, is named *Firien* and the wood *Firienholt*; and where it is told that 'in living memory none had ever dared to enter' Dunharrow. Perhaps this synopsis II and accompanying notes immediately preceded H.[36] The addition 'or the Halifirien' is not obviously later than the rest of this note on Dunharrow; it was presumably rejected at once, for in the companion typescript C of 'Minas Tirith' the names of all the beacons are in the final form, ending with 'the Halifirien on the borders of Rohan' (p. 233).

On the same piece of paper as synopsis II is a small sketch-map very hastily drawn in ink; this is reproduced on p. 258. At the top is Edoras at the entrance to the long valley of Harrowdale, through which flows the Snowbourn, rising in the Starkhorn at the head of the valley. The distance from the Starkhorn to Edoras is marked as 75 miles; on the First Map (IVE, VII.319), where the valley runs south-west, the distance between Edoras and the mountain against which is written 'Dunharrow' is also 75 miles.[37] About half-way up the valley the path taken by Théoden and the Riders, following the course of the mountain-stream, is seen descending into Harrowdale from the west; this path crosses the stream before it joins the Snowbourn (whereas in all early versions of the opening of 'The Muster of Rohan', including

258   THE WAR OF THE RING

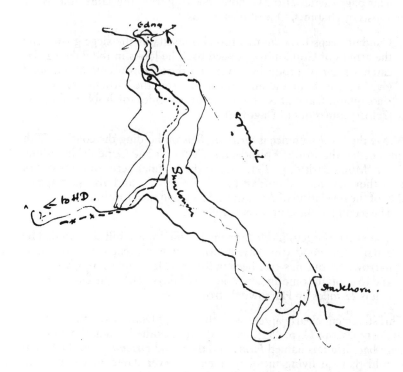

Harrowdale

BOOK FIVE BEGUN AND ABANDONED   259

the typescript H, the stone bridge is over the Snowbourn itself), and
turns north towards Edoras, ending at a place marked by a small circle
but without a name. The circle is enclosed within two lines forming an
oval shape. It can be seen in the original that the lower line is the
course of the Snowbourn as first drawn, and that the upper line was
put in with a subsequent stroke. However these markings, and the
detached crescent line above them, are to be interpreted, there can be
no doubt that this is the site of Dunharrow; both from the fact that the
path leads to it, and from the statement in the time-scheme D (p. 141):
'Théoden comes out of west into Harrowdale *some miles above
Dunharrow*, and comes to Dunharrow before nightfall.'

As regards the distances, if the Starkhorn is 75 miles from Edoras,
then Dunharrow on this map is considerably less than 22 miles from
Edoras (as stated in the note on the same page, cited above), indeed
scarcely more than half as far; but perhaps the discrepancy can be
accounted for by supposing that it was 22 miles on foot by a winding
track, whereas the 75 miles is shown as a linear distance between two
points.

An explanation of this curious stage in the evolution of the
geography of Harrowdale can be found by combining the evidence of
synopsis II, the time-scheme D, and the narrative opening of 'The
Muster of Rohan' in the typescript H. Abandoning the idea that
Dunharrow was a cavernous hold opening onto the green mountain-
field that was called the Lap of Starkhorn (p. 245), and that within it
there was a huge feasting-hall, to be used that very night to celebrate
the King's return, my father at the same time moved its site far down
the valley towards Edoras, and made it a cave or caves in a hill
('Firien') some 50 miles or so from the Starkhorn.

A third outline ('III') also sets out a scheme for Book V by chapters,
but does not proceed very far.

(III)   Book V
    Ch. 1.   Gandalf and Pippin reach Minas Tirith (Feb. 6 morning).
They see Denethor. Reasons for the beacons: (a) news from scouts
in Ithilien. (b) news reached Denethor on Feb. 5 that fleets of
Southrons had set sail. Gondor musters its forces. Pippin sees full
moon rising and wonders where Frodo is. No sign of Rohan.
    2.   Théoden comes to Dunharrow. Pukel men. (Feb. 6 [> 5]).
Beacons and messengers [*added:* morning 6]. Tidings of orc-
invasions of Wold. Théoden rides out on night of Feb. 8 [> 6].
Éomer and Éowyn ride with him. Gamling is left in command in
Westfold. The old seneschal of Edoras in Eastfold. [Aragorn and
Éomer ride north to beat off orcs. They come back >] Éomer rides
north to beat off orcs. He comes back and rejoins main body,

260   THE WAR OF THE RING

reporting that Ents and Lórien Elves have destroyed the northern diversion. They all ride to Minas Tirith. Where is Aragorn? He went with his rangers over the mountains.

3.   Great Darkness. Faramir returns (8). Host of Morghul crosses River (9). Southron fleets assail the south of Gondor (10 [> 9]). Gondor defeated and besieged (10 [> 9]). Gandalf in White Tower does not yet reveal his power or ...... [?name].

Final assault on Minas Tirith [added: [11 >] 10 night]. Nazgûl appear. Pelennor wall is taken. Sudden charge of Rohan breaks siege. Théoden and Éowyn destroy Nazgûl and Théoden falls [struck out: Feb. 12]. Aragorn arrives (having crossed the mountains with his rangers, he drove off the Southrons). Aragorn enters Minas Tirith and meets Denethor and Faramir.

4.   [Added: 12] Gandalf and Aragorn and Éomer and Faramir defeat Mordor. Cross into Ithilien. Ents arrive and Elves out of North. Faramir invests Morghul and main force comes to Morannon. Parley.

A suggestion that Aragorn should cross the mountains into Gondor is found in the notes E on p. 243; in these notes is found also the first mention of the coming of Rangers from the North, referred to also in the narratives F and G (pp. 247, 249). The Púkel-men entered in F (p. 245), where they are called *Hoker-men, Hocker-men*; in G they are *Pookel-men* (p. 248), and in typescript H *Pukelmen* (p. 251).

The text that I give next, 'IV', is reproduced on p. 261. This is a very battered page[38] of great interest, since it carries what is undoubtedly the earliest drawing of Minas Tirith, around which is written an outline in faint pencil. The line that runs up to the right of the White Tower indicates the mountain behind the city, with the name *Mindolluin* written across the summit. Whether my father already conceived the 'Hill of Guard' to be joined to the mountain mass by a shoulder cannot be said.

The outline reads as follows (with contractions expanded and some punctuation added):

(IV)   Gandalf and Pippin reach Minas Tirith dawn. Description of Minas Tirith and its huge 'cyclopean' concentric walls – it is in fact a fort and town the size of a small mountain. It has 7 circles with 7 – 6 – 5 – 4 – 3 – 2 – 1 gates before the White Tower is reached.

They are challenged on the borders of the Cityland, Pelennor,[39] about which ruins of an old wall ran. Gandalf [?carries messages] from Rohan and speaks some pass[?word] and they let him by in wonder. So he rides up to the 6th court and dismounts. There Pippin is re..... They pass into High City (Taurost) and so come before Denethor who at first does not recognize Gandalf.

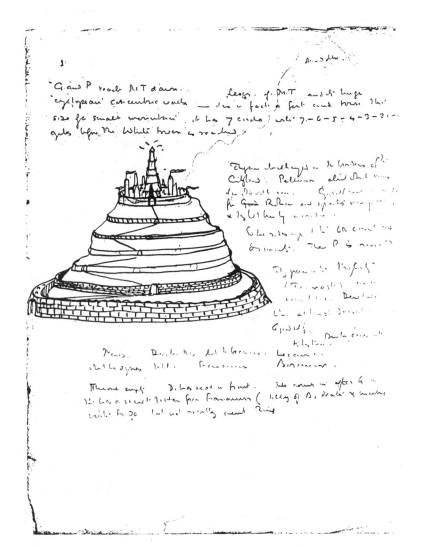

The earliest sketch of Minas Tirith

262   THE WAR OF THE RING

Denethor comes out to his [?throne]. News. Denethor has lit
the beacons because   what his spies tell. Faramir. Boromir.
Throne empty. Denethor has seat in front. He comes in after
Gandalf arrives. He has a secret letter from Faramir (telling of
Boromir's death and meeting with Frodo, but not overtly
mentioning Ring).

This seems to have been my father's first setting down on paper of his
conception of Minas Tirith.

The next two outlines ('V' and 'VI') were developed from III, and
are very closely related: they were certainly written at the same time.
From the rejected sentence in VI 'He has a secret' it is seen that my
father had IV in front of him, for in that text appears 'He has a secret
letter from Faramir'. The rejected reference in V to 'Dunharrow under
the Halifirien' relates this outline to the note on Dunharrow in II (see
p. 257). There is thus good reason to think that V and VI derive from
1944 rather than 1946, and it is notable that in V appears the first
glimpse of the story that would emerge as the passage of the Paths of
the Dead.

(V)   Book V
Gandalf and Pippin ride to Minas Tirith (3–4, 4–5 arriving
at sunrise on 6). Interview with Denethor – reasons for the
beacons: a great fleet from south is approaching mouths of
Anduin. Also messages from secret scouts in Ithilien report that
'storm is about to burst'.
    Muster of Gondor (Forlong the Fat etc.). Pippin on the battle-
ments sees the full moon; and thinks of Frodo.
    Théoden reaches Dunharrow [struck out: under the Hali-
firien] (Feb. 5 evening). Púkel-men. They find muster already
begun and not at Edoras. Rangers have come! Gandalf had been
at Edoras and issued orders: Nazgûl crossed the plain (3–4 and
on 4). Beacons are reported that night. Messengers arrive in
morning. Théoden prepares to ride. Gamling in charge at
Helm's Deep. Galdor the old seneschal[40] of Edoras in Eastfold.
Éowyn rides with Éomer and Théoden.
    Théoden sets out at nightfall (6). At Edoras they hear tidings
of invasion of Wold. ? Éomer rides off north but rejoins main
host later with news that the Ents have come out of Fangorn
and destroyed this N. diversion. They pass on at all speed into
Anórien.
    Aragorn is not there. He had fallen into converse with the
messengers of Gondor and getting guides from the men of
Harrowdale had passed into the mountains with his Rangers.
    Great darkness over land (Feb. 8). Faramir comes. Host of
Morghul crosses Great River at Osgiliath (night of 8) and assails

BOOK FIVE BEGUN AND ABANDONED 263

Gondor (9). At same time S[outhron] fleets come up the Great River and send a host into Lebennin, while another host from Morannon crosses River to north on a boat-bridge and links with the Morghul-host. Gondor is defeated in night battle 9–10. Gandalf in White Tower does not yet reveal himself. [*In margin:* Gandalf looks in Palantír?] Black hosts gather about the wall of Pelennor. Morning of 10 Nazgûl are seen: men fly. At sunrise on 10 there is a sound of horns. Charge of Rohan. Rout of the enemy. [*Scribbled in margin:* Éomer wounded.] Théoden is slain by Nazgûl; but he is unhorsed[41] and the enemy is routed. [*Added:* Gandalf leads charge in white.] Théoden is laid in state in tomb of kings. [*Struck out:* Great grief of Merry. Meeting of Merry and Pippin.]

[*Added:* News comes that fleet is coming up River. . . . . .] News comes from South that a great king has descended out of the mountains where he had been entombed, and set such a flame into men that the mountaineers (where the purer blood of Gondor lingered?) and the folk of Lebennin have utterly routed the Southrons, and burned [> taken] their ships. The fleet sailing up the River is an ally! Aragorn reaches Osgiliath by ship like a great king of old. (Frodo's vision?)[42] Meeting of Gandalf and Aragorn and Faramir at Osgiliath evening of 10.

Closely related to outline V is the following text ('VI'), which I incline to think was written second.

(VI)   Gandalf and Pippin ride to Minas Tirith (3–4, 4–5, 5–6) arriving at the Outer Wall of Pelennor at daybreak and seeing sunrise on the White Tower on morning of Feb. 6. On night of 5–6 they see the beacons flare up, and are passed by messengers riding to Rohan. Pippin sees moonrise about 9 p.m.

Description of Minas Tirith and its 7 concentric walls and gates. Gandalf and Pippin come into the presence of Denethor. Empty throne. Denethor has a seat in front. [*Struck out:* He has a secret] They exchange news. Reasons of Beacons: news of scouts in Ithilien that 'storm is coming'; Southrons are marching in; most of all – a great fleet from South is approaching the mouths of Anduin. Muster of Rohan [*read* Gondor] is going apace – catalogue.

(7) Great Darkness spreads from East. Faramir returns. Pippin on the battlements.

Théoden reaches Dunharrow (5 evening). Merry sees Púkel-men. They find Muster has already begun, owing to special instructions by Gandalf, who had stayed at Edoras on 4 and owing to passage of Nazgûl. Rangers have come! [*Struck out:* Aragorn and Éomer already there?] That night the beacon lights are reported. In morning messengers arrive from Gondor.

264   THE WAR OF THE RING

Théoden gets ready to ride. Éowyn and Éomer go with him. [*Struck out:* But Aragorn (after secret converse with Aragorn takes Merry]

Here outline VI ends, but the lower half of the page is taken up by a map, which is redrawn in part and discussed in a note at the end of this chapter.

NOTES

1 The illegible word might be *already*, in which case my father omitted the words *been riding*. The word I have given as *four* might be read as *five*.

2 The words *by nightfall tonight* are perfectly plain, but my father must have intended something else, since it was now several hours after nightfall. In the outlines V and VI (pp. 262–3) the messengers from Minas Tirith reach Edoras the following morning (6 February).

3 As in text B, the moon rises 'round and full out of the eastern shadows' ('now almost at the full,' RK). — At this stage the beacons were fired on the last night of Gandalf's ride; in the final form it was on the night preceding the last (the journey taking four nights), and so when Pippin woke in the dawn beside the wall of the Pelennor 'Another day of hiding and a night of journey had fleeted by' (RK p. 20). This sentence was added to the text of the chapter much later.

4 Possibly this means 'longer than the time that they had in fact taken'.

5 Here and subsequently, and again in text B, the river's name is written *Snowborn*, but at two of the occurrences in A the *u* was inserted.

6 At this point my father drew in the text a very simple little sketch of the 'upland field' set into the mountain's side, essentially the same as the lower of the two sketches on the page reproduced on p. 239, but without the falling stream.

7 My father first wrote 'ale of Háma', i.e. his 'funeral-ale', funeral feast (cf. *bridal* from *bride-ale*, marriage feast). He changed this to ... *ale of Háma*, intending some compound term of the same sense, but I cannot decipher it.

8 This is a reference to Théoden's words to Merry and Pippin at the end of 'The Road to Isengard': 'May we meet again in my house! There you shall sit beside me ...'

9 This contradicts the statement a few lines above that 'Éowyn comes forth and greets Théoden and Aragorn.' The story that Aragorn (with Legolas and Gimli) had gone on ahead and

BOOK FIVE BEGUN AND ABANDONED   265

reached Dunharrow before Théoden is not present in text B, which undoubtedly followed A; it appears however in the time-schemes C and D (pp. 140–1).

10   *Halbarad* first appeared in *The Lord of the Rings* as the name of Shadowfax: see VII.152, 390.

11   The Sea of Nurnen, the Nargil Pass, and the River Harnen all appear on the First Map (Map III, VII.309). — The text ends with a reference to Umbar that I cannot decipher.

12   *Éowyn* was struck out, and *wine!* written in the margin; which I take to mean that Éowyn was not seated, for she bore the wine.

13   The queries might mean that my father was uncertain of the correctness of his interpretation of the pencilled forms (in the one case it might be *Umbor* or *Umbar*; in the other the second vowel of *Nargil, Nargul* cannot now be read under the ink overlay). But this does not seem very likely. Both these names appear in text A (p. 237), where *Nargil* is clear, though *Umbar* could be read as *Umbor*. *Umbar* and *Haven of Umbar* appear on the First Map (VII.309) and on the map that I made in 1943; and on the latter the pass through the southern mountains of Mordor is named *Nargil* (on the First Map the name was pencilled in roughly and is hard to read, but was apparently *Narghil*, VII.310).

14   As originally drawn, a pass over the mountains in this region is clearly defined on the First Map: see Map IV^A, square P11 (VII.314), connecting to Map III, square Q11 (VII.309). Here the Blackroot rises in an oval lake. With the superimposed portion Map IV^{D-E} (VII.319) the connections become unclear, especially since a different convention was used in the representation of the mountains, but at any rate there is no clear indication of a pass. The 1943 map retains the oval lake and the broad pass, but its relation to the First Map is here difficult to interpret (VII.320). Possibly it was to this feature that my father referred in his note on that map (VII.321 note 1): 'The White Mountains are not in accord with the story'. On late maps, as is to be expected, no pass breaks the line of the mountains.

15   In the *Guide to the Names in The Lord of the Rings* (*A Tolkien Compass*, ed. Lobdell, p. 200) my father noted of the name *Púkel-men*: 'It represents Old English *púcel* (still surviving as *puckle*), one of the forms of the *puk-* stem (widespread in England, Wales, Ireland, Norway and Iceland) referring to a devil, or to a minor sprite such as Puck, and often applied to ugly misshapen persons.'

16   In place of this, RK has: '... a winding line of Riders crossing the ford and filing along the road towards the camp prepared for them. Only the king and his guard were going up into the Hold.'

17   RK has here: 'Such was the dark Dunharrow, the work of long-forgotten men'; cf. text H, p. 251.

266 THE WAR OF THE RING

18 At this point my father's writing suddenly becomes very much more rapid and rough.

19 Cf. 'The King of the Golden Hall' in VII.447, where Aragorn says: 'If I live, I will come, Lady Éowyn, and then maybe we will ride together.'

20 I think that Éowyn's naming her father *Éothain* is most likely to be a mere slip, for *Éomund* father of Éomer and Éowyn was established (VII.393 etc.), and *Éothain* was the name of Éomer's squire (VII.400–2); but see further p. 350 and note 13. In LR Appendix A (II) it is said that Eomund, chief Marshal of the Mark, was slain in the year 3002 in pursuit of Orcs on the borders of the Emyn Muil.

21 Old English *fyrgen*, *firgen* 'mountain'; the word *fyrgen-holt* 'mountain-wood' occurs in *Beowulf*, line 1393. — Afterwards, when the Firien had become the Dwimorberg and the Firienholt the Dimholt, the Firienfeld remained (RK p. 67).

22 This name undoubtedly begins with *An*, and the word preceding it is almost certainly 'in'; equally certainly it is this same name that appears below, as the land of the prince Benrodir. The remaining letters of the name are uninterpretable as they stand, but their vague shapes do not exclude 'Anárion', and this name, found on the First Map (VII.309) of the region south of Minas Tirith, appears in the notes E on p. 243: 'A fleet has put out ... and sailed up the Anduin and reached Anárion' (see further p. 244).

23 This lacuna is where the page is torn across, cutting through a line of text. It might perhaps be read, but very uncertainly, as 'from the vale of Morthond and his ... sons, dark-haired, grey-eyed'.

24 *Nosdiligand*: the second and third letters of this name are not perfectly clear, but can hardly be other than *os*. Without striking through the first syllable my father wrote another form above, apparently *Northiligand*.

25 The illegible words might just possibly be 'fugitives' and 'representing'.

26 My father called it a 'catalogue': pp. 229, 263.

27 These messages, distinct of course from those just referred to, must have been sent from Isengard or Helm's Deep.

28 The illegible word might possibly be 'morn(ing)'.

29 It is not clear whether 'Reach battle Feb. 15' refers to the Ents or to the Rohirrim; but in any case the Ents were certainly present after the siege of Minas Tirith was relieved ('Elves and Ents drive Orcs back'; cf. also outline II §4 'Elves of Lórien and Ents come from North', and similarly outline III §4). Thus the original idea that 'tree-giants' (see VI.410), or Treebeard (see VII.211, 214), played a part in the breaking of the siege survived at least in the

BOOK FIVE BEGUN AND ABANDONED   267

idea that Ents were present in the last stage of the war in the South, though this would never receive narrative form. See further pp. 343, 345–6, 361.

30   Cf. the notes given in VII.448: 'Probably Éowyn should die to avenge or save Théoden.' These notes contain also the suggestion · that the mutual love of Éowyn and Aragorn should be removed.

31   This is the date given in the time-scheme D (p. 182); see the Note on Chronology following.

32   The last two letters of this name might be read as *du*, sc. *Mordu*.

33   With this cf. the outline 'The Story Foreseen from Fangorn' (VII.438): 'Then return to Frodo. Make him look out into impenetrable night. Then use phial ... By its light he sees the forces of deliverance approach and the dark host go out to meet them'; also p. 230 in this book.

34   Cf. the outline given in VII.448: 'They pass by round Lórien' (on the homeward journey), with the later addition (VII.451 note 18): 'No. They learn (in Rivendell?) that Nazgûl razed Lórien ...'

35   Old English *haliern* (*hálig-ern* or *-ærn*) 'holy place, sanctuary'. Cf. my father's note on *Dunharrow* in the *Guide to the Names in The Lord of the Rings* (*A Tolkien Compass*, ed. Lobdell, p. 183): '*Dunharrow*. A modernisation of Rohan *Dúnhaerg* "the heathen fane on the hillside", so-called because this refuge of the Rohir-rim at the head of Harrowdale was on the site of a sacred place of the old inhabitants (now the Dead Men). The element *haerg* can be modernised in English because it remains an element in place-names, notably *Harrow (on the Hill).*'

36   Outline II was written on the same thin yellowish paper as was used for text H of 'The Muster of Rohan' and text C of 'Minas Tirith' (the two pages in the 'midget type'). This paper was also used for the time-schemes C, D, and S. See note 38.

37   On my father's later large-scale map of Rohan, Gondor and Mordor (on which my map published in RK was based) the distance from Edoras to Dunharrow (at the head of Harrowdale) is 16 miles and from Edoras to the Starkhorn 19 miles.

38   Outline IV was written on the same paper as that referred to in note 36.

39   *Pelennor*: see p. 277.

40   *Galdor* was preceded by *Ealdor*.

41   In outlines I, II and III it is said that Théoden and Éowyn (who is not mentioned here) 'slew' or 'killed' or 'destroyed' the King of the Nazgûl.

42   Frodo's vision of a ship with black sails and a banner bearing the emblem of a white tree (FR p. 379) was added afterwards to the text of 'The Mirror of Galadriel'.

268   THE WAR OF THE RING

Note on the map accompanying outline VI

This map, drawn fairly rapidly in pencil (with the rivers in blue crayon), covers the White Mountains and the lands to the south of them; it is laid out like the First Map in squares of 2 cm. side. In my redrawing I have numbered the uppermost horizontal line of squares O 9–14 according to the First Map, although there is some discrepancy, and continued this numbering throughout, where the discrepancy becomes much greater. This is done deliberately in order to emphasize the curiously anomalous nature of this map among my father's later maps to *The Lord of the Rings*. Comparison with the First Map (VII.309, 319) and those published in LR will show substantial shifts in the geographical relations: thus Ethir Anduin is further to the east, directly south of Rauros, and the Havens of Umbar are shown as much less far to the south, and east of Tolfalas. On no other map is this so.

I strongly suspect that (for whatever reason) my father made this map from memory, and that it played no further part in the geographical evolution; and I think that its starting-point and primary purpose was to depict the region (pencilled more heavily than other parts of the map) between Harrowdale and the source of Morthond: with the emergence of the story that Aragorn passed *through* the Mountains into Gondor the map of *The Lord of the Rings* needed to be altered to show that there was no pass in this region (see note 14 above). It will be seen that the southern rivers have been substantially changed, though by no means reaching the final form: Morthond of the First Map is now named Ringlo, while the new Morthond flows east into the delta of Anduin. Erech is marked, south of the rising of Morthond, as is also Pelargir on Anduin (neither of which is mentioned in any of these outlines).* Harrowdale is shown running south-east, as on the little map reproduced on p. 258.

The map as squared out on the page extended through five vertical lines of squares east of Osgiliath (cf. VII.309), but these were apparently left blank. Subsequently my father attached a moveable portion covering O 13–14, P 13–15, and at the same time very roughly drew in the outlines of the mountains encircling Mordor, which here form more nearly a complete wall on the east than on any other map. The Dark Tower is shown as standing on a 'peninsula' thrust out southwards from the Ash Mountains, with Mount Doom to the north-west of it, very much as on the Second Map as originally drawn,

---

* Pelargir was first placed at the top of the delta of Anduin. On the First Map (VII.309) a pencilled dot within a circle was placed beside Anduin at the point where rivers flow in from east and west on R 13: this is obviously Pelargir, and was no doubt entered at this time. Another pencilled dot within a circle was put in to the east of the original Morthond on First Map Q 12 (just to the right of the *i* of *Enedwaith*), and this is evidently Erech.

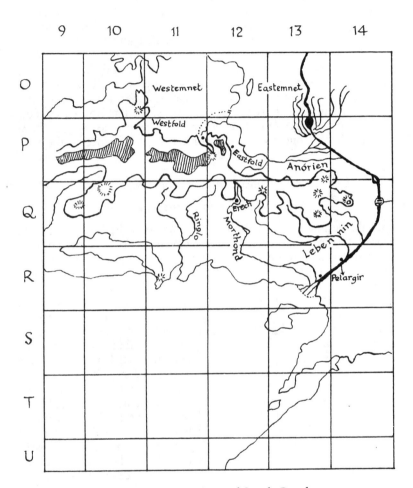

The White Mountains and South Gondor

270   THE WAR OF THE RING

pp. 435, 438. I have not attempted to redraw this added portion, for
the pass into Mordor (here called Kirith Gorgor) was apparently
moved eastwards from the position in which it was first drawn,
resulting in a confusion of lines that I cannot interpret; and Osgiliath
was now moved a good way to the north, so that it lies north-east of
Minas Tirith (as is shown on the Second Map, p. 434, and on my large-
scale map of Rohan, Gondor and Mordor published in RK, but not on
my general map accompanying LR). On this attached portion the
Dead Marshes are named, but not the Nomenlands; the rapids in
Anduin are still called *Sarn Ruin*. The course of Anduin below Rauros
was changed on the new P 14 to flow as it does on the First Map (see
VII.319) in a wide easterly curve, not in a straight line south-east (and
thus the mouths of Entwash had to be shifted to the east). This
supports my suggestion that the present map was drawn from
memory: in this one area it was corrected by reference to the First
Map.

Note on the Chronology

(i) Pippin and Frodo see the Full Moon

It would be interesting to know just what was the 'most awkward
error in the synchronization ... of movements of Frodo and the others'
that arrested the progress of *The Lord of the Rings* in October 1944
(see p. 234). It seems to me most likely to have been their relative
'positions' at the time of the Full Moon on 6 February.

I think it is clear that the time-schemes C, D, and S belong with the
work set out in this chapter, and indeed that they were closely associated with the chronological problem that my father had encountered:
see pp. 141–2, 234–5. In scheme C (p. 140) Gandalf and Pippin came
to Minas Tirith at sunset on Feb. 5. They had left Dol Baran on the
night of Feb. 3–4, passed Feb. 4 'in hiding' (presumably at Edoras),
ridden through the night of Feb. 4–5, and then after a short rest had
'abandoned secrecy' and ridden all through the next day (Feb. 5) to
reach the city at sunset. It seems likely that the original brief narrative
opening (A) of 'Minas Tirith', in which as they rode 'still the world of
grey and green rushed by and the sun rose and sank', was associated
with this scheme, and that it was abandoned because my father
decided that Gandalf did not in fact ride by day (see pp. 231–2). In the
pencilled continuation of that opening (p. 231) the new story had
entered: it is night, two days since Pippin 'saw the sun glinting on the
roof of the king's great house', and the 'third riding', thus the night of
Feb. 5–6. They see the beacons and the westbound messengers, but the
moon is not mentioned; and it is obvious that in this story they will
arrive at the wall of the Pelennor in the morning (Feb. 6). This is the
story in scheme D (p. 141), except that there the beacons and the
messengers are seen on the second night of the ride (Feb. 4–5). In that

BOOK FIVE BEGUN AND ABANDONED 271

scheme the Full Moon 'rises about 9.20 p.m. and sets about 6.30 a.m. on Feb. 7. Gandalf rides all night of 5–6 and sights Minas Tirith at dawn on 6th.'

It was a datum of Frodo's journey that he came before the Black Gate at dawn of Feb. 5, leaving at nightfall; and he was in Ithilien (the episode of the stewed rabbit) and was taken by Faramir to Henneth Annûn on Feb. 6 (the night of Full Moon, which Frodo saw in the small hours of Feb. 7 setting over Mindolluin). In my father's letter of 16 October 1944 he said that among the alterations made to resolve 'the dislocated chronology' he had increased the journey from the Morannon by a day; this alteration was made to scheme D, and was present in scheme S as first written (see pp. 141–2). But the alteration was made by pushing Frodo's journey back by a day, so that he came before the Morannon on Feb. 4; he still comes to Henneth Annûn on the 6th. Therefore, when he looked out from the Window of the West and saw the moon setting, Gandalf and Pippin were already in Minas Tirith; the time-schemes are explicit (and it was presumably on this basis that in outline III, p. 259, Pippin in Minas Tirith on the evening of the 6th 'sees the full moon rising and wonders where Frodo is'; similarly in outline V, p. 262, and also in the outline given in the next chapter, p. 276).

In the second draft (B) of the opening of 'Minas Tirith' (p. 232) Pippin on the night of Feb. 5(–6) saw the full moon rising out of the eastern shadows as he rode with Gandalf; and in the third draft (C, in 'midget type', p. 233) Pippin wonders where Frodo might be, 'little thinking that Frodo on that same night saw from afar the white snows under the moon.' Surely my father's intention here was to relate Pippin's thought to Frodo's at Henneth Annûn (as in RK); but there was a day out. Was this the chronological problem?

On the face of it, apparently not; for the modifications made to the chronology did not correct it. On the other hand, that my father was concerned with precisely this question is seen from an isolated page of notes on diverse subjects, one of which casts some very cloudy light on the matter:

> Whole of Frodo's and Sam's adventures must be set back *one day*, so that Frodo sees moon-set on morning (early hours) of Feb. 6, and Faramir reaches Minas Tirith on night of the 7th, and Great Darkness begins on 7th. (This can be done by making Frodo and Sam only wander 4 days in the Emyn Muil.) The next night Frodo would see from far away the full moon set beyond Gondor and wonder where he was in the mists of the West, and the war-beacons would be hid from him in the darkness of the world.

This is very difficult to understand. Frodo's adventures are to be set back by a day, and he will see the setting of the moon (not yet quite at the full) from Henneth Annûn in the later night of Feb. 5–6, when

272   THE WAR OF THE RING

Pippin was on the last lap to Minas Tirith, and thought of him. But then why is it not till the next night (Feb. 6–7) that Frodo thinks of Pippin (if 'him' is Pippin), and why is it on this night that the beacons of Gondor are burning?

(ii) Théoden comes to Harrowdale

In the second version (B) of 'The Muster of Rohan' (p. 237) Aragorn agrees with Théoden, as they enter Harrowdale, that the moon was full the night before, and he says that they have been four (changed from five) days on the road, so that six remained before the day appointed for the muster at Edoras. In time-scheme C (p. 140) Théoden reaches Helm's Deep from Isengard soon after dawn on Feb. 4, and he leaves Helm's Deep on Feb. 5 (when also 'Aragorn rides on ahead with Gimli and Legolas': this appears in the third narrative C, p. 241). Nothing further is said about Théoden's movements in time-scheme C; but if the two texts are combined we get the following chronology:

Feb. 4   Théoden reaches Helm's Deep soon after dawn
Feb. 5   Théoden leaves Helm's Deep
Feb. 6   Full Moon
Feb. 7   Théoden reaches Harrowdale at dusk
Feb. 13 Date appointed for the muster

If this is correct, the 'four days on the road' include the day spent at Helm's Deep.

In the third version C (p. 240) Éomer says that the moon was full on the night before the last, that five days have passed on the journey, and that five remain until the muster; and all this is repeated in the next version (F) in which the passage appears (pp. 244–5). In these versions the journey has taken one day more, as it appears:

Feb. 5   Théoden leaves Helm's Deep
Feb. 6   Full Moon
Feb. 7
Feb. 8   Théoden reaches Harrowdale.

Time-scheme D (pp. 141, 182) gives the following chronology (with which the fully 'synoptic' scheme S agrees):

Feb. 4–5 Aragorn rides by night to Edoras, which he reaches in the morning, and passes up Harrowdale
Feb. 5   Théoden leaves Helm's Deep
Feb. 6   Full Moon rises about 9.20 p.m. Théoden comes to Dunharrow before nightfall
(Feb. 7 Théoden prepares to ride to Gondor. Messengers from Minas Tirith arrive
Feb. 8   Théoden rides from Edoras)

This is the chronology of the typescript text H (pp. 251–2), to the extent at least that the moon is full (rising four hours after dark) on the

BOOK FIVE BEGUN AND ABANDONED 273

night of Théoden's arrival in Harrowdale: the journey through the mountains now took only two days. It is not the chronology of *The Tale of Years* in LR, in which Théoden set out from Helm's Deep on March 6 but did not reach Dunharrow until March 9.

The date appointed for the muster at Edoras as deduced above from the original narrative openings of the chapter, Feb. 13 (a week after the full moon of Feb. 6), is presumably to be associated with the change in the second manuscript of 'The Road to Isengard' from 'before the waning of the moon' to 'at the last quarter of the moon' (see pp. 27, 40). In the text H (p. 252) Éomer says to the King that 'Tomorrow ere evening you shall come to Edoras and keep tryst with your Riders'; with this perhaps cf. outline I (p. 255): 'Messages must bid Rohirrim assemble at Edoras as soon as may be after the Full Moon of Feb. 6.'

III

MINAS TIRITH

'I hope after this week actually to – write,' my father wrote to Stanley Unwin on 21 July 1946 (*Letters* no. 105); and it is clear that he did – at any rate on 7 December of that year he said that he was 'on the last chapters' (whatever that may have meant). Another synopsis of the proposed content of 'Book V' shows much further development in the narrative of the opening chapters, and I incline to think that it belongs to 1946 and was set down as a guide to the new work now beginning; I therefore give it here rather than with the outlines that I believe to date from 1944 (pp. 252 ff.). My father had now re-ordered earlier chapters, and so numbered the first of Book V in this synopsis '44' (not '41': see p. 226 note 49).[1] The text was written in pencil and then overwritten in ink: the underlying text was far briefer, but is barely legible except at the end, where the overwriting ceases.

Book V

Ch. 44 (1). Gandalf (and Pippin) rides to Minas Tirith and see[s] Denethor. Pippin on walls. Coming in of last allies. Great Darkness begins that night.

45. King and Aragorn (with Merry, Legolas, Gimli) ride to the Hornburg. Overtaken by the Sons of Elrond[2] and 30 Rangers seeking Aragorn (probably because of messages sent by Galadriel to Elrond). King rides to Dunharrow by mountain roads. Aragorn (Legolas and Gimli) and Rangers go by open road. Aragorn reveals he has looked in Palantír, and seeks the Paths of the Dead. King arrives at Dunharrow dusk 2 days later[3] and finds Aragorn has gone on Paths of the Dead. Errand riders of Gondor come. Muster of Rohan takes place in Harrowdale (by Gandalf's orders) not Edoras, and King sets out next morning for Edoras.

46. Pippin on walls. Several days later when Host of Morghul is victorious. News comes through of flanking attacks on Lórien and by Harad in South. A great army has crossed into Wold of Rohan. They fear Rohirrim will not come. Dark grows but even so the Nazgûl cause a greater darkness. Gandalf shines in the field. Pippin sees the light of him as he and Faramir rally men. But at last the enemy are at the gates, and the Nazgûl fly

MINAS TIRITH

275

over the city. Then just as gate is giving way they hear the horns of Rohan!

47. Go back to Merry. Charge of Rohan. Orcs and Black Riders driven from gate. Fall of Théoden wounded, but he is saved by a warrior of his household who falls on his body. Merry sits by them. Sortie saves King who is gravely wounded. Warrior found to be Éowyn. The Hosts of Morghul reform and drive them back to the gate. At that moment a wind rises, dark is rolled back. Black ships seen. Despair. Standard of Aragorn (and Elendil). Éomer's wrath. Morghul taken between 2 forces and defeated. Éomer and Aragorn meet.

48. Gandalf and Denethor learn of the defeat of the flank attacks by Shadow Host[4] and by Ents. They cross Anduin victorious and invest Minas Morghul. Gandalf and Aragorn come to Morannon and parley.

49. Return to Frodo and Sam.

At this point the overwriting in ink ceases – perhaps because my father saw that at this rate he was going to be very hard put to it to complete the story in 'Book Five and Last' (p. 219). In the pencilled underlying text he had had this programme for the last seven chapters:

48. Gandalf comes to the Black Gate.
49. Frodo and Sam come to Orodruin.
50. .... and return.
51. Feast at Minas Tirith.
52. Funeral at Edoras.
53. Return to Rivendell. Meeting with Bilbo.
54. Sam's Book and the passing of all Tales.

It was perhaps immediately before he turned to the chapter 'Minas Tirith' again that my father set down a further and very precise outline, which follows here (the figures refer of course to the dates in the month of February).

Gandalf and Pippin ride to Minas Tirith (3/4, 4/5, arriving at sunrise on 6). Pass Fords of Isen and reach mouth of Deeping Coomb about 2 a.m. (4). Come at daybreak to Edoras. Gandalf remains there during daylight. 2nd Nazgûl passes over Rohan (it left Mordor about midnight 3/4 but spies out plain and flies low over Edoras in early morn[ing]).[5] Gandalf rides again on night of 4/5 and passes into Anórien, where he lies hid in hills during daylight (5). Riding for third night (5/6) they see the beacons flare out, and are passed by messengers on swift horses speeding from Minas Tirith to Edoras. They reach the Pelennor Wall at first dawn, and after speech with guards pass through

276   THE WAR OF THE RING

and sight Minas Tirith in the sunrise (6). They pass up through the 7 concentric walls and gates to the White Tower. Pippin sees white houses and domes on the slopes of the mountain above the city. Gandalf explains they are the 'houses of the kings' – i.e. dead tombs. (Before the gate of the White Tower they see the ruin of the Tree, and Fountain?) They are admitted to the audience chamber, and see the throne. Denethor comes in, and does not sit in the throne, but on a smaller chair lower down and in front. Interview with Denethor and his grief at news of Boromir. They learn reason of beacons: a great fleet has been sighted coming from Umbar to mouths of Anduin. Also messages from spies etc. in Ithilien report that 'storm is about to burst'. Denethor is vexed that no aid has come from Rohan. Gandalf explains the situation. Also warns Denethor that help may even now be delayed as almost certainly Rohan will be attacked on eastern flank north of Emyn Muil. He counsels Denethor to muster what he can at once. 'The muster has already begun,' said Denethor. (Forlong the Fat etc., but too few come from Lebennin owing to threat of sea-attack.)

Pippin on the battlements has talk with a sentinel. He sees the moonrise on night of 6 (about 8.45 p.m.) and thinks of Frodo.[6]

Aragorn takes Legolas and Gimli and Merry and proposes that what is left of the Company shall be reunited. He says his heart now urges him to speed, for the time of his own revealing approaches. They may have a hard and dangerous journey, for now the real business is beginning, beside which the battle of the Hornburg is but a skirmish by the way. They agree and Aragorn and his company leave Dolbaran ahead of the king at about midnight. Merry rides with Aragorn, and Gimli with Legolas. They go fast and reach Westfold at daybreak (4) and [*struck out at once:* do not turn aside but go straight] see the 2nd Nazgûl flying.

A great deal of the first part of this derives directly from earlier outlines, but by no means all (thus it is here that the great tombs of Minas Tirith are first mentioned, and it is here that Pippin's friend of the Citadel guard – Beregond in RK – first appears). The concluding portion of the outline, however, telling that Aragorn with Merry, Legolas and Gimli left together from Dol Baran ahead of the king about midnight, reaching Westfold at dawn of the following day and not so very many hours after Gandalf, is an odd and surprising development.[7] But it seems to have been abandoned at once, without further issue.

MINAS TIRITH 277

Taking up the opening chapter 'Minas Tirith' again, my father followed closely the abandoned opening (the text C in 'midget type') so far as it went, and the new text still differs from RK pp. 19–21 in the points mentioned on p. 233, except that the leader of the men at the Pelennor Wall is now Ingold, not Cranthir.[8] Written for most of its length rapidly but generally legibly in ink, the draft extends almost to the end of the chapter; and from the point in the story where C ended (in the conversation with the men repairing the wall), for which my father had only very sketchy notes, he advanced confidently through the account of Minas Tirith seen across the 'townlands', the structure of the city, the entry of Gandalf and Pippin, the 'audience' with Denethor, and Pippin's meeting with Beregond (not yet nor for a long time so named). This draft underwent countless changes afterwards, yet from its first writing the story was present in all essentials of narrative structure, of atmosphere, and of tone. In what follows it can be assumed that every significant feature of description and conversation in the chapter was present in the draft unless something is said to the contrary. On the other hand I do not record all the small touches that were added in later: for example, Denethor does not in the draft text lay down his rod in order to lift the horn from his lap; Pippin is not said to receive back his sword and put it in its sheath; chairs are brought for Gandalf and Pippin, not a chair and a stool; the room in which they were lodged had only one window, not three; and so on.

As noted earlier, the text C stops just before Gandalf tells Cranthir / Ingold that 'you are overlate in repairing the wall of the Pelennor' (p. 233; RK p. 21), so that this name does not appear. In the new draft Gandalf, in his words with Ingold, speaks of 'the wall of Pelennor' – but it appears immediately afterwards that this was the name of the wall itself:

Gandalf passed now into the wide space beyond the Pelennor. So the men of Gondor called the wall that was built long ago after Ithilien fell into the hands of the Enemy.

The name appears also in several of the outlines that I have attributed to 1944 and given in the last chapter: 'Pelennor wall' (p. 260), 'the wall of Pelennor' (p. 263), 'the Outer Wall of Pelennor' (p. 263), but in the light of the present draft these are ambiguous; on the other hand, in outline IV (p. 260) occurs 'the Cityland, Pelennor, about which ruins of an old wall ran', which is not at all ambiguous. On the face of it, my father twice changed his mind about the meaning of this name; for in RK (p. 22) the wall is named *Rammas Echor* and the Pelennor is again the name of the 'fair and fertile townlands' of Minas Tirith (see pp. 287–8).

The description in the draft continues:

It went in a wide circle from the mountains' feet and back to

278   THE WAR OF THE RING

them, always distant some seven leagues from the First Gate of the City that looked eastward. Thus it enclosed the fair and fertile townlands on the long green slopes falling to the River, and at its easternmost point overlooked from a frowning bank the marshy levels. There it was loftiest and most guarded, for on a walled causeway the road from the fords of Osgiliath, a league away, came in through a great gate between two towers. But few men save herdsmen and tillers dwelt in the townlands, for the most part of the people of Gondor dwelt in the seven circles of the city of Minas Tirith, or in the deep vales of the mountains' borders; and away southward in Lebennin the land of Seven Rivers lived a hardy folk between the mountains and the mouths of Anduin and the Sea; and they were reckoned men of Gondor, yet their blood was mixed and if their stature and faces told the truth came more from those men who dwelt in the dark hills in the Dark Years ere the coming of the kings.

But now the light of day grew, and Pippin looked up ...

Thus the townlands were at first conceived altogether differently, as a great half-circle centred on the city and always with a radius of seven leagues, whereas in RK the enclosing wall was at its furthest point four leagues from the city and at its nearest little more than one.[9] In this draft text there is no mention of Emyn Arnen, of the Harlond, of Lossarnach, of Belfalas, or of Imrahil of Dol Amroth, and Lebennin is still 'the land of Seven Rivers' (see VII.310–12, and pp. 252, 254 in this book).

Pippin's first sight of Minas Tirith and Gandalf's encounter with the guards at the Great Gate is very much as in RK (p. 23), except that in the following passage from RK the bracketed part is absent:

but to his right great mountains reared their heads, [ranging from the West to a steep and sudden end, as if in the making of the land the River had burst through a great barrier, carving out a mighty valley to be a land of battle and debate in times to come. And there where the White Mountains of Ered Nimrais came to their end] (and) he saw, as Gandalf had promised, the dark mass of Mount Mindolluin ...

Also, the Tower of Ecthelion is here called the Tower of Denethor (see p. 281).

In the draft text the description of Minas Tirith is as follows:

For the manner of Minas Tirith was such that it was builded upon seven levels each carved in the hill, and each had a wall, and in each wall was a gate. But the gates were not made in a line, for the outer and lowest gate was in the east, but the next

MINAS TIRITH

279

faced half south and the third half north, and so on, so that the pave[d] way that led up without break or stair turned first this way and [then] that way across the face of the hill, until the seventh gate was reached that led to the great court and citadel on the levelled summit about the feet of the crowning tower. And that gate also looked due east, being there seven hundred feet above the plain before the walls, and the tower on the summit was three hundred feet from base to pinnacle. A strong citadel indeed it was and not to be taken by a host of men if there were any within that could hold weapons, unless some enemy could come behind and scale Mindolluin and so come behind upon the shoulder that joined the Hill of Guard to the mountain mass. But that shoulder which was at the height of the fifth wall was walled right up [to] the precipice that overhung it, and there stood the great domed tombs of bygone kings and lords, at once memorials and fortresses if need should come.

In the original hasty sketch of Minas Tirith reproduced on p. 261 the gates appear to be arranged in two lines meeting at the uppermost level, the one proceeding from the Great Gate (1 – 3 – 5 – 7), and the other proceeding from the second gate (2 – 4 – 6 – 7).[10] In the text just cited the configuration described in RK is present, with the Great Gate facing east, the second gate south-east, the third north-east, and so on up to the entrance to the Citadel, again facing east. On this page of the draft (reproduced on p. 280) my father drew a plan in which this arrangement is shown. The upper figure on the page is in fact two conjoined: the smaller area at the upper left (marked with 'M.T.' and 'summit of Mindolluin') was that first made, and this was struck out with three transverse lines. — It will be seen that the 'vast pier of rock whose huge out-thrust bulk divided in two all the circles of the City save the first' (RK p. 24), causing the mounting road to pass through a tunnel each time it crossed the line from the Great Gate to the Citadel, was not yet present.

Pippin's sense of the diminishment and decay of Minas Tirith, with its great silent houses, is told in the draft in words closely similar to those of the passage in RK (p. 24);[11] but the accoutrement of the guards of the Seventh Gate is thus described:

The guards of the gate were robed in white, and the[ir] helms were of strange shape, shining like silver, for they were indeed of *mithril*, heirlooms from the glory of old days, and above either cheekpiece were set the wings of sea-birds. Upon the breast of their surcoats were embroidered in white a tree blossoming like snow and above it a silver crown.

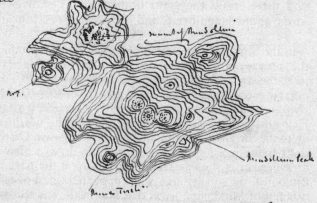

Minas Tirith and Mindolluin

MINAS TIRITH 281

It is added here that beside the guards of the Citadel one other wore this livery of the heirs of Elendil: 'the warden of the door of the hall of the kings aforetime where now dwelt the Lord Denethor'; and at the door there is one 'tall guard' ('the tall silent door-wardens', RK). Perhaps the change in the colour of the livery from white to black was on account of the white tree embroidered on the coats.

The dead Tree in the court of the Fountain, with Pippin's recollection of Gandalf's words *Seven stars and seven stones and one white tree*, and Gandalf's warning to him to bear himself discreetly before Denethor, survived into the final text with very little change; but Gandalf says only of Denethor and Boromir: 'He loved him greatly, too much, perhaps', and does not add 'and the more so because they were unlike' (yet later, when they have left Denethor, he says, much as in RK: 'He is not quite as other men, Pippin, and whatever be his ancestry by some chance the blood of the men of Westernesse runs true in him, as it does in his other son Faramir, and yet not in Boromir whom he loved most. They have long sight.'). And of Aragorn he says that 'if he comes it may be in some way that no one expects. And Denethor at least does not expect him in any way, *for he does not know that he exists.*'

The great hall was conceived from the first almost exactly as the description of it stands in RK (p. 26): the great images between the pillars, reminding Pippin of 'the kings of Argonath',[12] the empty throne, the old man in the stone chair gazing at his lap. Only the carved capitals of the pillars are not mentioned; on the other hand the floor of the hall is described: 'But the floor was of shining stone, white-gleaming, figured with mosaics of many colours' (see p. 288). The name of Denethor's father, Ecthelion, entered here, with only momentary hesitation (earlier in the draft the White Tower is called the Tower of Denethor, not as in RK the Tower of Ecthelion; p. 278).[13]

When Pippin cried 'that is the horn that Boromir always wore!' this dialogue follows in the draft:

'Verily,' said Denethor. 'And in my turn I wore it, and so did each eldest son of our house far back into the mists of time, before the failing of the kings, since [Mardil >] Faragon father of Mardil hunted the wild oxen of Araw[14] in the far fields of Rhûn. But we heard it blowing dimly in the North twelve days ago,[15] and now it will blow no more.'

'Yes,' said Pippin. 'I stood beside him as he blew it, and it shook the woods; but no help came. Only more orcs.'

Pippin's account of Boromir's death, his offer of his service to Denethor, and the swearing of the oath were very largely achieved in

282   THE WAR OF THE RING

the draft text,[16] save in one notable point: it is Gandalf, not Denethor, who speaks the words of the oath: '"Take the hilts," said Gandalf, "and speak after me." The old man laid the sword along his lap and Pippin laid his hand on the hilts and said slowly after Gandalf ...' The oath and its acceptance were scarcely changed from the original formulation in the draft, except only in the point that Denethor did not there name himself 'Steward of the High King'.

The words between Denethor and Gandalf that follow (RK p. 29), and Pippin's perception of the tension between them, and of Gandalf's greater power (though veiled), reached immediately the final text in almost every point; but Pippin's reflection on Gandalf's age and being took this form: 'Whence and what was Gandalf: when and in what far time and place [was he born >] did he come into the world and would he ever die?' His passing thought 'Treebeard had said something about wizards, but even then he had not thought of Gandalf as one of them' does not appear; it is not said that 'it was Denethor who first withdrew his gaze'; and Denethor says only 'for though the Stones are lost', without adding 'they say'.

In the margin of the page that bears this passage my father wrote: 'For his wisdom did not consider Gandalf, whereas the counsels of Denethor concerned himself, or Gondor which in his thought was part of himself'. There is no indication where this was to be placed, but I think that it would follow 'Pippin perceived that Gandalf had greater power, and deeper wisdom – and a majesty that was veiled.'

The interview with Denethor ended far more abruptly in the draft than in RK (pp. 30–1): at Denethor's words 'Let your wrath for an old man's seeming folly run off, and return to my comfort' there follows only: '"I will return as soon as may be," said Gandalf. "But I crave sometime words with you alone." And he strode from the hall with Pippin running at his side.'

After Gandalf had left the house in which they were lodged Pippin encountered a man clad in grey and white who named himself Beren son of Turgon (Beregond son of Baranor, clad in black and white, in RK). In their opening conversation and visits to Shadowfax and the buttery a number of small alterations and additions were made to the narrative later, but all are slight points: for example, Beren says to Pippin that 'It is said that you are to be treated as a guest for this day at the least', and that 'Those who have had heavy duty – and *guests* – take somewhat to refresh their strength in the mid-morning'; Pippin does not express his disappointment at seeing no inns in Minas Tirith; and the following curious dialogue was afterwards removed (cf. RK p. 34):

'... For now I may say that strange accents do not mar fair speech, and hobbits are well-spoken folk.'

'So Denethor, I mean the high Lord, said.'

MINAS TIRITH 283

'Did he indeed?' said Beren. 'Then you have received a mark of favour such as few guests have got from him.'

The keeper of the buttery was named *Duilas* (?), with a later pencilled alteration to *Garathon*.[17] Pippin tells Beren: 'I am only a boy in the reckoning of our people, for I am only twenty years old and we are not held to be grown-up as we say in the Shire for a dozen years more.'[18]

As Beren and Pippin looked out from the walls, 'Away down in the vale-bottom 7 leagues or so as the eye leaps, the Great River now flowed grey and glittering, coming out of the north-west and curving south-west till it was lost to view round the shoulders of the mountains in a haze and shimmer' (see pp. 288–9), whereas it is distant 'five leagues or so' in RK (p. 36): on this difference see p. 278. Immediately after this the original draft jumps, in relation to RK, from 'far beyond which lay the Sea fifty leagues away' to '"What do I see there?" asked Pippin, pointing due eastward down to the river'; thus the entire passage is lacking in which Pippin sees the traffic of waggons crossing the Pelennor and turning south, and Beregond explains to him that they are taking 'the road to the vales of Tumladen and Lossarnach, and the mountain-villages, and then on to Lebennin.' But from this point the conversation of Beren/Beregond and Pippin to its conclusion, as it stands in RK (pp. 36–40), was achieved, roughly indeed, but with scarcely any significant detail lacking, and often very close to the final text: the darkness in the East,[19] the passage of the Nazgûl far overhead, Beren's account of the battles for the crossings at Osgiliath,[20] of Denethor's far sight,[21] of the approach of the great fleet manned by the corsairs of Umbar,[22] of Faramir, and his invitation to Pippin to join his company for that day.

At this point the story told in the draft becomes altogether different from that of RK, and I give the remainder (very roughly written) of this earliest text in full:

Gandalf was not in the lodging, and Pippin went with Beren of the Guard, and he was shown to the others of the third company and welcomed by them, and made merry with them, taking his midday meal among them in a little hall near the north wall, and going here and there with others until the evening meal, and the closing hour, and the lowering of standards. Then he himself after the manner of Gondor soon went to his bed. Gandalf had not come or left any message. He rolled into bed and soon slept. In the night he was awakened by a light and saw Gandalf in the room outside the alcove. He was pacing to and fro. 'When will Faramir return?' he heard him mutter, as he peered out of the dark window. Then Pippin went to sleep again.

284   THE WAR OF THE RING

The next day still no commands came from Denethor. 'He is full of cares and busyness,' said Gandalf, 'and for the moment you are out of his mind. But not for good! He does not forget. Make use of your leisure while you can. Have a look round the City.'[23]

Beren was on duty and Pippin was left alone; but he had learned enough to find his way to the hatches at midmorning. For the rest of the time until noon he walked in the sixth circle, and visited Shadowfax, taking him some morsels that he had saved, which Shadowfax graciously accepted. In the afternoon Pippin walked down the ways of the City to the lowest circle and the great East Gate.

People stared much at him as he passed, and he would hear calls behind him, and those out of doors cried to others within to come see Mithrandir's halfling; but to his face most were courteous, saluting him gravely after the manner of Gondor with outstretched hand and a bowing of the head. For who he was and much concerning him was now noised through Minas Tirith.

He came at last by windy ways and many fair alleys and arches to the lower circles where there [were] many smaller houses. And here and there he saw children – and he was glad, for to his eyes it had seemed that too many of the folk of Minas Tirith were old. He passed a larger house with a pillared porch and steps and boys were playing there. As soon as he saw him one of the boys leapt down the steps into the street and stood in front of Pippin, looking him up and down.

'Well met,' said the lad. 'Are you not a stranger?'

'I was,' said Pippin. 'But they say I am now a man of Gondor.'

'Man!' said the boy. 'How old are you, and what is your name? I am ten already and soon shall be five feet high. Look, I am taller than you. But then my father is a soldier, one of the tallest.[24] I shall be a soldier too. What is your father?'

'Which question shall I answer first?' said Pippin. 'My father is like me a hobbit not a man, and he owns the land and fields round Whitwell near Tuckborough on the edge of the Westfarthing in the Shire. I am 21 years old[25] so I pass you there, though I am but four feet four, and that is reckoned a good height in my land, and I do not hope to better it much. For I shall not grow upward much before I come of age; though maybe I shall thicken and put on some weight, or should, if food were plentiful for travellers in the wild places.'

MINAS TIRITH   285

'Twenty-one,' said Gwinhir, and whistled. 'Why, you are quite old. Still, I wager I could stand you on your head, or lay you on your back.'

'Maybe you could if I let you,' said Pippin with a laugh. 'We know a trick or two of wrestling in my little country. But I do not much like standing on my head; what, if it came to a sticking point, and nothing else would serve, I have a sword, master Gwinhir.'

'A sword, have you?' said Gwinhir. 'Then you must be a soldier. Though you don't look like one.'

'I am and I do not indeed,' said Pippin. 'But when you have seen more than 10 years, if you live long enough, young friend, and survive the days that are coming, you will learn that folk are not always what they seem. Why, you might take me for a kind-hearted fool of a stranger lad. But I am not. I am a hobbit and the devil of a hobbit, companion of wizards, friend of Ents, member of the Company of Nine of whom your lord Boromir was one, of the ... of the Nine I should say, and I was at the battle of the Bridge of Moria and the sack of Isengard, and I wish for no wrestling or rough play. So let me be lest I bite.'

'Ai, Ai,' said Gwinhir. 'You do sound fierce, a ferret in the garb of a rabbit. But you have left your boots behind, master, maybe because you have outgrown them too quickly. Come on, good ferret, bite if you like,' and he ... up his fists. But at that moment a man came out from the door and sprang down into the street and grabbed the lad by the back of his tunic.

'What is this, Gwinhir, you ruffling young fool,' said the man. 'Will you waylay anything in the street that seems smaller than yourself? Will you not choose something larger? Shame on a son of mine, brawling before my doors like a young orc.'

'Nay, nay, not like an orc, Master Thalion, if that be your name,' said Pippin. 'I have seen enough orcs and all too close to be in any error. Here is nothing but a warlike lad spoiling for something to do. Will you not let him walk with me a while, and be my guide? For I am new come and there is much to see while the sun still shines. ....'

'I have already heard that the halflings are courteous of speech, if that one that came hither with Mithrandir is a sample,' said Thalion.[26] 'Yes indeed, the young ruffian shall go with you if you wish. Go now and keep a fair tongue in your head,' he said to Gwinhir, giving him a smart blow on his seat. 'But see that he returns ere the closing hour and the dusk.'

286   THE WAR OF THE RING

'I wanted a game,' said Gwinhir to Pippin as they set off. 'There are few lads of my age in this quarter, and such as there are are no match for me. But my father is stern, and I was near to a beating just now. When he says "orc" 'tis an ill omen for one's back. But you got me off very finely, and I thank you. What shall I show you?'

'I do not know,' said Pippin, 'but I am going to the East Gate, and we shall see.'

As they drew near the East Gate there was much sound of running and bustle, and Pippin thought he heard horns and trumpets blowing. For a moment his heart beat for he thought it might be a signal that war had begun. But Gwinhir cried out. 'They are come. Some of the folk from beyond the walls that have been rumoured. Hasten now, they'll be riding [?in by] the East Gate.

Here the draft ends, abandoned. Why my father rejected this story one can only surmise; a clue is perhaps to be found at the point in the text where Pippin, at the end of his first day (6 February) in Minas Tirith (spent in the company of Beren and other men of the Guard), 'after the manner of Gondor soon went to his bed' (p. 283). Here my father added a note on the manuscript in pencil, reminding himself to look up what had been said of the weather in the story of Frodo and Sam in Ithilien, and saying that 'if possible' the sunset of 6 February should be 'ominous': 'Darkness began next morning, a fiery haze.' When he wrote this he may have intended to rewrite the story only to the extent that Pippin should see the 'ominous' sunset as he went back to his lodging on the first night, and then when he woke next morning the great pall should have overspread the sky: in deepening darkness he would make his way down to the Great Gate, and encounter the aggressive Gwinhir. Or it may be that it was when writing this note that he decided to change the structure of the story, and abandoned the draft. At any rate, he evidently decided that it would be better to compress the whole story of this chapter into a single day, concluded by the first presage of the Darkness approaching and the smouldering sunset at the closing of the gates, when the last of the men of the Outlands had entered the City. Chronological considerations may have played a part in this.

He now turned back to the point where Beren invited Pippin to join his company for that day, and began anew. This new drafting was written in soft pencil at great speed, and would be hard indeed to interpret and often altogether illegible were the new text not so close to the final form: the story becomes that of RK in virtually every point[27] and largely in the same words. But it peters out shortly before the end

MINAS TIRITH

287

of the chapter, at the words 'But the dying sun set it all afire and Mindolluin was black against a dull smoulder' (RK p. 44).

Beren now becomes *Barathil*, changed in the course of the writing of the text to *Barithil*; his father's name does not appear. His son was named Bergil from the first. The Street of the Lampwrights has the Elvish name *Rath a Chalardain* (*Rath Celerdain* in RK); and Pippin is called *Ernil a Pheriannath* (*i* for *a* in RK).

The 'Homeric catalogue', as my father called it (p. 229), of the reinforcements entering Minas Tirith[28] from the Outlands was written out twice, the first form being jumbled and unclear, and at the second writing (beginning after the arrival of Forlong, at the words 'And so the companies came and were hailed and cheered ...', RK p. 43) it becomes remarkably close to the form in RK. I have the strong impression that the new names that appear here were devised in the composition of this text. Forlong the Fat, however, had appeared several times previously, pp. 229, 262, 276. He was here first said to be, as in RK, 'lord of the vale of Lossarnach',[29] but *Lossarnach* was struck out and replaced by 'the Ringlo away in Lebennin' (see Map III in VII.309). Yet this is immediately contradicted in both forms of the text, where we find just as in RK 'the men of Ringlo Vale behind Dervorin, son of their lord, striding on foot: three hundreds.' In the first form the vale is called Imlad-Ringlo. Duinhir and his five hundred bowmen from the Blackroot Vale (Morthond Vale and Imlad Morthond in the first form) is named (but not his sons, Duilin and Derufin in RK). After them come the men of 'Dor-Anfalas [*changed from* Belfalas], the Langstrand far away': see again Map III in VII.309, where 'Belfalas (Langstrand)' is the region afterwards named Anfalas. Their lord is Asgil-Golamir (Golasgil in RK). Then the hillmen of Lamedon, a name that first appears here; the fisher-folk of the Ethir; and Hirluin the Fair from the green hills of Pinnath Gelin, also first occurring here (but he is at first said to be from Erech). The Prince of Dol Amroth, kinsman of the Lord of Minas Tirith, bears the token of a golden ship and a silver swan; but he is given no name.

There is no other initial drafting extant (except for a roughly pencilled slip giving the revised conclusion of the conversation with Denethor, RK pp. 30–1). The first complete text is a typescript: I think it all but certain that my father made this before he proceeded much, if any, further in the narrative.

The title of the chapter as typed was: *Book V   Chapter XLIV: Peregrin enters the service of the Lord of Minas Tirith*. For the most part the differences between the original draft and RK noticed above (pp. 277–83 and notes) were retained in this text: some but by no means all of these were changed in pencil on the typescript. Thus Gandalf's ride still took three nights, not four. The description of the 'townlands' of Minas Tirith remains as it was (pp. 277–8), with the sole

288   THE WAR OF THE RING

difference that the *Pelennor* now becomes the name of the townlands, and the wall is named *Ramas Coren* (changed in pencil to *Rammas Ephel*).[30] On the other hand, the passage cited on p. 278 concerning the River is now present as in RK, except for the sentence 'And there where the White Mountains of Eredfain came to their end' (changed on the typescript to Ered Nimrais). The White Tower remains the Tower of Denethor; and the description of Minas Tirith remains as it was in the draft, with no material difference save in the height of the Tower, here said to be two hundred, not three hundred feet. Thus the great out-thrust pier of rock was still absent, and it was not introduced into this text. On the reverse of the preceding typescript page is a plan of the city, reproduced on p. 290; here appears the name *Rath Dínen*, and also *Othram or City Wall*, of the wall of the outermost circle, pierced by the Great Gate.[31]

In the account of the great hall the description of the floor is retained from the draft, and that of the capitals introduced, thus:

Monoliths of black marble, they rose to great capitals carved in many figures of strange beasts and leaves; and far above in shadow the wide vaulting gleamed with dull gold. The floor was of polished stone, white-gleaming, inset with flowing traceries of many colours.

This was repeated in the following typescript; but in the final typescript, from which the text in RK was printed, the sentence was compressed: '... gleamed with dull gold, inset with flowing traceries of many colours.' Since there is no indication on the second typescript that any change was intended, it seems certain that this was a casual 'line-jumping' error, causing the 'flowing traceries' to be ascribed to the vaulting.

Denethor now names the father of Mardil *Orondil* (*Faragon* in the draft, *Vorondil* in RK). It is still Gandalf, not Denethor, who speaks the words of the oath which Pippin repeats; but the conclusion of the conversation between Gandalf and Denethor (also found in preliminary drafting, p. 287) is now present, and differs from the form in RK only in that after Gandalf's words 'Unless the king should come again?' he continues: 'That would be a strange conclusion. Well, let us strive to keep some kingdom still against that event!'

Barathil, Barithil of the second draft (p. 287) is now *Barithil*, becoming in the course of the typing of this text *Berithil*; he is the son of Baranor, as is Beregond in RK. The man at the buttery hatch is now Targon, as in RK.

In the description of the view eastward from the walls of Minas Tirith the Anduin is still some seven leagues away, and as it bends 'in a mighty sweep south and west again' it is still 'lost to view *round the shoulders of the mountains* in a haze and shimmer' (p. 283). The

MINAS TIRITH

289

italicized words were afterwards struck from the typescript; the reason for this can be seen from a comparison of Map III in VII.309 with the large map of Rohan, Gondor and Mordor in *The Return of the King*, where the view of the Great River from Minas Tirith is not impeded by the eastern end of the mountains. The passage in RK which was absent from the draft, describing the traffic across the Pelennor, is now present and reaches the final form in every point, save only that Berithil here says: 'That is the road to the vales of Tumladen and Glossarnach' (see note 29); but this was changed in pencil to *Lossarnach*, and later in the text Forlong the Fat is named 'lord of Lossarnach'.[32]

Of the part of the text covered by the second draft (pp. 286–7) there is little to note, since the final form was already very largely achieved. In the 'catalogue' of the peoples of the Outlands the lord of Anfalas (so named) is now Golasgil, as in RK, but the prince of Dol Amroth is still not further identified. The conclusion of the chapter, not found in the draft, is here almost exactly as in RK. After the words (RK p. 45) 'The lodging was dark, save for a little lantern set on the table' my father first typed: 'Beside it was a scribbled note from Gandalf', but he barred this out immediately and substituted 'Gandalf was not there'. The chapter ends: 'No, when the summons comes, not at sunrise. There will be no sunrise. The darkness has begun.'

NOTES

1   Book V, Chapter 1 'Minas Tirith' is the 44th chapter in *The Lord of the Rings*. 'The Departure of Boromir' had now been separated off from 'The Riders of Rohan', 'Flotsam and Jetsam' from 'The Voice of Saruman', and 'The Forbidden Pool' from 'Journey to the Cross-roads'.

2   This is the first appearance of the Sons of Elrond (see VII.163–4, and p. 297 in this book).

3   According to time-schemes D and S (p. 272) Aragorn reached Edoras and went up Harrowdale on the morning of February 5, while Théoden came to Dunharrow at nightfall of the 6th.

4   This is the first reference to the part played by the Dead Men of Dunharrow. For the earliest hint of the story see outline V on p. 263: 'News comes from South that a great king has descended out of the mountains where he had been entombed, and set such a flame into men that the mountaineers ... and the folk of Lebennin have utterly routed the Southrons and burned [> taken] their ships.'

5   This was the Nazgûl (as the chronology was at this time) sent out from Mordor after Pippin looked into the *palantír* of Orthanc, passing high overhead and unseen 'about an hour after midnight'

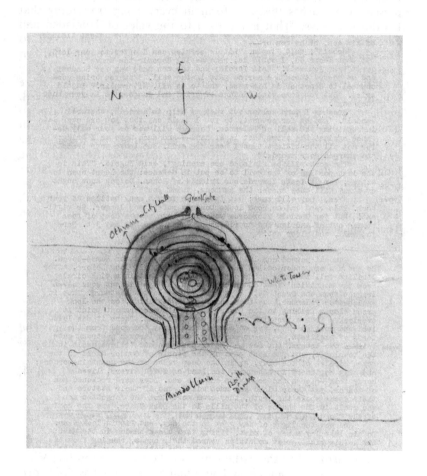

Plan of Minas Tirith

MINAS TIRITH 291

when Frodo, Sam and Gollum had not long left the pit among the slag-mounds: see pp. 119–20.

6   *Pippin on the battlements ... sees the moonrise on night of 6 ... and thinks of Frodo*: see p. 271.

7   I presume that the rejected words at the end of the outline 'do not turn aside but go straight (on)' mean that they passed the mouth of the Deeping Coomb and did not go up to the Hornburg. According to time-scheme D (p. 140) Gandalf reached Edoras at dawn on February 4, and he stayed there throughout the daylight hours. If Aragorn and his companions rode on at all speed making for Edoras, without any long halt, they would have caught him up!

8   Thus the passage in which Pippin thinks of Frodo remains the same as in text C, though with a difference in wording: 'little thinking that Frodo would see from far away the white snows under that same moon as it set beyond Gondor.' Gandalf's journey still takes three nights, not four as in RK.

9   On the First Map (Map III in VII.309) the distance from Minas Tirith to Osgiliath is about 70 miles (more than 23 leagues); and on the map made in October 1944 that I have redrawn on p. 269 it is still about 50 miles (which, since in the present draft the fords of Osgiliath were a league from the Pelennor wall, would give a radius of some 15 and a half leagues). In the note that my father wrote about my 1943 version of the First Map (see VII.322 note 1) he said that 'the distance across the vale of Anduin [should be] *much* reduced, so that Minas Tirith is close to Osgiliath and Osgiliath closer to Minas Morgul'; and the distance from the city to the Rammas Echor in the direction of Osgiliath is 10 miles on my map published in RK (on the original map on which mine was based 12 miles, agreeing with 'four leagues' in the text of RK, p. 22).

10 In the drawing the seventh gate faces in the same direction (north-east?) as the second gate, but the drawing may be defective: gates 1 – 3 – 5 – 7 are in a line.

11 In the draft, when Gandalf and Pippin came to the Seventh Gate, 'the sun that looked down on Ithilien and Sam busy with his steaming pan and herbs glowed on the smooth walls and the marbled arch and pillars.' It was the morning of February 6, the day on which Frodo and Sam encountered Faramir and went to Henneth Annûn. In RK the sentence is different: 'the warm sun that shone down beyond the river, as Frodo walked in the glades of Ithilien ...' — for on the day that Gandalf and Pippin arrived in Minas Tirith (March 9) Frodo and Sam reached the Morgul-road at dusk.

12 This is the first appearance of the name Argonath (see VII.359–60, 362).

292   THE WAR OF THE RING

13   In LR (*The Tale of Years*) it was the Steward Ecthelion I who rebuilt the White Tower in the year 2698, more than three centuries before this time; Denethor's father Ecthelion was the second Steward of that name (which derives from the legend of the Fall of Gondolin: see II.212, footnote). — 'The tower of Denethor' was named in the chapter 'The Palantír', p. 77.

14   *Vorondil father of Mardil* in RK, p. 27; and see LR Appendix A (I, ii). — A space was left for the name of the god, apparently filled in immediately, first with *Ramr* which was struck out before completion, then with *Araw*. On *Araw* beside *Oromë* see the *Etymologies*, V.379, stem ORÓM.

15   *twelve days ago* (*thirteen days ago* in RK): see p. 150 and note 10. In *The Tale of Years* the dates are February 26 (death of Boromir) and March 9 (Gandalf reaches Minas Tirith).

16   Denethor says of Pippin's sword: 'Surely it is a sax wrought by our own folk in the North in the deep past?', where RK has 'blade' and 'kindred'. The word *sax* (Old English *seax*, dagger, short sword) was the final choice in the draft after rejection of 'blade', 'knife' and 'dagger'.

17   Many other pencilled alterations were made to this part of the manuscript, mostly to clarify the writing, which is here rather rough. Among these the following may be noted: as Beren and Pippin sat on the seat beside the battlement Beren said: 'We thought it was the whim our lord to take him a page boy', and this was changed by the addition of 'after the manner of the old kings that had dwarves in their service, if old tales be true.'

18   *only twenty years old* was changed in pencil to *little more than twenty years old*. In RK Pippin told Beregond that 'it will be four years yet before I "come of age", as we say in the Shire.'

19   Of the shadow in the East it is said in the draft: 'Maybe it was mountains looming like clouds on the edge of sight ... 100 miles away'; cf. RK p. 37: 'Perhaps it was mountains looming on the verge of sight, their jagged edges softened by wellnigh twenty leagues of misty air.'

20   Where in RK (p. 37) Beregond tells that the Fell Riders won back the crossings 'less than a year ago', and that after Boromir had driven the enemy back 'we hold still the near half of Osgiliath', in the draft Beren says: 'And the Fell Riders but a little while ago [?two] years or more won back the crossings and came [?over] into this western land. But Boromir drove them back. And still we hold the crossings.'

21   Beren says as in RK that 'some say that as he sits alone in his high chamber in the Tower at night ... he can even read somewhat of the mind of the Enemy'; he does not speak of 'wrestling', nor add the words 'And so it is that he is old, worn before his time.'

MINAS TIRITH

293

22 The coming of the great fleet from the south is referred to in all but one of the outlines given in the last chapter. In the draft Beren says of the Corsairs of Umbar that they have 'long forsaken the suzerainty of Gondor' ('long ceased to fear the might of Gondor', RK). And he says of the fleet: 'Now that will draw off much help that we might look to from Lebennin south away between the mountains and the Sea, where folk are numerous.' Thus Belfalas is not named, as it is in RK ('from Lebennin and Belfalas', p. 38). The name *Belfalas* was originally applied to the coastal lands in the west subsequently named *Anfalas* (*Langstrand*): this change was made to the First Map and the 1943 map (VII.309–10). Precisely where my father placed Belfalas when Anfalas was substituted is not clear, but his note correcting the 1943 map (VII.322 note 1) says: 'Lebennin should be Belfalas'. That Belfalas was in the region of the Mouths of Anduin might seem to be suggested by the passage describing the journey of the funeral boat in drafting for 'The Departure of Boromir' (VII.382): 'and the voices of a thousand seabirds lamented him upon the beaches of Belfalas'; but Belfalas seems to have retained its original sense up to this time, since it was replaced by Dor-Anfalas in drafting for the present chapter (p. 287). On the Second Map (by a later addition) it is placed as on the map published in LR (see pp. 434, 437).

23 At this point my father scribbled down some very rough notes in pencil, but the following paragraph ('Beren was on duty ...') was then written over them, so that they are hard to read: 'rude boy of the City Gates   password   *Gir.. edlothiand na ngalad melon i ni [?sevo] ni [?edran]*. Sees the hosts ride in from Lebennin.'

24 Written in the margin here: 'He is called Thalion, and my name is Ramloth.' Beneath *Ramloth* is written *Gwinhir*, and at the first occurrence of the boy's name in the actual narrative my father began *Ram*, changed it to *Arad*, and then wrote *Gwinhir*. — *Thalion* 'steadfast' was the 'surname' of Húrin.

25 *I am 21 years old:* see note 18.

26 Added here: 'But do not speak so darkly.' I do not know what this refers to. Perhaps Pippin's concluding sentence, consisting of three or four wholly illegible words, was equally obscure to Thalion.

27 The greeting of Gondor is still 'with outstretched hand', not 'with hands upon the breast'; and Pippin still says that he is 21 years old (see note 25).

28 For the earliest form of the 'catalogue', bearing little relation to this, see p. 252. The name Forlong the Fat is written on the manuscript of 'The Story Foreseen from Fangorn', p. 229, but this is obviously not contemporary with that outline.

294
THE WAR OF THE RING

29 G was written before *Lossarnach*, but struck out before *Lossarnach* was entered: see p. 289.

30 This passage was afterwards rejected and replaced by a carefully written rider, introducing the description as it stands in RK p. 22, with the name Rammas Echor, and mention of Emyn Arnen, the Harlond, Lossarnach, 'Lebennin with its five swift streams', and Imrahil of Dol Amroth 'in the great fief of Belfalas'. As this rider was first written, 'the quays and landings of the Harlond' were 'the quays and landings of Lonnath-Ernin'.

31 The two cross lines above and below the word 'Rider' reversed show through from the other side of the page: this is the rider referred to in note 30. — The reference to the sun looking down on 'Sam busy with his steaming pan and herbs' (see note 11) remained, but was altered in pencil to 'the warm sun that shone down beyond the River, as Frodo saying farewell to Faramir walked in the glades of Ithilien' (in RK the words 'saying farewell to Faramir' are absent). The altered text represents the synchronization discussed in the Note on Chronology below, whereby Frodo left Henneth Annûn on the same morning as Gandalf reached Minas Tirith.

32 The treatment in this text of other differences of detail between the original draft and RK may be mentioned here. The description of the livery and helms of the guards of the Citadel (p. 279) now becomes precisely as in RK; but Gandalf's words 'And Denethor at least does not expect him in any guise, for he does not know that he exists' remain. Denethor still declares that the horn was heard blowing upon the northern marches twelve days ago (note 15), and he still calls Pippin's sword a *sax* (note 16). Berithil is still clad in grey and white, and his reference to 'the old kings that had dwarves in their service' remains (note 17). Pippin tells him that he has 'not long passed twenty years' (note 18), and later tells Bergil that he is 'nearly twenty-one' (p. 284). Of the mountains in the East it is said that 'their jagged edges [were] softened by wellnigh a hundred miles of misty air' (note 19). Berithil says that 'the Fell Riders, but two years ago, won back the crossings' (note 20); his words about Denethor in the Tower are now precisely as in RK (note 21); and he says that the Corsairs of Umbar 'have long forsaken the friendship of Gondor', and again does not mention Belfalas as a source of aid to the city (note 22).

Note on the Chronology

In the chapter 'Journey to the Cross-roads' (pp. 175 ff.) Frodo and Sam left Henneth Annûn in the morning of February 7 and reached the Osgiliath road at dusk of that day. During the night of February 7–8

MINAS TIRITH

the air became heavy, and dark clouds moved out of the East during the morning of the 8th; they reached the Cross-roads at sunset, and saw the sun 'finding at last the hem of the great slow-rolling pall of cloud'.

In the present chapter Gandalf and Pippin arrived at Minas Tirith at sunrise on February 6, and in the note added to the original draft (see p. 286) my father said that the sunset of that day was to be ominous, with the Darkness beginning next morning, the 7th. There is thus a day out between 'Journey to the Cross-roads' and 'Minas Tirith'. (In the outlines for Book V given in the last chapter the Darkness begins on the 8th in outlines III and V, but on the 7th in outline VI.)

I cannot certainly explain this. Presumably my father had introduced a change in the chronology of the movements of Frodo and Sam in Ithilien, or at any rate intended to, and it may be that the rather obscure note given on p. 271 is connected with this: 'Whole of Frodo's and Sam's adventures must be set back *one day*, so that Frodo sees moon-set on morning (early hours) of Feb. 6, and Faramir reaches Minas Tirith on night of the 7th, and Great Darkness begins on 7th.' This gives the following relations (and see note 31 above):

Feb. 6 Frodo leaves Henneth Annûn; reaches Osgiliath road at dusk.

Gandalf reaches Minas Tirith. Ominous sunset.

Feb. 7 Great Darkness begins. Frodo reaches Cross-roads at sunset.

See further the note on chronology on pp. 321–2. — The final synchronization of the stories east and west of Anduin was differently achieved, with extension of Gandalf's ride to Minas Tirith from three nights to four (p. 264 note 3), and of Frodo's journey from Henneth Annûn from two days to three (p. 182). Thus in *The Tale of Years* in LR:

March 8 Frodo leaves Henneth Annûn.

March 9 Gandalf reaches Minas Tirith. At dusk Frodo reaches the Morgul-road [= Osgiliath road]. Darkness begins to flow out of Mordor.

March 10 The Dawnless Day. Frodo passes the Cross Roads.

IV

MANY ROADS LEAD EASTWARD (1)

The original draft ('A') for Chapter XLV (Book V Chapter 2, afterwards called 'The Passing of the Grey Company') was written in pencil in my father's roughest script, and extended only as far as Théoden's words about the Rangers: 'thirty such men will be a strength not to be counted by heads' (RK p. 48). At this stage, I think, he wrote a brief outline for the next part of the chapter which takes up from the point reached in A.

> The night was old and the East grey when they came at last to the Hornburg and there rested.
>
> Rangers say that messages reached them through Rivendell. They suppose Gandalf or Galadriel or both?
>
> Merry sat at the king's side in Hornburg, regrets that Pippin was away.
>
> They prepare to ride by secret ways to Dunharrow. Aragorn does not sleep but becomes restless. Takes the Orthanc stone to the tower of the Hornburg and looks in it.
>
> He comes out of the chamber looking very weary, and will say naught but goes to sleep till evening.
>
> 'There is evil news,' he said. 'The black fleet is drawing near to Umbar [sic]. That will disturb counsels. I fear we must part, Éomer. To meet again later. But not yet. How long will it take to Dunharrow?' 'Two days. If we ride on the 5th we shall reach there by evening of the 6th.'[1]
>
> Aragorn fell silent. 'That will do,' he said.

The reverse of this page is a contoured map of the White Mountains, ruled in squares of 2 cm. side, extending some 90 miles east and west of Edoras, with no features (other than mountain peaks) marked save the Morthond and the Stone of Erech in the south and Edoras and the Snowbourn in the north. Harrowdale here runs a little west of south, in contrast to the map redrawn on p. 258 where it runs southeast, and Erech is a very little east of south from Edoras (assuming that the map is oriented north-south). A pencilled note against the Stone of Erech gives a distance: '62 miles as crow flies from Dunharrow' (where the second figure seems to have been changed from 3); and in the margin is written: 'Scale 4 times main map'. Whichever map

MANY ROADS LEAD EASTWARD (I) 297

my father was referring to[2] this would mean that 1 mm. = 1.25 miles; and a dot pencilled in subsequently very near the head of Harrowdale and obviously representing the place of Dunharrow is at a distance of 51 mm. from the Stone of Erech (= 63.75 miles).[3]

He now returned to the opening of the chapter and overwrote the brief pencilled text in ink, so that it is obscured.[4]

The new draft ('B') in ink, as far as the point where the underlying pencilled text ends, reaches that of RK (pp. 46–8) in all but a few points. In the opening paragraph of the chapter it is said of Merry's possessions only that 'he had few things to pack', and this was bracketed; at the head of the page my father wrote: 'Hobbit packs lost at Calembel? replenished at Isengard' (for *Calembel* see the Index to Vol. VII, s.v. *Calenbel*). To Aragorn's words 'But why they come, and how many they are, Halbarad[5] shall tell us' Halbarad replies: 'Thirty we are, and the brethren Elboron and Elbereth are among them. More of us could scarcely be found in these dwindling days, as you well know; and we had to gather in haste. We came because you summoned us. Is that not so?' To which Aragorn replies: 'Nay, save in wish.'[6]

The coming of the sons of Elrond with the Rangers is referred to in the outline given on p. 274. It is interesting to see that the names first given to them, *Elboron* and *Elbereth*, were originally those of the young sons of Dior Thingol's Heir, the brothers of Elwing, who were murdered by 'the evil men of Maidros' host' in the attack on Doriath by the Fëanorians (*The Annals of Beleriand*, in IV.307, V.142); they were thus the great-uncles of the sons of Elrond. But the names *Elboron* and *Elbereth* of Dior's sons had been replaced by *Elrún* and *Eldún* (IV.325–6; V.147, 351–3; VI.68).

The new draft B continues on from the point reached in the pencilled opening, but the passage that immediately follows in RK (in which Elrohir son of Elrond delivers his father's message to Aragorn concerning the Paths of the Dead, and Aragorn asks Halbarad what it is that he bears) is entirely absent. The text continues (RK p. 48):

The night was old and the East grey when they rode at last up from the Deeping Coomb and came back to the Hornburg. There they were to lie and rest for a while and take counsel.

Merry slept, until he was roused by Legolas and Gimli. 'The sun is high,' said [Gimli >] Legolas. 'Everyone else is out and about. Come and look round. There was a great battle here only three nights ago. I would show you where the Huorn-forest stood.'

'Is there not time to visit the Caves?' said Gimli.

'I have given my word to go with you,' said Legolas. 'But let

298   THE WAR OF THE RING

that be later and do not spoil the wonder with haste. It is near the hour of noon, and after we have eaten we are to set out swiftly, or so I hear.'

Merry sighed; he was lonely without Pippin and felt that he was only a burden, while everybody was making plans for a business he did not much understand.

'Aragorn has a company of his own now,' said Gimli. '[He seems changed somewhat, and some dark care is on him. But [he] looks more like a king than Théoden himself.][7] They are stout men and lordly. The Riders look almost like boys beside them; for they are grim and worn for the most part, such as Aragorn was. But he seems changed somewhat: a kingly man if ever there was one, though some dark care or doubt sits on him.'

'Where is he?' said Merry.

'In a high chamber in the tower,' said Gimli. 'He has not rested or slept, I think. He went there soon after we came here, saying he must take thought, and only his kinsman Halbarad went with him.'

Merry walked about with Legolas and Gimli for a while, while they spoke of this and that turn of the battle; and they passed the ruined gate and the mounds of the fallen, and they stood upon the dike looking down the Coomb. The Dead Down stood black and tall and stony amid the trampled grass. The Dunlanders and other men of the garrison were busy here and there, on the dyke and in the fields or on the battered walls. At length they returned and went to the meal in the hall of the burg. There Merry was called and was set beside the King.

The conversation of Merry with Théoden, leading to the offer of his service and its acceptance, is virtually the same as in RK (pp. 50–1) and need not be cited. Then follows:

They spoke together for a while. Then Éomer said: 'It is near the hour we set for our departing. Shall I bid men sound the horns? And where is Aragorn? His place is empty and he has not eaten.'

The horns were sounded and men got ready to ride, the Riders of Rohan now in a great company, for the King was leaving but a small garrison in the Burg, and all that could be spared were riding to the muster with him. A thousand spears had already ridden away at night to Edoras; and yet now there

MANY ROADS LEAD EASTWARD (I) 299

were still some three hundred or more that had gathered from the fields about.

In a group by themselves were the Rangers. They were clad in dark grey and their horses were rough-haired. Hoods were over the[ir] helms. They [?wore] spear and bow and sword. There was nothing fine or splendid in their array, no sign or badge, save this only, that each cloak was pinned on the left shoulder by a silver brooch shaped like a rayed star.[8] Dark and sombre and proud men they looked.

Presently Éomer came out of the gate of the Burg, and with him came Halbarad and Aragorn. They came down the ramp and walked to the waiting horses. Merry sitting on his pony by the King was startled by Aragorn. He looked grim, grey-faced, weary, old, and leant a little on Halbarad.

'I have evil tidings, lord,' he said standing before the King. 'A grave peril unlooked for threatens Gondor. A great fleet is drawing near from the south, and will cut off all but scanty help from that region. From Rohan alone can they expect much help now. But I must take new counsel. I fear, lord, and Éomer my friend, we must part – to meet again, maybe, or maybe not. But how long will you take to reach Dunharrow?'

'It is now an hour after noon,' said Éomer. 'On the evening of the second day from now we should come there. That night the moon will rise full, and the muster that the King commanded will begin the day after.'[9]

Aragorn fell silent as if considering. 'Two days,' he said. 'It cannot be much speeded. Well, by your leave, lord, I will forsake this secrecy. The time for it is passed for me. I will eat now and then I and my rangers will ride as swift as steed may go direct to Edoras. We shall meet at Dunharrow ere we part. Farewell. May I commit my friend and charge Meriadoc to your care?'

'No need,' said Théoden, 'he has sworn himself to my service. He is my esquire.'

'Good,' said Aragorn. 'All that you do is kingly. Farewell.'

'Goodbye, Meriadoc,' said Gimli, 'but we're going with Aragorn. It seems that he needs us. But we'll meet again, I think. And yours for the present is the better road, I think. Jogging on a nice pony, while I cling on behind Legolas and try to keep pace with these Rangers!'

'Farewell,' said Merry regretfully.

A horn was sounded and the Riders set forth, and rode down

300 THE WAR OF THE RING

the Coomb, and turning swiftly west [*read* east] took a path that skirted the foothills for a mile or so and then turned back in among the hills and slopes and disappeared.

Aragorn watched until the King's men were far down the Coomb. Then he turned to Halbarad. 'I must eat,' he said, 'and then we must speed on our way. Come Legolas and Gimli. I would speak to you as I eat.'

'Well,' said Aragorn as he sat at the table in the hall. 'I have looked in the Stone, my friends. For my heart [foreboded that] told me that there was much to learn.'

'You looked in the Stone!' said Gimli, amazed, awestruck, and rather alarmed. 'What did you tell – him?'

'What did I tell him?' said Aragorn sternly, and his eyes glinted. 'That I had a rascal of a rebel dwarf here that I would exchange for a couple of good orcs, thank you! I thought I had the strength, and the strength I had. I said naught to him and wrenched the Stone from him to my own purpose. But he saw me, yes and he saw me in other guise maybe than you see me. If I have done ill I have done ill. But I do not think so. To know that I lived and walked the earth was something of a blow to his heart, and certainly he will now hasten all his strokes – but they will be the less ripe. And then I learned much. For one thing, that there are yet other Stones. One is at Erech and that is where we are going. [*Struck out:* At the Stone of Erech Men shall ... be seen.][10] Halbarad bears this message:

Out of the mountain shall they come their tryst keeping;
at the Stone of Erech their horn shall blow,
when hope is dead and the kings are sleeping
and darkness lies on the world below:
Three lords shall come from the three kindreds
from the North at need by the paths of the dead
elflord, dwarflord, and lord forwandréd,
and one shall wear a crown on head.[11]

And that is an old rhyme of Gondor which none have understood; but I think I perceive somewhat of its sense now. To the Stone of Erech by the paths of the Dead!' he said rising. 'Who will come with me?'

The last two sentences were inked in over pencil, and the rest of the text consists of jottings in ink and pencil. These begin:

So now all roads were running together to the East and the coming of the War. And even as Pippin stood at the Gate and

MANY ROADS LEAD EASTWARD (I)   301

saw the Prince of Dol Amroth ride into the city with his banners the King of Rohan came down out of the hills.

This is the beginning of 'The Muster of Rohan' in RK.[12] It is followed by a sketch of the Starkhorn, and then by rough drafting developing the conversation of Théoden and Éomer as they came into Harrowdale nearer to its form in RK. On the significance of this see pp. 306–7.

This draft was followed (as I judge, immediately) by another ('C'), numbered 'XLV' but without title, more clearly written, but not much advancing on its predecessor. At the beginning of the chapter, Merry 'had few things to bring, for the hobbits had lost their packs at Calembel (Calledin), and though Merry and Pippin had found some new ones at Isengard and had picked up a few necessaries, they made only a light bundle' (see p. 297). In the conversation of Legolas, Gimli and Merry at the Hornburg (RK p. 49) Legolas now speaks of the sons of Elrond, still named Elboron and Elbereth (and it is only now actually made clear who these were, cf. p. 297): 'Sombre is their gear like the others', but they are fair and gallant as Elven-lords. And that is not to be wondered at, for they are the own sons of Elrond of Rivendell.' From Merry's question 'Why have they come? Have you heard?' the conversation then proceeds as in RK, with Gimli quoting the message that came to Rivendell and ascribing it to Gandalf, and Legolas suggesting that it came more likely from Galadriel.[13] Aragorn's horse Roheryn, brought by the Rangers (RK p. 51) has not yet entered (when he left for Edoras he still rode Hasufel), nor is Merry's pony (Stybba in RK) yet given a name; but the sons of Elrond are described in the same words as in RK, and their armour of bright mail cloaked in silver-grey (thus apparently contradicting Legolas' earlier remark 'Sombre is their gear like the others' ', where in RK he says 'Less sombre is their gear than the others' ').

When Aragorn came from the gate of the Burg the new text follows the earlier closely (pp. 299–300), but he does not name the 'grave peril unlooked for' that threatens Gondor, and he no longer says 'We shall meet at Dunharrow ere we part', but 'I shall be gone ere you come there, if my purpose holds'. His account of his looking into the *palantír* of Orthanc is somewhat developed, though his sarcasm to Gimli remains; from his words 'If I have done ill I have done ill, but I do not think so' this text continues:

'To know that I lived and walked the earth was a blow to his heart, I deem, for he knew it not till now. But he has not forgotten the sword of Isildur or his maimed hand and the pain that lives ever with him. That in this very hour of his great designs the heir of Isildur should be revealed and the sword of

302   THE WAR OF THE RING

Elendil – for I showed him that – will disturb his counsels. Certainly now he will hasten all his strokes, but the hasty stroke goes often wild.

'And I learned much. For one thing, that there are other Stones yet preserved in this ancient land. One is at Erech. And thither we are going. To the Stone of Erech, if we can find and dare the Paths of the Dead.'

'The Paths of the Dead?' said Gimli. 'That has a fell name! Where does it lie?'

'I do not know yet,' said Aragorn. 'But I know much old lore of these lands, and I have learned much myself in many journeys; and I have a guess. To prove it we shall ride fast ere the day is much older. But harken, here is an old rhyme of my kindred, almost forgotten. It was not said openly, but Halbarad tells me that the message that came to Rivendell ended so. "Bid Aragorn remember the dark words of old:

Out of the mountain shall they come their tryst keeping;
At the Stone of Erech their horns shall blow ..."'

The only differences in this form of the verse from that in the previous draft B (p. 300) are: *horns* for *horn* in line 2; *lost* for *dead* in line 3; *shadow* for *darkness* in line 4; and *man* for *lord* in line 7.

This text C was very substantially altered, by pencilled changes, and by the substitution of rewritten pages to replace existing ones. I doubt that much time if any elapsed between the initial writing of the manuscript and the making of these changes: my impression is that the text as first written ended at this point, with 'the dark words of old', at almost the same point as the preceding draft B ended (p. 300), and that my father at once began to develop it further.

The points in which B differed from RK, mentioned in note 6, were now all altered to the final form (save that the name *Dúnadan* had not yet arisen); and while *Elboron* remained, *Elbereth* was changed to *Elrohir*. The passage (RK p. 48) in which Elrohir delivers Elrond's message to Aragorn, and Halbarad speaks the message of Arwen accompanying her gift, is still altogether lacking; but after the description of the Rangers (RK p. 51) the following was inserted:

Halbarad their leader carried a tall staff, upon which it seemed was a great standard, but it was close-furled and covered with a black cloth bound about it with many thongs.

A major rewriting[14] was inserted into the C manuscript at the point where Aragorn came from the gate of the Burg; the text of RK is now much more nearly approached, yet not reached, for Aragorn seeks knowledge of the Paths of the Dead, whereas in RK (p. 52) he does not.

'I am troubled in mind, lord,' he said, standing by the king's stirrup. 'Strange words have I heard and I see new perils afar off. I have laboured long in thought, and now I fear that I must change my purpose. But tell me, Théoden, what do you know in this land of the Paths of the Dead?'

'The Paths of the Dead!' said Théoden. 'Why do you speak of them?' Éomer turned and gazed at Aragorn, and it seemed to Merry that the faces of the Riders that sat within hearing turned pale at the words, and he wondered what they could mean.

'Because I would learn where they are,' said Aragorn.

'I do not know if indeed there be such paths,' said Théoden; 'but their gate stands in Dunharrow, if old lore be true that is seldom spoken aloud.'

'In Dunharrow!' said Aragorn. 'And you are riding thither. How long will it be ere you come there?'

'It is now two hours past noon,' said Éomer. 'Before the night of the second day from now we should come to the Hold. That night the moon will rise at the full, and the muster that the king commanded will begin the day after. More speed we cannot make, if the strength of Rohan is to be gathered.'

Aragorn was silent for a moment. 'Two days,' he murmured, 'and then the muster of Rohan will only be begun. But I see that it cannot now be hastened.' He looked up, and it seemed that he had made some decision; his face was less troubled.

'Well, by your leave, lord, I must take new counsel. For myself and my kindred, we will now be secret no longer. For me the time of stealth has passed. I will make ready now, and then with my own folk I will ride the straight and open way with all speed to Edoras, and thence to Dunharrow, and thence – who shall say?'

'Do as you will,' said Théoden. 'Your foes are mine; but let each fight as his wisdom guides him. Yet now I must take the mountain-roads and delay no longer. Farewell!'

'Farewell, Aragorn!' said Éomer. 'It is a grief to me that we do not ride together.'

'Yet in battle we may meet again, though all the hosts of Mordor should lie between,' said Aragorn.

'If you seek the Paths of the Dead,' said Éomer, 'then it is little

304   THE WAR OF THE RING

likely that we shall meet among living men. Yet maybe it is your
doom to tread strange ways that others dare not.'

'Goodbye, Aragorn!' said Merry. 'I did not wish to be parted
from the remnant of our Company, but I have entered the
King's service.'

'I could not wish you better fortune,' said Aragorn.

'Goodbye, my lad,' said Gimli. 'I am sorry, but Legolas and I
are sworn to go with Aragorn. He says that he needs us. Let us
hope the Company will be gathered again some day. And for the
next stage yours will be the better road, I think. As you jog on
your pony, think of me clinging here, while Legolas vies at
horse-racing with those fell Rangers yonder.'

'Till we meet again!' said Legolas. 'But whatever way we
chose, I see a dark path and hard before each of us ere the end.
Farewell!'

The text then continues with Merry's sad farewell, and the departure of the Riders down the Coomb (in this text spelt throughout
Combe), but Aragorn's words with Halbarad about Merry and the
Shire-folk are absent. Aragorn's account of the Orthanc-stone was
now rewritten again, with various minor changes bringing the text still
closer to that in RK (his words 'The eyes in Orthanc did not see
through the armour of Théoden' are however not present: see p. 77
and note 17). But in answer to Gimli's objection 'But he wields great
dominion, nevertheless, and now he will move more swiftly' he replies
in this revised version:

'The hasty stroke goes often astray,' said Aragorn. 'And his
counsels will be disturbed. See, my friends, when I had mastered
the Stone I learned many things. A grave peril I saw coming
unlooked-for upon Gondor from the South that will draw off
great strength from the defence of Minas Tirith. And there are
other movements in the North. But now he will hesitate,
doubting whether the heir of Isildur hath that which Isildur
took from him, and thinking that he must win or lose all before
the gates of the City. If so, that is well, as well as an evil case
may be.

'Another thing I learned. There are other Stones yet preserved
in this ancient land. One is at Erech. Thither I will go. To the
Stone of Erech, if we can find the Paths of the Dead.'

'The Paths of the Dead!' said Gimli. 'That is a fell name, and
little to the liking of the men of Rohan, as I saw. Where do they
lie, and why must we seek them?'

MANY ROADS LEAD EASTWARD (I) 305

'I do not yet know where they lie,' said Aragorn. 'But in Dunharrow it seems that we may learn the answer. To Dunharrow at the swiftest, then, I will go.'

'And you would have us ride with you?' said Legolas.

'Of your free will I would,' said Aragorn. 'For not by chance, I deem, are we three now left together of the Company. We have some part to play together. Listen! Here is an old rhyme of my kindred, almost forgotten, never understood.

The days are numbered; the kings are sleeping.
It is darkling time, the shadows grow.
Out of the Mountain they come, their tryst keeping;
at the Stone of Erech horns they blow.
Three lords I see from the three kindreds:
halls forgotten in the hills they tread,
Elflord, Dwarflord, Man forwandréd,
from the North they come by the Paths of the Dead![15]

Why does this point to us, you may ask. I deem it fits the hour too well for chance. Yet if more is needed: the sons of Elrond bring this word from their father in Rivendell: "Bid Aragorn remember the Paths of the Dead."

'Come then!' Aragorn rose and drew his sword and it flashed in the twilight of the dim hall of the Burg. 'To the Stone of Erech! I seek the Paths of the Dead! Come with me who will!'

Legolas and Gimli answered nothing, but they rose also and followed Aragorn from the hall. There on the green waited silently the hooded Rangers. Legolas and Gimli mounted. Aragorn sprang on Hasufel. Then Halbarad lifted a great horn and the blast of it echoed in Helm's Deep; and they leapt away, riding down the Combe like thunder, while all the men that were left on Dike or Burg stared in amaze.

The last page of the manuscript carries the words pencilled at the end of version B (p. 300): 'So now all roads were running together to the East ...', the paragraph that opens 'The Muster of Rohan' in *The Return of the King*.

At this point my father typed a fair copy, which I will call 'M',[16] very closely based on the manuscript C as revised. This text, numbered 'XLV', bore the title 'Many Roads Lead Eastward'. Only a few passages need be noted. I have mentioned (p. 304) that after the departure of Théoden from the Hornburg 'Aragorn's words with Halbarad about Merry and the Shire-folk are absent' in C revised; but the forerunner of the passage in RK (p. 53) now appears:

306   THE WAR OF THE RING

Aragorn rode to the Dike and watched till the king's men were far down the Combe. Then he turned to Halbarad. 'There go three that I love,' he said, 'and not least the hobbit, Merry, most dearly. For all our love and dooms, Halbarad, and our deeds of arms, still they have a great worth, that greatheart little people; and it is for them that we do battle, as much as for any glory of Gondor. And yet fate divides. Well, so it is. I must eat a little, and then we too must haste away ...'[17]

Secondly, after Aragorn's words, 'If so that is well, as well as an evil case can be' (p. 304) he now continues:

'... These deadly strokes upon our flanks will be weakened. And we have a little room in which to play.
'Another thing I learned. There is another Stone preserved in the land of Gondor *that he has not looked in*. It is at Erech. Thither I will go. ...'

And lastly, Aragorn now introduces the 'old rhyme' in these words: 'Listen! Here is an old rhyme-of-lore among my kindred, almost forgotten, never understood: it is but a shard of the rhymes of Malbeth, the last Seer of our folk in the north' (see note 15). The verse differs from the form in C revised (p. 305) in lines 2–4, which here read:

> *It is darkling time, the shadow grows.*
> *Out of the Mountain he comes, his tryst keeping;*
> *At the Stone of Erech his horn he blows.*

From the point where 'Aragorn sprang on Hasufel' the typescript M continues thus:

... Then Halbarad lifted a great horn, and the blast of it echoed in Helm's Deep, and with that they leapt away, riding down the Combe like thunder, while all the men that were left on Dike or Burg stared in amaze.

So now all roads were running together to the East to meet the coming of war and the onset of the Shadow. And even as Pippin stood at the Gate of the City and saw the Prince of Dol Amroth ride in with his banners, the King of Rohan came down out of the hills.
Day was waning. In the last rays of the sun the Riders cast long pointed shadows that went on before them. ...

The paragraph 'So now all roads were running together to the East ...' had been written at the ends of texts B and C (pp. 300, 305), from which it was already clear that my father had in mind a chapter

MANY ROADS LEAD EASTWARD (I)   307

that should fall into two parts: first, the story of the return of Théoden and Aragorn to the Hornburg and Aragorn's looking into the *palantír* of Orthanc, followed by the separate departures of Théoden and the Riders and of Aragorn and the Rangers; and second, the story of Théoden's coming to Dunharrow. The paragraph 'So now all roads were running together to the East' was devised as the link between them (and provided the title of the chapter in the typescript, which I have adopted here). In terms of RK, this 45th chapter of *The Lord of the Rings* consisted of 'The Passing of the Grey Company' (pp. 46–56) and 'The Muster of Rohan' (pp. 64 ff.); but all account of Aragorn and the Rangers after they had left the Hornburg was to be postponed.

By the time typescript M was made, much further work had been done on what it is convenient to call by the later title 'The Muster of Rohan', extending it from the point reached in October 1944, as detailed in Chapter II ('Book Five Begun and Abandoned'). I shall therefore postpone the second part of 'Many Roads Lead Eastward' to my next chapter; but the subsequent history of the first or 'Hornburg' part may be briefly noticed here. The typescript M, retitled 'Dunharrow', became the vehicle of much of the later development (doubtless at different times) as far as the departure of Aragorn and the Rangers from the Hornburg, with such changes as *Parth Galen* for *Calembel* (and a proposed name *Calembrith*), *Elladan* for *Elboron*, the introduction of the passage (RK p. 48) in which Elrohir and Halbarad deliver the messages from Elrond and Arwen ('the Lady of Rivendell'), and of Aragorn's account (RK p. 55) of the oathbreaking of the Men of the Mountains and the words of Isildur to their king. Nonetheless, the verse of Malbeth did not at this stage reach the alliterative form in RK:

'. . . Listen! This is the word that the sons of Elrond bring to me from their father in Rivendell, wisest in lore:
'"Bid Aragorn remember the Paths of the Dead. For thus spoke Malbeth the Seer:
When the land is dark where the kings sleep
And long the Shadow in the East is grown,
The oathbreakers their tryst shall keep,
At the Stone of Erech shall a horn be blown:
The forgotten people shall their oath fulfill.
Who shall summon them, whose be the horn?
For none may come there against their will.
The heir of him to whom the oath was sworn;
Out of the North shall he come, dark ways shall he tread;
He shall come to Erech by the Paths of the Dead."'

308   THE WAR OF THE RING

At the stage represented by the further development of this typescript with its manuscript additions my father added (as the pagination shows), in a roughly written continuation that is however close to the form in RK, the story of the coming of the Grey Company (not yet so called) to Dunharrow, and the meeting that night, and again next day at dawn, of Aragorn and Éowyn (RK pp. 56–9).[18] It is clear from the pagination that at this stage the muster in Harrowdale was still to be included in this chapter ('Dunharrow'); and that the passage of the Paths of the Dead was not yet told in this part of the narrative.

NOTES

1   A note in the margin of this text says 'Night of 3, day of 4th', i.e. they came to the Hornburg at dawn of the 4th of February. The chronology envisaged here was presumably that Théoden would leave the Hornburg early on the 5th. See note 9.

2   On the First Map 'Dunharrow' was the name of the mountain afterwards called Starkhorn (VII.319 and p. 240 in this book); the distance from that 'Dunharrow' to the spot added later to mark the position of the Stone of Erech (p. 268, footnote) is 18.5 mm or 92.5 miles. Precisely the same, though I think that this is by chance rather than design, is found on the anomalous map redrawn on p. 269 for the distance from Erech to a little mark in Harrowdale that probably represents Dunharrow. The Second Map (p. 434) gives (probably) 45 miles; and this is also the distance on my father's large-scale map of Rohan, Gondor and Mordor (and on my reproduction of it published in *The Return of the King*).

3   A wooden ruler that may have been the one used by my father at this time gives 50 mm. = 62.5 miles.

4   Taum Santoski has been able however to read a good deal of it, especially in the latter part of the text where the arrival of the Rangers is described: here there is no difference of any significance between the original draft and the overwriting in ink. Of the opening passage of the chapter less can be made out; but it can be seen that Aragorn, in answer to Legolas' question 'Where?' ('And then whither?' in RK) replied: 'I cannot say yet. We shall go to the Hold of Dunharrow, to Edoras I guess for the muster that the King ordered in [three > ?four] nights' time from now. But that may prove too tardy.' He seems not to have said anything equivalent to 'An hour long prepared approaches'; and in answer to his question 'Who will go with me?' it is Merry alone who replies: 'I will. Though I promised to sit by the King when he gets back in his house and tell him about the Shire.' To this Aragorn replies: 'That must wait, I fear – [?indeed] I fear it shall

MANY ROADS LEAD EASTWARD (I) 309

prove one of the fair things that will not come to flower in this bitter spring.'

5 For earlier applications of the name *Halbarad* see p. 236 and note 10.

6 A few other details in which the text differs from RK may be mentioned. Aragorn's reply to Merry's remark about his promise to Théoden remains as it was (note 4). In the encounter with the Rangers Merry's thoughts are not reported; Halbarad does not name himself *Dúnadan*; and neither Aragorn nor Halbarad dismount at first – not until the 'recognition' do they leap down from their horses.

7 The brackets are in the original.

8 In *The Tale of Years* (LR Appendix B) the entry for the year 1436 in the Shire Reckoning states that the King Elessar, coming to the Brandywine Bridge, gave the Star of the Dúnedain to Master Samwise. In my note 33 to *The Disaster of the Gladden Fields* in *Unfinished Tales* (pp. 284–5) I said that I was unable to say what this was. This is a convenient place to mention that after the publication of *Unfinished Tales* two correspondents, Major Stephen M. Lott and Mrs. Joy Mercer, independently suggested to me that the Star of the Dúnedain was very probably the same as the silver brooch shaped like a rayed star that was worn by the Rangers in the present passage (RK p. 51); Mrs. Mercer also referred to the star worn by Aragorn when he served in Gondor, as described in Appendix A (I.iv, *The Stewards*): 'Thorongil men called him in Gondor, the Eagle of the Star, for he was swift and keen-eyed, and wore a silver star upon his cloak.' These suggestions are clearly correct.

9 The chronology is now thus:

> *February 4* Théoden and Aragorn reach the Hornburg at dawn. In the afternoon Théoden and the Riders leave for Dunharrow, and soon after Aragorn and the Rangers leave for Edoras.
>
> At the Hornburg Éomer says: 'On the evening of the second day from now we should come there [to Dunharrow]. That night the moon will rise full.'
>
> *February 6* Full moon. Théoden arrives at Dunharrow at dusk.

10 In a later text (see p. 397) the black Stone of Erech, brought from Númenor, was not a *palantír*, but a *palantír* was preserved in the Tower of Erech. In the present text (and in the subsequent revisions, pp. 302, 304–5), on the other hand, the most natural interpretation of the words seems to be that the Stone of Erech was itself the *palantír*. On the sites of the *palantíri* as originally conceived see pp. 76–7. — Against Aragorn's speech is pencilled in the margin: 'He has not forgotten the sword of Isildur. Doubtless

310 THE WAR OF THE RING

he will think that I have got the treasure.' Cf. the subsequent text (p. 304): 'But now he will hesitate, doubting whether the heir of Isildur hath that which Isildur took from him.'

11 I have punctuated this verse according to the subsequent version of it, which is almost identical. In the fourth line my father wrote *over earth*, changing *earth* to *the world*, and I have substituted *on* for *over*, as in the following version. — *forwandréd*: worn and weary from wandering.

12 The original texts of the abandoned opening of 'The Muster of Rohan' began 'Day was (fading) waning'; the paragraph cited ('So now all roads were running together to the East ...') precedes 'Day was waning' in RK.

13 In the message that came to Rivendell the wording in this text is: *The Lord Aragorn has need of his kindred. Let the last of the Kings of Men in the North ride to him in Rohan*, where RK has *Let the Dúnedain* ... In a rejected form of this passage preceding it in the manuscript the wording is: *Let all that remain of the* [struck out: *Tarkil*] *Kings of Men ride to him in Rohan.*

Legolas' support for his opinion that it was Galadriel who sent the message, 'Did she not speak through Gandalf of the ride of the Grey Company from the North?', is absent here. The reference is to 'The White Rider' (TT p. 106) and Galadriel's verse addressed to Aragorn spoken to him by Gandalf in Fangorn:

> *Near is the hour when the Lost should come forth,*
> *And the Grey Company ride from the North.*
> *But dark is the path appointed for thee:*
> *The Dead watch the road that leads to the Sea.*

It was at this stage in the evolution of the story that Galadriel's message in verse to Aragorn was changed from its earlier and altogether different form: see VII.431, 448.

When the three companions went down from the broken gates they 'passed the new mounds of the fallen raised on the Gore' ('on the greensward', RK p. 50); and 'the Riders were assembling upon the Gore' ('on the green', RK p. 51). Cf. the description of the Hornburg in the chapter 'Helm's Deep' (TT p. 134): 'About the feet of the Hornrock it [the Deeping Stream] wound, and flowed then in a gully through the midst of *a wide green gore*'; also the drawing of Helm's Deep and the Hornburg in *Pictures by J. R. R. Tolkien*, no. 26.

14 An odd detail may be mentioned here. In his conversation with Legolas and Merry Gimli says in the C version, as first written: 'I played a game which I won by no more than one orc' (cf. RK p. 49). This was now altered to: 'and here Legolas and I played a game which I *lost* only by a single orc', and this survived into the first typescript. But in the second completed manuscript of 'The Road to Isengard', written long before this time, the text is

MANY ROADS LEAD EASTWARD (I)   311

precisely as in TT, p. 148: '"You have passed my score by one," answered Legolas.'

15   A rejected version of this form of the verse is also found in the manuscript: in this the first two lines read:

The Shadow falls; the kings are sleeping.
It is darkling time, all lights are low.

The remainder of the verse is the same as that given in the text. Although Aragorn describes it only as 'an old rhyme of my kindred', the words 'Three lords I see' perhaps suggest the utterance of a seer; and Aragorn attributes it in the following text (p. 306) to 'Malbeth, the last Seer of our folk in the North' (cf. RK p. 54, where he declares that the wholly different verse that he recites in this place was spoken by 'Malbeth the Seer, in the days of Arvedui, last king at Fornost'). — In none of these texts is there any indication of what the 'tryst' might be. In the outline given on pp. 274–5 there is mention of the defeat of the Haradwaith by 'the Shadow Host'.

16   The reason for calling the typescript 'M' is that as will be seen shortly it covers, in a single chapter (XLV), both the story of Aragorn at the Hornburg (preceded by texts A to C) and the story of the Muster of Rohan (preceded by texts A to L).

17   This was changed on the typescript to read: '"There go three that I love," he said, "and the halfling, Merry, most dearly. ... and for them also we do battle, not only for the glory of Gondor. And yet fate divides us. ..."'

18   It is said in this continuation that Aragorn came to Edoras 'at dusk on the next day' (February 5), and that they did not halt there but passed up Harrowdale and came to Dunharrow 'late at night'; and Aragorn says to Éowyn on the following morning (February 6) that Théoden and Éomer will not return 'until the day is old'. See note 9.

V

MANY ROADS LEAD EASTWARD (2)

When my father made the typescript (M) of the long chapter 'Many Roads Lead Eastward' he had not only written a good deal of what afterwards became 'The Passing of the Grey Company': he had also greatly extended the story that would later become 'The Muster of Rohan' from the opening abandoned in October 1944. A new text of the latter (following the last of the earlier ones, that in 'midget type' which I have called H, p. 250) takes up at the point where Éomer says 'Harrowdale at last!' (RK p. 65); this I will call 'J'. Tolerably clearly written in ink, it extends only as far as Merry's wonderment at the line of standing stones across the Firienfeld (RK p. 68), the last lines being roughly pencilled, and then peters out into a brief outline; but so far as it goes the first part of 'The Muster of Rohan' in RK was now achieved almost word for word, except just at the point where it breaks off.[1] The text ends thus:

At last they came to a sharp brink, and the climbing road passed into a low cutting between walls of rock and passed up a slope out onto a wide upland. The Firienfeld men called it, a green mountain field of grass and heath above the deep-delved valley, on the lap of the great mountains behind: the Starkhorn southward, and westward [read northward][2] the many-peaked mass of Iscamba[3] Irensaga [written above: Ironsaw], between which lower, but steep and grim, stood the black wall of the Dwimorberg, rising out of thick slopes of sombre firs/pines. Towards this marched from the very brink of the stairs to the dark edge of the wood a line a double line [sic] of standing stones. Worn and black, some leaning, some fallen, some cracked or broken, they were like old teeth. Where they vanished into the wood there was a dark opening into a cavern or recess in the [?western] side. Just within dimly seen was a tall standing pillar.

Merry looked at this strange line of stones and wondered what they could be. He

Éowyn says Aragorn has gone by the Paths of the Dead.

The huts and pavilions of the hold.

To the king's pavilion come the messengers of Gondor.

The king promises 7 thousand horse to ride as soon as may

MANY ROADS LEAD EASTWARD (2)   313

be. At same [time] messengers come from Eastemnet saying that an orc-host has crossed the river, below the Limlight.

It is a gloomy evening repast.

The morning is dull and overcast, and gets darker.

On this page, which is reproduced on p. 314, are two rapid pencilled sketches which amply illustrate the final conception of Harrowdale and Dunharrow.

It is to be remembered that at this time the further story of Aragorn and the Grey Company, their coming to Dunharrow and their entering the Gate of the Dead, was not present in the narrative: the present passage was to be the first account of the Dwimorberg, the Firienfeld, the line of standing stones, the Dimholt, and the great monolith before the Dark Door. When afterwards the structure of the narrative was changed my father largely retained this description in the chapter 'The Muster of Rohan' (RK pp. 67–8): he treated the coming of the Grey Company to Dunharrow two nights before the arrival of Théoden in a single sentence ('they passed up the valley, and so came to Dunharrow as darkness fell', RK p. 56), and said almost nothing of the scene – they 'sat at supper' with Éowyn, 'as Aragorn came to the booth where he was to lodge with Legolas and Gimli, and his companions had gone in, there came the Lady Éowyn after him and called to him', and that is all. The approach of the Company to the Dark Door next morning is described with a mysterious brevity: the double line of standing stones across the Firienfeld is mentioned cursorily, as if their existence were already known to the reader: 'A dread fell on them, even as they passed between the lines of ancient stones and so came to the Dimholt' (RK p. 59).

The text J was followed by another, 'K', beginning at the same point ('Harrowdale at last!'); this was clearly written in ink as far as the point where Éowyn says to Théoden: 'And your pavilion is prepared for you, lord, for I have had full tidings of you' (cf. RK p. 68). In this text the description of the Firienfeld runs as follows (the passage here set between asterisks was rejected, but is not marked in any way in the manuscript):

The Firienfeld men called it, a green mountain-field of grass and heath, high above the deep-delved valley [> course of the Snowbourn], on the lap of the great mountains behind: the Starkhorn southwards to the right, and [westward in front >] northward to the left the many-peaked mass of Irensaga Ironsaw, between which there faced them, darkly frowning, the grim black wall of Dwimorberg, rising out of thick slopes of sombre pines. *[Towards these woods >] Across the wide field there marched, from the brink of the stair to the dark edge of

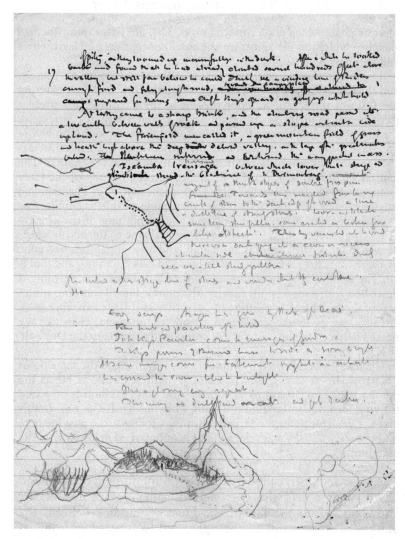

Starkhorn, Dwimorberg and Irensaga

MANY ROADS LEAD EASTWARD (2)   315

the woods, a double line of standing stones, worn and black. Some leaning, some fallen, some cracked or broken, they looked like rows of old and hungry teeth. Where they entered the wood there was a [dark opening >] way in the trees: just within dimly to be seen was a tall standing pillar and beyond it the dark opening of a cavern or great door.* Dividing the upland into two there marched a double line of standing stones that dwindled in the dusk and vanished into the trees. Those who followed that road came to a dark clearing amid the sighing gloom of the Firienholt,[4] and there like a shadow stood a single pillar of stone, and beyond a huge doorway in the side of the black cliff. Signs and figures were set about it that none could read, worn by the years and shrouded from the light.[5] In long memory none had dared to pass that door. Such was the dark Dunharrow, the work of long-forgotten men. ...

The text then continues very close indeed to RK (p. 68), ending with Éowyn's words to Théoden 'I have had full tidings of you', which do not stand at the foot of a page. The next words, '"So Aragorn has come," said Éomer' (RK p. 69), stand at the head of a new page, and there follows a manuscript pencilled in my father's most impossible handwriting, effectively indecipherable except insofar as later versions provide clues – as is however largely the case here. This further text can be regarded as a continuation of K. It carries the narrative of 'The Muster of Rohan' as far as the conclusion of Théoden's words with the errand-rider of Gondor, RK p. 73; and while it is naturally rough and hasty in expression, and would be greatly refined, the story was effectively present from the first. The following passage, however, I cite in full, following Éomer's words (cf. RK p. 70) 'For the road we have climbed is the approach to the Door. Yonder is the Firienholt. But what lies beyond no man knows.' For the earliest reference to the old man of Dunharrow see the notes ('E') given on p. 242.

'Only legend of old days has any report to make,' said Théoden. 'But if these ancient tales are to be believed, then the Door [?in] Dwimorberg leads to a secret way that goes under the mountains. But none have dared ever to explore it since Baldor son of Bregu dared to pass the Door, and came never back. Folk say that Dead Men out of ... Years guard the way and will suffer none to come to their secret halls. But at whiles they may be seen [?rush]ing out like shadows and down the Stony Road. Then the men of Harrowdale shut fast their doors and shroud their windows and are afraid. But seldom do the Dead come forth, and only at times of great peril.'

316   THE WAR OF THE RING

'Yet it is said in Harrowdale,' said Éowyn quietly, 'that they came forth in the moonless nights [?just past].'

'But why has Aragorn gone that way?' said Merry.

'Unless he has spoken to you his friend, then you have heard as much as we,' said Éowyn. 'But I thought that he had changed much since I saw him in Meduseld.[6] Fey he seemed to me, and as one that the Dead call.'

'Maybe,' said Théoden. 'Yet my heart tells me that he is a kingly man of high destiny. And take comfort in this, daughter, since comfort you seem to need in your grief for this passing guest. It is said that when the Eorlingas came first out of the North and passed up the Snowbourn seeking strong places of refuge in time of need, that Bregu and his son Baldor climbed the Stair of the Hold and [?passed] to the Door; and there there sat an old man aged beyond count of years, withered as old stone. Very like to the Púkel-men he was as he sat upon the threshold of the dark Door.

'Nothing he said until they sought to pass him and enter, and then a voice came out of him as if it were out of a stone, and to their amazement it spoke in their own tongue. *The way is shut.*

'Then they halted and looked at the old man whom [?the king] had at first taken for [??an image] such as stood at the turnings of the Stair. But he did not look at them. *The way is shut* the voice said again. *It was made by those who are Dead and [??for] the Dead [??to] keep until the time comes.*

'*And when will that be?* said Baldor.

'But no answer did he ever get. For the old man died in that hour and fell upon his face, and no other [??words] of the ancient dwellers in the mountains did [?our] folk ever learn. Yet maybe the time has come and Aragorn will pass.'

'And whether the time is [?come] or no,' said Éomer, 'none can discover save by daring the door. A [?true]-hearted man was Aragorn, and still against hope I hope to see his face once again. Yet our roads lie'   And then he paused, for there was a noise without of men's voices and the challenges of the king's guard.

Then Dúnhere entered and announced the coming of the messenger (or messengers)[7] of Gondor. In his opening words Dirgon, as he is called here (Hirgon in RK), says: 'Often you have aided us, but now the Lord Denethor begs for all your strength, and all your speed, lest Gondor fall. Then would the tide sweep over the fields of Calenardon.'[8] From Théoden's words 'And yet he knows that we are a scattered people and take time to gather in our riders' the text runs far

MANY ROADS LEAD EASTWARD (2)   317

more briefly than in RK to the end of his speech with the messenger. Dirgon does not speak again, and Théoden refers only, and briefly, to the war with Saruman and the lesser number of Riders that he can send; concluding 'Yet all is more advanced than I hoped. We may ride on the [?third] day from now.'

A further pencilled text ('L'), as fearsomely scrawled as K or worse, takes up after a short gap for which there is no drafting with Merry's words: 'I will not be left behind to be called for on return' (RK p. 73). It is curious that this text is headed 'XLVI' (without title), whereas the typescript M, obviously developed from L, includes this story of the departure of the Riders from Harrowdale as the conclusion of 'XLV: Many Roads lead Eastward'. I can only suppose that my father briefly intended to begin a new chapter with Merry's words, but thought better of it.

The opening of the text L is very close to RK pp. 73–5. The darkness that has spread out of the East and reached far into the western sky is described in the same words; the first messenger from Gondor is now named Hirgon, and the second (never named) is present – but this latter says of the darkness only: 'It comes from Mordor, lord. It began last night at sunset, and now the great cloud lies on all the [?land] between here and the Mountains of Shadow, and it is deepening. By the fire-signals war has already begun.' To this Théoden replies: 'Then the die is cast. There is no longer need or profit in hiding. We will muster at once and wait not. Those who are not here must be left behind or follow. ...'

Merry's story at this point was somewhat different from its form in RK. After his expostulation to Théoden ('Then tie me on to one, or let me hang on a stirrup ...') the text, hurled onto the paper, continues:

Théoden smiled. 'You shall ride before me on Snowmane [?rather than wander in the plains] of Rohan. Go now and see what the armourers have prepared for you.'

'It was the only request that Aragorn made,' said Éowyn. 'And it has been granted.'

With that she led him from the pavilion to a booth at some distance among the lodgings of the king's guard, and there a man brought out to her a small helm and a coat of mail and a shield like to the one that had been given to Gimli.[9] 'No mail we had to fit you nor time to forge a hauberk for you,'[10] she said, 'but here is a short jerkin of leather and a shield and a [?short] spear. Take them and bear them to good fortune. But now I have .... to look to. Farewell. But we shall meet again, my heart foretells, thou and I, Meriadoc.'

So it was that amid the gathering gloom the King of the Mark set out. Not many hours had passed, and now in the half-light

318 THE WAR OF THE RING

beside the grey rush of the Snowbourn he sat proudly on his white horse, and five [and] fifty hundreds of Riders, besides men ..... with spare horses bearing light burdens, [?were ranged]. They [?were to ride down] to Edoras and [?thence out and away] along the well-beaten road eastward, pass along the skirts of the hill[s] to [?Anórien] and the walls of Minas Tirith. Merry sat on his pony that was to bear him down the [?stony] valley, and after that he was to ride with the king or some other of his company.

A trumpet sang. The king raised his hand, and without any sound of voice, silently, without shout or song, the great ride began. The king passed along the lines followed by Merry and Éomer and the errand-riders of Gondor and Dúnhere, and then his guard of twelve picked spearmen. To Éowyn he had said farewell above in the Hold.

It is clear, from Théoden's 'You shall ride before me on Snowmane rather than wander in the plains of Rohan. Go now and see what the armourers have prepared for you', and from the words 'Merry sat on his pony that was to bear him down the stony valley, and after that he was to ride with the king or some other of his company', that at this stage Merry was to go with the Rohirrim to Minas Tirith openly, with the concurrence of Théoden, and without any assistance from Éowyn. This does not mean, of course, that Éowyn was not present among the Riders in disguise, although no covert reference is made to her in this original account of the departure from Harrowdale; and indeed her death before Minas Tirith·had been long foreseen (see VII.448; also the outline given on p. 256 and especially that on p. 275). In any case, a further draft for the story of the departure follows in text L:

First there went twelve of the king's household-men [?and] guard, picked spearmen. Tall and stern they looked to Merry, and one among them, less tall and broad than the others, glanced at the hobbit as he passed, and Merry caught the glint of clear grey eyes. He shivered a little, for it seemed to him that the face was of one that goes knowingly to death. The king followed with Éomer on his right and Dúnhere on his left. He had said farewell to Éowyn above in the Hold. Merry followed with the errand-riders of Gondor and behind went twelve more of the guard. Then in [?ordered] lines the companies of the riders turned and rode after them as was appointed. They passed down the road beside the Snowbourn, and through the hamlets of Upbourn and Underharrow where many sad faces looked from dark doors. And so the great ride to the East began,

MANY ROADS LEAD EASTWARD (2)   319

with which the songs of Rohan were busy for many lives of men thereafter.

Here the text L ends, and here the typescript M ends also.

In this second part of the chapter 'Many Roads lead Eastward' the typescript text shows great refinement in detail over these exceedingly rough and obviously primary drafts, but no texts are found to bridge them; and it seems possible that the developed form in M was actually achieved on the typewriter (there are in fact several passages that could suggest this). To a great extent the text of RK in 'The Muster of Rohan' was now present; but there remained still some differences, and among these I notice the following.[11]

Éowyn now says of the coming forth of the Dead (see p. 316): 'Yet it is said in Harrowdale that they came forth again in the moonless nights but little while ago, a great host in strange array, and none saw them return, they say.' The old man beside the Dark Door is still said to resemble one of the Púkel-men.[12] On the front of Hirgon's helm 'was wrought as an emblem a small silver crown' ('star' in RK). The second, unnamed errand-rider from Gondor says here of the darkness spreading out of Mordor: 'From my station by the beacon of Minrimmon I saw it rise', where in RK he says: 'From the hills in the Eastfold of your realm I saw it rise'. Notably, the conversation between Merry and Théoden now takes this form:

Théoden smiled. 'Rather than that I will bear you with me on Snowmane,' he said. 'I guessed your words before you spoke them. But at the least you shall ride with me to Edoras and look on Meduseld, for that way I shall go. So far Stybba can bear you: the great race will not begin till we reach the plains.'

'And over the plains with you to the end of the road your squire will ride,' said Éowyn. 'That you know in your heart, and others also have foreseen it. Come now, Meriadoc, and I will show you the gear that is prepared for you. It was the only request that Aragorn son of Arathorn made of us ere he departed.'

With that she led the hobbit from the king's pavilion to a booth among the lodges of the king's guard near by; and there a man brought out to her a small helm and a spear and round shield, and other gear.

The account of the departure follows that in text L (p. 318); the Rider who looked at Merry as he passed is still among the twelve household-men that preceded the host, 'somewhat less in height and girth than the others'; and nothing is said of what arrangement had been made for Merry after the departure of the host from Edoras.

320 THE WAR OF THE RING

The chapter 'Many Roads Lead Eastward' ended, both in manuscript and typescript, at the ride of the Rohirrim down Harrowdale: 'And so the great ride to the East began, with which the songs of Rohan were busy for many lives of men thereafter' (p. 319; RK p. 76). The conclusion of 'The Muster of Rohan' as it stands in RK was added later, but not much later (at least in terms of the progress of the narrative: what halts and of what duration took place in the writing of Books V and VI there seems no way of telling); it first appeared, in fact, as the opening of Chapter XLVII, 'The Ride of the Rohirrim', and I postpone it to that place (p. 349).

NOTES

1   On a rejected page in this manuscript, however, Théoden expresses some amazement at the scene in Harrowdale: 'The king looked with surprise about him, for there was a great concourse of men ... "What is the meaning of this?" asked the king. "Was not the muster set to begin tomorrow at Edoras?"' Then a man, unnamed, explains how this is due to Gandalf, and a note follows: 'Gandalf must tell the king as he rides off that he will order the muster at Dunharrow and speed it up. That will necessitate altering remarks about the full moon' (see the Note on Chronology below). This rejected page then concludes with a brief passage that depends on the note: 'So they saw that Gandalf must have done as he promised. The muster was here, not at Edoras, and already the greater part of the men of Rohan were assembled.'
    The words 'Gandalf must tell the king as he rides off' can only refer to his leaving Dol Baran on Shadowfax after the Nazgûl passed over; but no such change was in fact introduced in that place.
    At the foot of this rejected page is written: 'Éowyn tells of Aragorn's coming and his departure. The Paths of the Dead. The road of Monoliths.'
2   *westward* was, I think, no more than a slip. It was repeated in the following text (p. 313) but corrected, probably at once.
3   *Iscamba:* cf. Old English *camb* (Modern English *comb*), comb, crest (as of a cock, a helmet, etc.).
4   For the name *Firienholt* of the later *Dimholt* see p. 251 and note 21.
5   For the origin of this sentence see p. 246. It reappears in changed form in 'The Passing of the Grey Company' in RK (p. 59), where the Company halted before the Dark Door: 'Signs and figures were carved above its wide arch too dim to read, and fear flowed from it like a grey vapour.'

MANY ROADS LEAD EASTWARD (2)   321

6 The first part of the name of the Golden Hall is so scrawled that it could be read in almost any way, but it is clearly not *Winseld*, the earlier name, and is almost certainly the first occurrence of *Meduseld*.

7 Apparently there were two messengers, for while the writing is so fast that no detail of letter is entirely certain, my father seems to have written 'Men are here, errand-riders out of Gondor.' Théoden's reply could be equally well read as 'Let him come' or 'Let them come'. But only one man enters. — The war-arrow that he bears is green-feathered (black in RK).

8 The name *Calenard(h)on* emerged in the course of writing the chapter 'Faramir': see pp. 155–6, with notes 18 and 22.

9 The reference is to 'The King of the Golden Hall', TT p. 127: '[Gimli] chose a cap of iron and leather that fitted well upon his round head; and a small shield he also took. It bore the running horse, white upon green, that was the emblem of the House of Eorl.' This passage, in which is recounted also the arming of Aragorn and Legolas 'in shining mail', was added on a rider to the fair copy manuscript of 'The King of the Golden Hall'.

10 Thus the provision of a coat of mail for Merry, referred to in the preceding sentence, was immediately denied.

11 The following names and name-forms in the typescript may be mentioned. The *Firienholt* remains, for later *Dimholt*. *Brego* is now again spelt thus, not *Bregu*, but his son's name is here *Bealdor* (changed to *Baldor* on the typescript): both of these are Old English variants. The path down from the Dark Door ('the road of Monoliths', note 1) is again called 'the Stony Road', capitalised, as in the text K (p. 315). Hirgon speaks of *the Harad*, where RK has *the Haradrim*.

12 In RK (p. 71) the old withered man is said to have been once 'tall and kingly'. Cf. *The Lord of the Rings* Appendix F (*Of Men*): 'The Dunlendings were a remnant of the peoples that had dwelt in the vales of the White Mountains in ages past. The Dead Men of Dunharrow were of their kin.'

Note on the Chronology

In the last of the texts (H) of the abandoned opening of 'The Muster of Rohan' Théoden asked if the moon had not been full on the night before, and Éomer replied that on the contrary the moon would be full that night (pp. 251–2, 272–3). In the first of the later texts (J) Théoden himself says 'Tonight the moon will be full, and in the morning I shall ride to Edoras to the gathering of Rohan', and this remained into the typescript M.

In 'The Road to Isengard' the date of the muster at Edoras was changed over and over again according to the shifting chronology. For

322   THE WAR OF THE RING

the earliest texts see p. 27 and note 6; the second fair copy of that chapter had 'before the waning of the moon', changed to 'at the last quarter of the moon'. This was retained in the following typescript, but there changed subsequently to 'on the first day after the full moon' – which is the date in the present texts. (In 'The Road to Isengard' in TT, p. 150, the date of the muster is to be 'the second day after the full moon', and so at the beginning of 'The Muster of Rohan' in RK, p. 65, Théoden says: 'Last night the moon was full, and in the morning I shall ride to Edoras to the gathering of the Mark.')

In the note on text J (see note 1 above) it is said that 'Gandalf must tell the king as he rides off [from Dol Baran] that he will order the muster at Dunharrow and speed it up', and that this 'will necessitate altering remarks about the full moon.' I do not understand this. If my father was referring to the passage in 'The Road to Isengard' in which the date of the muster is set, this would seem to have no relevance: for Gandalf was proposing, in view of the coming of the Nazgûl, to *change* the arrangement that had been made and 'speed up' the muster.

All these later 'Muster of Rohan' texts agree that the moon was full on the night that Théoden came to Harrowdale (February 6); cf. p. 299 and note 9. This was the night following the day on which Gandalf and Pippin reached Minas Tirith at sunrise; the sunset of that day was 'ominous', and the Darkness began on February 7 (p. 295). With this the present texts agree: the second errand-rider from Gondor, arriving on the morning of the 7th, says that the Darkness 'began last night at sunset' (p. 317), and the departure of the Riders from Dunharrow takes place in deepening gloom. It is interesting to see that in text K, as Merry sat alone in his tent on the Firienfeld, 'Slowly night came on, and the half-seen heads of the mountains were crowned with small stars in the West, but the East was dark and shadowy, *and the moon did not appear until late at night*'; whereas in the typescript M (where it was still the night of full moon) the moon is not mentioned. The natural presumption is that the moon was hidden by the vast cloud spreading out of Mordor.

How my father was at this stage relating the full moon of February 6 to Frodo's movements is not clear to me. In *The Tale of Years* in LR the full moon was on March 7 (since Frodo left Henneth Annûn on March 8, and he saw the full moon setting before dawn on the morning of his departure: 'The Forbidden Pool', TT pp. 292–3), and Théoden came to Dunharrow on the evening of March 9; but with this the king's words in 'The Muster of Rohan', RK p. 65, 'Last night the moon was full', do not accord, and should have been 'Two nights ago'. This in turn would require alteration of the date set for the muster in 'The Road to Isengard' (see above).

VI

THE SIEGE OF GONDOR

My father's first start on this chapter was a brief, roughly pencilled text ('**A**') which he then wrote over in ink, so that a good deal is lost, especially of the latter part of it; but Taum Santoski has managed to recover quite enough to show that the ink overwriting ('**B**') followed it for the most part very closely. I shall here describe B rather than A, noting subsequently passages in which A is significantly different.

Text B (numberless and titleless) begins as does Chapter 4 in *The Return of the King* with 'Pippin was roused by Gandalf', and extends through the paragraph beginning 'It was dark and dim all day' (RK p. 80). After Pippin's question 'Why did you bring me here?' the text differs from that of RK:

'Because it was not safe to leave you behind,' answered the wizard. 'Safe for others, I mean. It is no safe place here for you or anyone else, as you'll probably soon discover. But you brought it on yourself.' Pippin said no more.

Before long he was walking with Gandalf back again down the long cold passage to the doors of the Tower Hall. Within Denethor sat in a grey gloom, like an old patient spider, Pippin thought, and looking as if he had not moved since he dismissed his new esquire the day before. He beckoned Gandalf to a seat, but Pippin was left standing for a while unheeded. Presently the old man turned to him with a cold smile, whether of mockery or welcome Pippin could not tell.

'And why have you come, Peregrin son of Paladin?' he said.

'I was told that you wanted me, sir,' said Pippin, 'to, well, to learn my new duties.'

'Ah yes,' said Denethor. 'It is to be hoped that you spent yesterday well and to your liking, if less in eating [*struck out:* and sleeping] than you might wish. Today you shall take your turn to wait on me. I have little more now to do, until my son Faramir returns with tidings. And if there comes no ill news and the great ones' (he looked at Gandalf) 'do not occupy all my leisure, you shall talk to me. Can you sing?'

Pippin's apologetic account of the songs he knew and his horror at the thought of singing a comic song of the Shire before the grim

324   THE WAR OF THE RING

Steward of Minas Tirith follows as in RK, as does Denethor's discussion with Gandalf, the arming and clothing of Pippin,[1] and the darkness over the city, up to 'as if all the Vale of Anduin waited for a ruinous storm.' Then follows:

His duties he found irksome and dull, so much so that he would even have welcomed a chance to sing one of his comic songs. But he was not asked to sing, and indeed few spoke to him at all.

Here the overwritten text B ends. In the underlying pencilled text A the discussion between Gandalf and Denethor did not concern Rohan, but was on the subject of the immediate strategy: though very little of it can be made out, the phrase 'Gandalf had already been urging on the Steward' and the name 'West Osgiliath' can be read. After Pippin had returned from the armoury it is said that he spent the day idly, 'for Denethor sat mostly behind closed doors'; and at some point during the day 'There was a clamour in the city. Faramir had returned. Pippin witnesses the greeting of Denethor and Faramir.'

The pencilled and the overwritten texts end at the same point on the page, although in substance they had diverged.

My father evidently doubted the rightness of beginning the chapter in this way, for at the head of the first page of this 'doubled' text he wrote in pencil: '? Begin with Pippin and Berethil[2] talking again on wall on eve[ning] of 9th. ...' This was in fact overwritten by part of the B text in ink, and as a result some further words of the note cannot be read; presumably therefore my father had (but only temporarily) abandoned the idea that the chapter might open differently.

At the end of the 'doubled' text the following notes were written in pencil:

? Sunset – a gleam far off. Gandalf says there is hope still in the West.

Next day there is a council and soon Faramir departs. Pippin has more talk with Berethil and hears that Faramir has gone to Osgiliath. Time passes slowly. Ill news comes on 11th March (next day) that there is a Fell Captain on the enemy's side. He has won the Crossings and Faramir is driven to Ramas Coren.[3] Still the darkness grows. It is like a slow disease, thought Pippin.

Some time on 9th Pippin must look out from the walls and see Nazgûl (6 or 7) flying over Pelennor, and see them pursue a few riders. But Gandalf rides out – and saves them. It is Faramir! Just in time. Great joy in City. Faramir sees Pippin as he comes up to the Citadel, and is astonished.

THE SIEGE OF GONDOR

325

In these notes is the first appearance of the final calendar, the month being now March instead of February. Whether it entered at this very time or somewhat earlier cannot be said: but the last actual date found in the texts is February 5–6 in the outline for a part of 'Many Roads Lead Eastward' given on p. 296, so that the change had at any rate been made not long since. The conception of the month 'lost' in Lórien had now been abandoned: see VII.367–9. The relative dates have however not been changed: in the note suggesting a different way of opening the chapter Pippin and Berethil are to be talking on the wall of the city 'on the evening of the 9th', which would be February 7 according to the former dating (see the Note on Chronology at the end of this chapter).

My father now returned to the idea of a different opening, and began a new draft ('C') in which the matter of the opening already written was omitted or compressed, and referred to only in retrospect. This draft was written in thick soft pencil, in ink over pencil, and in ink with pencilled corrections and clarifications, and is throughout a formidably difficult manuscript. I have no doubt that it all proceeded from the same time and impulse.

This new text is numbered 'XLVI', without title; it begins with the words 'It had been dark all day; from the sunless dawn until the evening the heavy gloom had deepened ...', and continues essentially as in RK pp. 80–1 as far as 'now he was one small soldier in a city preparing for a great assault, clad in the grim and sombre manner of the Tower of Guard'; but there is no reference to the errand of Berethil (Beregond) across the Pelennor, nor to the last gleam of the sun as it escaped from the pall of cloud (see below). Then follows:

For in the morning Denethor had summoned him, and bidden him to take up his duties as the lord's esquire; and he had been sent straight to the armouries where already clothes and gear were made ready for him by Denethor's command.

In some other time and place he might have taken pleasure in his new array, but he knew now too clearly that this was a deadly serious matter, and no masquerade in borrowed plumes. The small coat of black mail seemed heavy and burdensome, and the helmet with its wings weighed on his head. Black too was the tunic or surcoat that he now wore above his mail, except where upon the breast was broidered in white the device of the Tree. He had been permitted to retain the grey cloak of Lórien [added: when not on duty], but that was now cast aside on the seat beside him, for the air was close. He turned his gaze away from the darkling plain far below, and yawned, and then he sighed.

326   THE WAR OF THE RING

In Pippin's complaint to Berethil and their words about the Darkness, the failure of Faramir to return across the River and Gandalf's anxiety, and the sudden cry of the Nazgûl, the draft reaches the text of RK pp. 81–2 almost word for word (save only that Pippin does not name the Prince of Dol Amroth as present at the deliberations with Denethor, and he says that Gandalf left the council before the evening meal, where RK has 'noon-meal'); but when Pippin climbs on to the seat and looks out there enters the description of the last gleam of sun that shone also on the head of the ruined king at the Cross-roads, omitted at its place in RK (on the synchronisation see the note at the end of this chapter). Then again the draft reaches the final text in almost every turn of expression in the description of the Nazgûl swooping on the horsemen, the distant sound of Faramir's horn call, and the radiance of the White Rider racing towards them, as far as Pippin's wild shouting 'like an onlooker at a great race urging on a runner who is far beyond encouragement.' At this point my father stopped and set down a brief outline:

Gandalf saves Faramir. Faramir sees Pippin at gate of Citadel and wonders – Gandalf introduces them, and takes Pippin along to Denethor's council. So Pippin hears a lot and hears Faramir accept orders to go to Osgiliath. Denethor and Faramir marvel at Gandalf's power over Nazgûl. Gandalf says things are still not so bad – because the W[izard] King has not yet appeared. He reveals that he is a renegade of his own order ... [?from] Númenor. 'So far I have saved myself from him only by flight – for many an age he has lain in hiding or sleep while his master's power waned. But now he is grown more fell than ever. Yet it was foretold that he should be overthrown, in the end, by one young and gallant. But maybe that lies far in the future.'

He hears about Frodo and Sam. Also how Faramir crossed from Tol Varad (the Defended Isle) [> Men Falros] with three companions, and came on horse. The rest of the 'task force' he had despatched to the Pelennor Gate.

Last half of chapter must deal with situation after taking of Pelennor, the battle of Pelennor and the fall of the Gate.[4]

The draft continues with 'And now the swooping dark shadows were aware of the newcomer' (RK p. 83), and again the final form is closely approached, if with rougher and less full expression, through the coming of Faramir with Gandalf to the Citadel, his wonderment at seeing Pippin, and his story told in Denethor's private chamber. Only Pippin's emotion when he first saw Faramir was at this time different from the form in RK (pp. 83–4): the passage 'Here was one with an air

THE SIEGE OF GONDOR   327

of high nobility such as Aragorn at times revealed ...' is lacking (and remains absent in the following fair copy manuscript).

From the point where Faramir reached the story of his meeting with Frodo and Sam I give the draft text in full, for though in many respects it closely approaches that of RK there are also many differences, and some are very noteworthy.

As the tale of his meeting with Frodo and Sam was unfolded, Pippin became aware that Gandalf's hands were trembling as they clutched the carven wood; white they seemed now and very old, and as he looked at them suddenly with a thrill of fear he knew that Gandalf – Gandalf himself was afraid, mastering a great dread, and not yet daring to speak. At last when Faramir told how he had parted with the travellers and that they were resolved to take the road to Kirith Ungol his voice fell, and he shook his head and sighed. But Gandalf sprang up. 'Kirith Ungol and Morghul Vale,' he cried. 'The time, Faramir. When was this, do you say? Tell me, tell me. When did you part with them? When would they reach the Morghul Vale? When did this darkness begin? Do you not see – that it may be a sign that all is indeed lost?'

'I spoke with them yestermorn,'[5] said Faramir. 'It is nigh on [20 >] 7 leagues from Henneth Annûn to the road that runs from M[inas Morghul] to Osgiliath, [and from the nearest point up that road west [sic] of our landing place it is 5 or 6 leagues to the Vale of Dread >] and if they went straight southward then they would find the road some 5 or 6 leagues west of the Vale of Dread. But the darkness came soon; I deem [?under cover] of that very night, long ere they could reach the vale. Indeed I see your fear; but it is clear to me that the Enemy had long planned this war, and the hour was already determined and nought to do with the errand of the travellers.'

Gandalf paced up and down. 'Yesterday morn?' he said. 'Then you have been swift. How far hence is the place where you parted?'

'Maybe 75 leagues[6] as bird flies,' said Faramir. 'But I *am* swift. Yestereve I lay at Men Falros, the isle in the river northward which we hold in defence, and on the hither bank we keep horses. As the darkness drew on I saw that haste was needed. So I rode hither with the four men that could be horsed, and sent the rest of my company to strengthen the guard at the fords of Osgiliath. Have I done ill?'

'Ill!' said Denethor, and suddenly his eyes blazed. 'Why do

328   THE WAR OF THE RING

you ask? Do you need my judgement? Your bearing is lowly as is fitting, but it is long since you turned from your own way at my counsel. You have spoken skilfully and discreetly, but have I not seen your eyes fixed on Mithrandir, seeking to learn how much you should say? He has your heart in keeping.

'My son, your father is old, but he is not yet a dotard. I can see and hear as was my wont, and not much of what you have left unsaid or half said is now hidden. I know the answer to the riddling words and to other riddles besides. Now I understand the ...[7] of Boromir and his [?death].'

'If you [are] angry, father,' said Faramir, 'tell me what other courses you would have had me take.'

'You have done as I should have expected, for I know you well,' said Denethor. 'Ever your desire is to be lordly and generous as a king of old – gracious and gentle. And that well befits men of high lineage who sit in power amid peace. But in these black hours gentleness may be bought with death.'

'So be it,' said Faramir.

'So be it,' said Denethor; 'but not by your death only. The death also of your father and of all your people whom it will be your part to rule ere long – now Boromir is no more.' He paused, clutching his [?wand].

'Do you wish then,' said Faramir, 'that our places had been exchanged?'

'Yes, I wish that indeed,' said Denethor. 'Or no,' and then he shook his head; and rising suddenly laid his hand on his son's shoulder. 'Do not judge me harshly, my son,' he said, 'or think that I am harsh. Love is not blind. I knew your brother also. I would wish only that he had been in your place, if I were sure of one thing.'

'And what is that, my father?'

'That he was as strong in heart as you, and as trustworthy. That taking this thing he had brought it to me, and not fallen under thraldom. For Faramir, and you Mithrandir, amid all your far flung policies, there is another way that is not yours nor Boromir's. It is one thing to take and wield this power for one's own victory – you, Mithrandir, may think what you will of me –'

'What I think of you is at least one part of my mind that you do not seem to have read,' said Gandalf.

'As you will, but I have in this as much wisdom as yourself,' said Denethor. 'I would not use it. On the other hand, at this

THE SIEGE OF GONDOR

329

hour to send the bearer, and such a one, helpless into Mordor itself, or as my son to let him go with that burden to Kirith Ungol, that also seems to me folly patent.'

'What then is wisdom?' said Gandalf.

'To do neither,' answered Denethor. 'Certainly not to risk the maker recovering it to our final ruin. To keep it – hidden, deep hidden, yet not used – hidden beyond his grasp until at last [?either] he wins all by war and we are dead.[8] Would that I had that thing now: in the deep chambers of this citadel, and then we should not shake with dread ...'

The remainder of the conversation between Gandalf and Denethor reaches effectively the form in RK, p. 87 (but Gandalf says: 'had you taken this thing by force or daunting you would not have escaped'; 'if you had received this thing, it would have overthrown you', RK). The episode ends thus in the draft:

He turned to Faramir. 'What news from the garrison at Osgiliath?'

'I have sent the company from Ithilien to strengthen it, as I said,' replied Faramir. 'It will be there, I think, that the first assault will fall.'

He rose, and suddenly he swayed and leant upon his father. 'You are weary, my son,' said Denethor. 'You have not spoken of your ride from Men Falros – and the dreadful wings.'

'I do not wish to,' said Faramir.

'Then do not so,' said Denethor. 'Go now to sleep, and think that such things shall not come here within shot of our bows – not this night at least. Tomorrow will need new counsels.'

Gandalf's talk with Pippin after they returned to their lodging as it stands in RK (pp. 88–9) was closely approached here,[9] and I cite only one brief passage:

'... But in truth I believe that the news that Faramir brings has more hope in it than seemed at first. For if Frodo was still so far away yestermorn, then that which I hoped might be has probably happened. The Enemy has made war in haste *without* the Ring and thinking that it is with us. And even if all goes as he plans, and it will not if I can prevent it, he will have his eyes in many places, far from his own land. There is a gleam of hope there. So I told Aragorn when we rode to Rohan.[10] But still, I did not expect it so soon. Something else has happened to stir him.'

330   THE WAR OF THE RING

The draft text now races towards its more and more illegible conclusion. Some passages were added in ink, and these I include, marking them as such, since they clearly belong to much the same time. The last section opens with 'The next day came like a brown dusk' (RK p. 89), and continues very much as in the final text as far as the departure of Faramir to Osgiliath and the mutterings against Denethor.

'The Lord drives his son too hard, and now he must do duty for the one that is dead as well.' [*Added in ink:* But in truth Faramir went at his own will, and he it was that most swayed the council of the captains.][11] The council of the Lord had decided that with the threat in the South their force was too weak to make any stroke of war on their own part. They must man the defences and wait. Yet ever Faramir had urged that their outer defences must not be abandoned, and the River was the one that the Enemy should buy most dearly. It could not be crossed by a great host north of Men Falros because of the marshes, and away south in Lebennin it became too broad without many boats. So now he was gone again, taking such few men as Denethor would spare to strengthen the force that held the western ruins of Osgiliath. [*Added in ink:* 'But hold not too long so far afield,' said Denethor as he went out. 'Though you slay ten times your number at the crossing, the Enemy has more to spare. And your retreat will be hazardous. And do not forget that ... danger in the North. Not one army only will be sent at this time from the Black Gate.']

Hardly had he gone when a rider came in reporting that a host was approaching and ... had reached East Osgiliath. [*Added in ink:* and a Black Captain of great terror [?came] there out of Minas Morghul.] With that ominous news ended Pippin's third day in the Tower.

The next day the darkness, though perhaps little more, weighed yet heavier on men's minds, and it seemed that slowly fear grew. Late in the day evil news was brought by riders. The passage of the Anduin had been won. Faramir was retreating to the Pelennor Wall and the fort[s] that guarded the entrance of the causeway into the townlands; but he could not hold them long. He was much outnumbered and had 4 leagues or more of open land to cross with few defences when he must give back again.

'Mithrandir's help fails now,' said some. For Gandalf had ridden down to Osgiliath at Faramir's side.[12] But others said

THE SIEGE OF GONDOR　　　　331

'Nay, he has never given any, not of such a kind. He is not a captain of war.'

But late that night he returned riding with the last wains filled with wounded men. 'They have paid dearly for the causeway,' he said, 'although they had prepared all things well. They have been building barges and boats secretly in East Osgiliath to the ruin of Ithilien's trees. But the river is now half choked with them. But he has come whom I feared.' 'Not the Dark Lord,' cried Pippin. 'No, he will not come except in triumph,' said Gandalf. 'He wields others as his weapons. I speak of one whom you have met. The Wizard King, captain of those you called the Black Riders. Most fell of all the servants of the Dark Tower. But he has not [*struck out (?)*: yet] taken to winged steeds. [In him I am not overmatched, and yet still I am matched, for he was a member of our order before evil took him.][13] Now his fury and malice are grown to the full, and men fly before him. [*Written in ink at the head of the page*: But the Wizard King has not shown himself. He wields far behind a great fear that will drive his soldiers whither he will, even to cast themselves into the River that others [?can] walk on their bodies. But he will come forth yet.]'

So the storm broke at last.

The next day the causeway fort[s] fell and Faramir began his desperate retreat across the Pelennor, [*in ink, replacing a passage in pencil*: the enemy pouring through the wall behind and sweeping away the ... rearguard. Fires glowing red in the mist could be seen far off, and once and again [a] red flash and then slowly a dull rumble would come rolling across the darkened fields. The ... were destroying the wall and blasting great breaches in it so that they could enter at any point. Soon the tide of war [?would cross]. The companies of Gondor could be seen [?hastening] back. And with that out of the][14] And now the Nazgûl [?stooped again] and the retreat became a rout, and [?many] men threw away spear and shield and sword and ran shrieking, or flung themselves to the ground and were trampled.

Then there was a sortie from the city led by the Prince of Dol Amroth kinsman of Faramir and his folk, and Gandalf at his side. In the [?notch] of time they came up, and [?two] miles from the city drove back the enemy, making great slaughter, for the enemy cavalry were [?few] and [?little] ...; the Nazgûl [?would (not) stand] the onslaught of Gandalf, for their Captain was not with them.

332   THE WAR OF THE RING

So now the City prepared for a last siege. The Pelennor wall was abandoned, and all that could be [?withdrawn] behind the gates. Orcs and [?wild horsemen] roam[ed] the townlands lighting the black night with fires, and the more bold rode within earshot of watchers on the walls, crying with hideous voices, and many bore upon their spears the heads of men they had slain and hewn.

Here the draft C ends. It was followed by a fair copy manuscript ('D'), in which the text of RK was very largely achieved: but it took a great deal of further work to reach it. This manuscript can be seen as divided roughly between the part that was based on C, and the part that extended beyond the point where C ended. Like the draft, it is numbered 'XLVI', but has no title; and the chapter again begins with the words 'It had been dark all day.'

In the first part it is notable that while my father went to great pains with the detail of expression, and clearly intended it to stand, in all those passages in which Denethor showed himself less coldly obdurate and hostile to Faramir than he became in *The Return of the King* the original draft was followed closely. His sudden softening in response to Faramir's question 'Do you wish then that our places had been exchanged?' (p. 328) remains:

'Yes, I wish that indeed,' said Denethor. 'Or no.' And then he shook his head, and rising swiftly he laid his hand upon his son's bowed head. 'Do not judge me harshly, my son,' he said quietly, 'or believe me more harsh than I am. I knew your brother well also. Love is not blind. I could wish that Boromir had been at Henneth Annûn when this thing came there, only if I were sure of one thing.'

'Sure of what, my father?'

'That he was as strong in heart and selfless as you, my son. That taking this thing he would have brought it here and surrendered it, and not fallen swiftly under its thraldom. For, Faramir – and you too, Mithrandir, amid all your wide webs and policies – there is a third way, that is neither the folly of wizards nor the lust of warriors. ...'

It is certain that there was no element of embittered banter in these words, 'That he was as strong in heart and selfless as you, my son.' Denethor was coldly watchful as always of those he spoke to, but he expressed the true bearing of his mind. His gentler good-night to Faramir, with a suggestion of a comforting word (p. 329), remains; and in this brief passage it can be seen how Denethor's harshness towards Faramir was enforced in later revision by the slightest of

THE SIEGE OF GONDOR   333

touches: as in the movement from 'You are weary, my son' to 'You are weary, I see.'

Again, in the debate on the following day (p. 330), it is still Faramir who argues that an attempt must be made to hold the outer defences at the line of the Anduin (but so far does the new writing go towards the actual words of RK (pp. 89–90) that when my father came to revise the passage he had little more to do than to give the speeches to different speakers). In this version the speech made by Prince Imrahil (RK p. 90), warning of another host that may come from Mordor, is given to Gandalf, and it is Faramir who is adamant and concludes the debate with words that afterwards became his father's:

'Much must be risked in war,' said Faramir. 'But I will not yield the River and the fields of Pelennor unfought, unless my father commands me beyond denial.'

'I do not,' said Denethor. 'Farewell, and may your judgement prove just: at least so much that I may see you again. Farewell!'

When he rejected this account of what happened at that meeting of the council my father wrote in the margin of the page: 'This must be altered to make Faramir only go to please his father against his own counsel and to "take Boromir's place".' And on a slip of paper he wrote a brief statement of how, and why, the existing portrayal of Denethor's relations with Faramir must be changed:

The early conversation of Faramir and his father and motives must be altered. Denethor must be *harsh*. He must say he did wish Boromir had been at Henneth Annûn – for he *would* have been loyal to his father and brought him the Ring. (Gandalf may correct this.) Faramir grieved but patient. Then Denethor must be all for holding Osgiliath 'like Boromir did', while Faramir (and Gandalf?) are against it, using the arguments previously given to Denethor. At length in submission, but proudly, to please his father and show him that not only Boromir was brave [he] accepts the command at Osgiliath. Men in the City do not like it.

This will not only be truer to previous situation, but will explain Denethor's breaking up when Faramir is brought back *dying*, as it seems.

The first part of this passage was struck through, as far as 'Faramir grieved but patient', and the second part allowed to stand; but this was then rejected also. Finally the whole was marked with a tick, when my father at length decided that this was how it should in fact be.

Also on this slip is a note written independently: 'Something should

334   THE WAR OF THE RING

be said between Gandalf and Pippin about the scene between Faramir and his father', but this suggestion was not taken up.

Not only in these passages, but in almost all the points where the draft C differed from RK, the manuscript D, as my father first wrote it, retained his first conceptions.[15] When (in relation to further progress in the narrative) the very substantial alterations to this part of the chapter in D were carried out I cannot say for certain. After this, the text as it stands in RK was present in all essentials; but at this stage my father was still uncertain whether or not to adopt the 'longer opening', as he called it, in which the chapter opens with Gandalf's waking Pippin in their lodging (see pp. 324–5).[16]

Drafting for the latter part of the chapter is not as coherent and continuous as it is for the former. My impression is that having written the fair copy manuscript D on the basis of the draft C so far as it went, or so far as it usefully went, my father then simply went on with it, writing sections of draft *pari passu* with progress on the fair copy, which was itself in places the primary composition. There is no way of knowing over how long a period all this work was spread.

The last part of C, from 'The next day the darkness, though perhaps little more, weighed yet heavier on men's minds' (p. 330), where the draft text became very cursory and rushed, was developed to the form in RK (pp. 91 ff.): Gandalf does not now ride down to Osgiliath with Faramir, and the account of the barge-building in East Osgiliath and the fear of the Black Captain is given by the messenger; it is only at this news that Gandalf leaves the City, returning at mid-morning on the next day with the wains bearing the wounded, and there follows his conversation with Denethor (RK pp. 91–3), here set 'in a high chamber near the summit of the White Tower'. In this all is almost as in the final form; but Denethor, revealing the mail in which he was clad beneath his long cloak, says nothing of it (he does not reveal that he wears it night and day), and Gandalf still as in the draft (p. 331) reminds Pippin who the Black Captain is: 'You have met him, Peregrin son of Paladin, though then he was far from home, veiled to your eyes, when he stalked the Ringbearer. Now he is come forth in power again, growing as his Master grows.' Gandalf now names him 'King of Angmar long ago', and this is the first appearance of the conception of the Kingdom of Angmar in the texts of *The Lord of the Rings*. To Denethor's 'Or can it be that you have withdrawn because you are overmastered?' (causing Pippin to fear that 'Gandalf would be stung to sudden wrath') the wizard answers 'lightly' ('softly' in RK); and after 'But our trial of strength is not come yet' he recalls a prophecy concerning the fate of the Lord of the Nazgûl different from that in the brief outline given on p. 326:

'. . . And if words spoken of old come true, he is not doomed to

THE SIEGE OF GONDOR   335

fall before warrior or wise [> men of war or wisdom]; but in the hour of his victory to be overthrown by one who has never slain a man [> by one who has slain no living thing]. ...'

In RK this becomes: 'not by the hand of man shall he fall, and hidden from the Wise is the doom that awaits him' (cf. RK p. 116). At the end of this conversation Denethor says: 'Some have unjustly accused you, Mithrandir, of delighting to bear ill news'; before 'unjustly' my father pencilled 'no doubt', but afterwards removed both qualifications.

For all the story of the sortie for the rescue of Faramir and the out-companies and the mounting of the siege there is preliminary drafting, in which almost all features of the final narrative were already present.[17] In the fair copy there is a remarkable addition pencilled in to the description of the Nazgûl circling over the City on the first day of the siege:

The Nazgûl came once more, slaves of the Nine Rings, and to each, since now they were utterly subject to his will, their Lord had given again that ring of power that he had used of old.

This survived into the first typescript, where it was afterwards replaced by the words in RK (p. 97): 'The Nazgûl came again, and as their Dark Lord now grew and put forth his strength, so their voices, which uttered only his will and his malice, were filled with evil and horror.'

In initial drafting for the last part of the chapter the central story of Denethor's madness can be seen emerging as my father wrote (torrentially, with scarcely-formed letters).

And Faramir lay in his chamber wandering in fever, dying as it was said, while his father sat beside him and heeded little the ending of the defence. It seemed to Pippin, who often watched by his side or at the door, that at last something had snapped in the proud will of Denethor: whether grief at the harsh words he spoke before Faramir rode out,[18] or the bitter thought that whatever now should happen in the war, his line too was ending, and even the House of the Stewards would fail, and a lesser house rule the last remnant of the kings of men.

So it was that without word spoken or any commission from the Lord, Gandalf took command of the defence. Wherever he came men's hearts were lifted and the winged shadows passed from memory. Tirelessly he went from Citadel to the Gate, from north to south about the wall, and yet – when he had gone the shadow seemed to close on men again, and vain it seemed to resist, to wait there for cold sword or cruel hunger [*sic*].

336   THE WAR OF THE RING

And so they passed out of a dim day of fear to the shadow of desperate night. Fire now raged in the lowest circle of the City. The garrison on the walls was well nigh cut off, those that indeed had not already fled. And then in the middle night the assault was loosed.

[Messengers came to the high tower and Denethor looked at them. 'The [?outer] circle is burning, lord,' they said, 'men are flying from the walls.' 'Why?' said Denethor. 'It is well to burn soon than late. I will go now to my own pyre. Farewell, Peregrin son of Paladin, your service has been short. I release you from it, unless you would still use your sword in defence of what is lost. Go now if you will to him that brought you here, to your death.'

He rose and bidding men take up Faramir's bed and follow him left the White Tower and paced slowly, pausing only for a moment at the ... tree, passed out of the Citadel, and going laid himself in the house of tombs under the shadow of Mindolluin with Pippin by his side.]

This passage that I have enclosed in square brackets was an addition to the manuscript, but it can be seen clearly from the manuscript that my father inserted it while he was actually writing the description of the black horseman and the destruction of the Gate. A later note scribbled against the passage reads: 'Pippin follows the cortège until it enters the tombs and then flies down in search of Gandalf. Meets Berithil and together they go through the city. Pippin arrives in time to see Gandalf and the Sorcerer King.'

The vanguard passed over narrow ways between the trenches and suffered loss where they bunched, but too few archers left on the walls. [?Front of war] not in the north or south, but a great weight came to the gate. The ground was choked with bodies but still they came on.

There Gandalf stood. And then over the hill in the flare of the fire a great Black Horseman came. For a moment he ... halted menacing, and lifted up a great ... sword red to the hilt. Fear fell on all .... Then great rams went on before, but the steel only shook and boomed. The Black Captain ..... lifted again his hand crying in a dreadful voice. In some forgotten tongue he spoke crying aloud words of power and terror. Thrice the rams boomed. Thrice he cried, and then suddenly the gate as if stricken by some blast burst [?asunder], and a great flash as of lightning, burst and fell, and in rode the Lord of the Nazgûl. But there waiting still before the gate sat Gandalf, and Shadowfax

THE SIEGE OF GONDOR

337

alone among the free horses of the earth did not [?quail] but stood rooted as an image of grey marble.

'You cannot pass,' said Gandalf. 'Go back to the black abyss prepared for you, and fall into nothingness that shall come upon your Master.'

The Black Rider [?lay *for* laid] back his hood and ..... crown that sat upon no visible head save only for the light of his pale eyes.[19] A deadly laughter [?rang] out.

'Old fool,' he said. 'Old fool. Do you not know death when you see it? Die now and curse in vain. This is my hour of victory.' And with that he lifted his great sword. [*Added:* And then suddenly his hand wavered and fell and it seemed that he shrank.] And [> For] in that very moment away behind in some courtyard of the city a cock crowed. Shrill and clear he crowed, recking nothing of wizardry or war, welcoming only the morning that far above the shadows of death was now coming once again.

And as if in answer there came from far away another note. Horns, horns, horns, great horns of the north wildly blowing. The riders of Rohan had come at last.

From short passages of further drafting, either separate or pencilled on the fair copy manuscript itself and then overwritten, the final form of the story was largely reached, and there is nothing to notice in this development. But as the fair copy was left to stand there remained a few differences from RK. The account of Pippin's watching beside Denethor and Faramir remained essentially as it was in the initial draft (see p. 335), where Denethor himself does not speak, and the cause of his devastation is expressed as a surmise of Pippin's: 'Grief maybe had wrought it: grief at the harsh words he spoke when Faramir returned [> remorse for the harsh words he spoke that sent Faramir out into needless peril],[20] and the bitter thought that, whatever might now betide in war, woe or victory beyond all hope, his line too was ending ...'

The description of the journey of the bearers of Faramir, with Denethor and Pippin, after they had passed through the gate of the Citadel, begins thus (cf. RK pp. 99–100):

Turning westward they came at last to a dark door, used only by the Lord of the City, for it opened on a winding way that descended by many curves down to the narrow land under the shadow of Mindolluin's precipice where stood the tombs of the Kings and their Stewards.

But from this point the text reaches effectively the form in RK in the

338   THE WAR OF THE RING

description of the descent to Rath Dínen, the Silent Street.[21] The passage just cited reappears in the first typescript of the chapter, with the addition that the door was 'in the rearward wall of the sixth circle'; but the final text was entered on the typescript in a rider, and here the name of the door appears: '*Fenn Fornen*, for it was kept ever shut save at times of funeral'.[22]

Pippin's encounter with Berithil as he fled from the horrifying scene in Rath Dínen begins differently from its form in RK (p. 101):

'Whither do you run, Master Peregrin?' he said.

'To find Mithrandir,' answered Pippin.

'Then have you left the service of the Lord so soon? We hold that it is the duty of those who wear the black and silver to remain in the Citadel of Gondor whatever else may chance, until death release them.'[23]

'Or the Lord,' said Pippin.

'Then he sends you on some errand that I should not hinder. But tell me, if you may, what goes forward? ...'

The text then continues as in RK; but Pippin was still permitted at this fateful moment a more Shire-like turn of phrase: 'Something is wrong with him', he says of Denethor (where in RK he says 'He is fey and dangerous'), and he tells Berithil: 'Don't bother about "orders" and all that!'

Lastly, it is worth remarking that the importance of the Prince of Dol Amroth was enlarged as the chapter evolved. In the draft C Pippin did not name him among the 'great persons' present at the council held before Faramir's return from Henneth Annûn (p. 326), and this remains the case in the fair copy D. The Prince's intervention in the deliberations before Faramir went to Osgiliath is absent in the first version of D (p. 333): it enters with the revision (where he is called 'Dol Amroth'). His bringing of Faramir to the White Tower was never added to D (note 17). And in drafting for the latter part of D he is not mentioned as accompanying Gandalf in his tireless permabulation of the City (p. 335) – the passage in which he is introduced here (RK p. 98), with the reference to there being 'Elvish blood in the veins of that folk, for the people of Nimrodel dwelt once in that land long ago', was in fact written into the D manuscript as an afterthought soon after my father had passed this point. At this stage the name *Imrahil* had still not emerged (see pp. 287, 289).

NOTES

1 The account of Pippin's livery is in every point as described in RK, save only that the silver star on the circlet of his helm is not mentioned.

THE SIEGE OF GONDOR   339

2   *Berethil* is clearly written so, *Berithil* in the first typescript of
    'Minas Tirith', p. 288; after further occurrences of *Berethil*,
    however, *Berithil* reappears.
3   *Ramas Coren*: earlier name of the Wall about the Pelennor (p.
    288).
4   I have inverted the order of the last two paragraphs of this
    outline.
5   On this and subsequent references to days and times see the Note
    on Chronology below.
6   75 leagues from Henneth Annûn to Minas Tirith: 25 leagues in
    RK. The distance on my father's large map of Rohan, Gondor
    and Mordor which I redrew in *The Return of the King* is about
    23 leagues. The figure 75 in the present text is however perfectly
    clear, although the following text D, directly based here on the
    present draft, has 25. On the First Map the distance can be very
    roughly computed to something in the region of 75 miles, and I
    suppose that my father, working very fast, simply wrote 'leagues'
    for 'miles'.
7   The illegible word seems to begin with *d* and might be *duty*, but
    the writing is so unclear that it might be *dealings*, or some other
    word. In the following text, where Denethor still says that he
    knows 'the answer to the riddling words', the sentence is replaced
    by 'Poor Boromir!' > 'Alas for Boromir!'
8   The word I have given as '[?either]' is in fact hard to interpret in
    any other way. Possibly the sentence was left unfinished. The
    following text has the reading of RK (p. 87), 'save by a victory
    so final that what then befell would not trouble us, the dead
    [> being dead].'
9   Pippin says of Frodo: 'Just think, he was alive at least up to this
    time yesterday, and not so far away across the River!' I do not
    know why Pippin should say 'at least up to this time yesterday',
    since Faramir had said that he had parted with Frodo and Sam
    'yestermorn'. The following text has: 'he was alive and talking to
    Faramir only yesterday'. — In Gandalf's reckoning of the time he
    says: 'Let me see, he would discover some four days ago that we
    had thrown down Saruman – and had the Stone,' where RK has
    'five'. See the Note on Chronology below.
10 The following text has: 'So I told Aragorn, on the day when we
    met again in Fangorn and rode down to Rohan.' The reference is
    to 'The White Rider', TT p. 100: 'For imagining war he has let
    loose war, believing that he has no time to waste ... So the
    forces that he has long been preparing he is now setting in
    motion, sooner than he intended.'
11 Cf. the original outline on p. 326: 'Pippin ... hears Faramir
    accept orders to go to Osgiliath.'
12 In RK (p. 91) Gandalf does not leave the City until news comes of
    Faramir's retreat to the wall of the Pelennor.

340   THE WAR OF THE RING

13   The square brackets are in the original.
14   Here the passage in ink breaks off; the sentence would have continued with the sortie from the Gate.
15   I note here a few details. All the references to date remain as in the draft. The distance from Henneth Annûn to Minas Tirith becomes 25 leagues (see note 6). Peregrin's friend is Berithil (see note 2; Beregond only entered at a late stage). The island in Anduin receives momentarily the name *Cairros*, changed immediately to *Andros* (and later to *Cair Andros*).
16   This appears from a note written on a slip in which the existing opening of the chapter (see p. 325) was rewritten. In this revision was introduced the fact of Berithil's having just returned from an errand over the Pelennor 'to *Bered Ondrath*, the guard-towers upon the entrance of the causeway'. This name was subsequently lost.
17   I notice here two features in which the narrative differed from that in RK, and a few other details. The account of Prince Imrahil's bringing Faramir to Denethor in the White Tower, and the light seen flickering in the high chamber (RK pp. 94–5), is absent not only from the initial draft but also from the fair copy D; and the last men to come into the City before the Gate was shut (RK p. 95), reporting the 'endless companies of men of a new sort' who held the northward road or had gone on into Anórien, are not said to be led by Ingold in the draft.
     In both draft and fair copy the 'wild Southron men' of RK (p. 95) are 'wild eastlanders'. The wall of the Pelennor is still called Ramas Coren in both texts where RK has 'the Rammas' (p. 95), with '(? Corramas)' added at the time of writing. In the sentence (RK p. 94) 'And in his arms before him on his horse he [the Prince] bore the body of his kinsman, Faramir son of Denethor' a word is written above 'kinsman' in the draft text which looks like 'cousin'; this seems to have been struck through. The genealogy of the house of Dol Amroth is found in LR, Appendix A (I, iv): Denethor married (late) Finduilas daughter of Adrahil of Dol Amroth. Elsewhere it is recorded (see *Unfinished Tales* p. 248) that Adrahil was the father of Imrahil, so that Imrahil (brother of Finduilas) was Faramir's uncle.
18   This is curious, because in the D manuscript as written (when it was Faramir who imposed his own will on the council in his demand to lead a force to Osgiliath) Denethor (as reported) spoke no harsh words to Faramir, and indeed bade him farewell with the words 'may your judgement prove just: at least so much that I may see you again' (p. 333). This may suggest that the later version of this episode was already in being, in which Denethor says: 'But I will not yield the River and the fields of the Pelennor unfought – not if there is a captain that will do my will, and quail

THE SIEGE OF GONDOR

341

not' (cf. RK p. 90).

19 The handwriting here is such that many words could not be interpreted at all in isolation, without context or other clues, but 'save only for the light of his pale eyes' seems tolerably clear. Cf. p. 365.

20 See note 18.

21 The name *Rath Dínen* appears on the plan of the city reproduced on p. 290 from the first typescript of the chapter 'Minas Tirith', where however the conception of it was decisively different.

22 Other names are written beside this rider: *Fenn Forn the Closed Door, Fenn uiforn the Ever Closed*, also *Uidavnen* and the word *davnan.*

23 These words, slightly changed, were afterwards spoken by Gandalf to Pippin at the beginning of the chapter 'The Pyre of Denethor' (RK p. 126).

Note on the Chronology

The new 'calendar' (i.e. with dates in March instead of February, see p. 325) can be equated with the old from the date of the first day of the Darkness, Pippin's second day in Minas Tirith, which had been February 7 and is now March 9. I presume that my father calculated this on the basis that all months now had thirty days. Thus proceeding from 26 December = 26 January, the day of Frodo's flight (see VII.368), there are the following equations: December 31 = February 1; January 1 = February 2; January 29 = February 30; January 30 = March 1; January 31 = March 2; February 1 = March 3.

The chronology, however, is still not that of LR (see *The Tale of Years*). At this stage Faramir says (on 9 March) that he had parted with Frodo and Sam at Henneth Annûn on the morning of the previous day ('in the morning two days ago', RK p. 85), and he says that the Darkness began to come over that night ('yestereve', RK). The relation between the two chronologies can be set out thus:

	The present chronology	*The chronology in LR*
March 7	Frodo taken by Faramir to Henneth Annûn.	Frodo taken by Faramir to Henneth Annûn.
March 8	Frodo leaves Henneth Annûn. Gandalf reaches Minas Tirith.	Frodo leaves Henneth Annûn.

342 THE WAR OF THE RING

March 9	The Dawnless Day. Faramir rescued on the Pelennor. Frodo reaches the Cross-roads.	Gandalf reaches Minas Tirith.
March 10	Faramir goes to Osgiliath.	The Dawnless Day. Faramir rescued on the Pelennor. Frodo reaches the Cross-roads.
March 11	Faramir retreats to the Causeway Forts.	Faramir goes to Osgiliath.

Thus the horns of the Rohirrim are heard at cockcrow on March 14 in the chronology of the present texts, but on March 15 in LR. At this stage Frodo still takes two days, not three, from Henneth Annûn to the Cross-roads (see p. 182), and Gandalf takes three nights, not four, from Dol Baran to Minas Tirith (see p. 264 note 3).

Gandalf, speaking to Pippin on the night of 9 March, reckons that it was now four days since Sauron discovered 'that we had thrown down Saruman – and had the Stone' (note 9), whereas in RK (p. 88), on 10 March, he reckons the time as five days. He is referring to 5 March (= February 3), and the difference is again due to the longer time taken on his ride.

VII

THE RIDE OF THE ROHIRRIM

A single manuscript page ('**A**') gives an outline for the narrative of this chapter. It was written in ink over a pencilled text – which at this stage had again and unhappily become my father's frequent method of composition. The figures introducing each paragraph are of course the dates in the month of March.

(9)   Théoden leaves Dunharrow on 9th. He rides 25 miles to Edoras. After a halt there and reviewing the garrison he sets out East. At first they go slow to conserve strength. Merry is given leave to go to war, and is assigned to ride with one of the king's guard: the one who seems young and light and so less burden to his steed. He is silent and never speaks. They halt not far from where the Snowbourn runs into Entwash 25 miles from Edoras – they bivouac in dense willow-thickets.

(10)   They ride steadily and halt now nearly 100 miles from Edoras.

(11)   They ride again. When 125 miles out about midday fugitives and late joining riders bring news of attacks in North, and of forces crossing above Sarn Gebir[1] into the Wold of Rohan. Théoden decides that he has left sufficient garrison (or all possible) in his strong places, and must ride on: soon the marshes of Entwash mouth will cover his flank. They cross into Anórien (of Gondor) and camp under Halifirien (160 [miles]). Mysterious drums are heard in the woods and hills. Théoden resolves to ride warily, and sends out scouts.

(12)   They halt some 230 miles on at dusk (64 miles or a day's ride from Pelennor). They camp in the skirts of the Forest of Eilenach out of which rises Eilenach Beacon. Scouts return with the errand-riders of Minas Tirith (who had ridden ahead but found entrance closed). There is a great camp of enemy under [Amon Dîn >] Min Rimmon about [25 >] 50 miles west of the Pelennor or about [40 >] 14 miles further on:[2] Orcs are roving along the road. Dark men of Eilenach come in. They decide to push on by night. Suddenly they see fires ahead and hear cries. A great *hoom hom* is heard. Ents! Treebeard cries Merry. The enemy camp is in confusion. Dark men of Eilenach

344   THE WAR OF THE RING

have attacked it, and suddenly coming out of North after a victory over Orcs in Wold ([250 >] 225 miles) Treebeard and a company of Ents. The Rohirrim come round to rear [and] sweep the remnants away N.W. into marshes. They halt under Min Rimmon and take counsel of war.

(13) Morning of 13th. Scouts report that siege is now [?strait] and great fires and engines are all about walls. They ride about 20 miles and [?hide] in the woods and hills of Amon Dîn ready to move at night and attack with dawn.

(14) At dawn they charge. Rammas has been destroyed at this point.

At the foot of the page, in pencil, is a list of distances: *Eilenach* 215 (written beneath: 219); *Min Rimmon* 245 (written beneath: 246); *Amon Dîn* 270; *Rammas* 294; *Minas Tirith* 306.[3] Beside this list is a note: 'Camp just west of Min Rimmon (243 miles) on night of 12th.'

The names of the beacons in their final forms and final order (which I count eastwards from Edoras) had appeared long before in the abandoned opening C of 'Minas Tirith' (p. 233; repeated in the first text of the chapter), but now the order has been changed:

Early texts of 'Minas Tirith' and LR		The present text	
1	Halifirien	1	Halifirien
2	Calenhad	2	Calenhad
3	Min Rimmon	3	Erelas
4	Erelas	4	Nardol
5	Nardol	5	Eilenach
6	Eilenach	6	Min Rimmon
7	Amon Dîn	7	Amon Dîn

I can offer no explanation for this other than the obvious but not entirely convincing one that my father had misremembered the order as it stood in the 'Minas Tirith' text, and that afterwards, looking back through the papers, he returned to it.

So in the outline A the Rohirrim camped on the night of March 12 'in the skirts of the Forest of Eilenach out of which rises Eilenach Beacon', and here 'the dark men of Eilenach' enter the story, forerunners of the Woses or Wild Men of the Woods, though nothing is said of them other than that they attacked the enemy camp (the drumming in the hills is heard, however, from the camp under Halifirien on the previous night, March 11). Thus the Forest of Eilenach is the forerunner of the Druadan Forest, but Eilenach Beacon is the fifth, and beyond it are still Min Rimmon and Amon Dîn.

Treebeard and the Ents reappear, coming south 'after a victory over Orcs in the Wold', and clearly they play a part in the attack on the camp

THE RIDE OF THE ROHIRRIM 345

(I take it that the meaning of the text at this point is 'Dark men of Eilenach have attacked it, and so also have Treebeard and a company of Ents suddenly coming out of the North'). In the early outlines for Book V there are several references to the southward march of the Ents after the destruction of the Orcs on the Wold (see p. 255 and note 29), but these all specifically refer to their arrival (together with Elves from Lórien) *after* the siege of Minas Tirith had been broken: there has been no suggestion that they appeared earlier, in Anórien.

Merry is here 'given leave to go to war, and is assigned to ride with one of the king's guard: the one who seems young and light and so less burden to his steed.' This is presumably the story that my father had in mind at the end of 'Many Roads Lead Eastward' (see p. 318), where one among the guard, noticeably slighter in build (and certainly Éowyn), looked at Merry as the ride began from Dunharrow: this Rider would be *assigned* to carry the hobbit.

Two pages of pencilled text are hard to place since they are very largely illegible on account of subsequent overwriting in ink; but they are very noteworthy, since from what little can be read it is seen that my father was here developing the story of the coming of the Ents into Anórien from the outline just given. The narrative envisaged clearly ran into difficulties, and was decisively abandoned, without any repercussions in the development of the chapter; for this reason it seems most probable that they should be placed here. The ink overwriting that so obscured them bears no relation to the pencilled text beneath.[4]

On one of these pages (which I take to be the first in order since the arrival of Treebeard appears, whereas on the other he is already present) Treebeard's call of *hoom hom* (or something similar) is heard; 'Merry sprang up. "Treebeard!" he cried. Treebeard comes with good news. The Ents and the Huorns had ..... the invaders on the Wold and driven them into the River.' Fragments of the following sentence refer to rumour of the ride of the Rohirrim having reached the Ents, and to their great march southwards to aid the king. 'Friendship and reward the king offered. But he asked only leave when war was over to return to Fangorn and there be troubled by ..... For reward he would take .....'

No more than broken fragments can be discerned in the remainder of this page, but these suggest uncertainty of direction. 'They plan to divide into three. The Ents would come on the camp from the north first while the main host ...'; 'and so come down to the plain [?somewhat] behind the camp between it and the leaguer of the city'; 'Or remove the host of orc-men'; and later: 'In that case the wild men slay orcs but also turn against king. But the riders brush them aside and reach Amon Dîn ...'

The other page begins thus: 'But the wild men were nowhere to be seen. At the first sight of the Ents they had cried out shrieks of fear and

346   THE WAR OF THE RING

fled back to vanish into the hills ..... what dark and distant legends
out of [?elder] days held their minds enthralled none could say. But
Treebeard soon found for himself what he needed .... a [?pool]
under the side of Amon Dîn fed by a spring [?above]. There he stood
and [?laved] himself while the king and his captains held council under
the trees.' After '"Both ... and warriors are needed, lord," said
Éomer' follows: 'Some few at least must have escaped eastward to give
warning of our approach.' Does this refer to the Wild Men?

From the rest of this page scarcely anything useful can be gleaned,
but the sentence 'The wild men lead them again along hill-paths' is
clear; which is puzzling, since there seems not to be enough text
intervening to explain the reversal of the story just given.

Nothing more is found anywhere touching on the appearance of the
Ents in Anórien, and the reason for their disappearance can only be
guessed at. It seems to me possible that something on the following
lines may lie behind it. The vast armies at the disposal of Mordor
made it a certainty that a host would be dispatched beyond Minas
Tirith into Anórien in order to block any attempt from Rohan to come
to the aid of the city: this could be said to be a datum of the story. But
an assault on the orc-camp would necessarily constitute a major
episode, and my father wanted such an episode at this juncture no
more than did the Rohirrim. The Wild Men, who (as 'the dark men of
Eilenach') had entered in outline A as attackers of the orc-camp, found
their rôle in leading the Rohirrim by forgotten roads through the hills
known only to themselves, so that the orc-camp was entirely circum-
vented. The Ents therefore had no clear function left to them. This is of
course pure speculation; there are no notes found pertaining to the
question. But at any rate the explanation cannot be that my father had
come to feel (independently of the immediate story as it was emerging
here) that Treebeard should not appear again in person until the
reunited Company met him once more on the homeward journey: see
p. 361.

My father had great difficulty with the question of how Merry went
to Minas Tirith, and indeed with finding a satisfactory opening to the
chapter. The previous chapter in the narrative sequence ('Many Roads
Lead Eastwards') had ended with the host of the Rohirrim passing
down Harrowdale; now something must be told of the halt at Edoras
– but at the same time he would prefer to pass over the uneventful first
days of the ride and begin the chapter at a later point.

His first solution, in a very brief and very rough text ('B'), was to
open with the Riders halted on the third night (March 11) below the
Halifirien, where, as in the outline A, the mysterious drums are heard
in the hills, and to introduce the halt at Edoras as a retrospect of
Merry's as he reviewed his situation, lying under the trees in the
darkness.

THE RIDE OF THE ROHIRRIM   347

It was so dark that Merry could see nothing as he lay rolled in his blankets; but though it was an airless windless night all about was the soft whisper of endless dark trees. He lifted his head. There it was again, a sound like faint drums in the wooded hills and mountain-steps to the south, drums that stopped and seemed to be answered from other places. He wondered if the watchmen heard it. Though he could not see them he knew that all round him were companies upon companies of the Riders. He could smell the horses in the dark, and hear now and again their stamping and shifting on the soft needle-clad ground. They were bivouacked in the pinewoods that clustered about the dark Halifirien: a great hill, flat-topped, standing out from the [?main] range beside the road from Edoras on the borders of Anórien.

He was tired but could not sleep. He had ridden now for three days since the dark morning of the muster at Dunharrow, and at each halt the darkness seemed to deepen, and his heart and spirits to fall lower. There was now no song or speech on the way in all the great host of Rohan. At Edoras they had halted for a while and then at last he obtained the king's permission to go on to battle with him. He now wondered why. It was arranged that he was to ride before one of the king's guard, and it seemed that the young man whom he had noticed had claimed him, since he was lighter of build than the others, so that his steed was less burdened. At any rate as they rode forth at last from Edoras Merry had been helped up to this man's seat, and there he had [?sat] ... while men were riding, but never a word did his companion utter, at mounting or dismounting or on the way.

All the last part of this text (from 'At Edoras they had halted ...') was struck out, and the following substituted: 'and already he wondered why he had been so determined to come against [?even] the king's command. Not a word more since the first day had Grímhelm spoken [?whether] at mounting or dismounting or on the road.'

My father had come to the conclusion that Merry had *not* been given permission by Théoden to come with the host of Rohan to Minas Tirith; and he had decided also – perhaps for this reason – that the halt at Edoras had best be recounted in direct narrative. He therefore began a new opening for the chapter in another extremely rough manuscript ('C'), entitled 'The Ride of the Rohirrim':

The king came to Edoras in the gathering dark, though it was but noon. There he halted and said farewell to his golden hall

348 THE WAR OF THE RING

and the people of his house. Merry begged not to be parted from him.

'This is no journey for Stybba,' said Théoden. 'We ride to war, and in such battle as we hope to make what would you do, Master Holbytla, sworn swordthain though you are and greater of heart than of ... ?'

'As for that, who can tell?' answered Merry. 'And why did you take me as swordthain if I was to be left behind when my lord rides to war?'

'If the battle were here we would see how you bore yourself,' said Théoden, 'but it is 100 leagues or more to Mundbeorg[5] where Denethor is lord. And the first thing for my swordthain to do is to hear the commands of his lord.'

Merry went out unhappy and looked at the lines of horses. The companies were already being ordered for the start. Suddenly a Rider came up to him, and spoke softly in a whisper. 'Where will wants not, a way opens, say we,' he said. 'So have I found myself.' Merry [?looked] ... rider of the king's guard whom he noticed before. 'You wish to go where the lord of the Eorlingas goes?'

'I do,' said Merry. 'Then you shall ride before me,' said the Rider. 'Such good will shall not be wasted. Say nothing more, but come.'

'Thank you indeed, thank you sir – I do not know your name.'

'Do you not?' said the Rider softly. 'Then call me [Cyneferth >] Grímhelm.'[6]

(9) So it was that when the king set forth again before Grímhelm sat Meriadoc the hobbit, and his great grey steed made little of the burden, for Grímhelm was less in build than most of the guard though lithe and well-knit in shape. That [?evening] they camped in the willow thickets where Snowbourn ... into Entwash 12 leagues or more east of Edoras.

The text then tails off into scrawled and partly illegible notes about the next two days' journey: on the third day, with the date March 11 (cf. outline A, p. 343), 'men rode in joining the muster late, and they brought rumours of war in the North and of Orcs crossing into the Wold above Sarn Gebir'; to which news Éomer said: 'Too late to turn back or aside.'

It was now, as the name Grímhelm shows, that the conclusion of the text B, with the story that Merry rode with the king's permission, was rejected (p. 347).[7]

THE RIDE OF THE ROHIRRIM 349

My father evidently decided now (probably, as I have suggested, because he did not wish to treat each day of the ride from Edoras in consecutive narrative) that this passage, recounting the king's denial of Merry's request and Grímhelm's stepping secretly into the breach, had best be placed at the end of 'Many Roads Lead Eastward' ('The Muster of Rohan'); and the next text ('D')[8] was marked 'Place this at the end of Chapter II of Book V'. The alliterative song *From dark Dunharrow in the dim morning* had not yet arisen. The 'young rider of the guard' still names himself Grímhelm, but with an alternative *Derning*, and a further suggestion *Dernhelm*. The conclusion of the passage in RK (p. 78, the end of 'The Muster of Rohan') is now present, with mention of the Folde and the Fenmarch, but whereas in RK four beacon-hills are named after Halifirien (Calenhad, Min-Rimmon, Erelas, Nardol) here there are only three: Calenhad, Erelas, Nardol, with omission of Min-Rimmon (see p. 344).

Rough workings for *From dark Dunharrow in the dim morning* are found, and the song was then incorporated into a further text ('E')[9] ('to be added to Chapter II of Book V'). The Rider who bears Merry is here still called Grímhelm (with 'Dernhelm?' written beside); and four beacon-hills are now named, but still with the omission of Min-Rimmon: Calenhad, Erelas, Nardol, Eilenach (because, when this was written, Eilenach had already been passed when the story told in 'The Ride of the Rohirrim' begins).

Finally, the alliterative song with the following text was copied in a fine manuscript and attached to the typescript M of 'Many Roads Lead Eastward': here the song is all but in final form.[10] There are now no differences from RK in the conclusion of the earlier chapter, except that Dernhelm remains 'a young rider of the guard'.[11]

The development of the new opening of 'The Ride of the Rohirrim' (i.e., when the story of the halt at Edoras had been removed) is particularly hard to analyse. There is here no continuous primary text followed by a continuous second version: my father wrote in a series of overlapping and partly discontinuous stages, some of which are in pencil overwritten in ink. I shall not attempt here to describe this complex in detail, especially since much of it is repetition, as my father sought to find a satisfactory articulation of existing elements in the story.

In the earliest brief text of this new start to the chapter (in pencil, but largely legible despite the overwriting) the host of the Rohirrim is 'bivouacked in the pinewoods that clustered about Minrimmon Beacon'. Merry hears a sound like faint drums in the wooded hills. They had been riding for four days, and were now less than a day's ride from the walls of the Pelennor. Scouts sent ahead had returned with the errand-riders of Gondor and reported that Minas Tirith was besieged, that another host was holding the approach to the City, and

350   THE WAR OF THE RING

that a part of that force was marching west along the road. 'Suddenly
Merry heard the soft whisper of Dernhelm again. Not a word more
had he spoken since Edoras, either at mounting or dismounting or
upon the way. "Come!" he said. "We ride again by night. Battle comes
to meet us."' Here this text ends. It is clear that 'Minrimmon Beacon'
has now replaced 'Eilenach Beacon' of the outline A (p. 343);[12] and in
the ink text written over it (with the chapter number 'XLVII') Min
Rimmon Beacon is 'a tall hill standing up from the long ridges of the
forest of Taur-rimmon'.

In a second pencilled text, again overwritten but again largely
legible, the scouts report that the enemy host was encamped on the
road 'between Amon Dîn and the walls'. Dernhelm is now more
communicative, for when the night riding has begun Merry ventures
to put a question to him, and gets an answer. 'Drums, Dernhelm. Do
you hear them, or am I dreaming? Is that the enemy?' Dernhelm
replies very much as does Elfhelm the Marshal in RK (p. 105) after he
stumbled over Merry in the dark, though more briefly: 'It is the wild
men of the hills. In many wooded vales they live secretly, but most in
this region, remnants of the Dark Years. They go not to war for
Gondor or the Mark, and ask but to live wild. But now the darkness
troubles them and the coming of orcs: they fear lest the Dark Years be
come again. Let us be thankful. For they have offered service to
Théoden. They are now our guides.' Here this text ends in its turn.

Ink overwriting advances the story: Éothain 'captain of the guard'[13]
stumbles over Merry lying on the ground, and it is he who tells Merry
about the meaning of the drums: 'Those are not orc-drums. You hear
the wild men of the hills: so they talk together. In many wooded vales
of these regions they live few and secretly.' Éothain makes no mention
of the use of poisoned arrows by the Wild Men, and nothing is told
here of any colloquy with one of them. The text concludes (from the
end of Éothain's words to Merry):

'... Let us be thankful; for they have offered service to
Théoden. They have spied on the enemy, and will guide us, they
say, by cunning paths.'

'Where?' said Merry.

'That we shall learn ere long, I doubt not,' said Éothain. 'But I
must hasten. The guard is to lead a flank march, and I must
soon be ready.' He vanished in the dark, and at that moment
'Come,' said the soft voice of Dernhelm in Merry's ear. 'We ride
again. I am ready.'

Soon Merry found himself riding again, slowly, warily. The
guard led the way but beside each horse walked with long
strides strange shapes of men, hardly to be seen in the gloom,
and yet somehow Merry was reminded of the Púkel-men of

THE RIDE OF THE ROHIRRIM 351

Dunharrow. Guided by these unlooked for friends they turned away southward towards the hills, filing among the trees, and then turning again moved further along hidden tracks through narrow dales and over the shoulders of dark hills.

No words were spoken. Hours seemed to pass, and yet still the night held on.

A new draft in ink (the one that was written over and so obscured the pencilled text concerning the Ents and the Wild Men, p. 345) takes up at the point where the captain of the guard (here left unnamed and referred to as 'X') stumbles over Merry. He tells him that the Wild Men of the Woods 'still haunt Rimmon Forest, it is said'; he does not mention their poisoned arrows, but he says that 'even now one of their headmen is being taken to the king.' From here the story moves confidently into the conversation of the king and Éomer with the headman Ghân-buri-Ghân (so named unhesitatingly from his first appearance), near the end of which this text ends. Already in this draft the final form is very nearly achieved, with Ghân-buri-Ghân's names for the orcs (*gorgûn*), and for Minas Tirith (*Stonehouses*).[14] Of the ancient road made by the men of Gondor through the hills he says this:

'... They went to Eilenach with great wains. Forgotten now, but not by wild men. Paths in hills and behind hills. Long road runs still under tree and grass behind Rimmon down to Dîn, and so back to horsemen road.'

It is to be remembered that at this stage the Rohirrim were bivouacked in the forest of Taur-rimmon, out of which rose the tall hill of Min Rimmon Beacon, and that the order of the last three beacons was Eilenach, Min Rimmon, Amon Dîn (see p. 344). It is natural therefore that Ghân-buri-Ghân should speak of the old wain-road to Eilenach running 'behind Rimmon down to Dîn' (see below).

Turning now to the first completed text, this manuscript begins as a fair copy of the draft work already described, but for the latter part of the chapter (from the end of the conversation with Ghân-buri-Ghân) it is based variously on overwritten pencilled text and independent passages of preliminary drafting in ink. In this manuscript the chapter as it stands in RK was largely reached, and there are only relatively minor matters to mention. It is numbered 'XL.VII' and titled '(i) The Ride of the Rohirrim'; beside this my father wrote afterwards 'and the Battle of the Pelennor Field', then struck it out.

The Rohirrim are still camped in 'Taur-rimmon Forest' from which rises Min Rimmon beacon. Ghân-buri-Ghân tells of the wains that went to Eilenach passing 'through Rimmon', where he clearly means 'the forest of Rimmon'; and he speaks as in the draft of the lost road

352   THE WAR OF THE RING

that lies 'there behind Rimmon and down to Dîn'. Changes made to
the manuscript in these passages produced the text of RK (pp. 104,
106–7), but this development is rather puzzling. The host now lies in
the Druadan Forest out of which rises Eilenach Beacon; and Ghân-
buri-Ghân now says that the wains went 'through Druadan to
Rimmon'; but his words about the old road remain unchanged from
the draft, 'there behind Rimmon and down to Dîn'. If we suppose that
after the order of the beacons had been changed the ancient wain-road
went all the way to Min Rimmon (and the change of 'They went
through Rimmon to Eilenach' to 'They went through Druadan to
Rimmon' was not casually made: my father wrote *Rimmon* twice and
twice crossed it out before finally settling on this name), it nonetheless
seems strange that Ghân-buri-Ghân, in the Druadan Forest, should
say 'there behind Rimmon', since Min Rimmon was now the third
beacon, not the sixth, and some seventy-five miles to the west of
Eilenach.

The Rider who stumbles over Merry is now again named Éothain
(see p. 350), but he is now 'captain of Éomer's company (éored)'. By
subsequent correction he becomes 'Déorwin, chief of the king's
knights since Háma's death', and he speaks to Merry of 'the Druedain,
Wild Men of the Woods', who 'still haunt Druadan Forest, it is said.'
The name *Druedain* is not found in the published LR (in the present
manuscript it was afterwards replaced by *Woses*), but reappears in
Unfinished Tales. At a later stage, the Rider who fell over Merry and
cursed him for a tree-root became Elfhelm, while Déorwin (Déorwine)
survived in the story, still as chief of the king's knights, to be slain in
the Battle of the Pelennor Fields, his name remembered in the song of
the Mounds of Mundburg (RK pp. 120, 125). Elfhelm makes his first
appearance by correction to the present manuscript, taking over from
Éomer the speech beginning 'We need no further guides ...' (RK
p. 109): here he is described as 'one of the captains'. In the typescripts
of the chapter, where he has replaced Déorwine as the stumbling
Rider, he is called 'captain of the company with which he [Merry] was
riding'; the change to 'the Marshal, Elfhelm' was made when the book
was in proof.

After Éomer's counsel that the Rohirrim should rest now and set out
again at night, and the words 'To this the king assented, and the
captains departed' (RK p. 109), my father set down a brief outline:

On the grass way they find Hirgon's body and dead horse –
facing back west. They are drawing near the Rammas when
they meet a runner in the dark and take him captive; but he
proves to be a soldier of Gondor that escaping through a
postern has slipped through the leaguer and run for 14 miles.
He falls dying of wounds and exhaustion. 'Too late you come!'

THE RIDE OF THE ROHIRRIM

353

he cried. 'The first circle is burning and abandoned. The Lord will not give heed to the defence. Great siege towers and engines. They are bringing up a huge Ram for the Gates.'

Then suddenly as he looked at the flame far off the heart swelled in Théoden, as of one who is fey, and without more counsel he seized a great horn and blew it, and all the horns in the host took up the challenge. Then without more debate the Rohirrim poured in upon the fields of Gondor like a great torrent.

This passage was struck through; and from this point the development becomes for a stretch entirely obscure, a mosaic of repetitions and overwritings leading to the final text; but this was not achieved until after the manuscript was completed – the pagination shows that a page was added in here subsequently. Before this, the story was still that Dernhelm rode as a member of the king's guard, in the leading *éored* (see note 17); with the addition on the added page of the statement (RK p. 110) that 'Elfhelm's company came next, and now Merry noticed that Dernhelm had left his place and in the darkness was moving steadily forward until at last he was riding just in rear of the king's guard' that story is seen to be abandoned: Dernhelm had been riding from Edoras in the second *éored*.

On the added page is a small map. This marks the Druadan Forest and Stonewain Valley, the Anórien road, Eilenach (in its final position as the sixth beacon) and Amon Dîn, the 'Grey Woods' south-east of Amon Dîn, Mindolluin, Minas Tirith, and Osgiliath. The island of Cair Andros is shown, though not named, and most notably the Anduin now bends strongly west below Osgiliath, so that the walls of the Pelennor run along its bank for a stretch, and then turns still more sharply southwards (but the hills of Emyn Arnen are not shown): on this see p. 438. In one respect only does this map differ from the large-scale map of Rohan, Gondor and Mordor, and that is in the relation of Minas Tirith to Osgiliath.[15] Here the road across the Pelennor runs due east to the Causeway Forts (marked with small circles), and Osgiliath is due east of the city, whereas on the large map it lies to the north-east, and the road runs likewise; see the Second Map, pp. 434, 438.

In the remainder of 'The Ride of the Rohirrim' the final form was achieved in this manuscript almost word for word:[16] the speech of Wídfara about the change in the wind, the disposition of the companies of the Rohirrim,[17] Merry's fear that the king would quail and turn back, his great cry (with echoes of the Old Norse *Völuspá*) 'Arise, arise, Riders of Théoden ...', and the likening of Théoden to 'Oromë the Great in the Battle of the Valar when the world was young.'

Lastly I must mention the interesting name *Forannest*. Isolated notes

354   THE WAR OF THE RING

show my father working out this name, without giving any indication of its reference,[18] and on a page of the earliest drafting for the chapter, written above and perhaps associated with the sentence 'They were less than a day's ride from the Rammas', *Forannest* appears again, followed by the words 'North entrance [?in]'. That *Forannest* (whatever the name actually means) was the 'north-gate in the Rammas' (RK p. 111) is made certain by an isolated slip[19] giving the distances, east of Edoras, of the Mering Stream and the seven beacons; for here, following Amon Dîn, appears *Forannest (Rammas Echor)*.

NOTES

1   *Sarn Gebir:* the rapids in Anduin.
2   In the pencilled text the enemy camp is near Amon Dîn, and the distances are greater: 245 or 250 miles to the halt in the Forest of Eilenach, 285 to Amon Dîn.
3   The distance from the Rammas to Minas Tirith given here (12 miles or 4 leagues) obviously refers to the distance from the city to the point in the wall where the Rohirrim entered (where the North Road from Anórien ran into the townlands); and while in RK (p. 22) the city was four leagues from the wall at the widest extent of the Pelennor (in the direction of Osgiliath) and the north gate in the Rammas rather less ('maybe ten miles or more', RK p. 111), my father had now abandoned the original conception that the Pelennor had at all points a radius of seven leagues (see pp. 277–8, 287). Cf. also the draft for 'The Siege of Gondor' (p. 330), where it is said that when Faramir was forced to abandon the Causeway Forts he had '4 leagues or more of open land to cross', i.e. across the Pelennor.

      On the Second Map a line of five dots (shown on the redrawing, p. 434) runs northwest from Minas Tirith. These might seem rather too far north of the mountains to represent the beacons; but that they do so is seen from the fact that the distance measured in a direct line from Edoras to that nearest Minas Tirith is 270 miles, to the next 245 miles, and to the next 218 miles. These are virtually the same as the distances given here for Edoras to Amon Dîn, Min Rimmon, and Eilenach. On the other hand the distance on the Second Map from Edoras to the Rammas is about 285 miles, and to Minas Tirith about 295.
4   My references to and citations from the overwritten pencilled texts, here and subsequently, are very largely based on the work done on them by Taum Santoski.
5   In the following text of this passage the distance from Edoras to Minas Tirith becomes 'a hundred and one leagues', changed at once to 'a hundred leagues and two', as in RK. On my father's large-scale map of Rohan, Gondor and Mordor the distance in a

THE RIDE OF THE ROHIRRIM 355

direct line is 302 miles, but he noted against a pencilled line connecting them '304'. — On the form *Mundbeorg* 'hill of protection' for *Mundburg* in LR see VII.449 note 7.

6 *Cyneferth* has the very common Old English name-element *cyne-* 'royal'; *Grímhelm* means 'visored helm', cf. *gríma* 'mask', the name of Wormtongue.

7 On a torn half-sheet, subsequently used for other writing on the reverse, are the remains of a time-scheme which is very difficult both to read and to place in sequence, especially since some dates are lost and can only be deduced from those that are left. It seems that Théoden here remains a whole day at Dunharrow before setting out on the 10th of March, and on the 11th, after news has come in of an Orc-host entering Rohan from north of the Emyn Muil, Éomer leaves the host, rejoining it on the 12th. Against March 10 (?) is written: 'Merry insists on going to war and is taken up by [Grim >] Dúnhere who rides with the King, *Éowyn*, and Éomer.' It is hard to know what to make of this. A possibility is that my father had briefly decided to abandon the story of the 'young rider of the guard' (Éowyn), for Éowyn will now come openly to Minas Tirith, while Merry, equally openly, is taken by Dúnhere, chief of the men of Harrowdale. In support of this is the abandoned name *Grim-* (for *Grímhelm*?), and perhaps the underlining of *Éowyn*. But this seems to me very unlikely. It seems more probable that this text represents *earlier* ideas for this element in the story: not only is Merry permitted to go with the host, but Éowyn rides also as a matter of course (in which case the name *Grim-* is without significance, for *Grímhelm* had not yet arisen). In support of this is the diversion of Éomer northwards, mentioned in several of the early outlines for Book V, but not subsequently.

8 This text was in fact 'doubled', pencil overwritten in ink; but much of the pencilled form was left clear, and it shows no significant difference from the version in ink.

9 In this first finished version of *From dark Dunharrow in the dim morning* line 2 reads (as also in the first workings) *fate defying rode Fengel's son*, alliterating on *f*, with *Thengel?* in pencil in the margin (*with thane and captain rode Thengel's son*, RK). Both *fengel* and *þengel* were Old English poetic words for 'king, prince', and since *Thengel* as the name of Théoden's father appears in early texts of 'The Riders of Rohan' and 'The King of the Golden Hall' (VII.399, 402, 441) the appearance of *Fengel* here may have been inadvertent.

Line 8 reads *where deep once he drank ere darkness fell*, changed to *where long he had lived ere the light faded*. In line 10 *faith compelled him* preceded *Fealty kept he*. Line 12, where the original workings had *five days and nights*, changed to *four*

356   THE WAR OF THE RING

nights and days, retains the latter (*five* in RK). Line 14 reads *through Folde and Fenmarch past Firienlode*: *Firienlode* is clearly a river, and so perhaps the original name of the Mering Stream, which flowed through the Firien Wood. In line 16 *Minas Tirith* is *Mundberg*(see note 5; *berg* and *beorg*, 'hill, mountain', were Old English variants).

10   This text still has *Four nights and days* for *Five*, and *Mundberg* for *Mundburg* (see note 9).

11   This was subsequently altered on the manuscript. I presume that my father's thought was that for Éowyn to be disguised as a member of the king's own guard, and distinct among them by slightness of build, would obviously make her presence more readily detected; but see p. 369.

12   Cf. the note at the end of outline A (p. 344): 'Camp just west of Min Rimmon on night of 12th'. — The phrase 'bivouacked in the pinewoods that clustered about (Minrimmon Beacon)' was first used of the Halifirien (p. 347). In the final form it would be used of Eilenach, when that became again the sixth beacon (RK p. 104).

13   The name *Éothain* now appears in a third application (see p. 247 and note 20), for this Éothain, captain of the guard, can hardly be the same Rider as Éomer's squire in 'The Riders of Rohan' (see p. 266 note 20).

14   The appearance and clothing of Ghân-buri-Ghân are not described: 'There sat Théoden and Éomer and before [them] on the ground was a strange squat shape of a man. Merry felt that he had seen him before, and suddenly he remembered: the Púkelmen of Dunharrow. Almost it seemed that here was one come to life. Looking about he saw that in a ring just outside the light squatted other similar figures, while Riders on guard stood in a circle behind.' Ghân-buri-Ghân 'spoke after a fashion the Common Speech as it was in Gondor.' At the point where this draft ends he replies to the king's offer of reward and friendship thus: 'No need. Ghân-buri-Ghân himself go with you [?lord]. If he leads into trap you will kill him. If he lead well then we say farewell and ask only to be left in the woods.'

15   Whereas on the large map the Anduin bends southward after Cair Andros and is running north-south at Osgiliath, on this map it continues south-east after Cair Andros and then swings back south-west to Osgiliath. No features are shown here other than the course of the River itself.

16   The fair copy was here written over a pencilled text. Most of this Taum Santoski has been able to read, and it is seen that the final text was already closely approached.

17   After 'The first *éored* drew up behind him [Théoden] and about him on either side' (RK p. 111) this text continues: 'Elfhelm was

THE RIDE OF THE ROHIRRIM 357

away on the right ...': thus the words 'Dernhelm kept close to the king, *though* (Elfhelm's company was away on the right)' are lacking. This implies that the story was still present that Dernhelm rode as a member of the leading *éored* with the king's household-men (RK p. 110), not as one of Elfhelm's company; see p. 353.

18 Rejected forms in these notes are *fornest, Anfornest*, together with words *nesta, nethra, nest*, the last with meanings (apparently: the writing is very obscure) 'heart, core'.

19 The reverse of this slip (which is the lower half of a torn page) carries the following text:

... war would be useless, disastrous .... something much simpler, smaller and more desperate.

'I see you have something in mind,' said Thorin. 'What is it?'

'Well, this first,' I answered: 'you will have to go on your quest *secretly*, and that means you must go yourself, without messengers or embassies, and go with only a few faithful kinsmen or followers of your house. But you will need something more. There is a piece missing from the plan.'

For I needed thought. Thorin's tale had roused memories in my mind. Many years before I had been to Dol Guldur, as you know. You will know what I mean since you know Bilbo's story. I remembered the unhappy dying dwarf in the pits of Dol Guldur and the torn map and old key. Except that he was of Durin's folk of Erebor (as the map showed) I had no idea who he was. Of some importance perhaps since he was bearing a Ring, though he might have come by it in many ways. None but the Dwarves, and only a few of them, know who were the possessors of their great rings. But I had other far more perilous business on hand, and after I escaped from Dol Guldur many urgent cares. I stowed the things away till perhaps time would show their meaning. Now it had done so. I saw that I [had] heard the last wandering words of Thráin II Thrór's son, though he could not speak his own name or his son's. By what toughness of resistance he had kept these small things hidden in his torments, I do not know. But I think that

Comparison with *The Quest of Erebor* in *Unfinished Tales* will show that these passages are the forerunners of two in that (see p. 332 for the first, p. 324 for the second). My father said (*Unfinished Tales* p. 11) that this account of Gandalf's 'was to have come in during a looking-back conversation in Minas Tirith'; the present text may perhaps be assigned therefore to a time when *The Lord of the Rings* was approaching completion, if not actually finished; and this is supported by the reference to Thráin II (see VII.160). Since the notes on distances are obviously

358   THE WAR OF THE RING

a secondary use of the page, it would follow that the name *Forannest* was not abandoned, but was merely not used in the published work.

It is strange that Gandalf says here of the unknown Dwarf in Dol Guldur that he was 'of some importance perhaps since *he was bearing a Ring*, though he might have come by it in many ways' – and the following sentence 'None but the Dwarves, and only a few of them, know who were the possessors of their great rings' must imply that it was one of the Seven Rings of the Dwarves. But the story that Thráin's ring was taken from him in the dungeons of Sauron goes back to the earliest sketch for 'The Council of Elrond': 'But Thráin of old had one that descended from his sires. We do not now know where it is. We think it was taken from him, ere you found him in the dungeons long ago' (VI.398). It is surely incredible that at this stage my father should have entertained the idea that Thráin had managed to retain his ring in Dol Guldur. I can only suppose therefore, though it is not a natural interpretation of the words 'he was bearing a Ring', that he meant that Thráin told Gandalf that he *had been* the bearer of one of the Seven Rings of the Dwarves – even though he was so far gone that 'he could not speak his own name or his son's.' In the later form of this passage in *The Quest of Erebor* Gandalf did not discover in Dol Guldur who the Dwarf was, yet he did learn that he had been the possessor of a great Ring: 'Nearly all his ravings were of that. *The last of the Seven* he said over and over again.'

VIII

THE STORY FORESEEN FROM
FORANNEST

I have called this outline 'The Story Foreseen from Forannest' (the north gate of the Pelennor Wall) because it takes up at the point in the narrative where the Rohirrim poured through the outwalls of Minas Tirith in that place. But it will be seen that a part was foreseen for Denethor in no way consonant with the story of his madness and suicide, and this outline must come therefore from before the writing of at any rate the latter part of 'The Siege of Gondor', in which that story entered as the original draft was in progress (pp. 335–6).

A briefer, rougher form of this outline is found, extending only as far as the coming of the Host of the West before the Morannon. This my father rejected immediately and began on the fuller outline given here. A few differences in the first form are given in the notes.

The second form of the outline was given a heading 'Gandalf, Rohan, and Aragorn'; this was added to the text subsequently.

15 [March]. Horns of Rohan heard in the morning. Great charge of the Rohirrim through breach in north of Ramas-Coren. Rohirrim reach field before Great Gate, and men of Minas Tirith throw out enemy. But Wizard King takes to air and becomes Nazgûl,[1] rallies host of Morghul, and assails king. Théoden falls from horse sorely wounded; he is saved by Merry and Éowyn, but sortie from Gate does not reach them in time, before Éowyn is slain.[2] Grief and wrath of Éomer.

Éomer leads Rohirrim in a second reckless charge; but at that moment there is a cry from the city. A black fleet is seen coming to Haramon.[3] Men are landing. Then as final despair comes on, and Rohirrim give back, [west >] south wind rolls back cloud, and noon-sun gleams through. Aragorn unfurls his great standard from ship-top. The crown and stars of Sun and Moon shine out.[4] Men cry that Elendil has come back to life or Nume....[5]

Éomer charges again and the enemy is routed and so Éomer and Aragorn meet again on the field 'though all the hosts of Mordor lay between'.[6]

360 THE WAR OF THE RING

By evening of 15th [*in pencil* > 14] in a bloodred sun victory is complete. All enemy is driven into or back over Anduin. Aragorn sets up his pavilion and standard outside gate, but will not enter city, yet. Denethor comes down to greet the victors. Théoden dies. He bids farewell to Gandalf, Aragorn, Éomer and Merry. Théoden and Éowyn laid for a time in the royal tombs.

Words of Aragorn and Denethor. Denethor will not yield Stewardship, yet: not until war is won or lost and all is made clear. He is cold and suspicious and ? mock-courteous. Aragorn grave and silent. But Denethor says that belike the Stewardship will run out anyway, since he seems like to lose both his sons. Faramir is sick of his wounds. If he dies then Gondor can take what new lord it likes. Aragorn says he will not be 'taken', he will take, but asks to see Faramir. Faramir is brought out and Aragorn tends him all that night, and love springs between them.[7]

Aragorn and Gandalf counsel immediate action. Gandalf does not hope to conquer Mordor or overthrow Sauron and his tower. 'Not in these latter days, nor ever again by force of arms.' Yet arms have their place; and sloth now might be ruinous. Gandalf advises at least the taking and destruction of Minas Morghul.[8]

[N.B. Sauron already troubled by news of the victory of the Ents on March 11th – Ents another detail left out of his plans – first hears of Frodo on 15 of March, and at the same time, by Nazgûl, of the defeat in Pelennor and the coming of Aragorn. He is wrathful and afraid, but puzzled, especially by news of Frodo. He sends the Nazgûl to Kirith Ungol to get Frodo, but thinks chiefly of his war, and suspecting that Gondor will follow up victory he plans a counter-attack and withdraws all his forces to Morannon and Kirith Gorgor.]

The hosts, as many as are unhurt, of Rohan and Gondor, with Rangers, set out on 16th [*in pencil* > 17] and cross Anduin, and find Osgiliath empty. On 17th they march on Minas Morghul and the van (Riders of Rohan and Rangers and Gandalf) reach it on 18th [*in pencil* > 19] noon and find it dark and deserted. They burn the fields and Gandalf destroys its magic.[9] They now plan to march on the Morannon. A guard is set on Road, lest an army come up from South, or Sauron lets any sortie out through Kirith Ungol (no very great force could come that way in a hurry). They have now, however, to go more slow, and keep all their host together, moving only at the speed

THE STORY FORESEEN FROM FORANNEST   361

of infantry. The footmen come up on 19th. On 20th they set out for Morannon (120 [*in pencil* > 100] miles by road). They march through empty lands unassailed 20, 21, 22, 23, 24 and reach Morannon – just as Frodo [is beginning the ascent of Orodruin > is crossing Kirith Gorgor >] draws near Orodruin. There they to joy and surprise are joined by Ents, with new forces (out of North, including Elves of Lórien).

[Ents had victory on 11 March. It appears that Treebeard was told by Eagles sent by Galadriel of the assault on Lórien and the crossing of host to the Wold of Rohan on 7th. Treebeard and many Ents set out at once at great speed and cover over 200 miles, coming down on the enemy camp at south end of Downs in Eastemnet on 11 March; they destroyed many and drove rest in rout back over Anduin, where they had made bridges of boats above Sarn Gebir (about where Legolas shot down Nazgûl) – but in too great disarray to destroy the pontoons. So Ents cross. Treebeard is here joined by Elves of Lórien. They pursue the enemy round north and east of Emyn Muil and come down on the Hard of Dagor-lad (300 miles and more from Down-end to Morannon by this route): they move swiftly but mostly at night, for away here the Darkness is not over sky, only a great blackness is seen in the South, extending in breadth from Rauros to Linhir.[10] They arrive at same time as Gandalf.]

Now follows the Parley [*added:* on 25th]. Aragorn and Éomer wind horns before the Morannon, and summon Sauron to come forth. There is no answer at first, but Sauron had already laid his plans and an embassy was already coming to the Black Gate. The Wizard King? He bears the Mithril coat and says that Sauron has already captured the messenger[11] – a *hobbit*. How does Sauron know? He would of course guess from Gollum's previous visits that a small messenger might be a *hobbit*. But it is probable that either Frodo *talked in his drugged sleep* – not of the Ring, but of his name and country; and that Gorbag had sent tidings. The messenger jeers at Gandalf for sending a weak spy into the land where he dare not go himself, since his wizardry is no match for the Master. Now Sauron has the messenger, and what happens to him depends on Gandalf and Aragorn. He sees their faces blench. And jeers again. 'So!' he says – 'he was dear to you, or his errand was vital? So much the worse for you. For he shall endure slow torment of years, and then be released when broken, unless you accept Sauron's terms.'

362   THE WAR OF THE RING

'Name the terms,' said Gandalf, and tears were in his eyes, and all thought he was defeated and would yield – and of course be cheated.

The terms are that the Hosts of Gondor and Rohan shall withdraw at once beyond Anduin. All land east of Anduin to be Sauron's for ever, solely; and west of Anduin as far as Misty Mountains shall be tributary to Mordor and swear vassalage: Gondor and Rohan: as far as the river Isen. The Ents shall help rebuild Isengard and be subject to its lord – not Saruman, but one more trustworthy!

Gandalf replies, 'Yea, and what surety have we that Sauron will keep his part? Let him yield first the prisoner.' (That is awkward for the ambassador as in fact Sauron has not got him! But he laughs.) 'Take it or leave it so,' he said.

'We will take it,' said Gandalf, '— this the mithril-coat in memory. But as for your terms we reject them utterly.' Horror of Pippin and Merry if they are present? 'For in any case you would not keep them. Do as you will. And let fear eat your heart -- for if you so much as set a thorn in the flesh of Frodo you shall rue it.' The ambassador laughs, and gives a dreadful cry. Flinging off his garments he vanishes; but at that cry the host prepared in ambush sally from the mountains on either side, and from the Teeth, and pour out of the Gate. The host of Gondor taken at unawares wavers, and the leaders are surrounded. [*Added in pencil:* All the Nine Nazgûl remounted[12] swoop down; but the Eagles come to give battle.]

At that moment (25th) the Ring goes into Crack of Doom and the mountain vomits, and Baraddur crashes, and all things done by Sauron are cast down, the Black Gates fall. The Host of Mordor is dismayed, and flees back for refuge into Kirith Gorgor. The victorious host of Gondor and Rohan pours in in pursuit.

[*Remainder of the text is in pencil:*] Gandalf knows that Ring must have reached fire. Suddenly Sauron is aware of the Ring and its peril. He sees Frodo afar off. In a last desperate attempt he turns his thought from the Battle (so that his men waver again and are pressed back) and tries to stop Frodo. At same time he sends the Wizard King as Nazgûl[13] to the Mountain. The whole plot is clear to him.   ? He blasts the Stone so that at that moment the Orthanc-stone explodes: it would have killed Aragorn had he had it in hand?

Gandalf bids Gwaihir fly swiftly to Orodruin.

THE STORY FORESEEN FROM FORANNEST 363

This account of the Parley before the Black Gate may be compared with that in the outline 'The Story Foreseen from Fangorn', written years before (pp. 229–30).

As I have said, this text certainly preceded at any rate the latter part of 'The Siege of Gondor', in view of what is told here of Denethor. On the other hand, it equally clearly followed the initial drafting of 'The Ride of the Rohirrim', since the Ents here crossed the Anduin north of the Emyn Muil after their victory in the Wold of Rohan and came south to the Morannon through the lands east of the River: their appearance in Anórien had already been rejected.[14] While I have necessarily treated these chapters as separate narrative entities, whose development from initial draft to virtually final form proceeded without interruption, I think it is in fact very probable that my father moved back and forth between them.

NOTES

1 *But Wizard King takes to air and becomes Nazgûl.* These words can only mean that *Nazgûl* refers specifically to the Ring-wraiths *as borne upon 'winged steeds'.* But my father cannot have intended this. I presume that since in this part of *The Lord of the Rings* the Ringwraiths were 'winged', and their power and significance for the story lies in their being 'winged', he had nonetheless made this equation, and so slipped into saying that when the Black Captain (Lord of the Nazgûl) himself mounted on one of the monstrous birds he 'became a Nazgûl'. This occurs again at the end of the outline.

2 On the death of Éowyn see p. 318.

3 At the equivalent point in the first form of the outline there is a note in the margin: 'Pelennor wall here only 10 miles away and the wall right above stream which bends round the Hills of Haramon.' *Haramon*, the original name of Emyn Arnen, appears on the Second Map: see pp. 353; 434, 438.

4 The first form of the outline has: 'Sungleam shines on the [Tree >] Crown and stars of Sun and Moon.'

5 The first four letters of this name are certain, but it can scarcely be *Númenor*; the likeliest interpretation is *Numerion*.

6 The first form of the outline has here: 'Enemy is caught between Aragorn and the Dúnedain and Éomer and so Éomer and Aragorn meet.' This is the first time that the name Dúnedain is met with *ab initio* in the texts.

7 Of this passage, from 'Aragorn sets up his pavilion and standard outside gate', there is very little in the first form of the outline: 'Denethor comes down to welcome Aragorn; but will not yield the Stewardship, until all is proven and war is lost or won.

364 THE WAR OF THE RING

Aragorn agrees.' Then follows: 'Aragorn and Gandalf counsel immediate action.'

8 This passage is the first germ of 'The Last Debate'.

9 The first form of the outline has 'They burn the poisoned fields'; and distances are given: 'Minas Tirith to Osgiliath 26 miles. West edge of Osgiliath to Minas Morghul [50 >] 60 miles?' (with 55 written above 60).

10 This is the first reference to Linhir (see pp. 436–7).

11 It is curious and confusing that Sauron's messenger should refer to Frodo as a 'messenger'.

12 Earlier in this outline my father had questioned whether the ambassador was not in fact the Wizard King himself, and he appears again at the end, dispatched by Sauron to Orodruin (his fate on the fields of the Pelennor was therefore not yet finally decided). Since at the end of the parley the ambassador casts off his garments and vanishes, he was certainly a Ringwraith; is this the meaning of 'All the Nine Nazgûl remounted'?

13 On the implication of *he sends the Wizard King as Nazgûl* – that *Nazgûl* means specifically the winged Wraiths – see note 1. On the other hand, *All the Nine Nazgûl remounted* (note 12) carries the opposite implication.

14 It cannot be actually demonstrated that the story of the coming of Treebeard and the Ents to Anórien did not follow, and supersede, their appearance at the Black Gate; but this seems extremely improbable.

IX

THE BATTLE OF THE PELENNOR FIELDS

I give first a remarkable writing entitled *Fall of Théoden in the Battle of Osgiliath*. It is clearly written in ink, with only a few changes made at the time of writing; there are also a small number of pencilled corrections, which I show as such.

Then Théoden gave a great shout 'Forth Eorlingas!' and spurred Snowmane rearing into the deeps of the great shadow. But few followed him; for his men quailed and grew sick in that ghastly shade, and many fell upon the ground. The light of his golden shield grew dim. Still he rode on, and darts flew thick about him. Many fell before his spear, and almost he had reached to the standard of the Haradoth [> Haradhoth], when suddenly he gave a great cry, and fell. A black arrow had pierced his heart. And at the same moment Snowmane stumbled forward and lay still. The great shadow descended. Slowly the huge vulture-form [> Slowly as a settling cloud it] came down, lifted its wings, and with a hoarse croaking cry settled upon the body of the fallen king, digging in its talons and stooping its long [*added*: naked] neck. Upon its back there sat a shape. Black robed it was, and above the robe there was a steel crown, borne by no visible head save where between crown and cloak there was a pale and deadly gleam as it were of eyes.[1] But Théoden was not alone. One had followed him: Éowyn daughter of Éomund, and all had feared the light of her face, shunning her as night fowl turn from the day. Now she leapt from her horse and stood before the shadow; her sword was in her hand.

'Come not between the Nazgûl and his prey,' said a cold voice, 'or he will bear thee away to the houses of lamentation, beyond all darkness where thy flesh shall be devoured and thy shrivelled mind be left naked.'

She stood still and did not blench. 'I do not fear thee, Shadow,' she said. 'Nor him that devoured thee. Go back to him and report that his shadows and dwimor-lakes[2] are powerless even to frighten women.' The great bird flapped its wings and leapt into the air, leaving the king's body, and falling upon her

366   THE WAR OF THE RING

with beak and claw. Like a shaft of searing light a pale sword cold as ice was raised above her head.

She raised her shield, and with a swift and sudden stroke smote off the bird's head. It fell, its vast wings outspread crumpled and helpless on the earth. About Éowyn the light of day fell bright and clear. With a clamour of dismay the hosts of Harad turned and fled, and over the ground a headless thing crawled away, snarling and snivelling, tearing at the cloak. Soon the black cloak too lay formless and still, and a long thin wail rent the air and vanished in the distance.

Éowyn stepped to the king. 'Alas, Théoden son of Thengel,'[3] she said. 'But you have turned the tide. See, they fly. The enemy is broken by fear. Never did an old Lord of Men die better. You shall sleep well, and no Shadow nor foul thing assail your bed.'

Then there was a sound of a great ...[4] and the men of Minas Tirith and of the Mark released from the Shadow swept up, the light reborn was strong on their swords and spears. They drove the enemy into the River. Some stayed by their king.

I think that my father wrote this well before the period of composition we have now reached, and I would be inclined to associate it (very tentatively) with the outline sketches for Book V, where the event described here is several times referred to, and especially with Outlines III and V. In these, in contrast to what is said in I and II (p. 256), there is no mention of Éowyn's wounding or death: 'Théoden and Éowyn destroy Nazgûl and Théoden falls' (III, p. 260); 'Théoden is slain by Nazgûl; but he is unhorsed and the enemy is routed' (V, p. 263). Although in my father's narrative sketches silence is a bad guide, it is possible that these brief statements are nonetheless to be associated with what is certainly a notable feature of the present text, that there is no suggestion that Éowyn was in any way hurt in the encounter with the Lord of the Nazgûl or after (while Théoden is felled and dies without speaking). A difficulty with this view is that in Outline V the Nazgûl King is 'unhorsed', whereas in 'The Fall of Théoden in the Battle of Osgiliath' his descent on a 'huge vulture-form' is at the centre of the story. Since the 'vultures' are referred to as 'winged steeds', it is possible that the word 'unhorsed' was used in this sense, though that does not seem very likely.

It is obvious that no part was foreseen for Merry in the great event; and it seems that (in strong contrast to the final story, RK p. 117) it was the beheading of the great bird that in itself caused the defeat and flight of the Lord of the Nazgûl, deprived of his steed.

Whatever its relative dating, the piece certainly gives an impression of having been composed in isolation, a draft for a scene that my

THE BATTLE OF THE PELENNOR FIELDS 367

father saw vividly before he reached this point in the actual writing of the story. When he did so, he evidently had it before him, as is suggested by the words of the Lord of the Nazgûl (cf. RK p. 116).

When my father came to write the story of the Battle of the Pelennor Fields he all but achieved the form in which it stands in *The Return of the King* in a single manuscript ('**A**'). He adopted here the method of building up the completed narrative through massive correction and interpolation of his initial text; and the greater part if not all of this work clearly belongs to the same time. Beneath the writing in ink on the first page of this manuscript there is however a pencilled text, and this bears further on the subject of Théoden and the Lord of the Nazgûl.

This underlying text is largely illegible on account of the ink overwriting, which is closely-packed, but from what can be seen it seems not to have differed greatly (the opening paragraph of the chapter, mostly legible, is very close to the ink version on top of it) – as far as the passage where the golden shield of Théoden is dimmed, horses reared and screamed, and men falling from their horses lay upon the ground. But then follows: 'And through the ranks of the enemy a wide lane opened.' The rest of the pencilled text is almost entirely lost, but isolated words and phrases can be made out: 'There came riding ..... a great ..... [*struck out:* The Black Captain] ..... stood ..... the Black Captain robed ..... and above the robes was a crown ..... ' This can scarcely mean anything other than that the Lord of the Nazgûl did *not* descend upon the battle borne upon the back of a great vulture.

Various statements have been made on this subject, beginning with that in Outline V, cited above, that the Nazgûl was 'unhorsed'. In the rough draft of 'The Siege of Gondor' (p. 331) Gandalf, speaking to Pippin of the Wizard King, says that 'he has not [*struck out(?): yet*] taken to winged steeds'; in the outline 'The Story Foreseen from Forannest' (p. 359) 'the Wizard King takes to the air and becomes Nazgûl'; and of course there is the evidence of 'The Fall of Théoden in the Battle of Osgiliath'. That my father should at this stage have abandoned, however briefly, the story of the Winged Nazgûl descending upon Théoden is certainly surprising; but it seems plain that he did so.

The first manuscript A has no title, and was paginated continuously with 'The Ride of the Rohirrim'; a subsequent fair copy manuscript ('**B**') was afterwards given the number and title 'XLVIII The Battle of the Pelennor Fields'. The opening passage in A is distinct from the form in RK:

But it was no orc-chief or brigand that led the assault on Gondor. Who knows whether his Master himself had set a date

368   THE WAR OF THE RING

to the darkness, designing the fall of the City for that very hour and needing light for the hunting of those that fled, or fortune had betrayed him and the world turned against him? None can tell. Dismayed he may have been, cheated of victory even as he grasped it. Cheated, not yet robbed. He was still in command, wielding great power, Lord of the Nazgûl. He had many weapons. He left the Gates and vanished.

There is no mention of Dernhelm in the passage 'He [Théoden] slackened his speed a little, seeking new foes, and his knights came behind him. Elfhelm's men were among the siege-engines ...', where RK has 'and his knights came about him, and Dernhelm was with them.' This shows, I think, that Dernhelm was still conceived to have been riding with the king's knights throughout the journey from Edoras.[5]

When the Lord of the Nazgûl says to Éowyn[6] 'No living man may hinder me!' she replies, as the text was first written: 'I am no living man. You look upon a woman. Éowyn I am, Éomund's daughter. You stand between me and my kin. Begone! For though I have slain no living thing, yet I will slay the dead [> yet I will slay the Undead].' This rests on the earlier form of the prophecy concerning the Lord of the Nazgûl: 'he is not doomed to fall before men of war or wisdom; but in the hour of his victory to be overthrown by one who has slain no living thing' (pp. 334–5). This was changed on the manuscript to: 'Begone, if thou be not deathless! For living or dark undead, I will hew thee, if thou touch me.'

In the passage that follows, Éowyn's hair is described as 'shorn upon her neck', and this survived through the fair copy B into the first typescript, where it was changed to the reading of RK (p. 116): 'her bright hair, released from its bonds'. And Merry's thought is directly reported: 'I must do something. If only I can get away from those eyes!'

After the great cry of the Lord of the Nazgûl as he departed there follows: 'And far up above [?the] Nazgûl hearing that cry were filled with great terror, and fled away to Baraddur bearing ill tidings.' This was not taken up into the fair copy (B).[7]

At Théoden's death the text here is briefer, and no reference is made to the taking up of the banner from its dead bearer and the sign made by the king that it be given to Éomer: 'Grief and dismay fell upon Éomer as he leaped from the saddle and stood by the king. Slowly the old man opened his eyes again. "Hail, King of the Mark!" he said. ...' In the fair copy B the banner-bearer is named Guthwin (Guthláf in RK).

Of Merry's sword it was first said in this text: 'So passed the sword of the Barrow-downs, work of Westernesse. Glad would he have been to know its fate who wrought it slowly long ago, for the sorcerer-king

THE BATTLE OF THE PELENNOR FIELDS   369

he knew and the dread realm of Angmar in the ancient North, hating all his deeds.' The text of RK (pp. 119–20), 'who wrought it slowly long ago in the North-kingdom when the Dúnedain were young ...', was substituted, probably at once.[8]

The passage (RK p. 120) recording the burying of the carcase of the great beast and of Snowmane, with the horse's epitaph, is absent; and the great rain that came from the sea ('it seemed that all things wept for Théoden and Éowyn', recalling the grief for Baldr) likewise, being added in only on the first typescript. A page of the manuscript (A) in which the encounter of the Prince of Dol Amroth with the bearers of Théoden and Éowyn is described, and his discovery that Éowyn was still alive, was rejected and at once rewritten; in the rejected form occurs this passage in the words of the Prince (still given no other name) with the bearers:

'Bring him to the City,' he said. 'The gate is wide open, and by his own deed the way thither is made free.' And then he rose and looked on Éowyn and was amazed. 'Here is a woman!' he said. 'Do even the women of Rohan come to war in our aid?' he asked.

'It is the Lady Éowyn sister of King Éomer,' they said. 'And we do not know how she came here, but it seems that she took the place of one of his knights. [*Rejected at once:* Dernhelm ... a young kinsman of the king.] It is a grief beyond words to us.'

This is the only trace of the idea that Éowyn escaped detection by substituting herself for a young Rider among the king's knights actually named Dernhelm. No doubt it arose here and was abandoned here; probably because of the meaning of the name (*derne* 'hidden, secret'; cf. the earlier name by which Éowyn was to ride, *Grímhelm*, p. 355 note 6).

In the rewritten version of this passage the text of RK is reached, and here at last appears the name *Imrahil* of the Prince of Dol Amroth, entering apparently without any hesitation as to its form.

Among the horsemen of Gondor (RK p. 121) appears Húrin the Tall, 'Warden of the City', changed at once to 'Warden of the Keys'. In an immediately rejected version of the passage in which the new hosts streaming in from Osgiliath are described it was said of the Black Captain: 'He was gone, and the Nazgûl in fear had fled back to Mordor bearing ill tidings' (see note 7); but this was lost in the rewriting of the passage, where appear Gothmog lieutenant of Morghul,[9] the Variags of Khand (both names written without any precedent forms), and the black 'half-trolls' of Far Harad.[10]

The course of Anduin, as seen by the watchmen on the walls when the black fleet approached (RK p. 122), was first described thus:

370   THE WAR OF THE RING

For south away the river went in a knee about the out-thrust of the hills of Emyn Arnen in lower Ithilien,[11] and Anduin bent then in upon the Pelennor so that its outwall was there built upon the brink, and that at the nearest was no more than [five >] four miles from the Gates; [*added:* and quays and landings were made there for boats coming upstream from the Out-lands;] but thence the river flowed southeast for three leagues and all that reach could be seen in line by farsighted men on high. And they looking forth cried in dismay, for lo! up the reach of Arnen a black fleet could be seen ...

Striking out this passage my father noted against the first part of it: 'This is now told before in XLIV' (i.e. the chapter 'Minas Tirith'). He was referring to a rider introduced into the first typescript of that chapter (see p. 294 note 30) entirely recasting the original description of the Pelennor and the Outlands (pp. 278, 287) to its form in RK (p. 22), where the bend in Anduin about Emyn Arnen appears. This rider was already in existence, though obviously belonging to this phase of writing, as is seen from the name *Lonnath-ernin* of the landings, subsequently changed (presumably at this very juncture) to *Harlond*. In the present text the passage just cited was removed immediately, and the much briefer passage as found in this place in RK (p. 122) follows in the manuscript, with the name *Harlond*.[12]

The great banner of Aragorn is described in the same words as in RK (p. 123), except that in the sentence 'for they were wrought of gems *by Arwen daughter of Elrond*' the italicised words are absent. In the fair copy manuscript (B) 'by Finduilas Elrond's daughter'[13] was added in the margin, changed later to 'Arwen daughter of Elrond'. Aragorn is named 'Elessar, Isildur's heir'; and when men leapt from the ships to the quays 'There came Legolas and Gimli wielding his axe, and Halbarad with the standard, and Elboron and Elrohir with stars on their brow, and the dourhanded Dúnedain, Rangers of the North; and in the hand of Aragorn Branding was like a new fire kindled, Narsil reforged[14] as deadly as of old, and about his helm there was a kingly crown.' Thus *Elboron* still survived, for *Elladan* (see pp. 297, 302), the change being made on the fair copy. *Branding*, for *Andúril, Flame of the West*, remained until changed on the first typescript; while 'about his helm there was a kingly crown' was not replaced by 'upon his brow was the Star of Elendil' until the book was in proof.

At the end of the chapter as first written Duinhir of Morthond is named among the fallen, whereas in RK it is his sons, 'Duilin and his brother' (Derufin), who were trampled by the *mûmakil*.[15] Grimbold of Grimslade is not named (though he has appeared in 'The Ride of the Rohirrim'), and instead the sentence in which he is named in RK

THE BATTLE OF THE PELENNOR FIELDS   371

reads: 'Neither Hirluin the Fair would return to his green hills, nor Elfhelm to Eastfold [*written above:* Westfold],[16] nor Halbarad to the Northlands, dourhanded Ranger.'

In the alliterative song 'The Mounds of Mundburg' (not yet so named) there was much variation in the recording of those who died in the Battle of the Pelennor Fields. The earliest complete, though still very rough, form of the song reads:

As long after a maker[17] in Rohan said in his song:

> *We heard in the hills the horns ringing,*[18]
> *of swords shining in the South kingdom:*
> *steeds went striding to the Stoningland*
> *a wind in the morning, war at sunrise.*
> *There Théoden fell, Thengling mighty,*
> *life and lordship long had he wielded*
> *hoar king and high, Harding and Grimbold,*
> *Dúnhere and [Elfhelm >] Marculf, Déorwin the marshal.*
> *Hirluin the fair to the hills by the sea,*
> *nor Forlong the great to the flowering vales*
> *ever of Arnach in his own country*
> *returned in triumph, nor the tall bowman*
> *doughty Duinhir to the dark waters,*
> *meres of Morthond under mountain-shadows.*
> *Death in the morning and at day's ending*
> *lords took and lowly. Long now they sleep*
> *under grass in Gondor by the Great River.*
> *Red it ran then. Red was the sunset,*
> *the hills under heaven high snowmantled*
> *bloodred burning. Blood dyed the earth*
> *in the Field of Mundberg in the far country.*

Another rough text, moving nearer to the final form in some lines but petering out before the conclusion, has in the line corresponding to the 8th in the version just given *Dúnhere and [Elfhelm >] Guthwin, Déorwin the marshal.* Guthwin was the banner-bearer of the king (see p. 368). The first good text reaches the final form (with the name Rammas Echor in the last line) in all but the names of the dead Riders:

> *Harding and Guthwin,*
> *Dúnhere and Marculf, Déorwin and Grimbold,*
> *Herufare and Herubrand, Horn and Fastred,*
> *fought and fell there in a far country;*
> *in the mounds of Mundberg under mould they lie*
> *with their league-fellows, lords of Gondor.*[19]

372   THE WAR OF THE RING

NOTES

1 Cf. the initial drafting for the end of 'The Siege of Gondor' (p. 337): '... crown that sat upon no visible head save only for the light of his pale eyes.'

2 *dwimorlakes*: 'illusions, phantoms'. Old English *(ge)dwimor, -er*; cf. Wormtongue's name *Dwimordene* of Lórien in 'The King of the Golden Hall' (TT p. 118), and *Dwimorberg*. In the present chapter in RK (p. 116) Éowyn calls the Lord of the Nazgûl 'foul dwimmer-laik', *-laik* being the Old Norse ending *-leikr* corresponding to Old English *-lāc*, here 'modernised' as *-lake*.

3 *Théoden son of Thengel*: see p. 355 note 9.

4 The word is most naturally read as 'sound', in which case my father inadvertently repeated it instead of the word he had in mind, e.g. 'riding'.

5 The statement in 'The Ride of the Rohirrim' that 'Dernhelm had left his place and in the darkness was moving steadily forward until at last he was riding just in rear of the king's guard' (p. 353) was added after the writing of the present passage; see also p. 356 note 17.

6 Éowyn calls the Lord of the Nazgûl 'foul dwimmerlake', where *-lake* was changed subsequently to *-lord*. See note 2.

7 Cf. 'The Story Foreseen from Forannest', p. 360, in which it is said that Sauron heard from the Nazgûl of the defeat on the Pelennor and the coming of Aragorn.

8 For the first appearance of *Angmar* see p. 334, and of *Dúnedain* p. 363 note 6.

9 The name *Gothmog* is one of the original names of the tradition, going back to *The Book of Lost Tales*; Lord of Balrogs, slayer of Fëanor and Fingon.

10 *Khand, Near Harad*, and *Far Harad* were roughly entered on the Second Map.

11 *Emyn Arnen* has replaced *Haramon* (see p. 359 and note 3). On the origin of the great bend in the Anduin around the hills of Emyn Arnen see p. 438.

12 As first written, those who saw the black sails cried out: 'The Corsairs of Umbar! See! The Corsairs are coming. They have overrun Amroth and Belfalas and Lebennin are destroyed!'

13 In the First Age *Finduilas* was the daughter of Orodreth King of Nargothrond; she plays a major part in the *Túrinssaga*.

14 *Narsil reforged*: although it has been said that Aragorn gave the name *Branding* to the Sword of Elendil after its reforging (see VII.274 and note 19), its ancient name has never been told until now.

15 In the account of the men of the Outlands entering Minas Tirith given on p. 287 Duinhir is mentioned, but not his sons.

THE BATTLE OF THE PELENNOR FIELDS 373

16 In LR Elfhelm was not slain in the Battle of the Pelennor Fields, but survived to command the three thousand Riders of Rohan who were sent to 'waylay the West Road against the enemy that was in Anórien' (RK p. 158; the leader of this force was not named in the First Edition, but Elfhelm is named in both editions as among those who stood before the gates of Minas Tirith when the Captains of the West returned, RK p. 244).

17 *maker*: used in the long since lost sense 'poet'.

18 *We heard of the horns in the hills ringing* is a variant entered at the time of writing both in this text and in that following.

19 *Guthwin* was later changed to *Guthlaf* on this manuscript (see p. 368). *Herufare* is written so (for expected *-fara*) both here and (apparently) in a scrap of rough drafting for the passage; *Herefara* in RK.

X

THE PYRE OF DENETHOR

The original brief draft of this chapter ('A'), mercifully written fairly legibly in ink and not in pencil subsequently overwritten, extended from 'When the dark shadow at the Gate withdrew' as far as 'There was no guard at the gate of the Citadel. "Berithil has gone then," said Pippin' (RK p. 127). The final text was naturally not reached in every turn of expression or every detail, but apart from the absence of the meeting with Prince Imrahil as Gandalf and Pippin rode up from the Gate on Shadowfax there is no narrative difference of any significance.[1] At this point my father stopped and set down a brief outline ('B').

> ? Porter dead at Closed Door. ? They see fire and smoke below as they hurry down the winding road. Berithil has rebelled, and taking some of the guard has fought with the household men. Before they could gain entrance to the tomb, one of these dashed back and set a torch in the wood. But Berithil was just in time to save Faramir. But Denethor leaped back into the flames and was now dead. Gandalf closed the door. 'That ends a chapter!' he said. 'Let the Stewards burn – their days are over.' Light is growing fast. Faramir is borne away to the house where women were who remained in city to tend sick.

A large question mark was placed against the first part of this, and it was evidently rejected as soon as written and replaced by the following:

> ? Berithil and guard had gone and stopped the burning. Gandalf reasons with Denethor. 'I have seen' says Denethor 'ships coming up Anduin: I will no more yield to an upstart – and even if his claim be true of the younger line: I am Steward for the sons of Anárion not of Isildur – than [to] my dark foe.'

The development from this point is hard to be sure of, but I am almost certain that the next step was the following outline ('C'), written in ink around and through (but not over) a much rougher outline also in ink (briefer but essentially the same, with mention of the *palantír*):

> Gandalf and Pippin hear clash of arms as they hasten down

THE PYRE OF DENETHOR 375

the winding road to Rath Dínen. When they reach the Tombs they find Berithil holding the door alone against the household-men, who wish to obey Denethor's orders and come and set fire to the pyre. From within comes Denethor's voice commanding Berithil by his oaths to let them enter.

Gandalf sweeps aside the men and goes in. He upbraids Denethor, but Denethor laughs at him. Denethor has a *palantír*! He has seen the coming of Aragorn. But he has also seen the vast forces still gathered in Mordor, and says that victory in arms is no longer possible. He will *not* yield up the Stewardship 'to an upstart of the younger line: I am Steward of the sons of Anárion.' He wants things to be as they were – or not at all.

Gandalf demands the release of Faramir, and when Denethor attempts to slay him ('he shall not live to bow down!') Gandalf strikes the sword from his hand, and lets suddenly be seen his power so that even Denethor quails. Gandalf bids the men lift up Faramir and bear him from the chamber.

Denethor says 'At least so far my rule still holds that I may determine my own death.' He sets fire to the wood which is oil-drenched. Then he leaps onto the stone bed. He breaks the wand of his Stewardship and lays the pieces on his lap, and lies down taking the Stone between his hands. Then Gandalf leaves him. He closes the door and the flames roar within. They hear Denethor give a great cry, and then no more. 'So passes the Stewardship of Gondor!' said Gandalf. It is said that ever after, if anyone looked in that Stone, unless he had great strength of will, he saw only two old hands withering in flames. [*Added:* Gandalf bids Berithil and household men not to mourn – or be too downcast. Each side has tried to do their duty.]

They now bear Faramir to the house of the sick. As Gandalf and Pippin climb back up the road they hear the last shriek in the air of the Nazgûl. Gandalf stands still a moment. 'Some evil has befallen!' he says, 'which but for the madness of Denethor I could have averted. So far is the reach of the Enemy. But we know how his will had entry to the White Tower. *By the Stone.* Though he could not daunt Denethor or enslave him, he could fill him with despair, mistrust and unwisdom.' When Faramir is placed under care with Berithil as guard they meet the funeral cortège. Where is Merry? Pippin volunteers to try and find Merry.

Most of the essential ideas of the chapter were present here – and one that was rejected: Denethor knew who was aboard the black fleet

376   THE WAR OF THE RING

and what his coming meant (see pp. 378–9). This knowledge he derived from the *palantír*; and since it is present also in the brief preceding outline B the existence of the *palantír* in the White Tower must be presumed there also.[2]

At this stage, I think, my father began on a new text of the chapter ('D'), continuing as far as Gandalf's words concerning 'the heathen kings' (RK p. 129). The final text is here very closely approached[3] until near the end (which is very rough and has various alternative readings):

Then Gandalf showing now a marvellous strength leapt up on the faggots and raising the sick man bore him out of the deadly house; and as he was moved Faramir moaned and spoke his father's name.

Then Denethor stepped forward and the flame died in his eyes and he wept, and he said: 'Do not take my son from me. He calls for me.'

'He calls for you,' said Gandalf. 'But you cannot come to him save in one way. You must go out to the battle of your City putting away despair and risking death in the field; and he must struggle for life against hope in the dark ways of his fever. Then perchance you may meet again. / For unless you go out to the battle of your City putting away despair and risking death in the field you will never speak again with him in the waking world.'

'He will not wake again,' said Denethor. 'His house is crumbling. Let us die together.' / 'At least we can go to death side by side,' said Denethor. 'That lies not in the will of the Lord of this City or of any other,' said Gandalf. 'For you are not yet dead. And so do the heathen kings under the dominion of the Dark Lord, to slay themselves in pride and despair or to slay their kin for the easing of their own death.'

In RK this is followed by 'Then passing through the door he took Faramir from the deadly house and laid him on the bier on which he had been brought, and which had now been set in the porch. Denethor followed him ...'; for it is clear that Gandalf, bearing Faramir, had halted at Denethor's words 'Do not take my son from me!', and only now moved through the door. But in the text just given it is said that Gandalf bore Faramir 'out of the deadly house' as soon as he had lifted him from the pyre.

It was perhaps at this stage that my father wrote a single discontinuous page ('E') beginning with the words 'Gandalf now takes Faramir'. Here as in RK Denethor follows him; but no further words are spoken until, after a long hesitation while he looks on Faramir, he

THE PYRE OF DENETHOR

377

declares that he will rule his own end, and his death follows immediately. It is curious that Denethor is here said to die clasping the *palantír*, yet there is no drafting of the scene in which he reveals his possession of it.

Gandalf now takes Faramir.

Denethor now followed him to the door. And he trembled, looking in longing at his son and hesitating. Yet in the end his pride and wilfulness overmastered him and he was fey again. 'At least in this you shall not defy and snatch my power away,' he said. And stepping suddenly forth he seized a torch from the hand of one of his servants, and moving back thrust it among the wood, which being drenched in oil roared at once into flame and a black smoke filled the house. Then Denethor leaped again onto the table amid the fire and fume, and breaking the staff of his stewardship on his knee he cast it into the flames and laid himself back on his pillow clasping the *palantír* with both hands to his breast.

Gandalf in sorrow and horror turned his face away and came forth, closing the door. For a while he stood in thought silently upon the topmost step. And they heard the roar and crackle of the flames within; and then Denethor gave a great cry, and afterward spoke no more, nor was seen again by mortal man.

'So passes the Stewardship of Gondor!' said Gandalf. And he turned to Berithil and the lord's servants. 'Do not mourn overmuch,' he said. 'For the old days have passed for good or evil. And be not grieved with your own deeds. For all here, as I see it, have striven to do as they judged right, whether in obedience and the keeping of vows or in the breaking. For you servants of the Lord owed obedience only to your Lord, but Berithil owed also allegiance first to the Lord Faramir the captain of the guard. So let now all hate or anger that lies between you fall away and be forgotten. Bear away those who have fallen in this unhappy place. And we will bear Faramir to a place where he can die in peace if that is his doom, or find healing.'

So now Gandalf and Berithil taking up the bier that stood still in the porch before the doors set Faramir upon it and slowly bore him away to the houses of the sick, and the servants came behind bearing their fellows. And when they came at length through the closed door Gandalf bade Berithil who had the key to lock it. And as they passed into the upper circles of the City there was heard in the air the cry of the Lord of the Nazgûl as it

378   THE WAR OF THE RING

rose and passed away for ever. And they stood for a moment stricken with wonder.

This was followed (again with some doubt as to the sequence) by another discontinuous page ('F') that takes up in the course of Gandalf's reply to Denethor's words 'Do not take my son from me! He calls for me':

'... But he now must strive for life in the dark ways of his fever seeking healing; and you must go out to the battle of your city, risking death, if it must be, in the field. This you know well in your heart.'

But Denethor laughed. And going back to the table he lifted from it the pillow that he had lain on. And lo! in his hand he bore a *palantír*. 'Pride and despair!' he said. 'Did you think that [the] eyes of the White Tower were blind?' he said. [*Added in pencil, without direction for insertion:* This the Stone of Minas Tirith has remained ever in the secret keeping of the Stewards in the topmost chamber.] Nay, nay, I see more than thou knowest, Grey Fool ...'[4]

The page then continues very close to the final text (RK pp. 129–30), except in the view taken of Denethor's knowledge of Aragorn and the black fleet. In RK, as final proof that the power arrayed against Minas Tirith is too great for any withstanding, Denethor declares to Gandalf that 'even now the wind of thy hope cheats thee and wafts up Anduin a fleet with black sails.' He therefore does not know who is aboard. But (after Gandalf's reply 'Such counsels will make the Enemy's victory certain indeed') he goes on to accuse him of commanding Pippin 'to keep silence', and of installing him as a spy in his chamber; 'and yet in our speech together I have learned the names and purpose of all thy companions. So! With the left hand thou wouldst use me for a little while as a shield against Mordor, and with the right bring up this Ranger of the North to supplant me.' As the text stands in RK it is not clear what Denethor means by 'with the right hand'; for he does not know that it is the 'upstart' Aragorn who is coming up the Great River.

From the present text F, however, it is clear what Denethor did originally mean by 'with his right hand'. Here, he does not mention the black fleet in the first of these speeches; and in the second he makes no reference at all to Pippin – so that it is not from Pippin that he has learned of Aragorn's coming. But then he goes on: 'But I know your mind and its plots. Do I not see the fleets even now coming up Anduin! So with the left hand you would use me as a shield against Mordor, and with the right hand bring up this Ranger of the North to take my place.' Here it is obvious that he does know who is aboard (with

THE PYRE OF DENETHOR   379

his left hand, one might suppose, he gestures towards Osgiliath and with his right towards Pelargir); and he knew it from use of the *palantír*, as is expressly stated in the outline C (p. 375): 'Denethor has a *palantír*! He has seen the coming of Aragorn.'

This text (F) ends thus:

'But who saith that the Steward who faithfully surrenders shall have diminishment of love and honour! And at the last you shall not rob your son of his choice, slaying him in your proud wickedness while yet healing is in doubt. This you shall not do. Yield me now Faramir!'

It is hard to know what these last words imply, since at this point Gandalf must have already raised Faramir from the stone table and moved towards the door. It seems possible that some drafting has been lost, which would have made clearer the evolution of the final structure in this chapter.

At any rate, my father now began another text ('G'), for which he used the initial pages of D (p. 376), but soon diverged into new manuscript, roughly written but now completing the chapter; and here the substance and structure of RK was reached with few differences. The manuscript had originally no title, but at some point he wrote on it 'XLVIII The Pyre of Denethor': at that stage, presumably, he was treating 'The Ride of the Rohirrim' and 'The Battle of the Pelennor Fields' as one chapter (see pp. 351, 367). 'XLVIII' was subsequently changed to 'XLIX' and 'V.6'.[5]

As first written, the different view of Denethor's knowledge of Aragorn and the black fleet was preserved, though changed later on the manuscript to the final form (on this question see pp. 390–1). Gandalf still said 'So passes the Stewardship of Gondor' for 'So passes Denethor, son of Ecthelion'; and in his address to Berithil and the servants of Denethor who stood by he said: 'But Berithil of the guard owed allegiance first to his captain, Faramir, to succour him while he lived' (cf. p. 377). This was changed on the manuscript to read:

'... For you servants of the Lord owed obedience to him only. And he who says: "my master is not in his mind, and knows not what he bids; I will not do it", is in peril, unless he has knowledge and wisdom. But to Berithil of the guard such discernment was a duty, whereas[6] also he owed allegiance first to his captain, Faramir, to succour him while he lived.'

This was preserved in the fair copy ('H') that followed, and was not rewritten to the form in RK (p. 131) until the typescript stage was reached. At the end of this passage my father wrote, as in D, that Gandalf and Berithil bore Faramir to 'the houses of the sick', but he changed this to 'the Houses of Healing', with the Elvish name *Berin a*

380 THE WAR OF THE RING

Nestad, changed at once to *Bair Nestedriu*, both of which were struck out; but a little later in the chapter ('So now at last they passed into the high circles of the City, and in the light of morning they went towards the houses that were set apart for the tending of men hurt or dying', cf. RK p. 131) the name *Bair Nestedriu* reappears. In the fair copy H there is no Elvish name for the Houses of Healing in the first of these passages, but at the second the form *Bair Nestad* is found. In the first typescript, in this same passage, the name is *Edeb na Nestad*, which was struck through.

At this time the story was that Gandalf and Pippin rode through the Closed Door on their way to Rath Dínen (see note 3). Now, as Berithil and Gandalf bore the bier, 'behind them walked Pippin and beside him Shadowfax with downcast head'; and when they came back to the Door (here called 'the Steward's Door' as in RK; 'the Stewards' Door' in the fair copy) Gandalf sent Shadowfax back to his stable, dismissing him in the same words that in RK (p. 127) he used when they first came to the Door.

At the point in the narrative where the dome of the House of the Stewards in Rath Dínen cracked and fell, and 'then in terror the servants fled, and followed Gandalf', my father set down an outline, which was struck through.

Gandalf must say something about the Stone. How it was kept in Tower but only *kings* supposed to look in it.[7] Denethor in his grief when Faramir returned must have looked in it – hence his madness and despair. For though not yielding to Enemy (like Saruman) he got an impression of the Dark Lord's overwhelming might. The will of the Lord thus entered the Tower, confused all counsels, and kept Gandalf from the field. All this takes about 1½ hours to nearly 8 o'clock? So as they come out into the upper circles they hear the dreadful shriek of the Nazgûl's end. Gandalf forbodes evil. Does Gandalf look out from a high place? When [he] has put Faramir in the sick quarters with Berithil as his servant and guard, Gandalf and Pippin go back down towards the Gates and meet the cortège with bodies of Éowyn and Théoden.[8] Gandalf takes charge; but Pippin goes in search of Merry; and meets him wandering half blind. Eventually Gandalf and Pippin stand on battlement and watch progress of battle. Gandalf says he is not needed there so much as with the sick. Pippin (and Gandalf?) see the coming of Aragorn and the fleet. Eventually the captains return after victory at the Red Sunset.

Council must follow next day. Is any account of Aragorn's march put in at council?

THE PYRE OF DENETHOR 381

The text in this manuscript (G) was then continued to the end; and when my father came to record Gandalf's words about the *palantír* of Minas Tirith they took this form:

'... Alas! but now I perceive how it was that his will was able to enter among us into the very heart of this City.

'Long have I guessed that here in the White Tower, as at Orthanc, one of the great Stones of Sight was preserved. Denethor did not in the days of his wisdom ever presume to use it, nor to challenge Sauron, knowing the limits of his own powers. But in his grief for Faramir, distraught by the hopeless peril of his City, he must have dared to do this: to look in the Stone. He hoped maybe to see if help was drawing nigh; but the ways of the Rohirrim in the North were hidden; and he saw at first only what was preparing in the South. And then slowly his eye was drawn east, to see what it was willed that he should see. And this vision [*struck out:* true or false] of the great might of Mordor, fed the despair that was already in his heart until it rose and engulfed his mind.'

['That fits well with what I saw,' said Pippin. 'The Lord went away from the room where Faramir lay; and it was when he came back that I first thought he was changed, old and broken.'

'It was in the very hour that Faramir was brought back that many saw a strange light in the topmost chamber of the Tower,' said Berithil.

'Alas! then I guess truly,' said Gandalf.] 'Thus the will of Sauron entered into the Tower; and thus I have been delayed here. ...'

The passage that I have enclosed in square brackets was an addition, but pretty clearly one made at the time of writing. In the fair copy manuscript of 'The Siege of Gondor' the passage describing how Prince Imrahil brought Faramir to the White Tower after his rescue, how Denethor then went up to the secret room under the summit of the Tower, and how a light was seen flickering there (RK pp. 94–5), was absent: see p. 340 note 17. It was no doubt at this time that it was added. The fair copy H retains the form of the passage just given; it was not until later that it was revised to introduce Gandalf's guess that Denethor had looked many times into the *palantír*, and Berithil's corroboration 'But we have seen that light before, and it has been rumoured in the City that the Lord would at times wrestle in thought with his Enemy.' In the original manuscript of 'Minas Tirith' he had said to Pippin as they sat on the battlements that Denethor was reputed to be able to 'read somewhat of the mind of the Enemy' as he

382   THE WAR OF THE RING

sat in his high chamber at night, but he did not then add the words
'wrestling with him', nor 'And so it is that he is old, worn before his
time' (RK p. 37; p. 292 note 21). Thus Pippin's words, preserved in
RK, 'it was only when he returned that I first thought he was changed,
old and broken' were written when my father believed that it was only
now and for the first time that Denethor had dared to look into the
Seeing Stone of Minas Tirith.

NOTES

1 Gandalf says here: 'Is it not a law in the City that those who wear
   the black and silver must stay in the Citadel unless their lord leaves
   it?' And Pippin replies: 'He has left it.' For a previous use of this
   passage in a different context see p. 338 and note 23.
2 Cf. the original manuscript of the chapter 'Minas Tirith', p. 281:
   'And Denethor at least does not expect him in any way, *for he does
   not know that he exists.*' This in fact survived through all the
   typescripts and was only changed on the proof to the reading of
   RK: 'Though if he comes, it is likely to be in some way that no one
   expects, *not even Denethor.*'
3 A minor narrative difference is that when Gandalf and Pippin
   came to the Closed Door on Shadowfax they rode through it,
   though on the steep winding road beyond 'they could go only at a
   walk.' In RK Gandalf 'dismounted and bade Shadowfax return to
   his stable' (see p. 380).
4 When writing a very rapid draft my father would move from 'thou'
   to 'you' in the same speech, but his intention from the first was
   certainly that in this scene Denethor should 'thou' Gandalf, while
   Gandalf should use 'you'. In one passage confusion between 'thou'
   and 'you' remains in RK (Denethor's speech beginning 'Hope on
   then!', p. 129). Here in the fair copy manuscript my father wrote:
   'Do I not know that you commanded this halfling here to keep
   silence?'; subsequently he changed 'you commanded' to 'thou
   commandedst', but presumably because he disliked this form he
   changed the sentence to 'Do I not know that this halfling was
   commanded by thee ...' At the same time he added the sentence
   'That you brought him hither to be a spy within in my very
   chamber?', changing it immediately and for the same reason to
   'That he was brought hither ...' For some reason the 'you'
   constructions reappeared in the first typescript, and so remained.
5 'V.6', not 'V.7' as in RK, because 'The Passing of the Grey
   Company' and 'The Muster of Rohan' were still one chapter,
   'Many Roads Lead Eastward'. The fair copy manuscript (H) was
   also numbered 'XLIX' and 'V.6', with the title '(a) The Pyre of
   Denethor'.

THE PYRE OF DENETHOR   383

6   The meaning of *whereas* here is 'inasmuch as', 'seeing that'.
7   I take this to mean, in a colloquial sense of 'supposed', 'it was only
    the kings who were held to be permitted to look in it', rather than
    'it was only the kings who looked in it, as it was thought.'
8   The story now was that Éowyn was still alive: p. 369.

XI

THE HOUSES OF HEALING

On the same page that my father used for the original opening draft (A) of 'The Pyre of Denethor' (p. 374) he also wrote a brief passage for another place in the narrative, beginning: '"Well, Meriadoc, where are you going?" He looked up, and there was Gandalf.' This was, I feel certain, the opening of a new chapter; and since it stands first on the page, with the opening of 'The Pyre of Denethor' below it, it seems to me likely that my father for a moment thought to continue the narrative after 'The Battle of the Pelennor Fields' in this way. But however this may be, he subsequently on another page (numbered 'a') wrote a new opening ('A mist was in Merry's eyes of tears and of weariness when they drew near to the ruined Gates of Minas Tirith'), and joined this on to the first opening (now numbered 'b') already in existence. This first part ('a') of the brief composite text is already very close indeed to the opening of the chapter in RK; the second (earlier) part 'b' differs from the text of RK in that it is Gandalf, not Pippin, who finds Merry wandering in the streets of the City:

'Well, Meriadoc, where are you going?'

He looked up, and the mist before his eyes cleared a little,[1] and there was Gandalf. He was in a narrow empty street, and no one else was there. He passed his hand over his eyes. 'Where is the king?' he said, 'and Éowyn, and —' he stumbled and sat down on a doorstep and began to weep again.

'They have gone into the Citadel,' said Gandalf. 'You must have fallen asleep on your feet and taken a wrong turning. You are worn out, and I will ask no questions yet, save one: are you hurt, or wounded?'

'No,' said Merry, 'well, no, I don't think so. But I cannot use my right arm, not since I stabbed him. The sword has burned away like wood.'

Gandalf looked grave. 'Well, you must come with me. I will carry you. You are not fit to walk. They should not have let you. But then they did not know about you or they would have shown you more honour. But when you know more you will pardon them: many dreadful things have happened in this City.'

'Pardon them? What for?' said Merry. 'All I want is a bed if there's one to have.'

THE HOUSES OF HEALING   385

'You'll have that,' said Gandalf, 'but you may need more.' He looked grave and careworn. 'Here is yet another on my hands,' he sighed. 'After war comes the woe and hopeless oft seems the task of the healer.'

At this point the part 'b' ends and is followed by 'When the dark shadow at the Gate withdrew Gandalf still sat motionless', the opening of 'The Pyre of Denethor', as described above.

My father now wrote an outline, obviously before the story had proceeded further.

Pippin meets Merry wandering half blind and witless – (as in scene previously written: but *not* humorous). Merry also is taken to sickhouse (Faramir, Éowyn, Merry).

[King Théoden is laid on bier in Hall of the Tower covered with gold. His body is embalmed after the manner of Gondor. Long after when the Rohirrim carried it back to Rohan and laid it in the mounds, it was said that he slept there in peace unchanged, clad in the cloth of gold of Gondor, save that his hair and beard still grew but were golden, and a river of gold would at times flow from Théoden's Howe. Also a voice would be heard crying
> Arise, arise, Riders of Théoden
> Fell deeds awake. Forth Eorlingas!
when peril threatened.][2]

Now the Captains return. But Aragorn sets his pavilion in the field before the gate and will not enter without permission and sends in word begging leave to enter and speak with the Steward. They tell him that the Steward is dead by his own hand and the Lord Faramir sick, to death. Then he lays aside all the badges of Elendil, and enters as a plain man. Aragorn meets Pippin and Gandalf and asks after Merry. He is given news of Éowyn. Great joy of Éomer.

All that night Aragorn tends the sick, for the Kings of Gondor had both a craft and a power of healing, and by this [?latter] it was made clear that the true king was returned. Faramir opens his eyes and looks on Aragorn and love springs between them. Merry too recovers.

Counsel [*read* Council] of the Lords. Gandalf warns them that what Denethor had said is true: there was no final victory in arms against the Enemy. We fought here as best we could, because we had to; and it is so appointed in this world that resistance must be made to evil without final hope. But when we

386 THE WAR OF THE RING

take arms *to attack* we are using that power which is pre-eminently found in the Ring, and it would be logical to do as Denethor desired in that case: to use the Ring. So indeed we should probably [?now] have victory and overthrow Sauron. But only to set up another. So that in the end the result would be as evil, if different, or possibly worse, as if Sauron recovered the Ring. Therefore have I .....[3] recovery in order that for a great age victory should be otherwise.

But we must still use such power as we have. And not delay. Sauron must still be kept busy and deem we have the Ring.

Another page of outline-notes, very roughly pencilled, probably followed this.

Long sojourn of rest in Minas Tirith and coming of Finduilas?[4] [*written above:* and Galadriel].

Hobbits all go home via Rohan: funeral of Théoden, and then through Gap and up west of Misty Mountains to Rivendell and then home.

Yes, said Sam, as he closed the Book. That all happened a long time ago.

Aragorn will only enter as lord of the Forod, not as king.[5]

Lords ride in, and see Théoden lying in state. Where is Gandalf? He comes in late [*or* later] and tells of Théoden's fall,[6] and Yoreth's words.

They go to Houses of Healing, and Aragorn asks for *athelas*. He heals the sick. Yoreth says he must be king. After supper he heals many sick.

Council next day. Gandalf's advice. Merry wakes up feeling nearly well. While Council is [?on] Gimli, Legolas and Pippin talk. They ..... and hear of the love of Éowyn for Aragorn at Dunharrow. And of the great ride to Pelargir.

The lords ride east: 1000 Rohirrim, Dol Amroth and [?so on]. And a first force to hold Morgul. They ride into shadow of ambush. Peril.

A complete draft ('A') for the chapter now followed, written rapidly but legibly in ink. In the first part of the chapter there are passages of marked divergence from the story that followed. The manuscript A was followed by a fair copy 'B', for which some pages were taken out of A, including the opening page bearing the chapter number and title: 'Ch.L The Houses of Healing', the number changed subsequently to 'XLIX (b)'.[7]

The first divergence in A from RK comes with Gandalf's words

THE HOUSES OF HEALING   387

when he came on Pippin and Merry on the pavement of the main street up to the Citadel (RK p. 135):

> 'He should have been borne in honour into this City,' he said. 'Greater was the wisdom of Elrond than mine. For if I had had my way neither you nor he, Pippin, would have set out; and then far more grievous would the evils of this day have been. Faramir and Éowyn would be dead, and the Black Captain would be abroad to work ruin on all hope.'

This was repeated in the fair copy B, and (with loss of the final sentence 'Faramir and Éowyn would be dead ...') in the following typescripts: the change to 'He has well repaid my trust: for if Elrond had not yielded to me, neither of you would have set out' was not made until the book was in proof. This is decidedly strange: for the form of the Choosing of the Company in *The Fellowship of the Ring* (p. 289), in which it was through Gandalf's advocacy *against* Elrond that Merry and Pippin were included, had been reached long before in the second version of 'The Ring Goes South' (VII.164). Earlier than this, it is true, Gandalf had also been opposed to their inclusion ('Elrond's decision is wise', he had said, VII.115), but only here, and again in 'The Last Debate' (p. 415), is there any suggestion that it was Elrond who advocated their inclusion in opposition to Gandalf.

In the passage that follows, after the account of the 'leechcraft of Gondor' and the unknown malady named 'the Black Shadow' that came from the Nazgûl, the text of A is much briefer than that of RK (p. 136):

> And those that were so stricken fell slowly ever into a deeper dream, and from fever passed to a deadly cold and so died. But Faramir burned with a fever that would not abate.
>
> And an old wife, Yoreth ...

Thus there is no reference here to the morning wearing away and the day passing to sunset, while 'still Gandalf waited and watched and did not go forth'; and after Yoreth had uttered the old saying that 'The hands of the king are the hands of a healer' A diverges altogether from the later story.

> 'Mithrandir is wise and skilful,' said another. 'In this at least he is not a king,' said the old wife. 'He has done much for us, but rather his skill lies in the teaching of men, to do what they can or should.'
>
> But Gandalf seeing that all was done that could be done for the present arose and went out, and calling for Shadowfax rode away.

388   THE WAR OF THE RING

But Pippin and Berithil found themselves together little needed while the sick were yet in peril, and while such errands as were needful were done by the boys, Bergil and his friends, who had been saved from the wreck of the Rath a Chelerdain and sent up hither. So they went to the roof of the house that stood above the battlement of the wall, and they looked out. The battle now raged upon the fields; but it was far from the walls, and all the enemy had now been drawn away from the City; and they could not mark how fortune went: nought but a dust and a smoke in the distance away southward, and a far crying of horn and of trumpet. Yet so it was that Pippin with the farsighted eyes of his people was the first to descry the coming of the fleet.

'Look, look, Berithil!' he cried. 'The Lord was not all demented. He saw something in truth. There are ships on the River.'

'Yes,' said Berithil. 'But not such as he spoke of. I know the ...[8] of those ships and their sails. They come from Umbar and the havens of the Corsairs. Hark!'

And all about them men were crying in dismay: 'The Corsairs of Umbar!'

'You may say what you like and so may they,' said Pippin, 'but this I will say for my lord who is dead: I will believe him. Here comes Aragorn. Though how, and why in this way I cannot guess. Here comes the heir of Elendil!' he shouted; but no one, not even Berithil, took any heed of his small voice.

Yet true he proved. And at last it was known in the City. And all men were full of wonder. And so hope grew as the day rose to noon and waned, and at last it came to the red sunset. And watchers looking out saw all the fields before them dyed as with blood, and the sky above them was bloodred, and at last ere the red burned out to evening ash-grey over the fields of the Pelennor rode the captains in victory to the City.

Aragorn and Éomer and Imrahil now drew near the City with their captains and knights; and when they came before the Gates Aragorn said: 'Behold the setting of the sun in fire ...'

Aragorn's words are then as in RK p. 137, and his speech with Éomer that follows; but with Imrahil's intervention the original text diverges again:

And the Prince Imrahil said: 'Wise are your words, lord, if one who is kinsman of the house of the Stewards may venture to

THE HOUSES OF HEALING   389

give counsel. Yet I would not have you remain at the door like a beggar.'

'Then I will not,' laughed Aragorn. '[*added:* I will enter as one.] The banner shall be furled and the tokens no more displayed.' And he bade Halbarad [> Elladan][9] to furl the standard, and he removed the crown and stars[10] and gave them to the keeping of the sons of Elrond. And he entered the City on foot clad only in a grey mantle above his mail and bearing no other token save the green stone of Galadriel, and he said: 'I come only as Aragorn Lord of the Rangers of Forod.'[11]

And so the great captains of victory passed through the city and the tumult of the people, and mounted to the Citadel, and came to the Hall of the Tower seeking the Steward.

The description of Théoden lying in state follows as in RK (pp. 137–8), but then the story of his afterlife in the mound at Edoras is introduced and expanded from the outline given on p. 385; I cite it here from the fair copy B, where the text is all but identical to A except in the words heard from the mound.[12]

And thus, it was said in song, he remained ever after while the realm of Rohan endured. For when later the Rohirrim bore his body away to the Mark and laid it in the mounds of his fathers, there, clad in the cloth of gold of Gondor, he slept in peace unchanged, save only that his hair still grew and was turned to silver, and at times a river of silver would flow from Théoden's Howe. And that was a token of prosperity; but if peril threatened then at whiles men would hear a voice in the mound crying in the ancient tongue of the Mark:

> Arísath nú Rídend míne!
> Théodnes thegnas thindath on orde!
> Féond oferswithath! Forth Eorlingas!

Then follow the questions of Imrahil and Éomer in the Hall of the Tower, whereby they learn that 'the Steward is in the Houses of Healing' (thinking that this means Denethor), and Éomer learns that Éowyn is still living, just as in RK, except that when Éomer leaves the hall 'the others followed him' ('and the Prince followed him' RK), because Aragorn is present.

And when they came forth evening had come, with many stars. And even as the light waned Gandalf returned alone out of the East up the road from Osgiliath, glimmering in the twilight. And he went also to the Houses of Healing, and he met

390   THE WAR OF THE RING

the Lords before its doors. And they greeted him; and they said: 'We seek the Steward and it is said that he is in this house. ...'

In the passage that follows there are differences from RK, in that Aragorn does not only now appear as 'the cloaked man' come with Gandalf, unrecognised until he steps into the lantern-light. Thus Imrahil says: 'Shall it not be the lord Aragorn?', and Aragorn replies: 'No, it shall be the Lord of Dol Amroth until Faramir awakes. But it is my counsel that Mithrandir should rule us all in the days that follow and our dealings with the Enemy.' Then Gandalf speaks as in RK of his sole hope for the sick resting in Aragorn, and quotes the words of Yoreth.

When Aragorn encounters Berithil and Pippin at the door Pippin says: 'Trotter! How splendid. There, Berithil, you see Denethor was right after all.' The last sentence was struck out, and replaced by Pippin's words in RK (p. 139): 'Do you know, I guessed it was you in the black ships. But they were all shouting *Corsairs* and would not listen to me. How did you do it?' And when Imrahil says to Éomer 'Yet perchance in some other name he will wear his crown', Aragorn overhearing replies: 'Verily, for in the high tongue of eld I am Elessar, Elfstone, the renewer.'[13] Then lifting the green stone of Galadriel he says: 'But Trotter shall be the name of my house, if ever that be established; yet perhaps in the same high tongue it shall not sound so ill, and *tarakil*[14] I will be and all the heirs of my body.'

In the following passage the first section that I have enclosed in square brackets is so enclosed in the manuscript, with a query against it, though it was used in RK; the second section in square brackets has a line drawn round it in the manuscript with a mark of deletion and a query against it. In the fair copy the first is again put within square brackets, and the second does not appear.

And so they went in. [And as they passed towards the rooms where the sick were tended Gandalf told of the deeds of Éowyn and Meriadoc. 'For,' he said, 'long have I stood by them, and at first they spoke much in their sleep dreaming, before they sank into a yet deeper darkness. Also it is given to me to see many things afar off.] [And when there came a ...[15] cry from the fields I was near to the walls and looked out. And even as I did, the doom long foretold came to pass, though in a manner that had been hidden from me. Not by the hand of man was the Lord of the Nazgûl doomed to fall, and in that doom placed his trust. But he was felled by a woman and with the aid of a halfling;[16] and I heard the fading of his last cry borne away by the wind.']

It will be seen that there were major differences in the structure of the story as told in A from its form in RK. In the first place, the distant

THE HOUSES OF HEALING 391

view of the battlefield seen by Pippin and Berithil from the roof of the Houses of Healing is told in direct narrative, and thus the coming of the black fleet up Anduin is repeated from 'The Battle of the Pelennor Fields'. Since Pippin and Berithil were present at the House of the Stewards in Rath Dínen they had heard Denethor accuse Gandalf of intriguing to displace him: 'But I know your mind and its plots. Do I not see the fleets even now coming up Anduin! So with the left hand you would use me as a shield against Mordor, and with the right hand bring up this Ranger of the North to take my place' (p. 378). This knowledge Denethor had acquired from the *palantír*. The idea that Denethor knew that Aragorn was in command of the ships of the Corsairs was changed on the draft manuscript (G) of 'The Pyre of Denethor' (p. 379), and in the fair copy of that chapter, already as first written, his knowledge of Aragorn is derived as in RK from his conversations with Pippin: his sight of the black fleet becomes for him an overpowering proof of the futility of resistance to Mordor. The present text must therefore have preceded the fair copy of 'The Pyre of Denethor'.

In the form of the story in A Pippin has a reason for declaring that Aragorn is coming with the fleet ('There, Berithil, you see Denethor was right after all', p. 390) and for shouting 'Here comes the heir of Elendil!' when everyone was crying 'The Corsairs of Umbar!' (p. 388); in RK he can have no reason at all for his words to Aragorn ('Do you know, I guessed it was you in the black ships'), nothing but a strange presentiment.

In the second place, Gandalf leaves the Houses of Healing long before sunset and disappears on Shadowfax. Aragorn does not refuse to enter Minas Tirith with Éomer and Imrahil; and thus he is present at the door of the Houses of Healing when Gandalf comes back, returning alone 'up the road from Osgiliath' in the dusk (p. 389). Nothing is told of his errand (but I think it can be seen what it was from the B version of this part of the story, to be given shortly). In the changed story he did not leave the Houses of Healing until sunset, and his errand was to bring Aragorn in from outside the walls: this being a sudden decision inspired by the words of Yoreth. In the A version he does not appear to take any particular account of her words, and he leaves when he sees that 'all was done that could be done for the present'; yet when he returns he says as in RK that 'only in [Aragorn's] coming have I any hope for those that lie within', quoting the words of Yoreth.

A remarkable short text evidently belongs to this phase in the development of the story, as is seen from the fact that Aragorn has entered the city without Gandalf, who is looking for him. This text is found on an isolated slip in my father's worst handwriting, which he partly elucidated in pencil (with some queries), and slightly changed, in not quite his worst handwriting.

392   THE WAR OF THE RING

'Did you ride with the Rohirrim?' said Gandalf.

'Nay indeed,' said Legolas. 'A strange journey we have had with Aragorn by the Paths of the Dead, and we came here at the last in ships taken from our foes. Not often has one the chance to bring news to you, Gandalf!'

'Not often,' said Gandalf heavily. 'But my cares are many in these days, and my heart is sad. I am growing weary at last, Glóin's son, as this great matter draws to the final edge of its doom. Alas! alas! How our Enemy contrives evil out of our good. For the Lord of the City slew himself in despair seeing the black fleet approach. For the coming of the fleet and the sword of Elendil secured the victory but gave the last stroke of despair to the Lord of the City. But [?come], I must still labour. Tell me, where is Aragorn? Is he in these tents?'

'Nay, he has gone up into the City,' said Legolas, 'cloaked in grey and secretly.'

'Then I must go,' said Gandalf.

'But tell us in return one thing first,' said Gimli. 'Where are those young friends of ours who cost us such great pains? It is to be hoped that they were not [?worsted] and they are still alive.'

'One is lying grievously sick in the City after a great deed,' said Gandalf, 'and the other stays beside him.'

'Then may we come with you?' said Gimli.

'You may indeed!' said Gandalf.

This encounter on the fields of the Pelennor was lost, and nowhere else is Gandalf's meeting with Legolas and Gimli after they parted at Dol Baran recorded.

As the fair copy B was first written, Gandalf's earlier departure from the Houses of Healing and the scene in which Berithil and Pippin see the black fleet from the roof were retained;[17] but there are two significant differences. After Yoreth's words it is now said: 'But Gandalf *hearing this saying*, and seeing that all was done that could be done *by the leechcraft of Gondor*, arose and went out'; and the conversation of Berithil and Pippin is now changed:

'Look, look, Berithil!' he cried. 'The Lord did not see only visions of madness. Here come the ships up the River that he spoke of. What are they?'

'Alas!' answered Berithil. 'Now I can almost forgive his despair. I know the fashion of these ships and their sails, for that is the duty of all watchmen. They come from Umbar and the Haven of the Corsairs! Hark!'

THE HOUSES OF HEALING   393

And all about them men were now crying in dismay: 'The Corsairs of Umbar!'

Pippin's heart sank. It seemed bitter to him that after the joy of the horns at dawn hope should be destroyed again. 'I wonder where Gandalf has gone,' he thought. And then another question arose in his mind: 'Aragorn: where is he? He should have come with the Rohirrim, but he doesn't seem to have done so.'

'Berithil,' he said, 'I wonder: could there be any mistake? What if this was really Aragorn with the Broken Sword coming in the nick of time?'

'If so, he is coming in the ships of our enemies,' said Berithil.

It seems that Pippin's thought here, 'I wonder where Gandalf has gone' giving rise to the question 'Aragorn: where is he?', taken with the more explicit statement concerning Gandalf's departure, makes it certain that he had gone, as in the later story, to find Aragorn and (because 'the hands of the king are the hands of a healer') to bring him urgently to the Houses of Healing.[18] But why Gandalf did not return till dusk, after Aragorn had entered the city, is not explained.

At this point my father struck from the B manuscript all that followed 'and then passed to silence and a deadly cold, and so died' (RK p. 136; see p. 387) and replaced it with the text that stands in RK, with Gandalf leaving the Houses of Healing at sunset, his thought and purpose now perfectly plain: 'Men may long remember your words, Yoreth; for there is hope in them. Maybe a king has indeed returned to Gondor; or have you not heard the strange tidings that have come to the City?' To the point we have reached in A ('Also it is given to me to see many things afar off', p. 390) the fair copy B (apart from the passage concerning Théoden's Howe at Edoras already cited, and a few points that are mentioned in the notes) then has the text of RK.

The latter part of the chapter in A was written with remarkable fluency – or, at any rate, the text as it stands in this original draft[19] was scarcely changed afterwards. The only notable divergence from RK is found in the passage where Aragorn, Éomer, and Gandalf speak beside Éowyn's bed; for while the actual words of RK (p. 143) are present, what became Gandalf's speech is given to Aragorn. He begins: 'My friend, you had horses and deeds of arms ...', and continues to '... a hutch to trammel some wild thing in?' (where Gandalf ceases in RK), and then (without the sentence 'Then Éomer was silent, and looked on his sister, as if pondering anew all the days of their past life together') goes on, from the point where he begins in RK: 'I saw also what you saw. And few other griefs amid the ill chances of this world ...' Above 'said Aragorn' at the beginning of the speech my father wrote, almost certainly while still writing this

394   THE WAR OF THE RING

manuscript, 'Gandalf?'; and subsequently he made in pencil the changes that give the passage the form that it has in RK.

Beyond this there are only details to mention. The herb-master, in his discourse concerning the plant *kingsfoil*, declares it to be named *athelas* 'in the noble tongue, or to those who know somewhat of the Númenórean — ', 'Númenórean' being changed later both on A and on B to 'Valinorian' (and afterwards to 'Valinorean'); and Aragorn replies: 'I do so, and care not whether you say now *asea aranaite* or *kingsfoil*, so long as you have some.' The form *aranaite* became *aranion* on the final typescript.

When Aragorn leaves Merry (RK p. 146) he says: 'May the Shire for ever live unwithered and unchanged. For this, maybe, more than all else, I hope and labour';[20] the last part of this, from 'and unchanged', being struck from the fair copy.[21]

The chapter in A ended with Gandalf's words with the Warden of the Houses of Healing: '"They are a remarkable race," said the Warden, nodding his head. "Very tough in the fibre, I deem." "It goes deeper than the fibre," said Gandalf.' The conclusion of the chapter in RK is roughed out in a pencilled text that was subsequently over-written by material belonging to 'The Last Debate' (cf. note 19), but some of it can be read. Where the fair copy B has (as in RK) 'and so the name which it was foretold at his birth that he should bear was chosen by his own people', this first draft has 'and so his own choice was fulfilled [?in] the title chosen long before.' The final passage is largely illegible, but the following can be seen: 'And [?in the morning] when he had slept a little he arose and ..... called a council and the captains met in a chamber of the Tower ...' The fair copy ends as does the chapter in RK, with Aragorn leaving the city just before dawn and going to his tent; and pencilled beneath the last words of the text is this note: 'Aragorn will not go in the City again. So Imrahil, Gandalf and Éomer hold council [in the] tents with the sons of Elrond.'

NOTES

1   *and the mist before his eyes cleared a little*: this was added after the 'a' part of the text was written and joined on to 'b'.

2   This passage is enclosed within square brackets in the manu-script.

3   A first illegible word here almost certainly begins *res* and ends *ed*, but cannot as it stands be read as *resisted*. A second word could be 'the' or 'his'.

4   For a previous mention of Finduilas Elrond's daughter see p. 370.

5   Cf. the first narrative text (A) of the chapter, p. 389: 'I come only as Aragorn Lord of the Rangers of Forod.'

THE HOUSES OF HEALING   395

6 *and tells of Théoden's fall:* i.e. (I take it) the manner of Théoden's
   fall, of which Gandalf knew (cf. the second passage in square
   brackets on p. 390).

7 The first text A was paginated continuously on from 'The Pyre of
   Denethor', as also was the fair copy B. At some point my father
   wrote on the opening page of 'The Houses of Healing' (this page
   being common to both texts) the chapter number 'L', i.e.
   separating it from 'The Pyre of Denethor'; but the number 'XLIX
   (b)', following 'XLIX (a)' for 'The Pyre of Denethor' (see p. 382
   note 5), again makes them subdivisions of a single chapter,
   without an overall title.

8 The word might, just possibly, be 'crewmen'. B has 'fashion'
   (p. 392).

9 Halbarad was named among the slain in the original drafting of
   'The Battle of the Pelennor Fields' (p. 371).

10 *he removed the crown and stars:* the word 'and' was struck out;
   the replacement is illegible, but may be 'of' with another word
   struck out, i.e. 'crown of stars'. In B this becomes simply 'the
   crown'; altered on the first typescript to 'the crown of the North
   Kingdom', this survived into the proof, on which it was altered to
   'the Star of the North Kingdom'. Cf. 'The Battle of the Pelennor
   Fields', p. 370, where 'about his helm there was a kingly crown'
   was replaced on the proof by 'upon his brow was the Star of
   Elendil'.

11 Cf. RK p. 138 (at a different point in the narrative): 'I am but the
   Captain of the Dúnedain of Arnor'. In the fair copy manuscript,
   at the same point in the narrative as in RK, Aragorn says: 'I am
   but the Captain of the Rangers of Forod'.

12 In the first text A the verse is in modern English in the same words
   as in the outline on p. 385. In both A and B the passage is
   enclosed in square brackets.

13 In B the text remained almost the same: 'Verily, for in the high
   tongue of old I am Elessar, the Elfstone, and the Renewer', and
   this is the reading of the First Edition of LR. In the Second
   Edition *Envinyatar* was added before 'the Renewer'.

14 *tarakil:* the fourth letter *(a)* is not certain, but is very probable,
   especially in view of the form in B, where the text remained the
   same as in A but with *Tarakon* here. This was altered to
   Tarantar, which survived into the first typescript, where it was
   altered to *Telkontar* (> *Telcontar* on the proof).

15 The word begins with *gr(e)*, but is certainly not *great*. Possibly the
   word intended was *great*, but the last letters, which look like *ry*,
   were due to the following word *cry*.

16 On the doom of the Lord of the Nazgûl see pp. 334–5, 368.

17 It is said of Bergil and his friends in this version (see p. 388):
   'When the fire-bolts had fallen in the City they had been sent [to]

396   THE WAR OF THE RING

the upper circle; but the fair house in the Street of the Lamp-wrights had been destroyed.'

18   Cf. also the brief outline given on p. 386: 'Where is Gandalf? He comes in late and tells of Théoden's fall, *and Yoreth's words*.'

19   A part of the conclusion of the chapter, from '"He [Merry] lies nearby in this house, and I must go to him," said Gandalf' to 'For I have not slept in such a bed since I rode from Dunharrow, nor eaten since the dark before dawn' (RK pp. 145–6), is in fact extant in a preliminary pencilled text, subsequently over-written by a text in ink that belongs to the story of 'The Last Debate'. This draft, most of which has been read by Taum Santoski, shows no significant differences from the more finished version in A.

20   Cf. Aragorn's words to Halbarad at Helm's Deep, p. 306.

21   I collect here a few other details. For 'whether Aragorn had indeed some forgotten *power of Westernesse*' (RK p. 144) A, and at first B, had 'art or wizardry'. The name *Imloth Melui* in Yoreth's recollection of her youth (RK p. 142) appears thus from the first; and as in RK (p. 146) Aragorn says to Merry that the herb-master will tell him that tobacco is called '*westmansweed* by the vulgar, and *galenas* by the noble', where the pencilled draft that is extant for this portion of the chapter (note 19) has 'pipeweed' and 'sweet *galenas*'. For the name *galenas* see p. 38.

XII

THE LAST DEBATE

At some time before he began work on this chapter my father set down an outline entitled 'The march of Aragorn and defeat of [the] Haradrim.' This must have preceded 'The Battle of the Pelennor Fields', since the name *Haramon* appears, not *Emyn Arnen* (see p. 370 and note 11);[1] it was almost certainly a companion to the outline 'The Story Foreseen from Forannest' (pp. 359 ff.), but is obviously best given here. At the head of the page my father afterwards pencilled a note asking whether it might not be a good idea 'to have part of this told by a man of Morthond Vale', but nothing ever came of this. Pencilled changes made to the text are shown.

Aragorn takes 'Paths of the Dead' morning of 8 March, passes tunnels of mountains. (This tale will have to be told in brief later, probably at feast of victory in Minas Tirith – by Gimli and/or Legolas.) They see skeleton in armour of Bealdor son of Brego.[2] But except for dark and a feeling of dread meet no evil. The tunnels become the issuing caverns of Morthond. It is dusk [> afternoon] of 8 March when Aragorn and his company come out into the uplands of the head of the Vale of Morthond; and ride to Stone of Erech.[3] This was a black stone, according to legend brought from Númenor, set up to mark the meeting place of Isildur and Anárion with the last king of the dark men of the Mountains, who swore allegiance to the sons of Elendil, vowing to aid them and their kin for ever, 'even though Death should take us.' The stone was enclosed in a now ruined ring-wall and beside it the Gondorians had anciently erected a tower, and there had been kept one of the *palantíri*. No men went near the tower. Rumour of terror flies through the vales, for the 'King of the Dead' has come back – and behold behind the *living men* a great host of shadow-men, some riding some striding but all moving like the wind, are seen.

Aragorn goes to Erech at midnight, blows horns (and dim shadow horns echo him) and unfurls banner. The star on it shines in the dark. He finds the *palantír* (unsullied) buried in a vault. From Erech he sets out [*added:* dark] morn of March 9 [*added:* at 5 a.m.]. For [*read* From ?] Erech to Fords of Lameduin (say Linhir?) is 175 miles direct, about 200 by road.[4]

398   THE WAR OF THE RING

Great terror and wonder precedes his march. At Linhir on Lameduin men of Lebennin and Lamedon are defending passage of river against Haradwaith. Aragorn reaches Linhir at evening on March 10 after two days and night[s] forced riding with host of shadow behind in the deepening dark of Mordor. All fly before him. Aragorn crosses Lameduin into Lebennin at morning of March 11 and hastens to Pelargir [added: 100 miles].[5]

From this point the outline, becoming very rough, was struck out and replaced, immediately, by a new text on the reverse of the sheet of paper. At the head of this page is the following brief passage concerning Frodo and Sam, which (while certainly written at the same time as the outline of Aragorn's journey) probably already stood there:

Rescue of Frodo. Frodo is lying naked in the Tower; but Sam finds by some chance that the elven-cloak of Lórien is lying in a corner. When they disguise themselves they put on the grey cloaks over all and become practically invisible – in Mordor the cloaks of the Elves become like a dark mantle of shadow.

Then follows, returning to the outline:

Aragorn crosses into Lebennin on March 11th (morning) and rides with all speed to Pelargir – the Shadow Host follows. The Haradrim fly before him in dismay. Some hearing news of his coming in time get their ships off and escape down Anduin, but most are not manned. Early on 12th Aragorn comes on the fleet driving all before him. Many of the ships are stuffed with captives, and they are partly manned (especially the oars) by captives taken in raids on Gondor, or slave-descendants of captives taken long before. These revolt. So Aragorn captures many ships and mans them, though several are burned. He works feverishly because he knows that doom of Minas Tirith is near, if he does not come in time. That night the Shadow Host vanishes and goes back into the mountain valleys, and finally disappears into the Paths of the Dead and is never seen again to come forth.[6]

He sets out at 6 a.m. on 13 March, rowing. On the south plain of Lebennin the Anduin is very broad (5–7 miles) and slow. So with many oars they make about 4 miles an hour and by 6 a.m. on 14th are 100 miles on way. It is 125 miles by river from Pelargir to that place where Anduin takes a west-loop round the feet of Haramon, a great hill in South Ithilien, and

THE LAST DEBATE

399

bends into the Pelennor, so that here the Ramas-Coren is but 15 [> 5] miles from the City,[7] and stands right on the water brink. Just before that point the river course runs nearly North-South (slightly N.W.) and points straight towards Minas Tirith so that watchers can see that reach – about 10 miles long.[8]

On morning of the 15th [*written above:* 14] a wind rises [*added:* at dawn] and freshens from S.W. The cloud and gloom begins to roll back. They hoist sails and now go with [*struck out:* more] speed. About 9 a.m. they can be seen by watchers from Minas Tirith who are dismayed. As soon as Aragorn catches sight of the city, and of the enemy, he hoists his standard (the White Crown with the stars of Sun and Moon on either hand: Elendil's badge).[9] A sun-gleam from the S.E. lights it up and it shines afar like white fire. Aragorn lands and drives off enemy.

Especially notable here is the recurrence of the idea that appeared in 'Many Roads Lead Eastward' (pp. 300, etc.): there was a *palantír* at Erech (in the earlier chapter Aragorn seemed to say that the Stone of Erech was itself the *palantír*, p. 309 note 10). This Stone replaced that of Aglarond (pp. 76–8), so that there were still five *palantíri* in the South.

When my father came to write the chapter his intention – and achievement – was that in it should be recounted not only the debate of the commanders following the Battle of the Pelennor Fields but also the story of the journey of the Grey Company as recounted by Gimli and Legolas to Merry and Pippin – and that it should then carry the story on to the arrival of the Host of the West before the Morannon. The manuscript, or manuscript corpus, was originally entitled 'The Parley at the Black Gate'.[10] It was a huge labour to achieve the final arrangement, entailing draft upon draft upon draft, with the most complicated re-use of existing pages, or parts of them, as he experimented with different solutions to the structural problem. It is more than likely that when this great mass of manuscript and typescript left his hands it was already in dire confusion, and its subsequent ordering into wholly factitious textual entities made it seem that in 'The Last Debate' my attempt to discern the true sequence of the writing of *The Lord of the Rings* would finally founder. But it has proved otherwise, and since no significant element seems to have been lost out of the whole complex the sequence of development in fact emerges here at least as clearly as in some far less difficult parts of the narrative. But of course to describe in detail each textual pathway would demand far more space than can be allowed to it.

It seems that before my father began the coherent drafting of the

400   THE WAR OF THE RING

chapter – while he was in fact still writing 'The Houses of Healing' – he
set down a form of the speeches at the opening of the debate that had
arisen in his mind and would not be postponed.[11] Since a great deal of
this does not appear in RK I give it in full.

'My lords,' said Gandalf. ' "Go forth and fight! Vanity! You
may triumph on the fields of Pelennor for a day. But against the
Power that now arises there is no victory." So said the Steward
of this City before he died. And though I do not bring you
counsels of despair, yet ponder the truth in this. The people of
the West are diminished; far and wide the lands lie empty. And
it is long since your rule retreated and left the wild peoples to
themselves, and they do not know you; and [they] will come
seeking new lands to dwell in. Now were it but a matter of war
between Men, such as has been for many ages, I would say: You
are now too few to march East either in wrath or friendship, to
subdue or to teach. Yet you might take thought together, and
make such boundaries, and such forts and strongholds, as
could long be maintained and restrain the gathering tide [>
?wild]. But your war is not only against numbers, and swords
and spears, and untamed peoples. You have an Enemy of great
power and malice, and he grows, and he it is that fills all the
hearts of the wild peoples with hate, and directs and governs
that hatred, and so they are become no longer like waves that
may roll at whiles against your battlements, to be withstood
with valour and defeated with forethought. They are rising in a
great tide to engulf you. What then shall you do? Seek to
overthrow your Enemy.'

'Overlate should we begin that task!' said Prince Imrahil.
'[Had Minas Morgul been destroyed in ages past, and the watch
upon the Black Gate maintained   We slept, and no sooner had
he re-entered the Nameless Land]   We slept, and awoke to find
him already grown beyond our measure. And to destroy him we
must overthrow first all the allies that he has gathered.'

'That is true,' said Gandalf. 'And their numbers are too great,
as Denethor indeed saw. Therefore this war is without final
hope, whether you sit here to endure siege upon siege, or march
out to be overwhelmed beyond the River. Prudence would
counsel you to await onset in strong places, for so at least shall
the time before the end be made a little longer.

'But now into the midst of all these counsels of war comes the
Ring. Here is a thing which could command victory even in our
present plight.'

THE LAST DEBATE

401

'I have heard only rumour of this,' said Imrahil. 'Is it not said the One Ring of Sauron of old has come back to light, and that if he regain it then he will be as mighty as he was in the Dark Years?'

'It is said so and said truly,' answered Gandalf. 'Only he will be more mighty than of old and more secure. For there is no longer any land beyond the Sea from which help may come; [and those who dwell beyond even the West will not move, for they have committed the Great Lands to the keeping of Men.]'[12]

'But if we should find the Ring and wield it, how would it give us victory?' asked Imrahil.

'It would not do so all in a day,' answered Gandalf. 'But were it to come to the hand of some one of power [?or] royalty, as say the Lord Aragorn, or the Steward of this City, or Elrond of Imladrist,[13] or even to me, then he being the Ringlord would wax ever in power and the desire of power; and all minds he would cow or dominate so that they would blindly do his will. And he could not be slain. More: the deepest secrets of the mind and heart of Sauron would become plain to him, so that the Dark Lord could do nothing unforeseen. The Ringlord would suck the very power and thought from him, so that all would forsake his allegiance and follow the Ringlord, and they would serve him and worship him as a God. And so Sauron would be overthrown utterly and fade into oblivion; but behold, there would be Sauron still ..... but upon the other side, [a tyrant brooking no freedom, shrinking from no deed of evil to hold his sway and to widen it].'

'And worse,' said Aragorn. 'For all that is left of the ancient power and wisdom of the West he would also have broken and corrupted.'

'Then what is the use of this Ring?' said Imrahil.

'Victory,' said [Gandalf >] Húrin Warden of the Keys.[14] 'At least we should have won the war, and not this foul lord of Mordor.'

'So might many a brave knight of the Mark or the Realm speak,' said Imrahil. 'But surely more wisdom is required of lords in council. Victory is in itself worthless. Unless Gondor stand for some good, then let it not stand at all; and if Mordor doth not stand for some evil that we will not brook in Mordor or out of it, then let it triumph.'

'Triumph it will, say or do what we will, or so it seems,' said Húrin. 'But after many words still I do not hear what is our

402   THE WAR OF THE RING

present purpose. Surely, it is but a plain choice between staying here and marching forth. And if those who are wiser or more farsighted than I tell me there is no long[er] hope in waiting here, then I for one am for marching forth, and taking doom by the outstretched hand. So we may give it a wrench at the least before it grips us.'

'And in this at any rate I approve Húrin's words,' said Gandalf. 'For all my speech was leading to just such counsel. This is not a war for victory that cannot be won by arms.[15] I have rejected the use of the Ring, for that would make victory the same as defeat. I have (like a fool, said Denethor) set the Ring at a great risk that our Enemy will regain it, and so utterly overwhelm us; for to retain it would be to risk the certainty that ere the last throes came upon us one among us would take it, and so bring about at least as great an evil. But still we have set our hands to war. For resist we must while we have strength – and hope. But now our salvation, if any can be achieved, does not rest upon our deeds of arms, yet it may be aided by them. Not by prudence, as I say, of the lesser wars of Men. But by a boldness, even a rashness, that in other case would be folly. For our hope is still, though daily it grows fainter, that Sauron has not recovered the Ring, and while that is so he will be in doubt and fear lest we have it. The greater our rashness the greater his fear, and the more will his eye and thought be turned to us and not elsewhere where his true peril is. Therefore I say we should follow up this victory as soon as we may and move East with all such force as we have.'

'Yet still there must be prudence,' said Imrahil. 'There is scarce a man or horse alive among us that is not weary, even those that are not sick or hurt. And we learn that there is an army left unfought upon our north flank. We cannot wholly denude the city, or it will burn behind us.'

'True enough, I would not counsel it,' said Gandalf. 'Indeed for my design the force we lead East need not be great enough for any assault in earnest upon Mordor, so long as it is great enough to challenge a battle.'

Turning now to the primary manuscript of the chapter, this is itself a massive complex of rejected and retained material, but it cannot be satisfactorily separated into distinct 'layers', and I shall treat it as a single entity, referring to it as 'the manuscript'.

The opening achieves almost word for word the form in RK pp. 148–9, beginning 'The morning came after the day of battle' and

THE LAST DEBATE

403

continuing as far as Gimli's remark to Legolas: 'It is ever so with all the things that Men begin: there is a frost in spring, or a blight in summer, and they fail of their promise.' A servant of Imrahil then guided them to the Houses of Healing, where they found Merry and Pippin in the garden, 'and the meeting of those friends was a merry one.' The narrative then moves directly into the debate: as in RK (p. 154) Imrahil and Éomer went down from the city to the tents of Aragorn, and there conferred with Gandalf, Aragorn, Elrohir and Elladan. 'They made Gandalf their chief and prayed him to speak first his mind'; and as in RK he began by citing the words of Denethor before his death, bidding his listeners ponder the truth of them. But now he went on, following and condensing a passage in the draft just given:

'The peoples of the West are diminished; and it is long since your rule retreated and left the wild peoples to themselves; and they do not know you, and neither love nor fear will long restrain them. And you have an Enemy of great power and malice, who fills all their hearts with hatred, and governs and directs that hatred, so that they are no longer like waves that roll at whiles against your walls to be thrown back one by one: they are united, and they are rising as a great tide to engulf you.

'The Stones of Seeing do not lie, and not even the Lord of Barad-dûr can make them do so ...'

The remainder of Gandalf's speech, with the interventions of Imrahil,[16] Aragorn, and Éomer, was achieved through a series of drafts that need scarcely be considered more closely, except for one version of Gandalf's reply to Éomer (RK pp. 155–6). In this, after saying that the Dark Lord, not knowing whether they themselves possessed the Ring, would look for those signs of strife that would inevitably arise among them if they did, Gandalf goes on:

'Now it is known to you that I have set the Ring in peril. From Faramir we learn that it passed to the very borders of Mordor before this assault began, maybe on the first day of the darkness. And, my lords, it went by the way of Morgul. Slender indeed is the hope that the bearer can have escaped the perils of that way, of the horrors that wait there; still less is the hope that even if he comes through them to the Black Land he can pass there unmarked. Six days have gone, and hourly I watch the signs with great dread in my heart.'

'What are these signs that you look for, an enemy ... you on our ...' asked Imrahil.

404   THE WAR OF THE RING

'Darkness,' said Gandalf. 'That is my dread. And darkness began, and therefore for a while I felt a despair deeper than Denethor. But the darkness that is to be feared is not such as we have endured: it would need no clouds in the air; it would begin in our hearts feeling afar the power of the Ringlord, and grow till by sunlight or moonlight or under heaven or under roof all would seem dark to us. This darkness was but a device to make us despair and it has, as such deceits will, ... our enemy. The next sign is strife among the lords.'

A following draft reaches Gandalf's argument as it appears in RK, but here he adds to those signs that Sauron will have observed: 'He may also have seen in the Stone the death of Denethor, and since he judges all by himself he may well deem that a first sign of strife among his chief foes.' In the same text, after saying that 'we must at all costs keep his eye from his true peril', he adds: 'A single regiment of orcs set about Orodruin could seal our ruin' (in a subsequent version: 'A mere handful of orcs at watch on Orodruin would seal our doom').

At the end of the debate, following Aragorn's words (RK p. 158) 'no gates will endure against our Enemy if men desert them', an initial draft has a development that was not pursued:

Then even as they debated a rider came in search of Éomer. 'Lord,' he said, 'word has come from Anórien from the north-roads. Théoden King, when we rode hither, left men behind to watch the movements of enemy at Amon Dîn. They send word that there has been war far away in the Wold, and thence come strange tidings. For some say [the very woods have] that wild things of the woods have fallen on the orcs and driven them into the River and the rapids of Sarn Gebir. But the army that was on the road has heard this news, and also of our victory here, and is afraid, and is even now hastening back.'

'Ha!' said Éomer. 'If they dare to assail us they will rue it. If they seek to fly past they shall be smitten. We must cut off this finger of the Black Hand ere it is withdrawn.'

The numbers of those who should set out from Minas Tirith were differently conceived, for 'the great part of these should be horsed for swifter movement' (in contrast to RK: 'the great part of this force should be on foot, because of the evil lands into which they would go'): Éomer leading three thousand of the Rohirrim, Aragorn five hundred horse and fifteen hundred foot, and Imrahil a thousand horse and fifteen hundred foot; and there was no suggestion that any force of the Rohirrim were sent to 'waylay the West Road against the enemy that was in Anórien' (RK p. 158). The manuscript was however

THE LAST DEBATE   405

subsequently corrected and the muster as enumerated in RK introduced, with three thousand of the Rohirrim left behind.

After the words 'And he drew forth Branding and held it up glittering in the sun' (which is where in RK 'The Last Debate' ends), the original chapter then continues with a transition back to Legolas and Gimli: 'While the great captains thus debated and laid their designs, Legolas and Gimli made merry in the fair morning high up in the windy circles of Minas Tirith.' Legolas' sight of the gulls flying up Anduin follows, and the emotion that they stirred in him, are described in much the same words as in RK; but the conversation that follows is altogether different. At this stage no account had been given of the Paths of the Dead; in the outline at the beginning of this chapter (p. 397) my father had suggested that the story would be told 'at feast of victory in Minas Tirith', and had mentioned that in tunnels under the mountains the company saw the 'skeleton in armour of Bealdor son of Brego', but that except for the dark and a feeling of dread they met no evil.

There is at first both a draft and a more finished version; I give the latter, since it follows the former very closely.

'... No peace shall I have again in Middle-earth!'

'Say not so!' said Gimli. 'There are countless things still to see there, and great work to be done. But if all the Fair Folk, that are also wise, take to the Havens, it will become a duller world for those that are doomed to stay.'

'It is already rather dull,' said Merry, sitting and swinging his legs as he sat on the brink of the wall. 'At least it is for hobbits, cooped up in a stone city, and troubled with wars, while their visitors talk and nod together about their strange journey, and tell no one else about it. I last saw you at the Hornburg, and then I thought you were going to Dunharrow,[17] but up you come on ships out of the South. How did you do it?'

'Yes, do tell us,' said Pippin. 'I tried Aragorn, but he was too full of troubles, and just smiled.'

'It would be a long story fully told,' said Legolas, 'and there are memories of that road that I do not wish to recall. Never again will I venture on the Paths of the Dead, not for any friendship; and but for my promise to Gimli I would vow never to go into the White Mountains again.'

'Well, for my part,' said Gimli, '[wonder was stronger than fear >] the fear is past, and only wonder remains; yet it cannot be denied that it is a dreadful road.'[18]

'What are the Paths of the Dead?' said Pippin. 'I have never heard them named before.'

406 THE WAR OF THE RING

'It is a path through the Mountains,' began Gimli.

'Yes, I saw the door from a distance,' Merry broke in. 'It is up in Dunharrow, in the mountains behind Théoden's town and hall at Edoras. There is a long row of old stones leading across a high mountain field to a forbidding black mass, the Dwimorberg they call it, and there is a cave and a great opening at the foot of it, which nobody dares to enter. I think the Rohirrim believe that inside there dwell Dead Men, or their shadows, out of a past long before they came to that land.'

'So they told us,' said Legolas, 'and they forbade us to go in; but Aragorn could not be turned from it. He was in a grim mood. And that fair lady that lies now in the Houses below, Éowyn, wept at his going. Indeed at the last in the sight of all she set her arms about him imploring him not to take that road, and when he stood there unmoved, stern as stone, she humbled herself to kneel in the dust. It was a grievous sight.'

'But do not think that he was not moved,' said Gimli. 'Indeed, I think Aragorn himself was so deeply grieved that he went through all perils after like a man that can feel little more. He raised her up and kissed her hand, and then without a word we set out,[19] before the sun came over the black ridges of the mountain. I do not know how to put it into words, but even as we passed the last great standing stone a dread fell on me, of what I could not say, and my blood seemed running cold. I lifted my feet like lead across the threshold of that darkling door; and hardly had we passed within when a blindness of very night came upon us.

'Madness it would seem to try and take horses on such a road, but Aragorn said that we must attempt it, for every hour lost was perilous. We had to dismount and lead them, but I do not think they would have gone far, if it had not been for Legolas. He sang a song that went softly in the darkness, and though they sweated and trembled they did not refuse the road. I am speaking of our horses that the Rohirrim gave us;[20] the horses of the Rangers, it seemed, were so faithful to them that nothing would stay them if their masters were beside them.

'We had brought a few torches, and Elladan [> Aragorn] went ahead bearing one, and Elrohir [> Elladan] with another went at the rear. Bats flew over us, and [> We saw nothing, but] if we halted there seemed an endless whisper of voices all about, that sometimes rose into words, though not of any tongue that I have ever heard. Nothing assailed us, and yet steadily fear grew

THE LAST DEBATE 407

on us, as we went on. Most of all because we knew, how I know not but we knew, that we could not turn back: that all the black road behind us was packed with things that followed us but could not be seen.

'So it went on for some hours, and then we came to a sight that I cannot forget. The road, for so it was: no mere cavern-track, had been wide, so far as we could judge, and though it was utterly dark the air was clean. But now we came suddenly into a great empty space through which the way ran on. The dread was so great on me that I could hardly walk. Away to the left something glittered in the gloom as Aragorn's torch went by. ...

It will be seen that when my father transformed this story told by Gimli of the Paths of the Dead and placed it much earlier in the book (while in 'The Last Debate' merely referring to it as having been told to Merry and Pippin by Legolas: 'Swiftly then he told of the haunted road under the mountains,' RK p. 150), he retained Gimli as the one through whose experience the passage of the tunnels is described.

Gimli described the mailclad skeleton clutching at the door in almost the same words as are found in 'The Passing of the Grey Company' (RK pp. 60–1), with the addition that on the helm and the hilts of the sword there were 'north-runes'. But Aragorn here named the dead warrior:

'"Here lies Baldor son of Brego," he said, "first heir of that Golden Hall to which he never returned. He should be lying now under the flowers of Evermind[21] in the Third Mound of the Mark; but now there are nine mounds and seven green with grass, and through all the long years he has lain here at the door he could not open. But whither that door led, and why he wished to pass, none now shall ever know."

At this stage in the evolution of the book Théoden had told at Dunharrow how Baldor son of Brego passed the Dark Door and never returned (p. 315; cf. 'The Muster of Rohan' in RK, p. 70). But with the removal of the story of the Paths of the Dead from the present chapter to 'The Passing of the Grey Company', the discovery of the skeleton of Baldor came to stand *before* Théoden's words about him at Dunhar-row; and this I suppose was why my father changed the passage. It was certainly not because he concluded that Aragorn did not know who he was. In the passage in RK it is clear that he did know, though he did not name him; for he knew that he had lain there in the dark 'through all the long years' as the burial mounds of the Kings of the Mark were raised one by one.

408 THE WAR OF THE RING

There are now nine mounds and seven at Edoras.[22] In the original draft of this passage the text is interrupted at Aragorn's words 'Here lies Bealdor son of Brego' by a very roughly written list of the Kings of the Mark, set down in two columns, thus:

1	Eorl	10	[Bealdor > Folca >] Fréalaf Éowyn's
2	Brego		son (sister-son of king)
	(Bealdor)	11	[Brego >] Háma
3	Aldor	12	Walda
4	Fréa	13	Folca
5	Fréawine	14	Folcwine
6	Goldwine	15	Fengel
7	Déor	16	Thengel
8	Gram	17	Théoden
9	Helm		

The names Folca and Folcwine replaced rejected forms that I cannot make out. It will be seen that these are the names found in Appendix A (II, *The House of Eorl*) to *The Lord of the Rings*, with the sole exception of the eleventh king Háma (in LR the eleventh king was Brytta: this name has already appeared in early texts as the father of Brego, VII. 435, 445, but is here absent). Beneath is written a long series of Old English names, many of them those that appear in the list of kings above, together with others, such as *Beorn, Brytta, Hæleth, Léod, Oretta, Sigeric, Sincwine*, &c. I suppose that it is possible that this series of names was written first, though it stands second, and that the names of the kings in the numbered list were selected from it. At any rate, it looks very much as if it were at this very point that the First Line and the Second Line of the Kings of the Mark, and their names, came into being.[23]

Beside the names of the kings are written dates. My impression (not having studied the actual original page) is that only the dates of Fengel, Thengel, and Théoden belong with the writing of the manuscript page and the list of kings, but that these certainly do so. The dates are:

Fengel	born 1268, died 1353
Thengel	born 1298, died 1373
Théoden	born 1328, died 141[?8]

The last figure in the date of Theoden's death is unfortunately obscure, but is certainly not 9. The dates of these kings in LR are 2870–2953, 2905–2980, and 2948–3019, which in the Shire Reckoning become 1270–1353, 1305–1380, and 1348–1419. It is clear then that at this stage in the writing of *The Lord of the Rings* my father was working with a chronology that is esentially similar to that of LR in respect of Rohan – but the actual numerical years are given according to the Shire Reckoning.[24]

THE LAST DEBATE
409

Gimli does not record any words of Aragorn's to the Dead that followed:

'And so we turned away and left the dead untouched, and passed out of the hall that was his tomb, and hurried on, for behind us now fear seemed treading ever closer. And just when we felt that we could endure no more, and must either find an ending and escape, or else turn and run back in madness to meet the following fear, our last torch sputtered out.

'Of the next hour or hours I remember little, save a blind groping dread that pressed behind us, and a rumour that came behind like the shadow of the noise of endless feet, as horrible as the ghosts of men themselves. And we stumbled on till some of us were crawling on the ground like beasts.

'Then suddenly I heard the trickle of water ...

Allowing of course for the difference in mode of narration (e.g. 'Then Legolas turning to speak to me looked back, and I can remember still the glitter in his bright eyes before my face', cf. RK p. 61), the story of the emergence of the Company from the caverns and descent down the Vale of Morthond was little changed afterwards. Legolas takes up the narration at:

'The Dead were following,' said Legolas. 'A great grey host I saw come flowing behind us like a shadowy tide: shapes of men there were, and horses, and grey banners like shreds of cloud, and spears like winter thickets on a misty night. "The Dead are following," I said. "Yes, the Dead ride behind," said Elladan. "Ride on!"'

It seems that Gimli then takes up the tale again with 'And so we came at last out of the ravine as suddenly as if we had issued from a crack in a wall', for he refers to himself as 'Gimli of the Mountain' in his description of the ride to Erech. Elladan's answer to Gimli's question in RK 'Where in Middle-earth are we?' does not appear; it is here Gimli who describes the course of Morthond (with the explanation 'so I was after told'). He says that the river 'flows at last to sea past Barad Amroth[25] where dwells Prince Imrahil'; and he does not refer, as does Elladan in RK, to the significance of the name *Blackroot*. The ride to Erech is described thus:

'Bells I heard ringing in fear far below, and all the people fled before our faces; but we being in haste rode swiftly as though in pursuit, until our horses were stumbling weary, and [*struck out:* I at least,] even Gimli of the Mountain, was spent. And thus just ere the midnight hour – and black it was wellnigh as in the

410   THE WAR OF THE RING

caverns, for though we did not know it yet the darkness of
Mordor was creeping over us – just ere midnight we came to the
Hill of Erech.'

On the Darkness out of Mordor coming over the sky as the
Company rode to Erech see the Note on Chronology at the end of this
chapter. – The text at this point becomes the primary draft, and
continues:

'And what is that?' asked Merry.

'You should ask Aragorn,' said Gimli, 'or the brethren: they
know, as is fitting, all the lore of Gondor of old. It is a black
stone, they say, that old tales tell was brought[26] in ages past
from Númenor before its fall, when its ships would come to the
west shores of the world. And it was set upon a hill. And there-
on the King of the [struck out: Dark] Men of the Mountains had
sworn [> once swore] allegiance to the West; but afterwards the
[?Shadow] Men fell again under the dominion of Sauron. Isildur
came to the Stone of Erech, when he gathered strength to resist
the power of Mordor, and he summoned the Men of the
Mountains to come to his aid, and they would not.

'Then Isildur said to their king of that day: "Thou shalt be the
last. Yet if the West prove mightier than thy black Master, this
curse I set on thee and thy folk: to rest never till your oath is
fulfilled. For this war shall last down many ages, and you shall
be summoned once again ere the end." And they fled before the
wrath of Isildur, and did not dare to go forth to war on Sauron's
part. And they hid themselves in secret places in the mountains
and seldom came forth again, but slowly died and dwindled in
the barren hills.

This account of Gimli's to Merry and Pippin at Minas Tirith is the
forerunner of Aragorn's to Legolas and Gimli at the Hornburg (RK
p. 55). I think that it may very well have been at this point that the
story of the breaking of their oath to Isildur by the Men of the Mountains first emerged, and that it was now that Aragorn's words at the
Hornburg were enlarged to include it.
Gimli continues:

'But afterwards, in the days of Gondor's later power, men set
a ring-wall about the Stone of Erech, and built beside it on the
hilltop a tall dark tower, and there was guarded the seventh
Palantír, which now is lost.[27] The tower is ruinous and the
ring-wall is broken, and all about the land is empty, for none
will dwell near the Hill of Erech, because it is said that at times

THE LAST DEBATE   411

the Shadow-men will gather there, thronging about the ruined wall, and whispering. And though their tongue is now long forgotten, it is said that they cry "We are come!" and they wish to fulfill the broken oath and be at rest. But the terror of the Dead lies on that hill and all the land about.

'Thither in the blackness before the storm we came. And at last we halted. And Elladan blew his silver horn, and Elrohir unfurled the banner that at the Hornburg he bore still wrapped in grey [*later* > black];[28] and dark as it was the stars glinted on it, as it was spread on a wind like a breath of ghosts coming down from the mountains. Nothing could we see but the seven stars of Elendil, and yet we were aware of a great host gathered all about us upon the hill, and of the sound of answering horns, as if their echo came up out of deep caverns far away.

'But Aragorn stood by the banner and cried aloud. "The hour is come at last, and the oath shall be fulfilled. I go to Pelargir, and ye shall come behind me. And when all this land is clean, return, and be at peace! For I am Elessar, Isildur's heir of Gondor."

'Then there was a silence, and no whisper or rustle did we hear as the night wore away. We lay within the ruined ring-wall, and some slept; though we felt the terror of the Dead that hedged us round.

At this point a revised version begins, and I follow this, since it adheres very closely to the initial draft (see however notes 33, 34, and 35).

'Then followed the weariest journey that I have ever known, wearier than our hunting of orcs over wide Rohan on our feet; three days and nights and on into another day with little pause or rest.[29] No other mortal men could have endured it and fought at the end of it, save only the Dúnedain, these Rangers of the North. They are as tough as dwarves, I swear it, though none of my kin should believe me. Almost I wished I was an elf and had no need of sleep, or could both sleep and wake at once, as it seems that Legolas can.

'I was never in that land before, and I could not tell you much of our road, even if you wished to hear. But it is, I reckoned, some 60 leagues as birds fly from Erech, over Tarlang's Neck[30] into Lamedon, and so, crossing Kiril and Ringlo, to Linhir beside the waters of Gilrain, where there are fords that lead into

412   THE WAR OF THE RING

Lebennin. And from Linhir it is a hundred miles, if it is a step, to Pelargir on Anduin.[31]

'The next morning day did not dawn, as you will remember well, but it must have been before the sun rose above the vapours of Mordor that we set out again,[32] and east we rode to meet the gathering gloom; and ever close behind us came the Shadow Host, some riding, some striding, but all moving silently and with the same great speed, and when they overtook our horses, though we pressed them to their utmost, the Shadow Host swept about us wide on either flank, and some went on ahead.

'Terror and wonder ran on wings before us, and all that was left of the folk of Lamedon hid, or fled to the woods and hills.[33] Thus we came at nightfall of the second day from Erech to Linhir. There the men of Lamedon had been contesting the passage of Gilrain with a great strength of the Haradrim, and of their allies the Shipmen of Umbar, who had sailed up Gilrain-mouth and far up the waters of Anduin with a host of ships and were now ravaging Lebennin and the coast of Belfalas. But defenders and invaders alike fled at our approach. And thus we crossed into Lebennin unopposed, and there we rested, and sorely we needed it.

'Next day we made our greatest endeavour, for Aragorn was pressed with a great fear lest all that he did would prove too late. "I counted on two days more at the least," he said; "but those who challenge Sauron will ever fall short of their reckoning. Now already Minas Tirith is beset, and I fear it will fall ere we can come to its aid."

'So we rose ere night had passed, and went as swift as our stouthearted horses could endure over the flat plains of Lebennin; and behind us and about us the host of the Dead flowed like a grey tide.

'Great rumour of dismay went on before us. I do not know who set the tales on the wing, but as we learned after among both friends and foes the tidings ran wild: "Isildur has come back from the dead. The dead are come to war, but they wield living swords. [The Lord of the Ring has arisen!]"[34] And all the enemy who heard these things fled as best they could back to Anduin, for they had many ships there and great strength; and we hunted them out of the land: all that day and through the next night, with few brief halts, we rode. And so we came at the bitter last to the Great River again, and we knew ere we came

THE LAST DEBATE   413

that it was near, for there was salt in the air. The mouths of Anduin were indeed still far away south and west of us, but Anduin is even at Pelargir so great and wide that almost it seems a slow-flowing sea, and countless birds are on its shores.

'It was day, I guessed, by the veiled/hidden sun – the fourth since we left Dunharrow – when we reached those shores, and saw the fleets of Umbar. And then we had to fight, at last. But fear was our mightiest weapon. Many of those who learned of our coming had already gone aboard and thrust off and escaped down Anduin to the the Sea. But the enemy, whose main task it was to ravage South Gondor and prevent help going north to the City, had been too wide-scattered for all to escape so. And while they marched abroad their ships were left with small guard. But there were among them captains sent by Mordor, and orc-chieftains, and they were not so easily dismayed, and they endeavoured to hold their men to a defence. And indeed the Haradrim are a grim folk, and not easily daunted by shade or blade. But their resistance did not last long. For now seeing that we were indeed come to aid them, many of the more stouthearted men of the land gathered to Aragorn. And on the ships the slaves rebelled. For the Corsairs of Umbar had in their ships many new-captured prisoners, and the oarsmen were all slaves, many taken in Gondor in petty raids, or unhappy descendants of slaves made in years gone by. Before the fifth day was over we had taken well nigh all the fleet, save some ships that their masters set ablaze; and all the enemy that were not slain or drowned were gone flying over the [?borders] into the desert that lies north of Harad.[35]

Here the revised version stops, at the foot of a page, and my father struck out the whole page (which begins at 'So we rose ere night had passed', p. 412) and wrote a pencilled note:

No fight, but Shadows [?flow into] the ships and all men leap overboard except the chained captives. But Rangers went to each ship and comforted the captives.

He then rewrote the page – and this was obviously done immediately – beginning at the same words.

'So we rose ere night had passed, and went as swift as our stouthearted horses could endure over the green plains of Lebennin darkling under the shade of Mordor; and all about us the Host of the Dead flowed on like a grey tide. Still the rumour

414   THE WAR OF THE RING

of our coming went before us and all men were dismayed, and none neither foe nor friend would wait for our approach. For the darkness weighed on the allies of Mordor, not being orcs or folk bred in the Black Land, and those that could fled back to Anduin, where they had gathered many ships. Thus we hunted them from Gondor all that day and on through the next night, halting seldom and sleeping not at all, until we came at the bitter end to the Great River.'

'I knew it,' said Legolas, 'long ere we reached it, for there was salt in the air. And my heart was troubled for I thought that I drew near the Sea, but indeed the Mouths of Anduin were far away to the south. ... '

This is only the second time that Legolas has spoken since Gimli's story of the journey began. He speaks now of the great breadth of Anduin as Gimli had done (p. 413);[36] and (following the note at the end of the previous version of this section of the story) he goes on:

'... But fear was the only weapon that we needed, for the grey host passed on to every ship whether drawn up or anchored in the tide, and all the men that were in them fled, or leaped overboard, save the slaves of the oars that were chained, or captives under hold.'

Legolas describes how to each of the greater ships one of the Rangers went to comfort the captives, bidding them put aside fear and be free (RK p. 152).

'And when all the fleet was in our hands Aragorn went up on that ship which he took for his own and let sound many trumpets, and the Shadow Host withdrew to the shores, and stood in great array there silently, and there was a red light in the gloom, for some of the enemy had fired their ships ere they abandoned them.'

Aragorn's words to the Dead ('Now I will hold your oath all fulfilled') are close to those in RK (p. 153).[37] It is 'a tall figure of shadow', not as in RK said to be the King of the Dead, that steps forth and breaks his spear. The remainder of the story is very much as in RK, though here told by Legolas: the rest of the Company that night 'while others laboured', the release of the captives from the ships, the coming of the men of Lebennin (but Angbor of Lamedon is not named), the slow passage by oar up Anduin (but it was 'the fifth morning, that is the day before yesterday' that the fleet set out from Pelargir: see the Note on Chronology at the end of this chapter), Aragorn's fear that they would be too late ('for it is forty leagues and

THE LAST DEBATE 415

two by river from Pelargir to the landings under the Pelennor wall'), and the red glow to the north from the burning of Minas Tirith. Legolas' discourse ends, as does Gimli's in RK, with 'It was a great hour, and a great day, whatever may come after', to which Gimli replies: 'Yes, whatever come after. Yet for all our victory the faces of Gandalf and Aragorn look grave. I wonder what counsel they are taking in the tents below. For my part I wish it were all well over. Yet, whatever is still to do, I hope I may have part in it, for the honour of the folk of the Lonely Mountain.' To this was added later: '"And I for the folk of the Wood," said Legolas.' Then follows:

His [> Their] wish was granted. Two days later the army of the West that was to march forth was all assembled on the Pelennor. The host of orcs and easterlings had turned back out of Anórien and harried and scattered by the Rohirrim had fled with little fight towards Cair Andros ...

This is the beginning of 'The Black Gate Opens' in RK, but with a major difference from the subsequent story: for here Pippin as well as Merry was left behind.

... To their bitter grief the hobbits were not in that riding.
'Merry is not fit for such a journey yet,' said Aragorn, 'even if he could ride a swift steed. And you Peregrin will lighten his grief if you stay with him. So far you have kept even with one another as well as your fortunes allowed – and indeed if you did no more to the end of your days you have earned honour, and justified the wisdom of Elrond.[38] And indeed we are all in like peril. For though it may be our part to find a bitter end before the gate of Mordor, if we do so, then you will have your chance or necessity also of a last stand either here or wherever the black tide overtakes you. Farewell!'

And so despondently Merry and Pippin stood before the ruined gates of Minas Tirith with young Bergil and saw the great army mustered. Bergil was downcast and grieved at heart, for his father was commanded to march and lead a company of the men of Imrahil. For he having broken his oaths could no longer remain in the guard of the Citadel, until his case was judged.[39]

The trumpets rang and the host began to move. [First rode Aragorn and Gandalf and the sons of Elrond with the banner and the knights of Dol Amroth. Then came Éomer with the [?chosen] Riders, and afterwards came those of his men that were on foot, and men of Lebennin, and last the great com-

416   THE WAR OF THE RING

panies of Minas Tirith led by Imrahil.][40] And long after it had passed away out of sight down the great road to the Causeway the three stood there, until the last glint of the morning sun on spear and helm twinkled and was lost.

At this point my father decided that Pippin did in fact go with the host to the Black Gate, and he began anew at the words 'His [> Their] wish was granted' following the end of 'The Tale of Gimli and Legolas', continuing as before with 'Two days later the army of the West that was to march forth was all assembled on the Pelennor.' The text then continued both in initial draft and in a fair copy to the end of the story afterwards called 'The Black Gate Opens', with continuous pagination all the way through from the meeting of Gimli and Legolas with Imrahil before they went to the Houses of Healing. It is thus clear that the whole of the last part of Book V was in a completed (though not final) and coherent form before any structural reorganisation of the narrative took place. The structure was:

> Gimli and Legolas meet Imrahil and go to the Houses of Healing.
> The Last Debate.
> The Tale of Gimli and Legolas in the garden of the Houses of Healing.
> The journey to the Morannon and the Parley.

The next stage was the decision to reorganise the narrative so that 'Gimli's Tale' should stand independently – and therefore precede the Debate. To this end my father wrote a tentative conclusion for 'The Tale of Gimli and Legolas':

And so ended the tale of Legolas and Gimli concerning the ride of Aragorn by the Paths of the Dead, which long was recalled and sung in Gondor in after days, and it was said that never again were the Shadow-men seen by mortal men on mountain or in vale, [and the road from Dunharrow was free to all who were willing to take that way. Yet few did so, for the memory of fear abode there still; and none ever dared to open Baldor's door. *Struck out immediately:* A tomb they made for him in that dark place and so built it that none could come at that door.]

The passage that I have bracketed was replaced, probably at once, by the following:

but the stone of Erech stood ever alone, and on that hill no bird would alight nor beast feed; and the memory of fear still abode in the dark ways from Dunharrow, and few were willing to take that road; and none ever dared to open Baldor's door.

THE LAST DEBATE   417

Concomitantly with this the words 'Their wish was granted' (following the end of 'The Tale of Gimli and Legolas' and beginning the story of the march from Minas Tirith) were circled, with a direction to omit them if this 'end-piece' to the 'Tale' were added to it; and a note was scribbled on the manuscript beside the opening of the debate (p. 403): 'It might be better to take out the debate (shorten it) and put it at the beginning of the Parley chapter.' Thus the decision was taken to divide the chapter as it stood (entitled 'The Parley at the Black Gate', p. 399) into two: the first to be called 'The Paths of the Dead' and consisting solely of the tale told to Merry and Pippin in the garden of the Houses of Healing, the second to be called 'Parley at the Gate' and beginning with the debate in Aragorn's tent.

Relatively little adjustment of the existing material was needed to achieve this. From the point in the narrative where Gimli and Legolas found Merry and Pippin ('and the meeting of those friends was a merry one') my father simply dropped the transition to the debate (see p. 403) and continued with the conversation in the garden of the Houses of Healing (see p. 405 and RK p. 149): 'For a while they walked and talked, rejoicing for a brief space in peace and rest under the fair morning high up in the windy circles of the City.' The conversation leading into the 'Tale' was somewhat changed. In contrast to the earlier version Merry is no longer represented as being ignorant (as he could not have been) of Aragorn's passage under the mountains (see p. 405 and note 17). After Pippin's words 'Come, Legolas! You and Gimli have mentioned your strange journey with Trotter about a dozen times already this morning. But you haven't mentioned anything about it' this dialogue follows:

'I know some of the story and I guess some more,' said Merry. 'For I hear that you came in ships from the South. So I know that somehow you must have got through, though in Dunharrow all the people were afraid, and Éowyn I thought had been weeping. Come now! The sun is shining and we can bear it. Tell us about the Paths of the Dead!'

'The sun may shine,' said Gimli, 'still there are memories of that road that I do not wish to recall. Had I known what was before me I think that not for any friendship would I have taken those paths.'

'For my part,' said Legolas, 'I do not fear the Dead; but I hate the darkness under earth far from hope of the sky. It was a dreadful journey!'

'The Dead?' said Pippin. 'The Paths of the Dead? I have never heard of them before. Won't you tell us some more?'

'It is the name of a road that goes through the mountains,'

418   THE WAR OF THE RING

said Merry. 'I saw the Gate, as they call it, from a distance when I was in Dunharrow ...'

Merry then continues as he does in the earlier version, and is followed by Legolas and Gimli describing the departure and Éowyn's distress (cf. p. 406 and note 19):

'... I think the men of the Mark believe that inside there dwell the shadows of Dead Men, out of a past long before they came to that land.'

'So they told us,' said Legolas. 'And that lady who lies now below in the Houses, Éowyn, she begged Aragorn not to go in; but he could not be turned from it. He was in haste, and in a stern mood.'

'And at the last when she saw that he would go,' said Gimli, 'then she begged to come with us! Indeed she knelt before him. Yet she is a proud lady. I wondered much what it all might mean, and I was grieved; for she was young and much troubled. But he raised her up and kissed her hand and without more words we departed. Yet I saw that he, too, was greatly grieved.'

The earlier version was for the rest of its length very largely repeated: that is to say, the original pages were retained with their pagination altered and some passages rewritten. Legolas now plays a larger part in the narration, describing the ride to Erech (see pp. 409–10), at which point Gimli re-enters: '"Yes, indeed, and never shall I forget!" said Gimli, taking up the tale again. "For the terror of the Dead lay on the hill and all the land about it"'; he continues much as in RK pp. 62–3, but he does not say that Isildur set up the Stone of Erech at his landing ('It looked as if it had fallen from the sky, but it was brought out of the West, we were told'), and he still repeats the story (p. 411) that when the Shadow-men gathered about the Stone 'sometimes a cry would be heard in our speech:[41] "We have come!"' The tower and ring-wall on the Hill of Erech, and the *palantír*, have now disappeared.

For the second of the new chapters my father wrote a new opening, beginning (cf. p. 403) 'In the meanwhile Imrahil sent for Éomer and went down with him, and they came to the tents of Aragorn...' To this he added the existing pages of the manuscript recounting the course of the debate, which ended at 'And he drew forth Branding and held it up glittering in the sun' (p. 405), and then the manuscript of the story of the journey to the Morannon and the Parley. On the new opening he pencilled the title 'Parley at the Gate' and the chapter number 'LI', so that 'The Paths of the Dead' was 'L' (see note 10). The structure was now (see p. 416):

THE LAST DEBATE   419

The Paths of the Dead Gimli and Legolas go to the Houses of Healing, and Merry and Pippin hear the tale of the journey of the Grey Company from Dunharrow to the Battle of the Pelennor Fields.

Parley at the Gate 'The Last Debate', ending with Aragorn's drawing the sword of Elendil; the journey to the Morannon, and the parley with the Lieutenant of Barad-dûr.

It was probably now that my father made a typescript of the two chapters, the text diverging very little from the manuscript material as now reorganised;[42] but he treated them as subdivisions of a single chapter, without an overall title, and with the puzzling number 'XLIX' (see note 10): (i) 'The Paths of the Dead' and (ii) 'Parley at the Black Gate'.

The subsequent history of the chapter is textually exceedingly complicated, but I shall treat it briefly. The first typescript was very heavily revised, and two large sections of it were written out anew in a separate manuscript. The effect of all this was to bring the narrative closer in very many points to the texts in RK, and indeed much of the earlier part now required little more than grammatical alteration to bring Gimli's story to the direct author's narrative in 'The Passing of the Grey Company.'[43]

In the ride from Erech over Tarlang's Neck into Lamedon the deserted town of Calembel upon Ciril (so spelt, with C) appears,[44] and the blood-red sunset behind Pinnath Gelin (RK p. 63): the final chronology had now entered (see the Note at the end of this chapter). Angbor of Lamedon is now named, but the new text differs here from that of RK (p. 151):

'Then Aragorn said to Angbor their captain who alone stayed to meet him: "Behold! I am not the King of the Dead, but the Heir of Isildur, and I live yet for a while. Follow me, if you wish to see the end of this darkness and the downfall of Mordor."

'And Angbor answered: "I will gather all men that I may, and follow after you swiftly." His was a stout heart indeed, and I grieve that he fell beside me, as we clove our way from the Harlond.

In RK (p. 153) Angbor of Lamedon came to Pelargir but did not go up Anduin in the black fleet; he is last referred to by Aragorn in the debate in his tent (p. 157) as marching at the head of four thousand men from Pelargir through Lossarnach and expected soon to arrive at Minas Tirith.

To Legolas' words about the Sea (p. 414) he now adds his second reference to the gulls (RK p. 151): 'Alas! for the wailing of the gulls. Did not the Lady tell me to beware of them? For they cannot be

420   THE WAR OF THE RING

forgotten.' He is thinking of Galadriel's message to him, spoken by
Gandalf in Fangorn (TT p. 106):

> *Legolas Greenleaf long under tree*
> *In joy thou hast lived. Beware of the Sea!*
> *If thou hearest the cry of the gull on the shore,*
> *Thy heart shall then rest in the forest no more.*

For Galadriel's original message to Legolas, and its application, see
p. 22.

There is an interesting passage immediately following in this revised
version. In the version given on p. 413 there was fighting on the
shores, for 'there were captains sent by Mordor, and orc-chieftains,
and they were not so easily dismayed, and they endeavoured to hold
their men to a defence. And indeed the Haradrim are a grim folk, and
not easily daunted by shade or blade.' This was rejected, following a
note that there was in fact no fighting at Pelargir: '*But fear was the
only weapon that we needed*, for the grey host passed on to every ship
... and all the men that were in them fled, or leaped overboard'
(p. 414). My father now went back on this decision.

'I soon forgot them [the gulls] for my part,' said Gimli. 'For at
last we came to a battle. The Haradrim were driven now to
despair, and could fly no longer. There at Pelargir lay the fleets
of Umbar, fifty great ships and many smaller vessels beyond
count. Some few of our enemies reached their ships and put off,
seeking either to escape down the River or to reach the far
shores; and some they set fire to. But we came too swiftly upon
them for many to slip from us so. We were joined by some of the
hardier folk of Lebennin and the Ethir, but we were not many
when the corsairs turned to bay; and seeing our weakness their
hearts revived and they assailed us in their turn. There was stern
work there in the twilight by the grey waters, for the Shadow
Host halted and wavered, unwilling at the last, as it seemed, to
make war on Sauron. Then Aragorn let blow a horn and cried
aloud, saying that if they broke their oath a second time

Here my father stopped and rewrote the passage to a form not
essentially different from that in RK, where the Shadow Host is still
said to have 'hung back at the last', but with no explicit suggestion
that they were reluctant to fulfil the oath, and where for the living
there was no need for 'stern work in the twilight by the grey waters'.

At this time my father also wrote an experimental version 'with
entrance to the Door told at end of Chapter II of Book V' – that is, at
the end of 'Many Roads Lead Eastward'. This begins: 'But Aragorn
and his company rode across the high mountain-field upon which was
set the refuge of the Rohirrim; and the paths were laid between rows

THE LAST DEBATE   421

of standing stones hoar with age uncounted. The light was still grey, for the sun had not yet climbed over the black ridges of the Haunted Mountain ...' It must be presumed that the story of the coming of the Grey Company to Dunharrow, and Aragorn's parting from Éowyn, had now been added to 'Many Roads Lead Eastward' (see note 19). The text ends thus: '... a groping blindness overcame him, even Gimli Glóin's son the Dwarf, who had walked in many deep places under earth. So the Grey Company dared the forbidden door, and vanished from the land of living men.'

Although this shows that my father was pondering the possibility of removing some part of the story told in the Houses of Healing and rewriting it as direct narrative in its chronological place, the following typescript is a text of the whole 'Tale of Gimli and Legolas' incorporating all revision to that time, and ending with the words 'and none ever dared to move Baldor's bones' (cf. p. 416).

There followed a rough manuscript in which the first part of the 'Tale' was written out as direct narrative, to stand in its chronological place in the earlier chapter, thus greatly shortening the material of the end of Book V. A further typescript has the structure of 'The Last Debate' in RK, with the story of the passage of the Paths of the Dead removed and only mentioned as having been told, though here it was still Gimli who told it:

'Alas! I had heart only for myself,' said Gimli, 'and I do not wish to recall that journey.' He fell silent; but Pippin and Merry were so eager for news that at last he yielded and told them in halting words of the dreadful passage of the mountains that led to the black Stone of Erech. But when he came to the Day without Dawn he ceased. 'I am weary recalling that weariness, and the horror of the Dark,' he said.

'Then I will say on,' said Legolas.[45]

The structure of the narrative in RK had been at last achieved, with the debate in the tent of Aragorn following in the same chapter the end of the story told to Merry and Pippin in the Houses of Healing.[46] I see no way to determine at what stage all this later work was done.

NOTES

1 On Haramon see p. 359 and note 3. The reading 'the Hills of Haramon' (plural) in the outline 'The Story Foreseen from Forannest' is certain, in contrast to the 'great hill' referred to in the present text.

2 For Bealdor (Baldor) son of Brego see pp. 315–16, and on the spelling of the name p. 321 note 11.

422 THE WAR OF THE RING

3   A pencilled note in the margin reads: '25 miles. Dunharrow >
    Erech 55.' Presumably '25 miles' refers to the distance from the
    issue of the Paths of the Dead to the Stone of Erech. On the
    distance from Dunharrow to Erech see pp. 296–7 note 2.

4   By '(say Linhir?)' I suppose that my father meant that since the
    road to Pelargir crossed the Lameduin (later Gilrain) at Linhir,
    'Linhir' would do as well as 'Fords of Lameduin'. Linhir appears
    also in 'The Story Foreseen from Forannest' (p. 361); it is marked
    on the Second Map (see p. 437) at some distance above the head
    of the estuary of Lameduin, the direct distance from here to Erech
    on this map being 36 mm. or 180 miles.

5   From Linhir to Pelargir direct is 2 cm. or 100 miles on the Second
    Map.

6   The rejected portion of the outline has here: 'The Haradwaith try
    to fly. Some take ship back again down Anduin. But Aragorn
    overtakes them and captures most of the ships. Some are set fire
    to, but several manned by slaves and captives are captured.'
    (Then follows the passage about the Gondorian captives.) 'Ara-
    gorn embarks with men of South Gondor; the Shadow Host
    disperses, pursuing the Haradwaith about the vales.'

7   Cf. 'The Battle of the Pelennor Fields', p. 370: 'south away the
    river went in a knee about the out-thrust of the hills of Emyn
    Arnen in lower Ithilien, and Anduin bent then in upon the
    Pelennor so that its outwall was there built upon the brink, and
    that at the nearest was no more than [five >] four miles from the
    Gates.' In 'The Story Foreseen from Forannest' (p. 363 note 3)
    the Pelennor Wall is at this point ten miles away from the City.

8   On the Second Map it is 125 miles (the figure given in the text) up
    river from Pelargir to the angle of the 'knee' in Anduin (see note
    7), and thus the straight stretch of ten miles 'just before that
    point', visible from Minas Tirith, is the 'leg' below the 'knee'. In
    the further continuation of the passage from 'The Battle of the
    Pelennor Fields' cited in note 7 (see p. 370) the length of 'the
    reach of Arnen' is given as 'three leagues'; but on the Second
    Map, on which both these passages were based, it is substantially
    longer. In RK (p. 122) 'Anduin, from the bend at the Harlond, so
    flowed that from the City men could look down it lengthwise for
    some leagues.'

9   Cf. 'The Story Foreseen from Forannest' (p. 359): 'Then as final
    despair comes on, and Rohirrim give back, [west >] south wind
    rolls back cloud, and noon-sun gleams through. Aragorn unfurls
    his great standard from ship-top. The crown and stars of Sun and
    Moon shine out.'

10 The opening page of the manuscript bears the chapter-numbers
    'XLI', 'L', 'L(b)', and 'XLIX', all of which were struck out except
    the last. 'XLI' is an obvious slip (for 'LI'?), since the chapter could

THE LAST DEBATE   423

not possibly bear this number; but it is hard to see how it could be 'XLIX' either (see p. 386 and note 7).

11 This draft for the debate follows immediately on an abandoned sentence of 'The Houses of Healing', thus:

> Gandalf and Pippin then came to Merry's room and there saw Aragorn stand
> 'My lords,' said Gandalf. ...

The text that follows is written in ink over pencilled drafting for 'The Houses of Healing'.

12 This sentence is bracketed in the original, as also is that a little further on ('a tyrant brooking no freedom ...').

13 *Imladrist:* cf. p. 139 note 14 and p. 165 note 5.

14 My father struck out 'Gandalf' immediately. He then wrote 'Warden of the Keys' but put dots for the name, writing in 'Húrin' before he had gone much further. It would seem therefore that this was where the name arose, but since 'Húrin' appears in the first manuscript of 'The Battle of the Pelennor Fields' (p. 369) it seems clear that my father had merely forgotten momentarily here what name he had chosen for him.

15 Gandalf cannot have said this. Either *not* must be removed or *cannot > can.*

16 In a draft for this passage Imrahil called Dol Amroth *Castle Amroth*; this was repeated in a following draft, where it was changed to *Barad Amroth* (and finally *Barad > Dol).*

17 Merry of course knew that Aragorn did go to Dunharrow (cf. RK pp. 69–70; the final text of 'The Muster of Rohan' was now largely in being, p. 319). See p. 417.

18 This passage contrasts greatly with RK, where it is Gimli who will not speak of the Paths of the Dead, and Legolas who says 'I felt not the horror, and I feared not the shadows of Men, powerless and frail as I deemed them.' See p. 417.

19 I think that the parting of Aragorn and Éowyn would not have been recounted so fully by Legolas and Gimli here if the story of the coming of the Grey Company to Dunharrow already existed in the earlier chapter (RK pp. 56–9); see p. 308.

20 *our horses that the Rohirrim gave us:* 'horses', because Aragorn's horse was still Hasufel (pp. 301, 305–6); when Roheryn, his own horse brought from the North by the Rangers, was introduced, it was only Arod, the horse bearing Legolas and Gimli, that was of Rohan, and he alone is mentioned in the equivalent passage in RK ('The Passing of the Grey Company', p. 60).

21 In the early drafts for 'The King of the Golden Hall' the mounds of the kings at Edoras were first described as 'white with nodding flowers like tiny snowdrops', the flowers being subsequently *nifredil* (VII.442–3). In RK ('The Passing of the Grey Company', p. 61) Aragorn calls the flowers *simbelmynë*, but cf. 'The King of

424   THE WAR OF THE RING

the Golden Hall' (TT p. 111), where Gandalf says: 'Evermind they are called, *simbelmynë* in this land of Men, for they blossom in all the seasons of the year, and grow where dead men rest.'

22   In the first manuscript of 'The King of the Golden Hall' Legolas said of the barrows at Edoras: 'Seven mounds I see, and seven long lives of men it is, since the golden hall was built' (see VII.442 and 449 note 4). This was changed on that manuscript to the reading of TT (p.111): '"Seven mounds upon the left, and nine upon the right," said Aragorn. "Many long lives of men it is since the golden hall was built."'

23   If this is so, it was of course at this time that the first manuscript of 'The King of the Golden Hall' was emended to say that there were 'seven mounds upon the left, and nine upon the right' (see note 22).

24   The dates of the kings before the last three were so much changed and confused by overwriting that I can form no clear idea of what my father intended: it is at least plain, however, that they correspond in their pattern to those in LR – as adjusted for the Shire Reckoning.

25   *Barad Amroth*: see note 16. Later *Barad* was changed to *Dol.*

26   As first written, but immediately rejected, the text continued from this point: '... was brought from Númenor, and marks still the place where Isildur met the last king of the Dark Men of the Mountains, when he established the bounds of Gondor. And there he swore an oath, for Isildur and Elendil and his sons [*sic*] had the gift of tongues as many of the Númenóreans, and the tongues of men ..... [?of the wild] were known to him, for'

27   The ring-wall and tower on the Hill of Erech, in which was kept the *palantír*, are referred to in the outline given on p. 397; it is told there that Aragorn actually found the *palantír* of Erech, in a vault of the tower.

28   It is strange that it should be Elrohir who unfurled the banner (and bore it at the Hornburg), for from the first mention of the banner (p. 302) it was as in RK Halbarad the Ranger who bore it (and it was covered in a black cloth). — In RK (p. 63) no device could be seen on it in the darkness.

29   On this and subsequent references to the days of the journey see the Note on Chronology at the end of these Notes.

30   Tarlang's Neck is seen on the Second Map, though it is not named. For the geography of these regions see pp. 433 ff.

31   Sixty leagues in direct line from Erech to Linhir, and a hundred miles from Linhir to Pelargir, agrees with RK (p. 150): 'ninety leagues and three' from Erech to Pelargir.

32   *we set out again*: i.e. from Erech. — It is approximately here that the part of Gimli's story that was transferred to 'The Passing of the Grey Company' ends, and the part that remained actually

THE LAST DEBATE 425

reported in 'The Last Debate' begins; there is some overlap in RK (pp. 63, 151).

33 At this point there follows in the initial draft:

'... But when we came over Tarlang's Neck Elladan and two Rangers rode ahead and spoke to any that they could find willing to stay and listen to them, and told them that a great help was coming to them against the Shipfoes and the Southrons, and that it was not the King of the Dead but the heir of the Kings of Gondor that had returned. A few listened and believed, and at the crossings of Kiril we found food and fodder set for our need though no man had dared to stay beside it, nor any fresh horses for which we hoped.

34 The square brackets are in the original. The initial draft text has here:

'"... but they wield living swords." And some cried [*struck out:* though they knew not what it meant]: "The Lord of the Rings has arisen".'

In the margin of this page in the draft text my father subsequently wrote the following remarkable passage:

'Indeed all the folk of Lebennin call Aragorn that.'

'I wonder why?' said Merry. 'I suppose it is some device to draw the eyes of Mordor that way, to Aragorn, and keep them from Frodo'; and he looked east and shuddered. 'Do you think all his great labour and deeds will be in vain and too late in the end?' he said.

'I know not,' said Gimli. 'But one thing I know, and that is, not for any device of policy would Aragorn set abroad a false tale. Then either it is true and he has a ring, or it is a false tale invented by someone else. But Elrohir and Elladan have called him by that name. So it must be true. But what it means we do not know.'

There is nothing on this page of the draft, or indeed anywhere in the manuscript, that this can refer to but the cry 'The Lord of the Rings has arisen'. I have found only one scrap of writing that seems to bear on this. Under the text in ink of a piece of rough drafting (that referred to in note 39) for the beginning of the story of the march from Minas Tirith are a few furiously pencilled lines, parts of which can be read:

Galadriel must give her ring to Aragorn (..... to wed Finduilas?). Hence his sudden access of power .... [?that won't work. It will leave] Lórien defenceless also Lord of the Ring will be too ...

This raises many more questions than it answers; but it cannot be unconnected with the strange suggestion that in Lebennin Aragorn was called 'The Lord of the Ring(s)'. I do not know whether it is significant that in the first draft the *s* of *Rings* was not written

426   THE WAR OF THE RING

consecutively with *Ring*, but was added to the word – maybe immediately. This however only raises the question why, if Aragorn was called 'The Lord of the Ring' because it was thought that he possessed a Ring, did my father change it to 'The Lord of the Rings'? The only and rather desperate suggestion I can make is that he wished to mark the confusion of mind on the part of the people who uttered this cry (cf. 'though they knew not what it meant' in the draft text).

35 The initial draft has here: 'and all of the enemies that were not slain or drowned were flying away over the Poros into Lothland desert.' This name is not perfectly clear, but I take it as certain in view of the occurrence of Lothlann on the First Map (VII.309, 313); the form *Lothland* is found in the *Quenta Silmarillion* (V.264, 283). On the Second Map (p. 435) the region south of Mordor is named, but in pencil now so faint that it is hard to be sure of the name: the likeliest interpretation is 'Desert of Lostladen' (cf. the *Etymologies*, V.370, stem LUS).

36 Legolas says in this second version that the day they came to Pelargir was 'the fifth of our journey', whereas in the previous version (p. 413) 'it was the fourth since we left Dunharrow'; but I think that both expressions mean the same (see the Note on Chronology below).

37 The original primary draft reaches this point:
    'And when all was won Aragorn let sound a host of trumpets from the ship that he took for himself, and behold the Shadow host drew near to the shore, and all others fled away. But Aragorn set a line of torches along the shore and these they would not pass, and he spoke to the Dead Men: "Now I will count the oath fulfilled," he said, "when every stranger of Harad or of Umbar is hunted out of this land west of Anduin. When that is done go back and trouble never the valleys again – but go and be at rest."
    With this cf. the rejected portion of the outline given at the beginning of this chapter (note 6 above): 'The Shadow Host disperses, *pursuing the Haradwaith about the vales.*'

38 *and justified the wisdom of Elrond:* see p. 387.

39 In a rough draft for this passage Aragorn speaks to Berithil: 'It is not yet my part to judge you, Master Berithil. If I return I will do so with justice. But for this present you shall leave the guard in the Citadel and go out to war.'

40 The square brackets are in the original.

41 *in our speech* was corrected to *in the old speech of Númenor*, then changed back to *in our speech*.

42 Legolas now plays no part in the narration until Pelargir is reached.

43 The story in this version is expressly to be Gimli's: at the

THE LAST DEBATE   427

beginning, in response to Pippin's 'Won't you tell us some more?' he says: 'Well, if you must hear the tale, I will tell it briefly.' As in the unrevised typescript (note 42) Legolas says nothing until he breaks in on Gimli at his mention of the Great River ('I knew it long ere we reached it', p. 414); but by an alteration to this revised version he breaks silence at Gimli's words '[we] went as swiftly as our stouthearted horses could endure over the plains of Lebennin':

> 'Lebennin!' cried Legolas. All the while he had kept silence, gazing away southward, while Gimli spoke; but now he began to sing: *Silver flow the streams from Celos to Erui* ...

The text of his song is at once in the final form. In RK it is Legolas who tells the whole story up to this point, and Gimli who here takes it up.

44 The place where Kiril was crossed was named on the Second Map *Caerost on Kiril* (p. 437).

45 On the back of the last page of this typescript is the following remarkable passage, on which I can cast no light. It is written in a fine ornate script, together with other odds and ends of phrases in the same script, characteristic of my father's habit of 'doodling' in this way (cf. VII.379):

> Then spoke Elessar: Many Guthrond would hold that your insolence merited rather punishment than answer from your king; but since you have in open malice uttered lies in the hearing of many, I will first lay bare their falsehood, so that all here may know you for what you are, and have ever been. Afterwards maybe a chance shall be given you to repent and turn from your old evil.

46 The title that my father first chose for the chapter when the final structure had been reached was 'Tidings and Counsel': the 'tidings' of Gimli and Legolas, and the 'counsel' of Gandalf at the debate of the lords.

Note on the Chronology

In the outline 'The march of Aragorn and the defeat of the Haradrim' (pp. 397–9) the dates of Aragorn's journey are as follows:

March

8	(morning)	Enters the Paths of the Dead
	(midnight)	Comes to Erech
9	(early morning)	Leaves Erech under the Darkness from Mordor
10	(evening)	Reaches Linhir
11	(morning)	Crosses River Lameduin into Lebennin
12	(early morning)	Reaches Pelargir

428   THE WAR OF THE RING

13   (early morning)   Sets out up river from Pelargir
14   (early morning)   100 miles up river
15   (early morning)   Wind rises and sails hoisted on the ships;
                          c. 9 a.m. fleet is seen from Minas Tirith

The latter part of this chronology seems obviously unsatisfactory, in that the fleet is 100 miles up Anduin in the early morning of March 14, and yet nothing is said of any further journeying on the 14th: the last stretch is accomplished under sail on the morning of the 15th. Against this date (p. 399) my father wrote '14'; and in the companion outline 'The Story Foreseen from Forannest' (p. 360) the charge of the Rohirrim on the 15th was likewise changed to the 14th – which was the date in 'The Siege of Gondor', p. 342.

With the date of Aragorn's entering the Paths of the Dead cf. pp. 309 and 311, notes 9 and 18 (February 6 = March 8). The Dawnless Day is still March 9 (cf. p. 342).

In the manuscript of 'The Tale of Gimli and Legolas' this chronology is preserved – with March 14 as the date of the Battle of the Pelennor Fields. Thus Gimli tells that the Company came to Erech 'just ere the midnight hour – and black it was wellnigh as in the caverns, for though we did not know it yet the darkness of Mordor was creeping over us' (p. 410), and again (p. 412): 'The next morning day did not dawn' (in the margin of the manuscript the figure 9 is written here). 'At nightfall of the second day from Erech' they came to Linhir (and here 10 is written in the margin). They 'rose ere night had passed' (i.e. before dawn on March 11) and rode across Lebennin, 'all that day and through the next night'; and Gimli says that 'it was day, I guessed, by the hidden sun – the fourth since we left Dunharrow' (p. 413) when they reached the shores of Anduin at Pelargir, i.e. the morning of March 12. 'Before the fifth day was over we had taken well nigh all the fleet', which as will be seen in a moment means 'the fifth day of the journey', i.e. March 12.

The first version of the events at Pelargir ends here; in the second version Legolas says (note 36) that the day they reached Pelargir was 'the fifth of our journey' (March 12), that they rested that night 'while others laboured' – but also that the fleet set out up Anduin 'on the fifth morning, that is the day before yesterday' (March 13). This shows clearly that Legolas was distinguishing between 'the fifth day of our journey' (March 12) and 'the fifth morning since we left Dunharrow' (March 13) – so also in RK (p. 153) 'the sixth [morning] since we rode from Dunharrow' is the seventh day of the whole journey. Since it was now the day after the Battle of the Pelennor Fields, and the fleet left Pelargir on 'the day before yesterday', the battle took place on March 14.

The difference of this chronology from that of LR is therefore thus:

THE LAST DEBATE

The journey of Aragorn

Day	March	The present chronology	Chronology of LR
1	8	Reaches Erech at midnight	The same
2	9	The Dawnless Day	
3	10	Reaches Linhir	The Dawnless Day
4	11		Reaches Linhir
5	12	Reaches Pelargir	
6	13	Sets out from Pelargir	Reaches Pelargir
7	14	Battle of the Pelennor Fields	Sets out from Pelargir
8	15		Battle of the Pelennor Fields

In the chronology of the manuscript text Aragorn's journey from Dunharrow to Pelargir took four days and nights, reaching the Anduin on the fifth day, and setting out up river on the morning of the sixth day. In LR Aragorn took three days, not two, from Erech to Linhir, and so five days and nights to Pelargir. Thus in the manuscript (p. 411) Gimli says that from Erech 'then followed the weariest journey that I have ever known ... three days and nights and on into another day', whereas when in RK (p. 150) Legolas speaks of the great ride from Erech to Pelargir he says: 'Four days and nights, and on into a fifth, we rode from the Black Stone'.

Lastly, whereas in the manuscript text the Darkness out of Mordor came over the sky during the night of March 8, and 'the next morning day did not dawn', in RK (p. 151) 'one day of light we rode, and then came the day without dawn' (and in the earlier passage at the end of 'The Passing of the Grey Company', RK p. 63, in the evening of the day on which they left Erech at dawn 'the sun went down like blood behind Pinnath Gelin away in the West behind them', and 'the next day there came no dawn').

XIII

THE BLACK GATE OPENS

As I have explained in the last chapter (p. 416), the story of the journey to the Morannon, the parley with the Lieutenant of Barad-dûr, and the attack on the Host of the West in the slag-hills before the Gate, was written before my father made any move to break up and reorganize the presentation of the narrative in the single very long chapter, which would ultimately be distributed between 'The Passing of the Grey Company', 'The Last Debate', and 'The Black Gate Opens'.

For the conclusion of Book V he had in fact already written some time before a very full outline ('The Story Foreseen from Forannest', pp. 360–2), and this, when he came to write the narrative, he followed remarkably closely. Already present in the outline were the coming of the vanguard to Minas Morghul and the burning of the lands about, the silence that followed the summons to Sauron to come forth, the embassy from the Dark Tower already prepared, the display of Frodo's mithril coat, the blackmailing terms for the surrender of Frodo, Gandalf's refusal to treat and taking of the mithril coat, and the hosts lying ready in ambush. The chief differences from the final story were the coming of the Ents (with Elves of Lórien) to the Morannon (with an express declaration by the ambassador of Sauron that the Ents shall help to rebuild Isengard), uncertainty whether Merry and Pippin were present, and the person of the ambassador: doubtfully identified as the Wizard King (implying a different view of the outcome of his encounter with Éowyn and Merry in the Battle of the Pelennor Fields), but certainly a Nazgûl ('flinging off his garments he vanishes').

For the narrative there is both initial draft and fair copy, which doubtless belong to the same time, since the first two pages are common to both: from the point where the first text became quicker and rougher my father replaced it; but in the first draft the story as it stands in RK was already present in almost every point. Aragorn's dismissal of the faint-hearted (as it is described in *The Tale of Years*) was however (in both texts) Gandalf's, and the cause of their faint-heartedness more immediate (cf. RK p. 162):

... and they could descry the marshes and the desert that stretched north and west to the Emyn Muil. And now the Nazgûl swept down over them unceasingly, and often daring within bowshot of the earth they would plunge shrieking down,

THE BLACK GATE OPENS 431

and their fell voices made even the boldest blench. Some there were who were so unmanned that they could neither walk nor ride further north.

This survived into the fair copy, where it was replaced by the text of RK (p. 162), in which the Nazgûl did not closely approach the Host of the West until the final attack on the Slag-hills. In the draft text it is said that 'some 500 left the host' and went off south-west towards Cair Andros.

No more is said in the draft of the history of the Lieutenant of Baraddûr,[1] the nameless Mouth of Sauron, than that 'It is told that he was a living man, who being captured as a youth became a servant of the Dark Tower, and because of his cunning grew high in the Lord's favour ...' In the fair copy this was repeated, but was changed subsequently to: 'But it is said that he was a renegade, son of a house of wise and noble men in Gondor, who becoming enamoured of evil knowledge entered the service of the Dark Tower, and because of his cunning [and the fertile cruelty of his mind] [and servility] he grew ever higher in the Lord's favour ...' (these phrases being thus bracketed in the original). In RK (p. 164) the Mouth of Sauron 'came of the race of those that are named the Black Númenóreans'.[2]

NOTES

1 First written 'the Lieutenant of Morgul', but this may very probably have been no more than a slip.
2 A few other minor points may be mentioned together. The Morgul Pass (RK p. 161) is called 'the Pass of Kirith Ungol' in the fair copy, and the Pass of Cirith Gorgor (RK p. 162) is 'the Pass of Gorgoroth' in both texts, changed to 'the Pass of Kirith-Gorgor' in the fair copy. In the draft text Damrod of Henneth Annûn reappears again, with Mablung, as a leader of the scouts in Ithilien (RK p. 162); the host can see from their camp on the last night the red lights in the Towers of the Teeth; and in Gandalf's concluding words to the Mouth of Sauron (RK p. 167) he retains the words he used in the original outline (p. 362): 'Begone! But let fear eat your heart: for if you so much as set a thorn in the flesh of your prisoner you shall rue it through all ages.'

Note on the Chronology

In *The Tale of Years* in LR the following dates are given:
March 18 The Host of the West marches from Minas Tirith.
      19 The Host comes to Morgul-vale.
      23 The Host passes out of Ithilien. Aragorn dismisses the faint-hearted.

432   THE WAR OF THE RING

    24 The Host camps in the Desolation of the Morannon.
    25 The Host is surrounded on the Slag-hills.
In both manuscript texts the same indications of date are given, and in
the same words, as in RK, except in one point. The Host here left
Minas Tirith on 17 March (this date being written in the margin), and
since this was two days after 'the Last Debate', which itself took place
on the day after the battle, the date of the Battle of the Pelennor Fields
was here the 14th of March, not the 15th (see p. 428). In the present
versions, however, the difference of one day in the date of the departure
from Minas Tirith is soon lost, for this reason: where in RK (p. 160)
the first day's march ended five miles beyond Osgiliath, but 'the
horsemen pressed on and ere evening they came to the Cross Roads'
(i.e. 18 March), it is said here that '*Next day* the horsemen pressed on
and ere evening they came to the Cross Roads' (i.e. 18 March); and it
was again 'on the next day' that 'the main host came up' (with the date
'19' in the margin). Thus where it is said in RK (p. 161) 'The day after,
being the third day since they set out from Minas Tirith, the army
began its northward march along the road', it is here 'the fourth day',
with the date '20' written in the margin.

	The present version	*The Return of the King*
March 17	March begins, and ends at Osgiliath	
18	Horsemen reach the Cross Roads before evening	March begins, and ends near Osgiliath, but the horsemen go on and reach the Cross Roads before evening.
19	Main host comes to the Cross Roads	
20	The host begins northward march	

    It may be noted lastly that where in RK (p. 163) on the night of
24 March 'the waxing moon was four nights old', here it was 'but
three days from the full moon' on the night before the day on which
the Ring was destroyed.

XIV

THE SECOND MAP

Whenever this map was first made, it was certainly my father's working map during the writing of Book V of *The Lord of the Rings*.[1] The first stage in its making was carried out in black ink, but black ink was also used later, and since it was not drawn and lettered at its first making with the meticulousness of the earlier stages of the First Map it is scarcely possible to isolate the layers of accretion by this means. Red ink was also used for a few alterations, and in the final stage of its useful life corrections and additions were very roughly made in blue ink (also in blue crayon and pencil).

The single sheet of paper on which it was made is now, after so much use many years ago, limp, torn, wrinkled, stained, and rubbed, and some of the later pencillings can scarcely be seen. It is ruled in squares of 2 cm. side (= 100 miles), the squares being lettered and numbered according to the First Map. In my redrawing I have divided it into a western and an eastern portion, with the central vertical line of squares (14) repeated.

The attempt to redraw it posed difficulties. In places there is such a cobweb of fine crisscrossing and competing lines (the 'contours' are very impressionistic) as to bewilder the eye, and the redrawing had to be done while holding a lens; even so, I have certainly not followed every last wiggle with fidelity. Here and there it is hard to make out what the markings actually are or to interpret what they represent. In the region south of the White Mountains the map is so extremely crowded, and there are so many alterations and additions of names made at different times, that (since a primary aim of the redrawing is clarification) I have found it best to omit a number of names and explain the changes in the account of the map that follows; and for the same reason I have shown the new course of Anduin at Minas Tirith but not the new sites of Barad-dûr and Mount Doom. The redrawing is therefore avowedly inconsistent in what is shown and what is not, but I think inevitably so; and the following notes are an essential part of its presentation.

I refer to the map of Rohan, Gondor and Mordor published in *The Return of the King* as 'the large LR map'.

The account of the Rivers of Gondor written on this map has been given in Vol. VII (p. 312) in a discussion of peculiarities in the original conception of the southern rivers, but since in reducing my redrawing

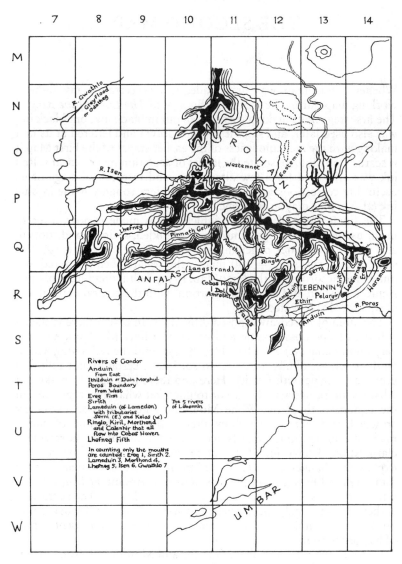

The Second Map (West)

THE SECOND MAP 435

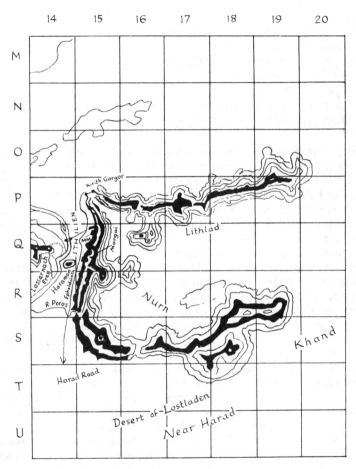

The Second Map (East)

436   THE WAR OF THE RING

to the size of the printed page the writing becomes extremely small I repeat it here:

Rivers of Gondor
Anduin
   From East
Ithilduin or *Duin Morghul*
Poros   Boundary
   From West
Ereg   First
Sirith
Lameduin   (of Lamedon) with tributaries
  Serni (E.) and *Kelos* (W.)
Ringlo, Kiril, Morthond and *Calenhir* that
  all flow into Cobas Haven
Lhefneg   Fifth

> The 5 rivers
> of Lebennin

In counting only the mouths are counted: *Ereg* 1, *Sirith* 2, *Lameduin* 3, *Morthond* 4, *Lhefneg* 5, *Isen* 6, *Gwathlo* 7

Ereg (later *Erui*) has now essentially its final place and course; *Sirith* likewise, but with no western tributary (*Kelos* on the large LR map) – the lines on the map in this valley are a dense maze and I have simplified them in the redrawing, but it is clear that there is only a single stream. *Lossarnach* seems to have been a much larger region than it is on the LR maps, but this may be due merely to the lettering of a long name in a small space.

Lameduin, while clearly written with final -*n* in the list of rivers (as also in the text given on pp. 397 ff.) is equally clearly written *Lamedui* on the map itself, and should perhaps have been so represented. It is also clear that there are three tributary streams marked, although only two, *Serni* and *Kelos*, are referred to in the list (and there is no place for another in 'the five rivers of Lebennin'); only the easternmost, *Serni*, is named on the map. All three join together at a place marked with a black dot (R 12), though this was at first given no name (see below).

Ringlo, Kiril, and *Morthond* have essentially the final courses; but Kiril is not a tributary of Ringlo as it is on the LR maps, and a fourth river, unnamed on the map but called *Calenhir* in the list of rivers, comes in from Pinnath Gelin to the westward. At the junction of the four streams the map is very hard to interpret: it is not clear which rivers have joined at the place marked by a black dot (Q 11) and which flow independently into Cobas Haven, the bay north of Dol Amroth. Beside the dot (in small lettering as if referring to the dot) was originally written *Lamedon*, which was struck through, and which I think was probably a simple error (in view of *Lameduin* many miles to the east). Above *Lamedon* was written *Linhir*, also struck through. The earliest reference to Linhir in the texts is found in the outline 'The

THE SECOND MAP

437

Story Foreseen from Forannest' (p. 361), where the Darkness out of Mordor is seen by the Ents as 'a great blackness ... extending in breadth from Rauros to Linhir': this could imply the earlier position, above Cobas Haven, but perhaps more probably the later, on Lameduin (Gilrain). The crossing of Ringlo was a later addition in red ink.

The name *Lamedon* was written a second time across R 13 (beneath *Serni* and above *Lebennin*), and this placing obviously consorts with the river-name *Lameduin*. In this position it was again struck out, *Lameduin* changed to *Gilrain*, and *Linhir* written against the dot on R 12 where the three streams join. *Lamedon* was later written in a third and final location (but see note 2) at the top of Q 12, across the upper waters of Kiril and Ringlo.

The emergence of the new geography can be traced in the texts. In the outline 'The march of Aragorn and defeat of the Haradrim' (see pp. 397–8 and note 4) occurs the following:

> Erech to Fords of Lameduin (say Linhir?) is 175 miles direct, about 200 by road. ... At Linhir on Lameduin men of Lebennin and Lamedon are defending passage of river against Haradwaith.

When this was written Lamedon still lay north of Ethir Anduin, a northward region of Lebennin, and 'the men of Lebennin and Lamedon' had withdrawn westwards to the line of the river, which they were attempting to hold. But already in the original drafts for the story of the ride of the Grey Company in 'The Last Debate' (see pp. 411–12) they passed 'over Tarlang's Neck into Lamedon', Lameduin has become Gilrain, and (as in RK, p. 151) it was the men of Lamedon who contested the passage of Gilrain against the Haradrim.[2]

The dot near the bottom right-hand corner of P 11 marks *Erech* (named on the original); this was an addition, as was the river flowing down from Erech to join the course of Morthond as originally marked on P–Q 11. To the dot on the river Kiril (Q 12), a later addition, is attached the pencilled name *Caerost on Kiril*; this was the forerunner of *Calembel*, where Kiril was crossed (RK p. 63). Neither *Caerost* nor *Calembel* is found in the original manuscript of 'The Last Debate' (see p. 419). The other dot on Q 12, east of the crossing of Ringlo, is marked with the pencilled name *Tarnost*, which so far as I know does not appear elsewhere.

The name Belfalas was a late addition (see p. 293 note 22); and a note added early to the map directs that *Pinnath Gelin* should be made into 'lower Green Hills'.

The name *Odotheg* 'Seventh' of Gwathlo or Greyflood was changed in pencil to *Odothui*; on this name see VII.311–12. The last letter of *Lhefneg* was also changed: most probably it was first written *Lhefned* and then immediately altered to *Lhefneg*, the form of the name in the list of rivers written on the map.

438   THE WAR OF THE RING

North of the White Mountains a line of dots on squares P 13, Q 13–14 represents the beacon hills; on this see p. 354 note 3.

Moving eastwards to Q 14, the original course of Anduin can be discerned on the original, running in a straight line from below the confluence of Ereg to where the river bends north-west below Osgiliath. The great elbow in Anduin here and the hills of Haramon that caused it were superimposed later in blue ink, *Haramon* being afterwards struck out and *Emyn Arnen* substituted (with some totally illegible name preceding it). In the original text of the chapter 'Minas Tirith' (p. 278) there was no mention of this feature. It is shown (but without the hills around which the river bends) on the little map drawn on a page added to the manuscript of 'The Ride of the Rohirrim' (p. 353); and it first appears in the texts in the outline 'The Story Foreseen from Forannest' (see p. 359 and note 3): 'the [Pelennor] wall right above the stream which bends round the Hills of Haramon'. The name *Emyn Arnen* appears in the drafting of 'The Battle of the Pelennor Fields' (p. 370). I have very little doubt that it was indeed the development of the story of the battle that brought the great bend in Anduin around the hills of Haramon / Emyn Arnen into being; for so the black fleet could be brought right under the wall of the Pelennor, and victory assured in the face of disaster by the exceedingly dramatic and utterly unlooked for arrival, on the very field, of Aragorn with the Rangers and the sons of Elrond, and all the men newly gathered from the southern fiefs.

Osgiliath is now north-east of Minas Tirith (see pp. 269–70, 353). A note on the map says that 'Minas Morgul must be rather more north' (cf. the plan reproduced on p. 181 and the large LR map).

Within the confines of Mordor a major change was made in the last stage of the use of this map. The great peninsula of high land (Q 16) thrust out southwards from the Ash Mountains, on which stood Barad-dûr, was struck through, and Barad-dûr was moved north-west (to P 16). This was where Orodruin had stood as the map was first drawn.[3] Orodruin was moved to stand near the bottom right-hand corner of P 15. I have in this case preserved the original site of Barad-dûr in my redrawing, for the alterations were carried out very roughly. Other additions of this time were the rough outline of the Sea of Nurnen, the names *Lithlad, Morgai*, and *Nurn*, and also *Gorgoroth* of the vale running back from the Morannon. *Gorgoroth* was struck out, and in its place was pencilled here the name *Narch Udûn*[4].

NOTES

1   The fact that the track of Frodo's journey from the Emil Muil to the Morannon (not shown on my redrawing) is very carefully marked and probably belongs to the first 'layer' does not demonstrate that in its making this map goes back to the writing of Book

THE SECOND MAP   439

IV. For one thing, it seems unlikely that my father would have made the map redrawn on p. 269 if the Second Map had been already in existence.

2 A name in scarcely visible pencilling that is almost certainly *Lamedon* can be seen written right across Q 11–12 (from below the *r* of *Morthond* to east of the crossing of Ringlo), which suggests that Lamedon was at first a larger region.

3 When Barad-dûr was moved to the site of Orodruin the original markings were obliterated.

4 The names *Harad Road*, *Near Harad* (and an arrow directing to *Far Harad*), *Desert of Lostladen* (see p. 426 note 35), *Khand* (see p. 369), and *Umbar* were scribbled in pencil or blue crayon.

INDEX

In this book the variables are so many that the arrangement of the index, if it is to be more than a simple list of forms, becomes to some degree a matter of choice; for on the one hand there was a great deal of alteration and substitution among the names themselves, while on the other their application changed as the narrative, and the geography, changed. Thus for example the *Stone of Erech* was originally a *palantír*, but when it became a stone brought from Númenor the *palantír* (or *Stone*) of Erech was for a time still present; *Kirith Ungol* and *Minas Morghul (Morgul)* were several times shifted in relation to each other; and the Lord of Westfold was in succession *Trumbold, Heorulf (Herulf), Nothelm, Heorulf, Erkenwald, Erkenbrand*, while *Westfold* was originally *Westmarch* and the original *Westfold* was a region in the west of the Misty Mountains. I hope at any rate that my attempt will be found accurate and serviceable for all the inconsistencies of presentation.

With constantly recurring names I have used the device employed in *The Return of the Shadow* and *The Treason of Isengard* whereby the word *passim* means that in a long run of references no more than one page here and there happens not to carry that name. Names occurring on the maps and on the pages reproduced from the original manuscripts are not indexed, and only exceptionally those in chapter-titles. Under the entry *Old English* are collected only special instances, and not of course the very large number of names in Rohan that are in fact Old English.

Adrahil of Dol Amroth 340
Adûnaic 161
Aglarond 28, 76–8, 399; *Caves of Splendour* 76–7; *Glittering Caves* 28, 77; *Caves of Helm's Deep, the Caves* 26–8, 297. The *palantír* of Aglarond 76–8, 399
Akallabêth 169
Aldor Third King of the Mark. 408
Ambarkanta 167
Amon Dîn The seventh beacon in Anórien. 233, 343–6, 350–1, 353–4, 404; *Dîn* 351–2. Earlier name *Amon Thorn* 232
Amon Hen 20, 59, 72, 118, 128; *Amon Henn* 128
Amon Lhaw 72
Amon Thorn See *Amon Dîn*.
Amroth See *Dol Amroth*.

INDEX **441**

Anárion 149, 153, 168, 397; *sons of* 374–5; name of region 243–4, 252, 254–5, 266

Anborn (1) Father of Falborn (precursor of Faramir). 136, 170. (2) Ranger of Ithilien. 154, 164, 169 (replaced *Falborn* (2)).

Andabund, Andrabonn 'elephant'. 136, and see 139. See *Múmak, Oliphaunt.*

Andros See *Cair Andros.*

Anduin 73, 85, 95, 98, 100–2, 110, 125, 128, 131, 133–4, 146–7, 149, 157, 182, 218, 229–30, 235, 243, 266, 268, 270, 275, 288, 295, 330, 333, 340, 353, 356, 360–3, 369–70, 372, 374, 378, 391, 398, 405, 412–14, 419, 422, 426, 428–9, 433, 436, 438; *Mouths of* 213, 246, 255, 262–3, 276, 278, 293, 413–14; *Vale of* 291, 324. See *(The) Delta, Ethir Anduin, (The) Great River.*

Andúril 'Flame of the West', Aragorn's sword. 370. Replaced *Branding*; see also *Elendil.*

Anfalas Fief of Minas Tirith. 287, 289, 293; *Dor-Anfalas* 287, 293; *Langstrand* 287, 293. See *Belfalas.*

Angbor Lord of Lamedon. 414, 419

Angmar 334, 369; *King of Angmar* 334

Angrenost Isengard. 44, 72, 79; also *Angost* 44, 72, 79

Annals of Beleriand 169, 297

Annon Torath See *Sern Aranath.*

Anórien 77, 141–2, 219, 231–4, 244, 253, 255, 262, 275, 318, 340, 343, 345–7, 353–4, 363–4, 373, 404, 415; *Anórien road*, see *Roads.*

Aragorn 3–5, 10–15, 17–22, 24–6, 37–9, 42, 47, 49–50, 52, 54, 56–60, 65, 67, 69–70, 72, 74–5, 77–8, 80, 124, 126, 140–1, 146–7, 149, 165, 219, 226, 229–30, 235–68 *passim*, 272, 274–6, 281, 291, (294), 296–321 *passim*, 327, 329, 339, 359–64, 370, 372, 375, 378–80, (382), 385–431 *passim*, 437–8. His standard 302, 359–60, 363, 370, 389, 397, 399, 411, 415, 422, 424. See *Elessar, Thorongil, Trotter.*

Arathorn Father of Aragorn. 15, 319

Araw The Vala Oromë. 281, 292

Argonath 132, 281, 291; *Pillars of the Kings* 132. See *Sarn Aran, Sern Aranath*; *Sarn Gebir* (1).

Arnach See *Lossarnach.*

Arnen See *Emyn Arnen.*

Arnor 395. See *North Kingdom.*

Arod Horse of Rohan. 78, 423

Arvedui 'Last King' of Arthedain. 311

Arwen 302, 307, 370; *Lady of Rivendell* 307. See *Finduilas* (2).

Asgil-Golamir Lord of Anfalas. 287. (Replaced by *Golasgil*.)

Ash Mountains 268, 438. See *Ered Lithui.*

Atani Edain, 'Fathers of Men'. 161

athelas Healing plant. 17, 386, 394. See *Kingsfoil.*

442   THE WAR OF THE RING

Avallóne   Haven in Tol Eressëa. 169
Avari   'The Unwilling', Elves who would not join the Great March from Kuiviénen. 158. *The Refusers* 157; *Wild Elves* 157

Bag End   45, 96
Baggins   Used by Gollum of Bilbo and Frodo. 111, 115
Baggins, Bilbo   45, 47, 49, 96, 115, 156, 194, 207, 219, 275, 357
Baggins, Frodo   17, 45, 50, 77–8, 81, 85–152 *passim*, 154, 156, 161, 163–8, 171–8, 182–226 *passim*, 229–30, 233–4, 241, 256–7, 259, 262–3, 267, 270–2, 275–6, 286, 291, 294–5, 322, 326–7, 329, 339, 341–2, 360–2, 364, 398, 425, 430(–1), 438
Bair Nestad, Bair Nestedriu   See *Berin a Nestad.*
Baldor   Son of Brego (second King of the Mark). 315–16, 321, 407, 416, 421; *Bealdor* 321, 397, 405, 408, 421
Baldr   Norse god (Balder). 369
Balrogs   372. See *Gothmog.*
Barad Amroth   409, 423–4; *Castle Amroth* 423. See *Dol Amroth.*
Barad-dûr   (in many instances spelt *Baraddur*) 64, 69–70, 72–3, 79–80, 119–20, 185, 189, 214, 219, 238, 241, 256, 362, 368, 403 (*Lord of*), 433, 438–9; *Lieutenant of Barad-dûr* 419, 430–1. The *palantír* of Barad-dûr 80 (*Ithil-stone*), 362, 404. See *Dark Tower.*
Barahir   (1) Father of Beren. 155. (2) Messenger from Minas Tirith to Théoden. 242, 244. See *Hirgon.*
Barangils   Men of the Harad, Southrons. 136
Baranor   Father of Berithil (Beregond). 282, 288
Barathil, Barithil   See *Berithil.*
Barren Hill   See *Death Down.*
Barren Lands   Before the Morannon. 140
Barrow-downs   209, 368
Battle Plain   85, (109), 111, (112). See *Dagorlad.*
Battles   See *Fords of Isen, Great Battle, Hornburg, Pelennor, Valar.*
Beacons   In Anórien. 77, 141, 231–4, 256–7, 259–60, 262–4, 270–2, 275–6, 317, 344, 351–2, 354, 438
Bealdor   See *Baldor.*
Beechbone   Ent. 53
Beleriand   155, 159, 161; see also 184, 187, and *Annals of Beleriand.*
Belfalas   (in different applications, see 293) 28, 41, 233, 236, 238, 252, 278, 287, 293–4, 372, 412, 437
Benrodir   Prince of Anárion (?). 252, 255, 266
Bëor   Father of Men. 157, 159
Beowulf   266
Bered Ondrath   The Causeway Towers. 340. See *Causeway.*
Beregond   Man of Minas Tirith. 276–7, 282–3, 288, 292, 325, 340. See *Berithil.*
Beren   (1) Beren One-hand. 155, 159, 184, 187, 218. (2) Man of

INDEX 443

Minas Tirith, precursor of Berithil, Beregond. (276), 282–4, 286, 292–3

Bergil Son of Berithil (Beregond). 287, 294, 388, 395, 415. See *Gwinhir*.

Berin a Nestad The Houses of Healing. 379–80; *Bair Nestad, Bair Nestedriu, Edeb na Nestad* 380

Berithil Man of Minas Tirith (replaced by *Beregond*). 288–9, 294, 336, 338–40, 374–5, 377, 379–81, 388, 390–3, (415), 426. Also *Berethil* 324–6, 339; earlier *Barathil, Barithil* 287–8

Bilbo Baggins See under *Baggins*.

Black Captain 330, 334, 336, 363, 367, 369, 387; *Fell Captain* 324. See *Angmar, Nazgûl, Wizard King*.

Black Fleet (including all references to the fleet after its capture) 275, 296, 359, 369–70, 372, 374–5, 378–80, 388, 390–3, 398–9, 415, 419, 428, 438; see also *Harad, Southrons*.

Black Gate(s) (including references to *the Gate*). The Morannon; originally name of the pass into Mordor (see 122). 113, 118–19, 122–3, 126–7, 130, 134, 138, 173, 190, 219, 271, 275, 330, 361–4, 400, 416, 419, 430; *North Gate* 213; *Parley at the (Black) Gate* 361–2, 416–17, 419, 430–1. See *Ennyn Dûr, Gates of Mordor, Morannon*.

Black Hand 404

Black Land Mordor. 403, 414

Black Mountains (including references to *the mountains*) 4, 8–10, 12–13, 22, 52, 56, 133, 137, 167. (Replaced by *White Mountains*.)

Black Númenóreans 431

Black Rider(s) 177, 187 (*Rider*), 275, 331, 337; *Fell Riders* 292, 294; *Black Horseman* 336

Blackroot, River 265, 409; *Blackroot Vale, Vale of Blackroot* 243–4, 253, 287. See *Morthond*.

Black Speech 20

Blessed Realm 164

Bodleian Library 193, 199, 221

Bombadil See *Tom Bombadil*.

Book of Lost Tales 372

Boromir 20, 22, 58, 101, 135–6, 139, 144–52, 154, 156, 160, 162–3, 165–7, 169, 229, 262, 276, 281, 285, 292, 328, (330), 332–3, 339; *Highwarden of the White Tower* 130; his horn 146–50, (165), 277, 281, 294

Branding Aragorn's sword. 14–15, 19–20, 370, 372, 405, 418. (Replaced by *Andúril*.)

Brandybuck, Caradoc Father of Meriadoc. 26, 35, 40–1

Brandybuck, Meriadoc (also *Merry*) 3–4, 6–7, 26, 35–41, 43, 47–50, 52–61, 66–8, 78, 80, 229, 236, 238, 240–8, 252, 263–4, 274–6, 296–312 *passim*, 316–19, 321–2, 343, 345–53, 355–6,

444 THE WAR OF THE RING

359–60, 362, 366, 368, 375, 380, 384–7, 390, (392), 394, 396, 399, 403, 405–7, 410, 415, 417–19, 421, 423, 425, 430; his pony 238, 240, 299, 301, 318 (and see *Stybba*); his sword 49, 59, 368, 384

Brandywine Bridge 309
Breaking of the Fellowship 22, 100–1, 142
Bree 38, 44, 52; *Bree-hill* 38; *Bree-folk* 38
Bregalad Ent. 25–6, 30–1, 39–40, 42–3, 49, 53, 55. See *Quickbeam*.
Brego Second King of the Mark, son of Eorl. 244, 321, 397, 405, 407–8, 421; *Bregu* 315–16, 321. Originally grandson of Eorl 243–4, son of Brytta 244
Broken Sword, The 393
Brytta Eleventh King of the Mark. 408; originally father of Brego, 244
Buckland 26, 35
Butterbur, Barnabas 39, 45; *Barliman* 45

Caerost on Kiril 427, 437. (Replaced by *Calembel* (2).)
Cair Andros Island in Anduin. 340, 353, 356, 415, 431. Earlier names *Tol Varad* 326; *Men Falros* 326–7, 329–30; *Cairros* 340; *Andros* 340
Cairros See *Cair Andros*.
Calembel (1) Lawn beneath Amon Hen (afterwards *Parth Galen*). 297, 301, 307. Other names *Calledin* 301; *Calembrith* 307. (2) Town in Lamedon. 419, 437 (see *Caerost*).
Calenard(h)on Rohan as a province of Gondor. 168, 316, 321; *Calenardan* 168. Earlier names *Elenarda* 155, 167; *Kalenarda* 155, 167, *Kalinarda* 156, 168
Calenhad The second beacon in Anórien. 233, 344, 349
Calenhir, River In Gondor. 436
Calledin See *Calembel* (1).
Carandrian Ent ('a rowan-ent'). (54), 55
Castle Amroth See *Barad Amroth*.
Causeway From Osgiliath to the Pelennor Wall. 278, 330–1, 416; *Causeway Forts (Towers)* 278, 330–1, 340, 342, 353–4, and see *Bered Ondrath*.
Caves of Helm's Deep See *Aglarond*.
Celeborn 112
Celos, River See *Kelos*.
Ceorl Rider of Rohan. 4–5, 8(–9)
Chronology (1) Within the narrative. 3–7, 21–2, 25–6, 41–2, 53, 57–60, 70, 73, 80–1, 85–6, 93, 100–3, 118–20, 126, 129–30, 134–5, 139–43, 145–6, 150, 166, 178–80, 182, 226, 231, 237, 240, 245, 255–6, 259–60, 262–4, 270–6, 286–7, 291–2, 294–6, 299, 308–9, 311, 321–2, 324–5 (change of month), 327, 339,

INDEX 445

341–4, 349, 355–6, 360–1, 397–9, 411–14, 426–9, 431–2. (2) Years of Middle-earth. 37–40, 45, 58, 309, 408, 424. (3) Of composition (external dating). 40, 44, 59, 77–8, 80–1, 85–6, 100, 104, 121, 131, 144, 151, 183–4, 218, 226, 231–5, 250–1, 255, 274

Cirdan 76, 78; *Kirdan* 77

Ciril, River See *Kiril.*

Cirith Gorgor See *Kirith Gorgor.*

Closed Door, The Leading to the Tombs in Minas Tirith. (337–8), 374, 377, 380, 382; *Steward's (Stewards') Door* 380. See *Fenn Fornen.*

Cobas Haven Bay north of Dol Amroth. 436–7

Common Speech 136, 144, 161–2, 356; *Common Tongue* 159–60, 162; *the ordinary language* 158–9

Company (of the Ring), The 85–6, 93, 98, 100–1, 112, 142, 145, 147, 166–7, 276, 304–5, 346, 387; *Company of Nine* 285; *the Fellowship* 79, 241

Corramas See *Ramas Coren.*

Corsairs of Umbar See *Umbar.*

Council of Elrond 149, 156

Crack of Doom 190, 362

Cranthir Man of Minas Tirith. 233, 277. (Replaced by *Ingold*.)

Cross-roads In Ithilien (also *Cross ways*). 121, 125, 132–5, 171, 177–80, 182, 184, 295, 326, 342, 432; the broken statue 132, 134–5, 171, 177, 326 (names for this, 132)

Cyneferth See *Dernhelm.*

Dagorlad 111–12, 256–7, 361. See *Battle Plain.*

Dale 157; *tongue of Dale* 159

Damrod Ranger of Ithilien. 136, 139, 151, 431; the name 160

Dark Door, The In the Dwimorberg, leading to the Paths of the Dead. (Including references to *the Door*) 313, 315–16, 319–21, 406–7, 420–1. See *Dead Men of Dunharrow.*

Dark Lord 49, 72, 122, 125, 145–6, 156, 195, 331, 335, 376, 380, 401, 403; *the Lord* 112, 380, 431. See *Sauron.*

Dark Men of Eilenach See *Eilenach.*

Dark Men of the Mountains See *Men of the Mountains.*

Darkness (out of Mordor), Great Darkness (and other references, as *shade of Mordor*) 177–9, 182, 260, 262–3, 271, 274–5, 286, 289, 295, 317, 319, 322, 324–7, 330, 334, 341, 347, 350, 361, 368, 398–9, 403–4, 410–14, 419, 422, 427–9, 437

Dark Tower 68, 71, 73, 77, 119, 124, 211, 268, 331, (360), 430–1; *the first Dark Tower* 127

Dark Years 207, 215, 223, 236, 238, 246, 278, 350, 401; *the Dark* 257; *days of Darkness* 159

446 THE WAR OF THE RING

Dawnless Day 179, 182, 295, 342, (412), 428–9; *Day without Dawn* 421

Dead Marshes (including references to *the Marshes*) 85, 93, 104–5, 107, 109–12, 115, 118–20, 128, 136, 185, 270, 330, 430

Dead Men (of Dunharrow), The Dead 267, 289, 310, 315–16, 319, 321, 406, 409, 411–14, 417–18, 426; *King of the Dead* 397, 414, 419, 425; *Gate of the Dead* 313, 418 (see *Dark Door*). See *Shadow Host, Paths of the Dead, Dunharrow.*

Death Down Below Helm's Deep. 40–1, 70; *Dead Down* 298; *Barren Hill* 41

Deeping Coomb (including many references to *the Coomb*, also spelt *Combe*) 10, 12–13, 17, 27, 29, 40, 42, 49, 54, 69–70, 72–3, 75, 78–9, 130, 140, 275, 291, 297–8, 300, 304–6

Deeping Stream 19, 24, 47, 310

Deeping Wall 11, 18, 21. See *Heorulf's Wall.*

Delta, The Of Anduin. 252–5, 268. See *Anduin, Ethir Anduin.*

Denethor (including references to *the Lord (of the City)*) 146, 148, 151, 153, 165, 167, 231, 236, 253, 255, 257, 259–60, 262–3, 274–7, 281–4, 287–8, 292, 294, 316, 323–30, 332–40, 348, 353, 359–60, 363, 374–82, 385–6, 388–92, 400, 402–4; the name 159–60. *The Tower of Denethor* 77, 130, 278, 281, 288, 292

Déor Seventh King of the Mark. 408

Déorwin(e) Rider of Rohan. 352; called *the Marshal* 371

Dernhelm Name of Éowyn disguised. 349–50, 353, 357, 368, 372; '*a young kinsman of the king*' 369. Earlier names *Cyneferth* 348, 355; *Grímhelm* 347–9, 355, 369; *Derning* 349

Derufin Son of Duinhir of Morthond Vale. 287, 370

Dervorin Son of the Lord of Ringlo Vale. 287

Dimgræf, Dimhale Helm's Deep. 23; *Dimgraf's gate* 23; *Dimhale's Door, Dimmhealh* 23

Dimholt Wood before the Dark Door of Dunharrow. 266, 313, 320–1. (Replaced *Firienholt*.)

Dín See *Amon Dín.*

Dior Thingol's Heir. 297

Dirgon Messenger from Minas Tirith to Théoden. 316–17. See *Hirgon.*

Díriel Ancient name used in Gondor. 161

Distances 12, 27, 36, 42, 68, 78–9, 119, 123, 125, 128, 132–3, 145, 252, 257, 259, 267, 278, 283, 291–2, 294, 296–7, 308, 327, 330, 339–40, 343–4, 348, 352, 354–5, 361, 363–4, 370, 397–9, 411–12, 414–15, 422, 424

Dol Amroth (including references to Imrahil as *Prince* or *Lord of Dol Amroth*) 252, 278, 287, 289, 294, 301, 306, 326, 331, 338, 340, 369, 386, 390, 415, 423–4; *Amroth* 372. See *Barad Amroth.*

INDEX

447

Dol Baran Last hill of the Misty Mountains (also *Dolbaran*). 72, 75, 79–81, 119–20, 129, 140, 142, 235, 270, 276, 320, 322, 342, 392

Dol Dúghol 122. See *Dol Guldur*.

Dol Guldur 122, 357–8

Dor-Anfalas See *Anfalas*.

Doriath 184, 187, 297

Downs In the Eastemnet. 361; *Down-end* 361

Dragons 217, 232

Druadan Forest 344, 352–3

Druedain The Wild Men of the White Mountains. 352. See *Wild Men*, *Woses*.

Dúath See *Ephel Dúath*.

Duilas See *Targon*.

Duilin Son of Duinhir of Morthond Vale. 287, 370

Duinhir Lord of Morthond Vale. 287, 370–2

Duin Morghul Stream flowing through Imlad Morghul, formerly called *Ithilduin*. 436. See *Morgulduin*.

Dúnedain 161–2, 310, 363, 369–70, 395, 411; *Dúnadan* 302, 309; *Star of the Dúnedain* (299), 309. See *Kings of Men*.

Dunharrow, the Hold (of Dunharrow) 69–70, 72, 141, 235–59 passim, 262–3, 265, 267, 272–4, 289, 296–7, 299, 301, 303, 305, 307–9, 311–13, 315–16, 318, 320–2, 343, 345, 347, 351, 355–6, 386, 396, 405–7, 413, 416–19, 421–3, 426, 428–9. Also the name of the mountain at the head of Harrowdale (later *Starkhorn*) 235–7, (238), 240, 242, 257, 308; *the Lap of Dunharrow* 238, 241. Former men of Dunharrow 236, 238, 241–4, 246, 251, 265, 267, 315–16, and see *Dead Men of Dunharrow*. *From dark Dunharrow in the dim morning* 349, 355–6

Dúnhere Rider of Rohan, chief of the men of Harrowdale. 316, 318, 355, 371

Dunland Region in the west of the Misty Mountains, at first called *Westfold*. 22–3, 27, 40–1, 236, 249, 253; *tongue of Dunland* 21, 159; *Dunlanders* 52 (origin of), 242, 247, 253, 298; *Dunlendings* 321. See *Westfold* (1).

Durin's folk 357

Dushgoi Orc name of Minas Morghul. 216–18, 226; *Lord(s) of Dushgoi* 216–17

Dwarves (general references) 14, 37–8, 153, 217, 292, 294, 357–8, 411; *Dwarflord* 300, 305

Dwimorberg 266, 312–13, 315, 372, 406. See *Haunted Mountain*.

Dwimordene Lothlórien. 372

Eagle(s) 219, 256, 361–2. See *Gwaihir*.

448   THE WAR OF THE RING

Ealdor   The seneschal of Edoras. (*256, 259*), 267. (Replaced by *Galdor*.)

Earendel   155 (*the half-elven*), 158–9, 168, 193, 203; *Earendel's star* 224, *the evening star* 210; *Alla (Aiya) Earendel Elenion Ankalima* 223

Eärnur   Last king of the line of Anárion. 153. See *Elessar* (1).

Eastemnet   236–7 (*East Emnet*), 243–4, 313, 361

Easterlings   244, 415

Eastfold   256, 259, 262, 319, 371

Eastlanders   340

Ecthelion   (1) A lord of Gondolin. 292. (2) *Ecthelion I*, Steward of Gondor. 292; *The Tower of Ecthelion* 278, 281. (3) *Ecthelion II*, Steward of Gondor, father of Denethor. 281, 292, 379

Edain   161. See *Atani*.

Edeb na Nestad   The Houses of Healing. See *Berin a Nestad*.

Edoras, Eodoras   (references up to 79 are almost all to the earlier form *Eodoras*) 3–6, 9, 12, 17–18, 22–3, 25, 27, 29, 40–1, 47–8, 51, 56, 58–60, 68–70, 73, 78–9, 102–3, 119–20, 140–2, 145–6, 182, 229, 232–3, 236–7, 240, 242, 245, 247, 249–50, 252, 254–7, 259, 262–4, 267, 270, 272–5, 289, 291, 296, 298–9, 301, 303, 308–9, 311, 318–22, 343–4, 346–50, 353–4, 368, 389, 406, 408, 423–4. The Mounds of Edoras 385, 389, 407–8, 423–4

Eilenach   The sixth (or fifth, see 344) beacon in Anórien. 233, 343–4, 349–54, 356; *Forest of Eilenach* 343–4, 354; *Dark Men of Eilenach* 343–6. Earliest form *Elenach* 232

Elbereth   (1) Varda. 210, 218. (2) Son of Dior Thingol's Heir. 297. (3) Son of Elrond. 297, 301–2. (Replaced by *Elrohir*.)

Elboron   (1) Son of Dior Thingol's Heir. 297. (2) Son of Elrond. 297, 301–2, 307, 370. (Replaced by *Elladan*.)

Eldamar   76. See *Elvenhome*.

Eldar   161

Elder Days   161

Elder People   Elves. 159, 169

Eldûn   Son of Dior Thingol's Heir. 297

Elenach   See *Eilenach*.

Elenarda   (1) 'Stellar Kingdom', the region of Ilmen. 167. (2) Applied to Rohan, preceding *Kalenarda* (see *Calenard(h)on*). 155, 167

Elendil   14, 19, 21, 149, 275, 359, 424; *sons of* 149, 397, 424, *heir(s), house, race of* 80, 155, 158, 247, 249, 281, 388, 391; *sword of Elendil* 253–4, 301–2, 392, 419 (see *Narsil*); *Star of Elendil* 370, 395, *seven stars of* 411, badges, tokens of 279, 281, 385, 389, 395, 399; the name 159–60

Elendilions   Descendants of Elendil. 76

Elessar   (1) Last king of the line of Anárion. 153. See *Eärnur*. (2) Aragorn. 309, 370, 390, 395, 411, 427. See *Elfstone*.

INDEX 449

Elf-friend(s) 157–9, 161, 168
Elfhelm Rider of Rohan. 352–3, 356–8, 371, 373; called *the Marshal* 350, 352
Elfstone Aragorn. 390, 395. See *Elessar*.
Elias Tobiasson First grower of pipeweed in the Shire. 36. See *Hornblower, Smygrave*.
Elladan Son of Elrond. 307, 370, 389, 403, 406, 409, 411, 425. (Replaced *Elboron* (2)).
Elostirion Osgiliath. 81, 122, 128, 132–3, 138, 229
Elrohir Son of Elrond. 297, 302, 307, 370, 403, 406, 411, 424–5. (Replaced *Elbereth* (3)).
Elrond 145, 156, 158, 165, 168, 207, 219, 223, 274, 301–2, (305), 307, 370, 387, 394, 401, 415, 426. See *Council of, Sons of, Elrond*.
Elros 158, 168
Elrûn Son of Dior Thingol's Heir. 297
Elven- *Elven-boat* 148, 163; *-blade* 194, 207, 209; *-cloak(s)* 92, 398; *-lords* 301; *rope* 175; *-speech, -tongue* 161–2; *-sword* 207. See *half-elven, High-elven*.
Elvenhome 157–60, 164, 169–70; *Bay of Elvenhome* 169. See *Eldamar*.
Elves Of Gildor's company 60; of Lórien 161, 168, 256, 260, 266, 345, 361, 398, 430. Divisions of the Elves 157, 168; in relation to Men 158; described by Sam 162–3; *Elflord* 300, 305; other references 77, 98, 109, 112, 131, 153, 155, 158–60, 184, 187, 213, 217, 224, 411. *Elves of the Woods, Middle Elves*, see *Lembi*; *Elves of Valinor* 158; *Exiled Elves* 157; *Western Elves* 161; *Wild Elves* 157. See *High Elves, Wood-elves; Eldar, Elder People, Fair Folk*.
Elvish (with reference to language) 35, 44, 50, 55, 158–61, 163, 202, 218, 287, 379–80; *Ancient Elvish of Elvenhome* 160; Elvish cited 218, 223, 293, 394. See *High-elven, Noldorin, Quenya*.
  (with other reference) 53, 134, 138, 151–2, 158, 163, 167, 169, 185, 190–1, 210, 216–17, 224, 338
Elwing 297
Emyn Arnen 278, 294, 353, 363, 370, 372, 397, 422, 438; *the reach of Arnen* (stretch of Anduin below the Harlond) 370, (399), 422. See *Haramon*.
Emyn Muil 87, 92–5, 98–102, 111–12, 118, 129, 133, 139, 165, 266, 271, 276, 355, 361, 363, 430, 438. See *Sarn Gebir* (1).
Enedwaith 268
Enemy, The 76, 97, 122–3, 158, 254, 277, 292, 327, 329–30, 375, 378, 380–1, 385, 390, 392, 400, 402–4
English 23, 123, 127, 129, 267; see *Old English*.
Ennyn Dûr The Gates of Mordor (name of the pass). 105, 113, 127. See *Black Gate(s), Gates of Mordor, Morannon*.

450   THE WAR OF THE RING

Ent(s) 4–6, 25–6, 30–1, 39, 41–2, 45, 47–62, (64), 66–8, 70, 79, 219, 255–6, 260, 262, 266–7, 275, 285, 343–6, 351, 360–4, (404), 430, 437; (language) 50, 55. *Entish* 50 (language), 56, half-*Entish* 50, 55. *Ent-house* 3; *Entmoot* 3–4, 7, 100. *Tree-giants* 266

Entwash, River 133, 343, 348; *mouths of Entwash* 270, 343

Entwood Fangorn. 30

Envinyatar The Renewer (Aragorn). 395

Eodoras See *Edoras.*

Eofored Second Master of the Mark (preceding Théodred). 22

Éomearc, Éomeark See *(The) Mark.*

Éomer 3, 6, 8, 10–11, 13–21, 25, 29, 41, 56, 62–5, 72, 78, 141, 226, 237–8, 240, 243–4, 246, (248), 252–6, 259–60, 262–4, 266, 272, 275, 296, 298–9, 301, 303, 309, 311–12, 315–16, 318, 321, 346, 348, 351–2, 355–6, 359–61, 363, 368, 385, 388–91, 393–4, 403–4, 415, 418; *King Éomer* 369

Éomund Father of Éomer and Éowyn. 266, 365, 368

éored Body of cavalry in Rohan. 13, 352–3, 356–7

Eorlingas People of Eorl, the Rohirrim. 9, 156, 236, 242, 247, 316, 348, 365, 385, 389

Eorl the Young 21, 24, 30, 155, 243–4, 408; *House of Eorl* (the Golden Hall) 77, 130, 236, (kindred) 321

Éothain Rider of Rohan. (1) Éomer's squire. 266, 356. (2) In other applications 247, 266; 350; 352, 356

Éowyn (1) Sister of Helm and mother of Fréalaf, tenth King of the Mark. 408. (2) Sister of Éomer. 70, 72, 79, 236, 242–4, 246–8, 255–6, 259–60, 262, 264–7, 275, 308, 311–13, 315–20, 345, 355–6, 359–60, 363, 365–6, 368–9, 372, 380, 383–7, 389–90, 393, 406, 417–18, 421, 423, 430

Ephel Dúath 122, 137, 176–7, 179–80, 195, (on *Ephel* see 137). Earlier names *Dúath* 106, 122; *Hebel Dúath* 122, 131, 133, 180. See *Mountains of Shadow.*

Epilogue 256. See *Sam's book*, under *Gamgee, Sam.*

Erebor The Lonely Mountain. 357; *The Quest of Erebor* 357–8

Erech (including many references to *the Stone* and *Hill of Erech*) 268, 287, 296–7, 300, 302, 304–9, 397, 399, 409–12, 416, 418–19, 421–2, 424, 427–9, 437; *Tower of Erech* 309, 397, 410, 418, 424. The *palantír* of Erech 300, 302, 304–6, 309, 397, 399, 410, 418, 424

Eredfain See *Ered Nimrais.*

Ered Lithui 128. See *Ash Mountains.*

Ered Nimrais The White Mountains. 103, 278, 288; earlier names *Hebel Uilos*, ~ *Orolos*, 137; *Hebel Nimrath* 156, 167, *Ered* ~ 137; *Ered Nimras* 168, *Ephel* ~ 137; *Ephel Nimrais* 137; *Eredfain* 288. See *White Mountains.*

Ereg, River See *Erui.*

INDEX

Erelas   The fourth (or third, see 344) beacon in Anórien. 233, 344, 349

Eressëa   169; *Tol Eressëa* 168, 170. See *Lonely Isle.*

Erkenbrand   Lord of Westfold. 10–11, 23–5, 40–1, 250. Replaced *Erkenwald* 24, 29, 40, 52, 60. See *Trumbold, Heorulf, Nothelm.*

Ernil a Pheriannath   'Prince of the Halflings', Peregrin Took. 287

Erui, River   In Gondor. 427, 436. Earlier form *Ereg* 436, 438

Ethir Anduin   268, 437; *the Ethir* 287, 420. See *Anduin, (The) Delta.*

Etymologies   In Vol. V, *The Lost Road.* 115, 139, 222, 292, 426

Evermind   Flower that grew on the Mounds of Edoras. 407, 424. See *simbelmynë.*

Exiled Elves   See *Elves.*

Eye, The   (in the Dark Tower) 104–5, 109, 189; *Orcs of the Eye* 105

Fair Folk   The Elves. 405

Falborn   (1) Precursor of Faramir. 136–7, 140, 145–9, 164–5, 170; becomes Boromir's brother 147. (2) Precursor of Anborn (2). 169

Fangorn (Forest)   3–4, 30, 53, 55, 59, 166, 262, 310, 339, 345, 420. See *Entwood.*

Faragon   Father of Mardil the Steward. 281, 288. (Replaced by *Orondil.*)

Faramir   45, 132, 136–7, 140–2, 144, 147–76 *passim*, 179, 182, 187, 197, 207, 209, 226, 231–4, 255, 260, 262–3, 271, 274, 281, 283, 291, 294–5, 323–4, 326–42, 354, 360, 374–7, 379–81, 385, 387, 390, 403; the name 160, 169; *the captain of the guard* 377

Far Harad   See *Harad.*

Fastred   Rider of Rohan. 371

Fathers of Men   155, 159, 161–2; *Fathers of the Three Houses* 159, 162; *Fathers of the Númenóreans* 158

Fëanor   76, 372; *Sons of Fëanor* 161, 169; *Fëanorians* 297

Feast at Edoras   45, 48, 58, 72; *at Dunharrow* 236, 240, 242, 247–8; the Feast-hall of Dunharrow 236, 240, 242–4, 248, 250, 259

Feast at Minas Tirith   275, 397, 405

Fell Captain, Fell Riders   See *Black Captain, Black Riders.*

Fellowship, The   See *Company (of the Ring).*

Fengel   (1) Substituted for *Thengel*, father of Théoden. 355. (2) Father of Thengel; fifteenth King of the Mark. 408

Fenmarch   Region of Rohan west of the Mering Stream. 349, 356

Fenn Fornen   The Closed Door (q.v.). 338; *Fenn Forn, Fenn Uiforn* 341. (In RK *Fen Hollen.*)

Ferny, Bill   219 (his pony).

Finduilas   (1) Daughter of Orodreth King of Nargothrond. 372. (2) Daughter of Elrond (precursor of Arwen). 370, 386, 394, 425. (3) *Finduilas of Dol Amroth*, wife of Denethor. 340

452 THE WAR OF THE RING

Fingon High King of the Noldor, slain in the Battle of Unnumbered Tears. 218, 372

Fire, The 134, 362. See *Orodruin*.

Firien Forerunner of the Dwimorberg. 251, 257, 259, 266; *Halifirien* 257, 262

Firienfeld The field of Dunharrow. 245, 251, 266, 312–13, 322

Firienholt The pinewood before the Door of Dunharrow. 251, 257, 266, 315, 320–1. (Replaced by *Dimholt*.)

Firienlode The Mering Stream (?). 356

Firien Wood On the border of Rohan and Gondor (in *Unfinished Tales* p.306 called *Firienholt*). 356

First Age 161, 372

Folca Thirteenth King of the Mark. 408

Folcwine Fourteenth King of the Mark. 408

Folde Region of Rohan near Edoras. 349, 356

Forannest The north gate in the Wall of the Pelennor. 353–4, 358–9

Fords of Isen (including references to *the Fords*) 4–5, 10, 12, 25, 27–8, 31, 39–43, 46–7, 50–1, 54, 56, 60, 68–70, 72, 79, 140, 275; *Isenford* 25, 48–9, 78–9. *Battles of the Fords of Isen* 29, 47, 52; *First Battle* 22, 51, 59; *Second Battle* 4–5, 8, 23, 51. See *Isen*.

Forgoil 'Strawheads', name of the Rohirrim among the Dunlanders. 21

Forlong (1) Name of Gandalf in the South (see *Fornold*). 153. (2) *Forlong the Fat*, Lord of Lossarnach. 153, 229, 262, 276, 287, 289, 293, 371

Fornobel See *Fornost*.

Fornold Name of Gandalf in the South. 153. (Replaced *Forlong* (1), replaced by *Incânus*.)

Fornost City on the North Downs, Norbury of the Kings. 76–8, 153–4, 311. The *palantír* of Fornost 76–8. Ealier name *Fornobel* 76, 154

Forod The North. *Lord of the (Rangers of) Forod*, Aragorn, 386, 389, 394–5

Frána Wormtongue. 55. See *Gríma*.

Fréa Fourth King of the Mark. 408

Fréalaf Tenth King of the Mark (see *Éowyn* (1)). 408

Fréawine Fifth King of the Mark. 408

Frodo Baggins See under *Baggins*.

fuilas See *galenas*.

Galadriel 22, 148, 160, 162–3, 168–9, 210, 219, 256, 274, 296, 301, 310, 361, 386, 420 (other references under *Phial* &c. below); *The Lady, The White Lady, The Lady of Lórien, The Lady of the Golden Wood* 150, 157, 160, 163, 203, 419

The Phial (star-glass, glass) of Galadriel 184–5, 187, 189–94,

INDEX 453

198–200, 203, 205–11, 214, 221, 223–4, 230, 267; *the Mirror* 189, 220, (263, 267); *the green stone* 389–90; Galadriel's Ring 425

Galbedirs 'Talking Trees'. 47, 50, 59. See *Lamorni, Ornómi.*

Galdor The seneschal of Edoras. 262, 267. (Replaced *Ealdor.*)

galenas pipeweed. 396; *green galenas* 38 (with other names *fuilas, marlas, romloth*). See *westmansweed.*

Gamgee (family name) 122–3. See *Goodchild.*

Gamgee, Andy Sam's uncle (first called *Obadiah Gamgee*). 95

Gamgee, Gaffer 89, 95, 122; *Ham, Hamfast* 122–3

Gamgee, Sam 50, 60, 68, 80–1, 85–106 *passim*, 109–11, 113, 115–16, 121–9, 131, 134–41, 144–6, 148–55, 158–60, 162–6, 169, 171–2, 175–8, 182–222 *passim*, 224, 226, 230, 235, 256, 271, 275, 286, 291, 294–5, 326–7, 339, 341, 386, 398; called *Samwise* 122, 127, 139, 158, 163, 211, 309. Sam's book 219, 256, 275, 386; his *Lament for Frodo* 185, 189

Gamling Rider of Rohan. 21, 24–5, 41, 256, 259, 262; *Gamling the Westmarcher* 21

Gandalf 3–6, 9, 11–12, 17–18, 22, 25–30, 35–81 *passim*, 96–7, 119–20, 126, 129–30, 138, 140–3, 145–6, 151–4, 167, 182, 213, 219, 226, 229–36, 242, 245–7, 249, 253–7, 259–60, 262–4, 270–1, 274–8, 281–4, 287–9, 291–2, 294–6, 301, 310, 320–342 *passim*, 357–62, 364, 367, 374–82, 384–7, 389–96, 400–4, 415, 420, 423–4, 427, 430–1. References to him in white or shining 229, 263, 274, 389; *the White Rider* 30, 229, 326. His other names 153; and see *Mithrandir.*

Gap of Rohan 3–5, 28, 42, 386

Garathon See *Targon.*

Gate of the Dead 313, 418. See *Dark Door, Dead Men of Dunharrow.*

Gate(s) of Mordor Originally name of the pass into Mordor (see 113). 104–6, 112–13, 128, 415; *Gates of the Land of Shadow* (chapter-title) 121. See *Black Gate(s), Ennyn Dûr, Morannon.*

Gazmog Orc of the Tower of Kirith Ungol. 212, 225. (Replaced by *Yagûl.*)

Ghân-buri-Ghân 351–2, 356

Gildor 53

Gil-galad 21

Gilrain, River In Gondor. 411–12, 422, 437; *Gilrain-mouth* 412. (Replaced *Lameduin.*)

Gilthoniel Varda. 218

Gimli 3–5, 13–15, 18, 20, 24–7, 37, 39, 47, 53–4, 59, 61–3, 65–7, 72, 78–9, 140–1, 146, 229, 238, 241, 243–4, 246, 249, 264, 272, 274, 276, 297–302, 304–5, 310, 313, 317, 321, 370, 386, 392, 397, 399, 403, 405–7, 409–10, 414–21, 423–9; *Glóin's son* 392, 421

454   THE WAR OF THE RING

Glamdring   Gandalf's sword. 223

Glittering Caves   See *Aglarond*.

Glóin   See *Gimli*.

Glossarnach   See *Lossarnach*.

Gnomes   158, 160, 169, 224. *Gnomish* 159, 161–2

Goblin(s)   18, 96, 213, 215; *Goblin-men* 52; *Goblin-wars* 224

God(s)   136, 168, 292, 401

Golasgil   Lord of Anfalas. 287, 289. (Replaced *Asgil-Golamir*.)

Golden Hall, The   3–4, 21, 29, 244, 321, 347, 407, 424; other references 56, 70, 231, 249, 270, and see *Eorl, Meduseld*.

Golden Wood, The   Lothlórien. 148, 158; *Lady of the Golden Wood* 150, 157

Goldwine   Sixth King of the Mark. 408

Gollum   78, 85–6, 89, 92, 95–129 *passim*, 132–8, 140–1, 151–5, 164, 169–203 *passim*, 206–9, 211–14, (217), 220–4, 291, 361. See *Smeagol*.

Gondolin   161, 169, 207, 224; *the Fall of Gondolin* 292

Gondor   21, 24, 49, 71–3, 76–8, 80, 95, 106, 122, 127, 135–6, 142–8, 151–4, 156, 158, 160–2, 165, 168, 170–1, 174, 180, 182, 219, 231–3, 235–6, 238, 241, 243–4, 246, 253, 256–7, 259–60, 262–3, 268, 271–2, 274, 278–9, 281–4, 286, 291, 293–4, 299–301, 304, 306, 309, 311–12, 315–19, 321–2, 331, 338, 343, 349–53, 356, 360, 362, 367, 369, 371, 375, 377, 379, 385, 387, 389, 392–3, 398, 401, 410–11, 413–14, 416, 424–5, 431, 436; *South(ern) Gondor* 253, 255, 413, 422; *the Realm* 401
    Languages of Gondor 136, 144, 159–62, 356; Kings of Gondor 238, 246, 263, 276, 278–9, 281–2, 292, 294, 337, 380, 383, 385, 425; customs 283–4, 293, 385; relations with the Rohirrim 155–6

Gondorian(s)   113, 135–7, 397, 422; *a dark Gondorian* 58

Goodchild   Name proposed to replace *Gamgee*. 122–3

Gorbag   Orc of Minas Morghul. 226, 361. (Replaced *Yagûl*.)

Gore, The   Below Helm's Deep. 310

Gorgor   = Gorgoroth. 137, 256

Gorgoroth   104, 116, 184, 190, 230, 438; *Pass of Gorgoroth* 431; *Battle of the Field of Gorgoroth* 21, 155

Gorgos   Eastern guard-tower of the pass into Mordor. 116

Gorgûn   Ghân-buri-Ghân's name for Orcs. 351

Gothmog   (1) In the First Age: Lord of Balrogs. 372. (2) Lieutenant of Morghul. 369.

Gram   Eighth King of the Mark. 408

Great Battle   The battle between Sauron and the Last Alliance of Elves and Men. 105; *the Battle, a great battle* 109, 112, 116

Great Darkness   See *Darkness out of Mordor*.

Great Lands   154, 158–9, 167–8, 401

Great One, The   Orc name for Sauron. 185

INDEX   455

Great River (including many references to *the River*) 50, 69, 116, 128, 133, 145–7, 150, 154, 177, 187, 214, 226, 233, 256, 260, 262–3, 278, 283, 288–9, 291, 294, 313, 326–7, 330–1, 333, 339–40, 345, 356, 363, 366, 370–1, 378, 388, 392, 400, 404, 412, 414, 420, 422, 427–8. See *Anduin*.

Great Sea   See *(The) Sea*.

Greenleaf   Legolas. 22, 420

Grey Company, The   (including references to *the Company*) 254, 308, 310, 313, 320, 397, 399, 409–10, 414, 419–21, 423, 428, 437

Greyflood River   437. See *Gwathlo, Odothui*.

Grey Havens   78, 219; *the Havens* 405. See *Mithlond*.

Grey Wanderer   Gandalf. 153. *Grey Pilgrim* 153; *Grey Fool* 378. See *Mithrandir*.

Grey Woods   South-east of Amon Dîn. 353

Gríma   Wormtongue. 355

Grimbold of Grimslade   Rider of Rohan. 370–1

Grímhelm   See *Dernhelm*.

Grishnákh   Orc of Mordor. 49, 59; *Grishnák* 59

Guthláf   Rider of Rohan, banner-bearer of Théoden. 368, 373. Earlier name *Guthwin* 368, 371, 373

Guthrond   See 427.

Guthwin   See *Guthláf*.

Gwaihir   362. See *Eagle(s)*.

Gwathlo, River   436–7. See *Greyflood, Odothui*.

Gwinhir   Boy of Minas Tirith, precursor of Bergil. 285–6, 293. Earlier name *Ramloth* 293

Hador (the Golden-haired)   Father of Men. 157, 159, 168; *people, folk of Hador* 168–9

Halbarad   (1) Shadowfax. 265. (2) Messenger from Minas Tirith to Théoden (sister-son of Denethor). 236, 242, 244. See *Hirgon*. (3) Ranger of the North. 297–300, 302, 304–7, 309, 370–1, 389, 395–6, 424

Haleth   Father of Men. 157, 159

Half-elven   155, 158

Half-high   36, 139, 145, 164, 166

Halfling(s)   139, 149, 166, 284–5, 311, 382, 390

Halifirien   (1) See *Firien*. (2) The first beacon in Anórien. 233, 257, 343–4, 346–7, 349, 356. See *Mindor Uilas*.

Háma   (1) Eleventh King of the Mark. 408. (Replaced by *Brytta*.) (2) Rider of Rohan. 5–6, 9, 22, 41, 236, 264, 352. See *Hamelow*.

Hamelow   The Mound of Háma. 41; *Hamanlow* 41

Harad   The South. 135–6, 142, 243, 366, 413, 426; = the people of Harad 274, 321; *ships of Harad* 226, 231, 256

456   THE WAR OF THE RING

Far Harad 369, 372, 439; *Near Harad* 372, 439; *Harad Road* 439

Haradhoth, Haradoth   People of Harad. 365

Haradrim   People of Harad. 254, 321, 397–8, 412–13, 420, 427, 437

Haradwaith   People of Harad. 58, 155, 229, 254, 311, 398, 422, 426, 437

Haramon, Hill(s) of   Earlier name of Emyn Arnen. 359, 363, 372, 397–8, 421, 438

Harding   Rider of Rohan. 371

Harlond   Quays on the west bank of Anduin at Minas Tirith. 278, 294, 370, (415), 419, 422. Earlier name *Lonnath-Ernin* 294, 370

Harnen, River   237, 265

Harns   = *Haradwaith, Haradrim* (?). 253–4

Harrowdale   77, 80, 141, 219, 231, 235–8, 240, 244–5, 249–51, 257, 259, 262, 267–8, 272–4, 289, 296–7, 301, 308, 311–13, 315–20, 322, 346, 355

Hasufel   Aragorn's horse of Rohan. 301, 305–6, 423

Haunted Mountain   The Dwimorberg. 421

Havens of Umbar   See *Umbar.*

Heathen Kings   376

Hebel Dúath   See *Ephel Dúath*; *Hebel Nimrath*, ~ *Orolos*, ~ *Uilos*, see *Ered Nimrais.*

Helm   Ninth King of the Mark. 10–11, 408

Helm's Deep   (including references to *the Deep*) 4–6, 10–12, 15–19, 21, 23, 25, 27, 29, 39, 41–2, 49, 52, 57–8, 68–72, 76, 78, 100, 120, 140, 238, 241, 248, 250–1, 262, 266, 272–3, 305–6, 310, 396. See *Dimgræf, Heorulf's Clough, Nerwet; Aglarond.*

Helm's Dike   (including references to *the Dike*) 13, 16–19, 22–3, 40–1, 298, 305–6. '*Inlets*' in the Dike 13, 15–19. See *Stanshelf.*

Helm's Gate, Helmsgate   (1) The fortress of Helm's Deep (replaced by *the Hornburg*). 10–11, 13, 17, 19. (2) Later sense, the entrance to Helm's Deep. 11. See *Heorulf's Hold.*

Helmshaugh   Helm's Deep. 11, 23

Henneth Annûn   119, 140–3, 154, 163–4, 166, 175, 178–9, 182, 271, 291, 294–5, 322, 327, 332–3, 338–42, 431; rejected Elvish names 164. *Pool of Annûn* 182. See *Window of the Sunset.*

Heorulf   Precursor of Erkenbrand. 8–11, 16–17, 19, 23–4; *Herulf* 8, 10–11, 17, 23; called *the Marcher* 10. See *Trumbold, Nothelm.*

Heorulf's Clough   Original name of Helm's Deep. 9–12, 23; *Herulf's Clough* 11; *Herelaf's Clough* 23; *the Clough* 11, 23, *the Long Clough* 23; *Theostercloh* 23

Heorulf's Hold   Original name of the Hornburg. 9–12, 17; *Herulf's Hold* 10, 23; *Herulf's Burg* 23. *Heorulf's Hoe* (properly the rock on which the fortress stood) 10–11, 23. See *Helm's Gate.*

Heorulf's Wall   The Deeping Wall. 19

INDEX   457

Herelaf's Clough   See *Heorulf's Clough.*

Herubrand   Rider of Rohan. 371

Herufare   Rider of Rohan. 371, 373; later from *Herefara* 373

Herugrim   Théoden's sword. 15

Herulf   See *Heorulf, Heorulf's Clough, Heorulf's Hold.*

High-elven   160–1, 169; *High Ancient Elven* 160; *High Elvish, high-elvish* 159–60

High Elves   157–8, 219; *High Men,* see *Men.*

High tongue   390, 395; *noble tongue* 394. See *Quenya.*

Hill of Guard   The hill of Minas Tirith. 260, 279. See *Tower of Guard.*

Hirgon   Messenger from Minas Tirith to Théoden. 316–17, 319, 321, 352. For earlier names see *Barahir* (2), *Dirgon, Halbarad* (2); and see *Messenger(s) from Minas Tirith.*

Hirluin the Fair   Lord of Pinnath Gelin. 287, 371

Hobbits   (general references) 36, 38–9, 66, 75–6, 123, 127, 150, 156, 160, 163, 241, 282, 284–5, 306, 388; the name 36, 44; *Hobbit-ells* 89, 99. See *Half-high, Halfling(s), Holbytla.*

Hobbit, The   223; referring to *The Lord of the Rings* 77

Hocker-men, Hoker-men   Earlier name of the Púkel-men. 245–6, 248, 260

Holbytla   Hobbit. 44, 348; *Holbytlan* (plural) 36; *Holbylta(n)* 36, 44

Hold of Dunharrow   See *Dunharrow.*

Horn   Rider of Rohan. 371

Hornblower, Tobias   First grower of pipeweed in the Shire. 37–40, 45; *Old Toby* 38, and as name of a pipeweed 45; replaced by *Tobold Hornblower,* 37, 39, 45. Family name 59. See *Elias Tobiasson, Smygrave.*

Hornburg, The   (including references to *the Battle of the Hornburg* and to *the Gates, the Burg, the Tower*) 5–7, 10, 18–19, 21–22, 25, (30), 40–2, 47, 52–3, 60, 70–3, 92, 95, 100–2, 120, 250, 257, 274, 276, 291, 296–9, 301–2, 305–11, 405, 410–11, 424. The *palantír* of the Hornburg 71–2. See *Helm's Gate, Heorulf's Hold.*

Hornpipe Shag   Name of a pipeweed. 45

Hornrock, The   310. See *Stanrock.*

Horsemasters   154; *Horse-marshals* 155; *Horsemen* (of Rohan) 56, 156, 229, 254, 351; *Horseboys* (Orc-name for Rohirrim) 213, also used of Orcs of Minas Morghul, 217

Houses of Healing   (374–5, 377, 379–80, 385); 379–80, 386, 389–93, 403, 406, 416–17, 419, 421; *Warden of* 394. See *Berin a Nestad.*

Huor   Brother of Húrin Thalion. 155

Huorns   6, 30–1, 40, 43, 46, 56–8, 69–70, 345; *Huorn-forest, Huorn wood* 39, 70, 297; other references 4, 16, 18, 22, 25–7, 47, 49, 51, 59, 404. See *Galbedirs, Lamorni, Ornómi.*

458 THE WAR OF THE RING

Húrin (1) Húrin Thalion. 155, 293. (2) Húrin the Tall, *Warden of the Keys* of Minas Tirith. 369, 401–2, 423; *Warden of the City* 369

Ilmen The region of the stars. 167. See *Elenarda*.

Imlad Morghul The vale of Morghul. 176, 223. See *Minas Morghul*.

Imlad Morthond The vale of Morthond. 287. See *Blackroot, Morthond*.

Imlad Ringlo The vale of Ringlo. 287. See *Ringlo*.

Imladrist Rivendell. 139, 165, 401, 423

Imloth Melui In Gondor (nowhere identified). 396

Imrahil Prince of Dol Amroth. 278, 294, 333, 338, 340, 369, 374, 381, 388–91, 394, 400–4, 409, 415–16, 418, 423; and see *Dol Amroth*.

Incânus Name of Gandalf in the South. 153. See *Forlong* (1), *Fornold*.

Ingold Man of Minas Tirith. 233, 277, 340. (Replaced *Cranthir*.)

Inland Sea The Sea of Nurnen (?). 243–4. See *Nurnen*.

Inram the Tall Man of Gondor, from the vale of Morthond (?). 252, 254

Irensaga 'Ironsaw', mountain at the head of Harrowdale. 312–13. See *Iscamba*.

Iron Door, The Underground entry into the Tower of Kirith Ungol. 226

Iscamba A name of the mountain Irensaga. 312, 320

Isenford See *Fords of Isen*.

Isengard (including references to the *Ring, Circle,* and *Gates* of Isengard) 4–8, 17, 21, 25–7, 31, 37, 39, 41–3, 45, 47–54, 56–9, 64, 68–75, 78–81, 92, 109–10, 119–20, 126, 129, 142, 235–7, 243, 247–9, 266, 272, 285, 297, 301, 362, 430. North gate of Isengard 39, 44–5, 47, 57–8

Isengarders 12, 51

Isen, River (including references to *the river*) 4, 8, 24, 28–31, 39–41, 43, 47–8, 51–2, 56–8, 68–9, 79, 230, 362, 436; and see *Fords of Isen*.

Isildur 21, 123, 149, 152–4, 304, 307, 310, 397, 410, 412, 418, 424; *heir of* 301, 304, 310, 370, 411, 419, *sons of* 374; *sword of Isildur* 301, 309; the name 159–60

Isildur's Bane 145, 149, 151, 164, 166

Ithil The Moon. 172

Ithilduin Former name of Duin Morghul. 436

Ithilien 133–6, 140–2, 145–7, 165, 170, 182, 190, 226, 252–4, 256, 259–60, 262–3, 271, 276–7, 286, 291, 294–5, 329, 331, 431; *lower Ithilien* 370, 422; *South Ithilien* 398

Ithil-stone The *palantír* of Minas Ithil. 80. See *Minas Morghul*.

Kalenarda, Kalinarda See *Calenard(h)on*.

INDEX 459

Kelos, River In Gondor. 436; *Celos* 427

Khand Land south-east of Mordor. 369, 372, 439. See *Variags*.

Khazâd The name of the Dwarves in their own language. 20

Khuzdul The language of the Dwarves. 20

King of the Dead See *Dead Men of Dunharrow*.

Kingsfoil The healing herb *athelas*. 394

Kings of Men Dúnedain. 310, 335

King Stones 98, 132, 137

Kirdan See *Cirdan*.

Kiril, River In Gondor. 411, 427, 436–7; *Ciril* 419; *crossings of Kiril* 425 (see *Caerost, Calembel* (2)).

Kirith Gorgor The great pass into Mordor, 'the Dreadful Pass', 'the Haunted Pass' (122). 121–2, 127, 270, 360–2, 431; *Cirith Gorgor* 122, 431

Kirith Naglath 'Cleft of the Teeth', proposed name for the Morannon. 137. See *Naglath Morn*.

Kirith Ungol (1) Original sense, the main pass into Mordor. 104–6, 111, 116, 121, 184, 220, 229; guard-towers of 106; translated *Spider Glen* 104, 184. (2) Cleft near the main pass. 106. (3) Pass below Minas Morghul. 113, 124. (4) Final sense, the high pass above the Morghul Vale (including references to the Stairs, the cleft, the pass, &c.). 101, 121, 124–6, 129, 136–7, 171, 173, 181–4, 186–7, 190–6, 198–200, 202, 208–9, 211–16, 218, 220–1, 223, 225–6, 252, 254, 256, 327, 329, 360, 431; *Ungol top* (Orc name) 216. For the tunnel (the Spider's lair) see *Shelob*.

The Tower of Kirith Ungol 113, 125–6, 183–4, 187, 190–1, 195, 199–200, 202, (207), 211–16, 218–20, 225–6, 398; *Ungol* (Orc name) 216

Lamedon 287, 398, 411–12, 414, 419, 436–7, 439. For changing application of the name see 436–7.

Lameduin, River In Gondor (later *Gilrain*). 398, 422, 427, 436–7; *Fords of Lameduin* 397, 422, 437; *Lamedui* 436

Lamorni 'Talking Trees'. 50, 60. See *Galbedirs, Ornómi*.

Lampwrights, Street of the In Minas Tirith. 287, 396. See *Rath a Chelerdain*.

Land of Seven Rivers 254, 278. See *Lebennin*.

Langstrand 287, 293, See *Anfalas*.

Last Alliance 129

Lebennin 229, 236, 243, 252, 254–5, 263, 276, 278, 283, 287, 289, 293–4, 330, 372, 398, 411–15, 420, 425, 427–8, 436–7; *five streams of Lebennin* 252, 254, 294, 436. See *Land of Seven Rivers*.

lebethron Tree of Gondor. 180. Earlier names *melinon, lebendron, lebethras* 176

Legolas 3–5, 13–15, 20, 22, 24–5, 27, 37, 40, 59, 66–7, 72, 78,

460   THE WAR OF THE RING

140–1, 146, 229, 238, 241, 243–4, 246, 249, 264, 272, 274, 276, 297–301, 304–5, 308, 310–11, 313, 321, 361, 370, 386, 392, 397, 399, 403, 405–7, 409–11, 414–21, 423–4, 426–9; *Greenleaf* 22, 420

lembas   86, 105, 139; *waybread, elvish bread* 130, 134, 138–9

Lembi   Elves of the Great Journey who never went to Valinor. 158. *The Lingerers* 157–8. Called also *Middle Elves, Elves of the Woods,* 157

Letters of J. R. R. Tolkien, The   45, 65, 77–8, 80, 85–6, 92, 100, 104, 115, 121–3, 127, 129, 131, 134, 136–7, 144, 147, 162, 170–1, 180, 183–4, 218–20, 233–4, 255, 274

Lewis, C. S.   104, 107, 137, 144, 171–2, 183–4

Lhammas, The   169

Lhefneg, River   In Gondor. 436–7. (Later *Lefnui.*)

Limlight, River   313

Lingerers, The   157–8. See *Lembi.*

Linhir   Town in Gondor on the river Lameduin (Gilrain). 361, 364, 397–8, 411–12, 422, 424, 427–9, 436–7

Lithlad   'Plain of Ash', in the north of Mordor. 127, 438

Little People   Hobbits. 167, 306

Lonely Isle   168–9. See *Eressëa.*

Lonely Mountain   415; *the Mountain* 409. See *Erebor.*

Longbottom   Village in the Southfarthing. 36–8; *Longbottom Leaf* (pipeweed) 37, 39, 45, 59

Long Lists   66, 76; *Long Rolls* 76

Lonnath-Ernin   See *Harlond.*

Lord of the Ring(s)   Applied to Aragorn. 412, 425–6

Lórien   89, 98, 148–9, 160–1, 163, 169, 214, 256, 260, 267, 274, 325, 345, 361, 372, 398, 425, 430. Time in Lórien 325; relation of Elves of Lórien to Galadriel 157, 168. See *Lothlórien.*

Lossarnach   Region of Gondor south-west of Minas Tirith (see 436). 153, 278, 283, 287, 289, 294, 419, 436; *Arnach* 371; *Glossarnach* 289, 294

Lostladen, Desert of   South of Mordor. 426, 439. See *Lothland.*

Lothland desert   South of Mordor. 426; *Lothlann* 426. See *Lostladen.*

Lothlórien   98, 159, 166, 168

Lugburz   The Dark Tower. 49, 213–14, 216–18. [In the Index to Vol. VII *Lugburz* is erroneously glossed 'Mordor'.]

Lune, Gulf of   76–7, 213

Mablung   Ranger of Ithilien. 136, 139, 145–6, 148, 151, 431; the name 159–60

Maidros   Son of Fëanor. 297

Malbeth the Seer   306–7, 311. Forms of the verse of Malbeth 300, 302, 305–7, 311

INDEX 461

Manorhall   In the Southfarthing. 36–7

Maps   First Map 12, 22, 41–2, 76, 78–80, 111–12, 115, 122–3, 127–8, 136, 240, 244, 257, 265–6, 268, 270, 287, 289, 291, 293, 308, 339, 426, 433; 1943 map 12, 42, 76, 78, 80, 111, 244, 265–6, 291, 293; Second Map 268, 270, 293, 308, 354, 363, 372, 422, 424, 426–7, 433–9; map of Rohan, Gondor and Mordor in RK (and its original) 112, 118, 267, 270, 289, 291, 308, 339, 353–4, 356, 433, 436, 438 (portion redrawn, Frodo's journey to the Morannon, 117–18).

Minor maps: Minas Morghul and the Cross-roads 180–1, 438; Harrowdale 257–9, 268; White Mountains and South Gondor 264, 268–70, 291, 308, 439; mountains between Edoras and Erech 296; map accompanying 'The Ride of the Rohirrim' 353, 438

Máraher   See *Mardil*.

Marculf   Rider of Rohan. 371

Mardil   The Good Steward. 153, 281, 288, 292; *Mardil's son* 156. Earlier name *Máraher* 153

Mark, The   Rohan. 21, 24, 27–8, 49, 246, 322, 350, 366, 389, 401, 407, 418; tongue of the Mark 35, 44, 389; *King, Lord, of the Mark* 41, 245, 247, 317 (Théoden), 368 (Éomer); *Kings of the Mark* 243–4, 407–8 (enumerated, 408). *Éomearc, Éomeark* 22; *Riddermark* 52

marlas   See *galenas*.

Marquette University   44, 235, 252

Marshal of the Mark, Chief   Éomund. 266

Master of the Mark, Second   22

Meduseld   316, 319, 321. (Replaced *Wínseld*.)

melinon   See *lebethron*.

Men   The divisions of Men 157 (*the High, Men of Light*; *Middle Men, Middle People*; *Men of (the) Shadow(s), Men of the Darkness*); speech of Men 21, 155, 157, 159–61 (*Man-speech* 160, *Mannish* 161); Men and Elves 158–9; and Sauron 45, 158; *Dominion of Men* 219 (Great Lands committed to Men 401); other references 45, 76–7, 109, 112, 134, 162, 184, 213, 219, 400, 402–3. See *Fathers of Men, Three Houses, Swart Men, Wild Men*.

Meneldil   Son of Anárion. 154

Men Falros   See *Cair Andros*.

Men of the Mountains   The Dead Men of Dunharrow. 307, 410; *Dark Men of the Mountains* 397, 410, 424; their King 397, 410, 424

Meriadoc Brandybuck, Merry   See under *Brandybuck*.

Mering Stream   The 'Boundary-stream' between Rohan and Gondor. 354, 356. See *Firienlode*.

Messenger(s) from Minas Tirith   Sent to ask Théoden for aid; also

462 THE WAR OF THE RING

errand-rider(s). 141, 231–4, 236, 244, 255–6, 259, 262–4, 270, 272, 274–5, 312, 315–17, 319, 321, 343, 349; and see *Hirgon*.

Methedras Last great peak of the Misty Mountains. 8

Middle Age Equivalent to the Second and Third Ages (cf. *the Middle Days* VII. 150). 219

Middle-earth 45, 167–8, 172, 217, 405, 409

Middle Elves See *Lembi*. *Middle Men*, *Middle People*, see *Men*.

Middle Stone, The The single pillar of stone before the Door of Dunharrow. 248, 250; see also 246, 312–13, 315, 406

Minas Anor 76, 154

Minas Ithil 76, 106, 125, 136, 152; see *Ithil-stone*.

Minas Morghul, Minas Morgul 71–2, 106, 113, 115–16, 123–6, 129, 132, 134, 136, 171, 173, 177, 180, 182–6, 192, 215, 217–18, 222, 225–6, 229–30, 256, 275, 291, 327, 330, 360, 364, 400, 430, 438; *Minas Morgol* 229. For changes in the site of Minas Morghul see 106, 113, 115–16, 124.

Morghul, Morgul 106, 213–14, 226, 260, 275, 386, 403, 431. (In the following references spelt here *Morghul* only.) *Morghulhost, Host(s) of Morghul* 182, 187, 192, 260, 262–3, 274–5, 359. *Lieutenant of Morghul* (Gothmog) 369, 431. *Vale, valley of Morghul, Morghul Vale* 176–7, 186–7, 327, 431, and see *Imlad Morghul*; *Morghul dale* 195; *Vale of Dread* 327; *Valley of the Wraiths* 180. *The Morghul Pass* 195, 431; *the main pass* 124, 192, 222. *Meads of Morghul* 202, (360, 364). *Morghul-road*, see *Roads*. The *palantír* of Minas Morghul (taken to Barad-dûr) 71–2, 76, 80 (*Ithil-stone*), 362, 404.

Minas Tirth (including many references to *the City*) 58, 70–3, 76, 79–80, 126, 129–30, 135, 138, 140–3, 145–7, 150–2, 155, 161, 164–8, 182, 219, 226, 229, 231–2, 234–5, 242, 244, 247, 249, 252–6, 259–60, 262–4, 266, 270–95 *passim*, 301, 304, 306, 318, 322, 324–5, 332–60 *passim*, 364, 366, 368–9, 372–405 *passim*, 410–19 *passim*, 422, 425, 428, 431–3, 438; *Tirith* 145, *Tirithman* 135; Minas Tirith described 278–9. See *Mundbeorg; Hill, Tower, of Guard*.

The Circles of the City 279, 284, 377, 405, 417; *first circle* 353, also *lowest* 284, 336, *outer(most)* 288, 336; *sixth circle* 284, 338; *upper circle* 396. *The Citadel* 276, 279, 281, 294, 324, 326, 329, 335–8, 374, 382, 384, 387, 389, 415, 426. *The Fountain* 276, *Court of the Fountain* 281.

The Gates: the outer and lowest gate 278, called *the Great Gate* 278–9, 286, 288, 359, *City Gates* 293, *East Gate* 284, 286, *First Gate* 278, and *the Gate(s)* 300, 306, 326, 332, 335–6, 340, 353, 359–60, 363, 368–70, 374, 380, 384–5, 388, 415, 422; other gates 278–9, 291; *the Seventh Gate* 279, 291.

The Hall of the Kings 281, great hall 281, 288, *Tower Hall, Hall of the Tower* 323, 385, 389. *The Tombs* 276, 279, 336–7,

INDEX 463

360, 375. *The Tower*, see *White Tower*. See also *Othram, Taurost*.

Prophetic verse of Minas Tirith 145, 149, 164–6, 328, 339. The *palantír* of Minas Tirith 71–2, 76, 231, 257, 263, 374–81, 391

Mindolluin, Mount 80, 130, 133, 138, 142, 172, 260, 271, (276), 278–9, 287, 336–7, 353. See *Tor-dilluin*.

Mindor Uilas Original name of the first beacon in Anórien (Halifirien). 233

Min Rimmon, Minrimmon The third (or sixth, see 344) beacon in Anórien. 233, 319, 343–4, 349–52, 354, 356; *Rimmon* 351–2. See *Rimmon (Forest)*.

Mirkwood 22, 122, 157; with reference to the spiders 184, 187, 217; *the Wood* 415; *Woodmen of Mirkwood* 242, 247, 249, 253

Mirror of Galadriel See *Galadriel*.

Misty Mountains (including references to *the mountains*) 8, 16, 21–2, 31, 43–4, 52, 68, 133, 230, 362, 386

Mithlond 76–7, 80–1; *Mithond* 77, 80, *Mithrond* 80–1. The *palantír* of Mithlond 76–8. See *Grey Havens*.

Mithrandir Gandalf. 153, 158, 163, 284–5, 328, 330, 332, 335, 338, 387, 390. See *Grey Wanderer*.

mithril (with reference to Frodo's mithril-coat) 92, 185, 190, 210, 219, 230, (257), 361–2, 430; (helms of the guards of the Citadel of Minas Tirith) 279

Monoliths, Road of The line of standing stones across the Firienfeld. 320–1; *the Stony Road* 315, 321

Moon, The 167, 172, 174, 359, 363, 399, 422. See *Ithil*. Phases of the Moon 16, 27, 40–1, 51, 81, 109, 131–5, 137, 140–3, 147, 152, 172, 174, 176, 180, 232, 237, 240, 245, 249, 251–2, 255, 259, 262–4, 270–3, 276, 295, 299, 303, 309, 316, 319–22, 432

Morannon The Black Gate; originally name of the pass into Mordor (see 122). 112, 118, 120, 122, 125, 127, 129–42 *passim*, 173, 260, 263, 271, 275, 359–61, 363, 399, 416, 418–19, 430, 432, 438. *Morennyn* 113, *Mornennyn* 112–13, 127, (names of the pass). See *Black Gate(s)*, *Gates of Mordor*, *Ennyn Dûr*, *Kirith Naglath*.

Mordor 48–50, 66, 68, 70–5, 77, 81, 85, 104–5, 107, 110–11, 115, 119–20, 122, 124, 136–7, 143, 148, 151–2, 154, 163, 165, 177, 179, 182–4, 215, 219–20, 226, 233, 247, 249, 254, 256, 260, 265, 268, 270, 275, 289, 295, 303, 317, 319, 322, 329, 333, 346, 359–60, 362, 369, 375, 378, 381, 391, 398, 401–3, 410, 412–14, 419–20, 425–9, 437–8. *Lord of Mordor* 401; *the pass into Mordor* 85, 104, 111, 270; *the mountains of Mordor* 265, 268. See *Gates of Mordor*; *Teeth of Mordor*; *Black Land*, *Nameless Land*.

Mordu (?) Sauron's messenger. 256, 267

464   THE WAR OF THE RING

Morennyn   See *Morannon.*
Morgai   438
Morghul, Morgul   See *Minas Morghul.*
Morgoth   168; *the Dark Power of the North* 161
Morgulduin   Stream flowing through Imlad Morghul. 180. See *Duin Morghul, Ithilduin.*
Moria   17, 20, 214; *the Bridge of Moria* 285
Mornennyn   See *Morannon.*
Morthond, River   268, 296, 397, 409, 436–7, 439; *Morthond Vale, Vale of Morthond* 254, 266, 287, (370), 397, 409; *meres of Morthond* 371. See *Blackroot, Imlad Morthond.*
Mountains of Shadow   106, 113, 115–16, 122, 182, 317; *the mountains* 112, 118, 124–5, 128–9, 131, 137, 173, 176, 180, 184, 187, 194, 207, 215, 292, 294. See *Ephel Dúath.*
Mountains of Terror   North of Doriath. 184, 187
Mount Doom   118, 190, 219, 268, 433; spelt *Mount Dûm* 118. See *Orodruin.*
Mount Fang   Translation of Elvish *Orthanc.* 35
Mugwort   Family name in Bree. 44
Mugworth   Village in the Southfarthing. 36, 44
Mûmak   Elephant of the Southrons. 136; plural *Mûmakil* 370. Earlier forms *Múmar, Múmund, Mâmuk* 136. See *Andabund, Oliphaunt.*
Mundbeorg   Name in Rohan of Minas Tirith. 348, 355; *Mundberg* 356, 371; later name *Mundburg* 355–6; alliterative song *The Mounds of Mundburg* 352, 371, 373

Naglath Morn   The Teeth of Mordor. 122, 137. Cf. *Kirith Naglath,* and see *Nelig Myrn, Teeth of Mordor.*
Naglur-Danlo   Orc of the Tower of Kirith Ungol. 212, 225
Nameless Land   Mordor. 196, 400
Nan Gurunír   The Wizard's Vale. 4–8, 26, 29, 31, 38, 43, 50–1, 59, 70, 72; later form *Nan Curunír* 41. See *(The) Wizard's Vale.*
Narch Udûn   Region behind the Morannon (later *Udûn*). 438
Nardol   The fifth (or fourth, see 344) beacon in Anórien. 233, 344, 349
Nargil Pass   In the southern mountains of Mordor. 237, 265; *Narghil Pass* 265; *Nargul Pass* 243–4, 265
Nargothrond   372
Narsil   The sword of Elendil. 370, 372. See *Elendil.*
Nazgûl   (All references are to the Winged Nazgûl) 48, 59, 71–3, 77, 109–10, 112, 118–20, 127, 141–2, 217, 219, 229, 231, (232, 249), 253, 255, 257, 260, 262–3, 267, 274–6, 283, 289, 320, 322, 324, 326, (329), 331, 335, 359–69, 372, 375, 380, 387, 430–1. *Nazgûl* used as if specifically = Ringwraith borne on wings 359, 362–4. See *Black Rider(s), Ringwraith(s).*

INDEX

465

King or *Lord of the Nazgûl* 256, (260, 263), 267, 334, 336, 363, (365), 366–8, 372, (375), 377, (380), 390, 395. Prophecy concerning him 326, 334–5, 368, 390, 395. See *Angmar, Black Captain, Wizard King*.

Near Harad See *Harad*.

Neleglos 'The White Tooth', Minas Ithil. 106, 113; replaced *Neleg Thilim*, 106

Nelig Myrn The Teeth of Mordor. 113, 122, 128; *Nelig Morn* 113, 122, 128. See *Naglath Morn*.

Nerwet Helm's Deep. 9, 23; *Nerwet Gate* 10. *Neolnerwet, Neol-nearu* 23

nifredil Flower on the burial mounds at Edoras. 423

Nimrodel Elf of Lórien. 338

Nindalf The Wetwang. 112, 118.

Nine Rings (of Men) 335 (repossessed by the Nazgûl).

Nobottle Village in the Westfarthing. 44

Noldor 76, 159–61, 168–9

Noldorin (language) 139, 169, 226

No Man's Land 111–12; *Noman-lands* 112, 120, 139; *Field of Nomen's Land* 229; *Nomenlands* 270; *the desert* 430

North Gate The Black Gate (Orc name). 213

North Kingdom The northern realm of the Dúnedain. 369, 395. See *Arnor*.

Northlands 371

North March (of Gondor) 167

Nosdiligand Lord of the people of the Delta. 252, 255, 266; *Northiligand* 266

Nothelm Name briefly replacing *Heorulf* (precursor of Erkenbrand). 11, 23

Númenor 72, 157–61, 164, 169–70, 309, 326, 363, 397, 410, 424; *the Fall of Númenor* 161, (title) 169; *old speech of Númenor* 426. See *Westernesse*.

Númenóreans 129, 153–5, 157–9, 161–2, 168–9, 424; *Black Nú-menóreans* 431. *Númenórean* (language) 159, 394

Nurn Region of Mordor. 438

Nurnen, Sea of 265, 438; called *the Inland Sea of Nurnen* 127, 236, and cf. 243–4.

Nûzu Orc of the Tower of Kirith Ungol. 212, 218

Odothui, River Seventh River (Greyflood); changed from *Odotheg*. 437

Old English 23, 36, 41, 44–5, 69, 122–3, 127, 138, 245, 257, 265–7, 292, 320–1, 355–6, 369, 372, 389, 408

Old Norse 353, 372

Oliphaunt 127, 129, 136–7, *Oliphant* 129. See *Andabund, Mûmak*.

Olórin Gandalf's name in the West, changed from *Olórion*. 153

466   THE WAR OF THE RING

Ondor Earlier name of Gondor. 155

Orcrist The sword of Thorin Oakenshield. 223

Orcs (including many compounds as *orc-drums, -laughter, -make, -path, -raid, -tower, -voices*) 3, 5, 9–10, 13–20, 22, 24, 26, 28, 40–1, 47, 49, 51, 54–5, 58–60, 105–6, 109, 119, 122, 124, 132, 134–5, 148, 150–1, 154, 165, 172, 184–6, 189–91, 195, 199–200, 207, 211–16, 218, 222–6, 237, 249, 253–6, 259, 266, 275, 281, 285–6, 300, 310, 313, 332, 343–6, 348, 350–1, 355, 367, 404, 411, 413–15, 420; *orch* 135. *Orc-men* 345. See *Goblins, Gorgûn.*

Ornómi 'Talking Trees'. 52, 54–6, 59; *Ornómar* 50, 60. See *Galbedirs, Lamorni.*

Orodras Original name of the second beacon in Anórien. 233

Orodreth King of Nargothrond. 372

Orodruin 275, 361–2, 364, 404, 438–9; *the Fire* 134, 362; *the Mountain* 362. See *Mount Doom.*

Oromë 292, 353. See *Araw.*

Orondil Father of Mardil the Steward. 288. See *Faragon, Vorondil.*

Orthanc 26, 31–3, 35, 39, 44, 47–8, 52–3, 55–6, 58, 61–79 passim, 119–20, 127, 129–30, 289, 301, 304, 307, 381. On the name see 35, and on the structure of Orthanc see 31–5, 61–2. The *palantír* of Orthanc (all references, including *Orthanc-stone, the Stone, the Glass, the Dark Crystal, the palantír,* &c.) 60, 64–7, 69–76, 78–81, 119–20, 126, 142, 274, 289, 296, 300–1, 304, 307, 339, 342, 362, 381

Osgiliath 69–72, 76, 79, 81, 115, 122, 128, 133, 135, 138, 147, 165, 175, 178, 182, 187, 213, 243, 247, 253, 255–6, 262–3, 268, 270, 278, 283, 291–2, 294–5, 324, 326, 329–30, 333–4, 338–40, 342, 353–4, 356, 360, 364, 369, 379, 389, 391, 432, 438. *East Osgiliath* 330–1, 334, *West Osgiliath* 324; *the Fords of Osgiliath* (213), 253, 278, 291, 327, *the Crossings* 283, 292, 294, 324. The *palantír* of Osgiliath 71–2, 76. *The Battle of Osgiliath* 365–7. See *Elostirion.*

Othram The City Wall of Minas Tirith. 288

Outlands The fiefs of Gondor. 286–7, 289, 370

Oxford 44, 193; *Oxford Dictionary* 116

palantír 65, 76, 79; of Orthanc 60, 67, 69, 75, 78, 80–1, 120, 126, 274, 289, 301, 307; of Barad-dûr 80; of Minas Tirith 231, 257, 263, 374–9, 381, 391; of Erech 309, 397, 399, 410, 418, 424. Plural *palantirs* 76–7, 81; *palantíri* 65, 78, 81, 309, 397, 399. See *Seeing Stones*; and for complete references to the *palantíri* however named see *Aglarond, Barad-dûr, Erech, Fornost, Hornburg, Minas Morghul, Minas Tirith, Mithlond, Orthanc, Osgiliath.*

Parley at the Black Gate See *Black Gate(s).*

INDEX   **467**

Parth Galen   20, 79, 307. See *Calembel* (1).

Paths of the Dead   262, 274, 297, 300, 302–5, 307–8, 312, 320, 392, 397–8, 405, 407, 416–17, 419, 421–3, 427–8; described 406–7, 409. See *Dead men of Dunharrow*.

Pelargir   Town on Anduin. 268, 379, 386, 398, 411–15, 419–20, 422, 424, 426–9

Pelennor   (1) The wall surrounding the 'townlands' of Minas Tirith. 277 (other early references, 260, 263, are ambiguous: see 277). (2) The 'townlands' (many references are to 'the wall of (the) Pelennor', 'the Pelennor wall'). 143, 233, 260, 263–4, 270, 275, 277, 283, 288–9, 291, 324–6, 330–3, 339–40, 342–3, 349, 353–4, 359–60, 363–4, 370, 372, 388, 392, 399–400, 415–16, 422, 438. *Townlands* 277–8, 287, 330, 332, 354; *Cityland* 260, 277. *Pelennor Gate* (at the Causeway?) 326; see also *Forannest*.
     Battle of the Pelennor Fields 153, 326, 352, 367, 371, 373, 399, 419, 428–30, 432, (438); and see *Osgiliath*.

Penannon   Original name of the third beacon in Anórien. 233

Peregrin Took, Pippin   See under *Took*.

Phial of Galadriel   See *Galadriel*.

Pictures by J. R. R. Tolkien   17, 44, 193, 250, 310

Pillars of the Kings   132. See *Argonath, King Stones*.

Pinnath Gelin   Hills north of Anfalas. 287, 419, 429, 436–7; unnamed 371

Pipeweed   (including references to *tobacco*) 36–9, 44–5, 47, 49, 58–9, 72–3, 162, 169, 396. Used by wizards 36–8, but not by orcs 49. See *galenas, westmansweed*.

Pool of Annûn   182

Poros, River   'Boundary'. 426, 436

Powers, The   The Valar. 157

Precious, The   The Ring. 97–9, 107, 109, 112, 186, 211; *precious* used by Gollum of himself 97, 109–10, 115, 193, 196, 198

Puck   265

Púkel-men   245, 251, 259–60, 262–3, 265, 316, 319, 350, 356; spelt *Pookel-men* 245–6, 248, 260. See *Hocker-men*.

Quendian   159 (*High Elvish Quendian*).

Quenta Silmarillion   157, 174, 426

Quenya   20, 139, 161. See *High tongue*.

Quickbeam   Ent. 26, 30, 49, 54. See *Bregalad*.

Ramas Coren   Earlier name of *Rammas Echor*. 288, 324, 339–40, 359, 399. Other names *Corramas* 340; *Rammas Ephel* 288; and see *Pelennor* (1).

Ramloth   See *Gwinhir*.

Rammas Echor   The wall about the Pelennor. 277, 291, 294, 354, 371; *the Rammas* 340, 344, 352–4

Rammas Ephel   See *Ramas Coren*.

468　　　THE WAR OF THE RING

Ranger(s)　(1) Of the North. 38, 49, 242, 244, 247, 249, 253–4, 260, 262–3, 274, 296–7, 299, 301–2, 304–5, 307–9, 360, 371, 378, 389, 391, 394–5, 406, 411, 413–14, 423–5, 438. (2) Of Ithilien. 136, 145–6

Rath a Chelerdain　'The Street of the Lampwrights' (q.v.) in Minas Tirith. 388; *Rath a Chalardain* 287; *Rath Celerdain* 287

Rath Dínen　'The Silent Street' in Minas Tirith. 288, 338, 341, 375, 380, 391

Rauros　118, 145, 147–8, 268, 270, 361, 437

Realm, The　Gondor. 401

Red Eye, The　Orc-emblem. 49, 132, 138

Refusers, The　See *Avari*.

Renewer, The　Aragorn. 390, 395. See *Envinyatar*.

Rhovanion　Wilderland. 253

Rhûn　The East. 281

Rhymes of Lore　65, 75–7, 306

Riddermark, The　52. See *(The) Mark, Rohan*.

Rider(s) of Rohan　4–5, 13, 16, 18, 22, 26, 28, 36, 40–2, 48, 50–1, 68, 92, 95, 102, 219, 226, 231, 238, 240, 242, 245, 250, 252, 256–7, 265, 273, 298–9, 303–4, 306–7, 309–10, 316–19, 322, 337, 345–9, 352–3, 356, 360, 369, 371, 373, 385, 413; Old English *Rídend* 389

Rimmon (Forest)　Forest about Min Rimmon Beacon. 351–2; *Taur-rimmon* 350–1. *Rimmon* used of the beacon-hill 351–2

Ringbearer, The　50, 105, 185, 229, 334; *the bearer* 329.

Ringlord, The　401, 404; *Ring-master* 105

Ringlo, River　In Gondor. 268, 287, 411, 436–7; *crossing of Ringlo* 437, 439; *Ringlo Vale* 287. See *Imlad Ringlo*.

Rings　48, 71, 73, 98, 156. Ring of Galadriel 425; Ring of Aragorn 425–6. See *Three Rings, Seven Rings, Nine Rings*.

Ring, The　50–1, 56, 67, 85–6, 98–9, 104–5, 109, 112, 115, 145, 151–2, (154), 160, 163–4, (167), 169, 173, 177, 185–7, 189–92, 195, 199, 211–15, 219, 224, 230, 256, 262, (304, 310), 329, (332), 333, 361–2, 386, 400–3, 432. *The One Ring* 98, 401; *the Ruling Ring* 151. *The War of the Ring* 71, 162; *The Ring* as title of the work 130, 136, 184; powers conferred by the Ring 186, 190–2, 212–14. See *(The) Precious*.

Ringwraith(s)　115, 120, 186, 363–4. See *Wraiths*.

Rivendell　76, 98, 139, 145, 218, 256, 267, 275, 296, 301–2, 305, 307, 310, 386. See *Imladrist*.

Roads　From Helm's Deep 27, 42, 72. From Isengard 31, 41, 43, 56, 68–9, 78. From Edoras to Minas Tirith 253, 318, 340, 347, 351 ('horsemen road'), 353–4, 373, 404; old wain-road in Anórien 351–2.

　From Minas Tirith into South Gondor 283; across the Pelennor to the Causeway 353, 389, 391, 416 (and see *Causeway*). From

INDEX

Osgiliath to Minas Morghul (*Morghul-road*, *Osgiliath road*) 135, 175–8, 182, 192, 291, 294–5, 327; *Wraith-road* over the pass above Minas Morghul 195, 222

Roads to the Black Gate 123, 128; south road through Ithilien 121, 123, 125, 128–9, 131–2, 135, 139, 151, 177, 360, 432, *Harad Road* 439

Rohan   4, 16, 35, 39, 42, 45, 50–2, 54, 68, 71, 80, 92, 95, 100, 102, 110, 126, 129–30, 141, 150, 152, 155–6, 158–9, 162, 166–7, 182, 219, 226, 229, 233, 235, 238, 243–5, 247, 249–51, 253–7, 259–60, 263, 274–6, 298–9, 301, 303–4, 306, 310–11, 317–21, 324, 329, 337, 339, 346–7, 355, 359–60, 362, 369, 371, 373, 385–6, 389, 408, 411, 423. Tongue of Rohan 35, 44, 155, 159, 243–4, 267, 389. *Rohan* = Men of Rohan 16, 18, 22, cf. *Rochann, Rohann* 22. See *(The) Mark*; *Riders of Rohan*; *Gap of Rohan, Wold of Rohan.*

Roheryn   Aragorn's horse. 301, 423

Rohir   Rohirrim. 24, 40, 56, 155, 157, 167–8, 236, 249

Rohiroth   Rohirrim. 22 (*Rochirhoth, Rohirhoth*), 24, 156–7, 168

Rohirrim   4–5, 22, 24, 40, 254–5, 266–7, 273–4, 318, 320, 342, 344–6, 349, 351–4, 359, 381, 385–6, 389, 392–3, 404–6, 415, 420, 422–3, 428. See *Eorlingas.*

Rohirwaith   Rohirrim. 22

romloth   See *galenas.*

Runes   138, 218; *north-runes* 407

Sam Gamgee   See under *Gamgee.*

Santoski, T. J. R.   308, 323, 354, 356, 396

Sarn Aran, Sern Erain   The Pillars of the Kings. 98. See *Sern Aranath.*

Sarn Gebir   (1) Old name of Emyn Muil. 85–6, 98–100, 111, 136, 139, 165. *Gates of Sarn Gebir*, the Pillars of the Kings, 98–9. (2) The rapids in Anduin. 343, 348, 354, 361, 404

Sarn Ruin   The rapids in Anduin. 270. See *Sarn Gebir* (2).

Saruman   6–8, 11, 21–2, 26, 29–30, 35, 37–9, 41, 43, 47–53, 55–6, 59, 61–7, 71–7, 79–80, 119–20, 126, 130, 240, 243, 249, 317, 339, 342, 362, 380. *Valley of Saruman*, see *Wizard's Vale. Saruman's staff* 64–5, 67

Sauron   21, 45, 48–50, 68, 72–4, 76–7, 79–80, (86), 95, 98, 105–6, (107), 110, 112, 122–3, (124), 127, 129, 135, 155, 179, 212, 214, (216, 218), 219, 229–30, 236, 238, 241, 243, 256–7, (300–1, 304, 306, 309–10, 326, 329, 339), 342, 358, 360–2, 364(–5), 372, 381, 386, 401–2, 404, 410, 412, 420, 430. *Mouth of Sauron* 431. See *Dark Lord.*

Saxon   123

Scāda Pass   In the White Mountains. 243–4, 251–3

Sea, The   36, 38, 150, 153, 155, 157–9, 168, 184, 187, 219, 278, 283, 293, 310, 369, 401, 409, 413–14, 419–20; *the Great Sea* 41

470 THE WAR OF THE RING

Seeing Stones The *palantíri*. 72–3, 75–6; also *Stones of Sight* 381, *Stones of Seeing* 403, *Stones* 72, 282, 300–1, 304 (in *Rhyme of Lore* 65, 281.) *The Seeing Stone, the Stone*: of Orthanc 70–5, 81, 119–20, 300, 304, 339, 342 (also *Orthanc-stone*); of Minas Tirith: 257, 375, 378, 380–2; of Barad-dûr 362, 404 (also *Ithil-stone*); of Erech 300, 302, 304–6, 309, 399. See *palantír*.

Sentinels, The See *(The) Silent Watchers*.

Sern Aranath The Pillars of the Kings. 99, 132, 137. *Sern Erain* 98; *Annon Torath* 132

Serni, River In Gondor. 436–7

Sern (Sairn, Sarnel) Ubed See 132, 137–8

Seven Rings of the Dwarves 357–8

Seven stars and seven stones and one white tree 65, 76, 281

Shadowfax 4, 9, 12, 28–9, (54), 126, 143, 232–3, 235, 265, 282, 284, 320, 336, 374, 380, 382, 387, 391

Shadow Host, Host of Shadow The Dead Men of Dunharrow. 275, 311, 398, 412, 414, 420, 422, 426; *the grey host* 414, 420; *Shadow-men* 397, 410–11, 416, 418, *Shadows of Men* 423, *Shadows* 406, 413

Shadow, The 306–7, 311; (the Lord of the Nazgûl) 365–6, 374, 385; *the Black Shadow*, malady caused by the Nazgûl, 387; *Men of (the) Shadow(s)*, see *Men*.

Shagram Orc of the Tower of Kirith Ungol. 218

Shagrat (1) Orc of Minas Morghul. 225 (replaced by *Yagûl*). (2) Orc of the Tower of Kirith Ungol. 216–18, 225 (replaced *Yagûl*).

Sharkûn See *Tharkûn*.

Shelob (115), 183 (the name *She-lob*), 199, 202, 207, 212–18, 222, 224–6. Earlier name *Ungoliant(e)* 196–200, 205–6, 209–11, 221–2. *The Great Spider* 191, 199, 222, *the Spider* 184, (196), 205–6, 208–9, 214, 218, 224. *Shelob's Lair* (including all references to the tunnel beneath Kirith Ungol) 124–5, 180, 184, 187, 190–2, 194–5, 197–200, 202–3, 205–17, 222–6. See *Spiders*; *Torech Ungol*.

Shire Reckoning (37–8), 45, 59, 309, 408, 424

Shire, The 37–8, 44, 59, 123, 219, 241, 256, 283–4, 292, 308, 323, 338, 394; *Shire-folk* 38, 304–5

Shorab or *Shorob* Gandalf's name in the East. 153

Silent Watchers, The In Minas Morgul. 123–6, 129; *the Watchers* 125, 216; *the Sentinels* 126; *the Night Watcher* 217

Silmarillion, The 169, 222

Silmaril, The (of Eärendel) 193, 203

simbelmynë The flower 'Evermind' (q.v.). 423–4

Sindarin 20, 161

Sirith, River In Gondor. 436

Slag-mounds Before the Morannon. 118–20, 140–2, 291; *Slag-heaps* 136; *Slag-hills* 430–2

INDEX   471

Smeagol Gollum. 97–8, 105, 109–12, 115–16, 124, 129, 196, 203, 223
Smial 45
Smygrave, Tobias First grower of pipeweed in the Shire. 37; *Smygraves* 37; the name 45. See *Elias Tobiasson, Hornblower.*
Snowbourn, River In Harrowdale. 238, 240–1, 245, 257, 259, 264, 296, 313, 316, 318, 343, 348; spelt *Snowborn* 235–7, 264
Snowmane Théoden's horse. 9, 15, 17, 246, 317–19, 365, 369
Sons of Elrond 274, 289, 297, 301, 305, 307, 389, 394, 415, 438; the brethren 410. See *Elbereth, Elboron; Elrohir, Elladan.*
Sons of Fëanor See *Fëanor.*
Sorcerer King, The See *(The) Wizard King.*
Southfarthing 36–7, 45, 58
South Kingdom Gondor. (72), 154, 371
Southland Harad. 237
Southrons 136, 140–1, 182, 260, 263, 289, 425; *Southron men* 135, 340; *fleets of Southrons, Southron fleets* 259–60, 263. *Southern men* 127, *men of the South* 137; *the Southerner at Bree* 52. See *Barangils, Haradwaith, Haradrim, Swertings.*
Spiders In the earlier story of Kirith Ungol. 104, 113, 125, 184–5, 187–94, 199, 220, 222. *Spider Glen*, see *Kirith Ungol.*
Stanrock, The Earlier name of the Hornrock. 10–11, 13, 16–19
Stanshelf Earlier name of Helm's Dike. 13, 23; Old English form *Stanscylf* 13, 23
Starkhorn Mountain at the head of Harrowdale. 242, 257, 259, 267, 301, 308, 312–13; *Lap of Starkhorn* 245–6, 259. Earlier name *Dunharrow*, q.v.
Star of the Dúnedain (299), 309; *star(s) of Elendil* 370, 395, 411; *of the North Kingdom* 395. Other references to the star(s) as device 338, 370, 389, 395, 397; 'stars of Sun and Moon' 359, 363, 399, 422
Stewards of Gondor 153, 168, 337, 374, 378; *House of the Stewards:* their line 335, 388; in Rath Dínen 380, 391. *The Steward* 282, 292, 324, 374–5, 379, 385, 389–90, 400–1; *the Stewardship* 360, 363, 375, 377, 379. See *(The) Closed Door.*
Sting 92, 185, 187–91, 193–4, 197–8, 205–7, 209–12, 222, 230
Stonehouses Ghân-buri-Ghân's name for Minas Tirith. 351.
Stones, The See *Seeing Stones.*
Stonewain Valley In Anórien. 353
Stoningland Gondor. 371
Stony Road See *Monoliths, Road of.*
Strawheads See *Forgoil.*
Street of the Lampwrights See *Rath a Chelerdain.*
Stybba Merry's pony of Rohan. 301, 319, 348
Sun, The 167, 174, 359, 363, 399, 422
Swart Men 105

472   THE WAR OF THE RING

Swertings   Men of the South. 127, 136–7, 144, 243, 252–4. See *Southrons*.

Talking Trees   47, 50, 55; *trees with voices* 55. See *Galbedirs, Lamorni, Ornómi*.
Tarakil   The name *Trotter* in Quenya. 390, 395; *Tarakon* 395; *Tarantar* 395; *Telkontar, Telcontar* 395
Targon   Keeper of the storehouse of Berithil's company of the Guard. 288. Earlier names *Duilas* 283, *Garathon* 283
Tarkil   Númenórean, Dúnadan. 310
Tarlang's Neck   Pass between the White Mountains and an outlying spur, west of Kiril. 411, 419, 424–5, 437
Tarnost   In South Gondor (south-east of the crossing of Ringlo). 437
Taurost   Name given to the 'High City' (Citadel) of Mina Tirith. 260
Taur-rimmon   See *Rimmon (Forest)*.
Teeth of Mordor   Towers of either side of the Morannon. 113, 122, 362; *Towers of The Teeth* 123, 131, 431. See *Naglath Morn, Nelig Myrn*.
Telcontar, Telkontar   See *Tarakil*.
Terch Ungol   'The Spider's Lair'. 202. See *Torech Ungol*.
Thalion   (1) Name of Húrin of Dor-lómin. 293. (2) Man of Minas Tirith, father of Gwinhir. (284), 285, 293
Tharkûn   Gandalf's name among the Dwarves ('Staff-man', *Unfinished Tales* p.397). 153. Earlier form *Sharkûn* 153
Théoden   (including many references to *the King*) 3–31 *passim*, 36–51 *passim*, 55–8, 62–3, 67–74, 77–9, 95, 100–1, 103, 119–20, 129, 140–1, 146, 155, 182, 219, 226, 231, 235–67 *passim*, 272–6, 289, 296, 298–322 *passim*, 343–60 *passim*, 365–9, 371–2, 380, 384–6, 389, 395–6, 404, 406–8. Legend of Théoden's Howe 385, 389, 393
     The King's Guard 9, 14–16, 265, 316–19, 343, 345, 347–51, 353, 355–6, 372, *knights* 352, 368–9, *household-men* 357
Théodred   Son of Théoden; Second Marshal of the Mask. 8, 22, 59
Theostercloh   See *Heorulf's Clough*.
Thengel   Sixteenth King of the Mark, father of Théoden. 355, 366, 372, 408. *Thengling*, son of Thengel, 371
Thingol   King of Doriath. 297
Thorin (Oakenshield)   357
Thorongil   Aragorn's name in Gondor. 309
Thráin son of Thrór   357–8
Three Houses of Men   157, 159–60, 162, 169; *of the Elf-friends* 161
Three Rings of the Elves   98
Thrihyrne   The three peaks above Helm's Deep. 12, 22. See *Tindtorras*.
Thrór   357; Thrór's map 357
Tighfield   Village in the Shire. 95

INDEX 473

Tindtorras   Earlier name of *Thrihyrne*. 8–10, 12, 22, 95
Tol Eressëa   See *Eressëa*.
Tolfalas   Island in the Bay of Belfalas. 268
Tol Varad   See *Cair Andros*.
Tom Bombadil   98, 209, 219
Took, Isengrim the First   38, 45; in LR *Isengrim II*, 45
Took, Paladin   Father of Peregrin. 26, 41, 323, 334–5
Took, Peregrin   (also *Pippin*) 3–4, 6, 26, 36, 39, 41, 48–50, 53, 55,
       57–60, 66–8, 72–81, 119–20, 130, 140–3, 229, 231–3, 241,
       246, 249, 255, 259–60, 262–4, 270–301 *passim*, 306, 322–7,
       329–31, 334–42, 362, 367, 374–5, 378, 380–92 *passim*, 399,
       403, 405, 407, 410, 415–17, 419, 421, 423, 427, 430. His age
       283–5, 292–4; his sword 49, 59, 277, 292, 294; his brooch of
       Lothlórien 49
Took(s)   45, 54
Tor-dilluin, Mount   Original name of Mindolluin. 77, 80
Torech Ungol   'The Spider's Hole', Shelob's Lair. 202; earlier form
       Terch Ungol 202
Tower of Guard   Minas Tirith. 138, 153, 325
Towers of the Teeth   See *Teeth of Mordor*.
Townlands   See *Pelennor*.
Treebeard   3, 6, 25–6, 30, 39–40, 43, 47–55, 57, 66–8, 76, 79, 266,
       282, 343–6, 361, 364; Treebeard in Anórien 343–6, 364
Tree-giants   See *Ents*.
Trolls   30; 223 (in *The Hobbit*)); half-trolls of Far Harad 369
Trotter   38, 49, 100, 246, 390, 417
Trumbold   Precursor of Erkenbrand. 8–9, 23. (Replaced by *Heorulf*.)
Tuckborough   Chief place of the Tookland. 26, 284
Tumladen, Vale of   In South Gondor, west of Minas Tirith. 283, 289
Tuor   155
Turgon   Man of Minas Tirith, father of Beren (2). 282
Túrin   155, 159, 218; *Túrinssaga* 372

Ufthak   Orc of the Tower of Kirith Ungol. 225. *Uftak Zaglûn*, see
       Zaglûn.
Umbar   255, 265, 276, 296, 388, 392, 426, 439; *Haven(s) of Umbar*
       265, 268, *Haven(s) of the Corsairs* 388, 392; *Corsairs of Umbar*,
       Corsairs 283, 293–4, 372, 388, 390–1, 393, 413, 420; *Shipmen
       of Umbar* 412, *fleets of Umbar* 413, 420; *Shipfoes* 425
Umbor   Passing form for *Umbar*. 243–4, 265; *Havens of Umbor* 243
Undead   368
Underharrow   Village in Harrowdale. 318
Unfinished Tales   79, 154, 180, 309, 340, 352, 357
Ungol   See *Kirith Ungol*.
Ungoliant(e)   Earlier name of Shelob (q.v.).
Unnamed, The   Sauron. 154

474   THE WAR OF THE RING

Upbourn   Village in Harrowdale. 318
Uruk-hai   22

Valar   136; *Battle of the Valar* 353; *those who dwell beyond the West* 401; *the Powers* 157. See *God(s)*.
Vale of Dread   327. See *Minas Morghul*.
Valinor   158, 164, 168; *Valinorian, Valinorean* 394
Valley of the Wraiths   180. See *Minas Morghul*.
Varda   174
Variags   The people of Khand. 369
Vorondil   Father of Mardil the Steward. 288, 292. See *Faragon, Orondil*.

Walda   Twelfth King of the Mark. 408
Warden of the City, of the Keys   See *Húrin* (2).
War of the Great Jewels   161
War of the Ring   71, 162
Watchers, The   See *(The) Silent Watchers*.
waybread   See *lembas*.
Weathertop   17
Wellinghall   Treebeard's house. 3
Westemnet   28
Westernesse   Númenor. 76, 155, 281, 368, 396
Westfarthing   284
Westfold   (1) Valleys in the west of the Misty Mountains (see *Dunland*). 8, 21–3, 41; *Westfolder* 21–2; *tongue of Westfold* 21. (2) In Rohan (see *Westmarch*). 10, 22, 40, 51–2, 59–60, 238, 245, 250–1, 256, 259, 276, 371; *Westfold Vale* 12, 21, 70; *Lord of Westfold* 24; *tongue of Westfold* 159
westmansweed   pipeweed. 396
Westmarch   Earlier name of Westfold (2). 17, 21; *Westmarch Vale* 21; *Westmarcher(s)* 8, 11, 19, 21, *Marcher* 10
Westron   161
West, The   (in various applications) 41, 45, 153, 155, 157, 162, 184, 187, 219, 271, 324, 400–1, 403, 410, 418; *Host(s) (army, forces) of the West* 229, 256, 359, 399, 415–16, 430–2; *Captains of the West* 373; *the western world* 159, 162. See *Window of the Sunset*.
Wetwang   112. See *Nindalf*.
White Council   77 (*the Council*).
White Crown   On Aragorn's standard. 399; *the Crown* 359, 363, 389, 395; *the Crown of the North Kingdom* 395
White Eye   The Moon. 109, 116; *White Face* 116, 180
White Hand   Emblem of Saruman. 20, 31
White Lady   Galadriel. 163
White Mountains   (including many references to *the mountains*) 137, 141, 155–6, 167, 232, 235, 237, 244, 251, 253, 260, 262–3, 265,

INDEX   475

268, 273, 277–8, 283, 288–9, 293, 296, 315–16, 321–2, 354, 397, 405–7, 410–11, 417, 421, 433, 438. Change of the name from *Black Mountains* 137. See *Ered Nimrais*.

White Rider   See *Gandalf*.

White Tower (of Minas Tirith)   (including references to *the Tower*) 139, 253, 256–7, 260, 263, 276, 279, 281, 288–9, 292, 294, 330, 334, 336, 338, 340, 375–6, 378, 380–1, 394, and see *Denethor, Ecthelion* (2). *The Tower Hall*, see *Minas Tirith*.

White Tree of Gondor   The dead Tree in Minas Tirith. 276, 281, 336; as device, and in the Rhyme of Lore, 65, 267, 279, 281, 325, 363

Whitwell   Village in the Shire near Tuckborough. 284

Widfara   Rider of Rohan. 353

Wild Elves   The Avari. 157

Wild Men   155, 157 (in Faramir's distinctions). Men of the western vales of the Misty Mountains (see *Westfold* (1)) 9–10, 16, 18–19, 21, *(wild) hill-men* 8, 20–1; the Druedain of Anórien 344–6, 350–2; of the East 105, 243–4, 340; of the South 340; *wild peoples* 400, 403

Williams, Charles   104, 107, 144, 171, 183–4

Window of the Sunset   Henneth Annûn. 164. *Window of the West* 164, 271; ~ *on the West* 132

Winseld   Earlier name of *Meduseld*. 321

Wise, The   335

Wizard King, The   326, 331, 359, 361–4, 367, 430; *the Sorcerer King* 336, 368. See *Angmar, Black Captain, Nazgûl*.

Wizard(s)   (other than references expressly to Gandalf and Saruman) 36–8, 47, 53, 60, 282, 285, 332, and see *(The) Wizard King*; *the Five Wizards* 64, 67; the order of Wizards (63), 326, 331

Wizard's Vale, The   4–6, 29, 79; *the Valley of Saruman* 7. See *Nan Gurunír*.

Wold of Rohan   244, 256, 259, 262, 274, 343–5, 348, 361, 363, 404

Wolfriders   9–10, 29, 51, 54

Wood-elves   96; *Elves of the Woods* 157 (see *Lembi*).

Woodmen of Mirkwood   See *Mirkwood*.

World, The   Middle-earth. 410

Wormtongue   3, 6, 9, 11, 26, 55, 58, 60, 63–6, 75, 78, 80, 355, 372. See *Frána, Gríma*.

Woses   344, 352. See *Druedain, Wild Men*.

Wraiths   107, 364; *Valley of the Wraiths* 180; *Wraith-road* 195, 222. See *Ringwraith(s)*.

Yagûl   (1) Orc of the Tower of Kirith Ungol. 225 (replaced by *Shagrat*). (2) Orc of Minas Morghul. 216–18, 225–6 (replaced by *Gorbag*). Spelt *Yagool* 217

Yellow Eye   The Sun. 116; *Yellow Face* 116, 180

476 THE WAR OF THE RING

Yoreth Woman of Gondor serving in the Houses of Healing (in LR spelt *Ioreth*). 386–7, 390–3, 396

Zaglûn Orc of Minas Morghul. 212–13, 225; *Uftak Zaglûn*, see 225. (Replaced in succession by *Shagrat, Yagûl, Gorbag.*)

> Write nothing in this margin but the number of your answer.

j

[A]. O sauron túle nukumna ...lantaner
and   came   humble(d)   they fell

turkildi nuhuinenna... tarkalion
under-shadow

ohta káre valannar... númeheruvi
war made   on-Powers   Lords-of-West

arda sakkante leneme ilúvatáren ...
Earth   rent   with-leave

ëari ullier ikilyanna ... númenóre
seas   should pour   into-chasm   Numenor

ataltane.
fell down

Kadō zigūrun zabathān unakkha ...
and so   humbled   he-came

ēruhīnim dubdam ugru-dalad ...ar-
fell   ?shadow beneath

pharazōnun azaggara avalōiyada...
was warring   against Powers

bārim an-adūn yurahtam dāira sū-
Lords of West   They rent   Earth   with

bēth-mā ēruvō... azrīya duphursā
assent   from Eru   the seas   should gush

akhāsada... anadūnē zīrān hikalba...
into Chasm   Anadune   the beloved   she fell

bawība dulgī ... balīk hazad annimru-
winds (were)   black   ships seven   of   ?

zīr azūlada ...
      eastwards

ii

[B] Agannālō burōda nēnud ... zāira
    death-shadow   very heavy   on us   longing

nēnud ... adūn izindi batān tāidō
on us   west   straight (right?) road   then (once?)

ayadda : idō katha batīna lōkhī.
it went   now   all   ways (are) bent

[A] Vahaiya sín andóre.
    far away   now (is)   Andore (Land of Gift)

[B] Ephalak idō Yōzāyan.
    far away   now   Gift-land

[B] Ephal-ephalak idō hi Akallabēth.
    for far away   now   She that hath fallen

[A] Haiya vahaiya sín atalante.
    for far away   now (is)   the Down-fallen.

SAURON DEFEATED

J. R. R. TOLKIEN

Sauron Defeated

THE END OF THE THIRD AGE

The History of
The Lord of the Rings

PART FOUR

THE NOTION CLUB PAPERS
and
THE DROWNING OF ANADÛNÊ

Christopher Tolkien

CONTENTS

Foreword   *page* ix

PART ONE: THE END OF THE THIRD AGE

I	The Story of Frodo and Sam in Mordor	3
II	The Tower of Kirith Ungol	18
III	The Land of Shadow	31
IV	Mount Doom	37
V	The Field of Kormallen	44
VI	The Steward and the King	54
VII	Many Partings	61
VIII	Homeward Bound	75
IX	The Scouring of the Shire	79
X	The Grey Havens	108
XI	The Epilogue	114
	Appendix: Drawings of Orthanc and Dunharrow	136

PART TWO: THE NOTION CLUB PAPERS

Introduction	145
Foreword and List of Members	155
The Notion Club Papers Part One	161
The Notion Club Papers Part Two	222
Major Divergences in Earlier Versions of Part Two	
(i) The earlier versions of Night 66	299
(ii) The original version of Lowdham's 'Fragments'	309
(iii) The earlier versions of Lowdham's 'Fragments' in Adunaic	311

SAURON DEFEATED

(iv) Earlier versions of Edwin Lowdham's
Old English text   313

(v) The page preserved from Edwin Lowdham's
manuscript written in Númenórean script   318

PART THREE: THE DROWNING OF ANADÛNÊ

(i) The third version of *The Fall of Númenor*   331
(ii) The original text of *The Drowning of Anadûnê*   340
(iii) The second text of *The Drowning of Anadûnê*   357
(iv) The final form of *The Drowning of Anadûnê*   387
(v) The theory of the work   397
(vi) Lowdham's Report on the Adunaic Language   413

Index   441

ILLUSTRATIONS

Arundel Lowdham's 'Fragments'	frontispieces
The Tower of Kirith Ungol	*page* 19
Mount Doom	42
First copy of the King's letter	130
Third copy of the King's letter	131
Orthanc I	138
Orthanc II	139
Orthanc III	139
Dunharrow I	140
Dunharrow II	141
Title-page of *The Notion Club Papers*	154
The surviving page of Edwin Lowdham's manuscript:	
Text I, *recto*	319
Text I, *verso*	320
Text II	321

Note:
Owing to the limitations of printing on 'India' paper, it has been necessary to reproduce in black and white the originally coloured frontispiece illustrations.

To
TAUM SANTOSKI

FOREWORD

With this book my account of the writing of *The Lord of the Rings* is completed. I regret that I did not manage to keep it even within the compass of three fat volumes; but the circumstances were such that it was always difficult to project its structure and foresee its extent, and became more so, since when working on *The Return of the King* I was largely ignorant of what was to come. I shall not attempt a study of the history of the *Appendices* at this time. That work will certainly prove both far-ranging and intricate; and since my father soon turned again, when *The Lord of the Rings* was finished, to the myths and legends of the Elder Days, I hope after this to publish his major writings and rewritings deriving from that period, some of which are wholly unknown.

When *The Lord of the Rings* had still a long way to go – during the halt that lasted through 1945 and extended into 1946, *The Return of the King* being then scarcely begun – my father had embarked on a work of a very different nature: *The Notion Club Papers*; and from this had emerged a new language, Adunaic, and a new and remarkable version of the Númenórean legend, *The Drowning of Anadûnê*, the development of which was closely entwined with that of *The Notion Club Papers*. To retain the chronological order of writing which it has been my aim to follow (so far as I could discover it) in *The History of Middle-earth* I thought at one time to include in Volume VIII, first, the history of the writing of *The Two Towers* (from the point reached in *The Treason of Isengard*) and then this new work of 1945–6, reserving the history of *The Return of the King* to Volume IX. I was persuaded against this, I am sure rightly; and thus it is in the present book that the great disparity of subject-matter appears – and the great difficulty of finding a title for it. My father's suggested title for Book VI of *The Lord of the Rings* was *The End of the Third Age*; but it seemed very unsatisfactory to name this volume *The End of the Third Age and Other Writings*, when the 'other writings', constituting two thirds of the book, were concerned with matters pertaining to the Second Age (and to whatever Age we find ourselves in now).

X SAURON DEFEATED

Sauron Defeated is my best attempt to find some sort of link between the disparate parts and so to name to the whole.

At a cursory glance my edition of *The Notion Club Papers* and *The Drowning of Anadûnê* may appear excessively complicated; but I have in fact so ordered them that the works themselves are presented in the clearest possible form. Thus the final texts of the two parts of the *Papers* are each given complete and without any editorial interruption, as also are two versions of *The Drowning of Anadûnê*. All account and discussion of the evolution of the works is reserved to commentaries and appendages which are easily identified.

In view of the great disparity between Part One and Parts Two and Three I have thought that it would be helpful to divide the Index into two, since there is scarcely any overlap of names.

I acknowledge with many thanks the help of Dr Judith Priestman of the Bodleian Library, and of Mr Charles B. Elston of Marquette Unversity, in making available photographs for use in this book (from the Bodleian those on pages 42 and 138–41, from Marquette those on pages 19 and 130). Mr John D. Rateliff and Mr F. R. Williamson have very kindly assisted me on particular points in connection with *The Notion Club Papers*; and Mr Charles Noad has again generously given his time to an independent reading of the proofs and checking of citations.

This book is dedicated to Taum Santoski, in gratitude for his support and encouragement throughout my work on *The Lord of the Rings* and in recognition of his long labour in the ordering and preparation for copying of the manuscripts at Marquette, a labour which despite grave and worsening illness he drove himself to complete.

Since this book was set in type Mr Rateliff has pointed out to me the source of Arundel Lowdham's allusion to 'the Pig on the Ruined Pump' (p. 179), which escaped me, although my father knew the work from which it comes well, and its verses formed part of his large repertoire of occasional recitation. It derives from Lewis Carroll, *Sylvie and Bruno*, chapter X – where however the Pig sat beside, not on, the Pump:

> *There was a Pig, that sat alone,*
> *Beside a ruined Pump.*
> *By day and night he made his moan:*

FOREWORD

It would have stirred a heart of stone
To see him wring his hoofs and groan,
Because he could not jump.

In *Sylvie and Bruno Concluded*, chapter XXIII, this becomes the first verse of a poem called *The Pig-Tale*, at the end of which the Pig, encouraged by a passing Frog, tries but signally fails to jump to the top of the Pump:

Uprose that Pig, and rushed, full whack,
Against the ruined Pump:
Rolled over like an empty sack,
And settled down upon his back,
While all his bones at once went 'Crack!'
It was a fatal jump.

On a very different subject, Mr Noad has observed and communicated to me the curious fact that in the Plan of Shelob's Lair reproduced in *The War of the Ring*, p. 201, my father's compass-points 'N' and 'S' are reversed. Frodo and Sam were of course moving eastward in the tunnel, and the South was on their right. In my description (p. 200, lines 16 and 20) I evidently followed the compass-points without thinking, and so carelessly wrote of the 'southward' instead of the 'northward' tunnels that left the main tunnel near its eastern end.

PART ONE

THE END OF THE THIRD AGE

I

THE STORY OF FRODO AND SAM
IN MORDOR

Long foreseen, the story of the destruction of the Ring in the fires of
Mount Doom was slow to reach its final form. I shall look back first
over the earlier conceptions that have appeared in *The Return of the
Shadow* and *The Treason of Isengard*, and then give some further
outlines of the story.

The conception of the Fiery Mountain, in which alone the Ring
could be destroyed, and to which the Quest will ultimately lead, goes
back to the earliest stages in the writing of *The Lord of the Rings*. It
first emerged in Gandalf's conversation with Bingo Bolger-Baggins,
predecessor of Frodo, at Bag End (VI.82): 'I fancy you would have to
find one of the Cracks of Earth in the depths of the Fiery Mountain,
and drop it down into the Secret Fire, if you really wanted to destroy
it.' Already in an outline that almost certainly dates from 1939
(VI.380) the scene on the Mountain appears:

> At end
> When Bingo [> Frodo] at last reaches Crack and Fiery Mountain *he
> cannot make himself throw the Ring away.* ? He hears Necro-
> mancer's voice offering him great reward – to share power with
> him, if he will keep it.
>   At that moment Gollum – who had seemed to reform and had
> guided them by secret ways through Mordor – comes up and
> treacherously tries to take Ring. They wrestle and Gollum *takes
> Ring* and falls into the Crack.
>   The mountain begins to rumble.

Two years later, in a substantial sketch of the story to come ('The
Story Foreseen from Moria') it was still far from clear to my father just
what happened on the Mountain (VII.209):

> Orodruin [*written above:* Mount Doom] has three great fissures
> North, West, South [> West, South, East] in its sides. They are very
> deep and at an unguessable depth a glow of fire is seen. Every now
> and again fire rolls out of mountain's heart down the terrific
> channels. The mountain towers above Frodo. He comes to a flat
> place on the mountain-side where the fissure is full of fire – Sauron's
> well of fire. The Vultures are coming. He *cannot* throw Ring in. The
> Vultures are coming. All goes dark in his eyes and he falls to his

4   SAURON DEFEATED

knees. At that moment Gollum comes up and wrestles with him, and takes Ring. Frodo falls flat.

Here perhaps Sam comes up, beats off a vulture and hurls himself and Gollum into the gulf?

Subsequently in this same outline is found:

They escape [from Minas Morgol] but *Gollum follows*.
It is *Sam* that wrestles with Gollum and [?throws] him finally in the gulf.

Not long after this, in the outline 'The Story Foreseen from Lórien' (VII.344), my father noted that 'Sam must fall out somehow' (presumably at the beginning of the ascent of Mount Doom) and that Frodo went up the mountain alone:

Sam must fall out somehow. Stumble and break leg: thinks it is a crack in ground – really Gollum. [?Makes ?Make] Frodo go on alone.
Frodo toils up Mount Doom. Earth quakes, the ground is hot. There is a narrow path winding up. Three fissures. Near summit there is Sauron's Fire-well. An opening in side of mountain leads into a chamber the floor of which is split asunder by a cleft.
Frodo turns and looks North-west, sees the dust of battle. Faint sound of horn. This is Windbeam the Horn of Elendil blown only in extremity.
Birds circle over. Feet behind.

Since the publication of *The Treason of Isengard* there has come to light an outline that is obviously closely related to this passage from 'The Story Foreseen from Lórien' (which does not necessarily mean that it belongs to the same time) but is very much fuller. This I will refer to as I. The opening sentences were added at the head of the page but belong with the writing of the text.

(I)   Sam falls and hurts leg (really tripped by Gollum). Frodo has to go alone. (Gollum leaps on Sam as soon as Frodo is away.)

Frodo toils on alone up slope of Mt.Doom. Earth quakes; the ground becomes hot. There is a narrow path winding up. It crosses one great fissure by a dreadful bridge. (There are three fissures (W. S. E.).) Near the summit is 'Sauron's Fire-well'. The path enters an opening in the side of the Mt. and leads into a low chamber, the floor of which is split by a profound fissure. Frodo turns back. He looks NW and sees dust and smoke of battle? (Sound of horn – the Horn of Elendil?) Suddenly he sees birds circling above: they come down and he realizes that they are Nazgûl! He crouches in the chamber-opening but still dare not enter. He hears feet coming up the path.

THE STORY OF FRODO AND SAM IN MORDOR   5

At same moment Frodo suddenly feels, many times multiplied, the impact of the (unseen) *searching eye*; and of the enchantment of the Ring. He does not wish to enter chamber or to throw away the Ring. He hears or feels a deep, slow, but urgently persuasive voice speaking: offering him life, peace, honour: rich reward: lordship: power: finally a share in the Great Power – *if* he will stay and go back with a Ring Wraith to Baraddur. This actually terrifies him. He remains immovably balanced between resistance and yielding, tormented, it seems to him a timeless, countless, age. Then suddenly a new thought arose – not from outside – a thought born inside *himself*: *he* would keep the Ring himself, and be master of all. Frodo King of Kings. Hobbits should rule (of course he would not let down his friends) and Frodo rule hobbits. He would make great poems and sing great songs, and all the earth should blossom, and all should be bidden to his feasts. *He puts on the Ring!* A great cry rings out. Nazgûl come swooping down from the North. The *Eye* becomes suddenly like a beam of fire stabbing sheer and sharp out of the northern smoke. He struggles now to take off the Ring – and fails.

The Nazgûl come circling down – ever nearer. With no clear purpose Frodo withdraws into the chamber. Fire boils in the Crack of Doom. All goes dark and Frodo falls to his knees.

At that moment Gollum arrives, panting, and grabs Frodo and the Ring. They fight fiercely on the very brink of the chasm. Gollum breaks Frodo's finger and gets Ring. Frodo falls in a swoon. Sam crawls in while Gollum is dancing in glee and suddenly pushes Gollum into the crack.

Fall of Mordor.

Perhaps better would be to make Gollum repent in a way. He is utterly wretched, and commits suicide. Gollum has it, he cried. No one else shall have it. I will destroy you all. He leaps into crack. Fire goes mad. Frodo is like to be destroyed.

Nazgûl shape at the door. Frodo is caught in the fire-chamber and cannot get out!

Here we all end together, said the Ring Wraith.

Frodo is too weary and lifeless to say nay.

You first, said a voice, and Sam (with Sting?) stabs the Black Rider from behind.

Frodo and Sam escape and flee down mountain-side. But they could not escape the running molten lava. They see Eagles driving the Nazgûl. Eagles rescue them.

Make issue of fire *below* them so that bridge is cut off and *a sea of fire bars their retreat* while mountain quivers and crumbles. Gandalf on *white* eagle rescues them.

6   SAURON DEFEATED

Against the sentence 'He is utterly wretched, and commits suicide' my father subsequently wrote *No.*

Another outline, which I will call II, is closely related to outline I just given. It is written in ink over a briefer pencilled text, very little of which can be read – partly because of the overwriting, partly because of the script itself (my father could not read the conclusion of the first sentence and marked it with dots and a query).[1]

(II)   Frodo now feels full force of the Eye .... ? He does not want to enter Chamber of Fire or throw away the Ring. He seems to hear a deep slow persuasive voice speaking: offering life and peace – then rich reward, great wealth – then lordship and power – and finally a share of the Great Power: if he will take Ring intact to the Dark Tower. He rejects this, but stands still – while thought grows (absurd though it may seem): he will keep it, wield it, and himself have Power alone; be Master of All. After all he is a great hero. Hobbits should become lords of men, and he their Lord, King Frodo, Emperor Frodo. He thought of the great poems that would be made, and mighty songs, and saw (as if far away) a great Feast, and himself enthroned and all the kings of the world sitting at his feet, while all the earth blossomed.

(Probably now Sauron is aware of the Ring and its peril, and this is his last desperate throw to halt Frodo, until his messenger can reach Orodruin.)

Frodo puts on Ring! A great cry rings out. A great shadow swoops down from Baraddur, like a bird. The Wizard King is coming. Frodo feels him – the one who stabbed him under Weathertop. He is wearing Ring and has been seen. He struggles to take off Ring and cannot. The Nazgûl draws near as swift as storm. Frodo's one idea is to escape it, and without thinking of his errand he now flies into the Chamber of Fire. A great fissure goes across it from left to right. Fire boils in it. All goes dark to Frodo and he falls on his knees. At that moment *Gollum* arrives panting and grabs at the Ring. That rouses Frodo, and they fight on the brink of the chasm. Gollum breaks Frodo's finger and gets Ring. Frodo falls in swoon. But Sam who has now arrived rushes in suddenly and pushes Gollum over the brink. Gollum and Ring go into the Fire together. The Mountain boils and erupts. Barad-dur falls. A great dust and *a dark shadow* floats away NE on the rising SW wind. Frodo suddenly thinks he can hear and smell Sea. A dreadful shuddering cry is borne away and until it dies far off all men and things stand still.

Frodo turns and sees door blocked by the Wizard King. The mountain begins to erupt and crumble. Here we will perish together, said the Wizard King. But Frodo draws Sting. He no longer has any fear whatsoever. He is master of the Black Riders. He

THE STORY OF FRODO AND SAM IN MORDOR   7

commands the Black Rider to follow the Ring his master and drives it into the Fire.

Then Frodo and Sam fly from the chamber. Fire is pouring out of the mountain-side by three great channels W, SE, S, and makes a burning moat all round. They are cut off.

Gandalf, of course, now knows that Frodo has succeeded and the Ring has perished. He sends Gwaihir the Eagle to see what is happening. Some of the eagles fall withered by flame?[2] But Gwaihir sweeps down and carries off Sam and Frodo back to Gandalf, Aragorn, etc. Joy at the reunion – especially of Merry and Pippin?

There seems to be no certain way in which to date this text, but the reference to the coming of the Wizard King from Barad-dûr shows at any rate that his fate on the Pelennor Fields had not yet arisen. I incline to think that it is relatively late, and would associate it tentatively with the end of the outline 'The Story Foreseen from Forannest' (VIII.362):

Gandalf knows that Ring must have reached fire. Suddenly Sauron is aware of the Ring and its peril. He sees Frodo afar off. In a last desperate attempt he turns his thought from the Battle (so that his men waver again and are pressed back) and tries to stop Frodo. At same time he sends the Wizard King as Nazgûl to the Mountain. The whole plot is clear to him. ...

Gandalf bids Gwaihir fly swiftly to Orodruin.

With this cf. the words of outline II just given: 'Probably now *Sauron is aware of the Ring and its peril*, and this is his *last desperate throw to halt Frodo*'; and 'Gandalf, of course, now knows that Frodo has succeeded and the Ring has perished. He sends Gwaihir the Eagle to see what is happening.'

I turn now to other outlines that preceded any actual narrative writing of Book VI. The first of these, Outline III, also only came to light recently; it is a somewhat disjointed page, with deletions and additions, but all belonging to the same time. I believe that time to be the brief period of work (October 1944) when my father began writing 'Minas Tirith' and 'The Muster of Rohan', and wrote also many outlines for Book V; with the opening of the present text cf. VIII.260: '[12] Gandalf and Aragorn and Éomer and Faramir defeat Mordor. Cross into Ithilien. Ents arrive and Elves out of North. Faramir invests Morghul and main force comes to Morannon. Parley.' It will be seen that the story of the fighting and slaughter in the Tower of Kirith Ungol had not yet arisen.

(III)   They pass into Ithilien [12 >] 11[3] [and turn >] Éomer and Faramir invest Minas Morghul. The rest turn / north to Morannon. Joined by Ents and Elves out of Emyn Muil. Camp on [*added:* S. edge (of)] Battle Plain [14 >] evening of 12. Parley. Messengers

8   SAURON DEFEATED

[*sic*] of Sauron. Gandalf refuses. [*Added*: begins assault on Morannon.]

Sam rescues Frodo night of 11/12. They descend into Mordor. [Gollum comes after them. They see a vast host gathering in Kirith Gorgor, and have to lie hid (12). 12/13 They go on and are tracked by Gollum. *This was struck out and replaced by the following*:] Frodo from the high tower holds up phial and as if with Elvish sight[4] sees the white army in Ithilien. On the other side he sees the vast secret host of Mordor (not yet revealed) gathered on the dead fields of Gorgor. ? Sauron delays to take Frodo because of the defeat at Gondor.

Mt.Doom (Orodruin) stands in plain at inner throat of Kirith Gorgor, but a complete darkness comes over land, and all they can see is Mt.Doom's fire and far away the Eye of Baraddur. They cannot find a path? It is not until night of 12 that they reach rocky slopes above the levels of Kirith Gorgor. There they see an immense host camped: it is impossible to go further. They remain in hiding during 13 – and are tracked down by Gollum. Suddenly the whole host strikes camp and pours away leaving Mordor empty. Sauron himself has gone out to war.[5] They cross plain and climb Mt.Doom. Frodo looks back and sees the white army driven back.

Frodo captured on night 10/11. But Shagrat persuades Gorbag not to send message at once,[6] until he's had a look for the *real* warrior still loose. Orcs scatter and hunt in Kirith Ungol (11). Sam at last finds way in – he has to go back and down pass[7] – then he finds quite a small fort[8] of many houses and a gate and a path leading up to the cliff. It is not until [evening >] night of 11 that he manages to get in.

Rescue of Frodo early on 12. Shagrat sends message to Lugburz. [*Added*: How do messages work. Signal from Tower to Eye. News.] Nazgûl arrives at Tower and takes coat of mail and [clothes etc. >] a sword to Baraddur (12).

Frodo and Sam hide in rocks. The Gorgor plain is covered with armies. They are in despair, for crossing is impossible. Slowly they work their way north to where the defile narrows, to a point nearer Mt.Doom [> Dûm].[9]

Another outline (IV) describes the capture of Frodo and his rescue by Sam from the Tower of Kirith Ungol; and this is yet another text of which I was not aware until recently. Like outline II it is written in ink over an underlying, and much briefer, pencilled text. It was written, very obviously at the same time, on the reverse of a page that carries a rejected preliminary version (also in ink over pencil) of the outline 'The march of Aragorn and defeat of the Haradrim' given in VIII.397–9, which preceded the writing of 'The Battle of the Pelennor Fields' and very probably accompanied the outline 'The Story Foreseen from

THE STORY OF FRODO AND SAM IN MORDOR   9

Forannest' (see VIII.397). This preliminary version of 'The march of Aragorn and defeat of the Haradrim', which contains remarkable features, is given at the end of this chapter (p. 14).

In this outline IV Gorbag is expressly the 'Master of the Tower', whereas in the fair copy manuscript of 'The Choices of Master Samwise' he is the Orc from Minas Morghul, as in RK. It is notable however that at his first appearance in this text he is the Orc from Minas Morghul, changed immediately to Shagrat – which is however marked with a query. This query suggests to me that after so much changing back and forth of the names of these beauties (see VIII.225, note 46) my father could not remember what decision he had come to, and did not at this time check it with the manuscript of the end of Book IV (cf. the case of 'Thror' and 'Thrain', VII.159–60). The same uncertainty is seen in outline III above (see note 6).

(IV)   Frodo is captured night of 10–11. Mar.12 Frodo in prison. (Sauron is distracted by news of the Ents and defeat of his forces in Eastemnet by Ents and Elves of Lórien.)

No message is sent for some time to Dark Tower – partly because of general . . . .[10] Frodo is stripped, and the *Mithril* coat is found.

[Gorbag >] Shagrat (?) covets this, and tries to stop Gorbag sending message: at first pleading need of searching for confederate. But quarrel breaks out, and Shagrat and Gorbag fight and their men take sides. Sam at last finds way in – by a front gate overlooking Mordor – and a steep descent down into a long narrow dale or trough beyond which is a lower ridge.[11] In end Gorbag (Master of the Tower) wins, because he has more men, and Shagrat and all his folk are slain. Gorbag then sends tidings to Baraddur together with the Mithril coat – but overlooks Lórien cloak.[12] Gorbag has only very few men left, and has to send two (since one won't go alone for fear of the missing spy) to Baraddur. Sam slips in and slays one of Gorbag's remaining two at the gate, another on stair, and so wins his way in to the Upper Chamber. There he finds Gorbag. Sam takes off his Ring and fights him and slays him. He then enters Frodo's chamber. Frodo lying bound and naked; he has recovered his wits owing to a draught given him by orcs to counter poison – but he has talked in his delirium and revealed his name and his country, though not his errand.[13] Frodo is filled with fear, for at first he thinks it is an orc that enters. Then hatred for the bearer of the Ring seizes him like a madness, and he reproaches Sam for a traitor and thief. Sam in grief; but he speaks kindly, and the fit passes and Frodo weeps. This is night of 13th. Sam and Frodo escape from Tower on 14th.

It might be a good thing to increase the reckoning of time that Frodo, Sam and Gollum took to climb Kirith Ungol by a day, so that Frodo is not taken until night of 11–12. Quarrel between Orcs on 12th and sending of message that night or morning of 13th when

10   SAURON DEFEATED

Gorbag is victorious. Sam gets in on 13th. Otherwise Sam will have to spend all 11, 12 and part of 13 trying to get into Tower.

Make Sam get in before fight and get mixed up with it. And so let Sam hear message sent to Baraddur?

The last outline (V), while written independently of IV, evidently belongs closely with it, and has the same story of the Tower of Kirith Ungol – Gorbag is the captain of the garrison, and Sam slays him. This text, giving the first detailed account of the journey of Frodo and Sam to Mount Doom, is identical in appearance to 'The Story Foreseen from Forannest' and was clearly a companion to it.

At the head of the page are written these notes on distances, which were struck through:

> Minas Tirith to Osgiliath (W. end) 24–5 miles. Width of city [*written above:* ruin] 4 miles. East end of Osgiliath to Minas Morghul about 60 miles (52 to Cross Roads?). Minas Morghul to top of Kirith Ungol (and pass below Tower) 15 miles on flat. Kirith Ungol to crest of next (lower) ridge beyond Trough is about 15 miles.

The opening paragraph of the main text is enclosed in square brackets in the original. All the changes shown were made subsequently in pencil, including the reduction of most of the dates by a day.

(V) [Gorbag sends swift runner to Baraddur on morn(ing) of 13th. He does not reach plain and make contact with any horseman until end [> morn(ing)] of 14th? A rider reaches Baraddur on 15th [> night of 14], and at same time by Nazgûl news of the defeat before Gondor and the coming of Aragorn is brought to him [Sauron].[14] He sends the Nazgûl to Kirith Ungol to learn more. The Nazgûl discovers Tower full of dead and the prisoner flown.]

Sam rescues Frodo and slays Gorbag on 14th [> 13]. Frodo and Sam escape: when clear of the Tower, they disguise themselves in orc-guise. In this way they reach the bottom of the Trough at night on 14th [> 13]. They are surprised that there seems no guard and no one about; but they avoid the road. (A steep stair-path leads down from Tower to join the main road from Minas Morghul over Kirith Ungol pass to the Plain of Mordor and so to Baraddur.) The darkness is that of night.[15]

On 15th [> 14] March they climb the inner ridge – about 1000 feet at most, sheer on W. side, falling in jumbled slopes on E. side. They look out on the Plain of Mordor, but can see little owing to dark [*added:* but the clouds are blown away]. Though by the wizardry of Sauron the air is clear of smokes (so that his troops can move) it hangs like a great pall in the upper air. It seems largely to issue from Orodruin – or so they guess, where far away (50 miles) under the pall there is a great glow, and a gush of flame. Baraddur

THE STORY OF FRODO AND SAM IN MORDOR   11

(further and S. of the Mountain) is mantled in impenetrable shadow. Still, Frodo and Sam can see that all plain is full of troops. Hosts of fires dot the land as far as they can see. They cannot hope to cross. Frodo decides to try and find a point where the open land is narrower, in or nearer to Kirith Gorgor. They descend into Trough again and work north. They begin to count their food anxiously. They are very short of water. Frodo weak after poison – though the orcs gave him something to cure it, and *lembas* seems specially good as antidote; he cannot go fast.[16] They manage 10 miles along Trough.

On 16th [> 15] they continue to crawl along Trough, until they are some 25–30 miles north of Kirith Ungol.

On 17th [> 16] they climb ridge again, and lie hid. They hardly dare move again even in the gloom, since they can see below them great hosts of warriors marching into the defile out of Mordor. Frodo guesses they are going to war and wonders what is happening to Gandalf etc. [*Added:* No, most of troops are now *coming back in*.]

On 19th [> 18] being desperate they go down and hide in the rocks at the edge of the defile. At last Sauron's troop-movements cease. There is an ominous silence. Sauron is waiting for Gandalf to come into trap. Night of 19–20 [> 18–19] Frodo and Sam try to cross the defile into Ered-Lithui. (About this time let Sam have suspicion that Gollum is still about, but say nothing to Frodo?)

After various adventures they get to Eredlithui at a point about 55 miles NW of Orodruin. 20 (part), 21, 22, 23 they are working along slopes of Eredlithui.[17]

On 24th their food and water is all spent – and Frodo has little strength left. Sam feels a blindness coming on and wonders if it is due to water of Mordor.

24th. Frodo with a last effort – too desperate for fear – reaches foot of Orodruin and on 25 begins the ascent. There is a constant rumble underground like a war of thunder. It is night. Frodo looks round fearing the ascent – a great compulsion of reluctance is on him. He feels the weight of the Eye. And behold the mantle of shadow over Baraddur is drawn aside: and like a window looking into an inner fire he sees the Eye. He falls in a faint – but the regard of the Eye is really towards Kirith Gorgor and the coming battle, and it sweeps past Orodruin.

Frodo recovers and begins ascent of Mt.Doom. He finds a winding path that leads up to some unknown destination; but it is cut across by wide fissures. The whole mountain is shaking. Sam half-blind is lagging behind. He trips and falls – but calls to Frodo to go on: and then suddenly Gollum has him from behind and chokes his cries. Frodo goes on alone not knowing that Sam is not behind, and is in danger. Gollum would have killed Sam but is suddenly

12   SAURON DEFEATED

filled with fear lest Frodo destroy Ring. Sam is half throttled, but he struggles on as soon as Gollum releases him.

Here the text ends, and at the end my father wrote in pencil: 'Carry on now with old sketch.' Possibly he was referring to outline II (p. 6), although there seems reason to think (p. 7) that that outline belongs to much the same time as the present text.

★

The chronology of writing

I take it as certain that my father took up *The Lord of the Rings* again, after the long halt at the end of 1944, in the latter part of 1946: this was when he returned to the abandoned openings of the chapters 'Minas Tirith' and 'The Muster of Rohan'. For the subsequent chronology of writing there is little evidence beyond the rather obscure statements in his letters. On 30 September 1946 (*Letters* no.106, to Stanley Unwin) he said that he 'picked it up again last week' and wrote a further chapter, but there is really no knowing what this was; and on 7 December 1946 (*Letters* no.107, to Stanley Unwin) he wrote: 'I still hope shortly to finish my "magnum opus": the Lord of the Rings: and let you see it, before long, or before January. I am on the last chapters.'

In an unpublished letter to Stanley Unwin of 5 May 1947 he wrote: 'It [Farmer Giles] is hardly a worthy successor to "The Hobbit", but on the real sequel life hardly allows me any time to work'; and in another of 28 May 'I have not had a chance to do any writing.' On 31 July 1947 (*Letters* no.109) he was saying: 'The thing is to finish the thing as devised and then let it be judged'; and a further eight months on (7 April 1948, *Letters* no.114, to Hugh Brogan) he wrote: 'Only the difficulty of writing the last chapters, and the shortage of paper have so far prevented its printing. I hope at least to finish it this year …' Then, on 31 October 1948 (*Letters* no.117, again to Hugh Brogan), he said, 'I managed to go into "retreat" in the summer, and am happy to announce that I succeeded at last in bringing the "Lord of the Rings" to a successful conclusion.'

The only other evidence that I know of is found in two pages on which my father made a list of candidates for an academic post with notes on their previous experience. Against several of the names he noted both date of birth and present age, from which it is clear that the year was 1948. On the reverse of one of these pages is drafting for the passage in 'The Land of Shadow' in which Frodo and Sam see the darkness of Mordor being driven back (RK p. 196); the second part is overwritten with drafting for the discussion of food and water in 'The Tower of Kirith Ungol' (RK p. 190), while the reverse of it carries very rough sketching of the discovery of Frodo by Sam in the Tower.

THE STORY OF FRODO AND SAM IN MORDOR 13

Thus in December 1946 he was 'on the last chapters' of *The Lord of the Rings*, and hoped to finish it 'before January'; but in 1948 he was drafting the opening chapters of Book VI. The explanation must be, I think, that by the end of 1946 he had completed or largely completed Book V, and so (in relation to the whole work) he could feel that he was now 'on the last chapters'; and greatly underestimating (as he had so often done before) how much needed to be told before he reached the end, he thought that he could finish it within the month. But 1947 was largely unproductive, as the letters imply; and Book VI was not written until 1948.

NOTES

1   The few words and sentences that I can make out are sufficient to show that the story in the underlying text was substantially the same. The ink overwriting ends before the pencilled text does, and the last sentence of the latter can be read: 'Thorndor sweeps down and carries off Sam and Frodo. They rejoin the host on Battle Plain.' The naming of the rescuing eagle *Thorndor* (earlier form of *Thorondor*) is very surprising, but is perhaps to be explained as an unconscious reminiscence (when writing at great speed) of the rescue of Beren and Lúthien in *The Silmarillion*.

2   Cf. the fate of the Nazgûl in RK (p. 224): 'And into the heart of the storm ... the Nazgûl came, shooting like flaming bolts, as caught in the fiery ruin of hill and sky they crackled, withered, and went out.'

3   The dates are still in February. For the change in the month see VIII.324–5; and with the chronology of this text cf. that given in VIII.226.

4   Cf. the outline 'The Story Foreseen from Fangorn' (VII.438): 'Then return to Frodo. Make him look out onto impenetrable night. Then use phial which has escaped ... By its light he sees the forces of deliverance approach and the dark host go out to meet them.' On this I remarked (VII.440, note 15): 'The light of the Phial of Galadriel must be conceived here to be of huge power, a veritable star in the darkness.'

5   *Sauron himself has gone out to war*: despite the apparent plain significance of the words, it is impossible that my father should have meant that Sauron was no longer present in the Dark Tower.

6   *Gorbag* replaced *Yagûl* as the name of the Orc from Minas Morghul in the fair copy manuscript of 'The Choices of Master Samwise' (see VIII.225, note 46). Here 'Shagrat persuades Gorbag not to send message at once' suggests that Gorbag is the Orc from the Tower, whereas a few lines later 'Shagrat sends message to Lugbúrz'; see further outline IV, p. 9.

14   SAURON DEFEATED

7   *he has to go back and down pass:* i.e., Sam had to go back out of the tunnels and up to the pass, then down the other side of it (cf. RK pp. 173–5).

8   *quite a small fort:* I think that this means, not 'only a *small* fort', but 'an actual fort, if not very large, not simply a tower'.

9   For the spelling *Mount Dûm* see VII.373, VIII.118.

10   My father could not read the pencilled words here and wrote queries against them.

11   This is the first description of the Morgai (which is marked and named on the Second Map, VIII.435, 438).

12   The outline 'The march of Aragorn and defeat of the Haradrim', closely associated with the present text, has a brief passage about the rescue of Frodo concerned with the cloak of Lórien (VIII.398):

> Rescue of Frodo. Frodo is lying naked in the Tower; but Sam finds by some chance that the elven-cloak of Lórien is lying in a corner. When they disguise themselves they put on the grey cloaks over all and become practically invisible – in Mordor the cloaks of the Elves become like a dark mantle of shadow.

13   Cf. 'The Story Foreseen from Forannest' (VIII.361):

> He [the ambassador of Sauron to the Parley] bears the Mithril coat and says that Sauron has already captured the messenger – a *hobbit*. How does Sauron know? He would of course guess from Gollum's previous visits that a small messenger might be a *hobbit*. But it is probable that either Frodo *talked in his drugged sleep* – not of the Ring, but of his name and country; and that Gorbag had sent tidings.

14   A pencilled X is written against this sentence. Cf. 'The Story Foreseen from Forannest' (VIII.360): 'Sauron ... first hears of Frodo on 15 of March, and at the same time, by Nazgûl, of the defeat in Pelennor and the coming of Aragorn. ... He sends the Nazgûl to Kirith Ungol to get Frodo ...'

15   Against this paragraph is written in the margin: 'Frodo's horror when Sam comes in and looks like a goblin. Hate for the Ringbearer seizes him and bitter words of reproach for treachery spring to his lips.'

16   In the margin is written here: 'Ring a great burden, worse since he had been for a while free of it.'

17   Beside these dates is written '10 miles, 15, 15, 15'.

★

The rejected preliminary version of 'The March of Aragorn and defeat of the Haradrim'

I have mentioned (pp. 8–9) that on the reverse of the page bearing outline IV (describing the capture and rescue of Frodo) is the original

THE STORY OF FRODO AND SAM IN MORDOR   15

form of the outline given in VIII.397–9, entitled 'The march of
Aragorn and defeat of the Haradrim'. This is a very puzzling text, and
I give it in full. It was in fact written in three forms. The first is a
pencilled text (**a**) as follows:

Aragorn takes Paths of the Dead early on March 8th. Comes out
of the tunnel (a grievous road) and reaches head of the Vale of
Morthond at dusk. He blows horns [*struck out:* and unfurls
standard] to amazement of the people; who acclaim [him] as a king
risen from the Dead. He rests three hours and bidding all to follow
and send out the war-arrows he rides for the Stone of Erech. This is
a stone set up between the mouths of Lamedui and the Ethir Anduin
delta to commemorate the landing of Isildur and Anárion. It is
about 275 miles by road from the issuing of the Paths of the Dead.
Aragorn rides 100 miles and reaches the Ringlo Vale (where men
are assembling) on March 9. There he gathers news and men. He
rides after short rest into Lamedon (10) and then goes to

Here this version was abandoned and a new start made, also in pencil,
at 'Aragorn takes Paths of the Dead'; but this text (**b**) was overwritten
in ink and can only be read here and there. The overwritten form (**c**)
reads thus:

Aragorn takes Paths of the Dead morn(ing) 8 March, passes
tunnels of the mountains and comes out into the head of Morthond
Vale at dusk. Men of the Dale are filled with fear for it seems to
them that behind the dark shapes of the living riders a great host of
shadowy men come nearly as swift as riders. Aragorn goes on
through night and reaches Stone of Erech at morn(ing) on March 9.
Stone of Erech was black stone fabled to have been brought from
Númenor, and set to mark the landing of Isildur and Anárion and
their reception as kings by the dark men of the land. It stood on the
shores of Cobas, near the outflow of Morthond, and about it was a
ruined wall within which was also a ruined tower. In the vault under
the tower forgotten was one of the Palantir[i]. From Erech a road
ran by [the] sea, skirting in a loop the hills of Tarnost, and so to
Ethir Anduin and the Lebennin.

At Stone of Erech Aragorn unfurls his standard (Isildur's) with
white crown and star and Tree and blows horns. Men come to him.
(The Shadow-men cannot be seen by day.) Aragorn learns that what
he saw in Palantir was true indeed: Men of Harad have landed on
the coasts near the Ethir, and their ships have sailed up the estuary
as far as Pelargir. There the men of Lebennin have made a block –
on the basis of an ancient defence. The Haradwaith are ravaging the
land. It is nearly 350 miles by coast road from Erech to Pelargir.
Aragorn sends out swift riders north into the Dales, summoning
what men remain to march on Pelargir. He does not himself take

16   SAURON DEFEATED

coast-road, since it is infested, but after a rest he sets out at dusk of March 9 – and goes like wind by rough paths over Linhir and so to Fords of Lameduin (about 150 miles away). The Shadow Host is seen to follow. He crosses Morthond at Linhir, passes into Ringlo Vale, and sets all land aflame for war. He reaches Lameduin evening of March 10. Men are assembled there, and are resisting an attempt of the Haradwaith to cross Lebennin > NW. Aragorn and the Shadow Host come out of the dark with the white star shining on the banner and the Haradwaith are terrified. Many drowned in the river Lameduin. Aragorn camps and crosses Lameduin into Lebennin and marches on Pelargir morn(ing) of 11 March. The terror of 'the Black King' precedes him, and the Haradwaith try to fly: some ships escape down Anduin, but Aragorn comes up driving Haradwaith before him. The Shadow Host camps on shores of Anduin before Pelargir on evening of March 11th. By night they set fire in guarded ships, destroy the Haradwaith and capture 2 vessels. On morn(ing) of 12th they set out up Anduin, with Haradwaith captains rowing.

The extraordinary thing about this, of course, is the site of Erech. It seems plain beyond any question from all the evidence presented in *The War of the Ring* (see especially the chapter 'Many Roads Lead Eastward (1)') that from its first emergence Erech was in the southern foothills of Ered Nimrais, near the source of Morthond: Erech stands self-evidently in close relationship with the Paths of the Dead. Why then did my father now move it, first (in a) to the coast between the mouths of Lameduin and Ethir Anduin, and then (in b and c) to Cobas Haven (north of Dol Amroth: see the Second Map, VIII.434)? I am unable to propose any explanation.

The geography of the c-version is at first sight hard to follow. In a Aragorn's route can be understood: all that is said here is that he rode from the head of Morthond Vale 'for the Stone of Erech'; he reaches the Ringlo Vale, and then continues into Lamedon (which at this stage lay east of the river Lameduin: see VIII.437). The distance of 275 miles from the issuing of the Paths of the Dead to Erech 'between the mouths of Lamedui and the Ethir Anduin delta' is however much too great, and was perhaps an error for 175. (On the form *Lamedui* see VIII.436.) In version c, however, Aragorn leaves Erech 'on the shores of Cobas, near the outflow of Morthond', and 'goes like wind by rough paths *over Linhir and so to Fords of Lameduin* (about 150 miles away). ... *He crosses Morthond at Linhir, passes into Ringlo Vale* ... *He reaches Lameduin.*' As it stands this makes no sense; but the explanation is that his journey is described twice in the same passage. The first statement is comprised in the words 'He goes like wind by rough paths over Linhir, and so to Fords of Lameduin (about 150 miles away).' The second statement is 'He crosses Morthond at

THE STORY OF FRODO AND SAM IN MORDOR   17

Linhir, passes into Ringlo Vale ... He reaches Lameduin.' This must mean that Linhir is here in the earlier position, above Cobas Haven (see VIII.437).

It is said in c that the coast road from Erech skirted in a loop 'the Hills of Tarnost'. This name is written in pencil against a dot on the square Q 12 of the Second Map, at the northern extremity of the hills between the rivers Lameduin and Ringlo (see VIII.434, 437, where I said that so far as I then knew the name *Tarnost* does not occur elsewhere).

Lastly, in the concluding lines of b, which were not overwritten, the name *Haradrians* is given to the Haradwaith.

II

THE TOWER OF KIRITH UNGOL

It seems that my father returned to the story of Frodo and Sam more than three years after he had 'got the hero into such a fix' (as he said in a letter of November 1944, VIII.218) 'that not even an author will be able to extricate him without labour and difficulty.' As one of the outlines given in the preceding chapter shows, however, he had continued to give thought to the question, and while Book V was still in progress he had discovered the essential element in Sam's rescue of Frodo: the quarrel of Shagrat and Gorbag in the Tower of Kirith Ungol, leading to the mutual slaughter of almost all the orcs both of the Tower and of Minas Morgul before Sam arrived (p. 9).

His first draft ('A') of the new chapter extended as far as the point where Sam, descending the path from the Cleft, sees the two orcs shot down as they ran from the gateway of the Tower, and looking up at the masonry of the walls on his left realises that to enter in 'the gate was the only way' (RK p. 178). In this draft the text of RK was largely achieved, but not in all respects. In the first place, the chapter begins thus: 'For a while Sam stood stunned before the closed door. Far within he heard the sounds of orc-voices clamouring ...' It is clear that he was not physically stunned, as he was in the final story. On this see pp. 21–2.[1]

Secondly, when Sam, groping his way back from the under-gate in the tunnel, wondered about his friends (RK p. 173), 'Out in the world it was the dark before dawn on the twelfth of March in Shire-reckoning, the third day since he and Frodo came to the Cross Roads, and Aragorn was drawing near to Anduin and the fleet of Umbar, and Merry was beginning the third day of his ride from Dunharrow, and the forest of Druadan lay before him; but in Minas Tirith Pippin stood sleepless on the walls [?waiting] for [the] Causeway Forts had fallen and the enemy was coming.'

Thirdly, the fortress of Kirith Ungol was at first conceived as rising 'in four great tiers', not three as in RK (p. 176), and its strange structure, as it were flowing down the mountain-side, is sketched on the page of the draft (reproduced on p. 19) beside the description in the text; this description, originally in pencil but overwritten in ink, runs as follows:

And in that dreadful light Sam stood aghast; for now he could see the Tower of Kirith Ungol in all its strength. The horn that

The Tower of Kirith Ungol

20   SAURON DEFEATED

those could see who came up the pass from the West was but its topmost turret. Its eastern face stood up in four great tiers from a shelf in the mountain wall some 500 feet below. Its back was to the great cliff behind, and it was built in four pointed bastions of cunning masonry, with sides facing north-east and south-east, one above the other, diminishing* as they went up, while about the lowest tier was a battlemented wall enclosing a narrow courtyard. Its gate open[ed] on the SE into a broad road. The wall at the [?outward] .... was upon the brink of a precipice.

    *[The bottom one was probably projected some 50 yards from the cliff, the next 40, the next 30, the top 20 – and on the top [or tip] of it was the turret-tower. Their heights were 50 ft., 40 ft., 30 ft., 20 ?]

With black blank eyes the windows stared over the plains of Gorgoroth and Lithlad; some [?form(ed)] a line of red-lit holes, climbing up. Maybe they marked some stair up to the turret.

With a sudden shock of perception Sam realized that this stronghold had been built not to keep people out of Mordor, but to keep them in! It was indeed in origin one of the works of Gondor long ago: the easternmost outpost of the defence of Ithilien and Minas Ithil, made when after the overthrow of Sauron, in the days of the Last Alliance, the Men of the West kept watch upon the evil land where still his creatures lurked. But as with the Towers of the Teeth that watch[ed] over Kirith Gorgor, Nargos and ? [sic][2], so here too the watch and ward had failed and treachery had yielded up the Tower to the Ringwraiths. [?And] now for long it had been occupied by evil things. And since his return to Mordor Sauron had found it useful.

The pencilled passage that follows the end of the overwriting in ink reads as follows:

... keep watch upon the evil land where still his creatures lurked. But as with the Towers of the Teeth upon Kirith Gorgor, so here the watch and ward had failed and treachery had yielded up the Tower. But Sauron too had found it useful. For he had few servants and many slaves. Still its purpose was as of old to keep people in.

Sam looked and he saw how the tower commanded the main road from the pass behind; the road he was on was only a narrow way that went corkscrewing down into the darkness and seemed to join a broad way from the gate to the road.

THE TOWER OF KIRITH UNGOL

21

This page was removed from the original draft text A on account of the illustration (the only one that my father ever made of the Tower of Kirith Ungol), which was squared off with rough lines, and placed with the second fair copy manuscript (E), although by then the fortress was built in three tiers not four.

This original draft continues on to its end thus, and in this appears the most important difference from the story of RK (pp. 176–8):

There was no doubt of the path he must take, but the longer he looked the less he liked it. He put on the Ring again and began to go down. Now he could hear the cries and sounds of fighting again. He was about halfway down when out of the dark gate into the red glow came two orcs running. They did not turn his way but were making for the main road, when they fell and lay still. Apparently they had been shot down by others from the wall of the lower course or from the shadow of the gate.[3] After that no more came out. Sam went on. He came now [to] the point where [the] descending path hugged the lower wall of the tower as it stood out from the rock behind. There was a narrow angle there. He stopped again, glad of the excuse; but he soon saw that there was no way in. There was no purchase in the smooth rock or [?jointed] masonry and 100 feet above the wall hung beetling out. The gate was the only way.

Here the first draft stops. Thus the entire passage in RK (p. 177) in which Sam is tempted to put on the Ring and claim it for his own, his mind filling with grandiose fantasies (deriving from those of Frodo on Mount Doom in outlines I and II, pp. 5–6), is lacking; but at the point where the draft ends my father wrote (clearly at the same time): *Sam must not wear Ring*. No doubt it was this perception that caused him to abandon this text.

He began at once on a second draft, 'B', for most of its length written legibly in ink, with the number 'LII'[4] and the title 'The Tower of Kirith Ungol'. This opened in the same way as did A (p. 18): 'For a while Sam stood stunned before the closed door. Far within he heard the sounds of orc-voices clamouring...' In the fair copy manuscript of 'The Choices of Master Samwise' it had been said (following the original draft) that 'Sam hurled himself against it, and fell', changed in pencil to 'Sam hurled himself against the bolted plates, and fell to the ground.' This was repeated in the first typescript of that chapter; only in the second typescript was the word 'senseless' introduced. The explanation of this is that while writing the present draft B of 'The Tower of Kirith Ungol' my father was struck by a thought which he noted in the margin of the page, telling himself that he 'must leave time for Frodo to recover and to fight'[5] and that in order to achieve this

22   SAURON DEFEATED

'Sam must *swoon* outside the undergate.' It was no doubt at this time that he changed the opening of B:

> For a while Sam stood dumb before the closed door. Then desperate and mad he charged at the brazen door, and fell back stunned; down into darkness he sank. How long it lasted he could not tell; but when he came to himself still all was dark.

Against the passage in the draft A referring to other events in the world at that hour (p. 18) my father noted: 'Make Frodo and Sam one day more in Epheldúath. So Frodo is captured night of 12, when Merry was in Druadan Forest and Faramir lay in fever and Pippin was with the Lord, but Aragorn was manning his fleet.' In B the passage now becomes:

> Out westward in the world it was deep night upon the twelfth of March by Shire-reckoning, three days since he and Frodo had passed the peril of Minas Morgul; and now Aragorn was manning the black fleet on Anduin, and Merry in the Forest of Druadan was listening to the Wild Man, while in Minas Tirith the flames were roaring and [the great assault upon the Gates had begun >] the Lord sat beside the bed of Faramir in the White Tower.

Against 'March' in this passage my father scribbled in the margin: 'Make Hobbit names of months.'

At the point where Sam at the crest of the pass looked out over Mordor to Orodruin ('the light of it ... now glared against the stark rock faces, so that they seemed to be drenched with blood', RK p. 176) my father halted briefly and wrote the following note across the page:

> Change in the Ring as it comes in sight of the furnace where it was made. Sam feels *large* – and naked. He knows that he must *not* use the Ring or challenge the Eye; and he knows he is not big enough for that. The Ring is to be a desperate burden and no help from now onwards.

The Tower of Kirith Ungol is still built in four tiers, not three, and the note concerning the dimensions of the bastions was retained (see p. 20), though the dimensions were changed:

> [The bottom tier projected some 40 yards from the nearly perpendicular cliff, the second 30, the third 20, the topmost 10; and their height diminished similarly, 80 ft., 70 ft., 60 ft., 40 ft., and the topmost turret some 50 ft. above the top of .... mountain wall.]

The road from Minas Morgul over the Pass of Morgul is said here to pass 'through a jagged cleft in the inner ridge out into the valley of Gorgor on its way to the Dark Tower'; the name *Morgai* had not yet been devised (cf. RK p. 176). *Gorgor* was changed, probably im-

THE TOWER OF KIRITH UNGOL   23

mediately, to *Gorgoroth* (cf. VIII.256). The Towers of the Teeth were at first not named in this text, but *Narchost and Carchost* was added in subsequently.

Following the note on the subject of the Ring just given, this draft now effectively reaches the text of RK in the account of Sam's temptation and his refusal of it, as far as the point where A ended ('The gate was the only way', RK p. 178). From this point B becomes rough and is partly in outline form.

Sam wonders how many orcs lived in the Tower with Shagrat and how many men Gorbag had [*marginal note:* Make Gorbag's men more numerous in last chapter of Book IV][6] and what all the fighting was about. 'Now for it!' he cried. He drew Sting and ran towards the open gate – only to feel a shock, as if he had run into some web like Shelob's but *invisible*. He could see no obstacle, but something too strong for his will to overcome barred the way. Then just inside the gate he saw the Two Watchers. They were as far as he could see in the gloom like great figures sitting on chairs, each had three bodies, and three heads, and their legs facing inward and outward and across the gateway. Their heads were like vulture-faces, and on their knees were laid clawlike hands.[7] They were carved of black stone, it seemed, moveless, and yet they were aware; some dreadful spirit of evil vigilance dwelt in them. They knew an enemy, and forbade his entry (or escape). Greatly daring, because there was now nothing else to do, Sam drew out the phial of Galadriel. He seemed to see a glitter in the jet-wrought eyes of the Watchers, but slowly he felt their opposition melt into fear. He sprang through, but even as he did so, as if it was some signal given by the Watchers, far up in the Tower he heard a shrill cry.

In RK (p. 179), even as Sam sprang through the gateway, 'he was aware, as plainly as if a bar of steel had snapped to behind him, that their vigilance was renewed. And from those evil heads there came a high shrill cry that echoed in the towering walls before him. Far up above, like an answering signal, a harsh bell clanged a single stroke.' In the margin of the present text, against the foregoing passage, is a note: 'Or make Watchers close with a snap. Sam is in a trap once more.'

The courtyard was full of slain orcs. Some lay here and there, hewn down or shot, but many lay still grappling one another, as they throttled or stabbed their opponents. Two archers right in

24   SAURON DEFEATED

the gateway – probably those who shot down the escaping orcs – lay pierced from behind with spears. [Sting, Sam noticed, was only shining faintly.]

Sam rushed across the court, and to his relief found the door at the base of the Tower ajar. He met no one. Torches are flaring in brackets. A stair, opening on right, goes up. He runs up it, and so out into the narrow yard before the second door. 'Well!' he said to himself, his spirits rising a little, 'Well! It looks as if Shagrat or Gorbag was on my side and has done my job for me. There's nobody left alive!' And with that he halted, suddenly realizing the full meaning of what he had said: nobody was left alive. 'Frodo! Frodo!' he called, forgetful of all else, and ran to the second door. An orc leaps out at him [in margin: Two orcs].

Sam kills the [> one] orc and the other runs off yelling for Shagrat. Sam climbs warily. The stair now rises at the back of the entrance passage, and climbs right up to the Turret (the Brazen Gate enters about on a level with the courtyard?). Sam hears voices, and stalks them. The orc is pattering away up the stairs. 'Shagrat!' he calls. 'Here he is, the other spy.' Sam follows. He overhears the orc reporting to Shagrat. Shagrat is lying wounded by dead body of Gorbag. All Gorbag's men have been killed, but they have killed all Shagrat's but these two.

An isolated slip of paper seems very likely to be the continuation of this outline, and the first sketching of the new story of the escape from the Tower. The writing declines towards the end into such a scrawl that many words and phrases are impossible to make out.

Shagrat has in vain tried to get messages away to Baraddûr. The Quarrel arose about the treasures. Gorbag coveted the mithril coat, but pretended that they must search for the missing spy first. He sent his men to capture wall and gate, and demanded mithril coat. But Shagrat won't agree. Frodo was thrust in chamber of turret and stripped. Shagrat gives him some medicine and begins to question him. Shagrat puts things together to send to Baraddur (Lugburz). Gorbag tries to fight way in and slay Frodo.

Gorbag and Shagrat fight.

When Shagrat hears news (although orc says the other spy is not a large warrior) he is frightened, as he is wounded. He makes the treasures into a bundle and tries to creep off. He must get to Lugburz. So when Sam leaps out with phial and shining sword he flees. Sam pursues; but gives up for he [?hears] Frodo

THE TOWER OF KIRITH UNGOL 25

[?crying]. He sees Shagrat far below rushing out of gate – and does not at first realize the misfortune of news getting to Lugburz. The orc left behind is tormenting Frodo. Sam rushes in and slays him.

Scene of yielding up Ring. Frodo has lost his cloak and ....[8] He has to dress in the orc's clothes [or in orcs' clothes]. Sam does likewise but keeps cloak and Sting. Frodo has to have orc-weapons. The sword is gone.[9] He tells Sam about the fight. They make their plans.

The opposition of the Watchers. The Tower seems full of evil. Cry goes up as they escape. And as if in answer a Nazgûl comes dropping down out of the black sky, [?shining .... ?with] a fell red, and perches on the wall. Meanwhile they dash down the road, and as soon as they can leave it and climb into the shelter of the rocks near bottom of trough. They wonder what to do.

Food.[10] Drink. They had found Frodo's sack and ..... [?in corner] rummaged – but orcs would not touch *lembas*. They gathered up what was left of it, in broken fragments. Orcs must drink. [?They see] [a] well in the courtyard. Sam tastes it – says Frodo not to risk it. It seems all right. They fill their water bottles. It is now 13th of March, make it 14th? They reckoned they have [?enough] for about a week with care or at a desperate pinch ten days. How far is it.

They climb to lower ridge and find they dare not go across the plain at that point – where it is broad and full of enemies.

The Nazgûl [?explores] Tower and sees there is [??trouble] and flies off. Frodo thinks it best to go north to where the plain narrows – he had seen sketch of Mordor in Elrond's house – and away from Kirith Ungol to which [??attention is now directed]. He bemoans fact that Shagrat had got away with *tokens*.

Chapter ends with the Nazgûl shining red circling over Tower [??and he cries as] ..... of orcs begin to search the [?pass] and the road and lands about.

I believe that at this stage my father began the chapter again, and this was the first completed manuscript ('D'). It was numbered 'LII' but given a new title 'The Orc-tower'; the number was later changed to 'L' (which I cannot explain) and the title 'The Tower of Kirith Ungol' (which it had borne in the draft B) restored.

New initial drafting begins at the point where Sam enters the gate of the Tower, but up to this point the final text was now written out on the basis of the drafts A and B described above, in a form only

26   SAURON DEFEATED

differing in a few minor points from that in RK. The chapter now opens exactly as it does in the published work (see p. 22), and Sam now has to climb back over the stone door leading into the passage to the under-gate, since he still cannot find the catch (note 1). The events 'out westward in the world' are described in the same words as in RK (with the addition, after 'Pippin watched the madness growing in the eyes of Denethor', of 'and Gandalf laboured in the last defence'); but the date ('noon upon the fourteenth day of March' in RK) is now 'morning upon the thirteenth day of March'. The name *Morgai* appears as an early addition to the text (p. 22). The Tower now has three tiers, and the note about the dimensions of the bastions, still present (see pp. 20, 22), was accommodated to this: the tiers now projected 40, 30 and 20 yards from the cliff, and their heights were 80, 70, and 60 feet, changed at the time of writing to 100, 75, and 50 feet. 'The top was 25 feet above Sam, and above it was the horn-turret, another 50 feet.'[11]

From ' "That's done it!" said Sam. "Now I've rung the front-door bell!" ' a draft text ('C') takes up. This is written in a script so difficult that a good deal of it would be barely comprehensible had it not been closely followed in the fair copy D.[12] The final story was now reached, and there is little to record of these texts. At the point in the narrative where Sam climbed up to the roof of the third (topmost) tier of the Tower there is a little diagram in D showing the form of the open space (not clearly seen in the drawing reproduced on p. 19): rectangular at the base but with the sides drawing together to a point (cf. the 'pointed bastions' referred to in the description of the Tower), roughly in the shape of a haystack. To the statement that the stairhead was 'covered by a small domed chamber in the midst of the roof, with low doors facing east and west' D adds 'Both were open': this was omitted in the second manuscript ('E'), perhaps inadvertently. The name of the sole surviving orc beside Shagrat is *Radbug* in both C and D (*Snaga* in RK; see LR Appendix F, p. 409), *Radbug* being retained in the final story as the name of an orc whose eyes Shagrat says that he had squeezed out (RK p. 182); in C the orcs whom Sam saw running from the gate and shot down as they fled are *Lughorn* and *Ghash* > *Muzgash* (*Lagduf* and *Muzgash* in D, as in RK). Where in RK Snaga declares that 'the great fighter' (Sam) is 'one of those bloody-handed Elves, or one of the filthy *tarks*', and that his getting past the Watchers is '*tark's* work',[13] C has 'that's Elvish work'; D has 'one of these filthy wizards maybe' and 'that's wizard's work' ('wizard' being changed in pencil to '*tark*', which appears in the second manuscript E as written).

Only in one point does the story as told in the draft C differ from that in D. When Gorbag rouses himself from among the corpses on the roof Sam sees in the latter, as in RK (p. 183), that he has in his hand 'a broad-headed spear with a short broken haft'; in C on the other hand he has 'a red [?and shining] sword. It was his own sword, the one he

THE TOWER OF KIRITH UNGOL   27

left by Frodo.' With this cf. text B (p. 25 and note 9): 'Frodo has to have orc-weapons. The sword is gone.'

Sam's song as he sat on the stair in the horn-turret was much worked on.[14] I give it here in the form that it has in D, which was preceded by rougher but closely similar versions.

> *I sit upon the stones alone;*
> *the fire is burning red,*
> *the tower is tall, the mountains dark;*
> *all living things are dead.*
> *In western lands the sun may shine,*
> *there flower and tree in spring*
> *is opening, is blossoming:*
> *and there the finches sing.*
>
> *But here I sit alone and think*
> *of days when grass was green,*
> *and earth was brown, and I was young:*
> *they might have never been.*
> *For they are past, for ever lost,*
> *and here the shadows lie*
> *deep upon my heavy heart,*
> *and hope and daylight die.*
>
> *But still I sit and think of you;*
> *I see you far away*
> *Walking down the homely roads*
> *on a bright and windy day.*
> *It was merry then when I could run*
> *to answer to your call,*
> *could hear your voice or take your hand;*
> *but now the night must fall.*
> *And now beyond the world I sit,*
> *and know not where you lie!*
> *O master dear, will you not hear*
> *my voice before we die?*

The second verse was altered on the manuscript:

> *For they are gone, for ever lost,*
> *and buried here I lie*
> *and deep beneath the shadows sink*
> *where hope and daylight die.*

At the same time the last two lines of the song became:

> *O Master, will you hear my voice*
> *and answer ere we die?*

28   SAURON DEFEATED

In this form the song appears in the second manuscript E. At a later stage it was rewritten on this manuscript to become virtually a different song, but still retaining almost unchanged the second half of the original first verse, which now became the opening lines:

> *In western lands the Sun may shine;*
> *there flower and tree in Spring*
> *are opening, are blossoming,*
> *and there the finches sing.*

Further correction of these lines on the manuscript produced the final form (RK p. 185).

A last point concerns the ladder: 'Suddenly the answer dawned on Sam: the topmost chamber was reached by a trap-door in the roof of the passage', RK p. 185. In my account of the fair copy manuscript of 'The Choices of Master Samwise' I did not describe a development in the last words of Shagrat and Gorbag that Sam overheard before they passed through the under-gate of the Tower (TT p. 351). In the draft text, only Shagrat speaks:

> 'Yes, up to the top chamber,' Shagrat was saying, 'right at the top. No way down but by the narrow stair from the Look-out Room below. He'll be safe there.'

In the fair copy this was retained, but Shagrat begins 'Yes, that'll do' (as if the suggestion had come from Gorbag), and 'the ladder' was substituted for 'the narrow stair'. It is thus seen that this element in the story was already present when Book IV was completed. The further development in the conversation of the orcs, in which Gorbag argues against Shagrat's proposal, and Shagrat declares that he does not trust all of his own 'lads', nor any of Gorbag's, nor Gorbag himself (and does not mention that the topmost chamber was reached by ladder), was added to the first typescript of 'The Choices of Master Samwise' at this time, as is seen from the fact that rough drafting for it is found on a page carrying drafts for passages for 'The Land of Shadow'. Curiously, my father wrote at the head of this: 'No way up but by a ladder', as if this idea had only now emerged.[15]

NOTES

1   When Sam came back to the stone door of the orc-passage 'on the inner side he found the catch' (whereas in RK he could not find it and had to climb over). This was retained in the second draft B.

2   For earlier names of the Towers of the Teeth see the Index to *The War of the Ring*, entries *Naglath Morn*, *Nelig Myrn*. The name *Nargos* here is a reversion to one of the original names (*Gorgos* and *Nargos*) of the towers guarding Kirith Ungol, when that was

THE TOWER OF KIRITH UNGOL   29

still the name of the chief pass into Mordor: see VII.344 and note 41.

3   These two orcs, who survived into the final text (RK p. 178), originally appeared in outline IV (p. 9) as messengers sent to Barad-dûr. At that time there was no suggestion that they did not make good their errand.

4   At this stage, presumably, 'The Pyre of Denethor' and 'The Houses of Healing' constituted the two parts of Chapter XLIX (VIII.386), while the remainder of Book V was divided between L and LI (the fair copy manuscript of 'The Black Gate Opens' is numbered LI).

5   In the event, of course, Frodo did not fight, and no draft of this period suggests that he did. Possibly at this stage, before he had come to write the new story of the rescue of Frodo, my father was still thinking in terms of the original plot in 'The Story Foreseen from Lórien', when Frodo was more active (VII.335 ff.).

6   In the fair copy manuscript of 'The Choices of Master Samwise' Sam asked himself: 'How many are there? Thirty, forty, or more?' The change to 'Thirty of forty from the tower at least, and a lot more than that from down below, I guess' (TT p. 344) was made on the first typescript of the chapter. – In outline IV (p. 9) the orcs of the Tower are the more numerous.

7   Cf. the original conception of the Sentinels guarding the entrance to Minas Morgul in 'The Story Foreseen from Lórien' written years before (VII.340–1): 'It was as if some will denying the passage was drawn like invisible ropes across his path. He felt the pressure of unseen eyes. ... The Sentinels sat there: dark and still. They did not move their clawlike hands laid on their knees, they did not move their shrouded heads in which no faces could be seen ...' See also the diagrammatic sketch of the Sentinels in VII.348.

8   The illegible word might possibly be *jewel* (i.e. the brooch of his elven-cloak).

9   *The sword is gone:* this is Sam's sword from the Barrow-downs; cf. 'The Choices of Master Samwise' (TT p. 340): ' "If I'm to go on," he said, "then I must take your sword, by your leave, Mr. Frodo, but I'll put this one to lie by you, as it lay by the old king in the barrow ..." ' See pp. 26–7.

10 This passage concerning their provision of food and water is marked to stand earlier – no doubt after the words 'They make their plans'. The illegible words in the sentence following 'Food. Drink.' could conceivably be read as *stick thrust*, i.e. 'They had found Frodo's sack and stick thrust in corner, rummaged.'

11 A few other differences of detail are worth recording. Where in RK (p. 176) the text reads: 'not even the black shadows, lying deep where the red glow could not reach, would shield him long

30   SAURON DEFEATED

from the night-eyed orcs' D continues: 'that were moving to and fro.' This was taken up from the draft B, and remained into the second manuscript of the chapter (E), where it was removed. – Sam's rejection of the temptation to claim the Ring as his own was expressed thus: 'The one small garden of a free gardener was all his need and due, not a garden swollen to a realm; his own hands to command, not the hands of others. Service given with love was his nature, not to command service, whether by fear or in proud benevolence.' – After the words 'He was not really in any doubt' (RK p. 177) there follows in D: 'but he was lonely and he was not used to it, or to acting on his own.' To this my father subsequently added, before striking it all out, 'Since no one else was there he had to talk to himself.'

12   Some passages are absent from the draft C, but not I think because pages are lost: rather D becomes here the initial narrative composition. Thus the passage in RK p. 181 from 'Up, up he went' to ' "Curse you, Snaga, you little maggot" ' is missing; and here the D text becomes notably rougher and full of corrections in the act of writing. The very rough draft C stops near the beginning of Sam's conversation with Frodo in the topmost chamber (RK p. 187), and from that point there are only isolated passages of drafting extant; but the latter part of D was much corrected in the act of writing, and was probably now to a large extent the primary composition.

13   Cf. LR Appendix F (RK p. 409): in Orkish Westron '*tark*, "man of Gondor", was a debased form of *tarkil*, a Quenya word used in Westron for one of Númenorean descent'.

14   For my father's original ideas for the song that Sam sang in this predicament see VII.333.

15   When Frodo and Sam passed out through the gate of the Tower Frodo cried: *Alla elenion ancalima! Alla* was not changed to *Aiya* until the book was in type (cf. VIII.223, note 29).

III

THE LAND OF SHADOW

It seems plain that 'The Land of Shadow' was achieved swiftly and in a single burst of writing; the draft material (here compendiously called 'A') consists largely of very roughly written passages immediately transferred to and developed in the first continuous manuscript ('B'), which was given the number 'LIII' (see p. 25) and the title 'Mount Doom', subsequently changed to 'The Land of Shadow'. Only in a few passages did my father go momentarily down an unsuccessful turn in the story.

The first of these concerns the overhearing by Sam and Frodo of the conversation of orcs in the valley beneath the Morgai, which was at first conceived very differently from the story in RK (pp. 202–3). The draft text A is here, as throughout, exceedingly difficult to read.

Presently [three >] two orcs came into view. They were in black without tokens and were armed with bows, a small breed, black-skinned with wide snuffling nostrils, evidently trackers of some kind. .... they were talking in some hideous unintelligible speech; but as they passed snuffling among the stones scarcely 20 yards from where the hobbits lurked Frodo saw that one was carrying on his arm a black mail-shirt very like the one that he had abandoned. He sniffed it as [he] went as if to recall its scent. All at once lifting his head he let out a cry. It was answered, and from the other direction (from Kirith Ungol now some miles behind) ... large fighting orcs came up with shields .... [?painted] with the Eye.

A [?babble] of talk in the common tongue now broke out. 'Nar,' said the tracker, 'not a trace further along. Nor o' this smell, but we're not [?easy]. Somebody that has no business here has been about. Different smell, but a bad smell: we've lost that too, it went up into the mountains.'

'A lot of use you little snufflers are,' grunted a bigger orc. 'I reckon eyes are better than your snotty noses. Have you seen anything?'

'What's to look for?' grunted the tracker.

Amid much further orcish dissension in confused drafting the final story emerges, with two orcs only, a soldier and a small tracker: my

32   SAURON DEFEATED

father had some trouble in deciding which offensive remark belonged to which speaker.

Drafting for the passage in which Sam described to Frodo all that had happened (RK p. 204) runs thus:

When he had finished Frodo said nothing for some time, but took Sam's hand and pressed it. At length he stirred. 'So this is what comes of eavesdropping, Sam,' he said. 'But I wonder if you'll ever get back. Perhaps it would have been safer to have been turned into a toad as Gandalf threatened. Do you remember that day, Sam,' he said, 'and clipping the edges under the window?'

'I do, Mr. Frodo. And I bet things are in [a] nasty mess there now with [?that] Lobelia and her Cosimo,[1] begging your pardon. There'll be trouble if ever we get back.'

'I shouldn't worry about that if I were you,' said Frodo. 'We've got to go on again now. East, East, Sam, not West. I wonder how long it will be before we are caught and all this slinking and toiling will be over?'

It is curious that Sam, speaking darkly of the state of affairs in the Shire, should ascribe it to Lobelia and Cosimo Sackville-Baggins. In the original sketch of the Mirror of Lothlórien, when it was King Galdaran's Mirror, and when it was Frodo who saw the visions of the Shire, he was to see 'Cosimo Sackville-Baggins very rich, buying up land'; but there is no mention of Cosimo in the first narrative of the scene (VII.249, 253).

Frodo's entrusting of Sting and the Phial of Galadriel to Sam entered in the first manuscript (B) in this form:

'You must keep the Lady's gift for me, Sam,' he said, 'I've nowhere to store it now, except in my hand, and I need both in the dark. And you must keep Sting too, since I have lost your sword. I have got an orc-blade, but I do not think it is my part to strike any blows again.'

It was at this time, as it appears, that my father came to a new perception of the lands in the north-western extremity of Mordor, and saw that the vale behind the Morannon was closed also at the southward end by great spurs that thrust out from Ephel Dúath and Ered Lithui. As first written in B, Frodo told Sam this concerning his knowledge of Mordor (cf. RK p. 204):

'No very clear notion, Sam,' said Frodo. 'In Rivendell before I set out I saw old maps made before the Dark Lord came back

THE LAND OF SHADOW   33

here, and I remember them vaguely. I had a little secret plan with names and distances: it was given to me by Elrond, but that has gone with all my other things. I think it was ten leagues or even a dozen from the Bridge to the Narrows, a point where the western and northern ranges send out spurs and make a sort of gate to the deep valley that lies behind the Morannon. The Mountain stands out alone on the plain, but nearer the northern range. Nearly fifty miles I think from the Narrows, more, of course, if we have to keep to the edge of the hills on the other side.'

In a revised version of this Frodo says: 'I guess, not counting our wasted climb, we've done say [twenty miles >] six or seven leagues north from the Bridge since we started.' The final version in this manuscript gives seven leagues as the distance they have traversed, 'ten leagues or so' from the Bridge to the meeting of the mountain-spurs, and still fifty miles from there to Mount Doom. In RK these distances are twelve leagues, not seven; twenty leagues, not ten; and sixty miles, not fifty: see further the Note on Geography at the end of this chapter.

When Frodo and Sam at last set eyes on the north-western confines of Mordor as seen from the south (RK p. 205) the names *Durthang* and *Carach Angren 'the Iron Jaws'* appear in the original draft, but the valley behind Carach Angren is named *the Narch*.[2] The draft text is here partly illegible, but enough can be read to show that the landscape was perfectly clear to my father's eyes as soon as he reached this point in the narrative. In the B text the name *Isenmouthe* appears, though the valley behind is still called 'the deep dark valley of Narch.'[3]

A notable feature in the original draft of the story is that there is no mention of Gollum (see RK p. 206). While Frodo slept Sam went off by himself and found water, as in RK, but then 'the rest of that grey day passed without incident. Frodo slept for [?hours]. Sam did not wake him, but trusting once more to "luck" slept for a long while beside him.' Gollum enters in the B text in these words:

At that moment he thought he caught a glimpse of a black form or shadow flitting among the stones above, near to Frodo's hiding. He was almost back to his master before he was sure. There was Gollum indeed! If his will could have given him strength for a great bound Sam would have sprung straight on his enemy's back; but at that moment Gollum became aware of him and looked back. Sam had a quick glimpse of two pale eyes now filled with a mad malevolent light, and then Gollum, jumping from rock to rock with great agility, fled away onto the ridge and vanished over its crest.

34   SAURON DEFEATED

The end of the chapter, the story of Frodo and Sam being forced to join the orc-band coming down from Durthang and their escape from it in the confusion at the road-meeting near the Isenmouthe, was achieved in all but minor details unhesitatingly.[4]

NOTES

1   For Cosimo Sackville-Baggins, later Lotho, see VI.283, VII.32.

2   It was while working on the latter part of 'The Land of Shadow' that my father first mapped this new conception of the north-western extremity of Mordor, on a slip of paper that bears on the reverse drafting for the story of the forced march of Frodo and Sam in the troop of orcs moving from Durthang to the Isenmouthe. On this little sketch-map the closed vale between the Morannon and the Isenmouthe is named *The Narch*, subsequently overwritten *Udûn*. In my description of the Second Map in VIII.438 I noted that the vale was first marked *Gorgoroth*, but that this was struck out, 'and in its place was pencilled here the name *Narch Udûn*.' It is in fact clear that *Narch* alone was first written, and that *Udûn* was intended as a replacement.

3   This was changed later to 'the deep dale of Kirith Gorgor', and then to 'the deep dale of Udûn' (see note 2).

4   A few such details from the earliest form of the conclusion of the chapter may be mentioned. The orc 'slave-drivers' are called 'two of the large fierce *uruks*, the fighting-orcs', and this seems to be the first time that the word was used (though the name *Uruk-hai* had appeared long since, VII.409, VIII.22, see also p. 436); and it is said that 'one of the slave-drivers *with night-sighted eyes* spied the two figures by the roadside.' Where in RK this orc says 'All your folk should have been inside Udûn before yesterday evening' he says here 'inside the Narch-line'; and following his words 'Don't you know we're at war?' he adds: 'If the elvish folk get the best of it, they won't treat you so kindly.'

Note on the Geography

In the first draft of the chapter, when Frodo and Sam climbed to the crest of the Morgai and looking out eastwards saw Mount Doom, it was 'still 30 miles away, perhaps, due East from where the hobbits stood.' In the B text, in the following manuscript, and in the final typescript for the printer, the distance became 'seven leagues or more', and was only altered to 'forty miles at least' (RK p. 200) at a late stage. It is impossible to relate '30 miles', still less 'seven leagues', to any of the maps. On the Second Map the distance due East from the Morgai to Mount Doom (in its second, more westerly, position, see VIII.438) is just under 50 miles, while on the Third Map (the last general small-scale map that my father made) it became 80 miles. On the

THE LAND OF SHADOW 35

large-scale map of Rohan, Gondor and Mordor the distance is somewhat under 60 miles, as Mount Doom was first placed; but when it was moved further to the west it became about 43 miles (under 40 in my redrawing of the map published in *The Return of the King*), with which the text of RK agrees.

The distance from the Morgai bridge below Kirith Ungol to the Isenmouthe was roughly estimated from memory by Frodo (p. 33) as 'ten leagues or even a dozen' (30–36 miles); and 'ten leagues at least' remained into the final typescript before being changed to the figure in RK (p. 204), 'twenty leagues at least'. The Second Map does not allow of precise measurement of the distance from the Morgai bridge to the Isenmouthe, since the conception of the closing of the vale behind the Morannon by spurs of Ephel Dúath and Ered Lithui had not arisen when it was made, but it could be minimally calculated as between 30 and 40 miles; on the large-scale map it becomes 56 miles or just under 19 leagues, agreeing with the twenty leagues of RK.

Frodo's estimation of the distance from the Isenmouthe to Mount Doom as about fifty miles likewise remained through all the texts until replaced at the very end by sixty. This distance is roughly 50 miles on the Second Map, about 80 on the Third Map, and 62 on the large-scale map as Mount Doom was first placed; when it was moved further west the distance from the Isenmouthe became 50 miles. The change of 50 to 60 at the end of the textual history of RK is thus, strangely, the reverse of the development of the map.

In the original draft Sam and Frodo joined the road to the Isenmouthe 'after it had already run down some 4 miles from the orc-hold of Durthang and turned away somewhat northward so that the long descent behind was hidden from them [?hurrying] on the stony road. They had been going an hour and had covered perhaps some 3 miles without meeting any enemy when they heard what they had all along dreaded ...' In B 'they came at last to the road where, after descending swiftly from Durthang, it became more level and ran under the ridge towards the Isenmouthe, a distance of perhaps ten miles.' As in A, they had only been on the road for an hour when they were overtaken by the orcs, and it is added in B at this point 'it was maybe six miles yet before the road would leave its high shelf and go down into the plain.' In the following manuscript and in the final typescript for the printer the hobbits still reached the road 'at the point where it swung east towards the Isenmouthe ten miles away', and it was still after only an hour on the road that they halted, and were shortly afterwards overtaken. On the typescript my father emended 'ten miles' to 'twenty miles', and 'an hour' to 'three hours', but the final reading of RK was 'after doing some twelve miles, they halted.' On the large-scale map the track of Frodo and Sam up the valley below the Morgai is marked, and the point where their track joined

36   SAURON DEFEATED

the road from Durthang is 20 miles from the Isenmouthe; the change in the text was thus very probably made to accommodate it to the map. The change whereby the hobbits had gone for three hours or twelve miles along the road before being overtaken clearly followed from the increased distance to the Isenmouthe, in order to reduce the time that Frodo and Sam had to submit to the punishing pace set by the orcs before they escaped.

Note on the Chronology

Dates are written in the margins of the original texts of this chapter. At this stage the chronology of the journey from Kirith Ungol can be set out thus:

March 14   Dawn: Frodo and Sam climb down into the valley below the Morgai. Wind changes and the darkness begins to be driven back.

  Night of March 14–15: They sleep below the crest of the Morgai; Sam sees a star.

March 15   They reach the top of the Morgai and see Mount Doom; descend and continue up the valley; overhear the two orcs quarrelling.

  Night of March 15–16: They continue up the valley northward.

March 16   They spend the day in hiding in the valley.

  Night of March 16–17: They continue up the valley.

March 17   In hiding. They see Durthang and the road descending from it. Gollum reappears.

  Night of March 17–18: They take the road from Durthang and are forced to join the orc-company.

This chronology accords with the date March 14 of the Battle of the Pelennor Fields (see VIII.428–9); in both the drafting A and the first manuscript B of the chapter 'It was the morning of the fourteenth of March ... Théoden lay dying on the Pelennor Fields.' Here in RK (p. 196) it was the morning of March 15; and all the dates as given above are in the final story one day later.

IV

MOUNT DOOM

The original draft of the chapter 'Mount Doom' was written continuously with the first completed manuscript B of 'The Land of Shadow', which at this stage was called 'Mount Doom' (see p. 31); but the division into two chapters was soon made.

The latter part of the original single chapter (which I will continue to call 'B') is remarkable in that the primary drafting constitutes a completed text, with scarcely anything in the way of preparatory sketching of individual passages, and while the text is rough and full of corrections made at the time of composition it is legible almost throughout; moreover many passages underwent only the most minor changes later. It is possible that some more primitive material has disappeared, but it seems to me far more probable that the long thought which my father had given to the ascent of Mount Doom and the destruction of the Ring enabled him, when at last he came to write it, to achieve it more quickly and surely than almost any earlier chapter in *The Lord of the Rings*. He had known from far back (see p. 3) that when Frodo (still called 'Bingo') came to the Crack of Doom he would be unable to cast away the Ring, and that Gollum would take it and fall into the chasm. But how did he fall? In subsequent outlines Sam's part was pondered. My father knew that Sam was attacked by Gollum on the way up the Mountain and delayed, so that Frodo made the final ascent alone; and he knew that Gollum got hold of the Ring by taking Frodo's finger with it. But for a long time he thought that it was Sam who, finally making his way to the Chamber of Fire, pushed Gollum with the Ring into the abyss. In none of the later outlines given in Chapter I did he achieve the final articulation of the story; but there seems good reason to think that these belong to the period of the writing of Book V, and if my chronological deductions are correct (see pp. 12–13), he had had plenty of time to 'find out what really happened' before he came actually to describe the final moments of the Quest.

As I have said, the final form of 'Mount Doom' was quite largely achieved in the first draft (B), and I give the following brief passage (interesting also for another reason) as exemplification (cf. RK p. 223):

'Master!' he cried. Then Frodo stirred, and spoke with a clear voice, indeed a voice clearer and more powerful than Sam had

38   SAURON DEFEATED

ever heard him use, and it rose above the throb and turmoils of
the chasm of Mount Doom, echoing in the roof and walls.

'I have come,' he said. 'But I cannot do what I have come to
do. I will not do it. The Ring is mine.' And suddenly he vanished
from Sam's sight. Sam gasped, but at that moment many things
happened. Something struck Sam violently in the back, his legs
were knocked from under him and he was flung aside striking
his head against the stony floor. He lay still.

And far away as Frodo put on the Ring the Power in
Baraddur was shaken and the Tower trembled from its foundations to its proud and bitter crown. The Dark Lord was suddenly
aware of him, the Eye piercing all shadows looked across the
plain to the door in Orodruin, and all the plot [> devices] was
laid bare to it. Its wrath blazed like a sudden flame and its fear
was like a great black smoke, for it knew its deadly peril, the
thread upon which hung its doom. From all its policies and
webs its mind shook free, and through all its realm a tremor ran,
its slaves quailed, and its armies halted and its captains suddenly
steerless bereft of will wavered and despaired. But its thought
was now bent with all its overwhelming force upon the
Mountain; and at its summons wheeling with a ...ing cry in a
last desperate race there flew, faster than the wind, the Nazgûl,
the Ringwraiths, with a storm of wings they hurtled towards
Mount Doom.

Frodo's words 'But *I cannot do* what I have come to do' were
changed subsequently on the B-text to 'But *I do not choose now to do*
what I have come to do.' I do not think that the difference is very
significant, since it was already a central element in the outlines that
Frodo would *choose* to keep the Ring himself; the change in his words
does no more than emphasize that he fully willed his act. (In the
second text of the chapter, the fair copy manuscript 'C',[1] Sam cried
out just before this not merely 'Master!' as in the first text and in RK
but 'Master! Do it quick!' – these words being bracketed probably at
the time of setting them down.)

This passage is notable in showing the degree to which my father
had come to identify the Eye of Barad-dûr with the mind and will of
Sauron, so that he could speak of 'its wrath, its fear, its thought'. In
the second text C he shifted from 'its' to 'his' as he wrote out this
passage anew.

Some other differences in the original text are worth recording. On
the morning after they escaped from the orc-band marching to the
Isenmouthe, following Frodo's words 'I can manage it. I must' (RK
p. 211) text B at first continued:

MOUNT DOOM

In the end they decided to crawl in such cover as they could towards the north-range [and then turn south >] until they were further from the vigilance on the ramparts, and then turn south.

As they went from hollow to hollow or along cracks in the stony ground, keeping always if they could some screen between them and the north, they saw that the most easterly of the three roads went also in the same direction. It was in fact the road to the Dark Tower, as Frodo guessed.

He looked at it. 'I shall wear myself out in a day of this crawling and stooping,' he said. 'If we are to go on we must risk it. We must take the road.'

Here my father stopped, struck this out, and replaced it by a passage very close to that in RK, where it is Sam who sees that they can go no further in this fashion and must risk taking the road to the Dark Tower.

Another slight difference in the original text follows Frodo's words to Sam on the morning on which they left the road and turned south towards Mount Doom: 'I can't manage it, Sam. It is such a weight to carry, such a weight' (RK p. 214).

Sam knew what he meant, but seeking for some encouragement amid despair he answered: 'Well, Mr Frodo, why not lighten the load a bit. We're going that way as straight as we can make.' He pointed to the Mountain. 'No good taking anything we're not sure to need.'

Like a child, distracted from its trouble by some game of make-believe, Frodo considered his words seriously for a moment. Then 'Of course,' he said. 'Leave everything behind we don't want. Travel light, that's the thing, Sam!' He picked up his orc-shield and flung it away, and threw his helmet after it; and undoing his heavy belt cast it and the sword and sheath with it clattering on the ground. Even his grey cloak he threw away.

Sam looked at him with pity.

This was struck out immediately and replaced by the text of RK, in which Sam suggests that he should bear the Ring for a while. But neither in the text B nor in the fair copy C is there mention of the phial of Galadriel or of the little box that she gave to Sam.[2]

The height of Mount Doom was at first differently conceived: 'It was indeed some 3000 feet or so from foot to the .... broken crater at its crown. A third of that height now lay below him ...' Text C still differs from RK (p. 218): 'The confused and tumbled shoulders of its great sprawling base rose for maybe three[3] thousand feet above the

40   SAURON DEFEATED

plain, and above them was reared, *almost as high again*, its tall central cone, like a vast oast or chimney capped by a jagged crater. But already Sam stood *half way up* the base ...' (where RK has 'half as high again' and 'more than half way up'). My father's drawing, reproduced in *Pictures by J. R. R. Tolkien* no. 30, and in this book on p. 42, from a small page that carries also a scrap of drafting for this part of the chapter, seems to show the final conception, with the cone 'half as high again' in relation to the 'base'; but in this drawing the door of the Sammath Naur is at the foot of the cone, whereas in all versions of the text the climbing road came 'high in the upper cone, but still far from the reeking summit, to a dark entrance'.[4]

When Gollum fell upon Sam as he carried Frodo up the road, both in the original text and in the fair copy C Sam not only tore the backs of his hands as he crashed forward (RK p. 220) but also cut his forehead on the ground. In B, against the words 'But Sam gave him no more heed. He suddenly remembered his master. He looked up the path and could not see him' (RK p. 222) my father wrote in the margin: 'his head was bleeding?' This was not taken up in C, but a little earlier, after the words 'Sam's hand wavered. His mind was hot with wrath and the memory of evil' (RK p. 221) C has: 'Blood trickled down his forehead.' Both these references to Sam's bleeding forehead were later struck from C. It is not clear to me what my father had in mind here. At first sight there might seem to be a connection with Sam's blindness in outline V (p. 11): 'Sam feels a blindness coming on and wonders if it is due to water of Mordor ... Sam half-blind is lagging behind', but that seems to have been introduced to explain how it was that when Gollum attacked Frodo went on unaware of what had happened; whereas here the blood in Sam's eyes was the result of Gollum's attack, and he himself urged Frodo to go on. Possibly the cutting of his forehead was intended to explain why Sam could not see Frodo when he looked up the path, and was removed when my father came to the point when Sam was again felled by Gollum in the Sammath Naur: 'He was dazed, and blood streaming from his head dripped in his eyes' (RK p. 223).

When Sam urged Frodo to go on up alone while he dealt with Gollum Frodo replied, both in B and C: 'The Quest shall now be all fulfilled', where in RK he said: 'This is the end at last.'

At the end of the chapter, after the words 'Down like lashing whips fell a torrent of black rain' (RK p. 224), the first text moves at once to ' "Well, this is the end, Sam," said a voice by his side.' Here my father wrote in the margin soon after: 'Put in here (or in next chapter?) vision of the cloudwrack out of Baraddur [?growing] to shape of a vast black [?man] that stretches out a menacing unavailing arm and is blown away.' The word 'man' is very unclear but I cannot see how else it could be read. Later at this point in the manuscript he wrote 'Fall of Ringwraiths' with a mark of insertion, and the passage 'And into the

MOUNT DOOM

heart of the storm, with a cry that pierced all other sounds ...' appears in C.

Lastly, Sam's feelings were thus described in B: 'If he felt anything in all that ruin of the world, it was perhaps most of all a great joy, to be servant once again, and know his master [*added:* and surrender to him the leadership].' This was repeated in C, but rejected and replaced by the reading of RK. In Frodo's final words he did not, in the original text, speak of forgiving Gollum.[5]

NOTES

1 The fair copy manuscript C is entitled 'Mount Doom' and numbered 'LIV' (see pp. 31, 37), the number changed subsequently to 'LII' (see p. 25).

2 Sam's vain use of the Phial when he entered the Sammath Naur (RK p. 222) appears in B. The addition concerning the Phial and the box was made later to text C.

The passage in which Sam remembered paddling in the Pool at Bywater with the children of Farmer Cotton (RK p. 216) is also absent from B. This is one of the few passages in this chapter for which a separate draft is found (before its introduction into text C), and here the names of the Cotton children are seen emerging.

3 *three* was changed in pencil to *two* on the manuscript (C), but *three* survived.

4 In both B and C, despite the earlier statement (as in RK p. 219) that the road came 'high in the upper cone ... to a dark entrance', it is said in the passage corresponding to that in RK p. 222 that the road 'with a last course passed *across the base of the cone* and came to the dark door', where in RK 'with a last eastward course [it] passed *in a cutting along the face of the cone* and came to the dark door'.

In B there is a little sketch of Mount Doom which my father struck through, and here the entrance to the Sammath Naur is placed about a third of the way up the cone (which is here shorter in relation to the base than in the drawing reproduced on p. 42). The road here disappears round the eastern side of the cone, below the door, and seems (the drawing is hard to make out) to reappear further up, coming from the left (east) and ending at the door.

5 A couple of points concerning names in this chapter may be mentioned. In the opening paragraph both B and C have 'He heard the scuffling and cries die down as the troops passed on into the Narch', where RK has 'passed on through the Isenmouthe'; see p. 33. The name *Sammath Naur* does not appear in B, but enters in C without any initial hesitation as to its form.

Mount Doom

MOUNT DOOM

43

Note on the Chronology

The chronology was still a day behind that of RK (see p. 36). At nightfall of the day on which they escaped from the orc-band at the Isenmouthe my father wrote in the margin of text B '18 ends'; this was March 19 in RK (in *The Tale of Years* 'Frodo and Samwise escape and begin their journey along the road to the Barad-dûr'). The reference to the passing of the Cross Roads by the Captains of the West and the burning of the fields of Imlad Morghul (so spelt) is however present in B at the same point as in RK (p. 212): see VIII.432.

In B, against the words 'There came at last a dreadful evening; and even as the Captains of the West drew near the end of the living lands, the two wanderers came to an hour of blank despair' (cf. RK p. 212), my father wrote 'end of 22'. This was the same date as in RK, and thus there follows in the original text 'Five days had passed since they escaped the orcs' (i.e. March 18–22), where RK has 'Four'.

V

THE FIELD OF KORMALLEN

In the first draft of this chapter my father again achieved for most of its length an extraordinarily close approach to the final form, and this is the more remarkable when one considers that he had no plan or outline before him. There had been many mentions of a great feast to follow the final victory (VII.212, 345, 448; VIII.275, 397), but nothing had ever been said of it beyond the fact that it was to take place in Minas Tirith.[1] That this text ('A') was indeed the first setting down on paper of the story and that nothing preceded it seems obvious from the nature of the manuscript itself, which has all the marks of primary composition.[2] It was followed by a fair copy manuscript ('B'), bearing the number and title 'LV   The Field of Kormallen', which was also pencilled in later on A.

Not until the end of the minstrel's song of Frodo of the Nine Fingers and the Ring of Doom did the first text A diverge in any narrative point, and little even in expression, from the form in RK. There are however several interesting details.

One of these concerns the Eagles. As the passage (RK p. 226) describing their coming above the Morannon was first written it read:

There came Gwaihir, the Wind-lord, and Lhandroval his brother, greatest of all the eagles of the north, mightiest of the descendants of [*added:* Great > old] Thorondor who built his eyries in the immeasurable peaks of Thangorodrim [*changed immediately to* the Encircling Mountains] when Middle-earth was young.

In the *Quenta* §15 (IV.137) it is told that after the Battle of Unnumbered Tears 'Thorndor King of Eagles removed his eyries from Thangorodrim to the northward heights of the Encircling Mountains [*about the plain of Gondolin*], and there he kept watch, sitting upon the cairn of King Fingolfin.' In the *Quenta Silmarillion* of 1937 there is no mention of the Eagles dwelling on Thangorodrim, and at the time of the fall of Fingolfin in his duel with Morgoth, before the Battle of Unnumbered Tears, Thorondor came for the rescue of the king's body 'from his eyrie among the peaks of Gochressiel' (i.e. the Encircling Mountains; V.285, §147). On the other hand, in the abandoned story 'Of Tuor and the Fall of Gondolin' given in *Unfinished Tales*, a story that I believe to have been written in 1951, Voronwë speaks to Tuor of

THE FIELD OF KORMALLEN   45

'the folk of Thorondor, who dwelt once even on Thangorodrim ere Morgoth grew so mighty, and dwell now in the Mountains of Turgon since the fall of Fingolfin' (p. 43).

Gwaihir the Windlord had of course appeared often before this in *The Lord of the Rings* (for long *Gwaewar*, but becoming *Gwaihir* in the course of the writing of 'The White Rider', VII.430). In the *Quenta Silmarillion* (see V.301) Gwaewar had been one of the three eagles that came to Angband for the rescue of Beren and Lúthien; the earliest form of that passage reads:

Thorondor led them, and the others were Lhandroval (Wide-wing) and Gwaewar his vassal.

The following text (also belonging to 1937) has:

Thorondor was their leader; and with him were his mightiest vassals, wide-winged Lhandroval, and Gwaewar lord of the wind.

In a revision of the passage which can be dated to 1951 *Gwaewar* was changed to *Gwaihir*. As I have noticed in V.301, the names of the vassals of Thorondor were suppressed in the published *Silmarillion* (p. 182) on account of the present passage in RK, but this was certainly mistaken: it is clear that my father deliberately repeated the names. As in so many other cases in *The Lord of the Rings*, he took the name *Gwaewar* for the great eagle, friend of Gandalf, from *The Silmarillion*, and when *Gwaihir* replaced *Gwaewar* in *The Lord of the Rings* he made the same change to the eagle's name in *The Silmarillion*. Now he took also *Lhandroval*[3] to be the name of Gwaihir's brother; and added a new name, *Meneldor* (RK p. 228).

At the fall of the Black Gate Gandalf said only: 'The Realm of Sauron is ended'; but to this my father added, probably immediately: 'So passes the Third Age of the World.' This was placed within brackets, and 'The Ringbearer has fulfilled his Quest' written in the margin.

To Gwaihir Gandalf said: 'You will not find me a burden any greater than when you bore me from Zirakinbar where my old life burned away.' *Zirakinbar* remained through all the texts of the chapter and was only changed to *Zirakzigil* on the galley proof. On these names see VII.174 and 431 with note 6.

Another difference in A which survived long (into the final type-script of the chapter) was the absence of Sam's expression of astonishment at seeing Gandalf at his bedside ('Gandalf! I thought you were dead! But then I thought I was dead myself. ...', RK p. 230).

The date of the Field of Kormallen (as the name was spelt until the final typescript) was expressed by Gandalf thus in A:

'Noon?' said Sam, puzzling his brains. 'Noon of what day?'
'The third day of the New Year,' said Gandalf, 'or if you like

46   SAURON DEFEATED

the twenty-eighth day of March in the Shire-reckoning. But in Gondor the New Year will always begin upon the 25th of March when Sauron fell, and when you were brought out of the fire to the King. ...'[4]

If March 25th was New Year's Day, the 28th was the fourth day of the New Year in Gondor, and my father wrote 'fourth' above 'third', without however striking out 'third'. In pencil he wrote 'seventh' against this, and 'the last day' above 'the twenty-eighth day', although this would give 31 days to the month. His reason for this is obscurely indicated by a note in the margin: 'More time required for [?gathering] of goods, say' (i.e., 'say the seventh').[5]

In the fair copy B as written Gandalf said 'The Seventh of the New Year; or if you like, the last day of March in the Shire-reckoning'; this was changed later to 'The Fourteenth of the New Year' and 'the sixth day of April in the Shire-reckoning'. Even allowing 31 days to the month, the sixth of April would be the thirteenth day of the New Year, and 'sixth' was afterwards changed to 'seventh', and finally to 'eighth', as in RK. I do not know precisely what considerations impelled my father so greatly to prolong the time during which Sam and Frodo lay asleep.

Their first conversation with Gandalf ends thus in A:

'What shall we wear?' said Sam, for all he could see were the old and tattered clothes that they had journeyed in, lying folded on the ground beside their beds.

'The clothes that you were found in,' said Gandalf. 'No silks and linen, nor any armour or heraldry, could be more honourable. But afterwards we shall see.'

This survived through all the texts to the galley, where 'The clothes that you were found in' was changed to 'The clothes that you journeyed in'. It was not until the Second Edition of 1966 that the passage was altered and extended, by changing Gandalf's words to 'The clothes that you wore on your way to Mordor.[6] Even the orc-rags that you bore in the black land, Frodo, shall be preserved', and by his return of the Phial of Galadriel and the box that she gave to Sam (RK pp. 230–1; cf. p. 39 and note 2).

The crying of praise as Frodo and Sam came to the Field of Kormallen underwent many changes. In all the texts of the chapter Old English phrases cried by the Riders of Rohan were mingled. The form of the 'Praise' in A runs thus (with some punctuation added from the B-text, which is closely similar):

Long live the halflings! Praise them with great praise! Cuio i Pheriannath anann, aglar anann! Praise them with great praise!

THE FIELD OF KORMALLEN   47

Hale, hale cumath, wesath hale awa to aldre. Fróda and Samwís! Praise them! Kuivië, kuivië! laurea'esselínen![7] Praise them!

In the fair copy B the Old English words were changed to *Wilcuman, wilcuman, Fróda and Samwís!* and the Quenya words became *Laitalle, laitalle, andave laita!* In the first typescript the Old English *Uton herian holbytlan!* was added before *Laitalle, laitalle;* and in the second (final) typescript the Quenya words became *A laituvar, laituvar, andave laita!* This was then changed on the typescript to *A laita te, laita te! Andave laituvalme!* Thus the form as it appears on the galley proof is:

Long live the Halflings! Praise them with great praise! Cuio i Pheriannath anann! Aglar anann! Praise them with great praise! Wilcuman, wilcuman, Fróda and Samwís! Praise them! Uton herian holbytlan! A laita te, laita te! Andave laituvalmet! Praise them! The Ringbearers, praise them with great praise!

The final text of the 'Praise', as it appears in RK, was typed onto the galley proof.

From the end of the minstrel's song (RK p. 232) the original text A runs thus:

And then Aragorn stood up and all the host rose, and they passed to a pavilion made ready, there to eat and drink and make merry.

But as Sam and Frodo stepped down with Aragorn from the throne Sam caught sight of a small man-at-arms as it seemed in the silver and sable of the guards of the king: but he was small and he wondered what such a boy was doing in such an army. Then suddenly he exclaimed: 'Why, look Mr Frodo. Look here. Bless me if it's not Pippin, Mr Peregrin Took I should say. Bless me but I can see there's more tales than ours to hear. It'll take weeks before we get it all right.'

'Yes,' said Frodo. 'I can see myself locked up in a room somewhere making notes for days or Bilbo will be bitterly disappointed.'

And so they passed to the feast and at a sign from Aragorn Pippin went with them.[8]

The page carrying this text was rejected; on the back of it is an outline of the story to come (see p. 51, 'The Story Foreseen from Kormallen'). A replacement page was substituted, but again the development turned out to be unsatisfactory:

48   SAURON DEFEATED

But first Frodo and Sam were led apart and taken to a tent, and there their old raiment was taken off, but folded and set aside with honour; and clean linen was brought to them. But Gandalf came and with him went an esquire, no more than a small lad he seemed, though clad in the silver and sable of the king's guard, and to the wonder of Frodo and Sam they bore the sword and the elven-cloak and the mithril-coat that had been taken from them; and for Sam they brought a coat of gilded mail, and on Frodo's right hand upon the middle[9] and little fingers they set small rings of mithril set each with a gem like a star. But the wonder of all these things was as little to the wonder on Sam's face as he looked on the face of the esquire and knew him.

And he cried out: 'Why look, Mr. Frodo. Look here! Save me, if it isn't Pippin, Mr. Peregrin Took, I should say. Why bless us all, but I can see there's more tales to tell than ours. It will take weeks of talk before we get it all sized up.'

'It will indeed,' said Pippin. 'But at present it is time for a feast, and you must not keep it waiting. Later on, Frodo must be locked up in a tower in Minas Tirith till he's made notes of all our doings, or Bilbo will be dreadfully disappointed.'

This passage was at once reconstructed to remove Pippin from the scene, and Gandalf comes to the tent alone, as in RK (p. 233). When he has set the rings of mithril on Frodo's fingers the feast follows at once:

... and on Frodo's right hand, upon the middle and little fingers, he set fine rings of mithril, slender as threads of silk but bearing each a small gem shining like a star.[10] And when they were made ready, and circlets of silver were set upon their heads, they went to the feast, and sat with Gandalf, and there was Aragorn and King Éomer of Rohan and all the Captains of the West, and there too were Legolas and Gimli.

[*Struck out at once:* 'That's six of the Company,' said Sam to Frodo. 'Where are the o(thers)] But when wine was brought there came in an esquire to serve the Kings of Gondor and Rohan, or so he seemed, and he was clad in the silver and sable of the guards of the King; but he was small, and Sam wondered what such a boy was doing in an army of mighty men. [*Then follows Sam's recognition of Pippin, as above.*]

'It will indeed,' said Pippin, 'and we'll begin as soon as this feast is ended. In the meantime you can try Gandalf. He's not as

THE FIELD OF KORMALLEN   49

close as he used to be, though he laughs now more than he talks.'

And so at last the glad day ended; and when the sun was gone and the crescent moon[11] rode slowly above the mist of Anduin and flickered through the fluttering leaves, Frodo and Sam sat amid the night-fragrance of fair Ithilien, and talked deep into the night with Pippin and Gandalf and Legolas and Gimli.

At last Gandalf rose. 'The hands of the King are hands of healing, dear friends,' he said. 'But you went near to the very brink of death, and though you have slept long and blessedly, still it is now time to rest again. Not you only, Frodo and Sam, but you Peregrin also. For when they lifted you from under the slain it is said that even Aragorn despaired of you.'

Probably at once, this was emended throughout to make Merry also present (see note 8), and the last part of it (Gandalf's parting words) was in turn rejected. In very rough further drafting the final text was approached, though not achieved, in the manuscript A. Gimli's speech (RK p. 234) at this time ended thus:

'... And when I heaved that great carcase off you, then I made sure you were dead. I could have torn out my beard. And that was but a week ago. To bed now you go. And so shall I.'

From this it is seen that it was 'the seventh day of the New Year': see p. 46.[12] The draft continues to its end thus:

'And I,' said Legolas, 'shall walk in the woods of this fair land, which is rest enough. And in days to come, if my Elven lord will allow it, some of our folk shall remove hither, for it is more lovely than any lands they have yet dwelt in;[13] and then it will be blessed for a while. But Anduin is near and Anduin leads down to the sea. To the sea, to the sea, and the white gulls crying, to the sea and the sea and the white foam flying,' and so singing he went away down the hill.

And then the others departed and Frodo and Sam went to their beds and slept; and in the morning the host prepared to return to Minas Tirith. The ships had come and they were lying under Cair Andros, and soon all would be set across the Great River, and so in peace and ease fare over the green swards of Anórien and to the Pelennor and the towers under tall Mindolluin, the city of the men of Gondor, last memory of Westernesse.

Thus the name *Kormallen* did not enter in the original text of the

50   SAURON DEFEATED

chapter, and it is not said that the Field was near to Henneth Annûn; but scribbled drafting put in later on the last page of the manuscript shows the final text emerging:

And in the morning they rose again and spent many days in Ithilien, for the Field of Kormallen where the host was encamped was near to Henneth Annûn, and they wandered here and there visiting the scenes of their adventures, but Sam lingered ever in some shadow of the woods to find maybe some sight of the Oliphaunt. And when he heard that in the seige of Gondor there had been fifty of them at the least, but all were dead, he thought it a great loss. And in the meanwhile the host rested, for they had laboured much and had fought long and hard against the remnant of the Easterlings and Southrons; and they waited also for those that were to return.

In the fair copy B the final text of the First Edition was present in all but a few points, most of which have been mentioned in the foregoing account and in the notes;[14] but an important change in the description of the dressing of Frodo and Sam before the feast (RK p. 233) was made in the Second Edition. As the text stood in the First Edition (going back unchanged to the fair copy manuscript B) it ran:

... For Sam he brought a coat of gilded mail, and his elven-cloak all healed of the soils and hurts that it had suffered; and when the Hobbits were made ready, and circlets of silver were set upon their heads, they went to the King's feast, and they sat at his table with Gandalf ...

In the Second Edition the passage was added in which Gandalf brought Sting and Sam's sword, and Frodo had to be persuaded to wear a sword and to accept back Sting. At this time also the reference was added to 'the Standing Silence' before the feast began.

NOTES

1   There had been a suggestion (VIII.397) that the tale of the passage of the Paths of the Dead should be told at the 'feast of victory in Minas Tirith', but that idea had of course been overtaken.

2   It may be that the first draft of 'The Field of Kormallen' was written before the fair copy manuscript of 'Mount Doom'. A pointer to this is the fact that where in RK (p. 228) 'a great smoke and steam belched from the Sammath Naur' A has 'a great fire belched from the cave': see p. 41 note 5.

3   The first draft A has the spelling *Lhandroval* at all occurrences, but the fair copy B has *Landroval*, as in RK.

THE FIELD OF KORMALLEN   51

4   Both in A and B it is Frodo who asks 'What king, and who is he?' On the first typescript Sam's question 'What shall we wear?' was transferred to Frodo, but in the final typescript given back to Sam.

5   Perhaps to be compared is the sentence in 'The Steward and the King', RK pp. 241–2: 'Merry was summoned [*from Minas Tirith*] and rode away with the wains that took store of goods to Osgiliath and thence by ship to Cair Andros.'

6   Frodo was naked when Sam found him in the Tower of Kirith Ungol; he had to dress in 'long hairy breeches of some unclean beast-fell, and a tunic of dirty leather' (RK p. 189).

7   *laurea'esselínen* was changed at the time of writing to *ankalim'esselínen*.

8   At this stage, when only a little time had passed since the fall of Sauron, Merry would still have been in Minas Tirith; cf. note 5.

9   My father named the penultimate finger (the 'fourth finger' or 'ring-finger') the 'third finger'; so Frodo's 'third finger was missing' (RK p. 229).

10 The rings of mithril set on Frodo's fingers were retained in the fair copy B, where the passage was struck out.

11 The 'crescent moon' remained in B and in the first typescript, where it was changed to 'the round moon'.

12 It is strange that in B Gimli said here, not as in RK 'And it is only a day yet since you were first up and abroad again', but 'a few days' (this being corrected on the manuscript).

13 This sentence was retained in B and the first typescript, where it was struck out.

14 To these may be added the retention of the name *Narch* in 'And they passed over the Narch and Gorgoroth' (RK p. 228), subsequently emended to *Udûn*. At the end of the chapter it was said at first in B that 'when the month of May was passed seven days the Captains of the West set out again', but this was changed to 'when the month of May was drawing near', and at the same time the last sentence of the chapter was changed from 'for the King would enter his gates with the rising of the Sun' by the addition of the words 'it was the Eve of May, and (the King would enter . . .)'.

THE STORY FORESEEN FROM KORMALLEN

This page (see p. 47) was scribbled down in pencil in my father's most impossible handwriting. I have not marked with queries a number of words that I think are probable but not altogether certain, and I have expanded several names given only as initials. The first sentence was written separately from the rest of the outline, whether before or after.

Gimli explains how Pippin was saved.

52   SAURON DEFEATED

Next scene – The Host sets out from Cair Andros and [*read* in] the ships and passes into Gondor.

Scene shifts to Merry and to Faramir and Éowyn.

Return of King Elessar. His crowning. His judgements ..... of Berithil.

The hobbits wait. For there is to be a wedding. Elrond and Galadriel and Celeborn come and bring Finduilas.

The wedding of Aragorn and Finduilas.

Also Faramir and Éowyn.

The end of the Third Age is presaged. What the Rings had done. Their power waned. Galadriel and Elrond prepare to depart.

The hobbits return with Éomer to the funeral of Théoden and then on through the Gap of Rohan [?with ..... and the Dúnedain].

They come on Saruman and he is [?pardoned].

They come to Rivendell and see Bilbo. Bilbo gives him Sting and the coat. But he is getting old.

They come back to the Shire [*added in margin:* via Bree, pick up pony] and drive out Cosimo Sackville-Baggins. Lobelia is dead – she had a fit in [?quarrel]. Sam replants the trees. Frodo goes back to Bag End. All is quiet for a year or two. And then one day Frodo takes Sam for a walking [?tour] to the Woody End. And [?behold there go many] Elves. Frodo rides to the Havens and says farewell to Bilbo. End of the Third Age.

Sam's Book.

It is plain that my father wrote this outline while he was working on 'The Field of Kormallen', and indeed the precise stage in that work can probably be deduced: for Gimli's words at the end of the evening, in which he spoke of finding Pippin under the heap of slain, had not entered ('Gimli explains how Pippin was saved'). The precise placing of these notes in the history of the composition of Book VI gives them a particular interest. Several features of the end of the story now appear for the first time: as the marriage of Faramir and Éowyn; Bilbo's giving of the mithril-coat and Sting to Frodo ('forgetting that he had already done so', RK p. 265); the time of peace and quiet after the return of the hobbits to the Shire (but that 'Sam's casket restores Trees' had been known for a long time, VII.286); and Frodo's walk with Sam to the Woody End. But the death, before the return of the hobbits, of Lobelia Sackville-Baggins in a fit (of fury? – the word I have given as *quarrel* is scarcely more than a guess) was not permanent: she would be resurrected, survive her imprisonment during the troubles of the Shire, and end her days in a much more enlightened fashion.

This outline is as elliptical as were so many of my father's sketches of the further course of the story, concentrating on particular elements and ignoring or only hinting at others; and it is hard to know what

THE FIELD OF KORMALLEN 53

narrative idea underlay the words 'Frodo rides to the Havens and says farewell to Bilbo'. Many years before (VI.380) he had written that when 'Bingo' returned to the Shire he would make peace, and would then 'settle down in a little hut on the high green ridge – until one day he goes with the Elves west beyond the towers' (cf. also another note of that time, VI.379: 'Island in sea. Take Frodo there in end'). In the outline 'The Story Foreseen from Moria' (VII.212) he had concluded his synopsis thus:

XXVIII What happens to Shire?

Last scene. Sailing away of Elves [added: Bilbo with them] ...

XXIX Sam and Frodo go into a green land by the Sea?

In another note of that period (VII.287) he said: 'When old, Sam and Frodo set sail to island of West ... Bilbo finishes the story.' Probably about the time of the writing of 'The King of the Golden Hall' he had written (VII.451) that in old age Frodo with Sam had seen Galadriel and Bilbo. On the other hand, in his letter to me of 29 November 1944 (see VIII.219) he was entirely clear – and accurate – in his prevision:

> But the final scene will be the passage of Bilbo and Elrond and Galadriel through the woods of the Shire on their way to the Grey Havens. Frodo will join them and pass over the Sea (linking with the vision he had of a far green country in the house of Tom Bombadil).

Since this is of course the story in the last chapter of *The Lord of the Rings* it is strange indeed to find in the present text that he had departed from it – for 'Frodo rides to the Havens and says farewell to Bilbo' can obviously be interpreted in no other way. I suspect therefore that there is in fact no mystery: that in notes written at great speed my father merely miswrote 'Bilbo' for 'Sam'.

Remarkable also is the reference to the encounter with Saruman – the word *pardoned* here is not certain, but can hardly be read otherwise. That they would meet Saruman again on the homeward journey was an old idea (see 'The Story Foreseen from Moria', VII.212), but then it had taken place at Isengard, and the matter of that scene had of course been removed to a much earlier place in the narrative (VII.436). A later note (VII.287) says that 'Saruman becomes a wandering conjuror and trickster', but nothing further has been told of him since he was left a prisoner in Orthanc guarded by the Ents until now.

VI

THE STEWARD AND THE KING

My remarks about 'The Field of Kormallen' (p. 44) can be repeated of 'The Steward and the King': the preliminary draft ('A') of this chapter, though written roughly and rapidly, was changed very little afterwards. There are nonetheless a number of differences in detail.[1]

A had no title, but 'Faramir and Éowyn' was pencilled in subsequently. A fair copy manuscript 'B' followed, with the chapter-number 'LVI' but no title; to this text the title 'The Watchers on the Walls' was added in pencil, and this was changed to 'The Steward and the King'. In B the page-numbers run only as far as 'And she abode there until King Éomer came' (RK p. 243); at 'All things were now made ready in the City', at the top of a new page, a new numbering from '1' begins.

Of this chapter my father made a third, very fine manuscript 'C', numbering it 'LIV'. Beneath the title 'The Steward and the King' he pencilled '(i) The Steward'; but although there is a large space in the text after 'And she remained there until King Éomer came', where the new page-numbering begins in B, there is no second sub-title.

At the beginning of the chapter in A the Warden of the Houses of Healing, after the words 'He sighed and shook his head' (RK p. 237), continues:

'It may come thus to us all yet,' he said, 'choosing or not choosing. But in the meantime we must endure with patience the hours of waiting. It is not always the easier part. But for you, Lady, you will be the better prepared to face evil that may come in your own manner, if you do as the healers bid, while there is still time.'

This was rejected before the chapter had proceeded much further, for similar words were given to Faramir subsequently in the initial text (RK p. 238). And when the Warden looked out from his window and saw Faramir and Éowyn, finding in the sight a lightening of his care, it is said: 'For it had been reported to him that the Lord Aragorn had said "If she wakes to despair then she will die, unless other healing comes which I cannot give."'

The blue mantle set with stars which Faramir gave to Éowyn when the weather turned cold is in A said to have been made for his mother 'Emmeril', changed in the act of writing to 'Rothinel of Amroth, who

THE STEWARD AND THE KING   55

died untimely'. This name survived into the following manuscript B, where it was changed to Finduilas (see pp. 58–9).

The words of the Eagle that bore tidings to Minas Tirith of the fall of the Dark Tower were first reported thus:

The realm of Sauron hath ended and the Ring of Doom is no more and the King is victorious, he has passed through the Black Gate in triumph and all his enemies are fled.

The name *Kormallen* entered in this text. My father left a blank for the name as he wrote: 'And Éowyn did not go, though her brother sent word begging her to come to the field of   [between Henneth Annûn and Cair Andros]' (cf. RK p. 242 and p. 50 above), but he evidently wrote the name in the margin at once, since it appears in the text as written a few lines later.

In the conversation between Éowyn and Faramir that follows she said, in A, 'I love or have loved another.' This survived in B, where her words were changed to 'I hoped to be loved by another', and then at once to 'I wished'.

Somewhat later in the chapter (RK p. 244) Ioreth (now so spelt; hitherto Yoreth) names the hobbits *Periannath* (cf. *Ernil i Pheriannath* in the chapter 'Minas Tirith', RK p. 41, *Ernil a Pheriannath* VIII.287), and this survived into the First Edition of LR, changed to *Periain* in the Second.

There were substantial differences in the original account of Aragorn's coming to Minas Tirith and his coronation before the walls from the story in RK (pp. 244–6). The entry of Aragorn, Gandalf, Éomer, Imrahil and the four hobbits into the cleared space before the Gateway was very briefly described in A: there was no mention of the Dúnedain nor of Aragorn's apparel. The casket in which the White Crown was laid was not described ('of black *lebethron* bound with silver' B, as in RK; cf. VIII.180). When Faramir, surrendering his office as 'the Last Steward of Gondor', gave Aragorn the white rod Aragorn did not return it to him; he said nothing to Faramir at this point, and Faramir at once proclaimed: 'Men of Gondor, you have no longer a Steward, for behold one has returned to claim the kingship at last. Here is Aragorn son of Arathorn ...' Among Aragorn's titles Faramir names him 'chieftain of the Dúnedain of the North' and does not name him 'bearer of the Star of the North'. After the description of the crown there follows:

And Aragorn knelt, and Faramir upon the one hand and upon the other the Prince Imrahil set the crown upon his head, and then Gandalf laid his hand on Aragorn's shoulder and bade him arise. And when he arose all that beheld him gazed in silence ...

56   SAURON DEFEATED

and a light was about him. And then Faramir said 'Behold the King!' and he broke his white rod.

Lastly, when Aragorn came to the Citadel a marginal addition to A says that 'the banner of Tree Crown and Stars was raised above it' ('the banner of the Tree and the Stars' B, as in RK); see VIII.279, 389, 399.

The reference to the Dúnedain 'in silver and grey' and the description of Aragorn's black mail and white mantle clasped with a great green stone was added to B, but the 'star upon his forehead bound by a slender fillet of silver' did not enter until the Second Edition; similarly Faramir still proclaimed him 'chieftain of the Dúnedain of the North' ('of Arnor', Second Edition) and did not name him 'bearer of the Star of the North' in the First Edition (see VIII.299, 309; 389 and note 10).

Rough marginal additions to A make Aragorn return the white rod to Faramir with the words 'That office is not yet wholly at an end' (cf. RK p. 245: 'That office is not ended, and it shall be thine and thy heirs' as long as my line shall last'), and give a first draft of his wish that he should be crowned by those 'by whose labours and valour I have come to my inheritance'. Here the ceremony takes this form: 'Gandalf took the crown and bade Frodo and Sam lay their hands also upon it, and they set the White Crown of Gondor upon the head of Aragorn'; whereas in RK, at Aragorn's request, Frodo brought the crown to Gandalf, who then performed the crowning alone. In B the text of RK was reached at all points in this scene apart from the words of Elendil repeated by Aragorn when he held up the crown,[2] which take the form: *Et Ëarello Endorenna lendien. Símane maruvan, ar hildinyar, kenn' Iluve-metta!* A translation pencilled in later is virtually the same as that in RK (p. 246): 'Out of the Great Sea to Middle-earth have I come. Here will I abide, and my heirs, unto the ending of the world.' In the third manuscript C the words remained the same as in B, apart from *tenn'* (as in RK) for *kenn'*, but were subsequently changed to *Et Ëarello Endorenna nilendie. Sinome nimaruva yo hildinyar tenn' Ambar-metta!*

A notable visitor to Minas Tirith among the many embassies that came to the King is found in A:

... and the slaves of Mordor he set free and gave them all the lands about Lake Núrnen for their own. And last of all there came to him Ghân-buri-Ghân of the Wild Woods and two of the headmen, and they were clad in garments of green leaves to do honour to the king, and they laid their foreheads on his feet; but he bade them rise up and blessed them and gave them the Forest of Druadan for their own, so that no man should ever enter it without their leave.

THE STEWARD AND THE KING   57

This was not rejected on the manuscript, but it is not present in B. For the further history of the last encounter with the Wild Men of the Woods see pp. 61–2, 67–8.

Éowyn's words to Faramir (RK p. 248), saying that she must now return to Rohan with Éomer, but that after the funeral of Théoden she will return, are absent from A (but were added to B). The statements in RK that the Riders of Rohan left Minas Tirith on the eighth of May and that the sons of Elrond went with them are not found in any of the texts, and they remain absent in the First Edition; on the other hand the return of Elladan and Elrohir to Minas Tirith with the company from Rivendell and Lothlórien (RK p. 250) is already found in A. It is told in A that 'the Companions of the Ring lived with Gandalf in a house in the Citadel, and went to and fro as they wished; but Legolas sat most[ly] on the walls and looked south towards the sea.' That the house was in the Citadel was not repeated in B, which retained however the words concerning Legolas; these were lost, possibly unintentionally, in C.

In the story of the ascent of Mindolluin by Gandalf and Aragorn (RK pp. 248–50) there are some differences from the final form to mention. In the original text it is not said that they went up by night and surveyed the lands in the early morning, nor is there mention of the ancient path to the hallow 'where only the kings had been wont to go'; and Gandalf in his words to Aragorn does not speak of the Three Rings, but says:

'... For though much has been saved, much is passing away. And all these lands that you see, and those that lie about, shall be dwellings and realms of Men, whom you must guide. For this is the beginning of the Dominion of Men, and other kindreds will depart, dwindle, and fade.'

B has the final text in all this. In A Aragorn says 'I have still twice the span of other men'; this was retained through the following texts and not changed until the galley proof to the reading of RK (where there is a difference between the First and Second Editions: in the First he says 'I may have life far longer than other men', but in the Second 'I shall').

When Aragorn saw the sapling at the edge of the snow he cried, in A, *En túvien!*, which in B becomes *En a túvien!* This was retained in C but corrected to *En [?in]túviet*; on the final (typescript) text of the chapter this was retained, but then erased and *Yé! utúvienyes* written in its place. The passage continues in A, in extremely difficult handwriting:

'... I have found it, for here is a scion of Nimloth eldest of trees. And how comes it here, for it is not yet itself seven years old?'

58   SAURON DEFEATED

And Gandalf said: 'Verily here is a sapling of the line of
Telperion Ninquelóte that the Elves of Middle-earth name
Nimloth. Nimloth the fair of many names, Silivros and
Celeborn[3] and Galathilion of old. But who shall say how it
comes here in the hour that is appointed? But the birds of the air
are many, and maybe down the ages as lord followed lord . . . . .
in the City and the tree withered, here where none looked for it
the [?race] of Nimloth has [?flowered already] hidden on the
mountain, even as Elendil's race lay hid in the wastes of the
North. Yet the line of Nimloth is older far than your line, lord
Elessar.'

With the names that appear in this passage cf. the *Quenta Silmarillion* in V.209, §16:
    Silpion the one was called in Valinor, and Telperion and Ninquelótë
    and many names in song beside; but the Gnomes name him
    Galathilion.
A footnote to the text (V.210) adds:
    Other names of Silpion among the Gnomes are Silivros glimmering
    rain (which in Elvish form is Silmerossë), Nimloth pale blossom,
    Celeborn tree of silver . . .
B has here the text of RK, in which Aragorn does not name 'the Eldest
of Trees', and Gandalf says: 'Verily this is a sapling of the line of
Nimloth the fair; and that was a seedling of Galathilion, and that a
fruit of Telperion of many names, Eldest of Trees.' In *The Silmarillion*
chapter 5 (p. 59) it is told that Yavanna made for the Elves of Tirion
    . . . a tree like to a lesser image of Telperion, save that it did not give
    light of its own being; Galathilion it was named in the Sindarin
    tongue. This tree was planted in the courts beneath the Mindon and
    there flourished, and its seedlings were many in Eldamar. Of these
    one was afterwards planted in Tol Eressëa, and it prospered there,
    and was named Celeborn; thence came in the fullness of time, as is
    elsewhere told, Nimloth, the White Tree of Númenor.[4]
In A the sapling did not 'hold only lightly to the earth', but 'Aragorn
and Gandalf dug deep.'

In the account of the riding from Rivendell and Lórien at the end of
the chapter it is not said in any of the texts that Elrond brought the
sceptre of Annúminas and surrendered it to Aragorn; this was only
inserted on the final proof. Elrond's daughter is named Finduilas
(VIII.370, 386, 425; at this stage Faramir's mother was named
Rothinel, p. 54); and in A my father added, after 'Finduilas his
daughter', '[and daughter of Celebrian child of Galadriel].' This is the
first mention of Celebrian, by this or any name. In the last sentence of
the chapter in A Aragorn 'wedded Finduilas Halfelven'; this name
survived into B, where Faramir's mother Rothinel was changed to

THE STEWARD AND THE KING

59

Finduilas, and Elrond's daughter Finduilas was changed to Arwen, called Undómiel.[5]

NOTES

1 All names in RK not mentioned in my account can be presumed to be present already in A, with the exception of *Beregond*, which was only changed from *Berithil* on manuscript C. Thus Elfhelm is called 'Elfhelm the Marshal' (RK p. 244; cf. VIII.352); and the last king of the line of Anárion is Ëarnur, here first named (RK p. 245; cf. VIII.153). The rather puzzling reference to Min-Rimmon (RK p. 245: 'tidings had gone out into all parts of Gondor, from Min-Rimmon even to Pinnath Gelin and the far coasts of the sea') goes back to A.

2 The words of Elendil do not appear in A.

3 In A the name *Celeborn* is spelt with C; so also *Celebrian*. In this chapter and in the next the C spelling reverted to *K* in the finely-written third manuscripts, but on both it was then corrected back to C.

4 Cf. also the *Akallabêth* in *The Silmarillion*, p. 263, and *Of the Rings of Power and the Third Age, ibid.* p. 291.

5 Arwen first emerged in the fair copy of the following chapter, 'Many Partings': see p. 66.

Note on the Chronology

A curious point of chronology that arises in this chapter concerns the lapse of time between the departure of the host from Minas Tirith and the destruction of the Ring.

At the beginning of the chapter, against the words 'When the Captains were but two days gone', the figure '19' is written in the margin of A, i.e. March 19. This is the chronology described in VIII.432, according to which the march from Minas Tirith began on the 17th (the 18th in RK).

When in RK (p. 239) it is said that 'the fifth day came since the Lady Éowyn went first to Faramir', and that was the day of the destruction of the Ring and the fall of the Dark Tower, the same is said in A (and subsequent texts); and at the head of that page my father noted: 'F. sees E. on 19. 20, 21, 22, 23, 24, 25.' This day was therefore the 24th of March. But this is strange, since already in the first draft of 'The Field of Kormallen' Gandalf had declared that 'in Gondor the New Year will always begin on the 25th of March when Sauron fell …' (p. 46). In A, Éowyn says that this day was 'seven days since [Aragorn] rode away' (RK p. 240), which agrees with the date of March 24 for the destruction of the Ring. But my father changed 'seven', as he wrote, to 'nine', which would presumably give March 26 as the day of deliverance. He then changed 'nine' to 'eight', giving the

60   SAURON DEFEATED

25th as the day, and 'eight' is the reading in B and C, changed in C to 'seven' as in RK: this presumably implies that the date of the departure from Minas Tirith had been changed to the 18th. – On the significance of the date 25 March see T. A. Shippey, *The Road to Middle-Earth* (1982) pp. 151–2.

VII

MANY PARTINGS

The original draft of this chapter ('**A**') was paginated continuously with that of 'The Steward and the King' and bore no title. In comparison with its subsequent form my father's initial account of the 'many partings' was remarkably brief and spare; and though his handwriting is very difficult and here and there altogether illegible I shall give a substantial part of it in full, for it differs in very many points from the story in RK.

The opening, however, remained almost unchanged from first draft to final text (apart from *Queen Finduilas* for *Queen Arwen*), as far as ' "Then I beg leave to depart soon," said Frodo.' Then follows (with no mention of the Queen's gift):

'In three days we will go,' said Aragorn. 'For we shall ride with you great part of the way. We too have errands to do.'

And so it was that the King of Gondor and his Queen set out once more upon the North Roads, and many knights rode with them; and the Princes of Dol Amroth and of Ithilien; and King Éomer and his householdmen were also in that riding, for he had come to the wedding of his lord and brother. And with slow songs of the Mark they brought from the Halls [*probably for* Hallows] and his resting in Rath Dínen King Théoden upon a golden bier; and as one that still slept deeply they laid him upon a great wain with Riders of Rohan all about it, and his banner borne before. And Merry being his esquire, and a Knight of the Riddermark, rode upon the wain and kept the arms of the dead king. But for the other companions steeds were furnished according to their stature, and Frodo and Sam rode at the king's side with Gandalf upon Shadowfax; and with them also went Legolas and Gimli upon Hasufel[1] who had borne them so far.[2]

And slowly and at peace they passed into Anórien. And .... the Greywood[3] under Amon Dîn.

Here my father stopped and asked whether the homage of the Wild Men should be put here – referring, presumably, to the story in the original text of 'The Steward and the King', where Ghân-buri-Ghân and two of his headmen actually came to Minas Tirith (p. 56). He then

62   SAURON DEFEATED

wrote: 'and there stood Ghân-buri-Ghân by the eaves of the trees, and did them homage as they passed' (see p. 67). The text continues:

And so at last after many days (15?) they brought King Théoden back to his own land, and they came to Edoras, and there they stayed and rested; and never so fair and full of light was the Golden Hall, for no king of the City of the South had ever come thither before. And there they held the funeral of Théoden, and he was laid in a house of stone with many fair things, and over him was raised a great mound, the eighth of those upon the east side of the Barrowfields, and it was covered with green turves of grass [and] of fair Evermind. And then the Riders of the King's House rode about it, and one among them sang a song of Théoden Thengel's son that brought light to the eyes of the folk of the Mark and stirred the hearts of all, even those that knew not [that] speech. And Merry who stood at the foot of the mound wept.[4]

And when the burial was over and the last song was ended there was a great feast in the hall, and when they came to the time when all should drink to the memories of mighty men forth came Éowyn Lady of Rohan, golden as the sun and white as snow, and she brought forth the cup to Eomer King of the Mark, and he drank to the memory of Théoden. And then a minstrel sang naming all the kings of the [?Mark] in their order, and last King Éomer; and Aragorn arose and [?wished him] hail [and] drank to him. And then Gandalf arose and bid all men rise, and they rose, and he said: 'Here is a last hail[5] ere the feast endeth. Last but not least. For I name now [one >] those who shall not be forgotten and without whose valour nought else that was done would have availed; and I name before you all Frodo of the Shire and Samwise his servant. And the bards and the minstrels should give them new names: *Bronwe athan Harthad* and *Harthad Uluithiad*, Endurance beyond Hope and Hope unquenchable.'[6]

And to those names men drank in honour; but Sam went very red, and murmured to Frodo: 'I don't know what my Dad would think of the change: he was always against outlandish names. "The gentry can do as they please," he said, "with their Roriuses and Ronshuses, but for plain folk something shorter wears better." But even if I could say the name, I think it don't suit. My hope ... . low, Mr. Frodo, ...'[7]

The announcement by Éomer of the betrothal of Faramir and

MANY PARTINGS 63

Éowyn and the words of Éowyn with Aragorn are particularly hard to read, but the passage does not differ significantly from that in RK (pp. 255–6). The text then continues:

And after the feast those that were to go took leave of King Éomer, and Faramir abode with him, for he would not be far from Éowyn any longer. And Finduilas also remained and took leave of her father and brethren. But Aragorn rode on with the companions, and they passed on to Helm's Deep and there rested. And then Legolas repaid his vow to Gimli and went into the Glittering Caves; and when he returned he was silent, for he said that only Gimli could find fit words. 'And now,' said he, 'we will go to Fangorn', at which Gimli looked little pleased.

And so they passed .... to Isengard and saw how the Ents had busied themselves, for all the stone circle was removed and was planted with trees, but in the midst of the orchards Orthanc rose up still, tall and [? unapproachable]. And there was Treebeard and other Ents to welcome them, and he praised all their deeds, of which it seemed he had full tidings. 'But Ents played their part,' said he. 'And there would have been no Golden Hall to return to but for Treebeard and his folk. For we caught a great army of those – *burarum* – those orcs that were coming down through the Wold and we drove them away. Or otherwise the king of the grassland would [?have never] ridden far.'

And Gandalf praised his work, and at last he said farewell with many long words, saying that he had added some new lines. And when Merry and Pippin at last said farewell he .... them and said 'Well, my merry folk! Take a draught before you go!' And they said 'Yes, indeed!' And he looked at them over the bowl, and he said 'Take care! For you have already grown since I saw you!' And they laughed, and then he [?went] sad, and he said 'And don't forget that if you ever hear news of the Entwives you must send word to us.' And Aragorn said 'The East lands now lie open.' But Treebeard shook his head and said that it was far away.

But Legolas and Gimli here said goodbye, and went into Fangorn, and from there they purposed [? to journey] together to their own countries. 'Alas, that our lands lie so far apart! But we will send word to Rivendell.' And Elrond looked at them and said: 'Send rather to the Shire.'

Then they rode to the Gap of Rohan, and Aragorn took leave of them in that very place where Pippin had looked in the Palantír. And Pippin said 'I wish we could have one to see all

64 SAURON DEFEATED

our friends.' 'But one only now remains,' said Aragorn ....,
'and the king must keep that. But forget not that my realm lies
now also in the North; and later on I may come again.'

And so slowly they passed in[to] the waste lands west of the
mountains and fared north, and summer wore away; and
Galadriel and Celeborn and their folk passed over the Dimrill
Stair and went back to Lórien. But Elrond and Gandalf and the
hobbits came back at last to Rivendell.

The chapter ends in this earliest form with very rough sketching of
the time that the hobbits spent with Bilbo, but most of the essentials of
the final form are present. The chief difference lies in Bilbo's gifts:
'Then Bilbo gave Frodo his coat and sword, and he gave Sam a lot of
books of lore, and he gave Merry and Pippin a lot of good advice.'
Bilbo's verse (*The Road goes ever on and on*) is lacking, but that there
should be a verse at this point is indicated on the manuscript.
Gandalf's intimation that he would go with the hobbits 'at least as far
as Bree' is lacking; and at the departure from Rivendell Elrond's words
of farewell to Frodo, though the same as in RK (suggesting that 'about
this time of the year' he should 'look for Bilbo in the woods of the
Shire'), were heard also by the others: 'And they did not fully
understand what he meant, and Gandalf of course would not explain.'
The text then runs straight on into what would become the opening of
the next chapter, 'Homeward Bound'.

This first manuscript was greatly enlarged by the insertion of new
material. The story of the visit to Isengard was elaborated, and
Treebeard's account of the release of Saruman from Orthanc now
enters – the necessary prelude, of course, to the encounter with
Saruman and Wormtongue on the northward journey of the remaining company. There are a number of differences from the text of RK,
but they are minor.[8] The farewell speeches of Treebeard with Celeborn and Galadriel now appear, differing from the final form only in
the Quenya phrase: *O vanimar vanimalion ontari* (see note 16).

A long rider takes up at the words 'Then they rode towards the Gap
of Rohan' (cf. RK p. 260), and the departure of Aragorn is told in
almost the same words as in RK; but Galadriel said to him: 'Elfstone,
through darkness you have come to your desire. Use well the days of
light', and Celeborn said: 'Kinsman, farewell, but your doom is like to
mine; for our treasure shall outlast us both' (see pp. 124–5 and note 16).

The story of the meeting with Saruman, which had been very
obliquely referred to in 'The Story Foreseen from Kormallen' ('They
come on Saruman and he is [?pardoned]', p. 52), was now fully told,
but with a number of differences, one very notable. No indication is
given of where or when the encounter took place: after the company
had crossed the Isen they 'passed into the waste land west of the

MANY PARTINGS

65

mountains, and they turned north, and summer wore away. And many days afterward they overtook an old man leaning on a staff ...' See further p. 69.

To Saruman's remark 'I am seeking a way out of his realm' Gandalf at first replies:

'Then you are going the wrong way [*bracketed:* as seems to be your doom], unless you wish to pass into the utter North and there freeze to death. For from the Sea in the West to Anduin and thence many days' march east is the realm of the King, and east ere long it will spread beyond the water of Rúnaeluin.'[9]

Without striking this out my father replaced it by:

'Then you have far to go,' said Gandalf, 'and should be going eastward. Yet even so you would have to travel far, and find the border of his realm ever marching up behind you.'

This was struck through, and the final text here is: ' "Then you have far to go," said Gandalf, "and I see no hope in your journey. ..." '

Wormtongue still names himself *Frána*, not *Gríma* (cf. VII.445, VIII.55). Most curious is my father's remarkably different initial conception of Saruman's response to Merry's generosity (the sentence that I have bracketed was presumably rejected):

'Mine, mine, yes, and dearly paid for,' said Saruman, clutching at the pouch. And then suddenly he seemed touched. 'Well, I thank you,' he said. '[You do not crow, and your kind looks maybe are not feigned.] You seem an honest fellow, and maybe you did not come to crow over me. I'll tell you something. When you come to the Shire beware of Cosimo, and make haste, or you may go short of leaf.'

'Thankyou,' said Merry, 'and if you get tired of wandering in the wild come to the Shire.'

My father knew that Saruman acquired his supply of pipe-weed from the Shire (see VIII.59, note 8). There is no certain indication that he had at this stage begun to conceive of any more far-reaching relations between Saruman and Cosimo Sackville-Baggins, but in the original draft of 'The Scouring of the Shire' this idea was very fully present (see p. 84). On the other hand, it is a very notable feature of that draft that Saruman was *not* present in person in the Shire and did not preside over the last stages of its spoliation.

Since as will be seen subsequently the whole of the conclusion of *The Lord of the Rings* from 'Many Partings' to the 'Epilogue' was written in one continuous draft, it seems perfectly possible that all this new material was introduced into the original draft of 'Many Partings'

66   SAURON DEFEATED

after the first draft of 'The Scouring of the Shire' had been written. If this is so, it was very probably when writing and developing the present passage that my father first conceived of Saruman's visit to the Shire (as in the story itself the decision to do so also arose in Saruman's mind at this juncture, RK p. 298); possibly it was in fact Merry's extraordinarily artless invitation (though immediately abandoned, as will be seen in a moment) that was the germ of the story.

Precisely what my father had in mind when he wrote Saruman's words here, 'When you come to the Shire beware of Cosimo, and make haste, or you may go short of leaf', I do not know. It certainly shows that Saruman knew what was going on there, but equally certainly it was intended to be taken as good advice on Saruman's part to repay Merry for his gift. But my father marked Merry's reply with a large query, and at once, on the same page, recognising that the pride, bitterness and malevolence of Saruman could never be pierced by such a gesture on the part of Merry Brandybuck, he wrote the passage that stands in RK (p. 262): 'This is but a repayment in token. You took more, I'll be bound ...'

The first draft A was followed by a much-needed fair copy 'B', and that (as in 'The Steward and the King') by a third text 'C' in my father's most handsome script. B was subsequently given the number and title 'LVII Many Partings'.[10] While the final form of the chapter was very largely achieved in B, there remain a number of minor differences from the text of RK; I mention here some of the more noteworthy, and collect a few further details in note 16.

It was in B that the name *Arwen* at last emerged. In the opening paragraph of the chapter in this text the Queen was named *Ellonel*, but this was at once changed back to *Finduilas*, and she is *Finduilas* at the two following occurrences (and *Evenstar* in 'But wear this now in memory of Elfstone and Evenstar with whom your life has been woven,' RK p. 253). It must have been at this point that my father determined that her name was not *Finduilas*, and that he must find out what it was; for on a page of rough drafting for sentences in the opening of the chapter he is seen experimenting with other names, as *Amareth, Emrahil*. He wrote *Elrond Elladan Elrohir Emrahil, Finduilas > Emrahil*, and beside this (evidently to avoid the clash with *Imrahil*) *Imrahil > Ildramir*; but then, clearly and firmly, *Arwen Undómiel*. Immediately after this in text B as written Éomer says to Gimli 'But now I will put Queen Arwen Evenstar first' (RK p. 253).

In a first form of Arwen's words to Frodo she says: 'Mine is the choice of Lúthien, and I have chosen as she at last', the words 'at last' being omitted in a second version of the passage; and of her gift to him she says in B:

'... But in my stead you shall go, Ringbearer, when the time comes, and if you then desire it: for your wounds have been

MANY PARTINGS 67

grievous and your burden heavy. But you shall pass into the West until all your wounds and weariness are healed. [*Struck out at once:* Take this token and Elrond will not refuse you.' And she took from her hair a white gem like a star] Take with you the Phial of Galadriel and Círdan will not refuse you. But wear this now in memory of Elfstone and Evenstar with whom your life has been woven!' And she took a white gem . . .

In the third manuscript C the text of RK was reached.

Merethrond, the Great Hall of Feasts in Minas Tirith (RK p. 253) is said in B to be 'in the Citadel' (a statement omitted in C). On a page of rough drafting for this passage my father dashed off a little plan of the Citadel. This is shown as a circle with seven small circles (towers) at equal distances within the circumference, one of these standing beside the entrance. Beyond the Court of the Fountain is marked, at the centre, the White Tower and Hall of the Kings, and beyond that again, on the west side of the Citadel, the King's House. To the right (north) of the White Tower is the Hall of Feasts. The outlines of other buildings are roughed in between the towers.

When Aragorn and Éomer came to the Hallows 'they came to the tomb that had been built in Rath Dínen' (where C has the reading of RK, 'the tombs in Rath Dínen'); and returning with the bier they 'passed through the City, where all the people stood in silence; but the knights of Rohan that followed the bier sang in their own tongue a lament for the fallen' (so in A, p. 61, 'with slow songs of the Mark'). This was changed to 'the knights of Rohan . . . walked also in silence, for the time for song was not yet come' (cf. RK p. 253).

The encounter with Ghân-buri-Ghân (see pp. 61–2) was further developed, re-using the original passage in the previous chapter (p. 56) where Ghân-buri-Ghân came to Minas Tirith:

. . . and they came to the Grey Wood under Amon Dín. And there beside the road in the shadow of the trees stood Ghân of the Wild Woods and two of his headmen beside him, and they were clad all in garments of green leaves to do honour to the king. For Ghân-buri-Ghân said: 'He was great king; he drove away dark with bright iron. And now men of Stonehouses have king, he will not let dark come back.' And he and his headmen laid their foreheads upon Aragorn's feet; and he bade them rise up, and he blessed them, and gave them the Forest of Druadan to be their own, so that no man should ever enter it without their leave. Then they bowed and vanished into the trees.

This was struck through, and a version replacing it is found written on the last page of text B of 'The Steward and the King', almost as in

68 SAURON DEFEATED

RK (p. 254), in which the Wild Men remain invisible and only their drums are heard. In this version the heralds added: 'and whoso slays one of his people slays the king's friends.'

All the names of the Kings of the Mark, recited by the minstrel in the Golden Hall, are now given, but my father missed out *Folcwine*, great-grandfather of Théoden: this was a mere slip, since Folcwine appears in the earliest list of the kings (VIII.408), and without him there are only seven mounds on the east side of the Barrowfield. But the omission escaped notice, and Folcwine was not inserted until the Second Edition. The eleventh king (*Háma* in the original list) now becomes *Léof* (changed to *Léofa* in the Second Edition).[11]

In the parting of Merry from Éomer and Éowyn (RK p. 256) they address him as 'Meriadoc of the Shire and of the Mark' – the name *Holdwine* ('of the Mark') was only introduced on the galley proof; and Éomer says this of the gift of the horn, which he does not attribute to Éowyn:

'... but you will take naught but the arms that were given to you. This I suffer, because though we are of other lands and kind, still you are to me a dear kinsman whose love can only be requited with love. But this one gift I beg you now to take ...'

The horn is described in the same words as in RK; but then follows:

'This is an heirloom of our house,' said Éowyn, 'and in the deeps of time it was made for our forefathers by the dwarves [*struck out:* of Dale], and Eorl the Young brought it from the North.'

The statement that the horn 'came from the hoard of Scatha the Worm' entered on the galley proof.

The meeting with Treebeard reaches in this text B the form in RK at almost all points. Treebeard's denunciation of the Orcs runs here: *henulka-morimaite-quingatelko-tingahondo-rakkalepta-saurikumba*.[12] A curious point is that Gandalf says here 'The Third Age begins', which was repeated in C but there emended to 'The New Age begins' as in RK. With this may be compared my father's letter of November 1944 (*Letters* no. 91, also VIII.219): 'So ends the Middle Age and the Dominion of Men begins', and, further back, Saruman's speech to Gandalf in Isengard (VII.150): 'The Elder Days are gone. The Middle Days are passing. The Younger Days are beginning'; but in 'The Story Foreseen from Kormallen' (p. 52) is found 'The end of the Third Age is presaged' and 'End of the Third Age'.

Gandalf's response to Treebeard's report that he had allowed Saruman to go free remains as it was in A (see note 8): Treebeard now says 'A snake without fangs may crawl where he will', but this does not yet prompt Gandalf to the observation that Saruman 'had still one

MANY PARTINGS

69

tooth left ... the poison of his voice', which entered in C. Gimli, in his farewell, still concludes as in A (p. 63): 'Alas! that our lands lie so far apart. But we will send word to Rivendell when we may'; to which Elrond now replies: 'Send rather to Gondor, or else to the Shire!'

Again as in A (note 8), Treebeard does not say when the release of Saruman had taken place, and this remained into the First Edition; in the Second Edition 'Yes, he is gone' was changed to 'Yes, he is gone seven days.'[13]

The actual encounter with Saruman now differed virtually not at all from RK, but the placing of it was somewhat different in the First Edition from the revised version in the Second. The text of the First Edition ran thus (RK pp. 260–1):

> Soon the dwindling company came to the Isen, and crossed over it, and came into the waste lands beyond, and then they turned northwards, and passed by the borders of Dunland. And the Dunlendings fled and hid themselves, for they were afraid of Elvish folk, though few indeed ever came to their country. But the travellers did not heed them, for they were still a great company and were well provided with all that they needed; and they went on their way at their leisure, setting up tents when they would; and as they went the summer wore away.
>
> After they had passed by Dunland and were come to places where few folk dwelt, and even birds and beasts were seldom to be seen, they journeyed through a wood climbing down from the hills at the feet of the Misty Mountains that now marched on their right hand. As they came out again into open country they overtook an old man leaning on a staff ...

As noted above, in the Second Edition Treebeard told Gandalf that Saruman had been gone seven days; and in the revision of the passage just cited the First Edition text 'After they had passed by Dunland and were come to places where few folk dwelt, and even birds and beasts were seldom to be seen, they journeyed through a wood ...' was altered to 'On the sixth day since their parting from the King they journeyed through a wood ...' By this change the company was still in Dunland when they came upon Saruman, and a little later in the narrative, after 'I fancy he could do some mischief still in a small mean way' (RK p. 263), my father added in the Second Edition: 'Next day they went on into northern Dunland, where no men now dwelt, though it was a green and pleasant country' (northern Dunland, rather than the country north of Dunland, now becoming the uninhabited region).

From this point, the end of the Saruman episode, the text B continues:

September came in with a golden morning shimmering above

70　　　SAURON DEFEATED

silver mists; and looking out they saw away to the east the sun catching three peaks that thrust up through floating cloud into the sky: Caradhras, Celebras, and Fanuiras.[14] They were near once more to the Gates of Moria. And now came another parting ...

This must mean that it was on the first of September that they saw the Mountains of Moria. This was developed by a late emendation to C to the reading of the First Edition:

September came in with golden days and silver nights. At last a fair morning dawned, shimmering above gleaming mists; and looking from their camp on a low hill the travellers saw away in the east the Sun catching three peaks that thrust up into the sky through floating clouds: Caradhras, Celebdil, and Fanuidhol. They were near to the Gates of Moria.

Here now for seven days they tarried, for the time was at hand for another parting ...

In the Second Edition this passage (from 'September came in ...') was extended by references to the Swanfleet river, the falls, and the ford by which the company crossed.[15]

In various small points B received further alteration in the story of the sojourn of the hobbits in Rivendell, but effectively the final form was now reached.[16]

NOTES

1　*Hasufel* was presumably no more than a slip of memory, though it survived until emended on the third manuscript. Hasufel was Aragorn's horse of Rohan, and the horse that carried Legolas and Gimli was Arod.

2　Pippin is not mentioned, but in a rejected form of the passage it is said that he 'rode with the Prince of Ithilien, for he was the esquire of the Steward.'

3　*the Greywood*: previously named ('Grey Woods') only on a small map in a draft text of 'The Ride of the Rohirrim', VIII.353.

4　Here there is a mark of insertion, probably referring to verses that would be given at this point (although there are no verses here in the second and third manuscripts: see note 16).

5　In *wished him hail* (if correctly read) in the preceding sentence *hail* means 'health, happiness, welfare'; in Gandalf's *Here is a last hail* the word seems to be used elliptically, as if 'Here is a last drinking (of) hail'.

6　The word that I give as *athan* is very unclear and uncertain.

7　Gandalf's praise of Frodo and Sam, and this engaging glimpse of

MANY PARTINGS

71

the Gaffer amid the ceremoniousness of Edoras, had disappeared in the second text. *Ronshus* is evidently his clipped form of *Gerontius*, the name of the Old Took; and I suppose that he attached the 'learned' or high-falutin ending *-us* to Rory (Brandybuck). But the Gaffer's views were not entirely lost. When discussing with Frodo the name of his eldest child ('The Grey Havens', RK p. 306) Sam said: 'I've heard some beautiful names on my travels, but I suppose they're a bit too grand for daily wear and tear, as you might say. The Gaffer, he says: "Make it short, and then you won't have to cut it short before you can use it."' – Sam's final remark is unfortunately altogether illegible; the word preceding *low* might possibly be *getting*, or *pretty*, but the word preceding that is certainly not *was*.

8   The two sentinel trees that grew now where the gates of Isengard had stood do not appear. The words of Aragorn and Gandalf with Treebeard after his mention of the destruction of the Orcs (whom he apostrophises only in English adjectives) in the Wold were different from those in RK (p. 258), though a part of this dialogue was used a little later in the final text:

> 'We know it,' said Aragorn, 'and never shall it be forgotten, nor your storming of Isengard, and it is our hope that your forest may grow again in peace. There is room and to spare west of the mountains.'
> 'Forest may grow,' said Treebeard sadly; 'woods may spread, but not Ents; there are no Entings now.'
> 'Never at least while the Mark and Gondor remain,' said Gandalf; 'and that will have to be very long indeed to seem long to Ents. But what of your most important task, Fangorn? ...'

Treebeard does not say how long it was since Saruman had gone (see p. 69); and Gandalf does not tell him that Saruman had found his soft spot and persuaded him by 'the poison of his voice', but says merely 'Well, he's gone then, and that is all there is to be said' (reminiscent of his resigned 'Well, well, he is gone' when he heard from Legolas at the Council of Elrond of Gollum's escape, FR p. 269). Quickbeam does not appear in the handing over of the keys to Orthanc: ' "It is locked," said Treebeard, "locked by Saruman, and here are the keys," and he gave three black keys to Aragorn.'

9   *Rúnaeluin*: the last four letters are not perfectly clear, but this seems much the most probable interpretation. Can *Rúnaeluin* be the Sea of Rhûn?

10 The third manuscript C was given the chapter-number 'LV'. This reduction of the numbers by two begins with 'The Tower of Kirith Ungol' (p. 25).

72   SAURON DEFEATED

11   In the First Edition, while the eleventh king is named *Léof* by the
      minstrel in Edoras in 'Many Partings', in the list of the Kings of
      the Mark in Appendix A (II) the eleventh king is *Brytta*, with no
      explanation given. In the Second Edition the explanation was
      added: 'He was called by his people *Léofa*, for he was loved by
      all; he was openhanded and a help to all the needy.'

12   The English adjectives in B are the same as those in RK: 'evileyed,
      blackhanded, bowlegged, flinthearted, clawfingered, foulbellied,
      bloodthirsty'. In C the words *quingatelko* and *rakkalepta* were
      omitted, and then *henulka* and *saurikumba* were struck out and
      tingahondo changed to *sincahondo*. Finally *sincahondo* was
      changed on the printer's typescript to *sincahonda* as in RK.

13   On a copy of the First Edition that my father used to make
      alterations for incorporation in the Second Edition he added to the
      section 'The Chief Days from the Fall of the Barad-dûr to the End
      of the Third Age' in Appendix B the entry '*August 15*   Treebeard
      releases Saruman', but this was not for some reason included in
      the Second Edition. See the Note on Chronology below.

14   On the names *Celebras* and *Fanuiras* see VII.174, 306.

15   The course of this river was marked already on the First Map
      (VII.305), flowing down from the Misty Mountains to join the
      Greyflood above Tharbad. It was not referred to in the text of the
      First Edition, but was named the *Glanduin* in Appendix A (I, iii,
      first paragraph). The accidents or misunderstandings that be-
      devilled its representation on the map accompanying *The Lord of
      the Rings* are detailed in *Unfinished Tales* pp. 263–5.

16   It is not said in B that the only part of the hobbits' story that
      really interested Bilbo was the account of the crowning and
      marriage of Aragorn; nor that he had forgotten that he had
      already given Sting and the mithril-coat to Frodo; nor that his
      books of lore had red backs. All these changes entered in the third
      manuscript C. The books were labelled *Translations from the
      Elvish, by B. B. Esquire*; *Esquire* was removed on the galley
      proof.

      I record here various other details, mostly concerning names, in
      which B differed from RK.

      The reference to Merry as 'a Knight of the Riddermark' was
      retained from A (p. 61) and then struck out. On *Hasufel* for *Arod*
      see note 1.

      The alliterative verses of the song of the Riders of Rohan as
      they rode round Théoden's barrow were only introduced on a
      rider to the fourth text, the typescript for the printer, together
      with the passage preceding them in which the song of the Riders
      brought to mind 'the voice of Eorl crying above the battle upon
      the Field of Celebrant', and 'the horn of Helm was loud in the
      mountains'. The king's minstrel, who made the song, was

MANY PARTINGS

Gleowin in B, *Gléowine* in C; and *the Barrowfields* of A become *the Barrowfield* in B.

In Éomer's farewell words to Merry (RK p. 256) he speaks of his deeds 'upon the fields of Mundberg', emended on C to *Mundburg* (see VIII.355–6).

Treebeard's name of Lórien was spelt *Laurelindórinan*, and this survived into the First Edition, becoming *Laurelindórenan* in the Second. He still says to Galadriel and Celeborn *O vanimar vanimalion ontari* (p. 64), *O* being changed to *A* on text B and *ontari* to *nostari* on C. The comma after *vanimar* was added in the Second Edition. In VIII.20 I mentioned late notes of my father's on the fragments of other languages found in *The Lord of the Rings*, which for the greater part of the book are so hastily written as to be mostly unusable. His translation of *O vanimar, vanimálion nostari* can however be made out (in the light of the Quenya words themselves): 'fair ones begetters of fair ones', and with this is a note '*nosta* beget'; cf. the *Etymologies* in Vol.V, stems BAN, NŌ, ONO.

Wormtongue's name remained *Frána* (p. 65) in B and C, but was changed to *Gríma* on the final typescript; and Gandalf still calls Butterbur *Barnabas* (RK p. 265).

Note on the Chronology

In the original draft A of this chapter there were scarcely any indications of chronology: Aragorn tells Frodo (p. 61) that they will depart from Minas Tirith in three days' time, but this only relates to the end of 'the days of rejoicing', of indeterminate length; and it was fifteen days' journey from Minas Tirith to Rohan.

In B Aragorn tells Frodo that they will leave in seven days, and that 'in three days now Éomer will return hither to bear Théoden back to rest in the Mark', as he duly did; and all this is retained in *The Lord of the Rings*, together with the fifteen days of the journey to Rohan. But neither B nor C give much more indication than did the original draft of the time taken over the stages of the journey from Edoras to Rivendell, and it may be that my father did not attend to the matter closely until the final preparation of the book. It is a curious fact that the chronology of 'The Chief Days from the Fall of the Barad-dûr to the End of the Third Age' in Appendix B (and which is the same in this respect in both editions) does not agree with the text of 'Many Partings' in respect either of Éomer's return in relation to the setting out for Edoras or of the time taken on that journey. In the chronology of 'The Chief Days' Éomer returned to Minas Tirith on July 18, and the riding from the City with King Théoden's wain took place on the following day, July 19, not four days later as in 'Many Partings'; while

74   SAURON DEFEATED

the arrival at Edoras is dated August 7, eighteen days later, not fifteen
as in the text.

As I have noted already, no indication of date was given for the
meeting of Saruman with the travellers as they rode north even in the
First Edition; in the Second Edition the passage was altered to say that
the meeting took place on the sixth day since they parted from the
King, and they were still in Dunland (see p. 69). But in fact this dating
was already present in the First Edition, in the chronology of 'The
Chief Days' in *The Tale of Years:*

August 22   They come to Isengard; they take leave of the King of
the West at sunset.

August 28   They overtake Saruman; Saruman turns towards the
Shire.

As the third text C was written it was still on September 1 that the
travellers saw the Mountains of Moria, but late emendation (see p. 70)
produced, or satisfied, the chronology of 'The Chief Days':

September 6   They halt in sight of the Mountains of Moria.

September 13   Celeborn and Galadriel depart, the others set out
for Rivendell.

On September 21, the day before Bilbo's birthday, Gandalf and the
hobbits returned to Rivendell, having taken (being mounted) a much
shorter time than they took to reach Moria on their outward journey,
nine months before.

VIII

HOMEWARD BOUND

The original draft A of 'Many Partings' continued on into the opening of 'Homeward Bound' (see p. 64), but my father drew a line of separation, and began a new pagination, probably at an early stage. At the same time he scribbled in a title for the new chapter: 'Homecoming'. This text runs on with continuous pagination right through to the end of *The Lord of the Rings*, and included the Epilogue.

This last of the first drafts ends the work in style: if not the most difficult of all the manuscripts of *The Lord of the Rings* it certainly has few rivals. As far as the Battle of Bywater (see p. 93) it gives the impression of having been written in one long burst, and with increasing rapidity. Ideas that appear in earlier reaches of the text are contradicted later without correction of the former passages. In the part of it that corresponds to 'Homeward Bound' and the beginning of 'The Scouring of the Shire', however, the text does not present excessive difficulty, chiefly because the final form of the story was not very substantially changed from that in the original draft, but also because my father's handwriting, while very rough throughout, declined only gradually as the text proceeded.

I break the text here into three chapters as in RK. Throughout, the original draft is of course called 'A'. Of the tale of the visit to *The Prancing Pony* there is not a great deal to record. It opens thus (RK p. 268):

So now they turned their faces for home; and though they rode now they rode but slowly. But they were at peace and in no haste, and if they missed their companions of their adventures, still they had Gandalf, and the journey went well enough when once they passed beyond Weathertop. For at the Fords of Bruinen Frodo halted and was loth to ride through, and from here on to Weathertop he was silent and ill at ease; but Gandalf said nothing.

And when they came to the hill he said 'Let us hasten', and would not look towards it. 'My wound aches,' he said, 'and the memory of darkness is heavy on me. Are there not things, Gandalf, that cannot ever be wholly healed?'

'Alas, it is so,' said Gandalf.

'It is so I guess with my wounds,' said Frodo. ...

76   SAURON DEFEATED

This page of A (carrying the end of the later 'Many Partings' and the beginning of 'Homeward Bound') was replaced, in all probability very soon, by a new page with a chapter number, 'LVIII', and in this the opening passage draws nearer to that in RK: the date of the crossing of the Fords of Bruinen is given (the sixth of October, as in RK), and Frodo speaks of his pain there, not below Weathertop; but he says: 'It's my shoulder, my wound aches. And my finger too, the one that is gone, but I feel pain in it, and the memory of darkness is heavy on me.'[1]

When Butterbur came to the door of *The Prancing Pony* he did not, as in RK, misunderstand Nob's cry 'They've come back' and come rushing out armed with a club:

And out came Barnabas wiping his hand on his apron and looking as bustled as ever, though there seemed few folk about, and not much talk in the Common Room; indeed he looked in the dim lamplight rather more wrinkled and careworn.

'Well, well,' he said, 'I never expected to see any of you folk again and that's a fact: going off into the wild with that Trotter . . .'

Whatever response Butterbur made to Gandalf's request 'And if you have any tobacco we'll bless you. Ours has long since been finished' is not reported. When Butterbur objects (RK p. 272) that he doesn't want 'a whole crowd of strangers settling here and camping there and tearing up the wild country' Gandalf tells him:

'. . . There's room enough for realms between Isen and Greyflood, and along the shores between Greyflood and Brandy-wine. And many folk used to dwell north away, a hundred miles and more from you, on the North Down[s] and by Nenuial or Evendimmer, if you have heard of it. I should not wonder if the Deadmen's Dike is filled with living men again. Kings' Norbury is its right name in your tongue. One day the King may come again.'[2]

Apart from these passages the text of 'Homeward Bound' in RK was virtually present in the draft text,[3] though naturally with many small changes in the dialogue still to come, until the end of the chapter: here there is a notable difference in the story. The conversation of the hobbits as they left Bree is much as in RK, but without Merry's reference to pipe-weed and without Gandalf's reference to Saruman and his interest in the Shire:

'I wonder what he [Butterbur] means,' said Frodo.

HOMEWARD BOUND

'I can guess some of it at any rate,' said Sam gloomily. 'What I saw in the Mirror. Trees cut down and all, and the old gaffer turned out. I ought to have turned back sooner.'

'Whatever it is it'll be that Cosimo at the bottom of it,' said Pippin.

'Deep but not at the bottom,' said Gandalf.

This stands near but not at the foot of a page. Across the empty space my father wrote this note:

Gandalf should stay at Bree. He should say: 'You may find trouble, but I want you to settle it yourselves. Wizards should not interfere in such things. Don't crack nuts with a sledge-hammer, or you'll crack the kernels. And many times over anyway. I'll be along some time.'

The empty space had perhaps been intended to mark a pause; at any rate this note was written in later (though not much later), since the text continues on the following page and Gandalf has not left the hobbits: he is present at and plays a part in the encounter with the gate-guards on the Brandywine Bridge (at the beginning of the next chapter in RK, 'The Scouring of the Shire': pp. 79–80).

They passed the point on the East Road where they had taken leave of Bombadil, and half they expected to see him standing there to greet them as they went by. But there was no sign of him, and there was a grey mist over the Barrow-down[s] southward and a deep veil hid the Old Forest far away.

Frodo halted and looked wistfully south. 'I should like to see the old fellow again. I wonder how he's getting on.'

'As well as ever, you may be sure,' said Gandalf. 'Quite untroubled, and if I may say so not at all interested in anything that has happened to us. There will be time later to visit him. If I were you I should press on for home now, or we'll not come to Brandywine Bridge till the gates are locked.'

'But there aren't any gates,' said Merry, 'at least not on the Road. There's the Buckland Gate of course.'

'There weren't any gates, you mean,' said Gandalf. 'I think you'll find some now.'

They did. It was long after dark when tired and wet they came to the Brandywine and found the way barred at both ends of the Bridge . . .

The first draft was followed by a fair copy ('**B**') of 'Homeward Bound' with that title, and then by a fine and elegant manuscript ('**C**').

78   SAURON DEFEATED

Already in B the final form of the chapter was achieved at almost every point.[4]

NOTES

1 The reason for the change was that the recurrence of the pain of Frodo's wound should depend on the date, not on the place. See further p. 112, notes 3 and 4.

2 The name *Nenuial* first occurs here. The curious (but certain) form *Evendimmer* I cannot explain; *Evendim* (and *Fornost Erain*) appear in the second text of the chapter.

3 The return of Bill the Pony is recorded by Butterbur in almost the same words as in RK (cf. VII.448, VIII.219). – Two other minor points may be mentioned here. Gandalf's sword (RK p. 272) is called *Orcrist* (the name of the sword of Thorin Oakenshield): this was a mere slip, which however survived into the third manuscript of the chapter, where it was changed to *Glamdring*. The entrance into Bree by the road from Weathertop was called 'the East-gate', and only changed to 'the South-gate' on the typescript for the printer; cf. the plan of Bree, VI.335.

4 In his parting words to the hobbits Gandalf says in B: 'I am not coming to the Shire. You must settle its affairs yourselves. To bring me in would be using a sledgehammer to crack nuts.' With the last sentence cf. the note, written on text A, given on p. 77. – *Trotter* and *Cosimo* survived into the third manuscript C and were only then changed to *Strider* and *Lotho*; *Barnabas* survived into the final typescript and was corrected on that to *Barliman*.

IX

THE SCOURING OF THE SHIRE

As has been seen in the last chapter, the long draft text A moves on into what became 'The Scouring of the Shire' without break; Gandalf's departure to seek out Tom Bombadil, where the chapter break would come, was not yet present. When the travellers came to the Brandywine Bridge their reception was just as in RK, but Sam's shouted 'I'll tear your notice down when I find it' is followed by:

'Come along now!' said the wizard. 'My name is Gandalf. And here is a Brandybuck, a Took, a Baggins, and a Gamgee, so if you don't open up quick there will be more trouble than you bargain for, and long before sunrise.'

At that a window slammed, and a crowd of hobbits poured out of the house with lanterns, and they opened the far gate, and some came over the Bridge. When they looked at the travellers they seemed more frightened than ever.

'Come, come,' said Merry, recognizing one of the hobbits. 'If you don't know me, Hob Hayward, you ought to. ...'

Before the narrative had proceeded much further the text was corrected and Gandalf's words were given to Frodo: ' "Come along now!" said Frodo. "My name is Frodo Baggins. And here is a Brandybuck, a Took, and a Gamgee..." '

The questioning of Hob Hayward (RK p. 277) is a tangle of names and titles. So far as I can see, it ran thus as first written, with some changes made immediately:

'I'm sorry, Mr. Merry, but we have orders.'
'Whose orders?'
'The Mayor's, Mr. Merry, and the Chief Shirriff's.'
'Who's the Mayor?' said Frodo.
'Mr. [Cosimo >] Sackville of Bag-End.'
'Oh is he, indeed,' said Frodo. 'And who's the Chief Shirriff?'
'Mr. [Baggins >] Sackville of Bag-End.'
'Oh, indeed. Well, I'm glad he's dropped the Baggins at least. And he'll leave Bag-End too if I hear any more nonsense.'

A hush fell on the hobbits beyond the gate. 'It won't do no good to talk that way,' said Hob. 'He'll get to hear of it. And if you make so much noise you'll wake up the Big Man.'

80 SAURON DEFEATED

'I'll wake him up in a way that'll surprise him,' said Gandalf. 'If you mean that your precious Mayor is employing ruffians out of the wild, then we've not come back too soon.' He leaped from his horse and put his hand to the gate and tore the notice from it, and threw it on the path in the faces of the hobbits.[1]

This was the last appearance of Gandalf before the final leave-taking at the Grey Havens.[2] 'Gandalf' was changed here to 'Frodo', and 'horse' to 'pony', and it was presumably at this point that the note given on p. 77 ('Gandalf should stay at Bree ...') was written on the manuscript. It will be seen in what follows that in this original version of the story Frodo played a far more aggressive and masterful part in the events than he does in RK, even to the slaying of more than one of the ruffians at Bywater and their leader at Bag End, despite his words to Sam already present in the first manuscript of 'The Land of Shadow' (p. 32; RK p. 204): 'I do not think it is my part to strike any blows again' (see the added sentence given in note 23).

The account of the hobbits' lodging that night in the guard-house by the Brandywine Bridge is much as in the final form, but lacks a few details (as Hob Hayward's remark that stocks of pipe-weed had been 'going away quietly' even before Frodo and his companions left the Shire, and the remonstrance of other hobbits against Hob's indiscretion, RK p. 279). It is Frodo, not Merry, who threatens Bill Ferny and gets rid of him. In the story of their 'arrest' at Frogmorton[3] 'one of the Shirriffs' told them that on the orders of the Chief Shirriff (see note 1) they were to be taken to the *Lock-holes* in Michel Delving (cf. RK p. 280), which is where the term first appears (see pp. 98–9). It turns out that, unlike the later story, Robin Smallburrow was actually the leader of the band of Shirriffs (see p. 95):

To the discomfiture of the Shirriffs Frodo and his companions all roared with laughter. 'Go on,' said Frodo. 'Robin Smallburrow, you're Hobbiton-bred. Don't be silly. But if you're going our way we'll go with you as quiet as you could wish.'

'Which way be you going, Mister Baggins?' said Shirriff Smallburrows,[4] a grin appearing on his face which he quickly smoothed away.

'Hobbiton, of course,' said Frodo. 'Bag End. But you needn't come any further than you wish.'

'Very well, Mr. Baggins,' said the Shirriff, 'but don't forget we've arrested you.'

Sam's conversation with Robin Smallburrows was concluded more abruptly in A (cf. RK pp. 281–2):

'... You know how I went for a Shirriff seven years ago, before

THE SCOURING OF THE SHIRE   81

all this. Gave you a chance of walking round the Shire and seeing folk and hearing the news, and keeping an eye on the inns. But we all has to swear to do as the Mayor bids. That was all right in the days of old Flourdumpling. Do you remember him? – old Will Whitfoot of Michel Delving. But it's different now. Yet we still has to swear.'

'You shouldn't,' said Sam, 'you should cut out the Shir-riffing.'

'Not allowed to,' said Robin.

'If I hear "not allowed" much oftener,' said Sam, 'I'm going to get angry.'

'Can't say I'd be sorry to see it,' said Robin, and he dropped his voice. 'Tell you the truth, your coming back and Mr. Frodo and all is the best that's happened in a year. The Mayor's in a fine taking.'

'He'll be in a fine getting before many days are over,' said Sam.

The Shire-house⁵ at Frogmorton was as bad as the gate-houses. ...

It was Frodo, not Merry, who made the Shirriffs march in front on the journey from Frogmorton, and there is no mention of his looking 'rather sad and thoughtful' as his companions laughed and sang. The incident of the old 'gaffer' by the wayside who laughed at the absurd scene, and Merry's refusal to allow the Shirriffs to molest him, is absent;⁶ but when the Shirriffs gave up their forced march at the Three-Farthing Stone while Frodo and his friends rode on to Bywater, the leader saying that they were breaking arrest and he could not be answerable, it was again Frodo, not Pippin, who said 'We'll break a good many things yet, and not ask you to answer.'

The horror especially of Frodo and Sam when they came to Bywater and saw what had been done there is told in A very much as in the final form; but from Sam's words 'I want to find the Gaffer' (RK p. 283) I give the text in full, for differences now begin to multiply, and before long the story evolves in a way totally unlike that of the final form of the chapter. By this point my father's handwriting is of extraordinary difficulty, and gets worse; it has been a struggle to elucidate it even to the extent that it is printed here. I have supplied much of the punctuation, and I have silently entered omitted words where these are obvious, corrected words given wrong endings, and so forth.

'It'll be dark, Sam, before we can get there,' said Frodo. 'We'll get there in the morning. One night now won't make any difference.'

82   SAURON DEFEATED

'I wish we'd turned down into Buckland first,' said Merry. 'I
feel trouble's ahead. We'd have heard all the news there and got
some help. Whatever Cosimo's been up to it can't have gone far
in Buckland. Bucklanders wouldn't stand any dictating from
him!'

All the houses were shut and no one greeted them. And they
wondered why, till coming to the Green Dragon, almost the last
house on the Hobbiton side, they were astonished and disturbed
to see four ill-favoured men lounging at the street-end. Squint-
eyed fellows like the one they saw at Bree. 'And at Isengard too,'
muttered Merry. They had clubs in their hands and horns in
their belts. When they saw the travellers they left the wall they
had been leaning on and walked into the road, blocking the
way.

'Where do you think you're going?' said one. 'This ain't the
road to Michel Delving. And where's the perishing Shirriffs?'

'Coming along nicely,' said Frodo. 'A bit footsore maybe.
We'll wait for them.'

'Garn, I told the Boss [> Big Sharkey] it was no good sending
the little fools. We ought to have a'gone, but the Boss [>
Sharkey] says no, and .... [> the Boss let him have his
way.][7]

'And if you had gone, what difference would that have made,
pray?' said Frodo quietly. 'We are not used to footpads in this
country, but we know how to deal with them.'

'Footpads, eh,' said the man, 'so that's your tone, is it? I'll
learn you manners if you ain't careful. Don't you trust too much
to the Boss's kind heart. [*Added in margin:* He's all right if you
treat him right, but he won't stand talk of that sort.] He's soft
enough. But he's only a hobbit. And this country needs something a bit bigger to keep it in order. It'll get it, too, and before
the year's out, or my name's not Sharkey. Then you'll learn a
thing or two, you little rat-folk.'

'Well,' said Frodo, 'I find that very interesting. I was thinking
of waiting here and calling in the morning, but now I think I had
better call on the Boss at once, if you mean my cousin Mr.
Cosimo. He'd like to know what's afoot in good time.'

The squinting man laughed. 'Oh, he knows alright though he
pretends not to. When we've finished with bosses we get rid of
them. And of anyone who gets in our way, see?' [*Added in
margin, as a replacement or variant:* 'O, Cosimo,' he said, and
he laughed again and looked sidelong at his mates. 'Ah, Boss

THE SCOURING OF THE SHIRE

Cosimo! [*Struck out:* He knows all right, or he did.] Don't you worry about him. He sleeps sound, and I shouldn't try and wake him now. But we're not going to let you pass. We get enough of .... in our way.']

'Yes, I see,' said Frodo. 'I'm beginning to see a great deal. But I fear you're behind the times and the news here, Ruffian Sharkey. Your day's over. You come from Isengard, I think. Well, I have myself come from the South, and this news may concern you. The Dark Tower has fallen, there is a King in Gondor, Isengard is no more, and Saruman is a beggar in the wilderness. You are the fingers of a hand that has been cut off, and arm and body too are dead. The King's messengers will be coming soon up the Greenway, not bullies of Isengard.'

The man stared at him, taken aback for a moment. Then he sneered. 'Swagger it, swagger it, little cock-a-whoop on your pony,' he said. 'Big words and fat lies won't scare us. King's messengers?' he said. 'When I see them I'll take notice maybe.'

This was too much for Pippin. As he thought of the minstrel upon Kormallen and the praise of all the fair host, and here this squint-eyed rascal calling the Ringbearer little cock-a-whoop. [*sic*]

He flashed out his sword and rode forward, casting aside his cloak so that the silver and sable of Gondor which he still wore could be seen. 'We are the King's messengers,' he said. '[And I'm the squire of Frodo of the Nine Fingers, Knight of Gondor, and down you go in the road on your knees or we'll deal with you. >] And I am the esquire of the Lord of Minas Tirith, and here is Frodo of the Nine Fingers renowned among all peoples of the West. You're a fool. Down on your knees in the road, or I'll set this troll's bane in you.' His sword glinted red in the last rays of the sun. Merry and Sam drew and rode up beside him; but Frodo made no move.

The man and his fellows taken aback by the weapons and the sudden fierce speech gave way and ran off up the road to Hobbiton, but they blew their horns as they ran.

'Well, we've come back none too soon,' said Merry.

'Not a day too soon,' said Frodo. 'Poor Cosimo. I hope we haven't sealed his doom.'

'What do you mean, Frodo?' said Pippin. 'Poor Cosimo? ... I'd seal his doom if I could get at him.'

'I don't think you understand it all quite,' said Frodo. 'Though you should. You've been in Isengard. But I've had

84   SAURON DEFEATED

Gandalf to talk to, and we've talked much on the long miles. Poor Cosimo! Well, yes. He's both wicked and silly. But he's caught in his own net. Can't you see? He started trading with Saruman and got rich secretly and bought up this and that on the quiet, and then he's [?hired] these ruffians. Saruman sent them to "help" him, and show him how to build and [??repair] ... all ...   And now of course they're running things in his name – and not in his name for long. He's a prisoner [?really] in Bag End, I expect.'

'Well, I am staggered,' said Pippin. 'Of all the ends to our journey this is the last I expected: to fight half-orcs in the Shire itself to rescue Cosimo the Pimple of all people!'[8]

'Fight?' said Merry. 'Well, it looks like it. But we're after all only 4 hobbits even if we're armed. We don't know how many ruffians there are about. I think we may really need the sledgehammer for this nut after all.'[9]

'Well, we can't help Cousin Pimple tonight,' said Frodo. 'We must find cover for the night.'

'I've an idea, Mr. Frodo,' said Sam. 'Let's go to old Jeremy Cotton's.[10] He used to be a stout fellow, and he has a lot of lads, all friends of mine.'

'What, Farmer Cotton down South Lane?' said Frodo. 'We'll try it!' They turned and a few yards back rode into the lane, and in a quarter of a mile came to the gates. Though it was early all the farmhouse was dark, and not a dog barked. ' "Not allowed", I suppose,' grunted Sam. They knocked on the door, twice. Then slowly a window was opened just above and a head peered out.

'Nay, it's none o' them ruffians,' whispered a voice. 'It's only hobbits.'

'Don't you pay no heed anyway, Jeremy,' said a voice (the farmer's wife by the sound of it). 'It'll only bring trouble, and we've had enough.'

'Go away, there's good fellows,' said the farmer hoarsely. 'Not the front door anyway. If there's anything you want badly come round to the back first thing in the morning before they're about. There's a lot in the street now.'

'We know that,' said Frodo. 'But we've sent them off. It's Mr. Frodo Baggins and friends here. We've come back. But we want shelter for a night. The barn will do.'

'Mr. Frodo Baggins?' gasped the farmer. 'Aye, and Sam with him,' added Sam.

THE SCOURING OF THE SHIRE 85

'All right! But don't shout,' said the farmer. 'I'm coming down.'

The bolts were drawn back stealthily and it crossed Sam's mind that he had never known that door to be locked let alone bolted before. Farmer Cotton put a head round and looked at them in the gloaming. His eyes grew round as he looked at them and then grave. 'Well,' he said, 'voices sound all right, but I wouldn't a' knowed you. Come in.' There was dim light in the passage, and he scanned their faces closely. 'Right enough,' he said, and laughed with relief. 'Mr. Baggins and Sam and Mr. Merry and Mr. Pippin. Well, you're welcome, more than welcome. But it's a sorry homecoming. You've been away too long.'

'What's come of my gaffer?' said Sam anxiously.

'Not too well, but not too bad,' said Farmer Cotton. 'He's in one of [?they new] Shire-houses, but he comes to my backdoor and I sees he's better fed than some of the poor things. He's not too bad.'

Sam drew a breath of relief. 'Shire-houses,' he said. 'I'll burn the lot down yet.'

They went into the kitchen and sat down by the fire, which the farmer blew up to a blaze. 'We go to bed early these days,' he said. 'Lights o'night bring unwelcome questions. And these ruffians, they lurk about at night and lie abed late. Early morning's our best time.'

They talked for a while and learned that Frodo's guesses had been near the mark. There were some twenty ruffians quartered in Hobbiton, and Cosimo was up at Bag End; but was never seen outside of it. 'His ma, they took her and put her in the Lockholes at Michel Delving three [?months] ago,' said the farmer. 'I'm less sorry for her than I am for some as they've took. But she did stand up to them proper, there's no denying. Ordered them out of the house, and so they took her.'

'Hm,' said Frodo. 'Then I am afraid we've brought you trouble. For we've threatened four of them and sent them off. The chief of them is one Sharkey by his own naming. I feared there were more. They blew horns and went off.'

'Ah, I heard 'em,' said the farmer. 'That's why we shut down. They'll be after you soon enough, unless you've scared 'em more than I guess. Not but what I think they'd run quick enough from anything of their own size. We'd clear 'em out of the country if only we'd get together.'

86 SAURON DEFEATED

'Have they got any weapons?'

'They don't show 'em, no more than whips, clubs, and knives, enough for their dirty work,' said the farmer. 'But maybe they have. Some have got bows and arrows, anyhow, and shoot [?pretty quick] and straight. They've shot three in this district to my knowledge.' Sam ground his teeth.

There came a great bang at the front door. The farmer went quietly down the passage putting out the light and the others followed him. There was a second louder bang. 'Open up you old rat, or we'll burn you out,' shouted a hoarse voice outside.

'I am coming,' said the farmer, all of a [?quake.] 'Slip up and see how many there is,' said Sam. And he [?rattled the chains] and . . . . ed the bolts as the farmer ran up the stairs and back.

'I should say a dozen at the least, but all the lot, I guess,' he said.

'All the better,' said Frodo. 'Now for it.'

The four hobbits stood back to the wall towards which the door swung. The farmer [?unbolted] the bolts, turned the key, and then [?slipped back] up the stairs. The door swung open and in [?peered] the head and shoulders of Sharkey. They let him come in; and then quickly Frodo drove the point of his sword into his neck. He fell, and there was a howl of rage outside. 'Burn them, burn them,' voices cried, 'go and get fuel.' 'Nar, dig them out,' said two, and thrust into the passage. They had swords in their hands, but Frodo now behind the door swung it suddenly in the face of the rear one, while . . . Sam ran Sting through the other.[11] Then the hobbits leaped out. The ruffian who had been down on his face was [?leaning against the doorpost]. He fled, blood pouring from his nose. The farmer . . . took the sword from the fallen ruffian and stood guard at the door. The hobbits ranged about the yards stealthily. They came on two ruffians bringing wood from the woodpile and . . . . ed and killed them before they knew they were attacked. 'It is like a rat hunt,' said Sam. 'But that's only four and one with a broken nose.'

At that moment they heard Merry shouting, 'Gondor to the Mark', and they ran and found him in a corner of the stack yard with four ruffians [?pressing] on him, but held at bay by his sword. They had only knives and clubs. Frodo and Sam came running from one side and Pippin from another. The ruffians fled blowing horns, but one more fell to Frodo's sword before he could escape.

THE SCOURING OF THE SHIRE 87

They heard the farmer calling. They ran back. 'One less,' said Farmer Cotton. 'I got him as he ran. The rest have run off down the lane blowing like a hunt.'

'That's six altogether,' said Frodo. 'But no doubt the horns will bring more. How many are there in the neighbourhood?'

'Not many,' said the farmer. 'They mostly bide here or at Michel Delving, and go anywhere's there's any dirty work. No more of [?them's] come in since last spring. I ... say there's not much [more than] a hundred in the whole Shire. If we could only join together.'

'Then let's start tonight,' said Frodo. 'Rouse up the folk. Put lights in the houses. Get out all the lads and grown hobbits. Block the road south and send out scouts round the place.'

It was not long before all Bywater was alive and awake again. Lights shining in windows and people at their doors. And there were even cheers for Mr. Frodo. Some lit a bonfire at the Road Bend[12] and danced round it. It was after all not more than [the] six[th of] October[13] on a fair evening of late autumn. Others went off to spy the land round about.

Those that went up Hobbiton way said that there was quite a hubbub there. News of Mr. Frodo's return had come in and folk were coming out. The ruffians seemed to have left the place clear. 'Bolted towards Michel Delving where they've made the Lockholes into a fortress, that's what they've a' done, I guess,' said Farmer Cotton. 'But they'll come back. There's no way from the West.[14] They don't go down the Tuckborough way. They've never given in there. And they've [?beaten] up more than one ruffian in the Took-house.[15] There is a kind o' siege going on.'

'We'll send word to them. Who'll go?' No answer.

'I'll go of course,' said Pippin. 'It's my own country. I'm proud of it. It's not more than 14 miles, as the crow flies or as Took goes who knows all the ways, from here where I stand to the Long Smial of [?Tuckborough] where I was born.[16] Anyone come with me? Well, never mind. I'll be bringing some [?stout] Tooklanders this way in the morning.'

Frodo sent out other messengers to all hamlets and farms near enough for folk to be willing to run to them.

Nothing more that night.

In the morning from Hobbiton and Bywater and round about there were about 100 fullgrown hobbits gathered together with sticks, staves, knives, pitchforks and mattocks and axes and

88   SAURON DEFEATED

scythes. Messages came in to say that a dozen or more ruffians
had been seen going west to Michel Delving the evening before.
Then a hobbit ran in to say that about fifty Tooklanders had
come in on ponies to the East Road junction and a couple of
hundred were marching up behind. 'Whole country's up, like a
fire,' he said. 'It's grand! Right glad we are you came back, Mr.
Frodo. That's what we needed.'

Frodo now had forces enough. He had [?the] block .. .... the
East .....[17] and put a lot of them behind the hedge on each side
of the way. They were under Pippin's command. 'I don't know
what you think,' he said to Merry and Sam. 'But it seems to me
that either the ruffians are all going to gather in Michel Delving
and fight it out there: in that case we'll have to raise the Shire
and go and dig them out; or more likely they'll come back in full
force this way to their precious Boss. It's forty miles if it's a foot
to Michel Delving. Unless they get ponies (which wouldn't help
much) or have got horses they can't come back for a day or
two.'
    'They'll send a messenger,' said Sam, 'and wait somewhere till
their friends arrive; that'll speed things up a bit. Even so I don't
see how they can do it till the day after tomorrow at quickest.'
    'Well then,' said Frodo, 'we'd best spend the time by going to
Hobbiton and have a word with Cousin Cosimo.'
    'Right you are, Mr. Frodo,' said Sam, 'and I'll look up the
gaffer.'
    So leaving Pippin in charge on the Road and Farmer Cotton
in Bywater, Frodo, Sam and Merry rode on to Hobbiton. It was
one of the saddest days of their lives. The great chimney rose up
before them, and as they came in sight of the village they saw
that the old mill was gone and a great red brick building
straddled the stream. All along the Bywater road every tree was
felled, and little ugly houses with no gardens in [?desert] ..... of
ash or gravel. As they looked up the hill they gasped. The old
farm on the right had been turned into a [?long ?big] work-
shop or [?building] with many new windows. The chestnuts
were gone. Bagshot Row was a yawning sand-pit, and Bag End
up beyond could not be seen for a row of sheds and ugly huts.[18]
    [*The following was struck out and replaced immediately:* A
[?surly dirty] ill-favoured hobbit was lounging at the new
mill-door. He was [?smut]-faced and [?chewing]. 'As good a
small model of Bill Ferny as I've seen,' said Sam.

THE SCOURING OF THE SHIRE   89

Ted Sandyman did not seem to recognize them but stared at them with a leer until they had nearly passed.

'Going to see the Boss?' he said. 'It's a bit early. But you'll see the notice on the gate. Are you the folks that have been making all the row down at Bywater? If you are, I shouldn't [?try] the Boss. He's angry. Take my advice and sheer off. You're not wanted. We've got work to do in the Shire now and we don't want noisy riffraff.'

'You don't always get what you want, Ted Sandyman,' said Sam. 'And I can tell you what's coming to you, whether you like it or no: a bath.' He jumped from his pony and before the astonished Ted knew what was coming Sam hit him square on the nose, and lifting him with an effort threw him over the bridge with a splash.]

A dirty surly-looking hobbit was lounging on the bridge by the mill. He was grimy-faced and grimy-handed, and was chewing. 'As good a small copy of Bill Ferny as you could ask for!' said Sam. 'So that's what Ted Sandyman admires, is it. I'm not surprised.'

Ted looked at him and spat. 'Going to see the Boss?' he said. 'If you are you're too early. He don't see no visitors till eleven, not even them as thinks themselves high and mighty. And he won't see you anyway. You're for the Lockholes, where you belong. Take my advice and sheer off before they come for you. We don't want you. We've work to do in the Shire now.'

'So I see,' said Sam. 'No time for a bath, but time for wall-propping. Well, never you mind, Ted, we'll find you something to do before this year's much older. And in the meantime keep your mouth shut. I've a score to pay in this village, and don't you make it any longer with your sneers, or you'll foot a bill too big for you to pay.'

Ted laughed. 'You're out o' date, Mr. Samwise, with your elves and your dragons. If I were you I'd go and catch one of them ships that [are] [?always] sailing, according to your tale. Go back to Babyland and rock your cradle, and don't bother us. We're going to make a big town here with twenty mills. A hundred new houses next year. Big stuff coming up from the South. Chaps who can work metals, and make big holes in the ground. There'll be forges a-humming and [?steamwhistles] and wheels going round. Elves can't do things like that.'

Sam looked at him, and his retorts died on his lips. He shook his head.

90   SAURON DEFEATED

'Don't worry, Sam,' said Frodo. 'He's day-dreaming, poor
wretch. And he's right behind the times. Let him be. But what
we shall do with [him] is a bit of a worry. I hope there's not
many caught the disease.'

'If I had known all the mischief Saruman had been up to,' said
Merry, 'I'd have stuffed my pouch down his throat.'

They went sadly up the winding road to Bag End. The Field of
the Party was all hillocks, as if moles had gone mad in it, but by
some miracle the tree was still standing, now forlorn and nearly
leafless.[19] They came at last to the door. The bell-chain dangled
loose. No bell could be rung, no knocking was answered. At last
they pushed and the door opened. They went in. The place
stank, it was full of filth and disorder, but it did not appear to
have been lived in for some time. 'Where is that miserable
Cosimo hiding?' they said. There was nothing living to be found
in any room save mice and rats.

'This is worse than Mordor,' said Frodo. 'Much worse in
some ways.' 'Ah,' said Sam, 'it goes home as they say, because
this is home, and it's all so, so mean, dirty [and] shabby. I'm
very sorry, Mr. Frodo. But I'm glad I didn't know before. All the
time in the bad places we've been in I've had the Shire in mind,
and that's what I've rested on, if you take my meaning. I'd not
have had a hope if I'd known all this.'

'I understand,' said Frodo. 'I said much the same to Gandalf
long ago.[20] Never mind, Sam. It's our task to put it all right
again. Hard work, but we'll not mind. Your box will come in
useful.'

'My box?' said Sam. 'Glory and sunshine, Mr. Frodo, but of
course. She knew, of course she knew. Showed me a bit in the
Mirror. Bless her. I'd well-nigh forgotten it. But let's find that
Boss first.'

'Hi you, what're you doing? Come out of it!' A loud voice
rang out. They ran to the door and saw a large man, bowlegged,
squinteyed, [?painfully ??bent] coming up the field from
one of the sheds. 'What in Mordor do you mean by it?' he
shouted. 'Come out of it. Come here, you Shire-rats. I [?saw]
you.'

They came out and went to meet him. When they drew near
enough for him to see them he stopped and looked at them, and
to Frodo it seemed that he was .... [?and] a little afraid. 'We're
looking for the Boss,' he said, 'or so I think you call him. Mr.
Cosimo of Bag End. I'm his cousin. I used to live here.'

THE SCOURING OF THE SHIRE 91

'Hi lads, hi, [?come here],' shouted the man. 'Here they are. We've got 'em.'

But there was no answer.

Frodo smiled. 'I think, Ruffian Sharkey, [?we] should cry "We've got him"? If you're calling for your other ruffians I'm afraid they've made off. To Michel Delving, I'm told. I am told you sleep sound.[21] Well, what about it now.' The hobbits drew their swords and pressed near him; but he backed away. Very orc-like all his movements were, and he stooped now with his hands nearly touching the ground. 'Blast and grind the fools,' he said. 'Why didn't they warn me?'

'They thought of themselves first, I expect,' said Frodo, 'and anyway you've given strict orders that your sleep is not to be disturbed. It's on every notice. Come. I want to see the Boss. Where is he?'

The man looked puzzled. Then he laughed. 'You're looking at him,' he said. 'I'm the Boss. I'm Sharkey all right.'

'Then where is Mr. Cosimo of Bag End?'

'Don't ask me,' said the man. 'He saw what was coming, and he legged it one night. Poor booby. But it saved us the trouble of wringing his neck. We'd had enough of him. And we've got on better without him. He hadn't the guts of his ma.'

'I see,' said Frodo. 'So you ruffians from Isengard have been bullying this country for a year, and [??pretending] to be Mayor and Shirriff and what not, and eating most of the food and ...ing folk and setting up your filthy hutches. What for?'

'Who are you,' said the man, 'to "what for" me? I'm the Boss. And I do what I like. These little swine have got to learn how to work and I'm here to learn 'em. Saruman wants goods and he wants provisions, and he wants a lot of things lying idle here. And he'll get them, or we'll screw the necks of all you little rats and take the land for ourselves.'

'Isengard is a ruin and Saruman walks as a beggar,' said Frodo. 'You've outlived your time, Ruffian Sharkey. The Dark Tower has fallen and there is a King in Gondor, and there is a King also in the North. We come from the King. I give you three days. After that you are outlaw, and if you're found in this Shire you shall be killed, as you killed the [?wretch] Cosimo. I see in your eye that you lie, and in your hands that you strangled him. Your way leads downhill and [to] the East. Quick now!'

The orc-man looked at them with such a leer of hatred as they had not seen even in all their adventures. '... you're liars like all

92   SAURON DEFEATED

your kind. Elf-friends and . . . . And four to one, which makes you so bold.'

'Very well,' said Frodo, 'one to one.' He took off his cloak. Suddenly he shone, a small gallant figure clad in mithril like an elf-prince. Sting was in his hand;[22] but he was not much more than half Sharkey's stature. Sharkey had a sword, and he drew it, and in a [?fury] hewed double-handed at Frodo. But Frodo using the advantage of his size and [?courage] ran in close holding his cloak as a shield and slashed his leg above the knee. And then as with a groan and a curse the orc-man [?toppled] over him he stabbed upwards, and Sting passed clean through his body.

So died Sharkey the Boss [?on the] . . . . where Bilbo's garden had been. Frodo [??crawling] from under him looked at him as he wiped Sting on the grass. 'Well,' he said, 'if ever Bilbo hears of this he'll believe the world has really changed! When Gandalf and I sat here long ago, I think that at least one thing I could never have guessed would be that the last stroke of the battle would be at this door.'[23]

'Why not?' said Sam. 'Very right and proper. And I'm glad that it was yours, Mr. Frodo. But if I may say so, though it was a grand day at Kormallen, and the happiest I have known, I never have felt that you got as much praise as you deserve.'

'Of course not, Sam,' said Frodo. 'I'm a hobbit. But why grumble? You've been far more neglected yourself. There's never only one hero in any true tale, Sam, and all the good folk are in others' debt. But if one had to choose one and one only, I'd choose Samwise.'

'Then you'd be wrong, Mr. Frodo,' said Sam. 'For without you I'm nothing. But you and me together, Mr. Frodo: well, that's more than either alone.'

'It's more than anything I've heard of,' said Merry. 'But as for the last stroke of battle, I'm not so sure. You've finished the beastly Boss, while I only looked on. I've a [?feeling] from the horns in the distance you'll find that Pippin and the Tooks have had the last word. Thank heaven my . . . . . is Took Brandybuck.'

It was as he said. While they had dealt with the Boss things had flared up in Bywater. The ruffians were no fools. They had sent a man on a horse to [?within] horn cry of Michel Delving (for they had many horn-signals). By midnight they had all assembled at Waymoot,[24] 18 miles west of the Bywater Road [?crossing]. They had [?horses of their own] on the White

THE SCOURING OF THE SHIRE 93

Downs and rode like the fire. They charged the road-barrier at 10 a.m. but fifty were slain. The others had scattered and escaped. Pippin had killed [?five] and was wounded himself.

So ended the [??fierce] battle of Bywater, the only battle ever fought in the Shire. And it has at least a chapter all to itself in all standard histories.

It was some time before the last ruffians were hunted out. And oddly enough, little though the hobbits were inclined to believe it, quite a number turned out to be far from incurable.

This ends a page, and with it the now fearsomely difficult writing comes to an end: for the next page is perfectly legible, and this better script continues to the end of the draft, which is also the end of *The Lord of the Rings*. The pagination is continuous, however, and the likeliest explanation seems to be that there was simply a break in composition at this point.

The division between 'The Scouring of the Shire' and 'The Grey Havens' occurs at a point in RK that has nothing corresponding in the original draft, but it is convenient to make a break here, after one further paragraph concerning the fate of the 'ruffians', and to give the further continuation of the draft in the following chapters.

If they gave themselves up they were kindly treated, and fed (for they were usually half-starved after hiding in the woods), and then shown to the borders. This sort were Dunlanders, not orc-men/halfbreeds, who had originally come because their own land was wretched, and Saruman had told them there was a good country with plenty to eat away North. It is said that they found their own country very much better in the days of the King and were glad to return; but certainly the reports that they spread (enlarged for the covering of their own shame) of the numerous and warlike, not to say ferocious, hobbits of the Shire did something to preserve the hobbits from further trouble.

It is very striking that here, virtually at the end of *The Lord of the Rings* and in an element in the whole that my father had long meditated, the story when he first wrote it down should have been so different from its final form (or that he so signally failed to see 'what really happened'!). And this is not only because the original story took a wrong direction, as it turned out, when all four of the 'travellers' went to Farmer Cotton's house, nor because he did not perceive that it was Saruman who was the real 'Boss', Sharkey, at Bag End, but most of all because Frodo is portrayed here at every stage as an energetic and commanding intelligence, warlike and resolute in action; and the

94   SAURON DEFEATED

final text of the chapter had been very largely achieved when the changed conception of Frodo's part in the Scouring of the Shire entered.

It is perhaps a minor question, to try to resolve how my father was developing the idea of 'Sharkey' as he wrote this text, but it is certainly not easy to do so. The statements made are as follows:

– The chief of the orcish men at Bywater said (p. 82) that he had told the Boss that it was no good sending hobbits, and that the men ought to have gone, but the Boss had said no. This was changed to make the man say that he had given this advice to 'Big Sharkey', but Sharkey had said no, and 'the Boss let him have his way'.

– Later in the same conversation, this man says: 'It'll get it too, and before the year's out, or my name's not Sharkey.' Then Frodo calls him (p. 83) 'Ruffian Sharkey'.

– When the ruffians came to Farmer Cotton's house it was 'Sharkey' who peered in at the door; and Frodo slew him with his sword.

– The man who accosted the hobbits at Bag End (whose orc-like character is much emphasised) is called by Frodo 'Ruffian Sharkey' (p. 91).

– Frodo tells this man that he wants to see the Boss; to which he replies: 'I'm the Boss. I'm Sharkey all right.'

– Subsequently Frodo again calls him 'Ruffian Sharkey'; and he slays him with Sting in single combat.

As the text stands there can be no solution to this unless it is supposed that my father changed his conception as he wrote without altering the earlier passages. This would probably mean that the name 'Sharkey', whatever its basis as a name, was transferred from the squint-eyed rascal at Bywater when my father saw that 'the Boss' (Cosimo Sackville-Baggins) was being used now purely nominally by some more ruthless and sinister presence at Bag End: this was 'Sharkey'.[25] Then, suddenly, after the present draft was completed, my father saw who it really was that had supplanted Cosimo, and Saruman took over the name 'Sharkey'.[26]

At any rate, it is altogether certain that Saruman only entered the Shire in person in the course of the development of the present chapter. On the other hand, his previous baleful association with Cosimo Sackville-Baggins was present in the original draft, as is seen from Frodo's remarks at Bywater (p. 84) and Merry's at Bag End (p. 90: 'If I had known all the mischief Saruman had been up to, I'd have stuffed my pouch down his throat').

It required much further work to attain the story as it stands in *The Return of the King*, and the vehicle of this development was the complicated second manuscript 'B', which was numbered 'LIX' and at first given the title 'The Mending of the Shire'. It seems very probable that Saruman's presence at Bag End had already arisen when my

THE SCOURING OF THE SHIRE 95

father began writing this text, and the references to 'Sharkey' are as in RK; but while in detail and in wording it advances far towards the final form he was still following A in certain features, and the major shift in the plot (whereby the fight at Farmer Cotton's house was removed) took place in the course of the writing of the manuscript.

Before that point in the story is reached the most notable feature is that Frodo retains his dominance and his resolute captaincy. The incident of the old 'gaffer' who jeered at the band of Shirriffs on their forced march from Frogmorton entered in B, but it was Frodo, not Merry, who sharply ordered their leader to leave him alone. The leader was still, and explicitly, Robin Smallburrow ('"Smallburrow!" said Frodo. "Order your fellows back to their places at once"'); but his displacement by the officious and anonymous leader took place in the course of the writing of this manuscript.[27]

There was a notable development in B of Frodo's exposition to Pippin concerning Cosimo and Saruman and the pass to which the Shire has been brought (see pp. 83–4). This was removed (cf. RK p. 285) when, on a rider inserted into B, it became Farmer Cotton who recounted from personal knowledge the recent history; but Cotton, of course, did not know who Sharkey was, and presumably would not have been much enlightened to learn that he was Saruman.

'I don't think you understand it quite,' said Frodo. 'Though you were at Isengard, and have heard all that I have since. Yes, Poor Cosimo! He has been a wicked fool. But he's caught in his own net now. Don't you see? Saruman became interested in us and in the Shire a good while ago, and began spying. [*Added:* So Gandalf said.] A good many of the strange folk that had been prowling about for a long while before we started must have been sent by him. I suppose he got into touch with Cosimo that way. Cosimo was rich enough, but he always did want more. I expect he started trading with Saruman, and getting richer secretly, and buying up this and that on the quiet. [*Added:* Saruman needed supplies for his war.]'

'Ah!' said Sam, 'tobacco, a weakness of Saruman's. [> 'Yes!' said Pippin. 'And tobacco for himself and his favourites!] I suppose that Cosimo must have got his hands on most of it. And on the South-farthing fields, too, I shouldn't wonder.'

'I expect so,' said Frodo. 'But he soon got bigger ideas than that. He began hiring [> He seems to have hired] ruffians; or Saruman sent them to him, to "help him". Chimneys, tree-hacking, all those shoddy little houses. They look like imitations of Saruman's notions of "improvement". But now, of course, the ruffians are on top ...'

96   SAURON DEFEATED

The text then becomes that of RK; but after Frodo's admonition on the subject of killing (RK p. 285) it continues thus, following and expanding A (p. 84):

'It depends on how many of these ruffians there are,' said Merry. 'If there are a lot, then it will certainly mean fighting, Frodo. And it isn't going to be as easy after this. It may prove a nut tough enough for Gandalf's sledgehammer. After all we're only four hobbits, even if we're armed.'

'Well, we can't help Cousin Pimple tonight,' said Pippin; 'we need to find more out. You heard that horn-blowing? There's evidently more ruffians near at hand. We ought to get under cover soon. Tonight will be dangerous.'

'I've an idea,' said Sam. 'Let's go to old Cotton's. He always was a stout fellow, and he's a lot of lads that were all friends of mine.'

'D'you mean Farmer Cotton down South Lane?' said Frodo. 'We'll try him!'

They turned, and a few yards back came on South Lane leading out of the main road; in about a quarter of a mile it brought them to the farmer's gates.

In the story of their arrival at the farm, their welcome there and conversation with Farmer Cotton, my father followed A (pp. 84–6) closely, with some minor expansion but no movement away from the draft narrative (except that the imprisonment of Lobelia Sackville-Baggins is made longer: ' "They took his ma six months ago," said Cotton, "end o' last April" '). But from the bang on the front door the story changes:

There came at that moment a loud bang on the door. Farmer Cotton went softly down the passage, putting out the light. The others followed. There was a second louder bang.

'Open up, you old rat, or we'll burn you out!' shouted a hoarse voice outside. Mrs. Cotton in a nearby room stifled a scream. Down the stairs that led into the kitchen five young hobbits came clattering from the two upper rooms where they slept. They had thick sticks, but nothing more.

'I'm coming,' shouted the farmer, rattling the chains and making a to-do with the bolts. 'How many is there?' he whispered to his sons. 'A dozen at least,' said Young Tom, the eldest, 'maybe all the lot.'

'All the better,' said Frodo. 'Now for it! Open up and then get back. Don't join in, unless we need help badly.'

THE SCOURING OF THE SHIRE 97

The four hobbits with swords drawn stood back to the wall against which the door swung. There came a great blow on the lock, but at that moment the farmer drew the last bolt, and slipped back with his sons some paces down the passage [*added: and round the corner out of sight*]. The door opened slowly and in peered the head of the ruffian they had already met. He stepped forward, stooping, holding a sword in his hand. As soon as he was well inside, the hobbits, who were now behind the opened door, flung it back with a crash. While Frodo slipped a bolt back, the three others leaped on the ruffian from behind, threw him down on his face and sat on him. He felt a cold blade of steel at his neck.

'Keep still and quiet!' said Sam. 'Cotton!' called Merry. 'Rope! We've got one. Tie him up!'

But the ruffians outside began attacking the door again, while some were smashing the windows with stones. 'Prisoner!' said Frodo. 'You seem a leader. Stop your men, or you will pay for the damage!'

They dragged him close to the door. 'Go home, you fools!' he shouted. 'They've got me, and they'll do for me, if you go on. Clear out! Tell Sharkey!'

'What for?' a voice answered from outside. 'We know what Sharkey wants. Come on, lads! Burn the whole lot inside! Sharkey won't miss that boob; he's no use for them as makes mistakes. Burn the lot! Look alive and get the fuel!'

'Try again!' said Sam grimly.

The prisoner now desperately frightened screamed out: 'Hi, lads! No burnings! No more burnings, Sharkey said. Send a messenger. You might find it was you as had made a mistake. Hi! D'you hear?'

'All right, lads!' said the other voice. 'Two of you ride back quick. Two go for fuel. The rest make a ring round the place!'

'Well, what's the next move?' said Farmer Cotton. 'At least they won't start burning until they've ridden to Bag-end and back: say half an hour, allowing for some talk. The murdering villains! Never thought they'd start burning. They burned a lot of folk out earlier, but they've not done [any] for a long while. We understood the Boss had stopped it. But see here! I've got the wife and my daughter Rosie to think of.'

'There's only two things to be done,' said Frodo. 'One of us has got to slip out and get help: rouse the folk. There must be

98   SAURON DEFEATED

200 grown hobbits not far away. Or else we've got to burst out
in a pack with your wife and daughter in a huddle, and do it
quick, while two are away and before more come.'

'Too much risk for the one [that] slips out,' said Cotton.
'Burst out together, that's the ticket, and make a dash up the
lane.'

The concluding passage, from 'There's only two things to be done,'
was written in a rapidly degenerating scribble, and the text ends here,
not at the foot of a page. The story of the attack on the farmhouse had
already shifted strongly away from that in the original draft (in which
Frodo and Sam slew two of the marauders at the front door and four
others were killed in the yard before the remainder fled); and at this
point my father decided that he had taken a wrong turning. Perhaps he
could not see any credible way in which they could burst out of the
house (with the young Cottons and their mother in the midst) and
through the ring of men unscathed. At any rate, the whole of this part
of the B text, from ' "D'you mean Farmer Cotton down South Lane?"
said Frodo' (p. 96), was removed from the manuscript and replaced by
a new start, with Frodo's saying in response to Sam's suggestion that
they all go to Farmer Cotton's: 'No! It's no good getting "under
cover" ', as in RK (p. 286), where however it is Merry who says this. It
is Frodo also, not Merry, who answers Pippin's question 'Do what?'
with 'Raise the Shire! Now! Wake all our people!', and tells Sam that
he can make a dash for Cotton's farm if he wants to; he ends 'Now,
Merry, you have a horn of the Mark. Let us hear it!'

The story of the return of the four hobbits to the middle of Bywater,
Merry's horn-call, Sam's meeting with Farmer Cotton and his sons, his
visit to Mrs. Cotton and Rose, and the fire made by the villagers, is
told in virtually the same words as in RK (pp. 286–8), the only
difference being that it was on the orders of Frodo, not of Merry, that
barriers were set up across the road at each end of Bywater. When
Farmer Cotton tells that the Boss (as he is still named throughout B,
though emended later to 'the Chief') has not been seen for a week or
two B diverges a little from RK, for Tom Cotton the younger
interrupts his father at this point:

'They took his ma, that Lobelia,' put in Young Tom. 'That'd
be six months back, when they started putting up sheds at Bag
End without her leave. She ordered 'em off. So they took her.
Put her in the Lock-holes. They've took others that we miss
more; but there's no denying she stood up to 'em bolder than
most.'

'That's where most of them are,' said the farmer, 'over at
Michel Delving. They've made the old Lock-holes into a regular

THE SCOURING OF THE SHIRE 99

fort, we hear, and they go from there roaming round, "gathering". Still I guess that there's no more than a couple of hundred in the Shire all told. We can master 'em, if we stick together.'
'Have they got any weapons?' asked Merry.

This perhaps implies that the *Lock-holes* were a prison in the days before any 'ruffian' came to the Shire. Subsequently Young Tom's story of Lobelia was removed from this part of the narrative, and replaced by Pippin's question 'Hobbiton's not their only place, is it?', which leads into Farmer Cotton's account of where else the 'ruffians' hung out beside Hobbiton, as in RK (p. 288), and a different idea of the origin of the Lock-holes: 'some old tunnels at Michel Delving'.

Merry's question 'Have they got any weapons?' leads, as in RK, to Farmer Cotton's account of the resistance of the Tooks, but without his reference to Pippin's father (Paladin Took), the Thain, and his refusal to have anything to do with the pretensions of Lotho (Cosimo):

'There you are, Frodo!' said Merry. 'I knew we'd have to fight. Well, they started it.'
'Not exactly,' said Farmer Cotton, 'leastways not the shooting. Tooks started that. You see, the Tooks have got those deep holes in the Green Hills, the Smiles[28] as they call 'em, and the ruffians can't come at 'em ...'

With Frodo still firmly in the saddle at Bywater, Merry rode off with Pippin to Tuckborough (as he does not in RK). After they had gone, Frodo reiterated his injunction against any killing that could be avoided (as in RK, p. 289), but then continued: 'We shall be having a visit from the Hobbiton gang very soon. It's over an hour since we sent the four ruffians off from here. Do nothing, until I give the word. Let them come on!' In RK it is Merry who gives the warning that the men from Hobbiton will soon be coming to Bywater, and he concludes 'Now I've got a plan'; to which Frodo merely replies 'Very good. You make the arrangements.' The arrival of the men, and the trapping of them beside the fire where Farmer Cotton was standing apparently all alone, follows exactly as in the final story, except that it is of course Frodo, not Merry, who accosts the leader; and when this encounter is over, and the men bundled off into one of their own huts, Farmer Cotton says 'You came back in the nick, Mr. Frodo.'

Then follows Cotton's account to Sam of the condition of the Gaffer ('he's in one of them new Shire-houses, Boss-houses I call 'em'), and Sam's departure to fetch him, virtually as in RK (p. 291). Once again, it is Frodo not Merry who posts look-outs and guards, and he goes off alone with Farmer Cotton to his house: 'He sat with the family in the kitchen, and they asked a few polite questions, but were far more concerned with events in the Shire. In the middle of the talk in burst

100   SAURON DEFEATED

Sam, with the Gaffer.' The farmer's account of the 'troubles', ending
with Young Tom's story of the carting off of Lobelia to the Lock-holes
(RK p. 291–3), was inserted into B on a long rider; and at this time
Frodo's earlier suppositions about how it all began (p. 95) and Young
Tom's earlier remarks about Lobelia (p. 98) were removed.[29]

The incursion of the Gaffer into the Cottons' kitchen is told as in
RK (pp. 293–4); but then follows in B:

> In the morning early they heard the ringing call of Merry's
> horn, and in marched nearly a hundred of Tooks and other
> hobbits from Tuckborough and the Green Hills. The Shire was
> all alight, they said, and the ruffians that prowled round
> Tookland had fled; east to the Brandywine mostly, pursued by
> other Tooks.
>
> There were now enough forces for a strong guard on the East
> Road from Michel Delving to Brandywine, and for another
> guard in Bywater. When all that had been settled and put in the
> charge of Pippin, Frodo and Sam and Merry with Farmer
> Cotton and an escort of fifty set out for Hobbiton.

The text then continues with the story of their coming to Hobbiton
and meeting with Ted Sandyman, and their entry into Bag End, told
almost word for word as in RK (pp. 296–7);[30] and ends with the
advent of Saruman and his murder by Wormtongue (on which see pp.
102–3). The text B ends just as does the chapter in RK, with Merry's
saying 'And the very last end of the War, I hope', Frodo's calling it 'the
very last stroke', and Sam's saying 'I shan't call it the end, till we've
cleared up the mess.' But there is thus no Battle of Bywater!

The Battle is found on inserted pages that are numbered as
additional ('19a, 19b') to the consecutive pagination of the text just
described. If this pagination means that these pages were written and
inserted subsequently, and it is hard to see what else it could mean, it
might seem that my father (still following the story in A, in which the
visit to Hobbiton preceded the battle, p. 92) had driven on to the end
of the Bag End episode without realising that the story of the Battle of
Bywater had yet to be told. But this seems incredible. Far more likely
he saw, as he wrote the story of the visit to Hobbiton, that the order of
the narration in A must be reversed, so that the chapter would end
with the last stroke of the War 'at the very door of Bag End'; but he
postponed the battle, and inserted it subsequently into the text already
continuously paginated.

Whenever this was done, the existing text (in which the dispositions
for defence next morning were followed at once by the visit to
Hobbiton) was altered to that of RK (p. 294), and the approach of
the men along the road from Waymoot and their ambush on the
high-banked road to Bywater was told almost as in the final story: the

THE SCOURING OF THE SHIRE 101

few differences in this passage are chiefly caused by Merry's having gone to Tuckborough with Pippin. The messenger from the Tookland does not refer to the Thain (see p. 99), and tells that 'Mr. Peregrin and Mr. Merry are coming on with all the folk we can spare'; it was Nick Cotton, not Merry, who had been out all night and reported the approach of the men, whom he estimated to number 'fifty or more' ('close on a hundred', RK); and when the Tooks came in 'the ringing call of Merry's horn was heard.' But from the point where the way back out of the ambush was blocked against the ruffian men, when the hobbits pushed out more carts onto the road, the B text diverges remarkably from the story told in RK:

A voice spoke to them from above. 'Well,' said Frodo, 'you have walked into a trap. Your fellows from Hobbiton did the same, and are all prisoners now. Lay down your weapons! Then go back twenty paces and sit down. Any who try to break out will be shot.'

Many of the men, in spite of the curses of their more villainous mates, at once obeyed. But more than a score turned about and charged back down the lane. Hobbit archers at gaps in the hedges shot down six before they reached the waggons. Some of them gave up, but ten or more burst through and dashed off, and scattered across country making for the Woody End it seemed.

Merry blew a loud horn-call. There were answering calls from a distance. 'They won't get far!' he said. 'All that country is now alive with hunters.'

The dead ruffians were laden on waggons and taken off and buried in an old gravel-pit nearby, the Battle Pits as they were called ever afterwards. The others were marched off to the village to join their fellows.

So ended the Battle of Bywater, 1419, the [only >] last battle fought in the Shire, and the only battle since the Greenfields, 1137,[31] away up in the North Farthing. In consequence, although it only cost six ruffian lives and no hobbits it has a chapter to itself in all the standard histories, and the names of all those who took part were made into a Roll and learned by heart. The very considerable rise in the fame and fortunes of the Cottons dates from this time.

The connection with the visit to Hobbiton was made in these words:

When all was settled, and a late midday meal had been eaten, Merry said: 'Well now, Frodo, it's time to deal with the Chief.'

102 SAURON DEFEATED

Farmer Cotton collected an escort of some fifty sturdy hobbits, and then they set out on foot for Bag End: Frodo, Sam, Merry and Pippin led the way.

The words 'When all was settled' are used now to refer to the ending of the battle and the disposal of the dead and captured ruffians; previously (p. 100) they had referred to the arrangements made to meet the approaching enemy.

The story of the meeting with Saruman at Bag End was written out twice in B, the first form soon declining into a scribble when my father thought better of the opening of the episode. The first opening I give here:

'No doubt, no doubt. But you did not, and so I am able to welcome you home!' There standing at the door was Saruman, looking well-fed and a great deal less wretched than before; his eyes gleamed with malice and amusement.

A sudden light broke on Frodo. 'Sharkey!' he said. Saruman laughed. 'So you've heard that, have you? I believe all my men used to call me that in the better times. They were so devoted. And so it has followed me up here, has it? Really I find that quite cheering.'

'I cannot imagine why,' said Frodo. 'And what are you doing here anyway? Just a little shabby mischief? Gandalf said he thought you were still capable of that.'

[*Struck out:* 'Need you ask?' said Saruman.] 'You make me laugh, you hobbit lordlings,' said Saruman. 'Riding along with all these great people so secure and so pleased with yourselves; thinking you have done great things and can now just come back and laze in the country. Saruman's home can be ruined, and he can be turned out. But not Mr. Baggins. Oh, no! He's really important.

'But Mr. Baggins is a fool all the same. And can't even mind his own affairs, always minding other people's. To be expected of a pupil of Gandalf. He must dawdle on the way, and ride twice as far as he need. The Shire would be all right. Well, after our little meeting I thought I might get ahead of you and learn you a lesson. It would have been a sharper lesson if only you had dawdled longer. Still I have done a little that you'll find it hard to mend in your time. It'll be a warning to you to leave other folk alone, and not to be so cocksure. And it will give me something quite pleasant to think about, to set against my own injuries.'

THE SCOURING OF THE SHIRE 103

The second version of the episode in B is virtually as in RK, except that it entirely lacks any reference to the dreadful corpse of Saruman and the mist that rose above it and loomed 'as a pale shrouded figure' over the Hill of Hobbiton; and this passage did not enter until my father wrote it in on the page proofs of *The Return of the King*.

A note that he pencilled against the episode in a copy of the First Edition is interesting:

Saruman turned back into Dunland[32] on Aug. 28. He then made for the old South Road and then went north over the Greyflood at Tharbad, and thence NW. to Sarn Ford, and so into the Shire and to Hobbiton on Sept. 22: a journey of about 460 [miles] in 25 days. He thus averaged about 18 miles a day – evidently hastening as well as he could. He had thus only 38 days in which to work his mischief in the Shire; but much of it had already been done by the ruffians according to his orders – already planned and issued before the sack of Isengard.

September 22 is the date given in *The Tale of Years* for Saruman's coming to the Shire, and October 30 for the coming of the 'travellers' to the Brandywine Bridge.

At a late stage of work on the B text (but before the insertion of the long rider in which Farmer Cotton recounts the history of the Shire since Frodo and his companions left, see p. 100 and note 29) my father perceived that Frodo's experience had so changed him, so withdrawn him, as to render him incapable of any such rôle in the Scouring of the Shire as had been portrayed. The text as it stood required no large recasting; the entirely different picture of Frodo's part in the events was brought about by many small alterations (often by doing no more than changing 'Frodo' to 'Merry') and a few brief additions. Virtually all of these have been noticed in the foregoing account.

A third, very fine manuscript ('C') followed B, and here the text of RK was reached in all but a few passages, most of these being very minor matters. It was on this manuscript that Cosimo Sackville-Baggins became Lotho, and the references to the Thain were introduced (see pp. 99, 101). The number of men at the Battle of Bywater had been enlarged to 'more than seventy', and the battle had become much fiercer, with the trapped men climbing the banks above the road and attacking the hobbits, already as C was first written; by later emendation the numbers of the men and of the slain on both sides were further increased. The original reading of C 'Merry himself slew the largest of the ruffians' was altered to '. . . the leader, a great squint-eyed brute like a huge orc'; with this cf. the description of the orc-man 'Sharkey' at Bag End in the A version, pp. 90–1. Lastly, an important addition was made to C concerning Frodo: 'Frodo had been

104   SAURON DEFEATED

in the battle, but he had not drawn sword, and his chief part had been
to prevent the hobbits in their wrath at their losses from slaying those
of their enemies who threw down their weapons' (RK pp. 295–6).

There lacked now only the passage describing the departure of the
spirit of Saruman, and his corpse.

NOTES

1   Subsequently the passage was corrected in pencil. The question
'Who's the Mayor?' was given to Merry, and the answer became
'The Boss at Bag End'; Frodo's 'And who's the Chief Shirriff?'
received the same answer. Then follows: 'Boss? Boss? You mean
Mr. Cosimo, I suppose.' 'I suppose so, Mr. Baggins, but we have
to say just The Boss nowadays.'
Further on, where in RK (p. 279) it is said that 'The new
"Chief" evidently had means of getting news', A has 'the New
Mayor [?or] Chief Shirriff'; but this was changed to 'the Boss or
Chief Shirriff'. When 'arrested' at Frogmorton Frodo and his
companions are told that 'It's [Mayor's >] the Chief Shirriff's
orders', where RK (p. 280) has 'It's the Chief's orders'.

2   But see p. 111.

3   The village was named *Frogbarn*, with *Frogmorton* written above
as an alternative (and *Frogmorton* occurs in the text subsequently); and the date of their ride from the Brandywine Bridge was
'the fifth of November in the Shire-reckoning', with '1st' (the date
in RK) written above. The village was 'about 25 miles from the
Bridge' ('about twenty-two miles' in RK).

4   The name *Smallburrow* was written so, as in RK, at the first
occurrence, but thereafter *Smallburrows*.

5   'Shire-house' is used in A for 'Shirriff-house' in RK. Sam asks
what the term means, and Robin Smallburrows replies: 'Well,
you ought to know, Sam. You were in one last night, and didn't
find it to your liking, we hear.'

6   See p. 95.

7   The text here is very difficult. Above '(I told) the Boss' my father
first wrote 'Long Tom' before changing this to 'Big Sharkey'. The
end of the ruffian's remarks as first written cannot be read: 'but
the Boss says no, and [?Long Tom] ..... way' (just possibly 'goes
his way').

8   There is a note on the manuscript here which is partly illegible:
' .... only Cosimo .... What happened to Otho?' In 'Three
is Company' (*The Fellowship of the Ring* p. 75) it is said that
Otho Sackville-Baggins 'had died some years before, at the ripe
but disappointed age of 102', and this goes back to an early stage.

9   See the note given on p. 77 ('Gandalf should stay at Bree ...').

THE SCOURING OF THE SHIRE   105

10   In RK Farmer Cotton is named Tom.

11   Sting had been given to Sam by Frodo in 'The Land of Shadow' (p. 32; RK p. 204); but Frodo wields Sting in his combat at Bag End with the chief of the orc-men (p. 92). In a passage that was introduced in the Second Edition Frodo was induced to receive it back at the Field of Cormallen (see p. 50).

12   *the Road Bend*: the westward turn in the road to Hobbiton at Bywater Pool. On the large-scale map of the Shire that I made in 1943 (VI.107) the bend is more marked and more nearly a right angle than it is on the small map in *The Fellowship of the Ring*.

13   *October* is a slip for *November*: see note 3.

14   By 'There's no way from the West' Farmer Cotton meant, I suppose, that there was no other way back from Michel Delving but by taking the East Road, since the ruffians could not or would not pass through the Tookland.

15   There are a couple of pages of roughly pencilled text which repeat, with minor alterations and extensions, this section of the chapter in A, made perhaps because my father recognised the near-illegibility of the original, and these pages have provided help in elucidating it here and there (characteristically, the words or phrases that defy elucidation in the original text are expressed differently in the second). At this point the pencilled text has: 'They've caught a ruffian or two and thrashed 'em in the Tookus' (*Tookus* < *Took-house*, as *workhouse* became *workus*).

16   I do not know whether *the Long Smial* is to be equated with *the Took-house*. – This is the first appearance of the word *smial*, which seems clearly to be written thus, although in the second text of 'The Scouring of the Shire' it is written *Smiles* (see p. 99 and note 28). Since Pippin was born in the Long Smial, it must be the forerunner of the Great Smials. These were at Tuckborough (Pippin speaks in Fangorn Forest of 'the Great Place of the Tooks away back in the Smials at Tuckborough', TT p. 64), but the name as written here is not in fact *Tuckborough*: it looks more like *Tuckbery* (not *Tuckbury*). However, there are many words wrongly written in this manuscript (in the next line of the text, for instance, the word I have given as '[?stout]' can really only be interpreted as 'stood').

17   The text could conceivably be interpreted as 'he had the block on the East [Road] strengthened', although no road-block on the East Road has been mentioned. The second, pencilled text of this part of the chapter (see note 15) has here: 'He had a block made on the Road at the waymeet.' This text gives out a few lines beyond this point.

18   It is interesting to look back at early references to the destruction in the Shire. In a note probably belonging to the time of the outline 'The Story Foreseen from Moria' (VII.216) my father

106 SAURON DEFEATED

wrote: 'Cosimo has industrialised it. Factories and smoke. The Sandymans have a biscuit factory. Iron is found'; and in the earliest reference to the Mirror in Lothlórien Frodo was to see 'Trees being felled and a tall building being made where the old mill was. Gaffer Gamgee turned out. Open trouble, almost war, between Marish and Buckland on one hand – and the West. Cosimo Sackville-Baggins very rich, buying up land' (VII.249; cf. also VII.253, where there is a reference to the tall chimney being built on the site of the old mill).

In 'The old farm on the right' one should possibly read 'left' for 'right'; cf. my father's painting of Hobbiton, and the words of the final text of 'The Scouring of the Shire' (RK p. 296): 'The Old Grange on the west side had been knocked down, and its place taken by rows of tarred sheds.'

19 Later in this manuscript (p. 108) the Tree in the Party Field had been cut down and burned.

20 The reference is to 'The Shadow of the Past' (FR p. 71): 'I feel that as long as the Shire lies behind, safe and comfortable, I shall find wandering more bearable: I shall know that somewhere there is a firm foothold, even if my feet cannot stand there again.'

21 *I am told you sleep sound:* cf. the words of the orc-man at Bywater, speaking of Cosimo (an addition to the text, p. 83): 'He sleeps sound, and I shouldn't try and wake him now.'

22 Earlier in this narrative Sam wielded Sting: p. 86 and note 11.

23 At the top of the page on which Frodo's words appear my father wrote: 'Ah, and you said in Mordor you'd never strike another blow,' said Sam. 'Just shows you never know.' See p. 80.

24 *Waymoot: Waymeet* in RK. My original large-scale map of the Shire made in 1943 (VI.107) has *Waymoot*, as also that published in *The Fellowship of the Ring*; but the second manuscript of 'The Scouring of the Shire' has *Waymeet*. Presumably my father changed his mind about the form but neglected the map.

25 It is not explained how Frodo knew that this person, when he met him at Bag End, was called 'Sharkey'.

26 Cf. Saruman's words at the end of the chapter (p. 102): 'I believe all my men used to call me that in the better times. They were so devoted' (RK: 'All my people used to call me that in Isengard, I believe. A sign of affection, possibly'). The footnote to the text in RK p. 298 'It was probably Orkish in origin: *Sharkū* [Second Edition *Sharkû*], "old man"' was not added until the book was in page proof.

27 A rewritten account of the arrest at Frogmorton and Sam's conversation with Robin Smallburrow was inserted into manuscript B. This is almost as in RK, but as first written Robin's reply to Sam's question 'So that's how the news of us reached you, was it?' was different:

THE SCOURING OF THE SHIRE 107

'Not directly. A message came down from the Chief at Bag End, about two hours ago, that you were to be arrested. I reckon someone must have slipped down from the Bridge to Stock, where there's a small gang of his Men. Someone went through Frogmorton on a big horse last night.'

This was changed at once to the text of RK (p. 282), but with 'One [runner] came in from Bamfurlong last night'. *Bamfurlong* was the reading of the First Edition here. In the Second Edition it was changed to *Whitfurrows* (which though shown on the map of the Shire was never mentioned in the text of the First Edition), and the name *Bamfurlong* was given to Maggot's farm in 'A Short Cut to Mushrooms' (FR p. 100): 'We are on old Farmer Maggot's land' of the First Edition became 'This is Bamfurlong; old Farmer Maggot's land.'

28   Cf. *the Long Smial* in A (note 16). A draft for the present passage has: 'those deep places the Old Smiles in the Green Hills'. I would guess that my father introduced *Smiles* as being the most natural spelling if the old word had survived into Modern English, but then abandoned it (it was changed to *Smials* on the B text) as being capable of an absurd interpretation. Cf. Appendix F (II, 'On Translation'): '*smial* (or *smile*) "burrow" is a likely form for a descendant of *smygel*'.

29   This rider was inserted at a late stage, for as in RK Merry interrupts Farmer Cotton with a question ('Who is this Sharkey?'); thus he was no longer away in Tuckborough with Pippin, but had assumed his rôle as commander of the operations at Bywater.

30   The only differences worth noting are that the trees had been felled along the Bywater Road 'for fuel for the engine'; and that a few men were still present in the huts at Hobbiton, who 'when they saw the force that approached fled away over the fields.'

31   It is said in the Prologue to *The Lord of the Rings* that 'before this story opens' 'the only [battle] that had ever been fought within the borders of the Shire was beyond living memory: the Battle of Greenfields, S.R.1147, in which Bandobras Took routed an invasion of Orcs.' The date 1137 was corrected to 1147 on the text C. – See p. 119.

32   In the First Edition the meeting with Saruman took place after the company had left Dunland: see p. 69.

X

THE GREY HAVENS

The original writing down of the last chapter of *The Lord of the Rings* was the continuation of the long uninterrupted draft text ('A') that extends back through 'The Scouring of the Shire' and 'Homeward Bound' (see pp. 75, 79), and which I left at the end of the Battle of Bywater on p. 93. That text continues:

And so the year drew to its end. Even Sam could find no fault with Frodo's fame and honour in his own country. The Tooks were too secure in their traditional position – and after all their folkland was the only one that had never given in to the ruffians – and also too generous to be really jealous; yet it was plain that the name of Baggins would become the most famous in Hobbit-history.

From this point the text of A, rough but now fully legible, differs chiefly from the final form of the chapter not in what is actually told nor in how it is told but in the absence of several significant features and a good deal of detail that were added in later. For example, while the rescue of Lobelia Sackville-Baggins from the Lockholes in Michel Delving and the disposition of her property is told much as in RK, there is no mention of Fredegar Bolger; and nothing is said of the hunting out of the gangs of men in the south of the Shire by Merry and Pippin. Frodo became the Mayor, not the Deputy Mayor, although the difference was only one of title, since he made it a condition of his acceptance that Will Whitfoot should become Mayor again 'as soon as the mess is cleared up'; and his inactivity in the office is not mentioned. As my father first set it down the account in RK (pp. 302–4) of the work of restoration and repair, of Sam's planting of young trees, of the fruitfulness of the year 1420,[1] and of Sam's marriage to Rose Cotton was very largely reached. In this text there is no reference to 'Sharkey's Men', and the jocular name given in Bywater to the restored Bagshot Row was 'Ruffians' End'. The seed in Galadriel's box is described as 'like a nut or a dried berry', its colour golden-yellow; Sam planted it in the Party Field 'where the tree had been burned' (see p. 90).

There is in A no reference to Frodo's first illness in March of 1420, when in Sam's absence Farmer Cotton found him on his bed 'clutching a white gem that hung on a chain about his neck' (the gift of Arwen recorded in 'Many Partings'). The passage in RK (p. 305) describing

THE GREY HAVENS   109

the finery and magnificence of Merry and Pippin, in contrast to the 'ordinary attire' of Frodo and Sam, is lacking, and so the further reference to the white jewel that Frodo always wore is also absent. Since my father had written a couple of pages earlier that 'Even Sam could find no fault with Frodo's fame and honour in his own country', the sharply contrasting picture in RK is of course lacking: 'Frodo dropped quietly out of all the doings of the Shire, and Sam was pained to notice how little honour he had in his own country. Few people knew or wanted to know about his deeds and adventures . . .'

Frodo's illness on the sixth of October 1420, the date of the attack of the Ringwraiths at Weathertop two years before, is recorded, but not that in March 1421. The naming of Sam's eldest daughter *Elanor* ('born on 25 March as Sam duly noted') on Frodo's suggestion is told, and the big book with red leather covers is described, without however any mention of the title page and the sequence of Bilbo's rejected titles; the writing in the book ended at Chapter 77 (the number being marked with a query).[2]

The last part of the chapter was set down with great sureness, though not all elements in the final story were immediately present. At the meeting of Frodo and Sam with the Elves in the Woody End there is no mention of the Great Rings of Elrond and Galadriel;[3] at Mithlond Círdan the Shipwright does not appear (but enters in a later marginal addition), nor is Gandalf said to bear the Third Ring; and Frodo's sight of the 'far green country under a swift sunrise' is absent (though this also is roughed in marginally; the linking of Frodo's passage over the Sea 'with the vision he had of a far green country in the house of Tom Bombadil' had been referred to in my father's letter of November 1944, see p. 53). I give here the text of A from the coming of the company to Mithlond:

And when they had passed the Shire by the south skirts of the White Downs they came to the Far Downs and the Towers and looked on the Sea; and rode down at last to Mithlond the Grey Havens in the long firth of Lūne. And there was a ship lying at the haven, and upon the quays stood one robed also in white. It was Gandalf, and he welcomed them; and they were glad for then they knew that he also would take ship with them.

But Sam was now sad at heart, and it seemed to him that if the parting would be bitter, even worse would be the lonely ride home. But even as they stood there and were ready to go aboard, up rode Merry and Pippin in great haste. And amid his tears Pippin laughed. 'You tried to give us the slip once before and failed, Frodo, and this time you have nearly done it, but you've failed again.' 'It was not Sam this time who gave you away,' said Merry, 'but Gandalf himself.'

110   SAURON DEFEATED

'Yes,' said Gandalf. 'It will be better to ride back three together than one alone. Well, here at last, dear friends, on the shores of the Sea comes an end of our fellowship in Middle-earth. Go in peace; and I will not say, do not weep, for not all tears are an evil.'

Then Frodo kissed Merry and Pippin and last of all Sam, and went aboard, and the sails were drawn up, and the wind blew, and slowly the ship sailed away down the [?pale] Gulf of Lune. And it was night again; and Sam looked on the grey sea and saw a shadow on the waters that was lost in the West. And he stood a while hearing the sigh and murmur of the waves on the shores of Middle-earth, and the sound of it remained in his heart for ever, though he never spoke of it. And Merry and Pippin stood silent beside him.

The long ride back to the Shire is told in almost the same words as in *The Return of the King*. And thus the Third Age was brought to its final end, in this most memorable of partings, without hesitation and with assured simplicity; the unmistakeable voices of Merry and Pippin, the still more unmistakeable voice of Gandalf in his last words on Middle-earth, and the beginning of the voyage that was bearing away into the True West the hobbits, Bilbo and Frodo, leaving Sam behind.

A manuscript of the chapter as a separate entity ('B') followed, subsequently numbered 'LX' and entitled 'The Grey Havens'. It was written before the changed view of Frodo's reputation in the Shire had entered, but with emendations and additions it reached the final form in almost all the features in which A differed from it. My father did not yet realise, however, that Fredegar Bolger languished in the Lockholes along with Will Whitfoot and Lobelia Sackville-Baggins; and of Lobelia it was said in a first draft of the passage concerning her that 'She never got over the news of poor Cosimo's murder, and she said that it was not his fault; he was led astray by that wicked Sharkey and never meant any harm.'

Frodo's first illness was still absent as B was originally written, and when it was introduced it was in these words:

Sam was away on his forestry work in March, and Frodo was glad, for he had been feeling ill, and it would have been difficult to conceal from Sam. On the twelfth of March[4] he was in pain and weighed down with a great sense of darkness, and could do little more than walk about clasping the jewel of Queen Arwen. But after a while the fit passed.

THE GREY HAVENS 111

An idea that was never carried further appears in a hastily scribbled passage on this manuscript, apparently intended for inclusion before 'Little Elanor was nearly six months old, and 1421 had passed to its autumn' (RK p. 306):

At midsummer Gandalf appeared suddenly, and his visit was long remembered for the astonishing things that happened to all the bonfires (which hobbit [?children] light on midsummer's eve). The whole Shire was lit with lights of many colours until the dawn came, and it seemed that the fire [??ran wild for him] over all the land so that the grass was kindled with glittering jewels, and the trees were hung with red and gold blossom all through the night, and the Shire was full of light and song until the dawn came.

No other trace of this idea is found. Perhaps my father felt that when Gandalf declared that his time was over he meant no less.[5]

The title page of the Red Book of Westmarch first appears in B, with Bilbo's titles written one above the other and all struck through (which was the meaning of the word 'so' in 'crossed out one after another, so:', RK p. 307):

Memoirs of An Amateur Burglar
My Unexpected Journey
There and Back Again   and What Happened After
Adventures of Five Hobbits
The Case of the Great Ring (compiled from the records
    and notes of B. Baggins and others)
What the Bagginses Did in the War of the Ring
(here Bilbo's hand ended and Frodo had written:)
The
Downfall
of
The Lord of the Rings
and
The Return of the King
(as seen by B. and F. Baggins, S. Gamgee, M. Brandybuck, P. Took,
    supplemented by information provided by the Wise)

In the typescript that followed B the following was added:

Together with certain excerpts from Books of Lore
translated by B. Baggins in Rivendell[6]

In B appeared the Three Rings of the Elves on the fingers of their bearers, but they were not yet named. It was not until the book was in galley proof that 'Vilya, mightiest of the Three' was added to the description of Elrond's Ring, Gandalf's Ring was named 'Narya the

112   SAURON DEFEATED

Great', and that of Galadriel became 'Nenya, the ring wrought of *mithril*'.

Lastly, both in A and in B my father set within square brackets, his usual sign of doubt, certain of Frodo's words to Sam in the Woody End, thus: 'No, Sam. Not yet anyway, not further than the Havens. [Though you too were a Ringbearer, if only for a little while: your time may come.]'

NOTES

1 Absent from the account of the year 1420 is the sentence in RK, p. 303: 'All the children born or begotten in that year, and there were many, were fair to see and strong, and most of them had a rich golden hair that had before been rare among hobbits.' This entered in the first typescript text. See p. 134, note 12.

2 In the following text the last, unfinished chapter in the Red Book was numbered '72', and on the first typescript this was changed to '80', as in RK.

3 The chant to Elbereth began thus:

> *O Elbereth Gilthoniel*
> *Silivren pennar oriel!*
> *Gilthoniel O Elbereth ...*

Cf. VI.394. This was repeated in the second text of the chapter, but *oriel* was emended to *íriel*. This in turn was repeated on the first typescript, and then the opening was changed to its form in RK:

> *A! Elbereth Gilthoniel*
> *silivren penna míriel*
> *o menel aglar elenath ...*

To Bilbo's question (RK p. 309) 'Are you coming?' Frodo replies here: 'Yes, I am coming, *before the wound returns*. And the Ringbearers should go together.' Frodo was speaking of the sickness that had come on him on October the sixth, the date of his wounding at Weathertop, in each of the following years. It was now 22 September (Bilbo's birthday); on the twenty-ninth of the month the ship sailed from the Grey Havens. On the third anniversary of the attack at Weathertop *The Lord of the Rings* ends, for it was on that day, according to *The Tale of Years*, that Sam returned to Bag End.

4 The date was corrected to the thirteenth of March on the following typescript text. This in the final chronology was the anniversary of the poisoning of Frodo by Shelob, as noted in *The Tale of Years*. Frodo's third illness, in the following year, also fell on March 13, according to *The Tale of Years*.

5 But he had perhaps intended that a final visit by Gandalf to the Shire should be recorded; as Gandalf said when he parted from the

THE GREY HAVENS
113

hobbits in the note on the draft manuscript of 'Homeward Bound' (p. 77): 'I'll be along some time.'

6   In the two typescript texts of the chapter the crossings-out were omitted, and Bilbo's first title 'Memoirs of an Amateur Burglar' was replaced by 'My Diary'. 'What Happened After' was still shown as an addition, and the words 'and friends' were added after 'Bagginses' in Bilbo's final title; in the margins of both typescripts my father noted that the corrections were to be printed as such, representing the original title-page. The final form of the page was introduced on the galley proof.

XI

THE EPILOGUE

The words that end *The Lord of the Rings*, ' "Well, I'm back," he said', were not intended to do so when my father wrote them in the long draft manuscript A which has been followed in the previous chapters. It is obvious from the manuscript that the text continued on without break;[1] and there is in fact no indication that my father thought of what he was writing as markedly separate from what preceded. I give now this last part of A: very rough, but legible throughout. The ages of Sam's children were added, almost certainly at the time of writing: Elanor 15, Frodo 13, Rose 11, Merry 9, Pippin 7.

And one evening in March [*added:* 1436][2] Master Samwise Gamgee was taking his ease by a fire in his study, and the children were all gathered about him, as was not at all unusual, though it was always supposed to be a special treat.

He had been reading aloud (as was usual) from a big Red Book on a stand, and on a stool beside him sat Elanor, and she was a beautiful child more fair-skinned than most hobbit-maids and more slender, and she was now running up into her 'teens; and there was Frodo-lad on the heathrug, in spite of his name as good a copy of Sam as you could wish, and Rose, Merry, and Pippin were sitting in chairs much too big for them. Goldilocks had gone to bed, for in this Frodo's foretelling had made a slight error and she came after Pippin, and was still only five and the Red Book rather too much for her yet. But she was not the last of the line, for Sam and Rose seemed likely to rival old Gerontius Took in the number of their children as successfully as Bilbo had passed his age. There was little Ham, and there was Daisie in her cradle.

'Well dear,' said Sam, 'it grew there once, because I saw it with my own eyes.'

'Does it grow there still, daddy?'

'I don't see why it shouldn't, Ellie. I've never been on my travels again, as you know, having all you young folk to mind –

THE EPILOGUE

115

regular ragtag and bobtail old Saruman would have called it. But Mr. Merry and Mr. Pippin, they've been south more than once, for they sort of belong there too now.'

'And haven't they grown big?' said Merry. 'I wish I could grow big like Mr. Meriadoc of Buckland. He's the biggest hobbit that ever was: bigger than Bandobras.'

'Not bigger than Mr. Peregrin of Tuckborough,' said Pippin, 'and he's got hair that's almost golden. Is he Prince Peregrin away down in the Stone City, dad?'

'Well, he's never said so,' said Sam, 'but he's highly thought of, that I know. But now where were [we] getting to?'

'Nowhere,' said Frodo-lad. 'I want to hear about the Spider again. I like the parts best where you come in, dad.'

'But dad, you were talking about Lórien,' said Elanor, 'and whether my flower still grows there.'

'I expect it does, Ellie dear. For as I was saying, Mr. Merry, he says that though the Lady has gone the Elves still live there.'

'When can I go and see? I want to see Elves, dad, and I want to see my own flower.'

'If you look in a glass you'll see one that is sweeter,' said Sam, 'though I should not be telling you, for you'll find it out soon enough for yourself.'

'But that isn't the same. I want to see the green hill and the white flowers and the golden and hear the Elves sing.'

'Then maybe you will one day,' said Sam. 'I said the same when I was your age, and long after, and there didn't seem no hope, and yet it came true.'

'But the Elves are sailing away still, aren't they, and soon there'll be none, will there, dad?' said Rose; 'and then all will be just places, and very nice, but, but ...'

'But what, Rosie-lass?'

'But not like in stories.'

'Well, it would be so if they all was to sail,' said Sam. 'But I am told they aren't sailing any more. The Ring has left the Havens, and those that made up their mind to stay when Master Elrond left are staying. And so there'll be Elves still for many and many a day.'

'Still I think it was very sad when Master Elrond left Rivendell and the Lady left Lórien,' said Elanor. 'What happened to Celeborn? Is he very sad?'

'I expect so, dear. Elves are sad; and that's what makes them so beautiful, and why we can't see much of them. He lives in his

116   SAURON DEFEATED

own land as he always has done,' said Sam. 'Lórien is his land, and he loves trees.'

'No one else in the world hasn't got a Mallorn like we have, have they?' said Merry. 'Only us and Lord Keleborn.'[3]

'So I believe,' said Sam. Secretly it was one of the greatest prides of his life. 'Well, Keleborn lives among the Trees, and he is happy in his Elvish way, I don't doubt. They can afford to wait, Elves can. His time is not come yet. The Lady came to his land and now she is gone;[4] and he has the land still. When he tires of it he can leave it. So with Legolas, he came with his people and they live in the land across the River, Ithilien, if you can say that, and they've made it very lovely, according to Mr. Pippin. But he'll go to Sea one day, I don't doubt. But not while Gimli's still alive.'

'What's happened to Gimli?' said Frodo-lad. 'I liked him. Please can I have an axe soon, dad? Are there any orcs left?'

'I daresay there are if you know where to look,' said Sam. 'But not in the Shire, and you won't have an axe for chopping off heads, Frodo-lad. We don't make them. But Gimli, he came down to work for the King in the City, and he and his folk worked so long they got used to it and proud of their work, and in the end they settled up in the mountains up away west behind the City, and there they are still. And Gimli goes once every other year to see the Glittering Caves.'

'And does Legolas go to see Treebeard?' asked Elanor.

'I can't say, dear,' said Sam. 'I've never heard of anyone as has ever seen an Ent since those days. If Mr. Merry or Mr. Pippin have they keep it secret. Very close are Ents.'

'And have they never found the Entwives?'

'Well, we've seen none here, have we?' said Sam.

'No,' said Rosie-lass; 'but I look for them when I go in a wood. I would like the Entwives to be found.'

'So would I,' said Sam, 'but I'm afraid that is an old trouble, too old and too deep for folks like us to mend, my dear. But now no more questions tonight, at least not till after supper.'

'But that won't be fair,' said both Merry and Pippin, who were not in their teens. 'We shall have to go directly to bed.'

'Don't talk like that to me,' said Sam sternly. 'If it ain't fair for Ellie and Fro to sit up after supper it ain't fair for them to be born sooner, and it ain't fair that I'm your dad and you're not mine. So no more of that, take your turn and what's due in your time, or I'll tell the King.'

THE EPILOGUE   117

They had heard this threat before, but something in Sam's voice made it sound more serious on this occasion. 'When will you see the King?' said Frodo-lad.

'Sooner than you think,' said Sam. 'Well now, let's be fair. I'll tell you all, stay-uppers and go-to-bedders, a big secret. But don't you go whispering and waking up the youngsters. Keep it till tomorrow.'

A dead hush of expectancy fell on all the children: they watched him as hobbit-children of other times had watched the wizard Gandalf.

'The King's coming here,' said Sam solemnly.

'Coming to Bag End!' cried the children.

'No,' said Sam. 'But he's coming north. He won't come into the Shire because he has given orders that no Big Folk are to enter this land again after those Ruffians; and he will not come himself just to show he means it. But he will come to the Bridge. And —— ' Sam paused. 'He has issued a very special invitation to every one of you. Yes, by name!'

Sam went to a drawer and took out a large scroll. It was black and written in letters of silver.

'When did that come, dad?' said Merry.

'It came with the Southfarthing post three days ago [*written above:* on Wednesday],' said Elanor. 'I saw it. It was wrapped in silk and sealed with big seals.'

'Quite right, my bright eyes,' said Sam. 'Now look.' He unrolled it. 'It is written in Elvish and in Plain Language,' said Sam. 'And it says: *Elessar Aragorn Arathornsson the Elfstone King of Gondor and Lord of the Westlands will approach the Bridge of Baranduin on the first day of Spring, or in the Shire-reckoning the twenty-fifth day of March next, and desires there to greet all his friends. In especial he desires to see Master Samwise Mayor of the Shire, and Rose his wife, and Elanor, Rose, Goldilocks and Daisie his daughters, and Frodo, Merry, and Pippin and Hamfast his sons.* There you are, there are all your names.'

'But they aren't the same in both lists,' said Elanor, who could read.

'Ah,' said Sam, 'that's because the first list is Elvish. You're the same, Ellie, in both, because your name is Elvish; but Frodo is *Iorhail*, and Rose is *Beril*, and Merry is *Riben* [> *R..el* > *Gelir*], and Pippin is *Cordof*, and Goldilocks is *Glorfinniel*, and Hamfast is *Marthanc*, and Daisy [*so spelt*] is *Arien*. So now you know.'

118   SAURON DEFEATED

'Well that's splendid,' said Frodo, 'now we all have Elvish names, but what is yours, dad?'

'Well, that's rather peculiar,' said Sam, 'for in the Elvish part, if you must know, what the King says is *Master Perhail who should rather be called Lanhail*, and that means, I believe, "Samwise or Halfwise who should rather be called Plain-wise". So now you know what the King thinks of your dad you'll maybe give more heed to what he says.'

'And ask him lots more questions,' said Frodo.

'When is March the 25th?' said Pippin, to whom days were still the longest measures of time that could really be grasped. 'Is it soon?'

'It's a week today,' said Elanor. 'When shall we start?'

'And what shall we wear?' said Rose.

'Ah,' said Sam. 'Mistress Rose will have a say in that. But you'll be surprised, my dears. We have had warning of this a long time and we've prepared for the day. You're going in the most lovely clothes you've ever seen, and we're riding in a coach. And if you're all very good and look as lovely as you do now I shouldn't be at all surprised if the King does not ask us to go with him to his house up by the Lake. And the Queen will be there.'

'And shall we stay up to supper?' said Rose, to whom the nearness of promotion made this an ever-present concern.

'We shall stay for weeks, until the hay-harvest at least,' said Sam. 'And we shall do what the King says. But as for staying up to supper, no doubt the Queen will have a word. And now if you haven't enough to whisper about for hours, and to dream about till the sun rises, then I don't know what more I can tell you.'

The stars were shining in a clear sky: it was the first day of the clear bright spell that came every year to the Shire at the end of March, and was every year welcomed and praised as something surprising for the time of the year.

All the children were in bed. Lights were glimmering still in Hobbiton and in many houses dotted about the darkening countryside. Sam stood at the door and looked away eastward. He drew Mistress Rose to him and held her close to his side. 'March 18th [> 25th]',[5] he said. 'This time seventeen years ago, Rose wife, I did not think I should ever see thee again. But I kept on hoping.'

THE EPILOGUE   119

['And I never hoped at all, Sam,' she said, 'until that very day; and then suddenly I did. In the middle of the morning I began singing, and father said "Quiet lass, or the Ruffians will come," and I said "Let them come. Their time will soon be over. My Sam's coming back." And he came.']⁶

'And you came back,' said Rose.

'I did,' said Sam; 'to the most belovedest place in all the world. I was torn in two then, lass, but now I am all whole. And all that I have, and all that I have had I still have.'

Here the text as it was written ends, but subsequently my father added to it the following:

They went in and shut the door. But even as he did so Sam heard suddenly the sigh and murmur of the sea on the shores of Middle-earth.

It cannot be doubted that this was how he intended at that time that *The Lord of the Rings* should end.

A fair copy ('**B**') followed, and this was headed 'Epilogue', without chapter-number; subsequently 'Epilogue' was altered to 'The End of the Book', again without number. The changes made to the original draft were remarkably few: very minor adjustments and improvements in the flow of the conversation between Sam and his children, and the alteration or enlargement of certain details.

Merry Gamgee now knows that Bandobras Took 'killed the goblin-king': the reference is to 'An Unexpected Party' in *The Hobbit*, where it is told that the Bullroarer 'charged the ranks of the goblins of Mount Gram in the Battle of the Green Fields, and knocked their king Golfimbul's head clean off with a wooden club.' Of the sailing of the Elves Sam now says, not that 'they aren't sailing any more', but that 'they are not sailing often now', and he continues: 'Those that stayed behind when Elrond left are mostly going to stay for good, or for a very long time. But they are more and more difficult to find or to talk to.' Of Ents he observes that they are 'very close, very secret-like, and they don't like people very much'; and of the Dwarves who came from Erebor to Minas Tirith with Gimli he says 'I hear they've settled up in the White Mountains not very far from the City', while 'Gimli goes once a year to see the Glittering Caves' (in Appendix A III, at end, it is said that Gimli 'became Lord of the Glittering Caves').

The King's letter now begins *Aragorn Arathornsson Elessar the Elfstone*; and the date of his coming to the Brandywine Bridge was now 'the eighth day of Spring, or in the Shire-reckoning the second of April', since my father had decided, already while writing A (see note 5), that the 25th of March was not the day on which the King would

120   SAURON DEFEATED

come to the Bridge, but the day on which *The Lord of the Rings* came
to an end.[7]

Daisie Gamgee's name is now *Erien* (*Arien* in A); and in the King's
letter he calls Sam *Master Perhail who should rather be called
Panthail*, which Sam interprets as 'Master Samwise who ought to be
called Fullwise'.

Other changes were made to B later, and these were taken up into
the third and final text 'C' of this version of the 'Epilogue', a
typescript. To this my father gave the revised title of B, 'The End of the
Book', with a chapter-number 'LVIII',[8] but he then struck out both
title and number and reverted to 'Epilogue.' The text now opens thus:

One evening in the March of 1436 Master Samwise Gamgee
was taking his ease by the fire in his study, and his children were
gathered round him, as was not at all unusual. Though it was
always supposed to be a special occasion, a Royal Command, it
was one more often commanded by the subjects than by the
King.

This day, however, really was a special occasion. For one
thing it was Elanor's birthday;[9] for another, Sam had been reading aloud from a big Red Book, and he had just come to the very
end, after a slow progress through its many chapters that had
taken many months. On a stool beside him sat Elanor . . .

Sam now says of the Entwives: 'I think maybe the Entwives don't
want to be found'; and after his words 'But now no more questions
tonight' the following passage was introduced:

'Just one more, please!' begged Merry. 'I've wanted to ask
before, but Ellie and Fro get in so many questions there's never
any room for mine.'

'Well then, just one more,' said Sam.

'About horses,' said Merry. 'How many horses did the Riders
lose in the battle, and have they grown lots more? And what
happened to Legolas's horse? And what did Gandalf do with
Shadowfax? And can I have a pony soon?' he ended breathlessly.

'That's a lot more than one question: you're worse than
Gollum,' said Sam. 'You're going to have a pony next birthday,
as I've told you before. Legolas let his horse run back free to
Rohan from Isengard; and the Riders have more horses than
ever, because nobody steals them any longer; and Shadowfax
went in the White Ship with Gandalf: of course Gandalf
couldn't have a' left him behind. Now that'll have to do. No
more questions. At least not till after supper.'

THE EPILOGUE 121

The letter of the King now begins *Aragorn Tarantar* (at which Sam explains 'that's Trotter') *Aranthornsson* &c. *Tarantar* was altered on the typescript to *Telcontar* ('that's Strider'): see VIII.390 and note 14. Rose's name in Elvish becomes *Meril* (for *Beril*), and Hamfast's *Baravorn* (for *Marthanc*); the Elvish name of Daisy (so spelt in C) reverts to *Arien* (for *Erien*), the form in A.

Though never published, of course, this version of the Epilogue is, I believe, quite well known, from copies made from the text at Marquette University. My father would never in fact have published it, even had he decided in the end to conclude *The Lord of the Rings* with an epilogue, for it was superseded by a second version, in which while much of Sam's news from beyond the Shire was retained its framework and presentation were radically changed.[10] Of this there are two texts. The first is a good clear manuscript with few corrections; it has neither title nor chapter-number. The second is a typescript, which though made by my father followed the manuscript very closely indeed; this is entitled 'Epilogue', with the chapter-number 'X' (i.e. of Book Six). I give here the text of the typescript in full.

The second version of the Epilogue

EPILOGUE

One evening in the March of 1436 Master Samwise Gamgee was in his study at Bag End. He was sitting at the old well-worn desk, and with many pauses for thought he was writing in his slow round hand on sheets of loose paper. Propped up on a stand at his side was a large red book in manuscript.

Not long before he had been reading aloud from it to his family. For the day was a special one: the birthday of his daughter Elanor. That evening before supper he had come at last to the very end of the Book. The long progress through its many chapters, even with omissions that he had thought advisable, had taken some months, for he only read aloud on great days. At the birthday reading, besides Elanor, Frodo-lad had been present, and Rosie-lass, and young Merry and Pippin; but the other children had not been there. The Red Book was not for them yet, and they were safely in bed. Goldilocks was only five years old, for in this Frodo's foretelling had made a slight error, and she came after Pippin. But she was not the last of the line, for Samwise and Rose seemed likely to rival old Gerontius Took as successfully in the number of their children as Bilbo had in the number of his years. There was little Ham,

122   SAURON DEFEATED

[and there was Daisy still in her cradle >] and Daisy, and there was Primrose still in her cradle.[11]

Now Sam was 'having a bit of quiet'. Supper was over. Only Elanor was with him, still up because it was her birthday. She sat without a sound, staring at the fire, and now and again glancing at her father. She was a beautiful girl, more fair of skin than most hobbit-maidens, and more slender, and the firelight glinted in her red-gold hair. To her, by gift if not by inheritance, a memory of elven-grace had descended.[12]

'What are you doing, Sam-dad[13] dear?' she said at last. 'You said you were going to rest, and I hoped you would talk to me.'

'Just a moment, Elanorellë,' said Sam,[14] as she came and set her arms about him and peered over his shoulder.

'It looks like Questions and Answers,' she said.

'And so it is,' said Sam. 'Mr. Frodo, he left the last pages of the Book to me, but I have never yet durst to put hand to them. I am still making notes, as old Mr. Bilbo would have said. Here's all the many questions Mother Rose and you and the children have asked, and I am writing out the answers, when I know them. Most of the questions are yours, because only you has heard all the Book more than once.'

'Three times,' said Elanor, looking at the carefully written page that lay under Sam's hand.

Q. *Dwarves, &c.* Frodo-lad says he likes them best. What happened to Gimli? Have the Mines of Moria been opened again? Are there any Orcs left?

A. *Gimli:* he came back to work for the King, as he said, and he brought many of his folk from the North, and they worked in Gondor so long that they got used to it, and they settled there, up in the White Mountains not far from the City. Gimli goes once a year to the Glittering Caves. How do I know? Information from Mr. Peregrin, who often goes back to Minas Tirith, where he is very highly thought of.

Moria: I have heard no news. Maybe the foretelling about Durin is not for our time.[15] Dark places still need a lot of cleaning up. I guess it will take a lot of trouble and daring deeds yet to root out the evil creatures from the halls of Moria. For there are certainly plenty of Orcs left in such places. It is not likely that we shall ever get quite rid of them.

THE EPILOGUE

Q. *Legolas.* Did he go back to the King? Will he stay there?

A. Yes, he did. He came south with Gimli, and he brought many of his people from Greenwood the Great (so they call it now). They say it was a wonderful sight to see companies of Dwarves and Elves journeying together. The Elves have made the City, and the land where Prince Faramir lives, more beautiful than ever. Yes, Legolas will stay there, at any rate as long as Gimli does; but I think he will go to the Sea one day. Mr. Meriadoc told me all this, for he has visited the Lady Éowyn in her white house.

Q. *Horses.* Merry is interested in these; very anxious for a pony of his own. How many horses did the Riders lose in the battles, and have they got some more now? What happened to Legolas's horse? What did Gandalf do with Shadowfax?

A. *Shadowfax* went in the White Ship with Gandalf, of course. I saw that myself. I also saw Legolas let his horse run free back to Rohan from Isengard. Mr. Meriadoc says he does not know how many horses were lost; but there are more than ever in Rohan now, because no one steals them any longer. The Riders also have many ponies, especially in Harrowdale: white, brown, and grey. Next year when he comes back from a visit to King Éomer he means to bring one for his namesake.

Q. *Ents.* Elanor would like to hear more about them. What did Legolas see in Fangorn; and does he ever see Treebeard now? Rosie-lass very anxious about Entwives. She looks for them whenever she goes in a wood. Will they ever be found? She would like them to be.

A. Legolas and Gimli have not told what they saw, so far as I have heard. I have not heard of any one that has seen an Ent since those days. Ents are very secret, and they do not like people much, big or little. I should like the Entwives to be found, too; but I am afraid that trouble is too old and deep for Shire-folk to mend. I think, maybe, Entwives do not want to be found; and maybe Ents are now tired of looking.

'Well dear,' said Sam, 'this top page, this is only today's batch.' He sighed. 'It isn't fit to go in the Book like that. It isn't a bit like the story as Mr. Frodo wrote it. But I shall have to make

124   SAURON DEFEATED

a chapter or two in proper style, somehow. Mr. Meriadoc might help me. He's clever at writing, and he's making a splendid book all about plants.'

'Don't write any more tonight. Talk to me, Sam-dad!' said Elanor, and drew him to a seat by the fire.

'Tell me,' she said, as they sat close together with the soft golden light on their faces, 'tell me about Lórien. Does *my* flower grow there still, Sam-dad?'

'Well dear, Celeborn still lives there among his trees and his Elves, and there I don't doubt your flower grows still. Though now I have got you to look at, I don't hanker after it so much.'

'But I don't want to look at myself, Sam-dad. I want to look at other things. I want to see the hill of Amroth where the King met Arwen, and the silver trees, and the little white niphredil, and the golden elanor in the grass that is always green. And I want to hear Elves singing.'

'Then, maybe, you will one day, Elanor. I said the same when I was your age, and long after it, and there didn't seem to be no hope. And yet I saw them, and I heard them.'

'I was afraid they were all sailing away, Sam-dad. Then soon there would be none here; and then everywhere would be just places, and'

'And what, Elanorellë?'

'And the light would have faded.'

'I know,' said Sam. 'The light is fading, Elanorellë. But it won't go out yet. It won't ever go quite out, I think now, since I have had you to talk to. For it seems to me now that people can remember it who have never seen it. And yet,' he sighed, 'even that is not the same as really seeing it, like I did.'

'Like really being in a story?' said Elanor. 'A story is quite different, even when it is about what happened. I wish I could go back to old days!'

'Folk of our sort often wish that,' said Sam. 'You came at the end of a great Age, Elanorellë; but though it's over, as we say, things don't really end sharp like that. It's more like a winter sunset. The High Elves have nearly all gone now with Elrond. But not quite all; and those that didn't go will wait now for a while. And the others, the ones that belong here, will last even longer. There are still things for you to see, and maybe you'll see them sooner than you hope.'

Elanor was silent for some time before she spoke again. 'I did not understand at first what Celeborn meant when he said

THE EPILOGUE   125

goodbye to the King,' she said. 'But I think I do now. He knew that Lady Arwen would stay, but that Galadriel would leave him.[16] I think it was very sad for him. And for you, dear Sam-dad.' Her hand felt for his, and his brown hand clasped her slender fingers. 'For your treasure went too. I am glad Frodo of the Ring saw me, but I wish I could remember seeing him.'

'It was sad, Elanorellë,' said Sam, kissing her hair. 'It was, but [it] isn't now. For why? Well, for one thing, Mr. Frodo has gone where the elven-light isn't fading; and he deserved his reward. But I have had mine, too. I have had lots of treasures. I am a very rich hobbit. And there is one other reason, which I shall whisper to you, a secret I have never told before to no one, nor put in the Book yet. Before he went Mr. Frodo said that my time maybe would come. I can wait. I think maybe we haven't said farewell for good. But I can wait. I have learned that much from the Elves at any rate. They are not so troubled about time. And so I think Celeborn is still happy among his trees, in an Elvish way. His time hasn't come, and he isn't tired of his land yet. When he is tired he can go.'

'And when you're tired, you will go, Sam-dad. You will go to the Havens with the Elves. Then I shall go with you. I shall not part with you, like Arwen did with Elrond.'

'Maybe, maybe,' said Sam kissing her gently. 'And maybe not. The choice of Lúthien and Arwen comes to many, Elanorellë, or something like it; and it isn't wise to choose before the time.

'And now, my dearest, I think that it's time even a lass of fifteen spring-times should go to her bed. And I have words to say to Mother Rose.'

Elanor stood up, and passed her hand lightly through Sam's curling brown hair, already flecked with grey. 'Good night, Sam-dad. But'

'I don't want *good night but*,' said Sam.

'But won't you show it me first? I was going to say.'

'Show you what, dear?'

'The King's letter, of course. You have had it now more than a week.'

Sam sat up. 'Good gracious!' he said. 'How stories do repeat themselves! And you get paid back in your own coin and all. How we spied on poor Mr. Frodo! And now our own spy on us, meaning no more harm than we did, I hope. But how do you know about it?'

126   SAURON DEFEATED

'There was no need for spying,' said Elanor. 'If you wanted it kept secret, you were not nearly careful enough. It came by the Southfarthing post early on Wednesday last week. I saw you take it in. All wrapped in white silk and sealed with great black seals: any one who had heard the Book would have guessed at once that it came from the King. Is it good news? Won't you show it me, Sam-dad?'

'Well, as you're so deep in, you'd better be right in,' said Sam. 'But no conspiracies now. If I show you, you join the grown-ups' side and must play fair. I'll tell the others in my own time. The King is coming.'

'He's coming here?' Elanor cried. 'To Bag End?'

'No, dear,' said Sam. 'But he's coming north again, as he hasn't done since you was a mite.[17] But now his house is ready. He won't come into the Shire, because he's given orders that no Big Folk are to enter the land again after those Ruffians, and he won't break his own rules. But he will ride to the Bridge. And he's sent a very special invitation to every one of us, every one by name.'

Sam went to a drawer, unlocked it, and took out a scroll, and slipped off its case. It was written in two columns with fair silver letters upon black. He unrolled it, and set a candle beside it on the desk, so that Elanor could see it.

'How splendid!' she cried. 'I can read the Plain Language, but what does the other side say? I think it is Elvish, but you've taught me so few Elvish words yet.'

'Yes, it's written in a kind of Elvish that the great folk of Gondor use,' said Sam. 'I have made it out, enough at least to be sure that it says much the same, only it turns all our names into Elvish. Yours is the same on both sides, Elanor, because your name *is* Elvish. But Frodo is *Iorhael*, and Rose is *Meril*, and Merry is *Gelir*, and Pippin is *Cordof*, and Goldilocks is *Glorfinniel*, and Hamfast is *Baravorn*, and Daisy is *Eirien*. So now you know.'

'How wonderful!' she said. 'Now we have all got Elvish names. What a splendid end to my birthday! But what is your name, Sam-dad? You didn't mention it.'

'Well, it's rather peculiar,' said Sam. 'For in the Elvish part, if you must know, the King says: "Master *Perhael* who should be called *Panthael*". And that means: Samwise who ought to be called Fullwise. So now you know what the King thinks of your old father.'

THE EPILOGUE

'Not a bit more than I do, Sam-dad, *Perhael-adar*[18] dearest,' said Elanor. 'But it says the second of April, only a week today![19] When shall we start? We ought to be getting ready. What shall we wear?'

'You must ask Mother Rose about all that,' said Sam. 'But we *have* been getting ready. We had a warning of this a long time ago; and we've said naught about it, only because we didn't want you all to lose your sleep of nights, not just yet. You have all got to look your best and beautifullest. You will all have beautiful clothes, and we shall drive in a coach.'

'Shall I make three curtsies, or only one?' said Elanor.

'One will do, one each for the King and the Queen,' said Sam. 'For though it doesn't say so in the letter, Elanorellë, I think the Queen will be there. And when you've seen her, my dear, you'll know what a lady of the Elves looks like, save that none are so beautiful. And there's more to it even than that. For I shall be surprised if the King doesn't bid us to his great house by Lake Evendim. And there will be Elladan and Elrohir, who still live in Rivendell – and with them will be Elves, Elanorellë, and they will sing by the water in the twilight. That is why I said you might see them sooner than you guessed.'

Elanor said nothing, but stood looking at the fire, and her eyes shone like stars. At last she sighed and stirred. 'How long shall we stay?' she asked. 'I suppose we shall have to come back?'

'Yes, and we shall want to, in a way,' said Sam. 'But we might stay until hay-harvest, when I must be back here. Good night, Elanorellë. Sleep now till the sun rises. You'll have no need of dreams.'

'Good night, Sam-dad. And don't work any more. For I know what your chapter should be. Write down our talk together – but not to-night.' She kissed him, and passed out of the room; and it seemed to Sam that the fire burned low at her going.

The stars were shining in a clear dark sky. It was the second day of the bright and cloudless spell that came every year to the Shire towards the end of March, and was every year welcomed and praised as something surprising for the season. All the children were now in bed. It was late, but here and there lights were still glimmering in Hobbiton, and in houses dotted about the night-folded countryside.

Master Samwise stood at the door and looked away eastward. He drew Mistress Rose to him, and set his arm about her.

128　　　SAURON DEFEATED

'March the twenty-fifth!' he said. 'This day seventeen years ago, Rose wife, I didn't think I should ever see thee again. But I kept on hoping.'

'I never hoped at all, Sam,' she said, 'not until that very day; and then suddenly I did. About noon it was, and I felt so glad that I began singing. And mother said: "Quiet, lass! There's ruffians about." And I said: "Let them come! Their time will soon be over. Sam's coming back." And you came.'

'I did,' said Sam. 'To the most belovedest place in all the world. To my Rose and my garden.'

They went in, and Sam shut the door. But even as he did so, he heard suddenly, deep and unstilled, the sigh and murmur of the Sea upon the shores of Middle-earth.

★

In this second Epilogue Sam does not read out the King's letter (since Elanor could read), but associated with it (as is seen from the name-forms *Eirien, Perhael, Panthael*) are three 'facsimiles' of the letter, written in *tengwar* in two columns.

The first of these ('I') is reproduced on p. 130. It is accompanied by a transliteration into 'plain letters' of both the English and the Sindarin. The transliteration of the English does not precisely correspond to the *tengwar* text, for the former omits *Arathornsson*, and adds *day* where the *tengwar* text has 'the thirty-first of the Stirring'. The words *and Arnor, ar Arnor* were added in to both the *tengwar* texts and are lacking in the transliterations. As my father wrote them they read as follows:

Aragorn Strider The Elfstone, King of Gondor and Lord of the Westlands, will approach the Bridge of Baranduin on the eighth day of Spring, or in the Shire-reckoning the second day of April. And he desires to greet there all his friends.
In especial he desires to see Master *Samwise*, Mayor of the Shire, and *Rose* his wife; and *Elanor, Rose, Goldilocks*, and *Daisy* his daughters; and *Frodo, Merry, Pippin* and *Hamfast* his sons.

To Samwise and Rose the King's greeting from Minas Tirith, the thirty-first day of the Stirring, being the twenty-third of February in their reckoning.
A · E ·

Elessar Telcontar: Aragorn Arathornion Edhelharn, aran

THE EPILOGUE   129

Gondor ar Hîr i Mbair Annui, anglennatha i Varanduiniant
erin dolothen Ethuil, egor ben genediad Drannail erin
Gwirith edwen. Ar e aníra ennas suilannad mhellyn în
phain: *edregol* e aníra tírad i Cherdir *Perhael* (i sennui
Panthael estathar aen) Condir i Drann, ar *Meril* bess dîn,
ar *Elanor, Meril, Glorfinniel,* ar *Eirien* sellath dîn; ar
Iorhael, Gelir, Cordof, ar *Baravorn,* ionnath dîn.

A *Pherhael* ar am *Meril* suilad uin aran o Minas
Tirith nelchaenen uin Echuir.

A · E ·

The change of pen after *ar Elanor* was no doubt made in order to fit
the Sindarin text onto the page.

The second 'facsimile' ('II'), not accompanied by a transliteration
and not reproduced here, is very similar to I, but *and Arnor, ar Arnor*
is part of the texts as written, there is no variation in the boldness of
the lettering, and the texts end at the words *his sons, ionnath dîn,*
followed by the initials A · E ·, so that there is here no mention of the
date and place of the letter.

The third of these pages ('III'), preserved with the typescript text of
the second Epilogue and accompanied by a transliteration, is reproduced on p. 131. In this case the use of vowel-*tehtar* above consonants in the Sindarin text greatly reduced its length. The English text is
the same as in I, but the note of the date is different: 'From Minas
Tirith, the twenty-third of February 6341' [= 1436]. The Sindarin text
differs from that of I and II in the word order:

Aragorn Arathornion Edhelharn anglennatha i Varanduiniant
erin dolothen Ethuil (egor ben genediad Drannail erin Gwirith
edwen) ar ennas aníra i aran Gondor ar Arnor ar Hîr iMbair
Annui [*written* Anui][20] suilannad mhellyn in phain . . .

The note of date at the end of the Sindarin text reads:

a Pherhael ar am Meril suilad uin aran o Minas Tirith
nelchaenen ned Echuir: 61.[21]

It emerges from the account of his works that my father wrote for
Milton Waldman in 1951 that the second version of the Epilogue was
written at a very late stage. In this account he included what he called
'a long and yet bald résumé' of the story of *The Lord of the Rings*; this
was omitted in *Letters* (no. 131), and I give here its closing passages.

The 'Scouring of the Shire' ending in the last battle ever fought there
occupies a chapter. It is followed by a second spring, a marvellous
restoration and enhancement of beauty, chiefly wrought by Sam
(with the help of gifts given him in Lórien). But Frodo cannot be
healed. For the preservation of the Shire he has sacrificed himself,
even in health, and has no heart to enjoy it. Sam has to choose

First copy of the King's letter

Third copy of the King's letter

132   SAURON DEFEATED

between love of master and of wife. In the end he goes with Frodo on a last journey. At night in the woods, where Sam first met Elves on the outward journey, they meet the twilit cavalcade from Rivendell. The Elves and the Three Rings, and Gandalf (Guardian of the Third Age) are going to the Grey Havens, to set sail for the West, never to return. Bilbo is with them. To Bilbo and Frodo the special grace is granted to go with the Elves they loved – an Arthurian ending, in which it is, of course, not made explicit whether this is an 'allegory' of death, or a mode of healing and restoration leading to a return. They ride to the Grey Havens, and take ship: Gandalf with the Red Ring, Elrond (with the Blue) and the greater part of his household, and Galadriel of Lórien with the White Ring, and with them depart Bilbo and Frodo. It is hinted that they come to Eressëa. But Sam standing stricken on the stone quay sees only the white ship slip down the grey estuary and fade into the darkling West. He stays long unmoving listening to the sound of the Sea on the shores of the world.

Then he rides home; his wife welcomes him to the firelight and his first child, and he says simply 'Well, I've come back.'[22] There is a brief epilogue in which we see Sam among his children, a glance at his love for Elanor (the Elvish name of a flower in Lórien) his eldest, who by a strange gift has the looks and beauty of an elven-maid; in her all his love and longing for Elves is resolved and satisfied. He is busy, contented, many times mayor of the Shire, and struggling to finish off the Red Book, begun by Bilbo and nearly completed by Frodo, in which all the events (told in The Hobbit and The Lord [of the Rings]) are recorded. The whole ends with Sam and his wife standing outside Bag-end, as the children are asleep, looking at the stars in the cool spring sky. Sam tells his wife of his bliss and content, and goes in, but as he closes the door he hears the sighing of the Sea on the shores of the world.

It is clear from the words 'we see Sam among his children' that my father was referring to the first version of the Epilogue.

He was persuaded by others to omit the Epilogue from The Lord of the Rings. In a letter to Naomi Mitchison of 25 April 1954 (Letters no. 144) he wrote:

Hobbit-children were delightful, but I am afraid that the only glimpses of them in this book are found at the beginning of vol. I. An epilogue giving a further glimpse (though of a rather exceptional family) has been so universally condemned that I shall not insert it. One must stop somewhere.

He seems both to have accepted and to have regretted that decision. On 24 October 1955, a few days after the publication of The Return of the King, he wrote to Katherine Farrer (Letters no. 173):

THE EPILOGUE

133

I still feel the picture incomplete without something on Samwise and Elanor, but I could not devise anything that would not have destroyed the ending, more than the hints (possibly sufficient) in the appendices.

NOTES

1 The 'Epilogue' text begins at the head of a page, but this is merely because the words ' "Well, I'm back," he said' stand at the foot of the preceding one.

2 '1436' was pencilled in subsequently. Apparently my father first wrote 'And one evening Master Samwise ...', but changed this at once to 'And one evening in March Master Samwise ...' This does not suggest the passage of many years since the sailing of the ship from Mithlond, but that such was the case is immediately plain in the same opening sentence ('and the children were all gathered about him'); the absence of a date in the text as first written must therefore be casual and without significance.

3 *Keleborn*: immediately above the name was spelt *Celeborn*; here, the *K* was changed from *C* in the act of writing the letter.

4 On the development of the legends of Galadriel and Celeborn see *The History of Galadriel and Celeborn* in *Unfinished Tales*, Part Two §IV.

5 *March 18th [> 25th]*: the King had declared in his letter that he would be coming to the Brandywine Bridge on March 25; Elanor had said that that was 'a week today'; and as my father wrote this concluding passage Sam said to Rose at the door of Bag End 'March 18th'. On the change to the 25th, apparently made immediately, see note 7.

6 The brackets are in the original.

7 The change in the King's letter from March 25 to April 2 was in fact, and at first sight very oddly, an emendation made on the B text. This question of the dates is minor, complicated, and explicable. When my father wrote the text A the great day of the King's coming north to the Brandywine Bridge was to be the 25th of March, the date of the destruction of the Ring and the downfall of Sauron (see pp. 59–60); and Elanor said (p. 118) that that was 'a week today', so that the occasion of Sam's conversation with his children recorded in the Epilogue was March 18. When Sam and Rose stood outside Bag End that night Sam said: 'March 18th. Seventeen years ago ...' (p. 118). My father changed '18' to '25' on the manuscript A (and probably at the same time added in the words '*This time* (seventeen years ago)') because he decided, just at that point, that the end of *The Lord of the Rings* (in its Epilogue) should fall on that date (possibly also because he recalled that it was Elanor's birthday, which had of

134   SAURON DEFEATED

course been chosen for the same reason); but he failed to postpone the date in the King's letter earlier in A (p. 117).

Writing out the fair copy B, in which he followed A very closely, he momentarily forgot this decision, and repeated the date in A of the King's coming to the Bridge, March 25. Subsequently, while writing B, he realised that this was now erroneous, and changed it to April 2; so at the end of B Sam says (as he had in A): 'March the twenty-fifth! This time seventeen years ago ...'

Elanor's answer to Pippin's question 'When is the second of April?' was changed subsequently on B from 'a week today' to 'a week tomorrow', which is the reading in the typescript C. This, however, was erroneous, since it gives March thirty-one days; 'a week today' was restored in the second version of the Epilogue, p. 127.

8   Chapter-number 'LVIII': the basis of the revised numbering of the chapters of Book Six is not clear to me. The sequence ran from LII 'The Tower of Kirith Ungol' (p. 25) to LX 'The Grey Havens' (p. 110), but on some of the chapters these numbers were reduced by two; here the reduction is by three.

9   Elanor's birth on 25 March (1421) was mentioned in the original draft of 'The Grey Havens', p. 109.

10   In this second version Sam is making notes, which are cited and which are an essential part of the Epilogue, for the filling of the empty pages at the end of the Red Book; and it seems odd that the title 'The End of the Book', so suitable to the second version, should have been used, and rejected, on texts B and C of the first (pp. 119–20).

11   This emendation was made on the typescript only. In 'The Longfather-tree of Master Samwise' in Appendix C Daisy Gamgee was born in 1433 and Primrose in 1435; Bilbo Gamgee was born in the year of the Epilogue, 1436, and was followed by three further children, making thirteen in all.

12   A footnote to the record of the birth of Elanor in *The Tale of Years* states: 'She became known as "the Fair" because of her beauty; many said that she looked more like an elf-maid than a hobbit. She had golden hair, which had been very rare in the Shire; but two others of Samwise's daughters were also golden-haired, and so were many of the children born at this time.' Cf. the reference in 'The Grey Havens' to the golden-haired children born in the Shire in the year 1420 (RK p. 303; see p. 112, note 1).

13   *Sam-dad*: this address to Sam by his children entered in text B of the first version.

14   In the manuscript 'said Sam' is followed by 'sucking his pen-holder'; this was probably omitted inadvertently, as were other phrases afterwards picked up and reinserted in the typescript.

THE EPILOGUE   135

15 Sam was no doubt thinking of the end of Gimli's song in Moria, by which he was greatly struck (FR p. 330):

> There lies his crown in water deep,
> Till Durin wakes again from sleep.

Or else of Gimli's words when Frodo and Sam looked with him into Mirrormere: 'O Kheled-zâram fair and wonderful! There lies the crown of Durin till he wakes.' ' "What did you see?" said Pippin to Sam, but Sam was too deep in thought to answer' (FR p. 348).

16 Elanor's words refer to RK p. 260 ('Many Partings'): 'But Celeborn said: "Kinsman, farewell! May your doom be other than mine, and your treasure remain with you to the end!" ' For the original form of Celeborn's farewell to Aragorn see p. 64.

17 I do not know of any other reference to this northern journey of Aragorn in the early years of his reign.

18 In the manuscript (which had *ai* forms, later emended, in the names *Iorhail, Perhail, Panthail*) Elanor calls her father *Panthailadar*.

19 *only a week today:* see note 7, at end.

20 My father's transliteration has *ar ennas i aran Gondor ar Arnor ar Hîr iMbair Annui aníra* ...

21 61 = 16, i.e. year 16 of the Fourth Age, which means that the Fourth Age began in 1421 (see Appendix D to *The Lord of the Rings*, at end).

22 In all the texts of 'The Grey Havens' from the earliest draft Sam said to Rose when he returned to Bag End 'Well, I'm back.' 'Well, I've come back' does not mean the same thing.

APPENDIX

Drawings of Orthanc and Dunharrow

When I wrote Volume VIII, *The War of the Ring*, it entirely and most regrettably escaped my memory that there are several unpublished drawings of Orthanc and Dunharrow in the Bodleian Library. As these are of much interest I reproduce them belatedly here, as a final appendix to the history of *The Lord of the Rings*.

The upper drawing on the page called here 'Orthanc I' shows a conception essentially similar to that of the little sketch 'Orthanc 3' reproduced in VIII.33 and described in the first manuscript of the chapter 'The Voice of Saruman', VIII.61. In this, the tower was founded on a huge arch spanning the great cleft in the rock; flights of stairs led up on two sides to a narrow platform beneath the arch, whence further stairs ran up 'to dark doors on either side, opening in the shadow of the arch's feet'. But in the present drawing the rock of Orthanc is enormously much greater in relation to the tower than in 'Orthanc 3'; the tower has only three tiers (seven in 'Orthanc 3' and in the description associated with it, VIII.32–3); and the horns at the summit are very much smaller.

In the lower drawing on this page, showing the Circle of Isengard in Nan Gurunír between the mountains' arms, is seen the feature described in the original drafting of the chapter 'The Road to Isengard' but rejected from the first completed manuscript (VIII.43, note 23): the western side of the Circle was formed by the mountain-wall itself. The dark letter C was a change made later to the faintly pencilled name of the Wizard's Vale, *Nan Gurunír* becoming *Nan Curunír*.

The page 'Orthanc II' carries two designs for 'Orthanc's roof'; and on 'Orthanc III' the final conception is seen emerging, in which the 'rock' of Orthanc becomes itself the 'tower'. The drawing on the right has in fact been previously published: it was used in *The Lord of the Rings Calendar 1977*, and so appears in *Pictures by J. R. R. Tolkien*, no. 27 (see VIII.44, note 26).

The two pages of drawings of Dunharrow are not easy to interpret, more especially 'Dunharrow I' (for the early conceptions of Dunharrow and the first sketches see VIII.235 ff.). Of 'Dunharrow I' it can at least be said that this idea of the approach to the Hold was never described in words. Apparently, the path winding up from the valley passed near the top of the cliff through the great door in the foreground and entered a steeply ascending tunnel, climbing up by

APPENDIX

137

stairs inside the cliff, the head of which can be seen emerging from a large opening or hole in the flat land above. The single menhir, first mentioned in the text F of the original work on the chapter 'The Muster of Rohan' (VIII.246) as standing in the rock-ringed floor of the Hold, is seen; but since there is no sign of the lines of standing stones across the upland (nor of the Púkel-men at the turns in the climbing path) I would be inclined to place this drawing after the earliest drafts of the chapter and the little sketches reproduced in VIII.239 but before the writing of the text F.

A very puzzling feature of this drawing is the wavy line at bottom left, hiding one of the bends in the climbing path.

The upper drawing on the page 'Dunharrow II' has a general likeness in the lie of the mountain side to the coloured drawing reproduced as the first frontispiece (but which should have been the second) to *The War of the Ring*, but there the resemblance ceases. In that other picture a double line of huge standing stones crosses the upland from the brink of the cliff to a dark cleft in the mountain, where the road so marked out disappears; and I suggested (VIII.250) that the dark cleft is ' "the gate of the Hold", the "Hold" itself, the "recess" or "amphitheatre" with doors and windows in the cliff at the rear, being in this picture invisible.' In the present drawing the Púkel-men are seen at the turns of the path coming up from the valley; at the top of the cliff the road continues to wind, but the turns are now marked by pointed stones. There is then a straight stretch across the upland field, unmarked by stones; and the road passing (apparently) between two stones or pillars leads into the Hold, in which the door into the cliff behind can be seen. In the left-hand lower drawing the Púkel-men reappear, and in the right-hand drawing a double line of cone-shaped stones leads across the upland and into the Hold, with a single stone standing in the middle of the 'amphitheatre'.

My guess is that the upper drawing on this page shows a stage in the development of the conception of Dunharrow when the Púkel-men had emerged, but not the double line of stones: these are seen at the moment of their emergence in one of the lower sketches. In relation to the manuscript evidence, 'Dunharrow I' would then belong with, but actually precede, the text F of 'The Muster of Rohan', in which both the Púkel-men (then called the Hoker-men) and the lines of stones are present.

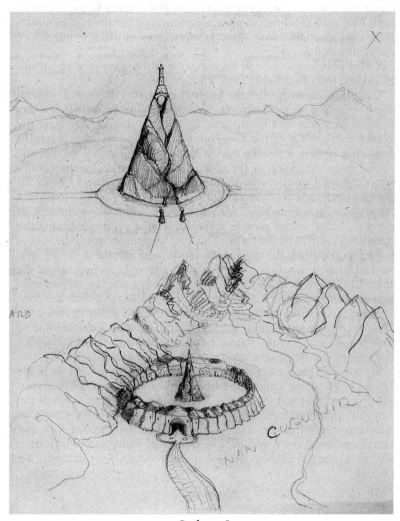

Orthanc I

APPENDIX

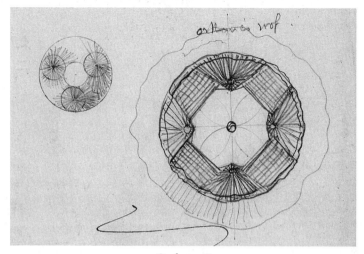

Orthanc II

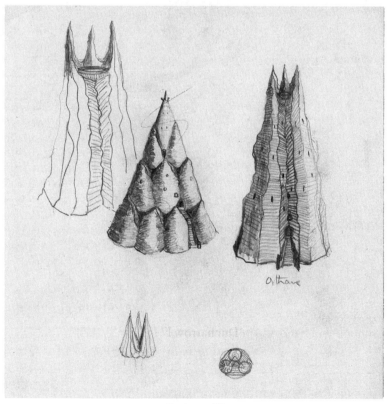

Orthanc III

Dunharrow I

APPENDIX

Dunharrow II

PART TWO

THE NOTION CLUB PAPERS

THE NOTION CLUB PAPERS

Introduction

On 18 December 1944, when *The Lord of the Rings* had reached the end of what would become *The Two Towers* (and a few pages had been written of 'Minas Tirith' and 'The Muster of Rohan' at the beginning of Book V), my father wrote to me (*Letters* no. 92) that he had seen C. S. Lewis that day: 'His fourth (or fifth?) novel is brewing, and seems likely to clash with mine (my dimly projected third). I have been getting a lot of new ideas about Prehistory lately (via Beowulf and other sources of which I may have written) and want to work them into the long shelved time-travel story I began. C. S. L. is planning a story about the descendants of Seth and Cain.' His words are tantalizingly difficult to interpret; but by 'clash with mine' he surely meant that the themes of their books ran rather close.[1]

Whatever lies behind this, it is seen that he was at this time turning his thoughts to a renewed attempt on the 'time-travel story', which would issue a year later in *The Notion Club Papers*. In his letter to Stanley Unwin of 21 July 1946 (*Letters* no. 105) he said that he hoped very shortly 'actually to – write', to turn again to *The Lord of the Rings* where he had left it, more than a year and a half before: 'I shall now have to study my own work in order to get back to it,' he wrote. But later in that same letter he said:

> I have in a fortnight of comparative leisure round about last Christmas written three parts of another book, taking up in an entirely different frame and setting what little had any value in the inchoate *Lost Road* (which I had once the impudence to show you: I hope it is forgotten), and other things beside. I hoped to finish this in a rush, but my health gave way after Christmas. Rather silly to mention it, till it is finished. But I am putting *The Lord of the Rings*, the *Hobbit* sequel, before all else, save duties that I cannot wriggle out of.

So far as I have been able to discover there is no other reference to *The Notion Club Papers* anywhere in my father's writings.

But the quantity of writing constituting *The Notion Club Papers*, and the quantity of writing associated with them, cannot by any manner of means have been the work of a fortnight. To substantiate this, and since this is a convenient place to give this very necessary information, I set out here the essential facts of the textual relations of all this material, together with some brief indication of their content.

146   SAURON DEFEATED

As the development of *The Notion Club Papers* progressed my
father divided it into two parts, the second of which was never
completed, and although he ultimately rejected this division[2] I have
found it in every way desirable to preserve it in this book. Part One
was 'The Ramblings of Michael Ramer: *Out of the Talkative Planet*',
and this consists of a report in direct speech of the discussions at two
successive meetings[3] of 'the Notion Club' at Oxford far in the future
at the time of writing. On the first of these occasions the conversation
turned on the problem of the vehicle, the machine or device, by which
'space-travellers' are transported to their destination, especially in
respect of its literary credibility in itself and its effect on the story
contained within the journeys; on the second, of which the report is
much longer, one of the members, Michael Ramer, expounded his
ideas concerning 'true dreams' and his experiences of 'space-travel' in
dream.

The earliest manuscript, here called 'A', is a complete text of Part
One. It is roughly written and hastily expressed, there is no title or
explanatory 'scene-setting', and there are no dates; but while the text
would undergo much expansion and improvement, the essential
structure and movement of the dialogue was already largely present.

The second manuscript, 'B', is also a complete text of Part One,
but is much fuller than A, and (with many changes and additions)
advances far towards the final form. Here also the two meetings, as the
text was first written, have no dates, and the numbers given to the
meetings imply a much longer history of the Club than is suggested for
it subsequently. For the elaborate title or prolegomenon to this version
see pp. 148–9.

The third manuscript, 'C', is written in a fine script, but is not quite
complete: it extends to Ramer's words 'So there does appear to be at
least one other star with attendant planets' (p. 207), and it is clear that
no more was written of this text (which, incidentally, it would have
taken days to write).

A typescript 'D', made by my father, is the final form of Part One. In
one section of the text, however, D seems to have preceded C, since it
has some B readings which were then changed to those of C; but the
final form of the text is scarcely ever in doubt, and even where it is the
differences are entirely trivial. Where C ends, the typescript follows B,
the place of transition being marked on the B manuscript. (A second
typescript – not, I think, made by my father – was begun, but
abandoned after only a few pages; this has no independent value.)

Part Two, 'The Strange Case of Arundel Lowdham', records a
number of further meetings of the Notion Club, continuous with those
of Part One. This second Part is largely devoted to the intrusion of the
Matter of Númenor into the discussions of the Notion Club, but of
this there are only two texts, a manuscript ('E') and a typescript ('F').

THE NOTION CLUB PAPERS 147

Both end at the same point, with the next meeting of the Club arranged and dated, but never written.

The typescript F is a complex document, in that my father rejected a substantial section of it ('F 1') as soon as he had typed it, replaced it ('F 2'), and then continued on to the end, the structure of the text being thus F 1, F 1 > F 2, F 2 (see p. 237 and note 37).

For both Parts, but especially for Part Two, there is a quantity of rough, discontinuous drafting, often scarcely legible.

While Part Two was being further developed (that is, after the completion of the manuscript E so far as it went) the Adunaic* language emerged (as it appears), with an abandoned but elaborate account of the phonology, and *pari passu* with *The Notion Club Papers* my father not only wrote a first draft of an entirely new version of the story of Númenor but developed it through further texts: this is *The Drowning of Anadûnê*, in which all the names are in Adunaic.

How is all this to be equated with his statement in the letter to Stanley Unwin in July 1946 that 'three parts' of the work were written in a fortnight at the end of 1945? Obviously it cannot be, not even on the supposition that when he said 'a fortnight' he greatly underestimated the time. Though not demonstrable, an extremely probable explanation, as it seems to me, is that at the end of that fortnight he stopped work in the middle of writing the manuscript E, at the point where *The Notion Club Papers* end, and at which time Adunaic had not yet arisen. Very probably Part One was at the stage of the manuscript B.[4] On this view, the further development of what had then been achieved of Part One, and more especially of Part Two (closely associated with that of the Adunaic language and the writing of *The Drowning of Anadûnê*), belongs to the following year, the earlier part of 1946. Against this, of course, is the fact that the letter to Stanley Unwin in which my father referred to the *Papers* was written in July 1946, but that letter gives no impression of further work after 'my health gave way after Christmas'. But it is to be remembered that *The Lord of the Rings* had been at a halt for more than a year and a half, and it may well be that he was deeply torn between the burgeoning of Adunaic and Anadûnê and the oppression of the abandoned *Lord of the Rings*. He did not need to spell out to Stanley Unwin what he had in fact been doing! But he said that he was 'putting *The Lord of the Rings* before all else', which no doubt meant 'I am *now going to put it* before all else', and that included Adunaic. To the interrupted *Notion Club Papers* he never returned.

The diverse and shifting elements in all this work, not least the complex but essential linguistic material, have made the construction

---

Adunaic is always so spelt at this time (not *Adûnaic*), and I write it so throughout.

148   SAURON DEFEATED

of a readily comprehensible edition extremely difficult, requiring much experimentation among possible forms of presentation. Since *The Notion Club Papers* are now published for the first time, the final typescripts D of Part One and F of Part Two must obviously be the text printed, and this makes for difficulties of presentation (it is of course very much easier to begin with an original draft and to relate it by consecutive steps to a final form that is already known). The two Parts are separated, with notes following each Part. Following the text of the *Papers* I give important sections that were rejected from or significantly changed in the final text, earlier forms of the 'Númenórean' fragments that 'came through' to Arundel Lowdham and of the Old English text written by his father, and reproductions of the 'facsimiles' of that text with analysis of the *tengwar*.

Although the final text of Part Two of the *Papers* and *The Drowning of Anadûnê* were intimately connected,[5] especially in respect of Adunaic, any attempt to combine them in a single presentation makes for inextricable confusion; the latter is therefore treated entirely separately in the third part of this book, and in my commentary on Part Two of the *Papers* I have not thought it useful to make continual reference forward to *The Drowning of Anadûnê*: the interrelations between the two works emerge more clearly when the latter is reached.

There are some aspects of the framework of the *Papers*, provided by the Foreword of the Editor, Mr. Howard Green, and the list of members of the Notion Club, which are better discussed here than in the commentary.

The Foreword

The original manuscript A of Part One, as already noticed, has no title or introductory statement of any kind, but begins with the words 'When Ramer had finished reading his latest story ...' The first page of B begins thus:

Beyond Lewis
or
Out of the Talkative Planet

Being a fragment of an apocryphal Inklings' Saga, made by some imitator at some time in the 1980s.

Preface to the Inklings

While listening to this fantasia (if you do), I beg of the present company not to look for their own faces in this mirror. For the mirror is cracked, and at the best you will only see your countenances distorted, and adorned maybe with noses (and other features) that are not your

THE NOTION CLUB PAPERS 149

own, but belong to other members of the company —
if to anybody.

Night 251
When Michael Ramer had finished reading his latest story ...

This was heavily emended and then struck through, and was replaced
by a new, separate title-page (made when B had been completed):

Beyond Probability[6]
or
Out of the Talkative Planet

———

The Ramblings of Ramer
being Nights 251 and 252 of *The Notion Club Papers*

[Little is known about this rare book, except that
it appears to have been written after 1989, as an
apocryphal imitation of the *Inklings' Saga Book*. The
author identifies himself with the character called in the
narrative Nicholas Guildford; but Titmouse has shown
that this is a pseudonym, and is taken from a mediaeval
dialogue, at one time read in the Schools of Oxford. His
real identity remains unknown.]

An aside to the audience. While listening to this hotch-
potch (if you do), I beg of the present company not to
look for their own faces in my mirror. For the mirror is
cracked ...

This is followed by a list of the persons who appear (see p. 151). It
seems clear that at the stage when the text B was written my father's
idea was far less elaborate than it became; intending perhaps, so far
as the form was concerned, no more than a *jeu d'esprit* for the
entertainment of the Inklings — while the titles seem to emphasise that
it was to be, in part, the vehicle of criticism and discussion of aspects
of Lewis's 'planetary' novels. Perhaps he called to mind the witty and
ingenious method that Lewis had devised for his criticism of *The Lay
of Leithian* in 1930 (see *The Lays of Beleriand*, p. 151). — So far as I
can see, there is no indication that at this stage he envisaged the form
that Part Two of the *Papers* would take, and definite evidence to the
contrary (see pp. 281–2).

There are several drafts for a more circumstantial account of the
Papers and of how they came to light, preceding the elaborate form in
the final text that follows. They were found at the University Press
waiting to be pulped, but no one knew how they had got there; or they
were found 'at Messrs. Whitburn and Thoms' publishing house'.[7]

150 SAURON DEFEATED

The mediaeval dialogue from which the name Nicholas Guildford is derived is *The Owl and the Nightingale*, a debate in verse written between 1189 and 1216. To the Owl's question, who shall decide between them, the Nightingale replies that *Maister Nichole of Guldeforde* is the obvious choice, since he is prudent, virtuous, and wise, and an excellent judge of song.

The List of Members

At the top of a page that preceded the manuscript A and is almost certainly the first setting down of the opening passage of Night 60 of the *Papers* (see p. 211, note 7) my father wrote these names:

Ramer Latimer Franks Loudham Dolbear

Beneath *Ramer* he wrote 'Self', but struck it out, then 'CSL' and 'To', these also being struck out. Beneath *Latimer* he wrote 'T', beneath *Franks* 'CSL', beneath *Loudham* 'HVD' (Hugo Dyson), and beneath *Dolbear* 'Havard'.

This is the only actual identification of members of the Notion Club with members of the Inklings that is found. The name *Latimer* (for *Guildford*) remained that of the Club's 'reporter' in manuscript A; it is derived from Old French *latinier* ('Latiner', speaker of Latin), meaning an interpreter. *Loudham* (so spelt in A and B, and initially in the manuscript E of Part Two) would obviously be Dyson even without 'HVD' written beneath (see Humphrey Carpenter, *The Inklings*, pp. 212–13); and since *Franks* (only becoming *Frankley* in the third text C) is here Lewis, I suppose that my father felt that the name was appropriate to his character. The other two names were presumably 'significant', but I do not know what the significance was. *Dolbear* is an uncommon surname, but there was a chemist's shop in Oxford called Dolbear & Goodall, and I recollect that my father found this particularly engaging; it may be that he simply found in Dolbear the chemist a comic appropriateness to Havard, or to Havard as he was going to present him. *Ramer* is very puzzling; and here there is no certain identification with one of the Inklings in the list. The various dictionaries of English surnames that I have consulted do not give the name. The only suggestion that I can make is that my father derived it from the dialectal verb *rame*, with these meanings given in the *Oxford English Dictionary*: 'to shout, cry aloud, scream; keep up the same cry, continue repeating the same thing; obtain by persistent asking; repeat, run over'; cf. also the *English Dialect Dictionary*, ed. Joseph Wright (with which he was very familiar: he called it 'indispensable', *Letters* no. 6), *ream* verb 3, also *raim*, *rame*, etc., which gives similar meanings, and also 'to talk nonsense, rave'. But this seems far-fetched.

At any rate, this list is interesting as suggesting that my father started out with the idea of a series of definite 'equivalences', distorted no doubt but recognisable. But I think that this plan very quickly dissolved, because he found that it would not suit his purpose; and not

THE NOTION CLUB PAPERS   151

even in the earliest text does there seem to be any clearer association with individual Inklings than there is in the final form of the *Papers*, with the possible exception of Lowdham. In A his interventions are limited to jocular facetiousness, and the interest that in the later form of Part One (pp. 199–201) he shows in 'Old Solar' and in Ramer's names of other worlds is in A given to Dolbear (and then in B to Guildford).

It would not suit my father's purpose, because in 'The Ramblings of Ramer' he wished to allow his own ideas the scope, in the form of a discussion and argument, that they would never have had in fact, in an actual meeting of the Inklings. The professional knowledge and intellectual interests of the members of the Notion Club are such as to make this symposium possible. On p. 149 I have given the second version of a title-page, in which after the author's 'aside to the audience', warning them 'not to look for their own faces in my mirror', there follows a list of the members of the Club. At this stage only six members were listed (plus Cameron); and of these six, Ramer is Professor of Finno-Ugric, Guildford is a Comparative Philologist, and Loudham has 'special interests in Icelandic and Anglo-Saxon', while the chemist Dolbear 'concerns himself with psychoanalysis and related aspects of language'. At this stage Frankley is a lecturer in French, changed to the Clarendon Reader in English Literature, 'with a taste for the Romance literatures and a distaste for things Germanic', while the statement of Jeremy's position and interests is much as in the final list. Ramer, Jeremy, Guildford and Frankley all have 'a taste for romances of travel in Space and Time.'

The enlarged list of members in the final form (pp. 159–60), most of whom do not have even walk-on parts, served the purpose, I suppose, of creating an impression of a more amorphous group surrounding the principals. The polymathy of the monk Dom Jonathan Markison extends to some very recondite knowledge of Germanic origins, while Ranulph Stainer appears in Part Two as a sceptical and rather superior onlooker at the strange proceedings. The surname of the apparently speechless undergraduate John Jethro Rashbold is a translation of *Tolkien* (*Toll-kühn*: see *Letters* no. 165 and note 1). In Part Two appears 'old Professor Rashbold at Pembroke', the Anglo-Saxon scholar described by Lowdham as 'a grumpy old bear' (p. 256 and note 72). There are no doubt other hidden puns and jokes in the list of members.

In my view it would be useless to seek even any 'intellectual equivalence' with historical persons, let alone portraiture (for a list of those who came often – but not all at the same period – to the Inklings, with brief biographies, see Humphrey Carpenter, *The Inklings*, Appendix A). The fact that Lowdham is 'loud' and makes jokes often at inappropriate moments derives from Dyson (but he was wittier than Lowdham), yet Lowdham is the very antithesis of Dyson in his learning and interests; no doubt Frankley's *horror borealis* is a reminiscence of

152   SAURON DEFEATED

Dyson also, though it is profoundly un-Dysonian to have read mediaeval works on Saint Brendan (p. 265). In earlier drafts of the list of members Dolbear has no position in the University, and with his red hair and beard and his nickname in the Club (see *Letters* no. 56) he can be seen as a sort of parody of Havard. But these things are marginal to the ideas expounded and debated in the *Papers*; essentially, the members of the Notion Club are fictions, and become more obviously so in Part Two.

Scarcely a sentence remained entirely unchanged between text A and text D of Part One, but in my notes all this development is largely ignored when (as for the most part it is) it is a matter of improvement in the expression or of amplification of the argument. Similarly, the ascription of speeches to speakers underwent many changes in the earlier texts, but in general I do not record them.

I do not enter in this book into any critical discussion of the topics and issues raised in 'The Ramblings of Michael Ramer'. This is partly because I am not well qualified to discuss them, but also because they fall somewhat outside the scope and aim of *The History of Middle-earth*, which is above all to present accurate texts accurately ordered (so far as I am able) and to elucidate them comparatively, within the context of 'Middle-earth' and the lands of the West. With very limited time at my disposal for this book I have thought that I could better devote it in any case to clarification of the complexities of the 'Númenórean' material. The notes are therefore very restricted in scope and are often trivial in relation to the content of the discussion, being mostly concerned with the elucidation of references that may be obscure and not easily tracked down, with comparison of earlier forms of certain passages, and with citation of other writings of my father's. I do not suppose that many readers of this book will be unacquainted with the novels of C. S. Lewis, *Out of the Silent Planet* (1938), *Perelandra* (1943), and *That Hideous Strength* (1945), but I have provided a few explanations and references.

Why my father abandoned *The Notion Club Papers* I do not know. It may be that he felt that the work had lost all unity, that 'Atlantis' had broken apart the frame in which it had been set (see pp. 281–2). But I think also that having forced himself to return to *The Lord of the Rings*, and having brought it to its end, he was then deflected into the very elaborate further work on the legends of the Elder Days that preceded the actual publication of *The Lord of the Rings*. However it was, the Notion Club was abandoned, and with it his final attempt to embody the riddle of Ælfwine and Eadwine in a 'tale of time'. But from its forgotten *Papers* and the strange figure of Arundel Lowdham there emerged a new conception of the Downfall of Númenor, embodied in a different tradition, which would come to constitute a major element in the *Akallabêth* many years later.

THE NOTION CLUB PAPERS

NOTES

1 In a note to this passage in my father's letter Humphrey Carpenter remarks: 'Lewis's next published novel after *That Hideous Strength* and *The Great Divorce* was *The Lion, the Witch and the Wardrobe*. Tolkien is, however, almost certainly referring to some other book of Lewis's that was never completed.' *The Great Divorce* was published in 1946; Lewis was reading it aloud in April and May 1944 (*Letters* no. 60, 69, 72).

It may be mentioned here that my father had evidently discussed with Lewis the matter of 'true dreams': an important element in the plot of *That Hideous Strength* is Jane Studdock's 'tendency to dream real things', in the words of Miss Ironwood (Chapter 3, §iii), and this can hardly be a mere coincidence. It is presumably not coincidental either that there should be so many references to 'Numinor' in *That Hideous Strength* (published in 1945); see p. 303 and note 15.

2 On the final text D of Part One the heading of the first page (after 'Leaves from the Notion Club Papers'):'Part I / The Ramblings of Michael Ramer / *Out of the Talkative Planet*' was struck out. The final text F of Part Two has no heading at the beginning. A pencilled title page apparently accompanying the manuscript E has 'Leaves from the Notion Club Papers / II / The Strange Case of Arundel Lowdham'.

3 A very brief report of an earlier meeting was added at the beginning of the text in the course of the development of Part One.

4 A pointer to this is the fact that in B the name is spelt *Loudham* throughout; in E it begins as *Loudham* but becomes *Lowdham* in the course of the writing of the manuscript; in C it is *Lowdham* from the first. See further p. 282.

5 Cf. the close relation of the manuscript of *The Lost Road* and the original text of *The Fall of Númenor*, V.9.

6 *Beyond Probability* is a pun on the title of Lewis's book *Beyond Personality*, which had been published in 1944.

7 That *Whitburn* (*and Thoms*) is a play on the name *Blackwell*, the Oxford bookseller and publisher, is seen from the fact that the firm was originally *Basil Blackwell and Mott*.

Leaves

from the

NOTION
CLUB
PAPERS

edited by
Howard Green

Second edition

MMXIV.

Leaves from

THE NOTION CLUB PAPERS

FOREWORD

These Papers have a rather puzzling history. They were found after the Summer Examinations of 2012 on the top of one of a number of sacks of waste paper in the basement of the Examination Schools at Oxford by the present editor, Mr. Howard Green, the Clerk of the Schools. They were in a disordered bundle, loosely tied with red string. The outer sheet, inscribed in large Lombardic capitals:

ꝺОᴄꞮОꝸ ᴄꝆꙌᴃ ꝑꜽꝑᴇꝆꙅ,

attracted the notice of Mr. Green, who removed them and scrutinized them. Discovering them to contain much that was to him curious and interesting, he made all possible enquiries, without result.

The Papers, from internal evidence, clearly had no connexion with any examinations held or lectures given in the Schools during Mr. Green's many years of office. Neither did they belong to any of the libraries housed in the building. Advertisement has failed to find any claimant to ownership. It remains unknown how the Papers reached the waste-paper sack. It seems probable that they had at some time been prepared for publication, since they are in many places provided with notes; yet in form they are nothing more than an elaborate minute-book of a club, devoted to conversation, debate, and the discussion of 'papers', in verse or prose, written and read by its members, and many of the entries have no particular interest for non-members.

The minutes, or reports, covered probably about 100 meetings or 'nights' during the years of last century, approximately 1980 to 1990. It is, however, not the least curious fact about these Papers that no such club appears ever to have existed. Though certain resemblances are inevitable between a group of imaginary academic persons and their real contemporaries, no such persons as those here depicted, either with such names, or

156 SAURON DEFEATED

such offices, or such tastes and habits, can be traced in the Oxford of the last generation, or of the present time.

The author appears in one or two passages, and in the occasional notes, to identify himself with the character called in the dialogues Nicholas Guildford. But Mr. J. R. Titmass, the well-known historian of twentieth-century Oxford, who has given all possible assistance to the present editor, has shown that this is certainly a fictitious name and derived from a mediaeval dialogue at one time read in the Schools of Oxford.

On examination the bundle was found to contain 205 foolscap pages, all written by one hand, in a careful and usually legible script. The leaves were disarranged but mostly numbered. The bundle contains the entries for Nights 51 to 75, but they are defective and several leaves appear to have been lost; some of the longer entries are incomplete. It is probable that three other bundles, containing Nights 1–25, 26–50, 76–100, once existed. Of the missing sections, however, only a few scattered sheets were found in the sack, and these, so far as can be discerned, belonged originally to the entries 1–25. Among them was a crumpled and much corrected sheet, of a different paper, containing a list of members.

The total on this scale would have made a volume of considerable bulk, but its size will be overestimated, if calculation is based on the length of the extracts here printed. Many Nights are represented only by a few lines, or by short entries, of which Nights 54 and 64 have been included as specimens. As a rule these short items have been omitted, unless they bear closely on the longer reports here selected and presented to those interested in literary curiosities.

Note to the Second Edition

Mr. W. W. Wormald of the School of Bibliopoly, and Mr. D. N. Borrow of the Institute of Occidental Languages, found their curiosity aroused by the published extracts, and asked Mr. Green for permission to examine the manuscript of the Papers. They have now sent in a joint report, which raises some interesting points.

'Paper of this kind,' they write, 'is, of course, very difficult to trace or to date. The sheets submitted to us are of a poor quality much inferior to the paper now in general use for such purposes. Without venturing on a definite opinion, we record our sus-

THE NOTION CLUB PAPERS   157

picion that these sheets are much older than the dates of the supposed meetings of the Club, perhaps 40 to 50 years older, belonging, that is, to the period during or just after the Six Years' War. This suspicion is supported by various items of internal evidence, notably the idiom of the dialogues, which is old-fashioned and does not represent with any fidelity the colloquial language either of the nineteen-eighties or of the present time. We conclude, then, that *The Notion Club Papers* were written sixty years ago, or more.

'It remains, nonetheless, on this hypothesis a puzzling fact that the Great Explosion of 1975 is referred to, and even more precisely, the Great Storm, which actually occurred on the night of Thursday, June 12th, 1987;[1] though certain inaccuracies appear in the account given of the progress and effects of the latter event. Mr. Green has proposed to us a curious explanation of this difficulty, evidently suggested to him by the contents of the Papers: the future events were, he thinks, "foreseen". In our opinion a less romantic but more probable solution is this: the paper is part of a stock purchased by a man resident in Oxford about 1940. He used the paper for his minutes (whether fictitious or founded on fact), but he did not use all his stock. Much later (after 1987) he copied out his matter again, using up the old paper; and though he did not make any general revision, he moved the dates forward and inserted the genuine references to the Explosion and the Storm.'

Mr. Green rejoins: 'This is one of the most fantastic "probable solutions" I have yet met, quite apart from the unlikelihood of an inferior paper being stored for about fifty years and then used for the same purpose again. The writer was not, I think, a very young man; but the handwriting is certainly not that of an old man. Yet if the writer was not young in 1940, he must have been old, very old, in 2000. For it is to that date, not to 1987, that we must look. There is a point that has escaped the notice of Messrs. Wormald and Borrow: the old house, no. 100 Banbury Road, the last private dwelling house in that block, was in fact the scene of "hauntings",* a remarkable display of poltergeist activity, between the years 2000 and 2003, which only ended when the house was demolished and a new building, attached to the Institute of National Nutrition, erected on the site. In the year 2003 a person possessed of the paper, the

---

* See Night 61, p. 179.

158   SAURON DEFEATED

pen-habits,* and the idiom of the period of the Six Years' War would have been an oddity that no pseudonym could conceal from us.

'In any case, the Storm is integral to all the entries from Night 63 to Night , [sic] and is not just "inserted". Messrs. Wormald and Borrow must either neglect their own evidence and place the whole composition after 1987, or else stick to their own well-founded suspicions of the paper, the hand,* and the idiom, and admit that some person or persons in the nineteen-forties possessed a power of "prevision".

'Mr. Titmass informs me that he cannot find any record in the nineteen-forties of the names given in the list. If therefore, any such club existed at that earlier period, the names remain pseudonyms. The forward dating might have been adopted as an additional screen. But I am now convinced that the Papers are a work of fiction; and it may well be that the predictions (notably of the Storm), though genuine and not coincidences, were unconscious: giving one more glimpse of the strange processes of so-called literary "invention", with which the Papers are largely concerned.'

MEMBERS OF THE NOTION CLUB

The Notion Club, as depicted, was informal and vague in outline. A number of characters appear in the dialogues, some rarely or fitfully. For the convenience of readers the List of Members found among the Papers is here printed, though several of the persons named do not appear in this selection. The order is not alphabetical and seems intended to represent some kind of seniority: the first six names were written earlier and larger; the rest were added at various times and in different inks, but in the same hand. There are also later entries inserted after some of the names, recording details of their tastes or history. A few further details, gleaned from the Papers them- selves, have been added in brackets.

---

*Mr. Wormald himself, something of an expert in such matters, before he proposed his 'probable solution', ventured the opinion that the handwriting of the Papers in general character went with the old-fashioned idiom and belonged to the same period. The use of a pen rather than a typewriter would indeed, in itself, already have been most unusual for a man of 1990, whatever his age.

THE NOTION CLUB PAPERS 159

MICHAEL GEORGE RAMER. Jesus College. Born 1929 (in Hungary). Professor of Finno-Ugric Philology; but better known as a writer of romances. His parents returned to England when he was four; but he spent a good deal of time in Finland and Hungary between 1956 and 68. [Among his interests are Celtic languages and antiquities.]

RUPERT DOLBEAR. Wadham. Born 1929. Research Chemist. Has many other interests, notably philosophy, psychoanalysis, and gardening. [A close friend of Ramer. He is redhaired and redbearded, and known to the Club as Ruthless Rufus.]

NICHOLAS GUILDFORD. Lincoln. Born 1937. Archaeologist. The Club reporter; because he likes it and knows shorthand. [He is seldom recorded as reading anything to the Club, and it is then not reported; but he appears to have written several novels.]

ALWIN ARUNDEL LOWDHAM. B.N.C. Born 1938. Lecturer in English Language. Chiefly interested in Anglo-Saxon, Icelandic, and Comparative Philology. Occasionally writes comic or satirical verse. [Known as Arry.]

PHILIP FRANKLEY. Queen's. Born 1932. A poet, once well-known as a leader of the Queer Metre movement; but now just a poet, still publishing volumes of collected verse; suffers from *horror borealis* (as he calls it) and is intolerant of all things Northern or Germanic. [He is, all the same, a close friend of Lowdham.]

WILFRID TREWIN JEREMY. Corpus Christi. Born 1942. University Lecturer in English Literature. He specializes in Escapism, and has written books on the history and criticism of *Ghost-stories*, *Time-travel*, and *Imaginary Lands*.

James Jones. Born 1927. Has been a schoolmaster, journalist, and playwright. Is now retired, living in Oxford, and divides his time between producing plays and his hobby of private printing. A very silent man, but assists the Reporter with his retentive memory.

Dr. Abel Pitt. Trinity. Born 1928. Formerly Chaplain of Trinity College; now Bishop of Buckingham. Scholar, occasional poet.

Colombo Arditi. St. John's. Born 1940. Tempestosa Professor of Italian. Is fond of (and not unskilled in) singing (basso), swimming, and the game of bowls. Collects books and cats.

160   SAURON DEFEATED

Dom Jonathan Markison, O.S.B.[2] New College, Master of St. Cuthbert's Hall. [Polymath.]

Sir Gerard Manface. All Souls. Lawyer. Mountaineer; much travelled. Has many children, for whom he wrote many (unpublished) books and tales. [Seldom appears. A special friend of Frankley, but not resident in Oxford.]

Ranulph Stainer. University College. Born 1936. Professionally an expert in banking and economics; privately devoted to the history and practice of music, and has composed several works, major and minor, including one (moderately successful) opera: *Midas.*

Alexander Cameron. Exeter. Born 1935. Modern historian, specially interested in Spanish and South American history. Collects coins and stamps. Plays a pianola. [No one remembers his being invited to join the Club, or knows why he comes; but he appears from time to time.]

John Jethro Rashbold. Magdalen. Born 1965. Undergraduate. Classical scholar; apprentice poet. [Introduced by Frankley, to whom he is much attached.]

Note. It is represented as the habit of the Club for all members to initial the record of any meeting at which they were present, whether they are reported as speaking or not. Presumably the initialling, which in the extant Papers is in the same hand as the text, took place after N.G.'s report has been seen and passed, and before the fair copy was made. Mr. Cameron's initials never appear.

THE NOTION CLUB PAPERS 161

Leaves from
The
NOTION CLUB PAPERS

[PART ONE][3]

Night 54. Thursday, November 16th, 1986.[4]

A wet night. Only Frankley and Dolbear arrived (Dolbear's house). Dolbear reports that Philip never said a word worth recording, but read him an unintelligible poem about a Mechanical Nightingale (or he thought that was the subject). Frankley reports that Rufus was drowsy and kept on chuckling to himself. The only clearly audible remark that he made was *going off the deep end, I think*. This was in reply to an enquiry about Michael Ramer, and whether D. had seen him lately. After F. had read a poem (later read again) called *The Canticle of Artegall* they parted. R.D. P.F.[5]

[One or two minor entries, defectively preserved, are here omitted.]

Night 60. Thursday, February 20th, 1987.[6] [Defective at the beginning. Ramer's story is lost.]

[When Michael Ramer had finished] reading his story, we sat in silence for a while. He had not read us anything for a long time; in fact he had seldom appeared at meetings for a year or more. His excuses for absence, when he gave any, had been vague and evasive. On this occasion the Club was better attended than usual, and no more easy to please. That hardly accounted for Ramer's nervousness. He is one of our oldest members, and was at one time one of our most frequent performers; but to-night he read hastily, boggling and stumbling. So much so that Frankley made him read several sentences over again, though these interruptions, which only made matters worse, are omitted above. Now he was fidgetting.

'Well?' he said at last. 'What do you think of it? Will it do?'

A few of us stirred, but nobody spoke.

'Oh, come on! I may as well get the worst over first. What have *you* got to say?' he urged, turning to Guildford in the next chair.

'I don't know,' Guildford answered reluctantly. 'You know how I dislike criticizing ...'

162   SAURON DEFEATED

'I've never noticed it before,' said Frankley.

'Go on, Nicholas!' laughed Lowdham. 'You dislike it about as much as Philip dislikes interrupting.'

'At any rate I don't criticize unfinished sentences,' said Guildford. 'If I'd not been interrupted, I was going to say *I dislike criticizing off-hand, and still in the heat of listening.*'

'In the chill's your more usual temperature,' said Lowdham.[7]

'Most unfair! I'm a voracious reader, and I like stories.'

A chorus of incredulous shouts followed, but Guildford could just be heard amending his words, first to *I read a good many tales and like most of them*, and finally to *I do like some stories, including one or two of Ramer's.* 'But it's much more difficult,' he went on at last, 'to say anything about the *liking*, especially so soon. Liking is often much more complex than dislike. And it's less necessary to say anything about it in a hurry. The feeling of liking has a very lasting flavour; it can wait, it's often better for being stored for a bit. But defects stick out all hard and painful, while one's still close at hand.'

'For those who have the knack of seeing them in *every* literary landscape,' Ramer interposed.

'There are minor ones,' Guildford went on unperturbed, 'that may, of course, get forgotten, or be overlooked by familiarity; but they are better removed while fresh.'

'The sort that Philip corrects at once while you are reading?' said Ramer.

'Yes,' said Guildford. 'But there are more serious faults than his anacolutha and split infinitives that may also get passed, if the thing's allowed to harden. It may be painful for the author to have the blindness of paternal love removed, but it seems the most useful thing to do on the spot. What's the good of sitting here, hearing things before they're in print, if all we're to do is to pat the father's back and murmur: *Any child of yours is welcome, Mr. Ramer. Your fiftieth, is it? Well, well! How they do all take after their dear father, don't they?*'

Lowdham laughed. 'And what you're longing to say, I suppose, is: *Why don't you wipe the brat's nose, and get its hair cut?*'

'*Or strangle it!*' said Ramer impatiently.

'No, seriously,' Guildford protested, 'I only objected to parts, not to the whole of your latest infant, Michael. Only to the first chapter and the end of the last one, really. But there! I suppose no one has ever solved the difficulty of arriving, of getting to another planet, no more in literature than in life. Because the

THE NOTION CLUB PAPERS (PART ONE)   163

difficulty is in fact insoluble, I think. The barrier cannot and will not ever be passed in mortal flesh. Anyway, the opening chapters, the journey, of space-travel tales seem to me always the weakest. Scientifiction, as a rule: and that is a base alloy. Yes it is, Master Frankley, so don't interrupt! Just as much as the word is an ill-made portmanteau: rotten for travelling with. And that goes for your machine, too, Ramer. Though it's one of the better failures, perhaps.'

'Thankyou for that!' Ramer growled. 'But it's just like you, Nicholas, to pick on the frame, which is an awkward necessity of pictures, and easy to change anyway, and say nothing about what's inside it. I suppose you must have seen something to praise inside: we know how painful you find praising anything. Isn't that the real reason why you postpone it?'

'Nonsense!' said Guildford. 'I thought what was inside was very good, if you must have it. Though I felt there was something very odd about it.'

'I'm sure you did!'

'I mean *odd* coming from you. And in its setting. For you won't get away with that framed excuse. A picture-frame is not a parallel. An author's way of getting to Mars (say) is part of *his* story of *his* Mars; and of *his* universe, as far as that particular tale goes. It's part of the picture, even if it's only in a marginal position; and it may seriously affect all that's inside.'

'Why should it?' said Frankley.

'Well, if there are space-ships at all in your imagined universe, you'll fail to sell it to me, for one thing,' said Guildford.

'That's carrying your anti-machine mania too far,' said Lowdham. 'Surely poor writers can include things *you* don't like in their stories?'

'I'm not talking about dislike at the moment,' Guildford returned. 'I'm talking about *credibility*. I don't like heroic warriors, but I can bear stories about them. I believe they exist, or could. I don't think space-ships do, or could. And anyway, if you pretend that they do, and use them for space-journeys in the flesh, they'll land you in space-ship sort of adventures. If you're spaceship-minded and scientifictitious, or even if you let your characters be so, it's likely enough that you'll find things of that order in your new world, or only see sights that interest such folk.'

'But that isn't true,' Frankley objected. 'It's not true of this story of Ramer's.'

'It's generally true, all too ghastly true,' said Guildford. 'But

164   SAURON DEFEATED

of course there is a way of escape: into inconsistency, discord. Ramer takes that way, like Lindsay,[8] or Lewis, and the better post-Lewis writers of this sort of thing. You *can* land on another world in a space-ship and then drop that nonsense, if you've got something better to do there than most of the earlier writers had. But personally I dislike that acutely. It makes the scientifictitious bunkum all the worse by contrast. Crystal torpedoes, and "back-rays", and levers for full speed-ahead (faster than light, mark you), are bad enough inside one of those hideous magazines – Dead Sea fruit with gaudy rinds; but in, say, *A Voyage to Arcturus** they are simply shocking. All the more so for being unnecessary. David Lindsay had at least two other better methods up his sleeve: the séance connexion; or the suggestion of the dark tower at the end. Thank goodness, there was at any rate no return by crystal torpedo in that tale!'[9]

'But the trick in *Out of the Silent Planet*, getting the hero kidnapped by space-ship villains, so as to explain how an interesting man ever got inside one, was not bad,' said Frankley. 'And the stupid villainy of the space-ship folk was essential. They behaved as such people would, and the plot depends on that.'

'Not bad, I agree,' said Guildford. 'Still it was, as you say, a trick. And not first rate, not if you want sheer literary credibility, the pure thing, rather than an alloy with allegory and satire. Ramer is not after any such Lewisite alloy; and I think his device of letting an intelligent artist get into a contraption by accident, not knowing what it is, is a mere trick. But what I really object to, in any such tale, however tinged, is the pretence that these contraptions could exist or function at all. They're indefinitely less probable – as the carriers of living, undamaged, human bodies and minds – than the wilder things in fairy-stories; but they pretend to be probable on a more material mechanical level. It's like having to take Heath-Robinsons seriously.'

'But you've got to have some kind of removal van,' said Frankley, 'or else do without this kind of story. They may not be

---

* This book had recently been rescued from oblivion by Jeremy's book on *Imaginary Lands*. See the account of his reading parts of this to the Club, above, Nights 30, 33, 40 [not preserved]. Most of the members are fairly well-read in twentieth-century books of travel in Space and Time. N.G.

THE NOTION CLUB PAPERS (PART ONE) 165

your sweetmeat, Nicholas, but I've got a tooth for them; and I'm not going to be done out of them by you.'

'You can wallow in Scientifiction mags, for all I care,' said Guildford; 'but I've got to have literary belief in my removal van, or I won't put my furniture into it. I have never met one of these vehicles yet that suspended my disbelief an inch off the floor.'

'Well, your disbelief evidently needs a power-crane,' said Frankley. 'You should look at some of the forgotten Old Masters, like Wells, if you've ever heard of him. I admit that what his first men found in the Moon was a bathos after the journey. But the machine and the journey were splendid. I don't of course, believe in a gravitation-insulator outside the story, but inside the story it worked, and Wells made damned good use of it. And voyages can end in grubby, vulgar, little harbours and yet be very much worth while.'

'It wouldn't be easy to miss the name of Wells with Jeremy always about,' said Guildford. 'And I *have* read *The First Men in the Moon*, and *The Time Machine*. I confess that in *The Time Machine* the landfall was so marvellous that I could have forgiven an even more ridiculous transport – though it would be difficult to think of one! All the same, the machine was a blemish; and I'm quite unconvinced that it was a necessary one. And if it had been removed – the effect on the whole thing! Enormous enhancement even of that remarkable tale.

'No doubt authors are in as great a hurry to get there as we are; but eagerness doesn't excuse carelessness. And anyway, we're older. We may allow the primitives their ingenuousness: we can't imitate it. Isn't it always so? What might do once won't do any longer. I used to read with gusto romances in which the hero just pushed off into the Blue, over mountains and deserts, without water supplies. But now I feel that procedure is slipshoddy.'

'There's no such word,' said Frankley.

'Shut up!' said Lowdham.

'I want my man to have his adventures in the Blue, as much as ever, but I want to be made to feel that the author has faced the difficulties and not ignored them, or fudged them. It's usually all the better for the tale in the long run.

'Certainly I'll admit that if I allow Wells his "cavorite",[10] then he makes good use of it. If I'd been a boy when the tale was new, I should have allowed it and enjoyed it. But I can't allow it

166   SAURON DEFEATED

now. I'm post-Wells. And we're not criticizing him but Ramer, for using at this much later date a rather similar device. Any one who touches space-travel now has got to be much more convincing: if indeed a convincing machine is at present possible. Command of power has prodigiously increased, but the problems have become more complex, and not simpler. Scientists can't destroy simple faith and hope still to keep it for themselves. A gravitation-insulator won't do. Gravity can't be treated like that. It's fundamental. It's a statement by the Universe of where you are in the Universe, and the Universe can't be tricked by a surname with *ite* stuck on the end, nor by any such abracadabra.

'And what of the effect on a man of being hurled out of one gravitational field through zero into another? Even on so elementary a journey as one to the Moon?'

'Oh! difficulties of that sort will be got over all right,' said Frankley. 'At least that is what most of the scientists say who are concerned with space-projects.'

'Scientists are as prone to wishful thinking (and talking) as other men, especially when they are thinking about their own romantic hopes and not yours,' said Guildford. 'And they like opening vague, vast, vistas before gapers, when they are performing as public soothsayers.'

'I'm not talking about that kind,' said Frankley. 'There are quiet unpublicized people, quite scientific medicos, for instance, who'll tell you that your heart and digestive arrangements, and all that, would function all right, even at, say, zero gravity.'

'I dare say they will,' said Guildford. 'Though I still find it difficult to believe that a machine like our body, made to function under definite earth-conditions, would in fact run on merrily when those were greatly changed – and for a long time, or permanently. Look how quickly we wilt, even on this globe, if we're transferred to unusual heights or temperatures. And the effect on you of greatly *increased* gravity is rather hushed up, isn't it?* Yet after all that is what you'd be most likely to get at the other end of your journey.'

'That's so,' said Lowdham. 'But people of this blessed century think primarily of travelling and speed, not of destination, or

---

* Not, of course, in Scientifiction. There it is usually exorcized by mere abracadabra in bogus 'scientific' form.   N.G.

THE NOTION CLUB PAPERS (PART ONE) 167

settling. It's better to travel "scientifically", in fact, than to get anywhere; or the vehicle justifies the journey.'

'Yes, and it is *speed* that really bothers me,' said Guildford, 'more than these other difficulties. I don't doubt the *possibility* of sending a rocket to the Moon. The preparations were knocked back by the Great Explosion,[11] but they say they're under way again. I'll even admit the eventual possibility of landing undamaged human goods on the lunar landscape – though what they'll do there is dubious. But the Moon is very parochial. Rockets are so slow. Can you hope to go as fast as light, anything like as fast?'

'I don't know,' said Frankley. 'It doesn't seem likely at present, but I don't think that all the scientists or mathematicians would answer that question with a definite *no*.'

'No, they're very romantic on this topic,' said Guildford. 'But even the speed of light will only be moderately useful. Unless you adopt a Shavian attitude and regard all these light-years and light-centuries as lies, the magnitude of which is inartistic. If not, you'll have to plan for a speed greater than light; much greater, if you're to have a practical range outside the Solar System. Otherwise you will have very few destinations. Who's going to book a passage for a distant place, if he's sure to die of old age on the way?'

'They still take tickets on the State Railways,' said Lowdham.

'But there's still at least a chance of arriving before death by coach or train,' said Guildford. 'I don't ask for any greater degree of probability from my author: just a possibility not wholly at variance with what we know.'

'Or think we know,' Frankley murmured.

'Quite so,' Guildford agreed. 'And the speed of light, or certainly anything exceeding it, is on that basis incredible: if you're going to be "scientific", or more properly speaking "mechanical". At any rate for anyone writing now. I admit the criteria of credibility may change; though as far as I can see, genuine Science, as distinct from mechanical romance, narrows the possibilities rather than expands them. But I still stick to my original point: the "machine" used sets the tone. I found space-ships sufficiently credible for a raw taste, until I grew up and wanted to find something more useful on Mars than ray-guns and faster vehicles. Space-ships will take you to that kind of country, no doubt. But I don't want to go there. There's no need now to travel to find it.'

168   SAURON DEFEATED

'No, but there is an attraction in its being *far away*, even if it's nasty and stupid,' said Frankley. 'Even if it's the same! You could make a good story – inevitably satirical in effect, perhaps, but not really primarily so – out of a journey to find a replica of Earth and its denizens.'

'I daresay! But aren't we getting a bit mixed?' said Lowdham. 'Nick's real point, which he seems to have forgotten as well as the rest of us, was incoherence – discord. That was really quite distinct from his dislike, or his disbelief in mechanical vehicles; though actually he dislikes them, credible or not. But then he began confusing *scientific probability* with *literary credibility*.'

'No, I didn't and I don't,' said Guildford. 'Scientific probability *need* not be concerned at all. But it *has* to be, if you make your vehicle mechanical. You cannot make a piece of mechanism even sufficiently credible in a tale, if it seems outrageously incredible *as a machine* to your contemporaries – those whose critical faculties are not stunned by the mere mention of a machine.'

'All right, all right,' said Lowdham. 'But let's get back to the incoherence. It's the discord between the objects and the findings of the better tales and their machines that upsets you. And I think you have something there. Lewis, for instance, used a space-ship, but he kept it for his villains, and packed his hero the second time in a crystal coffin without machinery.'

'Half-hearted,' said Guildford. 'Personally, I found the compromise very unconvincing. It was wilfully inefficient, too: poor Ransom[12] got half toasted, for no sound reason that I could see. The power that could hurl the coffin to Venus could (one would have thought) have devised a material that let in light without excessive heat. I found the coffin much less credible than the Eldils,[13] and granted the Eldils, unnecessary. There was a page or two of smoke-screen about the outward journey to Perelandra, but it was not thick enough to hide the fact that this semi-transparent coffin was after all only a material packing-case, a special one-man space-ship of unknown motive power. It was necessary to the tale, of course, to have safe delivery of Ransom's living terrestrial body in Venus: but this impossible sort of parcel-post did not appeal to me as a solution of the problem. As I say, I doubt if there is a solution. But I should prefer an old-fashioned wave of a wizard's wand. Or a word of power in Old Solar[14] from an Eldil. Nothing less would suffice: a miracle.'

THE NOTION CLUB PAPERS (PART ONE)   169

'Why have anything at all?' little Jeremy asked suddenly. So far he had sat curled up on the floor, as near to the fire as he could get, and he had said nothing, though his black birdlike eyes had hopped to and fro from speaker to speaker. 'The best stories I know about imaginary times and lands are just stories about them. Why a wizard? At least, why a wizard, outside the real story, just to waft you into it? Why not apply the *Once-upon-a-time* method to Space? Do you need more than author's magic? Even old Nick won't deny authors the power of seeing more than their eyes can. In his novels he lets himself look into other people's heads. Why not into distant parts of Space? It's what the author has really got to do, so why conceal it?'

'No, of course I don't deny authors their right of invention, *seeing*, if you like to call it that,' said Guildford.

At that point Dolbear stirred and seemed about to wake up; but he only settled more comfortably into his chair, and his loud breathing went on, as it had since the early part of Ramer's story.

'But that's a different kind of story, Jeremy,' objected Frankley. 'Quite good in its way. But I want to travel in Space and Time myself; and so, failing that, I want people in stories to do it. I want contact of worlds, confrontation of the alien. You say, Nick, that people cannot leave this world and live, at least not beyond the orbit of the Moon?'

'Yes, I believe they could not, cannot, and never will.'

'Very well then, all the more reason for having stories about *they could* or *they will*. Anybody would think you'd gone back to all that old-fashioned stuff about escapism. Do you object to fairy-tales?'

'No, I don't. But they make their own worlds, with their own laws.'

'Then why can't I make mine, and let its laws allow space-ships?'

'Because it won't then be your private world, of course,' said Guildford. 'Surely that is the main point of that kind of story, at an intelligent level? The Mars in such a story *is* Mars: the Mars that is. And the story is (as you've just admitted) a substitute for satisfaction of our insatiable curiosity about the Universe as it is. So a space-travel story ought to be made to fit, as far as we can see, the Universe as it is. If it doesn't or doesn't try to, then it

170   SAURON DEFEATED

does become a fairy-story – of a debased kind. But there is no need to travel by rocket to find Faërie. It can be anywhere, or nowhere.'

'But supposing you did travel, and did find Fairyland?' asked Ramer, suddenly. For some time now he had been staring at the fire, and had seemed to take very little interest in the battle that had been going on about him. Jeremy gaped at him, and jumped to his feet.

'But not by space-ship surely!' he cried. 'That would be as depressingly vulgar as the other way about: like an awful story I came across once, about some men who used a magic carpet for cheap power to drive a bus.'

'I'm glad to get *you* as an ally!' laughed Guildford. 'For you're a hardened sinner: you read that bastard stuff, scientific-tion, not as a casual vice, but actually as a professional interest.'

'The stuff is extremely interesting,' said Jeremy. 'Seldom as art. Its art level is as a rule very low. But literature may have a pathological side – still you've heard me on all that often enough. On this point I'm with you. Real fairy-stories don't pretend to produce impossible mechanical effects by bogus machines.'

'No. And if Frankley wants fairy-tales with mechanized dragons, and quack formulas for producing power-swords, or anti-dragon gas, or scientifictitious explanations of invisibility, well, he can have 'em and keep 'em. No! For landing on a new planet, you've got your choice: miracle; magic; or sticking to normal probability, the only known or likely way in which any one has ever landed on a world.'

'Oh! So you've got a private recipe all the time, have you?' said Ramer sharply.

'No, it's not private, though I've used it once.'

'Well? Come on! What is it?'

'Incarnation. By being born,' said Guildford.[15]

At that point Dolbear woke up. He yawned loudly, lifted his heavy lids, and his blue-bright eyes opened wide under his red brows. He had been audibly sleeping for a long while,* but we

---

* He often slept loudly, during a long reading or discussion. But he would rouse up in the middle of a debate, and show that he had the odd faculty of both sleeping and listening. He said that it was a time-saving habit that long membership of the Club had forced him to acquire. N.G.

THE NOTION CLUB PAPERS (PART ONE)   171

were used to the noise, and it disturbed us no more than the sound of a kettle simmering on the fire.

'What have you got to say to that, Ramer?' he asked. He shot a sharp glance at him, but Ramer made no reply. Dolbear yawned again. 'I'm rather on Nick's side,' he said. 'Certainly about the first chapter in this case.'

'Well, that was read at the beginning, before you settled down for your nap,' said Lowdham.

Dolbear grinned. 'But it was not that chapter in itself that interested me,' he said. 'I think most of the discussion has been off the point, off the immediately interesting point. The hottest trail that Nicholas got on to was the *discord*, as you said yourself, Arry.[16] That's what you should follow up now. I should feel it strongly, even if space-ships were as regrettably possible as the Transatlantic Bus-service. Michael! Your real story is *wholly* out of keeping with what you called the frame. And that's odd in you. I've never felt such a jar before, not in any of your work. I find it hard to believe that the machine and the tale were made by the same man. Indeed, I don't think they were. You wrote the first chapter, the space-voyage, and also the homecoming (rather slipshod that, and my attention wandered): you *made it up*, as they say. And as you've not tried your hand at that sort of thing before, it was not much above the average. But I don't think you wrote the story inside. I wonder what you've been up to?'

'What are you driving at?' said Jeremy. 'It was typical Ramer all through, nearly every sentence was hall-marked. And even if he wanted to put us off with borrowed goods, where could he get them from?'

'You know his itch to re-write other people's bungled tales,' said Lowdham. 'Though certainly he's never tried one on us before, without telling us.'

'I know all that,' said Jeremy, hopping about angrily. 'I mean: where could he get this tale from? If he has found any printed space-travel story that I don't know, then he's been doing some pretty hot research. I've never met anything like it at all.'

'You're missing my point,' said Dolbear. 'I shouldn't have said *wrote*. I should have said *made up, invented*. I say again: I wonder what you've been up to, Ramer?'

'Telling a story,' answered Ramer glumly, staring at the fire.

'Yes,' said Dolbear. 'But don't try to do that in the nursery sense, or we'll have to roast you.' He got up and looked round

172   SAURON DEFEATED

at us all. His eyes looked very bright under bristling brows. He turned them sharply on Ramer. 'Come!' he said. 'Come clean! Where's this place? And how did you get there?'

'I don't know where it is,' said Ramer quietly, still staring at the fire. 'But you're quite right. I went there. At least ... well, I don't think our language fits the case. But there is such a world, and I saw it – once.' He sighed.

We looked at him for a long while. All of us – except Dolbear, I think – felt some alarm, and pity. And on the surface of our minds blank incredulity, of course. Yet it was not quite that: we did not feel the underlying emotion of incredulity. For apparently all of us, in some degree, had sensed something odd about that story, and now recognized that it differed from the norm like seeing does from imagining. I felt that it was like the difference between a bright glimpse of a distant landscape: threadlike waters really falling; wind ruffling the small green leaves and blowing up the feathers of birds on the branches, as that can be seen through a telescope: limited but clear and coloured; flattened and remote, but moving and real – between that and any picture. Not, it seemed to me, an effect to be explained simply by art. And yet – the explanation offered was nonsense outside the pages of a romance; or so I found that most of us felt at that moment.

We tried a few more questions, but Ramer would not say any more that night. He seemed disgruntled, or tired; though we had not scoffed. To relieve the tension, Frankley read us a short poem he had recently written. It was generous of him, for it was a good piece; but inevitably it fell rather flat. It is, however, pretty well-known now, as it appeared as the opening poem of his 1989 volume: *Experiments in Pterodactylics*.

We broke up soon after he had read it.

'Ramer,' I said at the door, 'we *must* hear some more about this, if you can bear it. Can't you come next week?'

'Well, I don't know,' he began.

'O don't go off to New Erewhon again just yet!' cried Lowdham, a bit too jocularly. [I don't think so. A.A.L.] 'We want more News from Nowhere.'[17]

'I did not say it was Nowhere,' said Ramer gravely. 'Only that it was Somewhere. Well, yes, I'll come.'

I walked part of the way home with him. We did not talk. It was a starry night. He stopped several times and looked up at

THE NOTION CLUB PAPERS (PART ONE)   173

the sky. His face, pale in the night, had a curious expression, I thought: like a man in a strange country trying to get the points of the compass, and wondering which way his home lies.

In the Turl[18] we parted. 'I think what the Club really needs is not more stories – yet,' I said. 'They need, I specially want, some description of the method, if you could manage it.' Ramer said nothing. 'Well, good night!' I said. 'This has been one of the great Club evenings, indeed! Who'd have thought that in starting up that literary hare about the most credible way of opening a space-tale I'd blunder on the lair of a real winged dragon, a veritable way of travelling!'

'Then you do believe me?' said Ramer. 'I thought that all of you but Dolbear thought I was spoofing, or else going batty. You in particular, Nick.'

'Certainly not spoof, Michael. As for battiness: well, in a sense, your claim is a batty one, even if genuine, isn't it? At least, it is, if I've any inkling of it. Though I've nothing to go on but impressions, and such hints as I've managed to get out of Rufus about your recent doings. He's the only one of us that has seen much of you for quite a time; but I rather fancy that even he does not know a great deal?'

Ramer laughed quietly. 'You're a hound, I mean a sleuth-hound, by nature, Nicholas. But I am not going to lay down any more trail tonight. Wait till next week! You can then have a look at my belfry and count all the bats. I'm tired.'

'Sleep well!' I said.

'I do,' said Ramer. 'Very well indeed. Good night!'

MGR. NG. AAL. PF. WTJ. RD. JJ.

Night 61.   Thursday, February 27th, 1987.[19]

A week later we were all together again, in Frankley's rooms this time; and even Cameron had come. As will be seen, he actually made a remark on this occasion, more than his stock 'Thanks for a very enterrtaining evening.' It was generally understood that Ramer was going to read a paper on *Real Space-travel*.

He was the last to arrive, and we were pleasantly surprised to see that he looked quite well, quite normal, and had not even the rather haggard look he used to have after writing a paper. He spends a frightful lot of late hours on such things, and burns more paper than he keeps.

174   SAURON DEFEATED

Arry Lowdham[20] tapped him all over and pretended to be disappointed by the result. 'No models!' he cried. 'No plans of cylinders, spheres, or anything! Not even a Skidbladnir for a pocket-handkerchief!'[21]

'Now, none of that Nordic stuff, please!' groaned Frankley, who regards knowledge of his own language at any period before the Battle of Bosworth as a misdemeanour, and Norse as a felony.[22]

'No, not even a paper,' said Ramer.

'Why not?' we all cried.

'Because I haven't written one.'

'Oh I say!' we protested. 'Then you were spoofing all the time?' said Lowdham.

'No,' said Ramer. 'But I'm not going to read a paper. I didn't write one, because it would have been a great sweat; and I wasn't sure that you'ld really want to hear any more about it all. But if you do, I'm ready to talk.'

'Come on!' we said. Frankley shoved him down into a chair, and gave him a tankard of beer, and a box of matches – for him to strike, hold over a dead pipe, and throw away, as usual.

'Well,' he said after a short silence. 'It begins some way back. And the threads may seem a bit disconnected at first. The origins were literary, of course, like the discussion last week. I've always wanted to try a space-travel story, and have never dared. It was one of my earliest ambitions, ever since *Out of the Silent Planet* appeared, when I was a small boy. That puts it back a bit.'

'Yes, 1938,' said Cameron,[23] whose memory is like that. I doubt if he has ever read the book. The memoirs of minor modern diplomats are more in his line. The remark was his sole contribution.

'I never did write one,' said Ramer, 'because I was always bothered by the machinery, in a literary sense: the way of getting there. I didn't necessarily object to machines; but I never met and couldn't think of any credible vehicle for the purpose. I really agree very much with Nicholas on that point.'

'Well, you tried a pretty ordinary machine on us in that tale,' said Frankley.

'And seemed pretty disgruntled with me for objecting to it,' said Guildford.

'I was not really disgruntled,' said Ramer. 'A bit put out,

THE NOTION CLUB PAPERS (PART ONE)   175

perhaps, as one is when one's disguise is pierced too quickly. Actually I was interested in the way you all felt the discord: no more than I did myself. But I felt that I had to tell that story to somebody, to communicate it. I wanted to get it out. And yet, and yet now I'm rather sorry. Anyway, I put it in that quickly-made cheap frame, because I didn't want to discuss the way I came by it – at least not yet. But Ruthless Rufus with his "third degree" has landed me here.'

'Yes, he has!' said Dolbear. 'So get on with your confession!'

Ramer paused and considered. 'Well, thinking about methods of getting across Space, I was later rather attracted by what you may call the telepathic notion – merely as a literary device, to begin with. I expect I got the idea from that old book you lent me, Jeremy: *Last Men in London*, or some name like that.[24] I thought it worked pretty well, though it was too vague about the *how*. If I remember rightly, the Neptunians could lie in a trance and let their minds travel. Very good, but *how* does the mind travel through Space or Time, while the body is static? And there was another weakness, as far as I was concerned: the method seemed to need rational creatures with minds at the other end. But I did not myself particularly want to see – or I should say at that stage, perhaps, write about – what Lewis called *hnau*.[25] I wanted to see things and places on a grand scale. That was one thread.

'Another thread was dreams. And that had a literary origin, too, partly. Because Rufus and I have long been interested in dreams, especially in their story-and-scene-making, and in their relation to waking fiction. But as far as I could judge such things, it did seem to me that a pretty good case had been made out for the view that in dream a mind can, and sometimes does, move in Time: I mean, can observe a time other than that occupied by the sleeping body during the dream.'

'But of course it can, and without sleeping,' said Frankley. 'If we were confined to the present, we couldn't think at all, even if we could perceive or feel.'

'But I mean *moving* not by memory, or by calculation, or by invention, as the waking mind can be said to *move*; but as a perceiver of the external, of something new that is not yet in the mind. For if you can see, in other times than the time of dreaming, what you never saw in waking life, so that it is not in your memory – seeing the future, for instance, would be a clear

176 SAURON DEFEATED

case, and it cannot reasonably be doubted that that occurs –
then obviously there is a possibility of real first-hand seeing of
what is "not there", not where your body is.'

'Not even your eyes?' said Frankley.

'Ah,' said Ramer, 'that is of course a point. I shall come to
that later. It is probably a case of "translation"; but leave it for
a bit. I was thinking of dreaming chiefly, though I don't suppose
the possibility is really limited to that state. Only, if you live in a
never-ending racket of sense-impressions, other more distant
noises have to be very loud to be heard. And this *movement*, or
transference of observation: it is clearly not limited to Other
Time; it can occur in Other Space, or in both. A dreamer is not
confined to the events of Other Time occurring in his bedroom.'

'But wouldn't you expect to be limited to the places where
you yourself *have been*, or *will be*, in Other Time?' asked
Guildford.

'That's not the general human tradition about visions,' said
Ramer. 'Nor is it borne out by authenticated modern instances.
And it is not my experience, as you will see. But naturally I
thought about that point. I think, actually, that it is clear that
the mind can be in two places at one time: two or more; once
you have made it more than one, the figure is, perhaps, not very
important. For I suppose, as far as the mind goes, you can't get
nearer to saying where it is than to say where its attention is.
And that, of course, may be decided by various causes, internal
and external.

'You can get a sort of literary parallel. I think it is a pertinent
one, actually; for I don't think literary invention, or fancy, is
mixed up in all this by accident. When you are writing a story,
for instance, you can (if you're a vivid visualizer, as I am, and
are clearly visualizing a scene) *see* two places at once. You can
see (say) a field with a tree and sheep sheltering from the sun
under it, and be looking round your room. You are really seeing
both scenes, because you can recollect details later. Details of
the waking scene not attended to, because you were *abstracted*:
there's no doubt of that. I should as certainly add: details of the
inner scene, blurred because you were to some extent *distracted*.

'As far as my own visualizing goes, I've always been impressed by how often it seems independent of my will or planning
mind (at the moment). Often there is no trace of composing a
scene or building it up. It comes before the mind's eye, as we
say, in a way that is very similar to opening closed eyes on a

THE NOTION CLUB PAPERS (PART ONE)   177

complete waking view.*[26] I find it difficult, usually quite impossible, to alter these pictures to suit myself, that is my waking purpose. As a rule I find it better, and in the end more right, to alter the story I'm trying to tell to suit the pictures. If the two really belong together – they don't always, of course. But in any case, on such occasions you are really seeing double, or simultaneously. You tend to associate the two views, inner and outer, though the juxtaposition of them may be, usually is, their only connexion. I still associate a view of a study I no longer possess and a pile of blue-and-yellow-covered exam-scripts (long burnt, I hope) with the opening scene of a book I wrote years ago: a great morain high up in the barren mountains.'

'I know', said Jeremy, 'the foot of the Glacier in *The Stone-eaters*.'[27]

'I think a connexion could be made out between those two scenes,' said Frankley.

'It's very difficult to find any two things that the story-making faculty cannot connect,' said Ramer. 'But in this case the story-scene came into my head, as it is called, long before the examination reality. The two are connected only because I was re-visualizing, revisiting, the Glacier-foot very strongly that day.'

'That doesn't quite get rid of some connexion other than coinciding in time,' said Frankley.

'Well, never mind. They did coincide,' said Ramer. 'And that is my point at the moment. The mind can be in more than one place at a given time; but it is more properly said to be where its attention is. And that, I suppose, is in one place only: for most human minds, or at any rate for my mind.

'But I'm afraid this is a digression. To go back to dreams. Of course, the memory of such true dreams, or free dreams, is notoriously rarish and chancy, and also scrappy as a rule. But it is not legitimate, it is pretty plainly wrong, to assume that what is ordinarily remembered by ordinary people of their dreaming is either most of the total, or the most important part of it. And the will to remember can be strengthened, and the memory can

---

* Ramer said later: 'It is still more like re-viewing in memory a place that one has really been to; it is like *memory* in its quality as compared with *sightseeing*, but on the first occasion of its arising in the mind it does not seem to be "remembering".'   N.G.

178   SAURON DEFEATED

be enlarged. Rufus has had a good deal of experience in that direction, and he has helped me from time to time.'

Dolbear stirred and opened his eyes. 'So his suspicion was not due to pure literary criticism of discords?' said Frankley.

'Well, I haven't the faintest idea of what Michael is driving at, yet – if that's what you mean,' said Dolbear. 'Or rather, I understand what he's saying and more or less agree with it, but what it has to do with that vision of, of what was it?'

'Emberü,' said Ramer. 'I don't yet see,' Dolbear ended.[28]

'Well, here is a third thread,' Ramer went on. 'I had the notion, as others probably have too, that for movement or travelling the mind (when abstracted from the flood of sense) might use the memory of the past and the foreshadowing of the future that reside in all things, including what we call "inanimate matter". Those are not the right words, but they'll have to do: I mean, perhaps, the causal descent from the past, and the casual probability in the present, that are implicit in everything. At any rate, I thought that might be one of the mind's vehicles.[29] But an incarnate mind seemed rather a problem to me.'

'Not a very new one!' said Guildford.

Ramer laughed. 'Don't be too hard on me,' he said. 'I'm not at all original. And anyway my problem was practical rather than philosophical. I was puzzled about *jumping*. I didn't see how it could be done. I'm not a philosopher, but an experimenter, a man driven by desires – if not very fleshly ones, still very incarnate ones. Being an *incarnate* mind, I am conditioned by Time and Space, even in my curiosities; though being a *mind*, I want to get beyond the range of my own body's senses and history.

'Of course, you might imagine the mind, by some special effort of its own, doing something analogous to the body's leaping from place to place, especially in a less trammelled state like sleep, or trance. But I thought the analogy probably false – for a living man, anchored even in trance to the body, however long and thin the rope. The mind may be neither in Time nor Space, except in so far as it is specially associated with a body; but while you're alive the bond holds, I thought. Mind-body: they jump together, or neither jumps at all.

'I hardly need to say again that by *jump* I do not mean the movement of thought to objects already in its grasp, or memory: shifting instantaneously from, say, considering the peculiar

THE NOTION CLUB PAPERS (PART ONE)   179

configuration of Rufus's face to thinking of Table Mountain (which I once saw). I wanted to observe new things far off in Time and Space beyond the compass of a terrestrial animal.'

'And so,' said Lowdham, 'like the Pig on the Ruined Pump, day and night you made your moan, because you could not jump?'[30]

'Exactly,' said Ramer; 'for of course by this time I was really thinking more about travelling myself than writing a travel-story. But I didn't want to die. And I thought that all I could do was to refine my observation of other things that have moved and will move: to inspect the history of things whose paths have, at some point of time and space, crossed the path of my body.

'The mind uses the memory of its body. Could it use other memories, or rather, records? What kind of record of past events and forms could there be? In the time-sequence the disintegration of a form destroys the memory – or the special record – of the history of that form, unless it has got into a mind first. The fragments, right down to the smallest units, no doubt preserve the record of their own particular history, and that may include some of the history of the combinations that they've entered into. But take a haunted house, for instance.'

'Take a house!' interrupted Jeremy. 'All houses are haunted.'

'I agree,' said Ramer. 'But I'm using the words, as they're commonly used, to mean a house where some particular detail of the haunting has become specially perceptible; how or why that occurs is another question.'

'But *haunting*, and *atmosphere* (which I suppose is what Jeremy means), are something added by accident of history,' objected Frankley. 'They're not part of the house itself, *qua* house.'

'I'm not sure I understand you,' said Ramer. 'But I'm quite sure that I personally am not interested in 'housiness' in itself, but in this or that thing which you may class as a house, part of which (the most interesting part to me) is its history. If I say No. 100 Banbury Road,[31] I mean the shape which you call house *and* all that you call the accidents of its history: what it is at present. So do you. And if you destroy an actual house *qua* house, you also destroy, or dissipate, the special haunting. If a haunted house were pulled to pieces, it would stop being haunted, even if it were built up as accurately as possible again. Or so I think, and so-called 'psychical' research seems to bear

180   SAURON DEFEATED

me out. In a way analogous to life in a body. If all the king's horses and all his men had put Humpty Dumpty together again, they'ld have got, well, an egg-shell.'

'But you can go a long way, short of destruction, without wholly banishing atmosphere or quite laying ghosts,' said Jeremy. 'Bricking up windows, changing staircases, and things like that.'

'Quite right,' said Lowdham. 'There was one poor ghost I heard of, and when they raised the floor of his favourite corridor, he went on walking on the old level. So people in the passage below could see the old fellow's feet trudging along under the ceiling. That's how they discovered he had holes in his soles. Don't laugh!' he said indignantly. 'It's a most melancholy case, and well authenticated.'

'I dare say!' said Ramer. 'But quite apart from such forlorn ghosts, and Arry's authorities (whoever they may be), I expect there are in fact lots of neglected chances of historical research, with proper training; especially among old houses and things more or less shaped by man. But that was not my chief interest. I wanted to travel a long way.

'So I tried various experiments, on myself; various forms of training. It's difficult to concentrate, chiefly because it's difficult to get quiet enough. The body makes such a noise itself, quite apart from the din of sensations coming from outside. I wanted to discover if my mind had any power, any trainable latent power, to *inspect* and *become aware* of the memory or record in other things, that would be in them anyway, even if not inspectable by me. For, I suppose, what we call memory, human memory, is both the power to inspect and be aware of the record within us, *and* the record that would be there anyway. The power of inspection and awareness is always there; and so is the material and record, I suppose, unless it is smashed up. Though the inspector cannot always get at the records. We aren't in full control of ourselves, even, so obviously it wouldn't be easy to deal with other things.'

'But the mind seems also to have its own storehouses, as well as keys of inspection, doesn't it?' said Guildford. 'I mean, it can remember past inspections, and retains what it has noted.'

'Yes, I think so,' said Ramer; 'but it is difficult, of course, when you're dealing with a mind-body, an association in which neither can do anything without having some effect on the other. I don't think an incarnate mind ever gets really free of its

THE NOTION CLUB PAPERS (PART ONE)   181

body, wherever it strays, until a man dies, if then. However, I went on trying to train myself for this kind of, well, historical inspection and awareness. I don't think I have any special talent for it. I don't *know*, for so few people seem to have tried it. But I fancy that Jeremy, for instance, has more of a bent in this direction than I have.

'It is difficult, and it's also frightfully slow. Less slow, of course, with things that have organic life, or any kind of human associations: but they don't carry you very far. It's slow, and it's *faint*. In inorganic things too faint to surmount the blare of waking sense, even with eyes shut and ears stopped.

'But here the threads begin to join. Remember, I was also training my memory on dreams at the same time. And that is how I discovered that the other experiments affected them. Though they were blurred, blurred by the waking senses beyond recognition, I found that these other perceptions were not wholly unnoted; they were like things that are passed over when one is abstracted or distracted, but that are really "taken in". And, asleep, the mind, rootling about, as it does, in the day's leavings (or the week's), would inspect them again with far less distraction, and all the force of its original desire. I dare say it enjoyed it.

'But it couldn't make much of it. By which I suppose I mean that I couldn't remember much about such inspections, although I was now becoming pretty good at remembering large passages of more vivid and pictorial dreams. And that means I suppose also, that my mind was not able (at least not without more practice) to translate the notes into the terms of the senses which I can handle when awake. All the same, I used to get at that time very extraordinary geometric patterns presented to me, shifting kaleidoscopically but not blurred; and queer webs and tissues, too. And other non-visual impressions also, very difficult to describe; some like rhythms, almost like music; and throbs and stresses.

'But all the time, of course, I wanted to get off the Earth. That's how I got the notion of studying a meteorite, instead of mooning about with houses, ruins, trees, boulders, and all sorts of other things. There is a very large meteorite in a park, Gunthorpe Park in Matfield,[32] where I lived as a boy, after we came back from abroad; even then it had a strange fascination for me. I wondered if it could have come from Malacandra. I took to hobnobbing with it again, in the vacs. Indeed, I made

182 SAURON DEFEATED

myself ridiculous and an object of suspicion. I wanted to visit the stone alone at night – to lessen the distractions; but I was not allowed to: closing hours were closing hours. So I gave that up. It seemed to be quite without results.'

'So the poor old stone was left all alone?' said Lowdham.

'Yes,' said Ramer. 'It was. It is a very long way indeed from home, and it *is* very lonely. That is, there is a great loneliness in it, for a perceiver to perceive. And I got a very heavy dose of it. In fact I can't bear to look at such things now. For I found, about the end of the long vac. two years ago, after my final visit, that there *had* been results. It had evidently taken some time to digest them, and even partially translate them. But that is how I first got away, out beyond the sphere of the Moon, and very much further.'

'Travelling on a dream-meteor!' said Frankley. 'Hm! So that's your method, is it?'

'No,' said Ramer. 'Not if you mean how I got the news of Emberü that I put into my tale.[33] But I did work back into the meteorite's history, I think; though that sort of vehicle does not readily give any place or time references that can be related to our waking point. I did get, all the rest of that term, and I still do get occasionally, some very odd dreams or sleep-experiences: painful often, and alarming. Some were quite unpictorial, and those were the worst. Weight, for instance. Just Weight with a capital W: very horrible. But it was not a weight that was pressing on *me*, you understand; it was a perception of, or sympathy in, an experience of almost illimitable weight.[34] And Speed too. Heavens! waking up from that one was like hitting a wall, though only a wall of light and air in my bedroom, at a hundred miles a second – or rather, like knowing about it.

'And Fire! I can't describe that. Elemental Fire: fire that is, and does not consume, but is a mode or condition of physical being. But I caught sight of blazing fire, too: some real pictures. One, I think, must have been a glimpse of the meteorite hitting our air. A mountain corroded into a boulder in a few seconds of agonizing flame. But above, or between, or perhaps through all the rest, I knew endlessness. That's perhaps emotional and inaccurate. I mean Length with a capital L, applied to Time; unendurable length to mortal flesh. In that kind of dream you can know about the feeling of aeons of constricted waiting.

'Being part of the foundations of a continent, and upholding immeasurable tons of rock for countless ages, waiting for an

THE NOTION CLUB PAPERS (PART ONE)   183

explosion or a world-shattering shock, is quite a common situation in parts of this universe. In many regions there is little or no "free will" as we conceive it. Also, though they are large and terrific, events may be relatively simple in plan, so that catastrophes (as we might call them), sudden changes as the end of long repeated series of small motions, are "inevitable": the present holds the future more completely. A perceiving but passive mind could see a collapse coming from an immense distance of time.

'I found it all very disturbing. Not what I wanted, or at least not what I had hoped for. I saw, anyway, that it would take far too much of a mortal human life to get so accustomed to this kind of vehicle that one could use it properly, or selectively, at will. I gave it up. No doubt, when any degree of control was achieved, my mind would no longer have been limited to that particular vehicle or chunk of matter. The waking mind is not confined to the memories, heredity, or senses, of its own normal vehicle, its body: it can use that as a platform to survey the surroundings from. So, probably, it could, if it ever mastered another vehicle: it could survey, in some fashion, other things where the meteorite (say) came from, or things it had passed in its historical journey. But that second transference of observation would certainly be much more difficult than the first, and much more uncertain and inefficient.

'So I turned more than ever to dream-inspection, trying to get "deeper down". I attended to dreams in general, but more and more to those least connected with the immediate irritations of the body's senses. Of course, I had at times experienced, as most people have, parts of more or less rationally connected dreams, and even one or two serial or repeating dreams. And I have had also the not uncommon experience of remembering fragments of dreams that seemed to possess a "significance" or emotion that the waking mind could not discern in the remembered scene.[35] I was not at all convinced that this "significance" was due to obscured symbols, or mythical values, in the dream-scenes; or at least I didn't and don't think that that is true of most of such dream-passages. Many of these "significant patches" seemed to me much more like random pages torn out of a book.'

'But you didn't wriggle out of Rufus's clutches that way, did you?' said Guildford. 'He'll analyse a whole book as cheerfully as a page.'

184   SAURON DEFEATED

'It depends on the contents,' said Ramer. 'But I'll come back to that. For at about that time something decisive happened. It seemed to sweep away all other trials and experiments; but I don't think they were really wasted. I think they had a good deal to do with precipitating the, well, catastrophe.'

'Come on, come on! What was it?' said Dolbear. He stopped snoring and sat up.

'It was most like a violent awakening,' said Ramer. He was silent for almost a minute, staring at the ceiling as he lay back in his chair.

At last he went on. 'Imagine an enormously long, vivid, and absorbing dream being shattered – say, simultaneously by an explosion in the house, a blow on your body, and the sudden flinging back of dark curtains, letting in a dazzling light: with the result that you come back with a rush to your waking life, and have to recapture it and its connexions, feeling for some time a shock and the colour of dream-emotions: like falling out of one world into another where you had once been but had forgotten it. Well, that was what it was like *in reverse*; only recapturing the connexions was slower.

'I was awake in bed, and I *fell wide asleep*: as suddenly and violently as the waker in my illustration. I dived slap through several levels and a whirl of shapes and scenes into a connected and remembered sequence. I could remember all the dreams I had ever had, of that sequence. At least, I remember that I could remember them while I was still "there", better than I can "here" remember a long sequence of events in waking life. And the memory did not vanish when I woke up, and it hasn't vanished. It has dimmed down to normal, to about the same degree as memory of waking life: it's edited: blanks indicating lack of interest, some transitions cut, and so on. But my dream-memories are no longer fragments, no longer like pictures, about the size of my circle of vision with fixed eyes, surrounded with dark, as they used to be, nearly always. They are wide and long and deep. I have visited many other sequences since then, and I can now remember a very great number of serious, free, dreams, my deep dreams, since I first had any.'

'What a lumber-room!' said Lowdham.

'I said *my serious dreams*,' said Ramer. 'Of course, I can't, don't want to, and haven't tried to remember all the jumble of marginal stuff – the rubbish the analysts mostly muck about

THE NOTION CLUB PAPERS (PART ONE) 185

with, because it's practically all they've got – no more than you try to recollect all the scribbling on blotting-paper, the small talk, or the idle fancies of your days.'

'How far have you gone back?' Lowdham asked.

'To the beginning,' Ramer answered.

'When was that?'

'Ah! That depends on what you mean by *when*,' said Ramer. 'There are seldom any data for cross-timing as between waking and dreaming. Many dreams are in, or are concerned with, times remote from the standpoint of the body. One of those dreams might be said to occur before it started; or after. I've no idea how far I've gone *back* in that sense, backward in the history of the universe, you might say. But sticking to the waking time, then I suppose I cannot have begun dreaming until I had begun to be: that is, until the creation of my mind, or soul. But I doubt if any ordinary time-reference has any real meaning with regard to that event considered in itself; and the word *dreaming* ought to be limited to the ... er ... spare-time, off-duty, activities of an incarnate mind. So I should say my dreaming began with the entry of my mind into body and time: somewhere in the year 1929. But that fifty-odd years of our time *could* contain various indefinite lengths of experience, or operation, or journeying. My earlier experiments were not necessary, except perhaps to help in the precipitation of memory, as I said. My mind "asleep" had long done that sort of thing very much better.'

He paused, and we looked at him, some of us a bit queerly. He laughed. 'Don't imagine me walking about "in a dream", as people say. The two modes are no more confused than before. If you had two homes in quite different places, say in Africa and Norway, you'd not usually be in doubt which one you were staying in at any given time, even if you could not remember the transition. No, at the worst my situation is only like that of a man who has been reading a deeply interesting book, and has it "on his mind", as he goes about his affairs. But the impression can pass off, or be put aside, as in the case of a book. I need not think about my dreams, if I don't wish to, no more than I need think about any book or re-read it.'

'You say *re-read*. Can you will, now when awake, to go back to any particular dream, to repeat it or go on with it?' asked Frankley. 'And can you remember your waking life while in a dream?'

186   SAURON DEFEATED

'As to the last question,' Ramer replied, 'the answer is: in a sense *yes*. As clearly as you can remember it while writing a story, or deeply engrossed in a book. Only you can't give direct attention to it. If you do, you wake up, of course.

'The other question's more difficult. Dreams are no more all of one sort than the experiences of waking life; less so in fact. They contain sensations as different as tasting butter and understanding a logical argument; stories as different in length and quality as one of Arry's lower anecdotes and the Iliad; and pictures as unlike as a study of a flower-petal and those photographs of the explosion in the Atomic Reservation in the seventies,[36] which blew the Black Hole in the States. Dreams happen, or are made, in all sorts of ways. Those that people mostly remember, and remember most of, are marginal ones, of course, or on the upper levels . . .'

'Margins? Upper levels? What d'you mean?' snapped Jones,[37] breaking in, to our surprise. 'Just now you spoke of diving. When do we get to the bottom?'

'Never,' Ramer laughed. 'Don't take my words too literally, at any rate no more literally than I suppose you take the *sub* in *subconscious*. I'm afraid I haven't thought out my terminology very carefully, James; but then I didn't mean to talk about these things to you, not yet. I've been put on the mat. I think I meant *deep* as in *deeply interested*; and down, lower, upper, and all the rest have crept in afterwards, and are misleading. Of course there isn't any *distance* between dreams and waking, or one kind of dream and another; only an increase or decrease of abstraction and concentration. In some dreams there's no distraction at all, some are confused by distractions, some just *are* distractions. You can lie "deep" and sodden in body-made dreams, and receive clear visions in "light" sleep (which might seem on the very margin of waking). But if I use "deep" again you'll know that I mean dreams as remote as may be from disturbance, dreams in which the mind is seriously engaged.

'By the marginal ones I meant those that are produced when the mind is playing, idling, or fooling, as it often is, mooning aimlessly about among the memories of the senses – because it's tired, or bored, or out of mental sorts, or worried by sense-messages when its desires or attention are elsewhere; the devil's tattoo of dreaming as compared with the piano-playing. Some minds, perhaps, are hardly capable of anything else, sleeping or waking.

THE NOTION CLUB PAPERS (PART ONE) 187

'And the machinery may go on ticking over, even when the mind is not attending. You know how you've only got to do something steadily for hours – like picking blackberries, say – and even before you're asleep the manufacture of intricate trellises of briars and berries goes on in the dark, even if you're thinking of something else. When you begin to dream you may start by using some of those patterns. I should call that "marginal". And anything else that is largely due to what is actually going on, in and around the body: distraction complexes in which such things as "noises off", indigestion, or a leaking hot-water-bottle play a part.

'Asking if you can re-visit that stuff is like asking me if I can will to *see* (not make) rain tomorrow, or will to be waked up *again* by two black cats fighting on the lawn. But if you're talking about serious dreams, or visions, then it's like asking if I shall walk back up the road again last Tuesday. The dreams are for your mind events. You can, or might – waking desire has some effect, but not much – go back to the same "places" and "times", as a spectator; but the spectator will be the you of now, a later you, still anchored as you are, however remotely, to your body time-clock here. But there are various complications: you can re-inspect your memories of previous inspections, for one thing; and that is as near to dreaming the same dream over again as you can get (the closest parallel is reading a book for a second time). For another thing, thought and "invention" goes on in dreams, a lot of it; and of course you can go back to your own work and take it up again – go on with the story-making, if that is what you were doing.'

'What a busy time we all seem to have been having without knowing it,' said Lowdham. 'Even old Rufus may not be quite such a sloth as he looks. Anyway you've given him a jolly good excuse to fall back on. "Goodbye all! I'm off to my dream-lab to see if the retorts are bubbling," says he, and he's snoring in two ticks.'

'I leave the bubbling retorts to you,' said Dolbear, opening his eyes. 'I am afraid I've not yet got down to such high levels as Michael, and I muck about still with the marginal stuff, as he calls it. Tonight at any rate I've been having a bit of a dream: in the rootling stage, I suppose, owing to the distraction of this discussion going on round my body. I got a picture of Ramer, equipped with Frankley's long nose, trying to extract whiskey out of a bottle; he couldn't pour it out, as he had no arms, only

188   SAURON DEFEATED

a pair of black wings, like a devil in a stuffed M.A. gown.'

'The whiskey-bottle was not derived from the sense-data in this room,' said Lowdham.

'Now I can sympathize with the psychoanalysts,' said Frankley, rising and getting a bottle out of the cupboard. 'The difficulty they must have in sorting out dreams from the malicious inventions of the patient's waking mind!'

'No difficulty with Rufus,' said Lowdham. 'The drink-urge explains most of him. And I don't think he's got a Censor, sleeping or waking.'

'Hm! I'm glad I'm so transparent,' said Dolbear. 'Not everyone is so simple, Arry. You walk in disguises, even when awake. But they'll slip, my lad, one day. I shouldn't wonder if it was fairly soon.'[38]

'Lor!' said Lowdham. 'Have I come out in a false beard and forgotten it, or something?' But at that moment he caught a glint in Dolbear's eye, and stopped suddenly.

'Go on, Michael, and don't take any notice of them!' said Jeremy.

'Shall I?' he asked, absentmindedly drinking the whiskey that Frankley had put at Dolbear's elbow.

'Of course!' we said. 'We are fortified now.'

'Well, seriously,' he went on, 'I don't think the marginal stuff is very interesting in normal people: it's so ravelled, and more bother to unravel than it's worth. It's very much like the idleness and foolery of the waking mind. The chief distinction is, I think, that when a man's awake he's attending more to the foolery; and when he's asleep his attention is probably already far away: so the foolery is less good of its kind. But as for his mind being *busy*, Arry: I only said, if you remember, that your life *could* contain a lot of dream-work or events. I don't think it usually does. Minds can be lazy on their own account. Even for the energetic ones sleep is largely a rest. But of course, for a mind rest is not oblivion, which is impossible for it. The nearest it can get to that is passivity: the mind can be very nearly passive, contemplating something worthy of it, or what seems worthy. Or it can take the kind of holiday we call "a change", doing something different to the work imposed on it by needs or duties when it is awake. If it has by nature, or has acquired, some dominant interest – like history, or languages, or mathematics – it may at times work away at such things, while

THE NOTION CLUB PAPERS (PART ONE)   189

the old body is recuperating. It can then construct dreams, by no means always pictorial. It can plan and calculate.

'My mind, like many others, I imagine, makes up stories, composes verse, or designs pictures out of what it has got already, when for some reason it hasn't at the moment a thirst to acquire more. I fancy that all waking art draws a good deal on this sort of activity.[39] Those scenes that come up complete and fixed that I spoke of before, for instance; though some of them, I believe, are visions of real places.

'And that strong feeling of hidden significance in remembered fragments: my experience now, though it is still very imperfect, certainly bears out my guess, as far as my own dreams go. My significant fragments were actually often pages out of stories, made up in quieter dream-levels, and by some chance remembered. Occasionally they were bits of long visions of things not invented.

'If long ago you'd either read or written a story and forgotten it, and then in an old drawer you came on a few torn pages of it, containing a passage that had some special function in the whole, even if it had no obvious point in isolation, I think you'ld get very similar feelings: of hidden significance, of lost connexions eluding you, and often of regret.'

'Could you give us any examples?' asked Jeremy.

Ramer thought for a moment. 'Well,' he said, 'I could have done so. I've placed several of my fragments in their proper setting now. But the difficulty is that when once you've got the whole story, you tend very soon to forget which part of it was the bit you used to remember torn out. But there are a couple that I still remember, for I only placed them recently; and I still remember my disappointment. The whole stories are often not particularly good or interesting, you know; and the charm of the fragments is often largely in being unfinished, as sometimes happens in waking art. The sleeping mind is no cleverer than itself; only it can be less distracted and more collected, more set on using what it has.

'Here's one case: it's only interesting as an illustration. *A row of dark houses on the right, going up a slight slope. Their backs had little gardens or yards fenced with hedges, and a narrow path behind them. It was miserably dark and gloomy. Not a light in the houses, not a star, no moon. He was going up the path for no particular reason, in a heavy aimless mood. Near the top of the slope he heard a noise: a*

190   SAURON DEFEATED

*door had opened at the back of one of the houses, or it had
closed. He was startled and apprehensive. He stood still. End
of fragment.*
What would you expect the emotion to be that this aroused?'

'Like going round to the back-door after closing-time and
hearing that just being shut as well?' suggested Lowdham.

'It sounds reasonable enough,' agreed Ramer with a laugh.
'Actually it was a happiness that brings tears, like the thrill of
the sudden turn for good in a dangerous tale; and a kind of dew
of happiness was distilled that spilled over into waking, lasted
for hours, and for years was renewed (though diminishingly) on
recollection.

'All my waking mind could make of it was that the picture
was sombre. It did rather remind me of – or rather, I identified
it, in spite of some misfit, with a row of cottages near where I
lived as a small boy. But that did not explain the joy. And, by
the way, if it had really been a picture of that row, there should
have been a pump just at the top of the slope. I put it in. I see it
now in dark silhouette. But it was not there in my earliest
recollection, not in the original version. Also, I was only the *he*
of the scene in the way one does (or I do) identify oneself
variably with this or that character in a tale, especially with
regard to the point of vision. The scene was observed more or
less from *his* point of view, though I (the producer) was just
behind (and a little above) *him* – until he stopped. At the
emotion-point I took his place.

'The story that scene came out of is known to me now; and
it's not very interesting. Apparently it's one I made up years
ago,[40] somewhere in the fifties, at a time when, while awake, I
wrote lots of things of the sort. I won't bother you with it all: it
had a long and complicated plot,[41] mainly dealing with the Six
Years' War; but it wasn't very original, nor very good of its
kind. All that matters at the moment is that this scene came just
before a lovers' reunion, beyond the hope of either the man or
the woman. On hearing the noise he halted, with a premonition
that something was going to happen. The woman came out of
the door, but he did not recognize her till she spoke to him at the
gate. If he hadn't halted, they would have missed one another,
probably for ever. The plot, of course, explained how they both
came to be there, where neither of them had been before; but
that doesn't matter now. The interesting thing is that the
remembered fragment, for some reason, ended with the sound

THE NOTION CLUB PAPERS (PART ONE)   191

of the door and the halting; but the *emotion* left over was due to part of the story immediately following, which was not remembered pictorially at all. But there was no trace of the emotions of still later parts of the story, which did not finally have a happy ending.

'Well, there it is. Not very exciting, but suggestive, perhaps. Do you want the other case?'

Dolbear gave a loud snore. 'Hark at him!' said Lowdham. 'I expect he's analysed you enough already, and doesn't want any more of your juvenilia to interrupt his slumber.'

'Oh go on, Ramer!' said Jeremy. 'Let's have it!'

'It's your evening, and we asked for it,' said Guildford. 'Carry on!'

'Well, here's another picture,' said Ramer.

A pleasant small room: a fire, a lot of books, a large desk; a golden light from a lamp. He is sitting at the desk. The dreamer's attention, from slightly above his head, is concentrated on the circle of light, but is vaguely aware of dim figures away in front, moving about, taking books from shelves, reading in corners. He is looking at an open book at his left hand, and making notes on a paper. General air of cheerfulness and quiet. He pauses and looks up as if thinking, knocking his pipe-stem between his teeth. He turns a leaf of the book – and sees a new light, makes a discovery; but the fragment ends.

What do you make of that?'

'He'd solved the acrostic with the aid of a dictionary?' said Frankley.

'Emotion: Jack-Hornerism, quiet bibliophilous gloating?' said Lowdham.

'No!' said Ramer. 'Though you're getting warm, Arry. But the emotion associated was *worry*, with a heavy hang-over into waking hours of a dull sense of loss, as heavy as anything you felt in childhood when something precious was broken or lost.'

'Well, New Readers now go back to Chapter One,' said Lowdham. 'What is it?'

'Rather more unusual than the first case, so I'll tell it more fully,' said Ramer. 'He was the librarian in a small university. The room was his office-study: quite comfortable, but it had a glass wall on one side, through which he could overlook the main hall of the library. He was feeling cheerful, for a few years back a local magnate had left the university a splendid book-

192   SAURON DEFEATED

collection, and most of his money for the enlargement and upkeep of the library. The library had become important; so had he, and his salary as curator of the endowed collection was generous. And after a lot of delay a new wing had been built, and the books transferred. For some time he'd been carefully re-examining the more interesting items. The book to his left was a volume made up of various manuscript-fragments bound together, probably in the sixteenth century, by some collector or pilferer.

'In the remembered bit of the dream I knew I had been able to read the page before he turned over, and that it was not English; but I could remember no more than that – except that I was delighted, or he was. Actually it was a leaf, a unique fragment of a MS. in very early Welsh, before Geoffrey,[42] about the death of Arthur.

'He turned to look at the back of the leaf – and he found, stuck between it and the next, a document. It turned out to be a will made by the Donor. This book of fragments was one of the last things the magnate had acquired, just before his death. The will was later than the proved and executed will by nearly two years. It was in form, and witnessed, and it did not mention the university, but directed that the books should be dispersed and sold, and the proceeds should go to found a Chair of Basic English in London; while the rest of the estate should go to a nephew, previously passed over.

'The librarian had known the magnate, and had often been to his house: he had helped in cataloguing his collection. He saw that the witnesses were two old servants that had died soon after their master. The emotions are easy to understand: the librarian was proud of his library, a scholar, a lover of real English, and the father of a family; but he was also an honest man. He knew that the Donor had disliked the new Vice-Chancellor very much; also that the nephew was the Donor's next of kin, and poor.'

'Well, what did he do with the will?' said Jeremy.

'On second thoughts he thought it best to stuff it in the old oak chest?' said Lowdham.

'I don't know,' said Ramer. 'Of course it would have been easy and probably quite safe to suppress the will. But I found I had never finished the tale properly, though plenty of sequels could be invented. I found one or two ideas, not worked out, floating at the end. One was that the librarian went to the

THE NOTION CLUB PAPERS (PART ONE)   193

Vice-Chancellor, who begged him to keep his discovery quiet; he gave way, and was later blackmailed by the Vice-Chancellor himself. But evidently that hadn't seemed satisfactory, or I'd lost interest in the whole thing beyond the recorded situation. I left a good many such yarns incomplete at that time.

'There's little merit in these stories, as you see. But they do illustrate one or two points about fragmentary memory, and about dream-storywriting. For it is not, of course, writing, but a sort of realized drama.'

'Elvish Drama,'[43] Jeremy interposed; 'there's something about it ...' But we had heard him on that topic before. 'Ramer has the floor!' we cried.

'Well anyway,' Ramer went on: 'the whole story as it is told becomes visible and audible, and the composer is inside it – though he can take his stand in some odd positions (often high up), unless he puts himself into the play, as he can at any moment. The scenes *look* real, but are feigned; and the composition is not complete like a "slice of life": it can be given in selected scenes, and compressed (like a drama). Also it can, when you're working over it again or merely re-inspecting it, be reviewed in any order and at varying speeds (like re-reading or reconsidering a book). I think that is one, though only one, of the reasons why the memory of such dreams, when any survives at all, is so often dissolving or jumbled. The dreamer is aware, of course, that he is author and producer, at any rate while he is at work asleep; but he can get far more absorbed by his work than a waking man is by any book or play that he is either writing or reading; and he can feel the emotions very strongly – excessively sometimes, because they are heightened by the excitement of combining authorship with an acting part; and in memory they may be exaggerated still more through getting dislocated, abstracted from the sounds and scenes that would explain them.

'The cases I've cited are without any symbolism. Just plain emotional situations. I can't say much about symbolic or mythical significances. Of course they exist. And really I can only put them back one stage. For the dreamer can work on myth, and on fairy-tale, quite as much as on novelette. I did. I do. And with a more complete text, so to speak, the excerpted scenes are often much easier to understand, and the functions of the symbols are plainer – but their final solution recedes.

'There are good dreams, apparently of the sort I mean, quoted in books. My own were not so good: the ones I used to

194   SAURON DEFEATED

remember when awake, that is; they were only significant fragments, more statically pictorial, seldom dramatic, and usually without figures of humane shape.[44] Though I sometimes retained the memory of significant words or sentences without any scenery: such as *I am full of sovereign remedies*. That seemed a wise and satisfactory utterance. I have never yet found out why.

'Here are some of my fragments of this kind. There is the empty throne on the top of a mountain. There is a Green Wave, whitecrested, fluted and scallop-shaped but vast, towering above green fields, often with a wood of trees, too; that has constantly appeared.[45] I saw several times a scene in which a wide plain lay before the feet of a steep ridge on which I stood; the opposing sky was immense, rising as a vertical wall, not bending to a vault, ablaze with stars strewn almost regularly over all its expanse. That is an omen or presage of catastrophe. A dark shape sometimes passes across the sky, only seen by blotting out the stars as it goes. Then there is the tall, grey, round tower on the sheer end of the land. The Sea cannot be seen, for it is too far below, too immeasurably far; but it can be smelt. And over and over again, in many stages of growth and many different lights and shadows, three tall trees, slender, foot to foot on a green mound, and crowned with an embracing halo of blue and gold.'

'And what do you think they all mean?' asked Frankley.

'It took me quite a time, far too long, to explain the very minor story of the librarian,' said Ramer. 'I could not embark tonight on even one of the immense and ramified legends and cosmogonies that these belong to.'

'Not even on the Green Wave?' said Lowdham;[46] but Ramer did not answer him.

'Are the Blessed Trees religious symbolism?' asked Jeremy.

'No, not more than all things mythical are; not directly. But one does sometimes see and use symbols directly religious, and more than symbols. One can pray in dreams, or adore. I think I do sometimes, but there is no memory of such states or acts, one does not revisit such things. They're not really dreams. They're a third thing. They belong somewhere else, to the other anchorage, which is not to the Body, and differ from dreams more than Dream from Waking.

'Dreaming is not Death. The mind is still, as I say, anchored to the body. It is all the time inhabiting the body, so far as it is *in*

THE NOTION CLUB PAPERS (PART ONE)   195

anywhere. And it is therefore in Time and Space: attending to them. It is meant to be so. But most of you will agree that there has probably been a change of plan; and it looks as if the cure is to give us a dose of something higher and more difficult. Mind you, I'm only talking of the seeing and learning side, not for instance of morality. But it would feel terribly *loose* without the anchor. Maybe with the support of the stronger and wiser it could be celestial; but without them it could be bitter, and lonely. A spiritual meteorite in the dark looking for a world to land on. I daresay many of us are in for some lonely Cold before we get back.

'But out of some place beyond the region of dreams, now and again there comes a blessedness, and it soaks through all the levels, and illumines all the scenes through which the mind passes out back into waking, and so it flows out into this life. There it lasts long, but not for ever in this world, and memory cannot reach its source. Often we ascribe it to the pictures seen on the margin radiant in its light, as we pass by and out. But a mountain far in the North caught in a slow sunset is not the Sun.

'But, as I said, it is largely a rest-time, Sleep. As often as not the mind is inactive, not making things up (for instance). It then just inspects what is presented to it, from various sources – with very varying degrees of interest, I may say. It's not really frightfully interested in the digestion and sex items sent in by the body.'

'What is *presented* to it, you say?' said Frankley. 'Do you mean that some of the presentments come from outside, are *shown* to it?'

'Yes. For instance: in a halting kind of way I had managed to get on to other vehicles; and in dream I did it better and more often. So other minds do that occasionally to me. Their resting on me need not be noticed, I think, or hardly at all; I mean, it need not affect me or interfere with me at all; but when they are doing so, and are in contact, then my mind can use *them*. The two minds don't tell stories to one another, even if they're aware of the contact. They just are in contact and can learn.*[47] After

---

* See the further discussion of this point on the following Night 62. N.G. [Only a fragment of that meeting is preserved, and the only part that could correspond to this note is as follows. ' "How can the dreamer distinguish them?" said Ramer. "Well, it seems to me that

196   SAURON DEFEATED

all, a wandering mind (if it's at all like mine) will be much more
interested in having a look at what the other knows than in
trying to explain to the stranger the things that are familiar to
itself.'

'Evidently if the Notion Club could all meet in sleep, they'ld
find things pretty topsy-turvy,' said Lowdham.

'What kind of minds visit you?' asked Jeremy. 'Ghosts?'

'Well, yes of course, ghosts,' said Ramer. 'Not departed
human spirits, though; not in my case, as far as I can tell.
Beyond that what shall I say? Except that some of them seem to
know about things a very long way indeed from here. It is not a
common experience with me, at least my awareness of any
contact is not.'

'Aren't some of the visitors malicious?' said Jeremy. 'Don't
evil minds attack you ever in sleep?'

'I expect so,' said Ramer. 'They're always on the watch,
asleep or awake. But they work more by deceit than attack. I
don't think they are specially active in sleep. Less so, probably.
I fancy they find it easier to get at us awake, distracted and not
so aware. The body's a wonderful lever for an indirect influence
on the mind, and deep dreams can be very remote from its
disturbance. Anyway, I've very little experience of that kind –
thank God! But there does come sometimes a frightening ... a
sort of knocking at the door: it doesn't describe it, but that'll

the chief divisions are *Perceiving* (free dreams), *Composing and
Working*, and *Reading*. Each has a distinctive quality, and confusion is
not as a rule likely to occur, while it is going on; though the waking
mind may make mistakes about disjointed memories. The divisions
can be subdivided, of course. *Perceiving* can be, for instance, either
inspections and visits to real scenes; or apparitions, in which one may
be deliberately visited by another mind or spirit. *Reading* can be
simply going over the records of any experiences, messing about in the
mind's library; or it can be perceiving at second hand, using minds,
inspecting *their* records. There's a danger there, of course. You might
inspect a mind and think you were looking at a record (true in its own
terms of things external to you both), when it was really the other
mind's composition, *fiction*. There's *lying* in the universe, some very
clever lying. I mean, some very potent fiction is specially composed to
be inspected by others and to deceive, to pass as record; but it is made
for the malefit of Men. If men already lean to lies, or have thrust aside
the guardians, they may read some very maleficial stuff. It seems that
they do."']

THE NOTION CLUB PAPERS (PART ONE)   197

have to do. I think that is one of the ways in which that horrible sense of *fear* arises: a fear that doesn't seem to reside in the remembered dream-situation at all, or wildly exceeds it.

'I'm not much better off than anyone else on this point, for when that fear comes, it usually produces a kind of dream-concussion, and a passage is erased round the true fear-point. But there are some dreams that can't be fully translated into sight and sound. I can only describe them as resembling such a situation as this: working alone, late at night, withdrawn wholly into yourself; a noise, or even a nothing sensible, startles you; you get prickles all over, become acutely self-conscious, uneasy, aware of isolation: how thin the walls are between you and the Night.

'That situation may have various explanations here. But out (or down) there sometimes the mind is suddenly aware that there *is* a Night outside, and enemies walk in it: one is trying to get in. But there are no walls,' said Ramer sombrely. 'The soul is dreadfully naked when it notices it, when that is pointed out to it by something alien. It has no armour on it, it has only its being. But there is a guardian.

'He seems to command precipitate retreat. You could, if you were a fool, disobey, I suppose. You could push him away. You could have got into a state in which you were attracted by the Fear. But I can't imagine it. I'ld rather talk about something else.'

'Oh!' said Jeremy. 'Don't stop there! It's been mostly digressions since the meteorite. My fault largely. Won't you go on?'

'I should like to, if the Club can bear it. A little longer. I only meant: I'ld rather get back to the visions and the journeys. Well, apart from such dangers – which I've not experienced often or thought much about – I think that what one calls "interests" are sometimes actually stimulated, or even implanted by contacts. As you might get a special interest in China, through being visited by a Chinaman, especially if you got to know him and something of his mind.'

'Have you gone to any Celestial China?' asked Frankley. 'Or anywhere more interesting than your invented tales: something more like Emberü?'

'I've never *gone* anywhere,' said Ramer, 'as I've tried to explain. But I suppose I could say that I've *been* in places, and I'm still busy trying to sort out my observations. If you mean

198   SAURON DEFEATED

places off the Earth, other heavenly bodies: yes, I've seen several besides Emberü, either through other minds, or by vehicles and records; possibly by using light.* Yes, I've been to several strange places.

'The one I told you about, Green Emberü,[48] where there was a kind of organic life, rich but wholesome and longeval: that was where I landed when I first fell wide asleep. It seems a long while ago now. It is still very vivid to me, or was until last week.' He sighed.

'I cannot remember the original again now, somehow; not when awake. I've an idea that writing these memories up, re-telling them in waking life and terms, blurs or erases them in waking memory; overlays them into palimpsests. One can't have it both ways. Either one must bear the pains of not communicating what one greatly desires to share, or one must remain content with the translation. I wrote that account for you, and all I'll have now is that, and stirrings and faint traces of what lies beneath: the vision of Emberü!

'It's the same with Ellor. Ellor!' he murmured. 'Ellor Eshúrizel! I drew it once in words as best I could, and now it *is* words. That immense plain with its silver floor all delicately patterned; the shapely cliffs and convoluted hills. The whole world was designed with such loveliness, not of one thought, but of many in harmony; though in all its shapes there was nowhere any to recall what we call organic life. There "inanimate nature" was orderly, symmetrical, unconfused, yet intricate, beyond my mind's unravelling, in its flowing modulations and recollections: a garden, a paradise of water, metal, stone, like the interwoven variations of vast natural orders of flowers. Eshúrizel! Blue, white, silver, grey, blushing to rich purples were its themes, in which a glint of red was like an apocalyptic vision of essential Redness, and a gleam of gold was like the glory of the Sun. And there was music, too. For there were many streams, water abundant – or some fairer counterpart, less wayward, more skilled in

---

* Jones says that Ramer explained: 'I think that as the *seeing* in free dream is not done with eyes, it is not subject to optical laws. But light can be used, like any other mode of being. The mind can, as it were, travel back up-stream, as it can go back into the historical record of other things. But it seems tiring: it requires a great energy and desire. One can't do it often; nor can one go to an indefinite distance of Time and Space.' N.G.

THE NOTION CLUB PAPERS (PART ONE)   199

the enchantment of light and in the making of innumerable sounds. There the great waterfall of Öshül-küllösh fell down its three hundred steps in a sequence of notes and chords of which I can only hear faint echoes now. I think the En-keladim dwell there.'[49]

'The En-keladim?' asked Jeremy softly. 'Who are they?'

Ramer did not answer. He was staring at the fire. After a pause he went on. 'And there was another world, further away, that I came to later. I won't say very much. I hope to look on it again, and longer: on Minal-zidar the golden, absolutely silent and quiescent, a whole small world of one single perfect form, complete, imperishable in Time, finished, at peace, a jewel, a visible word, a realization in material form of contemplation and adoration, made by what adoring mind I cannot tell.'

'Where is Minal-zidar?' asked Jeremy quietly.

Ramer looked up. 'I don't know where or when,' he answered. 'The travelling mind does not seem very interested in such points, or forgets to try and find out in the absorption of beholding. So I have very little to go on. I did not look at the sky of Minal-zidar. You know, if you were looking at the face of somebody radiant with the contemplation of a great beauty or a holiness, you'd be held by the face for a very long time, even if you were great enough (or presumptuous enough) to suppose that you could see for yourself. Reflected beauty like reflected light has a special loveliness of its own – or we shouldn't, I suppose, have been created.

'But in Ellor there seemed to be lights in the sky, what we should call stars, not suns or moons, and yet many were much larger and brighter than any star is here. I am no astronomer, so I don't know what that may imply. But I suppose it was somewhere far away, beyond the Fields of Arbol.'[50]

'Fields of Arbol?' said Lowdham. 'I seem to have heard that before. Where do you get these names from? Whose language are they? Now that would really interest me, rather than geometry and landscape. I should use *my* chances, if ever I got into such a state, for language-history.'[51]

'Arbol is "Old Solar" for the Sun,' said Jeremy.[52] 'Do you mean, Ramer, that you can get back to Old Solar, and that Lewis* did not merely invent those words?'

---

* Referring to *Out of the Silent Planet* and *Perelandra*, which we had all read some time ago, under pressure from Jeremy (while he was

200   SAURON DEFEATED

'Old Solar?' said Ramer. 'Well, no. But of course I was quoting Lewis, in saying Fields of Arbol. As to the other names, that's another matter. They're as firmly associated with the places and visions in my mind as *bread* is with Bread in your minds, and mine. But I think they're *my* names in a sense in which *bread* is not.*

'I daresay it depends on personal tastes and talents, but although I'm a philologist, I think I should find it difficult to learn strange languages in a free dream or vision. You *can* learn in dreams, of course; but in the case of real visions of new things you don't talk, or don't need to: you get the meaning of minds (if you meet any) more directly. If I had a vision of some alien people, even if I heard them talking, their *sense* would drown or blur my reception of their *sounds*; and when I woke up, if I remembered what had been said, and tried to relate it, it would come out in English.'

'But that wouldn't apply to pure names, proper nouns, would it?' said Lowdham.

'Yes, it would,' said Ramer. 'The voice might say *Ellor*, but I should get a glimpse of the other mind's vision of the place. Even if a voice said *bread* or *water*, using "common nouns", I should be likely to get, as the core of a vague cloud (including tastes and smells), some particular glimpse of a shaped loaf, or a running spring, or a glass filled with transparent liquid.

'I daresay that you, Arry, are more phonetical, and more sound-sensitive than I am, but I think even you would find it difficult to keep your ear-memory of the alien words unblurred

writing his book on *Imaginary Lands*). See note to Night 60, p. 164. Jeremy was an admirer of the *Public-house School* (as he himself had dubbed them), and soon after he became a Lecturer he gave a series of lectures with that title. Old Professor Jonathan Gow had puffed and boggled at the title; and J. had offered to change it to *Lewis and Carolus, or the Oxford Looking-glass*, or *Jack and the Beanstalk*; which did not smooth matters. Outside the Club J. had not had much success in reviving interest in these people; though the little book of anonymous memoirs *In the Thirsty Forties, or the Inns and Outs of Oxford* attracted some notice when it came out in 1980. N.G.

* Lowdham says that Ramer told him after the meeting that he thought *Minal-zidar* meant Poise in Heaven; but *Emberü* and *Ellor* were just names. *Eshúrizel* was a title, signifying in an untranslatable way some blend or scheme of colours; but *Öshül-küllösh* meant simply Falling Water. N.G.

THE NOTION CLUB PAPERS (PART ONE)   201

by the impact of the direct meaning in such dreams. If you did, then very likely it would be only the sounds and not the sense that you'ld remember.

'And yet ... especially far away outside this world of Speech, where no voices are heard, and other naming has not reached ... I seem to hear fragments of language and names that are not of this country.'

'Yes, yes,' said Lowdham. 'That's just what I want to hear about. What language is it? You say not Old Solar?'

'No,' said Ramer, 'because there isn't any such tongue. I'm sorry to disagree with your authorities, Jeremy; but that is my opinion. And by the way, speaking as a philologist, I should say that the treatment of language, intercommunication, in tales of travel through Space or Time is a worse blemish, as a rule, than the cheap vehicles that we were discussing last week. Very little thought or attention is ever given to it.[53] I think Arry will agree with me there.'

'I do,' said Lowdham, 'and that's why I'm still waiting to hear where and how you got your names.'

'Well, if you really want to know what these names are,' said Ramer, 'I think they're my *native* language.'

'But that is English, surely?' said Lowdham. 'Though you were born in Madagascar, or some strange place.'

'No, you ass! Magyarország, that is Hungary,' said Ramer. 'But anyway, English is *not* my native language. Nor yours either. We each have a native language of our own – at least potentially. In working-dreams people who have a bent that way may work on it, develop it. Some, many more than you'ld think, try to do the same in waking hours – with varying degrees of awareness. It may be no more than giving a personal twist to the shape of old words; it may be the invention of new words (on received models, as a rule); or it may come to the elaboration of beautiful languages of their own in private: in private only because other people are naturally not very interested.

'But the inherited, first-learned, language – what is usually mis-called "native" – bites in early and deep. It is hardly possible to escape from its influence. And later-learned languages also affect the natural style, colouring a man's linguistic taste; the earlier learned the more so. As Magyar does mine, strongly – but all the more strongly, I think, because it is in many ways closer to my own native predilections than English is. In language-invention, though you may seem to build only out of

202 SAURON DEFEATED

material taken from other acquired tongues, it is those elements most near to your native style that you select.

'In such rare dreams as I was thinking about, far away by oneself in voiceless countries, then your own native language bubbles up, and makes new names for strange new things.'

'Voiceless countries?' said Jeremy. 'You mean regions where there is nothing like our human language?'

'Yes,' said Ramer. 'Language properly so called, as we know it on Earth – token (perceived by sense) plus significance (for the mind) – that is peculiar to an embodied mind; an essential characteristic, the prime characteristic of the fusion of incarnation. Only *hnau*, to use Jeremy's Lewisian word again, would have language. The irrational couldn't, and the unembodied couldn't or wouldn't.'

'But spirits are often recorded as *speaking*,' said Frankley.

'I know,' Ramer answered. 'But I wonder if they really do, or if they make you hear them, just as they can also make you see them in some appropriate form, by producing a direct impression on the mind. The clothing of this naked impression in terms intelligible to your incarnate mind is, I imagine, often left to you, the receiver. Though no doubt they can cause you to hear words and to see shapes of their own choosing, if they will. But in any case the process would be the reverse of the normal in a way, outwards, a translation from meaning into symbol. The audible and visible results might be hardly distinguishable from the normal, even so, except for some inner emotion; though there is, in fact, sometimes a perceptible difference of sequence.'

'I don't know what spirits can do,' said Lowdham; 'but I don't see why they cannot make actual sounds (like the Eldil in *Perelandra*): cause the air to vibrate appropriately, if they wish. They seem able to affect "matter" directly.'

'I dare say they can,' said Ramer. 'But I doubt if they would wish to, for such a purpose. Communication with another mind is simpler otherwise. And the direct attack seems to me to account better for the feelings human beings often have on such occasions. There is often a shock, a sense of being touched in the quick. There is movement from within outwards, even if one feels that the cause is outside, something other, not you. It is quite different in quality from the reception of sound inwards, even though it may well happen that the thing communicated directly is not strange or alarming, while many things said in the ordinary incarnate fashion are tremendous.'

THE NOTION CLUB PAPERS (PART ONE) 203

'You speak as if you *knew*,' said Jeremy. 'How do you know all this?'

'No, I don't claim to *know* anything about such things, and I'm not laying down the law. But I feel it. I *have* been visited, or spoken to,' Ramer said gravely. 'Then, I think, the meaning was direct, immediate, and the imperfect translation perceptibly later: but it was audible. In many accounts of other such events I seem to recognize experiences similar, even when far greater.'

'You make it all sound like hallucination,' said Frankley.

'But of course,' said Ramer. 'They work in a similar way. If you are thinking of diseased conditions, then you may believe that the cause is nothing external; and all the same something (even if it is only some department of the body) must be affecting the mind and making it translate outwards. If you believe in possession or the attack of evil spirits, then there is no difference in process, only the difference between malice and good-will, lying and truth. There is Disease and Lying in the world, and not only among men.'

There was a pause. 'We've got rather away from Old Solar, haven't we?' said Guildford at last.

'No, I think what has been said is very much to the point,' said Ramer. 'Anyway, if there is, or even was, any Old Solar, then either Lewis or I or both of us are wrong about it. For I don't get any such names as *Arbol* or *Perelandra* or *Glund*.[54] I get names much more consonant with the forms I devise, if I make up words or names for a story composed when awake.

'I think there might be an Old Human, or Primitive Adamic – certainly was one, though it's not so certain that all our languages derive from it in unbroken continuity; the only undoubted common inheritance is the aptitude for making words, the compelling need to make them. But the Old Human could not possibly be the same as the Prime Language of other differently constituted rational animals, such as Lewis's Hrossa.[55] Because those two embodiments, Men and Hrossa, are quite different, and the physical basis, which conditions the symbol-forms, would be *ab origine* different. The mind-body blends would have quite different expressive flavours. The expression might not take vocal, or even audible form at all. Without symbols you have no language; and language begins only with incarnation and not before it. But, of course, if you're going to confuse language with forms of *thought*, then you can

204   SAURON DEFEATED

perhaps talk about Old Solar. But why not Old Universal in that case?[56]

'However, I don't think the question of Old Solar arises. I don't think there are any other *hnau* but ourselves in the whole solar system.'

'How can you possibly know that?' asked Frankley.

'I think I know it by looking,' Ramer answered. 'I only once anywhere saw what I took to be traces of such creatures, but I'll tell you about that in a minute.

'I'll grant you that there is a chance of error. I have never been very interested in people. That's why when I first began to write, and tried to write about people (because that seemed to be the thing done, and the only thing that was much read), my efforts were so footling, as you see, even in dream. I'm now abnormally little interested in people in general, though I can be deeply interested in this or that unique individual; and the fewer I see the better I'm pleased. I haven't scoured the Fields of Arbol seeking for them! I suppose in dream I might have ignored or overlooked them. But I don't think it's at all likely. Because I like solitude in a forest and trees not manhandled, it does not follow that I shall overlook the evidence of men's work in a wood, or never notice any men I meet there. Much the reverse!

'It's true that I've not seen the solar planets often, nor explored them thoroughly: that's hardly necessary in most cases, if you're looking for any conceivable organic life resembling what we know. But what I *have* seen convinces me that the whole system, save Earth, is altogether barren (in our sense). Mars is a horrible network of deserts and chasms; Venus a boiling whirl of wind and steam above a storm-racked twilit core. But if you want to know what it looks and sounds like: a smoking black Sea, rising like Everest, raging in the dusk over dim drowned mountains, and sucking back with a roar of cataracts like the end of Atlantis – then go there! It is magnificent, but it isn't Peace. To me indeed very refreshing – though that's too small a word. I can't describe the invigoration, the acceleration of intellectual interest, in getting away from all this tangle of ant-hill history! I am *not* a misanthrope. To me it's a more inspiring and exacting, a much more responsible, perilous, lonely venture: that Men are in fact *alone* in EN.[57] In EN. For that is the name to me of this sunlit archipelago in the midst of the Great Seas.

'We can cast our own shadows out on to the other islands, if

THE NOTION CLUB PAPERS (PART ONE)   205

we like. It's a good and lawful form of invention; but an invention it is and proceeds out of Earth, the Talkative Planet. The only *hnau* ever to dwell in red *Gormok* or in cloud-bright *Zingil*[58] will be put there by us.'

'What reason have you for thinking that you've seen them at all, and not other places in remoter Space?' asked Frankley.[59]

'Well, I went to them in a more questioning mood,' said Ramer, 'and I looked for such signs as I could understand. They were planets. They went round the Sun, or a sun, in more or less the ways and times the books say, so far as I could observe. And the further heavens had much the same pattern, just the same to my little knowledge, as they have here. And old *Eneköl*, Saturn,[60] is unmistakable; though I suppose it is not quite impossible that he has his counterpart elsewhere.'

'Won't you describe what you saw there?' said Frankley. 'I once tried to describe a Saturnian landscape myself,*[61] and I should like to know if you support me.'

'I do, more or less,' said Ramer. 'I thought so at once when I landed there, and I wondered if you had been there too, or had heard some reliable news – though you may not remember it when awake. But it is getting late. I am tired, and I am sure you all are.'

'Well, something to wind up with!' Jeremy begged. 'You haven't really told us very much news yourself yet.'

'I'll try,' said Ramer. 'Give me another drink, and I'll do my best. As I haven't had time, when awake, either to name or to translate half of the shapes and sensations, it is impossible for me to do more than suggest the thing. But I'll try and tell you about one adventure among my deep dreams: or high ones, for this occurred on one of the longest journeys I have ever had the opportunity or the courage for. It illustrates several curious things about this sort of venture.

'Remember that dream-sequences dealing with astronomical exploration or space-travel are not very frequent in my collection. Nor in any one's, I should think. The chances of making such voyages are not frequent; and they're ... well, they take a bit of daring. I should guess that most people never get the chance and never dare. It is related in some way to *desire*, no

---

* In *The Cronic Star*. This appeared in his volume *Feet of Lead* (1980). One of the critics said that this title, taken with the author's name, said all that was necessary.   N.G.

206   SAURON DEFEATED

doubt; though which comes first, chance or wish, is hard to say
– if there's any real question of priority in such matters. I mean:
my ancient attraction to waking stories about space-travel, was
it a sign that I was really already engaged on exploration, or a
cause of it?

'In any case I have only made a few journeys, as far as I yet
know; few, that is, compared with other activities. My mind
"adream" is perhaps not daring enough to fit waking desire; or
perhaps the interests I'm most conscious of awake are not really
fundamentally so dominant. My mind actually seems fonder of
mythical romances, its own and others'. I could tell you a great
deal about Atlantis, for instance; though that is not its name to
me.'

'What *is* its name?' asked Lowdham sharply, leaning forward
with a curious eagerness; but Ramer did not answer the
question.

'It's connected with that Fluted Wave,'[62] he said; 'and with
another symbol: the Great Door, shaped like a Greek π with
sloping sides.[63] And I've seen the En-keladim, my En-keladim,
playing one of their Keladian plays: the Drama of the Silver
Tree:[64] sitting round in a circle and singing in that strange, long,
long, but never-wearying, uncloying music, endlessly unfolding
out of itself, while the song takes visible life among them. The
Green Sea flowers in foam, and the Isle rises and opens like a
rose in the midst of it. There the Tree opens the starred turf like
a silver spear, and grows, and there is a New Light; and the
leaves unfold and there is Full Light; and the leaves fall and
there is a Rain of Light. Then the Door opens – but no! I have
no words for that Fear.'

He stopped suddenly. 'That's the only thing I've ever seen,' he
said, 'that I'm not sure whether it's invented or not.[65] I expect
it's a composition – out of desire, fancy, waking experience, and
"reading" (asleep and awake). But there is another ingredient.
Somewhere, in some place or places, something like it really
happens, and I have seen it, far off perhaps or faintly.

'My En-keladim I see in humane forms of surpassing and
marvellously varied beauty. But I guess that their true types, if
such there be, are invisible, unless they embody themselves by
their own will, entering into their own works because of their
love for them. That is, they are *elvish*. But very different from
Men's garbled tales of them; for they are not lofty indeed, yet
they are not fallen.'

THE NOTION CLUB PAPERS (PART ONE)   207

'But wouldn't you reckon them as *hnau*?' asked Jeremy. 'Don't they have language?'

'Yes, I suppose so. Many tongues,' said Ramer. 'I had forgotten them. But they are not *hnau*; they are not bound to a given body, but make their own, or take their own, or walk silent and unclad without sense of nakedness. And their languages shift and change as light on the water or wind in the trees. But yes, perhaps *Ellor Eshúrizel* – its meaning I cannot seize, so swift and fleeting is it – perhaps that is an echo of their voices. Yes, I think Ellor is one of their worlds: where the governance, the making and ordering, is wholly in the charge of minds, relatively small, that are not embodied in it, but are devoted to what we call matter, and especially to its beauty. Even here on Earth they may have had, may have still, some habitation and some work to do.

'But I'm still wandering. I must go back to the adventure that I promised to tell. Among my few travel-sequences I recall one that seemed to be a long inspection (on several occasions) of a different solar system. So there does appear to be at least one other star with attendant planets.[66] I thought that as I wandered there I came to a little world, of our Earth's size more or less – though, as you'll see, size is very difficult to judge; and it was lit by a sun, rather larger than ours, but dimmed. The stars too were faint, but they seemed to be quite differently arranged; and there was a cloud or white whorl in the sky with small stars in its folds: a nebula perhaps, but much larger than the one we can see in Andromeda. Tekel-Mirim[67] it was, a land of crystals.

'Whether the crystals were really of such great size – the greatest were like the Egyptian pyramids – it is hard to say. Once away from Earth it is not easy to judge such things without at least your body to refer to. For there is no scale; and what you do, I suppose, is to focus your attention, up or down, according to what aspect you wish to note. And so it is with speed. Anyway, there on Tekel-Mirim it was the inanimate matter, as we should say, that was moving and growing: into countless crystalline formations. Whether what I took for the air of the planet was really air, or water, or some other liquid, I am not able to say; though perhaps the dimming of sun and stars suggests that it was not air. I may have been on the floor of a wide shallow sea, cool and still. And there I could observe what was going on: to me absorbingly interesting.

'Pyramids and polyhedrons of manifold forms and sym-

208   SAURON DEFEATED

metries were growing like ... like geometric mushrooms, and growing from simplicity to complexity; from single beauty amalgamating into architectural harmonies of countless facets and reflected lights. And the speed of growth seemed very swift. On the summit of some tower of conjoined solids a great steeple, like a spike of greenish ice, would shoot out: it was not there and then it was there; and hardly was it set before it was encrusted with spikelets in bristling lines of many pale colours. In places forms were achieved like snowflakes under a microscope, but enormously larger: tall as trees some were. In other places there were forms severe, majestic, vast and simple.

'For a time I could not count I watched the "matter" on Tekel-Mirim working out its harmonies of inherent design with speed and precision, spreading, interlocking, towering, on facet and angle building frets and arabesques and frosted laces, jewels on which arrows of pale fire glanced and splintered. But there was a limit to growth, to building and annexation. Suddenly disintegration would set in – no, not that, but reversal: it was not ugly or regrettable. A whole epic of construction would recede, going back through shapeliness, by stages as beautiful as those through which it had grown, but wholly different, till it ceased. Indeed it was difficult to choose whether to fix one's attention on some marvellous evolution, or some graceful devolving into – nothing visible.

'Only part of the matter on Tekel-Mirim was doing these things (for "doing" seems our only word for it): the matter that was specially endowed; a scientist would say (I suppose) that was of a certain chemical nature and condition. There were floors, and walls, and mighty circles of smooth cliff, valleys and vast abysses, that did not change their shape nor move. Time stood still for them, and for the crystals waxed and waned.

'I don't know why I visited this strange scene, for awake I have never studied crystallography, not even though the vision of Tekel-Mirim has often suggested that I should. Whether things go in Tekel-Mirim exactly as they do here, I cannot say. All the same I wonder still what on earth or in the universe can be meant by saying, as was said a hundred years ago (by Huxley, I believe) that a crystal is a "symmetrical solid shape assumed spontaneously by lifeless matter".[68] The free will of the lifeless is a dark saying. But it may have some meaning: who can tell? For we have little understanding of either term. I leave it there. I merely record, or try to record, the events I saw, and

THE NOTION CLUB PAPERS (PART ONE)   209

they were too marvellous while I could see them in far Tekel-Mirim for speculation. I'm afraid I've given you no glimpse of them.

'It was on one occasion, returning – or should I say "back-dreaming"? – from Tekel-Mirim, that I had the adventure that I'll close with. Speed, as I said, like size is very difficult to judge with no measure but vague memories of earth-events far away. Maybe I had been speeding up, that is moving quickly down Time in Tekel-Mirim, so as to get as long a story or sequence as I could. In Tekel-Mirim I must have been not only far away in Space but in a time somewhat before my earth-time, or I should have overrun the point for my withdrawal. For I had to withdraw on that visit earlier than my body usually summons me. A determination of my own will, set before I went to sleep, had fixed a time of waking, for an appointment. And the hour was coming near.

'It is no good harking back, when you do not want to repeat but to see on; and so I withdrew, with my mind still so filled with the wonder of Tekel-Mirim that I could not even adream, and still less awake, recall the transitions or the modes of travelling, until my attention was loosened from my recollections and I found that I was looking at a twinkling sphere. I knew that I had seen it, or something like it, on one of my other journeys; and I was tempted to examine it again. But time was running on, and dimly, like a remote shred of a dream (to one awake) I was aware of my body beginning to stir unwillingly, feeling the returning will. So there and then I "harked back" suddenly with as great an effort as I could manage; and at the same time I closed in to look for a while at this strange ball.

'I found a horrible disorderly shifting scene: a shocking contrast to Tekel-Mirim, and after Emberü and Ellor intolerable. Dark and light flickered to and fro over it. Winds were whirling and eddying, and vapours were rising, gathering, flashing by and vanishing too quick for anything to be discerned but a general ragged swirl. The land, if that is what it was, was shifting too, like sands in a tide, crumbling and expanding, as the sea galloped in and out among the unsteady edges of the coast. There were wild growths, woods you could hardly say; trees springing up like mushrooms, and crashing and dying before you could determine their shapes. Everything was in an abominable flux.

'I came still closer. The effort to attend carefully seemed to

210 SAURON DEFEATED

steady things. The flicker of light and dark became much slower; and I saw something that was definitely a small river, though it waggled a little, and broadened and narrowed as I looked at it. The trees and woods in its valley held their shapes now for some time. Then *"Hnau* at last!" I said to myself; for in the vale, down by the river among the trees I saw shapes, unmistakable shapes of houses. At first I had thought that they were some kind of quick-growing fungus, until I looked more steadily. But now I saw that they were buildings, but still fungus-buildings, appearing and then falling to pieces; and yet their agglomeration was spreading.

'I was still rather high above it all, higher than a man in a very tall tower; but I could see that the place was crawling or rather boiling with *hnau* of some sort – if they were not very large ant-creatures, endowed with amazing speed: darting about, alone or in bunches, bewilderingly; always more and more of them. Often they went shooting in or out like bullets along the tracks that led to the horrible, crumbling, outgrowing sore of house-shapes.

' "This really is frightful!" I thought. "Is this a diseased world, or is it a planet really inhabited by may-fly men in a sort of tumultuous mess? What's come to the land? It's losing most of its hair, going bald, and the house-ringworm goes on spreading, and starting up in fresh patches. There's no design, or reason, or pattern in it." And yet, even as I said this, I began to see, as I looked still more carefully, that there were in fact some shapes that did suggest crude design, and a few now held together for quite a long while.

'Soon I noticed down by the river, near the heart of the agglomeration, where I had observed it beginning, several constructions that endured. Two or three had some real form, not without an echo of beauty even to one fresh from Tekel-Mirim. They continued standing, while the ringworm ate its way further and further around them.

' "I must have a really close look," I thought; "for if there are *hnau* here, it is important, however nasty they may be; and I must take some notes. Just a look, and then I must be off. Now, what is that thing like a great fluted mushroom with an odd top? It hasn't been here as long as some of the other larger things." With that I came right down.

'Of course, if one really concentrates on things – especially to observe their static forms, not their changes, as I'd been doing in

THE NOTION CLUB PAPERS (PART ONE) 211

Tekel-Mirim – then they tend to halt, as it were. The speed is in you, when you're not tied to a time-clock of a body. So as I bent my attention, I lost all the acceleration that the excitement of Tekel-Mirim had induced. Things stood still for a moment, rock-hard.

'I was gazing at the Camera.[69] I was about thirty feet above the ground in Radcliffe Square. I suppose I had at first been seeing the Thames Valley, at a huge speed; and then, slower and slower, Oxford since I don't know when, since the beginning of the University probably.

'The clock on Saint Mary's struck 7 a.m. – and I woke up for my appointment. To go to Mass. It was the morning of the feast of Saint Peter and Saint Paul, June 29th 1986, by our reckoning. That's all for tonight! I must go to bed.'

'Well, I must be off too,' said Cameron. 'Thanks for a very enterrtaining evening!'

MGR. NG. PF. AAL. RD. WTJ. RS. JJ. JJR.

NOTES

1   The Great Storm of June 12th, 1987: my father's 'prevision' was only out by four months. The greatest storm in living memory struck southern England, causing vast damage, on October 16th, 1987. It is curious in the light of this to read Mr. Green's remarks (p. 158): 'it may well be that the predictions (notably of the Storm), though genuine and not coincidences, were unconscious: giving one more glimpse of the strange processes of so-called literary "invention", with which the Papers are largely concerned.'

2   O.S.B.: 'Order of Saint Benedict'.

3   For the title as typed in the final text D, but subsequently rejected, see p. 153 note 2.

4   In A and B the report of Night 54 is absent (cf. Mr. Green's Foreword, p. 156: 'Many Nights are represented only by a few lines, or by short entries, of which Nights 54 and 64 have been included as specimens').

5   I cannot explain *The Canticle of Artegall*. Irish *arteagal* = 'article'; and an isolated note of my father's reads: 'My/The Canticle of Night in Ale', 'Artegall', 'article Artegall'. But this does not help very much.

6   In B Night 60 is Night 251, without date (see p. 149).

7   I have mentioned (p. 150) a page that preceded text A and carries the identifications of members of the Notion Club with members of the Inklings. On this page are found two brief, abandoned

212   SAURON DEFEATED

openings for *The Notion Club Papers*. In the first Ramer asks Latimer (predecessor of Guildford) for his opinion of his story. With ' "Yes, I suppose it'll do," I answered' this opening breaks off, and is followed by:

> When I had finished reading my story, we sat in silence for a while. 'Well?' I said. 'What do you think of it? Will it do?' Nobody answered, and I felt the air charged with disapproval, as it often is in our circle, though on this occasion the critical interruptions had been fewer than usual. 'Oh, come on. What have *you* got to say? I may as well get the worst over,' I urged turning to Latimer. He is not a flatterer.
>
> 'Oh yes, it'll do, I suppose so,' he answered reluctantly. 'But why pick on me? You know I hate criticizing offhand and still in the heat of listening – or the chill.'

Here this second opening was abandoned. It is presumably to be connected with the word 'Self' written under *Ramer* at the head of the page (p. 150).

8   David Lindsay, author of *A Voyage to Arcturus*, published in 1920, to which Guildford refers subsequently (see note 9).

9   Cf. my father's letter to Stanley Unwin of 4 March 1938, concerning *Out of the Silent Planet* (*Letters* no. 26):

> I read 'Voyage to Arcturus' with avidity – the most comparable work, though it is both more powerful and more mythical (and less rational, and also less of a story – no one could read it merely as a thriller and without interest in philosophy religion and morals).

10   *Cavorite* was the substance 'opaque to gravitation' devised by the scientist Cavor in H. G. Wells's *The First Men in the Moon* (1901).

11   For 'the Great Explosion' see Mr. Green's Foreword, p. 157, and p. 186.

12   *Ransom:* Dr. Elwin Ransom was the Cambridge philologist who in *Out of the Silent Planet* went under duress to Mars (Malacandra), and in *Perelandra* went to Venus by the mediation of the Oyarsa of Malacandra (see next note).

13   At the beginning of *Perelandra* the *Eldils* are described thus:

> For Ransom had met other things in Mars besides the Martians. He had met the creatures called *eldila*, and specially that great eldil who is the ruler of Mars or, in their speech, the *Oyarsa* of *Malacandra*. The eldila are very different from any planatary creatures. Their physical organism, if organism it can be called, is quite unlike either the human or the Martian. They do not eat, breed, breathe, or suffer natural death, and to that extent resemble thinking minerals more than they resemble anything we should recognise as an animal. Though they appear on planets and may even seem to our senses to be

THE NOTION CLUB PAPERS (PART ONE)   213

sometimes resident in them, the precise spatial location of an eldil at any moment presents great problems. They themselves regard space (or 'Deep Heaven') as their true habitat, and the planets are to them not closed but merely moving points – perhaps even interruptions – in what we know as the Solar System and they as the Field of Arbol.

14 *Old Solar*: cf. *Perelandra* Chapter 2, in which Ransom speaks to Lewis before his journey to Venus begins:

'... I rather fancy I am being sent because those two black-guards who kidnapped me and took me to Malacandra, did something which they never intended: namely, gave a human being a chance to learn that language.'

'What language do you mean?'

'*Hressa-Hlab*, of course. The language I learned in Mala-candra.'

'But surely you don't imagine they will speak the same language on Venus?'

'Didn't I tell you about that?' said Ransom ... 'I'm surprised I didn't, for I found out two or three months ago, and scientifically it is one of the most interesting things about the whole affair. It appears we were quite mistaken in thinking *Hressa-Hlab* the peculiar speech of Mars. It is really what may be called Old Solar, *Hlab-Eribol-ef-Cordi*.'

'What on earth do you mean?'

'I mean that there was originally a common speech for all rational creatures inhabiting the planets of our system: those that were ever inhabited, I mean – what the eldils call the Low Worlds. ... That original speech was lost on Thulcandra, our own world, when our whole tragedy took place. No human language now known in the world is descended from it.'

For Ramer's observations on this subject see p. 203 and note 55.

15 In the original text A (still followed in B) Dolbear, waking up, says with reference to these words of Guildford's ('Incarnation. By being born'): 'Then try reincarnation, or perhaps transcarnation without loss of memory. What do you say, Ramer?'

16 *Arry*, for *Arundel*, became the name by which Lowdham was known in text C; in the earliest lists of members of the Notion Club he was simply *Harry Loudham*. For the significance of this see pp. 233–4, 281–2.

17 *New Erewhon*: *Erewhon* (= 'Nowhere') is the title of a satire by Samuel Butler (1872). *News from Nowhere*: a fantasy of the future by William Morris (1890).

18 *Turl Street* or *the Turl* is a narrow street running between High Street and Broad Street in Oxford, onto which open the gates of Ramer's college Jesus, Guildford's college Lincoln, and Exeter College.

214   SAURON DEFEATED

19 In B Night 61 is Night 252, without date (see p. 149).
20 B has *Harry Loudham*: see note 16.
21 In the 'Prose Edda' the Icelander Snorri Sturluson tells of Skidbladnir:
    'Skíðblaðnir is the best of ships and made with great skill ... Certain dwarves, the sons of Ívaldi, made Skíðblaðnir and gave the ship to Freyr; it is so large that all the Æsir [gods] can man it with their weapons and equipment of war, and it has a favourable wind so soon as the sail is set, wherever it is bound; but when it is not going to sea it is made of so many pieces and with such great cunning that it can be folded up like a napkin and kept in one's pouch' (*Snorra Edda, Gylfaginning* §42).
22 The Battle of Bosworth Field (1485), in which King Richard III was defeated and slain by Henry Tudor (Henry VII). A has here 'at any period before the accession of Richard II' (1377). On Frankley's *horror borealis* see pp. 151–2, 159.
23 *'Yes, 1938,' said Cameron:* in A this observation is given to Loudham, and rather surprisingly Latimer's comment is much as Guildford's in the final text: 'whose memory is like that. I doubt if he ever read the book. Memoirs of the courts of minor 18th century monarchs are his natural browsing-ground.' Yet at this earliest stage Loudham's interest in Norse was perhaps already present, since it is he who makes the joke about Skidbladnir immediately before. As B was written the remark was still attributed to Loudham, and Guildford's comment remains the same as in A; later Loudham was changed to Franks (the earlier name of Frankley) and then to Cameron. See pp. 281–2.
24 *Last Men in London* by Olaf Stapledon (1932).
25 *hnau:* rational embodied beings.
26 I have added the footnote from the third manuscript C; it is not in the final typescript D, but was perhaps omitted inadvertently.
27 In A there is no reference to the Glacier or any mention of what the scene in the book was; but a later addition in the margin runs:
    and the chief difference (since both were now inner) is that the one is tinged with sadness for it is past, but the other, the Glacier, is not so tinged, has only its own proper flavour, because it is not past or present with reference to the world.
28 In A Dolbear does not speak at this point; Ramer says: 'And the will to remember can be strengthened; and the memory enlarged. (Dolbear helped me in that: I suppose that is what made him so suspicious.) Now here comes another thread.' Thus neither *Emberü* nor any other name appear here in A; in B the name is *Gyönyörü*, changed subsequently to *Emberü*.
29 Following this, the text of Ramer's remarks in A and B is different from that in the final form. I give the B version:

THE NOTION CLUB PAPERS (PART ONE) 215

A living body can move in space, but not without an effort (as in a leap), or a vehicle. A mind can move more freely and very much quicker than a living body, but not without effort of its own kind, or without a vehicle. [*Added:* This is distinct from the instantaneous movement of thought to objects already in its grasp as memory.] And Space and Time do exist as conditions for it, especially while it is incarnate, and certainly if it is (largely for that reason) interested in them and studying them. How and how far in either dimension can it jump, without a vehicle? I asked myself. It probably cannot travel in empty Space, or eventless Time (which is the duration of empty Space): it would not be aware of it, if it did, anyway. How far can it jump over it? How can it jump at all?

The mind uses the memory of its body ...

30 For the source of Lowdham's allusion to the Pig on the Ruined Pump see the Foreword.

31 The Banbury Road leads north out of the centre of Oxford. I do not think that there was any special reason for the choice of this particular late Victorian house (the reference to it only enters in C, where my father first wrote 'No. *x* Banbury Road', changing this subsequently to 'No. 100'). Mr. Green, the putative editor of the *Papers* refers in his Foreword (p. 157) to poltergeist activity at this house in the early years of the twenty-first century.

32 *Gunthorpe Park in Matfield:* so far as I can discover, the only Matfield in England is in Kent, but there is no Gunthorpe Park in its vicinity.

33 *Emberü:* A has here: 'Not if you mean for getting such news as I put into that tale you've heard', and no name appears; B has, as at the previous occurrence (note 28) *Gyönyörü > Emberü.*

34 My father once described to me his dream of 'pure Weight', but I do not remember when that was: probably before this time.

35 Of this experience also my father spoke to me, suggesting, as does Ramer here, that the significance did not lie in the remembered passage itself. See Ramer's subsequent remarks on this topic, pp. 189 ff.

36 See pp. 157, 167. A has here: 'pictures as unlike as seeing a small flower growing and a whole world shattered'; B places the great explosion 'in the sixties'.

37 The intervention of James Jones (see p. 159) first appears in C. In B Ramer's explanation of what he meant by *deep dreams* is given in a footnote by Guildford ('Ramer said later ...').

38 In B Dolbear replies differently to Lowdham ('If I was to reveal some of the situations I've seen you in, Harry my lad'). His pregnant remarks 'You walk in disguises, even when awake. But they'll slip, my lad, one day. I shouldn't wonder if it was fairly soon' entered in the C text.

216   SAURON DEFEATED

39 A continues from this point:
> ... on this sort of activity – the best bits and passages, especially, those that seem to come suddenly when you're in the heat of making. They sometimes fit with an odd perfection; and sometimes good in themselves don't really fit.

B has here:
> ... on this sort of activity. Those scenes that come up complete and fixed, that I spoke of before, for instance. I think that those really good passages that arise, as it were, suddenly when you're abstracted, in the heat of making, are often long-prepared impromptus.

40 *it's one I made up years ago:* i.e., made up in dream.

41 In A, and (at first) in B, Ramer interpreted the first of his 'fragments' far more elaborately, giving the entire plot of the story. This is, as Ramer admitted, 'not very interesting'; and as B was first written Loudham says (in answer to Ramer's 'Do you want another case?') 'Not particularly, unless it's better than the last, which I don't expect.'

42 Geoffrey of Monmouth (died in 1155), author of *The History of the Kings of Britain*, a chief contribution to the popularity, outside the Celtic lands, of King Arthur and 'the Matter of Britain'. Such a manuscript leaf as this in Ramer's dream-narrative would be of superlative importance in the study of the Arthurian legend.

43 *Elvish Drama.* In A it is Ramer himself who speaks of 'elf-drama' ('it is not writing but elf-drama'), and again in B, which has:
> '... For it is not of course writing, but a sort of realized drama. The Elvish Drama that Lewis speaks of somewhere.'
>
> 'Not Lewis, said Jeremy. 'It comes in one of those essays of the circle, but it was by one of the minor members.'

The passage in question comes from the essay *On Fairy-Stories*, which my father had delivered at the University of St. Andrews in 1939, but which was not published until two years after the writing of *The Notion Club Papers*, in the memorial volume *Essays Presented to Charles Williams* (Oxford 1947). The passage is interesting in relation to Ramer's discourse and I cite a part of it:
> Now 'Faërian Drama' – those plays which according to abundant records the elves have often presented to men – can produce Fantasy with a realism and immediacy beyond the compass of any human mechanism. As a result their usual effect (upon a man) is to go beyond Secondary Belief. If you are present at a Faërian drama you yourself are, or think that you are, bodily inside its Secondary World. The experience may be very similar to Dreaming and has (it would seem) sometimes (by men) been confounded with it. But in Faërian drama you

THE NOTION CLUB PAPERS (PART ONE)   217

are in a dream that some other mind is weaving, and the knowledge of that alarming fact may slip from your grasp. To experience *directly* a Secondary World: the potion is too strong, and you give to it Primary Belief, however marvellous the events. You are deluded – whether that is the intention of the elves (always or at any time) is another question. They at any rate are not themselves deluded. This is for them a form of Art, and distinct from Wizardry or Magic, properly so called.

J. R. R. Tolkien, *The Monsters and the Critics and Other Essays*, 1983, p. 142; cf. also p. 116 in that edition of the essay ('In dreams strange powers of the mind may be unlocked . . .').

44   *of humane shape*: texts B, C, and D all have *humane*; cf. p. 206 ('humane forms') and note 55 below.

45   Cf. my father's letter to W. H. Auden of 7 June 1955 (*Letters* no. 163):

> . . . the terrible recurrent dream (beginning with memory) of the Great Wave, towering up, and coming in ineluctably over the trees and green fields. (I bequeathed it to Faramir.) I don't think I have had it since I wrote the 'Downfall of Númenor' as the last of the legends of the First and Second Age.

By 'beginning with memory' I believe that my father meant that the recurrence of the dream went as far back in his life as his memory reached. – Faramir told Éowyn of his recurrent dream of the Great Wave coming upon Númenor as they stood on the walls of Minas Tirith when the Ring was destroyed ('The Steward and the King', in *The Return of the King*, p. 240).

46   This remark of Lowdham's is absent from B and first enters in C; cf. note 38.

47   In B the footnote at this point does not derive as in the final text largely from Mr. Green but entirely from Nicholas Guildford, citing Ramer: 'Later Ramer enlarged on this point, in the course of a discussion of the various kinds of "deep dreams", and how the dreamer could distinguish them. He divided them . . .' What follows is closely similar to the later version of the note, but it ends thus: ' "Made for the Malefit of Men," he said. "To judge by the ideas men propagate now, their curious unanimity, and obsession, I should say that a terrible lot of men have thrust aside the Guardians, and are reading very maleficial stuff." N.G.' There was thus at this stage no reference to 'Night 62' (see p. 222 and note 2).

The word *maleficial* is occasionally recorded, but *malefit*, occuring in both versions of this note, is a coinage echoing *benefit*, as if ultimately derived from Latin *malefactum* 'evil deed, injury'.

48   The world *Emberü* has not been named in A (see notes 28, 33), but at this point Ramer says in A: 'The one I told you about,

218   SAURON DEFEATED

Menelkemen' (Quenya, 'Sky-earth'). In this original text the description of Menelkemen is (though briefer) that given in the final text of Ellor Eshúrizel, 'that immense plain with its floor of silver', ending with the account of the great waterfall, here called Dalud dimran (or perhaps dimron), with Eshil dimzor written above and Eshil külü (> külö) in the margin. There is no mention here of the En-keladim. At the end of the description of Menelkemen Jeremy asks 'Where is it, do you think?', which in the final text he asks after Ramer's description of the third world, Minal-zidar (p. 199).

In B (as originally written) Ramer says 'The one I told you about, Emberü the golden', and here the description of Emberü is that of Minal-zidar in the final version:

'... I wrote that account (not the frame) some time ago, and all I'll have now is that, and stirrings and faint traces of what lies beneath: the first vision of Emberü: golden, absolutely silent and quiescent, a whole small world of perfect form, imperishable in Time ...'

This description of Emberü ends, as does that of Minal-zidar in the final text, with 'made by what adoring mind I cannot tell'; then follows: 'And there was Menel-kemen.'

At this point in B my father stopped, struck out what he had written about 'the first vision of Emberü', and wrote instead: 'the first vision of Emberü: that immense plain with its silver floor all delicately patterned ...' – which in the final text is the description of Ellor Eshúrizel. Here the great waterfall is called Öshül-külö, and Ramer says: 'I think the Enkeladim dwell there.' My father then inserted in B, after 'the first vision of Emberü', the words ' "It is the same with Ellor. Ellor!" he murmured. "Ellor Eshúrizel! I drew it once in words as best I could, and now it is words. That immense plain with its silver floor ...'; and (all these changes being made at the time of composition) introduced at the end of the description of Ellor the third world, 'Minal-zidar the golden'.

Thus the images were developed and separated into distinct 'world-entities' in rapid succession. In A Menelkemen is the only world that Ramer describes, the world of the story that he had read to the Notion Club, the inorganic, harmonious world of metal, stone, and water, with the great waterfall. In B the world that Ramer described in his story is Emberü (replacing Gyönyörü of the earlier parts of the manuscript), the silent 'golden' world; but this was changed immediately (reverting to A) to make Emberü 'that immense plain with its silver floor', and then changed again to make this description that of a second world, Ellor Eshúrizel, while the 'golden' world becomes a third scene, Minal-zidar. The final stage was to call the first world Green

THE NOTION CLUB PAPERS (PART ONE)   219

Emberü, 'where there was a kind of organic life, rich but wholesome and longeval.'

49 On the *En-keladim* see p. 206 and notes 64, 65, and pp. 397, 400.

50 *the Fields of Arbol*: the Solar System in Lewis's novels (see note 13).

51 In A it is Dolbear, not Loudham, who asks: 'Where do you get all these names from? Who told you them? That [would] interest me more really than the geometry and landscape. I should, of course as you know, use my chance if I got into such a state for language-research.' In B this was still said by Dolbear, changed to Guildford and then to Loudham. See p. 151.

52 At this point both A and B continue with an account of Jeremy's attempt to arouse interest in the works of Lewis and Williams, which in the final text is put into a footnote of Guildford's here. I give the text of B, which follows that of A very closely but is clearer.

'*Arbol* is "Old Solar" for the Sun,' said Jeremy. 'Do you mean that you can get back to Old Solar, [*struck out:* or Old Universal,] and that Lewis was right?'

Jeremy was our Lewis-expert, and knew all his works, almost by heart. Many in Oxford will still remember how he had, a year or two before, given some remarkable lectures on Lewis and Williams. People had laughed at the title, because Lewis and all that circle had dropped badly out of fashion. Old Bell-Tinker, who was still Chairman of the English Board then, had boggled and puffed at it. 'If you must touch such a subject,' he snorted, 'call it Lewis and cut it Short.'

Jeremy had retorted by offering to change the title to 'Lewis and Carolus or the Oxford Looking-glass'. 'Or "Jack and the Beanstalk", if you like,' he added, but that was too recondite a joke for the English Board. I believe, before Jeremy spoke up, few even of the Twentieth Century experts could have named any work of Williams, except perhaps *The Octopus*. That was still occasionally played, because of the great revival of missionary interest after the Far-eastern martyrdoms in the sixties. *The Allegory of Love* was all of Lewis that the academicians ever mentioned (as a rule unread and slightingly). The other minor lights were only known by the few who read old C. R. Tolkien's little books of memoirs: *In the Roaring Forties*, and *The Inns and Outs of Oxford*. But Jeremy had made most of our club read some of those people (the Public-house School as it was called); though beside Jeremy only Ramer and Dolbear bothered with Tolkien père and all the elvish stuff.

'"Old Solar"?' said Ramer. 'Well, no. . . .

'Old Bell-Tinker' derives his name from a book of translations of

220 SAURON DEFEATED

Anglo-Saxon literature by Bell and Tinker. His very bad joke 'call it Lewis and cut it Short' refers to the *Latin Dictionary* by Lewis and Short. The title of Jeremy's lectures, which aroused laughter, is omitted, but was presumably the same as in the final text, *The Public-house School* (because the Inklings met in pubs). 'Few bothered with Tolkien père and all the elvish stuff' was doubtless no more than a self-deprecating joke – but implies that the 'elvish stuff' had at least been published! (cf. p. 303 and note 14). *In the Roaring Forties* is a pun on the name of the regions of the southern oceans, between forty and fifty degrees south, where there are great winds.

53 Since Ramer's criticism of the standard of linguistic invention characteristic of tales of space-travel and time-travel follows immediately on his denial that there could be any such language as Old Solar, he appears to be including Lewis in his criticism. Some years before, however, in his letter to Stanley Unwin of 4 March 1938 (*Letters* no. 26), my father had said of *Out of the Silent Planet*:

The author holds to items of linguistic invention that do not appeal to me ...; but this is a matter of taste. After all your reader found my invented names, made with cherished care, eye-splitting. But the linguistic inventions and the philology on the whole are more than good enough. All the part about language and poetry – the glimpses of its Malacandrian nature and form – is very well done, and extremely interesting, far superior to what one usually gets from travellers in untravelled regions. The language difficulty is usually slid over or fudged. Here it not only has verisimilitude, but also underlying thought.

54 *Glund:* the name of Jupiter in Old Solar (also *Glundandra*).

55 *I think there might be an Old Human, or Primitive Adamic ...*: A has here: 'But I think there might be, certainly was, an Old Humane or Adamic. But it could not possibly be the same as the Prime Language of Hrossa, *Hressa-hlab*.' This was retained in B (with Old Human for Old Humane: see note 44). The *Hrossa* were one of the three totally distinct kinds of *hnau* found on Malacandra; the language of the Hrossa was *Hressa-hlab*, which is 'Old Solar': see note 14.

56 *Old Universal:* see the beginning of the passage given in note 52.

57 *En:* this name appears already in A, with various predecessors, *An, Nor, El*, all struck out immediately.

58 *Gormok, Zingil:* in A Ramer's name for Mars is the Elvish word *Karan* ('red'); Venus was *Zingil* in A, though immediately replacing another name that cannot be read.

59 In A it is Jeremy who speaks at this point, asking: 'How do you know you've been there?' And Ramer replies: 'I don't: I have seen the places, not been there. My body's never travelled. I have seen

THE NOTION CLUB PAPERS (PART ONE)   221

the places either indirectly through other records, as you could say you'd seen Hongkong if you'd looked at many long accurate coloured films of it; or directly by using light. But how I know what the places are is another matter.'

60   Saturn is not mentioned in A. B has: 'And *Gyürüchill*, Saturn, is unmistakable'. *Gyürüchill* was changed to *Shomorú*, and then to *old Eneköl*.

61   *The Cronic Star* (in the footnote by Guildford at this point): Saturn (in astrology the leaden planet). *Cronic* is derived from *Kronos*, the Greek god (father of Zeus) identified by the Romans with Saturn; wholly distinct etymologically from *chronic*, derived from Greek *chronos* 'time'.

62   On the 'Fluted Wave' see p. 194.

63   In A Ramer says here: 'I could tell you about Atlantis (though that's not its name to me, nor Númenor): it is connected with that Fluted Wave. And the Door 𝝅 [which is connected with the Meg(alithic) >] of the Megalithic is too.' In B he speaks as in the final text, but says again 'though that's not its name to me, nor Númenor' – the last two words being later strongly struck out, and Loudham's question (asked with 'a curious eagerness') 'What *is* its name?' inserted (when the peculiar association of Lowdham with Númenor had entered: see notes 38, 46). In the final text of the *Papers* the emergence of the name *Númenor* is postponed until Part Two (p. 231).

64   A has here: 'But I've seen my Mârim [*changed probably at once to* Albarim] playing one of their Albar-plays: the drama of the Silver Tree.' In A the name *En-keladim* has not occurred (see note 48). With 'the Drama of the Silver Tree' cf. the citation from *On Fairy-Stories* given in note 43.

65   In A Ramer says: 'I don't think that's invented: not by me anyway. It seems to take place on this earth in some time or mode or [?place].' In A he goes straight on from 'Atlantis' to his final story.

In B Ramer comments on the Drama of the Silver Tree as in the final text, as far as 'something like it really happens, and I have seen it, far off perhaps or faintly.' Then follows:

I guess that the true types of my Enkeladim are invisible, unless they turn their attention to you. That is, they are Eldilic in Lewis's terms, in some lesser rank [*added:* or perhaps like Tolkien's Unfallen Elves, only they were embodied].

All this was struck out, and replaced on a rider by the final text, as far as 'entering as it were into their own works because of their love for them.' Then follows: 'that is, that they are of a kind other than Lewis's Eldila (even of lesser rank); and yet not the same as Tolkien's Unfallen Elves, for those were embodied.'

The original B text continues with 'I think [Emberü >] Ellor is

222   SAURON DEFEATED

one of their worlds ...', as in the final form. Against *Ellor* is a footnote:

> Ramer said that it was queer how the syllable cropped up: first in Tolkien's Eldar, Eldalie, then in Lewis's Eldil, and then in his Ellor. He thought it *might* be an 'elvish' or Keladian word. The Enkeladim are language-makers. NG.

66 Here the fair copy manuscript C ends, and the typescript D from here on follows B (see p. 146).

67 In A the name was *Tekel-Ishtar*, becoming *Tekel-Mirim* before the manuscript was completed.

68 Thomas Huxley, *Physiography*, 1877, cited in the *Oxford English Dictionary*.

69 The Radcliffe Camera, a great circular domed building standing in Radcliffe Square, Oxford, on the south side of which stands St. Mary's church and on the north side the Bodleian Library. *Camera* is used in the Latin sense 'arched or vaulted roof or chamber' (Latin *camera* > French *chambre*, English *chamber*).

[PART TWO][1]

Night 62.[2]   Thursday, March 6th, 1987. [Of this meeting only half a torn sheet is preserved. The relevant part will be found in the note to Night 61, p. 195. There appears to have been further discussion of Ramer's views and adventures.]

Night 63.   Thursday, March 13th, 1987. [Only the last page of the record of this meeting is preserved. The discussion seems to have proceeded to legendary voyages of discovery in general. For the reference to the *imram* see Night (69).][3]

[Good] night Frankley!'

Lowdham seemed to feel a bit guilty about his ragging; and when the meeting finally broke up, he walked up the High with Ramer and myself. We turned into Radcliffe Square.[4]

'Played the ass as usual, Ramer,' said Lowdham. 'Sorry! I felt all strung up: wanted a fight, or a carouse, or something. But really I was very interested, especially about the *imram*.[5] Underneath we Nordics[6] have some feelings, as long as the Dago-fanciers will only be reasonably polite.' He hesitated. 'I've had some rather odd experiences – well, perhaps we'll talk about it some other time. It's late. But in the vac. perhaps?'

THE NOTION CLUB PAPERS (PART TWO)   223

'I shall be going away,' said Ramer, a trifle coldly, 'till after Easter.'

'Oh well. But do come to the meetings next term! You must have lots more to tell us. I'll try and be good.'

It was a cool clear night after a windy day. It was starry in the west, but the moon was already climbing. At B.N.C.[7] gate Lowdham turned. The Camera looked vast and dark against the moonlit sky. Wisps of long white cloud were passing on an easterly breeze. For a moment one of them seemed to take the shape of a plume of smoke issuing from the lantern of the dome.

Lowdham looked up, and his face altered. His tall powerful figure appeared taller and broader as he stood there, gazing, with his dark brows drawn down. His face seemed pale and angry, and his eyes glittered.

'Curse him! May the Darkness take him!' he said bitterly. 'May the earth open ——' The cloud passed away. He drew his hand over his brow. 'I was going to say,' he said. 'Well, I don't remember. Something about the Camera, I think. Doesn't matter. Good night, chaps!' He knocked, and passed in through the door.

We turned up along the lane. 'Very odd!' I said. 'What a queer fellow he is sometimes! A strange mixture.'

'He is,' said Ramer. 'Most of what we see is a tortoise-shell: armourplate. He doesn't talk much about what he really cares for.'

'For some reason the last two or three meetings seem to have stirred him up, unsettled him,' I said. 'I can't think why.'

'I wonder,' said Ramer. 'Well, good night, Nick. I'll see you again next term. I hope to start attending regularly again.' We parted at the Turl end of the lane.

PF. RD. AAL. MGR. WTJ. JJR. NG.

Night 64.   Thursday, March 27th, 1987.[8]

There was only one meeting in the vacation. Guildford's rooms. Neither Ramer nor Lowdham were present (it was a quiet evening). Guildford read a paper on Jutland in antiquity; but there was not much discussion. [No record of the paper is found in the minutes.]

PF. WTJ. JM. RS. JJ. RD. NG.

224   SAURON DEFEATED

Night 65.   Thursday, May 8th, 1987.[9]

This was the first meeting of Trinity term. We met in Frankley's rooms in Queen's. Jeremy and Guildford arrived first (in time); others arrived one by one at intervals (late). There was nothing definite on for the evening, though we had hoped for some more talk from Ramer; but he seemed disinclined to say anything further. Conversation hopped about during the first hour, but was not notable.

Lowdham was restless, and would not sit down; at intervals he burst into a song (with which he had, in fact, entered at about half past nine). It began:

> *I've got a very Briny Notion*
> *To drink myself to sleep.*

It seldom progressed further, and never got beyond:

> *Bring me my bowl, my magic potion!*
> *Tonight I'm diving deep.*
> *down! down! down!*
> *Down where the dream-fish go.*

It was not well received, least of all by Ramer. But Lowdham subsided eventually, into a moody silence – for a while.

About ten o'clock the talk turned to neologisms; and Lowdham re-entered in their defence, chiefly because Frankley was taking the other side. (No. Pure love of truth and justice. AAL)

Lowdham to Frankley: 'You say you object to *panting*, which all the younger people use now for *desire* or *wish*?'

'Yes, I do. And especially to *having a great pant for* anything; or worse *having great pants for* it.'

'Well, I don't think you've got any good grounds for your objection: nothing better than novelty or unfamiliarity. New words are always objected to, like new art.'

'Nonsense! Double nonsense, Arry!' said Ramer.[10] 'Frankley is complaining precisely because new words are *not* objected to. And anyway, I personally object to lots of old words, but I have to go on using 'em, because they're current, and people won't accept my substitutes. I dislike many products of old art. I like many new things but not all. There is such a thing as merit, without reference to age or to familiarity. I took to *doink* at once: a very good onomatopoeia for some purposes.'

'Yes, *doink* has come on a lot lately,' said Lowdham. 'But it's not brand-new, of course. I think it's first recorded, in the Third

THE NOTION CLUB PAPERS (PART TWO)   225

Supplement to the N.E.D.,[11] in the fifties, in the form *dŏing*: seems to have started in the Air Force in the Six Years' War.'[12]

'And it's an onomatopoeia, mark you,' said Frankley. 'It's easy to appraise the merits of that kind of word, if you can call it a real word. Anyway, adopting that is not at all on all fours with misusing an established word, robbing Peter to relieve the poverty of Paul: lexicographical socialism, which would end by reducing the whole vocabulary to one flat drab Unmeaning, if there were no reactionaries.'

'And won't anybody give poor Peter his pants back?' Lowdham laughed. 'He's got some more pairs in the cupboard, you'll see. He'll just have to take to wearing modern *whaffing* and *whooshing*. And why not? Do you object to Language, root and branch, Pip? I'm surprised at you, and you a poet and all.'

'Of course I don't! But I object to ruining it.'

'But are you ruining it? Is it any worse off with *panting: whaffing* than with *longing: panting*? This is not only the way language is changed, it is how it was made. Essentially it consists in the contemplation of a relationship "sound : sense; symbol : meaning". It's not only when this is new (to you at any rate) that you can appraise it. At inspired moments you can catch it, get the thrill of it, in familiar words. I grant that an onomatopoeia is a relatively simple case: *whaff*. But "*to pant for* equals *to long for*" contains the same element: new phonetic form for a meaning. Only here a second thing comes in: the interest, pleasure, excitement, what you will, of the relation of old sense to new. Both are illumined, for a time, at any rate. Language could never have come into existence without the one process, and never have extended its grasp without the other. Both must go on! They will, too.'

'Well, I don't like this example of the activity,' said Frankley. 'And I detest it, when philologues talk about Language (with a capital L) with that peculiarly odious unction usually reserved for capitalized Life. That we are told "must go on" – if we complain of any debased manifestations, such as Arry in his cups. He talks about Language as if it was not only a Jungle but a Sacred Jungle, a beastly grove dedicated to Vita Fera,[13] in which nothing must be touched by impious hands. Cankers, fungi, parasites: let 'em alone!

'Languages are *not* jungles. They are gardens, in which sounds selected from the savage wilderness of Brute Noise are turned into words, grown, trained, and endued with the scents

226   SAURON DEFEATED

of significance. You talk as if I could not pull up a weed that
stinks!'

'I do not!' said Lowdham. 'But, first of all, you have to
remember that it's not *your* garden – if you must have this
groggy allegory: it belongs to a lot of other people as well, and
to them your stinking weed may be an object of delight. More
important: your allegory is misapplied. What you are objecting
to is not a weed, but the soil, and also any manifestations of
growth and spread. All the other words in your refined garden
have come into being (and got their scent) in the same way.
You're like a man who is fond of flowers and fruit, but thinks
loam is dirty, and dung disgusting; and the uprising and the
withering just too, too sad. You want a sterilized garden of
immortelles, no, paper-flowers. In fact, to leave allegory, you
won't learn anything about the history of your own language,
and hate to be reminded that it has one.'[14]

'Slay me with pontifical thunder-bolts!' cried Frankley. 'But
I'll die saying *I don't like pants for longings*.'

'That's the stuff!' laughed Lowdham. 'And you're right of
course, Pip. Both are right: the Thunder and the Rebel. For the
One Speaker, all alone, is the final court of doom for words, to
bless or to condemn. It's the agreement only of the separate
judges that seems to make the laws. If your distaste is shared by
an effective number of the others, then *pants* will prove – a
weed, and be thrust in the oven.

'Though, of course, many people – more and more, I
sometimes feel, as Time goes on and even language stales – do
not judge any longer, they only echo. Their native language, as
Ramer would call it, dies almost at their birth.

'It's not so with you, Philip my lad; you're ignorant, but you
have a heart. I dare say *pants* just doesn't fit your native style. So
it has always been with full men: they have had their hatreds
among the words, and their loves.'

'You talk almost as if you'd seen or heard Language since its
beginning, Arry,' said Ramer, looking at him with some surprise. It was a long time since Lowdham had let himself go at
such length.

'No! Not since its beginning,' said Lowdham, while a strange
expression came over his face. 'Only since – but ... Oh well!'
He broke off and went to the window. It was dark but clear as
glass in the sky, and there were many white stars.

The conversation drifted again. Starting from the beginnings

THE NOTION CLUB PAPERS (PART TWO)   227

of Language, we began to talk about legends of origins and cultural myths. Guildford and Markison began to have an argument about Corn-gods and the coming of divine kings or heroes over the sea, in spite of various frivolous interjections from Lowdham, who seemed curiously averse to the turn of the talk.

'The Sheaf personified,'* said Guild[ford. Here unfortunately one leaf is missing.] . . . . . .

[Jeremy] . . . . 'as you said. But I don't think one can be so sure. Sometimes I have a queer feeling that, if one could go back, one would find not myth dissolving into history, but rather the reverse: real history becoming more mythical – more shapely, simple, discernibly significant, even seen at close quarters. More poetical, and less prosaic, if you like.

'In any case, these ancient accounts, legends, myths, about the far Past, about the origins of kings, laws, and the fundamental crafts, are not all made of the same ingredients. They're not wholly inventions. And even what is invented is different from mere fiction; it has more roots.'

'Roots in what?' said Frankley.

'In Being, I think I should say,' Jeremy answered; 'and in human Being; and coming down the scale, in the springs of History and in the designs of Geography – I mean, well, in the pattern of our world as it uniquely is, and of the events in it as seen from a distance. A sort of parallel to the fact that from far away the Earth would be seen as a revolving sunlit globe; and that is a remote truth of enormous effect on us and all we do, though not immediately discernible on earth, where practical men are quite right in regarding the surface as flat and immovable for practical purposes.

'Of course, the pictures presented by the legends may be partly symbolical, they may be arranged in designs that compress, expand, foreshorten, combine, and are not at all realistic or photographic, yet they may tell you something true about the Past.

'And mind you, there are also real details, what are called facts, accidents of land-shape and sea-shape, of individual men and their actions, that are caught up: the grains on which the stories crystallize like snowflakes. There was a man called Arthur at the centre of the cycle.'

* [See Night 66, p. 236.]

228   SAURON DEFEATED

'Perhaps!' said Frankley. 'But that doesn't make such things as the Arthurian romances real in the same way as true past events are real.'

'I didn't say *in the same way*,' said Jeremy. 'There are secondary planes or degrees.'

'And what do you know about "true past events", Philip?' asked Ramer. 'Have you ever seen one, when once it was past? They are all stories or tales now, aren't they, if you try to bring them back into the present? Even your idea of what you did yesterday – if you try to share it with anyone else? Unless, of course, you can go back, or at least see back.'

'Well, I think there's a difference between what really happened at our meetings and Nicholas's record,' said Frankley. 'I don't think his reports erase the true history, whether they're true in their fashion to the events or not. And didn't you claim to be able sometimes to re-view the past as a present thing? Could you go back into Guildford's minutes?'

'Hmm,' Ramer muttered, considering. 'Yes and no,' he said. 'Nicholas could, especially into the scenes that he's pictured or re-pictured fairly solidly and put some mental work into. We could, if we did the same. People of the future, if they only knew the records and studied them, and let their imagination work on them, till the Notion Club became a sort of secondary world set in the Past: they could.'

'Yes, Frankley,' said Jeremy, 'you've got to make a distinction between lies, or casual fiction, or the mere verbal trick of projecting sentences back by putting the verbs into the past tense, between all that and *construction*. Especially of the major kind that has acquired a secondary life of its own and passes from mind to mind.'

'Quite so!' said Ramer. 'I don't think you realize, I don't think any of us realize, the force, the daimonic force that the great myths and legends have. From the profundity of the emotions and perceptions that begot them, and from the multiplication of them in many minds – and each mind, mark you, an engine of obscured but unmeasured energy. They are like an explosive: it may slowly yield a steady warmth to living minds, but if suddenly detonated, it might go off with a crash: yes: might produce a disturbance in the real primary world.'

'What sort of thing are you thinking of?' said Dolbear, lifting his beard off his chest, and opening his eyes with a gleam of passing interest.

THE NOTION CLUB PAPERS (PART TWO) 229

'I wasn't thinking of any particular legend,' said Ramer. 'But, well, for instance, think of the emotional force generated all down the west rim of Europe by the men that came at last to the end, and looked on the Shoreless Sea, unharvested, untraversed, unplumbed! And against that background what a prodigious stature other events would acquire! Say, the coming, apparently out of that Sea, riding a storm, [of] strange men of superior knowledge, steering yet unimagined ships. And if they bore tales of catastrophe far away: battles, burned cities, or the whelming of lands in some tumult of the earth – it shakes me to think of such things in such terms, even now.'

'Yes, I'm moved by that,' said Frankley. 'But it's large and vague. I'm still stuck a good deal nearer home, in Jeremy's casual reference to King Arthur. There you have a sort of legendary land, but it's quite unreal.'

'But you'll allow, won't you,' said Ramer, 'that the Britain of Arthur, as now imagined, even in a debased when-knights-were-bold sort of form, has some kind of force and life?'

'Some kind of literary attraction,' said Frankley. 'But could you go back to King Arthur's Camelot, even on your system? Of which, by the way, I'm not yet convinced: I mean, what you've told us seems to me very likely no more than an exceptionally elaborate, and exceptionally well-remembered form of what I call "dreaming" simply: picture-and-story-spinning while asleep.'

'And anyway: if legend (significant on its own plane) has gathered about history (with its own importance), which would you go back to? Which would you see, if you saw back?' asked Guildford.

'It depends on what you yourself are like, and on what you are looking for, I imagine,' Ramer answered. 'If you were seeking the story that has most power and significance for human minds, then probably that is the version that you'ld find.

'Anyway, I think you could – I think I could go back to Camelot, *if* the conditions of my mind and the chances of travel were favourable. The chances are not, as I told you, more than very slightly affected by waking desire. An adventure of that sort would *not* be the same thing as re-viewing what you'ld call Fifth-century Britain. Neither would it be like making a dream-drama of my own. It would be more like the first, but it would be more active. It would be much less free than the second. It would probably be more difficult than either. I fancy it might be

230   SAURON DEFEATED

the sort of thing best done by one or two people in concert.'

'I don't see how that would help,' said Frankley.

'Because different people have different views, or have individual contributions to make: is that what you mean?' asked Guildford. 'But that would be just as true of historical research or "backsight".'

'No, it wouldn't,' said Jeremy. 'You're mixing up history in the sense of a story made up out of the intelligible surviving evidence (which is not necessarily truer to the facts than legend) and "the true story", the real Past. If you really had a look back at the Past as it was, then everything would be there to see, if you had eyes for it, or time to observe it in. And the most difficult thing to see would be, as it always is "at present", the pattern, the significance, yes, the moral of it all, if you like. At least that would be the case, the nearer you come to our time. As I said before, I'm not so sure about that, as you pass backward to the beginnings. But in such a thing as a great story-cycle the situation would be different: much would be vividly real and at the same time ... er ... portentous; but there might be, would be, uncompleted passages, weak joints, gaps. You'd have to consolidate. You might need help.'

'You might indeed!' said Frankley. 'Riding down from Camelot (when you had discovered just where that was) to most other places on the legendary map, you'd find the road pretty vague. Most of the time you'd be lost in a fog! And you'd meet some pretty sketchy characters about the court, too.'

'Of course! And so you would about the present court,' said Markison, 'or in any Oxford quadrangle. Why should that worry you? Sketchy characters are more true to life than fully studied ones. There are precious few people in real life that you know as well as a good writer knows his heroes and villains.'

'Riding down to Camelot. Riding out from Camelot,' murmured Lowdham. 'And there was a dark shadow over that too. I wonder, I wonder. But it is still only a tale to me. Not all legends are like that. No, unfortunately. Some seem to have come to life on their own, and they will not rest. I should hate to be cast back into some of those lands. It would be worse than the vision of poor Norman Keeps.'

'What on earth is he talking about now?' said Guildford.

'The cork's coming out pretty soon, I think,' grunted Dolbear without opening his eyes.

'Oh, Norman Keeps is our barber,'[15] said Frankley. 'At least

THE NOTION CLUB PAPERS (PART TWO)   231

that's what Arry and I call him: no idea what his real name is. Quite a nice and moderately intelligent little man: but to him everything beyond a certain vague distance back is a vast dark barren but utterly fixed and determined land and time called The Dark Ages. There are only four features in it: Norman Keeps (by which he means baronial castles, and possibly the house of any man markedly richer than himself); Them Jameses (meaning roughly I suppose the kings One and Two); The Squires (a curious kind of bogey-folk); and The People. Nothing ever happened in that land but Them Jameses shutting up The People in the Keeps (with the help of The Squires) and there torturing them and robbing them, though they don't appear ever to have possessed anything to be robbed of. Rather a gloomy legend. But it's a great deal more fixed in a lot more heads than is the Battle of Camlan!'[16]

'I know, I know,' said Lowdham loudly and angrily. 'It's a shame! Norman Keeps is a very decent chap, and would rather learn truth than lies. But Zigūr[17] pays special attention to the type. Curse him!'

Conversation stopped, and there was a silence. Ramer and Guildford exchanged glances. Dolbear opened his eyes quietly without moving his head.

'Zigūr?' said Jeremy, looking at Lowdham. 'Zigūr? Who is he?'

'No idea, no idea!' said Lowdham. 'Is this a new game, Jerry? Owlamoo,[18] who's he?' He strode to the window and flung it open.

The early summer night was still and glimmering, warmer than usual for the time of year. Lowdham leant out, and we turned and stared at his back. The large window looked west, and the two towers of All Souls' stuck up like dim horns against the stars.

Suddenly Lowdham spoke in a changed voice, clear and ominous, words in an unknown tongue; and then turning fiercely upon us he cried aloud:

Behold the Eagles of the Lords of the West! They are coming over Nūmenōr![19]

We were all startled. Several of us went to the window and stood behind Lowdham, looking out. A great cloud, coming up slowly out of the West, was eating up the stars. As it approached it opened two vast sable wings, spreading north and south.

232　　　　SAURON DEFEATED

Suddenly Lowdham pulled away, slammed the window down, and drew the curtains. He slumped into a chair and shut his eyes.

We returned to our seats and sat there uncomfortably for some time without a sound. At last Ramer spoke.

'Númenōr? Númenōr?' he said quietly. 'Where did you find that name, Arundel Lowdham?'

'Oh, I don't know,' Lowdham answered, opening his eyes, and looking round with a rather dazed expression. 'It comes to me, now and again. Just on the edge of things, you know. Eludes the grasp. Like coming round after gas. But it's been turning up more often than usual this spring. I'm sorry. Have I been behaving oddly or something, not quite my old quiet friendly self? Give me a drink!'

'I asked,' said Ramer, 'because Númenōr is my name for Atlantis.'[20]

'Now that *is* odd!' began Jeremy.

'Ah!' said Lowdham. 'I wondered if it might be. I asked you what your name was that night last term; but you didn't answer.'

'Well, here's a new development!' said Dolbear, who was now wide awake. 'If Arry Lowdham is going to dive where the dreams go and find the same fish as Ramer, we shall have to look into the pool.'

'We shall,' said Jeremy; 'for it's not only Ramer and Arry. I come into it too. I knew I had heard that name as soon as Arry said it.[21] But I can't for the life of me remember where or when at the moment. It'll bother me now, like a thorn in the foot, until I get it out.'

'Very queer,' said Dolbear.

'What do you propose to do?' said Ramer.

'Take your advice,' said Jeremy. 'Get your help, if you'll give it.'

'Go into memory-training on the Rufus-Ramer system and see what we can fish up,' said Lowdham. 'I feel as if something wants to get out, and I should be glad to get it out – or forget it.'

'I'm a bit lost in all this,' said Markison. 'I've missed something evidently. Philip has told me a bit about the Ramer revelations last term, but I'm still rather at sea. Couldn't you tell us something, Lowdham, to make things a little clearer?'

'No, really, I'm feeling frightfully tired,' said Lowdham. 'You had better read up the records, if Nick has written them out

THE NOTION CLUB PAPERS (PART TWO)   233

yet.[22] I expect he has. He's pretty regular, and pretty accurate, if a bit hard on me. And come along to the next meeting. And we'd better make that in a fortnight's time, I think. You can have my room, if you think you can all get in. We'll see what we have got by then. I've nothing much to tell yet.'

The conversation then dropped back uncertainly towards the normal, and nothing further occurred worth noting.

As we went out Lowdham said to Ramer: 'D'you think I could come round and talk to you, and to Rufus, some time soon?'

'Yes,' said Ramer. 'The sooner the better. You come too, Jeremy.'

MGR. PF. RD. JM. JJ. RS. AAL. WTJ. NG.

Night 66.   Thursday, May 22nd, 1987.

A crowded evening. Lowdham's rather small room was pretty packed. The idea of Arry 'seeing things' was sufficiently astonishing to attract every member who was in Oxford. (Also I am supposed to keep more bottles in my cupboard than some that I could name. AAL)

Lowdham seemed in a bright and rather noisy mood again; reluctant to do anything but sing. Eventually he was quietened and got into a chair.

'Well now,' said Markison, 'I've read the records. I can't say I've made my mind up about them yet; but I'm very interested to hear how you come into such business, Arry. It doesn't seem in your line.'

'Well, I'm a philologist,' said Lowdham, 'which means a misunderstood man. But where I come in is, I think, at the point you've mentioned: at *Arry*. The name Arry, which some of you are pleased to attach to me, is *not* just a tribute to my vulgar noisiness, as seems assumed by the more ignorant among you: it is short not for Henry or Harold, but for Arundel. In full *Alwin Arundel Lowdham* your humble jester, at your service.'

'Well, what has that got to do with it?' said several voices.

'I'm not quite sure yet,' said Lowdham. 'But my father's name was Edwin.'[23]

'Illuminating indeed!' said Frankley.

'Not very, I think,' said Lowdham. 'Not illuminating, but puzzling. My father was an odd sort of man, as far as I

234   SAURON DEFEATED

remember. Large, tall, powerful, dark. Don't stare at me! I'm a reduced copy. He was wealthy, and combined a passion for the sea with learning of a sort, linguistic and archaeological. He must have studied Anglo-Saxon and other North-western tongues; for I inherited his library and some of his tastes.

'We lived in Pembrokeshire, near Penian:[24] more or less, for we were away a large part of the year; and my father was always going off at a moment's notice: he spent a great deal of his time sailing about Norway, Scotland, Ireland, Iceland, and sometimes southward to the Azores and so on. I did not know him well, though I loved him as much as a small boy can, and used to dream of the time when I could go sailing with him. But he disappeared when I was only nine.'

'Disappeared?' said Frankley. 'I thought you told me once that he was lost at sea.'

'He disappeared,' said Lowdham. 'A strange story. No storm. His ship just vanished into the Atlantic. That was in 1947, just forty years ago next month. No signals (he wouldn't use wireless, anyway). No trace. No news. She was called *The Éarendel*.[25] An odd business.'

'The seas were still pretty dangerous at that time, weren't they?' said Stainer. 'Mines all over the place?'

'Not a spar at any rate was ever found,' said Lowdham. 'That was the end of *The Éarendel*: a queer name, and a queer end. But my father had some queer fancies about names. I am called Alwin Arundel, a mouthful enough, out of deference to prudence and my mother, I believe. The names he chose were Ælfwine Éarendel.

'One of the few conversations I remember having with him was just before he went off for the last time. I had begged to go with him, and he had said NO, of course. "When can I go?" I said.

' "Not yet, Ælfwine," he said. "Not yet. Some time, perhaps. Or you may have to follow me."

'It was then that it came out about my names. "I modernized 'em," he said, "to save trouble. But my ship bears the truer name. It does not look to Sussex,[26] but to shores a great deal further off. Very far away indeed now. A man has more freedom in naming his ship than his own son in these days. And it's few men that have either to name."

'He went off next day. He was mad to be at sea again, as he had been kept ashore all through the Six Years' War,[27] from the summer of 1939 onward, except I believe just at the Dunkirk

THE NOTION CLUB PAPERS (PART TWO)   235

time in 1940. Too old – he was fifty when the war broke out, and I was only a year; for he had married late – too old, and I fancy a good deal too free and unbiddable to get any particular job, and he had become fiercely restless. He only took three sailors with him,[28] I think, but of course I don't know how he found them, or how they ever managed to get off, in those days of tyranny. I fancy they just cleared out illegally, somehow. Whither, I wonder? I don't think they meant to return. Anyway I never saw him again.'

'I can't see the connexion of this thread at all yet,' said Guildford.

'Wait a bit!' said Ramer. 'There is a connexion, or we think so. We've discussed it. You'd better let Arundel have his say.'

'Well – as soon as he'd gone ... I was only nine at the time, as I said, and I had never bothered much about books, let alone languages, naturally at that age. I could read, of course, but I seldom did ... as soon as my father had gone, and we knew that it was for good, I began to take up with languages, especially making them up (as I thought). After a time I used to stray into his study, left for years it was, just as it had been when he was alive.

'There I learned a lot of odd things in a desultory way, and I came across some sort of a diary or notes in a queer script. I don't know what happened to it when my mother died. I only found one loose leaf of it among the papers that came to me. I've kept it for years, and often tried and failed to read it; but it is mislaid at present. I was about fourteen or fifteen when I got specially taken with Anglo-Saxon, for some reason. I liked its word-style, I think. It wasn't so much what was written in it as the flavour of the words that suited me. But I was first introduced to it by trying to find out more about the names. I didn't get much light on them.

'*Éadwine* friend of fortune? *Ælfwine* elf-friend? That at any rate is what their more or less literal translation comes to. Though, as most of you will know (except poor Philip), these two-part names are pretty conventional, and not too much can be built on their literal meaning.'

'But they must originally have been made to have a meaning,' said Ramer. 'The habit of joining, apparently at random, any two of a list of beginners and enders, giving you Spear-peace and Peace-wolf and that sort of thing, must have been a later development, a kind of dried-up verbal heraldry. *Ælfwine* any-

236   SAURON DEFEATED

way is one of the old combinations. It occurs outside England, doesn't it?'

'Yes,' said Lowdham. 'And so does *Éadwine*. But I could not see that any of the many recorded Ælfwines were very suitable: Ælfwine, grandson of King Alfred, for instance, who fell in the great victory of 937; or Ælfwine who fell in the famous defeat of Maldon, and many others; not even Ælfwine of Italy, that is Albuin son of Auduin, the grim Langobard of the sixth century.'[29]

'Don't forget the connexion of the Langobards with King Sheaf,'[30] put in Markison, who was beginning to show signs of interest.

'I don't,' said Lowdham. 'But I was talking of my earliest investigations as a boy.'

'Nor the repetition of the sequence: Albuin son of Auduin; Ælfwine son of Éadwine; Alwin son of Edwin,' said Ramer.[31]

'Probably deliberately imitated from the well-known story of Rosamund,'[32] objected Philip Frankley. 'Arry's father must have known it. And that's quite enough to explain Alwin and Ælfwine, when you're dealing with a family of Nordic philologues.'

'Perhaps, O Horsefriend of Macedon!'[33] said Lowdham. 'But it doesn't take in *Éarendel*. There's little to be found out about that in Anglo-Saxon, though the name is there all right. Some guess that it was really a star-name for Orion, or for Rigel.[34] A ray, a brilliance, the light of dawn: so run the glosses.[35]

> *Éalá Éarendel engla beorhtost*
> *ofer middangeard monnum sended!'*

he chanted. ' "Hail Earendel, brightest of angels, above the middle-earth sent unto men!" When I came across that citation in the dictionary I felt a curious thrill, as if something had stirred in me, half wakened from sleep. There was something very remote and strange and beautiful behind those words, if I could grasp it, far beyond ancient English.

'I know more now, of course. The quotation comes from the *Crist*; though exactly what the author meant is not so certain.[36] It is beautiful enough in its place. But I don't think it is any irreverence to say that it may derive its curiously moving quality from some older world.'

'Why *irreverent*?' said Markison. 'Even if the words do refer to Christ, of course they are all derived from an older pre-christian world, like all the rest of the language.'

'That's so,' said Lowdham; 'but *Éarendel* seems to me a

THE NOTION CLUB PAPERS (PART TWO)   237

special word. It is not Anglo-Saxon;[37] or rather, it is not *only* Anglo-Saxon, but also something else much older.

'I think it is a remarkable case of linguistic coincidence, or congruence. Such things do occur, of course. I mean, in two different languages, quite unconnected, and where no borrowing from one to the other is possible, you will come across words very similar in both sound and meaning. They are usually dismissed as accidents; and I daresay some of the cases are not significant. But I fancy that they may sometimes be the result of a hidden symbol-making process working out to similar ends by different routes. Especially when the result is beautiful and the meaning poetical, as is the case with *Éarendel*.'

'If I follow all this,' said Markison, 'I suppose you are trying to say that you've discovered *Éarendel*, or something like it, in some other unconnected language, and are dismissing all the other forms of the name that are found in the older languages related to English. Though one of them, *Auriwandalo*, is actually recorded as a Langobardic name, I think. It's odd how the Langobards keep cropping up.'

'It is,' said Lowdham, 'but I am not interested in that at the moment. For I do mean that: I have often heard *éarendel*, or to be exact *ëarendil*, *e-a-r-e-n-d-i-l*, in another language, where it actually means Great Mariner, or literally Friend of the Sea; though it also has, I think, some connexion with the stars.'

'What language is that?' said Markison, knitting his brows. 'Not one I've ever come across, I think.' (He has 'come across' or dabbled in about a hundred in his time.)

'No, I don't suppose you've ever met it,' said Lowdham. 'It's an unknown language. But I had better try and explain.

'From the time of my father's departure I began to have curious experiences, and I have gone on having them down the years, slowly increasing in clearness: visitations of linguistic ghosts, you might say. Yes, just that. I am not a *seer*. I have, of course, pictorial dreams like other folk, but only what Ramer would call marginal stuff, and few and fleeting at that: which at any rate means that if I see things I don't remember them. But ever since I was about ten I have had words, even occasional phrases, ringing in my ears; both in dream and waking abstraction. They come into my mind unbidden, or I wake to hear myself repeating them. Sometimes they seem to be quite isolated, just words or names. Sometimes something seems to "break my dream"[38] as my mother used to say: the names seem to be

238   SAURON DEFEATED

connected strangely with things seen in waking life, suddenly, in some fleeting posture or passing light which transports me to some quite different region of thought or imagination. Like the Camera that night in March, Ramer, if you remember it.

'Looking at a picture once of a cone-shaped mountain rising out of wooded uplands, I heard myself crying out: "Desolate is Minul-Tārik, the Pillar of Heaven is forsaken!" and I knew that it was a dreadful thing. But most ominous of all are the Eagles of the Lords of the West. They shake me badly when I see them. I could, I could – I feel I could tell some great tale of Nūmenor.

'But I'm getting on too fast. It was a long time before I began to piece the fragments together at all. Most of these "ghost-words" are, and always were, to all appearance casual, as casual as the words caught by the eye from a lexicon when you're looking for something else. They began to come through, as I said, when I was about ten; and almost at once I started to note them down. Clumsily, of course, at first. Even grown-up folk make a poor shot, as a rule, at spelling the simplest words that they've never seen, unless they have some sort of phonetic knowledge. But I've still got some of the grubby little note-books I used as a small boy. An unsystematic jumble, of course; for it was only now and again that I bothered about such things. But later on, when I was older and had a little more linguistic experience, I began to pay serious attention to my "ghosts", and saw that they were something quite different from the game of trying to make up private languages.

'As soon as I started looking out for them, so to speak, the ghosts began to come oftener and clearer; and when I had got a lot of them noted down, I saw that they were not all of one kind: they had different phonetic styles, styles as unlike as, well – Latin and Hebrew. I am sorry, if this seems a bit complicated. I can't help it: and if this stuff is worth your bothering about at all, we'd better get it right.

'Well, first of all I recognized that a lot of these ghosts were Anglo-Saxon, or related stuff. What was left I arranged in two lists, A and B, according to their style, with a third rag-bag list C for odd things that didn't seem to fit in anywhere. But it was language A that really attracted me; it just suited me. I still like it best.'

'In that case you ought to have got it pretty well worked out by now,' said Stainer. 'Haven't you got a *Grammar and Lexicon of Lowdham's Language A* that you could pass round? I

THE NOTION CLUB PAPERS (PART TWO)   239

wouldn't mind a look at it, if it isn't in some hideous phonetic script.'

Lowdham stared at him, but repressed the explosion that seemed imminent. 'Are you deliberately missing the point?' he said. 'I've been painfully trying to indicate that I do *not* believe that this stuff is "invented", not by me at any rate.

'Take the Anglo-Saxon first. It is the only known language that comes through at all in this way, and that in itself is odd. And it began to come through *before* I knew it. I recognized it as Anglo-Saxon only after I began to learn it from books, and then I had the curious experience of finding that I already knew a good many of the words. Why, there are a number of ghost-words noted in the very first of my childish note-books that are plainly a beginner's efforts at putting down spoken Old English words in modern letters. There's *wook, woak, woof* = crooked, for instance, that is evidently a first attempt at recording Anglo-Saxon *wōh*.

'And as for the other stuff: A, the language I like best, is the shortest list. How I wish I could get more of it! But it's *not* under my control, Stainer. It's not one of my invented lingoes. I have made up two or three, and they're as complete as they're ever likely to be; but that's quite a different matter. But evidently I'd better cut out the autobiography and jump down to the present.

'It's now clear to me that the two languages A and B have got nothing to do with any language I've ever heard, or come across in books in the ordinary way. Nothing. As far as it is possible for any language, built out of about two dozen sounds, as A is, to avoid occasional resemblances to other quite unrelated tongues: nothing. And they have nothing to do with my inventions either. Language B is quite unlike my own style. Language A is very agreeable to my taste (it may have helped to form it), but it is independent of me; I can't "work it out", as you put it.

'Any one who has ever spent (or wasted) any time on composing a language will understand me. Others perhaps won't. But in making up a language you are free: too free. It is difficult to fit meaning to any given sound-pattern, and even more difficult to fit a sound-pattern to any given meaning. I say *fit*. I don't mean that you can't assign forms or meanings arbitrarily, as you will. Say, you want a word for *sky*. Well, call it *jibberjabber*, or anything else that comes into your head

240   SAURON DEFEATED

without the exercise of any linguistic taste or art. But that's code-making, not language-building. It is quite another matter to find a relationship, sound plus sense, that satisfies, that is when made *durable*. When you're just inventing, the pleasure or fun is in the moment of invention; but as you are the master your whim is law, and you may want to have the fun all over again, fresh. You're liable to be for ever niggling, altering, refining, wavering, according to your linguistic mood and to your changes of taste.

'It is not in the least like that with my ghost-words. They came through made: sound and sense already conjoined. I can no more niggle with them than I can alter the sound or the sense of the word *polis* in Greek. Many of my ghost-words have been repeated, over and over again, down the years. Nothing changes but, occasionally, my spelling. They don't change. They endure, unaltered, unalterable by me. In other words they have the effect and taste of real languages. But one can have one's preferences among real languages, and as I say, I like A best.

'Both A and B I associate in some way with the name *Númenor*. The rag-bag list has got pretty long as the years have gone on, and I can now see that, among some unidentified stuff, it contains a lot of echoes of later forms of language derived from A and B. The Númenorean tongues are old, old, archaic; they taste of an Elder World to me. The other things are worn, altered, touched with the loss and bitterness of these shores of exile.' These last words he spoke in a strange tone, as if talking to himself. Then his voice trailed off into silence.

'I find this rather hard to follow, or to swallow,' said Stainer. 'Couldn't you give us something a bit clearer, something better to bite on than this algebra of A and B?'

Lowdham looked up again. 'Yes, I could,' he said. 'I won't bother you with the later echoes. I find them moving, somehow, and instructive technically: I am beginning to discern the laws or lines of their change as the world grew older; but that wouldn't be clear even to a philologist except in writing and with long parallel lists.

'But take the name *Númenóre* or *Númenor* (both occur) to start with. That belongs to Language A. It means Westernesse, and is composed of *núme* "west" and *nóre* "folk" or "country". But the B name is *Anadûnê*, and the people are called *Adûnâim*, from the B word *adûn* "west". The same land, or so I think, has

THE NOTION CLUB PAPERS (PART TWO)   241

another name: in A *Andōre* and in B *Yōzāyan*,[39] and both mean "Land of Gift".

'There seems to be no connexion between the two languages there. But there are some words that are the same or very similar in both. The word for "sky" or "the heavens" is *menel* in Language A and *minil* in B: a form of it occurs in *Minul-tārik* "Pillar of Heaven" that I mentioned just now. And there seems to be some connexion between the A word *Valar*, which seems to mean something like "The Powers", we might say "gods" perhaps, and the B plural *Avalōim* and the place-name *Avallōni*. Although that is a B name, it is with it, oddly enough, that I associate Language A; so if you want to get rid of algebra, you can call A Avallonian, and B Adunaic. I do myself.

'The name *Ëarendil*, by the way, belongs to Avallonian, and contains *ëare* "the open sea" and the stem *ndil* "love, devotion": that may look a bit odd, but lots of the Avallonian stems begin with *nd*, *mb*, *ng*, which lose their *d*, *b*, or *g* when they stand alone. The corresponding Adunaic name, apparently meaning just the same, is *Azrubēl*. A large number of names seem to have double forms like this, almost as if one people spoke two languages. If that is so, I suppose the situation could be paralleled by the use of, say, Chinese in Japan, or indeed of Latin in Europe. As if a man could be called Godwin, and also Theophilus or Amadeus. But even so two different peoples must come into the story somewhere.

'Well there you are. I hope you are not all bored. I could give you long lists of other words. Words, words, mostly just that. For the most part significant nouns, like *Isil* and *Nīlū* for the Moon; fewer adjectives, still fewer verbs, and only occasional connected phrases. I love these languages, though they are only fragments out of some forgotten book. I find both curiously attractive, though Avallonian is nearest to my heart. Adunaic with its, well, faintly Semitic flavour belongs more nearly to our world, somehow. But Avallonian is to me beautiful, in its simple and euphonious style. And it seems to me more august, more ancient, and, well, sacred and liturgical. I used to call it the Elven-Latin. The echoes of it carry one far away. Very far away. Away from Middle-earth altogether, I expect.' He paused as if he was listening. 'But I could not explain just what I mean by that,' he ended.

There was a short silence, and then Markison spoke. 'Why did you call it Elven-Latin?'[40] he asked. 'Why Elven?'

242   SAURON DEFEATED

'I don't quite know,' Lowdham answered. 'It seems the nearest English word for the purpose. But certainly I didn't mean *elf* in any debased post-Shakespearean sort of sense. Something far more potent and majestic. I am not quite clear what. In fact it's one of the things that I most want to discover. What is the real reference of the *ælf* in my name?

'You remember that I said Anglo-Saxon used to come through mixed up with this other queer stuff, as if it had some special connexion with it? Well, I got hold of Anglo-Saxon through the ordinary books later on: I began to learn it properly before I was fifteen, and that confused the issue. Yet it is an odd fact that, though I found most of these words already there, waiting for me, in the printed vocabularies and dictionaries, there were some – and they still come through now and again – that are not there at all. *Tíwas*,[41] for instance, apparently used as an equivalent of the Avallonian *Valar*; and *Nówendaland*[42] for *Númenóre*. And other compound names too, like *Fréafíras*,[43] *Regeneard*,[44] and *Midswípen*.[45] Some were in very archaic form: like *hebaensuil* "pillar of heaven", or *frumaeldi*; or very antique indeed like *Wihawinia*.'[46]

'This is dreadful,' sighed Frankley. 'Though I suppose I should be grateful at least that Valhalla and Valkyries have not made their appearance yet. But you'd better be careful, Arry! We're all friends here, and we won't give you away. But you will be getting into trouble, if you let your archaic cats out of your private bag among your quarrelsome philological rivals. Unless, of course, you back up their theories.'[47]

'You needn't worry,' said Lowdham. 'I've no intention of publishing the stuff. And I haven't come across anything very controversial anyway. After all Anglo-Saxon is pretty near home, in place and time, and it's been closely worked: there's not much margin for wide errors, not even in pronunciation. What I hear is more or less what the received doctrine would lead me to expect. Except in one point: it is so slow! Compared with us urban chirrupers the farmers and mariners of the past simply mouthed, savoured words like meat and wine and honey on their tongues. Especially when declaiming. They made a scrap of verse majestically sonorous: like thunder moving on a slow wind, or the tramp of mourners at the funeral of a king. We just gabble the stuff. But even that is no news to philologists, in theory; though the realization of it in sound is something mere theory hardly prepares you for. And, of course, the

THE NOTION CLUB PAPERS (PART TWO)   243

philologists would be very interested in my echoes of very archaic English, even early Germanic – if they could be got to believe that they were genuine.

'Here's a bit that might intrigue them. It's very primitive in form, though I use a less horrific notation than is usual. But you had better see this.' He brought out from his pocket several scraps of paper and passed them round;

> *westra lage wegas rehtas, wraikwas nu isti.*

'That came through years ago,[48] long before I could interpret it, and it has constantly been repeated in various forms:

> *westra lage wegas rehtas, wraikwas nu isti.*
> *westweg wæs rihtweg, wóh is núþa*

and so on and on and on, in many snatches and dream-echoes, down from what looks like very ancient Germanic to Old English.

> *a straight way lay westward, now it is bent.*

It seems the key to something, but I can't fit it yet. But it was while I was rummaging in an Onomasticon,[49] and poring over the list of Ælfwines, that I got, seemed to *hear* and *see*, the longest snatch that has ever come through in that way. Yes, I said I wasn't a *seer*; but Anglo-Saxon is sometimes an exception. I don't see pictures, but I see letters: some of the words and especially some of the scraps of verse seem to be present to the mind's eye as well as to the ear, as if sometime, somewhere, I had seen them written and could almost recall the page. If you turn over the slips I gave you, you'll see the thing written out. It came through when I was only sixteen, before I had read any of the old verse; but the lines stuck, and I put them down as well as I could. The archaic forms interest me now as a philologist, but that's how they came through, and how they stand in my note-book under the date October 1st 1954. A windy evening: I remember it howling round the house, and the distant sound of the sea.

> *Monath módaes lust mith meriflóda*
> *forth ti foeran thaet ic feorr hionan*
> *obaer gaarseggaes grimmae holmas*
> *aelbuuina eard uut gisoecae.*
> *Nis me ti hearpun hygi ni ti hringthegi*
> *ni ti wíbae wyn ni ti weoruldi hyct*
> *ni ymb oowict ellaes nebnae ymb ýtha giwalc.*

244   SAURON DEFEATED

It sounds to me now almost like my own father speaking across
grey seas of world and time:

> My soul's desire over the sea-torrents
> forth bids me fare, that I afar should seek
> over the ancient water's awful mountains
> Elf-friends' island in the Outer-world.
> For no harp have I heart, no hand for gold,
> in no wife delight, in the world no hope:
> one wish only, for the waves' tumult.

'I know now, of course, that these lines very closely resemble
some of the verses in the middle of *The Seafarer*, as that strange
old poem of longing is usually called. But they are not the same.
In the text preserved in manuscript it runs *elþéodigra eard* 'the
land of aliens', not *aelbuuina* or *ælfwina* (as it would have been
spelt later) 'of the Ælfwines, the Elven-friends'. I think mine is
probably the older and better text – it is in a much older form
and spelling anyway – but I daresay I should get into trouble, as
Pip suggests, if I put it into a "serious journal".[50]
'It was not until quite recently that I picked up echoes of some
other lines that are not found at all among the preserved
fragments of the oldest English verses.[51]

> *Þus cwæð Ælfwine Wídlást Éadwines sunu:*
> *Fela bið on Westwegum werum uncúðra,*
> *wundra and wihta, wlitescéne land,*
> *eardgeard ælfa and ésa bliss.*
> *Lýt ænig wát hwylc his langoð síe*
> *þám þe eftsíðes eldo getwæfeð.*

'Thus spake Ælfwine the Fartravelled son of Éadwine:
There is many a thing in the west of the world unknown to
men; marvels and strange beings, [a land lovely to look on,]
the dwelling place of the Elves and the bliss of the Gods.
Little doth any man know what longing is his whom old
age cutteth off from return.
'I think my father went before Eld should cut him off. But
what of Éadwine's son?
'Well, now I've had my say for the present. There may be
more later. I am working at the stuff – as hard as time and my
duties allow, and things may happen. Certainly I'll let you
know, if they do. For now you have endured so much, I expect
you will want some more news, if anything interesting turns up.

THE NOTION CLUB PAPERS (PART TWO)   245

If it's any comfort to you, Philip, I think we shall get away from Anglo-Saxon sooner or later.'

'If it's any comfort to you, Arry,' said Frankley, 'for the first time in your long life as a preacher you've made me faintly interested in it.'

'Good Heavens!' said Lowdham. 'Then there must be something *very* queer going on! Lor bless me! Give me a drink and I will sing, as the minstrels used to say.

> *Fil me a cuppe of ful gode ale,*
> *for longe I have spelled tale!*
> *Nu wil I drinken or I ende*
> *that Frenche men to helle wende!*'[52]

The song was interrupted by Frankley. Eventually a semblance of peace was restored, only one chair being a casualty. Nothing toward or untoward occurred for the remainder of the evening.

AAL. MGR. WTJ. JM. RD. RS. PF. JJ. JJR. NG.

Night 67.   Thursday, June 12th, 1987.[53]

We met in Ramer's rooms in Jesus College. There were eight of us present, including Stainer and Cameron, and all the regulars except Lowdham. It was very hot and sultry, and we sat near the window looking into the inner quadrangle, talking of this and that, and listening for the noises of Lowdham's approach; but an hour passed and there was still no sign of him.

'Have you seen anything of Arry lately?' said Frankley to Jeremy. 'I haven't. I wonder if he's going to turn up at all tonight?'

'I couldn't say,' said Jeremy. 'Ramer and I saw a good deal of him in the first few days after our last meeting, but I haven't set eyes on him for some time now.'

'I wonder what he's up to? They say he cancelled his lectures last week. I hope he's not ill.'

'I don't think you need fret about your little Elf-friend,' said Dolbear. 'He's got a body and a constitution that would put a steamroller back a bit, if it bumped into him. And don't worry about his mind! He's getting something off it, and that will do him no harm, I think. At least whatever it does, it will do less harm than trying to cork it up any longer. But what on earth it all is – well, I'm still about as much at sea as old Edwin Lowdham himself.'

246　　SAURON DEFEATED

'Sunk, in fact,' said Stainer. 'I should say it was a bad attack of repressed linguistic invention, and that the sooner he brings out an Adunaic Grammar the better for all.'

'Perhaps,' said Ramer. 'But he may bring out a lot more besides. I wish he would come!'

At that moment there was the sound of loud footsteps, heavy and quick, on the wooden stairs below. There was a bang on the door, and in strode Lowdham.

'I've got something new!' he shouted. 'More than mere words. Verbs! Syntax at last!' He sat down and mopped his face.

'Verbs, syntax! Hooray!' mocked Frankley. 'Now isn't that thrilling!'

'Don't try and start a row, O Lover of Horses[54] and Horseplay!' said Lowdham. 'It's too hot. Listen!

'It's been very stuffy and thundery lately, and I haven't been able to sleep, a troublesome novelty for me; and I began to have a splitting headache. So I cleared off for a few days to the west coast, to Pembroke. But the Eagles came up out of the Atlantic, and I fled. I still couldn't sleep when I came back, and my headache got worse. And then last night I fell suddenly into a deep dark sleep – and I got this.' He waved a handful of papers at us. 'I didn't come round until nearly twelve this morning, and my head was ringing with words. They began to fade quickly as soon as I woke; but I jotted down at once all I could.

'I have been working on the stuff every minute since, and I've made six copies. For I think you'll find it well worth a glance; but you fellows would never follow it without something to look at. Here it is!'

He passed round several sheets of paper. On them were inscribed strange words in a big bold hand, done with one of the great thick-nibbed pens Lowdham is fond of. Under most of the words were glosses in red ink.[55]

I

(A) O　　*sauron*　*túle*　*nukumna* ... *lantaner*　*turkildi*
　　and　　?　　came　humbled　...　fell　　　?

　　nuhuinenna ... *tar-kalion*　*ohtakáre*　*valannar* ...
　　under shadow ...　　?　　　war made　on Powers ...

　　númeheruvi　*arda*　*sakkante*　*lenéme*　*ilúvatáren* ...
　　Lords-of-West　Earth　rent　with leave of　?　...

THE NOTION CLUB PAPERS (PART TWO) 247

> *ëari   ullier   ikilyanna   ... númenóre   ataltane*
> seas   should flow   into chasm ... Numenor   fell down

* * *

> (B) *Kadō   zigūrun   zabathān   unakkha ... ēruhīnim*
> and so   ?   humbled   he-came ...   ?

> *dubdam   ugru-dalad   ... ar-pharazónun   azaggara*
> fell   ?shadow under ...   ?   was warring

> *avalōiyada   ... bārim   an-adūn   yurahtam   dāira*
> against Powers ... Lords   of-West   broke   Earth

> *sāibēth-mā   ēruvō   ... azrīya   du-phursā   akhāsada*
> assent-with   ?-from ... seas   so-as-to-gush into chasm

> *... anadūnē   zīrān   hikallaba   ... bawība   dulgī*
> ... Numenor   beloved   she-fell down ... winds   black

> *... balīk   hazad   an-nimruzīr   azūlada*
> ... ships   seven   of ?   eastward

II

> (B) *Agannālō   burōda   nēnud ...   zāira   nēnud*
> Death-shadow   heavy   on-us ...   longing (is) on-us

> *... adūn   izindi   batān   tāidō   ayadda: īdō*
> ... west   straight road   once   went   now

> *kātha   batīna   lōkhī*
> all   roads   crooked

> (A) *Vahaiya   sín   Andóre*
> far away   now (is) Land of Gift

> (B) *Ēphalak   īdōn   Yōzāyan*
> far away   now (is) Land of Gift

> (B) *Ēphal   ēphalak   īdōn   hi-Akallabēth*
> far   far away   now (is)   She-that-hath-fallen

> (A) *Haiya   vahaiya   sín   atalante.*[56]
> far   far away   now (is)   the Downfallen.

'There are two languages here,' said Lowdham, 'Avallonian and Adunaic: I have labelled them A and B. Of course, I have put them down in a spelling of my own. Avallonian has a clear simple phonetic structure and in my ear it rings like a bell, but I

248   SAURON DEFEATED

seemed to feel as I wrote this stuff down that it was not really
spelt like this. I have never had the same feeling before, but this
morning I half glimpsed quite a different script, though I
couldn't visualize it clearly. I fancy Adunaic used a very similar
script too.

' "I believe these are passages out of some book," I said to
myself. And then suddenly I remembered the curious script in
my father's manuscript. But that can wait. I've brought the leaf
along.

'These are only fragmentary sentences, of course, and not by
any means all that I heard; but they are all that I could seize and
get written down. Text I is bilingual, though they are not
identical, and the B version is a little longer. That's only because
I could remember a bit more of it. They correspond so closely
because I heard the A version, a sentence at a time, with the B
version immediately following: in the same voice, as if someone
was reading out of an ancient book and translating it bit by bit
for his audience. Then there came a long dark gap, or a picture
of confusion and darkness in which the word-echoes were lost
in a noise of winds and waves.

'And then I got a kind of lamentation or chant, of which I
have put down all that I can now remember. You'll notice the
order is altered at the end. There were two voices here, one
singing A and the other singing B, and the chant always ended
up as I have set it out: A B B A. The last word was always
Atalante. I can give you no idea of how moving it was, horribly
moving. I still feel the weight of a great loss myself, as if I shall
never be really happy on these shores again.

'I don't think there are any really new words here. There are a
lot of very interesting grammatical details; but I won't bother
you with those, interesting as they are to me – and they seem to
have touched off something in my memory too, so that I now
know more than is actually contained in the fragments. You'll
see a lot of query marks, but I think the context (and often the
grammar) indicates that these are all names or titles.

'*Tar-kalion*, for instance: I think that is a king's name, for I've
often come across the prefix *tar* in names of the great, and *ar* in
the corresponding Adunaic name (on the system I told you
about) is the stem of the word for "king". On the other hand
turkildi and *ēruhīnim*, though evidently equivalent, don't mean
the same thing. The one means, I think, 'lordly men', and the
other is rather more startling, for it appears to be the name of

THE NOTION CLUB PAPERS (PART TWO)   249

God the Omnipotent with a patronymic ending: in fact, unless I am quite wrong, "Children of God". Indeed, I need not have queried the words *ēruvō* and *ilúvatáren*: there can't really be any doubt that *ēruvō* is the sacred name *Ēru* with a suffixed element meaning "from", and that therefore *ilúvatáren* means the same thing.

'There is one point that may interest you, after what we were saying about linguistic coincidence. Well, it seems to me a fair guess that we are dealing with a record, or a legend, of an Atlantis catastrophe.'

'Why *or*?' said Jeremy. 'I mean, it might be a record *and* a legend. You never really tackled the question I propounded at our first meeting this term. If you went back would you find myth dissolving into history or history into myth? Somebody once said, I forget who, that the distinction between history and myth might be meaningless outside the Earth. I think it might at least get a great deal less sharp on the Earth, further back. Perhaps the Atlantis catastrophe was the dividing line?'

'We may be able to deal with your question a great deal better when we've got to the bottom of all this,' said Lowdham. 'In the meantime the point I was going to bring up is worth noting. I said "Atlantis" because Ramer told us that he associated the word Númenor with the Greek name. Well, look! here we learn that Númenor was destroyed; and we end with a lament: *far, far away, now is Atalante*. *Atalante* is plainly another name for Númenor-Atlantis. But only after its downfall. For in Avallonian *atalante* is a word formed normally from a common base *talat* "topple over, slip down": it occurs in Text I in an emphatic verbal form *ataltane* "slid down in ruin", to be precise. *Atalante* means "She that has fallen down". So the two names have approached one another, have reached a very similar shape by quite unconnected routes. At least, I suppose the routes are unconnected. I mean, whatever traditions may lie behind Plato's *Timaeus*,[57] the name that he uses, Atlantis, must be just the same old "daughter of Atlas" that was applied to Calypso. But even that connects the land with a mountain regarded as the pillar of heaven. Minul-Tārik, Minul-Tārik! Very interesting.'

He got up and stretched. 'At least I hope you all think so! But, good lord, how hot and stuffy it is getting! Not an evening for a lecture! But anyway, I can't make much more out of this with only words, and without more words. And I need some pictures.

'I wish I could *see* a little, as well as hear, like you, Ramer. Or

250   SAURON DEFEATED

like Jerry. He's had a few glimpses of strange things, while we worked together; but he can't hear. My words seem to waken his sight, but it's not at all clear yet. Ships with dark sails. Towers on sea-washed shores. Battles: swords that glint, but are silent. A great domed temple.[58] I wish I could see as much. But I've done what I can. *Sauron. Zigūrun, Zigūr.* I can't fathom those names. But the key is there, I think. *Zigūr.*'

'*Zigūr!*' said Jeremy in a strange voice.[59] We stared at him: he was sitting with his eyes closed, and he looked very pale; beads of sweat were on his face.

'I say, what's the matter, Jerry?' cried Frankley. 'Open the other window, Ramer, and let's have some more air! I think there's a storm brewing.'

'*Zigūr!*' cried Jeremy again, in a remote strained voice. 'You spoke of him yourself not long ago, cursing the name. Can you have forgotten him, Nimruzīr?'[60]

'I had forgotten,' Lowdham answered. 'But now I begin to remember!' He stood still and clenched his fists. His brow lowered, and his eyes glittered. There was a glimmer of lightning far away through the darkening window. Away in the west over the roofs the sky was going dead black. There came a distant rumour of thunder.

Jeremy groaned and laid his head back.

Frankley and Ramer went to him, and bent over him; but he did not seem to notice them. 'It's the thunder, perhaps,' said Frankley in a low voice. 'He seemed all right a few minutes ago; but he looks pretty ghastly now.'

'Leave him alone,' growled Dolbear. 'You'll do no good hovering over him.'

'Would you like to lie down on my bed?' said Ramer. 'Or shall I get the car out and run you home?'

'Are you feeling ill, old man?' said Frankley.

'Yes,' groaned Jeremy without moving. 'Deathly. But don't trouble me! Don't touch me! *Bā kitabdahē!*[61] Sit down. I shall speak in a moment.'

There was a silence that seemed long and heavy. It was then nearly ten o'clock, and the pale sky of summer twilight was pricked by a few faint stars; but the blackness crawled slowly onwards from the West. Great wings of shadow stretched out ominously over the town. The curtains stirred as with a presage of wind, and then hung still. There was a long mutter of thunder ending in a crack.

THE NOTION CLUB PAPERS (PART TWO)   251

Lowdham was standing erect in the middle of the floor, looking out of the window with staring eyes. Suddenly:

'*Narīka 'nBāri 'nAdūn yanākhim*,'[62] he shouted, lifting up both his arms. 'The Eagles of the Lords of the West are at hand!'

Then all at once Jeremy began to speak. 'Now I see!' he said. 'I see it all. The ships have set sail at last. Woe to the time! Behold, the mountain smokes and the earth trembles!'

He paused, and we sat staring, oppressed as by the oncoming of doom. The voices of the storm drew nearer. Then Jeremy began again.

'Woe to this time and the fell counsels of Zigūr! The King hath set forth his might against the Lords of the West. The fleets of the Nūmenoreans are like a land of many islands; their masts are like the stems of a forest; their sails are golden and black. Night is coming. They have gone against Avallōni with naked swords. All the world waiteth. Why do the Lords of the West make no sign?'[63]

There was a dazzle of lightning and a deafening crash.

'Behold! Now the black wrath is come upon us out of the West. The Eagles of the Powers of the World have arisen in anger. The Lords have spoken to Ēru, and the fate of the World is changed!'[64]

'Do you not hear the wind coming and the roaring of the sea?' said Lowdham.

'Do you not see the wings of the Eagles, and their eyes like thunderbolts and their claws like forks of fire?' said Jeremy. 'See! The abyss openeth. The sea falls. The mountains lean over. *Urīd yakalubim!*' He got up unsteadily, and Lowdham took his hand, and drew him towards him, as if to protect him. Together they went to the window and stood there peering out, talking to one another in a strange tongue. Irresistibly I was reminded of two people hanging over the side of a ship. But suddenly with a cry they turned away, and knelt down covering their eyes.

'The glory hath fallen into the deep waters,' said Jeremy weeping.

'Still the eagles pursue us,' said Lowdham. 'The wind is like the end of the world, and the waves are like mountains moving. We go into darkness.'[65]

There was a roar of thunder and a blaze of lightning: flashes north, south, and west. Ramer's room flared into a blistering light and rocked back into darkness. The electric light had

252   SAURON DEFEATED

failed. At a distance there was a murmur as of a great wind coming.

'All hath passed away. The light hath gone out!' said Jeremy.

With a vast rush and slash rain came down suddenly like waterfalls out of the sky, and a wind swept the city with wild wings of fury; its shriek rose to a deafening tumult. Near at hand I heard, or I thought I heard, a great weight like a tower falling heavily, clattering to ruin. Before we could close the windows with the strength of all hands present and heave the shutters after them, the curtains were blown across the room and the floor was flooded.

In the midst of all the confusion, while Ramer was trying to find and light a candle, Lowdham went up to Jeremy, who was cowering against the wall, and he took his hands.

'Come, Abrazān!'[66] he said. 'There is work to do. Let us look to our folk and see to our courses, before it is too late!'

'It is too late, Nimruzīr,' said Jeremy. 'The Valar hate us. Only darkness awaits us.'

'A little light may yet lie beyond it. Come!' said Lowdham, and he drew Jeremy to his feet. In the light of the flickering candle that Ramer now held in a shaking hand, we saw him drag Jeremy to the door, and push him out of the room. We heard their feet stumbling and clattering down the stairs.

'They'll be drowned!' said Frankley, taking a few steps, as if to follow them. 'What on earth has come over them?'

'The fear of the Lords of the West,' said Ramer, and his voice shook. 'It is no good trying to follow them. But I think it was their part in this story to escape from the very edge of Doom. Let them escape!'

And there this meeting would have ended, but for the fact that the rest of us could not face the night and dared not go.

For three hours we sat huddled up in dim candle-light, while the greatest storm in the memory of any living man roared over us: the terrible storm of June 12th 1987,[67] that slew more men, felled more trees, and cast down more towers, bridges and other works of Man than a hundred years of wild weather.*

* The centre of its greatest fury seems to have been out in the Atlantic, but its whole course and progress has been something of a puzzle to meteorologists – as far as can be discovered from accounts it seems to have proceeded more like blasts of an explosion, rushing eastward and slowly diminishing in force as it went.   N.G.

THE NOTION CLUB PAPERS (PART TWO)   253

When at last it had abated in the small hours, and through the rags of its wild retreat the sky was already growing pale again in the East, the company parted and crept away, tired and shaken, to wade the flooded streets and discover if their homes and colleges were still standing. Cameron made no remark. I am afraid he had not found the evening entertaining.

I was the last to go. As I stood by the door, I saw Ramer pick up a sheet of paper, closely covered with writing. He put it into a drawer.[68]

'Good night – or good morning!' I said. 'We should be thankful at any rate that we were not struck by lightning, or caught in the ruin of the college.'

'We should indeed!' said Ramer. 'I wonder.'

'What do you wonder?' I said.

'Well, I have an odd feeling, Nick, or suspicion, that we may all have been helping to stir something up. If not out of history, at any rate out of a very powerful world of imagination and memory. Jeremy would say "perhaps out of both". I wonder if we may not find ourselves in other and worse dangers.'

'I don't understand you,' I said. 'But at any rate, I suppose you mean that you wonder whether they ought to go on. Oughtn't we to stop them?'

'Stop Lowdham and Jeremy?' said Ramer. 'We can't do that now.'

MGR. RD. PF. RS. JM. NG.   Added later AAL. WTJ.

Night 68.   June 26th, 1987.

Frankley's rooms. A small attendance: Frankley, Dolbear, Stainer, Guildford.

There is not much to record. Most of the Club, present or absent, were in one way or another involved in examinations, and tired, and more bothered than is usual at this season.*

---

* The extraordinary system of holding the principal examinations of the year in the summer, which must have been responsible for an incalculable amount of misery, was still in force. During the period of 'reforms' in the forties there was talk of altering this arrangement, but it was never carried out, though it was one of the few thoroughly desirable minor reforms proposed at the time. It was the events of the summer of 1987 that finally brought things to a head, as most of the examinations had that year to be transferred to the winter, or held again after the autumn term.   N.G.

254 SAURON DEFEATED

Things had been rather shaken up by the storm. It had come in the seventh week, right in the middle of the final examinations; and amongst a lot of other damage, the Examination Schools had been struck and the East School wrecked.

'What a time we've been having, ever since old Ramer started to attend again!' said Frankley. 'Notion Club! More like the Commotion Club! Is there any news of the Commoters?'

'D'you mean Lowdham and Jeremy?' said Stainer. 'Promoters, I should say! I've never seen anything better staged – and with Michael Ramer, as a kind of conniving chorus. It was wonderfully well done!'

'Wonderfully!' said Dolbear. 'I am lost in admiration. Think of their meteorological information! Superb! Foreseeing like that a storm not foretold, apparently, by any station in the world. And timing it so beautifully, too, to fit in neatly with their prepared parts. It makes you think, doesn't it? – as those say, who have never experienced the process. And Ramer says flatly that he was bowled over, altogether taken by surprise. Whatever you may think of his views, it would be very rash to assume that he was lying. He takes this affair rather seriously. "Those two are probably dangerous," he said to me; and he wasn't thinking merely of spoofing the Club, Stainer.'

'Hm. I spoke too hastily, evidently,' said Stainer, stroking his chin. 'Hm. But what then? If not arranged, it was a very remarkable coincidence.'

'Truly remarkable!' said Dolbear. 'But we'll leave that question open for a bit, I think; coincidence or connexion. They're both pretty difficult to accept; but they're the only choices. Pre-arrangement is impossible – or rather it's a damned sight more improbable, and even more alarming. What about these two fellows, though? Has anything been heard of them?'

'Yes,' said Guildford. 'They're alive, and neither drowned nor blasted. They've written me a joint letter to lay before the Club. This is what they say:

Dear Nick,
    We hope every one is safe and sound. We are. We were cast up far away when the wind fell, but we're dry again at last; so now we're off, more or less in the words of the old song, 'on some jolly little jaunts to the happy, happy haunts where the beer flows wild and free'. In due course (if ever) we'll let our colleges have our addresses.   A.A.L.

THE NOTION CLUB PAPERS (PART TWO)   255

That is the end of Arry's great big fist. Jeremy adds:

> We are researching. More stuff may come through, I think.
> What about a vacation meeting? Just before the racket of
> term. What about Sept. 25th? You can have my rooms. Yrs.
> W.T.J.'

'What about the racket of the vacation!' said Frankley.
'They're damned lucky not to be in the schools[69] this year, or
they'ld have to come back, wherever the wind may have blown
them. Any idea where that was, Nick?'

'No,' said Guildford. 'The postmark is illegible,[70] and there's
no address inside. But what about the proposed meeting? I
suppose most of us will be about again by then.'

September 25th was agreed to. At that moment Michael
Ramer came in. 'We've heard from them!' Frankley cried.
'Nicholas has had a letter. They're all right, and they're off on a
holiday somewhere: no address.'

'Good!' said Ramer. 'Or I hope so. I hope they won't wreck
the British Isles before they've finished.'

'My dear Ramer!' Steiner protested. 'What do you mean?
What can you mean? Dolbear has been preaching the open
mind to my incredulity. He had better talk to you. The other
extreme is just as bad.'

'But I haven't any fixed opinions,' said Ramer. 'I was merely
expressing a doubt, or a wild guess. But actually I am not really
very much afraid of any more explosions now. I fancy that that
force has been spent, for the present, for a long time to come
perhaps.

'But I *am* a little anxious about Arry and Wilfrid themselves.
They may quite well get into some danger. Still we can only wait
and see. Even if we could find them we could do no more. You
can't stop a strong horse with the bit between its teeth. You
certainly could not rein Arry in now, and Wilfrid is evidently
nearly as deeply in it as Arry is.

'In the meantime I have got something to show you. Arry
dropped a leaf of paper in my room that night. I think it is the
leaf of his father's manuscript that he told us about. Well – I've
deciphered it.'

'Good work!' said Guildford. 'I didn't know you were a
cryptographer.'

'I'm not,' Ramer laughed, 'but I have my methods. No, no –
nothing dreamy this time. I just made a lucky shot and landed

256   SAURON DEFEATED

on the mark. I don't know whether Arry had solved it himself
before he dropped it, but I think not; for if he had, he would
have included it in the stuff he showed us. It's quite plain what
held him up: it was too easy. He was looking for something
remote and difficult, while all the time the solution was right on
his own doorstep. He thought it was Nūmenorean, I guess; but
actually it is Old English, Anglo-Saxon, his own stuff!

'The script is, I suppose, Nūmenorean,[71] as Arry thought. But
it has been applied by someone to ancient English. The proper
names, when they're not Old English translations, are in the
same script, but the letters are then quite differently used, and
I shouldn't have been able to read them without the help of
Arry's texts.

'I wonder who had the idea of writing Anglo-Saxon in this
odd way? Old Edwin Lowdham seems at first a likely guess; but
I'm not so sure. The thing is evidently made up of excerpts from
a longish book or chronicle.'

'Well, come on!' cried Frankley. 'How you philologists do
niggle! Let's see it, and tell us what it says!'

'Here it is!' said Ramer, taking three sheets out of his pocket
and handing them to Frankley. 'Pass it round! I've got a copy.
The original is only a small octavo page as you see, written on
both sides in a large hand in this rather beautiful script.

'Now, I said to myself: "If this is in one of Arry's languages, I
can't do anything with it; no one but he can solve it. But he
failed, so probably it isn't. In that case, what language is it most
likely to be, remembering what Arry told us? Anglo-Saxon.
Well, that's not one of my languages, though I know the
elements. So when I'd made a preliminary list of all the separate
letters that I could distinguish, I trotted round to old Professor
Rashbold at Pembroke,[72] though I didn't know him personally.
A grumpy old bear Arry has always called him; but evidently
Arry has never given him the right sort of buns.

'He liked mine. He didn't care tuppence about what the stuff
said, but it amused him to try and solve the puzzle, especially
when he heard that it had defeated Arry. "Oh! Young Lowdham!" he said. "A clever fellow under that pothouse manner.
But too fly-away; always after some butterfly theory. Won't
stick to his texts. Now if *I* had had him as my pupil, I should
have put some stiffening into him." Well, starting out with my
guess that the stuff might be Anglo-Saxon, old Rashbold didn't
take long. I don't know his workings. All he said before I left

THE NOTION CLUB PAPERS (PART TWO)   257

was: "Never seen this script before; but I should say it was a consonantal alphabet, and all these diacritics are vowel-signs. I'll have a look at it." He sent it back to me this morning, with a long commentary on the forms and spellings, which I am not inflicting on you, except his concluding remarks.

'"To sum up: it is in Old English of a strongly Mercian (West-Midland) colour, ninth century I should say.[73] There are no new words, except possibly *to-sprengdon*. There are several words, probably names and not Old English, that I have not succeeded in getting out; but you will excuse me from spending more time on them. My time is not unlimited. Whoever made the thing knew Old English tolerably well, though the style has the air of a translation. If he wanted to forge a bit of Old English, why did not he choose an interesting subject?"

'Well, I solved the names, as I told you; and there you have the text as old Rashbold sent it back, with the names put in. Only as my typewriter has no funny letters I have used *th* for the old thorn-letter. The translation is Rashbold's too.[74]

Hi alle sǽ on weorulde oferliodon, sohton hi nyston hwet; ah ǽfre walde heara heorte westward .... forthon hit swé gefyrn arǽdde se Ælmihtiga thæt hi sceoldan steorfan 7 thás weoruld ofgeofan .... hi ongunnon murcnian .... hit gelomp seothhan thæt se fúla deofles thegn se the Ælfwina folc (Zigūr) nemneth wéox swíthe on middangearde 7 he geáscode Westwearena meht 7 wuldor .... walde héalecran stól habban thonne Earendeles eafera seolf ahte ...... Thá cwóm he, (Tarcalion) se cyning up on middangeardes óran 7 he sende sóna his érendwracan to (Zigūre): heht hine on ofste cuman to thes cyninges manrǽdenne to búganne. 7 he (Zigūr) lytigende ge-éadmedde hine thæt he cwóm, wes thæh inwitful under, fácnes hogde Westfearena théode ..... swé adwalde he fornéan alle tha (Numenor)iscan mid wundrum 7 mid tácnum .... 7 hi gewarhton micelne alh on middan (Arminalēth)[75] there cestre on thǽm héan munte the ǽr unawídlod wes 7 wearth nu to hǽthenum herge, 7 hi thér onsegdon unase[c]gendlic lác on unhálgum weofode ... Swé cwóm déathscua on Westfearena land 7 Godes bearn under sceadu féollon .... Thes ofer feola géra hit gelomp thæt (Tarcalione) wearth ældo onsǽge, thý wearth he hréow on móde 7 thá walde he be (Zigūres) onbryrdingum (Avalloni) mid ferde gefaran. Weron Westfearena scipferde swéswe

258　　　SAURON DEFEATED

unarímedlic égland on there sǽ .... ah tha Westfrégan gebédon hi to thǽm Ælmihtigan 7 be his léafe tosprengdon hi tha eorthan thæt alle sǽ nither gutan on efgrynde, 7 alle tha sceopu forwurdan, forthon seo eorthe togán on middum gársecge .... swearte windas asteogon 7 Ælfwines seofon sceopu eastweard adrǽfdon.

Nu sitte we on elelonde 7 forsittath tha blisse 7 tha eadignesse the iú wes 7 nu sceal eft cuman nǽfre. Ús swíthe onsiteth déathscua. Ús swíthe longath ..... On ærran mélum west leg reht weg, nu earon alle weogas wó. Feor nu is léanes lond. Feor nu is Neowollond[76] thæt geneotherade. Feor nu is Dréames lond thæt gedrorene.

All the seas in the world they sailed, seeking they knew not what; but their hearts were ever westward .... because so had the Almighty ordained it of old that they should die and leave this world .... they began to murmur .... It afterwards came to pass that the foul servant of the devil, whom the people of the ?Ælfwines name (Zigūr), grew mightily in middle-earth, and he learned of the power and glory of the *Westware* (Dwellers in the West) .... desired a higher throne than even the descendant of Earendel possessed ...... Then he, King (Tarcalion) landed on the shores of middle-earth, and at once he sent his messengers to (Zigūr), commanding him to come in haste to do homage to the king; and he (Zigūr) dissembling humbled himself and came, but was filled with secret malice, . purposing treachery against the people of the Westfarers ..... Thus he led astray wellnigh all the (Numenore)ans with signs and wonders .... and they built a great temple in the midst of the town (of Arminalēth) on the high hill which before was undefiled but now became a heathen fane, and they there sacrificed unspeakable offerings on an unholy altar ... Thus came death-shade into the land of the Westfarers and God's children fell under the shadow .... Many years later it came to pass that old age assailed (Tarcalion); wherefore he became gloomy in heart, and at the instigation of (Zigūr) he wished to conquer (Avallōni) with a host. The ship-hosts of the Westfarers were like countless islands in the sea .... But the West-lords prayed to the Almighty, and by his leave split asunder the earth so that all seas should pour down into an abyss and the ships should perish; for the earth gaped open in the midst of the ocean .... black winds arose and drove away Ælfwine's seven ships.

THE NOTION CLUB PAPERS (PART TWO)   259

Now we sit in the land of exile, and dwell cut off from the bliss and the blessedness that once was and shall never come again. The death-shade lies heavy on us; longing is on us . . . . . In former days west lay a straight way, now are all ways crooked. Far now is the land of gift. Far now is the ?prostrate land that is cast down. Far now is the land of Mirth that is fallen.

'Well, old Rashbold may not have found that interesting. But it depends what you're looking for. You people at any rate will find it interesting, I think, after the events of that night. You will notice that the original text is written continuously in bold-stroke hand (I don't doubt that the actual penman was old Edwin), but there are dividing dots at intervals. What we have is really a series of fragmentary extracts, separated, I should guess, by very various intervals of omission, extremely like Arry's snatches of Avallonian and Adunaic. Indeed this stuff corresponds closely to his (which in itself is very interesting): it includes all that he gave us, but gives a good deal more, especially at the beginning. You notice that there is a long gap at the same point as the break between his Text I and II.

'Of course, when old Rashbold said "the style has the air of a translation", he simply meant that the fabricator had not been quite successful in making the stuff sound like natural Anglo-Saxon. I can't judge that. But I daresay he is right, though his implied explanation may be wrong. This probably *is* a translation out of some other language into Anglo-Saxon. But not, I think, by the man who penned the page. He was in a hurry, or like Arry trying to catch the evanescent, and if he had had any time for translation he would have done it into modern English. I can't see any point in the Anglo-Saxon unless what he "saw" was already in it.

'I say "saw". For this stuff looks to me like the work of a man copying out all he had time to see, or all he found still intact and legible in some book.'

'Or all he could get down of some strongly visualized dream,' said Dolbear. 'And even so, I should guess that the hand that penned this stuff was already familiar with the strange script. It's written freely and doesn't look at all like the work of a man trying to copy something quite unknown. On your theory, Ramer, he wouldn't have had time, anyway.'

'Yes, it's a pretty puzzle,' said Frankley. 'But I don't suppose we shall get much forrarder[77] without Arry's help. So we must

260 SAURON DEFEATED

wait in patience till September, and hope for a light beyond the sea of Scripts. I must go. The scripts that are waiting for me are much longer and hardly more legible.'

'And probably more puzzling,' said Stainer. 'Surely there's no great mystery here, in spite of Ramer's attempts to create one. Here we have a specimen of old Edwin Lowdham's queer hobby: the fabrication of mythical texts; and the direct source of all Arry's stuff. He seems to have taken after his father, in more senses than one; though he's probably more inventive linguistically.'

'Really you're unteachable, Stainer,' said Dolbear. 'Why do you always prefer a theory that cannot be true, unless somebody is lying?'

'Who am I accusing of lying?'

'Well, wait until September, and then say what you've just said slowly and carefully to Arry, and you'll soon discover,' said Dolbear. 'If you've forgotten everything he said, I haven't. Good night!'

RD. PF. RS. MGR. NG.

Night 69. Thursday, 25 September, 1987.

There was a large meeting in Jeremy's rooms. Jeremy and Lowdham had reappeared in Oxford only the day before, looking as if they had spent all the vacation examining rather than holidaymaking. There were eight other people present, and Cameron came in late.

After the experiences of June 12th most of the Club felt a trifle apprehensive, and conversation began by being jocular, in consequence. But Lowdham took no part in the jesting; he was unusually quiet.

'Well, Jerry,' said Frankley at last, 'you're the host. Have you arranged any entertainment for us? If not, after so many weeks, I daresay several of us have got things in our pockets.'

'That means that you have at any rate,' said Jeremy. 'Let's have it! We want, or at least I want, some time to tell you about what we've been doing, but there's no hurry.'

'That depends on how long your account of yourselves is going to take,' said Stainer. 'Did you do anything except drink and dawdle about the countryside?'

'We did,' said Lowdham. 'But there's no special reason to suppose that you'ld be interested to hear about it, Stainer.'

THE NOTION CLUB PAPERS (PART TWO)   261

'Well, I'm here, and that indicates at least a faint interest,' said Stainer.

'All right! But if the Club really wants to hear us, then it's in for one or two meetings in which we shall take up all the time. Pip will burst, I can see, if he has to wait so long. Let him let his steam off first. What's it about, Horsey?'

'It'll explain itself, if the Club really wants to hear it,' said Frankley.

'Go on! Let's have it!' we said.

Frankley took a piece of paper out of his pocket and began.[78]

The Death of St. Brendan

At last out of the deep seas he passed,
    and mist rolled on the shore;
under clouded moon the waves were loud,
    as the laden ship him bore   4
to Ireland, back to wood and mire,
    to the tower tall and grey,
where the knell of Cluain-ferta's bell[79]
    tolled in green Galway.   8
Where Shannon down to Lough Derg ran
    under a rainclad sky
Saint Brendan came to his journey's end
    to await his hour to die.   12

'O! tell me, father, for I loved you well,
    if still you have words for me,
of things strange in the remembering
    in the long and lonely sea,   16
of islands by deep spells beguiled
    where dwell the Elven-kind:
in seven long years the road to Heaven
    or the Living Land did you find?'   20

'The things I have seen, the many things,
    have long now faded far;
only three come clear now back to me:
    a Cloud, a Tree, a Star.   24
We sailed for a year and a day and hailed
    no field nor coast of men;
no boat nor bird saw we ever afloat
    for forty days and ten.   28
We saw no sun at set or dawn,
    but a dun cloud lay ahead,

262   SAURON DEFEATED

and a drumming there was like thunder coming
    and a gleam of fiery red.   32

Upreared from sea to cloud then sheer
    a shoreless mountain stood;
its sides were black from the sullen tide
    to the red lining of its hood.   36
No cloak of cloud, no lowering smoke,
    no looming storm of thunder
in the world of men saw I ever unfurled
    like the pall that we passed under.   40
We turned away, and we left astern
    the rumbling and the gloom;
then the smoking cloud asunder broke,
    and we saw that Tower of Doom: 44
on its ashen head was a crown of red,
    where fires flamed and fell.
Tall as a column in High Heaven's hall,
    its feet were deep as Hell;   48
grounded in chasms the waters drowned
    and buried long ago,
it stands, I ween, in forgotten lands
    where the kings of kings lie low.   52

We sailed then on, till the wind had failed,
    and we toiled then with the oar,
and hunger and thirst us sorely wrung,
    and we sang our psalms no more.   56
A land at last with a silver strand
    at the end of strength we found;
the waves were singing in pillared caves
    and pearls lay on the ground;   60
and steep the shores went upward leaping
    to slopes of green and gold,
and a stream out of the rich land teeming
    through a coomb of shadow rolled.   64

Through gates of stone we rowed in haste,
    and passed, and left the sea;
and silence like dew fell in that isle,
    and holy it seemed to be.   68

THE NOTION CLUB PAPERS (PART TWO)   263

As a green cup, deep in a brim of green,
   that with wine the white sun fills
was the land we found, and we saw there stand
   on a laund between the hills   72
a tree more fair than ever I deemed
   might climb in Paradise:
its foot was like a great tower's root,
   it height beyond men's eyes;   76
so wide its branches, the least could hide
   in shade an acre long,
and they rose as steep as mountain-snows
   those boughs so broad and strong;   80
for white as a winter to my sight
   the leaves of that tree were,
they grew more close than swan-wing plumes,
   all long and soft and fair.   84

We deemed then, maybe, as in a dream,
   that time had passed away
and our journey ended; for no return
   we hoped, but there to stay.   88
In the silence of that hollow isle,
   in the stillness, then we sang –
softly us seemed, but the sound aloft
   like a pealing organ rang.   92
Then trembled the tree from crown to stem;
   from the limbs the leaves in air
as white birds fled in wheeling flight,
   and left the branches bare.   96
From the sky came dropping down on high
   a music not of bird,
not voice of man, nor angel's voice;
   but maybe there is a third   100
fair kindred in the world yet lingers
   beyond the foundered land.
Yet steep are the seas and the waters deep
   beyond the White-tree Strand.'   104

'O! stay now, father! There's more to say.
   But two things you have told:
The Tree, the Cloud; but you spoke of three.
   The Star in mind do you hold?'   108

264   SAURON DEFEATED

'The Star? Yes, I saw it, high and far,
   at the parting of the ways,
a light on the edge of the Outer Night[80]
   like silver set ablaze,   112
where the round world plunges steeply down,
   but on the old road goes,
as an unseen bridge that on arches runs
   to coasts than no man knows.'   116

'But men say, father, that ere the end
   you went where none have been.
I would hear you tell me, father dear,
   of the last land you have seen.'   120

'In my mind the Star I still can find,
   and the parting of the seas,
and the breath as sweet and keen as death
   that was borne upon the breeze.   124
But where they bloom those flowers fair,
   in what air or land they grow,
what words beyond the world I heard,
   if you would seek to know,   128
in a boat then, brother, far afloat
   you must labour in the sea,
and find for yourself things out of mind:
   you will learn no more of me.'   132

In Ireland, over wood and mire,
   in the tower tall and grey,
the knell of Cluain-ferta's bell
   was tolling in green Galway.   136
Saint Brendan had come to his life's end
   under a rainclad sky,
and journeyed whence no ship returns,
   and his bones in Ireland lie.   140

When Frankley stopped there was a silence. If he had hoped
for critical comments, adverse or favourable, he got none.

'Very odd indeed! Very odd!' said Lowdham at last. 'Have
you been in touch with our minds on the Ramer-system, Philip?
Anyway, when did you write that, and why?'

'There have been many more minds than yours, Arundel,
working on this theme, as has been pointed out before,' said
Ramer. 'Tell us about it, Philip!'

THE NOTION CLUB PAPERS (PART TWO)   265

'There's nothing much to tell,' said Frankley. 'I woke up about four days ago with the thing largely fixed, and the name Brendan running in my head. The first dozen lines were already made (or were still remembered), and some of the rest was too. The pictures were quite clear for a while. I read the *Navigatio Sancti Brendani*, of course, once upon a time, years ago, as well as that early Anglo-French thing, Benedeit's *Vita*. But I've not looked at them again – though perhaps if I did, I might find them less dull and disappointing than I remember them.'

'I don't think you would,' said Lowdham; 'they're rather dismal. Whatever merits they may have, any glimmer of a perception of what they are talking about is not one of them, trundling the magnificent theme to market like bunches of neatly cut and dried flowers. The Old French thing may be very interesting linguistically, but you won't learn much about the West from that.

'Still that seems to be where you got your Volcano and Tree from. But you've given them a twist that's not in your source. You've put them in a different order, I think, making the Tree further west; and your Volcano is not a hell-smithy, but apparently a last peak of some Atlantis.[81] And the Tree in St. Brendan was covered with white birds that were fallen angels. The one really interesting idea in the whole thing, I thought: they were angels that lived in a kind of limbo, because they were only lesser spirits that followed Satan only as their feudal overlord, and had no real part, by will or design, in the Great Rebellion. But you make them a third *fair* race.'

'And that bit about the "round world" and the "old road",' said Jeremy, 'where did you get that from?'

'I don't know,' said Frankley. 'It came in the writing. I got a fleeting picture, but it's faded now.'

'The Parting of the Ways!' muttered Lowdham. 'What do you know of that?'

'Oh, nothing. But, well – well, but you cannot really find or see Paradise by ship, you know.'[82]

'No,' said Lowdham. 'Not in the High Legends, not in those that have power. No longer. And it was seldom permitted anyway, even before.' He said no more, and we all sat still for a while.

The silence was finally broken by Markison. 'Well,' he said, 'I hope you're not going to take the line of St. Brendan to the

266   SAURON DEFEATED

monk: "you will learn no more of me." Have you two nothing more to say?'

'Yes indeed!' said Jeremy. 'But we've not been to Paradise.'

'Where have you been then?'

'We ended up at Porlock[83] on the 13th, that's last Saturday week,' said Jeremy.

'Why Porlock? Not a very exciting place, is it?'

'Not now, maybe,' Lowdham answered. 'You'll see a sort of reason for it, though. But if you mean: did we wittingly pick on Porlock? the answer is no.'

'We started off down in Cornwall, Land's End,' said Jeremy. 'That was just before the end of June.'

'Started off?' said Guildford. 'I got your letter on June 25th, but that still leaves a bit of a gap. We last saw you on the night of June 12th: not a date we're likely to forget in a hurry. What happened during the next ten days?'

'Was it as long as that?' said Lowdham blankly. 'I don't really know. We landed in a cove. I seem to remember the boat grinding on rocks and then being flung up on the shingles. We were damned lucky. She was holed and sinking, and we ought to have been drowned. Or did I dream it?' He knitted his brows. 'Bless me, if I'm sure. D'you remember, Trewyn?'[84]

'No,' said Jeremy, thinking. 'No, I don't. The first thing I can remember is your saying: "We'd better let Nick have a line to know that we haven't been drowned." Yes, yes of course: we'd been caught at sea in a storm of wind and lightning, and as you all knew we had gone sailing, we thought you might be anxious.'

'Don't you remember the night up in my rooms, the night of the great storm?' said Ramer.

'Yes, I remember bringing some texts round,' said Lowdham. 'And I remember the Eagles. But surely the storm came afterwards, after we had started on our research tour?'

'All right,' said Dolbear. 'Don't bother with all that now; there will be plenty of time to talk about it later. Get on with your own tale.'

'Well,' said Jeremy, 'we stuck to the west coasts as much as we could, staying by the sea, and walking as near to it as possible, when we did not go by boat. Arry is an able seaman, and you can still get small sailing craft in the West, and sometimes an old sailor to help who can still handle a boat

THE NOTION CLUB PAPERS (PART TWO)   267

without petrol. But after our wreck we did not sail again till we got round to North Devon. We actually crossed by boat from Bideford to South Wales in July, and then we went on to Ireland, right up the west coast of it by stages.

'We took a look at Scotland, but no further north than Mull. There seemed nothing for us there, no feel in the air at all. So we went back to Hibernia.[85] The great storm had left more traces there than anywhere, and not only in visible damage. There was a good deal of that, but much less than you would expect, and it did not interest us so much as the effect on the people and the stories that we found going about. People in Galway – well, for the matter of that, from Brandon Hill to Slieve League[86] – seemed to have been pretty well shaken by it, and were still scared for weeks afterwards. If the wind got up at all, as of course it did from time to time, they huddled indoors; and some would begin to trek inland.

'We both heard many tales of the huge waves "high as hills" coming in on the Black Night. And curiously enough, many of the tale-tellers agreed that the greatest waves were like phantoms, or only half real: "like shadows of mountains of dark black wicked water". Some rolled far inland and yet did little damage before, well, disappearing, melting away. We were told of one that had rolled clean over the Aran Isles[87] and passed up Galway Bay, and so on like a cloud, drowning the land in a ghostly flood like rippling mist, almost as far as Clonfert.

'And we came across one old man, a queer old fellow whose English was hardly intelligible, on the road not far from Loughrea.[88] He was wild and ragged, but tall and rather impressive. He kept pointing westward, and saying, as far as we could gather: "It was out of the Sea they came, as they came in the days before the days". He said that he had seen a tall black ship high on the crest of the great wave, with its masts down and the rags of black and yellow sails flapping on the deck, and great tall men standing on the high poop and wailing, like the ghosts they were; and they were borne far inland, and came, well, not a soul knows where they came.

'We could get no more out of him, and he went on westward and vanished into the twilight, and who he was or where he was going we did not discover either. Apart from such tales and rumours we had no real adventures. The weather was not too bad generally, and we walked a lot, and slept pretty well. A good many dreams came, especially in Ireland, but they were

268   SAURON DEFEATED

very slippery; we couldn't catch them. Arry got whole lists of
ghost-words, and I had some fleeting pictures, but they seldom
fitted together. And then, when we thought our time was up, we
came to Porlock.

'As we crossed over the Severn Sea[89] earlier in the summer,
Arry had looked back, along the coast to the south, at the shores
of Somerset, and he had said something that I couldn't catch.
It was ancient English, I think, but he didn't know himself: it
faded from him almost as soon as he had spoken. But I had a
sudden feeling that there was something important waiting for
us there, and I made up my mind to take him back that way
before the end of our journey, if there was time. So I did.

'We arrived in a small boat at Porlock Weir on Saturday,
September 13th. We put up at The Ship, up in Porlock itself; but
we felt drawn back shorewards, and as soon as we had fixed our
rooms we went out and turned westward, going up onto the
cliffs and along as far as Culbone and beyond. We saw the sun
set, dull, hazy, and rather grim, about half past six, and then we
turned back for supper.

'The twilight deepened quickly, and I remember that it
seemed suddenly to grow very chilly; a cold wind sprang up
from the land and blew out westward towards the dying sun;
the sea was leaden. We both felt tired and anxious, for no clear
reason: we had been feeling rather cheery. It was then that Arry
turned away from the sea and took my arm, and he said quite
clearly, and I heard him and understood him: *Uton efstan nú,
Tréowine! Me ofthyncth thisses windes. Mycel wén is Deniscra
manna to niht.*[90] And that seemed to break my dreams. I began
to remember, and piece together a whole lot of things as we
walked back to the town; and that night I had a long series of
dreams and remembered a good deal of them.'

'Yes,' said Lowdham, 'and something happened to me at that
moment, too. I began to *see* as well as to hear. Tréowine, that is
Wilfrid Trewyn Jeremy, and I seemed to have got into the same
dream together, even before we were asleep. The faces in the
hotel looked pale and thin, and the walls and furniture only half
real: other things and faces were vaguely moving behind them
all. We were approaching the climax of some change that had
begun last May, when we started to research together.

'Anyway, we went to bed, and we both dreamed; and we
woke up and immediately compared notes; and we slept again
and woke and did the same. And so it went on for several days,

THE NOTION CLUB PAPERS (PART TWO) 269

until we were quite exhausted. So at last we decided to go home; we made up our minds to come back to Oxford the next day, Thursday. That night, Wednesday, September 17th, something happened: the dreams coalesced, took shape, and came into the open, as you might say. It seemed impossible to believe when it was over that years had not slipped by, and that it was still Thursday, September 18th, 1987, and we could actually return here as we had planned. I remember staring incredulously round the dining-room, that seemed to have grown strangely solid again, half wondering if it was not some new dream-trick. And we went into the post-office and a bank to make sure of the date! Then we crept back here secretly, a week ago, and stayed in retreat until yesterday, conferring and putting together all we had got before we came out of hiding. I think I'll leave Trewyn to do the telling. He's better at it than I am; and he saw more, after the earlier scenes.'

'No!' said Jeremy. 'Alwin had better begin. The earlier part is his, more than mine. He remembers more of what was said by me than I do myself. Go on now, Arry!'

'Well', said Lowdham, 'it seemed to me like this. I woke with a start.[91] Evidently I had been dozing on a bench near the fire. The voices seemed to pour over me like a stream. I felt that I had been dreaming, something very odd and vivid, but I could not catch it; and for a minute or two the familiar scene in the hall seemed strange, and the English speech about me sounded alien and remote, although the voices were for the most part using the soft speech of western Wessex that I knew so well. Here and there I caught the tones of the Marchers from up beyond Severnmouth; and I heard a few speaking queerly, using uncouth words after the manner of those from the eastern shires.

'I looked down the hall, hoping to see my friend Tréowine Céolwulf's son. There was a great crowd in hall, for King Éadweard was there. The Danish ships were in the Severn Sea, and all the south shores were in arms. The heathen earls had been defeated away up in the west marches at Archenfield, but the pirates were still at large off the Welsh coast, trying to get food and supplies, and the Devenish men and Somersets[92] were on guard. There had been a bitter affray at Watchet a few nights before, but the Danish men had been driven off. Porlock's turn might come.

'I looked round at the faces of the men: some old and worn,

270   SAURON DEFEATED

some still young and keen; but they seemed dim, almost dreamlike in the wavering torches. The candles on the high table were guttering. A wind was blowing outside the great wooden hall, surging round the house; the timbers creaked. I felt tired. Not only because Tréowine and I had had a long spell of coastguard duty, and had had little sleep since the raid on Watchet; but I was tired of this woeful and dishevelled world, slipping slowly back into decay, as it seemed to me, with its petty but cruel wars, and all the ruin of the good and fair things there had been in my grandsires' days. The hangings on the wall behind the dais were faded and worn, and on the table there were but few vessels or candlesticks of gold and silver smithcraft that had survived the pillage of the heathen.

'The sound of the wind disturbed me and brought back to me old longings that I thought I had buried. I found myself thinking of my father, old Éadwine Óswine's son,[93] and the strange tales he had told me when I was a small lad and he a grizzled seaman of more than fifty winters: tales of the west coasts, and far islands, and of the deep sea, and of a land there was far away, where there was peace and fruitfulness among a fair folk that did not wither.

'But Éadwine had taken his ship, Éarendel, out into the deep sea long ago, and he never returned. What haven received him no man under heaven could tell. That was in the black winter, when Alfred went into hiding[94] and so many men of Somerset fled over sea. My mother fled to her kindred among the West Welsh[95] for a while, and I had seen only nine winters in this world, for I was born just before the holy Éadmund was done to death by the heathen.[96] I learned the Welsh tongue and much craft upon the wild waters, before I came back in full manhood to Somerset and the service of the good king in his last wars.[97]

'I had been in Íraland more than once; and wherever I went I sought tales of the Great Sea and what lay out upon it, or beyond, if haply it had any further shore. Folk had not much to tell for certain; but there was talk of one Maelduin[98] who had sailed to new lands, and of the holy Brendan and others. And some there were who said that there had been a land of Men away west in long days of yore, but that it had been cast down and those that escaped had come to Ériu[99] (so they called Íraland) in their ships, and their descendants lived on there, and in other lands about the shores of Gársecg. But they dwindled and forgot, and nought now was left of them but a wild strain in

THE NOTION CLUB PAPERS (PART TWO)   271

the blood of men of the West. "And you will know those that have it by the sea-longing that is on them," they said; "and it is many that it draws out west to their death or to come never back among living men".

'And I thought that maybe the blood of such men ran in my father's veins and my own, for our kin had long been settled at Glastonbury, where there was rumour of strange comers out of the sea in days of old. And the sound of the winds and seas on the west beaches was ever a restless music to me, at once a pain and a desire; and the pain was keener in Spring, and the desire stronger in Autumn. And now it was Autumn, and the desire was scarcely to be borne; for I was growing old. And the seas were wide. So I mused, forgetting once again where I was, but not sleeping.

'I heard the crash of waves on the black cliffs, and sea-birds wailing; snow fell. Then the sea opened before me, pale and boundless. And now the sun shone above me, and the land and the sound of it and the smell of it fell far behind. Tréowine was beside me, and we were alone, going west. And the sun came down and sank towards the sea before us, and still we sailed west, on towards the setting sun, and the longing in my heart drew me on against my fear and land-bound will. And so I passed into night in the midst of the deep waters, and I thought that a sweet fragrance was borne on the air.

'And suddenly I was brought back to Porlock and the hall of the king's thegn Odda. Men were calling out for a minstrel, and a minstrel I was, when the mood was on me. The king himself, stern Éadweard Alfred's son – tired before old age he looked – sent to me, bidding me sing or speak. He was a stern man, as I say, but like his father in having an ear, when he had the time, for the sound of the old measures. I rose and walked to the steps of the dais, and bowed.

'"*Westu hál, Ælfwine!*" said the king. "*Sing me nú hwæt-wegu: sum eald léoth, gif thu wilt.*"

'"*Ic can lýt on léothcræft, hláford,*" I said; "*ac this geworht'ic unfyrn thé to weorthmynde.*"

'And then I began, and let my voice roll out; but my mouth did not speak the words that I had purposed: of all that I had so carefully devised against the event, in the night watches or pacing on the cold cliffs, not a stave came out.

Hwæt! Éadweard cyning Ælfredes sunu
beorna béaggifa on Brytenríce

272   SAURON DEFEATED

> *æt Ircenfelda*[100] *ealdorlangne tír*
> *geslóg æt sæcce sweorda ecgum**

and all the rest, of such sort as kings look for: not a word of it.
Instead I said this:[101]

> *Monath módes lust mid mereflóde*
> *forth tó féran, thæt ic feor heonan*
> *ofer gársecges grimme holmas*
> *Ælfwina eard út geséce.*
> *Nis me tó hearpan hyge ne tó hringthege,*
> *ne tó wife wynn, ne tó worulde hyht,*
> *ne ymb ówiht elles, nefne ymb ýtha gewealc.*

Then I stopped suddenly, and stood confused. There was some
laughter, from those not under the king's eye, and a few
mocking calls. There were many folk in hall who knew me well,
and they had long been pleased to make a jest of my talk of the
Great Sea; and it now pleased them to pretend that I had spoken
of *Ælfwines eard*, as if I had a realm of my own out westward.

' "If England is not good enough, let him go find a better
land!" they cried. "He need go no further than Íraland, if he
longs for elves and uncouth wights, God save him! Or he can go
with the heathen to the Land of Ice that they say they have
found."

' "If he has no mind to sing for the raising of our hearts, let us
find a *scop* who will."

' "We have had enough of the sea," shouted one of the
Marchers. "A spell of Dane-hunting round the rim of Wales
would cure him."

'But the king sat gravely and did not smile, and many besides
were silent. I could see in his eyes that the words had touched
him, though I doubt not, he had heard others like them often
before.

' "Peace!" said old Odda of Portloca, master of the hall.
"Ælfwine here has sailed more seas than you have heard of, and

---

* Lowdham provides the following translations 'for Philip's benefit'.

'Greetings, Ælfwine,' said the king. 'Recite me something, some old
poem if you like.' 'I have little skill in poetry, my lord,' I said, 'but I
composed this in your honour a little while ago.'

'Lo! Éadweard the king, Alfred's scion, brave men's patron, in
Britain's island at Archenfield undying fame in battle reaped him with
reddened blades.'

For the translation of the next verses see Night 66, p. 244. N.G.

THE NOTION CLUB PAPERS (PART TWO)   273

the lands of the Welsh and Irish are not strange to him. With the king's leave let him say what his mood bids him. It is no harm to turn from these sorry shores for a while and speak of marvels and strange lands, as the old verse-makers often did. Will you not speak us something by the elder poets, Ælfwine?"

' "Not now, lord," I said; for I was abashed and weary, and I felt as a man in a dream who finds himself unclad in the market-place. "There are others in hall. Men of the Marches I hear by their speech; and they were used to boast of their songcraft, before the Danes came. With the king's leave I will sit."

'At that a man from among the Marchers leapt to his feet and got leave to speak; and lo! I saw it was my friend Tréowine. A small dark man he was, but he had a good voice, if a strange way with his words. His father Céolwulf, I had heard, claimed to come of the kin of the kings that sat at Tamworth[102] of old; but Tréowine had come south many years before. Ere I had found a seat, he had a foot on the step and had begun.

'His verse was in the old style, indeed it was the work of some old poet, maybe, though I had not heard it before, and many words were dark to us of later times; but he gave them out strong and true, now loud, now soft, as the theme asked, without help of harp. Thus he began, and soon all the hall was stone-still:

> *Hwæt! wé on geárdagum of Gársecge*
> *fyrn gefrugnon of feorwegum*
> *to Longbeardna londgemærum*
> *tha hí ær héoldon, íglond micel*
> *on North-théodum, nacan bundenne*
> *scírtimbredne scríthan gangan ...*

'But if it was dark to some of our younger men of Wessex, it will be as night to you, who have passed so much further down the streams of time, since the old poets sang in Angel of the grey North-seas; so I have cast it into the speech of your age. And I have done so, for by chance, or more than chance, this song had a part in what befell after, and its theme was knit up with my own thoughts, and it whetted my longing the more.

King Sheave[103]

In days of yore out of deep Ocean to the Longobards, in the land dwelling that of old they held in the isles of the North, a ship came sailing, shining-timbered, without oar or mast,

274   SAURON DEFEATED

eastward floating. The sun behind it sinking westward with flame kindled the fallow water. Wind was wakened. Over the world's margin clouds grey-helméd climbed slowly up, wings unfolding wide and looming, as mighty eagles moving onward to eastern Earth, omens bearing.

Men there marvelled, in the mist standing of the dark islands in the deeps of time: laughter they knew not, light nor wisdom; shadow was upon them, and sheer mountains stalked behind them, stern and lifeless, evil-haunted. The East was dark.

The ship came shining to the shore driven, and strode upon the strand, till its stern rested on sand and shingle. The sun went down. The clouds overcame the cold heavens. In fear and wonder to the fallow water sad-hearted men swiftly hastened, to the broken beaches, the boat seeking gleaming-timbered in the grey twilight. They looked within, and there laid sleeping a boy they saw breathing softly: his face was fair, his form lovely; his limbs were white, his locks raven golden-braided. Gilt and carven with wondrous work was the wood about him. In golden vessel gleaming water stood beside him; strung with silver a harp of gold beneath his hand rested; his sleeping head was softly pillowed on a sheaf of corn shimmering palely, as the fallow gold doth from far countries west of Angol. Wonder filled them.

The boat they hauled, and on the beach moored it high above the breakers, then with hands lifted from the bosom its burden. The boy slumbered. On his bed they bore him to their bleak dwellings, dark-walled and drear, in a dim region between waste and sea. There of wood builded high above the houses was a hall standing, forlorn and empty. Long had it stood so, no noise knowing, night nor morning, no light seeing. They laid him there, under lock left him lonely sleeping in the hollow darkness. They held the doors. Night wore away. New awakened, as ever on earth, early morning; day came dimly. Doors were opened. Men strode within, then amazed halted; fear and wonder filled the watchmen. The house was bare, hall deserted; no form found they on the floor lying, but by bed forsaken the bright vessel dry and empty in the dust standing. The guest was gone.

Grief o'ercame them. In sorrow they sought him, till the sun rising over the hills of heaven to the homes of men light came bearing. They looked upward, and high upon a hill hoar and treeless gold was glimmering. Their guest stood there with head

THE NOTION CLUB PAPERS (PART TWO)   275

uplifted, hair unbraided; harpstrings they heard in his hand ringing, at his feet they saw the fallow-golden corn-sheaf lying. Then clear his voice a song began, sweet, unearthly, words in music woven strangely in a tongue unknown. Trees stood silent, and men unmoving marvelling harkened.

Middle-earth had known for many ages neither song nor singer; no sight so fair had eyes of mortal, since the earth was young, seen when waking in that sad country long forsaken. No lord they had, no king, nor counsel, but the cold terror that dwelt in the desert, the dark shadow that haunted the hills and the hoar forest: Dread was their master. Dark and silent, long years forlorn lonely waited the hall of kings, house forsaken without fire or food.

Forth men hastened from their dim houses. Doors were opened, and gates unbarred. Gladness wakened. To the hill they thronged, and their heads lifting on their guest they gazed. Grey-bearded men bowed before him and blessed his coming their years to heal; youths and maidens, wives and children, welcome gave him. His song ended. Silent standing he looked upon them. Lord they called him; king they made him, crowned with golden wheaten garland: white his raiment, his harp his sceptre. In his house was fire, food and wisdom: there fear came not. To manhood he grew, might and glory.

Sheave they called him, whom the ship brought them, a name renowned in the North-countries ever since in song; but a secret hidden his true name was in tongue unknown of a far country, where the falling seas wash western shores, beyond the ways of men since the world worsened. The word is forgotten and the name perished.

Their need he healed, and laws renewed long forsaken. Words he taught them wise and lovely: their tongue ripened in the time of Sheave to song and music. Secrets he opened, runes revealing. Riches he gave them, reward of labour, wealth and comfort from the earth calling, acres ploughing, sowing in season seed of plenty, hoarding in garner golden harvest for the help of men. The hoar forest in his days drew back to the dark mountains; the shadow lifted, and shining corn, white ears of wheat, whispered in the breezes where waste had been. The woods blossomed.

Halls and houses hewn of timber, strong towers of stone steep and lofty, golden-gabled, in his guarded city they raised and roofed. In his royal dwelling of wood well-carven the walls were

276   SAURON DEFEATED

wrought; fair-hued figures filled with silver, gold, and scarlet, gleaming hung there, stories boding of strange countries, were one wise in wit the woven legends to thread with thought. At his throne men found counsel and comfort and care's healing, justice in judgement. Generous-handed his gifts he gave. Glory was uplifted. Far sprang his fame over fallow water; through Northern lands the renown echoed of the shining king, Sheave the mighty.

'When he ended there was loud applause – loudest from those who understood least, so that men should perceive how well they could thread the old songs; and they passed a horn to Tréowine's hand. But ere he drank, I rose up, and there where I stood I finished his song for him:

Seven sons he begat, sire[104] of princes, men great of mood, mighty-handed and high-hearted. From his house cometh the seed of kings, as songs tells us, fathers of the fathers, who before the change in the Elder Years the earth governed, Northern kingdoms named and founded, shields of their people: Sheave begat them: Sea-danes and Goths, Swedes and Northmen, Franks and Frisians, folk of the islands, Swordmen and Saxons, Swabians, Angles, and the Longobards, who long ago beyond Mircwudu a mighty realm and wealth won them in the Welsh countries, where Ælfwine, Éadwine's son in Italy was king. All that has passed!

'And with that, while men still stared – for there were many that knew my name and my father's – I beckoned to Tréowine, and we strode from the hall into the darkness and the wind.

'And there I think I must end for tonight,' said Lowdham, with a sudden change of tone and voice that startled us: we jumped like men waked suddenly from a dream. It seemed as if one man had vanished and another had sprung up in his place, so vividly had he presented Ælfwine to us as he spoke. Quite plainly I had seen him standing there, a man very like Arry but not the same – rather taller and less thick, and looking older and greyer, though by his account he was just Arry's age it seemed; I had seen the glittering of his eyes as he looked round and strode out. The hall and the faces I saw in a blur behind him, and Tréowine was only a dim shadow against the flicker of far candles as he spoke of King Sheave; but I heard the wind rushing above all the words.

THE NOTION CLUB PAPERS (PART TWO) 277

'Next meeting Tréowine and I will go on again, if you want any more of this,' said Lowdham. 'Ælfwine's tale is nearly done; and after that we shall flit more quickly, for we shall pass further and further from what Stainer would call History — in which old Ælfwine really walked, at least for the most part, I guess.

'If you haven't got a horn, fill me a mug! For I have done both Ælfwine's part and Tréowine's, and it is thirsty work, a minstrel's.'

Markison handed him a pewter tankard full. '*Béo thu blíthe æt thisse béorthege!*'[105] he said, for ancient English is only one of the innumerable things he knows.

Lowdham drained the tankard at a draught. And so ended the sixty-ninth night of the Notion Club. It was agreed to meet again in only one week's time, on October 2nd, lest the onset of term should hinder the further tales of Ælfwine and Tréowine.

WTJ. AAL MGR. RD. PF. RS. JM. JJR. NG.

Night 70.   Thursday, 2 October, 1987.

Here the typescript text ends, not at the foot of a page; and here the manuscript ends also, without the date-heading for the next meeting. It is certain that my father wrote nothing further. There are, however, two brief texts, written very fast in pencil but fortunately just about legible, which give a glimpse of what he had in mind. Though both obviously belong to the same time, it is not clear which preceded the other; the one that I give first was written on the back of a draft for the passage in E beginning 'It was then that Arry turned away from the sea' (p. 268).

The Danes attack Porlock that night. They are driven off and take refuge by swimming out to the ships and so to 'Broad Relic'.[106] A small 'cnearr'[107] is captured.

It is not well guarded. Ælfwine tells Tréowine that he has stores laid up. They move the boat and stock it the following night and set sail West.

The wind is from the East, and they sail on and on, and come to no land; they are exhausted, and a dreamlike death seems to be coming over them. They smell [? the] fragrance. *Swéte is blóstma bræþ begeondan sæ*[108] says Ælfwine, and struggles to rise. But the wind changes: great clouds come out of the West. 'Behold the Eagles of the Lords of the West coming over Númenor' said Ælfwine, and fell back as one dead.

278 SAURON DEFEATED

Tréowine sees the round world [?curve] below, and straight ahead a shining land, before the wind seizes them and drives them away. In the gathering dark [or dusk] he sees a bright star, shining in a rent in the cloud in the West. *Éalá Éarendel engla beorhtast.* Then he remembers no more.

'Whether what follows is my direct dream,' said Jeremy, 'or · the dreams of Tréowine and Ælfwine in the deeps of the sea I cannot say.'

I woke to find myself

Here this sketch tantalisingly breaks off. On the same page and fairly certainly written at the same time stands this note:

The theory is that the sight and memory goes on with *descendants* of Elendil and Voronwë (= Tréowine) but *not* reincarnation; they are different people even if they still resemble one another in some ways even after a lapse of many generations.

The second sketch is at first fuller (and may for that reason be thought to have followed the other), but then passes into an outline of headings and brief statements.

Danes attack that night but are driven off. Ælfwine and Tréowine are among those who capture a small ship that had ventured close inshore and stuck. The rest escape to 'Broad Relic'.

It is grey dawn ere all is over. 'Going to rest?' said Tréowine to Ælfwine. 'Yes, I hope so,' said Ælfwine, 'but not in this land, Tréowine! I am going – to seek a land, whence King Sheaf came, maybe; or to find Death, if that be not the name for the same place.'

'What do you mean?'

'I am sailing,' said Ælfwine. 'The wind blows westward. And here's a ship that knows the sea. The king himself has given it to me. I have handled many such before. Will you come? Two could make shift to sail her.'

'We should need more; and what of water and victual?'

'I have all prepared,' said Ælfwine, 'for this venture has long been brewing in my mind, and now at last chance and desire are matched. There is provision down in my house by the weir, and we'll find a couple of lusty men of Somerset whom I know. They'll go as far as Ireland at the least, and then we'll see.'

THE NOTION CLUB PAPERS (PART TWO)   279

'Yes, you'll find madmen enough there,' said Tréowine, 'but I'll go with you so far at the least.'

When it was dark on the following night Ælfwine brought along Ceola (of Somerset) and Geraint (of West Wales) and we stowed her, and thrust her off. The east wind freshened, and we set sail and drove out into the dark waters. There's no need to make long tale of it: we bent our course past the horns of Pembrokeshire and so out to sea. And then we had a change of weather, for a wild wind from the South-west drove us back and northward, and we hardly made haven upon a long firth in the South-west of Ireland. I'd never been there before, for I was younger than Ælfwine. We sat out the storm there, and got fresh supplies, and then Ælfwine spoke of his desire to Ceola and Geraint.

———

Tréowine sees the straight road and the world plunging down. Ælfwine's vessel seems to be taking the straight road and falls [*sic*] in a swoon of fear and exhaustion.

Ælfwine gets view of the Book of Stories; and writes down what he can remember.

Later fleeting visions.

Beleriand tale.

Sojourn in Númenor before and during the fall ends with *Elendil* and *Voronwë* fleeing on a hill of water into the dark with Eagles and lightning pursuing them. Elendil has a book which he has written.

His descendants get glimpses of it.

Ælfwine has one.

On the same slip of paper and written at the same time as this second text is a note saying that Edwin Lowdham's page 'should be in Anglo-Saxon *straight*, without some scraps of Númenórean', and that 'the Anglo-Saxon should *not* be written in Númenórean script'. Finally there stands this last note: 'At end Lowdham and Jeremy can revisualize some more fragments, but it is hardly needed, as Lowdham and Jeremy have a vivid dream of the Fall of Númenor.'

From the beginning of this history, the story of the Englishman Ælfwine, called also Eriol, who links by his strange voyage the vanished world of the Elves with the lives of later men, has constantly appeared. So in the last words of the *Quenta Noldorinwa* (IV.165) it is said:

To Men of the race of Eärendel have they [*the tales of the Quenta*] at times been told, and most to Eriol, who alone of the mortals of

280   SAURON DEFEATED

later days, and yet now long ago, sailed to the Lonely Isle, and came
back to the land of Leithien [*Britain*] where he lived, and remembered things that he had heard in fair Cortirion, the city of the Elves
in Tol Eressëa.

He is seen in Tavrobel of Tol Eressëa translating *The Annals of
Valinor* and *The Annals of Beleriand* from the work of Pengolod the
Wise of Gondolin, and parts of his Anglo-Saxon text are preserved
(IV.263, 281 ff.); the *Ainulindalë* was spoken to him by Rúmil of Tûn
(V.156); the *Lhammas* of Pengolod was seen by Ælfwine 'when he
came into the West' (V.167). To the *Quenta Silmarillion* his note is
appended (V.203): 'The work of Pengolod I learned much by heart,
and turned into my tongue, some during my sojourn in the West, but
most after my return to Britain'; after which follow the lines of
Ælfwine Wídlást that Arundel Lowdham heard, as Alboin Errol had
heard them: *Fela bið on Westwegum werum uncuðra, wundra ond
wihta, wlitescyne lond ...*
Crossing this theme, and going back to one form of the old story
Ælfwine of England (II.322 and note 42), was the story that Ælfwine
never set foot on the Lonely Isle. So in my father's sketches for those
further reaches of *The Lost Road* that he never wrote, Ælfwine on the
one hand (V.78) awakes on the beach of the Lonely Isle 'to find the
ship being drawn by people walking in the water', and there in Eressëa
he 'is told the Lost Tales'; but in other notes of that time (V.80), after
'the vision of Eressëa', the 'west wind blows them back', and they
come to shore in Ireland. In the note to the final version of the poem
The Song of Ælfwine (a version which I suggested was 'probably from
the years after *The Lord of the Rings*, though it might be associated
with the *Notion Club Papers* of 1945', V.100) it is told (V.103):

Ælfwine (Elf-friend) was a seaman of England of old who, being
driven out to sea from the coast of Erin, passed into the deep waters
of the West, and according to legend by some strange chance or
grace found the 'straight road' of the Elvenfolk and came at last to
the Isle of Eressëa in Elvenhome. Or maybe, as some say, alone in
the waters, hungry and athirst, he fell into a trance and was granted
a vision of that isle as it once had been, ere a West-wind arose and
drove him back to Middle-earth.

In the first of the sketches just given Ælfwine and Tréowine are in
sight of the 'shining land' when the wind drives them away; but in the
second my father once more sees Ælfwine in the Lonely Isle looking at
'the Book of Stories'. But the whole conception has now developed a
disturbing complexity: the Downfall of Númenor, the Straight Road
into the West, the ancient histories in unknown language and unknown script preserved in Eressëa, the mysterious voyage of Edwin
Lowdham in his ship *The Éarendel* and the single preserved page of his

THE NOTION CLUB PAPERS (PART TWO)   281

book in Anglo-Saxon, the 're-emergence' in his son Arundel (Éarendel) and his friend Wilfrid Trewin Jeremy of 'the sight and memory' of their forebears in distant ages communicated in dreams, and the violent irruption of the Númenórean legend into the late twentieth century – all framed within an elaborate foreseeing of the future (not without comic and ironic elements).

There is a slip of paper on which my father sketched out very rapidly ideas for what would become 'Part Two' of *The Notion Club Papers*; this was undoubtedly written before he began the writing of the manuscript E, but it is most conveniently given here.

Do the Atlantis story and abandon Eriol-Saga, with Loudham, Jeremy, Guildford and Ramer taking part.

After night 62.[109] Loudham, walking home with Guildford and Ramer, apologizes for appearing to scoff. They halt in Radcliffe Square and Loudham looks up at the Camera. It is starry, but a black cloud is coming up out of the West [*changed at once to* (but) caught like smoke in the moon a wisp of cloud seemed to be issuing from the lantern of the dome]. Loudham halts and looks up, passing [his] hand over his forehead. 'I was going to say,' he says, 'that – I don't know. I wonder.' He hopped into college and said no more.

Night 65. Truncated. It begins after lacuna. Conversation had been about myths, but Loudham had been restless, walking about twisting his handkerchief and making some unsuccessful jests.

Suddenly he went to the window. It was a summer night and he looked out, then spoke in a loud solemn voice. 'Behold the Eagles of the Lords of the West coming over Númenor.' We were startled. Some of us went and looked out. A great cloud was eating up the stars, spreading two vast dark wings south and north.

Loudham drew away. They discuss Númenor? Loudham's ancestry?

The words with which this sketch begins, 'Do the Atlantis story and abandon Eriol-Saga ...', are remarkable. In the first place, they seem to support the analysis of the way in which *The Notion Club Papers* developed that I have suggested at various points, and which I will state here in a more coherent form.

'Part One' of the *Papers* (not at this time conceived to be so) had reached the stage of the completed manuscript B (see p. 147 and note 4), and at this stage Harry Loudham was not seen as contributing greatly to the discussions of the Notion Club: a maker of jokes and

282   SAURON DEFEATED

interjections. Above all, he had no especial interest in the question of Atlantis or in names from unknown worlds. Examples of this have been pointed out in the notes to Part One.[110]

Only when the manuscript B was completed (and the text of 'Part One' of the *Papers* very largely achieved) did the thought enter: 'Do the Atlantis story.' With Loudham's standing beneath the Radcliffe Camera and staring up at the sky the whole course of the *Papers* was changed. Adjustments and additions were subsequently made to 'Part One', hinting at his peculiar 'affinity' with the legend of the downfall of the island empire, and changing the nature of his interests: for whereas in B Guildford could say of him (p. 214 note 23): 'Memoirs of the courts of minor 18th century monarchs are his natural browsing-ground', in the list of members of the Club given on p. 151 (made when B had been completed)[111] he has 'special interests in Icelandic and Anglo-Saxon'. And as the writing of 'Part Two' in the manuscript E proceeded he ceased to be Harry and became Arry, for Arundel (Éarendel).

But when my father wrote 'Do the Atlantis story' he also said that the 'Eriol-Saga' should be abandoned, although there is no mention of any such matter in the text of 'Part One'. The only explanation that I can see is that the 'Eriol-Saga' had been, up to this time, what my father had in mind for the further course of the meetings of the Notion Club, but was now rejecting in favour of 'Atlantis'.

In the event he did not do so; he found himself drawn back into the ideas that he had sketched for *The Lost Road* (see V.77–8), but now in a conception so intricate that one need perhaps look no further for an answer to the question, why were *The Notion Club Papers* abandoned?

NOTES

1   Pencilled at the head of the first page of the sole manuscript ('E') of 'Part Two' is 'The Strange [Investigation >] Case of Arundel Loudham', and the same title together with the number '[Part] II' is found on a separate title-page that seems to belong with E (p. 153 note 2). The second text of this Part, the typescript 'F', while distinct from the typescript D of Part One and with a separate pagination, has no title or heading before 'Night 62'.
    — *Loudham* is spelt thus in E at first, but becomes *Lowdham* in the course of the writing of the manuscript (p. 153 note 4).
2   In E there is no Night 62: see p. 195 (Guildford's footnote) and note 47.

THE NOTION CLUB PAPERS (PART TWO)   283

3 In E there is no head-note to Night 63 except the word 'defective', and thus no reference to 'the *imrám*'. In the final text, the typescript F, the number of the night to which the mention of the *imrám* is referred was left blank; I have added '69', since on that night Frankley read his poem on Saint Brendan (pp. 261 ff.). — The bracketed opening word 'Good', supposed to be absent in the original, was added by the editor.

4 *the High:* High Street; *Radcliffe Square*, see p. 222 note 69.

5 For 'especially about the *imrám*' E has 'especially about the Enkeladim', changed soon to 'the Imrám'. For references to the *Enkeladim (En-keladim)* in Part One see pp. 199, 206–7, 221 note 65; and for the *imrama* (tales of seavoyaging) see V.81–2.

6 *Nordics:* E has 'philologists' (but Ramer himself was a philologist).

7 *B.N.C.:* the common abbreviation of Brasenose College, whose gate is in Radcliffe Square. The 'lane' along which Ramer and Guildford walked after Lowdham had left them is Brasenose Lane, leading from Radcliffe Square to Turl Street (p. 213 note 18). — For *The Camera* in the following sentence see p. 222 note 69.

8 On the inclusion of Night 64 see the Editor's Foreword, p. 156.

9 In E as originally written the entire opening of Night 65 had been lost, and the text only takes up with '[Jeremy] ... "as you said. ..." ' — which is where in F the text takes up again after the loss of a page in the middle of the record of the meeting (p. 227). Thus in E the conversation concerning neologisms was at first lacking; it was added in to the manuscript subsequently.

10 In E it was Dolbear, not Ramer, who objected thus to Lowdham's remark. *Arry* (for *Harry*) entered in the course of the writing of E; see p. 213 note 16.

11 *N.E.D.: A New English Dictionary*, the actual title of the *Oxford English Dictionary* or *O.E.D.*

12 The expression *the Six Years' War* is used in the Foreword and several times in the text. In E my father called it here *the Second German War*.

13 *Vita Fera:* literally 'savage life' (*ferus* 'wild, untamed, savage, fierce').

14 Cf. p. 174: Frankley, according to Guildford, 'regards knowledge of his own language at any period before the Battle of Bosworth as a misdemeanour'.

15 *Norman Keeps* was an historical person, who expounded to my father the view of English history here recounted by Philip Frankley while plying his trade at the barbering establishment of Weston and Cheal in the Turl Street.

16 *Battle of Camlan:* the battle in which King Arthur and his nephew Modred fell.

284   SAURON DEFEATED

17   *Zigūr:* the Adunaic name of Sauron, which is the name that Lowdham uses in E here.

18   *Owlamoo:* This was in fact the name of a bogey conceived by my brother Michael (and of which my father made a picture, dated 1928, now in the Bodleian Library); but of course Lowdham intended no more than any old absurd name: in E he says 'Wallamaloo, who's he?'

19   *Nūmenōr:* so F at all occurrences here (the long mark over the *o* being added subsequently); E has *Númenor.*

20   *Nūmenōr is my name for Atlantis:* see p. 221 note 63.

21   *I knew I had heard that name as soon as Arry said it:* see pp. 306–7.

22   A footnote to the text in E at this point reads: 'The records were supposed to be written up and presented for correction at the end of each term. Before being passed they were initialled by all persons mentioned in them.   N.G.' Cf. the Note to the list of members of the Notion Club in F, p. 160.

23   *My father's name was Edwin:* in initial drafting (and in E as first written) Lowdham's father was called *Oswin Ellendel* (a 'modernisation' of *Elendil*) and he himself was *Alboin Arundel* (cf. Oswin Errol father of Alboin in *The Lost Road*, V.36 ff.). Oswin Loudham was at first to be a sailor by profession, or else the somewhat absentee Professor of Anglo-Saxon at Cambridge ('I believe he did know some Anglo-Saxon' said his son).

24   I have not been able to discover a place named Penian in Pembrokeshire.

25   *The Éarendel:* in E the ship was named *Éarendel Star.*

26   *It does not look to Sussex:* Arundel in Sussex (explained as Old English *hārhūn-dell,* 'hoarhound valley', the name of a plant) has of course no connection whatsoever with *Éarendel,* merely a likeness of sound.

27   E has 'the War of 1939' (see note 12).

28   *three sailors:* E has only 'And he'd had great difficulty in collecting any sort of crew.' Cf. the three mariners who accompanied Eärendel and Elwing on the voyage to Valinor in the *Quenta Silmarillion* (V.324, 327).

29   With this passage cf. V.37–8 and my commentary V.53–5.

30   *the connexion of the Langobards with King Sheaf:* see p. 227, and V.92 ff.

31   In E Ramer says: 'Nor the repetition of the sequence: *Alboin* son of *Audoin = Alwin* son of *Edwin.*' The addition in F of *Ælfwine son of Éadwine* is curious, since no actual Ælfwine son of Éadwine has been mentioned (merely the Old English forms of *Alwin* and *Edwin*). Possibly it should be understood that Ramer in his discussion with Lowdham before the present meeting

THE NOTION CLUB PAPERS (PART TWO)   285

(p. 235) had learnt of the verses ascribed to *Ælfwine Wídlást Éadwines sunu* (p. 244).

32 *Rosamund:* see V.54.

33 *O Horsefriend of Macedon!* A Lowdham joke on Frankley's first name (of which one is reminded immediately above), referring to King Philip of Macedon, father of Alexander the Great (Greek *phil-ippos* 'horse-loving').

34 *a star-name for Orion, or for Rigel:* see p. 301 and note 6.

35 *the glosses:* translations into Anglo-Saxon of individual words in Latin manuscripts. See my father's (draft) letter written in August 1967 to a correspondent known only as Mr. Rang (*Letters* no. 297), in which he gave a long account of the relation between Anglo-Saxon *Éarendel* and the *Eärendil* of his mythology. The relevant part of this letter is reprinted in II.266, but without the footnote to the words 'To my mind the Anglo-Saxon uses seem plainly to indicate that it was a star presaging the dawn (at any rate in English tradition)':

> Its earliest recorded A-S form is *earendil (oer-),* later *earendel, eorendel.* Mostly in glosses on *jubar = leoma;* also on *aurora.* But also in *Blickling Homilies* 163, *se níwa éorendel* applied to St John the Baptist; and most notably *Crist* 104, *éalá! éarendel engla beorhtast ofer middangeard monnum sended.* Often supposed to refer to Christ (or Mary), but comparison with Blickling Homilies suggests that it refers to the Baptist. The lines refer to a *herald,* and divine messenger, clearly not the *sóðfæsta sunnan léoma* = Christ.

The last words of this note refer to the following lines in the poem *Crist:*

> *Éalá Éarendel engla beorhtast*
> *ofer middangeard monnum sended,*
> *ond sóðfæsta sunnan léoma,*
> *torht ofer tunglas – þú tída gehwane.*
> *of sylfum þé symle inlíhtes.*

'... and true radiance of the sun, bright above the stars – thou of thy very self illuminest for ever every season.' — *The Blickling Homilies* are a collection of Old English sermons preserved in a manuscript at Blickling Hall in Norfolk.

36 E has 'what Cynewulf meant'. Of Cynewulf, author of the *Crist* and other poems, nothing is certainly known beyond his name, which he preserved by setting the runic letters composing it into short passages in the body of his poems, so that the actual names of the runes (as for example the W-rune was called *wynn* 'joy') have a meaning in the context.

37 From this point to the end of Night 66 there are not two but three texts to be considered (as already noted, p. 147), for this part of the typescript F was rejected and replaced by a new

286   SAURON DEFEATED

version, while both typescript versions differ radically from E in respect of Lowdham's linguistic discoveries. The divergences have many notable features, and the superseded versions are given separately, pp. 299 ff.

38 'That breaks my dream' was an expression of my mother's, meaning that something in waking life had suddenly reminded her of a passage in a dream. In the original version of Night 66 (p. 303) Jeremy says 'That breaks *my* dream!' when Lowdham's words suddenly recall to his mind the place where, in his dream, he had found the reference to Númenor. — The *Oxford English Dictionary* does not give the expression, and the only place that I have found it is in the *English Dialect Dictionary*, ed. Joseph Wright, *Break* 27 (3), with a reference to West Yorkshire.

39 *Yōzāyan:* this Adunaic name occurs in *Aldarion and Erendis* (*Unfinished Tales* p. 184): 'Do you not love the Yôzâyan?'

40 The term *Elf-latin* (also *Elven-latin*) occurs frequently in *The Lost Road* and *The Lhammas:* see the Index to Vol.V. Alboin Errol called the first language ('*Eressëan*') that 'came through' to him *Elf-latin,* but it is not explained why he did so.

41 *Tíwas: Tíw* was the name in Old English of the Germanic god equated with Mars (whence *Tuesday,* based on Latin *dies Martis*; French *Mardi*), and known in Old Norse as *Týr.* The name is generally derived from an earlier **Tiwaz,* cognate with Latin *deus* (< **deiwos*), and so meaning originally 'god'; in Old Norse the plural *Tívar* 'gods' is found, of which *Tíwas* (= 'Valar') is the unrecorded Old English equivalent that 'came through' to Lowdham.

42 *Nówendaland:* derived from the recorded Old English word *nówend* 'shipmaster, mariner'. For another occurrence of *Nówendaland* see p. 317.

43 *Fréafíras:* this word is found elsewhere (see p. 317) as a translation of the word *turkildi* in Lowdham's Fragment I (p. 246), which he translated 'lordly men' (p. 248): Old English *fréa* 'lord', often found also as the first element of compounds, and *fíras* 'men', a word used in Old English poetry (cf. IV.206, 208, 211–12).

44 *Regeneard:* this was no doubt used in reference to Valinor. In Old English the element *regn-* occurs in compounds with an intensive force ('greatness, power'), and also in proper names (as *Regenweald,* revived as *Reginald*). In the ancient Norse poems *Regin,* plural, meant the gods, the rulers of the world, and occurs in *Ragna-rök* 'the doom of the gods' (mistakenly transformed into 'the twilight of the gods' by confusion with the word *rökr* 'twilight'). Old English *eard* 'land, country, dwelling, home'; thus *Regeneard* 'God-home', Valinor.

45 *Midswípen:* a word *midja-sweipains* is found in Gothic,

THE NOTION CLUB PAPERS (PART TWO)   287

apparently meaning 'cataclysm, flood of the middle(-earth)', *midja* being a reduced form of *midjun-* as in Gothic *midjungards* (the inhabited world of men, 'Middle-earth'). This is clearly the basis of Lowdham's unrecorded Old English *Midswípen*.

46 *hebaensuil:* in later spelling *heofonsýl;* cf. the Old English text given on p. 314. *frumaeldi:* 'First Age'. I cannot certainly interpret *Wihawinia.*

47 In *The Lost Road* (V.43) Oswin Errol tells Alboin: 'But you'll get into trouble, if you let your cats out of the bag among the philologists – unless, of course, they back up the authorities.' Like Edwin Lowdham, Oswin Errol had studied Old English (V.44).

48 *westra lage wegas rehtas, wraikwas nu isti:* the line 'came through' also to Alboin Errol in *The Lost Road* (V.43), but ending *nu isti sa wraithas;* see p. 304.

49 *Onomasticon:* alphabetical list of proper names, especially of persons.

50 In *The Lost Road* Ælfwine chanted a form of these lines in the hall before King Edward the Elder (V.84), where they are not given in an archaic form but in the spelling of the manuscript of *The Seafarer* (see V.85):

> *Monað modes lust mid mereflode*
> *forð to feran, þæt ic feor heonan*
> *ofer hean holmas, ofer hwæles eðel*
> *elþeodigra eard gesece.*
> *Nis me to hearpan hyge ne to hringþege*
> *ne to wife wyn ne to worulde hyht*
> *ne ymb owiht elles nefne ymb yða gewealc.*

A prose translation is given (whereas Lowdham translates into alliterative verse): 'The desire of my spirit urges me to journey forth over the flowing sea, that far hence across the hills of water and the whale's country I may seek the land of strangers. No mind have I for harp, nor gift of ring, nor delight in women, nor joy in the world, nor concern with aught else save the rolling of the waves.'

In *The Seafarer* the text is somewhat different:

> *monað modes lust mæla gehwylce*
> *ferð to feran, þæt ic feor heonan*
> *elþeodigra eard gesece*

(which is then followed by five lines omitted in Ælfwine's version); *mæla gehwylce* 'on every occasion', *ferð (ferhð)* 'heart, spirit', i.e. literally 'the desire of my spirit urges my heart on every occasion to journey'. These alterations reappear in Lowdham's version here, and they depend, I imagine, on my father's judgement that the preserved text of *The Seafarer* is corrupt.

288   SAURON DEFEATED

The third line in *The Lost Road* text, *ofer hean holmas, ofer hwæles eðel*, not found in *The Seafarer*, is replaced in Lowdham's version by the less banal *ofer gársecges grimme holmas* (writing it in later spelling), 'over the grim waves of Gársecg (the ocean)'; for *Gársecg* see the references given in V.82.

The fourth line of Lowdham's version differs, as he points out, from that in *The Seafarer* in the reading *aelbuuina eard* (= later *ælfwina eard*) 'land of the Elf-friends' for *elþeodigra eard* 'land of strangers, aliens'; the substitution of *ælfwina* for *elþeodigra* requires the presence of the word *uut (út)* for metrical reasons. The text of *The Lost Road* follows *The Seafarer*.

In *The Notion Club Papers* Ælfwine's chant before the king (p. 272) is exactly as Lowdham's version here, but given in later spelling; see also p. 304.

51   These lines Alboin Errol recited to his father in *The Lost Road* (V.44) in precisely the same form, except that Ælfwine is not there called *Éadwines sunu*. For other appearances of these lines see V.55. In the translation the words 'a land lovely to look on' (*wlitescéne land*) have been added from the first typescript (see note 37): they were inadvertently omitted in the second.

52   Lowdham concludes his lecture in the manner of the ending of a medieval minstrel's romance, and with a swipe at Frankley. *or I ende:* 'before I end.'

53   From Night 67 onwards there are again only the manuscript E and the typescript F, the latter being the continuation of the revised typescript (see p. 147 and note 37 above).

54   *O Lover of Horses:* see note 33.

55   Lowdham's 'fragments' are inserted into the typescript on separate sheets. They are in two forms: a typescript, printed here, and a manuscript of two pages, reproduced as frontispieces to this book, representing Lowdham's copies 'in a big bold hand, done with one of the great thick-nibbed pens Lowdham is fond of', with 'glosses in red ink': for unglossed words there are however (unlike what Lowdham said of his copies, p. 248) no query marks. In the typescript text of the fragments the Avallonian and Adunaic words are given all in capital letters, but I print them here in italic, capitalising according to the manuscript version.

56   Comparison of the typescript text of the fragments printed here with the manuscript version reproduced as frontispieces will show that the only differences in actual word-forms are manuscript *hikalba* 'she fell' in I (B), where the typescript has *hikallaba*; manuscript *katha* 'all' in II, where the typescript has *kātha*; and manuscript *īdō* 'now' at all three occurrences in II, but *īdōn* at the last two in the typescript, with the gloss 'now (is)'. There are many minor differences in Lowdham's glosses.

THE NOTION CLUB PAPERS (PART TWO)   289

The typescript text of the fragments was no doubt made to accompany the final typescript F of the narrative, but it is not clear to me whether it preceded or followed the manuscript pages. Earlier forms of these pages are given on pp. 311–12. For the form of the fragments in E see p. 309.

57   Plato's dialogue *Timaeus* is the source (together with the long unfinished dialogue *Critias*) of the legend of Atlantis, the great island empire in the western ocean which, expanding aggressively against the peoples of the Mediterranean, was defeated by the Athenians, and was swallowed up 'in a single day and night' by the sea, leaving a vast shoal of mud that rendered the waters impassable in the region where Atlantis had been. According to Plato, the story was told (about the beginning of the sixth century B.C.) by an Egyptian priest to Solon the Athenian, and it came down thence by several intermediaries to Critias, a relative of Plato's, who tells the story in the two dialogues. In the *Critias* a long and extremely detailed account of Atlantis is given, of its great city, the temple of Poseidon with its colossal statue of the god, the wealth of the land in all resources of minerals, animals, timber, flowers and fruits, the horse-racing, the bull-sacrifice, the laws governing the realm. At the end of this account the narrator tells that the men of Atlantis fell away from the justice, wisdom and virtue of earlier generations, and that Zeus, perceiving their debasement and corruption, and wishing to punish them, called all the gods together and spoke to them; but at this point the *Critias* breaks off unfinished. The story of the war with the Greeks and the downfall of Atlantis is told, very briefly, in the other dialogue, the *Timaeus*.

The eldest child of Poseidon (tutelary god of Atlantis) by a mortal woman became the first king, and Poseidon named him Atlas, 'and after him the whole island and ocean were called Atlantis.'

Ultimately the name *Atlas* is that of the Titan who upheld the heavens on his head and his hands, according to Hesiod in the far western regions of the earth, near the dwelling of the Hesperides. He was the father of the Pleiades, and also, in Homer, of Calypso, on whose island Ogygia Odysseus was shipwrecked.

58   Cf. *The Lost Road*, where Audoin Errol, son of Alboin, speaks to himself of his dreams (V.52): 'Just pictures, but not a sound, not a word. Ships coming to land. Towers on the shore. Battles, with swords glinting but silent. And there is that ominous picture: the great temple on the mountain, smoking like a volcano.'

59   E has here: ' "... But I've done what I can. *Sauron* and *nahamna* remain to be solved." "Sauron!" said Jeremy in a strange voice.'

290   SAURON DEFEATED

Lowdham refers only to unknown Quenya words because, as will be seen more fully later, in E there was no Adunaic element in the fragments he received. The word *nahamna* preceded *nukumna* 'humbled' of the later text of the Quenya fragment (p. 246), and was uninterpretable also by Alboin Errol in *The Lost Road* (V.47).

60   The name *Nimruzīr* appears in Fragment I (B), 'seven ships of Nimruzīr eastward'. In E Jeremy addresses Lowdham as *Ëarendil*, changed subsequently to *Elendil*.

61   The Adunaic words *Bā kitabdahē!* are absent in E (see note 59).

62   In E Lowdham cries out: '*Es sorni heruion an!* The Eagles of the Lords are at hand!' This was changed later to 'The Eagles of the Powers of the West are at hand! *Sorni Nūmevalion anner!*' In an earlier, rejected version of the passage Lowdham's words were: '*Soroni númeheruen ettuler!*'

63   In E Jeremy speaks of 'the fell counsels of Sauron', not 'of Zigūr'. He says that 'Tarkalion has set forth his might', where F has 'the King', and the sails of the Númenórean ships are 'scarlet and black' ('golden and black', F). He ends in E: 'The world waits in fear. The Númenóreans have encompassed Avallon as with a cloud. The Eldar mourn and are afraid. Why do the Lords of the West make no sign?'

64   For 'The Lords have spoken to Ēru, and the fate of the World is changed' E has 'The Lords have spoken to Ilúvatar [> the Maker], and the counsel of the Almighty is changed, and the fate of the world is overturned.'

65   For the passage in F beginning 'See! The abyss openeth ...' E (as first written: the wording was changed in detail subsequently) has:

'Ah! Look! There is a chasm in the midst of the Great Seas and the waters rush down into it in great confusion. The ships of the Númenóreans are drowned in the abyss. They are lost for ever. See now the eagles of the Lords overshadow Númenor. The mountain goes up to heaven in flame and vapour; the hills totter, slide, and crumble: the land founders. The glory has gone down into the deep waters. Dark ships, dark ships flying into darkness! The eagles pursue them. Wind drives them, waves like hills moving. All has passed away. Light has departed!'
There was a roar of thunder and a blaze of lightning ...

Thus there is no mention in E of Lowdham and Jeremy moving to the window and 'talking to one another in a strange tongue.'

66   For *Abrazān* E has *Voronwë*, 'Steadfast', 'Faithful'; this was the name of the Elf who guided Tuor to Gondolin, *Unfinished Tales* pp. 30 ff. Cf. Jeremy's second name, Trewin (see note 84).

67   On 'the Great Storm' see p. 157 and note 1.

THE NOTION CLUB PAPERS (PART TWO) 291

68 The statement that Ramer picked up a piece of paper covered with writing and put it in a drawer is present in E as written. See note 70.

69 *in the schools:* acting as examiners in the final examinations, held at the end of the summer term (cf. Guildford's footnote on p. 253).

70 In E the letter was postmarked in London. — As E was written, the record of the meeting of Night 68 ended immediately after Guildford had read the letter aloud, with the words: 'We agreed to Thursday 25th of September', and is followed by Night 69 on that date. Thus, although at the end of Night 67 Guildford's statement that he saw Ramer pick up the leaf of Edwin Lowdham's manuscript and put it in a drawer was present in E as originally written, on Night 68 Ramer does not appear and the paper is not mentioned (which is why the account of Night 68 begins with the words 'There is not much to record' – words that should have been removed). In E Night 69 (the last meeting recorded in *The Notion Club Papers*) proceeds essentially as in F (pp. 260–77). The matter of 'Edwin Lowdham's page' on Night 68 was inserted into E, but the structure of the manuscript and its pagination show clearly that this was not done until the text of Night 69 had been completed.

71 In E Ramer's remarks about 'Edwin Lowdham's page' and his discovery that the language was Old English are very much the same as in F, but he gives an opinion about the dialect and date: 'He thought it was Númenórean, I guess. But actually it is just Old English – latish West Saxon, I think, but I'm no expert. The script is, I think, plainly Númenórean ...' See further notes 72 and 74.

72 *Rashbold* is a translation of *Tolkien*: see p. 151. Pembroke is the college to which the professorship of Anglo-Saxon is attached, its holder being *ex officio* a fellow of the college. — In E Professor Rashbold does not appear, and it is Ramer himself who deciphered, transcribed, and translated the page ('And here's the transcription, with such a translation as I could make').

73 Cf. the third Old English version of *The Annals of Valinor*, of which I noted (IV.290) that the language is that of ninth-century Mercia. There are several references in my father's letters to his particular liking for and sense of affinity with the West Midlands of England and its early language. In January 1945 he had said to me (*Letters* no. 95): 'For barring the Tolkien (which must long ago have become a pretty thin strand) you are a Mercian or Hwiccian (of Wychwood) on both sides.' In June 1955 he wrote to W. H. Auden (*Letters* no. 163): 'I am a West-midlander by blood (and took to early west-midland

292   SAURON DEFEATED

Middle English as a known tongue as soon as I set eyes on it)';
and in another letter of this time (*Letters* no. 165): '... it is, I
believe, as much due to descent as to opportunity that Anglo-
Saxon and Western Middle English and alliterative verse have
been both a childhood attraction and my main professional
sphere.'

74 The Old English version (not in the Mercian dialect, see note 71)
written to accompany the manuscript E is given on pp. 313–14,
and the representation of the original form of it in Edwin
Lowdham's *tengwar* on pp. 319–20. Of the subsequent Old
English (Mercian) version, printed here from F, my father began
a text in *tengwar* but abandoned it after a single page; this is
reproduced on p. 321.

75 *Arminalēth:* Adunaic name of the City of the Númenóreans,
found also in *The Drowning of Anadûnê.* In *The Fall of
Númenor* (§2) it was named *Númenos* (V.25, and in this book
p. 333). On the site of the temple see p. 384.

76 *Neowollond:* in Professor Rashbold's translation (p. 259) this is
rendered 'the ? prostrate land'; in the earlier Old English version
accompanying E, which was translated by Michael Ramer (note
72), the name (in the form *Niwelland*) is rendered 'the Land that
is fallen low' (pp. 314–15). Old English *neowol* (*néol, niwol*)
'prostrate, prone; deep, profound'; cf. the early names for
Helm's Deep, *Neolnearu, Neolnerwet,* VIII.23 note 6.

77 *forrarder:* 'further forward'.

78 On the texts and titles of this poem see the note on pp. 295–6,
where also the published version is given.

79 *Cluain-ferta:* Clonfert, near the river Shannon above Lough
Derg. The monastery was founded by Saint Brendan Abbot of
Clonfert, called the Navigator, about the year 559.

80 *a light on the edge of the Outer Night:* cf. the *Quenta
Silmarillion* (V.327): 'But [the Valar] took Vingelot [the ship of
Eärendel], and they hallowed it, and they bore it away through
Valinor to the uttermost rim of the world, and there it passed
through the Door of Night and was lifted up even into the
oceans of heaven.' The following line in the present text, *like
silver set ablaze,* is replaced in the final form of the poem
(p. 298, line 104) by *beyond the Door of Days.*

81 The passage Lowdham refers to is lines 33–52, where when 'the
smoking cloud asunder broke' they 'saw that Tower of Doom':
in the earliest text of the poem the mariners 'looked upon
Mount Doom' (p. 295).

82 Cf. the outline for *The Lost Road* in V.80, where 'Ælfwine
objects that Paradise cannot be got to by ship – there are deeper
waters between us than Garsecg. *Roads are bent:* you come
back in the end. No escape by ship.'

THE NOTION CLUB PAPERS (PART TWO)   293

83   *Porlock:* on the north coast of Somerset.

84   *Trewyn:* Jeremy's second name is spelt *Trewin* in the lists of members of the Notion Club. The Old English name is *Tréowine* (which Lowdham uses subsequently, p. 268), 'true friend'; cf. the Elvish name *Voronwë* 'Steadfast' by which Lowdham names him in the text E (note 66).

85   *Hibernia:* Ireland (see note 99).

86   *Slieve League* is a mountain on the coast of Donegal, *Brandon Hill* on the coast of Kerry; thus Lowdham means 'all down the west coast of Ireland'.

87   The *Aran Isles* lie across the entrance to Galway Bay.

88   *Loughrea:* a town and lake to the east of Galway.

89   *the Severn Sea:* the mouth of the Severn.

90   'Let us hasten now, Tréowine! I do not like this wind. There is a great likelihood of Danes tonight.'

91   The opening of Lowdham's story is closely based on the account in *The Lost Road* (V.83), although there Ælfwine's part is reported by the narrator, and it is his son Éadwine that he looks for in the hall, not his friend Tréowine. For a brief account of the historical setting in the years of King Edward the Elder (son of King Alfred), the defeat of the Danes at Archenfield in Herefordshire, and the raids on Watchet and Porlock, see V.80–1.

92   *Devenish men and Somersets: Devenish* is Old English *Defenisc* 'of Devon'; *Defnas, Defenas* 'men of Devon' is the origin of the name *Devon. Somersets* is from Old English *Sumorsǽte* 'men of Somerset' with the later plural ending added; as with *Defnas > Devon, Sumorsǽte* became the name of the region *Somerset.*

93   Edwin Lowdham's father has not been mentioned, but as is seen here he was Oswin Lowdham.

94   *Alfred went into hiding:* in the Isle of Athelney in Somerset, in 878.

95   *the West Welsh:* the people of Cornwall (Old English *Cornwealas* 'the Welsh in Cornwall' became the name of the region, *Cornwall*). On Ælfwine's mother, who came 'from the West', see II.313, V.85.

96   Saint Edmund, King of East Anglia, was defeated by the Danes in 869 and (according to the tenth century life of the king) murdered by them: he was tied to a tree and shot through with many arrows. The Danish raids in the region of the Severn took place in 914, and thus 'Ælfwine' was about 45 years old at this time (see V.80, 85), since he was born 'just before' the death of Saint Edmund. Arry Lowdham was born in 1938, and was now 48 or 49. Subsequently Guildford says (p. 276) that in his vision of Ælfwine in the hall at Porlock he had looked older than

294   SAURON DEFEATED

Lowdham, 'though by his account he was just of Arry's age it seemed'.

97   *the good king in his last wars:* King Alfred (died 899).
98   *Maelduin:* see V.81–2.
99   *Ériu:* the Old Celtic name **Iveriu* (whence Latin *Hibernia*) became Irish *Eriu* (accusative case *Eirinn*, Erin). From the same source is Old English *Íras, Íraland.*
100   *æt Ircenfelda:* Archenfield in Herefordshire; see V.80 (the Old English *Ircingafeld* given there is an earlier form).
101   *Monath módes lust . . .:* on these verses see note 50.
102   *Tamworth:* in Staffordshire: the chief residence of the Mercian kings.
103   *King Sheave:* for discussion of the legend of 'Sheaf' and notes on the text of the poem see V.91–6.

Among the manuscripts of *The Lost Road* material (see V.85 ff.) there are two texts of the poem, the one (which I will here call 'V') written out in verse lines, the other ('P') written as prose. In *The Lost Road* I printed V only, since the two versions differ only in a few minor details. In V there is a short narrative opening, in which it is told that Ælfwine chanted the poem; in P there is only a title, *King Sheave.*

In the manuscript E of *The Notion Club Papers* it is not Tréowine who recites the poem, as it is the typescript F:

At that one of the Marchers leaped to his feet and got leave to speak. Even before I had found a seat beside Tréowine, whom I espied far down the hall, the fellow had a foot on the step and had begun. He had a good voice, if a strange way with his words. Céolwulf, as I heard later, was his name, and he claimed to come of the blood of their kings that sat at Tamworth of old. His verse was in the old style . . .

This was changed in pencil to the later account. In E there is only a direction 'Here follows the Lay of King Sheave', which stands at the bottom of page 42 in the manuscript. The text continues on another page with 'When he ended there was loud applause . . . and they passed a horn of ale to Céolwulf's hand.' When I edited *The Lost Road* I did not observe that this page is numbered 46, while the manuscript P of *King Sheave* (in which the poem is written out as prose) is numbered 43 to 45. Thus the manuscripts V and P, which I took to be 'obviously closely contemporary' (V.87), were in fact separated by some eight years: a misjudgement based on the fact of the texts being placed together in my father's archive and their close similarity, although the evidence of the pagination is perfectly clear.

The manuscript P, then, was written in 1945 on the basis of the much earlier V, and was the text from which the typescript F given here was taken (with a few further changes); and all

THE NOTION CLUB PAPERS (PART TWO)   295

differences between the text given on pp. 273 ff. in this book and that on pp. 87 ff. in *The Lost Road* belong to 1945.

The last eight lines of the supplementary part of the poem (*The Lost Road* p. 91, lines 146–53, beginning 'Sea-danes and Goths ...'), which do not appear in the manuscript V, also belong apparently to the time of *The Notion Club Papers*.

104 The text P has *sires*, but both V and the typescript F of the *Papers* have *sire*.

105 *æt thisse béorthege:* Old English *béorðegu* 'beer-drinking'.

106 I cannot explain the reference of 'Broad Relic'.

107 *cnearr:* 'ship', a very rare Old English word probably taken from Norse, since it is only applied to vessels of the Vikings.

108 'Sweet is the breath of flowers beyond the sea.'

109 *After night 62:* this is the later Night 63.

110 See p. 214 note 23; p. 194 and note 46; p. 199 and note 51; p. 206 and note 63.

111 That this list, following the revised title-page given on p. 149, was made after the completion of manuscript B is seen from the name *Frankley* for earlier *Franks* (p. 150).

Note on 'The Death of Saint Brendan' with the text of the published form 'Imram'

A great deal of work went into this poem, with its elaborate versification: there are no less than fourteen closely-written pages of initial working, and there follow four finished manuscript texts preceding the typescript text printed on pp. 261–4. Much further work on it followed later. It is notable, however, that already in the earliest text the final form reached in *The Notion Club Papers* was very closely approached: there is in fact only one passage that shows a significant difference (and this was corrected already on the first manuscript to the later form). This concerns lines 43–53, where the earliest text reads:

> then the smoking cloud asunder broke
> and we looked upon Mount Doom:
> tall as a column in high Heaven's hall,
> than all mortal mountains higher,
> the tower-top of a foundered power,
> with crown of redgold fire.

> We sailed then on ...

The first text bears the title *The Ballad of St. Brendan's Death*. The second text, which as the pagination shows belongs with the manuscript E of *The Notion Club Papers*, is entitled *The Death of St. Brendan*. The third (with this title) and the fourth (without title) are finely written manuscripts, and the fifth (with the title *The Death of St.*

296   SAURON DEFEATED

Brendan pencilled in as shown on p. 261) is part of the typescript F of
The Notion Club Papers.

The poem, entitled *Imram* (Irish: 'sailing, voyaging') was once
previously printed, in the issue of the periodical *Time and Tide* for
3 December 1955 (where it was illustrated by a woodcut of Saint
Brendan and the great fishes by Robert Gibbings, originally made for
Helen Waddell's book of translations *Beasts and Saints*, 1934). Three
further typescripts, all with the title *Imram*, clearly belong to the later
time. I print here in its entirety the text as it was published in *Time and
Tide*, for that is now scarcely obtainable, and although the opening
and concluding verses underwent very little alteration my father
greatly changed most of the poem from its form in *The Notion Club
Papers.*

IMRAM

At last out of the deep sea he passed,
    and mist rolled on the shore;
under clouded moon the waves were loud,
    as the laden ship him bore   4
to Ireland, back to wood and mire
    and the tower tall and grey,
where the knell of Clúain-ferta's bell
    tolled in green Galway.   8
Where Shannon down to Lough Derg ran
    under a rain-clad sky
Saint Brendan came to his journey's end
    to find the grace to die.   12

'O tell me, father, for I loved you well,
    if still you have words for me,
of things strange in the remembering
    in the long and lonely sea,   16
of islands by deep spells beguiled
    where dwell the Elvenkind:
in seven long years the road to Heaven
    or the Living Land did you find?'   20

'The things I have seen, the many things,
    have long now faded far;
only three come clear now back to me:
    a Cloud, a Tree, a Star.   24

'We sailed for a year and a day and hailed
    no field nor coast of men;
no boat nor bird saw we ever afloat
    for forty days and ten.   28

THE NOTION CLUB PAPERS (PART TWO)   297

Then a drumming we heard as of thunder coming,
    and a Cloud above us spread;
we saw no sun at set or dawn,
    yet ever the west was red.   32

'Upreared from sea to cloud then sheer
    a shoreless mountain stood;
its sides were black from the sullen tide
    up to its smoking hood,   36
but its spire was lit with a living fire
    that ever rose and fell:
tall as a column in High Heaven's hall,
    its roots were deep as Hell;   40
grounded in chasms the waters drowned
    and swallowed long ago
it stands, I guess, on the foundered land
    where the kings of kings lie low.   44

'We sailed then on till all winds failed,
    and we toiled then with the oar;
we burned with thirst and in hunger yearned,
    and we sang our psalms no more.   48
At last beyond the Cloud we passed
    and came to a starlit strand;
the waves were sighing in pillared caves,
    grinding gems to sand.   52
And here they would grind our bones we feared
    until the end of time;
for steep those shores went upward leaping
    to cliffs no man could climb.   56
But round by west a firth we found
    that clove the mountain-wall;
there lay a water shadow-grey
    between the mountains tall.   60
Through gates of stone we rowed in haste,
    and passed, and left the sea;
and silence like dew fell in that isle,
    and holy it seemed to be.   64

'To a dale we came like a silver grail
    with carven hills for rim.
In that hidden land we saw there stand
    under a moonlight dim   68
a Tree more fair than ever I deemed
    in Paradise might grow:
its foot was like a great tower's root,
    its height no man could know;   72

SAURON DEFEATED

and white as winter to my sight
   the leaves of that Tree were;
they grew more close than swan-wing plumes,
   long and soft and fair.   76

'It seemed to us then as in a dream
   that time had passed away,
and our journey ended; for no return
   we hoped, but there to stay.   80
In the silence of that hollow isle
   half sadly then we sang:
softly we thought, but the sound aloft
   like sudden trumpets rang.   84
The Tree then shook, and flying free
   from its limbs the leaves in air
as white birds rose in wheeling flight,
   and the lifting boughs were bare.   88
On high we heard in the starlit sky
   a song, but not of bird:
neither noise of man nor angel's voice,
   but maybe there is a third   92
fair kindred in the world yet lingers
   beyond the foundered land.
But steep are the seas and the waters deep
   beyond the White-tree Strand!'   96

'O stay now, father! There is more to say.
   But two things you have told:
the Tree, the Cloud; but you spoke of three.
   The Star in mind do you hold?'   100

'The Star? Why, I saw it high and far
   at the parting of the ways,
a light on the edge of the Outer Night
   beyond the Door of Days,   104
where the round world plunges steeply down,
   but on the old road goes,
as an unseen bridge that on arches runs
   to coasts that no man knows.'   108

'But men say, father, that ere the end
   you went where none have been.
I would hear you tell me, father dear,
   of the last land you have seen.'   112

'In my mind the Star I still can find,
   and the parting of the seas,

THE NOTION CLUB PAPERS (PART TWO)   299

and the breath as sweet and keen as death
    that was borne upon the breeze.   116
But where they bloom, those flowers fair,
    in what air or land they grow,
what words beyond this world I heard,
    if you would seek to know,   120
in a boat then, brother, far afloat
    you must labour in the sea,
and find for yourself things out of mind:
    you will learn no more of me.'   124

In Ireland over wood and mire
    in the tower tall and grey
the knell of Clúain-ferta's bell
    was tolling in green Galway.   128
Saint Brendan had come to his life's end
    under a rain-clad sky,
journeying whence no ship returns;
    and his bones in Ireland lie.   132

MAJOR DIVERGENCES IN EARLIER VERSIONS OF THE NOTION CLUB PAPERS (PART TWO)

(i) The earlier versions of Night 66

I have mentioned previously that from Lowdham's words '*Éarendel* seems to me a special word. It is not Anglo-Saxon' (see p. 237 and note 37) there is a third text to be considered: for the part of the typescript F that follows from this point and extends to the end of Night 66 (p. 245) was rejected and replaced by another version. I shall refer to the rejected portion as 'F 1', and its replacement as 'F 2'. That this rewriting was carried out while the typescript was being made is seen from the fact that at the end of the rewritten section it is F 2 that continues to the end of the *Papers*.

For some distance the original manuscript E was followed closely in F 1 and for this part it is only necessary to give the text of the latter.

'In any case,' said Lowdham, '*Éarendel* is not Anglo-Saxon. Or rather, it is and it isn't. I think it is one of those curious cases of "linguistic coincidence" that have long puzzled me. I sometimes think that they are too easily dismissed as "mere accident". You know the sort of thing that you can find in any dictionary of a strange language, and which so excites the amateur philologists, itching to derive one tongue from another

300   SAURON DEFEATED

that they know better: a word that is nearly the same in form and meaning as the corresponding word in English, or Latin, or Hebrew, or what not. Like *mare* 'male' in the New Hebrides and Latin *maris, marem*.[1] Or the example that used to be given as a frightful warning in the old text-books: that *popol* means 'people' or 'popular assembly' in Tamil, but has no connexion whatever with *populus* and its derivatives, and is really derived, they say, from a Tamil word for a mat for the councillors to squat on.

'I dare say some of these things are mere chance, or at least not very significant. Yet I think it also happens that a word-form may be arrived at by different routes, in far separated times and places, and yet the result may be the product of a hidden symbol-making process working out to a similar end. Or in any case the "accident" may touch off, as it were, deeper or sleeping mind-echoes, so that the similar form thus acquires similar significance or emotional content. Every language has words in which its genius seems to come to flash-point, words whose form, though it remains within the general style, achieves a brilliance or a beauty of universal virtue.'

'If I follow all this, and I'm not at all sure that I do,' said Markison, 'I suppose you are trying to say that you've discovered *Éarendel* or something like it in some strange language. Is that so?'

'I think I come in for a moment here,' said Jeremy, who had been as restless as a bird on a twig ever since the word *Éarendel* had cropped up. 'We've been trying to strengthen our recollections under tuition; but I've not had much success yet. Still I have succeeded in connecting *Númenor* a little more clearly with a library,[2] with something I came across once when I was working on Ghost-stories. I can't get it more exact, or I couldn't. But a result of the effort to remember has been to drag up a good many vague dream-scenes of that rather troubled searching-for-something-missing variety: wandering about in libraries looking for a lost book, getting dusty and worried.

'Then two nights ago I got a dream of which I still remember one fairly clear passage. I took down a folder, or a cardboard case, from a high shelf, and in it I found a manuscript. It was in an ornamental and rather archaic hand, yet I seem to remember that I knew that it was not really old (by the paper, or the ink, or something), but belonged to this century. Here and there were passages in an unknown character.'

THE NOTION CLUB PAPERS (PART TWO)   301

'I've found that missing leaf of my father's book,' interposed Lowdham.[3] 'I've shown it to Jeremy, and he's quite certain that the character is the same. Though we've not succeeded in deciphering it. It's not any alphabet known to the books.'

'And what is more peculiar', said Jeremy, 'there is nothing at all to connect my dream-vision or dream-manuscript with Edwin Lowdham: the style of the hands is wholly different, though the letter-forms are the same. Old Edwin's is a large, black, broad-stroke round hand; mine was more delicate and pointed.

'Well, unfortunately I don't recollect anything very clear or connected about the contents of my dream-manuscript – I call it that because I begin to wonder if this dream is really founded on any waking experience at all – but it contained, I think, some kind of legendary history,[4] full of strange names all seeming to belong to the same language. This much I do remember: the name *Númenor* or *Númenóre* was frequent; and so was the name *Ëarendil*. Very nearly the same, you see, but actually spelt: *ë-a-r-e-n-d-i-l*, *Ëarendil*.

'So I think Arry must be right. It is a case of linguistic coincidence or congruence, and the key is not to be found in Anglo-Saxon. We need not bother with the connexions of English *Éarendel* in the other related languages, like the proper names *Ōrendel*, and *Aurvendill*, or Saxo's *Horwendillus*.'[5]

'But is not *Auriwandalo* actually recorded as a name in Langobardic?' said Markison, who has a finger in most pies of learning. 'Odd how the Langobards crop up.'

'It is,' said Lowdham.

'Hm, yes, and there is a connexion between these names and the stars,' said Jeremy. 'Didn't Thor throw Aurvendil's toe up into the sky, Arry?[6] And *Ëarendil* certainly had a connexion with a star in the strange tongue. Somehow I feel sure of that.'[7]

'Yes, that's so,' said Lowdham; 'but in the unknown language it was only a legendary connexion, not a linguistic one, I think. *Ëarendil* meant Sea-friend.[8] I am quite sure of that, because – well, perhaps I'd better go on where I left off.

'From the time of my father's departure ...

The following passage in E / F 1 was retained in the revised type-script F 2 (p. 237–8) as far as 'some great tale of Númenor' almost without change, and there is no need to repeat it. The only difference between the texts is in the name of the 'cone-shaped mountain', and this is a difference very important in determining the relation of the

302   SAURON DEFEATED

texts of *The Drowning of Anadûnê* to those of *The Notion Club
Papers*. Where F 2 has 'Desolate is *Minul-Tārik*, the Pillar of Heaven
is forsaken!' the name in E is *Menelminda*, changed in pencil to
Meneltyúla, while in F 1 it is *Menel-tûbel*, changed to *Menel-tûbil*.

From 'some great tale of Nūmenor', however, all three texts diverge
among themselves, and the major divergence is between the manuscript E and the first typescript F 1. I continue now therefore with the
text of E (cf. pp. 238 ff.).

'But most of the word-recollections are, as it were, casual; as
casual as the words caught by the eye from a lexicon when one
is looking for something else. It was a long time before I began
to note them down, and use them for the language I was
amusing myself by "making up". They did not fit, or rather they
took control and bent that language to their own style. In fact
it became difficult to tell which were my invented words and
which the ghost-words; indeed I've a notion that "invention"
gradually played a smaller and smaller part. But there was
always a large residue that would not work in.

'I soon found, as I got to know more, that some of the
ingredients were Anglo-Saxon, and other things: which I'll
mention in a minute. But when I weeded them out there was still
a large amount of words left over, and in worrying over these I
made a discovery. They belonged to another ghost-language,
and to one that was related to the other. I could perceive a good
many of the laws or rules of change: for the Númenórean style
was in most points the older, more archaic, while the other had
been altered (as if by contact with our western shores) to a style
much more like that of the older north-western tongues.'

'I don't follow all this,' said Stainer. 'Nor do I,' said both
Markison and Guildford. 'Give them some of the examples you
gave me, Arry,' said Ramer.

'Well,' said Lowdham hesitating, 'if I can remember any of
the examples where the relationship is clear to lay folk (it is
often rather complex). Yes, *lōme* is 'night' (but *not* 'darkness')
and *lōmelinde* is 'a nightingale': I feel sure of that. In the second
language it is *dūmh*, later *dū*; and *duilin*. I refer them to a
Primitive Western *dōmi, dōmilindē. Alda* means a 'tree' – it was
one of the earliest certain words I got – and *orne* when smaller
and more slender like a birch or rowan; in the second language I
find *galað*, and *orn* (plural *yrn*): I refer them to *galadā*, and *ornē*
(plural *ornei*). Sometimes the forms are more similar: the Sun
and Moon, for instance, appear as *Anār, Isil* beside *Anaur* (later

THE NOTION CLUB PAPERS (PART TWO)   303

Anor) and *Ithil*. I liked first the one language and then the other in different linguistic moods,[9] but the older seemed always the more august, somehow, the more, I don't know ... liturgical, monumental: I used to call it the Elven-latin; and the other seemed more resonant with the loss and regret of these shores of exile' – he paused – 'but I don't know why I say that.'

'But why *Elven*-latin?' asked Markison.

'I don't quite know,' said Lowdham. 'I certainly don't mean Elves in any of the more debased post-Shakespearean sort of ways. Actually the language is associated in my mind with the name *Eressë*: an island, I think. I often call it Eressëan.[10] But it is also associated with names like *Eldar*, *Eldalie* which seem to refer to, well, something like Ramer's *Enkeladim*.'[11]

'That breaks *my* dream!' cried Jeremy.[12] 'Of course! Now I know. It wasn't a library. It was a folder containing a manu-script, on a high shelf in Whitburn's second-hand room,[13] that funny dark place where all sorts of unsaleable things drift. No wonder my dreams were full of dust and anxiety! It must have been fifteen years ago since I found the thing there: *Quenta Eldalien, being the History of the Elves, by John Arthurson*[14] – in a manuscript much as I've described it. I took an eager but hasty glance. But I had no time to spare that day, and I could find no one in the shop to answer any enquiries, so I hurried off. I meant to come back, but I didn't, not for almost a fortnight. And – then the manuscript had vanished! They had no record of it, and neither old Whitburn nor anyone else there remembered ever seeing any such thing. I recall now what a catastrophe it seemed to me at the time; but I was very busy with other work, and soon forgot all about it.'

'It certainly looks as if more than one mind had been working back along similar lines,' said Ramer. 'Several minds indeed; for our expert is at fault for once. Lewis also mentions the name somewhere.'

'So he does!' cried Jeremy. 'In a preface, was it? But he was quoting from someone, I think, from a source that hasn't been traced. And he used the form *numinor*. All the other sources have *númenor*, or *númenórë* – that's so, isn't it, Arry?'[15]

'Yes,' said Lowdham. '*númē* is West, and *nórë* is kindred, or land. The ancient English was *Westfolde*, Hesperia.[16] But you wanted to know why *Elven*. Well, I got that from another line, too. You remember I mentioned that Anglo-Saxon used to come through mixed up with this other queer stuff? Well, I got hold

304   SAURON DEFEATED

of Anglo-Saxon through the ordinary books, of course, fairly early, and that confused the issue; though some words and names came through to me that are not in the dictionaries...'

From here to the end of Night 66 the version in the original manuscript E is very close to the final form (pp. 242–5), though some elements are lacking, notably Lowdham's description of the ancient slowness and sonorousness of diction (p. 242): following Frankley's 'Unless, of course, you back up their theories' Lowdham goes on: 'As a matter of fact, I think they do. At least, here is a bit that came through very early, long before I could interpret it; and it has been repeated over and over again in various forms:

Westra lage wegas rehtas   wraithas nu isti ...'[17]

The Old English lines beginning Monað módes lust are in later spelling, but have the same form as that in F 2 (see pp. 243–4 and note 50, and p. 272). There is no reference in E to the date of the 'coming through' of these lines, nor to its being an evening of high wind.

The remarkable feature of this original version is of course that Lowdham's two 'ghost-languages' were Quenya and Sindarin (or rather, the language that would come to be called Sindarin). Lowdham's account in this version thus maintains the linguistic experience of Alboin Errol in The Lost Road (cf. note 9): 'Eressëan as he called it as a boy ... was getting pretty complete. He had a lot of Beleriandic, too, and was beginning to understand it, and its relation to Eressëan' (V.45).

The first typescript version F 1 follows the manuscript E at the beginning of the section just given ('But most of these word-recollections ...', p. 302), in Lowdham's description of how the 'ghost-words' 'soon took control and bent my [invented] language to their own style'; but when he comes to tell that as he sifted the 'large residue [of words] that would not work in' he made a discovery, his discovery is totally different from that in the original text. This is where Adunaic first appeared. It may be that my father had been long cogitating this new language; but even if this is so, it would seem that it had not reached a form sufficiently developed to enter as Lowdham's 'second language' in manuscript E. In fact, I doubt that it is so. It seems to me to be overwhelmingly probable that Adunaic actually arose at this time (see further p. 147).

I give here the text of F 1 from this point (corresponding to the E text on p. 302 and the final text F 2 on p. 238).

'I found, when I got to know more, that some of the ingredients were Anglo-Saxon and other related things: I'll deal with that in a minute; it was not a large part. Working over the

THE NOTION CLUB PAPERS (PART TWO)   305

rest, collecting and sifting it, I made a discovery. I had got *two* ghost-languages: Númenorean A and B. Most of what I had got at an early period was B; later A became more frequent, but B remained the most common language, especially in anything like connected passages; A was chiefly limited to single words and names, though I think that a lot of it is incorporated in my invented language.

'As far as I could or can see, these languages are unrelated, though they have some words in common. But in addition to these tongues there remains a residue, and I now see that it consists of some echoes of other later tongues that are later than Númenorean A and B, but are derived from them or from their blending. I can discern some of the laws or lines of change that they show. For the Númenorean tongues, I feel, are archaic and of an elder world, but the others are altered and belong to Middle-earth.'

'I don't follow all this,' said Stainer. Most of us felt the same, and said so.

'Couldn't you give them some of the examples that you gave to me, Arry?' said Ramer. 'Some of the important names, and a word or two; it would be clearer with something definite to go on.'

Lowdham hesitated. 'I'll try,' he said. 'But I shan't be able to give many examples of the later changed forms; the relations would seldom be clear, even to philologists, without many instances side by side in writing.

'Well, take the name *Númenor* or *Númenóre*. That belongs to language A. It means Westernesse, and is composed of *núme* "west" and *nóre* "folk" or "country"; but the B name is *Anadún*, and the people are called *Adúnái*. And the land had another name: in A *Andóre*, and in B *Athánáti*; and both mean "land of gift". There seems no connexion between the two languages here; but in both *menel* means "the heavens". It occurs in the B name *Menel-túbil* that I mentioned just now. And there seems to be some connexion between the A word *Valar*, which appears to mean something like "gods", and the B plural *Avalói* and the place-name *Avallóni*.

'The name *Ëarendil*, by the way, belongs to language A, and contains *eäre* "the open sea" and the stem *ndil* "love, devotion". The corresponding B name is *Pharazír*, made of *pharaz* and the stem *iri-* [*changed in ink on the typescript to*: *Azrubél*, made of *azar* "sea" and the stem *bel-*]. A large number of the names seem

306   SAURON DEFEATED

to have double forms like this, almost as if one people spoke two languages. If that is so, I suppose the situation could be paralleled by the use of, say, Chinese in Japan, or indeed of Latin in Europe. As if a man could be called Godwin and also Theophilus or Amadeus. But even so, two different peoples must come into the story somewhere.

'I don't know if you want any more examples; but the words for the Sun and Moon in A are *Anar* and *Isil* (or in their oldest form *Anār* and *Ithīl*); and in B they are *Ūri* and *Nīlu*. These words survive in not much changed shapes in the later languages that I spoke of: *Anor (Anaur)* and *Ithil*, beside *Uir, Ȳr* and *Nil, Njūl*. Again the A and B forms seem unconnected; but there is a word that often occurs and is nearly the same in both: *lōme* in A, and *lōmi* in B. That means "night", but as it comes through to me I feel that it has no evil connotations; it is a word of peace and beauty and has none of the associations of fear or groping that, say, "dark" has for us. For the evil sense I do not know the A word. In B and its derivatives there are many words or stems, such as *dolgu, ugru, nūlu*.

'Well, there you are. I hope you are not all bored. I love these languages. I call them Avallonian and Adunaic.[18] I find first the one and then the other more attractive, in different linguistic moods; but A, the Avallonian, is the more beautiful, with the simpler and more euphonious phonetic style. And it seems to me the more august, somehow, the more ancient, and, well, sacred and liturgical. I used to call it the Elven-latin. But the Adunaic is more resonant with the loss and regret of Middle-earth, these shores of exile.' He paused, as if he heard echoes from a great distance. 'But I do not know why I say that,' he ended.

There was a short silence, and then Markison spoke. 'Why did you call it Elven-latin?' he asked. 'Why Elven?'

'It seemed to fit,' Lowdham answered. 'But certainly I didn't mean *elf* in any debased post-Shakespearean sort of sense. ...

The remainder of Night 66 is the same as in F 2 (pp. 242–5), except that, as in E, Lowdham's account of the ancient mode of utterance is absent.

It will be seen that in F 1, as in E, Wilfrid Jeremy interrupts to speak of his 'dream-manuscript' (p. 300), found in a library, in which occurred the names *Nūmenor* and *Ēarendil*: the unknown character of some passages in it was the same as that of the single leaf preserved from Edwin Lowdham's 'notes in a queer script' (p. 235), which Arundel Lowdham had now found again; but that this passage is

THE NOTION CLUB PAPERS (PART TWO) 307

entirely absent in F 2 (p. 237). Subsequently, in E, Jeremy returns to the subject ('That breaks *my* dream!', p. 303), remembering both that he found – in waking life, years before – the manuscript not in a library but in the second-hand room of a bookshop, and that the manuscript bore the title *Quenta Eldalien, being the History of the Elves, by John Arthurson*; and this leads to a mention of Lewis's use of the name *Numinor*. This second interruption of Jeremy's is *not* in F 1, which is on the face of it strange, since his first speech was surely intended to lead on to his second. A probable explanation of this is that my father decided to discard this element of Jeremy's manuscript (perhaps as complicating excessively the already complex conception) while he was making the typescript, and that this was one reason why he produced the revised version at this point. But Jeremy's remarks at the previous meeting (Night 65, p. 232: 'I come into it too. I knew I had heard that name as soon as Arry said it. But I can't for the life of me remember where or when at the moment. It'll bother me now, like a thorn in the foot, until I get it out') should have been removed.

NOTES

1 The genitive and accusative cases *maris, marem* are given because the nominative is *mas* ('male').

2 Jeremy is referring to the earlier passage (Night 65, p. 232) in which he claimed that he himself had heard the name *Númenor*, but could not remember when.

3 In the revised text F 2 there is no mention of the missing leaf having been found under Night 66 – naturally enough, since it was at this meeting that Lowdham referred to it as having been mislaid (p. 235). It was an odd oversight in E and F 1 that at the same meeting Lowdham both first mentions it and says that he cannot find it at the present time, and also declares that he has found it and discussed it with Jeremy. In F 2 he brings the leaf to the next meeting (p. 248).

4 E has here: '... the contents of the dream-manuscript – I call it that, because I doubt now whether this dream is really founded on any waking experience at all; though I don't somehow doubt that such a manuscript exists somewhere, probably in Oxford: it contains, I think, some kind of legendary history ...'

5 *Ōrendel* in German, *Aurvandill* in Norse, *Horwendillus* in Latinized form in the Danish History of Saxo Grammaticus (latter half of the twelfth century). The form in Norse is *Aurvandill*, but at the occurrences of the name both in E and F 1 my father spelt it *Aurvendill*. See note 6.

6 In the 'Prose Edda' of Snorri Sturluson a strange tale is told by the god Thor, how he 'carried Aurvandill in a basket on his back

308   SAURON DEFEATED

from the North out of Jötunheim [land of giants]; and he added for a token that one of his toes had stuck out of the basket and become frozen; and so Thor broke it off and cast it into the sky, and made a star of it, which is called *Aurvandilstá* [Aurvandil's Toe]' (*Snorra Edda, Skáldskaparmál* §17). Association of Aurvandill with Orion is the basis of the suggestions mentioned by Lowdham earlier (p. 236): 'Some guess that it [Éarendel] was really a star-name for Orion, or for Rigel' – Rigel being the very bright star in the left foot of Orion (as he is drawn in the old figure).

7   E has: 'And *Éarendil* certainly had a connexion with a star in the strange tongue: I seem to remember that: like the ship' – the last words being changed from 'And the ship was *Éarendel's Star*'. Earlier in E (p. 284 note 25) the ship was called *Éarendel Star*.

8   In E Lowdham translates *Éarendil* as 'Lover of the Great Seas'; in the final text F 2 as 'Great Mariner, or literally Friend of the Sea' (p. 237).

9   This passage is modelled on Alboin Errol's words to his father in *The Lost Road* (V.41), using the same examples, with the same distinction in respect of the word *lóme* ('night' but not 'darkness'), the same note that *alda* was one of the earliest words to appear, and the same remark that (in Alboin's words) 'I like first one, then the other, in different moods.'

10 *Eressëan* was Alboin Errol's name for his first language, 'Elf-latin'; the second was *Beleriandic*.

11 Cf. p. 221 note 65: the passage cited there from the B manuscript of Part One, in which 'Tolkien's Unfallen Elves' and 'Tolkien's Eldar, Eldalie' are referred to, though not struck out on that manuscript, must by now have been rejected; it is clear that Lowdham means that *Eldar, Eldalie* had 'come through' to him, and that he only knew them so. See further note 14.

12 See p. 286 note 38.

13 *Whitburn:* see p. 149 and note 7.

14 My father's father was Arthur Tolkien; he was referring of course to his manuscript of *The Silmarillion*, which had never been published but had washed up, forgotten and disregarded, in the second-hand room of a bookshop. The author of *The Silmarillion* is disguised by a pseudonym; for no reference can now be made to the works of *Tolkien*, least of all as having been published and known to members of the Notion Club (see the citation from manuscript B of Part One, p. 220 note 52 at end). — In a rejected form of this passage the title of the manuscript was not *Quenta Eldalien* but *Quenta Eldaron*.

15 Ramer's remark 'Lewis also mentions the name somewhere' is at first sight puzzling, since it was Lowdham's mention of *Eldar, Eldalie* that brought back to Jeremy's mind the manuscript by

THE NOTION CLUB PAPERS (PART TWO)   309

'John Arthurson' that he had once seen, and the name *Númenor* has not been mentioned for some time. But Ramer was following his own thought, that 'several minds' had been 'working back along similar lines' (and of course it was the name *Númenor* that had originally caught Jeremy's attention and finally led to his recollection of the manuscript). — Jeremy's words 'In a preface, was it?' presumably refer to Lewis's preface to *That Hideous Strength*: 'Those who would like to learn further about Numinor and the True West must (alas!) await the publication of much that still exists only in the MSS. of my friend, Professor J. R. R. Tolkien.' But then why does Jeremy say 'from a source that hasn't been traced', since the source, though unpublished, was stated by Lewis? Such an untiring researcher as Wilfrid Jeremy would have found out who J. R. R. Tolkien was, even if now forgotten!

By 'All the other sources' Jeremy presumably means his own recollection of the manuscript by 'John Arthurson' and the name that had 'come through' to Ramer (p. 232) and Lowdham.

There are a number of references to *Numinor* in *That Hideous Strength*, as: 'Merlin's art was the last survival of something older and different – something brought to Western Europe after the fall of Numinor' (Chapter 9, §v); again with reference to Merlin, 'something that takes us back to Numinor, to pre-glacial periods' (Ch.12, §vi); (Merlin) ' "Tell me, slave, what is Numinor?" "The True West," said Ransom' (Ch.13, §i); other references in Ch.13, §v.

16 *Westfolde* (*folde* 'earth, land, country') seems not to be recorded in Old English. This is the same as *Westfold* in *The Lord of the Rings*. – *Hesperia*: 'western land' (*hesperus* 'western', 'the evening star').

17 Above the *th* of *wraithas* is written *kw* (see p. 287 note 48).

18 In F 1 Lowdham's words about *Avallōni* in F 2 (p. 241) are absent ('Although that is a B name, it is with it, oddly enough, that I associate language A; so if you want to get rid of algebra, you can call A Avallonian, and B Adunaic'). Thus there is no explanation in F 1 why he calls the A language *Avallonian* despite the fact that *Avallōni* is a B name.

(ii) The original version of Lowdham's 'Fragments' (Night 67)

In the manuscript E Lowdham's fragments are, like Alboin Errol's in *The Lost Road* (V.47) in one language only, Quenya ('Eressëan'). Lowdham bursts in to Ramer's rooms and tells of his visit to Pembrokeshire just as he does in F (p. 246), but he does not bring copies of the text that has come to him – he asks Ramer for a large sheet of paper to pin up on a board. Then he says: 'Well, here it is! It's Númenórean or Eressëan, and I'll put the text that I can remember

310   SAURON DEFEATED

down first large, and the English gloss (where I can give any) underneath. It's fragmentary, just a collection of incomplete sentences.'

The first of the two fragments reads thus, as E was originally written
(the change of *ilu* to *eru* was very probably made at the time of
writing: for *ilu* 'the World' see IV.241–5):

ar   sauron   túle   nahamna ...   lantier   turkildi
and   ?   came   ?   ...   they-fell   ?

unuhuine   ... tarkalion ohtakāre   valannar ...
under-shadow ... ?   war-made   on-Powers ...

Herunūmen   [ilu >] eru   terhante ...   Ilúvatāren ...
Lord-of-West world   sunder-broke ...   of-God ...

ëari   ullier   kilyanna ... Nūmenōre ataltane.
seas   they-should-pour in-Chasm ... Numenor   down-fell.

It will be seen that the Elvish here, apart from the curious change
from *ilu* to *eru*, is identical in its forms with that of Alboin Errol's first
fragment; and the only differences in the glosses are 'of-God' for
Alboin's 'of-Ilúvatar', 'sunder-broke' for 'broke', and 'they-should-
pour' for 'poured'. A few changes were made subsequently: *lantier* >
lantaner, *eru* > *arda*, *terhante* > *askante*, and the addition of *lenēme*
'by leave' – the changed forms being found in the final version (p. 246)
with the exception of *askante*, where the final version has *sakkante*
'rent'.

Then follows (where in *The Lost Road* it is said: 'Then there had
seemed to be a long gap'): 'After that there came a long dark gap
which slipped out of memory as soon as I woke to daylight. And then I
got this:'

Malle   tēna   lende   nūmenna   ilya   sī   maller
road   straight went   westward   all   now   roads

raikar ... turkildi   rōmenna ...   nūruhuine
bent ...   ?   eastward ...   death-shadow

mēne   lumna   ... vahāya   sīn   atalante.
on-us   is-heavy   ... far-away now   ?

This is also very close to Alboin Errol's second passage. The word
tēna 'straight' was changed from *tēra* (as in *The Lost Road*), perhaps
in the act of writing; otherwise the only differences in the Quenya
words are *mēne lumna* for *mel-lumna* in *The Lost Road* (glossed
'us-is-heavy'), and *sīn* for *sin*, where Lowdham's gloss was changed
from 'now' (as in *The Lost Road*) to 'now-is'. This fragment appears
in Adunaic in the final version (Fragment II, p. 247), apart from the
words *vahaiya sín Andóre / atalante*.

In E Lowdham makes the same observations as in F (pp. 247–8) about

THE NOTION CLUB PAPERS (PART TWO)   311

his glimpse of the script, with the thought that these were passages out of a book; and he says likewise 'And then suddenly I remembered the curious script in my father's manuscript – but that can wait', without however adding, as he does in F, 'I've brought the leaf along', although at the end of the meeting, after the storm, Ramer picks up the leaf from the floor and puts it in a drawer (p. 291, notes 68 and 70). Lowdham remarks that 'there are some new words here', and that 'all except *nahamna* I at once guessed to be names'. He naturally has less to say in E about the language of the fragments than he does in F, noting only that he thought that *Tarkalion* was a king's name and that *Turkildi* was 'the name of a people: "lordly men", I think', and commenting on *Atalante* in very much the same words as in F, translating it as ' "It (or She) that is downfallen", or more closely "who has slipped down into an abyss" '.

(iii) The earlier versions of Lowdham's 'Fragments' in Adunaic (Night 67)

There are two manuscript pages of Lowdham's fragments in Quenya and Adunaic preceding those reproduced as frontispieces. The first of these pages, here called (1), has interlinear glosses in English in red ink; the second, (2), has not. In the Quenya fragment I (A) the development from the form found in E to the final form (pp. 246–7) can be observed, but there are only a few points to mention. The word *nahamna*, which neither Alboin Errol nor Lowdham could translate, became in (1) *kamindon*, still untranslatable but with the gloss *-ly* beneath, and in (2) *akamna*, changed to *nukumna*. The name *herunū-men* survived in (1) and (2), but was changed in the latter to *Nūmekundo* (*númeheruvi* in the final form).

The Adunaic fragments, I (B) and II (B), underwent a great deal of change, and I give here the text in (1), showing the changes made carefully to the text in ink, but ignoring scribbled pencilled emendations which are mostly very difficult to interpret.

Kadō	*zigūrun*	*zabathān*	[*hunekkū* >] *unekkū*	...	*eruhīn*
and so	?	humbled	he-came	...	?

udūbanim	*dalad*	*ugrus*	... *arpharazōn*
fell	under	horror? shadow? ...	?

azgaranādu	*avalōi-*[*men* >] *si*	... *bārun-adūnō*
was waging war?	Powers on	... the Lord of West

rakkhatū	*kamāt*	*sōbēthumā*	*eruvō*	... *azrē*
broke asunder	earth	assent-with	of God	... seas

nai [*phurusam* >] *phurrusim* *akhās-ada.*	*anadūni*	*akallabi.*
might-flow	Chasm-into	Westernesse fell in ruin.

312   SAURON DEFEATED

Adūnāim   *azūlada* ... *agannūlō*   *burudan*
The Adunai (Men of W.)   eastward ... death-shade   heavy-is

nēnum ... *adūn* *batān* *akhaini* *ezendi* *īdō* *kathī*
on-us ... West road lay straight lo! now all

batānī *rōkhī-nam* ... [*vahaia sīn atalante*] ... *ēphalek*
ways   bent-are ...   far away

īdōn   *akallabēth* ... [*haia vahaia sīn atalante*] ...
lo! now is   She-that-is-fallen ...

ēphal *ēphalek* *īdōn*   *athanātē*
far   far away   is now   Athanātē (the Land of Gift)

In the rejected typescript F 1 of Night 66 appears *Athānāti* (p. 305), where F 2 has *Yōzāyan* (p. 241).

In text (2) the final text of the fragments was very largely reached, but still with a number of differences. I list here all of these, in the order of the occurrence of the words in the final text, giving the final form first:

unakkha: *unakkha* > *yadda* > *unakkha*
dubdam: *dubbudam* > *dubdam*
ar-pharazōnun: *ar-pharazōn* > *ar-pharazōnun*
azaggara: *azagrāra*, with *azaggara* as alternative
bārim: *bārun*
yurahtam: *urahhata* > *urahta*
hikallaba (typescript), *hikalba* (manuscript): *hikallaba* > *hikalba*
bawība dulgī: *dulgu bawīb*
an-nimruzīr: *nimruzīr*
At the beginning of II *Adūnāim azūlada* retained from (1), then struck out
burōda nēnud: *buruda nēnu*
adūn izindi batān tāidō ayadda: *adūn batān ēluk izindi yadda*
īdō (manuscript) at last two occurrences, *īdōn* (typescript):   *īdōn*
hi-Akallabēth: *Akallabēth*

Eru. The appearance of the name *Eru* in these texts is interesting: Lowdham says (pp. 248–9) that he thinks that *ēruhīnim* in I (B) must mean 'Children of God'; that *ēruvō* 'is the sacred name *Ēru* with a suffixed element meaning "from"'; and that 'therefore *iluvatáren* means the same thing.' In a list of 'Alterations in last revision [of The Silmarillion] 1951' my father included *Aman, Arda, Eä, Eru*, and other names (V.338). It seems very probable that the name *Eru (Ēru)* – and *Arda* also – first emerged at this time, as the Adunaic equivalent of *Ilúvatar* (for the etymology of *Ēru* in Adunaic see p. 432). The

THE NOTION CLUB PAPERS (PART TWO)   313

appearance of *eru* in the E text (p. 310), replacing *ilu* 'world' and in turn displaced by *arda*, could be explained as the first emergence of *eru*, as a Quenya word, and with a different meaning.

(iv) Earlier versions of Edwin Lowdham's Old English text

Two texts of a longer Old English version are extant, the second of these, followed here, being a revision of the first but closely similar to it and accompanied by a translation. This version belongs with the manuscript E: there are no Adunaic names, and a complete facsimile of Edwin Lowdham's text in Númenórean script (*tengwar*) bears a page reference to the manuscript. In those passages where this version and the later one (pp. 257–8) can be compared many differences in the forms of words will be seen, for this does not represent the old Mercian dialect (see p. 291 note 71).

I give the text here as my father wrote it in a rapidly pencilled manuscript. The two sides of Edwin Lowdham's page in *tengwar* are reproduced on pp. 319–20; the *tengwar* text was directly based on the Old English that now follows, and (in intention) scarcely deviates from it. There are a very few minor differences in spelling between the two, including the last word, the name *Niwelland*, which in the *tengwar* text is given as *Neowolland* (p. 292 note 76).

Ealle sǽ on worulde hí oferlidon, sohton hí nyston hwæt ac ǽfre wolde hyra heorte westweard, forðamðe hí ofhyngrede wurdon ðǽre undéadlican blisse ðǽre *Eldalie* 7 swa hyra wuldor wéox swa ǽfre hyra langung 7 hyra unstilnes wurdon ðe má ætiht .... þá forbudon ða *Eldan* him on *Eresse* úp to cumanne, forðam hí mennisce wǽron 7 déadlice 7 þéahþe ða Wealdend him langes lífes úðon ne mihton hí alýsan hí of ðǽre woruldméðnesse ðe on ealle men ǽr ðam ende fǽreð 7 hí swulton efne hyra héacyningas, *Éarendles* yrfenuman, 7 hyra líffæc þúhte ðam *Eldum* scort. Forðon hit swá gefyrn arǽdde se Ælmihtiga ðæt hí steorfan sceoldon 7 þás woruld ofgyfan .... ac hí ongunnon murcnian, sægdon ðæt þis forbod him unryht þuhte. Þonne on dígle asendon hí scéaweras on *Avallon* ða dyrnan láre ðara *Eldena* to asméaganne; ne fundon ðeah nawðer ne rúne ne rǽd ðe him to bóte wǽron .... Hit gelamp siþþan ðæt se fúla Déofles þegn ðe Ælfwina folc *Sauron* nemneð wéox swíðe on middangearde 7 hé geaxode Westwarena miht 7 wuldor 7 ðæt hí gyt holde wǽren Gode; ongunnon úpahæfenlice swaðeah ... Þá gehyrde Westwarena cyning æt his sǽlidum be *Saurone* ðæt he wolde cyning béon ofer eallum cyningum 7 héalicran stól habban wolde ðonne *Éarendles* afera sylf ahte. Þonne sende hé *Tarcalion* se cyning bútan Wealdendra rǽde oþþe *Eldena* his ǽrendracan to *Saurone*, abéad him ðæt he on ofste on Westfoldan cwóme þǽr to ðæs cyninges manrǽdenne to búganne 7

314　　SAURON DEFEATED

hé *Sauron* lytigende geéadmédde hine ðæt he cwóm, wæs þeah inwitful under, fácnes hogode Westwarena þéode. Þá cwóm he úp æt sumum cyrre on *Rómelonde* ðære hýðe 7 sóna adwealde fornéan ealle ða *Númenóriscan* mid wundrum 7 mid tácnum; forðam he mihte mycel on gedwimerum 7 drýcræftum . . . . . . 7 hí geworhton mycelne ealh on ðam héan 'munte' ðe *Meneltyúla* – ðæt is to secganne Heofonsýl – hátte – se ðe ǽr wæs unawídlod; dydon ða hálignesse to hǽðenum hearge 7 þǽr onsægdon unasecgendlíce lác on unhalgum wéofode ... swa cwóm se déaþscúa on Westfarena land . . . .

Þæs ofer fela géara hit gelamp ðæt *Tarcalione* wearþ yldo onsǽge 7 þý wearð he hréow on móde 7 þa wolde he be *Saurones* onbryrdingum *Avallon* mid fyrde gefaran, forðamðe *Sauron* him sægde ðæt ða *Eldan* him on wóh éces lífes forwyrnden . . . . . wǽron Westwarena scipfyrda swaswa unarímedlic ígland on ðære sǽ 7 hyra mǽstas gelíce fyrgenbéamum on beorghliðum, 7 hyra here-cumbol gelíce þunorwolcnum; wǽron hyra segl blódréad 7 blacu . . . . . Nú sitte wé on elelande 7 forgytað ðære blisse ðe iú wæs 7 nú sceal eft cuman nǽfre. Ús swíðe onsitt Déaþscúa. Wóh biþ seo woruld. Feor nú is Niwelland ð.

I cannot explain the ð at the end of this text, which stands at the end of a line but not at the end of the page, and which must have a significance since the symbol for *th* concludes the version in *tengwar* (and concludes the page). The translation reads thus:

All the seas in the world they sailed, seeking they knew not what; but their hearts were turned ever westward, for they were become greatly desirous of the undying bliss of the Eldalie, and as their power and glory grew so was their longing and their unquiet ever the more increased . . . . Then the Eldar forbade them to land on Eresse, for they were of human kindred and mortal; and albeit the Powers had granted them long life, they could not release them from the weariness of the world that comes upon all men ere the end, and they died, even their high-kings, descendants of Éarendel; and their life-span seemed short to the Eldar. For thus had the Almighty ordained it, that they should die and leave this world . . . . But they began to murmur, saying that this prohibition seemed to them unjust. Then they sent out in secret spies to Avallon to explore the hidden knowledge of the Eldar; but they discovered neither lore nor counsel that was of any avail to them . . . .

It came to pass afterward that the foul servant of the Devil whom the people of the Ælfwinas call Sauron grew mightily in the Great Lands, and he learned of the power and glory of the Westware, and that they were still faithful to God, but were behaving arrogantly nonetheless ... Then the King of the Westware heard news from his

THE NOTION CLUB PAPERS (PART TWO) 315

mariners concerning Sauron, that he desired to be King over all Kings and to have a more exalted throne than even the heir of Éarendel himself possessed. Then he, Tarkalion the King, without counsel either of the Powers or of the Eldar, sent his ambassadors to Sauron, commanding him to come with all speed to Westfolde, there to do homage to the King. And Sauron, dissembling, humbled himself and came, being filled with malice beneath, and designing wickedness against the people of the Westware. He landed then one day at the haven of Rómelonde, and straightway he deluded well nigh all the Númenóreans with signs and wonders; for he had great craft in phantoms and in wizardry ... and they builded a great temple on that high mountain that was called Meneltyúla (that is to say the Pillar of Heaven), which before was undefiled, and there they did sacrifice unspeakable offerings upon an unholy altar ... thus came the Deathshadow upon the land of the Westware ....

Many years afterward it came to pass that old age assailed Tarkalion, so that he became exceedingly sad in mind, and he determined then (being goaded by Sauron) to invade Avallon with an army; for Sauron said to him that the Eldar refused to him the gift of everlasting life, wrongfully ..... The fleets of the Númenóreans were as uncounted islands in the sea and their masts were like unto tall trees upon the mountain-sides, and their war-banners like to thunder-clouds, and their sails were bloodred and black ....

Now we dwell in the land of exile and forget the bliss that once was and now shall come again never. Heavy lies upon us the Deathshadow. Bent is the world. Far now is the Land that is fallen low.

At the end the following bracketed sentence was added subsequently: '[that is Atalante which was before called Andor and Vinyamar and Númenor.]'

A remarkable feature of this text is the ascription to the *Eldar* of a ban on Númenórean landing in Eressëa, and still more the statement that Sauron told Tarkalion that the *Eldar* 'refused to him the gift of everlasting life'; on this see pp. 355–6.

Of names in this text the following may be noted. There is an Old English form *Eldan* for 'Eldar', with genitive plural *Eldena*, dative plural *Eldum*. For *Meneltyúla* (in the first draft of this version *Menelmindo*) see p. 302, and for *Heofonsýl* p. 242 and note 46. The statement that Sauron landed 'at the haven of *Rómelonde*' (in the first draft *Rómelónan*) is interesting: with *Rómelonde* 'East-haven' cf. the great harbour of *Rómenna* 'Eastward' in the later form of the legend. Also notable is the name *Vinyamar* of Númenor in the addition at the end of the translation: with this cf. *Vinya* 'the Young', 'the New Land' in *The Fall of Númenor* (V.19, 25, and in this book p. 332) and in *The*

316   SAURON DEFEATED

Lost Road (V.64). Later *Vinyamar* 'New Dwelling' became the name of the house of Turgon on the coast of Nevrast, before he removed to Gondolin (Index to *Unfinished Tales*).

With the sails of the Númenórean ships that were 'bloodred and black' cf. p. 290 note 63, where Jeremy sees them as 'scarlet and black' in E, but 'golden and black' in F.

There are several other Old English texts and scraps of texts extant. In one of these a much fuller account of the drowning of Númenor is given, to which I append a translation:

Ac þá þá Tarcaligeones foregengan dyrstlǽhton þæt híe on þæt land astígen and híe þǽr dydon micel yfel ond atendon Túnan þa burg, þá hréowsode Ósfruma and he gebǽd him to þam Ælmihtigan, and be þæs Scyppendes rǽde 7 léafe onhwierfed wearþ worulde gesceapu. Wearð Ósgeard from eorþan asundrod, 7 micel æfgrynde ætíewde on middum Gársecge, be éastan Ánetíge. 7 þa sǽ dufon niþer inn on þæt gin, ond mid þam bearhtme þara hréosendra wǽtera wearþ eall middangeard afylled; 7 þara wǽtergefealla se þrosm stanc up oþ heofon ofer þara écra munta héafdu.

Þǽr forwurdon eall Westfarena scipu, and adranc mid him eall þæt folc. Forwurdon éac Tarcaligeon se gyldena 7 seo beorhte Iligen his cwén, féollon bútú niþer swaswa steorran on þystro and gewiton seoþþan of eallra manna cýþþe. Micle flódas gelumpon on þam tíman and landa styrunga, and Westfolde þe ǽr Númenor hátte wearð aworpen on Gársecges bósm and hire wuldor gewát.

But when those who went before Tarcalion dared to go up into the land, and did there great evil and set fire to the city of Túna, then the Lord of the Gods grieved, and he prayed to the Almighty; and by the counsel and leave of the Creator the fashion of the world was changed. Ósgeard [Valinor] was sundered from the earth, and a great abyss appeared in the midst of Gársecg [the Ocean], to the east of Ánetíg [the Lonely Isle]. And the seas plunged down into the chasm, and all Middle-earth was filled with the noise of the falling waters; and the smoke of the cataracts rose up to heaven above the heads of the everlasting mountains.

There perished all the ships of the Westfarers, and all that people were drowned with them. There perished also Tarcalion the golden and bright Ilien his queen; they fell both like stars into the darkness and passed out of all men's knowledge. There were great floods in that time and tumults of the lands, and Westfolde, which before was named Númenor, was cast down into the bosom of Gársecg, and its glory perished.

Tol Eressëa, the Lonely Isle, is named *Ánetíg* in the Old English version of the earliest *Annals of Valinor* (IV.281, etc.). In that work Valinor was *Godéþel* changed to *Ésa-eard* (IV.283), *Ésa* being the

THE NOTION CLUB PAPERS (PART TWO)   317

genitive plural of *Ós* 'god', as here in *Ósgeard* (Valinor) and in *Ósfruma* 'Lord of the Gods' (Manwë). *Tarcaligeon, Iligen* are Old English spellings representing *Tarcalion, Ilien*.

Comparison of this text with *The Fall of Númenor* §§6–8 (pp. 336–7) will show a close relation between the two. I think it very probable that this text represents my father's original idea for the single preserved page of Edwin Lowdham's manuscript, before he decided that the page should consist, in Ramer's words (p. 259), of 'a series of fragmentary extracts, separated, I should guess, by very various intervals of omission'.

A portion of this text is also found written in *tengwar*, with an interlinear gloss in modern script. This, I think, was the first of the texts in *tengwar* (see the next section).

Other Old English names found in these papers are *Ealfæderburg* 'the mountain of Allfather (Ilúvatar)' as an alternative name for *Heofonsýl* 'Pillar of Heaven'; *Héafíras* 'High Men', of the Númenór-eans (cf. *Fréafíras* mentioned below); and *se Malsca*, of Sauron (cf. *Malscor*, a name of Morgoth found in a list of Old English equivalents of Elvish names associated with the *Quenta*, IV.209; an Old English noun *malscrung* 'bewitching, bewildering' is recorded).

Lastly may be mentioned a slip of paper giving the Quenya fragments in their original form (that is, in the form in which they are found in *The Lost Road* and preceding that in manuscript E, as is seen from *tēra* 'straight' for *tēna*, p. 310), with the usual English glosses and queries, but also with a translation into Old English (rapidly jotted down and hard to read):

> 7 Saweron cóm to hýþe. Gedruron Fréafíras under sceadu. Tarkal-ion wíg gebéad þam Héamægnum. Þa tocléaf Westfréa þas woruld be þæs Ælmihtigan léafe. 7 fléowon þa sǽ inn on þæt micle gin 7 wearþ Nówendaland ahwylfed.
>
> Géo læg riht weg westanweard, nú sind alle wegas [?forcrymbed]. Fréafíras éastweard. Déaþscúa ús líþ hefig on. Nú swiþe feor is seo Niþerhrorene.

It is curious to see that *nahamna* (marked as usual with a query in the modern English gloss) was translated to *hýþe* 'to haven'. The Old English words *be ... léafe* 'with leave' correspond to dots in the Elvish text (the word *lenēme* being introduced here later in E, p. 310). *Fréafíras* and *Nówendaland* are mentioned by Lowdham (p. 242 and -notes 42, 43) among names that have 'come through' to him which are not recorded in Old English. *Héamægnum: héah-mægen* 'great power'. *Westfréa* ('Lord of the West') was struck out and replaced by (appar-ently) *Regenríces Wealdend* ('Ruler of Valinor': cf. *Regeneard* p. 242 and note 44). No verb *(for)crymban* is recorded, but cf. Old English *crumb* 'crooked, bent', and *crymbing* 'curvature, bend'.

318 SAURON DEFEATED

(v) The page preserved from Edwin Lowdham's manuscript written in Númenórean script

My father's representations of this page are reproduced on pp. 319–21. The first form, here called Text I, is written on both sides of a single sheet as was Edwin Lowdham's, and represents the Old English text given on pp. 313–14; as already explained, this was written to accompany the account in the manuscript E. My father wrote it with a dipping pen, and where the ink ran pale parts of many letters, especially the fine strokes, are extremely faint in the original and disappear entirely in reproduction. To remedy this I have worked over a photocopy of the original and darkened the strokes to make them visible; and I have added line-numbers in the margins to make my commentary on the *tengwar* easier to follow.

Text II corresponds to the later Old English version in the typescript F, but it covers only one side of a sheet and extends only to the words *swé adwalde he for(néan)* (p. 257): at that point, as it appears, it was abandoned. This may or may not relate to my father's note (p. 279): 'the Anglo-Saxon should *not* be written in Númenórean script'.

The reproductions of these pages are followed by commentaries on the scripts, which differ in the two versions. These commentaries are reproduced from my manuscript, since it would be very much more difficult to print them.

Text I was written quickly and has a number of errors; Text II was more carefully done. Some pages of notes accompany the original texts, but these are very rough and difficult jottings and have not proved of much help in deducing the structure. There can be no doubt that these texts were to some degree experimental, especially in the use of the diacritic marks and in the application of the script to Old English.

In what I take to be the first of these *tengwar* texts (not reproduced), corresponding to part of the Old English text given on p. 316, the vowel-diacritics differ from the usage in Text I. Those used for *o* and *y* in Text I are here used for *u* and *o*, while *y* is rendered by that for *u* together with a single dot (= *i*), reflecting the historical origin of Old English *y* in many instances from *u* followed by *i* in the next syllable.

The surviving page of Edwin Lowdham's manuscript
Text I, recto

The surviving page of Edwin Lowdham's manuscript
Text I, verso

The surviving page of Edwin Lowdham's manuscript
Text II

322 SAURON DEFEATED

Text I

In the following analysis references to the text are by page and line-number, as '2:26' = line 26 of the verso page. The consonants are set out simply in alphabetical order, not according to phonetic function.

b ᵹ

c In Old English the letter *c* had 'front' and 'back' ('palatal' and 'velar') values, the front stop becoming [tš] as in *church* in later Old English. This distinction is represented here:

for the back stop, as in *ac* (1:2), *folc* (1:20); for the original front stop, as in *cyrre* (2:6-7, where the symbol is the last letter of line 6), *eces* (2:20). Thus the *c* in *undeadlican* (1:3) and in *deadlice* (1:7) is differently represented.

d For *ld* see *l*.

f In Old English the letter *f* was used in medial positions between voiced sounds to represent the voiced spirant [v]; thus 'v' will be found in many words where the Old English text has *f*, as *lifes* (1:8), *næfre* (2:26).

g In Old English the letter *g* (3) had not only front and back values but also stop and spirant. The back stop is represented here, as in *gode* (1:22); also in *ng*, where the nasal is indicated by a horizontal line above: *langung* (1:4).

The back spirant has the vertical rising not descending, as in *hogode* (2:6), *unhalgum* (2:14).

The front stop is represented. In late Old English this became [dž] as in *judge*; this appears in the words

THE NOTION CLUB PAPERS (PART TWO)   323

secganne (2:11), *unasecgendlice* (2:13-14), where *cg* is a
graph for *gg*, hence the mark of doubling placed below the
sign : ⬚ *secganne*.

The front spirant, which in Modern English has become *y*
initially or has combined to form diphthongs, has the vertical
rising, *ccl*, as in ⬚ *þegn* (1:19), ⬚ *~gearde*
(1:21), ⬚ *igland* (2:22), ⬚ *fyrgen* [cf. *Firien*
in *LR*] (2:22), ⬚ *segl* (2:24).

h   λ; d   The breath [h], only found initially, is represented by λ. The voiceless back spirant [χ] is represented by
d (cf. d under *g*), as in ⬚ *þeah* (1:17), ⬚ *ealh* (2:10),
⬚ *woh* (2:20).

ht may be represented by a combinatory sign ⬚ as in
⬚ *þuhte* (1:11), or ⬚ as in ⬚ *mihton* (1:8), accord-
-ing to the front or back position of the spirant (*cl, d*); but
the verticals may be written separately, as ⬚ *ahte* (1:26).

l   ⬚; *ld* ⬚ as in ⬚ *wuldor* (1:4)

m   ⬚

n   ⬚

þ   ⬚   (written ⬚ in *upahæfenlice* 1:22)

r   ⬚

s   ⬚ ; at the end of words often written as a curl, as for ex-
in ⬚ *facnes* (2:5). As in the case of *f*, in Old English
s was used in medial positions between voiced sounds to repre-
-sent the voiced spirant [z]. The only example of [z] in the
text is *alysan* (1:8), where it is written with the sign ⬚.

sc (becoming in the course of Old English [ʃ] as in *ship*)
is written with a combinatory sign ⬚ as in ⬚ *scort* ['short']
(1:11), ⬚ *deapscua* (2:15).

t þ For *ht* see *h*.

th h; ꝧ In Old English, as with *f/v, s/z*, the voiceless spirant (as in Modern English *thin*) and the voiced (as in *other*) appear in different positions in words, but in this case there were two symbols, the barred d 'ð' and the Runic 'þ' ('thorn'). These were not used, however, to distinguish the sounds.

The Old English text uses the signs indiscriminately, as is commonly the case in O.E. manuscripts; thus for example both þeah and ðeah occur. But it is curious that although the distinction between h and ꝧ was phonetic, between voiceless and voiced, no use is made of it: thus we find ·hiⱥ at 2:5 (where the text in modern script has þeah) but hoiⱥ at 1:17 (where it has ðeah).

v ꝧ On the frequent occurrence of ꝧ where the Old English word is spelt with an *f* see under *f*. The only other instance is abꝥ́ḿ *Avallon* (2:18).

w ȝ In ᚱᚾjⱥ *hreow* (2:17) the sign ᚢ '*u*' is used (see under *Vowels*).

hw is represented by ḥ as in ḥꝧ *hwæt* (1:1).

x ꝗ as in ȝjꝗ *weox* (1:20).

z ȝ See under *s*.

Vowels

Vowels are normally expressed by diacritic signs (*tehtar*):

a	/	i	.
æ	∴	o	ʾ
e	..	u	͡
		y	͜

These *precede* the consonant if placed *above* it and follow it if placed below, as in hꝺɲ̇ *ðære*, ꝕ̈ *ende*. The diacritics of *o* and *u* are not used in the subscript position.

The diacritics are very frequently borne on 'carriers', the short carrier ı being used for short vowels and the long carrier ȷ for long vowels (as *bj sǽ*, 1:1).

The Old English diphthongs are not represented by simple signs or diacritics: thus ⳡⳡⳡ *heorte* (1:2). The diphthong *ea* as representing [æa] is written with the diacritics of *æ* and *a*. as ⳡⳡⳡⳡ *westweard* (1:2); but *e+a* in ⳡⳡⳡⳡ *~gearde* (1:21).

The glide '*i, y*' is *a* in ⳡⳡⳡⳡⳡ *Meneltyúla* (2:11). ⳡⳡ *iú* (2:26).

In certain positions (chiefly in prefixes and finally) *a* is written as a letter, *ɑ*, though not invariably: so ⳡⳡ ⳡⳡⳡ *swa hyra* (1:4), ⳡⳡ ... ⳡⳡⳡⳡ *swa arædde* (1:12); also always *ɑ* in ⳡⳡⳡⳡⳡ *Sauron*. Long *a* has both letter and diacritic in ⳡⳡ *má* (1:5). Similarly *u* may be written as a letter, *u*, *û*; so ⳡⳡ *nú* (2:26), ⳡⳡⳡ *scúa* (2:27).

Other signs

Doubling is shown by two inclined strokes beneath the letter, or in the case of *ꞇ* within it : as ⳡⳡⳡ *Eresse* (1:6), ⳡⳡ *ealle* (1:1).

A horizontal line above the letter represents a nasal in such combinations as *nd, ng, mp,* as ⳡⳡ *ende* (1:9), ⳡⳡⳡⳡ *cyning* (1:23); in *nn* it therefore acts as a doubling sign, as ⳡⳡⳡ *þonne* (1:15).

The Old English sign ȝ *ond, and* 'and' is used (1:21 &c).

Errors

The text was written quickly, and there are a number of un-questionable errors, as for example : ⳡⳡⳡⳡ for ⳡⳡⳡⳡ *Éarendles* in 1:10, ⳡⳡ for ⳡⳡ *Eldum* in 1:11, ⳡⳡⳡⳡ '*Sauron*' in 2:4, ⳡⳡⳡⳡ for ⳡⳡⳡⳡ *gefaran* in 2:19. In some cases apparent errors may reflect indecision or rejected forms, as *y* for *r* in ⳡⳡⳡ *ǽfre* 1:4 (ⳡⳡⳡⳡ *næfre* 2:26), ⳡⳡⳡⳡ *unryht* 1:14, and ⳡȷ *he* for ⳡȷ *hí* twice in 1:1 and again in 1:2.

326   SAURON DEFEATED   V

Text II

In this form of the script the values of the *tengwar* are the same, the differences from Text I lying chiefly in the use of the vowel diacritics.   In Text II the diacritics follow the consonants; and while *i, o, u, y* remain the same those representing *a, æ, e* are now:

a   ∴

æ   ''

e   /

Thus *gefyrn* in Text I (1:12) is written ⟨tengwar⟩, but in Text II ⟨tengwar⟩ (line 2).

Further, the diacritics of *o* and *u* can be written subscript, as for example in ⟨tengwar⟩ *weorulde*, ⟨tengwar⟩ *oferliodon*, both in line 1.

As in Text I the Old English diphthong written *ea* but phonetically [æa] is represented by the diacritics of *æ* and *a*, thus ⟨tengwar⟩ *heara* in line 2; on the other hand, in ⟨tengwar⟩ *Westwearena* (lines 6-7) *ea* is represented by *e+a*.

In Text II long vowels can be shown by a subscript j; this is evidently the tail of the long carrier j. So ⟨tengwar⟩ *sǽ* (line 1), ⟨tengwar⟩ *þás* (3), ⟨tengwar⟩ ⟨tengwar⟩ *wéox swíðe* (6).

A problem lies in the representation of names. Ramer says of the text that the proper names, when they are not Old English translations, are in the same script, 'but the letters are then quite differently used'.   In the Old English text in modern script these names are set within brackets. In Text II appear only *Zigūr* (*Zigūre*) and *Tarcalion*, which are placed between marks of citation and represented thus:

line 5   ⟨tengwar⟩   *Zigūr*

line 10 ⟨tengwar⟩   *(to) Zigūre*

line 11 ⟨tengwar⟩   *Zigūr*

line 8   ⟨tengwar⟩   *Tarcalion*

THE NOTION CLUB PAPERS (PART TWO)   327

ᛒᛏ is here used with the value 'z'. (It is a feature of the script in Text II that ᚻ and 'ᛒᛏ (= 'th') are often but not always / with the vertical stroke extended downwards, to a greater or lesser degree: so ᛒᚾᚦᛗ (*forðon*, line 2), ᚷᛁᚦᛗ (*seoþþan*, line 4), ᚦᚢᛈ (*þæt*, line 3), but ᚻᚳᛞᛗ (*þegn*, line 5). In ᛒᛏ = 'z' the vertical is not extended downwards; but whether this distinction, not in any case very clearly marked, is significant I cannot say.)

The other consonants in *Zigūr*, and in *Tarcalion*, are not different from those used to represent the Old English; but the use of the diacritics is mysterious. In *Zigūr(e)* · = *i*, ⌐ = *u*, / = *e*, and a subscript ⌡ = long vowel, as in the rest of the text; but in one case of *Zigūr* a single dot is placed under *r*, in the other not. In *Tarcalion* single dots are placed under *r* and *n*; C̈ꞌ presumably represents *lio* (but with ·· = *i*), but there is no representation of the two occurrences of *a* in the name.

In this text there is only one clear error: this is the word ᛚᚷᚦ 'sté' in the last line of the page, for ᛚᚷ *swé* ('so'), written as ᛒᚷᚠ in line 2.

PART THREE

THE DROWNING
OF ANADÛNÊ

With the Third Version of
THE FALL OF NÚMENOR

And Lowdham's Report on
THE ADUNAIC LANGUAGE

THE DROWNING OF ANADÛNÊ

(i) The third version of The Fall of Númenor

Before coming to *The Drowning of Anadûnê* it is necessary to turn first to the original narrative of the legend of Númenor, which arose in close association with *The Lost Road* (see V.9). This, *The Fall of Númenor*, is extant (in addition to an initial sketch) in two versions, given in V.13 ff., which I called FN I and FN II, the second being closely similar to the first for the greater part of its length. Some subsequent work was done on this text during the period of the writing of *The Lord of the Rings*, including a rewriting of the passage describing 'the World Made Round' and a development of the concluding section concerning Beleriand and the Last Alliance (see V.31 ff.); but since the name *Ondor* appears in the latter passage it can be dated before February 1942, when *Ondor* became *Gondor* (VII.423); at that time my father was working on Book III of *The Lord of the Rings*.

Now there is a further text of *The Fall of Númenor* in fine manuscript, which I referred to but did not print in Vol.V; I noted there that 'this version, improved and altered in detail, shows however very little further advance in narrative substance,' and concluded therefore that it belongs to the same period as the revisions just referred to, i.e. to a relatively early stage in the writing of *The Lord of the Rings*. Since *The Drowning of Anadûnê* shows such an extraordinary departure from *The Fall of Númenor* I give the third version of the latter in full here, calling it 'FN III', to make comparison of the two works easier. I have again introduced the paragraph numbers that I inserted in the earlier versions; and various alterations that were made to FN III subsequently are shown as such.

The Last Tales

1. The Fall of Númenor

§1   In the Great Battle, when Fionwë son of Manwë overthrew Morgoth, the three houses of the Men of Beleriand were friends and allies of the Elves, and they wrought many deeds of valour. But men of other kindreds turned to evil and fought for Morgoth, and after the victory of the Lords of the West those that were not destroyed fled back east into Middle-earth. There many of their race wandered still in the unharvested lands, wild

332 SAURON DEFEATED FN III

and lawless, refusing the summons alike of Fionwë and of Morgoth to aid them in their war. And the evil men who had served Morgoth became their masters; and the creatures of Morgoth that escaped from the ruin of Thangorodrim came among them and cast over them a shadow of fear. For the gods [> Valar] forsook for a time the Men of Middle-earth who had refused their summons and had taken the friends of Morgoth to be their lords; and men were troubled by many evil things that Morgoth had devised in the days of his dominion: demons, and dragons and ill-shapen beasts, and the unclean orcs, that are mockeries of the creatures of Ilúvatar; and the lot of men was unhappy.

But Manwë put forth Morgoth, and shut him beyond the World in the Void that is without; and he cannot [> could not] return again into the World, present and visible, while the Lords are [> the Lords of the West were] enthroned. Yet his will remaineth, and guideth [> remained, and guided] his servants; and it moveth [> moved] them ever to seek the overthrow of the gods [> Valar] and the hurt of those that obey [> obeyed] them. When Morgoth was thrust forth, the gods [> Valar] held council. The Elves [> Eldar] were summoned to return into the West; and those that obeyed dwelt once more in Eressëa, the Lonely Isle; and that land was named anew Avallon: for it is hard by Valinor and within sight of the Blessed Realm. But to men of the three faithful houses rich reward was given. Fionwë son of Manwë came among them and taught them; and he gave them wisdom, and power, and life stronger than any others have of mortal race. [*Added:* and the span of their years, being un-assailed by sickness, was thrice that of Men of Middle-earth, and to the descendants of Húrin the Steadfast even longer years were granted, / even to three hundreds [> as is later told].][1]

§2 A land was made for them to dwell in, neither part of Middle-earth, nor of Valinor; for it was sundered from either by a wide sea, yet it was nearer to Valinor. It was raised by Ossë out of the depths of the Great Water, and it was established by Aulë and enriched by Yavanna; and the Eldar brought thither flowers and fountains out of Avallon, and they wrought gardens there of great beauty, in which at times the children of the Gods [> Valar] would walk. That land the Valar called Andor, the Land of Gift; and by its own folk it was at first called Vinya, the Young; but in the days of its pride they named it Númenor, that is Westernesse, for it lay west of all lands inhabited by mortals;

FN III   THE DROWNING OF ANADÛNÊ   333

yet it was far from the true West, for that is Valinor, the land of the Gods. But the glory of Númenor was thrown down [> overthrown] and its name perished; and after its ruin it was named in the legends of those that fled from it Atalantë, the Downfallen.

Of old the chief city and haven of that land was in the midst of its western coasts, and it was called Undúnië [> Andúnië],[2] because it faced the sunset. But the high place of the king was at Númenos in the heart of the land, the tower and citadel that was built by Elros son of Ëarendel [>Ëarendil], whom the gods and elves and men chose to be the lord [> who (was) appointed to be the first lord] of the Númenóreans. He was descended from the line of both Hador and Bëor, fathers of Men, and in part also from both the Eldar and the Valar, for Idril and Lúthien were his foremothers. But Elros and all his folk were mortal; for the Valar may not withdraw the gift of death, which cometh to men from Ilúvatar. [*This passage, from 'He was descended . . .', was struck out and replaced by the following rider:* 'Now Elrond, and Elros his brother, were descended from the line of both Hador and of Bëor, fathers of Men, and in part also both from the Eldar and the Valar, for Idril and Lúthien daughter of Melian were their foremothers. None others among Men of the Elder Days had kinship with the Elves, and therefore they were called Halfelven. The Valar indeed may not withdraw the gift of death, which cometh to Men from Ilúvatar, but in the matter of the Halfelven Ilúvatar gave them judgement. And this they judged: choice should be given to the brethren. And Elrond chose to remain with the Firstborn, and to him the life of the Firstborn was given, and yet a grace was added, that choice was never annulled, and while the world lasted he might return, if he would, to mortal men, and die. But to Elros, who chose to be a king of men, still a great span of years was granted, seven times that of mortal men; and all his line, the kings and lords of the royal house of Númenor, [*added:* being descended from Húrin,] had long life even according to the span of the Númenóreans, for some of the kings that sat at Númenos lived four hundred years. But Elros lived five hundred years, and ruled the Númenóreans four hundred years and ten. Thus, though long in life and assailed by no sickness, the men of Númenor were mortal still.] Yet the speech of Númenor was the speech of the Eldar of the Blessed Realm, and the Númenóreans conversed with the Elves, and were permitted to look upon Valinor from afar; for

334   SAURON DEFEATED   FN III

their ships went often to Avallon, and there their mariners were suffered to dwell for a while.

§3   In the wearing of time the people of Númenor grew great and glorious, in all things more like to the Firstborn than any other of the kindreds of Men; yet they were less fair and less wise than the Elves, though greater in stature. For the Númenóreans were exceedingly tall, taller than the tallest of the sons of men in Middle-earth. Above all arts they nourished ship-building and sea-craft, and became mariners whose like shall never be again, since the world has been diminished. They ranged from Eressëa in the West to the shores of Middle-earth, and came even into the inner seas; and they sailed about the North and the South and glimpsed from their high prows the Gates of Morning in the East. And they appeared among the wild men and filled them with wonder and dismay; for men in the shadows of the world deemed that they were gods or the sons of gods out of the West. Here and there the Númenóreans sowed good seed in the waste-lands, and they taught to the wild men such lore and wisdom as they could comprehend; but for the most part the men of Middle-earth feared them and fled; for they were under the sway of Sauron and the lies of Morgoth and they believed that the gods were terrible and cruel. Wherefore out of that far time are descended the echoes of legends both bright and dark; but the shadow lay heavy upon men, for the Númenóreans came only seldom among them and they tarried never long in any place. Upon all the waters of the world they sailed, seeking they knew not what, yet their hearts were set westward; and they began to hunger for the undying bliss of Valinor, and ever their desire and unquiet increased as their power and glory grew.

§4   The gods forbade them to sail beyond the Lonely Isle and would not permit them to land in Valinor; for the Númenóreans were mortal, and though the Lords of the West had rewarded them with long life, they could not take from them the weariness of the world that cometh at last, and they died, even their kings of the seed of Ëarendel, and their span was brief in the eyes of the Elves. And they began to murmur against this decree, and a great discontent grew among them. Their masters of knowledge sought unceasingly for secrets that should prolong their lives; and they sent spies to seek hidden lore in Avallon; and the gods were angered.

§5   Now it came to pass [added: in the days of Tar-kalion,

FN III   THE DROWNING OF ANADÛNÊ   335

and twelve kings had ruled that land before him,][3] that Sauron, servant of Morgoth, grew strong in Middle-earth; and he learned of the power and splendour of the Númenóreans, and of their allegiance to the gods; and he feared lest they should come and wrest from him the dominion of the East and rescue the men of Middle-earth from the Shadow. And the king from his mariners heard also rumour of Sauron, and it was reported that he would make himself a king, greater even than the king of Númenor. Wherefore, taking no counsel of the gods or of the Elves, Tar-kalion the king sent his messengers to Sauron and commanded him to come and do homage. And Sauron, being filled with malice and cunning, humbled himself and came; and he beguiled the Númenóreans with signs and wonders. Little by little Sauron turned their hearts towards Morgoth, his master; and he prophesied to them, and lied, saying that Morgoth would come again into the world. And Sauron spake to Tar-kalion, and to Tar-ilien his queen, and promised them life unending and the dominion of the earth, if they would turn unto Morgoth. And they believed him, and fell under the Shadow, and the greater part of their people followed them. And Tar-kalion raised a great temple to Morgoth upon the Mountain of Ilúvatar in the midst of the land; and Sauron dwelt there, and all Númenor was under his vigilance. [*This passage, from 'upon the Mountain of Ilúvatar ...', was struck out and replaced by the following:* in the midst of the city of Númenos,[4] and its dome rose like a black hill glowering over the land; and smokes issued from it, for in that temple the Númenóreans made hideous sacrifice to Morgoth, beseeching the Lord of Darkness to deliver them from Death. But the hallowed place of Ilúvatar was upon the summit of the Mountain Menelmin, Pillar of Heaven, in the midst of the land, and thither men had been wont to climb to offer thanksgiving. There only in all Númenor Sauron dared never to set his foot, and he forbade [any] to go there under pain of death. Few dared to disobey him, even if they so wished, for Sauron had many eyes and all the ways of the land were under his vigilance. But some there were who remained faithful, and did not bow to him, and of these the chief were Elendil the fair, and his sons Anárion and Isildur, and they were of the royal blood of Ëarendel, though not of the line direct.]

§6 But in the passing of the years Tar-kalion felt the oncoming of old age, and he was troubled; but Sauron said that

336   SAURON DEFEATED   FN III

the bounty of Morgoth was withheld by the gods, and that to obtain plentitude of power and freedom from death the king must be master of the West. And the fear of death was heavy upon Tar-kalion. Therefore at his command the Númenóreans made a great armament; and their might and skill had grown exceedingly in those days, for they had in these matters the aid of Sauron. The fleets of the Númenóreans were like a land of many islands, and their masts were like a forest of mountain-trees, and their banners like the streamers of a thunderstorm, and their sails were scarlet and black. And they moved slowly into the West, for all the winds were stilled, and all the world was silent in the fear of that time. And they encompassed Avallon; and it is said that the Elves mourned and sickness came upon them, for the light of Valinor was cut off by the cloud of the Númenóreans. Then Tar-kalion assailed the shores of Valinor, and he cast forth bolts of thunder, and fire came upon Túna, and flame and smoke rose about Taniquetil.

§7   But the gods made no answer. Then the vanguard of the Númenóreans set foot upon the forbidden shores, and they encamped in might upon the borders of Valinor. But the heart of Manwë was sorrowful and dismayed, and he called upon Ilúvatar, and took power and counsel from the Maker; and the fate and fashion of the world was changed. The silence of the gods was broken and their power made manifest; and Valinor was sundered from the earth, and a rift appeared in the midst of the Great Sea, east of Avallon.

Into this chasm the Great Sea plunged, and the noise of the falling waters filled all the earth, and the smoke of the cataracts rose above the tops of the everlasting mountains. But all the ships of Númenor that were west of Avallon were drawn down into the abyss, and they were drowned; and Tar-kalion the golden and bright Ilien his queen fell like stars into the dark, and they perished out of all knowledge. But the mortal warriors that had set foot upon the Land of the Gods were buried under fallen hills; there it is said they lie imprisoned in the Caves of the Forgotten until the day of Doom and the Last Battle.

§8   Then Ilúvatar cast back the Great Seas west of Middle-earth and the Empty Lands east of it, and new lands and new seas were made; and the world was diminished, for Valinor and Eressëa were taken from it into the realm of hidden things. And thereafter, however a man might sail, he could never again reach the True West, but would come back weary at last to the

FN III   THE DROWNING OF ANADÛNÊ   337

place of his beginning; for all lands and seas were equally distant from the centre of the earth. There was flood and great confusion of waters in that time, and sea covered much that in the Elder Days had been dry, both in the West and East of Middle-earth.

§9 Númenor, being nigh to the east of the great rift, was utterly thrown down, and overwhelmed in the sea, and its glory perished, and only a remnant of all its people escaped the ruin of those days. Some by the command of Tar-kalion, and some of their own will (because they still revered the gods and would not go with war into the West) had remained behind when the fleets set sail, and they sat in their ships upon the east coast of the land, lest the issue of war should be evil. Therefore, being protected for a while by the wall of their land, they avoided the draught of the sea; and many fled into the East, and came at length to the shores of Middle-earth.

Small remnant of all the mighty people that had perished were those that came up out of the devouring sea upon the wings of the winds of wrath, and shorn were they of their pride and power of old. But to those that looked out from the seaward hills and beheld their coming, riding upon the storm out of the mist and the darkness and the rumour of water, their black sails against the falling sun, terrible and strong they seemed, and the fear of the tall kings came into lands far from the sea.

§10 For lords and kings of men the Númenóreans became, and nigh to the western shores of Middle-earth they established realms and strong places. Some few were indeed evil, being of those who had hearkened to Sauron and still did not forsake him in their hearts; but the most were those of good will who had revered the gods and remembered the wisdom of old. Yet all alike were filled with the desire of long life upon earth, and the thought of death was heavy upon them. Their fate had cast them east upon Middle-earth, but their hearts still were westward. And they built mightier houses for their dead than for their living, and endowed their buried kings with unavailing treasure; for their wise men hoped still to discover the secret of prolonging life, and maybe of recalling it. Yet it is said that the span of their lives, which had of old been thrice that of lesser men, dwindled slowly; and they achieved only the art of preserving incorrupt the dead flesh of men. Wherefore the kingdoms of the western world became a place of tombs and

338   SAURON DEFEATED   FN III

were filled with ghosts. And in the fantasy of their hearts, amid the confusion of legends concerning half-forgotten things that once had been, they imagined in their thought a land of shades, filled with the wraiths of the things that are upon the mortal earth; and many deemed that this land was in the West and ruled by the gods, and that in shadow the dead should come · there, bearing with them the shadows of their possessions, who could in the body find the True West no more. Therefore in after days many would bury their dead in ships, setting them forth in pomp upon the sea by the west coasts of the ancient world.

§11   Now the blood of the Númenóreans remained most among men of those western lands and shores; and the memory of the primeval world abode most strongly there, where the old paths to the West had aforetime set out from Middle-earth. For the ancient line of the world remained in the mind of Ilúvatar, and in the thought of the gods, and in the memory of the world, as a shape and plan that has been changed and yet endureth. And it has been likened to a plain of air, or to a straight vision that bendeth not to the curving of the earth, or to a level bridge that rises slowly above the heavy air. Of old many of the exiles of Númenor could still see, some clearly and some more faintly, the paths to the True West; and they believed that at times from a high place they could descry the peaks of Taniquetil at the end of the Straight Road, high above the world. Therefore they built very high towers in those days, and their holy places were upon the tops of mountains, for they would climb, if it might be, above the mists of Middle-earth into the clearer air that doth not veil the vision of things far off.

§12   But ever the number of those that had the ancient sight dwindled, and those that had it not and could not conceive it in their thought scorned the builders of towers, and trusted to ships that sailed upon the water. But they came only to the lands of the new world, and found them like to those of the old and subject to death; and they reported that the world was round. For upon the Straight Road only the gods could walk, and only the ships of the Elves could journey; for being straight that road passed through the air of breath and flight and rose above it, and traversed Ilmen in which no mortal flesh can endure; whereas the surface of the earth was bent, and bent were the seas that lay upon it, and bent also were the heavy airs that were above them. Yet it is said that even of those Númenóreans of old who had the straight vision there were some who did not

FN III   THE DROWNING OF ANADÛNÊ   339

comprehend this, and they were busy to contrive ships that should rise above the waters of the world and hold to the imagined seas. But they achieved only ships that would sail in the air of breath. And these ships, flying, came also to the lands of the new world, and to the East of the old world; and they reported that the world was round. Therefore many abandoned the gods and put them out of their legends. But men of Middle-earth looked up with fear and wonder seeing the Númenóreans that descended out of the sky; and they took these mariners of the air to be gods, and some of the Númenóreans were content that this should be so.

§13   Yet not all the hearts of the Númenóreans were crooked; and knowledge of the days before the Downfall and of the wisdom descended from the Elf-friends, their fathers, was long preserved among them. And the wisest among them taught that the fate of Men was not bounded by the round path, nor set for ever upon the straight. For the round has no end, but no escape; and the straight is true, but has an end within the world, and that is the fate of the Elves. But the fate of Men, they said, is neither round nor ended, and is not complete within the world.

But even the wisdom of the wise was filled with sorrow and regret; and they remembered bitterly how the ruin was brought about and the cutting off of Men from their portion of the Straight Path. Therefore they avoided the shadow of Morgoth according to their power, and Sauron they held in hatred. And they assailed his temples and their servants, and there were wars among the mighty of Middle-earth, of which only the echoes now remain.

The concluding section (§14) of the earlier versions of *The Fall of Númenor* concerning Beleriand (see p. 331) was omitted in FN III.

Accepting the conclusion (see p. 331) that the version just given, as it was originally written, comes from a much earlier stage in the writing of *The Lord of the Rings* than do *The Notion Club Papers*, it seems almost certain that the alterations and additions made to it belong to the period of the *Papers* and *The Drowning of Anadûnê*. The chief evidence for this[5] lies in the addition to §5 stating that Tar-kalion was the thirteenth king of Númenor, and in the correction in §5 of the description of the temple: it was not on the Mountain of Ilúvatar, but 'in the midst of the city of Númenos' (see notes 3 and 4).

The most remarkable, and indeed astonishing, feature of these later additions to FN III is the statement in §2 that while 'the life of the Firstborn' was given to Elrond in accordance with his choice, 'yet a

340 SAURON DEFEATED FN III

grace was added, that choice was never annulled, and while the world lasted he might return, if he would, to mortal men, and die.' To my present knowledge no such thing is said elsewhere of the Choice of Elrond; and contrast Appendix A (I, i) to *The Lord of the Rings*: 'At the end of the First Age the Valar gave to the Half-elven *an irrevocable choice* to which kindred they would belong.' This passage in FN III concerning Elrond and Elros reappeared years later in the *Akallabêth*, but with this sentence removed (*The Silmarillion*, p. 261).

NOTES

1 On the threefold span of the Númenóreans see p. 378, §13. – *The descendants of Húrin the Steadfast*: presumably an inadvertence, for Huor, father of Tuor, father of Eärendil; but *Húrin* is repeated in the addition to §2. Cf. the note given in VII.6, 'Trotter is a man of Elrond's race descendant of Túrin', where *Túrin* is presumably a slip for *Tuor*.

2 *Undúnië*: *Andúnië* is the form in FN II, but on the amanuensis typescript made from FN II (V.31) the form was changed to *Undúnië*.

3 Tar-kalion became the fourteenth (not the thirteenth) king of Númenor by correction of the second text of *The Drowning of Anadûnê* (see p. 381, §20).

4 On uncertainty with regard to the site of the temple see p. 384, §32.

5 On the back of the slip carrying the long addition to §2 concerning Elrond and Elros are rough notes in which there is a reference to the Adunaic language; but these are not dateable.

(ii) The original text of The Drowning of Anadûnê

It will become very evident that *The Drowning of Anadûnê* was as closely associated with Part Two of *The Notion Club Papers* as was the original *Fall of Númenor* with *The Lost Road*. I shall give first the original draft, and postpone observations about it to the conclusion.

The draft is a typescript of extreme roughness, with a great many typing errors, and I have little doubt that my father, for some reason, and for the first time, composed a primary draft entirely *ab initio* on a typewriter, typing at speed. Certainly there is no trace among all this great collection of texts and notes of any still more 'primary' narrative (although there are preliminary sketches which are given later, pp. 397 ff.). I print it here essentially as it was typed, correcting the obvious errors and here and there inserting punctuation, but ignoring subsequent correction. Such correction is largely confined to the opening paragraphs, after which it ceases: it looks as if my father saw that it would be impossible to carry out a wholesale rewriting on a single-spaced typescript with narrow margins. In any case these corrections

DA I THE DROWNING OF ANADÛNÊ 341

were taken up into the second text, which I also give in full. One name that was consistently changed, however, is *Balāi* > *Avalāi*, as far as §16, where *Avalāi* appears in the typescript as typed. I have extended the marks of length over vowels throughout the text: my father's typewriter having no such marks, he inserted them in pencil, and often omitted them.

The numbered paragraphs have of course no manuscript warrant: I have inserted them to make subsequent reference and comparison easier. This first text has in fact little division into paragraphs, and my divisions are made largely on the basis of the following version.

I shall refer to this text subsequently as 'DA I'. It had no title as typed, but *The Drowning of Númenor* was pencilled in afterwards.

§1 Before the coming of Men there were many Powers that governed Earth, and they were Eru-bēnī, servants of God, and in the earliest recorded tongue they were called Balāi. Some were lesser and some greater. The mightiest and the chieftain of them all was Mēlekō.

§2 But long ago, even in the making of Earth, he pondered evil; he became a rebel against Eru, desiring the whole world for his own and to have none above him. Therefore Manawē his brother endeavoured to rule the earth and the Powers according to the will of Eru; and Manawē dwelt in the West. But Mēlekō remained, dwelling in hiding in the North, and he worked evil, and he had the greater power, and the Great Lands were darkened.

§3 And at the appointed time Men were born into the world, and they came in a time of war; and they fell swiftly under the domination of Mēlekō. And he now came forth and appeared as a Great King and as a god, and his rule was evil, and his worship unclean; and Men were estranged from Eru and from the Balāi, his servants.

§4 But there were some of the fathers of Men who repented, seeing the evil of King Mēlekō, and their houses returned with sorrow to the allegiance of Eru, and they were befriended by the Balāi, and they were called the Eruhil, the children of God. And the Balāi and the Eruhil made war on Mēlekō, and for that time they destroyed his kingdom and threw down his black throne. But Mēlekō was not destroyed and he went again for a while in hiding, unseen by Men. But his evil was still ever at work, and cruel kings and evil temples arose ever in the world, and the most part of Mankind were their servants; and they made war on the Eruhil.

342 SAURON DEFEATED DA I

§5 And the Balāi in grief withdrew ever further west (or if they did not so they faded and became secret voices and shadows of the days of old); and the most part of the Eruhil followed them. Though it is said that some of these good men, simple folk, shepherds and the like, dwelt in the heart of the Great Lands.

§6 But all the nobler of the Eruhil and those closest in the friendship of the Balāi, who had helped most in the war on the Black Throne, wandered away until they came to the last shores of the Great Seas. There they halted and were filled with dread and longing; for the Balāi for the most part passed over the sea seeking the realm of Manawē. And there instructed by the Balāi men learned the craft of ship-building and of sailing in the wind; and they built many small ships. But they did not dare to essay the deep waters, and journeyed mostly up and down the coasts and among the nearer isles.

§7 And it was by their ships that they were saved. For evil men multiplied in those days and pursued the Eruhil with hatred; and evil men inspired by the evil spirit of Mēlekō grew cunning and cruel in the arts of war and the making of many weapons; and the Eruhil were hard to put to it to maintain any land in which to dwell.

§8 And in those dark days of fear and war there arose a man among the Eruhil and his name was Earendil the Sea-friend, for his daring upon the sea was great. And it came into his heart that he would build a ship greater than any that had yet been built, and that he would sail out into the deep water and come maybe to the land of Manawē and there get help for his kinsfolk. And he let build a great ship and he called it Wingalōtē,[1] the Foam-flower.

§9 And when it was all ready he said farewell to his sons and his wife and all his kin; for he was minded to sail alone. And he said: 'It is likely that you will see me never again, and if you do not, then continue your war, and endure until the end. But if I do not fail of my errand, then also you may not see me again, but a sign you will see, and then have hope.'

§10 But Earendel[2] passed over the Great Sea and came to the Blessed Realm and spoke to Manawē.

§11 [Rejected at once: And Manawē said that he had not now the power to war against Mēlekō, who moreover was the rightful governor of Earth, though his right might seem to have been destroyed by his rebellion; and that the governance of the

DAI   THE DROWNING OF ANADÛNÊ   343

earth was now in the hands of] And Manawē said that Eru had forbidden the Balāi to make war by force; and that the earth was now in the hands of Men, to make or to mar. But because of their repentance and their fidelity he would give, as was permitted to him, a land for the Eruhil to dwell in if they would. And that land was a mighty island in the midst of the sea. But Manawē would not permit Earendil to return again amongst Men, since he had set foot in the Blessed Realm, where as yet no Death had come. And he took the ship of Earendil and filled it with silver flame and raised it above the world to sail in the sky, a marvel to behold.

§12   And the Eruhil on the shores of the sea beheld the light of it; and they knew that it was the sign of Earendil. And hope and courage was born in their hearts; and they gathered their ships, small and great, and all their goods, and set sail upon the deep waters, following the star. And there was a great calm in those days and all the winds were stilled. And the Eruhil came to the land that had been set for them, and they found it fair and fruitful, and they were glad. And they called that land Andōrē,[3] the land of Gift, though afterward it was mostly named Nūmenōrē, Westernesse.

§13   But not so did the Eruhil escape the doom of death that had been pronounced upon all Mankind; and they were mortal still; though for their fidelity they were rewarded by a threefold span, and their years were long and blissful and untroubled with sickness, so long as they remained true. And the Nūmenōreans grew wise and fair and glorious, the mightiest of men that have been; but their number was not great, for their children were few.

§14   And they were under the tutelage of the Balāi, and they took the language of the Balāi and forsook their own; and they wrote many things of lore and beauty in that tongue in the high tide of their realm, of which but little is now remembered. And they became mighty in all crafts, so that if they had had the mind they might easily have surpassed the evil kings of Middle-earth in the making of weapons and of war; but they were as yet men of peace; and of all arts they were most eager in the craft of ship-building, and in voyaging was the chief feat and delight of their younger men.

§15   But the Balāi as yet forbade them to sail westward out of sight of the western shores of Nūmenōr; and the Nūmenōr-eans were as yet content, though they did not fully understand

344   SAURON DEFEATED   DA I

the purpose of this ban. But the purpose was that the Eruhil should not be tempted to come to the Blessed Realm and there learn discontent, becoming enamoured of the immortality of the Balāi, and the deathlessness of all things in their land.

§16   For as yet the Balāi were permitted by Eru to maintain upon earth upon some isle or shore of the western lands still untrodden (it is not known for certain where; for Earendel alone of Men came ever thither and never again returned) an abiding place, an earthly paradise and a memorial of that which might have been, had not men turned to Mēlekō. And the Númenóreans named that land Avallondē the Haven of the Gods, for at times when all the air was clear and the sun was in the east they could descry, as them seemed, a city white-shining on a distant shore and great harbours and a tower; but only so when their own western haven, Andūniē of Númenōr, was low upon the skyline, and they dared not break the ban and sail further west. But to Númenōr the Avalāi came ever and anon, the children and the lesser ones of the Deathless Folk, some-times in oarless boats, sometimes as birds flying, sometimes in other fair shapes; and they loved the Númenóreans.

§17   And so it was that the voyages of the men of Western-esse in those days went east and not west from the darkness of the North to the heats of the South and beyond to the nether darkness. And the Eruhil came often to the shores of the Great Lands, and they took pity on the forsaken world of Middle-earth; and the young princes of the Númenóreans would come among the men of the Dark Ages, and they taught them language (for the native tongues of men of Middle-earth were yet rude and unshapen) and song, and many arts, such as they could compass, and they brought them corn and wine.

§18   And the men of Middle-earth were comforted, and in some places shook off somewhat the yoke of the offspring of Mēlekō; and they revered the memory of the Men out of the Sea and called them Gods, for in that time the Númenóreans did not settle or dwell in Middle-earth for long. For though their feet were set eastward their hearts were ever westward.

§19   Yet in the end all this bliss and betterment turned to evil again, and men fell, as it is said, a second time. For there arose a second manifestation of the power of darkness upon earth, and whether that was but a form of the Ancient or one of his old servants that waxed to new strength, is not known. And

DA I   THE DROWNING OF ANADÛNÊ   345

this evil thing was called by many names, but the Eruhil named
him Sauron, and men of Middle-earth (when they dared to
speak his name at all) named him mostly Zigūr the Great. And
he made himself a great king in the midst of the earth, and was
at first well-seeming and just and his rule was of benefit to all
men in their needs of the body; for he made them rich, whoso
would serve him. But those who would not were driven out into
the waste places. Yet Zigūr desired, as Mēlekō before, to be
both a king over all kings and as a god to men. And slowly his
power moved north and south, and ever westward; and he
heard of the coming of the Eruhil and he was wroth. And he
plotted in his heart how he might destroy Nūmenōr.

§20   And news came also to Nūmenōr and to Tarkalion the
king, Earendel's heir (for this title had all the kings of Nūmenōr,
and they were indeed descended in unbroken line from Elros the
son of Earendel), of Zigūr the Great, and how he purposed to
become master of all Middle-earth and after of the whole world.
And Tarkalion was angered, for the kings of Nūmenōr had
grown very glorious and proud in that time.

§21   And in the meanwhile evil, of which once long ago their
fathers had tasted, albeit they had after repented, awoke again
in the hearts of the Eruhil; for the desire of everlasting life and
the escape from death grew ever stronger upon them as their lot
in the land of Nūmenōr grew more blissful. And they began to
murmur in their hearts (and anon more openly) against the
doom of men; and especially against that ban which forbade
them to sail west or to visit the Blessed Realm.

§22   'For why should the Avalāi sit in peace unending there,'
said they, 'while we must die and go we know not whither,
leaving our own home; for the fault was not ours in the
beginning; and is not the author of evil Mēlekō himself one of
the Avalāi?'

§23   And the Avalāi knowing what was said, and seeing the
cloud of evil grow, were grieved, and they came less often to
Nūmenōr; and those that came spoke earnestly to the Eruhil;
and tried to teach them of the fashion and fate of the world,
saying that the world was round, and that if they sailed into the
utmost West, yet would they but come back again to the East
and so to the places of their setting out, and the world would
seem to them but a prison.

§24   'And so it is to those of your strange race,' said the
Avalāi. 'And Eru does not punish without benefit; nor are his

346   SAURON DEFEATED   DA I

mercies without sternness. For we (you say) are unpunished and dwell ever in bliss; and so it is that we do not die, but we cannot escape, and we are bound to this world, never again to leave it, till all is changed. And you (you murmur) are punished, and so it is that ye die, but ye escape and leave the world and are not bound thereto. Which therefore of us should envy the other?

§25 'Ye us maybe, for of you is required the greater trust, knowing not what lies before you in a little while. But whereas we know nothing of the mind of Eru in this (for he has not revealed anything of his purpose with you unto the Avalāi), we say to you that that trust, if you give it, will not be despised; and though it take many ages of Men, and is yet beyond the sight of the Avalāi, that Iluvatar the Father will not let those perish for ever who love him and who love the world that He has made.'

§26 But only a few of the Nūmenōreans harkened to this counsel. For it seemed hard to them, and they wished to escape from Death in their own day, and they became estranged from the Avalāi, and these came now no more to Nūmenōr save seldom and in secret, visiting those few of the faithful. Of whom the chief was one Amardil and his son Elendil (who was called also Earendil for his love of the sea, and for his father, though not of the elder line which sat upon the throne of Nūmenōr, was also of the blood of Earendil of old).

§27 But Tarkalion the king fell into evil mood, and the worship of Eru upon the high place the mountain of Meneltyūlā in the midst of the land was neglected in those days.

§28 But Tarkalion hearing of Sauron determined, without counsel of the Avalāi, to demand his allegiance and homage; for he thought that no king so mighty [could] ever arise as to vie with the lords of Nūmenōr; and he began in that time to smithy great hoard of weapons of war, and he let build great ships; and he sailed into the east and landed upon Middle-earth, and bade Sauron come and do homage to him. And Sauron came, for he saw not his time yet to work his will with Nūmenōr, and he was maybe not a little astonied at the majesty of the kings of men; and he was crafty. And he humbled himself and seemed in all things fair and wise.

§29 And it came into the heart of Tarkalion the King that for the better keeping of Sauron and his new promises of fealty he should be brought to Nūmenōr as his own hostage. And to

DA I THE DROWNING OF ANADÛNÊ 347

this Sauron assented willingly, for it chimed with his own desire. And Sauron looking upon Nūmenōr in the days of its glory was indeed astonied; but his heart within was all the more filled with hatred.

§30 Such was his craft and cunning that ere long he became closest to the counsels of the King; and slowly a change came over the land, and the hearts of the Faithful, the Avaltiri, were darkened.

§31 For with subtle arguments Sauron gainsaid all that the Avalāi had taught. And he bade them think that the world was not a closed circle; and that therein there were many lands yet for their winning, wherein was wealth uncounted; and even yet, when they came to the end thereof, there was the Dark without, out of which came all things. 'And Dark is the Realm of the Lord of All, Mēlekō the Great, who made this world out of the primeval darkness. And only Darkness is truly holy,' said he.

§32 And Tarkalion the King turned to the worship of the Dark and of Mēlekō the Lord thereof. And the Meneltyūlā was deserted in those days and none might ascend it under pain of death, not even those of the faithful who yet kept Eru in their hearts. But Sauron let build on a hill in the midst of the city of the Nūmenōreans, Antirion the Golden, a great temple; and it was in the form of a circle at the ground, and its walls were fifty feet thick, and they rose five hundred feet, and they were crowned with a mighty dome, and it was wrought all of silver, but the silver was black. And this was the mightiest of the works of the Nūmenōreans, and the most evil, and men were afraid of its shadow. And from the topmost of the dome, where was an opening or great louver, there issued ever and anon smoke, and ever the more often as the evil of Sauron grew. For there men sacrificed to Mēlekō with spilling of blood and torment and great wickedness; and ofttimes it was those of the faithful that were chosen as victims. But never openly on the charge that they would not worship Mēlekō; rather was cause sought against them that they hated the King or falsely that they plotted against their kin and devised lies and poisons.

§33 And for all this Death did not depart from the land. Rather it came sooner and more often and in dreadful guise. For whereas aforetime men had grown slowly old, and laid them down as to sleep in the end when they were weary at last of this world, now madness and sickness assailed them, and yet they were afraid to die and go out into the dark, the realm of the lord

348   SAURON DEFEATED   DA I

they had taken. And men made weapons in those days and slew
one another for little cause.

§34 Nonetheless it seemed that they prospered. For their
wealth increased mightily with the help of Sauron, and they built
ever greater ships. And they sailed to the Middle-earth to get
them new wealth; but they came no longer as the bringers of
gifts, but as men of war. And they hunted the men of Middle-
earth and enslaved them and took their goods; but they built
fortresses and great tombs upon the western shores in those
days. And men feared them, and the memory of the kindly kings
of the Elder Days faded in the world and was overlaid with
many a dread legend.

§35 Thus waxed Tarkalion the King to the mightiest tyrant
that had yet been seen in the world since the rule of Mēlekō;
and yet nonetheless he felt the shadow of death approach as his
days lengthened. And he was filled with anger and with fear.
And now came the hour that Sauron had planned. For he spoke
now to the King saying evil of Eru, that he was but a phantom, a
lie devised by the Avalāi to justify their own idleness and greed;
and that the Avalāi withheld the gift of everlasting life out of
avarice and fear lest the kings of men should wrest the rule
of the world and the Blessed Realm from them. 'And though
doubtless the gift of everlasting life is not for all, and only for
such as are worthy, being men of might and pride and great
lineage, still,' said Sauron, 'it is against all justice that this gift,
which is his least due, should be withheld from Tarkalion the
King, mightiest of the sons of Earth. To whom only Manawē
can compare, if even he.' And Tarkalion being besotted and also
under the shadow of Death, for his span was drawing to an end,
harkened to him, and devised war against the Avalāi. Long
was he in pondering this design, and it could not be hidden
from all.

§36 And in those days Amardil, who was of the royal house
as has been told, and faithful, and yet so noble and so well-
beloved of all save the most besotted of the people, that even in
the days of Sauron the King dared lay no hand on him as yet,
he learned of the secret counsels of the King, and his heart was
filled with sorrow and great dread. For he knew that Men could
not vanquish the Avalāi in war, and that great ruin must come
upon the world, if this war were not stayed. Therefore he called
his son Elendil Earendil and he said to him: 'Behold, the days
are dark and desperate; therefore I am minded to try that rede

DA I THE DROWNING OF ANADÛNÊ 349

which our forefather Earendil took: to sail into the West (be there ban or no ban) and speak to the Avalāi, yea even to Manawē himself if may be, and beseech his aid ere all is lost.'

'Would you then bewray the King?' said Elendil.

'For that very thing do I purpose to go,' said Amardil.

'And what then, think you, is like to befall those of your house whom you leave behind, when your deed becometh known?'

§37 'It must not become known,' said Amardil. 'I will prepare it in secret and I will set sail at first into the East, whither many ships daily set out, and then round about. But you and your folk, I counsel that you should prepare yourself ships and put on board all such things as your heart cannot bear to part with, and lie ready. But you should hold your ships in the eastern havens; and give out among men that you purpose, maybe, when all is ready to follow me into the East. And I think not that your going will be letted; for the house of Amardil is no longer so dear to our kinsman on the throne of Earendil that he will grieve over much if we seek to depart. But do not take many men with you, or he may become troubled because of the war that he now plots, for which he will need all the force that he hath. Do not take many, and only such as you may be sure that they are faithful. Even so open not your design to any.'

§38 'And what design is this that you make for me?'

'Until I return I cannot say. But to be sure it is like to be flight far from fair Andōrē that is now so defiled, and from our people; east or west the Avalāi alone shall say. But it is likely enough that you shall see me never again, and that I shall show you no sign such as Earendil our sire showed of old. But hold you ever in readiness, for the end of the world that we have known is at hand.'

§39 And it is said that Amardil set sail at night and went east and then about, and he took three servants with him, dear to his heart, and never again were they heard of by word or sign in this world; nor is there any tale or guess of their fate. But this much may be seen, that men could not be a second time saved by any such embassy; and for the treason of Nūmenōr there was no easy assoiling. But Elendil abode in the east of the land and held him secret and meddled not in the deeds of those days; and looked ever for the sign that came not. At whiles he would journey to the western shores of the land and gaze out at the sea, and sorrow and yearning was upon him, for he had loved his

350   SAURON DEFEATED   DA I

father – but further he was not suffered to go; for Tarkalion was now gathering his fleets in the havens of the west.

§40   Now aforetime in the isle of Númenōr the weather was ever fair, or leastways apt to the liking and needs of men, rain in due seasons and in measure, and sunshine, now warm now cooler, and winds from over the sea; and when the wind was in the west it seemed to many that it was filled with a fragrance, fleeting but sweet, heart-stirring, as of flowers that bloom for ever in undying meads and have no names on mortal shores. But now that too was changed. For the sky itself was darkened and there were storms of rain and hail in those days, and ever and anon the great ships of the Númenōreans would founder and return not to haven. And out of the West there would come at whiles a great cloud, shaped as it were an eagle with pinions spread to the North and to the South; and slowly it would creep up blotting out the sunset – for at that hour mostly was it seen; and then uttermost night would fall on Númenōr. And soon under the pinions of the eagles was lightning borne, and thunder rolled in the heaven, such a sound as men of that land had not before heard.

§41   Then men were afraid. 'Behold the Eagles of the Lords of the West coming over Númenōr!' they cried, and they fell upon their faces. And some would repent, but others hardened their hearts and shook their fists at heaven, and said: 'The Lords of the West have made the war. They strike the first blow, the next shall be ours.' And these words were spoken by the King and devised by Sauron.

§42   But the lightnings increased and slew men upon the hills and in the meads, and ever the darts of greatest fury smote at the dome of the Temple. But it stood firm.

§43   And now the fleets of the Númenōreans darkened the sea upon the west of the land, like an archipelago of mighty isles, and their masts were as forests, and their banners red as the dying sun in a great storm and as black as the night that cometh after. But the Eagles of the Lords of the West came up now out of the dayfall, in a long line one behind the other, as if in array of battle, and as they came their wings spread ever wider, until they embraced the heavens.

§44   But Tarkalion hardened his heart, and he went aboard his mighty ship Andalōkē and let spread his standard, and he gave the order for the raising of anchors.

DA I   THE DROWNING OF ANADÛNÊ   351

§45   And so the fleet of the Númenóreans set forth into the teeth of the storm, and they rowed resolutely into the West; for they had many slaves. And when the storm had abated the sky cleared, and a wind came up out of the East (by the arts of Sauron, some have said), and there was a false peace over all the seas and land while the world waited what should betide. And the fleets of the Númenóreans sailed out of sight of Andúnië and broke the ban, and held on through three nights and days; and they passed out of the sight of all watchers.

§46   And none can tell the tale of their fate, for none ever returned. And whether they came ever in truth to that haven which of old men thought that they could descry; or whether they found it not or came to some other land and there assailed the Avalāi, who shall say, for none know. For the world was changed in that time, and the memory of all that went before is become dim and unsure.

§47   But those that are wisest in discernment aver that the fleets of the Númenóreans came indeed to Avallondë and encompassed it about, but that the Avalāi made no sign. But Manawē being grieved sought the counsel at the last of Eru, and the Avalāi laid down their governance of Earth. And Eru overthrew its shape, and a great chasm was opened in the sea between Númenor and Avallondë and the seas poured in, and into that abyss fell all the fleets of the Númenóreans and were swallowed in oblivion. But Avallondë and Númenóre that stood on either side of the great rent were also destroyed; and they foundered and are no more. And the Avalāi thereafter had no local habitation on earth, nor is there any place more where memory of an earth without evil is preserved; and the Avalāi dwell in secret or have faded to shadows, and their power is minished.

§48   But Númenor went down into the sea, and all its children and fair maidens and its ladies, and even Tar-Ilien the Queen, and all its gardens and halls and towers and riches, its jewels and its webs and its things painted and carven, and its laughter and its mirth and its music and its wisdom and its speech, vanished for ever.

§49   Save only the very top of Meneltyūlā, for that was a holy place and never defiled, and that maybe is still above the waves, as a lonely isle somewhere in the great waters, if haply a mariner should come upon it. And many indeed after sought it, because it was said among the remnant of Númenor that those

352　　SAURON DEFEATED　　DA I

with holy sight had been able from the top of Meneltyūlā to see the haven of Avallondē, which otherwise only those could see who sailed far westward. And the hearts of the Nūmenōreans even after their ruin were still set westward.

§50　And though they knew that Nūmenōr and Avallondē were no more they said: 'Avallondē is no more and Nūmenōr is not; yet they were, and not in this present darkness; yet they were, and therefore still are in true being and in the whole shape of the world.' And the Nūmenōreans held that men so blessed might look upon other times than those of their body's life, and they longed ever to escape from the darkness of exile and see in some fashion the light that was of old. 'But all the ways are now crooked,' they said, 'that once were straight.'

§51　And in this way it came to pass that any were spared from the downfall of Nūmenōrē; and maybe that was the answer to the errand of Amardil. For those that were spared were all of his house and kin. For Elendil had remained behind, refusing the King's summons when he set out to war, and he went aboard ship, and abode there riding out the storm in the shelter of the eastern shore. And being protected by the land from the great draught of the sea that drew all down into the abyss, he escaped from death in that time. And a mighty wind arose such as had not before been, and it came out of the West, and it blew the sea into great hills; and fleeing before it Elendil and his sons in seven ships were carried far away, borne up on the crests of great waves like mountains of Middle-earth, and they were cast at length up far inland in Middle-earth.

§52　But all the coasts and seaward lands of Middle-earth suffered great ruin and change in that time. For the earth was sorely shaken, and the seas climbed over the lands and shores foundered, and ancient isles were drowned and new were uplifted, and hills crumbled and rivers were turned to strange courses.

§53　And here ends the tale to speak of Elendil and his sons who after founded many kingdoms in Middle-earth, and though their lore and craft was but an echo of that which had been ere Sauron came to Nūmenōr, yet did it seem very great to the men of the wild.

§54　And it is said that Sauron himself was filled with terror at the fury of the wrath of the Avalāi and the doom of Eru, for it was greater far than any that he had looked for, hoping only for the death of the Nūmenōreans and the defeat of their proud

DA I   THE DROWNING OF ANADÛNÊ   353

king. But he himself sitting in his black seat in the midst of his temple laughed when he heard the trumpets of Tarkalion sound for battle; and he laughed yet again when he heard afar the noise of the thunder; and a third time even as he laughed at his own thought (thinking what he would do now in Middle-earth, being rid of the Eruhil for ever) he was caught in the midst of his mirth, and his temple and his seat fell into the abyss.

§55 [*Rejected at once:* It was long before he appeared in visible form upon the earth again] But Sauron was not of mortal flesh, and though he was robbed of that form in which he had wrought evil for so long, as Zigūr the great, yet ere long he devised another; and he came back unto Middle-earth and troubled the sons of Elendil and all men beside. But that cometh not into the tale of the Downfall of Nūmenōr, Atalante the downfallen, as the exiles ever after named her whom they had lost, the land of Gift in the midst of the Sea.

★

There are two definitive clues to the date of this text. One is that at the foot of one of its pages are typed the words 'Ramer discusses the feeling of lost significance' (see pp. 183, 189); and the other is that the name of the Pillar of Heaven in Númenor is *Meneltyūlā*, which appears as a pencilled correction of the original name *Menelminda* in the manuscript E of Part Two of *The Notion Club Papers* (p. 302), while the next text of the *Papers* (the typescript F 1) has *Menel-túbel*, changed to *Menel-túbil*. It is thus certain that this first draft of *The Drowning of Anadûnê* was written in the course of work on Part Two of *The Notion Club Papers*, and can indeed be placed, presumably, precisely between the manuscript E and the typescript F 1.

Comparison with the text of the third version of *The Fall of Númenor* (FN III) given on pp. 331 ff. will show that this is an entirely new work, an altogether richer conception, and with many remarkable differences. But comparison with the much later *Akallabêth* (in the published *Silmarillion*, pp. 259–82) will also show that it is the direct ancestor of that work, to a much greater extent than *The Fall of Númenor*, although that also was used in the *Akallabêth*.

One of the most extraordinary features of this text lies in the conception of the *Balāi*, whom I shall call rather the *Avalāi*, since this name superseded the other before the typing of DA I was completed. At the beginning (§1) this is a name, 'in the earliest recorded tongue', of the *Eru-bēnī*, 'servants of God', who 'governed Earth'; 'some were lesser and some greater', and 'the mightiest and the chieftain of them

354 SAURON DEFEATED DA I

all was Mēlekō', brother of Manawē (see V.164, note 4). In §4 it is told that certain of the fathers of Men who repented, and who were named *Eruhil* 'Children of God', made war on Mēlekō in concert with the Avalāi and cast him down; but (§5) in grief at the evil works of Men the Avalāi withdrew ever westwards ('or if they did not so they faded and became secret voices and shadows of the days of old'), and the most part of the Eruhil followed them. And when they came to the shores of the Great Sea (§6) the Avalāi 'for the most part passed over the sea seeking the realm of Manawē', but the Eruhil of the western coasts were taught by the Avalāi the craft of ship-building.

After the coming of the Eruhil to Númenor 'they took the language of the Avalāi and forsook their own' (§14); and the Avalāi 'forbade them to sail westward out of sight of the western shores of Númenōr' (§15). The Avalāi dwelt somewhere in the West unknown to Men, who called that land *Avallondē*, translated 'the Haven of the Gods', for at times they could see a distant city far off in the West; and 'to Númenōr the Avalāi came ever and anon, the children and the lesser ones of the Deathless Folk, sometimes in oarless boats, sometimes as birds flying, sometimes in other fair shapes' (§16). Avalāi came to Númenor and attempted to persuade the Eruhil of the error of their thoughts (§§23–5); and when the fleets of Númenor came to Avallondē the Avalāi 'laid down their governance of Earth' (§47). At the Cataclysm Avallondē and Númenōrē were overwhelmed and swallowed up, 'and the Avalāi thereafter had no local habitation on earth ... and [they] dwell in secret or have faded to shadows, and their power is minished' (§47).

Who then are the Avalāi? Looking no further than the present text, the name must be said to represent the whole 'order' of deathless beings who, before the coming of Men, were empowered to govern the world within a great range or hierarchy of powers and purposes. Looking at it in relation to the earlier narrative, *The Fall of Númenor*, the distinction between 'Gods' and 'Elves' is here lost. In that work, after the Great Battle in which Morgoth was overthrown, 'the Elves were summoned to return into the West; and those that obeyed dwelt once more in Eressëa, the Lonely Isle; and that land was named anew Avallon: for it is hard by Valinor ...' (FN III §1, p. 332); and 'the speech of Númenor was the speech of the Eldar of the Blessed Realm, and the Númenóreans conversed with the Elves, and were permitted to look upon Valinor from afar; for their ships went often to Avallon, and there their mariners were suffered to dwell for a while' (FN III §2, p. 333). *The Fall of Númenor* was a vital and far-reaching extension of the legends embodied in the *Quenta Silmarillion*, but it was congruent with them. This earliest text of *The Drowning of Anadûnê*, in which the Elves are not distinctly represented, and Valinor and Eressëa are confused, is not.

Even more startling perhaps is the loss in this narrative of the

DA I   THE DROWNING OF ANADÛNÊ   355

conception that the world was made round at the Downfall of Númenor. Here, the Avalāi, coming to Númenor and attempting to teach the Eruhil 'of the fashion and fate of the world', declared to them 'that *the world was round*, and that if they sailed into the utmost West, yet would they but come back again to the East and so to the places of their setting out, and the world would seem to them but a prison' (§23); but when Sauron came to Númenor he 'gainsaid all that the Avalāi had taught. And he bade them think that *the world was not a closed circle*' (§31). Most striking is a hastily pencilled passage written alongside §§49–50, which was not taken up in the following text: 'For they believed still *the lies of Sauron that the world was plain* ['flat'; see footnote to p. 392], until their fleets had encompassed all the world seeking for Meneltyūla, and they knew that it was round. Then they said that the world was bent, and that the road to Avallondē could not be found, for it led straight on.' No direction is given for the insertion of this; but I think that it was intended to replace the sentence at the end of §50: ' "But all the ways are now crooked," they said, "that once were straight." '

In this connection the earlier version of the Old English text (the single preserved leaf of Edwin Lowdham's book) that accompanied the manuscript E of *The Notion Club Papers* (pp. 313–15) is interesting. In the Old English it was the *Eldar* who forbade the Númenóreans to land on Eresse (whereas in *The Fall of Númenor* it was the Gods who imposed the ban on sailing beyond Tol Eressëa, §4), because they were mortal, although it was 'the Powers' (*Wealdend*) who had granted them long life; and very remarkably Sauron declared to Tarkalion that 'the *Eldar* refused to him the gift of everlasting life'. The Númenóreans are here said to have 'sent out in secret spies to Avallon to explore the hidden knowledge of the Eldar' (a reminiscence of FN §4: 'they sent spies to seek hidden lore in Avallon'). The reference of *Avallon* is not explained in the Old English text, but it is surely the same as *Eresse* (in FN §1 Eressëa was renamed Avallon); yet Tarkalion determined to invade Avallon, because Sauron said that the Eldar had denied him everlasting life (whereas in FN §6 the fleets of the Númenóreans, having 'encompassed Avallon', 'assailed the shores of Valinor').

This Old English version came in point of composition between the completion of manuscript E of the *Papers* and the writing of DA I.[4] There is thus a development from a text in which both 'the Powers' and 'the Eldar' appear, but in which the Eldar have powers far greater and of a different order than could properly be ascribed to them, to a text (DA I) in which 'the Powers' (Valar) and 'the Eldar' are confused under the single term *Avalāi*; and in the Old English the name *Avallon* seems to be used confusedly (in contrast to the earlier *Fall of Númenor*), while in DA I *Avallondē* is a vague term, related to the vagueness of the name *Avalāi*.

356   SAURON DEFEATED   DA I

The further development and the significance of these extraordinary departures is discussed later: see pp. 391 ff. and 405 ff.

In this text DA I there are many other important developments in the legend of Númenor which were retained in the later story. The Ban now becomes more severe, for the Númenóreans are not permitted 'to sail westward out of sight of the western shores of Nūmenōr' (§15); the importance of the eastward voyages emerges, the coming of 'the Men out of the Sea' at first as teachers and enlighteners of the men of Middle-earth (§17), but afterwards as oppressors and enslavers (§34); and the 'Avalāi' are remembered as coming out of the West to Númenor, and attempting to avert the growing hostility to the Ban. The temple is now built, not on the Mountain sacred to Ilúvatar, but 'in the midst of the city of the Nūmenōreans, Antirion the Golden' (§32), and ascent of the Mountain is forbidden under pain of death. The 'Faithful' (named *Avaltiri*, §30) are referred to, and the story of Amardil (for later Amandil) and his son Elendil is told, with the statement that although Amardil was not of the elder line from which came the kings of Númenor, he also was descended from Eärendil (§§26, 36, 38). These are only the most striking new developments in the narrative, and moreover comparison with the *Akallabêth* will show that some of the prose itself remained unchanged into the final form.

It seems that in DA I Adunaic was at the point of emergence, with *Eru-bēnī*, *Avalāi*, and *Zigūr* (said to be the name of Sauron among the men of Middle-earth, §19).

NOTES

1   *Wingalōtē:* in the *Quenta* (Index to Vol.IV) the form was *Wingelot* > *Vingelot*, in the *Quenta Silmarillion* (Index to Vol.V) *Vingelot*. *Wingalōtē* was subsequently corrected to *Vingalōtē* on this typescript (see p. 377, §8).

2   The form *Earendel* occurs also in §§16, 20, but it was clearly no more than a casual reversion. Already in the manuscript E of Part Two of the *Papers* Wilfrid Jeremy notes that the name that he saw in his 'dream-manuscript' was *Earendil*, not *Earendel*.

3   *Andōrē: Andor* in *The Fall of Númenor* (§2) and *The Lost Road* (V.65).

4   The matter of 'Edwin Lowdham's page' was inserted into manuscript E of the *Papers* after the manuscript was completed so far as it went (see p. 291 note 70), and the name of the Pillar of Heaven in the accompanying Old English text was already *Meneltyúla* (p. 314; for earlier *Menelminda* in E), as in DA I, so that this name is not here indicative of relative date. On the other hand, in the Old English text Sauron built the great temple on the *Meneltyúla* itself,

DA II   THE DROWNING OF ANADÛNÊ   357

not in the midst of the city, which is good evidence that it was the earlier composition. So also, the ban upon landing on Eressëa in the Old English text (p. 313) was clearly a development from the original story in *The Fall of Númenor* (§4), that the Númenóreans must not sail beyond Eressëa, towards that in DA I that they must not sail beyond sight of the western coasts of Númenor.

(iii) The second text of The Drowning of Anadûnê

This text, 'DA II', is a typescript typed with care and almost free of error. A paper folded round it, in my father's writing, bears my name and the words 'Fair copy Anadûnê'. DA II represents so great an advance on and elaboration of DA I that (since it is almost free of alterations or hesitations during the original typing) it is hard to believe that no drafting intervened between the two, although there is no trace now of anything of the sort; but I do not think that I typed DA II (see p. 389, §28).

The title is *The Drowning of Anadûnê*. A fair number of alterations were pencilled on the typescript, and in addition several passages were rewritten or extended on typewritten slips attached to the body of the text. These are ignored in the text printed, but all changes of any substance are recorded in the commentary on DA II, pp. 376 ff.

I give the text in full, although this involves a certain amount of repetition especially in the latter part of the narrative, for the sake of clarity in the commentary and in making comparison with the *Akallabêth*. The paragraphs are numbered to provide convenient reference to DA I. In DA II both long marks and circumflex accents are used (inserted in pencil); the circumflex superseded the long mark, as is seen from the fact that it is found chiefly in corrected or added passages and on corrected names, and only here and there in the original text. The third text of *The Drowning of Anadûnê* uses the circumflex exclusively, and it is more convenient to do the same here.

THE DROWNING OF ANADÛNÊ

§1   Before the coming of Men there were many Powers that governed the Earth, and these were the Eru-bênî, servants of God. Many were their ranks and their offices; but some there were among them that were mighty lords, the Avalôi, whom Men remembered as gods, and at the beginning the greatest of these was the Lord Arûn.

§2   But it is said that long ago, even in the making of the Earth, the Lord Arûn turned to evil and became a rebel against Eru, desiring the whole world for his own and to have none above him. Therefore his brother Amân endeavoured to rule the Earth and the Powers according to the will of Eru; and Amân dwelt in the West.

358   SAURON DEFEATED   DA II

But Arûn remained on Earth, dwelling in hiding in the North, and he worked evil, and he had the greater power. And the Earth was darkened in that time, so that to Arûn a new name was given, and he was called Mulkhêr, the Lord of Darkness; and there was war between Mulkhêr and the Avalôi.

§3 At the appointed hour Men were born into the world, and they were called the Eru-hîn, the children of God; but they came in a time of war and shadow, and they fell swiftly under the domination of Mulkhêr, and they served him. And he now came forth and appeared as a Great King and as a god; and his rule was evil, and his worship unclean, and Men were estranged from Eru and from his servants.

§4 But some there were of the fathers of Men who repented, seeing the evil of the Lord Mulkhêr and that his shadow grew ever longer on the Earth; and they and their sons returned with sorrow to the allegiance of Eru, and they were befriended by the Avalôi, and received again their ancient name, Eruhîn, children of God. And the Avalôi and the Eruhîn made war on the servants of Mulkhêr; and for that time they destroyed his kingdom and threw down his temples. But Mulkhêr fled and brooded in the darkness without, for him the Powers could not destroy. And the evil that he had begun still sprouted like a dark seed in Middle-earth, bearing bitter grain, which though it were ever reaped and burned, was never at an end. And still cruel kings and unholy temples arose in the world, and the most part of Mankind were their servants; for Men were corrupt and still hankered in their hearts for the Kingdom of Arûn, and they made war on the Eruhîn and pursued them with hatred, wheresoever they might dwell.

§5 Therefore the hearts of the Eruhîn were turned westward, where was the land of Amân, as they believed, and an abiding peace. And it is said that of old there was a fair folk dwelling yet in Middle-earth, and Men knew not whence they came. But some said that they were the children of the Avalôi and did not die, for their home was in the Blessed Realm far away, whither they still might go, and whence they came, working the will of Amân in all the lesser deeds and labours of the world. The Eledâi they were named in their own tongue of old, but by the Eruhîn they were called Nimrî, the Shining Ones, for they were exceeding fair to look upon, and fair were all the works of their tongues and hands. And the Nimrî became sorrowful in the darkness of the days and withdrew ever

DA II   THE DROWNING OF ANADÛNÊ   359

westward; and never again was grass so green, nor flower so fair, nor water so filled with light when they had gone. And the Eruhîn for the most part followed them, though some there were that remained in the Great Lands, free men, serving no evil lord; and they were shepherds and dwelt far from the towers and cities of the kings.

§6 But those of the Eruhîn who were mightiest and most fair, closest in friendship with the Nimrî, most beloved by the Servants of God, turned their faces to the light of the West; and these were the children of the fathers that had been most valiant in the war upon Mulkhêr. And at the end of journeys beyond memory they came at last to the shores of the Great Seas. There they halted and were filled with great dread, and with longing; for the Nimrî passed ever over the waters, seeking the land of Amân, and the Eruhîn could not follow them.

Then such of the Nimrî as remained in the west of the world took pity on the Eruhîn, and instructed them in many arts; and the Eruhîn became wiser in mind, more skilled in hand and tongue, and they made for themselves many things that had not before been seen. In this way the dwellers on the shore learned the craft of ship-building and of sailing in the wind; and they built many fair ships. But their vessels were small, and they did not dare to essay the deep waters; for though their desire was to the unseen shores, they had not as yet the heart for the wastes of the Sea, and they sailed only about the coasts and among the hither isles.

§7 Yet it was by their ships that they were saved and were not brought to nought. For evil men multiplied in those days, and pursued the Eruhîn with hatred; and the men of Middle-earth, being filled with the spirit of Mulkhêr, grew cunning and cruel in the arts of war and the making of many weapons, so that the Eruhîn were hard put to it to maintain any land in which to dwell, and their numbers were diminished.

§8 In those dark days of fear there arose a man, and his daring upon the Sea was greater than that of all other men; and the Nimrî gave him a name and called him Ëarendil, the Friend of the Sea, Azrabêl in the language of the Eruhîn. And it came into the heart of Azrabêl that he would build a ship, fairer and more swift than any that men had yet made; and that he would sail out over deep water and come, maybe, to the land of Amân, and there get help for his kinsfolk. And with the help of the

360   SAURON DEFEATED   DA II

Nimrî he let build a ship, fair and valiant; white were its timbers, and its sails were white, and its prow was carven in the light of a silver bird; and at its launching he gave it a name and called it Rôthinzil, Flower of the Foam, but the Nimrî blessed it and named it also in their own tongue, Vingalôtë. This was the first of all the ships of Men to bear a name.

§9 When at last his ship was ready, then Azrabêl said farewell to his wife and to his sons and all his kin; for he was minded to sail alone. And he said to them: 'It is likely that ye will see me never again; and if ye do not, then harden your hearts, and cease not from war, but endure until the end. But if I do not fail of my errand, then also ye may not see me again; but a sign you will see, and new hope shall be given to you.'

§10 And it was at the time of evening that Azrabêl set forth, and he sailed into the setting sun and passed out of the sight of men. But the winds bore him over the waves, and the Nimrî guided him, and he went through the Seas of sunlight, and through the Seas of shadow, and he came at last to the Blessed Realm and the land of Amân and spoke unto the Avalôi.

§11 But Amân said that Eru had forbidden the Avalôi to make war again by force upon the kingdoms of Mulkhêr; for the Earth was now in the hands of Men, to make or to mar. Yet it was permitted to him, because of their fidelity and the repentance of their fathers, to give to the Eruhîn a land to dwell in, if they would. And that land was a mighty island in the midst of the sea, upon which no foot had yet been set. But Amân would not permit Azrabêl to return again among Men, since he had walked in the Blessed Realm where yet no death had come. Therefore he took the ship Rôthinzil and filled it with a silver flame, and raised it above the world to sail in the sky, a marvel to behold.

§12 Then the Eruhîn upon the shores of the Sea beheld the new light rising in the West as it were a mighty star, and they knew that it was the sign of Azrabêl. And hope and courage were kindled in their hearts; and they gathered all their ships, great and small, and their wives and their children, and all the wealth that they could bear away, and they set sail upon the deep waters, following the star. And there was a great calm in those days and all the winds were stilled. So bright was Rôthinzil that even at morning men could see it glimmering in the West; and in the cloudless night it shone alone, for no other star might come beside it. And setting their course towards it the

DA II   THE DROWNING OF ANADÛNÊ   361

Eruhîn came at last to the land that had been prepared for them, and they found it fair and fruitful, and they were glad. And they called that land Amatthânê the Land of Gift, and Anadûnê, which is Westernesse, Nûmenôrë in the Nimrian tongue.

§13   But not so did the Eruhîn escape the doom of death that had been pronounced upon all Mankind, and they were mortal still, although for their faithfulness they were rewarded by life of threefold span, and their years were full and glad and they knew no grief nor sickness, so long as they remained still true. Therefore the Adûnâi, the Men of Westernesse, grew wise and fair and glorious; but their numbers increased only slowly in the land, for though sons and daughters were born to them fairer than their fathers, and they loved their children dearly, yet their children were few.

§14   Thus the years passed, and the Adûnâi dwelt under the protection of the Avâlôi, and in the friendship of the Nimrî; and the kings and princes learned the Nimrian tongue, in which much lore and song was preserved from the beginning of the world. And they made letters and scrolls and books and wrote in them many things of wisdom and wonder in the high tide of their realm, of which all is now forgot. And they became mighty in all other crafts, so that if they had had the mind, they would easily have surpassed the evil kings of Middle-earth in the making of war and the forging of weapons; but they were become men of peace. In ship-building still was their chief delight, and this craft they followed more eagerly than all others; and voyaging upon the wide seas was the chief feat and adventure of their younger men.

§15   But the Avalôi forbade them to sail so far westward that the coasts of Anadûnê could no longer be seen; and the Adûnâi were as yet content, though they did not fully understand the purpose of this ban. But the purpose of Amân was that the Eruhîn should not be tempted to seek for the Blessed Realm, nor desire to overpass the limits set to their bliss, becoming enamoured of the immortality of the Avalôi and the land where all things endure.

§16   For as yet Eru permitted the Avalôi to maintain upon Earth, upon some isle or shore of the western lands (Men know not where), an abiding place, an earthly memorial of that which might have been, if Mulkhêr had not bent his ways nor Men followed him. And that land the Adûnâi named Avallôni, the Haven of the Gods; for at times when all the air was clear and

362   SAURON DEFEATED   DA II

the sun was in the east they could descry, as them seemed, a city white-shining on a distant shore, and great harbours, and a tower. But this only from the topmost peak of their island could the far-sighted see, or from some ship that lay at anchor off their western shores, as far as it was lawful for any mariner to go. For they did not dare to break the ban. And some held that it was a vision of the Blessed Realm that men saw, but others said that it was only a further isle where the Nimrî dwelt and the little ones that do not die; for mayhap the Avalôi had no visible dwelling upon Earth.

And certain it is that the Nimrî had some dwelling nigh unto Anadûnê, for thither they came ever and anon, the children of the Deathless Folk, sometimes in oarless boats, sometimes as birds flying, sometimes by paths that none could see; for they loved the Adûnâi.

§17   Thus it was that the voyages of the Adûnâi in those days went ever eastward and not west, from the darkness of the North to the heats of the South, and beyond the South to the Nether Darkness. And the Eruhîn came often to the shores of the Great Lands, and they took pity on the forsaken world of Middle-earth. And the princes of the Adûnâi set foot again upon the western shores in the Dark Years of Men, and none now dared withstand them; for most of the peoples of that age that sat under the shadow were now grown weak and fearful, And coming among them the sons of the Adûnâi taught them many things. Language they taught them, for the tongues of men on Middle-earth were fallen into brutishness, and they cried like harsh birds or snarled like the savage beasts. And corn and wine the Adûnâi brought, and they instructed men in the sowing of seed and the grinding of grain, in the shaping of wood and the hewing of stone, and in the ordering of life, such as it might be in the lands of little bliss.

§18   Then the men of Middle-earth were comforted, and here and there upon the western shores the houseless woods drew back, and men shook off the yoke of the offspring of Mulkhêr, and unlearned their terror of the dark. And they revered the memory of the tall Sea-kings, and when they had departed called them gods, hoping for their return; for at that time the Adûnâi dwelt never long in Middle-earth nor made any habitation of their own: eastward they must sail, but ever west their hearts returned.

DA II   THE DROWNING OF ANADÛNÊ   363

§19 Thus came the lightening of the shadow upon the Earth and the beginning of betterment, of which the songs of men preserve still the distant memory like an echo of the Sea. And yet in the end new good turned again to evil, and Men fell, as it is said, a second time. For there arose a second manifestation of the power of darkness upon Earth: a new shape of the Ancient Shadow, it may be, or one of its servants that drew power from it and waxed strong and fell. And this evil thing was called by many names; but its own name that it took in the arising of its power was Zigûr, Zigûr the Great. And Zigûr made himself a mighty king in the midst of the Earth; and well-seeming he was at first, and just, and his rule was of benefit to all men in the needs of the body. For he made them rich, whoso would serve him; but those who would not he drove out into the waste places. Yet it was the purpose of Zigûr, as of Mulkhêr before him, to make himself a king over all kings, and to be the god of Men. And slowly his power moved north and south, and ever westward; and he heard of the coming of the Eruhîn, and he was wroth, and he plotted in his heart how he might destroy Anadûnê.

§20 And tidings of Zigûr came also to Anadûnê, to Ar-Pharazôn the king, heir of Azrabêl; for this title had all the kings of Amatthânê, being descended indeed in unbroken line from Indilzar son of Azrabêl, and seven kings had ruled the Adûnâi between Indilzar and Ar-Pharazôn, and slept now in their deep tombs under the mount of Menel-Tûbal, lying upon beds of gold. For high and glorious had grown the kings of Amatthânê; and great and proud was Ar-Pharazôn, sitting upon his carven throne in the city of Ar-Minalêth in the noontide of his realm. And to him came the masters of ships and men returning out of the East, and they spoke of Zigûr, how he named himself the Great, and purposed to become master of all Middle-earth, and indeed of the whole world, if that might be. Great was the anger of Ar-Pharazôn when he heard these things, and he sat long in thought, and his mood darkened.

§21 For it must be told that evil, of which once long ago their fathers had partaken, albeit they had after repented, was not banished wholly from the hearts of the Eruhîn, and now again was stirring. For the desire of everlasting life, to escape from death and the ending of delight, grew ever stronger upon them as their lot in the land of Amatthânê grew more full of bliss. And the Adûnâi began to murmur, at first in their hearts

364   SAURON DEFEATED   DA II

and anon in words, against the doom of Men; and most of all against that ban which forbade them to sail into the West or to seek for the land of Amân and the Blessed Realm.

§22 And they said among themselves: 'Why do the Avalôi sit in peace unending there, while we must die and go we know not whither, leaving our own home and all that we have made? For the fault was not ours in the beginning, seeing that Mulkhêr was stronger and wiser than our fathers; and was not he, even the Lord Arûn, author of this evil, one of the Avalôi?'

§23 And the Nimrî reported these words to the Avalôi, and the Avalôi were grieved, seeing the clouds gather on the noontide of Amatthânê. And they sent messengers to the Adûnâi, who spoke earnestly to the king and to all who would listen to them, teaching them concerning the fashion and fate of the world.

'The doom of the world,' they said, 'One alone can change, who made it. And were you so to voyage that, escaping all deceits and snares, you came indeed to the Blessed Realm, little good would it do to you. For it is not the land of Amân that maketh its people deathless, but the dwellers therein do hallow the land; and there you should rather wither the sooner, as moths in a flame too bright and hot.'

But Ar-Pharazôn said: 'And doth not Azrubêl [sic] my father live? Or is he not in the land of Amân?'

To which it was answered: 'Nay, he is not there; though maybe he liveth. But of such things we cannot speak unto you. And behold! the fashion of the Earth is such that a girdle may be set about it. Or as an apple it hangeth on the branches of Heaven, and it is round and fair, and the seas and lands are but the rind of the fruit, which shall abide upon the tree until the ripening that Eru hath appointed. And though you sought for ever, yet mayhap you would not find where Amân dwelleth, but journeying on beyond the towers of Nimroth would pass into the uttermost West. So would you but come at the last back to the places of your setting out: and then the whole world would seem shrunken, and you would deem that it was a prison.

§24 'And a prison, maybe, it hath indeed become to all those of your race, and you cannot rest anywhere content within. But the punishments of Eru are for healing, and his mercies may be stern. For the Avalôi, you say, are unpunished, and so it is that they do not die; but they cannot escape and are bound to this world, never again to leave it, till all is changed. And you, you

DA II THE DROWNING OF ANADÛNÊ 365

say, are punished, and so it is that you die; but you escape, and leave the world, and are not bound thereto. Which of us therefore should envy the other?'

§25 And the Adûnâi answered: 'Why should we not envy the Avalôi, or even the least of the deathless? For of us is required the greater trust, knowing not what lieth before us in a little while. And yet we too love the world and would not lose it.'

And the messengers answered: 'Indeed the mind of Eru concerning you is not known to the Avalôi, and he hath not yet revealed it. But earnestly they bid you not to withhold again that trust to which you are commanded and your fathers returned in sorrow. Hope rather that in the end even the least of your desires shall have fruit. For the love of this Earth was set in your hearts by Eru, who made both it and you; and Eru doth not plant to no purpose. Yet many ages of men unborn may pass ere that purpose is made known.'

§26 But few only of the Adûnâi gave heed to this counsel. For it seemed hard to them and full of doubt, and they wished to escape from Death in their own day, not waiting upon hope; and they became estranged from the Avalôi, and would no longer receive their messengers. And these came now no more to Anadûnê, save seldom and in secret, visiting those few that remained faithful in heart.

Of these the chief was one Arbazân, and his son Nimruzân, great captains of ships; and they were of the line of Indilzar Azrabêlo, though not of the elder house, to whom belonged the crown and throne in the city of Arminalêth.

§27 But he Ar-Pharazôn the king fell into doubt, and in his day the offering of the first-fruits was neglected; and men went seldom to the hallow in the high place upon Mount Menel-Tûbal that was in the midst of the land; and they turned the more to works of handicraft, and to the gathering of wealth in their ships that sailed to Middle-earth, and they drank and they feasted and they clad themselves in silver and gold.

And on a time Ar-Pharazôn sat with his counsellors in his high house, and he debated the words of the messengers, saying that the shape of the Earth was such that a girdle might be set about it. 'For if we shall believe this,' he said, 'that one who goeth west shall return out of the East, then shall it not also be that one who goeth ever east shall come up at last behind the West, and yet break no ban?'

But Arbazân said: 'It may be so. Yet nought was said of how long the girdle might be. And mayhap, the width of the world is such that a man would wear the whole of his life, or ever he encompassed it. And I deem it for a truth that we have been set for our health and protection most westward of all mortal men, where the land of those that do not die lies upon the very edge of sight; so that he that would go round about from Anadûnê must needs traverse well nigh the whole girdle of the Earth. And even so it may be that there is no road by sea.' And it has been said that at that time he guessed aright, and that ere the shape of things was changed, eastward of Anadûnê the land stretched in truth from the North even into the uttermost South, where are ices impassable.

But the king said: 'Nonetheless we may give thought to this road, if it may be discovered.' And he pondered in his secret thought the building of ships of great draught and burden, and the setting up of outposts of his power upon far shores.

§28 Thus it was that his anger was the greater, when he heard those tidings of Zigûr the Mighty and of his enmity to the Adûnâi. And he determined, without counsel of the Avalôi or of any wisdom but his own, that he would demand the allegiance and homage of this lord: for in his pride he thought that no king could ever arise so mighty as to vie with the heir of Azrabêl. Therefore he began in that time to smithy great hoard of weapons of war, and he let build great ships and stored them with arms; and when all was ready he himself set sail into the East, and he landed upon Middle-earth; and he commanded Zigûr to come to him and to swear him fealty. And Zigûr came. For he saw not his time yet to work his will with Anadûnê; and he was maybe for the time astounded by the power and majesty of the kings of men, which surpassed all rumour of them. And he was crafty, well skilled to gain what he would by subtlety when force might not avail. Therefore he humbled himself before Ar-Pharazôn, and smoothed his tongue, and seemed in all things fair and wise.

§29 And it came into the heart of Ar-Pharazôn the king that, for the better keeping of Zigûr and his oaths of fealty, he should be brought to Anadûnê, and dwell there as a hostage for himself and all his servants. And to this Zigûr assented willingly, for it chimed with his desire. And Zigûr coming looked upon Anadûnê and the city of Ar-Minalêth in the days of its glory, and he was

DA II   THE DROWNING OF ANADÛNÊ   367

indeed astounded; but his heart within was filled the more with envy and with hate.

§30   Yet such was his cunning that ere three years were past he had become closest to the secret counsels of the king; for flattery sweet as honey was ever on his tongue, and knowledge he had of many hidden things; and all the counsellors, save Arbazân alone, began to fawn upon him. Then slowly a change came over the land, and the hearts of the Faithful grew full of fear.

§31   For now, having the ear of men, Zigûr with many arguments gainsaid all that the Avalôi had taught. And he bade men think that the world was not a circle closed, but there lay many seas and lands for their winning, wherein was wealth uncounted. And still, should they at the last come to the end thereof, beyond all lay the Ancient Darkness. 'And that is the Realm of the Lord of All, Arûn the Greatest, who made this world out of the primeval Darkness; and other worlds he yet may make and give them in gift to those that serve him. And Darkness alone is truly holy,' he said and lied.

§32   Then Ar-Pharazôn the king turned back to the worship of the Dark, and of Arûn-Mulkhêr the Lord thereof; and the Menel-tûbal was utterly deserted in those days, and no man might ascend to the high place, not even those of the Faithful who kept Eru in their hearts. But Zigûr let build upon a hill in the midst of the city of the Eruhîn, Ar-Minalêth the Golden, a mighty temple; and it was in the form of a circle at the base, and there the walls were fifty feet in thickness, and the width of their base was five hundred feet across the centre, and they rose from the ground five hundred feet, and they were crowned with a mighty dome; and it was wrought all of silver, but the silver was turned black. And from the topmost of the dome, where was an opening or great louver, there issued smoke; and ever the more often as the evil power of Zigûr grew. For there men would sacrifice to Mulkhêr with spilling of blood and torment and great wickedness, that he should release them from Death. And ofttimes it was those of the Faithful that were chosen as victims; but never openly on the charge that they would not worship Mulkhêr, rather was cause sought against them that they hated the king and were his rebels, or that they plotted against their kin, devising lies and poisons. And these charges were for the most part false, save that wickedness breeds wickedness, and oppression brings forth murder.

368   SAURON DEFEATED   DA II

§33   But for all this Death did not depart from the land. Rather it came sooner and more often and in dreadful guise. For whereas aforetime men had grown slowly old and laid them down in the end to sleep, when they were weary at last of the world, now madness and sickness assailed them; and yet they were afraid to die and go out into the dark, the realm of the lord that they had taken; and they cursed themselves in their agony. And men took weapons in those days and slew one another for little cause, for they were become quick to anger; and Zigûr, or those whom he had bound unto himself, went about the land setting man against man, so that the people murmured against the king and the lords and any that had aught that they had not, and the men of power took hard revenge.

§34   Nonetheless for long it seemed to the Adunâi that they prospered, and if they were not increased in happiness yet they grew more strong and their rich men ever richer. For with the aid of Zigûr they multiplied their wealth and they devised many engines, and they built ever greater ships. And they sailed with power and armoury to Middle-earth, and they came no longer as the bringers of gifts, but as men of war. And they hunted the men of Middle-earth and took their goods and enslaved them, and many they slew cruelly upon their altars. For they built fortresses and temples and great tombs upon the western shores in those days; and men feared them, and the memory of the kindly kings of the Elder Days faded in the world and was darkened by many a tale of dread.

§35   Thus Ar-Pharazôn the King of the land of the Star of Azrabêl grew to the mightiest tyrant that had yet been seen in the world since the reign of Mulkhêr, though in truth Zigûr ruled all from behind the throne. And the years passed, and lo! the king felt the shadow of Death approach as his days lengthened; and he was filled with rage and fear. And now came the hour that Zigûr had planned and long awaited. And Zigûr spoke to the king, saying evil of Eru, that he was but a phantom, a lie devised by the Avalôi to justify their own idleness and greed.

'For the Avalôi,' said he, 'withhold the gift of everlasting life out of avarice and fear, lest the kings of Men should wrest from them the rule of the world and take for themselves the Blessed Realm. And though, doubtless, the gift of everlasting life is not for all, but only for such as are worthy, being men of might and pride and great lineage, yet against all justice is it done, that this

DA II THE DROWNING OF ANADÛNÊ 369

gift, which is his least due, should be withheld from the King, Ar-Pharazôn, mightiest of the sons of Earth, to whom Amân alone can be compared, if even he.' And Ar-Pharazôn, being besotted, and walking under the shadow of Death, for his span was drawing to an end, harkened to Zigûr; and he began to ponder in his heart how he might make war upon the Avalôi. Long was he in preparing this design, and he spoke of it to few; yet it could not be hidden from all for ever.

§36 Now there dwelt still in the east of Anadûnê, nigh to the city of Ar-Minalêth, Arbazân, who was of the royal house, as has been told, and he was faithful; and yet so noble had he been and so mighty a captain of the sea that still he was honoured by all save the most besotted of the people, and though he had the hatred of Zigûr, neither king nor counsellor dared lay hand on him as yet. And Arbazân learned of the secret counsels of the king, and his heart was filled with grief and great dread; for he knew that Men could not vanquish the Avalôi in war, and that great ruin must come upon the world, if this war were not stayed. Therefore he called his son Nimruzân, and he said to him: 'Behold! the days are dark and desperate. Therefore I am minded to try that rede which our forefather Azrabêl took of old: to sail into the West (be there ban or no ban), and to speak to the Avalôi, yea, even to Amân himself, if may be, and beseech his aid ere all is lost.'

'Would you then bewray the King?' said Nimruzân.

'For that very thing do I purpose to go,' said Arbazân.

'And what then, think you, is like to befall those of your house whom you leave behind, when your deed becometh known?'

§37 'It must not become known,' said Arbazân. 'I will prepare my going in secret, and I will set sail into the East, whither daily many ships depart from our havens, and thereafter, as wind and chance may allow, I will go about through south or north back into the West, and seek what I may find.

'But you and your folk, my son, I counsel that you should prepare yourself other ships, and put aboard all such things as your hearts cannot bear to part with, and when the ships are ready you should take up your abode therein, keeping a sleepless watch. And you should lie in the eastern havens, and give out among men that you purpose, when you see your time, to set sail and follow me into the East. Arbazân is no longer so dear to our kinsman upon the throne that he will grieve over

370   SAURON DEFEATED   DA II

much, if we seek to depart for a season or for good. But let it not be seen that you intend to take many men, or he may become troubled because of the war that he now plots, for which he will need all the force that he may gather. Seek out rather the Faithful that are known to you, and let them lie ashore at call, if they are willing to go with you. But even to these men do not tell more of your design than is needful.'

§38 'And what shall that design be, that you make for me?' said Nimruzân.

'Until I return, I cannot say,' his father answered. 'But to be sure most like is it that you must fly from fair Amatthânê that is now defiled, and lose what you have loved, foretasting death in life, seeking a lesser land elsewhere. East or West, the Avalôi alone can say.

'And it may well prove that you shall see me never again, and that I shall show you no such sign as Azrabêl showed of old. But hold you ever in readiness, for the end of the world that we have known is now at hand.'

§39 And it is said that Arbazân set sail in a small ship at night, and steered first eastward and then went about and passed into the West. And he took three servants with him, dear to his heart, and never again were they heard of by word or sign in this world; nor is there any tale or guess of their fate. But this much may be seen that Men could not a second time be saved by any such embassy, and for the treason of Anadûnê there was no easy assoiling. But Nimruzân did all that his father had bidden, and his ships lay off the east coast of the land, and he held himself secret and did not meddle with the deeds of those days. At whiles he would journey to the western shores and gaze out upon the sea, for sorrow and yearning were upon him, for he had greatly loved his father; but nought could he descry but the fleets of Ar-Pharazôn gathering in the havens of the west.

§40 Now aforetime in the isle of Anadûnê the weather was ever apt to the liking and the needs of men: rain in due seasons and ever in measure, and sunshine, now warm now cooler, and winds from over the sea; and when the wind was in the West, it seemed to many that it was filled with a fragrance, fleeting but sweet, heart-stirring, as of flowers that bloom for ever in undying meads and have no names on mortal shores. But all this was now changed. For the sky itself was darkened, and there

DA II THE DROWNING OF ANADÛNÊ 371

were storms of rain and hail in those days, and violent winds; and ever and anon a great ship of the Adûnâi would founder and return not to haven, though never had such a grief betid before since the rising of the Star. And out of the West there would come at whiles a great cloud, shaped as it were an eagle, with pinions spread to the North and to the South; and slowly it would loom up, blotting out the sunset (for at that hour mostly was it seen), and then uttermost night would fall on Anadûnê. And anon under the pinions of the eagles lightning was borne, and thunder rolled in heaven, such a sound as men of that land had not heard before.

§41 Then men grew afraid. 'Behold the Eagles of the Lords of the West!' they cried; 'the Eagles of Amân are over Anadûnê!' and they fell upon their faces. And some few would repent, but the others hardened their hearts and shook their fists at heaven, and said: 'The Lords of the West have desired this war. They strike first; the next blow shall be ours.' And these words the king himself spoke, but Zigûr devised them.

§42 Then the lightnings increased and slew men upon the hills, and in the fields, and in the streets of the city; and a fiery bolt smote the dome of the Temple and it was wreathed in flame. But the Temple was unshaken; for Zigûr himself stood upon the pinnacle and defied the lightnings; and in that hour men called him a god and did all that he would. When therefore the last portent came they heeded it little; for the land shook under them, and a groaning as of thunder underground was mingled with the roaring of the sea; and smoke appeared upon the top of Menil-Tûbal [sic]. But still Ar-Pharazôn pressed on with his designs.

§43 And now the fleets of the Adûnâi darkened the sea upon the west of the land, and they were like an archipelago of a thousand isles; their masts were as a forest upon the mountains, and their sails were like a brooding cloud; and their banners were black and golden like stars upon the fields of night. And all things now waited upon the word of Ar-Pharazôn; and Zigûr withdrew into the inmost circle of the Temple, and men brought him victims to be burned. Then the Eagles of the Lords of the West came up out of the dayfall, and they were arrayed as for battle, one after another in an endless line; and as they came their wings spread ever wider, grasping all the sky; but the West burned red behind them, and they glowed like living blood beneath, so that Anadûnê was illumined as with a dying fire,

372   SAURON DEFEATED   DA II

and men looked upon the faces of their fellows, and it seemed to them that they were filled with wrath.

§44   Then Ar-Pharazôn hardened his heart, and he went aboard his mighty ship, Aglarrâma, castle of the sea; many-oared it was and many-masted, golden and sable, and upon it the throne of Ar-Pharazôn was set. Then he put on his panoply and his crown, and let raise his standard, and he gave the signal for the weighing of the anchors; and in that hour the trumpets of Anadûnê outrang the thunder.

§45   And so the fleets of the Adûnâi moved against the menace of the West; and there was little wind, but they had many oars, and many strong slaves to row beneath the lash. The sun went down, and there came a silence; and over the land and all the seas a dark stillness fell, while the world waited for what should betide. Slowly the fleets passed out of the sight of the watchers in the havens, and their lights faded upon the sea, and night took them; and in the morning they were gone. For at middle night a wind arose in the East (by Zigûr's art, it is said), and it wafted them away; and they broke the ban of the Avalôi, and sailed into forbidden seas, going up with war against the Deathless Folk, to wrest from them life everlasting in the circle of the world.

§46   And who shall tell the tale of their fate? For neither ship nor man of all that host returned ever to the lands of living men. And whether they came in truth to that harbour which of old the Adûnâi could descry from Menel-Tûbal; or whether they found it not, or came to some other land and there assailed the Avalôi, it is not known. For the world was changed in that time, and the memory of all that went before is unsure and dim.

§47   Among the Nimrî only was word preserved of the things that were; of whom the wisest in lore of old have learned this tale. And they say that the fleets of the Adûnâi came indeed to Avallôni in the deeps of the sea, and they encompassed it about; and still all was silent, and doom hung upon a thread. For Ar-Pharazôn wavered at the end, and almost he turned back; but pride was his master, and at last he left his ship and strode upon the shore. Then Amân called upon Eru, and in that hour the Avalôi laid down the governance of the Earth. But Eru showed forth his power, and he changed the fashion of the world; and a great chasm opened in the sea between Anadûnê and the Deathless Land, and the waters flowed down into it, and the noise and the smoke of those cataracts went up to

DA II   THE DROWNING OF ANADÛNÊ   373

heaven, and the world was shaken. And into the abyss fell all the fleets of the Adûnâi and were swallowed in oblivion. But the land of Amân and the land of his gift, standing upon either side of the great chasm in the seas, were also destroyed; for their roots were loosened, and they fell and foundered, and they are no more. And the Avalôi thereafter had no habitation on Earth, nor is there any place more where a memory of a world without evil is preserved; and the Avalôi dwell in secret, or have become as shadows and their power has waned.

§48   In an hour unlooked-for this doom befell, on the seventh evening since the passing of the fleets. Then suddenly there was a mighty wind and a tumult of the Earth, and the sky reeled and the hills slid, and Anadûnê went down into the sea with all its children, and its wives, and its maidens, and its ladies proud; and all its gardens and its halls and its towers, its riches and its jewels and its webs and its things painted and carven, and its laughter and its mirth and its music and its wisdom, and its speech, they vanished for ever. And last of all the mounting wave, green and cold and plumed with foam, took to its bosom Ar-Zimrahil the Queen, fairer than silver or ivory or pearls; too late she strove to climb the steep ways of Menel-Tûbal to the holy place, for the waters overtook her, and her cry was lost in the roaring of the wind.

§49   But indeed the summit of the Mountain, the Pillar of Heaven, in the midst of the land was a hallowed place, nor had it ever been defiled. Therefore some have thought that it was not drowned for ever, but rose again above the waves, a lonely island lost in the great waters, if haply a mariner should come upon it. And many there were that after sought for it, because it was said among the remnant of the Adûnâi that the far-sighted men of old could see from Menel-Tûbal's top the glimmer of the Deathless Land. For even after their ruin the hearts of the Adûnâi were still set westward.

§50   And though they knew that the land of Amân and the isle of Anadûnê were no more, they said: 'Avallôni is vanished from the Earth, and the Land of Gift is taken away, and in the world of this present darkness they cannot be found; yet they were, and therefore they still are in true being and in the whole shape of the world.' And the Adûnâi held that men so blessed might look upon other times than those of the body's life; and they longed ever to escape from the shadows of their exile and to see in some fashion the light that was of old. Therefore some

374 SAURON DEFEATED DA II

among them would still search the empty seas; 'but all the ways are crooked that once were straight,' they said.

§51 And in this way it came to pass that any were spared from the downfall of Anadûnê; and maybe this was the answer to the errand of Arbazân. For those that were spared were all of his house and kin, or faithful followers of his son. Now Nimruzân had remained behind, refusing the king's summons when he set out to war; and avoiding the soldiers of Zigûr that came to seize him and drag him to the fires of the Temple, he went aboard ship and stood out a little from the shore, waiting on the hour. There he was protected by the land from the great draught of the sea that drew all down into the abyss, and afterward from the first fury of the storm and the great wave that rolled outwards when the chasm was closed and the foundations of the sea were rocked.

But when the land of Anadûnê toppled to its fall, then at last he fled, rather for the saving of the lives of those that followed him than of his own; for he deemed that no death could be more bitter than the ruin of that day. But the wind out of the West blew still more wild than any wind that men had known; and it tore away sail and threw down mast and hunted the unhappy men like straws upon the water. And the sea rose into great hills; and Nimruzân, and his sons and people, fleeing before the black gale from twilight into night were borne up upon the crests of waves like mountains moving, and after many days they were cast away far inland upon Middle-earth.

§52 And all the coasts and seaward regions of the world suffered great ruin and change in that time; for the Earth was sorely shaken, and the seas climbed over the lands, and shores foundered, and ancient isles were drowned, and new isles were uplifted; and hills crumbled, and rivers were turned into strange courses.

§53 And here ends the tale to speak of Nimruzân and his sons who after founded many kingdoms in Middle-earth; and though their lore and craft was but an echo of that which had been ere Zigûr came to Anadûnê, yet did it seem very great to the wild men of the world.

§54 And it is said that Zigûr himself was filled with dread at the fury of the wrath of the Avalôi and the doom that Eru wrought; for it was greater far than aught that he had looked for, hoping only for the death of the Adûnâi and the defeat of their proud king. And Zigûr sitting in his black seat in the midst

DA II   THE DROWNING OF ANADÛNÊ   375

of his temple laughed when he heard the trumpets of Ar-Pharazôn sounding for battle; and again he laughed when he heard the thunder of the storm; and a third time, even as he laughed at his own thought (thinking what he would now do in the world, being rid of the Eruhîn for ever), he was taken in the midst of his mirth and his seat and his temple fell into the abyss.

§55   But Zigûr was not of mortal flesh, and though he was robbed of that shape in which he had wrought so great an evil, yet ere long he devised another; and he came back also to Middle-earth and troubled the sons of Nimruzân and all men beside. But that comes not into the tale of the Drowning of Anadûnê, of which all is now told. For the name of that land perished, and that which was aforetime the Land of Gift in the midst of the sea was lost, and the exiles on the shores of the world, if they turned to the West, spoke of Akallabê that was whelmed in the waves, the Downfallen, Atalantë in the Nimrian tongue.

★

I have shown (p. 353) that the original text of *The Drowning of Anadûne* (DA I) can be placed between the composition of the manuscript (E) of Part Two of *The Notion Club Papers* and the rejected section F 1 of the typescript, on the evidence of the name of the Pillar of Heaven: *Meneltyûlâ* in DA I (appearing as an emendation in E) but *Menel-tûbel* (>-*tûbil*) in F 1 (from here onwards, in comparative passages, I use the circumflex accent on all forms whatever the usage in the text cited). On the same basis the present text DA II belongs with F 1, since the Pillar of Heaven is here *Menel-Tûbal*, whereas the replacement section F 2 of the typescript of the *Papers* has *Minul-Târik*. Similarly DA II and F 1 agree in *Avalôi*, *Adûnâi* for F 2 *Avalôim*, *Adûnâim* (for the different forms of Adunaic names in F 1 and F 2 see pp. 240–1, 305).

On the other hand, DA II has *Anadûnê*, as does F 2, whereas F 1 has *Anadûn*; and F 1 had the Adunaic name of Eärendil as *Pharazîr*, changed on the typescript to *Azrubêl*, while DA II has *Azrabêl* from the first. In DA II appears the name *Amatthânê* of 'the Land of Gift', which supplanted the name in F 1, *Athânâti* (see p. 378, §12); F 2 has the final name, *Yôzâyan*.

From this comparison it is clear that the writing of DA II fell between the original and rewritten forms (F 1 and F 2) of Lowdham's account of Adunaic in Night 66 of *The Notion Club Papers*.

This greatly extended version of *The Drowning of Anadûnê* serves, looking further on, as an extraordinarily clear exemplification of my

376   SAURON DEFEATED   DA II *Commentary*

father's method of 'composition by expansion'. Separated by years and many further texts from the published *Akallabêth*, in DA II (most especially in the latter part of it) a very great deal of the actual wording of the *Akallabêth* was already present. The opening of DA II is totally distinct (for here the *Akallabêth* was expanded from *The Fall of Númenor*); but beginning with §12 (the sailing to Anadûnê following the Star) I calculate that no less than three-fifths of the precise wording of DA II was preserved in the *Akallabêth*. This is the more striking when one looks at it in reverse: for I find that, beginning at the same point in the *Akallabêth* (p. 260), only three-eighths of the latter (again, in precisely the same wording) are present in DA II. In other words, very much more than half of what my father wrote at this time was exactly retained in the *Akallabêth*; but very much less than half the *Akallabêth* was an exact retention from DA II.

A good deal of this expansion came about through the insertion (at different stages in the textual history) of phrases or brief passages into the body of the original text (and a small part of this belongs to the further textual history of *The Drowning of Anadûnê*). To a much greater extent the old narrative was transformed by the introduction of long sections of new writing. There were also significant alterations of structure.

There follows here a commentary, by paragraphs, on DA II, which includes all alterations of significance made to the text after it was typed, and also indications of the later expansions found in the *Akallabeth*.

Commentary on the second version

§1   In DA II the ambiguity of the term *Avalâi* in DA I is removed, and the *Avalôi* are 'mighty lords, whom Men remembered as gods', the Valar; while in §5 appear the *Nimrî* (Eldar). The phrase 'whom Men remembered as gods' was changed to 'who were before the world was made, and do not die'.

This opening paragraph had been very roughly rewritten on DA I nearly to its form in DA II, but for 'the Lord Arûn' the name was 'the Lord Kherû'.

§2   *his brother Amân* (DA I *Manawê*). In all the texts of *The Drowning of Anadûnê* Manwë is named *Amân*, and this is the sole reference of the name. *Aman* was one of the names that my father listed as 'Alterations in last revision [of *The Silmarillion*] in 1951' (see p. 312), and there seems good reason to suppose that *Amân* actually made its first appearance here, as the Adunaic name of Manwë.

§5   *some said that they were the children of the Avalôi and did not die.* In §16 the Nimrî are called, without any qualification of

DA II *Commentary* THE DROWNING OF ANADÛNÊ 377

'some said', 'the children of the Deathless Folk'. Cf. the opening of the *Quenta Silmarillion* (V.204, §2):

These spirits the Elves name the Valar, which is the Powers, and Men have often called them Gods. Many lesser spirits of their own kind they brought in their train, both great and small; and some of these Men have confused with the Elves, but wrongly, for they were made before the World, whereas Elves and Men awoke first in the World, after the coming of the Valar.

Though not mentioned in this passage, the conception of 'the Children of the Valar' is frequently encountered in the *Quenta Silmarillion*; and cf. especially *The Later Annals of Valinor* (V.110): 'With these great ones came many lesser spirits, beings of their own kind but of smaller might ... And with them also were later numbered their children ...' (see commentary on this, V.120–1).

Eledâi: this name is found elsewhere; see pp. 397 ff.

§7   *and were not brought to nought:* changed to 'and did not perish wholly from the Earth.'

§8   At the end of the opening sentence, '... than that of all other men', the following was added in:

for often he would launch his boat into the loud winds, or would sail alone far from the sight even of the mountains of his land, and return again hungry from the sea after many days.

Azrabêl: cf. the rejected section F 1 of the typescript of Part Two of the *Papers* (p. 305): '*Azrubêl*, made of *azar* "sea" and the stem *bel-*'. The form *Azrabêl* became *Azrubêl* in the course of typing the third text DA III; but there is a single occurrence of *Azrubêl*, as typed, in DA II (§23). On the significance of the two forms see p. 429.

Rôthinzil: this name is found in the *Akallabêth* (pp. 259–60).

Vingalôtë: in DA I *Wingalôtë*; becoming *Wingalôtë* in DA III, and reverting to *Vingalôtë* in the final text DA IV.

§11   The concluding passage, beginning 'But Amân would not permit Azrabêl ...', was changed to read:

Azrubêl did not return to bear these tidings to his kindred, whether of his own will, for he could not endure to depart again living from the Blessed Realm where no death had come; or by the command of Amân, that report of it should not trouble the hearts of the Eruhîn, upon whom Eru himself had set the doom of death. But Amân took the ship Rôthinzil and filled it with a silver flame, and set therein mariners of the Nimîr, and raised it above the world to sail in the sky, a marvel to behold.

378 SAURON DEFEATED DA II *Commentary*

The form *Nimîr*, for *Nimrî*, appears in the third text DA III.

§12 The name *Amatthânê* ('the Land of Gift') was typed in subsequently over an erasure, but the erased form can be seen to have had eight letters, beginning with *A* and probably ending with *e*. In the text F 1 of Part II of the *Papers* the Land of Gift was *Athānāti* (p. 305), and *Athanātē* occurs in an earlier form of Lowdham's fragment II, p. 312; thus the erased name here was obviously *Athānāte*. Subsequently the name *Amatthânê* appears in DA III as typed.

To this paragraph a typewritten slip was attached, changing the passage following the words 'they set sail upon the deep waters, following the star':

> And the Avalôi laid a peace on the sea for many days, and sent sunlight and a sailing wind, so that the waters glittered before the eyes of the Eruhîn like rippling glass, and the foam flew like shining snow before the stems of their ships. But so bright was Rôthinzil that even at morning men could see it glimmering in the West, and in the cloudless night it shone alone, for no other star might come beside it. And setting their course towards it, the Eruhîn came at last over leagues of sea and saw afar the land that was prepared for them, Zenn'abâr the Land of Gift, shimmering in a golden haze. Then they went up out of the sea and found a country fair and fruitful, and they were glad. And they called that land Gimlad, which is Starwards, and Anadûnê, which is Westernesse, Nûmenôrë in the Nimrian tongue.

This is virtually the text in the *Akallabêth* (pp. 260–1), apart of course from the names. *Zenn'abâr* was subsequently changed to *Zen'nabâr*, and then to *Abarzâyan* (which was the form in the third text DA III). The name *Amatthânê* was not lost, however: see p. 388, §23.

§13 The statement here and in DA I that the Eruhîn were rewarded by a life of threefold span goes back to a change made to FN II, §10 (V.28); cf. also Aragorn's words 'I have still twice the span of other men', p. 57, and the statement in Appendix A (I,i) to *The Lord of the Rings*: the Númenóreans were granted a span of life 'in the beginning thrice that of lesser Men'. For an account of my father's views on the longevity of the Númenóreans see *Unfinished Tales* pp. 224–5.

Between §13 and §14 there is a long passage in the *Akallabêth* in which Andúnië, the Meneltarma, Armenelos, and the tombs of the kings are referred to, and then the ancestry and choices of Elrond and Elros (this being closely derived from a long insertion to FN III §2: see pp. 333, 339–40).

DA II *Commentary* THE DROWNING OF ANADÛNÊ 379

§14 The opening sentence was changed to read:
Thus the years passed, and while Middle-earth went backward and light and wisdom failed there, the Adûnâi dwelt under the protection of the Avalôi, and in the friendship of the Nimrî, and increased in stature both of body and of mind. With 'the kings and princes learned the Nimrian tongue, in which much lore and song was preserved from the beginning of the world' cf. FN III §2 (p. 333): 'the speech of Númenor was the speech of the Eldar of the Blessed Realm'. In the *Akallabêth* the linguistic conception is more complex (p. 262): the Númenóreans still used their own speech, but 'their kings and lords knew and spoke also the Elven tongue [Sindarin], which they had learned in the days of their alliance, and thus they held converse still with the Eldar, whether of Eressëa or of the westlands of Middle-earth. And the loremasters among them learned also the High Eldarin tongue of the Blessed Realm, in which much story and song was preserved from the beginning of the world ...' See note 19 to *Aldarion and Erendis* in *Unfinished Tales*, p. 215.

§15 On the progressive restrictiveness of the Ban see p. 356 note 4.

§16 The vagueness of knowledge concerning the dwelling of the Avalôi ('upon some isle or shore of the western lands (Men know not where)') is retained from DA I, and the Adûnâi still name it 'the Haven of the Gods', *Avallôni*, for *Avallondē* in DA I. (In FN §1 the name *Avallon* was given to Tol Eressëa, 'for it is hard by Valinor'. In both versions of Lowdham's exemplification of Númenórean names in *The Notion Club Papers*, pp. 241, 305, he refers to the place-name *Avallôni* without suggesting where or what it might be; and in the second version F 2 he adds that although it is a name of his Language B, Adunaic, 'it is with it, oddly enough, that I associate Language A', Quenya. In both versions he calls Language A 'Avallonian'.) The Adûnâi named the land of the Avalôi 'the Haven of the Gods', *Avallôni*, '*for* at times ... they could descry ... a city white-shining on a distant shore, and great harbours, and a tower.' But there now enters in *The Drowning of Anadûnê* the idea of divergent opinions concerning this vision of a land to the west: 'And some held that it was a vision of the Blessed Realm that men saw, but others said that it was only a further isle where the Nimrî dwelt ... for mayhap the Avalôi had no visible dwelling upon Earth.' The latter opinion is supported by the author of *The Drowning of Anadûnê*, since 'certain it is that the Nimrî had some dwelling nigh unto Anadûnê, for thither they came ever and anon, the children of the Deathless Folk ...'
This was retained through the two further texts of *The*

380 SAURON DEFEATED DA II *Commentary*

Drowning of Anadûnê without any significant change save the loss of the words 'the children of the Deathless Folk' (see the note on §5 above). In the *Akallabêth* the true nature of the distant city is asserted: 'But the wise among them knew that this distant land was not indeed the Blessed Realm of Valinor, but was Avallónë, the haven of the Eldar upon Eressëa, easternmost of the Undying Lands' (pp. 262–3). See further the commentary on §47 below.

Before 'the Blessed Realm' the name *Zen'namân* was pencilled on the typescript, and again in §23; in both cases this was struck through. See the commentary on §47.

The reference to 'their own western haven, Andūniē of Nūmenōr' in DA I is now lost. Andúnië had appeared in FN (§2, p. 333): 'Of old the chief city and haven of that land was in the midst of its western coasts, and it was called Andúnië, because it faced the sunset'; this reappears in the *Akallabêth*, p. 261.

§17 In *none now dared withstand them* 'now' was changed to 'yet'; this is the reading of the *Akallabêth*, p. 263.

The whole of §§17–18 was retained in the *Akallabêth*, with the exception of the reference to the brutish speech of the men of Middle-earth (repeated in the following texts of *The Drowning of Anadûnê*). In the *Akallabêth* there appears here a reference to the far eastern voyages of the Númenóreans: 'and they came even into the inner seas, and sailed about Middle-earth and glimpsed from their high prows the Gates of Morning in the East'; this was derived from FN §3 (p. 334; see V.20, commentary on §3). With this cf. the opinion expressed in §27, that there was no sea-passage into the East.

§19 *of which the songs of men preserve still the distant memory like an echo of the Sea.* The song of *King Sheave* is doubtless to be understood as such an echo.

In the *Akallabêth* the first mention of the emergence of Sauron is postponed to a much later point in the narrative, and it is not until §21 that the old version begins to be used again, with the murmurings of the Númenóreans against the Doom of Men and the ban on their westward sailing.

In DA I *Zigūr* is the name which the men of Middle-earth gave to Sauron; it is not said that it was the name that he took for himself.

§20 *Amatthânê:* at the first occurrence in this paragraph the name was left to stand, but at the second (and again in §21) it was changed to *Zen'nabâr* (see under §12 above).

Indilzar: Elros, first King of Númenor. The name was changed to *Gimilzôr* (and so appears in the subsequent texts).

DA II *Commentary* THE DROWNING OF ANADÛNÊ   383

§27   *Menel-Tûbal* was here changed to *Menil-Tûbal*, and subsequently.

Of the debate of Ar-Pharazôn with Arbazân on the possibility of sailing east and so coming upon the land of Amân from the west, retained in the following texts, there is no vestige in the *Akallabêth*. On Arbazân's surmise that there might be no eastern passage by sea see under §17 above. It is perhaps possible that an idea of the geographical conception here can be gained from the two maps accompanying the *Ambarkanta* in IV.249, 251: for in the first of these there is very emphatically no sea-passage, and in the North and South there are 'ices impassable', while in the second there are straits by which ships might come into the furthest East. But even if this were so it could of course have no more than a 'pictorial' relevance, for the second map exhibits the convulsions after the breaking of Utumno and the chaining of Melkor in the First Battle of the Gods (*Quenta Silmarillion* §21, V.213).

§28   The story of Ar-Pharazôn's expedition into Middle-earth and the submission of Sauron is much enlarged in the *Akallabêth*, but this enlargement entered already in the third text DA III (see p. 389, §28).

§31   For 'he bade men think that the world was not a circle closed, but there lay many seas and lands for their winning' (retained in the following texts) the *Akallabêth* (p. 271) has: 'he bade men think that in the world, in the east and even in the west, there lay yet many seas and many lands for their winning'.

The concluding passage of §31, 'And that is the Realm of the Lord of All ...', was replaced by the following on a typewritten slip:

'And out of it the world was made; and the Lord thereof may yet make other worlds to be gifts to those who serve him, so that the increase of their power shall find no end.'

'And who is the lord of Darkness?' quoth Ar-Pharazôn.

And behind locked doors Zigûr spoke, and he lied, saying: 'It is he whose name is not now spoken, for the Avalôim have deceived you concerning him, putting forward the name of Eru, a phantom devised in the wickedness [> folly] of their hearts, seeking to chain Men in servitude to themselves. For they are the oracle of this Eru, which speaketh only what they will. But he that is their master and shall yet prevail will deliver you from this phantom; and his name is Arûn, Lord of All.'

Apart from names, this is almost the text of the *Akallabêth*.

§32   After the statement that Ar-Pharazôn 'turned back to the

384   SAURON DEFEATED   DA II *Commentary*

worship of the Dark' and that most of the people followed him, there enters in the *Akallabêth* (p. 272) the first mention of Amandil and Elendil, taking up the words of DA §26 and the opening sentences of §36 and greatly expanding them, with an account of the friendship of Ar-Pharazôn and Amandil in their youth, of Sauron's hatred of Amandil, and of his withdrawal to the haven of Rómenna.

The sentence 'and no man might ascend to the high place' was changed to 'for though not even Zigûr dared defile the high place, yet the king would let no man, upon pain of death, ascend to it'. The revised form appears in the *Akallabêth*, after which there is a long passage (pp. 272–3) concerning the White Tree of Númenor: of the king's reluctance to fell the Tree at Sauron's bidding, of Isildur's circumventing the guards about Nimloth and taking a fruit, narrowly escaping with many wounds, and of the king's then yielding to Sauron's demand. Then follows the description of the temple, not greatly changed from that in DA II, but with the addition that the first fire made on the altar was kindled with the wood of Nimloth. Of the White Tree of Númenor there is no mention in the texts of *The Drowning of Anadûnê*.

A puzzling reference to the site of the temple may be noticed here. This is in the final version of Edwin Lowdham's page in Old English, that appearing the typescript F 2 of Part Two of *The Notion Club Papers*. In the earlier Old English version (pp. 314–15) the temple was built 'on that high mountain that was called Meneltyúla (that is to say the Pillar of Heaven), which before was undefiled'. In the final version (pp. 257–8; certainly later than DA II, p. 375) it was built 'in the midst of the town of Arminalēth on the high hill which before was undefiled but now became a heathen fane'. Since the same words are used in both Old English texts the second version suggests a halfway stage, in which the temple was still built on the Pillar of Heaven (*on ðæm héan munte*), until now undefiled (*unawídlod*), but the Pillar of Heaven was in the midst of the city of Arminalēth. But this can scarcely be so, for already in DA I the story is present that the Meneltyúla was deserted, and that the temple was built on a hill in the midst of the city (Antirion).

In DA II both references to *Mulkhêr* were changed to *Arûn*, but *Arûn-Mulkhêr* was retained.

§35   For the passage following the words 'And Zigûr spoke to the king' the following (retained almost exactly in the *Akallabêth*) was substituted on a typewritten slip:

saying that his might was now so great that he might think to have his will in all things and be subject to no command or

DA II *Commentary* THE DROWNING OF ANADÛNÊ 385

ban. 'For behold! the Avalôim have possessed themselves of the land where there is no death; and they lie to you concerning it, hiding it as best they may, because of their avarice and their fear lest the kings of Men should wrest from them the Blessed Realm, and rule the world in their stead. And though, doubtless ...

§38 *Amatthânê* was here changed to *Anadûnê* (see under §§20, 23 above).

§39 In the *Akallabêth* (p. 276) there enters at this point an account of the treasures that were put aboad the ships at Rómenna, with the Seven Stones ('the gift of the Eldar') and the scion of Nimloth the White Tree.

§43 *their banners were black and golden:* in DA I the banners were 'red as the dying sun in a great storm and as black as the night that cometh after.' So in the manuscript E of Part Two of the *Papers* the sails of the Númenórean ships were 'scarlet and black', but 'golden and black' in the typescript F (p. 290 note 63; 'scarlet and black' also in FN III §6, 'bloodred and black' in the earlier Old English text, pp. 314–15).

§44 *Aglarrâma, castle of the sea:* in the *Akallabêth* the name of the great ship of Ar-Pharazôn is *Alcarondas*, with the same meaning.

§47 The radically different conception of the Cataclysm (from both *The Fall of Númenor* and the *Akallabêth*), here derived from the Nimrî but in DA I attributed merely to 'the wisest in discernment', in which the Land of Amân itself foundered, remained in the following texts: 'the fleets of the Adûnâi came indeed to Avallôni in the deeps of the sea, and they encompassed it about', and 'a great chasm opened in the sea between Anadûnê and the Deathless Land ... *But the land of Amân and the land of his gift,* standing upon either side of the great chasm [> rift] in the seas, *were also destroyed ...*'

Against the name *Avallôni* is pencilled *Zen'namân*, and this name appears written beside 'the Blessed Realm' in §§16, 23, though there struck out. At the end of §47 is written, but struck out, *Zen'namân* and *Zen'nabâr*, i.e. 'Land of Amân' and 'Land of Gift' (for *Zen'nabâr* see under §12 above). The references to *Avallôni* seem to amount to this: the distant city glimpsed across the sea was named by the Adûnâi *Avallôni* 'Haven of the Gods' *(Avalôi)* because they thought that it was a vision of the Blessed Realm (§16). Some said that this was not so: it was only an isle on which the Nimrî dwelt that they could see. The question is not resolved; but the name *Avallôni* was nonetheless used in §47 to refer to the Land of Amân. The statement that *Avallôni*

386 SAURON DEFEATED DA II *Commentary*

was 'encompassed' by the fleets of the Adûnâi is possibly to be associated with the words of §16, that the Avalôi dwelt 'upon *some isle* or shore of the western lands'.

Apart from the opinion held by some in Anadûnê that the land that they could see was an isle where the Nimrî dwelt, and the certainty that the Nimrî must have some dwelling near to Anadûnê, since they came there, Tol Eressëa is never referred to in *The Drowning of Anadûnê*.

The relation of the *Akallabêth* (pp. 278–9) to the earlier works in this passage is curious and characteristic. Just as in DA it is said that the fleets of Ar-Pharazôn 'came indeed to Avallôni ... and they encompassed it about', so in the *Akallabêth* they 'encompassed Avallónë'; but in the latter *Avallónë* is the eastern haven of Tol Eressëa, and the text continues: '*and all the isle of Eressëa*, and the Eldar mourned, for the light of the setting sun was cut off by the cloud of the Númenóreans.' My father was in fact turning back to *The Fall of Númenor* (§6, p. 336), which is almost the same here – but which has 'they encompassed Avallon', and lacks the words 'and all the isle of Eressëa': for in FN *Avallon* was the name of Eressëa itself.

The description of the 'changing of the fashion of the world' in the *Akallabêth* is almost exactly as in *The Drowning of Anadûnê*:

... and a great chasm opened in the sea between Númenor and the Deathless Lands, and the waters flowed down into it, and the noise and smoke of the cataracts went up to heaven, and the world was shaken. And all the fleets of the Númenóreans were drawn down into the abyss, and they were drowned and swallowed up for ever.

But whereas in *The Drowning of Anadûnê* this is followed by the statement that not only Anadûnê but the Land of Amân also disappeared into the great rift, in the *Akallabêth* my father again turned to *The Fall of Númenor* (§§7–8), telling that the king and his warriors who had set foot in the Blessed Realm were 'buried under falling hills' and 'lie imprisoned in the Caves of the Forgotten, until the Last Battle and the Day of Doom'; and then, that 'Ilúvatar cast back the Great Seas west of Middle-earth ... and the world was diminished, *for Valinor and Eressëa were taken from it into the realm of hidden things.*' Thus the radical difference in the conception of the loss of the True West between *The Drowning of Anadûnê* and the *Akallabêth* was a *reversion* to that of *The Fall of Númenor*.

The passage 'Ilúvatar cast back the Great Seas ...' was a revision (see V.32) of the original form of *The Fall of Númenor* (V.16; the second text FN II is virtually the same), in which the World Made Round was more unequivocally expressed: the

DA II *Commentary* THE DROWNING OF ANADÛNÊ   387

Gods 'bent back the edges of the Middle-earth, and they made it
into a globe ... Thus New Lands came into being beneath the
Old World, and all were equally distant from the centre of the
round earth ...'
This subject is further discussed on pp. 391 ff.

In the concluding sentence of §47 in DA II, 'and the Avalôi
dwell in secret, or have become as shadows and their power has
waned', my father was following DA I, where the name *Avalāi*
is ambiguously used; in the next text DA III the sentence was
changed (p. 391, §§46–7).

§48 *Ar-Zimrahil: Tar-Ilien* in DA I and in FN (§§5, 7); afterwards
Tar-Míriel, whose Adunaic name was Ar-Zimraphel (*Unfinished Tales* p. 224, *Akallabêth* pp. 269–70).

§§49–50 This passage, despite many small changes in the expression,
does not differ at all in its content from that in DA I, except for
the addition at the end of §50 of 'Therefore some among them
would still search the empty seas'. See further pp. 391 ff.

§51 After 'Nimruzân, and his sons and people' the words 'in their
seven ships' were added – presumably they had been omitted
unintentionally, since 'in seven ships' is present in DA I. In the
Akallabêth there were nine ships, 'four for Elendil, and for
Isildur three, and for Anárion two'. The sons of Elendil are not
named, nor their number given, in *The Drowning of Anadûnê*.

(iv) The final form of The Drowning of Anadûnê

The extensive alterations to the text of DA II detailed in the preceding
commentary were taken up into the third text, DA III, which was
typed on the same machine and the same paper as DA II. More
changes entered in DA III, and the completed typescript was then
further altered. Finally another typescript, DA IV, was made, identical
in appearance to the two preceding; in this the changes made to DA III
were taken up, but the completed text was scarcely emended. With DA
IV this phase in the development of the Númenórean legend comes to
an end.

There follows here an account, paragraph by paragraph, of the
alterations made between DA II, as emended, and the final form,
excluding only very minor changes (such as 'appointed time' for
'appointed hour' in §3). In general I do not distinguish between those
that entered in DA III and those that were made to it subsequently,
appearing in DA IV as typed.

§1 *Avalôi* became *Avalôim* throughout; this is the form in the final
text F 2 of Part Two of *The Notion Club Papers* (see p. 375).
Eru (*Eru-bênî, Eruhîn*) became *Êru* throughout. In the earlier

388   SAURON DEFEATED   DA III–IV

form of Lowdham's fragments the name has a short vowel (p. 311), but in the final form a long (p. 247).

§5 The opening sentence was changed to read: 'And out of the sorrows of the world the hearts of the Êruhîn were turned westward, for there, as they believed, was the land of Amân and abiding peace.'
Nimrî became Nimîr throughout.

§6 'filled with great dread, and with longing' > 'filled with longing'

§8 Azrabêl became Azrubêl throughout, at first by emendation of Azrabêl on DA III, and then as typed; see p. 377, §8.
Vingalôtë > Wingalôtë > Vingalôtë, see p. 377, §8.

§12 The Adunaic name of 'the Land of Gift' in DA III was Abarzâyan (see p. 378, §12), changed to the final form Yôzâyan, which appears in DA IV and in the final text F 2 of The Notion Club Papers (pp. 241, 247). It is thus seen that DA III preceded F 2.

§13 'so long as they remained still true' was omitted.
Adûnâi became Adûnâim throughout (cf. the note on Avalôi, Avalôim, §1 above).

§16 'to break the ban' > 'to break the ban of Amân'
'(a vision of the Blessed Realm) that men saw' > 'that men saw by grace'
'the children of the Deathless Folk' was omitted.

§19 'And yet in the end new good turned again to evil, and Men fell, as it is said, a second time' was omitted, the following sentence beginning 'But after an age there arose a second manifestation …'
'(he heard of the coming) of the Eruhîn' > 'of the Sea-kings out of the deeps'

§20 The name Minul-Târik of the Pillar of Heaven, replacing Menel-Tûbal (subsequently Menil-Tûbal) of DA II, first appears in DA III (see p. 375).

§21 'and now again was stirring' > 'and now the deep-planted seeds were stirring once again'

§23 For Amatthânê in DA II §§21, 23 (where it refers to 'the Land of Gift') the following texts have Anadûnê; but for the Blessed Realm in DA II §23 they have Amatthâni, the Blessed Realm. Thus Amatthânê, replaced in its application to Anadûnê in turn by Zen'nabâr, Abarzâyan, Yôzâyan, now reappears in the form Amatthâni as the name of Valinor; but Avallôni is retained in §§16, 47, 50. The etymology of Amatthâni is given in Lowdham's 'Report on Adunaic', p. 435.

DA III–IV   THE DROWNING OF ANADÛNÊ   389

§25 To the text of the typewritten rider attached to DA II and given on p. 382 the following was added in DA III after the words 'nor anywhere else within the girdle of the Earth': 'for it was not the Avalôim that named you in the beginning Êruhîn, the children of God.'
'who made both it and you' was omitted.

§26 *Arbazân* became *Aphanuzîr*, and *Nimruzân* became *Nimruzîr*, in DA III. Jeremy calls Lowdham *Nimruzīr* in *The Notion Club Papers*, pp. 250, 252, and the name appears in Lowdham's fragment I (B), p. 247, 'seven ships of Nimruzīr eastward'.

§27 After the words of Aphanuzîr (Arbazân) 'It may be so' he observes of the fraudulent argument of Ar-Pharazôn: 'Yet to go behind a command is not to keep it'; and in the passage following his speech the words 'where are ices impassable', first changed to '... is ice ...', were omitted.

§28 The story of the expedition of Ar-Pharazôn to Middle-earth was much enlarged on a typewritten page inserted into DA III. The new text is very close to that in the *Akallabêth* (p. 270), but lacks the reference to the Havens of Umbar:
... and when all was ready he himself set sail into the East. And men saw his sails coming up out of the sunset, dyed as with scarlet and gleaming with red gold, and fear fell on them and they fled far away. Empty and silent under the pale moon was the land when the King of Anadûnê [> Yôzâyan] set foot on the shore. For seven days he marched with banner and trumpet, and he came to a hill, and he went up and set there his pavilion and his throne; and he sat him down in the midst of the land, and the tents of his host were laid all about him like a field of proud flowers [> ranged all about him, blue, golden, and white, as a field of tall flowers]. Then he sent forth heralds and commanded Zigûr to come before him and swear to him fealty.
A recollection of mine in connection with this passage is perhaps worth mentioning. I remember my father, in his study in the house in North Oxford, reading me *The Drowning of Anadûnê* on a summer's evening: this was in 1946, for my parents left that house in March 1947. Of this reading I recall with clarity that the tents of Ar-Pharazôn were as a field of tall flowers of many colours. Since the passage only entered with the text DA III, and the naming of the colours of the flowers, 'blue, golden, and white', was pencilled onto the typescript, appearing in the final text DA IV as typed, my father was reading from DA III or DA IV. I have the strong impression that the Adunaic names were strange to me, and that my father read *The Drowning of*

390   SAURON DEFEATED   DA III–IV

Anadûnê as a new thing that he had written. This seems to support the suggestion I made earlier (p. 147) that the emergence of Adunaic and the evolution of a new form of the legend of the Downfall belong to the first half of 1946.

§30 This paragraph was rewritten to read:
> Yet such was the cunning of his mind, and the strength of his hidden will, that ere three years were passed he had become closest to the secret counsels of the King; for flattery sweet as honey was ever on his tongue, and knowledge he had of many things yet unrevealed to Men. And seeing the favour that he had of their lord, all the counsellors, save Aphanuzîr alone, began to fawn upon him. Then slowly a change came over the land, and the hearts of the Faithful were sorely troubled.

§31 At the end of the text on the replacement slip in DA II given on p. 383, §31, after 'his name is Arûn, Lord of All', was added: 'Giver of Freedom, and he shall make you stronger than they.'

§32 The description of the temple was changed on a retyped page of DA III by the alteration of the sentences following 'a mighty dome':
> And that dome was wrought all of silver and rose glittering in the sun, so that the light of it could be seen afar off; but soon the light was darkened and the silver became black. For in the topmost of the dome there was a wide opening or louver, and thence there issued a great smoke ...

To the second reference to Mulkhêr (> Arûn) in DA II was added 'Giver of Freedom' (cf. §31 above).

The final sentence of the paragraph became: 'These charges were for the most part false; yet those were bitter days, and wickedness begets wickedness.'

§36 The reply of Aphanuzîr (Arbazân) to Nimruzîr's question 'Would you then bewray the King?' was expanded to a form approaching that in the *Akallabêth* (p. 275):
> 'Yea, verily that I would,' said Aphanuzîr, 'if I thought that Amân needed such a messenger. For there is but one loyalty from which no man can be absolved in heart for any cause. And as for the ban, I will suffer in myself alone the penalty, lest all the Êruhîn become guilty.'

§38 'you must fly from fair Amatthânê that is now defiled, and lose what you have loved' > 'you must fly from the land of the Star with no other star to guide you; for that land is defiled. Then you shall lose what you have loved'

§39 'But this much can be seen that' was omitted.

DA III–IV THE DROWNING OF ANADÛNÊ 391

§41 '(the Eagles of Amân) are over Anadûnê!' > 'overshadow Anadûnê!'

§43 'one after another in an endless line' > 'advancing in a line the end of which could not be seen'

§§46–7 This passage in DA II was closely preserved in the final form, including the reference to the fleets of the Adûnâim coming to 'Avallôni in the deeps of the sea', apart from an insertion and alteration following 'For Ar-Pharazôn wavered at the end and almost he turned back' in §47:

> His heart misgave him when he looked upon the soundless shores and saw the Mountain of Amân shining, whiter than snow, colder than Death, silent, alone, immutable, terrible as the shadow of the light of God. But pride was now his master, and at last he left his ship, and strode upon the shore, claiming that land for his own, if none should do battle for it.

This passage was retained in the *Akallabêth* (p. 278), with *Taniquetil* for *the Mountain of Amân* and *Ilúvatar* for *God*.

Following 'the land of Amân and the land of his gift' (near the end of §47) was added 'Amatthâni and Yôzâyan' (see under §23 above).

The final sentence of §47 was changed to read: 'And the Avalôim thereafter had no habitation on Earth, and they dwell invisible; nor is there any place more where a memory of a world without evil is preserved.' See p. 387 (§47, at end).

§§49–50

This crucial passage was at first retained in DA III in exactly the form that it had in DA II (pp. 373–4) with one difference (apart from *Minul-Târik* for *Menil-Tûbal*): the end of §50 was changed to read: 'Therefore some among them would still search the empty seas, *hoping to come upon the Lonely Isle. But they found it not*: "for all the ways are crooked that once were straight," they said.' Already in §49 as it appears in DA I the summit of the Pillar of Heaven is called '*a lonely isle* somewhere in the great waters', if it were to be found rising above the surface of the sea.

Since apart from the statements in §16 that the Nimîr must have dwelt near Anadûnê, and that some said that it was the island of the Nimîr that could be seen, Tol Eressëa is otherwise conspicuous by its absence from *The Drowning of Anadûnê*, and *Avallôni* is a name of the Blessed Realm, it is clear that my father used the name *Lonely Isle* of the summit of the Pillar of Heaven on Anadûnê with a deliberate intention of ambiguity.

Additional typewritten pages were substituted for the conclusion (§§49–55) of the narrative in DA III, and §50 was extended

392   SAURON DEFEATED   DA III–IV

(§§49–50)

in a very remarkable way. The text was not further changed subsequently, and this is the final form of §§49–50 in *The Drowning of Anadûnê* (I give the passage in full for ease of comparison with the conclusion of the *Akallabêth* that follows):

Now the summit of Mount Minul-Târik, the Pillar of Heaven, in the midst of the land was a hallowed place, for there the Adûnâim had been wont to give thanks to Êru, and to adore him; and even in the days of Zigûr it had not been defiled. Therefore many men believed that it was not drowned for ever, but rose again above the waves, a lonely island lost in the great waters, if haply a mariner should come upon it. And many there were that after sought for it, because it was said among the remnant of the Adûnâim that the far-sighted men of old could see from the Minul-Târik the glimmer of the Deathless Land. For even after their ruin the hearts of the Adûnâim were still set westward; [§50] and though they knew that the world was changed, they said: 'Avallôni is vanished from the Earth, and the Land of Gift is taken away, and in the world of this present darkness they cannot be found; yet once they were, and therefore they still are in true being and in the whole shape of the world.' And the Adûnâim held that men so blessed might look upon other times than those of the body's life; and they longed ever to escape from the shadows of their exile and to see in some fashion the light that was of old. Therefore some among them would still search the empty seas, hoping to come upon the Lonely Isle, and there to see a vision of things that were.

But they found it not, and they said: 'All the ways are bent that once were straight.' For in the youth of the world it was a hard saying to men that the Earth was not plain* as it seemed to be, and few even of the Faithful of Anadûnê had believed in their hearts this teaching; and when in after days, what by star-craft, what by the voyages of ships that sought out all the ways and waters of the Earth, the Kings of Men knew that the world was indeed round, then the belief arose among them that it had so been made only in the time of the great Downfall, and was not thus before. Therefore they thought that, while the new world fell away, the old road and the path of the memory of the Earth went on towards heaven, as it were a mighty bridge invisible. And many were the rumours and tales among them concerning mariners and men forlorn upon the sea, who by some grace or fate had entered in upon

---

* *plain* is used in the lost sense 'flat'; but cf. the later spelling *plane* of the same word, and the noun *plain*.

DA III–IV   THE DROWNING OF ANADÛNÊ   393

(§§49–50)

the ancient way and seen the face of the world sink below
them, and so had come to the Lonely Isle, or verily to the
Land of Amân that was, and had looked upon the White
Mountain, dreadful and beautiful, ere they died.

In the *Akallabêth* a good deal of this passage was retained, but
given new bearings. I cite it here as it is printed in *The
Silmarillion*, pp. 281–2 (some editorial alteration at the beginning and end does not affect the sense of the passage).

Among the Exiles many believed that the summit of the
Meneltarma, the Pillar of Heaven, was not drowned for ever,
but rose again above the waves, a lonely island lost in the
great waters; for it had been a hallowed place, and even in the
days of Sauron none had defiled it. And some there were of
the seed of Eärendil that afterwards sought for it, because it
was said among loremasters that the farsighted men of old
could see from the Meneltarma a glimmer of the Deathless
Land. For even after the ruin the hearts of the Dúnedain were
still set westwards; and though they knew indeed that the
world was changed, they said: 'Avallónë is vanished from the
Earth and the Land of Aman is taken away, and in the world
of this present darkness they cannot be found. Yet once they
were, and therefore they still are, in true being and in the
whole shape of the world as at first it was devised.'

For the Dúnedain held that even mortal Men, if so blessed,
might look upon other times than those of their bodies' life;
and they longed ever to escape from the shadows of their exile
and to see in some fashion the light that dies not; for the
sorrow of the thought of death had pursued them over the
deeps of the sea. Thus it was that great mariners among them
would still search the empty seas, hoping to come upon the
Isle of Meneltarma, and there to see a vision of things that
were. But they found it not. And those that sailed far came
only to the new lands, and found them like to the old lands,
and subject to death. And those that sailed furthest set but a
girdle about the Earth and returned weary at last to the place
of their beginning; and they said: 'All roads are now bent.'

Thus in after days, what by the voyages of ships, what by
lore and star-craft, the kings of Men knew that the world was
indeed made round, and yet the Eldar were permitted still to
depart and to come to the Ancient West and to Avallónë, if
they would. Therefore the loremasters of Men said that a
Straight Road must still be, for those that were permitted to
find it. And they taught that, while the new world fell away,

394   SAURON DEFEATED   DA III–IV

(§§49–50)

the old road and the path of the memory of the West still went on, as it were a mighty bridge invisible that passed through the air of breath and of flight (which were bent now as the world was bent), and traversed Ilmen which flesh unaided cannot endure, until it came to Tol Eressëa, the Lonely Isle, and maybe even beyond, to Valinor, where the Valar still dwell and watch the unfolding of the story of the world. And tales and rumours arose along the shores of the sea concerning mariners and men forlorn upon the water who, by some fate or grace or favour of the Valar, had entered in upon the Straight Way and seen the face of the world sink below them, and so had come to the lamplit quays of Avallónë, or verily to the last beaches on the margin of Aman, and there had looked upon the White Mountain, dreadful and beautiful, before they died.

It will be seen that §49 and the first part of §50 (as far as 'But they found it not') in DA was largely retained in the *Akallabêth* (where however all this passage concerning the speculations of the Exiles was removed to the end of the work). But where DA has 'Avallôni is vanished from the Earth, and the Land of Gift is taken away' the *Akallabêth* has 'Avallónë is vanished from the Earth and the Land of Aman is taken away'. In DA Avallôni *is* the Land of Amân; in the *Akallabêth* it is the haven in Tol Eressëa (see p. 386). In DA those who searched the empty seas hoped to come upon 'the Lonely Isle', which is the summit of the Pillar of Heaven; in the *Akallabêth* they hoped to come upon 'the Isle of Meneltarma'.

In both versions the mariners who sailed west from Middle-earth seeking for the summit of Minul-Târik or Meneltarma discovered by their voyaging that the world was round; but in DA the words are 'that the world was indeed round', whereas in the *Akallabêth* they are 'that the world was indeed *made* round'.

In *The Fall of Númenor* it was explicit, the kernel of the legend of the Cataclysm, that the world was made round at the time of the Downfall (see pp. 386–7): this was the story, and within the story the rounding of the world at that time is a fact, unqualified. In *The Drowning of Anadûnê* the Nimîr (Eldar) had come to the Adûnâim and expressly taught that the world was *of its nature* round ('as an apple it hangeth on the branches of heaven', §23), but Zigûr coming had gainsaid it ('The world was not a circle closed', §31). In this work the author knows that the world is of its nature a globe; but very few of the Adûnâim had believed this teaching until the voyages of the survivors of the Downfall taught them that it was true (cf. the passage

DA III–IV THE DROWNING OF ANADÛNÊ 395

(§§49–50)

written on the original text DA I, p. 355: 'For they believed still the lies of Sauron that the world was plain, until their fleets had encompassed all the world seeking for Meneltyūlā, and they knew that it was round'). And so (as he recounts the tradition), rather than accept the true nature of the Round World, 'the belief arose among them that it had so been made only in the time of the great Downfall, and was not thus before.' So it was that the survivors of Anadûnê in the West of Middle-earth came to the conception of the Straight Road: '*Therefore they thought that, while the new world fell away, the old road and the path of the memory of the Earth went on towards heaven, as it were a mighty bridge invisible.*'

This is radically distinct from *The Fall of Númenor* (FN III §11, p. 338): 'For the ancient line of the world remained in the mind of Ilúvatar, and in the thought of the gods, and in the memory of the world, as a shape and plan that has been changed and yet endureth.' The author of *The Fall of Númenor* knows that 'of old many of the exiles of Númenor could still see, some clearly and some more faintly, the paths to the True West'; but for the rationalising author (as he may seem to be) of *The Drowning of Anadûnê* the Straight Road was a belief born of desire and regret.

The author of the *Akallabêth* had both works before him, and in this passage he made use of them both. I give again here the concluding passage of the *Akallabêth* with the sources shown (necessarily somewhat approximately): *The Drowning of Anadûnê* in italic, *The Fall of Númenor* (FN III §§8, 12) in roman between asterisks, and passages not found in either source in roman within brackets.

But they found it not. (And those that sailed far) *came only to the new lands, and found them like to the old lands, and subject to death.* (And those that sailed furthest set but a girdle about the Earth and returned) *weary at last to the place of their beginning;* and they said: '*All roads are now bent.*'

Thus in after days, what by the voyages of ships, what by (lore and) *star-craft, the kings of Men knew that the world was indeed* (made) *round,* (and yet the Eldar were permitted still to depart and to come to the Ancient West and to Avallónë, if they would.) *Therefore* (the loremasters of Men said that a Straight Road must still be, for those that were permitted to find it. And they taught) *that, while the new world fell away, the old road and the path of the memory of the* (West still) *went on, as it were a mighty bridge invisible* (that) *passed through the air of breath and of flight* ((which

396   SAURON DEFEATED   DA III–IV

(§§49–50)

were bent now as the world was bent),) *and traversed Ilmen which flesh unaided cannot endure,* (until it came to Tol Eressëa, the Lonely Isle, and maybe even beyond, to Valinor, where the Valar still dwell and watch the unfolding of the story of the world.) *And tales and rumours* (arose along the shores of the sea) *concerning mariners and men forlorn upon the water who, by some fate or grace* (or favour of the Valar,) *had entered in upon the* (Straight) *Way and seen the face of the world sink below them, and so had come to* (the lamplit quays of Avallónë, or verily to the last beaches on the margin of) *Aman, and there had looked upon the White Mountain, dreadful and beautiful, before they died.*

The intention that lay behind these aspects of *The Drowning of Anadûnê* is discussed in the next section (v).

§51   The description of the gale that followed the Cataclysm was rewritten in DA III to a form close to that in the *Akallabêth* (p. 280), but still retaining the seven ships (see p. 387, §51):

But when the land of Anadûnê toppled to its fall, then he [Nimruzîr] would have been drawn down and perished, and deemed it the lesser grief, for no wrench of death could be more bitter than the ruin of that day; but the wind took him, for it blew still from the West more wild than any wind that Men had known; and it tore away the sails, and snapped the masts, and hunted the unhappy men like straws upon the water; and the deeps rose up in towering anger.

Then the seven ships of Nimruzîr fled before the black gale out of the twilight of doom into the darkness of the world; and waves like moving mountains capped with snow bore them up amid the clouds, and after many days cast them away far inland upon Middle-earth.

On the text of DA IV *seven* was altered in a hastily scribbled change to *twelve*.

§55   At first the conclusion in DA III retained the form in DA II, but it was replaced by the following (with pencilled corrections as shown, appearing in DA IV as typed):

And the name of that land has perished; for neither did men speak of Gimlad, nor of Abarzâyan [> Yôzâyan] the Gift that was taken away, nor of Anadûnê upon the confines of the world; but the exiles on the shores of the Sea, if they turned towards the West, spoke of Akallabê [> Akallabêth] that was whelmed in the waves, the Downfallen, Atalantë in the Nimrian tongue.

Akallabêth is the form in Lowdham's fragments (pp. 247, 312).

*

THE DROWNING OF ANADÛNÊ 397

I have shown (p. 353) that the composition of the original draft DA I of *The Drowning of Anadûnê* fell between that of the sole manuscript E of Part Two of *The Notion Club Papers* and the first typescript F 1 of Night 66 in the *Papers*. The second text DA II fell between F 1 and the replacement F 2 (p. 375), as also did the third text DA III (p. 388, §12). The final text DA IV is the first in which the Adunaic name of 'the Land of Gift' is *Yôzâyan*, the form in F 2; it cannot be seen which of these two texts preceded the other, but this seems to be of slight importance. What is significant about these details, of course, is that they make it certain that the composition of *The Drowning of Anadûnê* was intertwined with and was completed within the same period as the further development of Part Two of *The Notion Club Papers*.

(v) The theory of the work

I turn now to the fundamental question, what is the significance of the extraordinary transformations of, and omissions from, the existing legends in the development of *The Drowning of Anadûnê*? I have headed this section *The theory of the work* because my father used the word in this connection, and because I believe and hope to show that there was a 'theory' behind it.

Before attempting to formulate an answer, there are three extremely curious texts to be considered. All three were written at great speed, dashed down in careless expression as words came to mind, and probably one after the other. Very obviously preceding the emergence of Adunaic, they are a series of sketches of the rapidly evolving conceptions that would underlie the new version of the Númenórean legend that my father was contemplating: the first of them is in fact headed *The theory of this version*.

This first essay, which I will call 'Sketch I', exceedingly rough and disjointed, led on to a second ('Sketch II') which followed I for some distance, enlarging and expanding it, but was then abandoned. It is convenient to give Sketch II first so far as it goes, and then the remainder of I.

Notes on this section will be found on pp. 410 ff.

Evil reincarnates itself from time to time – reiterating, as it were, the Fall.

There were 'Enkeladim' once on earth, but that was not their name in this world: it was *Eledāi* (in Númenórean *Eldar*).[1] After the First Fall they tried to befriend Men, and teach them to love the Earth and all things that grow in it. But evil also was ever at work. There were false Eldar: counterfeits and deceits made by evil, ghosts and goblins, but not always evil to look at. They terrified Men, or else deceived and betrayed them, and hence arose the fear of Men for all the spirits of the Earth.

398   SAURON DEFEATED

Men 'awoke' first in the midst of the Great Middle Earth (Europe and Asia), and Asia was first thinly inhabited, before the Dark Ages of great cold. Even before that time Men had spread westward (and eastward) as far as the shores of the Sea. The [Enkeladim >] Eledāi withdrew into waste places or retreated westward.[2]

The Men who journeyed westward were in general those who remained in closest touch with the true Eledāi, and for the most part they were drawn west by the rumour of a land in or beyond the Western Sea which was beautiful, and was the home of the Eledāi where all things were fair and ordered to beauty. This was so for there was a great island in the Ocean where the Eledāi had first 'awakened' when the world was made: that is complete and ready for their operations.

Thus it is that the more beautiful legends (containing truths) arose, of oreads, dryads, and nymphs; and of the Ljós-alfar.[3]

At length Men reached the western shores of the Great Lands, and were halted on the shores of the Sea. The shock and awe and longing of that meeting has remained in their descendants ever since, and the Great Sea and the setting sun has been to them the most moving symbol of Death and of Hope for Escape.

In the margin of the text of this page, which ends at this point, my father wrote: 'The Almighty even after the Fall allowed an earthly paradise to be maintained for a while; but the Eledāi were bidden to withdraw thither as men spread – if they would remain as they had been: otherwise they would fade and diminish.'[4]

In times remote, when Men, though they had now wandered for many many lives upon the face of the Earth, were yet young and untutored (save such few kindreds as had become knit in friendship with the western Eledāi, and their language had become enriched, and they knew verse and song and other arts), evil once again took visible shape. A great tyrant arose, first as the war-lord of a tribe, but he grew slowly to a mighty king, magician, and finally a god. In the midst [written above: North?] of the Great Lands was the seat of this terrible dominion, and all about men became enslaved to him. In that time Darkness became terrible. The black power slowly extended westward; for Melekō[5] knew that there lingered the most powerful and beneficent of the Eledāi, and that their friendship with Men was the greatest obstacle to his complete dominion.

Those among Men of the West who were most filled with sea-hunger began to make boats, aided and inspired (as in much else) by the Eledāi, and they began to essay the waters, at first with fear, but with growing mastery of wind and tide, and of themselves. But now war broke out, for the forces of Melekō threatened the lands of the west marches of the sea. The Men of the West were strong, and free, and the Easterlings of Melekō were driven back

THE DROWNING OF ANADÛNÊ 399

again and again. But this was only a respite, for the Easterlings were innumerable, and the attack was ever renewed with greater force; and Melekō sent phantoms and demons and spirits of evil into the western lands, so that these also might become intolerable and a time of dread, when men cowered in their houses and looked no more on the stars.

The Eledāi had long disappeared. Some said they had died, or faded into nothing; some that they had never been, and were but the inventions of old-time tales; some few that they had passed over the Sea to their land in the West.

A mariner arose in that time who was called Earendel, and he was king of Men upon the west shore of the Great Sea in the North of the world. He reported that once taken by a great wind he had been borne far out of his course and had indeed seen many islands in the regions of the setting sun – and one most remote from which there came a scent as of gardens of fair flowers. And it came to pass that all the Men of the West who had not died or fallen or fled into waste places were now hemmed in a narrow land, a large island some say, and they were assailed by Melekō, but only because their land was an isle, divided by a narrow water from the Great Lands, were they able still to hold out. Then Earendel took his ship and said farewell to his people. For he said it was his purpose to sail into the West and find the Eledāi and ask for their help. 'But I shall not return,' he said. 'If I fail then the sea will have me, but if I succeed then a new star will arise in heaven.'

And what deeds Earendel did upon his last voyage is not known for certain, for he was not seen again among living Men. But after some years a new star did indeed arise in the West, and it was very bright; and then many men began to look for the return of the Eledāi to their aid; but they were hard pressed by evil.

Here Sketch II ends as a continuously written text, but my father added some scribbled and disjointed notes at the end, which include this passage:

> Melekō was defeated with the aid of the Eledāi and of the Powers, but many Men had seceded to him. The Powers (under orders of Ilúvatar) withdrew the Eledāi to the Isle of Eresse, whose chief haven was westward, Avallon(de).[6] Those that remained in Middle-earth withered and faded. But faithful men of the Eruhildi (Turkildi) were also given an isle, between Eresse and Middle-earth.

Sketch I (written at extreme speed in soft pencil on small slips) was essentially the same as Sketch II, though much briefer, to the point where Earendel enters in the latter. In Sketch I, however, there was no reference to Earendel, and all that is told is that when there came a respite in the war with 'the tyrant' (who is not named in this text) 'and

400   SAURON DEFEATED

his Easterlings' the Men of the West set sail, having been instructed in
the art of ship-building by 'the last lingering Enkeladim' and they
landed 'on a large island in the midst of the Great Sea'. At the head of
the page my father noted: 'The first to set sail was Earendel. He was
never seen again.' Then follows (in very slightly edited form):

But there is another smaller isle out of sight to the West – and
beyond that rumour of a Great Land [?uninhabited] in the West.
This island is called Westernesse Númenor, the other Eressëa.
The religion of the Númenóreans was simple. A belief in a
Creator of All, Ilúvatar. But he is very remote. Still they offered
bloodless sacrifice. His temple was the *Pillar of Heaven*, a high
mountain in the centre of the island. They believed Ilúvatar to dwell
outside the world altogether; but symbolized that by saying he
dwelt in High Heaven.
[*Added:* But they believe he has under him Powers (Valar), some
at his special command, some residing in the world for its immediate government. These though *good* and servants of God are
inexorable, and . . . . hostile in a sense. They do not pray to them
but they fear and obey them (if ever any contact occur). Some are
Valandili (Lovers of the Powers).]
But they believe the world flat, and that 'the Lords of the West'
(Gods) dwell beyond the great barrier of cloud hills – where there is
no death and the Sun is renewed and passes under the world to rise
again.
[*Struck out:* His servants for the governance of the world were
Enkeladim and other greater spirits. *Added:* There were lesser
beings – especially associated with living things and with making . . .
– called Eldar.] These they asked for assistance in need. Some still
sailed to Eressëa. [*In margin:* Elendili] But the most did not, and
except among the wise the theory arose that the great spirits or
Gods (*not* Ilúvatar) dwelt in the West in a Great Land beyond the
sun. [*Bracketed:* The Enkeladim told them that the world was
round, but that was a hard saying to them.] Some of their great
mariners tried to find out.
They lived to a great age, 200 years or more, but all the more
longed for longer life. They envied the Enkeladim. They grew
mighty in ship-building, and began to adventure to sea. Some try to
reach the West beyond Eressëa but fail to return.
The Pillar of Heaven in neglected by all but a few. The kings build
great houses. The custom of sending their bodies adrift to sea in an
east wind grows up. The east wind begins to symbolize Death.[7]
Some sail back to the Dark Lands. There they are greeted with
awe, for they are very tall . . . . They teach true religion but
are treated as gods.
Sauron comes into being.

THE DROWNING OF ANADÛNÊ 401

He cannot prevail in arms against the Númenóreans who now have many fortresses in the West.

The text ends with a very rough sketch of the coming of Sauron and the Downfall. 'Sauron is brought to Númenor to do allegiance to Tarkalion'. He 'preaches a great sermon', teaching that Ilúvatar does not exist, but that the world is ruled by the Gods, who have shut themselves in the West, hating Men and denying them life. The one good God has been thrust out of the world into the Void; but he will return. In an added passage (but no doubt belonging to the time of the writing of the text) it is told, remarkably, that 'Sauron says *the world is round*. There is nothing outside but Night – and other worlds.'[8]

Sauron has 'a great domed temple' built on the Pillar of Heaven (see p. 384), and there human sacrifice takes place, the purpose of which is 'to add the lives of the slain to the chosen living'. The Faithful are persecuted, and chosen for the sacrifice; 'a few fly to Eressëa asking for help – but the Eressëans have departed or hidden themselves.' A vast fleet is prepared 'to assault Eressëa and go on to take the West Land from the Gods'; and the text ends with the bare statements that the fleet was sucked into the great chasm that opened, and that 'only those Númenóreans who had withdrawn east of the isle and refused to .... war were saved.' This is followed by a morass of names, including 'Elendil son of Valandil and his sons Árundil and Firiel', from which emerges 'Elendil and his sons Isildur and Anárion'. Finally there are some further notes: 'Sauron flees East also. The Pillar of Heaven is volcanic.[9] Sauron builds a great temple on a hill near where he had landed. The Pillar of Heaven also begins to smoke and he calls it a sign; and most believe him.'

The third text ('Sketch III') begins with a note on names: '*Ilūve Ilu:* Heaven, the universe, all that is (with and without the Earth); *menel:* the heavens, the firmament.'[10] Then follows:

In the beginning was *Eru* the One God (*Ilúvatar* the Allfather, *Sanavaldo* the Almighty). He appointed powers (*Valar*) to rule and order the Earth (*Arda*). One *Melekō*, the chief, became evil. There were also two kindreds of lesser beings, Elves : *Eldar* (**Eledāi*), and Men (*Hildi* = sons, or followers). The Eledāi came first, as soon as Arda became habitable by living things, to govern there, to perfect the *arts* of using and ordering the material of the Earth to perfection and beauty in detail, and to prepare the way for Men. Men (the Followers or Second Kindred) came second, but it is guessed that in the first design of God they were destined (after tutelage) to take on the governance of all the Earth, and ultimately to become Valar, to 'enrich Heaven', *Ilúve*. But Evil (incarnate in Melekō) seduced them, and they fell. They became immediately estranged from the Eldar and Valar. For Melekō represented their tutelage as usurpation by

402 SAURON DEFEATED

Eldar and Valar of Men's rightful heritage. God forbade the Powers to interfere by violence or might. But they sent many messages to Men, and the Eldar constantly tried to befriend Men and to teach them. But the power of Melekō increased, and the Valar retreated to the isle of *Eresse* in the Great Seas far west of the Great Lands (*Kemen*) – where they had always had as it were a habitation and centre in their early strife with Melekō.[11]

Melekō now (because evil decreased him, or to further his designs, or both) took visible shape as a Tyrant King, and his seat was in the North. He made many counterfeits of the Eledāi who were evil (but did not always so appear), and who cozened and betrayed Men, and so increased their fear and suspicion of the true Eldar.

There was war between the Powers and Melekō (the second war: the first had been in the making of the world, before Elves and Men were). Though all Men had 'fallen', not all remained enslaved. Some repented, rebelled against Melekō, and made friends of the Eldar, and tried to be loyal to God. They had no worship but to offer firstfruits to Eru on high places. They were not wholly happy, as Eru seemed far off, and they dared not pray to him direct; and so they regarded the Valar as gods, and so were often corrupted and deceived by Melekō, taking him or his servants (or phantoms) for 'gods'. But in the war against the seats of Melekō in the North there were *three kindreds* of good men (sons of God, *Eruhildi*) who were wholly faithful and never sided with Melekō. Among these there was *Earendel*, and he was alone of Men partly of the kindred of the Eledāi, and he became the first of Men to sail upon the Sea. In the days of the Second War when Men and the remaining Eledāi were hard pressed he set sail West. He said: 'I shall not return. If I fail you will hear no more of me. If I do not fail a new star will arise in the West.' He came to Eresse and spoke the embassy of the Two Kindreds before the Chief of the Valar, and they were moved. But Earendel was not suffered to return among living men, and his vessel was set to rise in the sky as a sign that his message was accepted. And Elves and Men saw it, and believed help would come, and were enheartened. And the Powers came and aided Elves and Men to overthrow Melekō, and his bodily shape was destroyed, and his spirit banished.

But the Powers now withdrew the Eldar to Eresse (where they had themselves dwelled, but now they had no longer any local habitation on earth, and seldom took shape visible to Elves or Men). Those who lingered in Kemen were doomed to fade and wither. But in Eresse was long maintained an earthly paradise filled with all beauties of growth and art (without excesses), the dwelling of the Eldar, a memorial of what Earth 'might have been' but for Evil. But the Men (Eruhildi) of the Faithful Houses were allowed (if they

THE DROWNING OF ANADÛNÊ 403

would) to go and dwell in another isle (greater but less fair) between Eresse and Middle-earth. Elros son of Earendel was their first king, in the land of Andor also called Númenor: so that the kings of the Númenóreans were called 'Heirs of Earendel'. Earendel was not only partly of Elf-kin but he was an Elf-friend (*Elendil*), whence the Kings of Númenor were also called *Elendilli (Ælfwinas)*. [*Marginal addition:* Elrond his other son elected to remain in Kemen and dwell with Men and the Elves that yet [?abode] in the West of Middle-earth.]

In that time the world was very forlorn and forsaken, for only fading Elves dwelt in the West of Middle-earth, and the best of Men (save others of the Eruhildi far away in the midst of Kemen) had gone westward. But even the Eruhildi of Númenor were mortal. For the Powers were not allowed to abrogate that decree of God after the fall (that Men should die and should leave the world not at their own will but by fate and unwilling); but they were permitted to grant the Númenóreans a threefold span (over 200 years).

And in Númenor the Eruhildi became wise and fair and glorious, the mightiest of Men, but not very numerous (for their children were not many). Under the tutelage of the Eressëans – whose language they adopted (though in course of time they altered it much) – they had song and poesy, music, and all crafts; but in no craft did they have such skill and delight as in ship-building, and they sailed on many seas. In those days they were permitted, or such of their kings and wise men who were favoured and called Elf-friends (*Elendilli*), to voyage to Eresse; but there they might come only to the haven of *Avallon(de)* on the east side of the isle and the city of [Túna >] Tirion on the hill behind, there to stay but a short while.[12] Though often the Elendilli craved to abide in Eresse this was not permitted to them by command of the Powers (received from God); for the Eruhildi remained mortal and doomed at the last to grow weary of the world and to die, even their high-kings the heirs of Earendel. And they were not suffered to sail beyond Eresse westward, where they heard rumour of a New Land, for the Powers were not willing that that land should as yet be occupied by Men. But the hearts of the Eruhildi felt pity for the forsaken world of Middle-earth, and often they sailed there, and wise men or princes of the Númenóreans would at times come among men in the Dark Ages and teach them language, and song, and arts, and bring to them corn and wine; and men of Middle-earth revered their memory as gods. And in one or two places nigh to the sea men of the western race made settlements and became kings and the fathers of kings. But at last all this bliss turned to evil, and men fell a second time.

For there arose a second manifestation of Evil upon Earth, whether the spirit of Melekō himself took new (though lesser) form,

404   SAURON DEFEATED

or whether it were one of Melekō's servants that had lurked in the
dark and now received the [? counsel] of Melekō out of the Void
and waxed great and wicked, tales differ. But this evil thing was
called by many names, and the Eruhildi called him *Sauron*, and he
sought to be both king over all kings, and to Men both king and
god. His seat was southward and eastward in Kemen, and his power
over Men (especially east and south) grew ever greater and moved
westward, driving away the lingering Eledāi and subjugating more
and more of the kindred of the Eruhildi who had not gone to
Númenor. And Sauron learned of Númenor and its power and
glory; and to Númenor in the days of Tarkalion the Golden (the
[21st >] tenth in the line from Earendel)[13] news came of Sauron and
his power, and that he purposed to take the dominion of all Kemen,
and of all the Earth after.

But in the meanwhile evil had been at work [?already] in the
hearts of the Númenóreans; for the desire of everlasting life and to
escape death grew ever stronger upon them; and they murmured
against the prohibition that excluded them from Eresse, and the
Powers were displeased with them. And they forbade them now
even to land upon the island. At this time of estrangement from
Eledāi and Valāi Tarkalion hearing of Sauron determined without
counsel of Eldar or Valar to demand the allegiance and homage of
Sauron. ... [*sic*]
    Númenor cast down.
    Eresse and the Eledāi removed from the world save in memory
and the world delivered to Men. Men of Númenórean blood could
still see Eresse as a mirage [?on] a straight road leading thither.
    The ancient Númenóreans knew (being taught by the Eledāi) that
the Earth was round; but Sauron taught them that it was a disc and
flat, and beyond was nothing, where his master ruled. But he said
that beyond Eresse was a land in the [?utter] West where the Gods
dwelt in bliss, and usurped the good things of the Earth.[14] And that
it was his mission to bring Men to that promised land, and
overthrow the greedy and idle Powers. And Tarkalion believed him,
being hungry for life undying.
    And the Númenóreans after the downfall still spoke of the
Straight Road that ran on when the Earth was bent. But the good
ones – those that fled from Númenor and took no part in the war on
Eresse – used this only in symbol. For by 'that which is beyond
Eresse' they meant the world of eternity and the spirit, in the region
of Ilúvatar.[15]

Here this text ends, with lines drawn showing that it was completed.
All the concluding passage (from 'The ancient Númenóreans knew
...'), concerning the shape of the world and the meaning of the
Straight Road, was struck through, the only part of the text so treated.

THE DROWNING OF ANADÛNÊ   405

It will be seen that in the latter part of Sketch III appear a number of phrases that survived into *The Drowning of Anadûnê* (such as 'men fell a second time', 'there arose a second manifestation (of Evil) upon Earth', 'this evil thing was called by many names').

It seems to me that there are broadly speaking two possible lines of explanation of my father's thinking at this time. On the one hand, many years had passed since the progressive development of 'The Silmarillion' had been disrupted, and during all that time the actual narrative manuscripts had lain untouched; but it cannot be thought that he had put it altogether out of mind, that it had not continued to evolve unseen. Above all, the relation between the self-contained mythology of 'The Silmarillion' and the story of *The Lord of the Rings* boded problems of a profound nature. This work had now been at a standstill for more than a year; but *The Notion Club Papers* was leading to the re-emergence of Númenor as an increasingly important element in the whole, even as the Númenórean kingdoms in Middle-earth had grown so greatly in significance in *The Lord of the Rings*.

It might seem at least arguable, therefore, that the departures from the 'received tradition' (not a line of which had been published, as must always be borne in mind) seen in my father's writing at this time represent the emergence of new ideas, even to the extent of an actual dismantling and transformation of certain deeply embedded concep-tions. Chief among these are the nature of the 'dwelling' of the Valar in Arda and the interrelated question of 'the shape of the world'; and the 'Fall of Men', seduced in their beginning by 'Mēlekō', but followed by the repentance of some and their rebellion against him.

On the other hand, it may be argued that these developments were inspired by a specific purpose in respect only of *The Drowning of Anadûnê*. Essentially this is the view that I myself take; but the other is not thereby excluded radically or at all points, for ideas that here first appear would have repercussions at a later time.

It will be seen that the 'sketches' just given are remarkably dissimilar in many points, although it is true that their haste and brevity, a certain vagueness of language, and my father's characteristic way of omitting some features and enlarging on others in successive 'outlines', make it often difficult to decide whether differences are more apparent than real. But I shall not in any case embark on any comparative analysis, for I think it will be agreed without further discussion that these 'sketches', taken with the opening texts of *The Drowning of Anadûnê*, give a strong impression of uncertainty on my father's part: they are like a kaleidoscopic succession of different patternings, as he sought for a comprehensive conception that would satisfy his aim.

But what was that aim? The key, I think, is to be found in the treatment of the Elves (*Ēnkeladim, Eledāi, Eldar, Nimrî* or *Nimîr*). For beyond a few very generalised ideas nothing is known of them: of

406   SAURON DEFEATED

their origin and history, of the Great March, of the rebellion of the Noldor, of their cities in Beleriand, of the long war against Morgoth. In the first text of *The Drowning of Anadûnê* this ignorance is extended beyond that of the 'sketches' to a total obscuration of the distinction between Valar and Eldar (see pp. 353–4), although in the second text the Eldar appear under the Adunaic name *Nimrî*. In the 'sketches' the isle of Eressëa (Eresse) appears, yet confusedly, for (in Sketch III) the Valar dwelt on Eresse, and it was to Eresse that Earendel came and spoke before 'the Chief of the Valar'; while in *The Drowning of Anadûnê* Tol Eressëa has virtually disappeared.

Where could such ignorance of the Elves be found but in the minds of Men of a later time? This, I believe, is what my father was concerned to portray: a tradition of Men, through long ages become dim and confused. At this time, perhaps, in the context of *The Notion Club Papers* and of the vast enlargement of his great story that was coming into being in *The Lord of the Rings*, he began to be concerned with questions of 'tradition' and the vagaries of tradition, the losses, confusions, simplifications and amplifications in the evolution of legend, as they might apply to his own – within the always enlarging compass of Middle-earth. This is speculation; it would have been helpful indeed if he had at this time left any record or note, however brief, of his reflections. But many years later he did write such a note, though brief indeed, on the envelope that contains the texts of *The Drowning of Anadûnê*:

> Contains very old version (in Adunaic) which is good – in so far as it is just as much different (in inclusion and omission and emphasis) as would be probable in the supposed case:
> (a) Mannish tradition
> (b) Elvish tradition
> (c) Mixed Dúnedanic tradition

The handwriting and the use of a ball-point pen suggest a relatively late date, and were there no other evidence I would guess it to be some time in the 1960s. But it is certain that what appears to have been the final phase of my father's work on Númenor (*A Description of Númenor, Aldarion and Erendis*) dates from the mid-1960s (*Unfinished Tales* pp. 7–8); and it may be that the *Akallabêth* derives from that period also.

At any rate, there is here unequivocal evidence of how, long afterwards, he perceived his intention in *The Drowning of Anadûnê*: it was, specifically, 'Mannish tradition'. It could well be that – while the 'sketches' preceded the emergence of Adunaic – the conception of such a work was an important factor in the appearance of the new language at this time.

It seems to me likely that by 'Elvish tradition' he meant *The Fall of Númenor*; and since 'Mixed Dúnedanic tradition' presumably means

THE DROWNING OF ANADÛNÊ 407

a mixture of Elvish and Númenórean tradition, he was in this surely referring to the *Akallabêth*, in which both *The Fall of Númenor* and *The Drowning of Anadûnê* were used (see pp. 376, 395–6).

I conclude therefore that the marked differences in the preliminary sketches reflect my father's shifting ideas of what the 'Mannish tradition' might be, and how to present it: he was sketching rapidly possible modes in which the memory, and the forgetfulness, of Men in Middle-earth, descendants of the Exiles of Númenor, might have transformed their early history.[16]

In *The Drowning of Anadûnê* the confusions and obscurities of the 'Mannish tradition' were in fact deepened, in relation to the preliminary sketches: in the submergence of the Elves under the general term *Avalái* in DA I, and in the virtual disappearance of Tol Eressëa, with the name 'Lonely Isle' given to the summit of the Pillar of Heaven sought by seafarers after the Downfall. It is seen too in the treatment of 'Avallon(de)': for in the sketches (see note 12) this name appears already in the final application, the eastward haven in Tol Eressëa, while in DA I the reference of *Avallondē* is obscure, and in the subsequent texts *Avallôni* is used of the Blessed Realm (see pp. 379 §16, 385 §47). My father seems not to have finally resolved how to present the Blessed Realm in this tradition; or, more probably, he chose to leave it as a matter 'unsure and dim'. In Sketch III it is told that after the banishment of Melekō from the world the Powers 'had no longer any local habitation on earth', and the Land of the Gods in the far West seems to be presented as a lie of Sauron's (see note 14). In *The Drowning of Anadûnê* (§16) those in Anadûnê who argued that the distant city seen over the water was an isle where the Nimrî (Nimîr) dwelt held also that 'mayhap the Avalôi(m) had no visible dwelling upon Earth'; yet later it is recounted (§47, and still more explicitly in the revision made to this passage, p. 391) that Ar-Pharazôn set foot on the Land of Amân, and after the Land of Amân was swallowed in the abyss 'the Avalôi(m) thereafter had no habitation on Earth'.

The attempt to analyse and order these shifting and fugitive conceptions will perhaps yield in the end no more than an understanding of what the problems were that my father was revolving in his mind. But since there is no reason to think that he turned to the subject of Númenor again, after he had forced himself to return to the plight of Sam Gamgee at the subterranean door of the Tower of Kirith Ungol, until many years had passed, it is interesting to see what he wrote of it in his long letter to Milton Waldman in 1951 (*Letters* no. 131): and I reprint two extracts from that letter here.

Thus, as the Second Age draws on, we have a great Kingdom and evil theocracy (for Sauron is also the god of his slaves) growing up in

408   SAURON DEFEATED

Middle-earth. In the West – actually the North-West is the only part clearly envisaged in these tales – lie the precarious refuges of the Elves, while Men in those parts remains more or less uncorrupted if ignorant. The better and nobler sort of Men are in fact the kin of those that had departed to Númenor, but remain in a simple 'Homeric' state of patriarchal and tribal life.

Meanwhile *Númenor* has grown in wealth, wisdom, and glory, under its line of great kings of long life, directly descended from Elros, Earendil's son, brother of Elrond. The *Downfall of Númenor*, the Second Fall of Man (or Man rehabilitated but still mortal), brings on the catastrophic end, not only of the Second Age, but of the Old World, the primeval world of legend (envisaged as flat and bounded). After which the Third Age began, a Twilight Age, a Medium Aevum, the first of the broken and changed world; the last of the lingering dominion of visible fully incarnate Elves, and the last also in which Evil assumes a single dominant incarnate shape.

The *Downfall* is partly the result of an inner weakness in Men – consequent, if you will, upon the first Fall (unrecorded in these tales), repented but not finally healed. Reward on earth is more dangerous for men than punishment! The Fall is achieved by the cunning of Sauron in exploiting this weakness. Its central theme is (inevitably, I think, in a story of Men) a Ban, or Prohibition.

The Númenóreans dwell within far sight of the easternmost 'immortal' land, Eressëa; and as the only men to speak an Elvish tongue (learned in the days of their Alliance) they are in constant communication with their ancient friends and allies, either in the bliss of Eressëa, or in the kingdom of Gilgalad on the shores of Middle-earth. They became thus in appearance, and even in powers of mind, hardly distinguishable from the Elves – but they remained mortal, even though rewarded by a triple, or more than a triple, span of years. Their reward is their undoing – or the means of their temptation. Their long life aids their achievements in art and wisdom, but breeds a possessive attitude to these things, and desire awakes for more *time* for their enjoyment. Foreseeing this in part, the gods laid a Ban on the Númenóreans from the beginning: they must never sail to Eressëa, nor westward out of sight of their own land. In all other directions they could go as they would. They must not set foot on 'immortal' lands, and so become enamoured of an immortality (within the world), which was against their law, the special doom or gift of Ilúvatar (God), and which their nature could not in fact endure.

. . .

But at last Sauron's plot comes to fulfilment. Tar-Calion feels old age and death approaching, and he listens to the last prompting of Sauron, and building the greatest of all armadas, he sets sail into

THE DROWNING OF ANADÛNÊ   409

the West, breaking the Ban, and going up with war to wrest from the gods 'everlasting life within the circles of the world'. Faced by this rebellion, of appalling folly and blasphemy, and also real peril (since the Númenóreans directed by Sauron could have wrought ruin in Valinor itself) the Valar lay down their delegated power and appeal to God, and receive the power and permission to deal with the situation; the old world is broken and changed. A chasm is opened in the sea and Tar-Calion and his armada is engulfed. Númenor itself on the edge of the rift topples and vanishes for ever with all its glory into the abyss. Thereafter there is no visible dwelling of the divine or immortal on earth. Valinor (or Paradise) and even Eressëa are removed, remaining only in the memory of the earth. Men may sail now West, if they will, as far as they may, and come no nearer to Valinor or the Blessed Realm, but return only into the east and so back again; for the world is round, and finite, and a circle inescapable – save by death. Only the 'immortals', the lingering Elves, may still if they will, wearying of the circle of the world, take ship and find the 'straight way', and come to the ancient or True West, and be at peace.

Three years later my father said in a letter to Hugh Brogan (18 September 1954, *Letters* no. 151):

Middle-earth is just archaic English for $\acute{\eta}$ $oἰκουμένη$, the inhabited world of men. It lay then as it does. In fact just as it does, round and inescapable. That is partly the point. The new situation, established at the beginning of the Third Age, leads on eventually and inevitably to ordinary History, and we here see the process culminating. If you or I or any of the mortal men (or hobbits) of Frodo's day had set out over sea, west, we should, as now, eventually have come back (as now) to our starting point. Gone was the 'mythological' time when Valinor (or Valimar), the Land of the Valar (gods if you will) existed physically in the Uttermost West, or the Eldaic (Elvish) immortal Isle of Eressëa; or the Great Isle of Westernesse (Númenor-Atlantis). After the Downfall of Númenor, and its destruction, all this was removed from the 'physical' world, and not reachable by material means. Only the Eldar (or High-Elves) could still sail thither, forsaking time and mortality, but never returning.

A week later he wrote to Naomi Mitchison (25 September 1954, *Letters* no. 154):

Actually in the imagination of this story we are now living on a physically round Earth. But the whole 'legendarium' contains a transition from a flat world (or at least an $oἰκουμένη$ with borders all about it) to a globe: an inevitable transition, I suppose, to a modern 'myth-maker' with a mind subjected to the same 'appearances' as ancient men, and partly fed on their myths, but taught that the

410 SAURON DEFEATED

Earth was round from the earliest years. So deep was the impression made by 'astronomy' on me that I do not think I could deal with or imaginatively conceive a flat world, though a world of static Earth with a Sun going round it seems easier (to fancy if not to reason).

The particular 'myth' which lies behind this tale, and the mood both of Men and Elves at this time, is the Downfall of Númenor: a special variety of the Atlantis tradition. ...

I have written an account of the Downfall, which you might be interested to see. But the immediate point is that before the Downfall there lay beyond the sea and the west-shores of Middle-earth an *earthly* Elvish paradise Eressëa, and *Valinor* the land of the *Valar* (the Powers, the Lords of the West), places that could be reached physically by ordinary sailing-ships, though the Seas were perilous. But after the rebellion of the Númenóreans, the Kings of Men, who dwelt in a land most westerly of all mortal lands, and eventually in the height of their pride attempted to occupy Eressëa and Valinor by force, Númenor was destroyed, and Eressëa and Valinor removed from the physically attainable Earth: the way west was open, but led nowhere but back again – for mortals.

NOTES

1   The name *Eledāi* occurs in DA II (and subsequent texts) §5, as the name of the Nimrî (Nimîr) in their own language. On Michael Ramer's *Enkeladim* see pp. 199, 206 and note 65, 303.

2   Sketch I has here: 'The Great Central Land, Europe and Asia, was first inhabited. Men awoke in Mesopotamia. Their fates as they spread were very various. But the Enkeladim withdrew ever west.'

3   *Ljós-alfar:* Old Norse, 'Light-elves', mentioned in the 'Prose Edda' of Snorri Sturluson.

4   Cf. DA II (and subsequent texts) §16: 'For as yet Eru permitted the Avalôi to maintain upon Earth ... an abiding place' (DA I 'an abiding place, an earthly paradise').

In my father's exposition of his work to Milton Waldman in 1951 there is a passage of interest in relation to the opening of this sketch (*Letters* no. 131, pp. 147–8):

In the cosmogony there is a fall: a fall of Angels we should say. Though quite different in form, of course, to that of the Christian myth. These tales are 'new', they are not directly derived from other myths and legends, but they must inevitably contain a large measure of ancient wide-spread motives or elements. After all, I believe that legends and myths are largely made of 'truth', and indeed present aspects of it that can only be received in this mode; and long ago certain truths and modes of this kind were discovered and must always reappear.

THE DROWNING OF ANADÛNÊ 411

There cannot be any 'story' without a fall – all stories are ultimately about the fall – at least not for human minds as we know them and have them.

So, proceeding, the Elves have a fall, before their 'history' can become storial. (The first fall of Man, for reasons explained, nowhere appears – Men do not come on the stage until all that is long past, and there is only a rumour that for a while they fell under the domination of the Enemy and that some repented.) The main body of the tale, the *Silmarillion* proper, is about the fall of the most gifted kindred of the Elves ...

Notable here is my father's reference to 'a rumour that for a while [Men] fell under the domination of the Enemy and that some repented', and see also the further citation from this letter on p. 408; with this cf. DA II (and subsequent texts) §§3–4:

At the appointed hour Men were born into the world, and they were called the Eru-hîn, the children of God; but they came in a time of war and shadow, and they fell swiftly under the domination of Mulkhêr, and they served him. ... But some there were of the fathers of Men who repented, seeing the evil of the Lord Mulkhêr and that his shadow grew ever longer on the Earth; and they and their sons returned with sorrow to the allegiance of Eru, and they were befriended by the Avalôi, and received again their ancient name, Eruhîn, children of God.

Of this there is no suggestion in the *Quenta Silmarillion* (V.274–6); cf. however the suggestions in Chapter 17 of the published *Silmarillion* ('that a darkness lay upon the hearts of Men (as the shadow of the Kinslaying and the Doom of Mandos lay upon the Noldor) [the Eldar] perceived clearly even in the people of the Elf-friends whom they first knew').

At the head of the following page of the text is a very rough and disjointed note in which are named the *Eruhildi*, sons of God, descended from Shem or Japheth (sons of Noah).

5 *Melekō*: a footnote to the text states: 'He had many names in different tongues, but such was his name among the Númenóreans, which means Tyrant.' This is the form of the name in DA I, but with long first vowel: *Mēlekō*.

6 *Eresse* is the form in the earlier version of Edwin Lowdham's Old English text, pp. 313–14. – On the haven of *Avallon(de)* see note 12. In 'whose chief haven was westward' read 'eastward'.

7 In *The Fall of Númenor* (§10) ship-burial came to be practised by the Exiles on the western coasts of Middle-earth.

8 This (presumably) contradicts the earlier, bracketed, statement in this same text (p. 400): 'The Enkeladim told them that the world was round, but that was a hard saying to them.' The statement here is of course the opposite of the story in *The Drowning of*

412   SAURON DEFEATED

Anadûnê (§§23, 31), where Sauron taught that the world was flat, contradicting the instruction of the messengers of the Avalôi(m). In Sketch III (p. 404) 'The ancient Númenóreans knew (being taught by the Eledāi) that the Earth was round; but Sauron taught them that it was a disc and flat, and beyond was nothing, where his master ruled.'

9   *The Pillar of Heaven is volcanic:* cf. Lowdham's comment on Frankley's poem (p. 265): 'Your Volcano is ... apparently a last peak of some Atlantis.'

10   On *Ilu, Ilúve*, see IV.241, V.47, 63, and the *Etymologies*, stem IL, V.361. The word *menel* first occurs here or in the manuscript E of Part Two of *The Notion Club Papers*, in the name *Menelminda* of the Pillar of Heaven (p. 302).

11   The first occurrence of the word *kemen* in the texts, but cf. the added entry stem KEM- in the *Etymologies*, V.363.

where they had always had as it were a habitation and centre in their early strife with Melekō: the legend that the isle on which the Valar dwelt before Morgoth overthrew the Lamps was also that on which Ulmo ferried the Elves to Valinor, and which Ossë anchored to the sea-bottom far out in the ocean, so that it was named 'the Lonely Isle'. The original form of the story is found in *The Book of Lost Tales* ('The Coming of the Elves', I.118 ff.) and then in the successive versions of 'The Silmarillion': the 'Sketch of the Mythology' from the 1920s (IV.12, 14, 45), the *Quenta Noldorinwa* (IV.80, 86), and the *Quenta Silmarillion* (V.208, 221–2).

12   In the earlier version of the Old English text of the surviving page of Edwin Lowdham's manuscript (pp. 313–14) the Númenóreans were forbidden to land on Eresse. Here they may visit the isle, but only briefly, and only the haven of Avallon(de) and the city of [Túna >] Tirion 'on the hill behind'; subsequently the Powers, in their displeasure, transmuted this into a prohibition against landing on Eresse at all (p. 404). On the reference to 'the city of [Túna >] Tirion on the hill behind' see note 16.

In notes added to Sketch II (p. 399), as well as in the present passage, 'Avallon(de)' appears as the name of the haven in Eresse, and this is where the final application of the name (later *Avallónë*) first appears (in FN III *Avallon* was still the name of the Lonely Isle, as it remained in the earlier Old English text referred to above).

13   *tenth in the line from Earendel*: this can be equated with the statement in DA II §20 (see the commentary, p. 381) if Earendel is himself numbered, as the first in the line though not the first king of Númenor.

14   This presumably implies that the idea of a land in the far West where the Gods dwelt was a lie of Sauron's. Earlier in the text

THE DROWNING OF ANADÛNÊ 413

(p. 402) it has been told that the Gods had dwelt in Eresse, but after the final overthrow of Melekō 'they had no longer any local habitation on earth' (cf. also Sketch I, p. 400: 'except among the wise the theory arose that the great spirits or Gods ... dwelt in the West in a Great Land beyond the sun'). See further p. 407.

15 Cf. VIII.164 and note 37.

16 A curious case is presented by the statement in Sketch III, p. 403, that 'the city of [Túna >] Tirion' was 'on the hill behind the haven of Avallon(de)'; for Tún(a), Tirion was of course the city of the Elves in Valinor. One might suppose that Homer nodded here; but in the earliest draft of an Old English text for 'Edwin Lowdham's page' (p. 316), which closely followed *The Fall of Númenor* §6, it is told that the Númenóreans, landing in Valinor, set fire to the city of Túna. The statement in Sketch III is therefore more probably to be taken as intentional, an example of a famous name handed down in tradition but with its true application forgotten.

(vi) Lowdham's Report on the Adunaic Language

This is a typescript made by my father that ends at the bottom of its seventeenth page, at which point he abandoned it (there is no reason to suppose that further pages existed but were lost). That it belongs with the final texts DA III and DA IV of *The Drowning of Anadûnê* is readily seen from various names and name-forms, as *Nimīr, Azrubēl, Adūnāim, Minul-Tārik, Amatthāni* (see p. 388, §§5, 8, 13, 20, 23).

In printing 'Lowdham's Report' I have followed my father's text very closely indeed, retaining his use of capitals, italics, marks of length, etc. despite some apparent inconsistency, except where corrections are obvious and necessary. The only point in which I have altered his presentation is in the matter of the notes. These (as became his usual practice in essays of this sort) he simply interspersed in the body of the text as he composed it; but as some of them are very substantial I have thought it best to collect them together at the end. I have added no commentary of my own.

It may be noted that the 'we' of Lowdham's introduction refers to himself and Jeremy; cf. Footnotes 2 and 6 on pp. 432–3.

ADUNAIC

It is difficult, of course, to say anything about the pre-history of a language which, as far as my knowledge goes, has no close relations with any other tongue. The other contemporary language that came through together with Adunaic in my earlier 'hearings', and which I have called Avallonian, appears to be

414   SAURON DEFEATED

distinct and unrelated, at least not 'cognate'. But I guess that originally, or far back beyond these records, Avallonian and Adunaic were in some way related. It is in fact clear now that Avallonian is the *Nimriyē* or 'Nimrian tongue' referred to in the very early Exilic text that we have managed to get concerning the Downfall. In that case it must be the language of the *Nimīr*, or a western form of it, and so be the ultimate source of the languages of Men in the west of the Old World. Perhaps I should rather say that the glimpses of the 'Nimrian tongue' that we have received show us a language, itself doubtless much changed, that is *directly* descended from the primeval Nimrian. From that Nimrian in a later stage, but still older than the Avallonian, the ancestor of Adunaic was partly derived.

But Adunaic must then for a long time have developed quite independently. Also I think it came under some different influence. This influence I call Khazadian; because I have received a good many echoes of a curious tongue, also connected with what we should call the West of the Old World, that is associated with the name Khazad. Now this resembles Adunaic phonetically, and it seems also in some points of vocabulary and structure; but it is precisely at the points where Adunaic most differs from Avallonian that it approaches nearest to Khazadian.

However, Adunaic evidently again later came into close contact with Avallonian, so that there is, as it were, a new layer of later resemblances between the two tongues: Adunaic for instance somewhat softened its harder phonetic character; while it also shows a fairly large number of words that are the same as the Avallonian words, or very similar to them. Of course, it cannot always be determined in such cases whether we are dealing with a primitive community of vocabulary, or with a later borrowing of Avallonian terms. Thus I am inclined to think that the Adunaic Base MINIL 'heaven, sky' is a primitive word, cognate with the Nimrian Base MENEL and not borrowed from it at a later time; although certainly, if *Menel* had been so borrowed, it would probably have acquired the form *Minil* [*struck out:* and the actual Adunaic noun *Minal* could be explained as an alteration to fit *Minil* into the Adunaic declensional system]. On the other hand it seems plain that the Adunaic word *lōmi* 'night' is an Avallonian loan; both because of its sense (it appears to mean 'fair night, a night of stars', with no connotations of gloom or fear), but also because it is quite

THE DROWNING OF ANADÛNÊ 415

isolated in Adunaic. According to Adunaic structure, as I shall try to exhibit it, *lōmi* would require either a biconsonantal Base LUM, or more probably a triconsonantal Base LAW'M; but neither of these exist in our material, whereas in Avallonian *lóme* (stem *lómi-*) is a normal formation from an Avallonian biconsonantal Base LOM.

I will try now and sketch the structure and grammar of Adunaic, as far as the material that we have received allows this to be done. The language envisaged is the language about the period of the Downfall, that is more or less during the end of the reign of King Ar-Pharazōn. From that period most of the records come. There are only occasional glimpses of earlier stages, or of the later (Exilic) forms of the language among the descendants of the survivors. Some of our chief texts, notably *The Drowning*, are in point of time of composition Exilic: that is they must have been put together at some time later than the reign of Ar-Pharazōn; but they are in a language virtually identical with the 'classical' Adunaic. This is probably due to two causes: their drawing on older material; and the continued use of the older language for higher purposes. For the actual daily speeches of the Exiles seem in fact to have changed and diverged quickly on the western shores. Of these changed and divergent forms we have only a few echoes, but they sometimes help in elucidating the forms and history of the older tongue.

*

General Structure.
The majority of the word-bases of Adunaic were *triconsonantal*. This structure is somewhat reminiscent of Semitic; and in this point Adunaic shows affinity with Khazadian rather than with Nimrian. For though Nimrian has many triconsonantal stems (other than the products of normal suffixion), such as the stem MENEL cited above, these are rarer in Nimrian, and are mostly the stems of *nouns*.

The vocalic arrangements within the base, however, do not much resemble Semitic; neither does Adunaic show anything strictly comparable to the 'gradations' of languages familiar to us, such as the *e/o* variation in the Indo-European group. In an Adunaic Base there is a Characteristic Vowel (CV) which shares with the consonants in characterizing or identifying the Base. Thus KARAB and KIRIB are distinct Bases and may have wholly unrelated meanings. The CV may, however, be modified in

416   SAURON DEFEATED

certain recognized ways (described below under the Vowels) which can produce effects not unlike those of gradation.

In addition to the *triconsonantal* Bases, there existed also in Adunaic a large number of *biconsonantal* Bases. Many of these are clearly ancient, though some may have been borrowed from Avallonian, where the biconsonantal Base is normal. These ancient biconsonantal Bases are probably an indication that the longer forms are in fact historically a later development. A few of the commonest verbal notions are expressed by biconsonantal forms, though the verb form of Adunaic is usually triconsonantal: thus NAKH 'come, approach', BITH 'say', contrasted with SAPHAD 'understand', NIMIR 'shine', KALAB 'fall', etc. [*Footnote 1*]

A number of ancient elements also exist: affixes, pronominal and numeral stems, prepositional stems, and so on, that only show *one* consonant. When, however, a 'full word', a noun for instance, has a uniconsonantal form, it must usually be suspected that an older second consonant has disappeared. Thus *pâ* 'hand' is probably derived from a Base PA3.

Consonants.

The following is a table of the Consonants which Adunaic appears originally (or at an earlier stage) to have possessed: [*Footnote 2*]

	(a) p-series	(b) t-series	(c) c-series	(d) k-series
STOPS				
1. *Voiceless:*	P.	T.	C.	K.
2. *Voiced:*	B.	D.	J.	G.
3. *Voiceless aspirated:*	Ph.	Th.	Ch.	Kh.
CONTINUANTS				
4. *Voiceless:*	–	S.	2.	H.
5. *Voiced (weak):*	W.	L, R, Z.	Y.	3. ?.
6. *Voiced: Nasals:*	M.	N.	–	9.

[*Footnote 3*]

The sounds of the C-series: C, J, Ch, 2 were front or 'palatal' consonants originally; that is roughly consonants of the K-series made in the extreme forward or *y*-position, and they might be so represented, but the above notation has been adopted, because their later development was to simple consonants. The

THE DROWNING OF ANADÛNÊ   417

sign 2 represents a voiceless hissed Y, that is the German *ich*-laut, or a rather stronger form of the voiceless Y often heard initially in such an English word as *huge*.

It will be noted that the T-series is the most rich, and possessed *three* voiced continuants. The T-series is probably the most frequently employed in Base-formation; and is certainly the most used in pronominal and formative elements (especially those of uniconsonantal form). The P-series is the poorest and possesses no voiceless hiss; but it is very probable that one anciently existed, a voiceless W (as English *wh*), but became H prehistorically.

H represents the voiceless back hissing sound, the *ch* of Welsh, Gaelic, and German (as in *acht*). 3 is the corresponding voiced spirant, or 'open' G.

Adunaic employs affixion in word-formation, though more sparingly than Avallonian; and in contrast to Avallonian employs prefixion more frequently than suffixion: the latter is sparingly used in forming stems (where the two elements become merged), but is more frequent in inflexion (where the two elements usually remain distinct). The primitive Adunaic combinations of consonants, in consequence, are due mainly to the contact of the basic consonants, and are predominantly of the form 'Continuant + some other consonant', or *vice versa*. This is so, because the predominant (but not exclusive) form of the Adunaic Bases, when triconsonantal, is X + Continuant + X; or X + X + Continuant, where X = any consonant.

A much employed method of derivation, however, is the lengthening or 'doubling' of one of the basic consonants. The consonant doubled is usually either the medial or final consonant of the Base, though in certain formations the initial may be doubled (only *one* of the basic consonants is so treated in any one word).

Similar to this method, and so to some extent competing with it in functions, is the infixion of an homorganic nasal before the final, or less frequently the medial, basic consonant: thus B to MB; D to ND; G to NG. This method cannot, of course, be distinguished from doubling in the case of the Nasals. It is doubtful if it originally occurred before the other continuants: the apparent cases of NZ may be due to *NJ, which became NZ, or to the analogy of such cases. [*Footnote 4*]

Adunaic, like Avallonian, does not tolerate more than a single

418　　　　　　　SAURON DEFEATED

basic consonant initially in any word (note that Ph, Th, Kh, are simple consonants). Unlike Avallonian it tolerates a large number of combinations medially, and there consonants in contact are very sparingly assimilated. Finally, in the 'classical' period Adunaic did not possess consonant-combinations, since affixes always ended in a vowel or a single consonant; while basic stems were always arranged in the following forms: ATLA, TAL(A) in the case of biconsonantal bases; AK(A)LAB(A), (A)KALBA in the case of triconsonantals. But the omission of short final A (not I or U), both in speech and writing, was already usual before the end of the classical period, with the consequence that a large number of consonant combinations became final.

The following list will show the normal development of the more primitive consonants in later Adunaic. The consonants are here set out in the order of the former table, and not according to the phonetic classification.

	(a)	(b)	(c)	(d)
1.	P.	T.	S.	K.
2.	B.	D.	Z.	G.
3.	Ph.	Th.	S.	Kh.
4.	–	S.	S.	H.
5.	W.	L, R, Z.	Y.	– (G). –.
6.	M.	N.	–	(N) [*Footnote 5*]

It will be observed that the consonants have not suffered any very material change except in the case of the C-series, which has become dental (apart from Y, which remains unchanged). With the development of C, Ch, Z to S may be compared the development of Latin fronted C in part of the Romance area; and the development of Indo-European K to S in Slavonic. Similarly the development of J (fronted G) to Z may be compared with the change of Indo-European fronted G and Gh to Z in Iranian and Slavonic. The assumption of a primitive C-series is based partly on scraps of internal evidence (such as the presence of an infixion NZ, whereas infixion of Nasal does not occur before the genuine consonants); partly on early forms, especially some scraps of an early inscription, [*Footnote 6*] which shows two different s-letters and z-letters. The treatment of Avallonian loans is also significant; in early loans the Avallonian Ty and Hy (approximately equivalent to the English *t*

THE DROWNING OF ANADÛNÊ   419

in *tune* and *h* in *huge*) both become s in Adunaic: as for instance Adunaic *sulum* 'mast', *sūla* 'trump' from Nimrian *kyulumā*, *hyōlā*, Avallonian *tyulma*, *hyóla*.

In the earlier language Ph, Th, Kh had plainly been aspirated stops, as in ancient Greek. This is most clearly seen when these sounds came into contact with others (see below). But it appears from various signs in the spelling, from the later developments in Exilic, and from the actual pronunciations of words coming through in audible form, that before the Downfall these aspirates had become strong spirants: F (bilabial), Þ (as English voiceless *th*), and X (the *ach*-sound originally belonging to H, with which Kh now coalesced in cases where H had not gone on to the breath-H). At the same time the combinations PPh, TTh, KKh became the 'affricates' PF, TÞ, KX, and then the long or double spirants FF, ÞÞ, XX. PTh and KTh appear to have become FÞ, XÞ.

H was originally, as noted above, the voiceless back-spirant; but in the classical language it had usually become the breath H. So, always initially, and medially between vowels. It never, however, becomes silent in these positions. [*Footnote 7*] The spirantal sound of H was retained before s [*added:* and where long or doubled HH] (where it later therefore coalesced with Kh); and in some 'hearings' it seems to occur before T and Th, though usually before consonants it is heard as a breathless puff, having the timbre of the preceding vowel. On the development of H in other contacts, see below.

The original consonants w and y were weak (consonantal forms of the vowels U and I). Medially they disappeared prehistorically before the vowels U and I respectively. But initially they were strengthened, becoming more spirantal (though w remained bilabial); so that the initial combinations WU and YI remained. The same strengthening occurred between vowels (where w and y had not been lost). After consonants both w and y remained weaker, like English w and y. Before consonants and finally they were vocalized and usually combined with the preceding vowels to form diphthongs (see the *Vowels*). [*Footnote 8*]

The sound ʔ [see Footnote 1] had no sign in Adunaic script, except in the archaic inscription referred to above [page 418 and Footnote 6]. Presumably it disappeared very early. It cannot be determined whether it had ever been used medially as a base-forming consonant. Probably not.

420   SAURON DEFEATED

3 became weakened, until in the classical period (parallel with the softening of the voiceless equivalent H to the breath-H) it merged with the adjacent vowels. This softening of the back spirants may be ascribed to Avallonian influence.

Initially 3 disappeared. Medially between vowels it disappeared also, and contractions often resulted (always in the case of like vowels, A3A to Ā); U3 + vowels became UW-, and I3 + vowel became IY-. Finally, or before a consonant, 3 became merged with the preceding vowel, which if short was consequently lengthened; as A3DA to ĀDA.

Assimilations in contact.

As noted above, these were only sparingly made, owing to the strong consciousness of the basic consonantal pattern in Adunaic. And even those assimilations most commonly made in actual speech are seldom represented in writing, except in the comparatively rare cases where the structure of the word was no longer recognized.

The nasals offer, however, a surprising exception to this conservative tendency, both in writing and speech. This is all the more remarkable, since the combinations MP, NT, NK seem not only easy to us, but are highly favoured in Avallonian. They were disliked in Adunaic, and tended to be changed even at the contact point of distinct words in composition: as *Amātthāni* from AMĀN + THĀNI 'the realm of Amān'.

The dental nasal N was in speech assimilated in position to following consonants of other series. It thus became M before P, Ph, B, and M; though notably NW remained unchanged (NW is a favoured combination in Avallonian); and 9 before K, Kh, G, H, 3. Where the nasal still remained a nasal, as in MB, NG, this change of position is often disregarded in writing.

After these changes in position the combinations of Nasal + Voiceless consonant all suffered change. In the combinations MP, MPh, NT, NTh, NK, NKh the nasal was first unvoiced, and then denasalized, the resulting combinations being PP, PPh, TT, TTh, KK, KKh. These changes were recognized as a rule in writing, though a diacritic was usually placed above the P, T, or K that resulted from a nasal; the evidence of the audible forms seems to show that this sign was etymological and grammatical, not phonetic. In old formations N + H became 9H and then HH (phonetically XX, long back voiceless spirant); but in contacts made after the weakening of H to breath-H, or remodelled after

THE DROWNING OF ANADÛNÊ 421

the event, NH remained and is heard as a voiceless NN with breath off-glide. NS became TS.

Since M did not become assimilated in position to following consonants there were the combinations MT, MTh, MK, MKh, MS, and MH. Parallel with the development described above these became PT, PTh, PK, PKh, PS, but no example of P-H for M-H is found. In the few cases of contact of M + H MH is written, and (as in the case of NH) a voiceless MM is heard.

Where the following consonant was voiced the changes are few (other than the changes in position described above). 3 after N or the infixed homorganic 9 does not disappear but becomes nasalized yielding 99, which became NG (phonetically 9G). NR, NL tended to become RR, LL, but usually with the retention of nasality (transferred to the preceding vowel), in speech; the change is not as a rule represented in writing, though such spellings as NRR, NLL are found. M3 became, in accordance with the general tendency of 3 to be assimilated to a preceding voiced sound, MM. MW became in speech MM (colloquially a preceding labial usually absorbs a following W), but this change is usually not shown in spelling.

Other assimilations are rarer and less remarkable. In speech there was a tendency for consonants in contact to be assimilated in the matter of voice; but this tendency is less strong than in, say, English, and is mostly disregarded in writing. Thus we usually find *Sapda* from Base SAPAD, and *Asdi* from Base ASAD, where *sabda* and *azda* may be spoken (though the z in such a form is only partly voiced and is not the same as the strongly buzzed sound of a basic Z).

The aspirates Ph, Th, Kh have naturally a strong unvoicing tendency on the sounds that follow, and transfer their aspiration or audible breath off-glide to the end of the group. Thus Ph + D, or T, or Th became PTh (or strictly PhTh). Thus from Base SAPHAD is derived *saphdān* 'wise-man, wizard', becoming later *sapthān* (phonetically, as described above, *safpān*). But such combinations are not very common, and in perspicuous forms (such, for example, as arise in verbal or noun inflexion, or in casual composition) were liable to be remodelled, especially after the change of the aspirates to spirants; thus *usaphda* 'he understood' for *usaptha*.

The continuants W, Y; L, R, Z are pronounced voiceless after the aspirates, but otherwise suffer no change. They are also

422 SAURON DEFEATED

unvoiced after s and H. Before H and s the continuants L, R, Z were unvoiced, but w and Y had already become vowels (U and I). M, N were unvoiced after the aspirates (while these remained as such), but not after other sounds; after the later developed spirants F, P, X the unvoicing of M, N was only partial.

After voiceless sounds 3 while it still remained an audible · consonant became H. After voiced sounds it was assimilated to these, so that for instance B3, D3 became BB, DD. As noted above N3, 93, became 99 and then NG.

After voiced sounds H was not voiced but tended to unvoice the preceding consonant. Similarly where it preceded a voiced continuant (as in HR, HM, HZ, etc.); but before B, D, G it tended to become voiced, that is to become the same as 3, and so to disappear, being merged in the preceding vowel.

The Adunaic Vowels.

Adunaic originally possessed only the three primary vowels: A, I, U; and the two basic diphthongs AI, AU.

Each Base possessed *one* of these vowels: A, I, U as one of its essential components; this I call the CV (Characteristic Vowel).

The normal place of the CV was between the first and second basic consonant: thus NAK-, KUL'B.

The 2-consonant Bases could also add the CV at the end; and the 3-consonant Bases could add it before the last radical: NAKA, KULUB. These forms with two basic vowels may be called the Full forms of the Base.

Various other forms or modifications occurred.

(i)   Prefixion of the CV: ANAK, UKULB, IGIML.

(ii)   Suffixion of the CV in 3-consonant Bases: KULBU, GIMLI.

(iii) Suppression of the CV in its normal place, in which case it must be present in some other place: -NKA, -KLUB, -GMIL.

This 'suppression' of the normal CV can only occur in 2-consonant Bases where it is also suffixed. It also requires that the CV shall be prefixed: ANKA, UKLUB, IGMIL; or (more rarely) that some other formative prefix ending in a vowel shall be present: DA-NKA, DA-KLUB, DA-GMIL.

These modifications are seldom combined: that is, a basic form does not usually have the CV repeated more than twice (as UKULBU, KULUBU); though such a form as UKULB could not originally stand in Adunaic as a word, some other vowel than the CV was taken as the ending (as UKULBA).

THE DROWNING OF ANADÛNÊ   423

One of the vowels of a basic stem must be either the CV or one of its normal modifications (described below); but the second vowel of the 'Full form' need not be the CV, but may be any one of the primary vowels (or their modification). Thus NAKA — NAKI, NAKU; KULUB — KULAB, KULIB. The prefixed vowel (as distinct from a separate formative prefix) must always be the CV; but the suffixed vowel may also vary: so KULBA, KULBI; GIMLA, GIMLU. [*Footnote 9*]

Every primary vowel A, I, U can show one of the following modifications:
(i)   Lengthening: Ā, Ī, Ū.
(ii) Fortification or A-infixion: Ā, AI, AU.
(iii) N-infixion: AN, IN, UN. [*Footnote 10*]
In the older language over-long vowels were recognized, and marked with a special sign, in my transcription represented by ^. These occurred: (i) as an actual basic modification: chiefly in 2-consonant Bases, and in any case only before the last basic consonant; (ii) as the product of the contraction of vowels, where one of the merged vowels was already long. Thus Base ZIR 'love, desire' produces both *zīr* and *zîr*; and also *zaira* and *zâir* 'yearning'.

Similar forms were sometimes produced by Bases with medial W, Y and lengthened CV: as Base DAWAR produces **dāw'r* and so *dâur* 'gloom'; *zāyan* 'land' produces plural **zāyīn* and so *zâin*.

Except in the oldest texts and 'heard' forms the diphthongs *ai, au* have become monophthongized to long (open) *ē* and *ō* respectively. The long diphthongs remained unchanged, and are usually heard, whatever their origin, as diphthongs with a long vowel as the first element, and a shorter one (always I or U) as the second element; though this second element is rather longer and clearer than in a normal diphthong: the intonation is 'rising-falling'.

The only source of *ē, ō* in Adunaic is the older diphthongs *ai, au*. The language consequently possesses no short *ĕ* or *ŏ*. Avallonian *ĕ* and *ŏ* are usually represented by *i* and *u*, respectively; though sometimes (especially in unstressed syllables before *r*, or where the Adunaic system favours it) both appear as *a*. In the earlier loans from Avallonian, presumably before the monophthongization of *ai, au*, Avallonian *ē* and *ō* appear as *ī* and *ū* respectively; but later they appear as *ē* and *ō*.

424   SAURON DEFEATED

Contact of vowels.

This can be produced (i) by the loss of a medial consonant, especially 3; (ii) in suffixion, especially in the addition of the inflexional elements: ĭ, ŭ, ă, āt, *im*, etc.

If one or both of the components is long then the product is a long diphthong or an over-long vowel.

U contracts with U; I with I; and A with A.

After U a glide consonant w is developed (so ŭ – ă, ŭ – ĭ to ŭwă, ŭwĭ), as described above. Similarly after I a Y is developed (so ĭ – ă, ĭ – ŭ to ĭyă, ĭyŭ).

Earlier Adunaic also possessed the long diphthongs: ÔI, ÔU, and ÊI, ÊU. These were all contraction products, and ÊU was rare. In the classical period ÔI (and ÊU) remained; but ÔU became the over-long simple vowel Ô, and similarly ÊI became Ê.

These diphthongs were mainly found in inflexional syllables, where they appear to be produced by adding such inflexional elements as *-i*, *-u* direct to the uninflected form (come to be regarded as the stem) instead of to the etymological stem. Thus the plural of *manō* 'spirit', from **manaw-*, or *manau, is *manôi*.

But similar forms can also be produced basically. Thus a Base KUY can produce by 'fortification' *kauy-* to *kōy*, *kôi*. A Base KIW can produce by 'fortification' *kaiw-* to *kēw*, *kêu*. It is possible that the inflexional forms are also, at least partly, of similar origin. If the plural inflexion was in fact originally YĪ not Ī (as it seems to be, because Y was lost before I medially) then the development would be so: *manaw, manau* + *yi* to *manōyi* to *manôi*; and similarly *izray, izrai* + *yī* to *izrēyī* to *izrêi* to *izrê*.

By the processes (i) of N-infixion, and consonant doubling; and (ii) of varying the position of the CV, and modifying it; and varying the vowels of the subordinate syllables, the Adunaic Bases, and especially those of 3-consonant form, were capable of an enormous number of derivative forms, without recourse to prefixion or suffixion. Naturally no single Base shows more than a few of the possible variations. In any case, any given derivative never shows two of the one *kind* of variation at the same time; for this purpose N-infixion and consonant doubling count as one kind of process; and Lengthening and A-fortification count as another. Alteration in the position of the CV, and variation of the subordinate vowels, can be combined with any other derivative process.

THE DROWNING OF ANADÛNÊ

Even with these limitations such Bases as KULUB and GIMIL can for example develop the following variants (among other possible forms):

KULBU, -A, -I; KULAB, KULIB, KULUB; UKLUB — *Kulbō, -ā, -ē, -ū, -ī; kōlab, kōlib, kōlub, kulōb, kuleb, kulāb, kulūb, kulīb; uklōb, uklūb*

Kullub, -ib, -ab (with variants showing *-ūb, īb, āb, ēb, ōb*); *kulubba, kulubbi, kulabbu, kulabba, kulabbi, kulibbu, kulibbi, kulibba; kulumba* (also *kulimba, kulamba,* etc., though N-infixion is usually found with the CV preceding the nasal); *uklumba;* etc.

GIMLI, -A, -U; GIMAL, GIMIL, GIMUL; IGMIL with parallel variations, such as GĒMIL, GIMĒL, IGMĒL, GIMMIL, GIMILLA, etc.

The apparent gradations produced by these changes are:

Basic A: a —— ā —— â
Basic I: i —— ī —— î; ē —— âi
Basic U: u —— ū —— û; ō —— âu.

Declension of nouns.

Nouns can be divided into two main classes: *Strong* and *Weak. Strong* nouns form the Plural, and in some cases certain other forms, by modification of the last vowel of the Stem. *Weak* nouns add inflexions in all cases.

The stems of strong nouns were doubtless originally all Basic stems in one or other of the fuller forms: as NAKA, GIMIL, AZRA; but the strong type of inflexion had spread to most nouns whose stem ended in a short vowel followed by a single consonant. No nouns with a monosyllabic stem are strong.

The stems of Weak nouns were either monosyllabic, or they ended in a lengthened or strengthened syllable (such as *-ā, -ān, -ū, -ōn, -ūr,* etc.), or they were formed with a suffix or added element.

It is convenient also to divide nouns into Masculine, Feminine, Common, and Neuter nouns; though there is not strictly speaking any 'gender' in Adunaic (there is no m. f. or n. form of adjectives, for example). But the *subjective* case, as it may be called, differs in the four named varieties in the singular; and is formed differently in the plural neuter from the method employed in the m. f. and c. This arises because the subjective was originally made with pronominal affixes, and Adunaic distinguishes gender (or rather sex) in the pronouns of the third person.

426   SAURON DEFEATED

All nouns are Neuter, except (i) Proper names of persons, and personifications; (ii) Nouns denoting male or female functions; and male or female animals, where these are specifically characterized: as 'master, mistress, smith, nurse, mother, son'; or 'stallion, bitch'.

Masculine or Feminine are the personifications of natural objects, especially lands and cities, which may have a neuter and a personalized form side by side. Often the 'personification' is simply the means of making a proper name from a common noun or adjective: thus *anadūni* 'western', *Anadūnē* f. 'Westernesse'. Abstractions may also be 'personified', and regarded as agents: so *Agān* m. 'Death', *agan* n. 'death'. In such cases, however, as *nīlō* n. 'moon', and *ūrē* n. 'sun', beside the personalized forms *Nīlū* m. and *Ūrī* f., we have not so much mere personification but the naming of real persons, or what the Adūnāim regarded as real persons: the guardian spirits of the Moon and the Sun, in fact 'The Man in the Moon' and 'The Lady of the Sun'.

Common are the noun *anā* 'homo, human being'; the names of all animals when not specially characterized; and the names of peoples (especially in the plural, as *Adūnāim*). [*Footnote 11*]

The stems of nouns can end in any single basic consonant, or in a vowel. It must be noted, however, that the original basic consonants w, y, 3 have become vocalized finally, and that these final forms tend to become regarded as the actual stems. So *pā* 'hand' probably from **pa3a*, pl. *pâi*; *khâu* and *khō* 'crow' from **khāw* and **khăw*; pls. *khāwī(m)* and *khôi* (the latter should historically be *khăwī*).

Long consonants or combinations of consonants do not occur finally in classical Adunaic. [*Footnote 12*] The stems of nouns consequently can end only in one (or no) consonant. Suffixal elements usually end in a vowel, or in dental stops: *t, th, d*; or in continuants, especially *s, z, l, r*, the nasals *n* and *m*; less commonly in consonants of the other series such as *h, g, p, ph, b*, though *k* is not uncommon.

Where, however, a noun has a basic stem there is no limitation. Thus *pūh* 'breath'; *rūkh* 'shout'; *nīph* 'fool'; *urug* 'bear'; *pharaz* 'gold'. Such 'basic' forms are not very common, except as neuters; and they are very rare as feminines (since specifically feminine words are usually made with the suffixes *-ī*, *-ē* from the masculine or common stem). The only frequent f.

THE DROWNING OF ANADÛNÊ 427

noun of this type is *nithil* 'girl'. The word *mīth* 'baby girl, maid-child' appears to be of this type, but is probably made with an affix *-th* (often met in feminines) from a base MIYI 'small'; cf. the m. form *mīk*, and the dual *miyāt* '(infant) twins'.

In compound nouns and names, however, a bare stem (often containing a lengthened or fortified vowel) is very frequent as a final element. In such formations, whatever the function of the stem used as a simplex, this final element very frequently has an agental force, and so requires the *objective* form in the preceding element (on the objective form see below). So *izindu-bēth* 'true-sayer, prophet'; *Azrubēl* p.n. 'Sea-lover'. Contrast the simplex *bēth* 'expression, saying, word'.

Masculine nouns usually have *ō*, *ŭ*, or *ă* in the final syllable. If they have affixed elements they end in *-ō*, or *-ū*; or in the favoured 'masculine' consonants *k*, *r*, *n*, *d* preceded by *ō*, *ŭ*, or *ă*.

Feminines usually have *ē*, *ĭ*, or *ă* in the final syllable; and if they have affixed elements (as is usual) they end in *-ē* or *-ĭ*; or in the favoured 'feminine' consonants *th*, *l*, *s*, *z* preceded by *ē*, *ĭ*, or *ă*.

Common nouns have 'neuter' stem forms, or favour the ending *-ā* or *-ă* in the final syllable.

Neuter nouns do not show *ī*, or *ū*, in the last syllable of their stems, nor do they employ suffixes that contain *ū*, *ō*, or *ī*, *ē*, as these are signs of the masculine and feminine respectively. [*Footnote 13*]

Nouns distinguish *three* numbers: *Singular*, *Plural*, and *Dual*. In most cases the Singular is the normal form, and the others are derived from it. There are, however, a good number of words with a more or less plural significance that are 'singular' (that is uninflected) in form, while the corresponding singulars are derived from them, or show a less simple form of the base. Thus *gimil* 'stars', beside the sg. *gimli* or *igmil* (the latter usually meaning a star-shaped figure, not a star in the sky). These plural-singulars are really collectives and usually refer to all the objects of their kind (either all there are in the world, or all there are in any specific place that is being thought or spoken of). Thus *gimil* means 'the stars of heaven, all the stars to be seen', as in such a sentence as 'I went out last night to look at the stars'; the plural of the singulars *gimli, igmil* — *gimlî, igmîl* — mean 'stars, several stars, some stars', and will in consequence be the only forms to be used with a specific numeral, as *gimlî hazid*

428   SAURON DEFEATED

'seven stars'. Similarly in the title of the *Avalē* or 'goddess' *Avradī*: *Gimilnitīr* 'Star-kindler', the reference is to a myth, apparently, of her kindling all the stars of heaven; *gimlu-nitīr* would mean 'kindler of a (particular) star'.

The Duals are collectives or pairs, and mean 'both' or 'the two'. Hence they never require the article. They are made with a suffix *-at*. The Dual is only normally used of things that go in natural or customary pairs: as shoes, arms, eyes. For the expression of, say, two separate shoes not making a pair Adunaic would use the *singular* noun with the numeral 'two' *satta* following. But in the older language things only belonging together casually, where we should say 'the two', are sometimes put into the dual.

The chief use in classical Adunaic of the Dual was to make pair-nouns when (a) two objects are generally associated, as 'ears'; or sometimes (b) when they are generally contrasted or opposed, 'day and night'. The first case gives no difficulty: so *huzun* 'ear', *huznat* 'the two ears (of one person)'. In the second case, if the two objects are sufficiently different to have separate names, then either (a) the two stems can be compounded and the dual inflexion added at the end; or occasionally (b) one only of the stems is used, the other being understood, or added separately in the singular. Thus for 'sun and moon' are found *ūriyat, ūrinīl(uw)at*, and *ūriyat nīlō*.

Nouns distinguish *two* forms or 'cases' in each number: 1. *Normal* 2. *Subjective*. In addition in the singular only there is an *Objective* form.

The *Normal* (N) shows no inflexion for 'case'.

It is used in all places where *Subjective* (S) or *Objective* (O) are not obligatory. Thus: (i) as the object of a verb. It never immediately precedes a verb of which it is the object. (ii) Before another noun it is either (a) in apposition to it, or (b) in an adjectival or possessive genitive relation. The first noun is the one in the genitive in Adunaic (adjectives normally precede nouns). For that reason cardinal numerals, which are (except 'one') all nouns, follow their noun: *gimlī hazid* = 7 of stars. The two functions: apposition, and genitival adjective, were normally distinguished by stress and intonation. [*Footnote 14*] (iii) Predicatively: *Ar-Pharazōnun Bār 'nAnadūnē* 'King Pharazon is Lord of Anadune'. (iv) As subject when it immediately precedes a fully inflected verb. In that case the verb must contain the

THE DROWNING OF ANADÛNÊ 429

requisite pronominal prefixes. If the subjective is used the verb need not have any such prefixes. Thus *bār ukallaba* 'the lord fell', or *bārun (u)kallaba*; the latter is rather to be rendered 'it was the lord who fell', especially where both subjective and pronominal prefix are used. (v) As the base to which certain adverbial 'prepositional' affixes are added; such as *ō* 'from', *ad*, *ada* 'to, towards', *mā* 'with', *zē* 'at'.

The *Subjective* (S) is used as the subject of a verb. As shown above the subjective need not be used immediately before a verb with pronominal prefixes; an object noun is never placed in this position. The S. also represents the verb 'to be' as copula; cf. (iii) above. When two or more nouns in apposition are juxtaposed in Adunaic only the last of the series receives the subjective inflexion: thus *Ar-Pharazōn kathuphazgānun* = 'King Ar-Pharazon the Conqueror'. Contrast *Ar-Pharazōnun kathuphazgān* = 'King Ar-Pharazon is (was) a Conqueror'.

The *Objective* form (O) is only used in compound expressions, or actual compounds. Before a verb-noun, or verb-adjective (participle), or any words that can be held to have such a sense, it is then in an objective-genitive sense. Thus *Minul-Tārik* 'Pillar of Heaven', the name of a mountain. Here *minul* is the O. form of *minal* 'heaven', since *tārik* 'pillar' here means 'that which supports'. *minal-tārik* would mean 'heavenly pillar', sc. a pillar in the sky, or made of cloud. Contrast *Azru-bēl* (where *azru* shows the O. form of *azra* 'sea') 'Sea-lover', with *azra-zāin*.

Plural nouns are seldom (and Dual nouns never) placed in such a position. When a plural noun is so used it always stands in *object* and not adjectival or possessive relation to the noun that follows, so that the plural nouns need no special objective form. The genitive of a plural noun can only be expressed with the prefix *an-* described in the note above [see Footnote 14]; thus *Ārū'nAdūnāi* 'King of the Anadunians'.

Plurality is expressed in Adunaic either by *ī* as the last vowel of the stem before the final consonant (in strong nouns), or by the suffixion of the element *-ī*. It is suggested above that the suffix originally had the form *-yī* [see page 424].

Duality is expressed by the suffix *-at*. There are no 'strong' forms.

430   SAURON DEFEATED

The *Subjective*: in Neuter nouns this is expressed by *a*-fortification of the last vowel of the stem, in the case of strong nouns: as *zadan* with the S. form *zadān*; in weak nouns the suffix -*a* is used. In Masculine nouns, strong or weak, the suffix -*un* is used; in Feminines the suffix -*in*; in Common nouns the suffix -*an*, or -*n*. In plurals it has the suffix -*a* in Neuters, and in all other nouns the suffix -*im*.

The *Objective* has either the vowel *u* in the last syllable of the stem, or else the suffix -*u*.

Examples of Declension

Nouns may be divided as noted above [see page 425] into Strong and Weak. In *Strong* nouns the cases and plural stems are formed partly by alterations of the last vowel of the stem (originally the variable vowel of the second syllable of basic stems), partly by suffixes; in the *Weak* nouns the inflexions are entirely suffixal.

The Strong nouns may again be divided into Strong I, and Strong II. In I the variable vowel occurs before the last consonant (Base form KULUB); in II the variable vowel is final (Base forms NAKA, KULBA).

Neuter Nouns

Strong I

Examples: *zadan*, house; *khibil*, spring; *huzun*, ear.

Singular	N.	zadan	khibil	huzun
	S.	zadān	khibēl	huzōn
	O.	zadun	khibul	huzun, huznu [*Footnote 15*]
Dual	N.	zadnat	khiblat	huznat
	S.	zadnāt	khiblāt	huznāt
Plural	N.	zadīn	khibīl	huzīn
	S.	zadīna	khibīla	huzīna

The Dual usually shows, as in the above examples, suppression of the final vowel before the suffix -*at*; but the final vowel of the N. form is often retained, especially where suppression would lead to the accumulation of more than two consonants, or where the preceding vowel is long: so usually *tārikat* 'two pillars'.

In all nouns the N. and S. of Duals was only distinguished in earlier texts. Before the Exilic periods the ending -*āt* was used

THE DROWNING OF ANADÛNÊ   431

for both N. and S. This doubtless was due to the coalescence of
N. and S. in the very numerous class Strong II.

Strong II

Examples: *azra*, sea; *gimli*, star; *nīlu*, moon.

Singular	N.	azra	gimli	nīlu
	S.	azrā	gimlē	nīlō
	O.	azru	gimlu	nīlu
Dual	N.	azrāt, -at	gimlat, -iyat	nīlat, -uwat
	S.	azrāt	gimlāt, -iyāt	nīlāt, -uwāt
Plural	N.	azrī	gimlī	nīlī
	S.	azrīya	gimlīya	nīlīya

Beside the normal plural *gimli* there exists, as noted above [see
page 427], also the plural with singular form *gimil* (declined like
khibil, only with no plural or dual forms), in the sense 'the stars,
all the stars' or 'stars' in general propositions. Other plurals of
this type are not uncommon: such as *kulub* 'roots, edible
vegetables that are roots not fruits', contrasted with *kulbī*
'roots' (a definite number of roots of plants).

The dual forms N. *azrat*; N. *gimlat*, S. *gimlāt*; N. *nīlat*, S.
nīlāt are archaic, but in accordance with the basic system of
Adunaic, and show a parallel suppression of the variable vowel
to that seen in *zadnat*, etc. The later forms are due to the growth
of the feeling that the final vowels of the N. forms *azra*, *gimli*,
nīlu are suffixal and invariable, so that -*āt* was added to the N.
form without suppression, producing *azrāt*, *gimilyat*, *nīluwat*.
Later forms show -*āt* in both N. and S. owing to the predomi-
nance numerically of the nouns with final -*a*.

Weak

Here belong monosyllabic nouns; and disyllabic nouns with
a long vowel or diphthong in the final syllable, such as *pūh*,
breath; *abār*, strength, endurance, fidelity; *batān*, road, path.

Singular	N.	pūh	abār	batān
	S.	pūha	abāra	batāna
	O.	pūhu	abāru	batānu
Dual	N.	pūhat	abārat	batānat
	S.	pūhāt	abārāt	batānāt

432   SAURON DEFEATED

Plural   N.   pūhī   abārī   batānī [*Footnote 16*]
           S.   pūhīya   abārīya   batānīya

Masculine, Feminine, and Common Nouns

M., F., and C. nouns only differ in the Singular Subjective, where the suffix -*n* is usually differentiated by the insertion of the sex or gender signs *u, i, a*. In later, but still pre-exilic, texts the Feminine Objective often takes the vowel *i* (so *nithli* for *nithlu*) owing to the association of the vowel *u* with the masculine. Feminine nouns are seldom of 'basic' form, that is few belong to Strong declension I*a*, since specifically feminine words are usually formed from the M[asculine]

Here Lowdham's 'Report' breaks off at the foot of a page (see p. 436). The 'footnotes' to the text now follow.

Footnote 1
In reckoning the number of consonants in a Base it must be observed that many bases originally began with weak consonants that later disappeared, notably the 'clear beginning' (or possibly the 'glottal stop') for which I have used the symbol ʔ. Thus Base ʔIR 'one, alone', from which is derived a number of words (e.g. *Ēru* 'God'), is a biconsonantal base.

Footnote 2
In so far as this table differs from the list of the actual consonants of our records, it is arrived at by deduction from the observable changes occurring in word-formation, from variations in spelling in the written documents 'seen' by Jeremy, from the treatment of Avallonian loan-words, and from the alteration of the older forms that have been occasionally noted.

Footnote 3
Adunaic did not possess, as independent Base-forming elements, nasals of the c- or k-series. The latter (here symbolized by 9), the sound of *ng* in English *sing*, occurs, however, as the form taken (a) by an 'infixed' nasal before consonants of the k-series, and (b) by the dental nasal N (not M) when it comes in contact with a consonant of the k-series in the process of word-formation. On 'infixion' see below [see p. 417 and Footnote 4]. Doubtless Adunaic originally possessed similarly a nasal of the c-series, but as these all became dentals, except Y, if it occurred at all, it could only occur in NY. In this combination,

THE DROWNING OF ANADÛNÊ 433

however, the Adūnāim appear to have used the same sign as for dental N.

Footnote 4

Nasal-infixion is of considerable importance in Avallonian; but does not seem to occur at all in Khazadian; so that this element in Adunaic structure may be due to Avallonian influence in the prehistoric period.

Footnote 5

This sound only occurs in the combination NG, for which Adunaic employed a single letter.

Footnote 6

Jeremy could not see this very clearly; it was perhaps already very old and partly illegible at the period to which his 'sight' was directed. We believe it to have been on some monument marking the first landing of Gimilzōr, son of Azrubēl, on the east coast of Anadūnē. It cannot have been quite contemporary, since the texts seem to speak of the Adunaic script as being only invented after they had dwelt some little time in the island. It is likely, nonetheless, to date from a time at least 500 years, and quite possibly 1000 years, before the time of Ar-Pharazōn. This is borne out both by the letter-forms and by the archaism of the linguistic forms. The length of the period during which the Adūnāim dwelt in Anadūnē cannot of course be computed at all accurately from our scrappy material; but the texts seem to show that (a) Gimilzōr was young at the time of the landing; (b) Ar-Pharazōn was old at the time of the Downfall; (c) there were twelve kings in between: that is practically 14 reigns [see p. 381, §20]. But members of the royal house seem often to have lived to be close on 300; while kings seem normally to have been succeeded by the *grandsons* (their sons were as a rule as old as 200 or even 250 before the king 'fell asleep', and passed on the crown to their own sons, so that as long and unbroken a reign as possible might be maintained, and because they themselves had become engrossed in some branch of art or learning). This means that the realm of Anadūnē may have lasted well over 2000 years.

Footnote 7

Apparent cases, such as the variation between pronominal *u-* and *hu-*, are due to the existence of two stems, one beginning

434   SAURON DEFEATED

with a weak consonant (3 or ?), the other with the intensified H-form.

Footnote 8

In composition or inflexion a 'glide' w was developed between u and a following vowel (other than u), and this developed into a full consonant in Adunaic. Similarly a y was developed between ı and a following vowel (other than ı). The best representation of Adunaic w in English letters is probably *w*; but I have used *v* in the Anglicizing of Adunaic names.

Footnote 9

Note that these variations are only permitted where the CV is in normal position; such forms as AN'KU, UKLIB are not permitted.

Footnote 10

These modifications are not held to change the identity of the CV, so that they can occur together with vowel-variation in subordinate syllables: thus from Base GIM'L a form GAIMAL is possible.

N-infixion, though not strictly a vocalic change, is included here because it plays a similar part in grammar and derivation to Lengthening. It only occurs before a medial or final radical (never as in Avallonian before the initial), and there is limited to occurrence before the Stops and z (on which see above [p. 417]).

Footnote 11

Common nouns can be converted into M. or F. when required by appropriate modifications or affixes; or, naturally, separate words can be used. Thus *karab* 'horse', pl. *karīb*, beside *karbū* m. 'stallion', *karbī* 'mare'; *raba* 'dog', *rabō* m. and *rabē* f. 'bitch'. *anā* 'human being', *anū* 'a male, man', *anī* 'a female'; beside *naru* 'man', *kali* 'woman'. *nuphār* 'parent' (dual *nuphrāt* 'father and mother' as a pair), beside *ammī*, *ammē*, 'mother'; *attū*, *attō* 'father'.

Footnote 12

In most of our records from approximately the time of the Downfall final -ă was in fact often omitted in speech, not only before the vocalic beginning of another word, but also (especially) finally (i.e. at the end of a sentence or phrase) and in other cases; so that the spoken language could have various final consonant combinations.

THE DROWNING OF ANADÛNÊ

435

Footnote 13

This use of *ŭ* and *ĭ* (and of *ō* from *au*, *ē* from *ai*) as m. and f. signs runs through all Adunaic grammar. *u* and *i* are the bases of pronominal stems for 'he' and 'she'. The use of the affixed elements -*ū* and -*ī* finally to mark gender (or sex): as in *karbū* 'stallion', or *urgī* 'female bear', is in fact probably a close parallel to such modern English formations as 'he-goat', 'she-bear'.

Footnote 14

In apposition each noun was separate and had an independent accent. In the genitive function the preceding or adjectival noun received a louder stress and higher tone, the second noun being subordinated. These combinations are virtual compounds. They are often in Adunaic script joined with a mark like a hyphen (–) or (=), or are actually compounded. Even when they are not conjoined the end of one noun is often assimilated to the following, as in *Amān-thāni* to *Amāt-thāni*, *Amatthāni* 'Land of Aman'. Adunaic has another way of expressing the genitive, where the nexus is not quite so close: by the adjectival prefix -*an*. Though this resembles the function of English 'of', it is not a preposition (Adunaic prepositions are in fact usually 'postpositions' following their noun); it is the equivalent of an inflexion or suffix. Thus *thāni anAmān*, usually *thāni 'nAmān* 'Land of Aman'. The same prefix occurs in *adūn* 'west, westward', *adūni* 'the West', *anadūni* 'western'. Other examples of the adjectival use are: *kadar-lāi* 'city folk', *azra-zāin* 'sea-lands, sc. maritime regions', *Ar-Pharazōn* 'King Pharazon'.

Footnote 15

The O. form *huznu*, borrowed from the nouns of Strong II and Weak, is frequently found in nouns whose final vowel is *u*. It occurs also in nouns with other final vowels (as *zadnu*), but less frequently.

Footnote 16

Dissyllabic nouns with a long final syllable (containing *a*) sometimes, especially in the older texts, make a strong plural by change of *a* to *i*, but not other strong forms: so *batin*, *batīna* 'roads'.

*

436 SAURON DEFEATED

Of further material on Adunaic in addition to 'Lowdham's Report' there is not a great deal, and what there is consists almost entirely of preliminary working, much of it very rough, for the text given above. From the point where it breaks off (at the beginning of the section on Masculine, Feminine, and Common Nouns, p. 432), however, drafting in manuscript is found for its continuation. The complexities of the passage of these nouns from 'strong' to 'weak' declension are rather obscurely arranged and presented, and there are illegibilities. I have been in two minds whether to print this draft; but on the whole it seems a pity to omit it. The form given here is somewhat edited, by removal of repetition, small clarifications of wording, omission of a few obscure notes, and the use of the macron throughout in place of the confusing mixture of macron and circumflex in the manuscript.

Masculine, Feminine, and Common nouns only differ in the Singular Subjective, where the suffix is M. *-un*, F. *-in*, C. *-(a)n*. Feminines also are very rarely 'basic', being nearly always formed with suffix from a masculine or common noun [see p. 426].

M. and F. nouns also have mainly become weak, since as a rule they show lengthening in the stem (final syllable) as a formative not an inflexional device.

Therefore corresponding to Neuter Strong I we have a small class I(a) as *tamar* 'smith', and a diminishing variety I(b) as *phazān* 'prince, king's son'. Corresponding to Neuter Strong II there is a small class II(a) of mainly common nouns as *raba* 'dog', and II(b) of nouns ending in *ū* (masc.), *ī* (fem.), *ā* (common); to which are joined nouns ending in *ō* (masc.) and *ē* (fem.) [on which see below]. These have usually become weak.

Strong I(a)

Examples: *tamar*, m. 'smith'; *nithil*, f. 'girl'; *nimir*, c. 'Elf'; *uruk*, c. 'goblin, orc.'

Singular	N.	tamar	nithil	nimir	uruk
	S.	tamrun	nithlin	nimran	urkan
	O.	tamur-	nithul-	nimur-	uruk-
		(tamru-)	(nithlu-)	(nimru-)	(urku-)
Dual		tamrăt	nithlăt	nimrăt	urkăt
Plural	N.	tamīr	nithīl	nimīr	urīk
	S.	tamrim	nithlim	nimrim	urkim

THE DROWNING OF ANADÛNÊ

I(b)

Examples: *phazān* 'prince'; *banāth* 'wife'; *zigūr* 'wizard'.

Singular	N.	phazān	banāth	zigūr
	S.	phazānun	banāthin	zigūrun
	O.	(phazūn-)	(banūth-)	(zigūr-)
		phazānu-	banāthu-	zigūru
Dual		phazānăt	banāthăt	zigūrăt
Plural	N.	phazīn	banīth	zigīr
	S.	phazīnim	banīthim	zigīrim

Here belong only masculines with *ā*, *ū* in final syllables and feminines with *ā*. And these may all be declined weak: plural *phazānī, -īm, banāthī, zigūrī*, etc.

II(a)

There are very few M., F., C. nouns here since such have normally long final stems and have become weak. Here belong chiefly archaic *naru* 'male', *zini* 'female' (beside *narū, zinī*), and nouns denoting animals, as *raba* 'dog'.

Singular	N.	naru	zini	raba
	S.	narun	zinin	raban
	O.	naru-	zinu-	rabu-
Dual		narăt	zinăt	rabăt
Plural	N.	narī	zinī	rabī
	S.	narīm	zinīm	rabīm

Nouns corresponding to II(b) have all become weak except *anā* 'human being', which makes plural *anī* beside weak *anāi*.

Singular	N.	anā	Dual	anāt	Plural	N.	anī
	S.	anān				S.	anīm
	O.	anū-					

Weak (a)

Here belong nouns ending in a consonant. These are seldom 'basic' (except as described above in compounds).
Examples: *bār* 'lord'; *mīth* 'little girl'; *nūph* 'fool' [but *nīph* p. 426].

438　　　　　　　SAURON DEFEATED

Singular	N.	bār	mīth	nūph
	S.	bārun	mīthin	nūphan (or m.f. *núphun*, *-in*)
	O.	bāru-	(mīthu-) mīthi-	nūphu- (f. nūphi-)
Dual		bārăt	mīthăt	nūphăt
Plural	N.	bārī	mīthī	nūphī
	S.	bārīm	mīthīm	nūphīm

Weak (b)

Here belong (i) masculines and feminines ending in *ū* and *ī* and common nouns in *ā*. Also (ii) a new class, masculines in *ō*, feminines in *ē*. These are not quite clear in origin. They appear to derive (a) from basic stems in *aw*, *ay*; (b) from *-aw*, *-ay* used as m. f. suffixes as variants of *u*, *i*; (c) from common nouns in *a* + m. *u*, f. *i*, instead of varying vowel. So *raba* > *rabau* > *rabō*. These are specially used in f., since *rabī* would appear the same as the common plural.

Examples: *nardū* 'soldier'; *zōrī* 'nurse'; *mānō* 'spirit'; *izrē* 'sweetheart, beloved'; *anā* 'human'. To this class (especially in plural) belong many names of peoples as *Adūnāi*.

Singular	N.	nardū	zōrī	mānō	izrē
	S.	nardūn	zōrīn	mānōn	izrēn
	O.	nardū-	zōrī- (arch. zōrīyu)	mānō-	izrē (izrāyu)
Dual		nardŭwăt	zōrĭyăt	mānōt (mānawăt)	izrēt (izrayăt)
Plural	N.	nardŭwī	zōrī	mānōi	(izrē) izrēnī
	S.	nardŭwīm	zōrīm	mānōim	(izrēm) izrēnīm

Other rough pages are interesting as showing that a major change in my father's conception of the structure entered as the work progressed: for the Adunaic noun at first distinguished five cases, Normal, Subjective, Gentitive, Dative, and Instrumental. To give a single example, in masculine nouns the genitival inflexion was *ō* (plural *ōm*); the dative *-s*, *-se* (plural *-sim*); and the instrumental *-ma* (plural *-main*), this being in origin an agglutinated post-position meaning 'with', and expressing an instrumental or comitative relation. At this stage the masculine *bār* 'lord' showed the following inflexional system (if I interpret it correctly):

| Singular | N. | bār | Dual | bārut | Plural | bāri |
| | S. | bārun | | bārut | | bārim |

THE DROWNING OF ANADÛNÊ

G.	bārō	bārōt	bāriyōm
D.	bārus	bārusit	bārisim
I.	bāruma	bārumat	bārumain

Of notes on other aspects of Adunaic grammar there is scarcely a trace: a few very rough jottings on the verb system are too illegible to make much of. It can be made out however that there were three classes of verbs: I Biconsonantal, as *kan* 'hold'; II Triconsonantal, as *kalab* 'fall down'; III Derivatives, as *azgarā-* 'wage war', *ugrudā-* 'overshadow'. There were four tenses: (1) aorist ('corresponding to English "present", but used more often than that as historic present or past in narrative'); (2) continuative (present); (3) continuative (past); (4) the past tense ('often used as pluperfect when aorist is used = past, or as future perfect when aorist = future'). The future, subjunctive, and optative were represented by auxiliaries; and the passive was rendered by the impersonal verb forms 'with subject in accusative'.

I have remarked before on the altogether unmanageable difficulty that much of my father's philological writing presents: I wrote in *The Lost Road and Other Writings* (V.342):

It will be seen then that the philological component in the evolution of Middle-earth can scarcely be analysed, and most certainly cannot be presented, as can the literary texts. In any case, my father was perhaps more interested in the processes of change than he was in displaying the structure and use of the languages at any given time – though this is no doubt due to some extent to his so often starting again at the beginning with the primordial sounds of the Quendian languages, embarking on a grand design that could not be sustained (it seems indeed that the very attempt to write a definitive account produced immediate dissatisfaction and the desire for new constructions: so the most beautiful manuscripts were soon treated with disdain).

'Lowdham's Report' is thus remarkable in that it was allowed to stand, with virtually no subsequent alteration; and the reason for this is that my father abandoned the further development of Adunaic and never returned to it. This is emphatically not to suggest, of course, that at the moment of its abandonment he had not projected – and probably quite fully projected – the structure of Adunaic grammar as a whole; only that (to the best of my knowledge) he wrote down no more of it. Why this should have been must remain unknown; but it may well be that his work was interrupted by the pressure of other concerns at the point where 'Lowdham's Report' ends, and that when he had leisure to return to it he forced himself to turn again to *The Lord of the Rings*.

In the years that followed he turned into different paths; but had he returned to the development of Adunaic, 'Lowdham's Report' as we have it would doubtless have been reduced to a wreck, as new

440 SAURON DEFEATED

conceptions caused shifts and upheavals in the structure. More than likely, he would have begun again, refining the historical phonology – and perhaps never yet reaching the Verb. For 'completion', the achievement of a fixed Grammar and Lexicon, was not, in my belief, the over-riding aim. Delight lay in the creation itself, the creation of new linguistic form evolving within the compass of an imagined time. 'Incompletion' and unceasing change, often frustrating to those who study these languages, was inherent in this art. But in the case of Adunaic, as things turned out, a stability was achieved, though incomplete: a substantial account of one of the great languages of Arda, thanks to the strange powers of Wilfrid Jeremy and Arundel Lowdham.

INDEX I

To Part One *The End of the Third Age*

This first index is made with the same degree of fulness as those to the previous volumes dealing with the history of the writing of *The Lord of the Rings*. As before, names are mostly given in a 'standard' form; and certain names are not indexed: those occurring in the titles of chapters etc.; those of the recipients of letters; and those appearing in the reproductions of manuscript pages. The word *passim* is again used to mean that in a long run of references there is a page here and there where the name does not occur.

Akallabêth 59

Amareth Transient name preceding *Arwen*. 66. See *Finduilas* (1).

Amon Dîn The seventh beacon in Anórien. 61, 67

Amroth (1) The Hill of Amroth in Lórien. (115), 124. (2) See *Dol Amroth.*

Anárion 15, 59

Anduin 16, 18, 22, 49, 65. See *Ethir Anduin, Great River.*

Angband 45

Annúminas Elendil's city on Lake Nenuial. 58 (the sceptre of Annúminas)

Anórien 49, 61

Aragorn 7, 10, 14–16, 18, 22, 47–9, 52, 54–9, 61–4, 67, 70–3, 117, 119, 121, 128, 135; called *Arathornsson* 117, 119, 121, 128, *Arathornion* 128

    The King 46–51, 55–6, 61, 64–5, 67–9, 74, 76, 83, 91, 93, 111, 116–28, 133–4; *The Return of the King* 111; *King of Gondor* 48, 61, 117, ~ *and Arnor* 128–9, *aran Gondor ar Arnor* 128–9, 135; *King of the West* 74; *Lord of the Westlands* 117, 128, *Hîr iMbair Annui* 129, 135.

    King's messengers 83; *King's guard(s)* 47–8; the King's letter to Samwise 117, 119–21, 125–8, 133; his coronation 55–6; his life-span 57

    See *Elessar, Elfstone; Trotter, Strider.*

Arathorn Father of Aragorn. 55. See *Aragorn.*

Arien Aragorn's translation of *Daisy* (Gamgee). 117, 120–1. [Cf. *Arien* the Sun-maiden in *The Silmarillion; Daisy < Days's eye*, in origin probably a kenning for the Sun, transferred to the flower.] See *Erien, Eirien.*

442   SAURON DEFEATED

Arnor 56, 128–9, 135. See *Aragorn*.

Arod Horse of Rohan. 70, 72; Legolas's horse 120, 123. See *Hasufel*.

Arwen 59, 61, 66, 108, 110, 124–5; called *Undómiel* 59, 66, *Evenstar* 66–7; *the Queen* 66, 118, 127. The white jewel, her gift to Frodo, 67, 108–10; the choice of Arwen 66, 125. For earlier names of Elrond's daughter see *Finduilas* (1).

Bag End 3, 52, 79–80, 84–5, 88, 90–1, 93–4, 97–8, 100, 102–7, 112, 117, 121, 126, 132–3, 135.

Baggins 79, 108; *Bagginses* 111, 113

Baggins, Bilbo 47–8, 52–3, 64, 72, 74, 92, 109–14, 121–2, 132. His mailcoat, see *mithril*; his books of lore 64, 72, 111, and see *Red Book of Westmarch*.

Baggins (and *Bolger-Baggins*), *Bingo* 3, 37, 53

Baggins, Frodo 3–14, 18, 21–2, 24–5, 27, 29–53 *passim*, 56, 61–2, 64, 66, 70–114 *passim*, 121–3, 125, 129, 132, 135; *Frodo of the Nine Fingers* 44, 83, *Frodo of the Ring* 125; Old English *Fróda* 47. His character in the Scouring of the Shire 80, 93, 95, 103; his sicknesses after his return 108–10, 112; the Praise of Frodo and Sam at Kormallen 46–7, and at Edoras 62, 70–1

Bagshot Row 88, 108; called *Ruffians' End* 108

Bamfurlong (1) Village in the Eastfarthing (replaced by Whitfurrows). 107. (2) Maggot's farm. 107

Bandobras Took See under *Took*.

Barad-dûr 5–11, 24, 29, 38, 40, 43. See *Dark Tower*, *(The) Eye*.

Baranduin, Bridge of 117, 128; *(i) Varanduiniant* 129. See *Brandywine*.

Baravorn Aragorn's translation of *Hamfast* (Gamgee). 121, 126, 129. (Replaced *Marthanc*.)

Barrow-downs 29, 77

Barrowfield At Edoras. 68, 73; *Barrowfields* 62, 73

Battle of Unnumbered Tears 44

Battle Plain 7, 13

Beregond Man of Minas Tirith. 59. See *Berithil*.

Beren 13, 45

Beril Aragorn's translation of *Rose* (Gamgee). 117, 121. (Replaced by *Meril*.)

Berithil Man of Minas Tirith. 52, 59. (Replaced by *Beregond*.)

Big Folk Men (as seen by hobbits). 117, 126

Bilbo Baggins See under *Baggins*.

Bill the Pony (52), 78

Black Gate 45, 55. See *Morannon*.

Black Land 46. See *Mordor*.

Black Rider(s) 5–7

Bodleian Library 136

INDEX I   **443**

Bolger, Fredegar   108, 110
Bombadil   See *Tom Bombadil*.
Boss, The   See *Sackville-Baggins, Cosimo*; subsequently the orc-man
   at Bag End 91–2, 94. (Replaced by *The Chief*).
Brandybuck   79, 92
Brandybuck, Meriadoc or *Merry*   7, 18, 22, 49, 51–2, 61–6, 68,
   72–3, 76–7, 79–86, 88, 90, 92, 94–104, 107–11, 115–16,
   123–4. Called *a Knight of the Riddermark* 61, 72; his horn 68,
   98, 100–1
Brandybuck, Rory   71; '*Rorius*' 62, 71
Brandywine, River   76–7, 100; *Brandywine Bridge* (including refer-
   ences to *the Bridge*) 77, 79–80, 103–4, 107, 117, 119–20, 126,
   133–4. See *Baranduin*.
Bree   52, 64, 76–8, 80, 82, 104
Bruinen, Fords of   75–6
Brytta   Eleventh King of the Mark. 72. See *Háma*; *Léofa*.
Buckland   82, 106, 115; *Buckland Gate* 77; *Bucklanders* 82
Butterbur, Barnabas   73, 76, 78; later name *Barliman* 78
Bywater   80–1, 87–9, 92, 94, 98–100, 106–8; *Bywater Pool* 41,
   105; *Bywater Road* 88, 92, 107 (see *Roads*); *Battle of Bywater*
   75, 93, 100–4, 108; *Battle Pits* 101

Cair Andros   Island in Anduin. 49, 51–2, 55
Captains of the West   43, 48, 51; *the Captains* 59
Carach Angren   'Jaws of Iron', the Isenmouthe. 33
Caradhras   70
Carchost   The eastward(?) of the Towers of the Teeth. 23
Causeway Forts   In the Pelennor Wall at the entrance of the road
   from Osgiliath. 18
Celebdil   One of the Mountains of Moria. 70. Earlier name *Celebras*
   70, 72
Celeborn (1)   'Tree of silver', a name of the White Tree of Valinor.
   58–9; *Keleborn* 59. Afterwards the Tree of Tol Eressëa, 58
Celeborn (2)   Lord of Lothlórien. 52, 64, 73–4, 115, 124–5, 133,
   135; *Keleborn* 116, 133
Celebrant, Field of   72
Celebras   See *Celebdil*.
Celebrían   Daughter of Celeborn and Galadriel, wedded to Elrond.
   58–9
Chamber of Fire   See *Sammath Naur*.
Chief, The   See *Sackville-Baggins, Cosimo*. *Chief Shirriff*, see *(The)*
   Shire.
Chronology   (1) Within the narrative. 7–11, 13–16, 18, 22, 25–6,
   36, 43, 45–6, 49, 51, 57, 59–61, 69–70, 72–4, 76, 78, 87,
   103–5, 109–10, 112, 117–19, 127–9, 133–4. (2) Years of
   Middle-earth (Shire-reckoning). 101, 107–9, 111–12, 114,

444   SAURON DEFEATED

120–1, 129, 134–5. (3) Of composition (external dating). 7, 12–13, 129

Círdan the Shipwright   67, 109

Cobas Haven   Bay north of Dol Amroth. 16–17; *Cobas* 15–16

Common Tongue   31; *Plain Language* 117, 126

Company (of the Ring), The   48; *Companions of the Ring* 57

Cordof   Aragorn's translation of *Pippin* (Gamgee). 117, 126, 129

Cormallen   See *Kormallen*.

Cotton, Farmer   41, 84–8, 93–9, 102–3, 105, 107–8, (119); named *Jeremy* 84, *Tom* 105; his wife 84, 96–8, (128); his children 41, 84, 96–8; *Tom Cotton* the younger 96, 98–100; *Nick Cotton* 101; *the Cottons* 101

Cotton, Rose   See *Gamgee, Rose* (1).

Cracks of Earth   3. *Crack (of Doom)* 3, 5, 37

Cross Roads   In Ithilien. 10, 18, 43

Dale   68

Dark Lord   32, 38. See *Sauron*.

Dark Men   15

Dark Tower   6, 9, 13, 22, 39, 55, 59, 83, 91; *the Tower* 38. See *Barad-dûr*.

Deadmen's Dike   Name of Fornost after its ruin. 76

Dead, The   15. See *Paths of the Dead*.

Denethor   26; *the Lord (of Minas Tirith)* 22, 83

Dimrill Stair   The pass beneath Caradhras (see VII.164). 64

Distances   10–11, 14–16, 33–6, 88, 92, 103–4

Dol Amroth   16; *the Prince of Dol Amroth* 61; *Amroth* 54

Druadan Forest, Forest of Druadan   18, 22, 56, 67

Dúnedain   52, 55–6

Dunharrow   18, 136–7; *the Hold* 136–7

Dunland   69, 74, 103, 107; *northern Dunland* 69; *Dunlanders* 93, *Dunlendings* 69

Durin   122, 135

Durthang   Orc-hold in the mountains west of Udûn, originally a fortress of Gondor. 33–6

Dwarves   68, 119, 122–3

Eagles   5, 7, 44, 55; *white eagle* 5. See *Gwaihir, Lhandroval, Meneldor, Thorondor*.

Eärnur   Last king of the line of Anárion. 59

Eastemnet   Rohan east of the Entwash. 9

Easterlings   50

East Road   77, 88, 100, 105; see *Roads*.

East, The   91; *the East lands* 63

Edoras   62, 71–4

Eirien   Final form of Aragorn's translation of *Daisy* (Gamgee). 126, 128–9. See *Arien, Erien*.

INDEX I   445

elanor Golden flower of Lórien. (114–15), 124, 132. For Sam's
daughter *Elanor* see under *Gamgee*.
Elbereth Varda. 112
Eldamar Elvenhome, the region of Aman in which the Elves dwelt.
58
Elder Days 68
Elendil 56, 58–9; *the Horn of Elendil (Windbeam)* 4
Elessar (The) Elfstone, Aragorn. 52, 58, 117, 119, 128. See *Aragorn*.
Elf-friends 92; *Elf-maid* 134, *Elf-prince* 92
Elfhelm the Marshal Rider of Rohan. 59
Elfstone, (The) Aragorn. 64, 66–7, 117, 119, 128; the green stone
56; Sindarin *Edhelharn* 128–9. See *Elessar*.
Elladan Son of Elrond. 57, 66, 127
Ellonel Transient name preceding Arwen. 66. See *Finduilas* (1).
Elrohir Son of Elrond. 57, 66, 127
Elrond 25, 33, 52–3, 58–9, 63–4, 66–7, 69, 109, 111, 115, 119,
124–5, 132; *Council of Elrond* 71. *Sons of Elrond* 57, (63); see
Elladan, Elrohir.
Elven- Elven-cloak 14, 29, 48, 50 (and see *Lórien*); -grace 122;
-light 125; -lord 49; -maid 132
Elves 7, 9, 14, 26, 52–3, 58, 89, 109, 111, 115–16, 119, 123–5,
127, 132
Elvish (with reference to language) 58, 72, 117–18, 121, 126, 132;
Elvish cited 30, 46–7, 51, 56–7, 62, 64, 68, 70, 72–3, 112,
128–9; (with other reference) 8, 26, 34, 69, 116, 125
Emmeril Original name of the wife of Denethor. 54. See *Finduilas*
(2).
Emrahil Transient name preceding *Arwen*. 66. See *Finduilas* (1).
Emyn Muil 7
Encircling Mountains (about the plain of Gondolin) 44. See
Gochressiel, (Mountains of) Turgon.
Ents 7, 9, 53, 63, 71, 116, 119, 123; *Entwives* 63, 116, 120, 123;
Entings 71
Éomer, King Éomer 7, 48, 52, 54–5, 57, 61–3, 66–8, 73, 123
Eorl the Young 68, 72
Éowyn 52, 54–5, 57, 59, 62–3, 68, 123; *Lady of Rohan* 62
Ephel Dúath 22, 32, 35
Erebor The Lonely Mountain. 119
Erech, Stone of Erech 15–17; the *palantír* of Erech 15
Ered Lithui The Ash Mountains. 11, 32, 35; *the north(ern) range*
33, 39
Ered Nimrais 16. See *White Mountains*.
Eressëa See *Tol Eressëa*.
Erien Replaced, and replaced by, *Arien*. 120–1. See *Arien, Eirien*.
Ethir Anduin 15–16; *the Ethir* 15
Etymologies In Vol.V, *The Lost Road*. 73

446   SAURON DEFEATED

Evendim, Lake   78, 127; *Evendimmer* 76, 78; *the Lake* 118. See *Nenuial*.

Evenstar   66–7. See *Arwen*.

Evermind   Flower that grew on the Mounds of Edoras. 62

Eye, The   (in the Dark Tower) 5–6, 8, 11, 22, 31, 38; see especially 38.

Fangorn   (1) Treebeard. 71. (2) Fangorn Forest. 63, 105, 123

Fanuidhol   One of the Mountains of Moria. 70. Earlier name *Fanuiras* 70, 72

Faramir   7, 22, 52, 54–9, 62–3, 123; *Prince of Ithilien* 61, 70; *Steward of Gondor* 55, 70

Far Downs   109

Farmer Gil ₃ of Ham   12

Ferny, Bill   80, 88–9

Fiery Mountain   3; *the Mountain* 3–7, 11, 33, 37–9; *the Secret Fire* 3. See *Mount Doom, Orodruin*.

Finduilas (1)   Daughter of Elrond (precursor of Arwen). 52, 58–9, 61, 63, 66; called *Half-elven* 58. Other transient names before *Arwen: Amareth, Ellonel, Emrahil*.

Finduilas (2)   of Dol Amroth, wife of Denethor. 55, 59. Earlier names *Emmeril, Rothinel*.

Fingolfin   44–5

Folcwine   Fourteenth King of the Mark. 68

Fornost Erain   City on the North Downs, Norbury of the Kings. 78

Fourth Age, The   135

Frána   Wormtongue. 65, 73. (Replaced by *Gríma*.)

Frodo Baggins   See under *Baggins*.

Frogmorton   Village in the Eastfarthing. 80–1, 95, 104, 106–7; earlier name *Frogbarn* 104

Galadriel   52–3, 58, 64, 73–4, (90), 108–9, 112, 125, 132–3; *the Lady* 32, 115–16. *The Phial of Galadriel, the Phial* 8, 13, 23–4, 32, 39, 41, 46, 67; the box, her gift to Sam 39, 41, 46, 52, 90, 108

Galathilion   The White Tree of Valinor. 58. Afterwards the Tree of Tirion, 58

Galdaran, King   Early name of the Lord of Lothlórien. 32

Gamgee   79

Gamgee, Bilbo   Sam's tenth child. 134

Gamgee, Daisy   Sam's eighth child, as first spelt *Daisie*. 114, 117, 120–2, 126, 128, 134. See *Arien, Eirien, Erien*.

Gamgee, Elanor   Sam's eldest child. (71), 109, 111, 114–18, 120–9, 132–5; nicknamed *Ellie*, and called by Samwise *Elanorellë*. See *elanor*.

Gamgee, Frodo   Sam's second child and eldest son. 114–18, 120–2, 126, 128; called also *Frodo-lad*, and nicknamed *Fro*. See *Iorhael*.

INDEX I   447

Gamgee, Gaffer (62), 71, 77, 81, 85, 88, 99–100, 106
Gamgee, Goldilocks Sam's sixth child. 114, 117, 121, 126, 128. See
   Glorfinniel.
Gamgee, Hamfast Sam's seventh child. 114, 117, 121, 126, 128;
   nicknamed *Ham.* See *Baravorn, Marthanc.*
Gamgee, Merry Sam's fourth child. 114–17, 119–21, 123, 126, 128.
   See *Gelir, Riben.*
Gamgee, Pippin Sam's fifth child. 114–18, 121, 126, 128, 134. See
   Cordof.
Gamgee, Primrose Sam's ninth child. 122, 134
Gamgee, Rose (1) Rose Cotton, Sam's wife. 97 (*Rosie*), 98, 108,
   114, 117–19, 121–2, 125, 127–8, (132), 133, 135. (2) Sam's
   third child. 114–18, 121, 123, 126, 128; called also *Rosie-lass.*
   See *Beril, Meril.*
Gamgee, Samwise or *Sam* 4–14, 18–53 *passim*, 56, 61–2, 64, 70–1,
   77, 79–81, 83–6, 88–90, 92, 95–129 *passim*, 132–5; Old English
   Samwís 47. The Praise of Frodo and Sam at Kormallen 46–7, and
   at Edoras 62, 70–1; his song in the Tower of Kirith Ungol 27–8,
   30; his sword from the Barrow-downs 25–7, 29, 32, 48, 50; his
   book 52; Galadriel's gift to him, see *Galadriel.* See *Lanhail,
   Panthael, Perhael.*
Gandalf 3, 5, 7–8, 11, 26, 32, 45–6, 48–50, 55–9, 61–5, 68–71,
   73–80, 84, 90, 92, 95–6, 102, 104, 109–12, 117, 120, 123, 132
   ('*Guardian of the Third Age*')
Gap of Rohan 52, 63–4
Gelir Aragorn's translation of *Merry* (Gamgee). 117, 126, 129.
   (Replaced *Riben.*)
Ghân-buri-Ghân 56, 61–2, 67; *Ghân* 67
Ghash See *Muzgash.*
Gilthoniel Varda. 112
Gimli 48–9, 51–2, 61, 63, 66, 69–70, 116, 119, 122–3, 135
Glamdring Gandalf's sword. 78. See *Orcrist.*
Glanduin, River 72. See *Swanfleet.*
Gléowine Minstrel of Théoden. 73 (and earlier form *Gleowin*).
Glittering Caves 63, 116, 119, 122
Glorfinniel Aragorn's translation of *Goldilocks* (Gamgee). 117, 126,
   129
Gnomes 58
goblin(s) 14, 119; *goblin-king* 119
Gochressiel 44. See *Encircling Mountains.*
Golden Hall, The 62–3, 68
Golfimbul Leader of the Orcs of Mount Gram (in *The Hobbit*). 119
Gollum 3–6, 8–9, 11–12, 14, 33, 36–7, 40–1, 71, 120
Gondolin 44
Gondor 8, 10, 20, 30, 46, 48–50, 52, 55–6, 59, 61, 69, 71, 83, 86,
   91, 117, 122, 126, 128–9, 135

448

SAURON DEFEATED

Gorbag Orc of Minas Morgul (but also of the Tower of Kirith Ungol, see 9). 8–10, 13–14, 18, 23–4, 26, 28

Gorgor 8 (*fields of Gorgor, the Gorgor plain*), 22 (*valley of Gorgor*); replaced by *Gorgoroth*. See *Kirith Gorgor*.

Gorgoroth 20, 23, 34, 51. See *Gorgor, Kirith Gorgor*.

Gorgos Eastern guard-tower of Kirith Ungol as the main pass into Mordor. 28

Gram, Mount 119. See *Golfimbul*.

Great River 49; *the River* 116. See *Anduin*.

Great Sea See *(The) Sea*.

Green Dragon The inn at Bywater. 82

Greenfields, Battle of 101, 107; ~ *of the Green Fields* 119

Green Hills In the Shire. 99–100, 107

Greenway 83

Greenwood the Great Later name of Mirkwood. 123

Greyflood, River 72, 76, 103

Grey Havens 53, 80, 109, 112, 132; *the Havens* 52–3, 112, 115, 125. See *Mithlond*.

Grey Wood (also *Greywood, Grey Woods*). Under *Amon Dîn*. 61, 67, 70

Gríma Wormtongue. 65, 73. (Replaced *Frána*.)

Gwaewar See *Gwaihir*.

Gwaihir 'The Windlord', Eagle of the North; earlier name *Gwaewar* (45). (1) In the Elder Days, vassal of Thorondor. 45. (2) In the Third Age, descendant of Thorondor. 7, 44–5

Gwirith April. 129

Half-elven See *Finduilas* (1).

Halflings 46–7. See *Periain, Periannath*.

Háma Eleventh King of the Mark. 68. (Replaced by *Brytta*, also named *Léofa*.)

Harad The South. *Men of Harad* 15

Haradwaith People of the South. 15–17; *Haradrians* 17

Harrowdale 123

Hasufel Aragorn's horse of Rohan. 61 (error for *Arod*), 70, 72

Havens, The See *Grey Havens*.

Hayward, Hob Hobbit; a guard at the Brandywine Bridge. 79–80

Helm Ninth King of the Mark. 72

Helm's Deep 63

Henneth Annûn 50, 55

High Elves 124

Hobbiton 80, 82–3, 85, 87–8, 99–101, 103, 105–7, 118, 127; *the Hill of Hobbiton* 103; *the Old Mill* 88, 106, *the Old Grange* (88), 106, *the bridge* 89

Hobbit, The 12, 119, 132

Holbytlan (Old English) Hobbits. 47

INDEX I

449

Holdwine Merry Brandybuck's name in Rohan. 68
Houses of Healing 54

Ildramir Transient name replacing *Imrahil*. 66
Imlad Morghul The vale of Morghul. 43
Imrahil 55, 66; and see *Dol Amroth, Ildramir*.
Ioreth Woman of Gondor. 55; earlier spelling *Yoreth* 55
Iorhael Aragorn's translation of *Frodo* (Gamgee). 126, 129; earlier
    spelling *Iorhail* 117, 135
Isengard 53, 63–4, 68, 71, 74, 82–3, 91, 95, 103, 106, 120, 123; *the
    Circle of Isengard* 136
Isenmouthe 33–6, 38, 41, 43. See *Carach Angren*.
Isen, River 64, 69, 76
Isildur 15; the standard of Isildur 15
Ithilien 7–8, 20, 49–50, 116; *Prince of Ithilien* (Faramir) 61, 70

Keleborn See *Celeborn* (1) and (2).
Kheled-zâram Mirrormere. 135
Kings' Norbury 76. See *Fornost Erain*.
King, The See *Aragorn*.
Kirith Gorgor The great pass into Mordor. 8, 11, 20, 34. [Kirith
    Gorgor originally not separated from Gorgor(oth): see 32–3.]
Kirith Ungol The high pass or cleft above the Morgul Vale. 8–10,
    (14, 18), 20, 22, 25.
    The Tower of Kirith Ungol guarding the pass (including
    references to *the Tower* and to *Kirith Ungol* in this sense) 7–10,
    12–14, 18, 20–7, 29–30, 51 (some references are imprecise,
    whether to the pass or the fortress, 11, 25, 31, 35–6). *The turret*
    (or *horn-turret*) of the Tower (visible from the western side of the
    pass) 18, 20, 22, 24, 26–7; *the under-gate, brazen door, brazen
    gate* 18, 21–2, 24, 26, 28; the fortress described 18–20, 22, 26.
    Original sense, the main pass into Mordor, 28
Kormallen, Field of 45–6, 49–50, 55, 83, 92; *Cormallen* 105

Lagduf Orc of the Tower of Kirith Ungol; earlier name *Lughorn*. 26
Lamedon 15–16
Lameduin, River 16–17; *Lamedui* 15–16; *Fords of Lameduin* 16;
    Mouths of Lamedui(n) 15–16
Landroval See *Lhandroval*.
Lanhail 'Plain-wise', Aragorn's name for Samwise. 118. See
    Panthael.
Last Alliance, The 20
Laurelindórenan The old Elvish name of Lórien used by Treebeard,
    earlier *Laurelindórinan*. 73
Lebennin 15–16
lebethron Tree of Gondor. 55
Legolas 48–9, 57, 61, 63, 70–1, 116, 120, 123

450   SAURON DEFEATED

lembas   11, 25

Léofa   Name given to Brytta, eleventh King of the Mark, earlier *Léof*. 68, 72

Letters of J. R. R. Tolkien, The   12, 18, 53, 68, 109, 129, 132; other letters 12

Lhandroval   'Wide-wing', Eagle of the North. (1) In the Elder Days, vassal of Thorondor. 45. (2) In the Third Age, descendant of Thorondor and brother of Gwaihir. 44–5, 50. Later form *Landroval* 50

Linhir   Town in Gondor, on the river Morthond. 16–17

Lithlad   'Plain of Ash', in the north of Mordor. 20

Lockholes   In Michel Delving. 80, 85, 87, 89, 98–100, 108, 110

Lórien   9, 14, 58, 64, 73, 115–16, 124, 129, 132. *Lórien-cloak, cloak of Lórien* 9, 14; other references to the cloaks 25, 29, 39, 48, 50

Lothlórien   32, 57, 106. See *Mirror of Lothlórien*.

Lugburz   The Dark Tower. 8, 13, 24–5

Lughorn   See *Lagduf*.

Lune, Firth of   109; *Gulf of Lune* 110

Lúthien   13, 45; the choice of Lúthien 66, 125

Maggot, Farmer   107 (see *Bamfurlong*).

mallorn   116; the *mallorn*-seed, gift of Galadriel, 108

Maps   First Map 72; Second Map 14, 16–17, 34–5; Third Map 34–5; map of Rohan, Gondor and Mordor 35; general map published in LR 72; maps of the Shire 105–7; sketch-map of N.W. Mordor 34; map accompanying 'The Ride of the Rohirrim' 70; plan of the Citadel of Minas Tirith 67

Marish, The   106

Mark, The   Rohan. 61–2, 67–8, 71, 73, 86, 98; *King(s) of the Mark* 62, 68, 72. See *(The) Riddermark*.

Marquette University   121

Marthanc   Aragorn's translation of *Hamfast* (Gamgee). 117, 121. (Replaced by *Baravorn*.)

Mayor, The   See *(The) Shire*.

Men   57; *Men of the West* 20; *Dominion of Men* 57, 68

Meneldor   Eagle of the North. 45

Merethrond   The Great Hall of Feasts in Minas Tirith. 67

Meriadoc Brandybuck, Merry   See under *Brandybuck*.

Meril   Aragorn's translation of *Rose* (Gamgee). 121, 126, 129. (Replaced *Beril*.)

Michel Delving   80–2, 85, 87–8, 91–2, 98–100, 105, 108

Middle Age   Equivalent to the Second and Third Ages. 68. *Middle Days* 68

Middle-earth   44, 56, 58, 110, 119, 128

Minas Ithil   20

INDEX I

451

Minas Morgul   18, 22, 29; earlier form *Minas Morghul* 7, 9–10, 13; *Morghul* 7; original form *Minas Morgol* 4. *Pass of Morgul* 22

Minas Tirith   10, 18, 22, 44, 48–51, 55–7, 59–61, 67, 73, 83, 119, 122, 128–9; *the City* 54, 58, 67, 73, 116, 119, 122–3; *the City of the South* 62; *the Stone City* 115; *the Lord (of Minas Tirith)* 22, 83. See *Mundburg, Stonehouses.*

   The Citadel 56–7, 67 (plan of, 67); *the White Tower* 22, 67; *Hall of the Kings, Court of the Fountain, the King's house,* 67; *Hall of Feasts,* see *Merethrond. The Hallows* 61, 67; *the Gates, Gateway* 22, 55

Mindolluin, Mount   49, 57; *the mountain* 58

Mindon, The   The tower of Ingwë in Tirion. 58

Min-Rimmon   The third beacon in Anórien. 59

Mirrormere   135. See *Kheled-zâram.*

Mirror of Lothlórien   32, 77, 90, 106

Misty Mountains   69, 72; *the mountains* 64–5, 71, 136

Mithlond   109, 133. See *Grey Havens.*

mithril   (of Frodo's mithril-coat) 9, 14, 24, 48, 52, 72, 92 (other references to the coat 8, 52, 64); (of the rings given to Frodo at Kormallen) 48, 51; (of the ring Nenya) 112

Moon, The   (phases) 49, 51

Morannon   7–8, 32–5, 44. See *Black Gate.*

Mordor   3, 5, 7–9, 11–12, 14, 20, 22, 29, 32–4, 40, 46, 56, 90, 106; *Plain of Mordor* 10; map(s) of Mordor in Elrond's house 25, 32–3. See *Black Land.*

Morgai   The inner ridge beyond the Ephel Dúath. 14, 22, 26, 31, 34–6; unnamed 9–11, 25. *The Trough* below the Morgai 10–11; the bridge over 33, 35

Morgoth   44–5

Moria   74, 122, 135, *Mines of Moria* 122; *Gates of Moria* 70; *Mountains of Moria* 70, 74

Morthond, River   16; *Morthond Vale, the Dale* 15–16; *source of Morthond* 16, *outflow of Morthond* 15–16

Mount Doom   3–4, 8, 10–11, 21, 33–9, 41; spelt *Mount Dûm* 8, 14; described 39–41. See *Fiery Mountain, Orodruin.*

Mundburg   Name in Rohan of Minas Tirith, earlier name *Mundberg.* 73

Muzgash   Orc of the Tower of Kirith Ungol; earlier name *Ghash.* 26

Naglath Morn, Nelig Myrn   The Teeth of Mordor. 28

Nan Gurunír   The Wizard's Vale; later form *Nan Curunír.* 136

Narchost   The westward(?) of the Towers of the Teeth. 23. (Replaced *Nargos.*)

Narch, The   Original name of the vale of Udûn. 33–4, 41, 51; *the Narch-line* 34

452 SAURON DEFEATED

Nargos Western guard-tower of Kirith Ungol as the main pass into Mordor, 28; one of the Towers of the Teeth, 20, 28 (replaced by *Narchost*).

Narrows, The The gap between the mountain-spurs enclosing the Narch. 33

Narya One of the Three Rings of the Elves, borne by Gandalf. 111; *the Red Ring* 132, *the Third Ring* 109

Nazgûl 4–8, 10, 13–14, 25, 38

Necromancer, The 3

Nenuial The lake in Arnor beside which Annúminas was built. 76, 78. See *Evendim*.

Nenya One of the Three Rings of the Elves, borne by Galadriel. 112; *the White Ring* 132

New Age, The The Fourth Age. 68

New Year (in Gondor) 45–6, 49, 59

Nimloth The White Tree of Valinor. 57–8. Afterwards the Tree of Númenor, 58

Ninquelótë The White Tree of Valinor (Sindarin *Nimloth*). 58

niphredil White flower of Lórien. (115), 124

Nob Servant at *The Prancing Pony*. 76

North Downs In Arnor. 76

Northfarthing 101

North, The 55–6, 58, 64–5, 68, 91, 122

Númenor 15; *White Tree of Númenor* 58 (*Nimloth*). See *Westernesse*.

Númenórean 30

Núrnen, Lake 56

Old English 46–7, 107

Old Forest 77

Oliphaunt 50

Orcrist The sword of Thorin Oakenshield, attributed to Gandalf. 78

Orc(s) (including compounds, as *orc-blade, orc-rags, orc-voices*) 8–11, 13, 18, 21, 23–32, 34–6, 38–9, 43, 46, 63, 68, 71, 103, 107, 116, 122; *orc-man, orc-men* 91–3, 103, 105–6, *half-orcs* 84; *orcish, orc-like* 31, 91, 94; orc-speech 31 (see *Orkish*).

Orkish (language) 30, 106

Orodruin 3, 6–8, 10–11, 22, 38. See *Fiery Mountain, Mount Doom*.

Orthanc 53, 63–4, 71, 136

Osgiliath 10, 51

palantír 15, 63; *palantíri* 15

Panthael 'Fullwise', Aragorn's name for Sanwise. 126, 128–9; earlier spelling *Panthail* 120, 135; *Panthail-adar* 135 (*adar* 'father'). See *Lanhail*.

Party Field, The At Bag End. 90, 106, 108

Paths of the Dead 15–16, 50; *the Dead* 15

INDEX I 453

Pelargir Town on Anduin. 15–16
Pelennor Fields, Pelennor 7, 14, 36, 49
Peregrin Took, Pippin See under *Took.*
Perhael Aragorn's translation of *Samwise* ('Half-wise'). 126, 128–9, (*a*) *Pherhael* 129; *Perhael-adar* 127 (*adar* 'father'); earlier spelling *Perhail* 118, 120, 135. See *Lanhail, Panthael.*
Periain Halflings. 55. (Replaced *Periannath* in Second Edition of LR.)
Periannath Halflings. 55; (*i*) *Pheriannath* 46–7, 55
Phial of Galadriel See *Galadriel.*
Pictures by J. R. R. Tolkien 40, 136
Pinnath Gelin Hills in the west of Gondor. 59
pipeweed (including references to *tobacco, leaf*) 65, 76, 80, 95
Prancing Pony, The 75–6
Púkel-men 137; earlier name *Hoker-men* 137

Queen, The See *Arwen.*
Quenta, The (*Quenta Noldorinwa*) 44
Quenta Silmarillion 44–5, 58
Quenya 30, 47, 64, 73
Quickbeam Ent. 71

Radbug Orc of the Tower of Kirith Ungol. 26
Rath Dínen 'The Silent Street' in Minas Tirith. 61, 67
Red Book of Westmarch 111; *the* (or *a*) *Red Book, the Book* (109), 112, 114, 120–3, 125–6, 132, 134
Rhûn, Sea of 71
Riben Aragorn's translation of *Merry* (Gamgee). 117. (Replaced by *Gelir.*)
Riddermark, The 61, 72. See *(The) Mark.*
Ringbearer, The (9), 14, 45, 66, 83, 112; *Ringbearers* 47, 112
Ringlo, River 17; *Ringlo Vale* 15–17
Rings, The 52 (of the Elves); *The Lord of the Rings* 111. See *Three Rings.*
Ring, The 3, 5–7, 9, 12, 14, 21–3, 25, 30, 37–9, 59, 133; *the Great Ring* 111; *the Ring of Doom* 44, 55; *Frodo of the Ring* 125; *Companions of the Ring* 57; *War of the Ring* 111
Ringwraith(s) 5, 20, 38, 40, 109
Rivendell 32, 52, 57–8, 63–4, 69–70, 73–4, 111, 115, 127, 132
Road goes ever on and on, The 64
Roads Coast road in South Gondor 15–17. Main road from Minas Morgul to Barad-dûr 10, 20–2; from Durthang to the Isenmouthe 35–6; from the Isenmouthe to Barad-dûr 39, 43.
  'North Roads' from Minas Tirith 61; the East Road 77–8, 88, 100, 105; the Bywater Road, leaving the East Road at the 'waymeet' (105), 87–8, 92, 96, 98, 100, 105, 107. The old South Road 103

454 SAURON DEFEATED

Rohan 48, 57, 70, 73, 120, 123; see *(The) Mark*, *(The) Riddermark.*
Riders *(of Rohan)* 46, 57, 61, 72, 120, 123; *Riders of the King's House* 62; *Knights of Rohan* 67; *Lady of Rohan* (Éowyn) 62. See *Gap, Wold, of Rohan.*
Rothinel of Amroth Wife of Denethor. 54, 58. (Replaced *Emmeril,* replaced by *Finduilas* (2).)
Ruffian(s) (in the Shire) 80, 83–8, 91–7, 99–105, 108, 117, 119, 126, 128
Rúnaeluin See 65, 71

Sackville-Baggins, Cosimo 32, 34, 52, 65–6, 77–9, 82–5, 88, 90–1, 94–5, 99, 103–4, 106, 110; called *Pimple* 84, 96; *the Boss* 82, 88–91, 94, 97–8, 104; *the Chief* 98, 101, 104, 107. (Replaced by *Lotho.*)
Sackville-Baggins, Lobelia 32, 52, (85, 91), 96, 98–100, 108, 110
Sackville-Baggins, Lotho 34, 78, 99, 103. (Replaced *Cosimo.*)
Sackville-Baggins, Otho 104
Sammath Naur The Chambers of Fire in Orodruin. 40–1, 50. *The Chamber of Fire, (fire-)chamber* 4–7, 37
Samwise Gamgee, Sam See under *Gamgee.*
Sandyman, Ted 89, 100. *Sandymans* 106
Sarn Ford 103
Saruman 52–3, 64–6, 68–9, 71–2, 74, 76, 83–4, 90–1, 93–5, 100, 102–4, 106–7, 115
Sauron 6–11, 13–14, 20, 38, 45–6, 51, 55, 59, 133; *ambassador of Sauron* 14; *Sauron's Fire-well* 3–4 (see *Sammath Naur*).
Scatha the Worm Dragon of Ered Mithrin (the Grey Mountains). 68
Sea, The 6, 15, 49, 53, 57, 59, 65, 109–10, 116, 119, 123, 128, 132; *the Great Sea* 56
Sentinels of Minas Morgul 29. See *(The) Watchers.*
Shadowfax 61, 120, 123
Shadow Host The Dead Men of Dunharrow. 16; *Shadowy men, Shadow-men* 15
Shagrat Orc, commander of the Tower of Kirith Ungol (but also from Minas Morgul, see 9). 8–9, 13, 18, 23–6, 28
Sharkey One of the Hobbiton ruffians. 82–3, 85–6, 94; Orc-man ('the Boss') at Bag End 91–2, 94, 103, 106; (with the same reference?) *Big Sharkey* 82, 94, 104; name of Saruman 93–5, 97, 102, 107–8, 110, *Sharkû* 106
Shelob 23, 112; *the Spider* 115
Shippey, T. A. The Road to Middle-earth. 60
Shire-reckoning 18, 22, 46, 104, 117, 119, 128 (and see *Chronology*); Sindarin *genediad Drannail* 129
Shire, The 32, 52–3, 62–6, 68–9, 74, 76, 78, 80–1, 84, 87–91, 93–5, 98–103, 105–12, 116–18, 121, 126–9, 132, 134; Sindarin *Drann* 129

INDEX I

Shire-folk 123, *Shire-rats* 90; *Shire-house(s)* 81, 85, 99, 104, *Shirriff-house* 104; *Shirriffs* 80–2, 95; *Chief Shirriff* 79–80, (91), 104; *Mayor* 79–81, 91, 104, 108, 117, 128, 132, Sindarin *Condir* 129; *Deputy Mayor* 108; *Thain* 99, 101, 103; *Scouring of the Shire* (not as chapter-title) 94, 103, 129

Shirriffs, Chief Shirriff   See *(The) Shire.*

Silivros   The White Tree of Valinor. 58

Silmarillion, The   13, 45, 58–9. See *(The) Quenta, Quenta Silmarillion.*

Silmerossë   The White Tree of Valinor. 58

Silpion   The White Tree of Valinor. 58

Sindarin   58, 128–9

Smallburrow, Robin   Also *Smallburrows* (80, 104). Hobbit, one of the Shirriffs. 80–1, 95, 104, 106

Smials   105, 107; *(Great) Smials* at Tuckborough 105; earlier *Long Smial* 87. 105, 107, *(Old) Smiles* 99, 105, 107

Snaga   Orc of the Tower of Kirith Ungol. 26, 30

Sons of Elrond   See *Elrond.*

Southfarthing   95, 117, 126; *Southfarthing post* 117, 126

South Lane   Lane leading from the Bywater Road to the Cottons' farm. 84, (87), 96, 98

South Road   103

Southrons   50

South, The   62, 83, 89

Spring   117, 119, 128; Sindarin *Ethuil* 129

Standing Silence   Before meals in Gondor. 50

Star of the North   55–6; star on Arangorn's brow 56; star(s) on his standard 15–16, 56

Steward of Gondor   See *Faramir.*

Sting   5–6, 23–5, (29), 32, 50, 52, (64), 72, 86, 92, 94, 105–6

Stirring   The season before Spring. 128; Sindarin *Echuir* 129

Stock   Village in the Marish. 107

Stonehouses   Ghân-buri-Ghân's name for Minas Tirith. 67

Strider   78, 121, 128. See *Telcontar.*

Swanfleet, River   70, (72). See *Glanduin.*

Tarantar   Trotter. 121

Tarkil   Númenórean. 30

Tark   Man of Gondor (Orc-name derived from *Tarkil*). 26, 30

Tarnost, Hills of   In South Gondor. 15, 17

Telcontar   Strider. 121, 128

Telperion   The White Tree of Valinor. 58

Thain of the Shire   90, 101, 103. See *Took, Paladin.*

Thangorodrim   44–5

Tharbad   72, 103

Thengel   Father of Théoden. 62

456   SAURON DEFEATED

Théoden   36, 52, 57, 61, 62, (67), 68, 72–3; *king of the grassland* 63. Lament for Théoden 72
Third Age, The   45, 52, 68, 110, (124); *Guardian of the Third Age* (Gandalf) 132. In different sense 68
Thorin Oakenshield   78
Thorondor   King of Eagles in the Elder Days 13, 44–5; earlier form *Thorndor* 13, 44
Thráin   9
Three-Farthing Stone   81
Three Rings (of the Elves)   (52), 57, 111, 132; *the Great Rings* 109. See *Narya, Nenya, Vilya.*
Thrór   9
Tirion   City of the Elves in Aman. 58
Tol Eressëa   The Lonely Isle. 58; *Eressëa* 132
Tom Bombadil   53, 77, 79, 109
Tooks   92, 99–101, 105, 108; *Took* 79, 87, 92; *Great Place of the Tooks* 105; *the Took-house* 87, 105, *Tookus* 105. See *(The) Tookland.*
Took, Bandobras   107, 115, 119; *the Bullroarer* 119
Took, Gerontius (the Old Took)   71, 114, 121; 'Ronshus' 62, 71
Took, Paladin   Thain of the Shire, father of Peregrin. 99
Took, Peregrin or *Pippin*   7, 18, 22, 26, 47–9, 51–2, 63–4, 70, 77, (79), 81, 83–8, 92–3, 95–6, 98–102, 105, 107–11, 115–16, 122, 135. *Knight of Gondor* 83
Took-house   See *Tooks.*
Tookland, The   100–1, 105; *Tooklanders* 87–8
Towers of the Teeth   20, 23, 28. See *Carchost, Narchost, Nargos.*
Towers, The   The White Towers on the Tower Hills. 53, 109
Tree, The   On Aragon's standard. 15, 56
Treebeard   63–4, 68–9, 71–3, 116, 123
Trotter   76, 78, 121. See *Tarantar.*
Trough, The   See *Morgai.*
Tuckborough   87, 99–101, 105, 107, 115
Tuor   44
Turgon, Mountains of   45. See *Encircling Mountains.*

Udûn   Vale between the Morannon and the Isenmouthe. 34, 51. Earlier name *the Narch.*
Umbar   *fleet of Umbar* 18; *the black fleet* 22
Undómiel   59, 66. See *Arwen.*
Unfinished Tales   44, 72, 133
Uruk-hai   34; *Uruks* 34. See also 436.

Valinor   58
Vilya   The mightiest of the Three Rings of the Elves, borne by Elrond. 111; *the Blue Ring* 132; *the Ring* (i.e. of Rivendell) 115

INDEX I

Voronwë Elf of Gondolin. 44
Vultures Steeds of the Winged Nazgûl. 3–4

War of the Ring 111; *the War* 100
Watchers, The At the gate of the Tower of Kirith Ungol. 23, 25–6
Waymoot Village in the Westfarthing where the roads from Sarn Ford and Little Delving joined the East Road. 92, 100, 106; *Waymeet* 106
Weathertop 6, 75–6, 78, 109, 112
West, The 67, 83, 132; *island of the West* 53; *King of the West* 74; *the True West* 110. See *Captains of, Men of, the West.*
Westernesse Númenor. 49
Westlands 117, 128. See *Aragorn.*
Westmarch See *Red Book of Westmarch.*
Westron 30
White army 8
White Crown 55–6; on Aragorn's standard 15, 56
White Downs 92–3, 109
White Mountains 119, 122; *the mountains* 15, 116; *the Dales* 15. See *Ered Nimrais.*
White Ship The ship that bore the Ringbearers from the Grey Havens. 120, 123, 132; other references to the ship 109–10, 133
White Tower See *Minas Tirith.*
White Tree of Númenor Nimloth. 58. (The sapling found on Mount Mindolluin 57–8.)
Whitfoot, Will Mayor of the Shire. 81, 108, 110; called *Flourdumpling* 81
Whitfurrows Village in the Eastfarthing (replaced *Bamfurlong*). 107
Wild Men, Wild Man (of Druadan Forest) 22, 61, 68; *Wild Men of the Woods* 57; *Ghân of the Wild Woods* 56, 67
Windbeam The horn of Elendil. 4
Wise, The 111
Wizards (not referring expressly to Gandalf or Saruman) 26, 77. *The Wizard King* 6–7; *the Wizard's Vale* 136 (see *Nan Gurunír*).
Wold (of Rohan) 63, 71
Woody End 52, 101, 109, 112
Wormtongue 64–5, 73, 100. See *Frána, Gríma.*

Yagûl Orc of Minas Morghul. 13. (Replaced by *Gorbag.*)
Yavanna 58
Yoreth See *Ioreth.*
Younger Days 68

Zirakzigil One of the Mountains of Moria (Silvertine). 45. Earlier name *Zirakinbar* 45

INDEX II

To Part Two *The Notion Club Papers* and
Part Three *The Drowning of Anadûnê*

In view of the great array of names occurring in these two parts of the book this second index is a little more restricted in scope than the first, especially in the reduction or omission of explanatory identification in many cases, and to some extent in the amount of cross-reference to related names. A number of names occurring in the Notes to Part Two that are casual and insignificant outside the immediate context have been omitted, but very few from the actual texts of the Papers. Inevitably the choice between omission and inclusion in such cases is rather arbitrary. In the case of names from the works of C. S. Lewis and from Michael Ramer's accounts of his experiences their provenance is indicated by '[Lewis]' and '[Ramer]', often without further explanation.

The exclusions mentioned in the note to Index I are made here also; and names are similarly given in 'standard' form, especially in the matter of accents and marks of length: thus the circumflex is generally used in Adunaic names.

Members of the Notion Club are included under the surname, and references include the initials of members and pages on which the person speaks but is not named. All names of streets, colleges and other buildings in Oxford are collected under the entry *Oxford*. O.E. = Old English.

Many names and groups of names have given exceptional difficulty in organisation and presentation, for there are here not only several languages, changing forms within the languages, rejections and replacements of names, but also shifting identities and intended uncertainty of reference.

Abarzâyan The Land of Gift. 378, 388, 396. (Replaced by *Yôzâyan*.)
Abrazân Lowdham's Adunaic name for Jeremy. 252, 290. See *Voronwë* (2).
Adûnâi Men of Westernesse. 305, 312, 361–6, 368, 371–5, 379, 385–6, 388, 438. See *Adûnâim*.
Adunaic 147–8, 241, 246–8, 259, 284, 286, 288, 290, 292, 304, 306, 309–13, 340, 356, 375–6, 379, 387–90, 397, 406, 413–39 (Lowdham's *Report*), 439–40; Lowdham's *Language B* or *Númenórean B* 238–41, 247–8, 305–6, 309, 379

INDEX II   459

Adunaic cited (including single words and stems) 240–1, 247–8, 250–1, 288, 290, 305–6, 377; 413–39 (the language described)

Adûnâim Men of Westernesse (replaced *Adûnâi* in narrative). 240, 312, 375, 382, 388, 391–2, 394, 413, 426, 433

Ælfwinas See *Elf-friends*.

Ælfwine Ælfwine the Mariner *(Eriol)*. 244, (269–70), 271–3, (274–5), 276–80, 285, 287–8, 292–4; called *Wídlást* 'Far-travelled' 244, 280, 285; his mother 270, 293; the tale of *Ælfwine of England* 280; *The Song of Ælfwine* 280

Other Englishmen named *Ælfwine* 236, 243; = Elendil 258; = Alboin the Lombard 236, 276; Lowdham's first name (changed to *Alwin*) 234, 236; the name itself 235, 242

Africa 185

Aglarrâma 'Castle of the Sea', the ship of Ar-Pharazôn. 372, 385. See *Andalóke, Alcarondas*.

Ainulindalë 280

Akallabêth 'She that has fallen' *(Atalante)*. 247, 312, 396, earlier *Akallabê* 375, 396. The work so titled 152, 340, 353, 356–7, 376–87, 389–96, 406–7

Albarim [Ramer] 221; *Albar-plays* 221. (Preceded *Enkeladim*.)

Alboin the Lombard 284; *Albuin* 236; *Ælfwine* 236, 276

Alcarondas 'Castle of the Sea', the ship of Ar-Pharazôn. 385

Aldarion and Erendis (The Tale of) 286, 379, 406

Alfred, King 236, 270–2, 293–4; *Ælfred* 271

Allfather See *Ilúvatar*.

Almighty, The 258, 290, 314, 316, 398, 401; O.E. *Ælmihtiga* 257–8, 313, 316–17; *Sanavaldo* 401

Alwin Lowdham's first name (changed from *Ælfwine*): see 234, 236, 269, 284

Amân (1) Adunaic name of Manwë (many references are to *the land of Amân*). 357–61, 364, 369, 371–3, 376–7, 381–3, 385–6, 388, 390–1, 393–4, 407, 420, 435; *Mountain of Amân* (Taniquetil) 391.

(2) *Aman*, the Blessed Realm. 312, 376, 393–4, 396

Amandil Father of Elendil. 356, 382, 384. See *Amardil, Arbazân, Aphanuzîr*.

Amardil Earlier name of Amandil. 346, 348–9, 352, 356, 382

Amatthânê The Land of Gift. 361, 363–4, 370, 375, 378, 380–1, 385, 388, 390. (Replaced by *Zen'nabâr*.) *Amatthâni* 'Land or Realm of Amân' (420, 435), the Blessed Realm, 388, 391, 413, 420, 435

Ambarkanta 383

Anadûnê Westernesse, Númenor. 147, 240, 247, 361–3, 365–6, 369–76, 378–9, 385–6, 388–9, 391–2, 395–6, 407, 426, 428, 433; *Anadûn* 305, 375; *Anadûni* 311; *Anadunians* 429

460   SAURON DEFEATED

Anar   The Sun. 302, 306; *Anaur, Anor* 302–3, 306

Anárion   335, 387, 401

Andalóke   'Long Serpent', the ship of Tarkalion. 350. ['The Long Serpent' was the name of the great ship of Olaf Tryggvason King of Norway.] See *Aglarrâma.*

Andóre   'Land of Gift'. 241, 247, 305, 310, 343, 349, 356; *Andor* 315, 332, 356, 403

Andromeda   Constellation. 207

Andúnië   Western haven in Númenor. 333, 340, 344, 351, 378, 380, 382; *Undúnië* 333, 340

Angel   Ancient home of the English. 273; *Angol* 274

Angles   276

Anglo-Saxon   (language) 151, 159, 220, 234–9, 242–3, 245, 255–6, 259, 279–82, 284–5, 291–2, 299, 301–4, 318. Other references under *Old English, English.*

Antirion the Golden   City of the Númenóreans. 347, 356, 381, 384. See *Tar Kalimos.*

Aphanuzîr   Amandil. 389–90. (Replaced *Arbazân.*)

Aragorn   378

Aran Isles   267, 293

Arbazân   Amandil. 365–7, 369–70, 374, 382–3, 389–90. (See *Aphanuzîr.*)

Arbol, Field of   [Lewis] The Solar System. 213; *Fields of Arbol* 199–200, 204, *Arbol* (the Sun) 199, 203, 219

Archenfield   In Herefordshire. 269, 272, 293–4; O.E. *(æt) Ircenfelda* 272, 294, *Ircingafeld* 294

Arda   246, 310, 312–13, 401, 405, 440

Arditi, Colombo   Member of the Notion Club. 159

Ar-Gimilzôr   Twenty-third King of Númenor. 381–2. See *Gimilzôr.*

Armenelos   City of the Númenóreans. 378

Arminalêth, Ar-Minalêth   City of the Númenóreans. 257–8, 292, 363, 365–7, 369, 381, 384; called *the Golden* 367. (Replaced by *Armenelos.*)

Ar-Pharazôn   (including references to *the King*) 247, 251, 290, 311–12, 363–72, 374–5, 381–6, 389–91, 407, 415, 428–9, 433, 435; *King Pharazôn* 428, 435. See *Tarkalion.*

Arthur, King   192, 216, 227, 229, 283; *Arthurian legend, romances* 216, 228

Arthurson, John   Pseudonym of J. R. R. Tolkien. 303, 307, 309

Arûn   Original name of Mulkhêr (Morgoth). 357–8, 364, 367, 376, 383–4, 390; *Arûn-Mulkhêr* 367, 384. Replaced *Kherū*, 376

Arundel   (1) See *Lowdham, Alwin Arundel.* (2) In Sussex. 284

Árundil   Passing name for a son of Elendil. 401

Ar-Zimrahil   Earlier name of Ar-Zimraphel. 373, 387. See *Tar-Ilien.*

Ar-Zimraphel   Queen of Ar-Pharazôn (*Tar-Míriel*). 387

Asia   398, 410

INDEX II   461

Atalante 'The Downfallen' (*Akallabêth*). 247–9, 310–12, 315, 333, 353, 375, 396
Athânâte, Athânâti The Land of Gift. 305, 312, 375, 378. (Replaced by *Amatthânê.*)
Athelney In Somerset. 293
Athenians 289; *Solon the Athenian* 289
Atlantic, The 234, 246, 252
Atlantis 152, 204, 206, 221, 232, 249, 265, 281–2, 284, 289, 409–10, 412
Atlas (1) The Titan, upholder of the heavens. 289; *daughter of Atlas* 249 (see *Calypso*). (2) First King of Atlantis. 289
Audoin the Lombard 284; *Auduin* 236; *Éadwine* 276
Aulë 332
Aurvandill (Aurvendill) Old Norse name cognate with *Éarendel*. 301, 307–8; *Aurvandil's Toe*, star-name, 301, 308. Cognate names in other languages 237, 301, 307
Avalâi Gods and Elves (see 353–4). 341, 344–9, 351–6, 376, 381, 387, 407. (Replaced *Balâi*.)
Avalê 'Goddess'. 428
Avalôi The Valar. 305, 311, 357–8, 360–82 *passim*, 385–8, 407, 410–12; *Children of the Avalôi* 358, 376. See *Avalôim*.
Avalôim The Valar (replaced *Avalôi* in narrative). 241, 247, 375, 382–3, 385, 387–9, 391, 407, 412
Avallon The Lonely Isle. 290, 313–15, 332, 334, 336, 354–5, 379, 386, 412
Avallondē 'Haven of the Gods', land of the Avalâi (Balâi). 344, 351–2, 354–5, 379, 407. See *Avallôni*.
Avallónë The Haven of the Eldar in Tol Eressëa. 380, 386, 393–6, 412; earlier form '*Avallon(de)*' 399, 403, 407, 411–13
Avallôni 'Haven of the Gods', land of the Avalôi(m). 241, 251, 257–8, 305, 309, 361, 372–3, 379, 385–6, 388, 391–2, 394, 407 (see especially 385–6)
Avallonian Lowdham's name for Quenya. 241–2, 247, 249, 259, 288, 306, 309, 379, 413–20, 423, 432–4; Lowdham's *Language A* or *Númenórean A* 238–41, 247–8, 305–6, 309, 379. See *Eressëan, Nimrian, Quenya.*
Avaltiri The Faithful in Númenor. 347, 356
Avradî Varda. 428. See *Gimilnitîr.*
Azores 234
Azrubêl Eärendil. 241, 305, 364, 375, 377, 388, 413, 427, 429, 433; earlier *Azrabêl* 359–60, 363, 366, 369–70, 375, 377, 388; *Azrabêlo* 365, 382, *Azrabêlôhin* 382, son of Azrabêl; the wife of Azrabêl 360. Earliest Adunaic name *Pharazîr* 305, 375

Balâi Name replaced by *Avalâi*. 341–4, 353
Barad-dûr 382

462   SAURON DEFEATED

Bârim an-adûn   Lords of the West. 247, 251; *Bârun-adûnô* Lord of the West 311

Beleriand   279, 331, 339, 406; *Annals of Beleriand* 280; *Men of Beleriand* 331; *Beleriandic* (language) 304, 308

Bell-Tinker   Oxford professor. 219–20

Bëor   333

Beowulf   (the poem) 145

Bideford   In Devon. 267

Black Throne, The   (341), 342

Blackwell, Basil   Oxford bookseller. 153. See *Whitburn and Thoms*.

Blessed Realm, The   332–3, 342–5, 348, 354, 358, 360–2, 364, 368, 377, 379–80, 385–6, 388, 391, 407, 409. *A Great Land beyond the sun* 400, (412), 413, *the West Land* 401

Blickling Homilies   285

Book of Lost Tales, The   412; *the Lost Tales* 280; *the Book of Stories* (in Tol Eressëa) 279–80

Borrow, D. N.   Oxford scholar interested in *The Notion Club Papers*. 156–8

Bosworth (Field), Battle of   174, 214, 283

Brandon Hill   On the coast of Kerry. 267, 293

Brendan, Saint   152, 261, 264–5, 270, 283, 292, 296, 299; *Abbot of Clonfert* 292; mediaeval works on 152, 265. *The Death of Saint Brendan* (poem) 261–4, 295; later version *Imram* 296–9

Britain   216, 229, 272, 280; O.E. *Brytenrice* 271

British Isles   255

Broad Relic   See 277–8, 295

Butler, Samuel   213; *Erewhon* 172, 213

Calypso   Daughter of Atlas. 249, 289; her isle *Ogygia* 289

Cambridge   212, 284

Camelot   229–30

Camera, The   See *Oxford*.

Cameron, Alexander   Member of the Notion Club. 151, 160, 173–4, 211, 214, 245, 253, 260

Camlan, Battle of   231, 283

Carpenter, Humphrey   (*The Inklings*) 150–1; (*Letters of J. R. R. Tolkien*) 153

Cataclysm, The   354, 385, 394, 396; O.E. *Midswípen* 242, 286–7; accounts of it 316, 336–7, 351, 372–3, 386

Caves of the Forgotten   336, 386

Celtic   159, 216; *Old Celtic* 294

Ceola   Companion of Ælfwine and Tréowine. 279

Céolwulf   (1) Father of Tréowine. 269, 273. (2) Preceded Tréowine as reciter of *King Sheave*. 294

Children of God   249, 258, 312, 341, 354, 358, 389, 411 (see *Eruhil, Eruhîn*); O.E. *Godes bearn* 257.

INDEX II

463

Children of the Gods, of the Valar   332, 377
China   197; Chinese 241, 306
Christ   236, 285; Christian (myth) 410
Clonfert, Abbey of   In Galway. 267, 292
Cloud, The   In The Death of St. Brendan. 261–3, 296–8
Clúain-ferta   Clonfert. 261, 264, 292, 296, 299
Corn-gods   227. See Sheaf.
Cornwall   266, 293; O.E. Cornwealas 293. See Wales, Welsh.
Cortirion   City of the Elves in Tol Eressëa. 280
Creator, The   316, 400; the Maker 290, 336; O.E. Scyppend 316
Crist   Old English poem. 236, 285
Culbone   In Somerset. 268
Cynewulf   Author of the Crist. 285

Danes   272–3, 277–8, 293; Sea-danes 276, 295. Danish 269, 293;
   O.E. Denisc 268; Danish History of Saxo 307
Dark Ages   (of Middle-earth) 344, 398, 403; Dark Years 362
Dark Lands   Middle-earth. 400
Darkness, the Dark   223, 347, 367–8, 384, 398, the Ancient Dark-
   ness 367; Lord, Power of Darkness 335, 344, 358, 363, (367),
   383; Nether Darkness 344, 362
Day of Doom   336, 386
Deathless Folk   372; Children of the Deathless Folk 344, 354, 362,
   377, 379–80, 388, lesser ones of ~ 344, 354; the Deathless 365
Deathless Land   372–3, 385, 392–3; Deathless Lands 386. See
   Undying Lands.
Death of Saint Brendan, The   See (Saint) Brendan.
Deep Heaven   [Lewis] Space. 213
Devil, The   231, 314; O.E. Déofol 257, 313
Devon   267, 293; Devenish 'of Devon' 269, 293
Dolbear, Rupert   Member of the Notion Club. (Including references
   to him by his nickname Rufus) 150–2, 159, 161, 169–73, 175,
   178–9, 183–4, 187–8, 191, 211, 213–15, 219, 223, 228, 230–3,
   245, 250, 253–5, 259–60, 266, 277, 283
Donegal   293
Door of Night   292. Door of Days 292, 298
Downfall, The   (Also The Downfall (Fall) of Númenor, of Anadûnê)
   152, 217, 279–80, (282), 339, 353, 355, 374, 390, 392, 394–5,
   401, 404, 407–10, 414–15, 419, 433–4. The Downfallen, see
   Atalante.
Drama of the Silver Tree   [Ramer] 206, 221
Drowning of Númenor, The   Title of the original text of The
   Drowning of Anadûnê. 341
Dúnedain   393; Dúnedanic 406
Dwellers in the West   See (The) West.
Dyson, H. V. D.   150–2

464   SAURON DEFEATED

Eä   The Universe. 312

Éadwine   (1) Father of Ælfwine the Mariner. 244, 270, 285, 288. (2) Son of Ælfwine (in *The Lost Road*). 292. (3) = Audoin the Lombard. 276. (4) = Edwin Lowdham. 244. The name itself 235--6

Eagle(s)   (All references are to the great clouds, and most to *The Eagles of the Lords (of the West), of the Powers, of Amân*) 231, 238, 246, 251, 266, 274, 277, 279, 281, 290, 350, 371, 391

Éarendel   In Old English. 236–7, 278, 284–5, 299–301, 308. Lowdham's second name (changed to *Arundel*) 234, 281–2. See *Aurvandill.*

Éarendel, The   Edwin Lowdham's ship. 234, 280, 284; *Earendel('s) Star* 284, 308. *Éarendel*, the ship of Éadwine father of Ælfwine the Mariner, 270

Eärendil the Mariner   237, 241, 285, 301, 305–6, 308, 333, 340, 342–3, 346, 349, 356, 359, 375, 393, 408; the wife of Eärendil 342. Earlier form *Eärendel* 257–8, 279, 284, 292, 313–15, 333–5, 342, 344–5, 356, 399–400, 402–4, 406, 412. *Eärendil* as second name of Elendil 346, 348; Lowdham so addressed by Jeremy 290. See *Azrubêl.*

Earth, (The)   168, 181, 198, 202, 204–5, 207–9, (213), 221, 227, 246–7, 249, 258, 274, 311, 335–8, 341–5, 348, 351, 353–4, 357–8, 360–6, 369, 372–4, 377, 379, 381–2, 387–98 *passim*, 401–12 *passim*. See *(The) Talkative Planet, Thulcandra.*

East Anglia   Kingdom of the East Angles. 293

Easterlings   398–400

East, The   274, 334–5, 337, 339, 345, 349, 351, 355, 363, 365–6, 369, 380–1, 383, 389, 409

Edward the Elder   King of England. 287, 293; O.E. *Éadweard* 269, 271–2; *the king* 273, 278, 288

Edmund, Saint   King of East Anglia. 293; O.E. *Éadmund* 270

Egyptian   207, 289

Eldalië   222, 303, 308, 313–14. See *Quenta Eldalien.*

Eldar   222, 290, 303, 308, 314–15, 332–3, 354–5, 376, 379–80, 385–6, 393–5, 397, 400–2, 404–6, 409, 411; O.E. *Eldan* 313–15. *Eldaic* 409

Eldarin   (tongue) 381; *High Eldarin* 379

Elder Days   152, 333, 337, 348, 368. *Elder World* 240; *Elder Years* 276

Eldil(s)   [Lewis] 168, 202, 212–13, 222; *Eldila* 212, 221; *Eldilic* 221

Eledâi   Eldar. 358, 377, 397–9, 401–5, 410, 412

Elendil   278–9, 284, 335, 346, 348–9, (350), 352, 356, 382, 384, 387, 401; with second name *Eärendil* 346, 348; his sons 335, 352–3, 387, 401. Lowdham so addressed by Jeremy 290. *Elendil = Elf-friend* 403; modernized *Ellendel* 284. See *Ælfwine, Nimruzân, Nimruzîr.*

INDEX II

465

Elendili 'Elf-friends'. 400; *Elendilli* 403

Elf-friend(s) 244–5, 280 288, 339, 403, 411; *Elven-friends* 244; O.E. *Ælfwinas (Ælfwines)* 244, 257–8, 272, 288, 313–14, 403

Elf-kin 403. *Elven-kind* 261, 296. *Elvenfolk* 280

Ellor [Ramer] 198–200, 207, 209, 218, 221–2; *Ellor Eshúrizel* 198, 207, 218; *Eshúrizel* 198, 200

Elrond 333, 339–40, 378, 403, 408

Elros 333, 340, 345, 378, 380–2, 403, 408. See *Indilzar, Gimilzôr*.

Elvenhome 280

Elven-Latin Quenya. 241, 286, 303, 306; *Elf-Latin* 286, 308

Elven tongue 379

Elves 216–17, 244, 272, 279–80, 290, 303, 331–6, 338–9, 354, 377, 401–3, 405–13; *Unfallen Elves* 221, 308; *History of the Elves* 303, 307; the word *Elf* 242, 306

Elvish (of language) 220, 222 [Ramer], 293, 310, 317, 382, 408; (with other reference) 206 [Ramer], 219–20, 406–7, 409–10. *Elvish Drama, Elf-drama* 193, 216; *Faërian Drama* 216

Elwing 284

Emberü [Ramer] 178, 182, 197–8, 200, 209, 214–15, 217–18, 221; *Green Emberü* 198, 218–19. (Replaced *Gyönyörü*.)

Empty Lands 336

En [Ramer] The Solar System. 204, 220

Eneköl [Ramer] The planet Saturn. 205, 221. (Replaced *Shomorú*.)

Enemy, The 411

England 159, 211, 215, 236, 272, 280, 291

English (language) 150, 159, 192, 200–1, 222, 237, 242, 259, 267, 300, 310–11, 317, 417–19, 421, 432, 434–5, 439; *ancient English,* or with reference to Old English, 236, 243–4, 256, 268–9, 277, 301, 303, 409

English Dialect Dictionary 150, 286

Enkeladim [Ramer] Elves. 199, 206–7, 218–19, 221, 283, 303; other than in Ramer's account 397–8, 400, 405, 410–11 (equated with *Eledâi, Eldar,* 397)

Éowyn 217

Eressë = *Eressëa.* 303, 313–14, 355, 399, 402–4, 406, 411–13

Eressëa and Tol Eressëa 280, 315–16, 332, 334, 336, 354–5, 357, 379–80, 386, 391, 394, 396, 400–1, 406–10. See *Lonely Isle.*

Eressëan (language) 286, 303–4, 308–9. *Eressëans* 401, 403. See *Avallonian, Nimrian, Quenya.*

Erin, Ériu See *Ireland.*

Eriol Ælfwine the Mariner. 279; *Eriol-saga* 281–2

Errol, Alboin In *The Lost Road.* 280, 284, 286–90, 304, 308–11

Errol, Audoin Son of Alboin Errol. 289

Errol, Oswin Father of Alboin Errol. 284, 287, (288, 308)

Eru Ilúvatar; also *Êru* (see 387–8, 432). 247, 249, 251, 290, 311–12, 341, 343–8, 351–2, 357–8, 360–1, 364, 367–8, 372,

466   SAURON DEFEATED

374, 377, 381–3, 387, 392, 401–2, 410–11, 432. In different sense, 'the world', 310, 313

Eru-bênî 'Servants of God', the Powers. 341, 353, 356–7, 387; *Êru-bênî* 387

Eruhil 'Children of God', Númenóreans. 341–5, 353–5. (Replaced by *Eruhîn*.)

Eruhildi 'Sons of God', Númenóreans. 399, 402–4, 411. (Replaced by *Eruhil*.)

Eruhîn 'Children of God', Númenóreans; also *Êruhîn* (see 387–8). 311, 358–63, 367, 375, 377–8, 387–90, 411; *Êruhînim* 247–8

Etymologies, The In Vol.V, *The Lost Road*. 412

Europe 229, 241, 306, 309, 398, 410

Exiles (of Númenor) 338, 353, 375, 393–6, 407, 411, 415. *Exilic* 414–15, 419, 430, 432

Faërie 170; *Faërian Drama* 216. *Fairyland* 170; *fairy-stories, fairy-tales* 164, 170, 193

Faithful, The In Númenor. 346–7, 356, 367, 370, 382, 390, 392, 401; cf. also 335, 348–9, 365, 369, 399, and see *Avaltiri*. *Faithful Houses of Men (Eruhildi)* 402

Fall of Men (called also *the First Fall*) 397–8, 401–3, 405, 408, 411; references to '*the Second Fall*' 344, 363, 388, 397, 403, 405, 408. *Fall of the Elves* 410–11

Faramir 217

Fathers of Men 333, 341, 354, 358, 411; cf. also 359–60, 363–5, 369

Field of Arbol See *Arbol*.

Finland 159

Finno-Ugric 151, 159

Fionwë Son of Manwë. 331–2

Firiel Passing name for a son of Elendil. 401

First Age, The 217, 287, 340; O.E. *frumældi* 242, 287

Firstborn, The The Elves. 333–4, 339

Followers Men. 401. See *Hildi*.

Frankley, Philip Member of the Notion Club. 150–1, 159–70, 172–9, 182, 185, 187–8, 191, 194–5, 197, 202–5, 211, 214, 222–30, 232–6, 242, 244–6, 250, 252–6, 259–65, 272, 277, 283, 285, 288, 295, 304, 412; called by Lowdham *Pip*, also *Horse-friend of Macedon, Lover of Horses, Horsey* (see 285); his poems 161, 172, 205, 211, 221, and *The Death of Saint Brendan* 261–5. Earlier name *Franks* 150, 214, 295

Franks 276

Fréafíras (O.E.) 'Lordly Men' (Númenóreans). 242, 286, 317; *Héafíras* 317. See *Turkildi*.

French 151, 222, 286; *Anglo-French* 265; *Old French* 150, 265; *Frenche men* 245

INDEX II 467

Frisians 276
Frodo 409

Gaelic 417
Galway 261, 264, 267, 296, 299; (town) 293; *Galway Bay* 267, 293
Gamgee, Sam 407
Gársecg (O.E.) The Ocean. 243, 258, 270, 272–3, 288, 292, 316
Gates of Morning 334, 380
Geoffrey of Monmouth 192, 216
Geraint Cornishman, companion of Ælfwine and Tréowine. 279
German 307, 417
Germanic 151, 159, 286; (language) 243
Gilgalad 408
Gimilnitîr 'Star-kindler', Varda. 428. See *Avradî.*
Gimilzôr Elros. 380, 382, 433. (Replaced *Indilzar.*) See *Ar-Gimilzôr.*
Gimlad 'Starwards', Númenor. 378, 396
Glastonbury 271
Glund [Lewis] The planet Jupiter. 203, 220; *Glundandra* 220
goblins 397
God 249, 310–11, 314, 391, 400–3, 408–9, 432; O.E. 313. See also *Children of God, Servants of God.*
Gods 241, 244, 305, 332–9, 344, 354–5, 357, 362, 376–7, 387, 395, 400–4, 408–9, 412–13; *Goddess* 428 (see *Avalê*); (*a, the*) *God* 341, 345, 358, 363, 371, 398, 401, 404, 407; *Land of the Gods* 333, 336, 407, 409; *First Battle of the Gods* 383; *Haven of the Gods,* see *Avallondë, Avallôni; Lord of the Gods* (Manwë) 316–17, O.E. *Ósfruma* 316–17; *Children of the Gods* 332, *sons of Gods* 334
     Norse Gods: Æsir 214, *Regin* 286, *Tívar* 286; Old English *Ése* 244 (singular *Ós* 317), *Tiwas* 242, 286 (= Valar)
Gondolin 280, 290, 316
Gondor 331
Gormok [Ramer] The planet Mars 205, 220. See *Karan.*
Goths 276, 295; *Gothic* (language) 286–7
Gow, Professor Jonathan 200
Great Battle At the end of the Elder Days. 331, 354
Great Door [Ramer] 206; *the Door* 206, 221
(Great) Explosion 157, 167, 186, 212, 215; *the Black Hole* 186
Great Lands Middle-earth. 314, 341–2, 344, 359, 362, 398–9, 402; *Great Central Land* 410. See *Kemen. A Great Land beyond the sun,* see *Blessed Realm.*
Great March (of the Elves) 406
Great Sea(s) 270, 272, 290, 308, 336, 342, 354, 359, 386, 398–400, 402; *Shoreless Sea* 229, *Western Sea* 398, ~ *Ocean* 289; also

468　　　SAURON DEFEATED

many references to *the Sea(s)*, not indexed. See *Gársecg. Great Seas* (of Space) 204

(Great) Storm 157–8, 211, 252, 254, 267, 290; *the Black Night* 267

Great Water The Great Sea. 332; *great waters* 351, 373, 391–3

Great Wave 217; *Green Wave* 194; *Fluted Wave* 206, 221

Greek 206, 221, 240, 249, 285, 409, 419; *Greeks* 289

Green, Howard Editor of The Notion Club Papers. 148, 155–7, 211–12, 215, 217, (283)

Guardians [Ramer] 196–7, 217

Guildford, Nicholas Member of the Notion Club and its reporter; often called *Nick*. 149–51, 156, 159–74, 176–8, 180, 183, 191, 195, 198, 200, 202, 205, 211–15, 217, 219, 221, 223–4, 227–33, 235, 245, 252–5, 260, 266, 272, 276–7, 281–4, 291, 293, 302. *Maister Nichole of Guldeforde* 150. (Replaced *Latimer.*)

Gunthorpe Park in Matfield 181, 215

Gyönyörü [Ramer] 214–15, 218. (Replaced by *Emberü.*)

Gyürüchill [Ramer] The planet Saturn. 221. (Replaced by *Shomorú.*)

Hador 333

Half-elven 333, 340

Havard, Dr. Robert 150, 152

Haven of the Gods See *Avallondē, Avallôni.*

Heathen, The Vikings. 270, 272; *the heathen earls* 269

Heaven 200, 261, 292, 296, 364, 381, 392, 395, 401; *High Heaven* 262, 295, 297, 400. See *Deep Heaven; Menel, Pillar of Heaven.*

Hebrew 238, 300

Hell 262, 297

Helm's Deep 292

Herefordshire 293–4

Herunúmen 'Lord of the West'. 310–11; *Númekundo* 311. *Númeheruvi* 'Lords of the West' 246, 311

Hesiod 289

Hesperia Western land. 303, 309. See *Westfolde.*

Hesperides 289

Hibernia Ireland. 267, 293–4

High Elves 409

Hildi 'sons, or followers', Men. 401. See *Eruhildi.*

Hnau [Lewis] 175, 202, 204–5, 207, 210, 214, 220

Hobbits 409

Homer 289, 413; *Homeric* 408; *the Iliad* 186

Hressa-hlab [Lewis] 213, 220. See *Old Solar.*

Hrossa [Lewis] 203, 220

Hungary 159, 201; *Magyarország* 201; *Magyar* 201

Huor 340

INDEX II
469

Húrin the Steadfast 332–3, 340
Huxley, Thomas 208, 222
Hwiccian 291. [*Hwicce*, a West Midland people whose name survives in the Forest of Wychwood.]

Iceland 234; *Land of Ice* 272. *Icelandic* 151, 159, 282; *Icelander* 214
Idril Wife of Tuor, mother of Eärendil. 333
Ilien See *Tar-Ilien*.
Ilmen The region above the air, region of the stars. 338, 394, 396
Ilu The World, the Universe. 310, 313, 401, 412; *Ilúve* 401, 412
Ilúvatar 246, 249, 290, 310, 312, 332–3, 335–6, 338, 346, 386, 391, 395, 399–401, 404, 408; *Allfather* 317, 401. *The Mountain of Ilúvatar* 317, 335, 339, 356, *the Mountain* 251, 289–90, 301, 373; O.E. *Ealfæderbeorg* 317; see *(The) Pillar of Heaven*.
Imrám (Irish) tale of seavoyaging, plural *Imráma*. 222, 283; (the poem) 296–9
Indilzar Elros. 363, 365, 380–2. (Replaced by *Gimilzôr*.)
Indo-European 415, 418
Inklings, The 148–51, 211, (216, 219), 220; *Inklings' Saga*, ~ *Saga-book* 148–9
Inner Seas (of Middle-earth). 334, 380
Iranian 418
Ireland 234, 261, 264, 267, 278–80, 293, 296, 299; O.E. *Íraland* 270, 272, 294; *Ériu* 270, 294, *Erin* 280, 294. See *Hibernia*.
Irish 211, 294, 296; *the Irish* 273, O.E. *Íras* 294
Isil The Moon. 241, 302, 306; *Ithil* 303, 306
Isildur 335, 384, 387, 401
Italy 236, 276

Japan 241, 306
Japheth Son of Noah. 411
Jeremy, Wilfrid Trewin Member of the Notion Club. 151, 159, 164–5, 169–71, 173, 175, 177, 179–81, 188–9, 191–4, 196–7, 199–203, 205, 207, 211, 216, 218–20, 223–4, 227–33, 245, 249–55, 260, 265–9, 277–9, 281, 283, 286, 289–90, 293, 300–1, 303, 306–9, 316, 356, 389, 413, 432–3, 440; called *Jerry* 231, 250; the name *Trewin* 290, 293, spelt *Trewyn* 266, 268–9, 293; his books 159, 164, 200. For Jeremy's '*alter ego*' in Anglo-Saxon England see *Tréowine*, in Númenor see *Abrazân, Voronwë*.
John the Baptist 285
Jones, James Member of the Notion Club. 159, 173, 186, 198, 211, 215, 223, 233, 245
Jötunheim Land of the Giants in Norse mythology. 308
Jutland 223
Jupiter (the planet) 220. See *Glund*.

470   SAURON DEFEATED

Karan [Ramer] The planet Mars. 220. (Replaced by *Gormok*.)
Keladian [Ramer; cf. *Enkeladim*] 206, 222
Kemen The Great Lands, Middle-earth. 402–4, 412
Kerry 293
Khazad The Dwarves. 414. *Khazadian* (language) 414–15, 433
Kherū See *Arûn*.
Kings of Men The Númenóreans. 337, 346, 348, 366, 368, 385,
    392–3, 395, 410
Kinslaying, The 411
Kirith Ungol, Tower of 407
Kronos Greek god (identified with Saturn). 221

Lamps, The The original lights of Middle-earth. 412
Land of Gift (Also *Land of his Gift*, i.e. the gift of Amân) 241, 247,
    259, 312, 332, 343, 353, 361, 373, 375, 378, 385, 388, 391–2,
    394, 397; *the Gift* 396; O.E. *léanes lond* 258. See *Andórë*;
    Athânâte, Amatthânê, Zen'nabâr, Abarzâyan, Yôzâyan.
Land of Ice See *Iceland*.
Land of the Star 368, 390. See *(The) Star of Eärendil*.
Land's End In Cornwall. 266
Langobards Lombards. 236–7, 284, 301; *Longobards* 273, 276;
    O.E. *Longbeardan* 273; *Langobardic* 237, 301
Last Alliance 331
Last Battle 336, 386
Latimer Member of the Notion Club (precursor of Guildford). 150,
    212, 214
Latin 150, 217, 220, 222, 225, 238, 241, 283, 285–6, 294, 300,
    306–7, 418. See *Elven-Latin*.
Lay of Leithian 149
Leithien Britain. 280
Letters of J. R. R. Tolkien, The 145, 147, 150–3, 212, 217, 220,
    285, 291–2, 381, 407–10
Lewis, C. S. 145, 148–50, 152–3, 164, 168, 175, 199–200, 202–3,
    213, 216, 219–22, 303, 307–9; with reference to his nickname
    Jack 200, 219. *Out of the Silent Planet* 152, 164, 174, 199, 212,
    220; *Perelandra* 152, 199, 202, 212–13; *That Hideous Strength*
    152–3, 309; other works 153, 219
Lhammas, The 280, 286
Light-elves 410; Old Norse *Ljós-alfar* 398
Lindsay, David 164, 212. *A Voyage to Arcturus* 164, 212
Living Land In *The Death of St. Brendan*. 261, 296
Lonely Isle, The (1) (Tol) Eressëa. 280, 316, 332, 334, 354, 394,
    396, 412; O.E. *Anetig* 316. (2) The summit of the Pillar of
    Heaven after the Downfall. 391–4, 407; *a lonely isle, ~ island*
    351, 373, 391–3
Lord of All (Mēlekō, Arûn) 347, 367, 383, 390

INDEX II 471

Lord of the Rings, The 145, 147, 152, 280, 309, 331, 339–40, 378, 405–6, 439
Lords of the West 231, 238, 246–7, 251–2, 258, 277, 281, 290, 331–2, 334, 350, 371, 400, 410; *the Lords* 251, 290, 332; O.E. *Westfrégan* 'West-lords' 258 (*Westfréa* 'West-lord' 317). See *Bârim an-adûn, Herunúmen*; *Eagles*.
Lost Road, The 145, 153, 280, 282, 284, 286–90, 292–5, 304, 308–10, 315, 317, 331, 340, 356
Lost Tales See *(The) Book of Lost Tales*.
Lough Derg In the Shannon. 261, 292, 296
Loughrea In Galway. 267, 293
Lowdham, Alwin Arundel Member of the Notion Club. References include his earlier name *Harry Loudham*, and the later *Arry* for *Arundel* (on the changes of his name see 153, 213, 233–4, 282–3). 146, 148, 150–3, 159, 162–3, 165–8, 171–4, 179–80, 182, 184–8, 190–2, 194, 196, 199–202, 206, 211, 213–17, 219, 221–7, 230–56, 259–61, 264–6, 268–77, 279–90, 292–4, 299–312, 317, 375, 378–9, 388–9, 396, 412–13, 440; his *Report on Adunaic* 413 ff. *Alboin* preceding *Alwin* 284. See *Ælfwine, Éarendel, Elendil, Nimruzîr*.
   Lowdham's invented languages 235, 238–40, 256, 302, 304–5
Lowdham, Edwin Father of A. A. Lowdham. 233–6, 245, 260, 280, 284, 287, 293, 301 (all other references are to his manuscript). Called *Éadwine* 244; original name *Oswin Ellendel* 284
   His manuscript and the single preserved page 148, 235, 248, 253, 255–9, 279–81, 291–2, 301, 306–7, 311, 313–27, 355–6, 381, 384, 411–13
Lowdham, Oswin Father of Edwin Lowdham. 293
Low Worlds [Lewis] Planets of the Solar System. 213
Lúthien 333

Macedon See *Frankley*.
Maelduin Irish voyager. 270, 294
Magyar See *Hungary*.
Malacandra [Lewis] The planet Mars. 181, 212–13, 220; *Malacandrian* 220. See *Mars*.
Manface, Sir Gerald Member of the Notion Club. 160
Maldon, Battle of 236
Manawē See *Manwë*.
Mandos, Doom of 411
Mannish (tradition) 406–7
Manwë 317, 331–2, 336, 376, 381. *Manawē* 341–3, 348–9, 351, 354, 376. See *Amân, Gods, Valar*.
Marchers 269, 272–3, 294; *Men of the Marches* 273; *West Marches* 269
Mârim [Ramer] 221. (Replaced by *Albarim*.)

472 SAURON DEFEATED

Markison, Dom Jonathan Member of the Notion Club. 151, 160, 223, 227, 230, 232–3, 236–7, 241, 245, 253, 265, 277, 300–3, 306

Mars (the planet) 163, 167, 169, 204, 212–13, 220; *Martian(s)* 212; (the god) 286. See *Gormok, Malacandra; Tiw.*

Mediterranean, The 289

Megalithic 221

Mēlekō Melkor-Morgoth. 341–2, 344–5, 347–8, 354, 398–9, 401–5, 407, 411–13; translated *Tyrant* 411. *Offspring of Mēlekō* 344

Melian 333

Melkor 383. See *Mēlekō.*

Menel The heavens. 241, 305, 401, 412, 414–5

Menelkemen [Ramer] 218

Menelmin The Pillar of Heaven. 335. Other abandoned names (in order of succession) *Menelminda* 302, 353, 356, 412, *Menelmindo* 315; *Meneltyúla* 302, 314–15, 346–7, 351–3, 355–6, 375, 384, 395; *Menel-túbel* 302, 353, 375, *Menel-túbil* 302, 305, 353, 375, *Menel-Túbal* 363, 365, 367, 372–3, 375, 383, 388, *Menil-Túbal* 371, 383, 388, 391. See *Minul-Tárik.*

Meneltarma The Pillar of Heaven. 378, 393–4; *Isle of Meneltarma* 393–4

Mercia Kingdom of the Mercians. 291. *Mercian* 291, 294; (dialect of Old English) 257, 292, 313. See *West Midlands.*

Merlin [Lewis] 309

Mesopotamia 410

Middle-earth 152, 241, 258, 275, 280, 287, 305–6, 316, 331–2, 334–9, 343–6, 352–3, 358, 361–3, 365–6, 368, 374–5, 379–80, 382–3, 386, 389, 394–6, 399, 403, 405–11, 439; *the Middle-earth* 236, 348, 387, *the Great Middle-earth* 398; O.E. *Middangeard* 236, 257, 285, 313, 316. See *Great Lands, Kemen.*

    Men of Middle-earth (in the age of Númenor) 332, 334, 339, 344–5, 348, 356, 359, 362, 368, 380, 403 (and see *Wild Men*); their tongues 344, 362, 380

Middle English 291

Minal-zidar [Ramer] 199–200, 218; translated *Poise in Heaven* 200

Minas Tirith 217

Minul-Tárik The Pillar of Heaven. 238, 241, 249, 302, 375, 388, 391–2, 394, 413, 428. See *Menelmin.*

Mircwudu 'Mirkwood', the Eastern Alps (see V.91). 276

Modred Nephew of King Arthur. 283

Moon, The 165–7, 169, 182, 241, 302, 306, 426; *moons* 199. See *Isil, Nílú.*

Morgoth 317, 331–2, 334–6, 339, 354, 406, 412; O.E. *Malscor* 317

Morris, William 213; *News from Nowhere* 172, 213

Mountain of Ilúvatar See *Ilúvatar.*

INDEX II
473

Mount Doom In *The Death of St. Brendan.* 292, 295
Mulkhêr 'Lord of Darkness' (358), Morgoth. 358–61, 363–4, 367–8, 384, 390, 411; *Arûn-Mulkhêr* 367, 384; offspring of *Mulkhêr* 362
Mull (Island of) Argyll, Scotland. 267

Neowollond, -land (O.E.) 'The Land that is fallen low' (315), *Atalante.* 258, 292, 313; *Niwelland* 292, 313–14.
Neptunians Inhabitants of Neptune. 175
Nevrast 316
New Hebrides 300
New Lands 387, 393, 395; *a New Land* (west of Eressëa) 403; the *New Land (Númenor)*, see *Vinya.* See *(The) World.*
Nîlû The Moon. 241, 306, 426; *Nil, Njūl* 306
Nimrî 'The Shining Ones' (Eldar). 358–62, 364, 372, 376, 378–9, 385–6, 388, 405–7, 410; later form *Nimîr* 377–8, 388, 391, 394, 405, 407, 410, 413–14, 436
Nimrian (tongue) 361, 375, 378–9, 396, 414–15, 419; *Nimriyê* 'Nimrian tongue' 414. See *Avallonian, Eressëan, Quenya.*
Nimloth The White Tree of Númenor. 384–5
Nimrûn, Towers of Unknown. 381; earlier *Nimroth* 364, 381
Nimruzân Elendil. 365, 369–70, 374–5, 382, 387, 389; his sons 374–5, 387. (Replaced by *Nimruzîr.*)
Nimruzîr Elendil. 247, 290, 312, 389–90, 396; Lowdham so addressed by Jeremy 250, 252
Noldor 406, 411
Nordic 174, 236; *Nordics* 222, 283
Norman Keeps An uninstructed barber. 230–1, 283
Norse, Old Norse 174, 214, 286, 295, 307, 410
Northmen 276
North, The 308, 334, 341, 344, 358, 362, 366, 383, 399, 402; *Isles of the North* 273; *North-seas* 273, *North-countries* 275, *Northern lands* 276
Norway 185, 234
Notion Club, the Club 146, 148, 150–2, 155, 157–61, 164, 170, 173, 196–7, 200, 211, 213, 218–19, 228, 253–4, 260–1, 277, 281–2, 284, 293, 308
Notion Club Papers Division into two parts 146–7, 153; original extent 156; suggested course of development 281–2
Nówendaland (O.E.) 'Land of Seafarers', Númenor. 242, 286, 317
Númenor 146–7, 217, 221, 231–2, 238, 240, 247, 249, 277, 279, 281, 284, 286, 290, 300–3, 305–7, 309–10, 315–16, 331–40, 343–7, 349–57, 379–80, 382, 384, 386, 395, 400–1, 403–10, 412 (other references under *(The) Downfall*). *A Description of Númenor* 406

474 SAURON DEFEATED

Númenóre 240, 242, 247, 310, 303, 305, 310, 343, 351–2, 354, 361, 378. *Numinor* [Lewis] 153, 303, 307, 309

Speech of Númenor 333, 343, 354, 361, 379; the number of Kings before Ar-Pharazôn 335, 339–40, 363, 381–2, 404, 412, 433; *the White Tree of Númenor*, see *Nimloth*. See *Anadûnê, Westernesse, Land of Gift*.

Númenórean (of language) 148, 240, 256, 279, 291, 302, 305, 309, 379, 381, 397; (of script) 256, 279, 291, 313, 318; (with other reference) 152, 281, 290, 315–16, 381, 385, 387, 397, 404–5, 407

Númenóreans 251, 258, 290, 292, 315, 317, 333–40, 343–4, 346–7, 350–2, 354–7, 378–82, 386, 400–1, 403–4, 408–13; O.E. *Númenoriscan* 257, 314. Called *Men out of the Sea* 344, 356, *Sea-kings* 362, 388; and see *Kings of Men, Adûnai, Adûnaim*.

Life-span of the Númenóreans 332–3, 337, 340, 343, 361, 378, 400, 403, 408, 433; religion 400; the Ban on their westward sailing 313–14, 333–4, 343–5, 351, 354, 356–7, 361–2, 364–5, 372, 379, 404, 408, 412

Númenos City of the Númenóreans. 292, 333, 335, 339. See *Armenelos, Arminalêth; Antirion, Tar Kalimos*.

Ocean, The 273, 317, 398. See *Gársecg*.
Odda of Portloca King's thegn under Edward the Elder. 271–2
Odysseus 289
Old English 148, 239, 243, 255, 257, 284–7, 291–5, 304, 309, 313, 315–18, 355–7, 381, 384, 412–13; other references under *Anglo-Saxon, English*.

Words or passages cited 236, 239, 242–4, 257–8, 268, 271–3, 277–8, 285–7, 292–5, 304, 313–14, 316–17, 384
Old Human (language) 203, 220; *Old Humane* 220; *Primitive Adamic* 203, 220, *Adamic* 220
Old Lands 393, 395. See *(The) World*.
Old Road, The See *(The) Straight Road*.
Old Solar [Lewis] 151, 168, 199–202, 204, 213, 219–20; *Hlab-Eribol-ef-Cordi* 213. See *Hressa-hlab*.
Old Universal (language) 204, 219–20
Ondor Earlier name of Gondor. 331
Orcs 332
Orion 236, 285, 308
Öshül-küllösh [Ramer] The waterfall in Ellor. 199–200; translated *Falling Water* 200. Earlier names 218
Ossë 332, 412
Óswine Father of Éadwine father of Ælfwine the Mariner. 270
Outer Night 264, 292, 298
Out of the Silent Planet See *Lewis, C. S.*

INDEX II

475

Owlamoo 231, 284
Owl and the Nightingale, The 150
Oxford 146, 149–50, 153, 155–7, 159–60, 200, 211, 213, 215, 219, 222, 230, 233, 260, 269, 307, 389
    Oxford University 152, 211; *University Press* 149. *The Schools:* faculties 149, 156; = examinations 255, 291; *Examination Schools* (building) 155, 254, *Clerk of the Schools* 155. *English Board* (Board of the Faculty) 219
    Streets, etc.: *High Street, the High* 213, 222, 283; *Turl Street, the Turl* 173, 213, 223, 283; *Broad Street* 213; *Brasenose Lane* 283; *Radcliffe Square* 211, 222, 281, 283; *Radcliffe Camera, the Camera* 211, 222–3, 238, 281–3; *Bodleian Library* 222, 284; *St. Mary's Church* 211, 222; *Banbury Road* 157, 179, 215
    Colleges: *All Souls'* 160, 231; *Brasenose (B.N.C.)* 159, 223, 283; *Corpus Christi* 159; *Exeter* 160, 213; *Jesus* 159, 213, 245; *Lincoln* 159, 213; *Magdalen* 160; *New College* 160; *Pembroke* 132, 256, 291; *Queen's* 159, 224; *St. John's* 159; *Trinity* 159; *University College* 160; *Wadham* 159
Oxford English Dictionary 150, 222, 283, 286; *New English Dictionary* 225, 283
Oyarsa [Lewis] The Eldil of Malacandra. 212

Paradise 263, 265–6, 292, 297, 409; *earthly paradise* 344, 398, 402, 410
Parting of the Ways, The In *The Death of St. Brendan.* 264–5, 298
Pembrokeshire 234, 279, 284, 309, *Pembroke* 246
Pengolod the Wise of Gondolin 280
Penian In Pembrokeshire. 234, 284
Perelandra [Lewis] The planet Venus. 168, 203; as title, see *Lewis, C. S.*
Pharazîr See *Azrubêl.*
    356, 373, 375, 384, 388, 391–4, 400–1, 407, 412, 429; O.E. *Heofonsýl* 287, 314–15, 317, archaic *Hebaensuil* 242; a Volcano 410, 412, and cf. 265, 289–90. *The Mountain (of Ilúvatar),* see *Ilúvatar;* and see *(The) Lonely Isle* (2), *Menelmin, Meneltarma, Minul-Târik.*
Pitt, Dr. Abel Member of the Notion Club. 159
Planet(s) 204–5, 210, 212–13; of another Solar System 207
Plato 249, 289; Dialogues: *Critias,* 289; *Timaeus* 249, 289
Pleiades Daughters of Atlas. 289
Porlock In Somerset. 266, 268–9, 271, 277, 293; *Porlock Weir* 268; O.E. *Portloca* 272
Poseidon 289
Powers, The (Valar) 241, 246–7, 310–11, 314–15, 341, 355, 357–8, 377, 399–404, 407, 410, 412; *Powers of the World* 251,

476   SAURON DEFEATED

of the West 290; wars of the Powers 402; O.E. *Waldend* 313, 355, *Héamægnu* 317. See *Avalôi, Avalôim, Gods, Valar.*
Primitive Adamic   See *Old Human.*
Prose Edda, Snorra Edda   See *Snorri Sturluson.*
Public-house School, The   Jeremy's name for writers of the Inklings. 200, 219–20

Quendian   439
Quenta Eldalien   'The History of the Elves'. 303, 307–8; *Quenta Eldaron* 308
Quenta Noldorinwa   279, 412; *the Quenta* 279, 317, 356
Quenta Silmarillion   280, 284, 292, 354, 356, 377, 383, 411–12. See *(The) Silmarillion.*
Quenya   218, 290, 304, 309–11, 313, 317, 379; Quenya words and passages cited 240–1, 246–9, 289–90, 302–3, 305–6, 308, 310, 317, 415, 419. See *Avallonian, Eressëan, Nimrian.*

Ragnarök   286
Ramer, Michael   Member of the Notion Club. 146, 148–53, 159, 161–4, 166, 169–224, 226, 228–9, 231–3, 235–8, 245–6, 249–57, 259–60, 264, 266, 277, 281, 283–4, 291–2, 302–3, 305, 308–9, 311, 317, 353, 410; his book *The Stone-eaters* 177, 214
Ransom, Dr. Elwin   [Lewis] 168, 212–13, 309
Rashbold, John Jethro   Member of the Notion Club. 151, 160, 211, 223, 245, 277
Rashbold, Professor   151, 256–7, 259, 291–2. On the name *Rashbold* see *Tolkien, J. R. R.*
Regeneard   (O.E.) Valinor. 242, 286, 317; *Regenrice* 317
Return of the King, The   217
Rigel   Star in Orion. 236, 285, 308
Ring, The   217, 382
Ringwraiths   382
Romance   (languages and literatures) 151, 418
Romans   221
Rómelonde   'East-haven' in Númenor. 314–15; earlier (in O.E. text) on *Rómelónan* 315. (Replaced by *Rómenna.*)
Rómenna   'Eastward', haven in Númenor. 315, 384–5; cf. 310
Rosamund   Wife of Alboin the Lombard. 236, 285
Rôthinzil   'Flower of the Foam', the ship of Azrubêl. 360, 377–8. See *Vingalótë.*
Rufus   See *Dolbear, Rupert.*
Rúmil of Tûn   280
Runes   (Old English) 285

Sanavaldo   The Almighty. 401
Satan   265

INDEX II   477

Saturn (the planet) 205, 221; *Saturnian* 205; (the god) 221. See *Eneköl, Gyürüchill, Shomorú.*

Sauron 246, 250, 284, 289–90, 310, 313–15, 317, 334–7, 339, 345–8, 350–3, 355–6, 380, 382–4, 393, 395, 400–1, 404, 407–9, 412; O.E. *se Malsca, Saweron* 317. See *Zigûr.*

Saxo Grammaticus Danish historian. 301, 307

Saxons 276

scop (O.E.) minstrel. 272

Scotland 234, 267

Sea-danes See *Danes.*

Seafarer, The Old English poem. 243–4, 272, 287–8, 304

Seas of sunlight, Seas of shadow 360

Second Age, The 217, 407–8

Second Kindred Men. 401

Semitic 241, 415

Servants of God 341, 353, 357, 359. See *Eru-bênî.*

Seven Stones The Palantíri. 385

Severn, River 293; *Severn Sea, Severn-mouth* 268–9, 293

Shadow, The 258, 334–5, 339, 362–3; *the Ancient Shadow* 363; *the Deathshadow* 247, 315, *-shade* 258–9, 312, O.E. *Déapscúa* 257-8, 314, 317

Shannon, River 261, 292, 296

Shaw, G. B. Shavian 167

Sheaf, The 227; *King Sheaf* 236, 278, 284, 294, *King Sheave* 273–6, 294, 380

Ship-burial 338, 400, 411

Shem Son of Noah. 411

Shomorú [Ramer] The planet Saturn. 221. (Replaced *Gyürüchill,* replaced by *Eneköl.*)

Shoreless Sea See *Great Sea(s).*

Silmarillion, The 308, 312, 376, 405, 411–12; (published work) 340, 353, 393, 411. See *Quenta Silmarillion.*

Sindarin 304, 379; Sindarin words cited 302, 306

Six Years' War 157–8, 190, 225, 234, 283; *Second German War* 283; *War of 1939* 284

Skidbladnir 174, 214

Slavonic 418

Slieve League On the coast of Donegal. 267, 293

Snorri Sturluson Icelandic historian, author of the *Prose Edda* (*Snorra Edda*) 214, 307–8, 410

Solar System 167, 204, 213, 219; another Solar System 207. See *Planet(s), Low Worlds; En.*

Somerset 268, 270, 278–9, 293; *Somersets* 'men of Somerset' 269, 293

Sons of God See *Eruhildi.*

South, The 334, 344, 362, 366, 383

478   SAURON DEFEATED

Space (including references to Space-ships, Space-travel) 146, 151, 163–4, 166–71, 173–6, 178–9, 195, 198, 201, 205–6, 209, 213, 215, 220. See *Deep Heaven*.

Staffordshire 294

Stainer, Ranulph Member of the Notion Club. 151, 160, 211, 223, 233–4, 238–40, 245–6, 253–5, 260–1, 277, 302, 305

Stapledon, Olaf 214; *The Last Men in London* 175, 214

Stars 199, 207, 237, 301, 427

Star of Eärendil (Azrubêl), The (278), 301, 308, 343, 360, 371, 376, 378, 399, 402; *Land of the Star* 368, 390. *The Star* (in *The Death of St. Brendan*) 261, 263–4, 296, 298

Starwards See *Gimlad*.

St. Brendan See *Brendan*.

Storm, The See *Great Storm*.

St. Peter and St. Paul, Feast of 211

Straight Road, The or *A* (into the Ancient West) 247, 279–80, 310, 312, 338, 393, 395, 404; *Straight Way* 243, 259, 394, 396, 409; *Straight Path* 339; O.E. *riht weg, reht weg* 243, 258; *the old road* 264–5, 298, 392, 394–5; *the ancient way* 392

Sun, The 195, 198–9, 205, 219, 302, 306, 400, 410, 413, 426; *suns* 199; another sun 205, 207. See *Anar, Arbol*.

Sussex 234, 284

Swabians 276

Swedes 276

Swordmen 276

Table Mountain (Cape Town) 179

Talkative Planet, The Earth. 127, 148–9, 153, 205. See *Thulcandra*.

Tamil Language of S.E. India and Ceylon. 300

Tamworth In Staffordshire. 273, 294

Taniquetil 336, 338, 391; *the Mountain of Amân* (Manwë) 391; *the White Mountain* 393–4, 396

Tar-Atanamir Thirteenth King of Númenor. 382

Tar-Calion See *Tarkalion*.

Tar-Ilien Earlier name of *Tar-Míriel*. 335, 351, 387; *Ilien* 316–17, 336; O.E. *Iligen* 316–17. See *Ar-Zimrahil*.

Tar Kalimos Elvish name of Arminalêth. 381

Tar-kalion (also *Tarcalion, Tar-Calion*, and including references to *the King*) 246, 248, 257–8, 290, 310–11, 313–17, 334–7, 339–40, 345–8, 350, 352–3, 355, 381, 401, 404, 408–9; O.E. *Tarcaligeon* 316–17; called *the Golden* 316, 336, 381, 404. See *Ar-Pharazôn*.

Tar-Míriel Queen of Tarkalion (Ar-Zimraphel). 387. See *Tar-Ilien*.

Tar-Palantir Twenty-fourth King of Númenor. 381–2

Tavrobel In Tol Eressëa. 280

Tekel-Mirim [Ramer] 207–211, 222; earlier name *Tekel-Ishtar* 222

INDEX II   479

Temple   The temple of Morgoth in Númenor. (1) On the Pillar of Heaven. 289, 315, 335, 339, 356, 384, 401. (2) In the City of the Númenóreans. 250, 258, 335, 339, 347, 350, 353, 356–7, 367, 371, 374–5, 384, 390. O.E. *alh* 257, *ealh* 314. The temple described 347, 367, 384, 390

tengwar   148, 292, 313–14, 317–27

Thames, River   (210); *Thames Valley* 211

Thangorodrim   332

Third Age, The   408–9

Thor   301, 307–8

Three Houses   (of the Men of Beleriand) 331–2; *the Faithful Houses, three kindreds* 402

Thulcandra   [Lewis] The Silent Planet, Earth. 213

Time, Time-travel   151, 159, 164, 169, 175–6, 178–9, 182, 195, 198–9, 201, 209, 215, 218, 220

Tirion   City of the Elves in Valinor. 403, 412–13

Titmass, J. R.   Historian of Oxford. 156, 158; earlier name *Titmouse* 149

Tiw   (O.E.) Germanic god equated with Mars; Old Norse *Týr*. 286. Plural *Tíwas, Tívar*, see *Gods*.

Tol Eressëa   See *Eressëa*.

Tolkien, Arthur   308 (see *Arthurson, John*).

Tolkien, C. R.   In *The Notion Club Papers*. 219

Tolkien, Edith   286

Tolkien, J. R. R.   In *The Notion Club Papers*. 150, (216), 219–22, 308–9; and see *Arthurson, John*. Referred to by C. S. Lewis 309. The name *Tolkien* translated *Rashbold* 151, 291
On Fairy-Stories 216–17, 221. See *Letters, (The) Lord of the Rings, Unfinished Tales*.

Tolkien, M. H. R.   284

Tower of Doom   In *The Death of St. Brendan*. 262, 292

Tree, The   In *The Death of St. Brendan*. 261, 263, 265, 296–8; *the White-tree Strand* 263, 298. *The White Tree of Númenor*, see *Nimloth*. *The Blessed Trees* [Ramer] 194; see *Drama of the Silver Tree*.

Tréowine   Friend and companion of Ælfwine the Mariner. 268–71, 273, 276–80, 293–4; Céolwulf's son 269, 273. See *Jeremy, Wilfrid Trewin*.

Trotter   340

True West, The   309, 333, 336, 338, 386, 395, 409; *the Ancient West* 393, 395, 409

Túna   City of the Elves in Valinor (see *Tirion*). 316, 336, 403, 412–13; *Tûn* 280

Tuor   290, 340

Turgon   316

Túrin   340

480 SAURON DEFEATED

Turkildi 'Lordly Men' (Númenóreans). 246, 248, 286, 310–11, 399.
See *Fréafíras*.
Two Kindreds Elves and Men. 402
Two Towers, The 145

Ulmo 412
Umbar, Havens of 389
Undúnië See *Andúnië*.
Undying Lands 380. See *Deathless Land*.
Unfinished Tales 286, 290, 316, 378–9, 381–2, 387, 406
Universe, The 163, 166, 169, 183, 185, 196, 208, 401
Ûrî The Sun. 306, 426; *Uir, Ŷr* 306
Utumno 383

Valāi Valar. 404
Valandil Named as father of Elendil. 401. *Valandili* 'Lovers of the
Powers', name given to certain Númenóreans. 400
Valar 241–2, 246, 252, 286, 292, 305, 310, 332–3, 340, 355,
376–7, 394, 396, 400–2, 404–6, 409–10, 412; *Chief of the Valar*
(Manwë) 402, 406; *Children of the Valar* 332, 377. See *Gods,
Powers*; *Children of the Gods*.
Valhalla 242
Valimar 409
Valinor 284, 286, 292, 316–17, 332–4, 336, 354–5, 379–80, 386,
388, 394, 396, 409–10, 412–13; *Land of the Gods*, see *Gods*;
O.E. *Ósgeard* 316–17, *Ésa-eard*, *Godépel* 316, and see
Regeneard. *Annals of Valinor* 280, 291, 316, 377
Valkyries 242
Venus (the planet) 168, 204, 212–13, 220. See *Perelandra, Zingil*.
Vikings 295. See *(The) Heathen*.
Vingalótë 'Foam-flower', the ship of Eärendil. 356, 360, 377, 388;
Wingalótë 342, 356, 377, 388; *Vingelot* 292, 356; *Wingelot* 356.
See *Rôthinzil*.
Vinya 'The Young', 'The New Land', Númenor. 315, 332
Vinyamar (1) Númenor. 315, (2) The house of Turgon in Nevrast.
316
Void, The 332, 401, 404
Volcano See *(The) Pillar of Heaven*.
Voronwë ('Steadfast, Faithful'). (1) Elf of Gondolin. 290. (2) Com-
panion of Elendil; identified with Tréowine; Jeremy so named by
Lowdham. 278–9, 290, 293.
Voyage to Arcturus, A See *Lindsay, David*.

Wales 272; *South Wales* 267; *West Wales* (Cornwall) 279
Watchet In Somerset. 269–70, 293
Wells, H. G. 165–6, 212. *The Time Machine* 165; *The First Men in
the Moon* 165, 212

INDEX II

Welsh 269, 273, 293; (language) 192, 270, 417; = Roman 276 (see V.91); *West Welsh*, the people of Cornwall, 270, 293

Wessex Kingdom of the West Saxons. 269, 273; *West Saxon* (dialect) 291

Westernesse Númenor. 240, 305, 311, 332, 343–4, 361, 378, 400, 409, 426. See *Anadûnê*.

Westfarers See *(The) West*.

Westfold In Rohan. 309

Westfolde (O.E.) Númenor. 303, 309, 313, 315–16

West Midlands (of England) 291; *West-midland* (dialect) 257, 291; *West-midlander* 291. See *Mercia*.

West, The 152, 251, 265, 280, 332, 334, 336–8, 341, 345, 349–52, 354–7, 359–60, 364–5, 369–72, 374–5, 378, 381, 383, 394–6, 399–402, 404, 407–9, 412–14. *Dwellers in the West* (O.E. *Westware*), *Westfarers* (O.E. *Westfaran*) = Númenóreans, 257–8, 313–16; *West Land* (Valinor) 401; *West of the World* (O.E. *Westwegas*) 244, 280; *Men of the West* 271, 398–400. See *Lords of the West*, *True West*.

Whitburn and Thoms Oxford publishing house and bookseller. 149, 153; *Whitburn* 303. See *Blackwell*.

White Mountain See *Taniquetil*.

White Tree of Númenor See *Nimloth*.

Wihawinia See 242, 287

Wild Men (of Middle-earth) 334, 374, *men of the wild* 352

Williams, Charles 219; *Carolus* 200, 216

Wingalótë, Wingelot See *Vingalótë*.

World, The (Passages bearing on the conception of The World Made Round at the Downfall of Númenor) 264–5, 278–9, 298, 331, 336–9, 345, 347, 352, 355, 364, 366–7, 381, 383, 386, 392–6, 400–1, 404, 408–12; and see *(The) Cataclysm*, *(The) Straight Road*.

The *New World* 338–9, 392–3, 395; the *Old World* 338–9, 387, 408–9, 414; and see *New Lands, Old Lands*. The *circle(s) of the world* 372, 409

Wormald, W. W. Oxford scholar interested in *The Notion Club Papers*. 156–8

Wychwood 291 (see *Hwiccian*).

Yôzâyan The Land of Gift. 241, 247, 286, 312, 375, 388–9, 391, 396–7. For earlier names see *Land of Gift*.

Yavanna 332

Zen'nabâr The Land of Gift. 378, 380, 385, 388; earlier *Zenn'abâr* 378. (Replaced by *Abarzâyan*.)

Zen'namân The Blessed Realm. 380, 385

Zeus 221, 289

482 SAURON DEFEATED

Zigûr Sauron. 231, 247, 250–1, 257–8, 284, 290, 311, 345, 353, 356, 363, 366–8, 371–2, 374–5, 380, 383–4, 389(–90), 392, 394 (and see 437).

Zingil [Ramer] The planet Venus. 205, 220